Great Britain & Ireland

2002

■ *Selection of hotels and restaurants*

Sélection d'hôtels et de restaurants ■

■ *Selezione di alberghi e ristoranti*

Auswahl an Hotels und Restaurants ■

Great Britain & Ireland

This 29th edition of The Red Guide Great Britain & Ireland offers a fully revised selection of hotels, guesthouses, restaurants and pubs. All the information in this book is tried and tested in complete anonymity by our team of dedicated, professional inspectors.

As always, we have carefully updated every detail, and new for this year we have added the symbol 🚸 *to our already comprehensive list of symbols, to show those hotels that have special facilities for children.*

And in line with the move to the European currency in January 2002, prices for those establishments listed in the Republic of Ireland are given in euro.

Something else to look out for is the **"Bib Gourmand"** *, highlighting those restaurants offering good food at moderate prices.*

The Red Guide is written for and by our readers, so don't forget to write to us with your comments. The complete Great Britain & Ireland Red Guide selection is also available on-line at
www.ViaMichelin.co.uk
and you can e-mail us with your comments to
theredguide-gbirl@uk.michelin.com

Contents

Choosing a hotel or restaurant

This guide offers a selection of hotels and restaurants to help motorists on their travels. In each category establishments are listed in order of preference according to the degree of comfort they offer.

Categories

	XXXXX	*Luxury in the traditional style*
	XXXX	*Top class comfort*
	XXX	*Very comfortable*
	XX	*Comfortable*
	X	*Quite comfortable*
		Traditional pubs serving food
		Other recommended accommodation (Guesthouses, farmhouses and private homes)
without rest.		*The hotel has no restaurant*
	with rm	*The restaurant also offers accommodation*

Peaceful atmosphere and setting

Certain establishments are distinguished in the guide by the red symbols shown below.

Your stay in such hotels will be particularly pleasant or restful, owing to the character of the building, its decor, the setting, the welcome and services offered, or simply the peace and quiet to be enjoyed there.

to ,	*Pleasant hotels*
XXXXX to X,	*Pleasant restaurants*
« Park »	*Particularly attractive feature*
	Very quiet or quiet, secluded hotel
	Quiet hotel
< sea	*Exceptional view*
<	*Interesting or extensive view*

The maps located at the beginning of each regional section in the guide indicate places with such peaceful, pleasant hotels and restaurants.

By consulting them before setting out and sending us your comments on your return you can help us with our enquiries.

Hotel facilities

In general the hotels we recommend have full bathroom and toilet facilities in each room. This may not be the case, however, for certain rooms in categories [house symbol] and [house symbol].

30 rm	*Number of rooms*
[lift symbol]	*Lift (elevator)*
[air conditioning symbol]	*Air conditioning*
TV	*Television in room*
[no smoking symbol]	*Establishment either partly or wholly reserved for non-smokers*
[modem symbol]	*Modem point in the bedrooms*
[wheelchair symbol]	*Rooms accessible to disabled people*
[children symbol]	*Special facilities for children*
[terrace symbol]	*Meals served in garden or on terrace*
[pool symbols]	*Outdoor or indoor swimming pool*
[exercise symbol] S	*Exercise room – Sauna*
[garden symbol]	*Garden*
[park symbol]	*Park*
[tennis symbol] 18	*Hotel tennis court – Golf course and number of holes*
[anchor symbol]	*Landing stage*
[fish symbol]	*Fishing available to hotel guests. A charge may be made*
[conference symbol] 150	*Equipped conference hall: maximum capacity*
[car symbol]	*Hotel garage (additional charge in most cases)*
P	*Car park for customers only*
[no dogs symbol]	*Dogs are excluded from all or part of the hotel*
Fax	*Telephone document transmission*
May-October	*Dates when open, as indicated by the hotelier*
season	*Probably open for the season – precise dates not available. Where no date or season is shown, establishments are open all year round.*
LL35 OSB	*Postal code*

Cuisine

Stars

Certain establishments deserve to be brought to your attention for the particularly fine quality of their cooking. ***Michelin stars*** *are awarded for the standard of meals served. For such restaurants we list three culinary specialities typical of their style of cooking to assist you in your choice.*

✿✿✿ **Exceptional cuisine, worth a special journey**

One always eats here extremely well, sometimes superbly. Fine wines, faultless service, elegant surroundings. One will pay accordingly!

✿✿ **Excellent cooking, worth a detour**

Specialities and wines of first class quality. This will be reflected in the price.

✿ **A very good restaurant in its category**

The star indicates a good place to stop on your journey. But beware of comparing the star given to an expensive « de luxe » establishment to that of a simple restaurant where you can appreciate fine cooking at a reasonable price.

The "Bib Gourmand"

Good food at moderate prices

You may also like to know of other restaurants with less elaborate, moderately priced menus that offer good value for money and serve carefully prepared meals.
We bring them to your attention by marking them with the **"Bib Gourmand"** ☺ *and* Meals *in the text of the Guide, e.g.* Meals 19.00/25.00.

Please refer to the map of star-rated restaurants ✿✿✿, ✿✿, ✿ and the **"Bib Gourmand"** ☺, *located at the beginning of each regional section in the guide.*

Prices

Prices quoted are valid for autumn 2001. Changes may arise if goods and service costs are revised. Hotels and restaurants in bold type have supplied details of all their rates and have assumed responsibility for maintaining them for all travellers in possession of this guide.

In some towns, when commercial or tourist events are taking place, the hotel rates are likely to be considerably higher.

Prices are given in £ sterling, except for the Republic of Ireland where euro are quoted. Where no mention s., t., *or* st. *is shown, prices may be subject to the addition of service charge, V.A.T., or both (V.A.T. does not apply in the Channel Islands).*

Your recommendation is self-evident if you always walk into a hotel guide in hand.

Meals

Meals 13.00/28.00	**Set meals**
	Lowest 13.00 *and highest* 28.00 prices for set meals – *including cover charge, where applicable*
Meals 19.00/25.00	*See page 7*
s.	*Service only included*
t.	*V.A.T. only included*
st.	*Service and V.A.T. included*
🍾 12.00	*Price of a bottle of house wine*
Meals a la carte	**A la carte meals**
20.00/35.00	*The prices represent the range of charges from a simple to an elaborate 3 course meal and include a cover charge where applicable*
	⌂: *Dinner in this category of establishment will generally be offered from a fixed price menu of limited choice, served at a set time to residents only. Lunch is rarely offered. Many will not be licensed to sell alcohol.*

Rooms

rm 50.00/90.00	*Lowest price* 50.00, *per room for a comfortable single and highest price* 90.00 *per room for the best double or twin*
suites	*Check with the hotelier for prices*
rm ☕ 55.00/85.00	*Full cooked breakfast (whether taken or not) is included in the price of the room*
☕ 6.00	*Price of breakfast*

Short breaks (SB)

Many hotels offer a special rate for a stay of two or more nights which comprises dinner, room and breakfast usually for a minimum of two people. Please enquire at hotel for rates.

Alcoholic beverages-conditions of sale

The sale of alcoholic drinks is governed in Great Britain and Ireland by licensing laws which vary greatly from country to country.

Allowing for local variations, restaurants may stay open and serve alcohol with a bona fide meal during the afternoon. Hotel bars and public houses are generally open between 11am and 11pm at the discretion of the licensee. Hotel residents, however, may buy drinks outside the permitted hours at the discretion of the hotelier.

Children under the age of 14 are not allowed in bars.

Deposits

Some hotels will require a deposit, which confirms the commitment of customer and hotelier alike. Make sure the terms of the agreement are clear.

Credit cards

Credits cards accepted by the establishment: MasterCard (Eurocard) – American Express – Diners Club – Visa – Japan Credit Bureau

Towns

✉ York	*Postal address*
401 M 27, ⑩	*Michelin map and co-ordinates or fold*
West Country G.	*See the Michelin Green Guide The West Country of England*
pop. 1057	*Population. (Crown copyright 1991. Published by permission of the Controller of Her Majesty's Sationery Office.)*
BX A	*Letters giving the location of a place on the town plan*
18	*Golf course and number of holes (handicap sometimes required, telephone reservation strongly advised)*
	Panoramic view, viewpoint
	Airport
	Shipping line
	Passenger transport only
	Tourist Information Centre

Standard Time

In winter standard time throughout the British Isles is Greenwich Mean Time (G.M.T.). In summer British clocks are advanced by one hour to give British Summer Time (B.S.T.). The actual dates are announced annually but always occur over weekends in March and October.

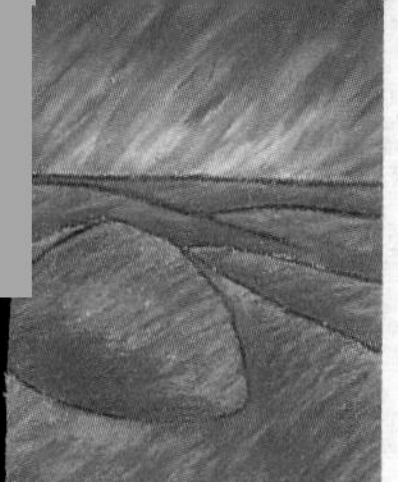

Sights

Star-rating

★★★	*Highly recommended*
★★	*Recommended*
★	*Interesting*
AC	*Admission charge*

Location

See	*Sights in town*
Envir.	*On the outskirts*
Exc.	*In the surrounding area*
N, S, E, W	*The sight lies north, south, east or west of the town*
A 22	*Take road A 22, indicated by the same symbol on the Guide map*
2 m.	*Mileage*

Local maps

May we suggest that you consult them

Should you be looking for a hotel or restaurant not too far from Leeds, for example, you can now consult the map along with the town plan.
The local map (opposite) draws your attention to all places around the town or city selected, provided they are mentioned in the Guide.
Places located within a range of 25 km/16 miles are clearly identified by the use of a different coloured background.
The various facilities recommended near the different regional capitals can be located quickly and easily.

Note:

Entries in the Guide provide information on distances to nearby towns.
Whenever a place appears on one of the local maps, the name of the town or city to which it is attached is printed in BLUE.

Example:

ILKLEY is to be found on the local map LEEDS

IKLEY *W. Yorks.* 402 O 22 – pop. 13 530
Myddleton ℘ (01943) 607277
Station Rd, LS29 8HA ℘ (01943) 602319
London 210 – Bradford 13 – Harrogate 13 – Leeds 16 – Preston 46

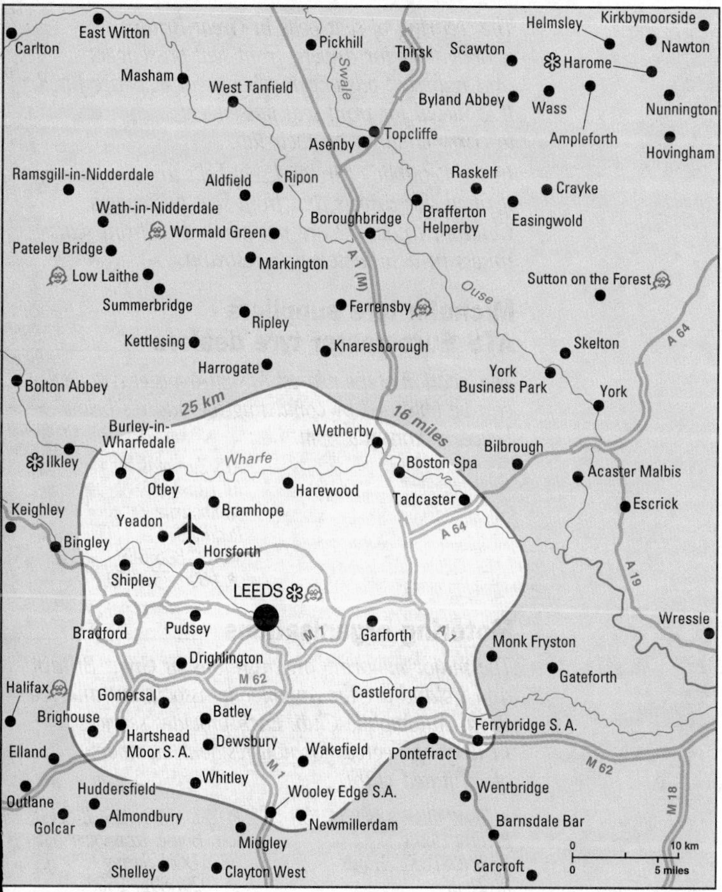

Carlton
East Witton
Masham
West Tanfield
Pickhill
Swale
Thirsk
Scawton
Helmsley
Kirkbymoorside
Nawton
Harome
Byland Abbey
Wass
Nunnington
Ampleforth
Hovingham
Topcliffe
Asenby
Ramsgill-in-Nidderdale
Aldfield
Ripon
Raskelf
Crayke
Wath-in-Nidderdale
Boroughbridge
Brafferton Helperby
Easingwold
Wormald Green
Pateley Bridge
Markington
A 1 (M)
Low Laithe
Summerbridge
Sutton on the Forest
Ouse
Ferrensby
Ripley
Kettlesing
Knaresborough
Skelton
A 64
Harrogate
York Business Park
York
Bolton Abbey
25 km
16 miles
Burley-in-Wharfedale
Wetherby
Bilbrough
Ilkley
Wharfe
Boston Spa
Acaster Malbis
Otley
Harewood
Tadcaster
Escrick
Keighley
Bramhope
Yeadon
A 64
Bingley
Horsforth
A 19
Shipley
LEEDS
Wressle
Bradford
Pudsey
M 1
Garforth
A 1
Monk Fryston
Drighlington
Gateforth
M 62
Halifax
Gomersal
Castleford
Batley
Brighouse
Ferrybridge S. A.
Hartshead Moor S. A.
Dewsbury
Elland
Wakefield
Pontefract
M 62
M 1
Whitley
Huddersfield
Wooley Edge S.A.
Wentbridge
M 18
Outlane
Almondbury
Newmillerdam
Golcar
Barnsdale Bar
Midgley
0
10 km
Carcroft
0
5 miles
Shelley
Clayton West

All the local maps are indicated on the thematic maps that precede each country

Car, tyres

The wearing of seat belts in Great Britain is obligatory for drivers, front seat passengers and rear seat passengers where seat belts are fitted. It is illegal for front seat passengers to carry children on their lap.

In the Republic of Ireland seat belts are compulsory, if fitted, for drivers and front seat passengers. Children under 12 are not allowed in front seats unless in a suitable safety restraint.

Michelin tyre suppliers
ATS Euromaster tyre dealers

The location of the nearest ATS Euromaster tyre dealer can be obtained by contacting the address below between 9am and 5pm.

ATS Euromaster
Jill Lane
Sambourne
Redditch
Worcs. B96 6ES
✆ 0800 750 850

Motoring organisations

The major motoring organisations in Great Britain and Ireland are the Automobile Association and the Royal Automobile Club. Each provides services in varying degrees for non-resident members of affiliated clubs.

AUTOMOBILE ASSOCIATION
Fanum House
BASINGSTOKE, Hants
RG21 2EA
✆ (08705) 448866

AUTOMOBILE ASSOCIATION
23 Suffolk Street
DUBLIN 2
✆ (01) 617 9950

ROYAL AUTOMOBILE CLUB
RAC House, Lansdowne Rd.
CROYDON, Surrey CR9 2JA
✆ (020) 8917 2500

ROYAL AUTOMOBILE CLUB
RAC IRELAND
New Mount House
22-24 Lower Mount St.
DUBLIN 2
✆ (01) 676 0113

Town plans

a ● a *Hotels – Restaurants*

Sights

Place of interest

Interesting place of worship

Roads

M 1 *Motorway*

4 4 *Junctions: complete, limited*

Dual carriageway with motorway characteristics

Main traffic artery

A 2 *Primary route (GB) and National route (IRL)*

One-way street – Unsuitable for traffic, street subject to restrictions

Pedestrian street – Tramway

Piccadilly P R *Shopping street – Car park – Park and Ride*

Gateway – Street passing under arch – Tunnel

15'5 *Low headroom (16'6" max.) on major through routes*

Station and railway

Funicular – Cable-car

B *Lever bridge – Car ferry*

Various signs

Tourist Information Centre

Church/Place of worship – Mosque – Synagogue

Communications tower or mast – Ruins

Garden, park, wood – Cemetery

9 *Stadium – Racecourse – Golf course*

Golf course (with restrictions for visitors) – Skating rink

Outdoor or indoor swimming pool

View – Panorama

Monument – Fountain – Hospital – Covered market

Pleasure boat harbour – Lighthouse

Airport – Underground station – Coach station

Ferry services:

- passengers and cars

Main post office

Public buildings located by letter:

C H J *County Council Offices – Town Hall – Law Courts*

M T U *Museum – Theatre – University, College*

POL. *Police (in large towns police headquarters)*

London

BRENT WEMBLEY *Borough – Area*

Borough boundary – Area boundary

Cette 29e édition du Guide Rouge Great-Britain & Ireland propose une sélection actualisée d'hôtels, maisons d'hôtes, restaurants et pubs. Elle est réalisée en toute indépendance par les Inspecteurs Michelin, des professionnels passionnés qui visitent les établissements, les testent dans un total anonymat et règlent leurs additions.

Les nombreuses informations, mises à jour avec le plus grand soin, seront complétées cette année par le symbole ⛹ qui signale des hôtels disposant d'équipements d'accueil particuliers pour les enfants.

Et pour accompagner le passage à la devise européenne en janvier 2002, les prix des établissements sélectionnés en République d'Irlande sont donnés en euros.

Un bon conseil : suivez le **"Bib Gourmand"** *. Il vous indiquera de nombreux restaurants où vous pourrez faire un repas soigné à prix modérés.*

Le Guide Rouge vit et progresse grâce à ses lecteurs. N'hésitez pas à nous écrire. Vous pouvez également nous faire part de vos commentaires à
theredguide-gbirl@uk.michelin.com
et consulter la sélection du Guide Rouge Great Britain & Ireland sur
www.ViaMichelin.co.uk

Sommaire

Le choix d'un hôtel, d'un restaurant

Ce guide vous propose une sélection d'hôtels et restaurants établie à l'usage de l'automobiliste de passage. Les établissements, classés selon leur confort, sont cités par ordre de préférence dans chaque catégorie.

Catégories

🏨🏨🏨🏨🏨	XXXXX	*Grand luxe et tradition*
🏨🏨🏨🏨	XXXX	*Grand confort*
🏨🏨🏨	XXX	*Très confortable*
🏨🏨	XX	*De bon confort*
🏨	X	*Assez confortable*
	🍺	*Traditionnel "pub" anglais servant des repas*
🏠		*Autres formes d'hébergement conseillées (Logis à la ferme, maison d'hôtes et cottages)*
without rest.		*L'hôtel n'a pas de restaurant*
	with rm	*Le restaurant possède des chambres*

Agrément et tranquillité

Certains établissements se distinguent dans le guide par les symboles rouges indiqués ci-après.
Le séjour dans ces hôtels se révèle particulièrement agréable ou reposant.
Cela peut tenir d'une part au caractère de l'édifice, au décor original, au site, à l'accueil et aux services qui sont proposés, d'autre part à la tranquillité des lieux.

🏨🏨🏨🏨🏨 à 🏨, 🏠	*Hôtels agréables*
XXXXX à X, 🍺	*Restaurants agréables*
« Park »	*Élément particulièrement agréable*
🐦 (rouge)	*Hôtel très tranquille ou isolé et tranquille*
🐦 (noir)	*Hôtel tranquille*
⋞ sea	*Vue exceptionnelle*
⋞	*Vue intéressante ou étendue*

Les localités possédant des établissements agréables ou tranquilles sont repérées sur les cartes au début de chacune des régions traitées dans ce guide. Consultez-les pour la préparation de vos voyages et donnez-nous vos appréciations à votre retour, vous faciliterez ainsi nos enquêtes.

L'installation

Les chambres des hôtels que nous recommandons possèdent, en général, des installations sanitaires complètes. Il est toutefois possible que dans les catégories 🏠 et ⌂, certaines chambres en soient dépourvues.

30 rm	*Nombre de chambres*
[symbole]	*Ascenseur*
[symbole]	*Air conditionné*
TV	*Télévision dans la chambre*
[symbole]	*Établissement entièrement ou en partie réservé aux non-fumeurs*
[symbole]	*Prise modem dans la chambre*
[symbole]	*Chambres accessibles aux handicapés physiques*
[symbole]	*Équipements d'accueil pour les enfants*
[symbole]	*Repas servis au jardin ou en terrasse*
[symbole] [symbole]	*Piscine : de plein air ou couverte*
[symbole] S	*Salle de remise en forme – Sauna*
[symbole]	*Jardin de repos*
[symbole]	*Parc*
[symbole] 18	*Tennis à l'hôtel – Golf et nombre de trous*
[symbole]	*Ponton d'amarrage*
[symbole]	*Pêche ouverte aux clients de l'hôtel (éventuellement payant)*
[symbole] 150	*Salles de conférences : capacité maximum*
[symbole]	*Garage dans l'hôtel (généralement payant)*
P	*Parking réservé à la clientèle*
[symbole]	*Accès interdit aux chiens (dans tout ou partie de l'établissement)*
Fax	*Transmission de documents par télécopie*
May-October	*Période d'ouverture, communiquée par l'hôtelier*
season	*Ouverture probable en saison mais dates non précisées. En l'absence de mention, l'établissement est ouvert toute l'année*
LL35 OSB	*Code postal de l'établissement*

La table

Les étoiles

Certains établissements méritent d'être signalés à votre attention pour la qualité de leur cuisine. Nous les distinguons par ***les étoiles de bonne table.*** *Nous indiquons, pour ces établissements, trois spécialités culinaires qui pourront orienter votre choix.*

✿✿✿ **Une des meilleures tables, vaut le voyage**

On y mange toujours très bien, parfois merveilleusement. Grands vins, service impeccable, cadre élégant... Prix en conséquence.

✿✿ **Table excellente, mérite un détour**

Spécialités et vins de choix... Attendez-vous à une dépense en rapport.

✿ **Une très bonne table dans sa catégorie**

L'étoile marque une bonne étape sur votre itinéraire. Mais ne comparez pas l'étoile d'un établissement de luxe à prix élevés avec celle d'une petite maison où, à prix raisonnables, on sert également une cuisine de qualité.

Le "Bib Gourmand"

Repas soignés à prix modérés

Vous souhaitez parfois trouver des tables plus simples, à prix modérés; c'est pourquoi nous avons sélectionné des restaurants proposant, pour un rapport qualité-prix particulièrement favorable, un repas soigné.

Ces restaurants sont signalés par le **"Bib Gourmand"** *et* Meals

Ex Meals 19.00/25.00.

Consultez les cartes des étoiles de bonne table ✿✿✿, ✿✿, ✿ *et des* **"Bib Gourmand"**, *placées au début de chacune des régions traitées dans ce guide.*

Les prix

Les prix que nous indiquons dans ce guide ont été établis en automne 2001. Ils sont susceptibles de modifications, notamment en cas de variations des prix des biens et services.

Dans certaines villes, à l'occasion de manisfestations commerciales ou touristiques, les prix demandés par les hôteliers risquent d'être considérablement majorés. Les prix sont indiqués en livres sterling (1 £ = 100 pence), sauf en République d'Irlande où ils sont donnés en euros. Lorsque les mentions **s., t.,** *ou* **st.** *ne figurent pas, les prix indiqués peuvent être majorés d'un pourcentage pour le service, la T.V.A., ou les deux (la T.V.A. n'est pas appliquée dans les Channel Islands). Les hôtels et restaurants figurent en gros caractères lorsque les hôteliers nous ont donné tous leurs prix et se sont engagés, sous leur propre responsabilité, à les appliquer aux touristes de passage porteurs de notre guide.*

Entrez à l'hôtel le guide à la main, vous montrerez ainsi qu'il vous conduit là en confiance.

Repas

Meals 13.00/28.00 — **Repas à prix fixe**
Minimum 13.00, *maximum* 28.00.
Ces prix s'entendent couvert compris

Meals 19.00/25.00 — *Voir page 21*

s. — *Service compris*

t. — *T.V.A. comprise*

st. — *Service et T.V.A. compris (prix nets)*

🍾 12.00 — *Prix pour une bouteille de vin de la maison*

Meals à la carte 20.00/35.00 — **Repas à la carte**
Le 1er prix correspond à un repas simple mais soigné, comprenant : petite entrée, plat du jour garni, dessert. Le 2e prix concerne un repas plus complet, comprenant : entrée, plat principal, fromage ou dessert. Ces prix s'entendent couvert compris.

⌂ : *Dans les établissements de cette catégorie, le dîner est servi à heure fixe exclusivement aux personnes ayant une chambre. Le menu, à prix unique, offre un choix limité de plats. Le déjeuner est rarement proposé. Beaucoup de ces établissements ne sont pas autorisés à vendre des boissons alcoolisées.*

Chambres

rm 50.00/90.00	*Prix minimum* 50.00 *d'une chambre pour une personne et prix maximum* 90.00 *de la plus belle chambre occupée par deux personnes*
suites	*Se renseigner auprès de l'hôtelier*
rm ☕ 55.00/85.00	*Le prix du petit déjeuner à l'anglaise est inclus dans le prix de la chambre, même s'il n'est pas consommé*
☕ 6.00	*Prix du petit déjeuner*

Short breaks (SB)

Certains hôtels proposent des conditions avantageuses ou «Short Break» pour un séjour minimum de 2 nuits. Ce forfait, calculé par personne, pour 2 personnes au minimum, comprend la chambre, le dîner et le petit déjeuner. Se renseigner auprès de l'hôtelier.

La vente de boissons alcoolisées

En Grande-Bretagne et en Irlande, la vente de boissons alcoolisées est soumise à des lois pouvant varier d'une région à l'autre. D'une façon générale, les restaurants peuvent demeurer ouverts l'après-midi et servir des boissons alcoolisées dans la mesure où elles accompagnent un repas suffisamment consistant. Les bars d'hôtel et les pubs sont habituellement ouverts de 11 heures à 23 heures. Néanmoins, l'hôtelier a toujours la possibilité de servir, à sa clientèle, des boissons alcoolisées en dehors des heures légales. Les enfants au-dessous de 14 ans n'ont pas accès aux bars.

Les arrhes

Certains hôteliers demandent le versement d'arrhes. Il s'agit d'un dépôt-garantie qui engage l'hôtelier comme le client. Bien faire préciser les dispositions de cette garantie.

Cartes de crédit

Cartes de crédit acceptées par l'établissement : MasterCard (Eurocard) – American Express – Diners Club – Visa – Japan Credit Bureau

Les villes

✉ York	*Bureau de poste desservant la localité*
401 M 27, ⑩	*Numéro des cartes Michelin et carroyage ou numéro du pli*
West Country G.	*Voir le guide vert Michelin The West Country of England*
pop. 1057	*Population*
BX A	*Lettres repérant un emplacement sur le plan*
⛳18	*Golf et nombre de trous (Handicap parfois demandé, réservation par téléphone vivement recommandée)*
✳ ⩤	*Panorama, point de vue*
✈	*Aéroport*
⛴	*Transports maritimes*
⛴	*Transports maritimes (pour passagers seulement)*
ℹ	*Information touristique*

Heure légale

Les visiteurs devront tenir compte de l'heure officielle. En Grande-Bretagne : une heure de retard sur l'heure française.

Les curiosités

Intérêt

★★★	*Vaut le voyage*
★★	*Mérite un détour*
★	*Intéressant*
AC	*Entrée payante*

Situation

See	*Dans la ville*
Envir.	*Aux environs de la ville*
Exc.	*Excursions dans la région*
N, S, E, W	*La curiosité est située :* *au Nord, au Sud, à l'Est, à l'Ouest*
A 22	*On s'y rend par la route A 22,* *repérée par le même signe sur le plan du Guide*
2 m.	*Distance en miles*

Les cartes de voisinage

Avez-vous pensé à les consulter ?

Vous souhaitez trouver une bonne adresse, par exemple, aux environs de Leeds ? Consultez la carte qui accompagne le plan de la ville.

La « carte de voisinage » (ci-contre) attire votre attention sur toutes les localités citées au Guide autour de la ville choisie, et particulièrement celles situées dans un rayon de 25 km/16 miles (limite de couleur).

Les « cartes de voisinage » vous permettent ainsi le repérage rapide de toutes les ressources proposées par le Guide autour des métropoles régionales.

Nota :

Lorsqu'une localité est présente sur une « carte de voisinage », sa métropole de rattachement est imprimée en BLEU sur la ligne des distances de ville à ville.

Example:

Vous trouverez ILKLEY sur la carte de voisinage LEEDS

ILKLEY *W. Yorks.* 402 O 22 – pop. 13 530
18 *Myddleton ☎ (01943) 607277*
Station Rd, LS29 8HA ☎ (01943) 602319
London 210 – Bradford 13 – Harrogate 13 – Leeds 16 – Preston 46

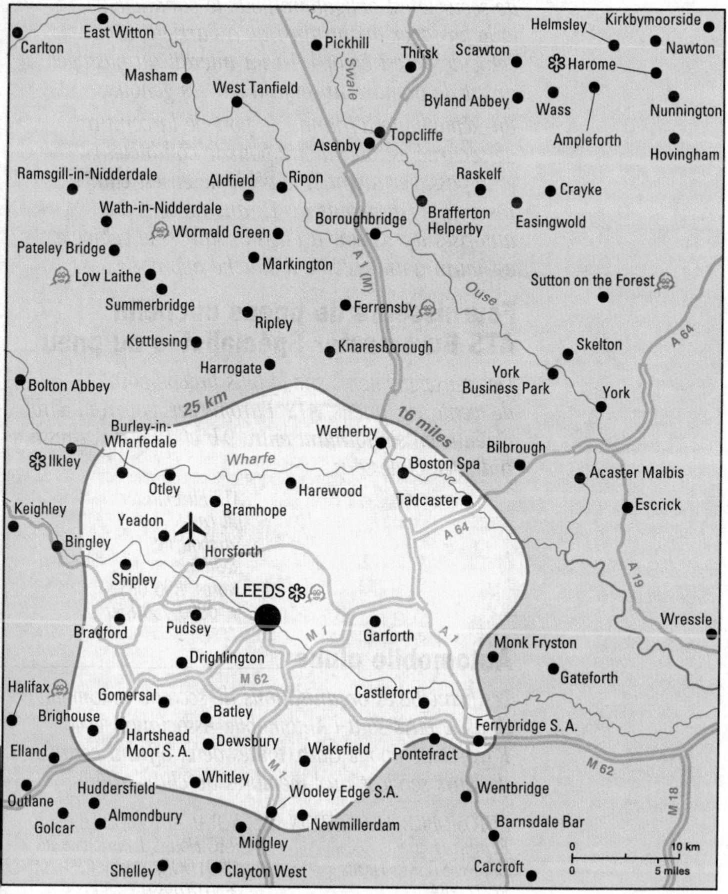

Toutes les «Cartes de voisinage» sont localisées sur la carte thématique située au début des pages de chaque pays

La voiture, les pneus

En Grande-Bretagne, le port de la ceinture de sécurité est obligatoire pour le conducteur et le passager avant ainsi qu'à l'arrière, si le véhicule en est équipé. La loi interdit au passager avant de prendre un enfant sur ses genoux.

En République d'Irlande, le port de la ceinture de sécurité est obligatoire pour le conducteur et le passager avant si le véhicule en est équipé. Les enfants de moins de 12 ans ne sont pas autorisés à s'asseoir à l'avant, sauf si le véhicule est muni d'un système d'attache approprié.

Fournisseurs de pneus michelin ATS Euromaster Spécialistes du pneu

Des renseignements sur le plus proche point de vente de pneus ATS Euromaster pourront être obtenus en s'informant entre 9 h et 17 h à l'adresse indiquée ci-dessous.

ATS Euromaster
Jill Lane
Sambourne
Redditch
Worcs. B96 6ES
✆ 0800 750 850

Automobile clubs

Les principales organisations de secours automobile dans le pays sont l'Automobile Association et le Royal Automobile Club, toutes deux offrant certains de leurs services aux membres de clubs affiliés.

AUTOMOBILE ASSOCIATION
Fanum House
BASINGSTOKE, Hants
RG21 2EA
✆ (08705) 448866

AUTOMOBILE ASSOCIATION
23 Suffolk Street
DUBLIN 2
✆ (01) 617 9950

ROYAL AUTOMOBILE CLUB
RAC House, Lansdowne Rd.
CROYDON, Surrey CR9 2JA
✆ (020) 8917 2500

ROYAL AUTOMOBILE CLUB
RAC IRELAND New Mount House
22-24 Lower Mount St.
DUBLIN 2
✆ (01) 676 0113

Les plans

ⓐ ● a	*Hôtels – Restaurants*

Curiosités

Bâtiment intéressant
Édifice religieux intéressant

Voirie

M 1	*Autoroute*
❹ ④	*- échangeurs : complet, partiel*
	Route à chaussées séparées de type autoroutier
	Grand axe de circulation
A 2	*Itinéraire principal (Primary route : GB) (National route : IRL)*
	Sens unique – Rue impraticable, réglementée
	Rue piétonne – Tramway
Piccadilly P	*Rue commerçante – Parking – Parking Relais*
	Porte – Passage sous voûte – Tunnel
15'5	*Passage bas (inférieur à 16'6") sur les grandes voies de circulation*
	Gare et voie ferrée
	Funiculaire – Téléphérique, télécabine
B	*Pont mobile – Bac pour autos*

Signes divers

	Information touristique
	Église/édifice religieux – Mosquée – Synagogue
	Tour ou pylône de télécommunication – Ruines
	Jardin, parc, bois – Cimetière
9	*Stade – Hippodrome – Golf – Patinoire*
	Golf (réservé)
	Piscine de plein air, couverte
	Vue – Panorama
	Monument – Fontaine – Hôpital – Marché couvert
	Port de plaisance – Phare
	Aéroport – Station de métro – Gare routière
	Transport par bateau :
	- passagers et voitures
	Bureau principal
	Bâtiment public repéré par une lettre :
C H	*- Bureau de l'Administration du Comté – Hôtel de ville*
M T U	*- Musée – Théâtre – Université, grande école*
POL. J	*- Police (commissariat central) – Palais de Justice*

Londres

BRENT WEMBLEY	*Nom d'arrondissement (borough) – de quartier (area)*
	Limite de « borough » – d'« area »

Questa 29ª edizione della Guida Rossa Gran Bretagne & Irlanda propone una selezione aggiornata di alberghi, B&B, ristoranti e pubs. E' realizzata in assoluta autonomia di giudizio dagli ispettori Michelin, persone competenti che visitano gli esercizi, li provano in totale anonimato e pagano sempre i loro conti.

Le numerose informazioni, aggiornate con cura, sono arricchite quest'anno dal simbolo 🚸 che segnala gli alberghi che dispongono di strutture specifiche di accoglienza per i bambini.

E per salutare l'introduzione della moneta unica europea nel gennaio 2002, i prezzi degli esercizi selezionati per la Repubblica d'Irlanda sono indicati in euro.

Un buon consiglio: seguito il **"Bib Gourmand"** ☺. *Vi indicherà numerosi ristoranti dove troverete pasti accurati a un prezzo contenuto.*

La Guida Rossa vive e si evolve grazie ai suoi Lettoi. Non esitate a scriverci, oggi anche via internet, presso l'indirizzo ***theredguide-gbirl@uk.michelin.com*** *o consultare l'intera selezione della Guida Rossa Gran Bretagna & Irlanda sul sito* ***www.Viamichelin.co.uk***

Sommario

La scelta di un albergo, di un ristorante

Questa guida propone una selezione di alberghi e ristoranti per orientare la scelta dell'automobilista. Gli esercizi, classificati in base al confort che offrono, vengono citati in ordine di preferenza per ogni categoria.

Categorie

	XXXXX	*Gran lusso e tradizione*
	XXXX	*Gran confort*
	XXX	*Molto confortevole*
	XX	*Di buon confort*
	X	*Abbastanza confortevole*
		Pub tradizionali con cucina
		Altra forme di alloggio consigliate (Pensioni, Fattorie e Case private)
without rest.		*L'albergo non ha ristorante*
	with rm	*Il ristorante dispone di camere*

Amenità e tranquillità

Alcuni esercizi sono evidenziati nella guida dai simboli rossi indicati qui di seguito. Il soggiorno in questi alberghi si rivela particolarmente ameno o riposante.

Ciò può dipendere sia dalle caratteristiche dell'edificio, dalle decorazioni non comuni, dalla sua posizione e dal servizio offerto, sia dalla tranquillità dei luoghi.

a ,	*Alberghi ameni*
XXXXX a X,	*Ristoranti ameni*
« Park »	*Un particolare piacevole*
	Albergo molto tranquillo o isolato e tranquillo
	Albergo tranquillo
≤ sea	*Vista eccezionale*
≤	*Vista interessante o estesa*

Le località che possiedono degli esercizi ameni o tranquilli sono riportate sulle carte che precedono ciascuna delle regioni trattate nella guida.

Consultatele per la preparazione dei vostri viaggi e, al ritorno, inviateci i vostri pareri; in tal modo agevolerete le nostre inchieste.

Installazioni

Le camere degli alberghi che raccomandiamo possiedono, generalmente, delle installazioni sanitarie complete. È possibile tuttavia che nelle categorie e alcune camere ne siano sprovviste.

30 rm	*Numero di camere*
	Ascensore
	Aria condizionata
	Televisione in camera
	Esercizio riservato completamente o in parte ai non fumatori
	Presa modem in camera
	Attrezzaturaper accoglienza e ricreazione dei bambini
	Camere di agevole accesso per portatori di handicap
	Pasti serviti in giardino o in terrazza
	Piscina: all'aperto, coperta
	Palestra – Sauna
	Giardino
	Parco
18	*Tennis appatenente all'albergo – Golf e numero di buche*
	Pontile d'ormeggio
	Pesca aperta ai clienti dell'albergo (eventualmente a pagamento)
150	*Sale per conferenze: capienza massima*
	Garage nell'albergo (generalmente a pagamento)
P	*Parcheggio riservato alla clientela*
	Accesso vietato ai cani (in tutto o in parte dell'esercizio
Fax	*Trasmissione telefonica di documenti*
May-October	*Periodo di apertura, comunicato dall'albergatore*
season	*Probabile apertura in stagione, ma periodo non precisato. Gli esercizi senza tali menzioni sono aperti tutto l'anno.*
LL35 OSB	*Codice postale dell'esercizio*

La tavola

Le stelle

*Alcuni esercizi meritano di essere segnalati alla vostra attenzione per la qualità particolare della loro cucina; li abbiamo evidenziati con le «**stelle di ottima tavola**».*
Per ognuno di questi ristoranti indichiamo tre specialità culinarie e alcuni vini locali che potranno aiutarvi nella scelta.

✿✿✿ **Una delle migliori tavole, vale il viaggio**

Vi si mangia sempre molto bene, a volte meravigliosamente. Grandi vini, servizio impeccabile, ambientazione accurata... Prezzi conformi.

✿✿ **Tavola eccellente, merita una deviazione**

Specialità e vini scelti...
Aspettatevi una spesa in proporzione.

✿ **Un'ottima tavola nella sua categoria**

La stella indica una tappa gastronomica sul Vostro itinerario.
Non mettete però a confronto la stella di un esercizio di lusso, dai prezzi elevati, con quella di un piccolo esercizio dove, a prezzi ragionevoli, viene offerta una cucina di qualità.

Il "Bib Gourmand"

Pasti accurati a prezzi contenuti

Per quando desiderate trovare delle tavole più semplici a prezzi contenuti abbiamo selezionato dei ristoranti che, per un rapporto qualità-prezzo particolarmente favorevole, offrono un pasto accurato.
Questi ristoranti sono evidenziali nel testo con il **"Bib Gourmand"** *e* Meals*, evidenziata in rosso, davanti ai prezzi.*
Ex. Meals 19.00/25.00.

Consultate le carte delle stelle ✿✿✿, ✿✿, ✿ e con il **"Bib Gourmand"**, *che precedono ciascuna delle regioni trattate nella guida.*

I prezzi

I prezzi che indichiamo in questa guida sono stati stabiliti nel l'autunno 2001 e potranno pertanto subire delle variazioni in relazione ai cambiamenti dei prezzi di beni e servizi.
Gli alberghi e i ristoranti vengono menzionati in carattere grassetto quando gli albergatori ci hanno comunicato tutti i loro prezzi e si sono impegnati, sotto la propria responsabilità, ad applicarli ai turisti di passaggio, in possesso della nostra guida.
In alcune città, in occasione di manifestazioni turistiche o commerciali, i prezzi richiesti dagli albergatori potrebbero risultare considerevolmente più alti. I prezzi sono indicati in lire sterline (1 £ = 100 pence) ad eccezione per la Repubblica d'Irlanda dove sono indicati in euro.
Quando non figurano le lettere s., t., *o* st. *i prezzi indicati possono essere maggiorati per il servizio o per l'I.V.A. o per entrambi. (L'I.V.A. non viene applicata nelle Channel Islands).*
Entrate nell'albergo o nel ristorante con la guida in mano, dimostrando in tal modo la fiducia in chi vi ha indirizzato.

Pasti

Meals 13.00/28.00	**Prezzo fisso** *Prezzo minimo* 13.00, *e massimo* 28.00. *Questi prezzi comprendono il coperto*
Meals 19.00/25.00	*Vedere p. 35*
s.	*Servizio compreso*
t.	*I.V.A. compresa*
st.	*Servizio ed I.V.A. compresi (prezzi netti)*
🍾 12.00	*Prezzo di una bottiglia del vino della casa*
Meals a la carte 20.00/35.00	**Alla carta** *Il 1° prezzo corrisponde ad un pasto semplice comprendente: primo piatto, piatto del giorno con contorno, dessert.* *Il 2° prezzo corrisponde ad un pasto più completo comprendente: antipasto, piatto principale, formaggio e dessert* *Questi prezzi comprendono il coperto*

⌂: *Negli alberghi di questa categoria, la cena viene servita, ad un'ora stabilita, esclusivamente a chi vi allogia. Il menu, a prezzo fisso, offre una scelta limitata di piatti. Raramente viene servito anche il pranzo. Molti di questi esercizi non hanno l'autorizzazione a vendere alcolici.*

Camere

rm 50.00/90.00	*Prezzo minimo* 50.00, *per una camera singola e prezzo massimo* 90.00 *per la camera più bella per due persone*
suites	*Informarsi presso l'albergatore*
rm ☕ 55.00/85.00	*Il prezzo della prima colazione inglese è compreso nel prezzo della camera anche se non viene consumata*
☕ 6.00	*Prezzo della prima colazione*

«Short Breaks» (SB.)

Alcuni alberghi propongono delle condizioni particolarmente vantaggiose o short break per un soggiorno minimo di due notti. Questo prezzo, calcolato per persona e per un minimo di due persone, comprende: camera, cena e prima colazione. Informarsi presso l'albergatore.

La vendita di bevande alcoliche

La vendita di bevande alcoliche in Gran Bretagna è regolata da leggi che variano considerevolmente da regione a regione. Eccezion fatta per varianti locali, i ristoranti possono rimanere aperti o servire bevande alcoliche con i pasti il pomeriggio. I bar degli hotel e i pub sono generalmente aperti dalle 11 alle 23, a discrezione del gestore. I clienti dell'hotel, comunque, possono acquistare bevande al di fuori delle ore stabilite se il direttore lo permette. Il bambini al di sotto del 14 anni non possono entrare nei bar.

La caparra

Alcuni albergatori chiedono il versamento di una caparra. Si tratta di un deposito-garanzia che impegna tanto l'albergatore che il cliente. Vi consigliamo di farvi precisare le norme riguardanti la reciproca garanzia di tale caparra.

Carte di credito

MC AE DC VISA JCB	*Carte di credito accettate dall'esercizio MasterCard (Eurocard) – American Express – Diners Club – Visa – Japan Credit Bureau*

Le città

✉ *York*	*Sede dell'ufficio postale*
401 M 27, ⑩	*Numero della carta Michelin e del riquadro o numero della piega*
West Country G.	*Vedere la Guida Verde Michelin The West Country of England*
pop. 1057	*Popolazione*
BX **A**	*Lettere indicanti l'ubicazione sulla pianta*
18	*Golf e numero di buche (handicap generalmente richiesto, prenotazione telefonica vivamente consigliata)*
✻ ⩤	*Panorama, vista*
✈	*Aeroporto*
⛴	*Trasporti marittimi*
⛴	*Trasporti marittimi (solo passeggeri)*
🛈	*Ufficio informazioni turistiche*

Ora legale

I visitatori dovranno tenere in considerazione l'ora ufficiale in Gran Bretagna: un'ora di ritardo sull'ora italiana.

Luoghi d'interesse

Grado di interesse

★★★	*Vale il viaggio*
★★	*Merita una deviazione*
★	*Interessante*
AC	*Entrata a pagamento*

Ubicazione

See	*Nella città*
Envir.	*Nei dintorni della città*
Exc.	*Nella regione*
N, S, E, W	*Il luogo si trova : a Nord, a Sud, a Est a Ovest*
A 22	*Ci si va per la strada A 22 indicata con lo stesso segno sulla pianta*
2 m.	*Distanza in miglia*

Le carte dei dintorni

Sapete come usarle?

Se desiderate, per esempio, trovare un buon indirizzo nei dintorni di Leeds, la « carta dei dintorni » (qui accanto) richiama la vostra attenzione su tutte le località citate nella Guida che si trovino nei dintorni della città prescelta, e in particolare su quelle raggiungibili nel raggio di 25 km/16 miles (limite di colore). Le « carte dei dintorni » coprono l'intero territorio e permettono la localizzazione rapida di tutte le risorse proposte dalla Guida nei dintorni delle metropoli regionali.

Nota:

Quando una località è presente su una « carta dei dintorni », la città a cui ci si riferisce è scritta in BLU nella linea delle distanze da città a città.

Esempio:

Troverete ILKLEY sulla carta dei dintorni di LEEDS

IKLEY *W. Yorks.* 402 O 22 – pop. 13 530
18 *Myddleton* ☎ *(01943) 607277*
☐ *Station Rd, LS29 8HA* ☎ *(01943) 602319*
London 210 – Bradford 13 – Harrogate 13 – Leeds 16 – Preston 46

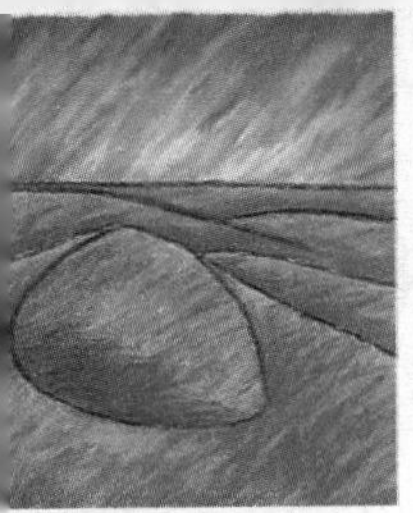

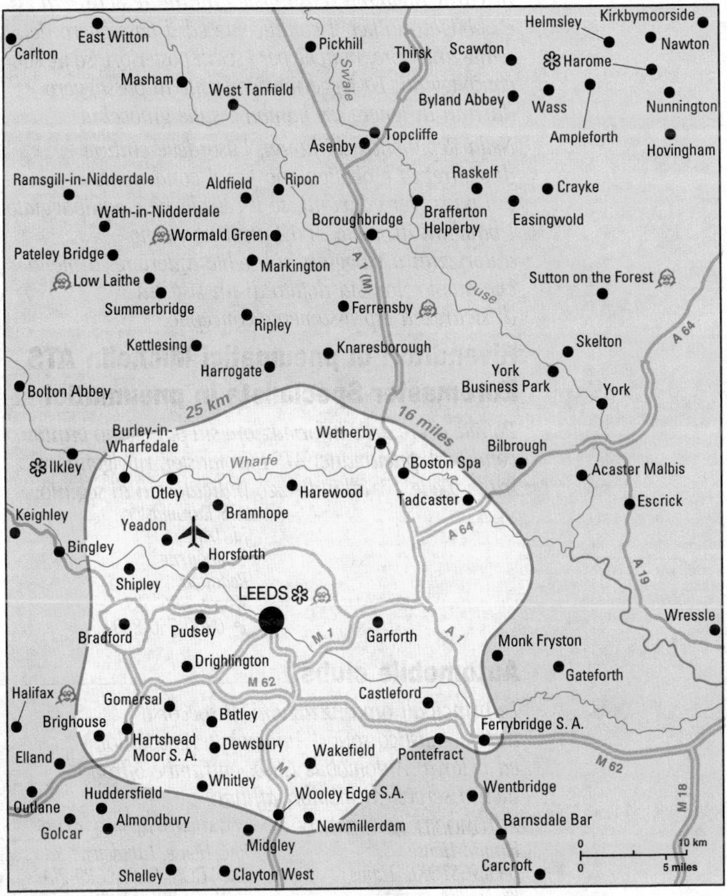

Carlton
East Witton
Masham
West Tanfield
Pickhill
Swale
Thirsk
Scawton
Helmsley
Kirkbymoorside
Nawton
Harome
Byland Abbey
Wass
Nunnington
Ampleforth
Hovingham
Asenby
Topcliffe
Ramsgill-in-Nidderdale
Aldfield
Ripon
Raskelf
Crayke
Wath-in-Nidderdale
Boroughbridge
Brafferton Helperby
Easingwold
Wormald Green
Pateley Bridge
Markington
A 1 (M)
Low Laithe
Sutton on the Forest
Ouse
Summerbridge
Ripley
Ferrensby
Kettlesing
Knaresborough
Skelton
A 64
Harrogate
York Business Park
York
Bolton Abbey
25 km
16 miles
Burley-in-Wharfedale
Wetherby
Bilbrough
Ilkley
Wharfe
Boston Spa
Acaster Malbis
Otley
Harewood
Tadcaster
Escrick
Keighley
Bramhope
Yeadon
A 64
Bingley
Horsforth
A 19
Shipley
LEEDS
Wressle
Bradford
Pudsey
M 1
Garforth
A 1
Monk Fryston
Drighlington
Gateforth
M 62
Halifax
Gomersal
Castleford
Batley
Brighouse
Hartshead Moor S. A.
Ferrybridge S. A.
Dewsbury
Elland
Wakefield
Pontefract
M 62
M 1
Whitley
Wentbridge
Outlane
Huddersfield
Wooley Edge S.A.
M 18
Almondbury
Newmillerdam
Barnsdale Bar
Golcar
Midgley
0
10 km
0
5 miles
Carcroft
Shelley
Clayton West

Tutte le «carte dei dintorni» sono indicate sulle carte tematiche che precedono ogni paese

L'automobile, I pneumatici

In Gran Bretagna, l'uso delle cinture di sicurezza è obbligatorio per il conducente ed il passeggero del sedile anteriore, nonchè per i sedili posteriori, se ne sono equipaggiati. La legge non consente al passaggero davanti di tenere un bambino sulle ginocchia.

Nella Repubblica d'Irlanda, l'uso delle cinture di sicurezza è obbligatorio per il conducente e il passeggero davanti, se il veicolo ne è equipaggiato. I bambini di meno di 12 anni non sono autorizzati a viaggiare sul sedile anteriore, a meno che questo non sia dotato di un sistema di sicurezza esprassamente concepito.

Rivenditori di pneumatici Michelin ATS Euromaster Specialista in pneumatici

Potrete avere delle informazioni sul piú vicino punto vendita di pneumatici ATS Euromaster, rivolgendovi, tra le 9 e le 17, all'indirizzo indicato qui di seguito:

ATS Euromaster
Jill Lane
Sambourne
Redditch
Worcs. B96 6ES
☎ 0800 750 850

Automobile clubs

Le principali organizzazioni di soccorso automobilistico sono l'Automobile Association ed il Royal Automobile Club: entrambe offrono alcuni servizi ai membri affiliati.

AUTOMOBILE ASSOCIATION
Fanum House
BASINGSTOKE, Hants
RG21 2EA
☎ (08705) 448866

AUTOMOBILE ASSOCIATION
23 Suffolk Street
DUBLIN 2
☎ (01) 617 9950

ROYAL AUTOMOBILE CLUB
RAC House, Lansdowne Rd.
CROYDON, Surrey CR9 2JA
☎ (020) 8917 2500

ROYAL AUTOMOBILE CLUB
RAC IRELAND
New Mount House
22-24 Lower Mount St.
DUBLIN 2
☎ (01) 676 0113

Le piante

@ ● a *Alberghi – Ristoranti*

Curiosità

Edificio interessante

Costruzione religiosa interessante

Viabilità

M 1 *Autostrada*

4 4 *- svincoli: completo, parziale*

Strada a carreggiate separate di tipo autostradale

Asse principale di circolazione

A 2 *Itinerario principale (Primary route : GB) (National Route : IRL)*

Senso unico – Via impraticable, a circolazione regolamentata

Via pedonale – Tranvia

.Piccadilly P R *Via commerciale – Parcheggio – Parcheggio Ristoro*

Porta – Sottopassaggio – Galleria

15'5 *Sottopassaggio (altezza inferiore a 16'6") sulle grandi vie di circolazione*

Stazione e ferrovia

Funicolare – Funivia, Cabinovia

B *Ponte mobile – Traghetto per auto*

Simboli vari

Ufficio informazioni turistiche

Chiesa/edificio religioso – Moschea – Sinagoga

Torre o pilone per telecomunicazioni – Ruderi

Giardino, parco, bosco – Cimitero

Stadio – Ippodromo – Golf – Pattinaggio

Golf riservato

Piscina all'aperto, coperta

Vista – Panorama

Monumento – Fontana – Ospedale – Mercato coperto

Porto per imbarcazioni da diporto – Faro

Aeroporto – Stazione della Metropolitana – Autostazione

Trasporto con traghetto:
- passeggeri ed autovetture

Ufficio centrale

Edificio pubblico indicato con lettera:

C H *- Sede dell'Amministrazione di Contea – Municipio*

M T U *- Museo – Teatro – Università, grande scuola*

POL. J *- Polizia (Questura, nelle grandi città) – Palazzo di Giustizia*

Londra

BRENT WEMBLEY *Nome del distretto amministrativo (borough) – del quartiere (area)*

Limite del « borough » – di « area »

Die 29. Ausgabe des Guide Rouge Great-Britain & Ireland empfiehlt Ihnen eine aktualisierte Auswahl an Hotels, Gästehäusern, Restaurants und Pubs. Sie wurde von unseren Inspektoren in völliger Unabhängigkeit erstellt. Sachkundige Fachleute, welche die Häuser anonym besuchen, testen und Ihre Rechnung selbst begleichen.

In diesem Jahr haben wir das Symbol ⚲ *zur Vervollständigung unserer reichhaltigen Informationen neu hinzugefügt. Das bedeutetdie Betriebe mit diesem Symbol bieten spezielle Einrichtungen und Angebote für Kinder.*

Zum Übergang auf die Europäische Währung im Januar 2002 wurden die Preise der empfohlenen Betriebe in der Republik Irland in Euros angegeben.

Eine gute Empfehlung: folgen Sie dem **"Bib Gourmand"** ☺. *Er führt Sie zu zahlreichen Restaurants in welchen man Ihnen eine sorgfältig zubereitete Mahlzeit zu günstigen Preisen serviert.*

Der Guide Rouge lebt und entwickelt sich mit Ihrer Hilfe weiter, zögern Sie nicht uns Ihre Hinweise zu schicken. Sie erreichen den Roten Michelin-Führer auch unter seiner E-Mail:
theredguide-gbirl@uk.michelin.com
Die Auswahl des Guide Rouge Great-Britain & Ireland finden Sie auch im Internet unter
www.ViaMichelin.co.uk

Inhaltsverzeichnis

Wahl eines Hotels, eines Restaurants

Die Auswahl der in diesem Führer aufgeführten Hotels und Restaurants ist für Durchreisende gedacht. In jeder Kategorie drückt die Reihenfolge der Betriebe (sie sind nach ihrem Komfort klassifiziert) eine weitere Rangordnung aus.

Kategorien

🏨🏨🏨🏨🏨	XXXXX	*Großer Luxus und Tradition*
🏨🏨🏨🏨	XXXX	*Großer Komfort*
🏨🏨🏨	XXX	*Sehr komfortabel*
🏨🏨	XX	*Mit gutem Komfort*
🏨	X	*Mit standard Komfort*
	🍺	*Traditionelle Pubs die Speisen anbieten*
⌂		*Andere empfohlene Übernachtungsmöglichkeiten (Gästehäuser, Bauernhäuser und Private Übernachtungsmöglichkeiten) und Pensionen*
without rest.		*Hotel ohne restaurant*
	with rm	*Restaurant vermietet auch Zimmer*

Annehmlichkeiten

Manche Häuser sind im Führer durch rote Symbole gekennzeichnet (s. unten). Der Aufenthalt in diesen ist wegen der schönen, ruhigen Lage, der nicht alltäglichen Einrichtung und Atmosphäre sowie dem gebotenen Service besonders angenehm und erholsam.

🏨🏨🏨🏨🏨 bis 🏨, ⌂	*Angenehme Hotels*
XXXXX bis X, 🍺	*Angenehme Restaurants*
« Park »	*Besondere Annehmlichkeit*
🐎	*Sehr ruhiges, oder abgelegenes und ruhiges Hotel*
🐎	*Ruhiges Hotel*
⋞ sea	*Reizvolle Aussicht*
⋞	*Interessante oder weite Sicht*

Die den einzelnen Regionen vorangestellten Übersichtskarten, auf denen die Orte mit besonders angenehmen oder ruhigen Häusern eingezeichnet sind, helfen Ihnen bei der Reisevorbereitung. Teilen Sie uns bitte nach der Reise Ihre Erfahrungen und Meinungen mit. Sie helfen uns damit, den Führer weiter zu verbessern.

Einrichtung

Die meisten der empfohlenen Hotels verfügen über Zimmer, die alle oder doch zum größten Teil mit einer Naßzelle ausgestattet sind. In den Häusern der Kategorien und kann diese jedoch in einigen Zimmern fehlen.

30 rm	*Anzahl der Zimmer*
	Fahrstuhl
	Klimaanlage
TV	*Fernsehen im Zimmer*
	Hotel ganz oder teilweise reserviert für Nichtraucher
	Modemanschluß im Zimmer
	Für Körperbehinderte leicht zugängliche Zimmer
	Spezielle Einrichtungen/Angebote für Kinder
	Garten-, Terrassenrestaurant
	Freibad, Hallenbad
	Fitneßraum – Sauna
	Liegewiese, Garten
	Park
18	*Hoteleigener Tennisplatz – Golfplatz und Lochzahl*
	Bootssteg
	Angelmöglichkeit für Hotelgäste, evtl. gegen Gebühr
150	*Konferenzräume: Höchstkapazität*
	Hotelgarage (wird gewöhnlich berechnet)
P	*Parkplatz reserviert für Gäste*
	Hunde sind unerwünscht (im ganzen Haus bzw. in den Zimmern oder im Restaurant)
Fax	*Telefonische Dokumentenübermittlung*
May-October	*Öffnungszeit, vom Hotelier mitgeteilt*
season	*Unbestimmte Öffnungszeit eines Saisonhotels. Die Häuser, für die wir keine Schließungszeiten angeben, sind im allgemeinen ganzjährig geöffnet*
LL35 OSB	*Angabe des Postbezirks (hinter der Hoteladresse)*

Küche

Die Sterne

Einige Häuser verdienen wegen ihrer überdurchschnittlich guten Küche Ihre besondere Beachtung. Auf diese Häuser weisen die Sterne hin.

Bei den mit «Stern» ausgezeichneten Betrieben nennen wir drei kulinarische Spezialitäten, die Sie probieren sollten.

✿✿✿ **Eine der besten Küchen : eine Reise wert**

Mar ißt hier immer sehr gut, öfters auch hervorragend, edle Weine, tadelloser Service, gepflegte Atmosphäre... entsprechende Preise.

✿✿ **Eine hervorragende Küche : verdient einen Umweg**

Ausgesuchte Menus und Weine... angemessene Preise.

✿ **Eine sehr gute Küche : verdient Ihre besondere Beachtung**

Der Stern bedeutet eine angenehme Unterbrechung Ihrer Reise.

Vergleichen Sie aber bitte nicht den Stern eines sehr teuren Luxusrestaurants mit dem Stern eines kleineren oder mittleren Hauses, wo man Ihnen zu einem annehmbaren Preis eine ebenfalls vorzügliche Mahlzeit reicht.

Der "Bib Gourmand"

Sorgfältig zubereitete, preiswerte Mahlzeiten

Für Sie wird es interessant sein, auch solche Häuser kennenzulernen, die eine sehr gute, Küche zu einem besonders günstigen Preis/Leistungs-Verhältnis bieten.

Im Text sind die betreffenden Restaurants durch rote Angabe **"Bib Gourmand"** *und* **Meals** *kenntlich gemacht, z.B.* **Meals** 19.00/25.00.

Preise

Die in diesem Führer genannten Preise wurden uns im Herbst 2001 angegeben. Sie können sich mit den Preisen von Waren und Dienstleistungen ändern. In einigen Städten werden bei kommerziellen oder touristischen Veranstaltungen von den Hotels beträchtlich erhöhte Preise verlangt.

Die Preise sind in Pfund Sterling angegeben (1 £ = 100 pence) mit Ausnahme der Republik Irland wo sie in Euros angegeben sind.

Wenn die Buchstaben s., t., *oder* st. *nicht hinter den angegebenen Preisen aufgeführt sind, können sich diese um den Zuschlag für Bedienung und/oder MWSt erhöhen (keine MWSt auf den Channel Islands).*

Die Namen der Hotels und Restaurants, die ihre Preise genannt haben, sind fett gedruckt. Gleichzeitig haben sich diese Häuser verpflichtet, die von den Hoteliers selbst angegebenen Preise den Benutzern des Michelin-Führers zu berechnen.

Halten Sie beim Betreten des Hotels den Führer in der Hand. Sie zeigen damit, daß Sie aufgrund dieser Empfehlung gekommen sind.

Mahlzeiten

Meals 13.00/28.00 — **Feste Menupreise**
Mindestpreis 13.00, *Höchstpreis* 28.00 *für ein angebotenes Menü*

Meals 19.00/25.00 — *Siehe Seite 49*

s. — *Bedienung inkl.*

t. — *MWSt inkl.*

st. — *Bedienung und MWSt inkl.*

🍾 12.00 — *Preis für eine Flasche Hauswein*

Meals a la carte 20.00/35.00 — **Mahlzeiten «à la carte»**
Der erste Preis entspricht einer einfachen aber sorgfältig zubereiteten Mahlzeit, bestehend aus kleiner Vorspeise, Tagesgericht mit Beilage und Nachstisch. Der zweite Preis entspricht einer reichlicheren Mahlzeit mit Vorspeise, Hauptgericht, Käse oder Nachtisch (inkl. Couvert)

⌂*: In dieser Hotelkategorie wird ein Abendessen normalerweise nur zu bestimmten Zeiten für Hotelgäste angeboten. Es besteht aus einem Menu mit begrenzter Auswahl zu festgesetztem Preis. Mittagessen wird selten angeboten. Viele dieser Hotels sind nicht berechtigt, alkoholische Getränke auszuschenken.*

Zimmer

rm 50.00/90.00 — *Mindestpreis 50.00, für ein Einzelzimmer und Höchstpreis 90.00 für das schönste Doppelzimmer*

suites — *Preise auf Anfrage*

rm ☕ 55.00/85.00 — *Übernachtung mit englischem Frühstück, selbst wenn dieses nicht eingenommen wird*

☕ 6.00 — *Preis des Frühstücks*

« Short breaks » (SB.)

Einige Hotels bieten Vorzugskonditionen für einen Mindestaufenthalt von zwei Nächten oder mehr (Short Break). Der Preis ist pro Person kalkuliert, bei einer Mindestbeteiligung von zwei Personen und schließt das Zimmer, das Abendessen und das Frühstück ein.

Ausschank alkoholischer Getränke

In Großbritanien und Irland unterliegt der Ausschank alkoholischer Getränke gesetzlichen Bestimmungen die von Land zu Land sehr verschieden sind. Restaurants können nachmittags geöffnet sein und alkoholische Getränke ausschenken, wenn diese zu einer entsprechenden Mahlzeit genossen werden. Hotelbars und Pubs sind generell von 11 Uhr vormittags bis 23 Uhr abends geöffnet: Hotelgäste können alkoholische Getränke jedoch auch außerhalb der Öffnungszeiten serviert werden.
Kindern unter 14 Jahren ist der Aufenthalt in Bars untersagt.

Anzahlung

Einige Hoteliers verlangen eine Anzahlung. Diese ist als Garantie sowohl für den Hotelier als auch für den Gast anzusehen.

Kreditkarten

Vom Haus akzeptierte Kreditkarten: MasterCard (Eurocard) – American Express – Diners Club – Visa – Japan Credit Bureau

Städte

✉ York	*Zuständiges Postamt*
401 M 27, ⑩	*Nummer der Michelin-Karte und Koordinaten des Planfeldes oder Faltseite*
West Country G.	*Siehe auch den grünen Michelinführer The West Country of England*
pop. 1057	*Einwohnerzahl*
BX A	*Markierung auf dem Stadtplan*
18	*Öffentlicher Golfplatz und Lochzahl (Handicap manchmal erforderlich, telefonische Reservierung empfehlenswert)*
✳ ⇐	*Rundblick, Aussichtspunkt*
✈	*Flughafen*
⛴	*Autofähre*
⛴	*Personenfähre*
ℹ	*Informationsstelle*

Uhrzeit

In Großbritannien ist eine Zeitverschiebung zu beachten und die Uhr gegenüber der deutschen Zeit um 1 Stunde zurückzustellen.

Sehenswürdigkeiten

Bewertung

★★★	*Eine Reise wert*
★★	*Verdient einen Umweg*
★	*Sehenswert*
AC	*Eintritt (gegen Gebühr)*

Lage

See	*In der Stadt*
Envir.	*In der Umgebung der Stadt*
Exc.	*Ausflugsziele*
N, S, E, W	*Im Norden (N), Süden (S), Osten (E), Westen (W) der Stadt*
A 22	*Zu erreichen über die Straße A 22*
2 m.	*Entfernung in Meilen*

Umgebungskarten

Denken Sie daran sie zu benutzen

Die Umgebungskarte erleichtert Ihnen die Suche nach einem Hotel oder Restaurant in der Nähe einer größeren Stadt.
Wenn Sie zum Beispiel eine gute Adresse in der Nähe von Leeds suchen, gibt Ihnen die Umgebungskarte schnell einen Überblick über alle Orte, die in diesem Führer erwähnt sind.
Innerhalb der in Kontrastfarbe gedruckten Grenze liegen Orte, die im in einer Entfernung von 25 km/16 miles zu erreichen sind.

Anmerkung:

All Orte die auf einer Nachbarschaftskarte verzeichnet sind haben im Ortsblock einen Hinweis. Der entsprechende Ortsname ist in diesem Falle in den Entfernungsangaben in „BLAU" gedruckt.

Beispiel:

Sie finden ILKLEY auf der Umgebungskarte von LEEDS

ILKLEY *W. Yorks.* 402 O 22 – pop. 13 530
Myddleton ℘ (01943) 607277
Station Rd, LS29 8HA ℘ (01943) 602319
London 210 – Bradford 13 – Harrogate 13 – Leeds 16 – Preston 46

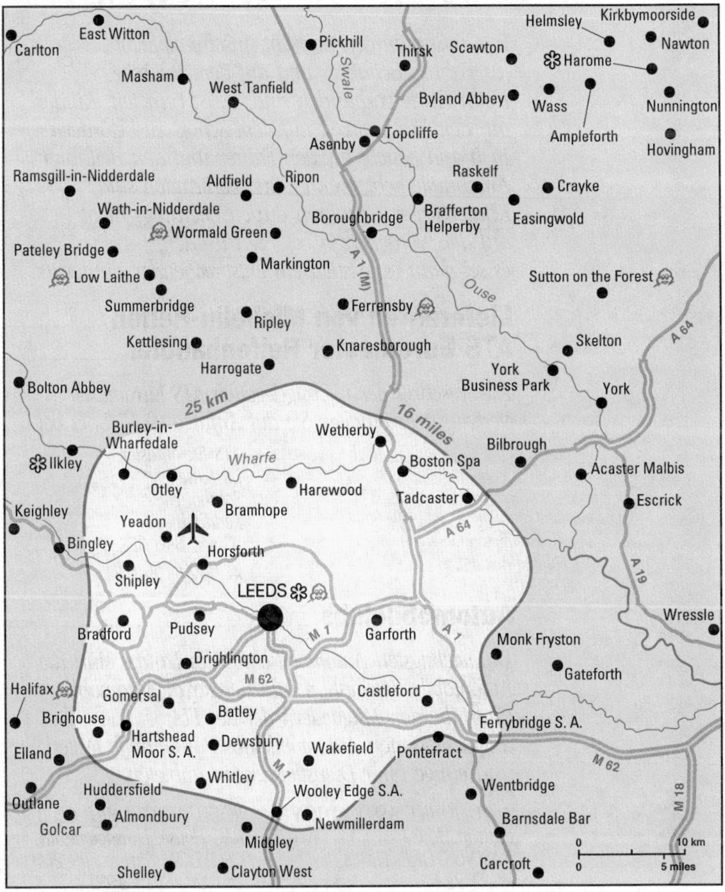

Carlton
East Witton
Masham
West Tanfield
Pickhill
Swale
Thirsk
Scawton
Helmsley
Kirkbymoorside
Nawton
Harome
Byland Abbey
Wass
Ampleforth
Nunnington
Hovingham
Topcliffe
Asenby
Ramsgill-in-Nidderdale
Aldfield
Ripon
Raskelf
Crayke
Easingwold
Wath-in-Nidderdale
Boroughbridge
Brafferton
Helperby
Wormald Green
Pateley Bridge
Markington
A 1 (M)
Low Laithe
Summerbridge
Ouse
Sutton on the Forest
Ferrensby
Ripley
Kettlesing
Knaresborough
Skelton
Harrogate
York
Business Park
York
A 64
Bolton Abbey
25 km
16 miles
Burley-in-
Wharfedale
Wetherby
Bilbrough
Ilkley
Wharfe
Boston Spa
Acaster Malbis
Otley
Harewood
Tadcaster
Escrick
Keighley
Bramhope
Yeadon
A 64
Bingley
Horsforth
A 19
Shipley
LEEDS
Bradford
Pudsey
M 1
Garforth
A 1
Wressle
Monk Fryston
Drighlington
Gateforth
M 62
Halifax
Gomersal
Castleford
Batley
Brighouse
Hartshead
Moor S. A.
Ferrybridge S. A.
Dewsbury
Elland
Wakefield
Pontefract
M 62
M 1
Whitley
Wentbridge
Huddersfield
Wooley Edge S.A.
M 18
Outlane
Almondbury
Newmillerdam
Barnsdale Bar
Golcar
Midgley
0
10 km
0
5 miles
Carcroft
Shelley
Clayton West

Die Umgebungskarten finden Sie auf der Themenkarte vor dem jeweilingen Land

Das Auto, die Reifen

In Großbritannien herrscht Anschnallpflicht für Fahrer, Beifahrer und auf dem Rücksitz, wenn Gurte vorhanden sind. Es ist verboten, Kinder auf den Vordersitzen auf dem Schoß zu befördern. In Irland besteht für den Fahrer und den Beifahrer Anschnallpflicht, wenn Gurte vorhanden sind, Kinder unter 12 Jahren dürfen allerdings nicht auf den Vordersitzen befördert werden, es sei denn es existiert ein entsprechender Kindersitz.

Lieferanten von Michelin-Reifen ATS Euromaster Reifenhändler

Die Anschrift der nächstgelegenen ATS Euromaster-Verkaufsstelle erhalten Sie auf Anfrage (9-17 Uhr) bei

ATS Euromaster
Jill Lane
Sambourne
Redditch
Worcs. B96 6ES
✆ 0800 750 850

Automobilclubs

Die wichtigsten Automobilsclubs des Landes sind die Automobile Association und der Royal Automobile Club, die den Mitgliedern der der FIA angeschlossenen Automobilclubs Pannenhilfe leisten und einige ihrer Dienstleistungen anbieten.

AUTOMOBILE ASSOCIATION
Fanum House
BASINGSTOKE, Hants
RG21 2EA
✆ (08705) 448866

AUTOMOBILE ASSOCIATION
23 Suffolk Street
DUBLIN 2
✆ (01) 617 9950

ROYAL AUTOMOBILE CLUB
RAC House, Lansdowne Rd.
CROYDON, Surrey CR9 2JA
✆ (020) 8917 2500

ROYAL AUTOMOBILE CLUB
RAC IRELAND
New Mount House
22-24 Lower Mount St.
DUBLIN 2
✆ (01) 676 0113

Stadtpläne

Hotels – Restaurants

Sehenswürdigkeiten

Sehenswertes Gebäude
Sehenswerter Sakralbau

Straßen

M 1 — *Autobahn*
4 4 — *- Anschlußstellen: Autobahneinfahrt und/oder-ausfahrt,*
Schnellstraße mit getrennten Fahrbahnen
Hauptverkehrsstraße
A 2 — *Fernverkehrsstraße (Primary route : GB) (National route : IRL)*
Einbahnstraße – Gesperrte Straße, mit Verkehrsbeschränkungen
Fußgängerzone – Straßenbahn
Piccadilly P — *Einkaufsstraße – Parkplatz, Parkhaus*
Tor – Passage – Tunnel – Park-and-Ride-Plätze
15'5 — *Unterführung (Höhe angegeben bis 16'6") auf Hauptverkehrsstraßen*
Bahnhof und Bahnlinie
Standseilbahn – Seilschwebebahn
B — *Bewegliche Brücke – Autofähre*

Sonstige Zeichen

Informationsstelle
Kirche/Gebetshaus – Moschee – Synagoge
Funk-, Fernsehturm – Ruine
Garten, Park, Wäldchen – Friedhof
9 — *Stadion – Pferderennbahn – Golfplatz – Eisbahn*
Golfplatz (Zutritt bedingt erlaubt)
Freibad – Hallenbad
Aussicht – Rundblick
Denkmal – Brunnen – Krankenhaus – Markthalle
Jachthafen – Leuchtturm
Flughafen – U-Bahnstation – Autobusbahnhof
Schiffsverbindungen: Autofähre
Hauptpostamt
Öffentliches Gebäude, durch einen Buchstaben gekennzeichnet:
C H J — *- Sitz der Grafschaftsverwaltung – Rathaus – Gerichtsgebäude*
M T U — *- Museum – Theater – Universität, Hochschule*
POL. — *- Polizei (in größeren Städten Polizeipräsidium)*

London

BRENT WEMBLEY — *Name des Verwaltungsbezirks (borough) – des Stadtteils (area)*
Grenze des « borough » – des « area »

Beer

Beer is one of the oldest and most popular alcoholic drinks in the world. Traditional draught beer is made by grinding malted barley, heating it with water and adding hops which add the familiar aroma and bitterness.
Beers in Britain can be divided into 2 principal types: Ales and Lagers which differ principally in their respective warm and cool fermentations. In terms of sales the split between the two is approximately equal. Beer can also be divided into keg or cask.

Keg beer – *is filtered, pasteurised and chilled and then packed into pressurised containers from which it gets its name.*

Cask beer – *or 'Real Ale' as it is often referred to, is not filtered, pasteurised or chilled and is served from casks using simple pumps. It is considered by some to be a more characterful, flavoursome and natural beer.*

There are several different beer styles in Britain and Ireland:

Bitter – *whilst it is the most popular traditional beer in England and Wales it is now outsold by lager.*
Although no precise definition exists it is usually paler and dryer than Mild with a high hop content and slightly bitter taste.

Mild – *is largely found in Wales, the West Midlands and the North West of England. The name refers to the hop character as it is gentle, sweetish and full flavoured beer.*
It is generally lower in alcohol and sometimes darker in colour, caused by the addition of caramel or by using dark malt.

Stout – *the great dry stouts are brewed in Ireland and are instantly recognisable by their black colour and creamy head. They have a pronounced roast flavour with plenty of hop bitterness.*

In Scotland the beers produced are full bodied and malty and are often known simply as Light, Heavy, or Export which refers to the body and strength of the beer.

Although Ireland is most famous for its stouts, it also makes a range of beers which have variously been described as malty, buttery, rounded and fruity with a reddish tinge.

Whisky

The term whisky is derived from th Scottish Gealic uisage beatha *and the Irish Gaelic* uisce beathadh, *both meaning "water of life". When spelt without an e it usually refers to Scotch Whisky which can only be produced in Scotland by the distillation of malted and unmalted barley, maize, rye, and mixtures of two or more of these. Often simply referred to as Scotch it can be divided into 2 basic types: malt whisky and grain whisky.*

Malt whisky – *is made only from malted barley which is traditionally dried over peat fires. The malt is then milled and mixed with hot water before mashing turns the starches into sugars and the resulting liquid, called wort, is filtered out. Yeast is added and fermentation takes place followed by two distilling processes using a pot still. The whisky is matured in oak, ideally sherry casks, for at least three years which affects both its colour and flavour. All malts have a more distinctive smell and intense flavour than grain whiskies and each distillery will produce a completely individual whisky of great complexity. A single malt is the product of an individual distillery. There are approximately 100 malt whisky distilleries in Scotland.*

Grain whisky – *is made from a mixture of any malted or unmalted cereal such as maize or wheat and is distilled in the Coffey, or patent still, by a continuous process. Very little grain whisky is ever drunk unblended.*

Blended whisky – *is a mix of more than one malt whisky or a mix of malt and grain whiskies to produce a soft, smooth and consistent drink. There are over 2,000 such blends which form the vast majority of Scottish whisky production.*

Irish Whiskey – *differs from Scotch whisky both in its spelling and method of production. It is traditionally made from cereals, distilled three times and matured for at least 7 years. The different brands are as individual as straight malt and considered by some to be gentler in character.*

La bière

La bière est l'une des plus anciennes et populaires boissons alcoolisées dans le monde. Pour produire la bière pression traditionnelle, on écrase l'orge maltée que l'on chauffe ensuite avec de l'eau à laquelle on ajoute le houblon. C'est ce qui lui donne son arôme et son goût amer bien connus.
Deux types de bières sont principalement vendues en Grande-Bretagne : les Ales *fermentées à chaud et les* Lagers *fermentées à froid. Elles se divisent en « keg beer » et en « cask beer ».*

Bière en keg : *elle est filtrée, pasteurisée et refroidie, puis versée dans des tonnelets pressurisés appelés kegs.*

Bière en cask *ou « Real Ale » : elle n'est ni filtrée, ni pasteurisée, ni refroidie mais tirée directement du tonneau à l'aide d'une simple pompe. Selon certains, cette bière, de qualité bien distincte, a plus de saveur et est plus naturelle.*

Types de bières vendues au Royaume-Uni et en Irlande :

Bitter – *C'est la bière traditionnelle la plus populaire en Angleterre et au pays de Galles mais ses ventes diminuent au profit des lagers. La Bitter est généralement plus pâle et son goût plus sec que la* Mild. *Son contenu en houblon est élevé et elle a un goût légèrement amer.*

La Mild *se consomme surtout au pays de Galles, dans le Midlands de l'Ouest et dans le Nord-Ouest de l'Angleterre. On l'appelle ainsi en raison de son goût moelleux légèrement douceâtre conféré par le houblon. Cette bière, généralement moins alcoolisée, est plus foncée par le caramel qui lui est ajouté ou par l'utilisation de malt plus brun.*

Stout – *les grandes marques de bières brunes sont brassées en Irlande et sont reconnaissables par leur couleur noire rehaussée de mousse crémeuse. Elles ont un goût prononcé de houblon grillé et une saveur amère.*

Celles produites en Écosse sont maltées; elles ont du corps et se dénomment le plus souvent Light, Heavy ou Export en référence au corps et à leur teneur en alcool.

Whisky

Le mot whisky est un dérivé du gaélique écossais uisage beatha *et du gaélique irlandais* uisce beathadh *signifiant tous deux « eau de vie ». Quand il est écrit sans* e, *il se réfère au whisky écossais qui ne peut être produit qu'en Écosse par la distillation de céréales maltées ou non comme l'orge, le maïs, le seigle ou d'un mélange de deux ou plus de ces céréales. Souvent appelé tout simplement Scotch il se réfère à deux types de whiskies : whisky pur malt ou whisky de grain.*

Le whisky pur malt est fait seulement à partir d'orge maltée qui est traditionnellement séchée au-dessus de feux de tourbe. Le malt est moulu et mélangé avec de l'eau chaude, puis le brassage transforme l'amidon en sucre; le moût est ensuite filtré. On y ajoute de la levure et après la fermentation on fait distiller deux fois dans un alambic. Le whisky est alors vieilli pendant au moins trois ans dans des fûts de chêne, ayant contenu de préférence du sherry, ce qui transforme son goût et sa couleur. Tous les whiskies pur malt ont un arôme particulier et une saveur plus intense que les whiskies de grain et chaque distillerie produit son propre whisky avec des qualités bien distinctes. Il y a environ une centaine de distilleries de whiskies pur malt en Écosse.

Le whisky de grain est fait d'un mélange de céréales, maltées ou non, comme le maïs ou le froment et est distillé dans un alambic de type Coffey suivant un procédé continu. Très peu de whiskies de grain sont consommés à l'état pur. On procède à des mélanges pour la consommation.

Blended whisky est le mélange d'un ou de plusieurs whiskies pur malt et de whiskies de grain afin de produire un alcool léger, moelleux et de qualité. Il existe plus de 2 000 marques de blended whiskies qui forment la majeure partie de la production écossaise.

Le whisky irlandais, différent du whisky écossais par sa fabrication, est traditionnellement produit à partir de céréales; il est ensuite distillé trois fois et vieilli pendant au moins sept ans. Certains le trouvent plus moelleux.

Birra

La birra è una delle bevande alcoliche più antiche e popolari. La tradizionale birra alla spina si ottiene macinando l'orzo, riscaldandolo con l'acqua e aggiungendo il luppolo, che le conferiscono l'aroma e il tipico sapore amaro.

Le birre britanniche si dividono in due tipi principali: Ales e Lagers, *che differiscono essenzialmente per la fermentazione, rispettivamente calda e fredda. In termini di vendita, i due tipi approssimativamente si equivalgono. La birra può anche dividersi in* keg *(lett,* barilotto*), e* cask *(lett* botte*).*

La keg beer *è filtrata, pastorizzata e raffreddata, e poi messa in contenitori pressurizzati, da cui deriva il nome.*

La cask beer, *o* Real Ale, *come viene comunemente indicata, non è filtrata, pastorizzata o raffeddata, ed è servita dalle botti, usando semplici pompe. Alcuni la considerano una birra più ricca di carattere e di gusto e più naturale.*

In Gran Bretagna e Irlanda, le birre si caratterizzano anche in base a « stili » diversi.

Le bitter *costituisce la birra tradizionalmente più popolare in Inghilterra e nel Galles, ma è ora « superata » dalla* lager. *Non esiste definizione specifica per la birra* bitter, *ma si può dire che si tratta in genere di una birra più pallida e secca della* mild, *dall'alto contenuto di luppolo e dal gusto leggermente amaro.*

La mild *è diffusa in Galles, West Midlands e Inghilterra nord-occidentale. Il nome richiama il carattere del luppolo, essendo delicata, dolce e dal gusto pieno. Contiene solitamente una limitata quantità di alcol ed è talvolta scura per l'aggiunta di caramello e per l'impiego di malto scuro.*

La secche stouts *vengono prodotte in Irlanda e sono immediatamente riconoscibili dal colore nero e dalla schiuma cremosa. Hanno una decisa fragranza di tostatura e un gusto amaro di luppolo.*

Whisky

Il termine whisky deriva dal gealico scozzese uisage beatha e dal gaelico irlandese uisce beathadh, che significano « acqua di vita ». Se scritto senza la e, indica di solito lo Scotch Whisky, che può essere unicamente prodotto in Scozia dalla distillazione di malto e orzo, granturco e segale, e dall'unione di due o più di questi ingredienti. Spesso chiamato semplicemente Scoveri, si divide in due tipi: malt whisky e grain whisky.

Il malt whisky viene prodotto unicamente con malto, tradizionalmente seccato su fuochi alimentati con torba. Il malto viene poi macinato e gli viene aggiunta acqua bollente prima che l'impasto muti gli amidi in zuccheri e il liquido che ne deriva, chiamato wort (mosto di malto), venga filtrato. Si amalgama poi il lievito e avviene la fermentazione, seguita da due processi di distillazione nell'alambicco. Il whisky è lasciato invecchiare in legno di quercia, idealmente in botti di sherry, per almeno tre anni, perchè acquisti colore e sapore. Ogni tipo di malt whisky ha un profumo più distintivo e un gusto più intenso del grain whisky. Ogni distilleria produce un whisky dal carattere individuale, che richiede un processo di grande complessità. Un solo malt whisky è il prodotto di una specifica distilleria. In Scozia, esistono circa 100 distillerie di malt whisky.

Il grain whisky è il risultato della fusione di qualsiasi cereale con o senza malto, come il granturco o il frumento, en viene distillato nel Coffey, o alambicco brevettato, grazie ad un processo continuo. È molto scarsa la quantità di grain whisky che si beve puro.

Il blended whisky nasce dalla fusione di più di un malt whisky, o da quella di malt e grain whiskies. Il risultato è una bevanda dal gusto delicato, dolce e pieno. Esistono più di 2000 whisky di questo tipo, che costituiscono la parte più consistente della produzione scozzese.

Bier

Bier ist eines der ältesten und beliebtesten alkoholischen Getränke der Welt. Das traditionelle Faßbier wird aus gemahlener und gemalzter Gerste hergestellt, die in Wasser erhitzt wird. Durch Beigabe von Hopfen werden das bekannte Aroma und der typische bittere Geschmack erzeugt.

Die Biersorten in Großbritannien unterteilen sich in zwei Hauptgruppen: Ales *und* Lagers, *wobei die Art der Gärung – im einen Fall warm, im anderen kalt – ausschlaggebend für das Endresultat ist. Beide Sorten haben hierzulande einen ungefähr gleichen Marktanteil. Da sich die meisten Brauvorgänge anfangs gleichen, entscheiden erst die Endphasen des Brauens, welche der verschiedenen Biersorten entsteht.*

Darüber hinaus kann das englische Bier auch nach der Art seiner Abfüllung in Keg- *bzw.* Cask-*Bier unterschieden werden:*

Keg beer *wird gefiltert, pasteurisiert, abgekühlt und anschlienßend in luftdichte, unter Druck gesetzte Metallbehälter gefüllt, von denen das Bier auch seinen Namen erhält.*

Cask beer, *gewöhnlich* Real Ale *genannt, wird weder gefiltert, noch pasteurisiert oder gekühlt, sondern mit einfachen (zumeist Hand-) Pumpen vom Faß gezapft.*

Es gibt folgende Biersorten in Großbritannien und Irland: Bitter ist das meistbekannte traditionelle Bier in England und Wales. Eine genaue Definition, was ein Bitter ausmacht, sucht man vergeblich; es ist gewöhnlich heller und trockener als das Mild, *hat einen hohen Hopfenanteil und einen leicht bitteren Geschmack. In den letzten Jahren hat das – meist importierte oder in Lizenz gebraute –* Lager *ihm jedoch den Rang abgelaufen.*

Mild *ist übergiegend in Wales, in den westlichen Midlands und Nordwestengland zu finden. Der Name bezieht sich auf den Hopfenanteil, der es zu einem milden, etwas süßlichen und vollmundigen Bier macht. Es hat einen geringeren Alkoholgehalt und besitz wegen der Zugabe von Karamel oder dunklem Malz bisweilen eine dunklere Farbe.*

Stouts *von hervorragendem trockenem Geschmack werden in Irland gebraut und sind unmittelbar an ihrer schwarzen Farbe und der cremigen Blume erkennbar. Sie haben einen ausgesprochen starken Geschmack nach bitterem Hopfen.*

In Schottland hergestellte Biere sind alkoholstark und malzig; sie sind oft einfach bekannt als: Light, Heavy oder Export *– Bezeichnungen, die auf Körper und Stärke des Bieres hinweisen.*

Whisky

Die Bezeichnung Whisky entstammt dem Gälischen, wo im Schottischen der Ausdruck uisage beatha, *im Irischen des Ausdruck* uisce beathadh *jeweils « Wasser des Lebens » bedeuten. Wird Whisky ohne ein e am Ende geschrieben, ist* Scotch Whisky *gemeint, der nur in Schottland aus gemalzter und ungemalzter Gerste, Mais, Roggen oder aus Mischungen zweier oder mehrerer dieser Zutaten gebrannt werden darf. Oft auch nur als* Scotch *bezeichnet, kann dieser in zwei Grundarten unterschieden werden:* malt whisky *und* grain whisky.

Malt (Malz) whisky *wird nur aus gemalzter Gerste hergestellt, die traditionell über Torffeuern getrocknet wird. Danach wird das Malz gemahlen und mit heißem Wasser vermischt, wonach in der Maische die Stärke in Zucker umgewandelt wird. Die dadurch entstandene Flüssigkeit, «* wort *» genannt, wird gefiltert und mit Hefe versetzt, was den Gärungsprozess einleitet. Anschließend folgen zwei Destillierungen im herkömmlichen Topf über offenem Feuer. Der Whisky reift danach mindestens drei Jahre lang in Eichenholz, idealerweise in Sherry-Fässern, was sich sowohl auf Farbe wie auf Geschmack des Whiskys auswirkt. Alle* malts *haben einen ausgeprägteren Geruch und intensiveren Geschmack als die* grain-*Whiskies; und jede Destillerie erzeugt einen völlig eigenen Whisky mit individueller Geschmacksnote und großer Komplexität. Ein sogenannter* single malt *enstammt aus einer einzigen Destillerie. Es gibt ungefähr 100 Malt Whisky-Destillerien in Schottland.*

Grain (Korn) whisky *wird aus Mischungen von gemalzten und ungemalzten Getreidesorten, wie Mais oder Weizen, hergestellt und wird in einem kontinuierlichen Prozeß in dem sogenannten « Coffey » destilliert. Nur sehr wenige Kornwhisky-Sorten sind nicht das Ergebnis von* blending, *dem Abstimmen des Geschmacks durch Mischung.*

Blended whisky *wird aus mehr als einer Sorte Malt Whisky oder aus Malt und Grain Whiskies gemischt, um ein weiches, geschamcklich harmonisches Getränk von beständiger Güte zu garantieren. Die über 2000 im Handel zu findenden* blends *stellen den Großteil der schottischen Whiskyerzeugung dar.*

Irish Whiskey *unterscheidet sich vom Scotch Whisky sowohl in der Schreibweise wie auch dem Herstellungsverfahren. Er wird traditionell aus Getreide hergestellt, wird dreifach destilliert und reift mindestens sieben Jahre lang. Die verschiedenen Sorten sind so individuell ausgeprägt wie reine Malt Whiskies und werden oft als weicher und gefälliger empfunden.*

Menu

Starred establishments
Les établissements à étoiles
Gli esercizi con stelle
Die Stern-Restaurants

✿✿✿

England

Bray-on-Thames *Waterside Inn*
London *Gordon Ramsay*

✿✿

England

Bath *Blinis*
Bray-on-Thames *Fat Duck*
Chagford *Gidleigh Park*
Cheltenham *Le Champignon Sauvage*
London *Capital*
- *Le Gavroche*
- *John Burton-Race*
- *The Square*
- *La Tante Claire*
Oxford *Le Manoir aux Quat' Saisons*
Winteringham *Winteringham Fields*

Ireland

Republic of Ireland
Dublin *Patrick Guilbaud*
– *Thornton's*

✿

England

Altrincham *Juniper*
Baslow *Fischer's at Baslow Hall*
Bath *Bath Priory*
- *Moody Goose*
Blackburn *Northcote Manor*
Blakeney *Morston Hall*
Bourton-on-the-Water *Lords of the Manor*
Bristol *Harveys*
Cambridge *Midsummer House*
Channels Islands
Guernsey *Café du Moulin*
Jersey *Longueville Manor*
- *Village Bistro*
Chester *Arkle*
East Grinstead *Gravetye Manor*
Emsworth *36 on the Quay*
Faversham *Read's*
Folkestone *La Terrasse*
Grantham *Harry's Place*
Grasmere *Michaels Nook*
Great Malvern *Croque-en-Bouche*
Helmsley *The Star Inn*
Ilkley *Box Tree*
Kenilworth *Simpson's*
Kington *Stagg Inn*
Leeds *Gueller*
- *Pool Court at 42*

London	*Aubergine*
-	*Chapter One*
-	*Chez Bruce*
-	*Chez Nico*
-	*City Rhodes*
-	*Club Gascon*
-	*Connaught*
-	*L'Escargot*
-	*Foliage*
-	*The Glasshouse*
-	*Mirabelle*
-	*Monsieur Max*
-	*Nahm*
-	*Nobu*
-	*The Oak Room Marco Pierre White*
-	*1 Lombard Street (Restaurant)*
-	*L'Oranger*
-	*Orrery*
-	*Pétrus*
-	*Pied à Terre*
-	*Putney Bridge*
-	*Rhodes in the Square*
-	*Richard Corrigan at Lindsay House*
-	*River Café*
-	*Roussillon*
-	*Tamarind*
-	*Zafferano*
-	*Zaika*
Longridge	*Paul Heathcote's*
Ludlow	*Hibiscus*
-	*Merchant House*
-	*Mr Underhill's at Dinham Weir*
Lyndhurst	*Le Poussin at Parkhill*
Newbury	*Vineyard*
New Milton	*Chewton Glen*
Norwich	*Adlard's*
Oakham	*Hambleton Hall*
Sheffield	*Old Vicarage*
Shepton Mallet	*Charlton House*
Shipston-on-Stour	*Chavignol at the Old Mill*
Shrewsbury	*Sol*
Stamford	*The Olive Branch*
Storrington	*Fleur de Sel*
Taplow	*Waldo's*
Taunton	*The Castle*
Tavistock	*Horn of Plenty*
Ullswater	*Sharrow Bay Country House*
Wells-next-the-Sea	*Rococo*
Wight (Isle of)	
Yarmouth	*The George*
Winchester	*Chesil Rectory*
Windermere	*Holbeck Ghyll*
Yeovil	*Priory House*

Scotland

Achiltibuie	*Summer Isles*
Auchterarder	*Andrew Fairlie at Gleneagles*
Balloch	*Georgian Room*
Castle Douglas	*Plumed Horse*
Dalry	*Braidwoods*
Edinburgh	*Martin Wishart*
Fort William	*Inverlochy Castle*
Glasgow	*Amaryllis*
Port Appin	*Airds*
Portpatrick	*Knockinaam Lodge*

Wales

Abergavenny	*Walnut Tree Inn*
Conwy	*Old Rectory Country House*
Llanwrtyd Wells	*Carlton House*
Machynlleth	*Ynyshir Hall*
Pwllheli	*Plas Bodegroes*

Ireland

Northern Ireland	
Bangor	*Shanks*
Belfast	*Restaurant Michael Deane*
Republic of Ireland	
Dublin	*Peacock Alley*
-	*The Commons*

"Bib Gourmand"

Good food at moderate prices

Repas soignés à prix modérés

Pasti accurati a prezzi contenuti

Sorgfältig zubereitete, preiswerte Mahlzeiten

Meals

England

Aldeburgh	*Lighthouse*
Alderley Edge	*The Wizard*
Bath	*Hole in the Wall*
Birmingham	*Metro Bar & Grill*
-	*Le Petit Blanc*
Blackpool	*September Brasserie*
Brighton and Hove	*Black Chapati*
-	*Terre à Terre*
Burford	*Jonathan's at the Angel brasserie*
Burnham Market	*The Restaurant (at Hoste Arms H.)*
Burnsall	*Devonshire Fell*
Cambridge	*22 Chesterton Road*
Carlisle	*Magenta's*
Channel Islands	
Jersey	*Green Island*
-	*Jersey Pottery*
Chelmsford	*Muddy Waters*
Chipping Campden	*Churchill Arms*
Cirencester	*Village Pub*
Coln St.Aldwyns	*The Courtyard Bar (at New Inn at Coln)*
Devizes	*George & Dragon*
Durham	*Bistro 21*
Faversham	*Dove Inn*
Four Marks	*Yew Tree*
Great Missenden	*Berts*
Halifax	*Design House*
Horncastle	*The Magpies*
Kendal	*Punch Bowl Inn*
Keyston	*Pheasant*
Knaresborough	*The General*
-	*Tarleton Inn (Bar/Brasserie)*
Ledbury	*The Malthouse*
Leeds	*Brasserie Forty Four*
-	*The Calls Grill*
-	*Leodis*
London	*L'Accento*
-	*Al Duca*
-	*Cafe Spice Namaste*
-	*Cantina Vinopolis (Brasserie)*
-	*I Cardi*
-	*Chada Chada*
-	*Chapter Two*
-	*Il Forno*
-	*Light House*
-	*Malabar*
-	*Metrogusto*
-	*Metrogusto*
-	*The Parsee*
-	*The Phoenix*
-	*Sabras*
-	*Sarkhel's*
-	*The Vale*
Long Melford	*Scutchers*
Loughborough	*Lang's*
Manchester	*Rhodes & Co*
Nayland	*White Hart Inn*
Newcastle upon Tyne	*Café 21*
-	*Café 21*
Oldham	*Brasserie (at White Hart Inn)*
Orford	*The Trinity*
Oxford	*Le Petit Blanc*
Pateley Bridge	*Dusty Miller*
Preston	*Simply Heathcotes*
Ripon	*Olives*
Ross-on-Wye	*Lough Pool Inn*

Rushlake Green	*Stone House*
St Albans	*Sukiyaki*
Salisbury	*Howard's House*
Sheffield	*Rafters*
-	*Thyme*
Skipton	*Angel Inn (Bar Brasserie)*
Southport	*Warehouse Brasserie*
Sowerby Bridge	*The Millbank*
Standish	*The Mulberry Tree*
Stanton	*Leaping Hare*
Storrington	*Old Forge*
Sutton on the Forest	*Rose & Crown*
Telford	*Hundred House*
Tetbury	*The Trouble House*
Turville	*Bull & Butcher*
Wells	*Ritchers*
West Malling	*The Swan*
Windsor	*Al Fassia*
Woodbridge	*The Captain's Table*

Scotland

Edinburgh	*Atrium*
-	*Rhodes & Co.*
Glasgow	*No. Sixteen*
Strathyre	*Creagan House*

Wales

Cardiff	*Gilby's*
-	*Woods Brasserie*
Knighton	*The Waterdine*
Llandudno	*Nikki Ip's*
Talbot Green	*Brookes*

Ireland

Northern Ireland

Belfast	*Aldens*
-	*Cayenne*
-	*Deanes Brasserie*
Holywood	*Fontana*

Republic of Ireland

Baltimore	*Customs House*
Cork	*Jacobs on the Mall*
Dingle	*The Chart House*
Dublin	*Jacobs Ladder*
-	*Mermaid Cafe*
Dungarvan	*The Tannery*
Dun Laoghaire	*Duzy's Café*
Kenmare	*An Leath Phingin*
-	*The Lime Tree*
Kilbrittain	*Casino House*
Kilkenny	*Zuni*
Kinsale	*Fishy Fishy Cafe*

Particularly pleasant Hotels
Hôtels agréables
Alberghi ameni
Angenehme Hotels

England

London	*The Berkeley*
-	*Claridge's*
-	*Dorchester*
-	*Mandarin Oriental Hyde Park*
-	*Ritz*
-	*Savoy*
New Milton	*Chewton Glen*
Taplow	*Cliveden*

Ireland *Republic of Ireland*

Straffan	*Kildare H. & Country Club*

England

Aylesbury	*Hartwell House*
Bath	*Lucknam Park*
-	*The Royal Crescent*
Ipswich	*Hintlesham Hall*
London	*Connaught*
Melton Mowbray	*Stapleford Park*
Oxford	*Le Manoir aux Quat' Saisons*

Scotland

Ballantrae	*Glenapp Castle*
Dunkeld	*Kinnaird*
Fort William	*Inverlochy Castle*

Wales

Llyswen	*Llangoed Hall*

Ireland *Republic of Ireland*

Dublin	*The Merrion*
Kenmare	*Park*
-	*Sheen Falls Lodge*

England

Abberley	*The Elms*
Amberley	*Amberley Castle*
Bath	*Bath Priory*
-	*Homewood Park*
Bolton Abbey	*Devonshire Arms Country House*
Bourton-on-the-Water	*Lords of the Manor*
-	*Lower Slaughter Manor*
Broadway	*Buckland Manor*
Castle Combe	*Manor House*
Chagford	*Gidleigh Park*

Channel Islands

La Pulente (Jersey)	*Atlantic*
Rozel Bay (Jersey)	*Chateau La Chaire*
St Saviour (Jersey)	*Longueville Manor*
East Grinstead	*Gravetye Manor*
Evershot	*Summer Lodge*
Gillingham	*Stock Hill Country House*
Grasmere	*Michaels Nook*
Leeds	*42 The Calls*
Littlehampton	*Bailiffscourt*
London	*Blakes*
-	*Capital*
-	*Charlotte Street*
-	*Cliveden Town House*

London	*Covent Garden*
-	*Durley House*
-	*The Goring*
-	*The Halkin*
-	*The Milestone*
-	*One Aldwych*
-	*Pelham*
Newbury	*Vineyard*
Oakham	*Hambleton Hall*
Royal Leamington Spa	*Mallory Court*
Sandiway	*Nunsmere Hall*
Scilly *(Isles of)*	
St Martin's	*St Martin's on the Isle*
Tresco	*The Island*
Seaham	*Seaham Hall*
Shepton Mallet	*Charlton House*
Sutton Coldfield	*New Hall*
Taunton	*The Castle*
Tetbury	*The Close*
-	*Calcot Manor*
Ullswater	*Sharrow Bay Country House*
York	*Middlethorpe Hall*

Scotland

Arisaig	*Arisaig House*
Auchterarder	*Aucherarder House*
Dunblane	*Cromlix House*
Edinburgh	*The Bonham*
-	*The Howard*
Eriska *(Isle of)*	*Isle of Eriska*
Glasgow	*One Devonshire Gardens*
Inverness	*Culloden House*
Newton Stewart	*Kirroughtree House*
Port Appin	*Airds*

Wales

Llandudno	*Bodysgallen Hall*
Llangammarch Wells	*Lake Country House*

Ireland *Republic of Ireland*

Cashel	*Cashel House*
Dublin	*The Clarence*
Gorey	*Marlfield House*
Mallow	*Longueville House*
Wicklow	*Tinakilly House*

England

Ambleside	*The Samling*
Bath	*Queensberry*
Brampton	*Farlam Hall*
Bridgnorth	*The Old Vicarage*
Burrington	*Northcote Manor*
Cheltenham	*On the Park*
Cuckfield	*Ockenden Manor*
Frome	*Babington House*
Hereford	*Castle House*
Horley	*Langshott Manor*
Kingsbridge	*Buckland-Tout-Saints*
King's Lynn	*Congham Hall*
Lewdown	*Lewtrenchard Manor*
London	*22 Jermyn Street*
Milford-on-Sea	*Westover Hall*
Oxford	*Old Parsonage*
Purton	*Pear Tree at Purton*
Rushlake Green	*Stone House*
St Mawes	*Tresanton*
Ullswater	*Old Church*
Wareham	*Priory*
Wellington	*Bindon Country House*
Wight *(Isle of)*	
Yarmouth	*The George*
Windermere	*Gilpin Lodge*
-	*Holbeck Ghyll*
Woodstock	*Feathers*

Scotland

Achiltibuie	*Summer Isles*
Arran *(Isle of)*	*Kilmichael Country House*
Gullane	*Greywalls*
Lewis & Harris *(Isle of)*	
Ardvourlie (Harris)	*Ardvourlie Castle*
Portpatrick	*Knockinaam Lodge*

Wales

Llandrillo	*Tyddyn Llan Country House*
Machynlleth	*Ynyshir Hall*
Swansea	*Fairyhill*
Talsarnau	*Maes-y-Neuadd*

Ireland *Republic of Ireland*

Arthurstown	*Dunbrody Country House*
Ballingarry	*Mustard Seed at Echo Lodge*
Cashel	*Zetland Country House*
Castlebaldwin	*Cromleach Lodge*
Craughwell	*St Clerans*
Glin	*Glin Castle*
Kanturk	*Assolas Country House*
Kinsale	*Perryville House (without rest)*
Shanagarry	*Ballymaloe House*

England

Blakeney *Morston Hall*
Chipping Campden *Malt House*
Coln St Aldwyns *New Inn at Coln*
Cranbrook *Kennel Holt*
Dartmouth *Nonsuch House*
Dulverton *Ashwick House*
Keswick *Swinside Lodge*
Porlock *Oaks*
Salisbury *Howard's House*
Staverton *Kingston House*
Swaffham *Strattons*
Teignmouth *Thomas Luny House (without rest)*
Tintagel *Trebrea Lodge*
Wight (Isle of) *Seaview*
Wiveliscombe *Langley House*

Scotland

Dunblane *Rokeby House*
Kelso *Edenwater House*
Kentallen *Ardsheal House*
Lochinver *The Albannach*
Maybole *Ladyburn*
Muir of Ord *Dower House*
Nairn *Boath House*
Perth *Dupplin Castle*
Tain *Glenmorangie House*

Wales

Betws-y-Coed *Tan-y-Foel Country House*
Llansanffraid Glan Conwy *Old Rectory Country House*

Ireland

Northern Ireland

Holywood *Rayanne House*

Republic of Ireland

Bagenalstown *Kilgraney Country House*
Lahinch *Moy House*
Riverstown *Coopershill*

England

Alnmouth *High Buston Hall*
Askrigg *Helm*
Aylmerton *Felbrigg Lodge*
Bath *Haydon House (without rest)*
Billingshurst *Old Wharf (without rest)*
Blockley *The Old Bakery*
Calne *Chilvester Hill House*
Carlisle *Number Thirty One*
Caxton *Church Farm*
Cockermouth *New House Farm*
- *Winder Hall*
Crackington Haven *Manor Farm*
Cranbrook *Old Cloth Hall*
Dover *Old Vicarage (without rest)*
East Hoathly *Old Whyly*
Faversham *Frith Farm House*
Honiton *Cokesputt House*
Ipswich *Woolverstone House*
Kirkby Malham *Holgate Head*
Lavenham *Lavenham Priory (without rest)*
Lewes *Millers (without rest)*
Lizard *Landewednack House*
Malpas *Tilston Lodge (without rest)*
Marazion *Ednovean Farm (without rest)*
Morpeth *Eshott Hall*
North Bovey *The Gate House*
Norton St. Philip *Monmouth Lodge (without rest)*
Petworth *Old Railway Station (without rest)*
Ripley *High Winsley Cottage*
St Blazey *Nanscawen Manor House (without rest)*
Seaford *Old Parsonage (without rest)*
Shrewsbury *Pinewood House (without rest)*
Stow-on-the-Wold *Rectory Farmhouse (without rest)*
Tavistock *Quither Mill*
- *Tor Cottage (without rest)*
Veryan *Crugsillick Manor*
Wareham *Gold Court House*
Woodstock *Shipton Glebe*
Yoxford *Church Farm (without rest)*

Scotland

Arran *(Isle of)*	*Apple Lodge*
Banchory	*Old West Manse*
Earlston	*Birkhill*
Edinburgh	*17 Abercromby Place (without rest)*
-	*27 Heriot Row (without rest)*
Fort William	*Crolinnhe (without rest)*
-	*The Grange (without rest)*
Glenborrodale	*Feorag House*
Inverness	*Millwood House (without rest)*
Islay *(Isle of)*	*Kilmeny Country Guest House*
Shetland Islands	*Buness House*
Skye *(Isle of)*	*Kinlochfollart*
Stathpeffer	*Craigvar (without rest)*

Wales

Bala	*Fron Feuno Hall (without rest)*
Dollgellau	*Abergwynant Hall*

Ireland

Northern Ireland

Dungannon	*Grange Lodge*

Republic of Ireland

Castlelyons	*Ballyvolane House*
Castlerea	*Clonalis House*
Cong	*Ballywarren House*
Galway	*Norman Villa (without rest)*
Kanturk	*Glenlohane*
Kenmare	*Sallyport House (without rest)*
Kilkenny	*Blanchville House*

Particularly pleasant Restaurants
Restaurants agréables
Ristoranti ameni
Angenehme Restaurants

XXXXX

England

London *The Restaurant (at Ritz H.)*

XXXX

England

Bray-on-Thames *Waterside Inn (with rm)*
London *Grill Room (at Dorchester H.)*
Taplow *Waldo's*
Winteringham *Winteringham Fields (with rm)*

XXX

England

Baslow *Fischer's at Baslow Hall (with rm)*
Cambridge *Midsummer House*
Dedham *Le Talbooth*
Emsworth *36 on the Quay*
London *Orrery*
- *Oxo Tower*
- *Le Pont de la Tour*
Moulsford *Beetle & Wedge (with rm)*
Newcastle upon Tyne *Fisherman's Lodge*
Romsey *Old Manor House*
Tavistock *Horn of Plenty (with rm)*
Welwyn Garden City *Auberge du Lac*

Scotland

Peat Inn *The Peat Inn (with rm)*

XX

England

Channel Islands
Guernsey *Café du Moulin*
Jersey *Jersey Pottery (Garden Rest)*
- *Suma's*
Derby *Darleys*
Eastbourne *Hungry Monk*
Goring *Leatherne Bottel*
Grantham *Harry's Place*
Lockington *Rockingham (with rm)*
London *J. Sheekey*
- *Quaglino's*
- *Rules*
Moreton-in-Marsh *Marsh Goose*
Nayland *White Hart Inn (with rm)*
Padstow *The Seafood (with rm)*
Pateley Bridge *Yorke Arms (with rm)*
Reading *Castle*
Yeovil *Little Barwick House (with rm)*

Scotland

Kingussie *The Cross (with rm)*
Skye (Isle of) *Three Chimneys & The House Over-By (with rm)*

Ireland

Republic of Ireland
Dalkey *Kish*

England

Burford *Jonathans at the Angel brasserie (with rm)*
Torquay *Mulberry House (with rm)*

Scotland

Spean Bridge *Old Pines (with rm)*

Ireland

Republic of Ireland
Kenmare *The Lime Tree*

England

Aylesbury *Bottle & Glass*
Barnard Castle *Rose & Crown (with rm)*
Broadhembury *Drewe Arms*
Cirencester *The Bell Inn*
- *Village Pub (with rm)*
Exeter *Nobody Inn*
Great Yeldham *White Hart*
Helmsley *The Star Inn (with rm)*
Henley-in-Arden *Crabmill*
Keyston *Pheasant*
Oundle *The Falcon Inn*
Skipton *Angel Inn (Bar/Brasserie)*
Stadhampton *Crazy Bear (with rm)*
Stow-on-the-Wold *Fox Inn (with rm)*
Winchester *Wykeham Arms (with rm)*
Witney *The Boot Inn*
Woburn *The Birch*

Wales

Caersws *Ty Siarad (with rm)*
Conwy *Groes Inn (with rm)*

Ireland

Northern Ireland
Donaghadee *Grace Neills*

England

Channel Islands, Isle of Man

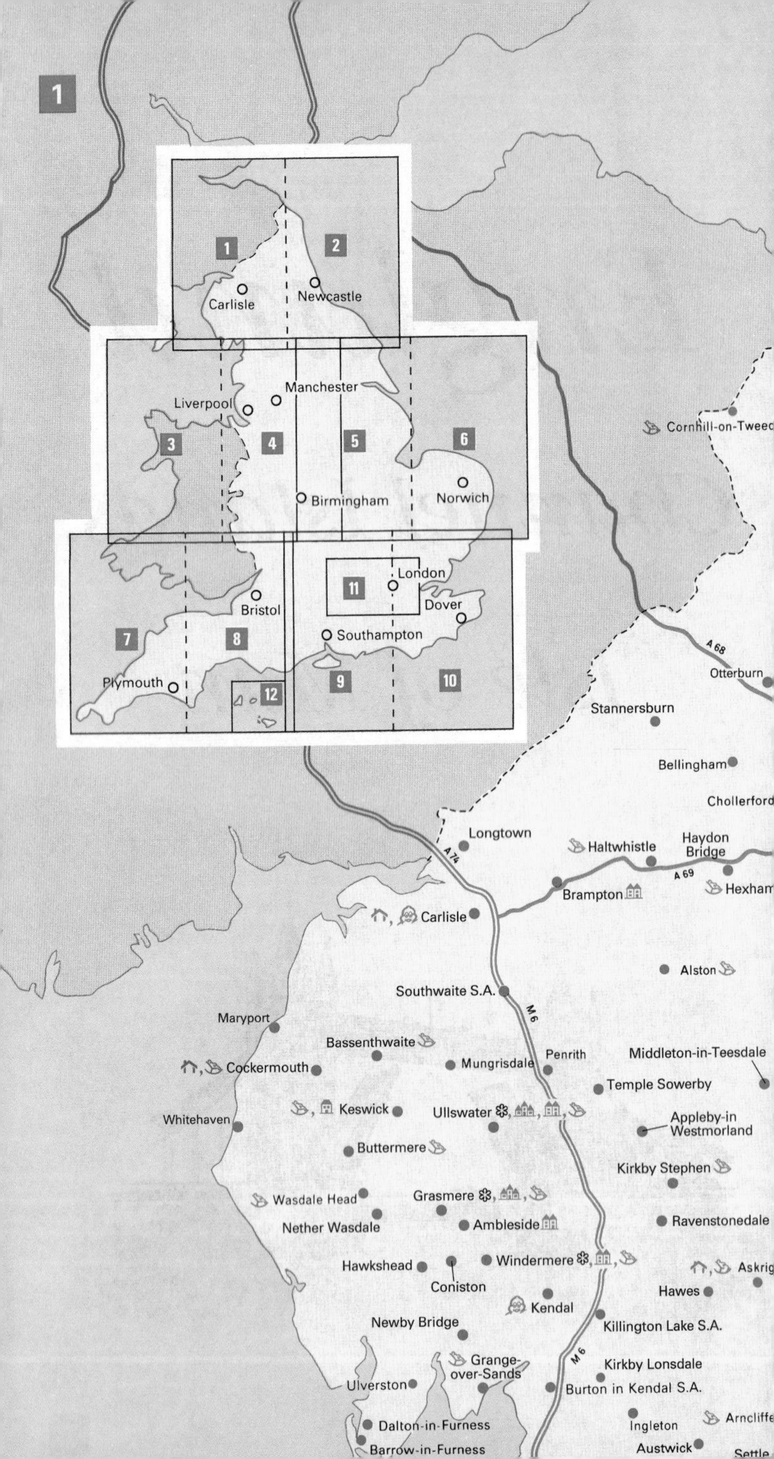

1
1
2
Carlisle
Newcastle
Manchester
Liverpool
3
4
5
6
Birmingham
Norwich
London
11
Dover
Bristol
Southampton
7
8
Plymouth
12
9
10
Cornhill-on-Tweed
A 68
Otterburn
Stannersburn
Bellingham
Chollerford
Longtown
Haltwhistle
Haydon Bridge
A 74
A 69
Hexham
Brampton
Carlisle
Alston
Southwaite S.A.
M 6
Maryport
Bassenthwaite
Penrith
Middleton-in-Teesdale
Mungrisdale
Cockermouth
Temple Sowerby
Keswick
Ullswater
Whitehaven
Appleby-in Westmorland
Buttermere
Kirkby Stephen
Wasdale Head
Grasmere
Nether Wasdale
Ambleside
Ravenstonedale
Hawkshead
Windermere
Askrig
Coniston
Hawes
Kendal
Killington Lake S.A.
Newby Bridge
M 6
Grange-over-Sands
Kirkby Lonsdale
Ulverston
Burton in Kendal S.A.
Dalton-in-Furness
Ingleton
Arncliffe
Barrow-in-Furness
Austwick
Settle

2

Place with at least

a hotel or restaurant ● Ripon
a pleasant hotel or restaurant
a quiet, secluded hotel
a restaurant with ✿, ✿✿, ✿✿✿, Meals

Localité offrant au moins

une ressource hôtelière ● Ripon
un hôtel ou restaurant agréable
un hôtel très tranquille, isolé
une bonne table à ✿, ✿✿, ✿✿✿, Meals

La località possiede come minimo

una risorsa alberghiera ● Ripon
Albergo o ristorante ameno
un albergo molto tranquillo, isolato
un'ottima tavola con ✿, ✿✿, ✿✿✿, Meals

Ort mit mindestens

einem Hotel oder Restaurant ● Ripon
ein angenehmes Hotel oder Restaurant
einem sehr ruhigen und abgelegenen Hotel
einem Restaurant mit ✿, ✿✿, ✿✿✿, Meals

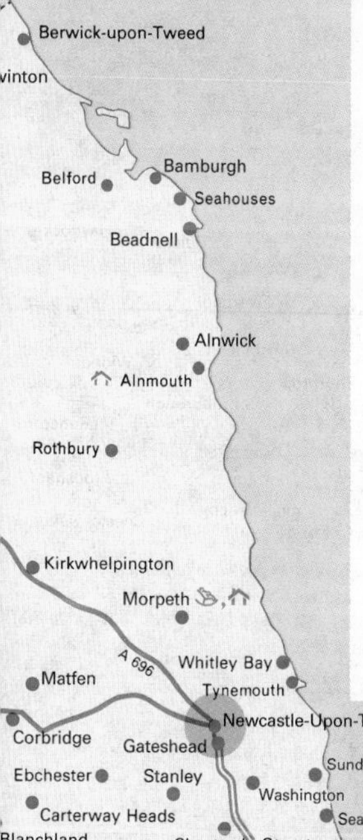

3

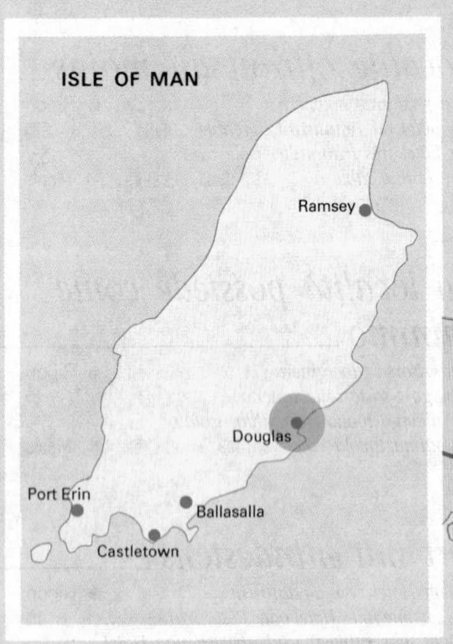

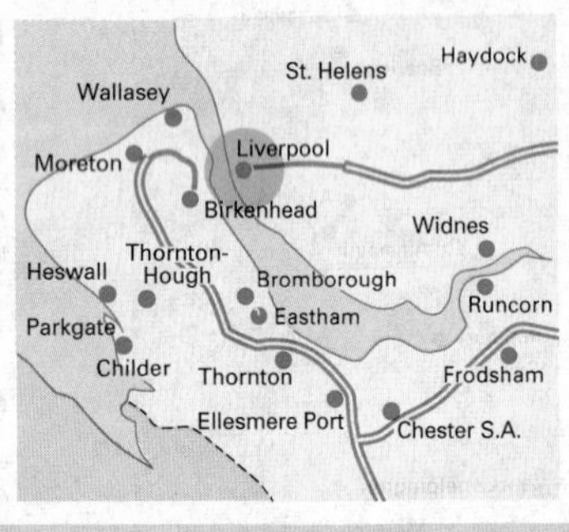

ST GEORGE'S CHANNEL

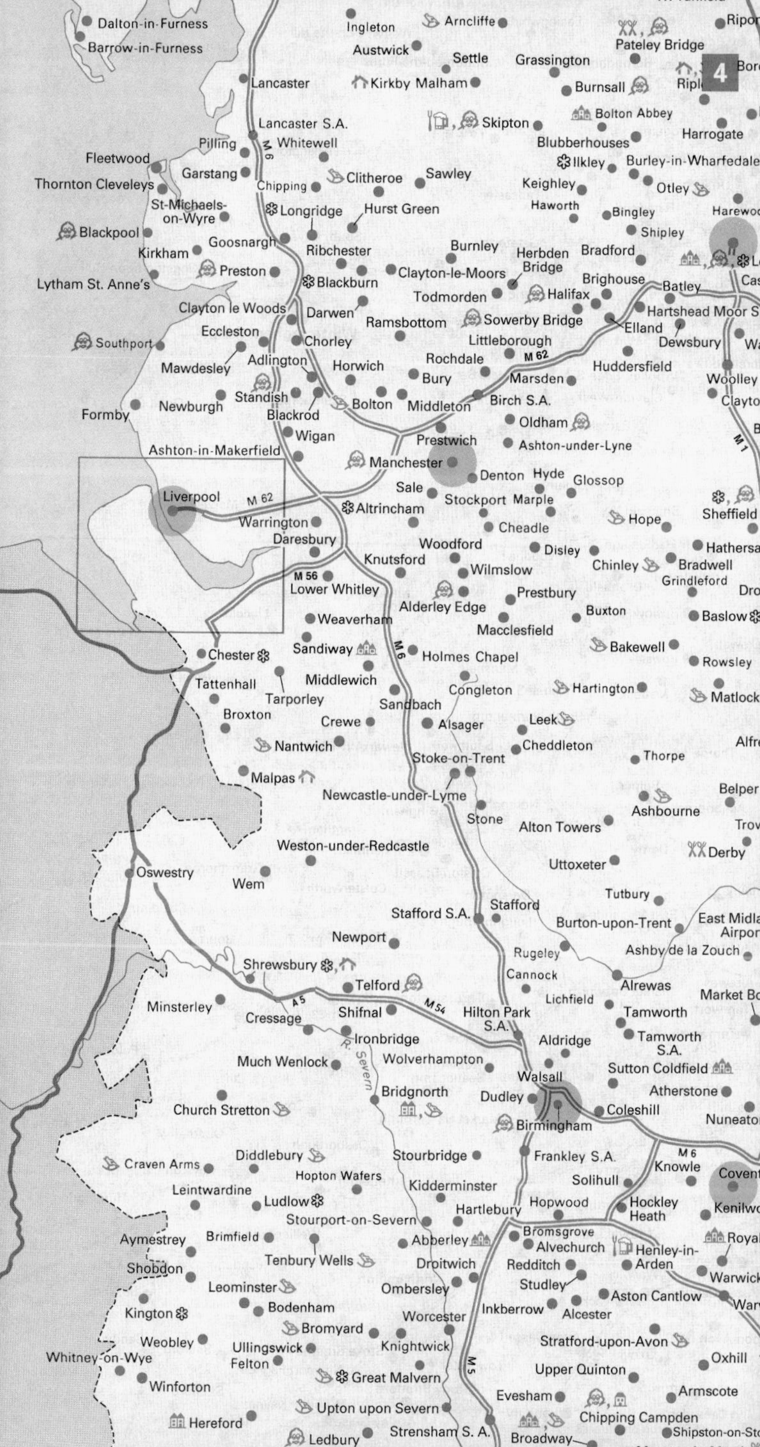
4
Dalton-in-Furness
Barrow-in-Furness
Ingleton
Arncliffe
Austwick
Settle
Grassington
Pateley Bridge
Ripon
Lancaster
Kirkby Malham
Burnsall
Bolton Abbey
Lancaster S.A.
Skipton
Harrogate
Pilling
Whitewell
Blubberhouses
M 6
Fleetwood
Garstang
Clitheroe
Sawley
Ilkley
Burley-in-Wharfedale
Thornton Cleveleys
Chipping
Keighley
Otley
St-Michaels-on-Wyre
Longridge
Hurst Green
Haworth
Bingley
Blackpool
Goosnargh
Shipley
Kirkham
Ribchester
Burnley
Herbden Bridge
Bradford
Preston
Clayton-le-Moors
Lytham St. Anne's
Blackburn
Brighouse
Batley
Todmorden
Halifax
Clayton le Woods
Darwen
Hartshead Moor S.A.
Ramsbottom
Sowerby Bridge
Elland
Southport
Eccleston
Chorley
Littleborough
Dewsbury
Adlington
Rochdale
M 62
Mawdesley
Horwich
Huddersfield
Bury
Marsden
Woolley
Standish
Newburgh
Bolton
Middleton
Birch S.A.
Formby
Blackrod
Oldham
Wigan
Prestwich
Ashton-in-Makerfield
Ashton-under-Lyne
M 1
Manchester
Denton
Hyde
Glossop
Sale
Liverpool
M 62
Stockport
Marple
Altrincham
Sheffield
Warrington
Cheadle
Hope
Daresbury
Woodford
Disley
Knutsford
Chinley
Bradwell
M 56
Wilmslow
Grindleford
Lower Whitley
Prestbury
Alderley Edge
Buxton
Weaverham
Baslow
Macclesfield
Chester
Sandiway
M 6
Holmes Chapel
Bakewell
Rowsley
Tattenhall
Middlewich
Congleton
Hartington
Matlock
Tarporley
Sandbach
Broxton
Crewe
Alsager
Leek
Nantwich
Cheddleton
Thorpe
Stoke-on-Trent
Malpas
Newcastle-under-Lyme
Belper
Ashbourne
Stone
Alton Towers
Weston-under-Redcastle
Derby
Oswestry
Uttoxeter
Wem
Tutbury
Stafford
Stafford S.A.
Burton-upon-Trent
East Midlands Airport
Newport
Rugeley
Ashby de la Zouch
Shrewsbury
Cannock
Telford
Alrewas
A 5
M 54
Lichfield
Minsterley
Shifnal
Hilton Park S.A.
Tamworth
Cressage
Ironbridge
R. Severn
Aldridge
Tamworth S.A.
Wolverhampton
Much Wenlock
Sutton Coldfield
Walsall
Bridgnorth
Atherstone
Dudley
Church Stretton
Coleshill
Nuneaton
Birmingham
Stourbridge
Frankley S.A.
M 6
Craven Arms
Diddlebury
Knowle
Hopton Wafers
Solihull
Kidderminster
Leintwardine
Ludlow
Hopwood
Hockley Heath
Hartlebury
Stourport-on-Severn
Bromsgrove
Aymestrey
Brimfield
Abberley
Alvechurch
Henley-in-Arden
Royal
Tenbury Wells
Droitwich
Redditch
Shobdon
Warwick
Leominster
Ombersley
Studley
Aston Cantlow
Bodenham
Inkberrow
Kington
Alcester
Bromyard
Worcester
Weobley
Stratford-upon-Avon
Ullingswick
Knightwick
Whitney-on-Wye
Felton
Oxhill
M 5
Upper Quinton
Great Malvern
Winforton
Armscote
Evesham
Upton upon Severn
Chipping Campden
Hereford
Broadway
Strensham S. A.
Shipston-on-Stour
Ledbury

5
Ripon
Pateley Bridge
Easingwold
Hovingham
Whitwell-on-the-Hill
Sutton-on-the-Forest
Boroughbridge
Ripley
Knaresborough
Harrogate
York
Wetherby
Burley-in-Wharfedale
Boston Spa
Otley
Tadcaster
Lockington
Bridlington
Brandesburton
Bingley
Harewood
Shipley
Beverley
Gateforth
South Cave
Wressle
Leeds
Castleford
Monk Fryston
Kingston-upon-Hull
Batley
Ferrybridge S.A.
Hartshead Moor S.A.
Elland
Pontefract
Dewsbury
Wakefield
Winteringham
Wentbridge
Woolley Edge S.A.
Barnsdale Bar
Clayton West
Scunthorpe
Great Grimsby
Barnsley
Doncaster
Rotherham
Sheffield
Hope
Blyth
Market Rasen
Louth
Hathersage
Retford
Marton
Bradwell
Grindleford
Woodhall S.A.
Dronfield
Worksop
Markham Moor
Baslow
Lincoln
Bakewell
Chesterfield
Horncastle
Rowsley
Mansfield
Matlock
Tibshelf S.A.
Woodhall Spa
South Normanton
Alfreton
Southwell
Newark-on-Trent
Thorpe
Gunthorpe
Boston
Sleaford
Belper
Ashbourne
Nottingham
Trowell S.A.
Bingham
Grantham
Derby
Langar
Redmile
Colston Bassett
Grimsthorpe
Holbeach
Tutbury
Castle Donington
Colsterworth
East Midlands Airport
Spalding
Loughborough
Ashby de la Zouch
Melton Mowbray
Bourne
Alrewas
Markfield
Market Bosworth
Tamworth
Thrussington
Stamford
Tamworth S.A.
Oakham
Leicester
Sutton Coldfield
Peterborough
Kibworth Beauchamp
Atherstone
Hinckley
Uppingham
King's Cliffe
Coleshill
Nuneaton
Corby
Stilton
Market Harborough
Chatteris
Oundle
Knowle
Desborough
Coventry
Kettering
Keyston
Hockley Heath
Kenilworth
Rugby
Thrapston S.A.
Huntingdon
Brampton
Royal Leamington Spa
St. Ives
Henley-in-Arden
Watford Gap S.A.
Wellingborough
Warwick
Daventry
Rushden
Buckden
Aston Cantlow
Northampton
Warwick S.A.
St. Neots
Caxton
Avon Dassett
Roade
Sandy
Oxhill
Stoke Bruerne
Bedford
Towcester
Newport Pagnell
Melbourn
Armscote
Stony Stratford
Shefford
Banbury
Milton Keynes
Shipston-on-Stour
Aspley Guise
Flitwick
Moreton-in-Marsh
Woburn
A1
M 62
A 63
M 1
M 18
R. Trent
A 17
M 69
M 6
A 14
M 40

NORTH SEA

Burgh-le-Marsh
Burnham Market
Brancaster Staithe
Wells-next -the-Sea
Blakeney
West Runton
Kelling
Cromer
Hunstanton
Little Walsinghan
Binham
Holt
Aylmerton
Snettisham
Great Snoring
Erpingham
Thorpe Market
Barney
Dersingham
Fakenham
North Walsham
Foulsham
Reepham
Long Sutton
Coltishall
Elsing
King's Lynn
Wroxham
East Dereham
A 47
Acle
Norwich
Swaffham
Great Yarmouth
Wymondham
Lowestoft
A 11
Pulham Market
Ely
Mildenhall
Diss
Stanton
Southwold
Thornham Magna
Barton Mills
Yoxford
Westleton
Bury St. Edmunds
Newmarket
Framlingham
Kelsale
A 14
Stowmarket
Cambridge
Snape
Aldeburgh
A 11
Needham Market
Duxford
Lavenham
Woodbridge
Orford
Long Melford
Monks Eleigh
Ipswich
Clare
Sudbury
Hadleigh
Capel St. Mary
Great Yeldham
Stoke-by-Nayland
Nayland
Dedham
Felixstowe

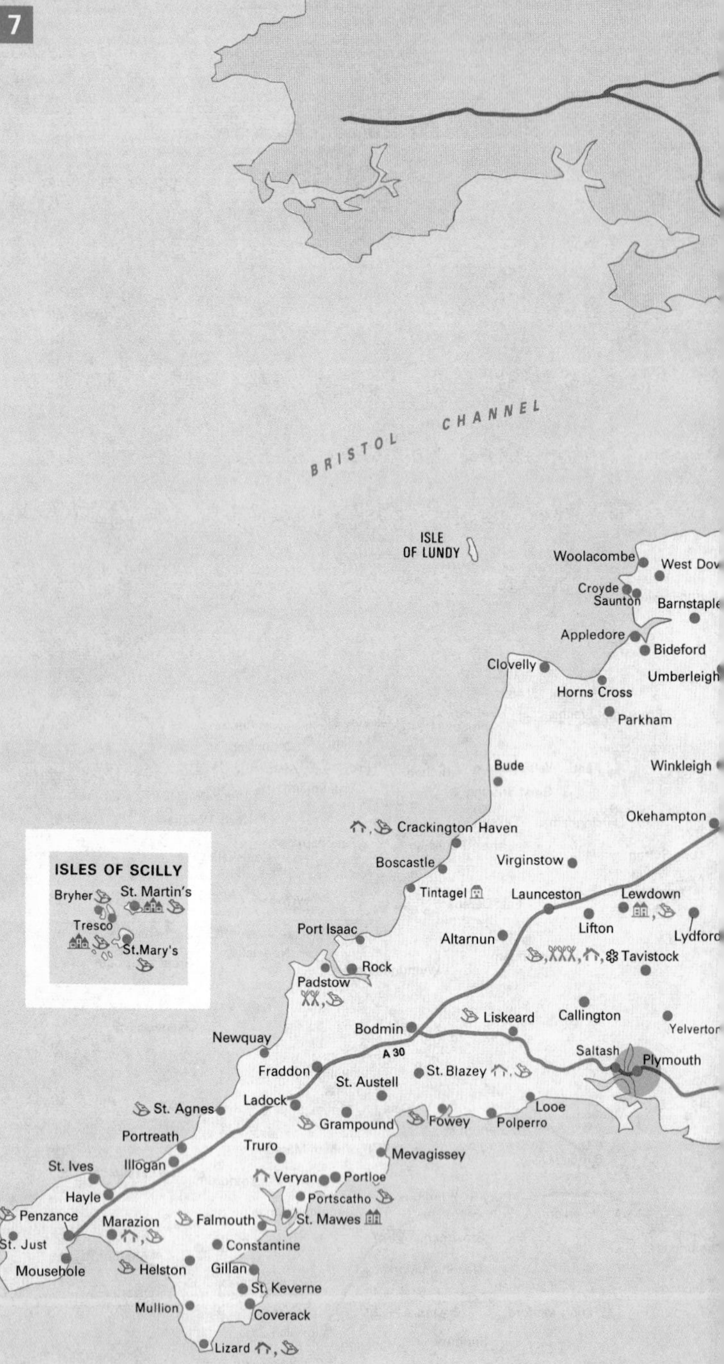

BRISTOL CHANNEL
ISLE OF LUNDY
Woolacombe
West Dov
Croyde
Saunton
Barnstaple
Appledore
Bideford
Clovelly
Umberleigh
Horns Cross
Parkham
Bude
Winkleigh
Okehampton
Crackington Haven
Boscastle
Virginstow
Tintagel
Launceston
Lewdown
Lifton
Lydford
Port Isaac
Altarnun
Tavistock
Rock
Padstow
ISLES OF SCILLY
Bryher
St. Martin's
Tresco
St.Mary's
Liskeard
Callington
Bodmin
Yelverton
Newquay
A 30
Saltash
Plymouth
Fraddon
St. Blazey
St. Austell
Ladock
Looe
St. Agnes
Grampound
Fowey
Polperro
Portreath
Truro
Mevagissey
Illogan
St. Ives
Veryan
Portloe
Hayle
Portscatho
Penzance
Marazion
Falmouth
St. Mawes
St. Just
Constantine
Mousehole
Helston
Gillan
St. Keverne
Mullion
Coverack
Lizard

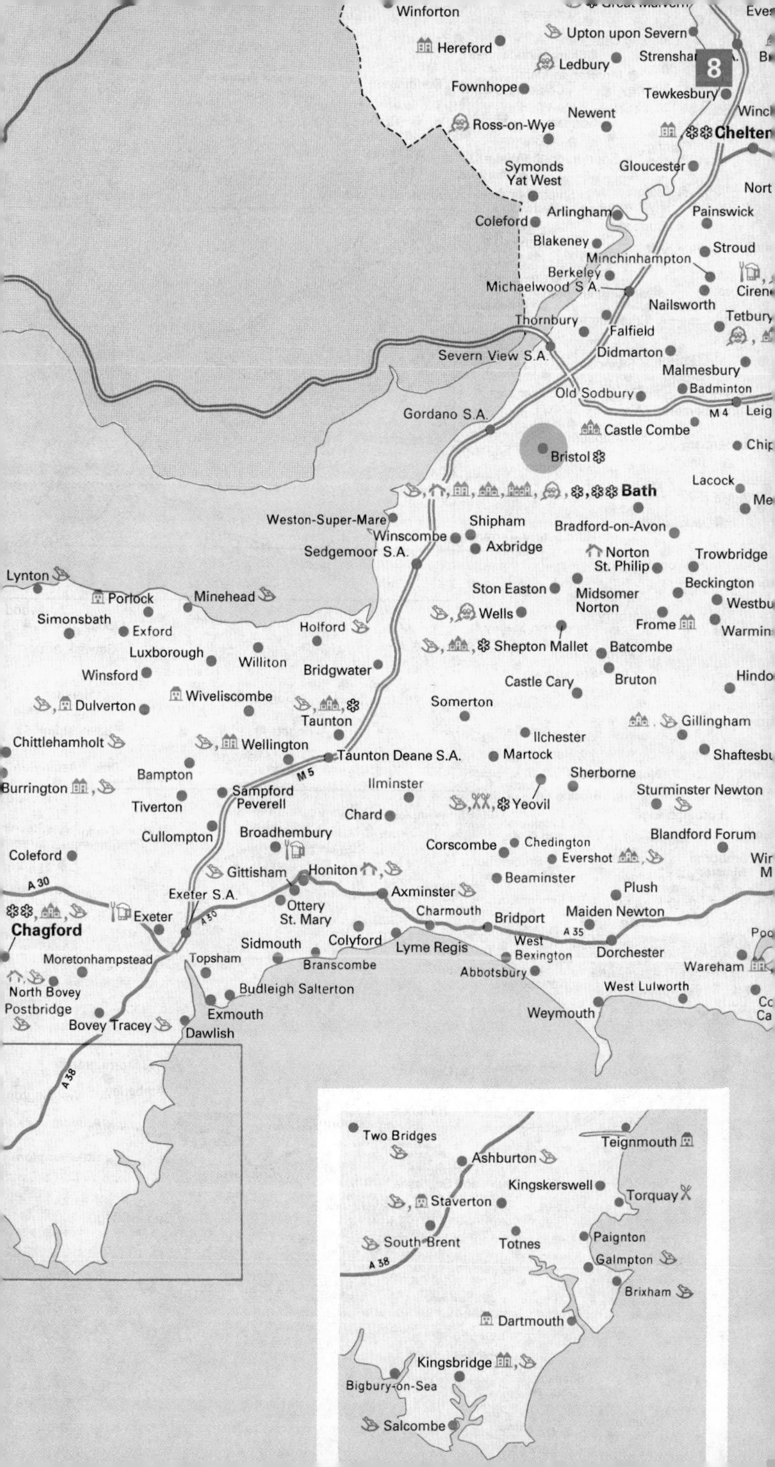

8
Winforton
Hereford
Upton upon Severn
Ledbury
Strensham
Fownhope
Tewkesbury
Newent
Ross-on-Wye
Cheltenham
Gloucester
Symonds Yat West
Coleford
Arlingham
Painswick
Blakeney
Stroud
Minchinhampton
Berkeley
Michaelwood S.A.
Nailsworth
Thornbury
Falfield
Tetbury
Severn View S.A.
Didmarton
Malmesbury
Old Sodbury
Badminton
M 4
Gordano S.A.
Castle Combe
Bristol
Lacock
Bath
Weston-Super-Mare
Shipham
Winscombe
Bradford-on-Avon
Sedgemoor S.A.
Axbridge
Norton St. Philip
Trowbridge
Lynton
Beckington
Porlock
Minehead
Ston Easton
Midsomer Norton
Simonsbath
Wells
Frome
Exford
Holford
Luxborough
Williton
Shepton Mallet
Batcombe
Winsford
Bridgwater
Bruton
Castle Cary
Wiveliscombe
Somerton
Dulverton
Taunton
Gillingham
Chittlehamholt
Ilchester
Wellington
Taunton Deane S.A.
Martock
Shaftesbury
Bampton
M 5
Sherborne
Burrington
Ilminster
Sturminster Newton
Sampford Peverell
Tiverton
Chard
Yeovil
Cullompton
Broadhembury
Blandford Forum
Corscombe
Chedington
Coleford
Evershot
Gittisham
Honiton
Beaminster
A 30
Exeter S.A.
Axminster
Plush
Ottery St. Mary
Charmouth
Exeter
Bridport
Maiden Newton
Chagford
A 30
West Bexington
A 35
Sidmouth
Colyford
Lyme Regis
Dorchester
Moretonhampstead
Topsham
Branscombe
Wareham
Abbotsbury
North Bovey
Budleigh Salterton
West Lulworth
Postbridge
Exmouth
Weymouth
Bovey Tracey
Dawlish
A 38
Two Bridges
Teignmouth
Ashburton
Kingskerswell
Torquay
Staverton
South Brent
Totnes
Paignton
Galmpton
A 38
Brixham
Dartmouth
Kingsbridge
Bigbury-on-Sea
Salcombe

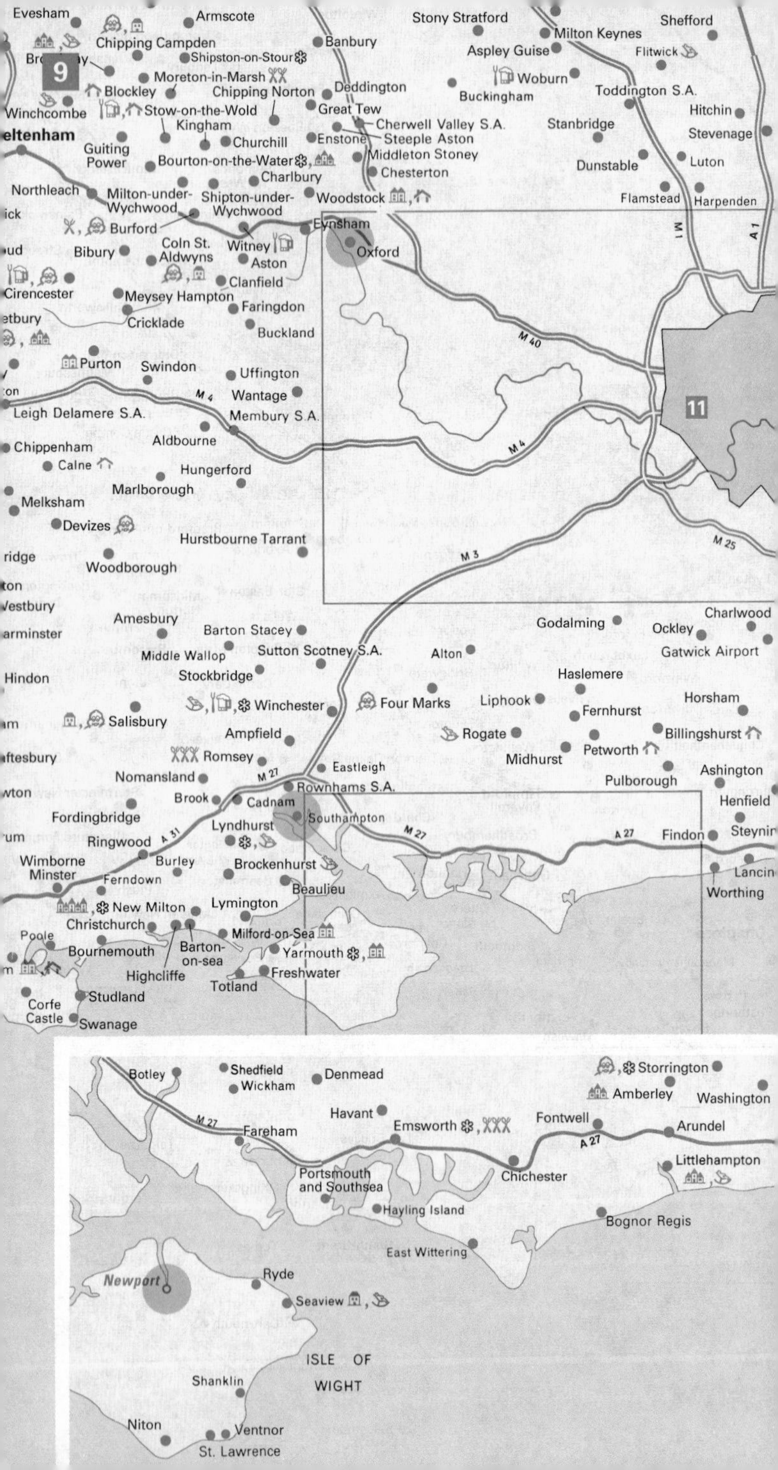
9
Evesham
Armscote
Chipping Campden
Shipston-on-Stour
Banbury
Moreton-in-Marsh
Blockley
Chipping Norton
Deddington
Winchcombe
Stow-on-the-Wold
Great Tew
Kingham
Cherwell Valley S.A.
Steeple Aston
Churchill
Enstone
Guiting Power
Bourton-on-the-Water
Middleton Stoney
Chesterton
Charlbury
Northleach
Milton-under-Wychwood
Shipton-under-Wychwood
Woodstock
Burford
Eynsham
Oxford
Bibury
Coln St. Aldwyns
Witney
Aston
Clanfield
Cirencester
Meysey Hampton
Faringdon
Cricklade
Buckland
Purton
Swindon
Uffington
Wantage
Leigh Delamere S.A.
Membury S.A.
Aldbourne
Chippenham
Calne
Hungerford
Marlborough
Melksham
Devizes
Hurstbourne Tarrant
Woodborough
Amesbury
Barton Stacey
Middle Wallop
Sutton Scotney S.A.
Stockbridge
Hindon
Winchester
Four Marks
Salisbury
Ampfield
Romsey
Eastleigh
Nomansland
Rownhams S.A.
Brook
Cadnam
Southampton
Fordingbridge
Lyndhurst
Ringwood
Burley
Brockenhurst
Wimborne Minster
Ferndown
Beaulieu
New Milton
Lymington
Christchurch
Milford-on-Sea
Poole
Bournemouth
Barton-on-sea
Yarmouth
Highcliffe
Freshwater
Totland
Studland
Corfe Castle
Swanage
Stony Stratford
Milton Keynes
Shefford
Aspley Guise
Flitwick
Woburn
Buckingham
Toddington S.A.
Hitchin
Stanbridge
Stevenage
Dunstable
Luton
Flamstead
Harpenden
M 1
A 1
M 40
M 4
M 3
M 25
M 27
A 31
A 27
11
Godalming
Charlwood
Ockley
Gatwick Airport
Alton
Haslemere
Horsham
Liphook
Fernhurst
Rogate
Billingshurst
Petworth
Midhurst
Ashington
Pulborough
Henfield
Findon
Worthing
Botley
Shedfield
Wickham
Denmead
Storrington
Amberley
Washington
Havant
Fareham
Emsworth
Fontwell
Arundel
Portsmouth and Southsea
Chichester
Littlehampton
Hayling Island
Bognor Regis
East Wittering
Newport
Ryde
Seaview
ISLE OF WIGHT
Shanklin
Niton
Ventnor
St. Lawrence

10

Clare
Sudbury
Hadleigh
Ipswich
M 11
Great Yeldham
Stoke-by-Nayland
Capel St. Mary
Nayland
Dedham
Felixstowe
Baldock
Wethersfield
Clavering
Thaxted
Manningtree
Harwich and Dovercourt
Stansted Airport
Wix
Coggeshall
Bishop's Stortford
Colchester
Great Dunmow
Braintree
Ware
Fuller Street
Feering
Clacton-on-Sea
M 11
Chelmsford
Maldon
M 25
Burnham-on-Crouch
Leigh-on-Sea
Basildon
Rochford
Horndon-on-the-Hill
Southend-on-Sea
LONDON
Canvey Island
North Stifford
Gravesend
Rochester
Medway S.A.
Cobham
M 20
Whitstable
Birchington
Margate
Sittingbourne
West Malling
Faversham
Ramsgate
Maidstone S.A.
Sandwich
Canterbury
Hunton
Maidstone
Lenham
M 25
M 23
Waltham
Deal
Pluckley
M 20
Wye
Horley
Edenbridge
Turners Hill
Royal Tunbridge Wells
Ashford
Dover
East Grinstead
Crawley
Cranbrook
Folkestone
Forest Row
Hartfield
Goudhurst
Tenterden
A 259
Hythe
A 23
Ticehurst
Hawkhurst
Cuckfield
Fletching
New Romney
Uckfield
Sedlescombe
Wittersham
Channel Tunnel
Haywards Heath
Halland
Rushlake Green
Rye
Newick
Battle
Hickstead
Herstmonceux
Winchelsea
Lewes
East Hoathly
Westfield
Hailsham
Hastings and St. Leonards
Brighton and Hove
Bexhill
Alfriston
Newhaven
Eastbourne
Seaford

ENGLISH CHANNEL

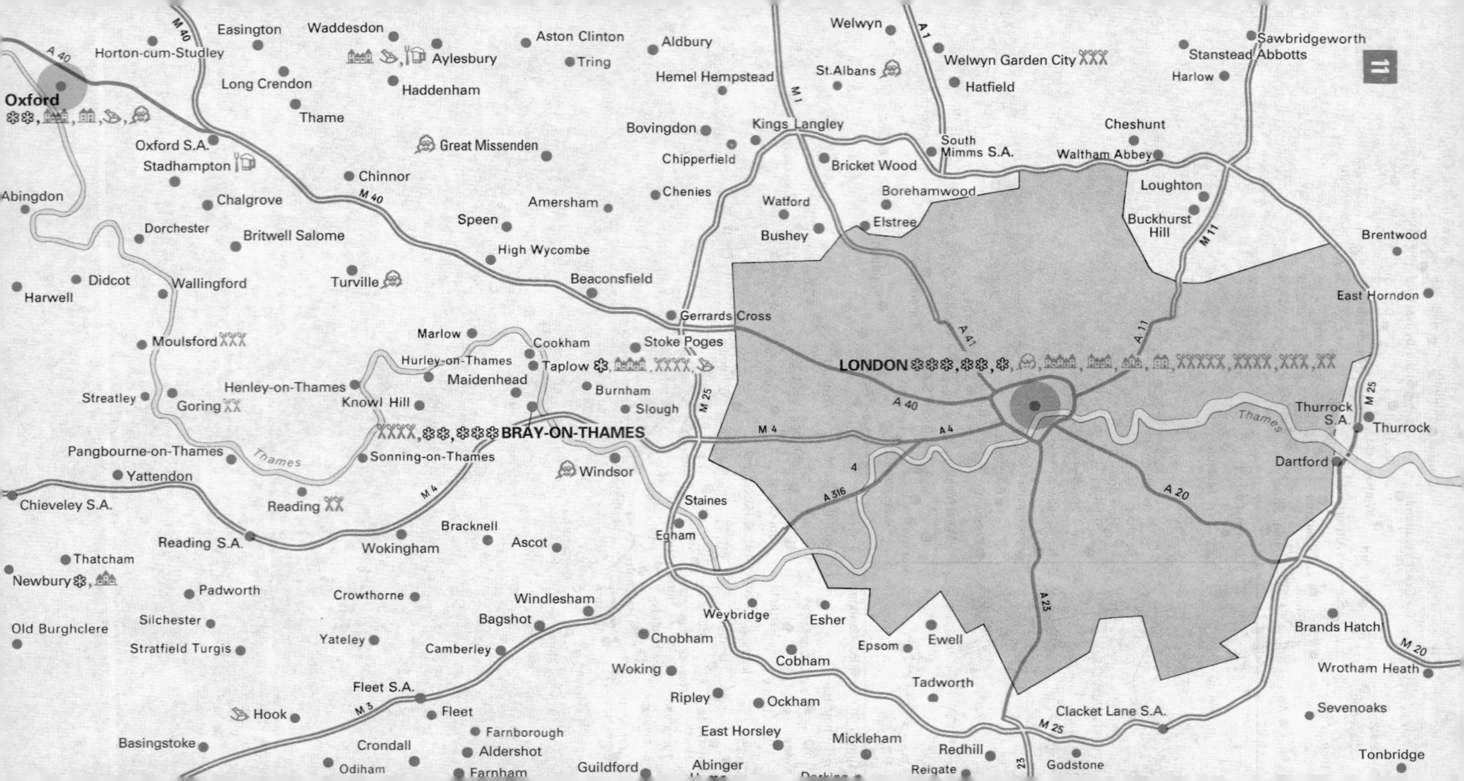

11
Oxford
Horton-cum-Studley
Easington
Waddesdon
Aston Clinton
Aldbury
Welwyn
Sawbridgeworth
Stanstead Abbotts
Aylesbury
Long Crendon
Haddenham
Tring
Hemel Hempstead
St.Albans
Welwyn Garden City
Hatfield
Harlow
Thame
Oxford S.A.
Stadhampton
Great Missenden
Bovingdon
Kings Langley
Chipperfield
South Mimms S.A.
Cheshunt
Waltham Abbey
Bricket Wood
Loughton
Abingdon
Chalgrove
Chinnor
Amersham
Chenies
Watford
Borehamwood
Buckhurst Hill
Dorchester
Britwell Salome
Speen
Elstree
Bushey
High Wycombe
Brentwood
Didcot
Harwell
Wallingford
Turville
Beaconsfield
East Horndon
Gerrards Cross
Marlow
Stoke Poges
Moulsford
Cookham
Hurley-on-Thames
Taplow
LONDON
Maidenhead
Streatley
Henley-on-Thames
Goring
Knowl Hill
Burnham
Slough
Thurrock S.A.
Thurrock
BRAY-ON-THAMES
Pangbourne-on-Thames
Sonning-on-Thames
Thames
Windsor
Dartford
Yattendon
Chieveley S.A.
Reading
Staines
Bracknell
Egham
Reading S.A.
Ascot
Wokingham
Thatcham
Newbury
Padworth
Crowthorne
Windlesham
Bagshot
Weybridge
Esher
Ewell
Brands Hatch
Silchester
Old Burghclere
Yateley
Chobham
Epsom
Stratfield Turgis
Camberley
Cobham
Woking
Wrotham Heath
Tadworth
Fleet S.A.
Ripley
Ockham
Hook
Fleet
Clacket Lane S.A.
Sevenoaks
Farnborough
East Horsley
Basingstoke
Crondall
Aldershot
Mickleham
Redhill
Tonbridge
Odiham
Farnham
Guildford
Abinger
Reigate
Godstone
A 40
M 40
M 1
A 1
M 11
A 41
A 11
A 40
M 4
A 4
4
A 316
A 20
A 23
M 25
M 20
M 3
23

Channel Islands

12

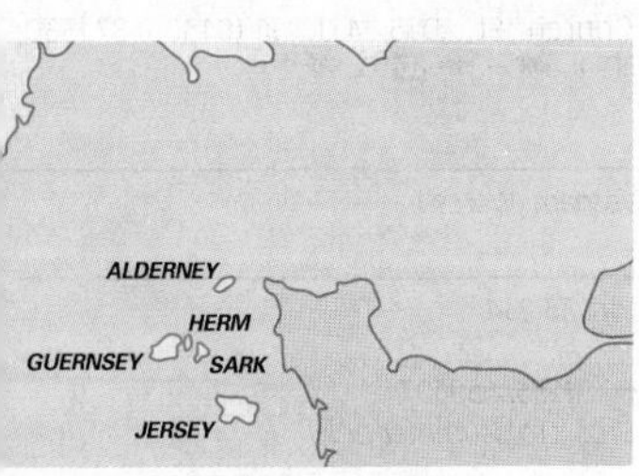

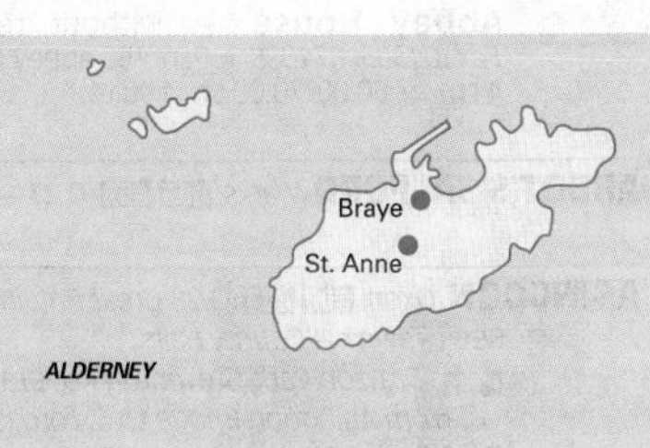

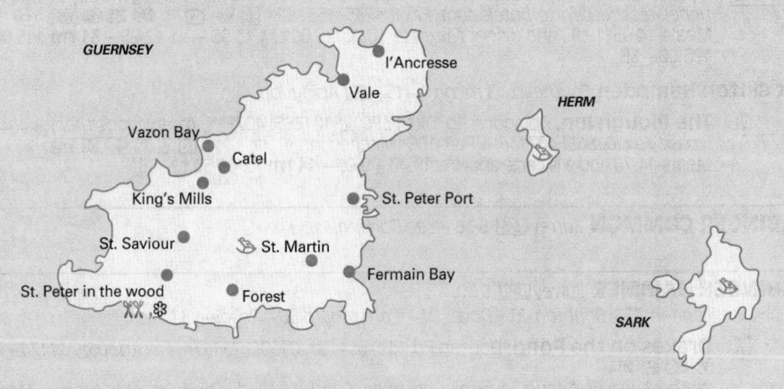

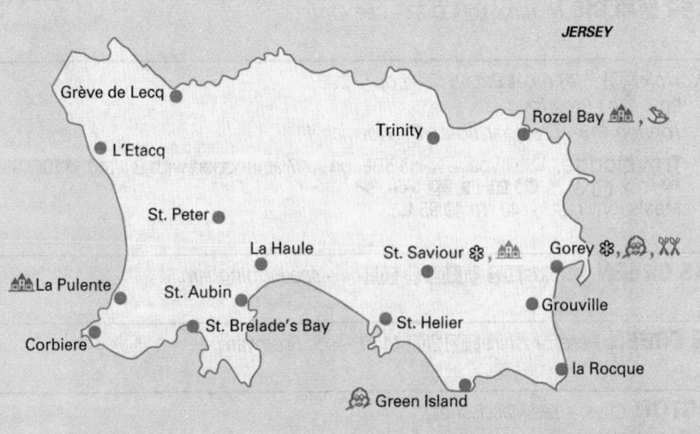

ABBERLEY *Worcs.* 403 404 M 27 – *pop. 654* – ✉ *Worcester.*
London 137 – Birmingham 27 – Worcester 13.

The Elms ⛭, WR6 6AT, West : 2 m. on A 443 ✆ (01299) 896666, *elmshotel@ukonline.co.uk*, *Fax (01299) 896804*, ≤, « Queen Anne mansion », ⛱, 🎾, ✗ – ⇹ rest, TV P – 🏠 40. MC AE D VISA. ✗
Meals 15.00/34.95 **t.** 🍾 16.00 – **21 rm** ☕ 110.00/225.00 **t.** – SB.

ABBOTSBURY *Dorset* 403 404 M 32 *The West Country G.* – *pop. 422.*
See : *Town★★ - Chesil Beach★★ - Swannery★* **AC** – *Sub-Tropical Gardens★* **AC**.
Env. : *St Catherine's Chapel★, ½ m. uphill (30 mn rtn on foot).*
Exc. : *Maiden Castle★★ (≤★) NE : 7½ m.*
London 146 – Exeter 50 – Bournemouth 44 – Weymouth 10.

Abbey House ⛭ without rest., Church St, DT3 4JJ, ✆ (01305) 871330, *Fax (01305) 871088*, « Part 15C abbey infirmary », ⛱ – ⇹ TV P. ✗
4 rm ☕ 60.00/70.00 **st.**, 1 suite.

ABBOT'S SALFORD *Warks.* 403 404 O 27 – *see Evesham (Worcs.).*

ABINGDON *Oxon.* 403 404 Q 28 *Great Britain G.* – *pop. 35 234.*
See : *Town★ – County Hall★.*
⛳18, ⛳9 *Drayton Park, Steventon Rd, Drayton* ✆ *(01235) 550607.*
⛴ *from Abingdon Bridge to Oxford (Salter Bros. Ltd) (summer only).*
ℹ *25 Bridge St* ✆ *(01235) 522711.*
London 64 – Oxford 6 – Reading 25.

Upper Reaches, Thames St, OX14 3JA, ✆ (0870) 4008101, *heritagehotels-abingdon.upper-reaches@forte-hotels.com*, *Fax (01235) 555182* – ⚓ ⇹ TV P. MC AE D VISA JCB
Meals 14.95/19.95 and dinner a la carte 16.00/25.00 **t.** 🍾 13.95 – ☕ 12.95 – **31 rm** 115.00/195.00 – SB.

at Clifton Hampden *Southeast : 3 m. on A 415* – ✉ *Abingdon.*

The Plough Inn, Abingdon Rd, OX14 3EG, ✆ (01865) 407811, *reservation@theploughinn.co.uk*, *Fax (01865) 407136*, « Part 16C thatched inn », ⛱ – ⇹ TV ♿ P. MC AE VISA. ✗
Meals 14.75 and a la carte approx. 18.40 🍾 9.95 – **11 rm** ☕ 69.50 **t.** – SB.

ABINGER COMMON *Surrey* 404 S 30 – *see Dorking.*

ABINGER HAMMER *Surrey* 404 S 30.
London 35 – Brighton 40 – Dover 91 – Portsmouth 50 – Reading 33.

✗✗ **Drakes on the Pond,** Dorking Rd, RH5 6SA, ✆ (01306) 731174, *Fax (01306) 731174* – ▤ P. MC AE VISA
closed 3 weeks August, 1 week Christmas, Sunday, Monday and Saturday lunch – **Meals** 19.00/32.50 **t.** 🍾 11.00.

ACASTER MALBIS *N. Yorks.* 402 Q 22 – *see York.*

ACLE *Norfolk* 404 Y 26 *Great Britain G.* – *pop. 2 208.*
Env. : *The Broads★.*
London 118 – Great Yarmouth 8 – Norwich 11.

Travelodge, Acle bypass, NR13 3BE, on A 47 at junction with B 1140 ✆ (01493) 751970 – ⇹ rm, TV ♿ P. MC AE D VISA JCB. ✗
Meals (grill rest.) – **40 rm** 49.95 **t.**

ACOCKS GREEN *W. Mids* 402 ⑩ 403 ㉒ 404 ⑳ – *see Birmingham.*

ACTON GREEN *Herefordshire* 403 404 M 27 – *see Bromyard.*

ADLINGTON *Ches.* – *see Macclesfield.*

ADLINGTON *Lancs.* 402 404 M 23 – *pop. 8 556.*
London 217 – Liverpool 35 – Manchester 21 – Preston 16.

Gladmar Country, Railway Rd, PR6 9RG, ☎ (01257) 480398, *Fax (01257) 482681,* – TV P. MC AE D VISA.
Meals (residents only) (dinner only) 14.50 **st.** 7.75 – **20 rm** 44.00/64.00 **st.**

AINTREE *Mersey.* 402 403 L 23 – *see Liverpool.*

ALBRIGHTON *Shrops.* 402 403 L 25 – *see Shrewsbury.*

ALCESTER *Warks.* 403 404 O 27 – *pop. 6 282.*
London 104 – Birmingham 20 – Cheltenham 27 – Stratford-upon-Avon 8.

Kings Court, Kings Coughton, B49 5QQ, North : 1 ½ m. on A 435 ☎ (01789) 763111, *info @kingscourthotel.co.uk, Fax (01789) 400242,* – TV P – 130. MC AE VISA
Meals a la carte 10.20/24.00 **t.** – **42 rm** 59.00/86.00 **st.**

Travelodge, Birmingham Rd, Oversley Hill Roundabout, B49 6AA, South : 1 m. at junction of A 46 with A 435 ☎ (01789) 766987, *Fax (01789) 766987* – rm, rest, TV P. MC AE D VISA JCB.
Meals (grill rest.) – **40 rm** 52.95 **t.**

Le Grand Londres (GREATER LONDON) est composé de la City et de 32 arrondissements administratifs (Borough) eux-mêmes divisés en quartiers ou en villages ayant conservé leur caractère propre (Area).

ALDBOURNE *Wilts.* 403 404 P 29 – *pop. 1 682.*
London 77 – Oxford 36 – Southampton 53 – Swindon 9.

XX **Raffles,** 1 The Green, SN8 2BW, ☎ (01672) 540700, *mary@raffles-restaurant.fsnet.co.uk, Fax (01672) 540038* – MC AE D VISA
closed 1 week spring, 2 weeks September, 26-31 December, Monday, Sunday dinner, lunch Tuesday and Bank Holidays – **Meals** 10.50 (lunch) and a la carte 15.80/27.20 **t.**

ALDBURY *Herts.* 404 S 28 – *pop. 891.*
London 39 – Aylesbury 12 – Luton 20 – Oxford 36.

Valiant Trooper, Trooper Rd, HP23 5RW, ☎ (01442) 851203, *Fax (01442) 851071,* – P. MC VISA
closed dinner Sunday and Monday – **Meals** a la carte 15.00/19.50 **t.**

ALDEBURGH *Suffolk* 404 Y 27 – *pop. 2 654.*
Thorpeness Golf Hotel, Thorpeness ☎ (01728) 452176.
152 High St ☎ (01728) 453637.
London 97 – Ipswich 24 – Norwich 41.

Wentworth, Wentworth Rd, IP15 5BD, ☎ (01728) 452312, *stay@wentworth-aldeburgh.co.uk, Fax (01728) 454343,* <, – TV P. MC AE D VISA
closed 1-5 January – **Meals** 13.00/16.00 **t.** 9.95 – **37 rm** 69.50/135.00 – SB.

Flint House without rest., Aldeburgh Rd, Friston, Saxmundham, IP17 1PD, Northwest : 2 ¾ m. on A 1094 ☎ (01728) 689123, *handsel@eidosnet.co.uk,* – TV P
3 rm 35.00/60.00 **st.**

X **The Lighthouse,** 77 High St, IP15 5AU, ☎ (01728) 453377, *sarafox@diron.co.uk, Fax (01728) 453377* – . MC VISA JCB
closed 2 weeks January and 1 week October – **Meals** 16.00 (dinner) and lunch a la carte 16.00/23.75 **t.**

X **152,** 152 High St, IP15 5AX, ☎ (01728) 454152, *Fax (01728) 452505,* – MC VISA JCB
closed 20 January-6 February, Monday in winter and Tuesday – **Meals** a la carte 15.95/23.40 **t.** 9.95.

X **Regatta,** 171-173 High St, IP15 5AN, ☎ (01728) 452011, *Fax (01728) 453324* – . MC AE VISA
closed Sunday dinner-Wednesday November-March, 25-26 December and Wednesday in October – **Meals** - Seafood specialities - a la carte 13.50/21.50 **t.** 9.50.

ENGLAND

ALDERLEY EDGE *Ches.* 402 403 404 N 24 – *pop. 5 280.*

Wilmslow, Great Warford, Mobberley ℘ (01565) 872148.

London 187 – Chester 34 – Manchester 14 – Stoke-on-Trent 25.

Alderley Edge, Macclesfield Rd, SK9 7BJ, ℘ (01625) 583033, *sales@alderley-edge-hotel co.uk, Fax (01625) 586343,* – TV P – 100. MC AE VISA.
Meals – (see ***The Alderley*** below) – 10.50 – **45 rm** 109.00/200.00 **t.**, 1 suite.

The Alderley (at Alderley Edge H.), Macclesfield Rd, SK9 7BJ, ℘ (01625) 583033, *sales@alderley-edge-hotel.co.uk, Fax (01625) 586343,* – P. MC AE VISA
Meals 15.50/25.50 and a la carte 30.70/39.80 **t.** 12.95.

The Wizard, Macclesfield Rd, SK10 4UB, Southeast : 1 ¼ m. on B 5087 ℘ (01625) 584000, *Fax (01625) 585105,* – P. MC AE VISA
closed Monday and Sunday dinner – **Meals** (light lunch)/dinner a la carte 18.25/27.25 **t** 11.00.

Est, Est, Est, 75 London Rd, SK9 7DY, ℘ (01625) 583993, *Fax (01625) 583814,* – . MC AE VISA JCB
closed 25-26 December – **Meals** - Italian - a la carte 11.00/25.60 9.95.

ALDERNEY 403 Q 33 and 230 ⑨ – *see Channel Islands.*

ALDERSHOT *Hants.* 404 R 30.

39 The High St ℘ (01252) 320968.

London 45 – Portsmouth 38 – Reading 22 – Winchester 32.

Potters International, 1 Fleet Rd, GU11 2ET, off A 325 ℘ (01252) 344000, *Fax (01252) 311611,* – rest, TV P – 350. MC AE VISA.
Meals (bar lunch Saturday) 17.50 (dinner) and a la carte 15.00/21.50 **st.** 9.50 – **95 rm** 110.00/195.00 **st.**

Travel Inn, Wellington Ave, GU11 1SQ, East : on A 323 ℘ (01252) 344063, *Fax (01252) 344073* – rm, rest, TV P. MC AE VISA.
Meals (grill rest.) – **60 rm** 41.95 **t.**

ALDFIELD *N. Yorks.* – *see Ripon.*

ALDRIDGE *W. Mids.* 402 403 404 O 26 – *pop. 16 862* – ✉ *Walsall.*

London 130 – Birmingham 12 – Derby 32 – Leicester 40 – Stoke-on-Trent 38.

Plan : see Birmingham p. 5

Fairlawns, 178 Little Aston Rd, WS9 0NU, East : 1 m. on A 454 ℘ (01922) 455122, *welcome@fairlawns.co.uk, Fax (01922) 743210,* – rest, TV P – 80. MC AE VISA.
Meals *(closed Bank Holidays)* 16.50/27.50 **st.** 12.50 – **44 rm** 67.50/117.50 **st.**, 6 suites – SB.

ALFRETON *Derbs.* 402 403 404 P 24 – *pop. 22 822.*

Shirland, Lower Delves ℘ (01773) 834935 – Ormonde Fields, Nottingham Rd, Codnor, Ripley ℘ (01773) 742987.

London 134 – Derby 13 – Nottingham 19 – Sheffield 27.

Travelodge, Old Swanwick Colliery Rd, DE55 1HJ, South : ¾ m. by A 61 at junction with A 38 ℘ (01773) 520040, *Fax (01773) 520040* – rm, rest, TV P – 50. MC AE VISA JCB.
Meals (grill rest.) – **60 rm** 39.95 **t.**

ALFRISTON *E. Sussex* 404 U 31 – *pop. 1 721* – ✉ *Polegate.*

London 66 – Eastbourne 9 – Lewes 10 – Newhaven 8.

Star Inn, High St, BN26 5TA, ℘ (01323) 870495, *heritagehotels_alfriston.star_inn@forte-hotels.com, Fax (01323) 870922,* « Part 14C coaching inn » – TV P – 30. MC AE VISA
Meals (bar lunch Monday-Saturday)/dinner 19.00/30.00 **t.** 12.50 – **37 rm** 60.00/100.00 **t.** – SB.

ALLESLEY *W. Mids.* 403 404 P 26 – *see Coventry.*

ALMONDBURY *W. Yorks.* 402 ⑲ – *see Huddersfield.*

ALNMOUTH *Northd.* 401 402 P 17 *Great Britain G. – pop. 586.*

Env. : *Warkworth Castle★ AC, S : 4 m. by B 1338 and A 1068.*

Alnmouth Village, Marine Rd ☎ (01665) 830370.

London 314 – Edinburgh 90 – Newcastle upon Tyne 37.

Marine House, 1 Marine Rd, NE66 2RW, ☎ (01665) 830349, *tanney@marinehouse.freeserve.co.uk, Fax (01665) 830349,* ← – ⊁ TV P. MC VISA JCB
closed 1 week Christmas and 2-25 January – **Meals** *(closed Monday-Friday)* (dinner only) 14.95 **st.** 7.95 – **13 rm** 49.00/66.00.

High Buston Hall without rest., High Buston, NE66 3QH, Southwest : 2 ¼ m. by B 1338 off A 1068 ☎ (01665) 830606, *highbuston@aol.com, Fax (01665) 830707,* ←, « Georgian house, antiques », – ⊁ P. ⊀
closed Christmas and New Year – **3 rm** 70.00/90.00 **st.**

ALNWICK *Northd.* 401 402 O 17 *Great Britain G. – pop. 7 419.*

See : *Town ★ – Castle★★ AC.*

Exc. : *Dunstanburgh Castle★ AC, NE : 8 m. by B 1340 and Dunstan rd (last 2½ m. on foot).*

Swansfield Park ☎ (01665) 602632.

2 The Shambles ☎ (01665) 510665.

London 320 – Edinburgh 86 – Newcastle upon Tyne 34.

Charlton House without rest., 2 Aydon Gdns, South Rd, NE66 2NT, Southeast : ½ m. ☎ (01665) 605185 – ⊁ TV P. ⊀
restricted opening in winter – **5 rm** 20.00/50.00.

at North Charlton *North : 6 ¾ m. by A 1 – ✉ Alnwick.*

North Charlton Farm without rest., NE67 5HP, ☎ (01665) 579443, *ncharlton@agricplus.net, Fax (01665) 579407,* ←, « Working farm », – ⊁ TV P. ⊀
3 rm 35.00/60.00 **st.**

at Newton on the Moor *South : 5½ m. by A 1 – ✉ Alnwick.*

Cook and Barker Inn with rm, NE65 9JY, ☎ (01665) 575234, *Fax (01665) 575234,* – ⊁ rest, TV P. MC AE VISA. ⊀
closed dinner 25 December – **Meals** 18.50 (dinner) and a la carte 15.90/26.95 **st.** 10.65 – **5 rm** 62.50/115.00 **st.**

at Swarland *South : 7 ¾ m. by A 1 – ✉ Alnwick.*

Swarland Old Hall without rest., NE65 9HU, Southwest : 1 m. on B 6345 ☎ (01670) 787642, *procter@swarlandoldhall.fsnet.co.uk, Fax (01670) 787642,* ←, « Working farm », – ⊁ TV P. ⊀
closed Christmas and April – **3 rm** 30.00/40.00 **st.**

at Eglingham *Northwest : 7 m. on B 6346 – ✉ Alnwick.*

Tankerville Arms, NE66 2TX, ☎ (01665) 578444, – ⊁ P. MC AE VISA
closed 25 December – **Meals** a la carte 12.75/19.65 **t.** 9.50.

ALREWAS *Staffs.* 402 403 404 O 25 – *pop. 4 409 – ✉ Burton-upon-Trent.*

London 127 – Birmingham 24 – Derby 32 – Stoke-on-Trent 30.

The Old Boat, Kings Bromley Rd, DE13 7DB, ☎ (01283) 791468, *sandner@oldboat.freeserve.co.uk, Fax (01283) 791468,* – ⊁ P. MC VISA JCB
Meals a la carte 15.65/20.10 **s.** 10.00.

ALSAGER *Ches.* 402 403 404 N 24 *Great Britain G. – pop. 13 435 – ✉ Stoke-on-Trent (Staffs.).*

Env. : *Little Moreton Hall★★ AC, NE : 4 m. by A 50 and A 34.*

London 180 – Chester 36 – Liverpool 49 – Manchester 32 – Stoke-on-Trent 11.

Manor House, Audley Rd, ST7 2QQ, Southeast : ¾ m. ☎ (01270) 884000, *mhres@compasshotels.co.uk, Fax (01270) 882483,* – ⊁ TV ♿ P – 200. MC AE VISA
Meals (bar meals Saturday lunch and Sunday dinner) 13.00/26.50 and a la carte **st.** 11.00 – **57 rm** 91.00/112.00 **st.** – SB.

Sappho Cottage without rest., 118 Crewe Rd, ST7 2JA, ☎ (01270) 882033, *reception@sappho-cottage.co.uk, Fax (01270) 883556,* – ⊁ TV P. ⊀
4 rm 30.00/50.00.

Wenn Sie ein ruhiges Hotel suchen,
benutzen Sie zuerst die Karte in der Einleitung
oder wählen Sie im Text ein Hotel mit dem Zeichen oder .

ALSTON *Cumbria* 401 402 M 19 – *pop. 2 065.*

Alston Moor, The Hermitage ℘ (01434) 381675.

The Alstonmorry Information Centre, Town Hall ℘ (01434) 382244.

London 309 – Carlisle 28 – Newcastle upon Tyne 45.

Lovelady Shield Country House, Nenthead Rd, CA9 3LF, East : 2 ½ m. on A 689 ℘ (01434) 381203, *enquiries@lovelady.co.uk, Fax (01434) 381515*, ≤, – rest, TV P. MC AE VISA JCB
Meals (dinner only and Sunday lunch) 33.00 **st.** 12.50 – **12 rm** 60.00/180.00 **st.** – SB.

Nent Hall Country House, CA9 3LQ, East : 2 ½ m. on A 689 ℘ (01434) 381584, *info @nenthallhotel.com, Fax (01434) 382668*, – TV P. MC VISA
closed 24-26 December – **Meals** (lunch by arrangement) 13.50/26.00 **t.** 10.50 – **17 rm** 42.00/72.00 **t.** – SB.

High Windy Hall, Middleton in Teesdale Rd, CA9 3EZ, Southeast : 4 m. on B 6277 ℘ (01434) 381547, *sales@hwh.u_net.com, Fax (01434) 382477*, ≤, – TV P. MC VISA JCB.
mid March-November – **Meals** (by arrangement) 22.50 **t.** 9.00 – **5 rm** 35.00/75.00 **t.** – SB.

ALTARNUN *Cornwall* 403 G 32 *The West Country G.* – *pop. 2 405* – ✉ *Launceston.*

See : *Church★.*

Env. : *Bodmin Moor★★, Laneast (St Sidwell's★), N : 2½ m. by minor roads.*

London 279 – Exeter 56 – Plymouth 34 – Truro 39.

Penhallow Manor Country House, PL15 7SJ, ℘ (01566) 86206, *stay@penhallow -manor.co.uk, Fax (01566) 86179*, – TV P. MC VISA.
closed 28 December-February – **Meals** (dinner only) 23.00 **t.** 10.50 – **6 rm** 60.00/ 120.00 **t.** – SB.

ALTON *Hants.* 404 R 30 – *pop. 16 005.*

Old Odiham Rd ℘ (01420) 82042.

7 Cross and Pillory Lane ℘ (01420) 88448.

London 53 – Reading 24 – Southampton 29 – Winchester 18.

Grange, London Rd, GU34 4EG, Northeast : 1 m. on A 3004 ℘ (01420) 86565, *info@alton grange.co.uk, Fax (01420) 541346*, – TV P – 80. MC AE VISA JCB.
closed 23 December-2 January – ***Truffles :*** **Meals** a la carte 24.65/31.85 **t.** 11.50 – **31 rm** 79.50/145.00 **t.**

ALTON TOWERS *Staffs.* 402 403 404 O 25.

London 158 – Birmingham 48 – Derby 23 – Stafford 24 – Stoke-on-Trent 13.

Alton Towers, ST10 4DB, ℘ (0870) 5001100, *info@alton-towers, Fax (01538) 704657*, ≤, « Fantasy themed », – rest, TV P – 200. MC AE VISA.
closed 25-30 December – ***Secret Garden :*** **Meals** (light lunch)/dinner a la carte 16.85/ 20.85 **t.** – 4.95 – **175 rm** 109.00/145.00 **t.**

ALTRINCHAM *Gtr. Manchester* 402 403 404 N 23 – *pop. 40 042.*

Altrincham Municipal, Stockport Rd, Timperley ℘ (0161) 928 0761 – Dunham Forest, Oldfield Lane ℘ (0161) 928 2605 – Ringway, Hale Mount, Hale Barns ℘ (0161) 904 9609.

20 Stamford New Rd ℘ (0161) 912 5931.

London 191 – Chester 30 – Liverpool 30 – Manchester 8.

Cresta Court, Church St, WA14 4DP, on A 56 ℘ (0161) 927 7272, *info@cresta-court. co.uk, Fax (0161) 926 9194*, – rest, TV P – 320. MC AE VISA
Meals (bar lunch Monday and Saturday) 15.95/25.00 **st.** 13.95 – 8.95 – **136 rm** 76.50/ 86.50 **st.** – SB.

Quality H., Langham Rd, WA14 2HT, Southwest : 1 m. by A 538 on B 5161 ℘ (0161) 928 7121, *admin@gb064.u-net.com, Fax (0161) 927 7560*, – rest, TV P – 160. MC AE VISA
Meals *(closed Saturday lunch)* 17.95 (dinner) and a la carte approx. 25.70 **st.** 11.95 – 10.75 – **89 rm** 95.00/105.00 **t.** – SB.

Premier Lodge, Manchester Rd, West Timperley, WA14 5NH, North : 2 m. on A 56 ℘ (0161) 962 7414, *Fax (0161) 962 3456* – rm, TV P – 50. MC AE VISA JCB.
Meals (grill rest.) – **48 rm** 46.95 **st.**

XXX **Juniper,** 21 The Downs, WA14 2QD, ☎ (0161) 929 4008, *reservations@juniper-restaurant.co.uk, Fax (0161) 929 4009* – ⊭ ▤. MC AE VISA JCB
closed 25-26 December, 1 week January, 2 weeks August, Saturday lunch, Sunday and Monday – **Meals** 18.00 (lunch) and a la carte 30.00/41.00 **t.** 16.00
Spec. Yeast soup, assiette of leeks. Roast saddle of rabbit, crab bisque. "Stella Artois" sorbet.

X **Snockers-On-The-Green,** 9 Goose Green, WA14 1DW, ☎ (0161) 929 8929, *chris@snockers.com* – MC AE ① VISA JCB
closed Monday dinner and Sunday – **Meals** 11.00/14.95 and dinner a la carte 22.00/30.25 **t.** 13.00.

at Hale *Southeast : 1 m. on B 5163 – ✉ Altrincham.*

X **Est, Est, Est,** 183 Ashley Rd, WA15 9SD, ☎ (0161) 928 1811, *Fax (0161) 928 3468* – ▤. MC AE ① VISA
Meals - Italian - a la carte 9.40/26.60 10.95.

at Halebarns *Southeast : 3 m. on A 538 – ✉ Altrincham.*

Marriott Manchester Airport, Manchester Airport, Hale Rd, WA15 8XW, ☎ (0161) 904 0301, *sfsh@lineone.net, Fax (0161) 980 1787,* Fб, ≘s, ▢, 🛲 – |≡|, ⊭ rm, ▤ TV ☏ P – 🎓 200. MC AE ① VISA JCB. ✻
The Four Seasons : **Meals** 15.95/22.95 and dinner a la carte 22.95/31.40 **st.** – ☕ 12.95 – **142 rm** 115.00 **st.** – SB.

ALVECHURCH *Worcs.* 403 404 O 26 – *pop. 5 829.*
London 113 – Birmingham 11 – Bromsgrove 6.

Alcott Farm without rest., Weatheroak, B48 7EH, Northeast : 2 ¾ m. by Radford Rd on Beoley rd (Icknield St) ☎ (01564) 824051, *Fax (01564) 829799,* 🛲, 🎾 – ⊭ TV P. ✻
4 rm ☕ 35.00/55.00.

ALVELEY *Shrops. – see Bridgnorth.*

ALWALTON *Cambs.* 402 404 T 26 – *see Peterborough.*

AMBERLEY *W. Sussex* 404 S 31 *Great Britain G. – pop. 525 – ✉ Arundel.*
Env. : *Bignor Roman Villa (mosaics★) AC, NW : 3½ m. by B 2139 via Bury.*
London 56 – Brighton 24 – Portsmouth 31.

Amberley Castle 🐚, BN18 9ND, Southwest : ½ m. on B 2139 ☎ (01798) 831992, *info@amberleycastle.co.uk, Fax (01798) 831998,* « 14C castle, 12C origins », 🛲, 🎾 – ⊭ TV P – 🎓 40. MC AE ① VISA. ✻
Queen's Room : **Meals** (booking essential) 17.50/45.00 **t.** 17.50 – ☕ 16.50 – **13 rm** 145.00/195.00 **t.**, 6 suites – SB.

AMBLESIDE *Cumbria* 402 **L 20** *Great Britain G. – pop. 2 905.*
Env. : *Lake Windermere★★ – Dove Cottage, Grasmere★ AC* **AY A** – *Brockhole National Park Centre★ AC, SE : 3 m. by A 591* **AZ**.
Exc. : *Wrynose Pass★★, W : 7½ m. by A 593* **AY** – *Hard Knott Pass★★, W : 10 m. by A 593* **AY**.
ℹ *Central Buildings, Market Cross ☎ (015394) 32582* **AZ** – *Main Car Park, Waterhead ☎ (015394) 32729 (summer only)* **BY**.
London 278 – Carlisle 47 – Kendal 14.

Plan on next page

The Samling 🐚, Ambleside Rd, LA23 1LR, South : 1 ½ m. on A 591 ☎ (015394) 31922, *info@thesamling.com, Fax (015394) 30400,* ≤ Lake Windermere and mountains, 🐚, 🛲, 🎾 – ⊭ rest, TV P. MC AE ① VISA. ✻
Meals (booking essential for non-residents) (dinner only and Sunday lunch) 35.00 **st.** 14.95 – **8 rm** ☕ 110.00/275.00 **st.**, 2 suites.

Rothay Manor, Rothay Bridge, LA22 0EH, South : ½ m. on A 593 ☎ (015394) 33605, *hotel@rothaymanor.co.uk, Fax (015394) 33607,* ≤, 🛲 – ⊭ rest, TV ♿ P. MC AE ① VISA JCB. ✻ **BY r**
closed 3 January-8 February – **Meals** 15.00/31.00 **t.** 13.00 – **16 rm** ☕ (dinner included) 104.00/192.00 **t.**, 2 suites – SB.

Ambleside Salutation, Lake Rd, LA22 9BX, ☎ (015394) 32244, *enquiries@hotelambleside.uk.com, Fax (015394) 34157,* Fб, ≘s – ⊭ TV P – 🎓 40. MC AE ① VISA JCB **AZ r**
Garden : **Meals** (dinner only) 16.50/19.50 **st.** 11.00 – **42 rm** ☕ 41.00/108.00 **st.** – SB.

AMBLESIDE GRASMERE

Borrans Rd . . . . **BY** 2
Broadgate . . . . **BZ** 3
Cheapside . . . . **AZ** 4
Church St. . . . . **AZ** 6
Compston St . . . . **AZ** 8
Easedale Rd. . . . . **BZ** 10
Kelsick Rd . . . . **AZ** 12
King St . . . . **AZ** 13
Lake Rd . . . . **AZ**
Market Pl . . . . **AZ** 14
North Rd . . . . **AZ** 17
Old Lake Rd . . . . **AZ** 20
St. Mary's Lane . . . . **AZ** 22
Smithy Brow . . . . **AZ** 23
Swan Hill . . . . **AY** 24

***Town plans:** roads most used by traffic and those on which guide listed hotels and restaurants stand are fully drawn; the beginning only of lesser roads is indicated.*

Borrans Park, Borrans Rd, LA22 0EN, ✆ (015394) 33454, *mail@borranspark.co.uk, Fax (015394) 33003*, ←, 🚗 – ⊁ TV & P. MC VISA JCB. ✗ BY a
Meals (booking essential to non-residents) (dinner only) 20.00 ⌶ 6.95 – **12 rm** ☐ 60.00/90.00 **st.** – SB.

Brathay Lodge without rest., Rothay Rd, LA22 0EE, ✆ (01539) 432000, *brathay@globalnet.co.uk* – ⊁ TV P. MC VISA JCB AZ e
21 rm 50.00/110.00 **t.**

Elder Grove without rest., Lake Rd, LA22 0DB, ✆ (015394) 32504, *info@eldergrove.co.uk, Fax (015394) 32504* – ⊁ TV P. MC VISA JCB AZ a
closed 24-26 December – **10 rm** ☐ 32.00/68.00 **t.**

Ambleside Lodge without rest., Rothay Rd, LA22 0EJ, ✆ (015394) 31681, *cherryho@globalnet.co.uk, Fax (015394) 34547*, 🚗 – ⊁ TV P. MC VISA JCB AZ x
18 rm ☐ 50.00/140.00 **t.**

Crow How ⛬, Rydal Rd, LA22 9PN, Northwest : ½ m. on A 591 ✆ (015394) 32193, *Fax (015394) 31770*, ←, 🚗 – ⊁ TV P. MC VISA BY x
Meals (dinner only) 16.95 **st.** ⌶ 10.95 – **9 rm** ☐ 45.00/69.00 **st.** – SB.

Rowanfield Country House ⛬, Kirkstone Rd, LA22 9ET, Northeast : ¾ m. ✆ (015394) 33686, *email@rowanfield.com, Fax (015394) 31569*, ← Lake Windermere and Coniston Old Man, 🚗 – ⊁ TV P. MC VISA. ✗ AZ u
closed late November-mid March except 24 December-1 January – **Meals** (by arrangement) 25.00 **st.** – **8 rm** ☐ 57.00/100.00 **st.** – SB.

Laurel Villa without rest., Lake Rd, LA22 0DB, ✆ (015394) 33240, *laurel/villa-ambleside@hotmail.com, Fax (015394) 33240* – ⊁ TV P. ✗ AZ s
8 rm ☐ 30.00/70.00 **st.**

Riverside ⛬ without rest., Under Loughrigg, LA22 9LJ, ✆ (015394) 32395, *hotel@riverside-ambleside.co.uk, Fax (015394) 32240*, 🚗 – TV P. MC VISA. ✗ BY s
closed 24 December-4 January – **5 rm** ☐ 30.00/80.00 **t.**

The Log House, Lake Rd, LA22 0DN, ✆ (015394) 31077 – ⊁. MC VISA BY v
Meals a la carte 23.50/32.45 **t.** ⌶ 13.50.

Glass House, Rydal Rd, LA22 9AN, ✆ (015394) 32137, *enquiries@theglasshouserestaurant.co.uk, Fax (015394) 31139*, « Converted 15C mill » – ⊁. MC VISA AZ v
closed 3 weeks January and 25-26 December – **Meals** (booking essential) a la carte 19.45/26.25 **t.** ⌶ 10.50.

Drunken Duck Inn with rm, Barngates, LA22 0NG, Southwest : 3 m. by A 593 and B 5286 on Tarn Hows rd ✆ (015394) 36347, *info@drunkenduckinn.co.uk, Fax (015394) 36781*, ←, « Part 16C » – ⊁ rest, TV P. MC AE VISA JCB. ✗
closed 25 December – **Meals** a la carte 14.00/33.00 **t.** ⌶ 10.00 – **13 rm** ☐ 60.00/120.00 **t.**

at Waterhead *South : 1 m. on A 591* – ✉ *Ambleside.*

Wateredge, Borrans Rd, LA22 0EP, ✆ (015394) 32332, *info.m@wateredgehotel.co.uk, Fax (015394) 31878*, ←, « Part 17C fishermen's cottages, lakeside setting », 🚗 – ⚓, ⊁ rest, TV P. MC AE ① VISA JCB BY o
closed 1 week Christmas – ***Wateredge Inn :*** **Meals** a la carte 12.95/20.40 **t.** ⌶ 10.50 – **21 rm** ☐ 45.00/110.00 **t.**

Regent, LA22 0ES, ✆ (015394) 32254, *info@regentlakes.co.uk, Fax (015394) 31474* – ⊁ TV P. MC VISA BY e
closed 1 week Christmas – **Meals** (bar lunch)/dinner 21.00/25.00 and a la carte 24.00/31.00 **t.** ⌶ 12.95 – **30 rm** ☐ 65.00/130.00 **t.** – SB.

at Clappersgate *West : 1 m. on A 593* – ✉ *Ambleside.*

Nanny Brow Country House ⛬, LA22 9NF, ✆ (015394) 32036, *reservations@nannybrowhotel.co.uk, Fax (015394) 32450*, ←, « Landscaped gardens », ⛏ – ⊁ TV P. MC AE VISA JCB BY u
Meals (booking essential) (dinner only) a la carte approx. 39.00 **t.** ⌶ 8.00 – **12 rm** ☐ (dinner included) 105.00/210.00 **t.**, 3 suites – SB.

Grey Friar Lodge, LA22 9NE, ✆ (015394) 33158, *greyfriar@veen.freeserve.co.uk, Fax (015394) 33158*, ←, « Antiques », 🚗 – ⊁ TV P. MC VISA JCB. ✗ BY n
closed mid December-mid January – **Meals** *(closed Monday)* (residents only) (dinner only) (set menu only) 18.50 **st.** ⌶ 9.50 – **8 rm** ☐ 36.00/88.00 **st.** – SB.

at Skelwith Bridge *West : 2½ m. on A 593* – ✉ *Ambleside.*

Skelwith Bridge, LA22 9NJ, ✆ (015394) 32115, *skelwithbr@aol.com, Fax (015394) 34254* – ⊁ rest, TV P. MC VISA JCB AY v
closed 13-23 December – ***The Bridge :*** **Meals** (dinner only and Sunday lunch) 10.25/21.50 **st.** ⌶ 10.25 – **29 rm** ☐ 50.00/90.00 **st.** – SB.

Greenbank without rest., LA22 9NW, on A 593 ✆ (015394) 33236, *greenbank@bigwig.net*, ←, 🚗 – ⊁ TV P. ✗ AY e
3 rm ☐ 34.00/48.00.

ENGLAND

at Elterwater *West : 4½ m. by A 593 off B 5343 – ✉ Ambleside.*

Langdale H. & Country Club, Great Langdale, LA22 9JD, Northwest : ½ m. on B 5343 ☎ (015394) 37302, Reservations (Freephone) 0500 051197, *info@langdale.co.uk, Fax (015394) 37694,* squash – rest, – 100. AE VISA. AY c
Purdeys : **Meals** (light lunch)/dinner 20.00/25.00 12.95 – **65 rm** 130.00/210.00 – SB.

Eltermere Country House, LA22 9HY, ☎ (015394) 37207, *colin@hensington.demon.co.uk, Fax (015394) 37540,* ←, – AE VISA JCB. AY i
Meals (dinner only) 25.00 **st.** 12.50 – **19 rm** (dinner included) 45.00/130.00 **st.** – SB.

at Little Langdale *West : 5 m. by A 593 – ✉ Langdale.*

Three Shires Inn, LA22 9NZ, ☎ (015394) 37215, *enquiry@threeshiresinn.co.uk, Fax (015394) 37127,* ←, – rest, VISA. AY z
closed January – **Meals** (bar lunch)/dinner 19.75 **st.** 9.50 – **10 rm** 35.00/86.00 **st.** – SB.

AMERSHAM (Old Town) *Bucks.* 404 S 28 – *pop. 21 711.*
Little Chalfont, Lodge Lane ☎ (01494) 764877.
Tesco's Car Park, London Road West ☎ (01494) 729492 (April-September).
London 29 – Aylesbury 16 – Oxford 33.

Crown, 16 High St, HP7 0DH, ☎ (0870) 4008103, *heritagehotels-amersham.crown@forte-hotels.com, Fax (01494) 431283,* « Part 16C former coaching inn », – AE VISA JCB.
Meals 15.95/21.95 and a la carte 22.00/34.00 **t.** 13.75 – 12.50 – **37 rm** 145.00/180.00 **st.** – SB.

King's Arms (Restaurant), High St, HP7 0DJ, ☎ (01494) 726333, *Fax (01494) 433480,* « Part 15C inn » – AE VISA JCB
closed 25-28 December, Sunday dinner and Monday – **Meals** 14.50/25.00 and a la carte 22.95/28.00 **t.** 10.20.

Gilbey's, 1 Market Sq, HP7 0DF, ☎ (01494) 727242, *gilbeysamersham@cs.com, Fax (01494) 431243,* – AE VISA
closed 24-27 December – **Meals** (booking essential) a la carte 18.85/24.95 **t.** 8.70.

AMESBURY *Wilts.* 403 404 O 30 *The West Country G. – pop. 6 333.*
Env. : *Stonehenge★★★ AC, W : 2 m. by A 303.*
Exc. : *Wilton Village★ (Wilton House★★ AC, Wilton Carpet Factory★ AC), SW : 13 m. by A 303, B 3083 and A 36.*
Redworth House, Flower Lane ☎ (01980) 622833.
London 87 – Bristol 52 – Taunton 66.

Travelodge, SP4 7AS, North : ¼ m. at junction of A 303 with A 345 ☎ (01980) 624966, *Fax (01980) 624966* – rm, AE VISA JCB.
Meals (grill rest.) – **48 rm** 52.95 **t.**

Mandalay without rest., 15 Stonehenge Rd, SP4 7BA, ☎ (01980) 623733, *Fax (01980) 626642,* – AE VISA JCB.
5 rm 38.00/46.00 **s.**

AMPFIELD *Hants.* 403 404 P 30 – *pop. 1 523 – ✉ Romsey.*
Ampfield (Par Three), Winchester Rd ☎ (01794) 368480.
London 79 – Bournemouth 31 – Salisbury 19 – Southampton 11 – Winchester 7.

Potters Heron, Winchester Rd, SO51 9ZF, on A 3090 ☎ (02380) 266611, *Fax (02380) 251359,* – rest, – 150. AE VISA
Meals (bar lunch Monday to Saturday)/dinner 19.95 and a la carte 18.40/28.75 **st.** 10.95 – 10.75 – **54 rm** 90.00/99.00 **st.** – SB.

Keats, Winchester Rd, SO51 9BQ, on A 3090 ☎ (01794) 368252 – AE VISA JCB.
closed Sunday, Monday and Bank Holidays – **Meals** - Italian - 11.20 (lunch) and a la carte 19.90/27.70 **t.** 11.20.

AMPLEFORTH *N. Yorks.* 402 Q 21 – *✉ York.*
London 237 – Leeds 53 – Middlesbrough 29 – York 24.

Shallowdale House, YO62 4DY, West : ½ m. ☎ (01439) 788325, *stay@shallowdalehouse.demon.co.uk, Fax (01439) 788885,* ← Gilling Gap, – VISA.
closed Christmas and New Year – **Meals** (by arrangement) 22.50 **st.** 12.50 – **3 rm** 44.00/80.00 **st.** – SB.

AMPNEY CRUCIS *Glos.* 403 404 O 28 – *see Cirencester.*

ANNITSFORD *Northd.* 401 P 18 – *see Newcastle upon Tyne (Tyne and Wear).*

ANSTY *W. Mids. – see Coventry.*

APPLEBY-IN-WESTMORLAND *Cumbria* 402 M 20 – *pop. 2 570 (inc. Bongate).*
Appleby, Brackenber Moor (017683) 51432.
Moot Hall, Boroughgate (017683) 51177.
London 285 – Carlisle 33 – Kendal 24 – Middlesbrough 58.

Appleby Manor Country House, Roman Rd, CA16 6JB, East : 1 m. by B 6542 and Station Rd (017683) 51571, *reception@applebymanor.co.uk, Fax (017683) 52888*, – TV P – 40. MC AE VISA.
closed 24-26 December – **Meals** a la carte 20.25/30.00 **st.** 11.00 – **30 rm** 81.00/122.00 **st.** – SB.

Tufton Arms, Market Sq, CA16 6XA, (017683) 51593, *info@tuftonarmshotel.co.uk, Fax (017683) 52761*, – TV P – 100. MC AE VISA JCB
Meals 23.00 (dinner) and a la carte 13.75/23.00 **t.** 9.50 – **19 rm** 55.00/145.00 **t.**, 2 suites – SB.

APPLEDORE *Devon* 403 H 30 *The West Country G. – pop. 2 187.*
See : *Town*★.
London 228 – Barnstaple 12 – Exeter 46 – Plymouth 61 – Taunton 63.

West Farm, Irsha St, EX39 1RY, West : ¼ m. (01237) 425269, *westfarm@appledore-devon.co.uk*, « 17C house », – rm, TV P.
closed Christmas-New Year – **Meals** (by arrangement) (communal dining) 25.00 **st.** – **3 rm** 52.50/80.00 **st.**

ARLINGHAM *Glos.* 403 404 M 28 – *pop. 377* – *Gloucester.*
London 120 – Birmingham 69 – Bristol 34 – Gloucester 16.

Old Passage Inn with rm, Passage Rd, GL2 7JR, West : ¾ m (01452) 740547, *info@fishattheoldpassageinn.com, Fax (01452) 741871*, – TV P. MC AE VISA.
closed 24-30 December – **Meals** - Seafood - *(closed Monday and Sunday dinner)* a la carte 25.25/33.00 **t.** 10.40 – **3 rm** 60.00/90.00 **st.**

ARMSCOTE *Warks..*
London 91 – Birmingham 36 – Oxford 38.

The Fox and Goose Inn with rm, CV37 8DD, (01608) 682293, *Fax (01608) 682293*, – TV P. MC AE VISA.
closed 1 January and 25-26 December – **Meals** a la carte 17.00/23.00 **t.** 10.00 – **4 rm** 38.00/80.00 **t.**

ARNCLIFFE *N. Yorks.* 402 N 21 – *pop. 79* – *Skipton.*
London 232 – Kendal 41 – Leeds 41 – Preston 50 – York 52.

Amerdale House, BD23 5QE, (01756) 770250, *Fax (01756) 770250*, – rest, TV P. MC VISA.
mid March-mid November – **Meals** (dinner only) 30.00 **st.** 12.95 – **11 rm** (dinner included) 82.50/169.00 **st.** – SB.

ARUNDEL *W. Sussex* 404 S 31 *Great Britain G. – pop. 3 033.*
See : *Castle*★★ *AC.*
61 High St (01903) 882268.
London 58 – Brighton 21 – Southampton 41 – Worthing 9.

Norfolk Arms, 22 High St, BN18 9AD, (01903) 882101, *nka/forestdale@forestdale.com, Fax (01903) 884275* – rest, TV P – 100. MC AE VISA
Meals (bar lunch Monday-Saturday)/dinner 17.85 **st.** 9.95 – **34 rm** 65.00/115.00 **st.** – SB.

Swan, 27-29 High St, BN18 9AG, (01903) 882314, *info@swan-hotel.co.uk, Fax (01903) 883759* – , rest, TV P. MC AE VISA.
Meals a la carte 13.70/18.90 **t.** 8.50 – **15 rm** 65.00/85.00 **t.**

Comfort Inn, Crossbush, BN17 7QQ, Southeast : 1 ¼ m. by A 27 on A 284 ✆ (01903) 840840, *admin@gb642.u_net.com, Fax (01903) 849849* – ⇔, ▤ rest, TV ♿ P – 30. MC AE DI VISA
Meals (dinner only) 10.75 and a la carte approx. 15.50 **st.** 11.95 – 8.75 – **53 rm** 49.50 **t.** – SB.

Travel Inn, Crossbush, BN18 9PQ, East : 1 m. on A 27 ✆ (01903) 882655, *Fax (01903) 884381* – ⇔, ▤ rest, TV ♿ P. MC AE DI VISA.
Meals (grill rest.) – **30 rm** 41.95 **t.**

at Burpham *Northeast : 3 m. by A 27 – ✉ Arundel.*

Burpham Country, BN18 9RJ, ✆ (01903) 882160, *Fax (01903) 884627*, ←, – ⇔ TV P. MC AE VISA JCB.
Meals *(closed Sunday and Monday)* (booking essential to non-residents) (dinner only) 21.00/25.00 **t.** 11.00 – **10 rm** 45.00/110.00 **t.** – SB.

George and Dragon, BN18 9RR, ✆ (01903) 883131 – ⇔. MC AE VISA JCB
closed 25 December and Sunday dinner – **Meals** (bar lunch Monday-Saturday)/dinner a la carte 24.25/30.40 **t.** 12.50.

at Walberton *West : 3 m. by A 27 off B 2132 – ✉ Arundel.*

Hilton Avisford Park, Yapton Lane, BN18 0LS, on B 2132 ✆ (01243) 551215, *reservations@avisford.stakis.co.uk, Fax (01243) 552485*, ←, heated, 18, , squash – ⇔ TV ♿ P – 350. MC AE DI VISA
Meals *(closed Saturday lunch)* (buffet lunch)/dinner 22.50/27.90 **t.** 13.50 – **134 rm** 109.00/129.00 **t.**, 5 suites – SB.

ASCOT *Windsor & Maidenhead* 404 R 29 – *pop. 15 761 (inc. Sunningdale).*
18 *Mill Ride, Ascot ✆ (01344) 886777.*
London 36 – Reading 15.

Royal Berkshire, London Rd, Sunninghill, SL5 0PP, East : 2 m. on A 329 ✆ (01344) 623322, *Fax (01344) 627100*, « Queen Anne mansion », , , , – ⇔ TV P – 80. MC AE DI VISA
Meals *(closed Saturday lunch)* (booking essential) 22.50/29.50 and dinner a la carte 19.90/44.95 **t.** 18.00 – 15.50 – **60 rm** 215.00/240.00 **t.**, 3 suites.

Berystede, Bagshot Rd, Sunninghill, SL5 9JH, South : 1 ½ m. on A 330 ✆ (0870) 400 8111, *heritagehotels-ascot.berystede@forte-hotels.com, Fax (01344) 873061*, heated, – ⇔, ▤ rest, TV P – 120. MC AE DI VISA
Meals *(closed Saturday lunch)* 17.50/40.00 and dinner a la carte 20.50/39.50 **t.** 14.50 – 12.50 – **89 rm** 175.00/195.00 **st.**, 1 suite – SB.

at Sunninghill *South : 1 ½ m. by A 329 on B 3020 – ✉ Ascot.*

Highclere, Kings Rd, SL5 9AD, ✆ (01344) 625220, *Fax (01344) 872528* – ⇔ rest, TV P. MC AE VISA JCB.
*closed 20 December-6 January***Meals** *(closed Sunday)* (residents only) (dinner only) a la carte 19.00/30.45 **t.** 11.50 – **11 rm** 90.00/120.00 **t.**

Jade Fountain, 38 High St, SL5 9NE, ✆ (01344) 627070, *Fax (01344) 627070* – ▤. MC AE DI VISA JCB
Meals - Chinese (Canton, Peking) - 24.50 and a la carte 18.00/24.00 **t.** 15.00.

ASENBY *N. Yorks. – see Thirsk.*

ASHBOURNE *Derbs.* 402 403 404 O 24 *Great Britain G. – pop. 6 300.*
Env. : *Dovedale★★ (Ilam Rock★) NW : 6 m. by A 515.*
13 Market Pl ✆ (01335) 343666.
London 146 – Derby 14 – Manchester 48 – Nottingham 33 – Sheffield 44.

Callow Hall, Mappleton Rd, DE6 2AA, West : ¾ m. by Union St (off Market Pl) ✆ (01335) 300900, *reservations@callowhall.co.uk, Fax (01335) 300512*, ←, « Victorian country house », , , – TV ♿ P. MC AE DI VISA.
closed 25-26 December and 1 January – **Meals** – (see ***The Restaurant*** below) – **15 rm** 85.00/165.00 **t.**, 1 suite – SB.

Hanover International, Derby Rd, DE6 1XH, Southeast : 1 m. following signs for the A 52 (Derby) ✆ (01335) 346666, *hanoversales@ashbourne.freeserve.co.uk, Fax (01335) 346549*, , , – ⇔ TV ♿ P – 200. MC AE DI VISA JCB.
Brasserie 209 : **Meals** a la carte 17.70/25.15 **st.** 11.00 – **48 rm** 85.00/100.00 **t.**, 2 suites – SB.

Lichfield House without rest., Bridge View, Mayfield, DE6 2HN, Northwest : 1 ¾ m. by A 52 (Leek rd) on B 5032 ☎ (01335) 344422, *elizabull@barclays.net*, – TV P.
closed 25-26 December – **3 rm** 35.00/50.00.

The Restaurant (at Callow Hall), Mappleton Rd, DE6 2AA, West : ¾ m. by Union St (off Market Pl) ☎ (01335) 300900, *Fax (01335) 300512* – P. VISA
closed Sunday dinner to non-residents, 25-26 December and 1 January – **Meals** (dinner only and Sunday lunch)/dinner 20.00/38.50 and a la carte 29.75/36.50 **t.** 14.75.

ASHBURTON *Devon* 403 I 32 *The West Country G.* – *pop. 3 660.*

Env. : *Dartmoor National Park★★.*

London 220 – Exeter 20 – Plymouth 25.

Holne Chase, TQ13 7NS, West : 3 m. on Two Bridges rd ☎ (01364) 631471, *info@holne-chase.co.uk, Fax (01364) 631453*, – TV P. VISA
Meals – (see ***The Restaurant*** below) – **9 rm** 95.00/150.00 **st.**, 7 suites 170.00 **st.** – SB.

Gages Mill, Buckfastleigh Rd, TQ13 7JW, Southwest : 1 m. on Buckfastleigh/Totnes rd ☎ (01364) 652391, *moore@gagesmill.co.uk, Fax (01364) 652391*, – rest, P.
March-mid November – **Meals** (by arrangement) 14.00 5.00 – **8 rm** 25.00/59.00.

The Restaurant (at Holne Chase H.), TQ13 7NS, West : 3 m. on Two Bridges rd ☎ (01364) 631471, *Fax (01364) 631453*, – P. VISA
Meals (booking essential) 20.00/34.50 **st.** 11.50.

at Holne *West : 4½ m. by Two Bridges rd* – ✉ *Ashburton.*

Wellpritton Farm, TQ13 7RX, Northeast : 1 m. ☎ (01364) 631273, *info@wellprittonfarm.com*, – P. VISA JCB
Meals (by arrangement) 12.50 **st.** – **5 rm** 25.00/40.00 **st.** – SB.

ASHBY DE LA ZOUCH *Leics.* 402 403 404 P 25 – *pop. 10 595.*

18 *Willesley Park, Measham Rd ☎ (01530) 411532* – *North St ☎ (01530) 411767.*

London 119 – Birmingham 29 – Leicester 18 – Nottingham 22.

Rajni, 48 Tamworth Rd, LE65 2PR, South : ½ m. on B 5006 ☎ (01530) 560349, *Fax (01530) 560347* – P. VISA JCB
closed 25 December – **Meals** - Indian - (lunch by arrangement)/dinner 28.75 and a la carte 12.90/24.45 8.20.

ASHFORD *Kent* 404 W 30 – *pop. 52 002.*

Channel Tunnel : Eurostar information and reservations ☎ (08705) 186186.

18 The Churchyard ☎ (01233) 629165 – The Visitor Centre, McArthur Glen designer outlet, Kimberly Way ☎ (01233) 628181.

London 56 – Canterbury 14 – Dover 24 – Hastings 30 – Maidstone 19.

Eastwell Manor, Eastwell Park, Boughton Lees, TN25 4HR, North : 3 m. by A 28 on A 251 ☎ (01233) 213000, *eastwell@btinternet.com, Fax (01233) 213017*, « Reconstructed period mansion in formal gardens », heated, – rest, TV P – 250. VISA
Meals 15.00/32.00 and a la carte 38.75/45.50 **t.** 14.00 – ***Pavilion Restaurant* :** **Meals** *(closed Sunday dinner)* 15.00 (lunch) and a la carte approx. 19.20/28.95 **t.** 12.50 – **20 rm** 170.00/265.00 **t.**, 3 suites – SB.

Ashford International, Simone Weil Ave, TN24 8UX, North : 1 ½ m. by A 20 ☎ (01233) 219988, *sales@ashfordinthotel.co.uk, Fax (01233) 647743*, – , rm, TV P – 400. VISA
closed 1 week Christmas – ***Alhambra* :** **Meals** *(closed Sunday and Saturday lunch)* 12.95/16.95 and a la carte 19.70/28.95 **t.** 10.95 – ***Mistral Brasserie* :** **Meals** *(closed Saturday lunch)* (carvery) 16.95 **t.** 10.95 – 9.95 – **199 rm** 99.00/129.00 **st.**, 2 suites – SB.

Holiday Inn Ashford Central, Canterbury Rd, TN24 8QQ, North : ¾ m. on A 28 ☎ (0870) 400 9001, *ashford@sc.com, Fax (01233) 643176*, – rm, TV P – 100. VISA JCB.
Meals 15.00/25.00 and a la carte 15.50/27.95 **st.** 11.00 – **103 rm** 99.00/179.00 **st.** – SB.

Pilgrims Rest, Canterbury Rd, Kennington, TN24 9QR, Northeast : 2 m. on A 28 ☎ (01233) 636863, *pilgrimsrest@fullers.co.uk, Fax (01233) 610119*, , – rm, rest, TV P – 70. VISA
Meals a la carte 12.45/19.15 **t.** 9.75 – 7.50 – **34 rm** 49.00/54.00 **t.**

Travel Inn, Hall Ave, Orbital Park, Sevington, TN24 0GA, Southeast : 3 m. by A 292 off A 2070 ☎ (01233) 500755, *Fax (01233) 500712* – , rm, rest, TV P. VISA.
Meals (grill rest.) – **60 rm** 41.95 **t.**

at Hothfield *Northwest : 3½ m. by A 20 – ✉ Ashford.*

Holiday Inn Garden Court, Maidstone Rd, TN26 1AR, North : 1 m. on A 20 ℘ (01233) 713333, *sales@holidayinn-ashford.freeserve.co.uk, Fax (01233) 712082,* – rm, – 80.
Meals (dinner only) a la carte 14.75/21.20 **st.** – 10.95 – **100 rm** 59.00/79.00 **st.** – SB.

Travel Inn, Maidstone Rd, Hothfield Common, TN26 1AP, North : ¾ m. on A 20 ℘ (01233) 712571, *Fax (01233) 713945* – rm, .
Meals (grill rest.) – **60 rm** 41.95 **t.**

ASHFORD-IN-THE-WATER *Derbs.* 402 403 404 O 24 – *see Bakewell.*

ASHINGTON *W. Sussex* 404 S 31 – *pop. 2 852* – ✉ *Pulborough.*
London 50 – Brighton 20 – Worthing 9.

Mill House, Mill Lane, RH20 3BZ, ℘ (01903) 892426, *mill1@netcomuk.co.uk, Fax (01903) 892855,* – – 40.
Meals (dinner only) 17.95/22.50 **st.** 10.95 – **10 rm** 49.00/89.00 **st.**

ASHTON-IN-MAKERFIELD *Gtr. Manchester* 402 M 23 – *pop. 28 105* – ✉ *Wigan.*
London 199 – Liverpool 19 – Manchester 20.

Premier Lodge, 53 Warrington Rd, WN4 9PJ, South : ½ m. on A 49 ℘ (0870) 7001572, *Fax (0870) 7001573* – rm, .
Meals (grill rest.) a la carte approx. 12.50 **t.** 7.80 – **28 rm** 46.95 **t.**

There is no paid advertising in this Guide.

ASHTON-UNDER-LYNE *Gtr. Manchester* 402 403 404 N 23 – *pop. 43 906.*
32 Market St ℘ (0161) 343 4343.
London 209 – Leeds 40 – Manchester 7 – Sheffield 34.

York House, York Pl, off Richmond St, OL6 7TT, ℘ (0161) 330 9000, *Fax (0161) 343 1613,* – – 40.
closed 1 week New Year – **Meals** *(closed Saturday lunch, Sunday and Bank Holidays)* 12.50/15.00 and a la carte 12.00/24.50 **t.** 10.35 – **34 rm** 40.00/83.00 **t.** – SB.

Woodlands without rest., 33 Shepley Rd, Audenshaw, M34 5DL, Southwest : 2 m. by A 635 and A 6017 on B 6169 ℘ (0161) 336 4241 – .
3 rm 40.00/60.00.

ASKRIGG *N. Yorks.* 402 N 21 – *pop. 1 002* – ✉ *Leyburn.*
London 251 – Kendal 32 – Leeds 70 – York 63.

Helm, Helm, DL8 3JF, West : 1 ½ m., turning right at No Through Rd sign after 1 m. ℘ (01969) 650443, *holiday@helmyorkshire.com, Fax (01969) 650443,* ≤ Wensleydale, « Part 17C stone cottage » – .
closed mid November-2 January – **Meals** (by arrangement) 19.50 **s.** 12.35 – **3 rm** 55.00/78.00 **s.** – SB.

ASPLEY GUISE *Beds.* 404 S 27 – *pop. 2 236.*
Woburn Sands, West Hill ℘ (01908) 582264 – Lyshott Heath, Ampthill ℘ (01525) 840252.
London 52 – Bedford 13 – Luton 16 – Northampton 22.

Moore Place, The Square, MK17 8DW, ℘ (01908) 282000, *info@mooreplace.co.uk, Fax (01908) 281888,* « Georgian mansion », – rest, – 40.
Meals *(closed Saturday lunch)* 13.50/24.95 **t.** 11.95 – **51 rm** 100.00/120.00 **t.**, 1 suite – SB.

ASTON *Devon* 403 404 P 28.
London 75 – Oxford 17 – Swindon 19.

Chimney Farmhouse without rest., Chimney, OX18 2EH, South : 2 m. ℘ (01367) 870279, *Fax (01367) 870279,* ≤, « Working farm », –
closed December and January – **3 rm** 35.00/60.00 **st.**

ASTON CANTLOW *Warks.* 403 404 O 27 – *pop. 1 843* – ✉ *Solihull.*

London 103 – Birmingham 21 – Stratford-upon-Avon 4 – Warwick 20 – Worcester 24.

The King's Head, Bearley Rd, B95 6HY, ☎ (01789) 488242, *Fax (01789) 488137,* « Part 15C », – P. MC AE VISA
Meals (booking essential) a la carte 16.35/24.85 **t.** 9.95.

ASTON CLINTON *Bucks.* 404 R 28 – *pop. 3 467* – ✉ *Aylesbury.*

London 42 – Aylesbury 4 – Oxford 26.

West Lodge without rest., London Rd, HP22 5HL, ☎ (01296) 630362, *jib@westlodge.co.uk, Fax (01296) 630151,* – TV P. MC AE VISA JCB.
7 rm 35.00/70.00 **st.**

ATHERSTONE *Warks.* 403 404 P 26 – *pop. 10 677.*

London 120 – Birmingham 22 – Coventry 15 – Leicester 30.

Chapel House with rm, Friar's Gate, CV9 1EY, ☎ (01827) 718949, *Fax (01827) 717702,* « Part Georgian former dower house », – rest, TV. MC VISA JCB.
closed 25-26 December – **Meals** *(closed Sunday dinner and Bank Holidays)* (lunch by arrangement)/dinner a la carte approx. 22.25 **t.** 10.75 – **13 rm** 55.00/90.00 **t.** – SB.

***Groß-London** (GREATER LONDON) besteht aus der City und 32 Verwaltungsbezirken (Borough). Diese sind wiederum in kleinere Bezirke (Area) unterteilt, deren Mittelpunkt ehemalige Dörfer oder Stadtviertel sind, die oft ihren eigenen Charakter bewahrt haben.*

AUSTWICK *N. Yorks.* 402 M 21 – *pop. 467* – ✉ *Lancaster (Lancs.).*

London 259 – Kendal 28 – Lancaster 20 – Leeds 46.

Austwick, LA2 8BY, ☎ (015242) 51224, *austwickh@cs.com, Fax (015242) 51796,* « Georgian mansion house », – TV P. MC VISA.
Meals 12.95/20.00 and a la carte 13.00/25.00 **t.** 10.75 – **11 rm** 40.00/90.00 **st.** – SB.

Wood View, The Green, LA2 8BB, ☎ (015242) 51268, – TV P. MC VISA
Meals (by arrangement) 16.00 – **6 rm** 35.00/64.00 **st.** – SB.

AVON DASSETT *Warks.* – *pop. 191* – ✉ *Leamington Spa.*

London 82 – Birmingham 37 – Coventry 22 – Oxford 34.

Crandon House without rest., CV47 2AA, Northeast : 1 ¼ m. by Fenny Compton rd on Farnborough rd ☎ (01295) 770652, *crandonhouse@talk21.com, Fax (01925) 770632,* , – TV P. MC VISA.
closed Christmas – **5 rm** 30.00/52.00.

AXBRIDGE *Somerset* 403 L 30 – *pop. 1 773.*

London 142 – Bristol 17 – Taunton 27 – Weston-Super-Mare 11.

The Parsonage without rest., Parsonage Lane, Cheddar Rd, BS26 2DN, East : ¾ m. on A 371 ☎ (01934) 733078, *Fax (01934) 733078,* – TV P.
3 rm 38.00/48.00 **st.**

AXMINSTER *Devon* 403 L 31 *The West Country G.* – *pop. 3 472.*

Env. : Lyme Regis★ - The Cobb★, SE : 5½ m. by A 35 and A 3070.

The Old Courthouse, Church St ☎ (01297) 34386.

London 156 – Exeter 27 – Lyme Regis 5.5 – Taunton 22 – Yeovil 24.

Fairwater Head Country House, Hawkchurch, EX13 5TX, Northeast : 5 ¼ m. by B 3261 and A 35 off B 3165 ☎ (01297) 678349, *reception@fairwaterhead.demon.co.uk, Fax (01297) 678459,* Axe Vale, – TV P. MC AE VISA
restricted opening in winter – **Meals** 13.50/29.50 **t.** 9.50 – **20 rm** 92.00/164.00 **t.** – SB.

at Membury *North : 4½ m. by A 35 and Stockland rd* – ✉ *Axminster.*

Lea Hill, EX13 7AQ, South : ½ m. ☎ (01404) 881881, *reception@leahillhotel.co.uk, Fax (01404) 881890,* , « Part 14C Devon longhouse », – TV P. MC AE VISA
closed 3 January-16 March – **Meals** *(closed Sunday)* (bar lunch)/dinner 24.95 **t.** 11.95 – **9 rm** 59.00/116.00 **t.**, 2 suites – SB.

AYCLIFFE *Darlington* – *see Darlington.*

AYLESBURY *Bucks.* 404 R 28 *Great Britain G. – pop. 58 058.*

Env. : *Waddesdon Manor★★, NW : 5½ m. by A 41 – Chiltern Hills★.*

Weston Turville, New Rd (01296) 424084 – Hulcott Lane, Bierton (01296) 393644.

8 Bourbon St (01296) 330559.

London 46 – Birmingham 72 – Northampton 37 – Oxford 22.

Hartwell House, Oxford Rd, HP17 8NL, Southwest : 2 m. on A 418 (01296) 747444, *info@hartwell-house.com, Fax (01296) 747450,* ≤, « Part Jacobean, part Georgian house, former residence of Louis XVIII », – rm, P – 80. VISA
Meals 22.00/46.00 **st.** – 17.50 – **33 rm** 140.00/225.00 **st.**, 13 suites 325.00/700.00 **st.** – SB.

Holiday Inn Aylesbury, Aston Clinton Rd, HP22 5AA, Southeast : 2 m. on A 41 (0870) 400 9002, *Fax (01296) 392211,* – rm, P – 100. AE VISA
Meals *(closed Saturday lunch)* 15.95 (dinner) and a la carte 17.35/29.15 **st.** 11.95 – 11.95 – **138 rm** 129.00 **t.**, 2 suites.

Holiday Inn Garden Court, Buckingham Rd, Watermead, HP19 3FY, North : 1 m. on A 413 (01296) 398839, *aylesbury@holidayinns.co.uk, Fax (01296) 394108,* – rm, P – 30. AE VISA JCB.
Meals (residents only) (dinner only) a la carte 16.00/20.00 – 8.50 – **40 rm** 82.00 **st.**

Bottle & Glass, Gibraltar, HP17 8TY, Southwest : 5 m. on A 418 (01296) 748488, *Fax (01296) 747673,* « 17C thatched inn » – P. AE VISA JCB
closed Sunday dinner – **Meals** - Seafood specialities - 19.95 (lunch) and a la carte 22.45/40.25 **t.** 10.50.

AYLMERTON *Norfolk* 404 X 25.

London 139 – Norwich 27.

Felbrigg Lodge, NR11 8RA, Southeast : 1 m. by Metton Rd (01263) 837588, *info@felbrigglodge.co.uk, Fax (01263) 838012,* – P. VISA JCB.
Meals (by arrangement) 27.50 **st.** – **4 rm** 60.00/140.00 **t.**

AYMESTREY *Herefordshire* 403 L 27 – *pop. 301.*

London 156 – Birmingham 54 – Hereford 17 – Shrewsbury 35 – Worcester 31.

Riverside Inn, HR6 9ST, (01568) 708440, *riverside@aymestrey.fsnet.co.uk, Fax (01568) 709058,* « 16C », – P. VISA JCB
closed 25 December – **Meals** a la carte 15.70/25.45 **t.** 9.95.

BADMINTON *South Gloucestershire* 403 404 N 29 – *pop. 2 167.*

London 114 – Bristol 19 – Gloucester 26 – Swindon 33.

Bodkin House, Petty France, GL9 1AF, Northwest : 3 m. on A 46 (01454) 238310, *info@bodkin-house-hotel.co.uk, Fax (01454) 238422* – rest, P. AE VISA.
Meals 21.95 and a la carte 17.00/22.00 **st.** 9.50 – **9 rm** 57.00/95.00 **st.** – SB.

BAGINTON *Warks.* 403 404 P 26 – *see Coventry.*

BAGSHOT *Surrey* 404 R 29 – *pop. 5 190.*

Windlesham, Grove End (01276) 452220.

London 37 – Reading 17 – Southampton 49.

Pennyhill Park, London Rd, GU19 5EU, Southwest : 1 m. on A 30 (01276) 471774, *pennyhillpark1@msn.com, Fax (01276) 473217,* ≤, « Gardens and parklands », heated, – rest, P – 150. AE VISA
St James : **Meals** - Italian - *(closed Saturday lunch)* 18.95 (lunch) and dinner a la carte 28.95/45.45 **t.** 22.00 – (see also ***The Latymer*** below) – 16.00 – **113 rm** 175.00/195.00 **s.**, 10 suites.

Travel Inn, London Rd, GU19 5HR, North : ½ m. on A 30 (01276) 473196, *Fax (01276) 451357,* – rm, rest, P. AE VISA.
Meals (grill rest.) – **40 rm** 41.95 **t.**

The Latymer (at Pennyhill Park H.), London Rd, GU19 5EU, Southwest : 1 m. on A 30 (01276) 471774, *pennyhillpark@msn.com, Fax (01276) 473217,* – P. AE VISA
closed Sunday and Monday – **Meals** (booking essential) (dinner only) 50.00 **st.** 23.50.

BAKEWELL *Derbs.* 402 403 404 O 24 *Great Britain G. – pop. 3 818.*

Env. : *Chatsworth★★★ (Park and Garden★★★) AC, NE : 2½ m. by A 619 – Haddon Hall★★ AC, SE : 2 m. by A 6.*

Old Market Hall, Bridge St (01629) 813227.

London 160 – Derby 26 – Manchester 37 – Nottingham 33 – Sheffield 17.

Rutland Arms, The Square, DE45 1BT, (01629) 812812, *rutland@bakewell.demon.co.uk, Fax (01629) 812309* – – 100. VISA JCB
Meals 9.95/19.50 **t.** 10.00 – **35 rm** 59.00/94.00 **t.** – SB.

Aitch's Wine Bar & Bistro, 4 Buxton Rd, DE45 1DA, (01629) 813895, *aitchwinebar@btconnect.com, Fax (01629) 815096* – VISA JCB
closed 25-26 December, 1 January, Sunday lunch and Sunday dinner in winter – **Meals** (booking essential) (light lunch) a la carte 20.20/27.40 **t.** 10.95.

at Great Longstone *North : 4 m. by A 619 off B 6001 – Bakewell.*

Croft Country House , DE45 1TF, (01629) 640278, *jthursby@ukonline.co.uk, Fax (01629) 640369,* – . VISA.
closed January-14 February – **Meals** (dinner only) 28.50 **t.** 10.50 – **9 rm** 63.00/121.00 **t.** – SB.

at Ashford-in-the-Water *Northwest : 1 ¾ m. by A 6 and A 6020 – Bakewell.*

Riverside House, Fennel St, DE45 1QF, (01629) 814275, *riversidehouse@enta.net, Fax (01629) 812873,* – . VISA.
Meals – (see ***The Riverside Room*** below) – **15 rm** 95.00/215.00 **t.** – SB.

The Riverside Room (at Riverside House), Fennel St, DE45 1QE, (01629) 814275, *Fax (01629) 812875* – . VISA
Meals 16.95/39.95 and a la carte 22.40/39.95 **t.** 15.25.

BALDERSTONE *Lancs. – see Blackburn.*

BALDOCK *Herts.* 404 T 28 – *pop. 9 232.*

London 40 – Bedford 20 – Cambridge 22 – Luton 16 – Milton Keynes 33.

Sleep Inn without rest., Radwell, SG7 5TR, Northwest : 2 m. by A 507 at junction 10 of A 1(M) (01462) 832900, *admin@glo100.u-net.com, Fax (01462) 832901* – . VISA.
62 rm 49.50 **t.**

BALLASALLA *Isle of Man* 402 G 21 – *see Man (Isle of).*

BALSALL COMMON *W. Mids. – see Coventry.*

BAMBER BRIDGE *Lancs.* 402 M 22 – *see Preston.*

BAMBURGH *Northd.* 401 402 O 17 *Great Britain G. – pop. 582.*

See : *Castle★ AC.*

London 337 – Edinburgh 77 – Newcastle upon Tyne 51.

Lord Crewe Arms, Front St, NE69 7BL, (01668) 214243, *lca@tinyonline.co.uk, Fax (01668) 214273* – rest, . VISA JCB
March-November – **Meals** *(closed lunch Monday-Friday)* a la carte 15.65/22.40 **t.** 9.95 – **18 rm** 40.00/99.00 **t.**

at Waren Mill *West : 2 ¾ m. on B 1342 – Belford.*

Waren House , NE70 7EE, (01668) 214581, *enquiries@warenhousehotel.co.uk, Fax (01668) 214484,* – – 30. VISA JCB
Meals (dinner only) 22.45 **st.** 14.75 – **8 rm** 90.00/140.00 **st.**, 2 suites – SB.

BAMPTON *Devon* 403 J 31 – *pop. 1 617.*

London 189 – Exeter 18 – Minehead 21 – Taunton 15.

Bark House, Oakfordbridge, EX16 9HZ, West : 3 m. by B 3227 on A 396 (01398) 351236, – rest,
restricted opening in winter – **Meals** (booking essential) (residents only) (dinner only) (set menu only) 25.00 **st.** 10.25 – **5 rm** 39.50/103.00 **st.** – SB.

BANBURY *Oxon.* 403 404 P 27 *Great Britain G. – pop. 39 906.*

Exc. : *Upton House★ AC, NW : 7 m. by A 422.*

Cherwell Edge, Chacombe ✆ (01295) 711591.

Spiceball Park Rd ✆ (01295) 259855.

London 76 – Birmingham 40 – Coventry 25 – Oxford 23.

Whately Hall, Horsefair, by Banbury Cross, OX16 0AN, ✆ (0870) 4008104, *heritagehotels-banbury.whatelyhall@forte-hotels.com, Fax (01295) 271736,* « Part 17C », – 80. MC AE VISA JCB.
Meals *(closed Saturday lunch)* 7.95/21.50 and a la carte 19.15/31.85 **st.** 9.95 – **66 rm** 105.00/115.00 **st.**, 6 suites – SB.

Banbury House, Oxford Rd, OX16 9AH, ✆ (01295) 259361, *banburyhouse@compuserve.com, Fax (01295) 270954* – rm, – 70. MC AE VISA.
closed 24 December-2 January – **Meals** (bar lunch)/dinner 19.00 **st.** 12.95 – 10.00 – **63 rm** 87.00/97.00 **st.** – SB.

at North Newington *West : 2 ¼ m. by B 4035 – ✉ Banbury.*

La Madonette Country Guest House without rest., OX15 6AA, ✆ (01295) 730212, *lamadonett@aol.com, Fax (01295) 730363,* – MC VISA JCB.
5 rm 45.00/65.00 **t.**

at Wroxton *Northwest : 3 m. by B 4100 on A 422 – ✉ Banbury.*

Wroxton House, Stratford Rd, OX15 6QB, ✆ (01295) 730777, *reservations@wroxtonhousehotel.com, Fax (01295) 730800* – – 40. MC AE VISA.
closed 1-3 January – **Meals** (dinner only and Sunday lunch)/dinner 17.00 a la carte 15.05/21.45 **st.** 12.00 – 9.95 – **32 rm** 85.00/105.00 **st.** – SB.

at Shenington *Northwest : 6 m. by B 4100 off A 422 – ✉ Banbury.*

Sugarswell Farm, OX15 6HW, Northwest : 2 ¼ m. on Edge Hill rd ✆ (01295) 680512, *Fax (01295) 688149,* « Working farm », –
Meals (by arrangement) (communal dining) 22.50/25.00 **st.** – **3 rm** 45.00/70.00 **st.**

BANTHAM *Devon – see Kingsbridge.*

BAWTRY *S. Yorks.* 402 403 404 Q 23 – *see Doncaster.*

BARFORD *Warks.* 403 404 P 27 – *see Warwick.*

BAR HILL *Cambs.* 404 U 27 – *see Cambridge.*

BARLBOROUGH *Derbs.* 402 403 404 Q 24 – *pop. 1 917.*

London 160 – Derby 45 – Lincoln 37 – Nottingham 30 – Sheffield 12.

Ibis, 3 Tallys End, Chesterfield Rd, S43 4TX, on A 619 ✆ (01246) 813222, Reservations (Freephone) 0800 897121, *Fax (01246) 813444* – – 35. MC AE VISA JCB
Meals (grill rest.) 11.50 – **86 rm** 42.00 **st.**

BARNARD CASTLE *Durham* 402 O 20 *Great Britain G. – pop. 6 084.*

See : *Bowes Museum★ AC.*

Exc. : *Raby Castle★ AC, NE : 6½ m. by A 688.*

Harmire Rd ✆ (01833) 638355.

Woodleigh, Flatts Rd ✆ (01833) 695320.

London 258 – Carlisle 63 – Leeds 68 – Middlesbrough 31 – Newcastle upon Tyne 39.

Demesnes Mill without rest., DL12 8PE, Southeast : ½ m. by The Bank and Gray Lane, through the playing field ✆ (01833) 637929, *millbb2@ic24.net, Fax (01833) 637974,* « Part 15C former cornmill on banks of River Tees », – MC VISA JCB
March-October – **3 rm** 40.00/75.00 **s.**

Homelands, 85 Galgate, DL12 8ES, ✆ (01833) 638757, *homelands@barnard-castle.fsnet.co.uk,* –
closed 23 December-2 January – **Meals** (by arrangement) 15.95 – **5 rm** 25.00/55.00.

Greta House without rest., 89 Galgate, DL12 8ES, ✆ (01833) 631193, *gretahousebc@btclick.com, Fax (01833) 631193,* –
3 rm 35.00/50.00 **s.**

Rokeby Close Farm without rest., Hutton Magna, DL11 7HN, Southeast : 6 m. by B 6277, A 66 on Hutton Magna rd ✆ (01833) 627171, *don.wilkinson@farmline.com, Fax (01833) 627662*, ⩽, « Collection of Hebridean sheep and Highland cattle », – TV P. ✻
3 rm 30.00/50.00 **t.**

at Greta Bridge *Southeast : 4½ m. by B 6277 off A 66 – ✉ Barnard Castle.*

Morritt Arms, DL12 9SE, ✆ (01833) 627232, *relax@themorritt.co.uk, Fax (01833) 627392*, « 17C former coaching inn », – TV P – 200. MC AE VISA
Copperfield : Meals 18.95 (dinner) and a la carte 14.95/24.65 **st.** 8.80 – ***Pallatts :*** Meals a la carte 14.95/21.65 **st.** 8.80 – **23 rm** 59.50/101.50 **st.**

The Coach House, DL12 9SD, ✆ (01833) 627201, *info@coachhousegreta.co.uk*, « 17C », – TV P. MC VISA JCB
Meals (by arrangement) 20.00 – **3 rm** 45.00/64.00.

at Romaldkirk *Northwest : 6 m. by A 67 on B 6277 – ✉ Barnard Castle.*

Rose and Crown with rm, DL12 9EB, ✆ (01833) 650213, *hotel@rose-and-crown.co.uk, Fax (01833) 650828*, « Part 18C coaching inn » – rest, TV P. MC VISA
closed 24-26 December – ***The Restaurant :*** Meals *(closed Sunday dinner)* 13.95/25.00 **st.** 10.95 – **10 rm** 62.00/86.00 **st.**, 2 suites – SB.

at Eggleston *Northwest : 6½ m. by A 67 on B 6278 – ✉ Barnard Castle.*

Cloud High without rest., DL12 0AU, on B 6278 ✆ (01833) 650644, *cloudhigh@btinternet.com, Fax (01833) 650644*, ⩽, – TV P. ✻
closed 20 December-10 January – **3 rm** 32.00/52.00 **s.**

BARNARD GATE *Oxon.* 403 404 P 28 – *see Witney.*

BARNEY *Norfolk* 404 W 25 – ✉ *Fakenham.*

London 187 – Cambridge 71 – King's Lynn 21 – Norwich 29.

Old Brick Kilns, Little Barney Lane, NR21 0NL, East : ¾ m. ✆ (01328) 878305, *enquire@old-brick-kilns.co.uk, Fax (01328) 878948*, – TV P. MC VISA. ✻
Meals (by arrangement) (communal dining) 15.00 **st.** 4.30 – **3 rm** 25.00/50.00 **st.** – SB.

BARNSDALE BAR *W. Yorks.* 402 404 Q 23 – ✉ *Pontefract.*

London 181 – Leeds 22 – Nottingham 53 – Sheffield 26.

Travelodge, WF8 3JB, on A 1 (southbound carriageway) ✆ (01977) 620711, *Fax (01977) 620711* – rm, rest, TV P. MC AE VISA JCB. ✻
Meals (grill rest.) – **56 rm** 39.95 **t.**

BARNSLEY *Glos.* 403 404 O 28 – *see Cirencester.*

BARNSLEY *S. Yorks.* 402 404 P 23 – *pop. 75 120.*

Wakefield Rd, Staincross ✆ (01226) 382856 – Silkstone, Field Head, Elmhirst Lane ✆ (01226) 790328 – Wombwell Hillies, Wentworth View, Wombwell ✆ (01226) 754433.
46 Eldon St ✆ (01226) 206757.
London 177 – Leeds 21 – Manchester 36 – Sheffield 15.

Ardsley House H. and Health Club, Doncaster Rd, Ardsley, S71 5EH, East : 2 ¾ m. on A 635 ✆ (01226) 309955, *sales@ardsley-house.co.uk, Fax (01226) 205374*, , , , – rm, rest, TV P – 450. MC AE VISA
Meals (bar lunch Saturday and Bank Holidays) 10.95/20.95 and dinner a la carte 22.75/34.30 **t.** 11.00 – 9.75 – **74 rm** 83.00/102.00 **t.** – SB.

Tankersley Manor, Church Lane, S75 3DQ, South : 6 ¼ m. on A 61 ✆ (01226) 744700, *tankersley@marstonhotels.com, Fax (01226) 745405*, – TV P – 340. MC AE VISA. ✻
Meals *(closed Saturday lunch)* 19.95 and dinner a la carte 20.00/30.00 **st.** 12.95 – **69 rm** 99.00/119.00 **st.** – SB.

Travel Inn, Maple Rd, Tankersley, S74 3DL, South : 6 ½ m. by A 61 at junction with A 616 ✆ (01226) 350035, *Fax (01226) 741524* – rm, rest, TV P. MC AE VISA. ✻
Meals (grill rest.) – **42 rm** 41.95 **t.**

Travelodge, Doncaster Rd, S70 3PE, East : 2 m. on A 635 ✆ (01226) 298799, *Fax (01226) 298799* – rm, TV P. MC AE VISA JCB. ✻
Meals (grill rest.) – **32 rm** 42.95 **t.**

BARNSTAPLE *Devon* 403 H 30 *The West Country G. – pop. 20 740.*
See : *Town★ - Long Bridge★.*
Env. : *Arlington Court★★ (Carriage Collection★) AC, NE : 6 m. by A 39.*
18, 9 *Chulmleigh, Leigh Rd ☎ (01769) 580519.*
36 Boutport St ☎ (01271) 374037.
London 222 – Exeter 40 – Taunton 51.

Imperial, Taw Vale Parade, EX32 8NB, ☎ (01271) 345861, *info@brend-imperial.co.uk, Fax (01271) 324448* – rest, rest, – 60. VISA
Meals 12.50/22.00 and a la carte 31.00/39.50 **st.** 10.00 – 10.00 – **63 rm** 69.00/110.00 **st.** – SB.

Barnstaple, Braunton Rd, EX31 1LE, West : 1 ½ m. on A 361 ☎ (01271) 376221, *info@barnstaplehotel.co.uk, Fax (01271) 324101*, , heated, – rest, rest, – 350. VISA
Meals 11.50/18.50 and a la carte 24.50/28.00 **st.** 8.75 – 9.50 – **60 rm** 50.00/85.00 **st.** – SB.

Travel Inn, Barum Gate, Whiddon Drive, EX32 8RY, on A 361 ☎ (01271) 377830, *Fax (01271) 377710* – rm, rest, . VISA JCB.
Meals (grill rest.) – **40 rm** 41.95 **t.**

Lynwood House with rm, Bishops Tawton Rd, EX32 9EF, South : 1 ½ m. by A 361 and Newport rd ☎ (01271) 343695, *info@lynwoodhouse.co.uk, Fax (01271) 379340* – rest, . VISA
Meals - Seafood - *(closed 25 December, 1 January, Saturday lunch and Sunday)* a la carte 24.50/39.00 **t.** 12.00 – **5 rm** 47.50/67.50 **t.** – SB.

at Bishop's Tawton *South : 2 ¾ m. by A 39 on A 377 – ✉ Barnstaple.*

Downrew House, EX32 0DY, Southeast : 1 ½ m. on Chittlehampton rd ☎ (01271) 342497, *downrew@globalnet.co.uk, Fax (01271) 323947*, ←, heated, , – rest, – 40. VISA JCB
Meals *(closed dinner Sunday and Monday)* (bar lunch Monday-Saturday)/dinner 22.50 and a la carte 17.50/25.00 **t.** 11.85 – **12 rm** 55.00/130.00 **t.** – SB.

Halmpstone Manor, EX32 0EA, Southeast : 3 m. by Chittlehampton rd ☎ (01271) 830321, *charles@halmpstonemanor.co.uk, Fax (01271) 830826*, ←, – rest, . VISA JCB
closed Christmas-New Year and February – **Meals** (set menu only) (lunch by arrangement)/dinner 30.00 **st.** 9.50 – **5 rm** 70.00/140.00 **st.**

BARROW-IN-FURNESS *Cumbria* 402 K 21 – *pop. 48 947.*
18 *Rakesmoore Lane, Hawcoat ☎ (01229) 825444* – 18 *Furness, Walney Island ☎ (01229) 471232.*
Forum 28, Duke St ☎ (01229) 894784.
London 295 – Kendal 34 – Lancaster 47.

Arlington House, 200-202 Abbey Rd, LA14 5LD, North : 1 m. ☎ (01229) 831976, *Fax (01229) 870990*, heated – . VISA.
closed 25-26 December – **Meals** *(closed Sunday)* (dinner only) a la carte 19.75/25.50 **t.** 7.50 – **8 rm** 65.00/85.00 **t.**

BARTON MILLS *Suffolk.* 404 V 26 – *pop. 832.*
London 72 – Cambridge 21 – Ipswich 37 – Norwich 40.

Travelodge, Fiveways Roundabout, IP28 6AE, on A 11 ☎ (01638) 717675, *Fax (01638) 717675* – rm, . VISA JCB.
Meals (grill rest.) – **40 rm** 52.95 **t.**

BARTON-ON-SEA *Hants.* 403 404 P 31.
London 108 – Bournemouth 11 – Southampton 24 – Winchester 35.

Oysters with rm, Marine Drive, BH25 7DZ, ☎ (01425) 627777, *oysters@ukonline.co.uk, Fax (01425) 617714*, ← Christchurch Bay, Isle of Wight and The Needles, – rest, rest, . VISA
closed first 2 weeks January – **Meals** - Seafood - *(closed Monday)* 14.95 (lunch) and a la carte 20.00/40.00 **t.** 13.50 – **3 rm** 60.00/75.00 **t.**

Wenn Sie ein ruhiges Hotel suchen,
benutzen Sie zuerst die Karte in der Einleitung
oder wählen Sie im Text ein Hotel mit dem Zeichen oder .

BARTON STACEY *Hants.* 403 404 P 30 – *pop. 741.*
London 76 – Andover 10 – Bath 60 – Salisbury 22 – Winchester 8.

Travelodge, SO21 3NP, North : 1 ¼ m. on A 303 (westbound carriageway) *(01264) 720260* – rm, TV, P. MC AE VISA JCB.
Meals (grill rest.) – **20 rm** 52.95 **t.**

BARTON UNDER NEEDWOOD *Staffs. – see Burton-upon-Trent.*

BARWICK *Somerset* 403 404 M 31 – *see Yeovil.*

BASILDON *Essex* 404 V 29 – *pop. 100 924.*
18 Clayhill Lane, Sparrow's Hearne (01268) 533297 – 9 Langdon Hills, Lower Dunton Rd, Bulphan (01268) 548444.
London 30 – Chelmsford 17 – Southend-on-Sea 13.

Holiday Inn, Cranes Farm Rd, SS14 3DG, Northwest : 2 ¼ m. by A 176 off A 1235 *(0870) 400 9003, Fax (01268) 530119,* – rm, TV, P – 300. MC AE VISA JCB.
Meals *(closed Saturday lunch)* 10.00/15.00 and dinner a la carte 18.40/26.90 **t.** 11.95 – 13.95 – **149 rm** 140.00 **t.** – SB.

Premier Lodge, Festival Leisure Park, Pipps Hill Road South, SS14 3DG, Northwest : 2 ¾ m. by A 176 off A 1235 *(0870) 7001376, Fax (0870) 7001377,* – rm, rest, TV, P. MC AE VISA.
Meals (grill rest.) a la carte approx. 12.50 **t.** 7.80 – **64 rm** 49.95 **t.**

Travel Inn, High Rd, Fobbing, SS17 9NR, Southwest : 2 ¼ m. by A 176 at junction with A 13 *(01268) 554500, Fax (01268) 581752* – rm, TV, P – 100. MC AE VISA
Meals (grill rest.) – **60 rm** 41.95 **t.**

Travel Inn, Felmores, East Mayne, SS13 1BW, North : 1 ½ m. on A 132 *(01268) 522227, Fax (01268) 530092* – rm, TV, P. MC AE VISA.
Meals (grill rest.) – **32 rm** 41.95 **t.**

at Wickford *North : 5 ¼ m. by A 132 – Basildon.*

Chichester, Old London Rd, Rawreth, SS11 8UE, East : 2 ¾ m. by A 129 *(01268) 560555, Fax (01268) 560580,* – rest, rest, TV, P. MC AE VISA.
closed 24-31 December – **Meals** *(closed Saturday lunch)* a la carte approx. 18.00 **t.** 9.90 – 8.95 – **33 rm** 75.00 **t.** – SB.

The Guide is updated annually so renew your Guide every year.

BASINGSTOKE *Hants.* 403 404 Q 30 – *pop. 77 837.*
18 Test Valley, Micheldever Rd, Overton (01256) 771737 – 18 Weybrook Park, Rooksdown Lane, Basingstoke (01256) 320347.
Willis Museum, Old Town Hall, Market Pl (01256) 817618.
London 55 – Reading 17 – Southampton 31 – Winchester 18.

Plan on next page

Audleys Wood, Alton Rd, RG25 2JT, South : 1 ½ m. on A 339 *(01256) 817555, audleyswood@thistle.co.uk, Fax (01256) 817500,* « Gothic Renaissance mansion », – rm, TV, P – 50. MC AE VISA. Z v
Meals *(closed Saturday lunch)* 18.00/21.50 (lunch) and a la carte 25.00/40.00 **st.** 15.00 – 11.50 – **70 rm** 156.00 **st.**, 2 suites – SB.

Hilton Basingstoke, Old Common Rd, Black Dam, RG21 3PR, *(01256) 460460, Fax (01256) 840441,* – rm, rest, TV, P – 150. MC AE VISA JCB Z i
Meals *(closed Saturday lunch)* (carvery) 14.50/19.50 and dinner a la carte 16.65/28.15 **t.** 12.50 – 11.00 – **141 rm** 150.00 **st.** – SB.

Fernbank without rest., 4 Fairfields Rd, RG21 3DR, *(01256) 321191, availability@fernbankhotel.co.uk, Fax (01256) 321191* – TV P. MC AE VISA. Y a
16 rm 65.00/90.00.

Travel Inn, Worting Rd, RG22 6PG, *(01256) 811477, Fax (01256) 819329* – rm, TV, P. MC AE VISA. Z c
Meals (grill rest.) – **71 rm** 41.95 **t.**

Travelodge, Winchester Rd, RG22 5HN, Southwest : 2 ¼ m. by A 30 *(01256) 843566* – rm, TV, P. MC AE VISA JCB. Z u
Meals (grill rest.) – **32 rm** 59.95 **t.**

BASINGSTOKE

Aldermaston Road . . . . Z 2
Beaconsfield Road . . . . Y 3
Buckland Avenue . . . . Z 5
Chequers Road . . . . Y 6
Church Street . . . . Y 7
Churchill Way . . . . Z 9
Churchill Way East . . . . Z 10
Council Road . . . . Y 12
Cross Street . . . . Y 13
Fairfields Road . . . . Y 14
Houndmills Road . . . . Z 17
London Street . . . . Y 19
New Road . . . . Y 20
Reading Road . . . . Z 22
Southern Ringway . . . . Z 23
Upper Church Street . . . . Y 24
Victoria Street . . . . Y 25
Walks (The) Shopping Centre . . . . Y
Winchester Street . . . . Y 27
Wote Street . . . . Y 28

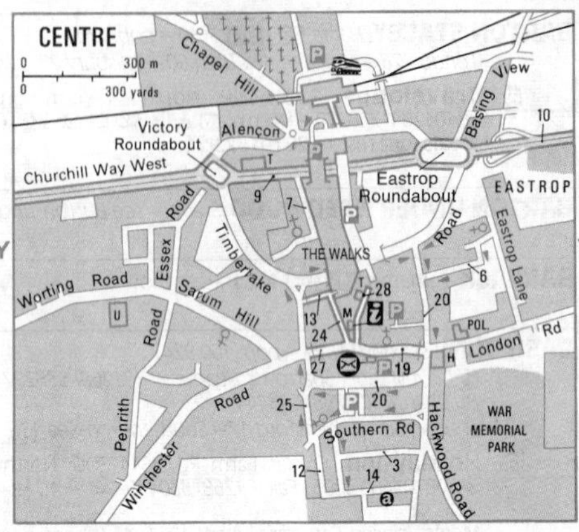

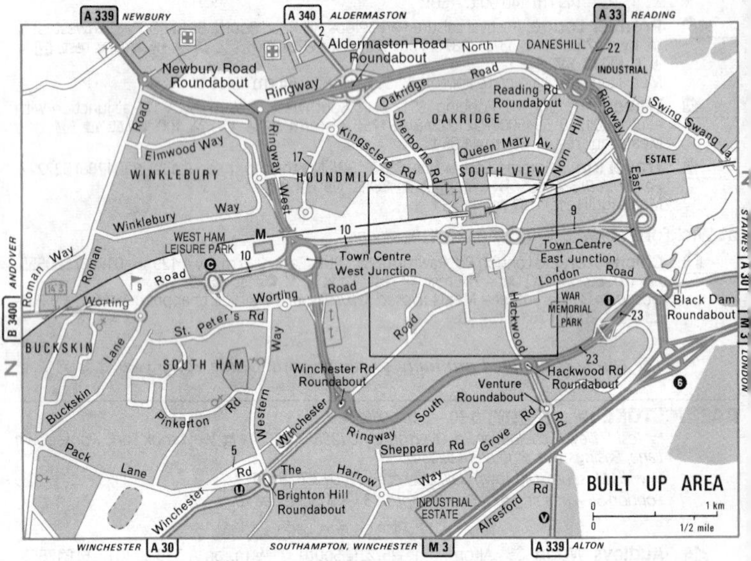

Remember the speed limits that apply in the United Kingdom, unless otherwise signposted.
- 60 mph on single carriageway roads
- 70 mph on dual carriageway roads and motorways

BASLOW *Derbs.* 402 403 404 P 24 *Great Britain G. – pop. 1 184 –* ✉ *Bakewell.*
See : *Chatsworth*** (Park and Garden***) AC.*
London 161 – Derby 27 – Manchester 35 – Sheffield 13.

Cavendish, DE45 1SP, on A 619 ☎ (01246) 582311, *info@cavendish-hotel.net, Fax (01246) 582312,* ≤ Chatsworth Park, « Collection of paintings and fine art », – rest, TV P – 25. MO AE O VISA.
The Gallery : Meals a la carte 24.75/32.65 17.50 – ***Garden Room :*** Meals a la carte 21.15/30.40 **t.** 13.75 – 12.55 – **23 rm** 95.00/145.00 **t.**, 1 suite.

XXX **Fischer's at Baslow Hall** with rm, Calver Rd, DE45 1RR, on A 623 ☎ (01246) 583259, *ms@fischers-baslowhall.co.uk, Fax (01246) 583818*, « Edwardian manor house, gardens » – ⚟ rest, TV ☎ P. MC AE ⓓ VISA JCB. ⚟
closed 25-26 December – **Meals** 24.00/48.00 **t.** 15.00 – 8.50 – **10 rm** 100.00/150.00 **t.**, 1 suite
Spec. Roast squab pigeon, confit of leg meat. Forest of Dean wild venison. Cappuccino coffee cup.

BASSENTHWAITE *Cumbria* 401 402 K 19 – *pop. 433.*

London 300 – Carlisle 24 – Keswick 7.

Armathwaite Hall ⚟, CA12 4RE, West : 1 ½ m. on B 5291, ✉ Keswick ☎ (017687) 76551, *reservations@armathwaite-hall.com, Fax (017687) 76220*, ≤ Bassenthwaite Lake, « Part 18C mansion in extensive grounds », ⚟, ⚟, ⚟, ⚟, ⚟, ⚟ – ⚟ ⚟ TV P – ⚟ 80. MC AE ⓓ VISA
Meals 16.95/37.95 and dinner a la carte **t.** 12.95 – **42 rm** 65.00/230.00 **t.** – SB.

The Pheasant, CA13 9YE, Southwest : 3 ¼ m. by B 5291 on Wythop Mill rd, ✉ Cockermouth ☎ (017687) 76234, *pheasant@easynet.co.uk, Fax (017687) 76002*, « 16C », ⚟ – ⚟ rest, P. MC VISA. ⚟
closed 25 December – **Meals** 15.75/21.95 and dinner a la carte 22.15/32.65 **t.** 12.95 – **16 rm** 65.00/150.00 **t.** – SB.

Ravenstone, CA12 4QG, South : 1 ½ m. on A 591 ☎ (017687) 76240, *info@ravenstone-hotel.co.uk, Fax (017687) 76733*, ≤, ⚟ – ⚟ rest, TV P. MC AE VISA
Meals (dinner only) 18.00/21.00 **st.** 9.50 – **20 rm** 40.00/100.00 **st.** – SB.

Ravenstone Lodge, CA12 4QG, South : 1 ½ m. on A 591 ☎ (017687) 76629, *ravenstone.lodge@talk21.com, Fax (017687) 76629*, ≤, ⚟ – TV P. MC VISA JCB
Meals (residents only) (dinner only) 16.50/20.50 **st.** 8.95 – **10 rm** 30.50/61.00 **st.**

at Ireby *North : 5 m. by A 591 on Ireby rd – ✉ Carlisle.*

Woodlands Country House ⚟, CA7 1EX, Northwest : ¼ m. on Mealsgate rd ☎ (016973) 71791, *hj@woodlnd.u-net.com, Fax (016973) 71482*, ⚟ – ⚟ TV P. MC VISA
closed January – **Meals** (by arrangement) 17.00 **st.** 8.50 – **7 rm** 38.00/70.00 **st.** – SB.

BATCOMBE *Somerset* 403 404 M 30 – *pop. 391* – ✉ *Shepton Mallet.*

London 130 – Bristol 24 – Bournemouth 50 – Salisbury 40 – Taunton 40.

Three Horseshoes Inn, BA4 6HE, ☎ (01749) 850359, *Fax (01749) 850615*, ⚟, ⚟ – P. MC VISA JCB
Meals a la carte 17.40/24.40 **t.** 11.00.

BATH

Bath & North East Somerset **403** **404** M 29 *The West Country G. – pop. 85 202.*

London 119 – Bristol 13 – Southampton 63 – Taunton 49.

TOURIST INFORMATION

Abbey Churchyard, Abbey Chambers ℘ (01225) 477101.

PRACTICAL INFORMATION

9, 9, 9, Tracy Park, Bath Rd, Wick ℘ (0117) 937 2251 – 18 Lansdown ℘ (01225) 422138 – 9 Entry Hill ℘ (01225) 834248.

SIGHTS

City★★★ – **Royal Crescent**★★★ **AV** *(No 1 Royal Crescent*★★ *AC* **AV A**) – *The Circus*★★★ **AV** – *Museum of Costume*★★★ *AC* **AV M7** – *Royal Photographic Society National Centre of Photography*★★ *AC* **BV M8** – *Roman Baths*★★ *AC* **BX D** – *Holburne Museum and Crafts Study Centre*★★ *AC* **Y M5** – *Pump Room*★ **BX B** - *Assembly Rooms*★ **AV** – *Bath Abbey*★ **BX** – *Pulteney Bridge*★ **BV** – *Bath Industrial Heritage Centre*★ *AC* **AV M1** – *Lansdown Crescent*★★ *(Somerset Place*★ *)* **Y** – *Camden Crescent*★ **Y** – *Beckford Tower and Museum AC (prospect*★ *)* **Y M6** – *Museum of East Asian Art*★ **AV M9** – *Orange Grove*★ **BX**.

Env. : *Claverton (American Museum*★★ *AC, Claverton Pumping Station*★ *AC) E : 3 m. by A 36* **Y**.

Exc. : *Corsham Court*★★ *AC, NE : 8 ½ m. by A 4 – Dyrham Park*★ *AC, N : 6 ½ m. by A 4 and A 46.*

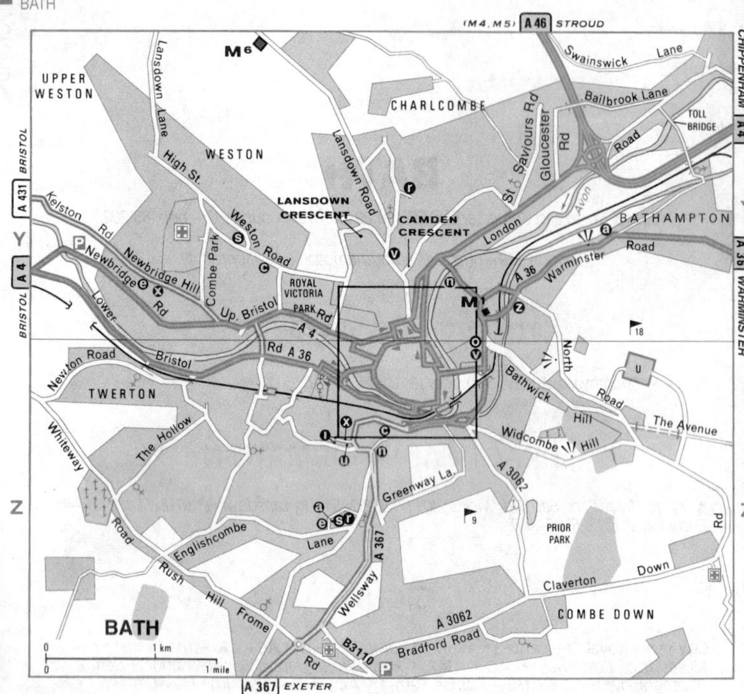

Bath Spa, Sydney Rd, BA2 6JF, (0870) 4008222, *fivestar@bathspa.u-net.com, Fax (01225) 444006*, « Part 19C mansion in landscaped gardens », – – 120. VISA JCB Y z
Alfresco : Meals 16.50 (lunch) and a la carte 20.70/34.65 **t.** 15.00 – ***Vellore :*** Meals (dinner only and Sunday lunch)/dinner 35.00 and a la carte 40.50/45.95 **t.** 19.00 – 14.75 – **98 rm** 190.00/210.00 **st.**, 5 suites – SB.

The Royal Crescent, 16 Royal Cres, BA1 2LS, (01225) 823333, *reservations@royalcrescent.co.uk, Fax (01225) 447427*, «Restored 18C town houses in magnificent Georgian crescent », – – 40. VISA JCB AV a
Pimpernels : Meals a la carte 22.00/51.00 **st.** 24.00 – 17.50 – **34 rm** 220.00 **st.**, 11 suites 420.00/800.00 **st.** – SB.

Bath Priory, Weston Rd, BA1 2XT, (01225) 331922, *bathprioryhotel@compuserve.com, Fax (01225) 448276*, « Gardens », heated, – VISA. Y c
Meals 27.50/45.00 **t.** 18.50 – **28 rm** 145.00/310.00 **t.** – SB
Spec. Pan-fried scallops, ginger velouté. Grilled lemon sole, smoked haddock tortellini. Chocolate fondant, malted milk ice cream.

Homewood Park, Hinton Charterhouse, BA2 7TB, Southeast : 6 ½ m. on A 36 (01225) 723731, *res@homewoodpark.com, Fax (01225) 723820*, « Part Georgian country house », heated, – rest, VISA JCB.
Meals 16.00/38.00 **st.** 16.00 – **17 rm** 109.00/215.00 **st.**, 2 suites – SB.

The Francis on the Square, Queen Sq, BA1 2HH, (0870) 4008223, *heritagehotels_bath.francis@forte-hotels.com, Fax (01225) 319715* – – 80. VISA AV i
Meals 21.95 and a la carte 20.00/30.00 **t.** 14.00 – 13.50 – **95 rm** 120.00/215.00 **st.** – SB.

Hilton Bath City, Walcot St, BA1 5BJ, (01225) 463411, *bathhnhngm@hilton.com, Fax (01225) 464393*, – – 220. VISA JCB BV i
Meals a la carte 9.90/32.40 **st.** 10.80 – 14.25 – **150 rm** 110.00/160.00 **st.** – SB.

BATH

Ambury .... BX 2
Argyle Street .... BV 3
Bennett Street .... AV 4
Bridge Street .... BVX 6
Broad Quay .... BX 7
Chapel Row .... AVX 9
Charles Street .... AX 10
Charlotte Street .... AV 12
Cheap Street .... BX 13
Churchill Bridge .... BX 14
Circus Place .... AV 16
Gay Street .... AV
Grand Parade .... BX 17
Great Stanhope Street .... AV 18
Green Street .... BV 21
Guinea Lane .... BV 23
Henry Street .... BX 24
Lower Borough Walls .... BX 26
Milsom Street .... BV
Monmouth Place .... AVX 28
Monmouth Street .... AX 30
New Bond Street .... BV 31
New Orchard Street .... BX 32
Nile Street .... AV 34
Northgate Street .... BVX 35
Old Bond Street .... BX 36
Orange Grove .... BX 38
Pierrepont Street .... BX 39
Quiet Street .... BV 41
Russell Street .... AV 42
Southgate Street .... BX 43
Stanley Road .... BX 45
Terrace Walk .... BX 46
Upper Borough Walls .... BX 48
Westgate Buildings .... AX 49
Westgate Street .... ABX 50
Wood Street .... AV 52
York Street .... BX 53

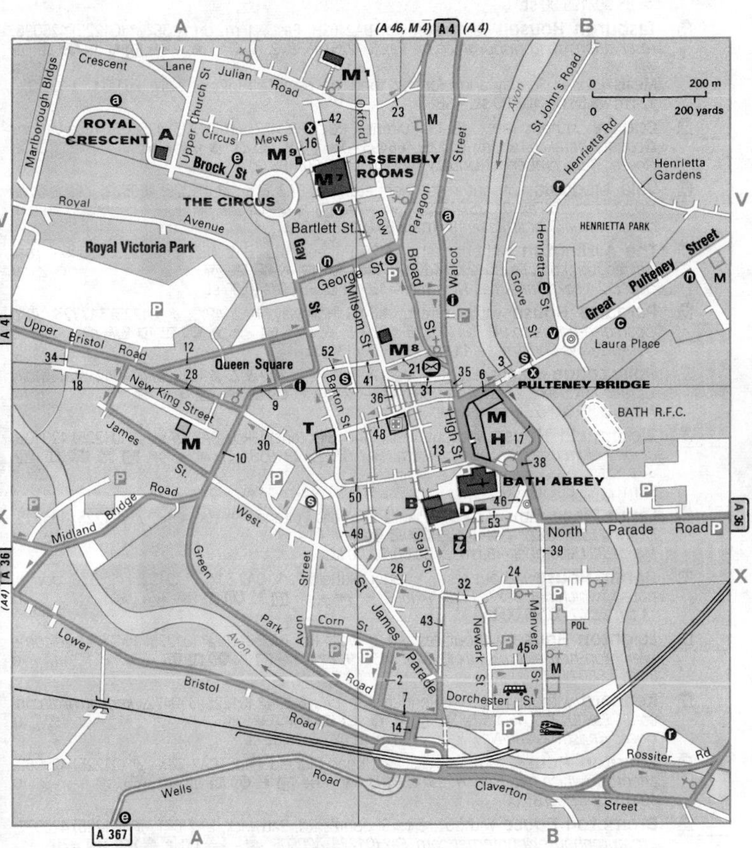

Queensberry, Russell St, BA1 2QF, ✆ (01225) 447928, *enquiries@bathqueensberry.com, Fax (01225) 446065,* – 𝌆 TV P – 30. MC VISA. AV x
closed 4 days Christmas – **Meals** – (see ***Olive Tree*** below) – ☕ 9.50 – **29 rm** 100.00/225.00 **t.** – SB.

Dukes, Great Pulteney St, BA2 4DN, ✆ (01225) 787960, *info@dukesbath.co.uk, Fax (01225) 787961,* « Georgian town house » – rest, TV P. MC VISA. BV n
Fitzroys : **Meals** (booking essential) 15.00 (lunch) and a la carte 22.00/35.00 **t.** 18.00 – ☕ 7.50 – **14 rm** 125.00/160.00 **st.**, 4 suites – SB.

Menzies Waterside, Rossiter Rd, Widcombe Basin, BA2 4JP, ✆ (01225) 338855, *waterside@menzies-hotels.co.uk, Fax (01225) 428941* – 𝌆, rm, TV P – 130. MC AE VISA BX r
Meals 9.95/17.00 and a la carte 19.85/28.40 **st.** 14.95 – **112 rm** 85.00/150.00 **st.** – SB.

Lansdown Grove, Lansdown Rd, BA1 5EH, (01225) 483888, *lansdown@marstonhotels.com, Fax (01225) 483838,* – – 80. Y v
Meals 14.95/23.00 **st.** 12.95 – **47 rm** 95.00/129.00 **st.**, 1 suite – SB.

Apsley House without rest., 141 Newbridge Hill, BA1 3PT, (01225) 336966, *info@apsley-house.co.uk, Fax (01225) 425462,* – . Y x
closed 3 days Christmas – **9 rm** 65.00/125.00 **st.**

The Windsor, 69 Great Pulteney St, BA2 4DL, (01225) 422100, *sales@bathwindsorhotel.com, Fax (01225) 422550* – . BV c
Meals - Japanese - *(closed Sunday lunch)* a la carte 10.00/25.00 **st.** 13.50 – **14 rm** 85.00/195.00 **st.**

Tasburgh House, Warminster Rd, BA2 6SH, East : 1 m. on A 36 (01225) 425096, *reservations@bathtasburgh.co.uk, Fax (01225) 463842,* , , – . Y a
Meals *(closed Sunday and Monday)* (booking essential) (dinner only) 25.00 **t.** 12.50 – **12 rm** 55.00/105.00 **st.** – SB.

County without rest., 18-19 Pulteney Rd, BA2 4EZ, (01225) 425003, *reservations@county-hotel.co.uk, Fax (01225) 466493* – . Z o
closed 23 December-10 January – **22 rm** 70.00/195.00.

Villa Magdala without rest., Henrietta Rd, BA2 6LX, (01225) 466329, *office@villamagdala.co.uk, Fax (01225) 483207,* – . BV r
closed 1 week Christmas – **18 rm** 65.00/130.00 **st.**

The Ayrlington without rest., 24-25 Pulteney Rd, BA2 4EZ, (01225) 425495, *mail@ayrlington.com, Fax (01225) 469029,* – Z v
closed 2 weeks Christmas-New Year – **12 rm** 75.00/110.00 **st.**

Paradise House without rest., 86-88 Holloway, BA2 4PX, (01225) 317723, *info@paradise-house.co.uk, Fax (01225) 482005,* , – . Z c
closed 2 days Christmas – **11 rm** 75.00/130.00.

Holly Lodge without rest., 8 Upper Oldfield Park, BA2 3JZ, (01225) 424042, *stay@hollylodge.co.uk, Fax (01225) 481138,* , – . Z x
7 rm 55.00/97.00 **st.**

Bloomfield House without rest., 146 Bloomfield Rd, BA2 2AS, (01225) 420105, *bloomfieldhouse@compuserve.com, Fax (01225) 481958,* , – . Z r
5 rm 55.00/105.00.

Laura Place without rest., 3 Laura Pl, Great Pulteney St, BA2 4BH, (01225) 463815, *Fax (01225) 310222* – . BV v
March-22 December – **8 rm** 60.00/92.00 **st.**

Dorian House without rest., 1 Upper Oldfield Park, BA2 3JX, (01225) 426336, *dorian.house@which.net, Fax (01225) 444699,* , – . Z u
11 rm 47.00/85,00 **t.**

Leighton House without rest., 139 Wells Rd, BA2 3AL, (01225) 314769, *welcome@leighton-house.co.uk, Fax (01225) 443079,* – . AX e
8 rm 50.00/79.00 **st.**

Kennard without rest., 11 Henrietta St, BA2 6LL, (01225) 310472, *kennard@dircon.co.uk, Fax (01225) 460054* – . BV u
closed Christmas and New Year – **13 rm** 48.00/98.00 **st.**

Cheriton House without rest., 9 Upper Oldfield Park, BA2 3JX, (01225) 429862, *cheriton@which.net, Fax (01225) 428403,* – . Z u
10 rm 52.00/85.00.

Brompton House without rest., St John's Rd, Bathwick, BA2 6PT, (01225) 420972, *bromptonhouse@btinternet.com, Fax (01225) 420505,* – . Y n
closed 21 December-14 January – **16 rm** 48.00/95.00 **t.**

Cranleigh without rest., 159 Newbridge Hill, BA1 3PX, (01225) 310197, *cranleigh@btinternet.com, Fax (01225) 423143,* – . Y e
closed 24-26 December – **8 rm** 50.00/85.00 **t.**

Travelodge without rest., 1 York Buildings, George St, BA1 2EB, (01225) 448999, *Fax (01225) 442061* – . BV e
66 rm 59.95 **t.**

Gainsborough without rest., Weston Lane, BA1 4AB, (01225) 311380, *gainsborough_hotel@compuserve.com, Fax (01225) 447411,* – . Y s
closed 23 December-3 January – **17 rm** 48.00/95.00 **st.**

Harington's, 8-10 Queen St, BA1 1HE, (01225) 461728, *post@haringtonshotel.co.uk, Fax (01225) 444804* – . . AV s
closed Christmas – **Meals** (light lunch only) a la carte approx. 14.45 8.50 – **13 rm** 68.00/108.00 **st.**

Haydon House without rest., 9 Bloomfield Park, off Bloomfield Rd, BA2 2BY, (01225) 444919, *stay@haydonhouse.co.uk, Fax (01225) 427351*, – TV. MC AE VISA JCB. Z a
5 rm 50.00/103.00 st.

Meadowland without rest., 36 Bloomfield Park, off Bloomfield Rd, BA2 2BX, (01225) 311079, *meadowland@bath92.freeserve.co.uk, Fax (01225) 311079*, – TV P. MC VISA. Z e
closed 23-28 December – **3 rm** 60.00/90.00 **st.**

Badminton Villa without rest., 10 Upper Oldfield Park, BA2 3JZ, (01225) 426347, *badmintonvilla@cableinet.co.uk, Fax (01225) 420393*, <, – TV P. MC VISA JCB. Z i
closed 22 December-1 February – **5 rm** 48.00/68.00 **st.**

Lavender House, 17 Bloomfield Park, off Bloomfield Rd, BA2 2BY, (01225) 314500, *lavenderhouse@btinternet.com, Fax (01225) 448564*, – TV. MC VISA JCB. Z s
Meals (by arrangement) 15.50/20.00 **s.** – **5 rm** 52.00/90.00.

Brocks without rest., 32 Brock St, BA1 2LN, (01225) 338374, *marion@brocksguesthouse.co.uk, Fax (01225) 334245* – TV. MC VISA. AV e
closed 25 and 31 December – **6 rm** 50.00/78.00 **t.**

Blairgowrie House without rest., 55 Wellsway, BA2 4RT, (01225) 332266, *blairgowrie.bath@ukgateway.net, Fax (01225) 484535* – TV. Z n
closed 25 December and 1 January – **3 rm** 44.00/58.00 **s.**

Oakleigh without rest., 19 Upper Oldfield Park, BA2 3JX, (01225) 315698, *oakleigh@which.net, Fax (01225) 448223* – TV P. MC AE VISA. Z i
3 rm 55.00/75.00 **st.**

XX **Blinis** (Blunos), 16 Argyle St, BA2 4BJ, (01225) 422510, *Fax (01225) 421764* – . MC AE VISA BV x
closed Sunday, Monday and lunch Tuesday – **Meals** 25.00/47.50 **t.** 22.00
Spec. Scrambled duck egg with Sevruga caviar, blinis and iced vodka. Tortellini of fresh eel with deep fried elvers. Slow braised honey-glazed belly of pork.

XX **Olive Tree** (at Queensberry H.), Russell St, BA1 2QF, (01225) 447928, *enquiries@bathqueensberry.com, Fax (01225) 446065* – . MC VISA AV x
closed 4 days Christmas, Sunday lunch and Bank Holiday Mondays – **Meals** 13.50/26.00 and a la carte 27.95/33.00 **t.** 12.50.

XX **Moody Goose** (Shore), 7A Kingsmead Sq, BA1 2AB, (01225) 466688, *moodygoose@excite.co.uk, Fax (01225) 466688* – . MC AE VISA AX s
closed 2 weeks January, Sunday and Bank Holidays except Good Friday – **Meals** 16.00/23.00 and dinner a la carte 28.00/33.50 **t.** 13.00
Spec. Foie gras parfait with roasted peach. Roast turbot, ravioli of crab, lime and coriander. Dark chocolate fondant with white chocolate and tarragon sorbet.

XX **Hole in the Wall,** 16 George St, BA1 2EH, (01225) 425242, *Fax (01225) 425242* – . MC AE VISA AV n
closed 25, 26 and 31 December and Sunday – **Meals** 8.50/21.50 and a la carte 22.75/26.75 **t.** 12.50.

XX **Rajpoot,** Rajpoot House, Argyle St, BA2 4BA, (01225) 466833, *asamad1@aol.com, Fax (01225) 444527* – . MC AE VISA BV s
closed 25-26 December – **Meals** - Indian - 7.25/28.00 and a la carte 18.00/28.00 **t.** 10.50.

XX **Sukhothai,** 90a Walcot St, BA1 5BG, (01225) 462463, *Fax (01225) 462463* – . MC AE VISA JCB BV a
closed Sunday lunch – **Meals** - Thai - 13.00/25.00 and a la carte 12.00/16.00 **t.** 9.50.

X **Woods,** 9-13 Alfred St, BA1 2QX, (01225) 314812, *Fax (01225) 443146*, – MC AE VISA AV v
closed 25-26 December – **Meals** 12.25/22.95 **t.** 12.00.

Richmond Arms, 7 Richmond Pl, Lansdown, BA1 5PZ, North : ¾ m. by Lansdown Rd off Richmond Rd (01225) 316725, *cuniflecth@aol.com*, Y r
closed Sunday dinner and Monday – **Meals** a la carte 17.00/19.00 **t.** 8.50.

at Colerne *(Wilts.) Northeast : 6 ½ m. by A 4 – Y – , Batheaston rd and Bannerdown Rd – Chippenham.*

Lucknam Park , SN14 8AZ, North : ½ m. on Marshfield rd (01225) 742777, *reservations@lucknampark.co.uk, Fax (01225) 743536*, <, « Palladian mansion in extensive parkland, walled garden », , , , , – rest, TV P – 40. MC AE VISA JCB.
Meals (light lunch)/dinner 45.00 **t.** 17.50 – 18.00 – **37 rm** 155.00/320.00 **t.**, 4 suites – SB.

at Bathford *East : 3½ m. by A 4 – Y – off A 363 – Bath.*

The Lodge without rest., Bathford Hill, BA1 7SL, (01225) 858467, *lodgethe@aol.com, Fax (01225) 858172*, heated, – TV P. MC
5 rm 65.00/110.00, 1 suite.

at Monkton Combe *Southeast : 4½ m. by A 36 – Y – ✉ Bath.*

Monkshill without rest., Shaft Rd, BA2 7HL, ☎ (01225) 833028, *monks.hill@virgin.net, Fax (01225) 833028,* ≤ Limpley Stoke Valley, « Antiques », – TV P. MC AE VISA JCB
closed Christmas and New Year – **3 rm** 55.00/80.00 **st.**

at Limpley Stoke (Lower) *Southeast : 5½ m. by A 36 – Y – off B 3108 – ✉ Bath.*

Cliffe, Cliffe Drive, Crowe Hill, BA2 7FY, ☎ (01225) 723226, *cliffe@bestwestern.co.uk, Fax (01225) 723871,* ≤, heated, – rest, TV P. MC AE D VISA JCB
Meals 12.75/14.25 (lunch) and a la carte 19.45/28.75 **st.** 12.95 – **11 rm** 80.00/100.00 **st.** – SB.

BATHFORD *Bath & North East Somerset* 403 404 M 29 – *see Bath.*

BATLEY *W. Yorks.* 402 O 22 – *pop. 48 030.*
London 205 – Leeds 9 – Manchester 40 – Middlesbrough 76 – Sheffield 31.

Alder House, Towngate Rd, WF17 7HR, Southwest : 1 m. by B 6123 ☎ (01924) 444777, *info@alderhousehotel.co.uk, Fax (01924) 442644,* – TV P – 80. MC AE D VISA
Meals *(closed Sunday dinner and Saturday lunch)* 12.00/18.95 **t.** 9.95 – **20 rm** 49.50/72.00 **t.** – SB.

Le Grand Londres (GREATER LONDON) est composé de la City et de 32 arrondissements administratifs (Borough) eux-mêmes divisés en quartiers ou en villages ayant conservé leur caractère propre (Area).

BATTLE *E. Sussex* 404 V 31 *Great Britain G. – pop. 5 235.*
See : *Town★ – Abbey and Site of the Battle of Hastings★ AC.*
88 High St ☎ (01424) 773721.
London 55 – Brighton 34 – Folkestone 43 – Maidstone 30.

PowderMills , Powdermill Lane, TN33 0SP, South : 1 ½ m. by A 2100 on Catsfield rd ☎ (01424) 775511, *powdc@aol.com, Fax (01424) 774540,* ≤, , « Part Georgian gunpowdermill, antiques », , , , – TV P – 250. MC AE D VISA
Orangery : **Meals** 15.50/25.50 and a la carte 25.50/35.00 **t.** 11.25 – **40 rm** 80.00/175.00 **t.** – SB.

Fox Hole Farm without rest., Kane Hythe Rd, TN33 9QU, Northwest : 2 ½ m. by A 2100 and A 271 on B 2096 ☎ (01424) 772053, *Fax (01424) 773771,* « 18C woodcutters cottage », , – TV P. MC VISA
3 rm 33.00/59.00 **st.**

BEACONSFIELD *Bucks.* 404 S 29 – *pop. 12 292.*
Beaconsfield Seer Green ☎ (01494) 676545.
London 26 – Aylesbury 19 – Oxford 32.

De Vere Bellhouse, Oxford Rd, HP9 2XE, East : 1 ¾ m. on A 40 ☎ (01753) 887211, *bellhouse@devere-hotels.co.uk, Fax (01753) 888231,* , , , , squash – TV P – 400. MC AE D VISA JCB
Archways : **Meals** *(closed Sunday dinner)* 15.50/32.00 and a la carte 25.15/31.75 **t.** 14.50 – ***Brasserie :*** **Meals** a la carte 19.50/23.50 **t.** 13.50 – **133 rm** 155.00/175.00 **t.**, 3 suites – SB.

at Wooburn Common *Southwest : 3½ m. by A 40 – ✉ Beaconsfield.*

Chequers Inn , Kiln Lane, HP10 0JQ, Southwest : 1 m. on Bourne End rd ☎ (01628) 529575, *info@chequers-inn.com, Fax (01628) 850124,* , – TV P – 45. MC D VISA.
Meals 17.95/26.95 and a la carte 28.15/39.15 9.50 – **17 rm** 97.50/102.50 **t.** – SB.

BEADNELL *Northd.* 401 402 P 17.
London 341 – Edinburgh 81 – Newcastle upon Tyne 47.

Beach Court without rest., Harbour Rd, NE67 5BJ, ☎ (01665) 720225, *info@beachcourt.com, Fax (01665) 721499,* ≤ Beadnell Bay – TV P. MC AE VISA JCB
closed 24 December-1 January – 4.95 – **3 rm** 44.50/99.00 **s.**

BEAMINSTER *Dorset* 403 L 31 – *pop. 2 769.*
Chedington Court, South Perrott ☎ (01935) 891413.
London 154 – Exeter 45 – Taunton 30 – Weymouth 29.

Bridge House, 3 Prout Bridge, DT8 3AY, ☎ (01308) 862200, *enquiries@bridge-house.co.uk, Fax (01308) 863700,* – rm, TV P. MC AE D VISA JCB
closed 28 December-1 January – **Meals** 11.00/29.00 **t.** 11.50 – **14 rm** 60.00/130.00 **t.** – SB.

BEARSTED *Kent* 404 V 30 – *see Maidstone.*

BEAULIEU *Hants.* 403 404 P 31 *Great Britain G.* – *pop. 726* – ✉ *Brockenhurst.*
See : *Town★★ - National Motor Museum★★ AC.*
Env. : *Buckler's Hard★ (Maritime Museum★ AC) SE : 2 m.*
London 102 – Bournemouth 24 – Southampton 13 – Winchester 23.

Montagu Arms, Palace Lane, SO42 7ZL, ☎ (01590) 612324, *enquires@montagu_arms.co.uk, Fax (01590) 612188,* , « Part 18C inn, gardens » – TV P – 40. MC AE D VISA.
Restaurant : **Meals** 29.95 (dinner) and a la carte 20.40/41.45 12.95 – ***Monty's Brasserie :*** **Meals** a la carte 14.00/23.40 **t.** 11.95 – **22 rm** 80.00/200.00 **t.**, 2 suites – SB.

at Bucklers Hard *South : 2½ m.* – ✉ *Brockenhurst.*

Master Builder's House, SO42 7XB, ☎ (01590) 616253, *res@themasterbuilders.co.uk, Fax (01590) 616297,* <, , « Located in 18C maritime village », – rm, TV P – 40. MC AE VISA.
Riverview : **Meals** 25.00/35.00 and a la carte 27.25/34.20 14.00 – ***Yachtsman Gallery :*** **Meals** a la carte 15.95/24.90 **t.** 14.00 – **23 rm** 120.00/165.00 **t.**, 2 suites – SB.

The Guide is updated annually so renew your Guide every year.

BECKINGTON *Somerset* 403 404 N 30 – *pop. 903* – ✉ *Bath (Bath & North East Somerset).*
London 110 – Bristol 27 – Southampton 54 – Swindon 37.

Travelodge, BA3 6SF, on A 36 ☎ (01373) 830251, *Fax (01373) 830251* – rm, TV & P. MC AE D VISA JCB.
Meals (grill rest.) – **40 rm** 49.95 **t.**

BEDFORD *Beds.* 404 S 27 – *pop. 73 917.*
Bedfordshire, Bromham Rd, Biddenham ☎ (01234) 261669 Y – *Mowsbury, Kimbolton Rd ☎ (01234) 216374.*
10 St Paul's Sq ☎ (01234) 215226.
London 59 – Cambridge 31 – Colchester 70 – Leicester 51 – Lincoln 95 – Luton 20 – Oxford 52 – Southend-on-Sea 85.

Plan on next page

Barns, Cardington Rd, MK44 3SA, East : 2 m. on A 603 ☎ (01234) 270044, *Fax (01234) 273102,* – TV P – 120. MC AE D VISA Y n
Meals *(closed 26 December-1 January, Bank Holidays and Saturday lunch)* a la carte 18.85/25.15 **st.** 11.00 – 11.50 – **48 rm** 95.00/150.00 **st.** – SB.

Bedford Swan, The Embankment, MK40 1RW, ☎ (01234) 346565, *info@bedfordswanhotel.co.uk, Fax (01234) 212009,* – , rest, TV P – 250. MC AE D VISA X a
Meals 11.50/16.50 and a la carte 18.90/25.30 8.00 – 8.95 – **109 rm** 85.00/89.50 **st.**, 1 suite – SB.

Travel Inn, Priory Country Park, Barkers Lane, MK41 9RQ, ☎ (01234) 352883, *Fax (01234) 325697* – rm, TV & P. MC AE D VISA. Y s
Meals (grill rest.) – **32 rm** 41.95 **t.**

at Elstow *South : 2 m. by A 6* – ✉ *Bedford.*

St Helena, High St, MK42 9XP, ☎ (01234) 344848, « Part 16C house », – P. MC AE D VISA Y r
closed 1 week Christmas, Saturday lunch, Sunday and Monday – **Meals** 25.00/30.00 **t.** 15.50.

at Houghton Conquest *South : 6½ m. by A 6* – Y – ✉ *Bedford.*

Knife and Cleaver, The Grove, MK45 3LA, ☎ (01234) 740387, *info@knifeandcleaver.com, Fax (01234) 740900,* , – rest, TV P. MC AE D VISA JCB.
closed 27-30 December – **Meals** *(closed Sunday dinner)* (bar lunch Saturday) 14.95 (lunch) and a la carte 19.40/34.95 **t.** 10.50 – **9 rm** 49.00/74.00 **t.**

BEDFORD

Alexandra Road . . . . X 3
Ampthill Road . . . . X 4
Ashburnham Road . . . . Y 6
Castle Road . . . . XY 7
Church Lane . . . . Y 9
Church Square . . . . X 10
Clapham Road . . . . Y 12
Commercial Road . . . . X 13
Eastcotts Road . . . . Y 15
Embankment The . . . . X 16
Ford End Road . . . . Y 18
Goldington Road . . . . X 19
Harpur Centre X
Harpur Street . . . . X 21
Hassett Street . . . . X 22
Haylands Way . . . . Y 24
High Street . . . . Y 25
Hillgrounds Road . . . . Y 26
Horne Lane . . . . X 27
Interchange Retail park . . . . . Y
Longholme Way . . . . Y 28
Loys Street . . . . X 30
Manton Lane . . . . Y 31
Newnham Avenue . . . . Y 33
Newnham Road . . . . X 34
Queen's Drive . . . . Y 36
River Street . . . . X 37
Rope Walk . . . . Y 39
St. Pauls Square . . . . X 40
Shakespeare Road . . . . Y 42
Silver Street . . . . X 43
Thurlow Street . . . . X 45
West End Lane . . . . Y 46

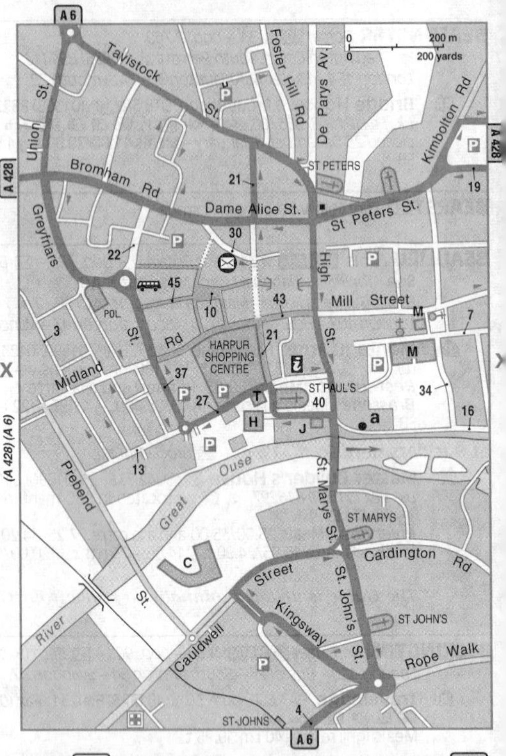

Great Britain and Ireland is now covered by an Atlas at a scale of 1 inch to 4.75 miles.

Three easy to use versions: Paperback, Spiralbound and Hardback.

A 6
Tavistock St.
Union St.
Foster Hill Rd
De Parys Av.
0 200 m
0 200 yards
Kimbolton Rd
A 428
ST PETERS
19
Bromham Rd
21
Dame Alice St.
St Peters St.
Greyfriars
30
22
High St.
Mill Street
M
7
45
43
10
POL
3
St.
Rd
HARPUR SHOPPING CENTRE
21
Midland
37
T
ST PAUL'S
40
34
16
27
H
J
a
X
(A 428) (A 6)
13
Prebend St.
Great Ouse
River
St Marys St.
ST MARYS
Cardington Rd
C
Street
St. John's St.
Kingsway
ST JOHN'S
Cauldwell
Rope Walk
ST-JOHNS
4
A 6

A 6 KETTERING
B 660
A 428
NORTHAMPTON
12
31
BEDFORD PARK
PUTNOE
Kimbolton Rd
Polhill Av.
24
36
9
GOLDINGTON
Goldington Rd
Ouse
18
42
A 428
Bromham Rd
Goldington
U
7
Barkers Lane
Riverfield Drive
Great
6
BEDFORD
33
RUSSELL PARK
New Cut
QUEEN'S PARK
18
s
PRIORY COUNTRY PARK
28
River
39
Cardington Rd
PRIORY BUSINESS PARK
Y
n
Kempston Rd
London Rd
JUBILEE PARK
15
26
Bedford Rd
Spring Rd
Ampthill Rd
Elstow Rd
Mile Rd
Harrowden Rd
Bedford Rd
CARDINGTON
B 531
r
25
Abbeyfields
Elstow Rd
46
The Highway
SHORTSTOWN
INTERCHANGE RETAIL PARK
ELSTOW
0 1 km
0 1/2 mile
LONDON BIRMINGHAM
A 421
B 530
A 6 LUTON
A 600 HICHTIN

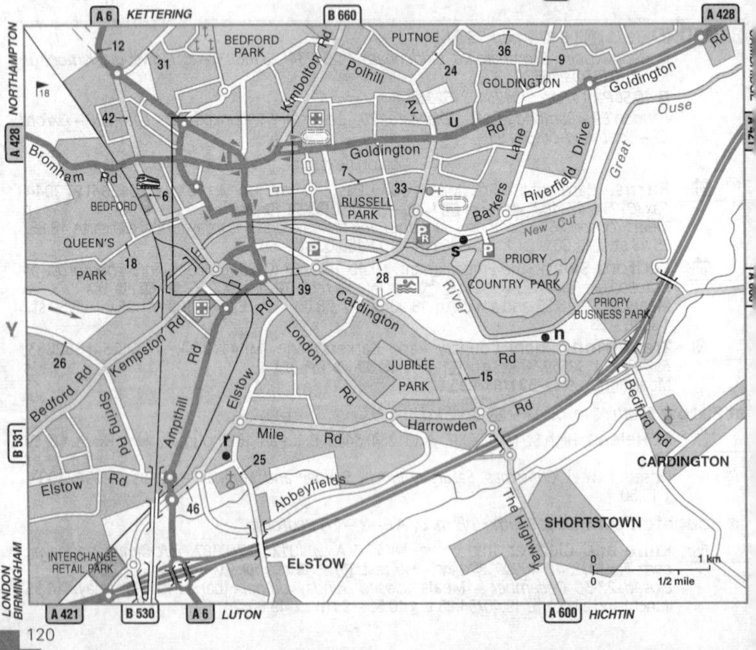

at Marston Moretaine *Southwest : 6¼ m. by A 6 – Y – off A 421 – ✉ Bedford.*

Travelodge, Beancroft Rd junction, MK43 0PZ, on A 421 ✆ (01234) 766755, *Fax (01234) 766755* – rm, TV & P. MC AE VISA JCB.
Meals (grill rest.) – **54 rm** 49.95 **t.**

Moreteyne Manor, Woburn Rd, MK43 0NG, ✆ (01234) 767003, *Fax (01234) 767003*, « 16C moated manor house », – P. MC AE VISA
closed 1 week spring, 1 week winter and Monday – **Meals** (booking essential) 16.50/28.50 **t.** 10.95.

at Milton Ernest *Northwest : 5 m. on A 6 – Y – ✉ Bedford.*

The Strawberry Tree, Radwell Rd, MK44 1RY, ✆ (01234) 823633, *Fax (01234) 825976*, « 18C thatched cottage », – P. MC VISA JCB
closed 2 weeks summer, 2 weeks winter, Monday, Tuesday, Saturday lunch and Sunday – **Meals** 34.00 (dinner) and lunch a la carte 29.50/33.50 **t.** 12.00.

at Bletsoe *Northwest : 6½ m. by A 6 – ✉ Bedford.*

North End Barns without rest., MK44 1QT, North : 1 m. on Riseley rd ✆ (01234) 781320, *Fax (01234) 781320*, « Working farm », , – TV & P. MC AE VISA JCB
8 rm 25.00/50.00 **s.**

BEESTON *Notts.* 402 403 404 Q 25 – *see Nottingham.*

BELFORD *Northd.* 401 402 O 17 – *pop. 1 177.*
Belford, South Rd ✆ (01668) 213433.
London 335 – Edinburgh 71 – Newcastle upon Tyne 49.

Blue Bell, Market Pl, NE70 7NE, ✆ (01668) 213543, *bluebel@globalnet.co.uk*, *Fax (01668) 213787*, – rest, TV & P. MC AE VISA
Meals (bar lunch Monday to Saturday)/dinner 23.00 and a la carte **t.** 10.95 – **17 rm** 44.00/98.00 **t.** – SB.

Purdy Lodge, Adderstone Services, NE70 7JU, on A 1 at junction with B 1341 ✆ (01668) 213000, *reception@purdylodge.co.uk*, *Fax (01668) 213111* – TV & P. MC AE VISA JCB
closed 25 December – **Meals** (bar lunch)/dinner a la carte 10.85/23.45 **st.** 9.50 – **20 rm** 41.95 **st.** – SB.

BELLINGHAM *Northd.* 401 402 N 18 – *pop. 1 164* – ✉ *Hexham.*
Boggle Hole ✆ (01434) 220530.
Fountain Cottage, Main St ✆ (01434) 220616.
London 315 – Carlisle 48 – Newcastle upon Tyne 33.

Westfield House, NE48 2DP, ✆ (01434) 220340, *info@westfield-house.net*, *Fax (01434) 220356*, – TV P. MC VISA.
Meals (by arrangement) 16.00 7.50 – **3 rm** 28.00/60.00 **st.** – SB.

BELPER *Derbs.* 402 403 404 P 24 – *pop. 18 213.*
London 141 – Derby 8 – Manchester 55 – Nottingham 17.

Makeney Hall Country House, Makeney, Milford, DE56 0RS, South : 2 m. by A 6 on Makeney rd ✆ (01332) 842999, *Fax (01332) 842777*, – , rest, TV & P – 150. MC AE VISA JCB
Meals *(closed Saturday lunch)* 13.95/19.90 and a la carte 19.90/34.00 **st.** 12.00 – 10.75 – **45 rm** 92.00/150.00 **st.** – SB.

The Green Room, 61 King St, DE56 1QA, ✆ (01773) 828800, *greenroombelper@aol.com*, *Fax (01773) 828184* – . MC AE VISA JCB
closed Sunday dinner and Monday – **Meals** 7.50/16.50 (lunch) and a la carte 22.90/27.25 **t.** 12.00.

at Shottle *Northwest : 4 m. by A 517 – ✉ Belper.*

Dannah Farm, Bowmans Lane, DE56 2DR, North : ¼ m. by Alport rd ✆ (01773) 550273, *reservations@dannah.demon.co.uk*, *Fax (01773) 550590*, « Working farm », , – TV P. MC VISA JCB.
closed Christmas – **Meals** (booking essential) (residents only except Saturday) (dinner only) 19.50/25.95 **st.** 11.50 – **6 rm** 57.50/79.00 **st.**, 2 suites.

BELSTONE *Devon* 403 I 31 – *see Okehampton.*

BEPTON *W. Sussex – see Midhurst.*

BERKELEY *Glos.* 403 404 M 28 *Great Britain G. – pop. 1 550.*
See : *Berkeley Castle★★ AC.*
Exc. : *Wildfowl and Wetlands Trust, Slimbridge★ AC, NE : 6½ m. by B 4066 and A 38.*
London 129 – Bristol 20 – Cardiff 50 – Gloucester 18.

Prince of Wales, Berkeley Rd, GL13 9HD, Northeast : 2 ½ m. by B 4066 on A 38 ☎ (01453) 810474, *Fax (01453) 511370,* – 200. VISA.
Meals - Italian - (bar lunch Monday to Saturday) (carving lunch Sunday)/dinner a la carte 15.40/22.65 – 6.50 – **43 rm** 54.00/69.00 **st.**

The Old School House, Canonbury St, GL13 9BG, ☎ (01453) 811711, *oldschoolhouse@btinternet.com, Fax (01453) 511761* – rest, VISA
Meals *(closed Sunday)* (booking essential to non-residents) (dinner only) a la carte 20.95/25.50 **t.** 11.95 – **8 rm** 58.00/70.00 **t.**, 1 suite – SB.

BERKSWELL *W. Mids.* 403 404 P 26 *– see Coventry.*

BERWICK-UPON-TWEED *Northd.* 401 402 O 16 *Great Britain and Scotland G. – pop. 13 544.*
See : *Town★ - Walls★.*
Env. : *Foulden★, NW : 5 m. – Paxton House (Chippendale furniture★) AC, W : 5 m. by A 6105, A 1 and B 6461.*
Exc. : *St Abb's Head★★ (<★), NW : 12 m. by A 1, A 1107 and B 6438 – SW : Tweed Valley★★ – Eyemouth Museum★ AC, N : 7½ m. by A 1 and A 1107 – Holy Island★ (Priory ruins★ AC, Lindisfarne Castle★ AC), SE : 9 m. by A 1167 and A 1 – Manderston★ (stables★), W : 13 m. by A 6105 – Ladykirk (Kirk o'Steil★), SW : 8½ m. by A 698 and B 6470.*
Goswick ☎ (01289) 387256 – Magdalene Fields ☎ (01289) 306384.
106 Marygate ☎ (01289) 330733.
London 349 – Edinburgh 57 – Newcastle upon Tyne 63.

Marshall Meadows Country House, TD15 1UT, North : 2 ¾ m. by A 1 ☎ (01289) 331133, *stay@marshallmeadows.co.uk, Fax (01289) 331438,* – 200. VISA JCB
closed 25-28 December – **Meals** 10.00/22.00 and a la carte 22.00/30.00 **st.** 9.95 – **18 rm** 75.00/85.00 **st.**, 1 suite – SB.

High Letham Farmhouse, TD15 1UX, West : 2 ¼ m. by A 6105 and A 1 on Low Cocklaw rd ☎ (01289) 306585, *hlfm@fantasyprints.co.uk, Fax (01289) 304194,* <, – VISA.
closed 24-26 December – **Meals** (by arrangement) (communal dining) 22.00 **st.** 8.00 – **3 rm** 44.00/68.00 **st.** – SB.

BEVERLEY *East Riding* 402 S 22 *Great Britain G. – pop. 23 632 – Kingston-upon-Hull.*
See : *Town★ - Minster★★ – St Mary's Church★.*
The Westwood ☎ (01482) 867190.
34 Butcher Row ☎ (01482) 867430.
London 188 – Kingston-upon-Hull 8 – Leeds 52 – York 29.

Tickton Grange, Tickton, HU17 9SH, Northeast : 3 ¾ m. on A 1035 ☎ (01964) 543666, *maggy@tickton-grange.demon.co.uk, Fax (01964) 542556,* – – 200. VISA.
restricted opening 25 December-3 January – **Meals** – (see ***Squires Dining Room*** below) – 8.50 – **17 rm** 65.00/85.00 **t.** – SB.

Squires Dining Room (at Tickton Grange), Tickton, HU17 9SH, Northeast : 3 ¾ m. on A 1035 ☎ (01964) 543666, *Fax (01964) 542556* – VISA
restricted opening 25 December-3 January – **Meals** 22.50/25.00 (dinner) and a la carte 20.00/30.00 **t.** 11.95.

at Walkington *Southwest : 3½ m. by A 164 on B 1230 – Beverley.*

Manor House with rm, Northlands, Newbald Rd, HU17 8RT, Northeast : 1 m. by Northgate on Beverley rd ☎ (01482) 881645, *derek@the-manorhouse.co.uk, Fax (01482) 866501,* « Late 19C house, conservatory », – VISA
closed 25 December-4 January – **Meals** *(closed Sunday and Bank Holidays)* (dinner only) 15.00 and a la carte 15.00/30.00 **t.** 13.95 – 11.50 – **7 rm** 80.00/110.00 **t.** – SB.

BEWDLEY *Worcs.* 402 403 404 N 26 *– see Kidderminster.*

BEXHILL *E. Sussex* 404 V 31 – *pop. 38 905.*

Cooden Beach ✆ (01424) 842040 – Highwoods, Ellerslie Lane ✆ (01424) 212625.

51 Marina ✆ (01424) 732208.

London 66 – Brighton 32 – Folkestone 42.

Leet Lychgates, 5a Church St, Old Town, TN40 2HE, ✆ (01424) 212193, *leet@tesco.net, Fax (01424) 212193* – . VISA JCB
closed Sunday-Tuesday – **Meals** (booking essential) (dinner only) 19.50 15.00.

BEYTON *Suffolk* 404 W 27 – *see Bury St. Edmunds.*

BIBURY *Glos.* 403 404 O 28 *Great Britain G. – pop. 570 – Cirencester.*

See : *Village*★.

London 86 – Gloucester 26 – Oxford 30.

Swan, GL7 5NW, ✆ (01285) 740695, *swanhot1@swanhotel-cotswolds.co.uk, Fax (01285) 740473,* « Attractively furnished inn with gardens and trout stream », – – 50. VISA JCB.
Signet Room : **Meals** (dinner only and Sunday lunch)/dinner 28.50 and a la carte approx. 39.00 **st.** 15.75 – ***Jankowski's Brasserie :*** **Meals** a la carte 14.65/20.65 **st.** 12.00 – **20 rm** 99.00/260.00 **st.** – SB.

Cotteswold House without rest., Arlington, GL7 5ND, on B 4425 ✆ (01285) 740609, *cotteswold.house@btclick.com, Fax (01285) 740609* – . VISA.
3 rm 35.00/48.00.

BIDEFORD *Devon* 403 H 30 *The West Country G. – pop. 13 066.*

See : *Bridge*★★ – *Burton Art Gallery*★ *AC.*

Env. : *Appledore*★, *N : 2 m.*

Exc. : *Clovelly*★★, *W : 11 m. by A 39 and B 3237 – Lundy Island*★★, *NW : by ferry – Rosemoor*★ – *Great Torrington (Dartington Crystal*★ *AC) SE : 7½ m. by A 386.*

Royal North Devon, Golf Links Rd, Westward Ho ✆ (01237) 473824 – Torrington, Weare Trees ✆ (01805) 622229.

to Lundy Island (Lundy Co. Ltd) (1 h 45 mn).

Victoria Park, Kingsley Rd ✆ (01237) 421853.

London 231 – Exeter 43 – Plymouth 58 – Taunton 60.

Yeoldon House, Durrant Lane, EX39 2RL, North : 1 ½ m. by B 3235 off A 386 ✆ (01237) 474400, *yeoldonhouse@aol.com, Fax (01237) 476618,* – . VISA
closed 24-26 December – **Meals** *(closed Sunday)* (dinner only) 21.50/27.50 **t.** 10.50 – **10 rm** 60.00/105.00 **st.**

Memories, 8 Fore St, Northam, EX39 1AW, North : 2 m. by B 235 off A 386 ✆ (01237) 473419, *Fax (01237) 473419* – . VISA JCB
closed 2 weeks in winter, Sunday and Monday – **Meals** (dinner only) a la carte 17.40/21.40 11.95.

at Instow *North : 3 m. by A 386 on B 3233 – Bideford.*

Commodore, Marine Par, EX39 4JN, ✆ (01271) 860347, *admin@the-commodore.freeserve.co.uk, Fax (01271) 861233,* Taw and Torridge estuaries, – rest, – 250. VISA.
Meals (dinner only and Sunday lunch)/dinner 22.00 and a la carte 20.00/51.00 **t.** 10.50 – **20 rm** (dinner included) 80.00/160.00 **t.** – SB.

BIGBURY-ON-SEA *Devon* 403 I 33 – *pop. 600 – Kingsbridge.*

London 196 – Exeter 42 – Plymouth 23.

Henley, Folly Hill, TQ7 4AR, ✆ (01548) 810240, *Fax (01548) 810240,* Bigbury Bay and Bolt Tail, – . VISA JCB
March-November – **Meals** (booking essential to non-residents) (dinner only) 20.00 **st.** 11.50 – **6 rm** (dinner included) 67.00/114.00 **st.** – SB.

BILBROUGH *N. Yorks.* 402 Q 22 – *see York.*

BILLESLEY *Warks.* – *see Stratford-upon-Avon.*

BILLINGSHURST *W. Sussex* 404 S 30 – *pop. 4 980.*
London 44 – Brighton 24 – Guildford 25 – Portsmouth 40.

Travelodge, Five Oaks, Staines St, RH14 9AE, North : 1 m. on A 29 ℘ (01403) 782711, *Fax (01403) 782711* – rm, rest, TV & P. MC AE D VISA JCB.
Meals (grill rest.) – **26 rm** 49.95 **t.**

Old Wharf without rest., Wharf Farm, Newbridge, RH14 0JG, West : 1 ¾ m. on A 272 ℘ (01403) 784096, *david.mitchell@farming.co.uk, Fax (01403) 784096,* ≤, « Restored canalside warehouse », , , , – TV P.
closed 2 weeks Christmas and New Year – **3 rm** 45.00/90.00 **s.**

BILSBORROW *Lancs. – see Garstang.*

BINFIELD HEATH *Oxon. – see Henley-on-Thames.*

BINGHAM *Notts.* 402 404 R 25 – *pop. 7 057.*
London 125 – Lincoln 28 – Nottingham 11 – Sheffield 35.

Yeung Sing, Market St, NG13 8AB, ℘ (01949) 831831, *Fax (01949) 838833* – TV P. MC AE VISA.
closed 25-26 December and 1 January – **Meals** – (see below) – **15 rm** 43.00/56.00 **t.**

XX **Yeung Sing** (at Yeung Sing H.), Market St, NG13 8AB, ℘ (01949) 831222, *Fax (01949) 838833* – P. MC AE VISA
closed 25-26 December and 1 January – **Meals** - Chinese (Canton) - (dinner only and Sunday lunch)/dinner 17.50 and a la carte 14.80/40.50 **st.** 12.00.

BINGLEY *W. Yorks.* 402 O 22 – *pop. 19 585* – ✉ *Bradford.*
St Ives Est. ℘ *(01274) 562436.*
London 204 – Bradford 6 – Skipton 13.

Five Rise Locks, Beck Lane, BD16 4DD, via Park Rd ℘ (01274) 565296, *info@five-rise-locks.co.uk, Fax (01274) 568828,* – TV P. MC VISA JCB
closed 27 December-3 January and Saturday lunch – ***Oxley's* : Meals** (lunch by arrangement) 13.00 and a la carte 13.25/19.75 **st.** 7.00 – **9 rm** 52.00/62.00 **st.** – SB.

Travel Inn, Bradford Rd, Sandbeds, BD20 5NH, Northwest : 1 ½ m. by A 650 ℘ (01274) 566662, *Fax (01274) 566114* – rm, rest, TV & P. MC AE D VISA.
Meals (grill rest.) – **40 rm** 41.95 **t.**

BINHAM *Norfolk* 404 W 25 – *pop. 281* – ✉ *Fakenham.*
London 123 – Cambridge 75 – King's Lynn 31 – Norwich 29.

Field House , Walsingham Rd, NR21 0BU, Southwest : 1 ½ m. on Walsingham rd ℘ (01328) 830639, « Georgian farmhouse », – TV P.
closed November-mid February – **Meals** (by arrangement) 19.00 **s.** – **3 rm** 45.00/70.00 **s.**

BINLEY *W. Mids. – see Coventry.*

BINTON *Warks. – see Stratford-upon-Avon.*

BIRCHINGTON *Kent* 404 X 29 – *pop. 9 859.*
London 71 – Dover 20 – Maidstone 40 – Margate 5.

Crown Inn (Cherry Brandy House), Ramsgate Rd, Sarre, CT7 0LF, Southwest : 4 m. on A 28 ℘ (01843) 847808, *crown@shepherd_neame.co.uk, Fax (01843) 847914,* – TV & P. MC AE VISA
Meals a la carte 13.40/23.95 **t.** 10.95 – **12 rm** 55.00/75.00 **t.** – SB.

BIRCH SERVICE AREA *Gtr. Manchester* 402 ㉒ 403 ③ 404 ⑩ – ✉ *Heywood (Lancs.).*

Travelodge, OL10 2HQ, M 62 (eastbound) between junctions 18 and 19 ℘ (0161) 655 3403, *Fax (0161) 655 3358* – rm, TV & P. MC AE D VISA JCB.
Meals (grill rest.) 43.00/66.00 **st.** 23.50 – **55 rm** 39.95 **t.**

Travelodge, OL10 2HQ, M 62 (westbound) between junctions 18 and 19 ℘ (0161) 643 9419 – rm, TV & P. MC AE D VISA JCB.
Meals (grill rest.) – **35 rm** 42.95 **t.**

BIRKENHEAD *Mersey.* 402 403 K 23 – *pop. 93 087.*

18 Arrowe Park, Woodchurch ✆ (0151) 677 1527 – 18 Prenton, Golf Links Rd, Prenton ✆ (0151) 608 1461.
Mersey Tunnels (toll).
to Liverpool and Wallasey (Mersey Ferries) frequent services daily.
Woodside Ferry Booking Hall ✆ (0151) 647 6780.
London 222 – Liverpool 2.

Plan : see Liverpool p. 3

Bowler Hat, 2 Talbot Rd, Prenton, CH43 2HH, Southwest : 2 ½ m. by A 552 on B 5151 ✆ (0151) 652 4931, *Fax (0151) 653 8127,* – TV P – 200. MO AE VISA
Blades : **Meals** *(closed Saturday lunch)* 10.95/19.95 and a la carte 13.20/27.15 **t.** 10.95 – **32 rm** 80.00/125.00 **t.** – SB.

River Hill, Talbot Rd, Prenton, CH43 2HJ, Southwest : 2 ¼ m. by A 552 on B 5151 ✆ (0151) 653 3773, *reception@theriverhill.co.uk, Fax (0151) 653 7162,* – TV P. MO AE VISA.
Meals (dinner only and Sunday lunch)/dinner 10.00/16.95 and a la carte 13.85/25.40 **t.** 9.95 – 5.95 – **14 rm** 54.50 **t.**

BIRMINGHAM

W. Mids. 403 404 O 26 *Great Britain G. – pop. 965 928.*

London 122 – Bristol 91 – Liverpool 103 – Manchester 86 – Nottingham 50.

TOURIST INFORMATION

Convention & Visitor Bureau, 2 City Arcade ℘ (0121) 643 2514, Fax (0121) 616 1038
Convention & Visitor Bureau, National Exhibition Centre ℘ (0121) 780 4321
Birmingham Airport, Information Desk ℘ (0121) 767 7145.
Visitor Information Centre, 130 Colmore Row ℘ (0121) 693 6300.

PRACTICAL INFORMATION

18 *Edgbaston, Church Road ℘ (0121) 454 1736,* **FX**.
18 *Hilltop, Park Lane, Handsworth ℘ (0121) 554 4463,* **CU**.
18 *Hatchford Brook, Coventry Road, Sheldon ℘ (0121) 743 9821.*
18 *Brandhall, Heron Road, Oldbury, Warley ℘ (0121) 552 7475,* **BU**.
9 *Harborne Church Farm, Vicarage Road, Harborne ℘ (0121) 427 1204,* **EX**.
Birmingham International Airport : ℘ (0121) 767 5511, E : 6½ m. by A 45 **DU**.

SIGHTS

See : *City★ – Museum and Art Gallery★★* **JZ M2** *– Barber Institute of Fine Arts★★ (at Birmingham University)* **EX** *– Cathedral of St. Philip (stained glass portrayals★)* **KYZ**.

Env. : *Aston Hall★★* **FV M**.

Exc. : *Black Country Museum★, Dudley, NW : 10 m. by A 456 and A 4123* **AU** *– Bournville★, SW : 4 m. on A 38 and A 441.*

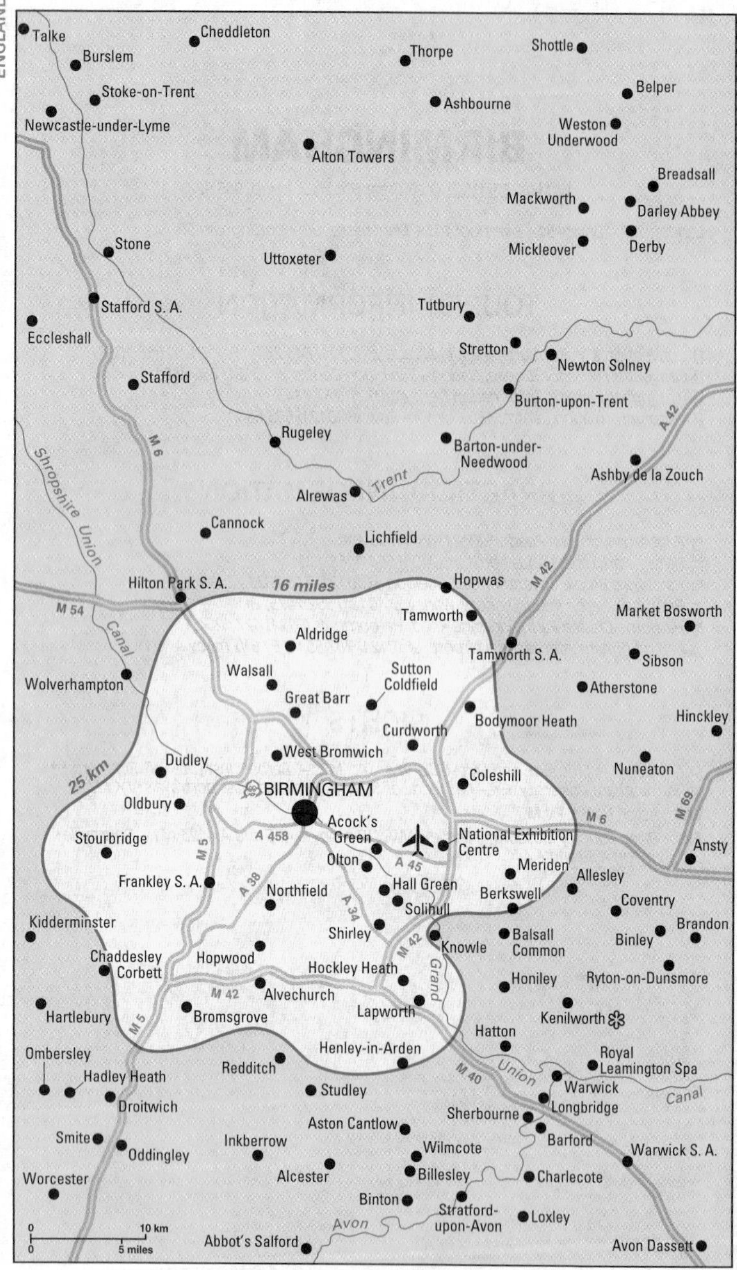

The Guide is updated annually so renew your Guide every year.

STREET INDEX TO BIRMINGHAM TOWN PLANS

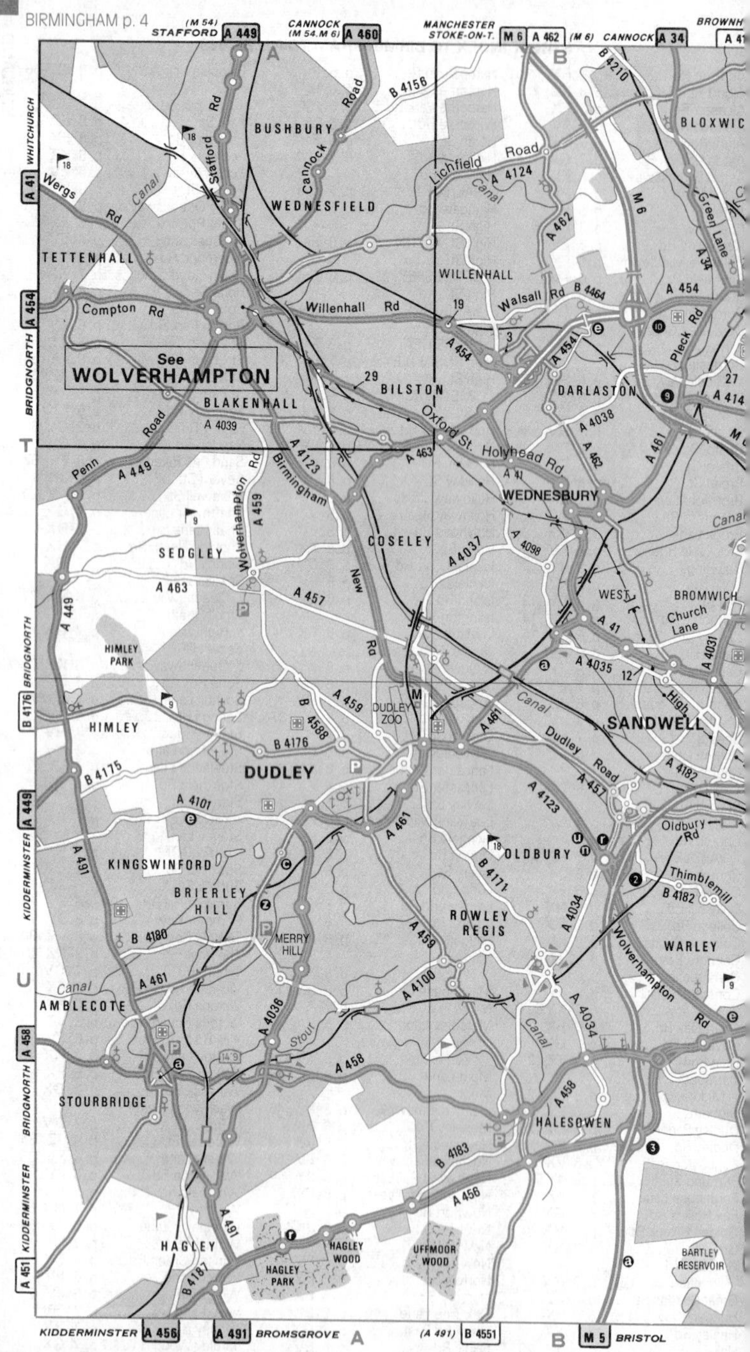
(M 54) STAFFORD A 449
CANNOCK (M 54.M 6) A 460
MANCHESTER STOKE-ON-T. M 6 A 462 (M 6) CANNOCK A 34
WHITCHURCH A 41
BRIDGNORTH A 454
BRIDGNORTH B 4176
KIDDERMINSTER A 449
BRIDGNORTH A 458
KIDDERMINSTER A 451
KIDDERMINSTER A 456 A 491 BROMSGROVE
(A 491) B 4551
M 5 BRISTOL
BUSHBURY
WEDNESFIELD
TETTENHALL
See WOLVERHAMPTON
BLAKENHALL
BILSTON
WILLENHALL
BLOXWICH
DARLASTON
WEDNESBURY
COSELEY
SEDGLEY
WEST BROMWICH
SANDWELL
HIMLEY PARK
HIMLEY
DUDLEY
DUDLEY ZOO
KINGSWINFORD
BRIERLEY HILL
MERRY HILL
OLDBURY
ROWLEY REGIS
WARLEY
AMBLECOTE
STOURBRIDGE
HALESOWEN
HAGLEY
HAGLEY PARK
HAGLEY WOOD
UFFMOOR WOOD
BARTLEY RESERVOIR
Wergs Rd
Compton Rd
Stafford Rd
Cannock Road
Lichfield Road
Willenhall Rd
Walsall Rd
Penn Road
Wolverhampton Rd
Birmingham New Rd
Oxford St.
Holyhead Rd
Dudley Road
Oldbury Rd
Thimblemill
Green Lane
Pleck Rd
Church Lane
High
Wolverhampton Rd
Canal
Stour
A 4039
A 4123
A 463
A 4124
A 462
A 454
A 4541
A 4038
A 461
A 41
A 414
A 4037
A 4098
A 459
A 457
A 4035
A 4031
A 4182
A 4101
A 491
A 4034
A 4100
A 4036
A 458
A 456
B 4156
B 4210
B 4464
B 4588
B 4176
B 4175
B 4171
B 4182
B 4180
B 4183
B 4187
M 6
19
3
29
27
12
A
B
T
U

BIRMINGHAM AND WOLVERHAMPTON
ENLARGED AREA

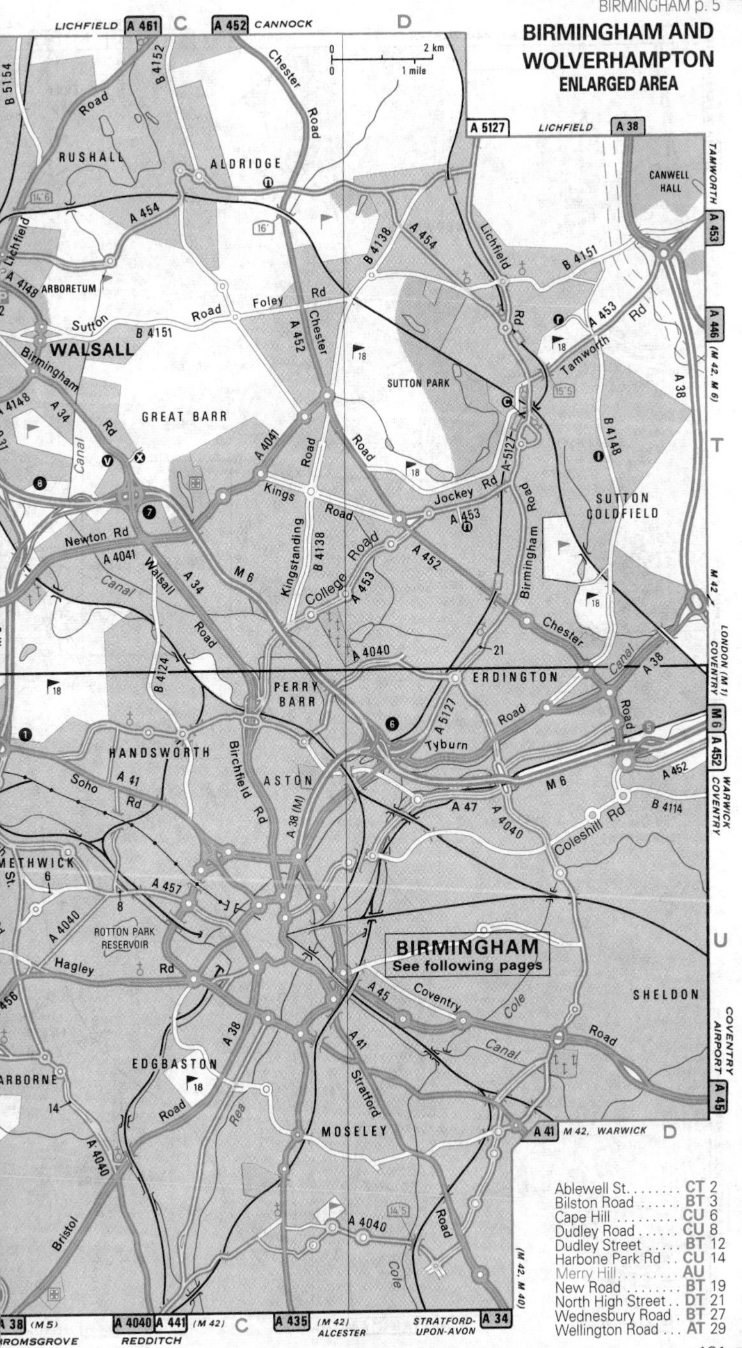

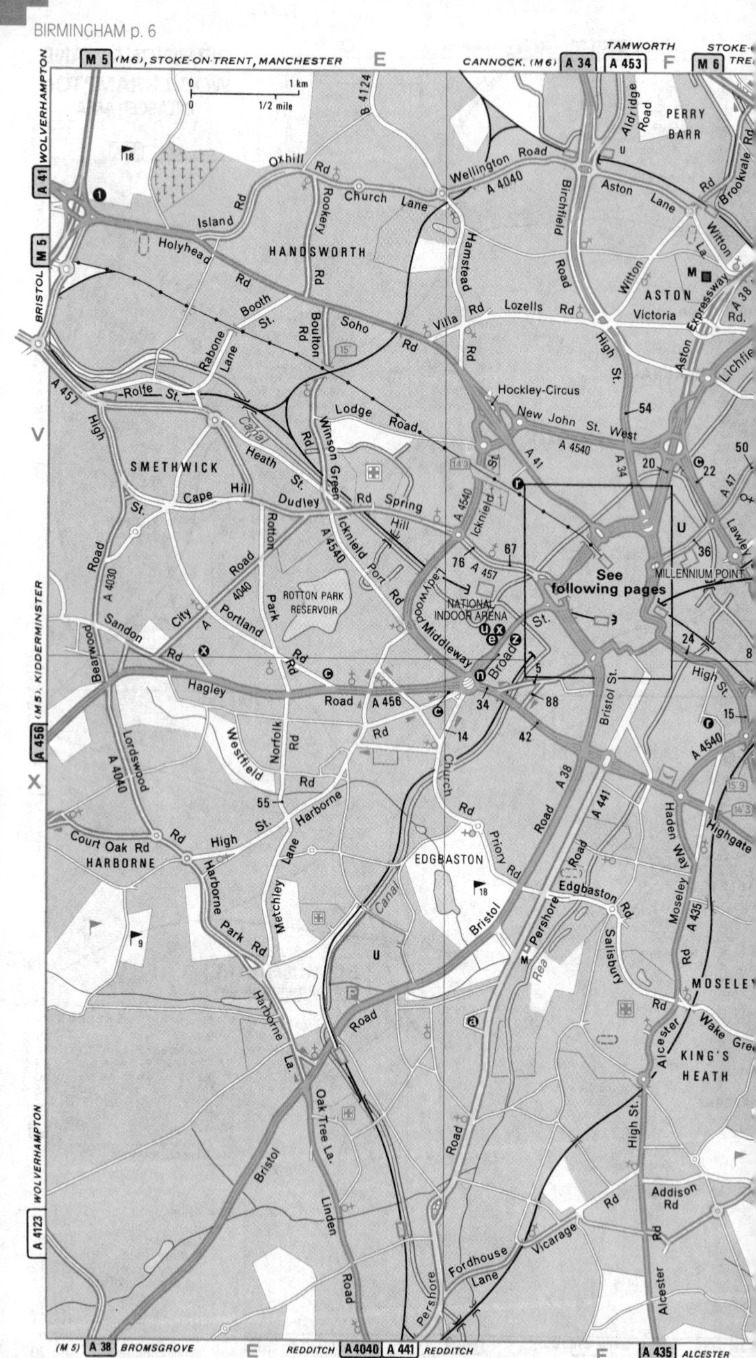
M 5 (M6), STOKE-ON-TRENT, MANCHESTER
CANNOCK. (M6) A 34
TAMWORTH A 453
M 6
A 41 WOLVERHAMPTON
BRISTOL M 5
A 456 (M 5). KIDDERMINSTER
A 4123 WOLVERHAMPTON
(M 5) A 38 BROMSGROVE
REDDITCH A4040 A 441 REDDITCH
A 435 ALCESTER
PERRY BARR
HANDSWORTH
ASTON
SMETHWICK
HARBORNE
EDGBASTON
MOSELEY
KING'S HEATH
ROTTON PARK RESERVOIR
NATIONAL INDOOR ARENA
MILLENNIUM POINT
See following pages
Hockley-Circus
Holyhead Rd
Soho Rd
Hagley Road A 456
Bristol Road
Pershore Rd
Alcester Rd
Harborne Park Rd
Edgbaston Rd
Lodge Road
Dudley Rd
Cape Hill

BUILT UP AREA

For Street Index see Birmingham p. 3

CENTRE

Albert St. . . . . KZ 2
Bull Ring Centre . . . . KZ
Bull St. . . . . KY 13
Corporation St. . . . . KYZ
Dale End. . . . . KZ 21
Hall St. . . . . JY 29
Holloway Circus. . . . . JZ 32
James Watt
Queensway. . . . . KY 35
Jennen's Rd . . . . KY 36
Ladywell Walk. . . . . KZ 37
Lancaster Circus. . . . . KY 39
Lancaster St. . . . . KY 41
Martineau Place
Shopping . . . . KZ
Masshouse Circus . . . . KY 43
Minories Shopping Centre . KY
Moat Lane . . . . KZ 44
Moor St. Queensway. . . . . . KZ 46
Navigation St.. . . . . JZ 49
New St. . . . . JKZ
Newton St. . . . . KY 53
Paradise Circus . . . . JZ 56
Paradise Forum
Shopping Centre . . . . JZ
Park St. . . . . KZ 57
Priory Queensway . . . . KY 59
St Chads Circus . . . . JKY 62
St Chads Ringway . . . . KY 63
St Martin's Circus . . . . KZ 64
Shadwell St. . . . . KY 70
Smallbrook Queensway . . . . KZ 71
Snow Hill Queensway . . . . . KY 73
Summer Row . . . . JY 77
Temple Row . . . . KZ 80
Waterloo St. . . . . JZ 84

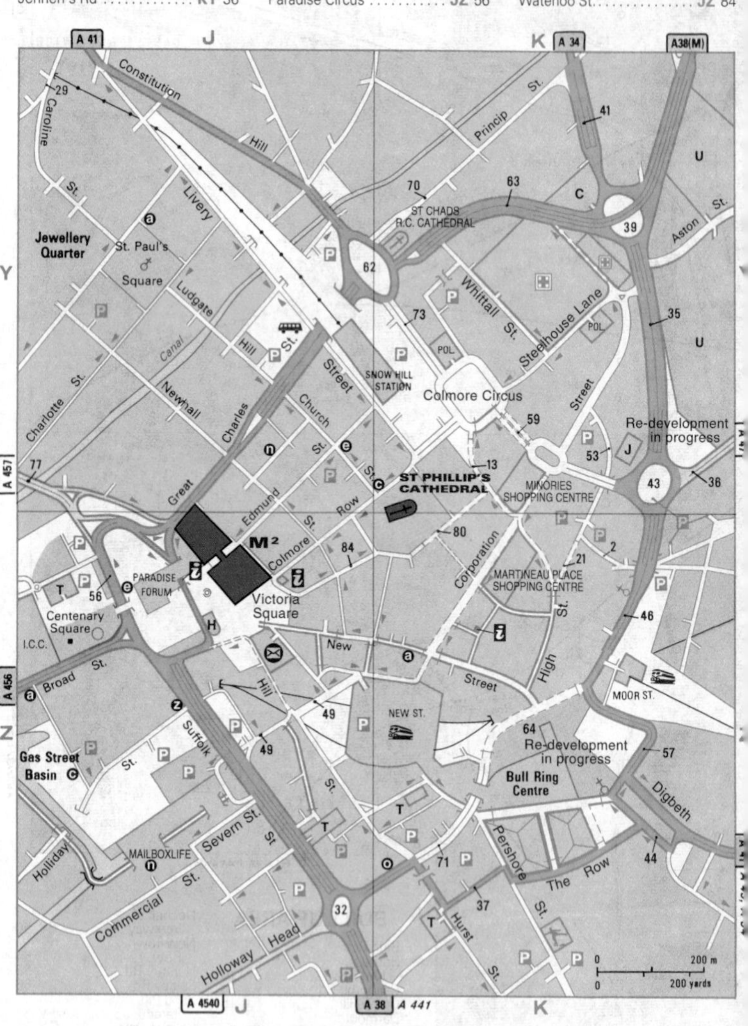

«Short Breaks»

Many hotels now offer a special rate for a stay of 2 nights which includes dinner, bed and breakfast.

Town plans : Birmingham pp. 3-8

Hyatt Regency, 2 Bridge St, B1 2JZ, (0121) 643 1234, *hrbirm@hrb.co.uk, Fax (0121) 616 2323,* – rm, – 250. VISA JCB. JZ a
Meals 13.50 (lunch) and a la carte 18.00/28.75 **st.** 14.50 – 13.25 – **315 rm** 175.00 **st.**, 4 suites.

Birmingham Marriott, 12 Hagley Rd, B16 8SJ, (0121) 452 1144, *Fax (0121) 456 3442,* – rm, – 30. VISA JCB FX c
Langtrys : **Meals** *(closed Sunday lunch)* 16.50 (lunch) and a la carte 23.50/32.00 **t.** 12.00 – (see also ***Sir Edward Elgar's*** below) – 14.45 – **94 rm** 149.00/195.00 **st.**, 4 suites – SB.

Hotel Du Vin, 25 Church St, B3 2NR, (0121) 236 0559, *info@birmingham.hotelduvin.com, Fax (0121) 236 0889,* « Converted Victorian hospital, contemporary wine themed interior », – rm, – 85. VISA. JY e
Bistro : **Meals** a la carte 26.25/31.25 **t.** 11.50 – 11.50 – **66 rm** 110.00/175.00 **t.**

Crowne Plaza Birmingham, Central Sq, B1 1HH, (0121) 631 2000, *Fax (0121) 643 9018,* – rm, – 150. VISA JZ z
closed 24-26 December – **Meals** *(closed Saturday lunch)* (carvery) 12.95/19.95 and a la carte 22.45/27.95 **st.** – 13.95 – **281 rm** 139.00/149.00 **st.**, 3 suites.

The Burlington, Burlington Arcade, 126 New St, B2 4JQ, (0121) 643 9191, *mail@burlingtonhotel.com, Fax (0121) 643 5075,* – rm, rest, – 400. VISA KZ a
closed 24-30 December – ***Berlioz :*** **Meals** 18.00/22.00 and a la carte 22.00/40.00 **t.** 13.50 – 13.50 – **107 rm** 135.00/145.00 **st.**, 5 suites.

Copthorne, Paradise Circus, B3 3HJ, (0121) 200 2727, *sales.birmingham@mill-cop.com, Fax (0121) 200 1197,* – rm, rest, – 180. VISA. JZ e
Goldsmiths : **Meals** (dinner only) a la carte 24.70/33.95 **t.** – ***Goldies :*** **Meals** 15.00 and a la carte 18.35/27.15 **t.** 13.50 – 13.95 – **209 rm** 150.00/170.00 **st.**, 3 suites – SB.

Jonathan's, 16-24 Wolverhampton Rd, Oldbury, B68 0LH, West : 4 m. by A 456 (0121) 429 3757, *sales@jonathans.co.uk, Fax (0121) 434 3107,* « Authentic Victorian furnishings and memorabilia » – , rest, – 100. VISA. BU e
Victorian Restaurant : **Meals** - English - *(closed Saturday lunch and 1 January)* (booking essential) 15.90 (lunch) and a la carte 32.50/35.00 **t.** 12.90 – ***Secret Garden :*** **Meals** *(closed Saturday and Sunday lunch, 1 January and Bank Holidays)* 9.50 (lunch) and a la carte 9.40/14.80 **t.** 12.00 – **46 rm** 98.00/125.00 **st.**, 2 suites – SB.

Birmingham Grand Moat House, Colmore Row, B3 2DA, (0121) 607 9988, *revbgd@queensmoat.co.uk, Fax (0121) 233 1465* – rm, rest, – 500. VISA JKY c
Hugo's : **Meals** a la carte 13.40/23.40 **st.** 11.95 – 11.50 – **170 rm** 120.00/140.00 **st.**, 3 suites – SB.

Posthouse Birmingham City, Smallbrook, Queensway, B5 4EW, (0870) 400 9008, *gm1841@forte-hotels.com, Fax (0121) 631 2528* – rm, – 630. VISA KZ o
Meals *(closed Saturday lunch)* (carvery rest.) 10.00/18.00 **st.** 11.95 – 13.95 – **280 rm** 129.00 **st.** – SB.

City Inn, 1 Brunswick Sq, Brindley Pl, B1 2HW, (0121) 643 1003, *birmingham.reservations@cityinn.com, Fax (0121) 643 1005,* – – 105. VISA. FV a
closed 24-31 December – ***City Café :*** **Meals** 12.80/15.95 and a la carte 20.20/32.20 **st.** 11.25 – 10.50 – **238 rm** 89.00 **st.**

Novotel, 70 Broad St, B1 2HT, (0121) 643 2000, *hlo77@accor-hotels.com, Fax (0121) 643 9796,* – rm, rest, – 300. VISA JCB FV e
Meals 10.00/25.00 and a la carte 14.00/28.00 **st.** 12.00 – 11.00 – **148 rm** 99.00 **st.** – SB.

Jurys Inn, 245 Broad St, B1 2HQ, (0121) 626 0626, *info@chamberlain.co.uk, Fax (0121) 626 0627* – , rest, – 400. VISA. FV z
Meals (carvery) 10.00/12.00 8.00 – 6.00 – **445 rm** 59.00 **st.**

Paragon, Alcester St, B12 0PJ, (0121) 627 0627, *info@chamberlain.co.uk, Fax (0121) 627 0628* – , rest, – 400. VISA. FX r
Meals (carving rest.) 10.00 3.75 – **250 rm** 49.00/59.00 **t.**

Asquith House, 19 Portland Rd, off Hagley Rd, Edgbaston, B16 9HN, (0121) 454 5282, *tina@asquith-house.com, Fax (0121) 456 4668,* « Victorian house », – . VISA. EX c
closed 25, 26 and 31 December and 1 January – **Meals** 17.95/35.95 and a la carte 16.40/22.70 **t.** 8.95 – **8 rm** 60.00/83.00 **t.**

Westbourne Lodge, 27-29 Fountain Rd, Edgbaston, B17 8NJ, (0121) 429 1003, *info@westbournelodge.co.uk, Fax (0121) 429 7436,* – rm, TV P. AE VISA JCB EV x
Meals *(closed Friday-Sunday)* (booking essential to non-residents) (bar lunch)/dinner 14.95/17.95 **t.** 10.00 – **24 rm** 52.00/75.00 **t.** – SB.

Copperfield House, 60 Upland Rd, Selly Park, B29 7JS, (0121) 472 8344, *info@copperfieldhousehotel.fsnet.co.uk, Fax (0121) 415 5655,* – rest, TV P. AE VISA JCB. FX a
closed Christmas and New Year – **Meals** *(closed Sunday)* (dinner only) a la carte 18.50/23.75 **t.** 9.00 – **17 rm** 62.50/85.00 **t.** – SB.

Travel Inn, Richard St, Waterlinks, B7 4AA, (0121) 333 6484, *Fax (0121) 333 6490* – rm, rest, TV P. AE VISA. FV c
Meals (grill rest.) (dinner only) – **60 rm** 41.95 **t.**

Travelodge, 1741 Coventry Rd, Yardley, B26 1DS, Southeast : 5 m. by A 41 on A 45 (0121) 764 5882, *Fax (0121) 764 5882* – rm, TV P. AE VISA. HX e
Meals (grill rest.) – **40 rm** 52.95 **t.**

Travelodge, 230 Broad St, B15 1AY, (0121) 644 5266, *Fax (0121) 644 5251* – TV AE VISA JCB. FV n
Meals (grill rest.) – **136 rm** 52.95 **t.**

Travel Inn, 20-22 Bridge St, B1 2JH, (0121) 633 4820, *Fax (0121) 633 4779* – rm, TV P – 40. AE VISA. JZ c
Meals (grill rest.) – **53 rm** 41.95 **t.**

Ibis, 1 Bordesley Park Rd, B10 0PD, (0121) 506 2600, *h2178@accor-hotels.com, Fax (0121) 506 2610* – TV P. AE VISA JCB GX e
Meals (dinner only) a la carte approx. 14.00 **st.** 9.25 – 3.95 – **87 rm** 39.95 **st.**

Days Inn without rest., 160 Wharfside St, The Mailbox, B1 1RL, (0121) 643 9344, *birmingham@daysinn.co.uk, Fax (0121) 643 2044* – TV AE VISA. JZ n
90 rm 62.50 **st.**

Sir Edward Elgar's (at Birmingham Marriott H.), 12 Hagley Rd, B16 8SJ, (0121) 452 1144, *Fax (0121) 456 3442* – P. AE VISA JCB FX c
closed Monday – **Meals** (dinner only and Sunday lunch)/dinner 32.50 and a la carte 29.75/39.95 **t.** 13.95.

Bank, 4 Brindleyplace, B1 2JB, (0121) 633 4466, *Fax (0121) 633 4465,* – AE VISA FV u
closed 26 December and 1 January – **Meals** 12.50 (lunch) and a la carte 23.50/34.65 **t.** 11.00.

La Toque D'Or, 27 Warstone Lane, Hockley, B18 6JQ, (0121) 233 3655, *didier@latoquedor.co.uk, Fax (01562) 754957,* « Former rolling mill » – AE VISA FV r
closed 1 week Easter, 2 weeks August, Christmas, New Year, Sunday, Monday, Tuesday after Bank Holidays and Saturday lunch – **Meals** - French - 15.50/23.50 **t.** 12.50.

Metro Bar and Grill, 73 Cornwall St, B3 2DF, (0121) 200 1911, *Fax (0121) 200 1611* – AE VISA JY n
closed Sunday – **Meals** (booking essential) a la carte 18.90/27.85 **t.** 10.95.

Henry's, 27 St Paul's Sq, B3 1RB, (0121) 200 1136, *Fax (0121) 200 1190* – AE VISA JY a
closed 25-26 December and Bank Holiday Monday – **Meals** - Chinese (Canton) - 16.50/38.00 and a la carte 16.20/36.80 **t.** 8.80.

Le Petit Blanc, Nine Brindleyplace, B1 2HS, (0121) 633 7333, *birmingham@lepetitblanc.co.uk, Fax (0121) 633 7444* – AE VISA FV x
closed 25 December – **Meals** 15.00 (lunch) and a la carte 24.70/29.90 **t.** 11.00.

at Hall Green *Southeast : 5 ¾ m. by A 41 on A 34 – Birmingham.*

Mizan, 1347 Stratford Rd, B28 9HW, (0121) 777 3185 – AE VISA JCB GX a
Meals - Indian - (dinner only and Thursday lunch)/dinner a la carte 9.90/16.45 **t.** 7.50.

at Birmingham Airport *Southeast : 9 m. by A 45 –* **DU** *– Birmingham.*

Holiday Inn Birmingham Airport, Coventry Rd, B26 3QW, on A 45 (0870) 4009007, *gm1029@forte-hotels.com, Fax (0121) 782 2476* – TV P – 130. AE VISA JCB
Meals *(closed Saturday and Sunday lunch)* 13.00/15.00 and dinner a la carte 21.85/30.40 **st.** 19.95 – 14.95 – **141 rm** 149.00 **st.**

Novotel, Passenger Terminal, B26 3QL, (0121) 782 7000, *H1158@accor-hotels.com, Fax (0121) 782 0445* – rm, TV – 35. AE VISA
Meals *(closed lunch Saturday, Sunday and Bank Holidays)* 14.50/20.00 and a la carte 16.50/27.40 **st.** 11.25 – 11.50 – **195 rm** 107.00 **st.**

at National Exhibition Centre *Southeast : 9½ m. on A 45* – **DU** – *Birmingham.*

Hilton Birmingham Metropole, Bickenhill, B40 1PP, (0121) 780 4242, *Fax (0121) 780 3923,* – rm, – 2000. AE VISA
Meals *(closed Saturday lunch)* (carvery) 18.00/28.50 **t.** 18.00 – ***Primavera :* Meals** - Italian - (dinner only) 31.95 and a la carte 32.15/43.95 **st.** 18.00 – 14.00 – **779 rm** 235.00/315.00 **st.**, 15 suites – SB.

Express by Holiday Inn without rest., Bickenhill, Parkway, B40 1QA, (0121) 782 3222, *sales.nec@ingram.hotel.co.uk, Fax (0121) 780 4224* – – 100. AE VISA JCB
179 rm 69.95.

at Acocks Green *Southwest : 5 m. by A 41* – *Birmingham.*

Westley, Westley Rd, B13 9YZ, (0121) 706 4312, *reservations@westley-hotel.co.uk, Fax (0121) 706 2824* – – 200. AE VISA GX c
accommodation closed 24-25 December – **Meals** (bar lunch Monday-Saturday)/dinner 14.95 and a la carte **st.** 10.50 – 9.00 – **35 rm** 75.00/86.00 **st.**, 1 suite.

at Northfield *Southwest : 6 m. by A 38* – **CU** – *Birmingham.*

Norwood, 87-89 Bunbury Rd, B31 2ET, via Church Rd (0121) 411 2202, *Fax (0121) 411 2202,* – . AE VISA.
closed 23 December-2 January – **Meals** (bar lunch)/dinner 19.95 – **18 rm** 62.50/67.50 **st.** – SB.

at Oldbury *West : 7¾ m. by A 456 on A 4123* – *Birmingham.*

Express by Holiday Inn without rest., Birchley Park, B69 2BD, (0121) 511 0000, *Fax (0121) 511 0051* – – 30. AE VISA JCB BU r
109 rm 60.00 **st.**

Travel Inn, Wolverhampton Rd, B69 2BH, on A 4123 (0121) 552 3031, *Fax (0121) 552 1012* – rm, rest, . AE VISA. BU u
Meals (grill rest.) – **40 rm** 41.95 **t.**

Travelodge, Wolverhampton Rd, B69 2BH, on A 4123 (0121) 552 2967 – rm, . AE VISA JCB. BU n
Meals (grill rest.) – **33 rm** 39.95 **t.**

at Great Barr *Northwest : 6 m. on A 34* – *Birmingham.*

Holiday Inn Birmingham, Chapel Lane, B43 7BG, (0870) 4009009, *gm1030@forte-hotels.com, Fax (0121) 357 7503,* – rm, – 120. AE VISA JCB CT x
Meals 13.00/15.00 and dinner a la carte 16.15/29.00 **st.** 11.95 – 13.95 – **192 rm** 129.00 **st.**

Express by Holiday Inn without rest., Birmingham Rd, B42 2BL, (0121) 358 4044, *Fax (0121) 358 4644* – . AE VISA. CT v
32 rm 55.00 **st.**

at West Bromwich *Northwest : 6 m. on A 41* – *Birmingham.*

Moat House Birmingham, Birmingham Rd, B70 6RS, (0121) 609 9988, *revbwb @queensmoat.co.uk, Fax (0121) 525 7403,* – rm, rest, – 180. AE VISA JCB BU c
Meals *(closed Saturday lunch)* a la carte 13.45/27.85 **t.** 11.95 – 11.50 – **168 rm** 118.00/135.00 **st.** – SB.

BIRMINGHAM AIRPORT *W. Mids.* 403 404 O 26 – *see Birmingham.*

BISHOP'S HULL *Somerset* – *see Taunton.*

BISHOP'S STORTFORD *Herts.* 404 U 28 – *pop. 28 403.*

Stansted Airport : (0870) 0000303, NE : 3½ m.

The Old Monastery, Windhill (01279) 655831.

London 34 – Cambridge 27 – Chelmsford 19 – Colchester 33.

The Cottage without rest., 71 Birchanger Lane, CM23 5QA, Northeast : 2 ¼ m. by B 1383 on Birchanger rd (01279) 812349, *Fax (01279) 815045,* « Part 17C and 18C cottages », – . VISA JCB.
closed Easter and Christmas-New Year – **15 rm** 40.00/70.00 **t.**

The Lemon Tree, 14-16 Water Lane, CM23 2LB, (01279) 757788, *Fax (01279) 757766* – . VISA JCB
closed 25-26 December, first week January, Sunday dinner and Monday – **Meals** 10.00/19.95 and a la carte 19.25/27.25 **t.** 10.95.

ENGLAND

at Hatfield Heath *(Essex) Southeast : 6 m. on A 1060 – ✉ Bishop's Stortford.*

Down Hall Country House, CM22 7AS, South : 1 ½ m. by Matching Lane ☎ (01279) 731441, *reservations@downhall.co.uk, Fax (01279) 730416,* ≤, « 19C Italianate mansion », rest, rest, – 220. VISA JCB
Ibbetsons : Meals *(closed Saturday lunch, Sunday and Monday)* 19.50 (lunch) and a la carte 33.75/45.25 **t.** 15.50 – ***Downham :*** Meals *(closed Saturday lunch)* 18.50/34.50 **t.** 15.50 – 15.95 – **100 rm** 128.00/188.00 **st.** – SB.

BISHOP'S TAWTON *Devon* 403 H 30 – *see Barnstaple.*

BLABY *Leics.* 402 403 404 Q 26 – *see Leicester.*

BLACKBURN *Blackburn* 402 M 22 – *pop. 105 994.*

18 Pleasington ☎ (01254) 202177 – 18 Wilpshire, 72 Whalley Rd ☎ (01254) 248260 – 9 Great Harwood, Harwood Bar ☎ (01254) 884391.

15-17 Railway Rd ☎ (01254) 53277.

London 228 – Leeds 47 – Liverpool 39 – Manchester 24 – Preston 11.

at Langho *North : 4½ m. on A 666 – ✉ Whalley.*

Mytton Fold, Whalley Rd, BB6 8AB, Northeast : 1 m. by A 666 on Whalley rd ☎ (01254) 240662, *mytton-fold.hotel@virgin.net, Fax (01254) 248119,* 18, – 250. VISA.
Meals (bar lunch Monday-Friday)/dinner 13.30/22.30 **st.** 11.45 – **28 rm** 52.00/82.00 **st.** – SB.

Petre Lodge, Northcote Rd, BB6 8BG, Northeast : ½ m. ☎ (01254) 245506, *aslambert@fsbdial.co.uk, Fax (01254) 245506,* « Former village primary school » – VISA JCB.
closed 23 December-4 January – **Meals** (residents only) (dinner only) a la carte 12.95/17.20 **st.** 5.50 – **10 rm** 50.00/60.00 **st.**

Northcote Manor (Haworth) with rm, Northcote Rd, BB6 8BE, North : ½ m. on A 59 at junction with A 666 ☎ (01254) 240555, *admin@northcotemanor.com, Fax (01254) 246568,* – rest, VISA.
Meals 10.00/25.00 (lunch) and a la carte 31.00/47.95 **t.** 15.00 – **14 rm** 100.00/130.00 **t.** – SB
Spec. Lancashire hot pot salad. Fillet of sea bass, cannelloni of fennel. Bakewell tart soufflé, vanilla ice cream.

at Clayton-le-Dale *North : 4 ¾ m. by A 666 on B 6245 – ✉ Blackburn.*

Shajan, Longsight Rd, BB1 9EX, Southwest : ½ m. on A 59 ☎ (01254) 813234 – VISA
closed 25 December – **Meals** - Indian - (buffet lunch Sunday) a la carte 13.50/23.30 **t.** 10.50.

at Mellor *Northwest : 4 m. by A 677 – ✉ Blackburn.*

Millstone, Church Lane, BB2 7JR, ☎ (01254) 813333, *millstone@shireinns.co.uk, Fax (01254) 812628* – – 25. VISA
Millers : Meals *(closed Saturday lunch)* a la carte approx. 22.50 **st.** 13.45 – **21 rm** 93.00/113.00 **st.**, 2 suites – SB.

at Balderstone *Northwest : 6½ m. by A 677 off A 59 – ✉ Blackburn.*

Premier Lodge, Myerscough Rd, BB2 7LE, on A 59 ☎ (0870) 7001330, *Fax (0870) 7001331* – rm, rest, VISA JCB.
Meals (grill rest.) (in bar) a la carte approx. 12.50 **t.** 7.80 – **20 rm** 46.95 **t.**

BLACKPOOL *Blackpool* 402 K 22 *Great Britain G.* – *pop. 146 262.*

See : *Tower★ AC AY A.*

18 Blackpool Park, North Park Drive ☎ (01253) 397910 **BY** – *9 Poulton-le-Fylde, Myrtle Farm, Breck Rd ☎ (01253) 892444.*

Blackpool Airport : ☎ (01253) 343434, S : 3 m. by A 584.

1 Clifton St ☎ (01253) 478222 – Pleasure Beach, Unit 25, Ocean Boulevard, South Promenade ☎ (01253) 403223.

London 246 – Leeds 88 – Liverpool 56 – Manchester 51 – Middlesbrough 123.

BLACKPOOL

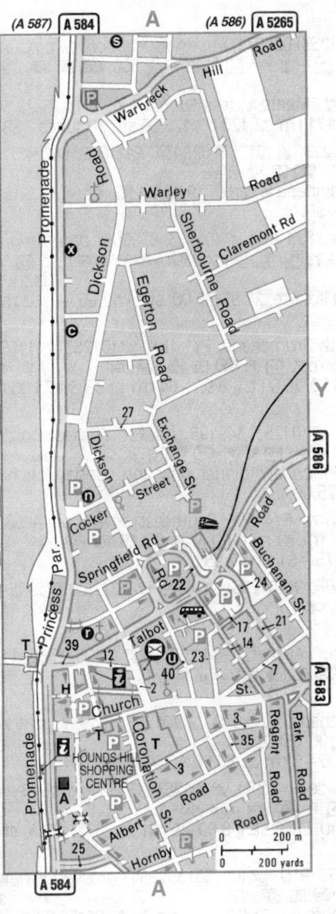

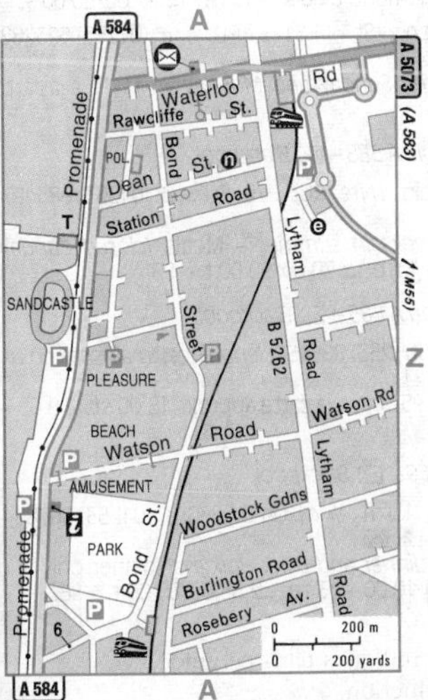

B FLEETWOOD A 587
Promenade
Queen's Promenade
A 584
Fleetwood Rd
A 587
Red Bank Rd
Devonshire Rd
B 5124
POL
Bispham Road
A 587
B 5265 Hill Road
LAYTON
Warbreck
Devonshire
St. Walburgas Rd
Drive
B 5266
B 5268
A 586 LANCASTER
A 586 Road
Talbot Road
B 5266 Newton
A 583
Hornby Road
Whitegate
West Park Drive
STANLEY
PARK
BLACKPOOL ZOO PARK
East Park Drive
Park
Dr. Road
A 583
Preston Old Rd
PRESTON A 583 (M 55)
Preston New Rd
B 5261
Road
Waterloo
A 5073
Lytham Road
St.
Marton Dr.
Hawes Side Lane
Vicarage Lane
Yeadon Way
(M 55)
Road
Watson
Lytham
Clifton Drive
Annes Road
Edge Rd
Common
Midgeland Road
Highfield Road
B 5262
A 5230
Lane
Gate
Squires
(M 55)
Y
Z
0 1 km
0 1/2 mile
A 584 ST. ANNES
B

ENGLAND

Imperial, North Promenade, FY1 2HB, ✆ (01253) 623971, *imperialblackpool@paramount-hotels.co.uk, Fax (01253) 751784,* ←, Fö, ≘, ▣ – |\$|, ✻ ▣ ✆ P – 🎪 500. MC AE ⓓ VISA ✻
AY
closed 26 September-3 October – ***Palm Court :*** Meals *(closed Sunday lunch)* 14.75/20.5 and dinner a la carte 24.20/31.75 **st.** 12.95 – **171 rm** ⇨ 120.00/175.00 **st.**, 10 suites – SB.

Hilton Blackpool, North Promenade, FY1 2JQ, ✆ (01253) 623434, *Fax (01253) 29437,* ←, ≘, ▣ – |\$| ✻, ▤ rest, ▣ ✆ ♿ P – 🎪 700. MC AE ⓓ VISA
AY
The Promenade : Meals 7.95/19.50 and dinner a la carte 19.95/24.95 **st.** 13.50 – ⇨ 10.50 – **268 rm** 165.00/185.00 **st.**, 6 suites – SB.

De Vere Heron's Reach, East Park Drive, FY3 8LL, ✆ (01253) 838866, *peter.wrigh@devere-hotels.com, Fax (01253) 798800,* Fö, ≘, ▣, 18, ✻, squash – |\$| ✻, ▤ rest, ▣ ✆ ♿ P – 🎪 600. MC AE ⓓ VISA. ✻
BZ
Park Brasserie : Meals 19.95 (dinner) and a la carte 22.85/38.00 **st.** 12.95 – **162 rm** ⇨ 95.00/120.00 **st.**, 2 suites – SB.

Libertys on the Square, Cocker Sq, North Promenade, FY1 1RX, ✆ (01253) 291155 *Fax (01253) 752271,* ←, Fö, ≘ – |\$|, ✻ rest, ▤ rest, ▣ P. MC AE ⓓ VISA. ✻
AY
Meals (dinner only and Sunday lunch)/dinner 8.50/20.00 **t.** 8.95 – **64 rm** ⇨ 39.50/73.00 **t.** – SB.

Old Coach House, 50 Dean St, FY4 1BP, ✆ (01253) 349195, *blackpool@theoldcoachhouse.freeserve.co.uk, Fax (01253) 344330,* ✻ – ✻ ▣ ✆ P. MC VISA JCB. ✻
AZ
Meals *(closed Tuesday to non-residents and Monday)* (dinner only and Sunday lunch)/dinner 12.50/23.50 **t.** 8.95 – **11 rm** ⇨ 45.00/75.00 **t.**

Premier Lodge, Whitehills Park, Hallam Way, FY4 5LY, Southeast : 4 m. on A 583 ✆ (0870) 7001514, *Fax (0870) 7001515* – |\$|, ✻ rm, ▤ rest, ▣ ♿ P. MC AE ⓓ VISA. ✻
Meals (grill rest.) a la carte approx. 14.20 **t.** 8.75 – **81 rm** 42.95 **t.**

Travel Inn, Yeadon Way, South Shore, FY1 6BF, ✆ (01253) 341415, *Fax (01253) 343805* – ✻ rm, ▤ rest, ▣ ♿ P – 🎪 40. MC AE ⓓ VISA. ✻
AZ
Meals (grill rest.) – **79 rm** 41.95 **t.**

Travel Inn, Squires Gate Lane, Blackpool Airport, FY4 2QF, ✆ (01253) 362411 *Fax (01253) 362413* – ✻ rm, ▤ rest, ▣ ♿ P. MC AE ⓓ VISA JCB. ✻
BZ
Meals (grill rest.) – **39 rm** 41.95 **t.**

Sunray, 42 Knowle Ave, off Queens Promenade, FY2 9TQ, ✆ (01253) 351937, *sunray@cwcom.net, Fax (01253) 593307* – ✻ rest, ▣ P. MC AE VISA
BY
April-November – **Meals** (by arrangement) 13.00 – **9 rm** ⇨ 30.00/60.00.

Burlees, 40 Knowle Ave, off Queen's Promenade, FY2 9TQ, ✆ (01253) 354535, *enquiries@burleeshotel.co.uk, Fax (01253) 354535* – ✻ ▣ P. MC VISA JCB. ✻
BY
March-mid November – **Meals** (by arrangement) 11.00 **st.** 8.00 – **9 rm** ⇨ 26.00/52.00 **st.** – SB.

Grosvenor View, 7-9 King Edward Ave, FY2 9TD, ✆ (01253) 352851, *grosvenor-view@yahoo.co.uk, Fax (01253) 352109* – ✻ ▣ P. MC AE VISA. ✻
AY
restricted opening in winter – **Meals** (by arrangement) 8.00 **s.** – **15 rm** ⇨ 17.00/50.00 **s.**

September Brasserie, 15-17 Queen St, FY1 1PU, ✆ (01253) 623282, *Fax (01253) 299455* – MC AE ⓓ VISA JCB
AY
closed 2 weeks in summer, 2 weeks in winter, Sunday and Monday – **Meals** a la carte 18.50/23.75 **t.** 10.95.

at Little Thornton *Northeast : 5 m. by A 586* – **BY** – *off A 588* – ✉ *Blackpool.*

River House ✻ with rm, Skippool Creek, Wyre Rd, FY5 5LF, ✆ (01253) 883497, *Fax (01253) 892083,* ←, ✻ – ▣ P. MC VISA
closed 25-26 December, 1 January and 2 weeks in summer – **Meals** *(closed Sunday)* (booking essential) 25.00 and a la carte 7.50 – **4 rm** ⇨ 70.00/90.00 **t.** – SB.

at Little Singleton *Northeast : 6 m. by A 586* – **BY** – *on A 585* – ✉ *Blackpool.*

Mains Hall ✻, 86 Mains Lane, FY6 7EV, ✆ (01253) 885130, *enquiries@mainshall.co.uk, Fax (01253) 894132,* ✻ – ✻ ▣ P. MC AE ⓓ VISA
Meals (bar lunch Monday-Saturday)/dinner 7.95 and a la carte approx. 15.00 **st.** 9.00 – **12 rm** ⇨ 60.00/100.00 **st.** – SB.

at Singleton *Northeast : 7 m. by A 586* – **BY** – *on B 5260* – ✉ *Blackpool.*

Singleton Lodge ✻, Lodge Lane, FY6 8LT, North : ¼ m. on B 5260 ✆ (01253) 883854, *Fax (01253) 894432,* ✻ – ▣ P – 🎪 60. MC AE ⓓ VISA
closed Bank Holidays – **Meals** *(closed Sunday dinner and Bank Holidays)* (dinner only and Sunday lunch)/dinner a la carte 14.75/21.50 **t.** 10.00 – **13 rm** ⇨ 55.00/80.00 **t.** – SB.

Les prix — Pour toutes précisions sur les prix indiqués dans ce guide, reportez-vous aux pages de l'introduction.

BLACKROD *Lancs.* 402 404 M 23 – *pop. 5 681.*
London 220 – Burnley 25 – Liverpool 31 – Manchester 16 – Preston 18.

Ramada Jarvis Bolton, Manchester Rd, BL6 5RU, Southeast : 1 ½ m. by B 5408 on A 6 ✆ (01942) 814598, *jibolton.rs@jarvis.co.uk, Fax (01942) 816026,* – rm, P – 250. MC AE VISA
Meals (bar lunch Saturday) a la carte 18.95/24.80 **st.** 14.00 – 10.95 – **91 rm** 100.00/110.00 **st.** – SB.

BLACKWATER *Cornwall* 403 E 33 – *see Truro.*

BLAKENEY *Glos.* 403 404 M 28.
London 134 – Bristol 31 – Gloucester 16 – Newport 31.

Viney Hill Country Guesthouse, Viney Hill, GL15 4LT, West : ¾ m. by A 48 ✆ (01594) 516000, *info@vineyhill.com, Fax (01594) 516018,* – P. MC AE VISA.
Meals (by arrangement) 17.00 **st.** 10.00 – **6 rm** 38.00/60.00 **st.** – SB.

BLAKENEY *Norfolk* 404 X 25 – *pop. 1 628* – ✉ *Holt.*
London 127 – King's Lynn 37 – Norwich 28.

Blakeney, The Quay, NR25 7NE, ✆ (01263) 740797, *reception@blakeney.hotel.co.uk, Fax (01263) 740795,* ←, – rest, P – 200. MC AE VISA
Meals (light lunch Monday to Saturday)/dinner 22.50 and a la carte 19.50/29.10 **t.** 9.00 – **60 rm** (dinner included) 82.00/240.00 **t.** – SB.

White Horse with rm, 4 High St, NR25 7AL, ✆ (01263) 740574, *Fax (01263) 741303* – P. MC AE VISA.
closed January – **Meals** (bar lunch and Sunday and Monday dinner) a la carte 20.40/24.20 **t.** 11.50 – **10 rm** 40.00/90.00 **t.**

at Cley next the Sea *East : 1½ m. on A 149* – ✉ *Holt.*

Cley Mill, NR25 7RP, ✆ (01263) 740209, *Fax (01263) 740209,* ←, « 18C redbrick windmill on saltmarshes », – P. MC VISA
Meals (by arrangement) (communal dining) 17.50 **st.** 11.00 – **7 rm** 72.00/84.00 **st.**

at Morston *West : 1½ m. on A 149* – ✉ *Holt.*

Morston Hall (Blackiston), The Street, NR25 7AA, ✆ (01263) 741041, *reception@morstonhall.com, Fax (01263) 740419,* – rest, P. MC AE VISA
closed January and 25-26 December – **Meals** (booking essential) (set menu only) (dinner only and Sunday lunch)/dinner 36.00 **st.** 12.00 – **6 rm** (dinner included) 140.00/220.00 **st.** – SB
Spec. Grilled scallops with parsley mash. Noisettes of lamb, ratatouille, béarnaise sauce. Millefeuille of summer pudding, Champagne sabayon.

BLANCHLAND *Northd.* 401 402 N 19 – *pop. 135* – ✉ *Consett (Durham).*
London 298 – Carlisle 47 – Newcastle upon Tyne 24.

Lord Crewe Arms, DH8 9SP, ✆ (01434) 675251, *lord@crewearms.freeserve.co.uk, Fax (01434) 675337,* « Part 12C Abbots's lodgings », – rest. MC AE VISA
Meals (bar lunch Monday-Saturday)/dinner 28.00 **t.** 9.00 – **19 rm** 80.00/110.00 **t.** – SB.

BLANDFORD FORUM *Dorset* 403 404 N 31 *The West Country G.* – *pop. 8 880.*
See : *Town*★.
Env. : *Kingston Lacy*★★ *AC, SE : 5½ m. by B 3082 – Royal Signals Museum*★, *NE : 2 m. by B 3082.*
Exc. : *Milton Abbas*★, *SW : 8 m. by A 354 – Sturminster Newton*★, *NW : 8 m. by A 357.*
18 *Ashley Wood, Wimbourne Rd ✆ (01258) 452253.*
1 Greyhound Yard ✆ (01258) 454770.
London 124 – Bournemouth 17 – Dorchester 17 – Salisbury 24.

Crown, West St, DT11 7AJ, ✆ (01258) 456626, *thecrownhotel@blandforddorset.freeserve.co.uk, Fax (01258) 451084,* – P – 200. MC AE VISA
closed Christmas – **Meals** *(closed Saturday lunch and Sunday dinner)* 16.95 and a la carte 16.20/23.45 **t.** 11.55 – **32 rm** 68.00/90.00 **t.** – SB.

at Chettle *Northeast : 7¼ m. by A 354* – ✉ *Blandford Forum.*

Castleman with rm, DT11 8DB, ✆ (01258) 830096, *chettle@globalnet.co.uk, Fax (01258) 830051,* ←, « Part 16C dower house with Victorian additions », – rest, P. MC VISA JCB.
closed February and 25-26 December – **Meals** (dinner only and Sunday lunch)/dinner a la carte 15.50/23.50 **t.** 9.00 – **8 rm** 45.00/75.00 **t.**

ENGLAND

at Farnham *Northeast : 7½ m. by A 354 – ✉ Blandford Forum.*

The Museum Inn with rm, DT11 8DE, ✆ (01725) 516261, *themuseuminn@supanet.co.uk, Fax (01725) 516949,* – TV P. MC VISA
closed 25 and 31 December – **Meals** (bookings not accepted) a la carte 17.40/28.40 **t.** 9.95 – **4 rm** 65.00/120.00 **t.**

BLEDINGTON *Glos.* 403 404 P 28 – *see Stow-on-the-Wold.*

BLETSOE *Cambs.* 404 S 27 – *see Bedford.*

BLOCKLEY *Glos.* 403 404 O 27 – *pop. 1 668 – ✉ Moreton-in-Marsh.*
London 91 – Oxford 34 – Birmingham 39.

The Old Bakery, High St, GL56 9EU, ✆ (01386) 700408, *Fax (01386) 700408,* <, « Converted Victorian cottage », – TV P. MC AE VISA JCB.
closed 2 weeks June, December and January – **Meals** (by arrangement) (set menu only) 12.00 – **3 rm** (dinner included) 90.00/200.00 **st.** – SB.

BLUBBERHOUSES *N. Yorks.* 402 O 22.
London 246 – Harrogate 17 – Leeds 21.

The Stone House Inn, Thruscross, HG3 4AH, North : 2 m. on Greenhow Rd ✆ (01943) 880325, *Fax (01943) 880325* – P. MC AE VISA
closed 25 December, Monday except Bank Holidays and Sunday dinner – **Meals** - South African specialities - a la carte 23.85/28.85 **t.**

BLUNSDON *Wilts.* 403 404 O 29 – *see Swindon.*

BLYTH *Notts.* 402 403 404 Q 23 – *pop. 1 867 – ✉ Worksop.*
London 166 – Doncaster 13 – Lincoln 30 – Nottingham 32 – Sheffield 20.

Charnwood, Sheffield Rd, S81 8HF, West : ¾ m. on A 634 ✆ (01909) 591610, *info@charnwoodhotel.com, Fax (01909) 591429,* – rest, TV P – 120. MC AE VISA JCB.
The Lantern : **Meals** 12.95/19.95 and a la carte 17.95/29.95 **t.** 10.95 – **33 rm** 55.00/90.00 **st.** – SB.

Travelodge without rest., Hilltop roundabout, S81 8HG, North : ¾ m. by B 6045 at junction of A 1 (M) with A 614 ✆ (01909) 591841, *Fax (01909) 591831* – TV P. MC AE VISA JCB.
39 rm 39.95 **t.**

BODENHAM *Herefordshire* 403 404 L 27.
London 140 – Birmingham 55 – Hereford 10 – Shrewsbury 48 – Worcester 25.

England's Gate Inn, HR1 3HU, North : ¾ m. ✆ (01568) 797286, *englandsgate@hotmail.com, Fax (01568) 797768,* – P. MC AE VISA JCB
closed Sunday dinner – **Meals** a la carte 13.20/21.45 **t.** 8.95.

BODMIN *Cornwall* 403 F 32 *The West Country G. – pop. 12 553.*
See : *St Petroc Church★.*
Env. : *Bodmin Moor★★ – Lanhydrock★★, S : 3 m. by B 3269 – Blisland★ (Church★), N : 5 ½ m. by A 30 and minor roads – Pencarrow★, NW : 4 m. by A 389 and minor roads – Cardinham (Church★), NE : 4 m. by A 30 and minor rd – St Mabyn (Church★), N : 5½ m. by A 389, B 3266 and minor rd.*
Exc. : *St Tudy★, N : 7 m. by A 389, B 3266 and minor rd.*
Shire House, Mount Folly Sq ✆ (01208) 76616.
London 270 – Newquay 18 – Plymouth 32 – Truro 23.

Mount Pleasant, Mount, PL30 4EX, East : 7 ¼ m. by A 30 on Warleggan rd ✆ (01208) 821342, *colette@capper61.fastnet.co.uk,* <, heated, – P. MC VISA JCB.
Easter-September – **Meals** (by arrangement) 16.00 – **5 rm** 45.00/70.00.

Bokiddick Farm without rest., Lanivet, PL30 5HP, South : 6 m. by A 30 following signs for Lanhydrock and Bokiddick ✆ (01208) 831481, *gillhugo@bokiddickfarm.co.uk, Fax (01208) 831481,* « Working farm », – TV P.
closed Christmas and New Year – **3 rm** 30.00/50.00.

BODYMOOR HEATH *Staffs.* 402 403 404 O 26 – *see Tamworth.*

BOGNOR REGIS *W. Sussex* 404 R 31 – *pop. 19 836.*

Belmont St. ☎ (01243) 823140.

London 65 – Brighton 29 – Portsmouth 24 – Southampton 36.

Premier Lodge, Shripney Rd, PO22 9PA, North : 3 m. on A 29 ☎ (01243) 822323, *Fax (01243) 841430* – rm, TV P – 80. MC AE VISA JCB.
Meals a la carte approx. 13.00 **t.** 8.95 – **24 rm** 42.95 **t.**

Inglenook, 255 Pagham Rd, Nyetimber, PO21 3QB, West : 2 ½ m. by B 2166 following signs for Pagham ☎ (01243) 262495, *reception@the-inglenook.com, Fax (01243) 262668,* « Part 16C », – TV P – 100. MC AE VISA
Meals 11.95/16.95 and a la carte 21.25/43.00 **t.** 11.50 – **18 rm** 45.00/200.00 **t.** – SB.

BOLDON *Tyne and Wear* 401 402 O 19 – *see Sunderland.*

BOLLINGTON *Ches.* 402 403 404 N 24 – *see Macclesfield.*

For maximum information from town plans: consult the conventional signs key.

BOLTON *Gtr. Manchester* 402 404 M 23 – *pop. 139 020.*

18 Regent Park, Links Rd, Chorley New Rd ☎ (01204) 844170 – 18 Lostock Park ☎ (01204) 843278 – 18 Boston Old Links, Chorley Old Rd, Montserrat ☎ (01204) 840050.

Town Hall, Victoria Sq ☎ (01204) 334400.

London 214 – Burnley 19 – Liverpool 32 – Manchester 11 – Preston 23.

Bolton Moat House, 1 Higher Bridge St, BL1 2EW, ☎ (01204) 879988, *cbbol@queens moat.co.uk, Fax (01204) 380777,* , , – , rest, TV P – 200. MC AE VISA.
Meals *(closed Saturday lunch)* 18.95 and a la carte 18.40/32.50 **t.** 13.95 – 11.50 – **132 rm** 115.00/145.00 **t.** – SB.

New Pack Horse, Nelson Sq, Bradshawgate, BL1 1DP, ☎ (01204) 527261, *info@pack horse.macdonald-hotels.co.uk, Fax (01204) 364352* – TV – 275. MC AE VISA.
Meals a la carte 9.75/25.00 **t.** 13.00 – **74 rm** 55.00/95.00 **st.**

at Egerton *North : 3½ m. on A 666 – ✉ Bolton.*

Egerton House, Blackburn Rd, BL7 9PL, ☎ (01204) 307171, *info@egerton.macdonald-hotels.co.uk, Fax (01204) 593030,* – TV P – 150. MC AE VISA JCB
Meals (dinner only and Sunday lunch)/dinner a la carte 16.50/29.25 **st.** 14.50 – 10.50 – **32 rm** 80.00/120.00 **st.** – SB.

at Bromley Cross *North : 3¼ m. by A 676 on B 6472 – ✉ Bolton.*

Last Drop Village, Hospital Rd, BL7 9PZ, Northwest : 1 m. by B 6472 ☎ (01204) 591131, *info@lastdrop-macdonald-hotels.co.uk, Fax (01204) 304122,* « Village created from restored farm buildings », , , , , squash – TV P – 700. MC AE VISA.
Meals *(closed Saturday lunch)* a la carte 16.95/25.00 **t.** 14.50 – 10.50 – **125 rm** 90.00/115.00 **t.**, 3 suites – SB.

at Edgworth *Northeast : 7 m. by A 676, B 6472 and B 6391 – ✉ Bolton.*

Quarlton Manor Farm , Plantation Rd,, BL7 0DD, Northeast : 1 ½ m. by Blackburn rd ☎ (01204) 852277, *Fax (01204) 852286,* , « Part 17C farmhouse », , – TV P
Meals 16.50/28.50 **t.** 8.00 – **4 rm** 44.00/88.00 **st.**, 1 suite – SB.

BOLTON ABBEY *N. Yorks.* 402 O 22 *Great Britain G. – pop. 117 – ✉ Skipton.*

See : *Bolton Priory★ AC.*

London 216 – Harrogate 18 – Leeds 23 – Skipton 6.

The Devonshire Arms Country House , BD23 6AJ, ☎ (01756) 710441, *sales@the devonshirearms.co.uk, Fax (01756) 710564,* , « Part 17C restored coaching inn, collection of fine art and antiques », , , , , , , – TV P – 90. MC AE VISA
The Burlington : **Meals** (dinner only and Sunday lunch) 45.00 **st.** 14.95 – (see also ***Devonshire Brasserie and Bar*** below) – **38 rm** 135.00/185.00 **st.**, 3 suites – SB.

Devonshire Brasserie and Bar (at The Devonshire Arms Country House), BD23 6AJ, ☎ (01756) 710710, *Fax (01756) 710564,* « Contemporary decor » – P. MC AE VISA
Meals (booking essential) a la carte 18.50/23.00 **st.** 12.95.

BOREHAMWOOD *Herts.* 404 T 29 – *pop. 29 837.*
London 10 – Luton 20.

Plan : see Greater London (North West) p. 9

Elstree Moat House, Barnet bypass, WD6 5PU, at junction of A 5135 with A ... *(020) 8214 9988, cbels@queensmoat.co.uk, Fax (020) 8207 3194,* – rm, P – 400. AE VISA JCB.
Meals *(closed Saturday lunch)* 14.50/19.50 and a la carte 20.00/30.00 12.95 – 11.50 –
131 rm 149.00/199.00 **t.** – SB.

BOROUGHBRIDGE *N.Yorks.* 402 P 21 – *pop. 1 903.*
Fishergate (01423) 323373 (summer only).
London 215 – Leeds 19 – Middlesbrough 36 – York 16.

Rose Manor, Horsefair, YO51 9LL, (01423) 322245, *rosemanorhotel@ukf.net Fax (01423) 324920,* – rm, P – 250. AE VISA.
closed 25-26 December – **Meals** 18.50 (dinner) and a la carte 18.15/23.85 **st.** 5.95 – **19 rm** 85.00/124.00 **st.**, 1 suite – SB.

Crown, Horsefair, YO51 9LB, (01423) 322328, *sales@crownboroughbridge.co.uk Fax (01423) 324512,* – rm, P – 180. AE VISA
Meals 19.95 and a la carte 20.50/23.50 **st.** 8.95 – **37 rm** 65.00/90.00 **st.** – SB.

thediningroom, 20 St James's Sq, YO51 9AR, (01423) 326426, *lisaastley@virginnet.co.uk, Fax (01423) 326426,* – VISA
closed 25 December, 1-22 January, Sunday dinner, Monday and Bank Holidays – **Meals** (booking essential) a la carte 15.95/25.00 **t.** 12.50.

at Brafferton Helperby *Northeast : 5 m. by B 6265 and Easingwold rd on Helperby rd* – *York*

Laurel Manor Farm without rest., YO61 2NZ, by Hall Lane (01423) 360436, *laurelmf@aol.com, Fax (01423) 360437,* « 18C farmhouse », – P
3 rm 35.00/70.00 **t.**

BORROWDALE *Cumbria* 402 K 20 – *see Keswick.*

BOSCASTLE *Cornwall* 403 F 31 *The West Country G.*
See : *Village*★.
Env. : *Church*★ – *Old Post Office*★.
London 260 – Bude 14 – Exeter 59 – Plymouth 43.

Bottreaux House, PL35 0BG, South : ¾ m. by B 3263 on B 3266 (01840) 250231, *bothotel@dircon.co.uk, Fax (01840) 250170* – P. AE VISA JCB
Meals *(closed Sunday)* (dinner only) a la carte approx. 17.00 **t.** 9.50 – **7 rm** 35.00/52.00 **t.** – SB.

Trerosewill Farm without rest., Paradise, PL35 0BL, South : 1 m. off B 3263 (01840) 250545, *trerosewill@talk21.com, Fax (01840) 250545,* ←, « Working farm », – P. VISA JCB.
March-October – **6 rm** 27.50/59.00.

BOSHAM *W. Sussex* 404 R 31 – *see Chichester.*

BOSTON *Lincs.* 402 404 T 25 *Great Britain G.* – *pop. 34 606.*
See : *St Botolph's Church*★.
Exc. : *Tattershal Castle*★, *NW : 15 m. by A 1121, B 1192 and A 153 – Battle of Britain Memorial Flight, RAF Coningsby*★, *NW : 14 m. on A 1121, B 1192 and A 153.*
Cowbridge, Horncastle Rd (01205) 362306.
Market Pl (01205) 356656.
London 122 – Lincoln 35 – Nottingham 55.

Travel Inn, Wainfleet Rd, PE21 9RW, North : 1 ½ m. on A 52 (01205) 362307, *Fax (01205) 366494* – rm, P – 35. AE VISA JCB.
Meals (grill rest.) – **34 rm** 41.95 **t.**

BOSTON SPA *W. Yorks.* 402 P 22 – *pop. 4 135.*
London 127 – Harrogate 12 – Leeds 12 – York 16.

Four Gables without rest., Oaks Lane, LS23 6DS, West : ¼ m. by A 659 (01937) 849031, *info@four.gables.co.uk, Fax (01937) 849031,* – P.
3 rm 34.00/58.00 **st.**

Spice Box, 152 High St, LS23 6BW, (01937) 842558, *Fax (01937) 849955* – AE VISA
closed 26 December-2 January, Sunday dinner and Monday lunch – **Meals** (dinner booking essential) 8.50/16.95 and a la carte 19.65/25.65 **t.** 10.75.

BOTLEY *Hants.* 403 404 Q 31 – *pop. 2 297* – ✉ *Southampton.*

Botley Park H. Golf & C.C., Winchester Rd, Boorley Green ☎ (01489) 780888 ext : 451.
London 83 – Portsmouth 17 – Southampton 6 – Winchester 11.

Botley Park H. Golf & Country Club, Winchester Rd, Boorley Green, SO32 2UA, Northwest : 1 1/2 m. on B 3354 ☎ (01489) 780888, *events.botleypark@macdonald-hotels.co.uk, Fax (01489) 789242,* squash – rest, – 250.
Meals (dancing Saturday evening) a la carte 19.50/30.00 **st.** 15.00 – **100 rm** 110.00/145.00 **st.** – SB.

BOUGHTON *Kent* – *see Faversham.*

BOURNEMOUTH *Bournemouth* 403 404 O 31 *The West Country G.* – *pop. 155 488.*

See : *Compton Acres★★ (English Garden ≤★★★) AC* **AX** – *Russell-Cotes Art Gallery and Museum★★ AC* **DZ** - *Shelley Rooms AC* **EX.**

Env. : *Poole★, W : 4 m. by A 338 – Brownsea Island★ (Baden-Powell Stone ≤★★) AC, by boat from Sandbanks* **BX** *or Poole Quay – Christchurch★ (priory★) E : 4 1/2 m. on A 35.*

Exc. : *Corfe Castle★, SW : 18 m. by A 35 and A 351 – Lulworth Cove★ (Blue Pool★) W : 8 m. of Corfe Castle by B 3070 – Swanage★, E : 5 m. of Corfe Castle by A 351.*

Queens Park, Queens Park West Drive ☎ (01202) 396198, **DV** – *Bournemouth and Meyrick Park, Central Drive ☎ (01202) 290307,* **CY.**

Bournemouth (Hurn) Airport : ☎ (01202) 364000, N : 5 m. by Hurn - **DV.**

Westover Rd ☎ (0906) 8020234.

London 114 – Bristol 76 – Southampton 34.

Plans on following pages

Bournemouth Highcliff Marriott, St Michael's Rd, West Cliff, BH2 5DU, ☎ (01202) 557702, *reservations.bournemouth@marriotthotels.co.uk, Fax (01202) 293155,* ≤, heated, – rm, – 350. **CZ z**
Meals 13.50/25.00 and a la carte 25.00/48.45 **st.** 15.95 – **154 rm** 126.00/226.00 **st.**, 3 suites – SB.

Royal Bath, Bath Rd, BH1 2EW, ☎ (01202) 555555, *royalbathhotel@devere-hotel.com, Fax (01202) 554158,* ≤, – – 400.
Meals (dinner only) 24.00 and a la carte 32.00/40.00 **t.** 14.95 – (see also ***Oscars*** below) – **133 rm** 135.00/210.00 **t.**, 7 suites – SB. **DZ a**

Carlton, East Overcliff, BH1 3DN, ☎ (01202) 552011, *carlton@menzieshotels.co.uk, Fax (01202) 299573,* ≤, heated, – rest, – 160. **EZ a**
Meals 13.50/27.50 and dinner a la carte 26.65/37.20 **st.** 14.95 – 12.95 – **68 rm** 120.00 **st.**, 5 suites – SB.

Norfolk Royale, Richmond Hill, BH2 6EN, ☎ (01202) 551521, *norfolkroyal@englishrosehotels.co.uk, Fax (01202) 299729,* – rest, – 90. **CY u**
The Orangery : **Meals** 13.50/22.50 and a la carte 25.00/38.40 **st.** 14.75 – **90 rm** 105.00/185.00 **t.**, 5 suites – SB.

Hilton Bournemouth, Westover Rd, BH1 2BZ, ☎ (01202) 557681, *reservations@bournemouth.stakis.co.uk, Fax (01202) 554918,* ≤, – rm, – 300. **DZ n**
Meals *(closed Saturday lunch)* 12.50 and dinner a la carte 22.00/42.00 **t.** 12.30 – 12.50 – **114 rm** 115.00/180.00 **st.**, 6 suites – SB.

Chine, Boscombe Spa Rd, BH5 1AX, ☎ (01202) 396234, *reservations@chinehotel.co.uk, Fax (01202) 391737,* ≤, heated, – rm, – 120. **DX e**
Meals *(closed Saturday lunch)* 15.50/19.95 **st.** 11.50 – **89 rm** (dinner included) 78.25/180.00 **t.**

Miramar, 19 Grove Rd, East Overcliff, BH1 3AL, ☎ (01202) 556581, *sales@miramar-bournemouth.com, Fax (01202) 291242,* ≤, – – 150. **DZ u**
Meals *(closed Saturday lunch)* 20.95 and a la carte 10.00/20.00 **t.** 9.95 – **44 rm** 57.50/160.00 **t.** – SB.

Connaught, West Hill Rd, West Cliff, BH2 5PH, ☎ (01202) 298020, *sale@theconnaught.co.uk, Fax (01202) 298028,* heated, – – 250. **CZ v**
Meals *(restricted opening Christmas and New Year)* (bar lunch Monday-Saturday)/dinner 19.50 **st.** 9.45 – **55 rm** 70.00/140.00 **st.**, 1 suite – SB.

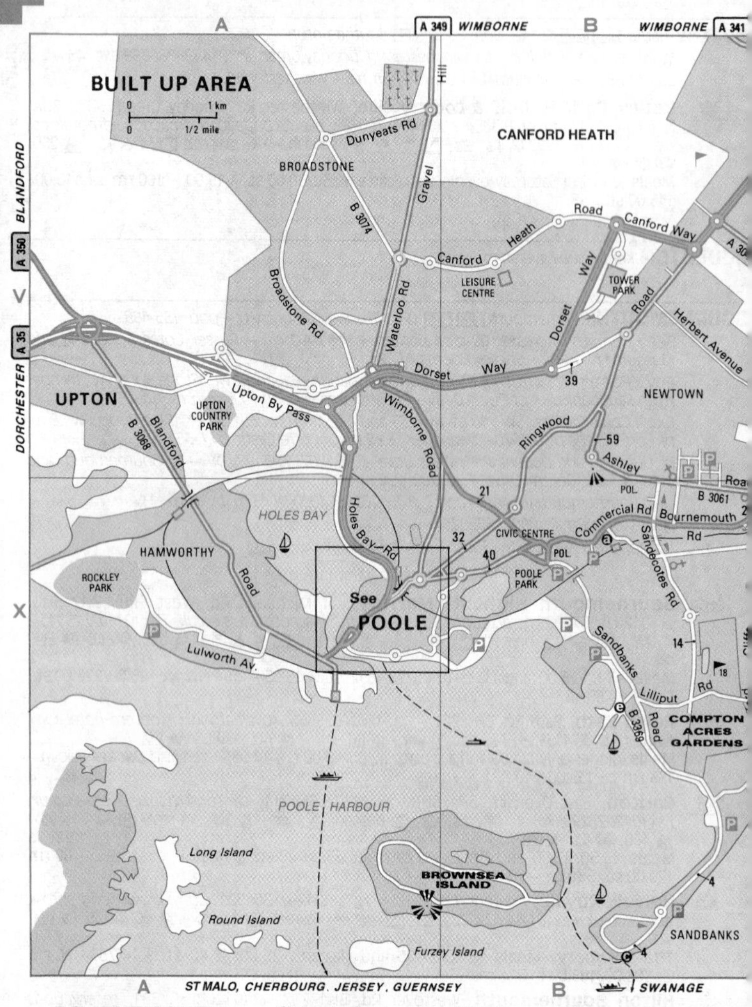

BOURNEMOUTH AND POOLE

Archway Road .... BX 2
Banks Road............. BX 4
Boscombe Overcliff Road .... EX 6
Boscombe Spa Road ..... DX 7
Branksome Wood Road.................. CY 9
Chessel Avenue .... EX 10
Clarendon Road .... CX 12
Commercial Road .... CY 13
Compton Avenue......... BX 14
Cranleigh Road........... EV 16
Durley Road.............. CZ 17
Ensbury Park Road .... CV 19
Exeter Road............. CDZ 20
Fernside Road............ ABX 21
Fir Vale Road............ DY 23
Gervis Place .... DY 24
Gloucester Road.......... EV 26
Hinton Road .... DZ 27
Lansdowne (The).......... DY 28
Lansdowne Road.......... DY 30
Leven Avenue .... CX 31
Longfleet Road........... BX 32
Madeira Road .... DY 34
Manor Road.............. EY 35
Meyrick Road .... EYZ 36
Old Christchurch Road .... DY
Old Wareham Road....... BV 39
Parkstone Road .... BX 40
Pinecliff Road .... CX 42
Post Office Road .... CY 43
Priory Road .... CZ 45
Queen's Road .... CX 46
Richmond Hill............ CY 47
Richmond Park Road ..... DV 48
Russell Cotes Road....... DZ 49
St. Michael's Road........ CZ 51
St. Paul's Road........... EY 52
St. Peter's Road.......... DY 53
St. Stephen's Road .... CY 55
St. Swithuns Road South .... EY 56
Seabourne Road.......... EV 57
Seamoor Road .... CX 58
Sea View Road........... BV 59
Southbourne Grove .... EX 61
Southbourne Overcliff Drive................... EX 62
Sovereign Shopping Centre EX
Square (The) .... CY
Suffolk Road .... CY 64
Surrey Road .... CX 66
Triangle (The) .... CY 67
Upper Hinton Road .... DZ 68
Wessex Way .... CX 70
West Cliff Promenade .... CZ 71
Western Road .... CX 73
Westover Road........... DZ 75

A 348 SOUTHAMPTON C A 347 FERNDOWN INTERNATIONAL AIRPORT D INTERNATIONAL AIRPORT E A 338

SOUTHAMPTON SALISBURY

Wimborne Road
BEAR CROSS
KINSON
Wimborne Rd
Stour
Hurn Road
Moors
Poole Lane Road
East Howe Lane
Leybourne Av.
Coombe Av.
Redhill Drive
REDHILL PARK
Redhill Av.
Rd
MOORDOWN
Castle
West Way
Road
A 3060 Lane
West
Ringwood Spur Rd
Stour
LISDOWN
Kinson
Columbia Road
A 347
Boundary Rd
19
East Way
CHARMINSTER
V
Road
Wimborne
WINTON
Queen's Park Avenue
Wessex Way
Castle Lane East
9
A 35 LYNDHURST
Road
U
Talbot Av.
Alma Rd
QUEEN'S PARK
18
KING'S PARK
Central Drive
Road
A 35
Glenferness Avenue
East Avenue
Wimborne
Charminster
48
Wessex Way
King's Park
Ashley Rd
16
Holdenhurst Rd
26
Christchurch
57
WEST SOUTHBOURNE
MEYRICK PARK
Road
SOVEREIGN SHOPPING CENTRE
66
31
Road 70
66
Rd
Parkwood Rd
61
Lindsay Rd
46
Christchurch
7
10
BOSCOMBE 6
6
62
The Avenue
Alumhurst Road
58
WESTBOURNE
BOURNEMOUTH
12
West Cliff Rd
X
73
KSOME ARK
42
POOLE BAY

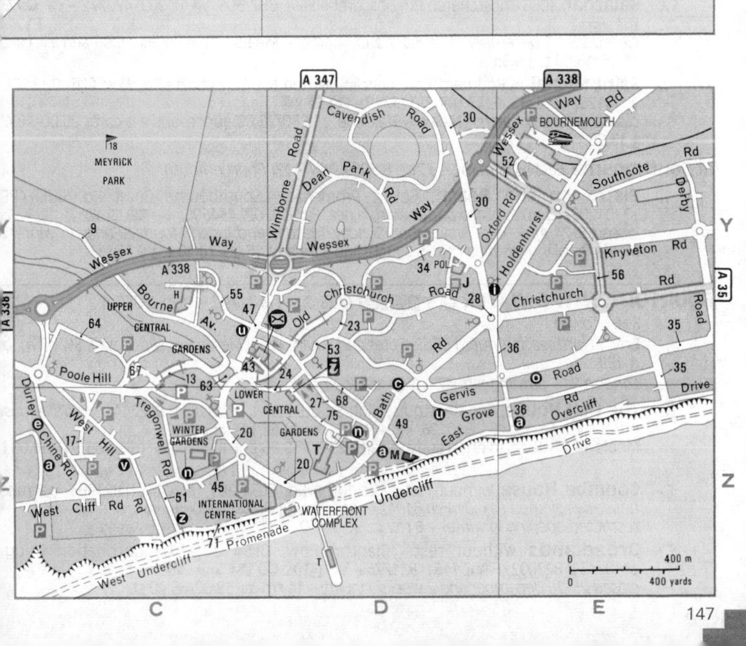

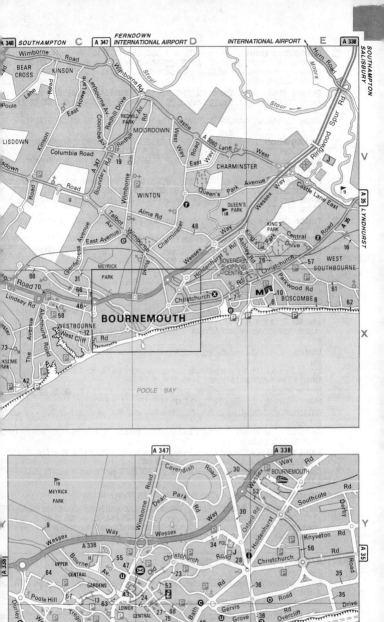

ENGLAND

Carrington House, Knyveton Rd, BH1 3QQ, (01202) 369988, *carrington@zoffan hotels.co.uk, Fax (01202) 292221*, – 300. VISA
Meals (bar lunch)/dinner 16.00 and a la carte 15.45/22.00 **st.** 5.95 – 9.50 – **145 rm** 85.00/110.00 **t.** – SB. DX

Durley Hall, Durley Chine Rd, BH2 5JS, (01202) 751000, *sales@durleyhall.co.uk Fax (01202) 757585*, heated, – rest, – 160. VISA CZ
Meals (buffet lunch Monday-Saturday)/dinner 18.50 **st.** 9.50 – **81 rm** 59.00/118.00 **st** – SB.

Collingwood, 11 Priory Rd, BH2 5DF, (01202) 557575, *info@hotel-collingwood.co.uk Fax (01202) 293219*, – rest, VISA CZ
Meals (bar lunch Monday-Saturday)/dinner 16.95 **t.** 8.50 – **53 rm** (dinner included 58.00/116.00 **t.** – SB.

Belvedere, 14 Bath Rd, BH1 2EU, (01202) 297556, *belvedere_hotel@msn.com Fax (01202) 294699* – – 80. VISA. DYZ
Meals (bar lunch Monday-Saturday)/dinner 14.50 and a la carte 13.50/20.40 **t.** 8.95 **61 rm** 49.00/104.00 **t.** – SB.

Tudor Grange without rest., 31 Gervis Rd, East Cliff, BH1 3EE, (01202) 291472 *Fax (01202) 311503*, – VISA EY
closed 24 December-2 January – **11 rm** 49.00/66.00 **t.**

Boltons, 9 Durley Chine Road South, West Cliff, BH2 5JT, (01202) 751517 *Fax (01202) 751629*, heated, – VISA CZ
Meals (dinner only) 12.50 **st.** 8.50 – **12 rm** 40.00/70.00 **st.** – SB.

Silver Trees without rest., 57 Wimborne Rd, BH3 7AL, (01202) 556040, *billsmithstree @aol.com, Fax (01202) 556040*, – VISA. CV
5 rm 27.00/46.00.

Oscars (at Royal Bath H.), Bath Rd, BH1 2EW, (01202) 555555, *Fax (01202) 554158* – VISA JCB DZ
closed Sunday dinner and Monday – **Meals** 13.00/32.00 and a la carte 21.00/51.00 **st** 14.50.

Clarks, 350-352 Charminster Rd, BH8 9RX, (01202) 240310, *Fax (01202) 523576* – VISA DV
closed 2 weeks January, 1 week June, Sunday, Monday and lunch Tuesday and Saturday – **Meals** 15.95 (lunch) and a la carte 24.45/30.85 **t.** 10.45.

Noble House, 3-5 Lansdowne Rd, BH1 1RZ, (01202) 291277 – VISA JCB
Meals - Chinese - 6.00/28.00 and a la carte 11.90/27.60 **t.** 9.50. DEY

Salathai, 1066 Christchurch Rd, Boscombe East, BH7 6DS, (01202) 420772 – VISA JCB EV
closed 25-26 December, 1 January and Sunday – **Meals** - Thai - 7.95/15.95 and a la carte 11.45/18.00 **t.** 9.95.

Saint Michel (at Bournemouth Highcliff Marriott H.), St Michael's Rd, West Cliff, BH2 5DU (01202) 315716, *Fax (01202) 315716* – VISA CZ
closed Saturday lunch – **Meals** - Brasserie - 13.50/25.00 (lunch) and a la carte 25.00/48.4 15.95.

at Southbourne *East : 3 ¾ m. by A 35 on B 3059* – EV – *Bournemouth.*

Bistro on the Beach, Solent Promenade, Southbourne Coast Rd, BH6 4BE (01202) 431473, *bistro.bridge@virgin.net, Fax (01202) 434606*, – VISA
closed 8-24 April, 4-27 November, Sunday-Tuesday and lunch Monday-Friday in winter – **Meals** (booking essential) 15.95 (lunch) and a la carte 15.95/28.10 **t.** 9.95.

BOURTON-ON-THE-WATER *Glos.* 403 404 O 28 *Great Britain G. – pop. 2 239.*

See : *Town*★.

Env. : *Northleach (Church of SS. Peter and Paul*★, *Wool Merchants' Brasses*★*), SW : 5 m. by A 429.*

London 91 – Birmingham 47 – Gloucester 24 – Oxford 36.

The Dial House, The Chestnuts, High St, GL54 2AN, (01451) 822244, *info@dialhouse hotel.com, Fax (01451) 810126*, – VISA JCB.
Meals 14.95/18.95 (dinner) and a la carte 23.00/30.95 **t.** 10.50 – **14 rm** 85.50/114.00 **t** – SB.

Coombe House without rest., Rissington Rd, GL54 2DT, (01451) 821966, *coombe house@virgin.net, Fax (01451) 810477*, – VISA JCB.
restricted opening in winter – **6 rm** 50.00/60.00 **st.**

Broadlands without rest., Clapton Row, GL54 2DN, by Coronation Bridge (01451) 822002, *Fax (01451) 821776* – VISA JCB.
closed 25-26 December and 2 weeks January – **11 rm** 38.00/65.00 **st.**

Lansdowne Villa without rest., Lansdowne, GL54 2AR, ✆ (01451) 820673, *lansdowne@star.co.uk, Fax (01451) 822099* – ⇔ TV P. MC VISA
12rm ☐ 33.00/56.00 st.

The Lawns without rest., Station Rd, GL54 2ER, ✆ (01451) 821195, *Fax (01451) 821195* – ⇔ TV P.
closed 24 December-10 January – **5 rm** ☐ 40.00/60.00 s.

at Great Rissington *Southeast : 3¼ m. – ✉ Cheltenham.*

Lamb Inn, GL54 2LP, ✆ (01451) 820388, *paul@thelamb-inn.com, Fax (01451) 820724,* « Part 17C Cotswold stone inn », – ⇔ rm, P. MC VISA
Meals a la carte 12.20/22.40 **t.** 9.95 – **14 rm** ☐ 45.00/90.00 **t.**

at Lower Slaughter *Northwest : 1¾ m. by A 429 – ✉ Cheltenham.*

Lower Slaughter Manor, GL54 2HP, ✆ (01451) 820456, *lowsmanor@aol.com, Fax (01451) 822150,* ←, « 17C manor house, gardens », – ⇔ rest, TV P – 25. MC AE VISA.
closed January – **Meals** 15.00/45.00 **t.** 25.00 – **13 rm** ☐ 175.00/400.00 **t.**, 3 suites.

Washbourne Court, GL54 2HS, ✆ (01451) 822143, *washbourne@classic.msn.com, Fax (01451) 821045,* « Part 17C house », – ⇔ rest, TV P. MC AE VISA JCB.
Meals 19.75/42.00 **t.** 15.40 – **19 rm** ☐ 105.00/280.00 **t.**, 9 suites – SB.

at Upper Slaughter *Northwest : 2¾ m. by A 429 – ✉ Cheltenham.*

Lords of the Manor, GL54 2JD, ✆ (01451) 820243, *lordsofthemanor@btinternet.com, Fax (01451) 820696,* ←, « Part 17C manor house », – ⇔ rest, TV P – 30. MC AE VISA JCB.
Meals 16.95/21.00 (lunch) and a la carte 39.50/50.00 **t.** 15.95 – **26 rm** ☐ 99.00/189.00 **st.**, 1 suite – SB
Spec. Roast John Dory, pickled lamb tongue. Organic salmon, smoked eel macaroni. Chocolate fondant, parsnip ice cream.

BOVEY TRACEY *Devon* 403 I 32 *The West Country G. – pop. 3 492 – ✉ Newton Abbot.*
See : *St Peter, St Paul and St Thomas of Canterbury Church*★.
Env. : *Dartmoor National Park*★★.
18 *Newton Abbot ✆ (01626) 52460.*
London 214 – Exeter 14 – Plymouth 32.

Edgemoor, Haytor Rd, TQ13 9LE, West : 1 m. on B 3387 ✆ (01626) 832466, *edgemoor@btinternet.com, Fax (01626) 834760,* – ⇔ rest, TV P – 50. MC AE VISA JCB
closed 1 week New Year – **Meals** (booking essential) 16.95/27.45 **t.** 8.45 – **16 rm** ☐ 57.50/100.00 **t.** – SB.

Front House Lodge, East St, TQ13 9EL, ✆ (01626) 832202, *fronthouselodge@aol.com, Fax (01626) 832202,* – ⇔ TV P. MC VISA JCB.
Meals (by arrangement) 12.00/18.00 7.00 – **5 rm** ☐ 27.00/60.00.

at Haytor *West : 2½ m. on B 3387 – ✉ Bovey Tracey.*

Bel Alp House, TQ13 9XX, on B 3387 ✆ (01364) 661217, *Fax (01364) 661292,* ← countryside, – ⇔ rest, TV P. MC AE VISA JCB
closed 20 December-10 January – **Meals** (booking essential to non-residents) (dinner only) 25.00/30.00 **st.** 9.00 – **6 rm** ☐ 75.00/150.00 **st.**

at Haytor Vale *West : 3½ m. by B 3387 – ✉ Newton Abbot.*

Rock Inn with rm, TQ13 9XP, ✆ (01364) 661305, *rockinn@eclipse.co.uk, Fax (01364) 661242,* « 18C », – ⇔ rm, TV P. MC AE VISA JCB
closed 25 December – **Meals** a la carte 21.65/25.15 **t.** 10.95 – **9 rm** ☐ 60.50/95.50 **t.** – SB.

BOVINGDON *Herts.* 404 S 28 – *pop. 4 491.*
London 35 – Aylesbury 29 – Maidenhead 21 – Oxford 31.

Bobsleigh, Hempstead Rd, HP3 0DS, on B 4505 ✆ (01442) 833276, *info@bobsleigh.macdonald-hotels.co.uk, Fax (01442) 832471,* heated, – TV P – 60. MC AE VISA JCB
Meals *(closed Monday lunch)* (Sunday dinner residents only) 15.95/22.95 and a la carte 28.35/32.35 **t.** 13.50 – **47 rm** ☐ 77.00/110.00 **st.** – SB.

BOW BRIDGE *Devon – see Totnes.*

BOWNESS-ON-WINDERMERE *Cumbria* 402 L 20 – *see Windermere.*

BRACKNELL *Bracknell Forest* 404 R 29 – *pop. 60 895.*
Downshire, Easthampstead Park, Wokingham ☎ (01344) 302030.
The Look Out, Discovery Park, Nine Mile Ride ☎ (01344) 354409.
London 35 – Reading 11.

Coppid Beech, John Nike Way, RG12 8TF, Northwest : 3 m. on B 3408 ☎ (01344) 303333, *sales@coppid-beech-hotel.co.uk, Fax (01344) 301200,* – rm, rest, – 350. *VISA* JCB
Rowans : **Meals** 17.50/24.95 and a la carte 26.85/46.95 **st.** 13.50 – ***Brasserie in the Keller :*** **Meals** *(closed Sunday)* (dinner only) a la carte 12.95/22.65 **st.** 12.75 – **203 rm** 165.00/185.00 **st.**, 2 suites – SB.

Grange Bracknell, Charles Sq, RG12 1DF, ☎ (01344) 474000, *bracknell@grangehotels.co.uk, Fax (01344) 302970* – rm, *VISA* JCB.
Meals (bar lunch Saturday, Sunday and Bank Holidays) 24.50 and a la carte 23.75/38.75 **st.** 12.95 – 15.00 – **88 rm** 225.00/265.00 **st.**, 32 suites.

Hilton Bracknell, Bagshot Rd, RG12 0QJ, South : 2 m. off A 322 ☎ (01344) 424801, *Fax (01344) 487454,* – , rest, – 260. *VISA* JCB
closed 26-31 December – **Meals** *(closed Saturday lunch)* (carvery lunch)/dinner a la carte approx. 22.50 **st.** 12.30 – 12.50 – **215 rm** 195.00/215.00 **st.** – SB.

Travel Inn, Arlington Sq, Wokingham Rd, RG42 1NA, West : ½ m. on B 3048 at "3.M." roundabout ☎ (01344) 319520, *Fax (01344) 319526* – rm, rest, *VISA*
Meals (grill rest.) – **61 rm** 41.95 **t.**

Travelodge without rest., London Rd, Binfield, RG4 2AA, Northwest : 2 ¾ m. on B 3408 ☎ (01344) 485940, *Fax (01344) 485940* – *VISA* JCB.
70 rm 69.95 **t.**

Les prix — Pour toutes précisions sur les prix indiqués dans ce guide, reportez-vous aux pages de l'introduction.

BRADFORD *W. Yorks.* 402 O 22 *Great Britain G.* – *pop. 289 376.*
See : *City★ – National Museum of Photography, Film and Television★.*
West Bowling, Newall Hall, Rooley Lane ☎ (01274) 724449 **BY** – *Woodhall Hills, Woodhall Rd, Calverley, Pudsley ☎ (0113) 256 4771,* – *Bradford Moor, Scarr Hill, Pollard Lane ☎ (01274) 771716* **BX** – *East Brierley, South View Rd ☎ (01274) 681023* **BX** – *Queensbury, Brighouse Rd, Queensbury ☎ (01274) 882155* **AY.**
Leeds and Bradford Airport : ☎ (0113) 250 9696, NE : 6 m. by A 658 **BX.**
Central Library, Prince's Way ☎ (01274) 753678.
London 212 – Leeds 9 – Manchester 39 – Middlesbrough 75 – Sheffield 45.

Plan of Enlarged Area : see Leeds

Hanover International, Mayo Ave, off Rooley Lane, BD5 8HZ, ☎ (01274) 406606, *sales@hanover-international.com, Fax (01274) 406600,* – rm, rest, – 800. *VISA* JCB **BY a**
Four Seasons : **Meals** (bar lunch Saturday) 10.95/19.50 and a la carte 23.15/33.70 **st.** 11.50 – 9.75 – **130 rm** 105.00 **st.**, 1 suite – SB.

Hilton Bradford, Hall Ings, BD1 5SH, ☎ (01274) 734734, *Fax (01274) 306146* – rm, rest, – 700. *VISA* **BZ e**
Meals (grill rest.) a la carte 15.40/26.70 **st.** 12.30 – 12.95 – **116 rm** 95.00/115.00 **st.**, 4 suites – SB.

Courtyard by Marriott Leeds/Bradford, The Pastures, Tong Lane, BD4 0RP, Southeast : 4 ¾ m. by A 650 and B 6135 on Tong Lane ☎ (0113) 2854646, *Fax (0113) 2853661,* – rm, rest, – 250. *VISA*. on Leeds town plan **BU e**
Meals a la carte 14.25/22.90 **st.** 11.75 – **53 rm** 91.50/112.00 **st.** – SB.

Guide Post, Common Rd, Low Moor, BD12 0ST, South : 3 m. by A 641 off A 638 ☎ (01274) 607866, *bookings@guideposthotel.net, Fax (01274) 671085* – rm, – 100. *VISA* on Leeds town plan **AU c**
Meals *(closed Saturday lunch)* a la carte 17.20/23.75 **st.** 9.95 – **43 rm** 67.50/97.50 **st.** – SB.

Novotel Bradford, Euroway Trading Estate, Merrydale Rd, BD4 6SA, South : 3 ½ m. by A 641 and A 6117 off M 606 ☎ (01274) 683683, *os10@accor-hotels.com, Fax (01274) 651342* – rm, – 300. *VISA* on Leeds town plan **AU a**
Meals 14.00 and a la carte 12.00/18.00 **st.** 9.95 – 9.50 – **127 rm** 55.00 **st.** – SB.

Travel Inn, Whitehall Rd, Cleckheaton, BD19 6HG, South : 5 ½ m. by A 650, A 6177, M 606 off A 58 ☎ (01274) 862828, *Fax (01274) 852973* – rm, rest, *VISA*. on Leeds town plan **BU c**
Meals (grill rest.) – **40 rm** 41.95 **t.**

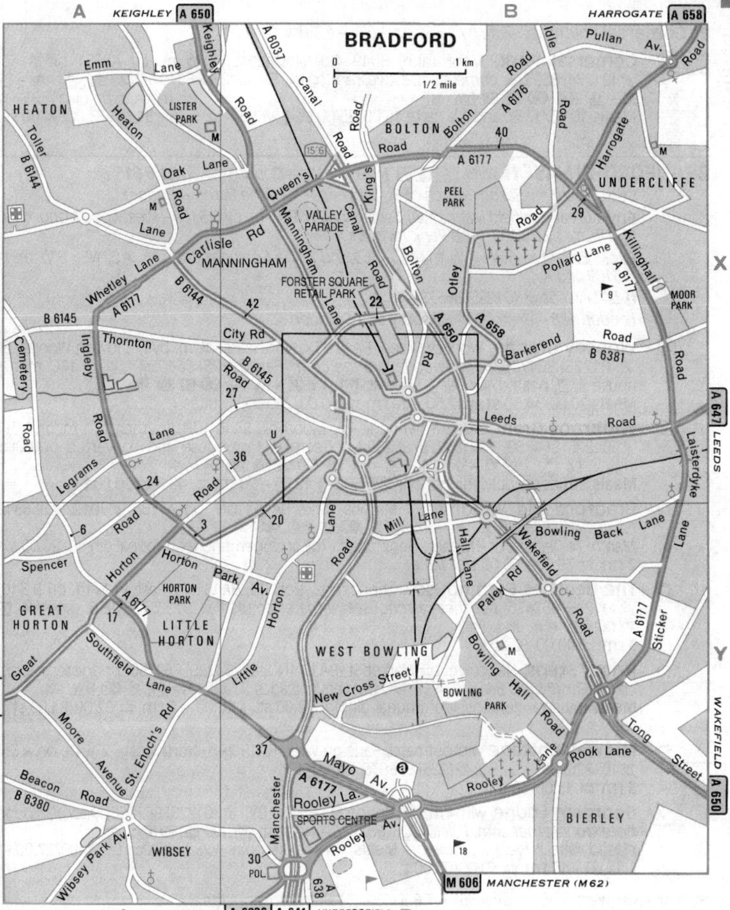

BRADFORD

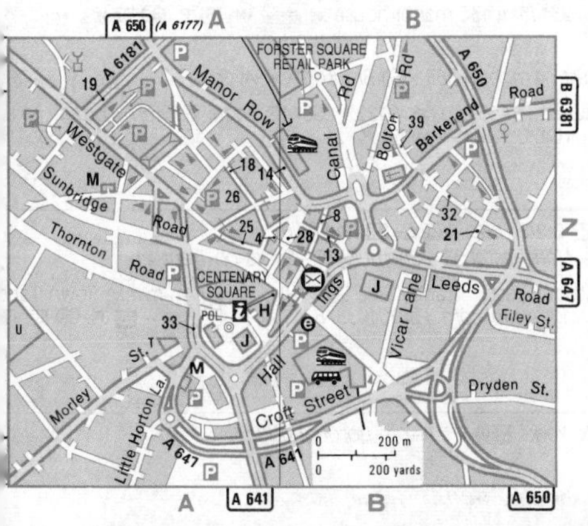

All Saints Road . . . . AY 3
Bank Street . . . . AZ 4
Beckside Road . . . . AY 6
Broadway . . . . BZ 8
Charles Street . . . . BZ 13
Cheapside . . . . BZ 14
Cross Lane . . . . AY 17
Darley Street . . . . AZ 18
Drewton Road . . . . AZ 19
Easby Road . . . . BY 20
East Parade . . . . BZ 21
Forster Square Retail Park . . . . BXY
Hamm Stasse . . . . BX 22
Horton Grange Road . . . . . . AX 24
Ivegate . . . . AZ 25
Kirkgate Centre . . . . AZ 26
Listerhills Road . . . . BX 27
Market Street . . . . BZ 28
Northcote Road . . . . BX 29
Odsal Road . . . . BY 30
Peckover Street . . . . BZ 32
Prince's Way . . . . AZ 33
Shearbridge Road . . . . BX 36
Smiddles Lane . . . . BY 37
Stott Hill . . . . BZ 39
Valley View Grove . . . . BX 40
White Abbey Road . . . . BX 42

ENGLAND

at Gomersal *Southeast : 7 m. by A 650 on A 651 – ✉ Bradford.*

Gomersal Park, Moor Lane, BD19 4LJ, Northeast : 1 ½ m. by A 651 off A 65… *℘ (01274) 869386, gomersal@bestwestern.co.uk, Fax (01274) 861042,* … 200. MO AE O VISA on Leeds town plan BU
Meals 10.95/17.50 and a la carte 15.00/25.00 **st.** 11.95 – 9.25 – **51 rm** 83.00/94.00 **st.**

BRADFORD-ON-AVON *Wilts.* 403 404 N 29 *The West Country G. – pop. 8 815.*

See : *Town★★ - Saxon Church of St. Lawrence★★ - Tithe Barn★ – Bridge★.*

Env. : *Great Chalfield Manor★ (All Saints★) AC, NE : 3 m. by B 3109 – Westwood Manor★ AC, S : 1½ m. by B 3109 – Top Rank Tory (≤★).*

Exc. : *Bath★★★, NW : 7 ½ m. by A 363 and A 4 – Corsham Court★★ AC, NE : 6 ½ m. by B 3109 and A 4.*

34 Silver St ℘ (01225) 865797.

London 118 – Bristol 24 – Salisbury 35 – Swindon 33.

Woolley Grange, Woolley Green, BA15 1TX, Northeast : ¾ m. by B 3107 on Woolley St *℘ (01225) 864705, info@woolleygrange.com, Fax (01225) 864059,* « 17C manor house », heated, – rest, 40. MO AE O VISA
Meals 20.00/34.50 **st.** 12.50 – **20 rm** 90.00/230.00, 3 suites.

Widbrook Grange, Trowbridge Rd, Widbrook, BA15 1UH, Southeast : 1 m. on A 363 *℘ (01225) 864750, Fax (01225) 862890,* « Georgian farmhouse and converted outbuildings », – rest, 25. MO AE O VISA JCB.
Meals (residents only) (dinner only) 25.50 **t.** 12.00 – **20 rm** 49.00/120.00 **t.**

Bradford Old Windmill, 4 Masons Lane, BA15 1QN, on A 363 *℘ (01225) 866842 Fax (01225) 866648,* ≤, – MO AE VISA.
March-24 December – **Meals** - Vegetarian - (by arrangement) (communal dining) 20.00 **s.** – **2 rm** 79.00/109.00 **s.**, 1 suite.

The Beeches Farmhouse without rest., Holt Rd, BA15 1TS, East : 1 ¼ m. on B 310… *℘ (01225) 863475, beeches-farmhouse@netgates.co.uk, Fax (01225) 863996,* – MO VISA JCB.
3 rm 40.00/60.00 **s.**

Priory Steps, Newtown, off Market St, BA15 1NQ, *℘* (01225) 862230, *priorysteps@clara.co.uk, Fax (01225) 866248,* ≤, « 17C weavers cottages », – MO VISA.
Meals (by arrangement) (communal dining) 22.00 **st.** 10.00 – **5 rm** 62.00/84.00 **st.** – SB.

Midway Cottage without rest., Farleigh Wick, BA15 2PU, Northwest : 2 ¾ m. on A 363 *℘ (01225) 863932, Fax (01225) 866836,* –
3 rm 35.00/50.00.

Georgian Lodge with rm, 25 Bridge St, BA15 1BY, *℘* (01225) 862268, *georgianlodgehotel@btinternet.com, Fax (01225) 862218* – rest, MO AE O VISA.
closed first 2 weeks January – **Meals** *(closed Monday lunch)* a la carte 20.00/27.00 **st** 11.00 – **10 rm** 30.00/95.00 **t.**

at Winsley *West : 2½ m. by A 363 off B 3108 – ✉ Bradford-on-Avon.*

Burghope Manor without rest., BA15 2LA, *℘* (01225) 723557, *burghope.manor@virgin.net, Fax (01225) 723113,* « 13C manor house », – MO AE VISA JCB.
5 rm 85.00/100.00 **st.**

at Monkton Farleigh *Northwest : 4 m. by A 363 – ✉ Bradford-on-Avon.*

Fern Cottage without rest., BA15 2QJ, *℘* (01225) 859412, *enquiries@fern-cottage.co.uk, Fax (01225) 859018,* « Part 17C », –
3 rm 40.00/60.00 **st.**

BRADWELL *Derbs.* 402 403 404 O 24 – *pop. 1 728 – ✉ Sheffield.*

London 181 – Derby 51 – Manchester 32 – Sheffield 16 – Stoke-on-Trent 41.

StoneyRidge without rest., Granby Rd, S33 9HU, West : ¾ m. via Town Lane *℘ (01433) 620538, toneyridge@aol.com, Fax (01433) 623154,* ≤, – MO AE O VISA JCB
4 rm 31.00/56.00.

BRAFFERTON HELPERBY *N. Yorks.* 402 P 21 – *see Boroughbridge.*

There is no paid advertising in this Guide.

BRAINTREE *Essex* 404 V 28 – *pop. 33 229.*

Kings Lane, Stisted (01376) 346079 – Towerlands, Panfield Rd (01376) 326802.

Town Hall Centre, Market Pl (01376) 550066.

London 45 – Cambridge 38 – Chelmsford 12 – Colchester 15.

Express by Holiday Inn without rest., Galley's Corner, Cressing Rd, CM7 8DJ, Southeast : 2 ¼ m. on B 1018 (01376) 551141, *Fax (01376) 551142* – 30.
47 rm 52.50 **st.**

Travel Inn, Galley's Corner, CM7 8GG, Southeast : 2 m. by B 1018 on A 120 (01376) 340914, *Fax (01376) 555087* – rm, rest.
Meals (grill rest.) – **40 rm** 41.95 **t.**

BRAMHOPE *W. Yorks.* 402 P 22 – *see Leeds.*

BRAMPTON *Cambs.* 402 404 T 27 – *pop. 4 673.*

London 72 – Bedford 22 – Cambridge 18 – Northampton 36.

Travel Inn, Brampton Hut, Great North Rd, PE28 4NQ, Northwest : 2 m. by B 1514 at junction of A 1 and A 14 (01480) 810800, *Fax (01480) 811298* – rm, rest. – 25.
Meals (grill rest.) – **80 rm** 41.95 **t.**

BRAMPTON *Cumbria* 401 402 L 19 *Great Britain G.* – *pop. 3 957.*

Env. : Hadrian's Wall★★, NW : by A 6077.

Talkin Tarn (016977) 2255 – Brampton Park, Huntingdon (01480) 434700.

Moot Hall, Market Sq (016977) 3433.

London 317 – Carlisle 9 – Newcastle upon Tyne 49.

Farlam Hall, CA8 2NG, Southeast : 2 ¾ m. on A 689 (016977) 46234, *farlamhall@dial.pipex.com, Fax (016977) 46683*, « Victorian country house, ornamental gardens » –
closed 25-30 December – **Meals** (booking essential to non-residents) (dinner only) 32.50 **t.** 13.75 – **12 rm** (dinner included) 130.00/270.00 **t.** – SB.

Kirby Moor Country House, Longtown Rd, CA8 2AB, North : ½ m. on A 6071 (016977) 3893, *info@kirbymoor-hotel.com, Fax (016977) 41847*, – rest.
Meals a la carte approx. 12.35/22.00 **st.** 10.35 – **7 rm** 45.00/70.00 **st.**

at Kirkcambeck *North : 7 ¾ m. by A 6071 and Walton rd – Brampton.*

Cracrop Farm without rest., CA8 2BW, West : 1 m. by B 6318 on Stapleton rd (016977) 48245, *cracrop@aol.com, Fax (016977) 48333*, « Working farm », – JCB.
closed 25 December – **4 rm** 25.00/55.00 **s.**

BRANCASTER STAITHE *Norfolk* 404 V 25.

London 131 – Cambridge 74 – Norwich 39.

The White Horse with rm, Main Rd, PE31 8BW, (01485) 210262, *reception@whitehorsebrancaster.co.uk, Fax (01485) 210930*, –
Meals a la carte 15.75/26.00 **t.** 9.70 – **8 rm** 65.00/90.00 **t.** – SB.

BRANDESBURTON *East Riding* 402 T 22 – *pop. 1 835* – *Great Driffield.*

London 197 – Kingston-upon-Hull 16 – York 37.

Burton Lodge, YO25 8RU, Southwest : ½ m. on Leven rd (01964) 542847, *burton@lodge5755.freeserve.co.uk, Fax (01964) 544771*, – rest. JCB
closed 25-26 December – **Meals** (residents only) (dinner only) 15.00 **st.** – **9 rm** 37.00/54.00 **st.** – SB.

BRANDON *Warks.* 403 404 P 26 – *see Coventry (W. Mids.).*

BRANDS HATCH *Kent* 404 (44) – *Dartford.*

Corinthian, Gay Dawn Farm, Fawkham, Dartford (01474) 707559.

London 22 – Maidstone 18.

Thistle Brands Hatch, DA3 8PE, on A 20 (0870) 3339128, *Fax (0870) 3339228*, – rm, rest. – 270. JCB
Genevieves : **Meals** a la carte 20.10/31.40 **st.** 11.95 – 11.50 – **121 rm** 125.00 **t.**

at Fawkham Green *East : 1½ m. by A 20 – ✉ Ash Green.*

Brands Hatch Place, DA3 8NQ, ✆ (01474) 872239, *Fax (01474) 879652*, squash – 120. *VISA*.
Meals 24.00 (dinner) and a la carte 19.00/35.00 **st.** 13.25 – 10.50 – **41 rm** 80.00/165.00 **st.** – SB.

BRANSCOMBE *Devon* 403 K 31 *The West Country G. – pop. 501 – ✉ Seaton.*
See : *Village*★.
Env. : *Seaton (≤★★), NW : 3 m – Colyton*★.
London 167 – Exeter 20 – Lyme Regis 11.

Masons Arms, EX12 3DJ, ✆ (01297) 680300, *reception@masonsarms.co.uk, Fax (01297) 680500*, « 14C inn » – rest, – 100. *VISA*
Meals (bar lunch)/dinner 24.00 and a la carte 12.95/21.50 **st.** 11.00 – **28 rm** 60.00/150.00 **st.** – SB.

BRAYE *Alderney (Channel Islands)* 403 Q 33 and 230 ⑨ – *see Channel Islands.*

BRAY-ON-THAMES *Windsor & Maidenhead* 404 R 29 – *pop. 8 121 – ✉ Maidenhead.*
London 34 – Reading 13.

Plan : see Maidenhead

Monkey Island, SL6 2EE, Southeast : ¾ m. by Upper Bray Rd and Old Mill Lane ✆ (01628) 623400, *monkeyisland@btconnect.com, Fax (01628) 784732*, ≤, « Island on River Thames », rest, – 120. *VISA*.
Meals a la carte 17.90/43.75 **t.** 25.00 – **25 rm** 130.00/205.00 **t.**, 1 suite.

Chauntry House, 1 High St, SL6 2AB, ✆ (01628) 673991, *res@chauntryhouse.com, Fax (01628) 773089*, – 30. *VISA* JCB X a
closed 26 December-2 January – **Meals** 22.00/35.00 and a la carte 22.00/40.00 **st.** 13.00 – **15 rm** 120.00/180.00 **st.** – SB.

Waterside Inn (Roux) with rm, Ferry Rd, SL6 2AT, ✆ (01628) 620691, *reservations@waterside-inn.co.uk, Fax (01628) 784710*, « ≤ Thames-side setting » – *VISA* JCB. X s
closed 26 December-31 January and 3-4 April – **Meals** - French - *(closed Tuesday except dinner June-August and Monday)* 33.50/74.00 and a la carte 67.00/99.50 **t.** 26.00 – **8 rm** 160.00/185.00 **st.**, 1 suite
Spec. Tronçonnettes de homard poêlées minute au Porto blanc. Filets de lapereau grillés aux marrons glacés. Soufflé chaud aux framboises.

Fat Duck (Blumenthal), High St, SL6 2AQ, ✆ (01628) 580333, *Fax (01628) 776188*, – *VISA* JCB X e
closed 24 December-8 January, Sunday dinner and Monday – **Meals** 25.75/58.00 and a la carte 58.00/75.00 **t.** 16.00
Spec. Crab biscuit, roast foie gras, marinated salmon and oyster vinaigrette. Saddle of lamb, lamb tongue and onion purée. Chocolate fondant, avocado risotto, coconut sorbet.

The Fish, Old Mill Lane, SL6 2BG, ✆ (01628) 781111, *Fax (01628) 623571*, – *VISA* X r
closed Sunday dinner – **Meals** - Seafood - 21.95 (lunch) and a la carte 28.00/34.00 **st.** 15.95.

BREADSALL *Derby – see Derby.*

BRENTWOOD *Essex* 404 V 29 – *pop. 49 463.*
18 Bentley G. & C.C., Ongar Rd ✆ (01277) 373179 – 18, 9 Warley Park, Magpie Lane, Little Warley ✆ (01277) 224891.
Pepperell House, 44 High St ✆ (01277) 200300.
London 22 – Chelmsford 11 – Southend-on-Sea 21.

Marygreen Manor, London Rd, CM14 4NR, Southwest : 1 ¼ m. on A 1023 ✆ (01277) 225252, *info@marygreenmanor.co.uk, Fax (01277) 262809*, – 50. *VISA*.
Meals 16.50/30.00 and a la carte 30.35/41.60 **t.** 13.00 – 12.00 – **54 rm** 123.50/219.00 **st.**, 1 suite.

Holiday Inn, Brook St, CM14 5NF, Southwest : 1 ½ m. on A 1023 (0870) 4009012, *Fax (01277) 264264*, rm, rest, 100.
Meals (grill rest.) a la carte approx. 15.00 13.95 – 13.95 – **150 rm** 110.00/159.00 **st.** – SB.

BRICKET WOOD *Herts..*

London 23 – Watford 4 – St Albans 4.

Travel Inn Metro, Moor Mill, Smug Oak Lane, AL2 3TY, (01727) 875557, *Fax (01727) 873289*, – rm,
Meals (grill rest.) – **56 rm** 49.95 **t.**

BRIDGNORTH *Shrops.* 402 403 404 M 26 *Great Britain G. – pop. 11 229.*

Exc. : *Ironbridge Gorge Museum★★ AC (The Iron Bridge★★ - Coalport China Museum★★ - Blists Hill Open Air Museum★★ - Museum of the River and Visitor Centre★) NW : 8 m. by B 4373.*

Stanley Lane (01746) 763315.

The Library, Listley St (01746) 763257.

London 146 – Birmingham 26 – Shrewsbury 20 – Worcester 29.

at Worfield *Northeast : 4 m. by A 454 – Bridgnorth.*

The Old Vicarage , WV15 5JZ, (01746) 716497, *admin@the-old-vicarage.demon.co.uk, Fax (01746) 716552*, « Edwardian parsonage », –
Meals *(closed Saturday lunch)* (booking essential) 18.50 (lunch) and dinner a la carte 22.50/35.00 **st.** 14.50 – **13 rm** 80.00/175.00 **st.**, 1 suite – SB.

at Alveley *Southeast : 7 m. by A 442 – Bridgnorth.*

Mill, Birdsgreen, WV15 6HL, Northeast : ¾ m. (01746) 780437, *Fax (01746) 780850*, – , rest, – 200.
Meals 12.75/23.50 and a la carte 21.50/30.80 **t.** 10.10 – 7.50 – **21 rm** 68.00/116.00 **t.** – SB.

BRIDGWATER *Somerset* 403 L 30 *The West Country G. – pop. 34 610.*

See : *Town★ – Castle Street★ – St. Mary's★ – Admiral Blake Museum★ AC.*

Env. : *Westonzoyland (St. Mary's Church★★) SE : 4 m. by A 372 – North Petherton (Church Tower★★) S : 3½ m. by A 38.*

Exc. : *Stogursey Priory Church★★, NW : 14 m. by A 39.*

Enmore Park, Enmore (01278) 671244.

50 High St (01278) 472652.

London 160 – Bristol 39 – Taunton 11.

Walnut Tree, North Petherton, TA6 6QA, South : 3 m. on A 38 (01278) 662255, *reservations@walnut-tree-hotel.co.uk, Fax (01278) 663946*, – rm, rest, – 120.
closed 26 December – ***Duke's :*** **Meals** a la carte 18.25/22.45 **t.** 9.95 – ***Duke's Bistro :*** **Meals** (bookings not accepted) a la carte 18.25/22.45 **t.** 9.95 – 9.00 – **31 rm** 75.00/86.00 **t.**, 1 suite – SB.

at Woolavington *Northeast : 5 m. by A 39 on B 3141 – Bridgwater.*

Chestnut House, Hectors Stone, Lower Road, TA7 8EQ, (01278) 683658, *jon@chestnuthouse.freeserve.co.uk, Fax (01278) 684333*, « Part 16C farmhouse », – rest,
Meals a la carte 17.50/25.00 10.00 – **6 rm** 45.00/70.00.

at Cannington *Northwest : 3½ m. by A 39 – Bridgwater.*

Blackmore Farm without rest., TA5 2NE, Southwest : 1 ½ m. by A 39 on Bradley Green rd (01278) 653442, *dyerfarm@aol.com, Fax (01278) 653427*, « Part 14C manor house, working farm », , –
3 rm 35.00/55.00 **st.**, 1 suite.

Particularly pleasant hotels and restaurants are shown in the Guide by a red symbol.
Please send us the names of anywhere you have enjoyed your stay.
Your **Michelin Guide** will be even better.

BRIDLINGTON *East Riding* 402 T 21 *Great Britain G. – pop. 31 334.*
Env. : *Flamborough Head★, NE : 5 ½ m. by B 1255 and B 1259 – Burton Agnes Hall★ AC SW : 6 m. by A 166.*
Belvedere Rd ☎ (01262) 672092 – Flamborough Head, Lighthouse Rd, Flamborough ☎ (01262) 850333.
25 Prince St ☎ (01262) 673474.
London 236 – Kingston-upon-Hull 29 – York 41.

Expanse, North Marine Drive, YO15 2LS, ☎ (01262) 675347, *expanse@brid.demon.uk Fax (01262) 604928,* ← – 200.
Meals 9.95/16.00 and dinner a la carte 18.55/23.65 **st.** 9.90 – **48 rm** 60.00/88.00 **st.** – SB.

BRIDPORT *Dorset* 403 L 31 *The West Country G. – pop. 7 278.*
Env. : *Parnham House★★ AC, N : 6 m. by A 3066 – Mapperton Gardens★, N : 4 m. by A 3066 and minor rd* – **Exc.** : *Lyme Regis★ – The Cobb★, W : 11 m. by A 35 and A 3052.*
Bridport and West Dorset, East Cliff, West Bay ☎ (01308) 422597.
32 South St ☎ (01308) 424901.
London 150 – Exeter 38 – Taunton 33 – Weymouth 19.

Roundham House, Roundham Gdns, West Bay Rd, DT6 4BD, South : 1 m. by B 3157 ☎ (01308) 422753, *cyprencom@compuserve.com, Fax (01308) 421500,* ←, – VISA JCB
closed January, February and Sunday – **Meals** (dinner only) 17.95 **t.** 9.30 – **8 rm** 38.00/70.00 **t.** – SB.

Britmead House without rest., West Bay Rd, DT6 4EG, South : 1 m. on B 3157 ☎ (01308) 422941, *britmead@talk21.com, Fax (01308) 422516,* – VISA JCB – **7 rm** 40.00/64.00 **st.**

Riverside, West Bay, DT6 4EZ, South : 1 ¾ m. by B 3157 ☎ (01308) 422011 *Fax (01308) 458808,* ←, – VISA
mid February-November – **Meals** - Seafood - *(closed Sunday dinner and Monday except Bank Holidays)* (booking essential) (restricted dinner February-March and October-November) a la carte 19.00/30.00 **t.** 10.50.

at Shipton Gorge *Southeast : 3 m. by A 35 – ✉ Bridport.*

Innsacre Farmhouse, Shipton Lane, DT6 4LJ, North : 1 m. ☎ (01308) 456137 *innsacre.farmhouse@btinternet.co.uk, Fax (01308) 456137,* « 17C », – VISA JCB
closed October and 24 December-2 January – **Meals** (by arrangement) 17.50 **t.** 11.50 – **4 rm** 65.00/80.00 **t.**

BRIGHOUSE *W. Yorks.* 402 O 22 – *pop. 32 198.*
Crow Nest Park, Coach Rd, Hove Edge ☎ (01484) 401121.
London 213 – Bradford 12 – Burnley 28 – Manchester 35 – Sheffield 39.

Posthouse Leeds Brighouse, Clifton Village, HD6 4HW, Southeast : 1 m. on A 644 ☎ (0870) 400 9013, *GM1736@forte-hotels.com, Fax (01484) 400068,* – rm – 200. AE VISA
Meals 10.00/17.50 and a la carte 18.25/27.45 **t.** 11.95 – 11.95 – **92 rm** 96.00/116.00 **t.** – 2 suites – SB.

Waterfront Lodge, Huddersfield Rd, HD6 1JZ, ☎ (01484) 715566, *Fax (01484) 715588* « Canalside setting » – rm, rest, AE VISA.
closed 25 December and 1 January – ***Prego :*** **Meals** - Italian - *(closed Monday lunch)* a la carte 19.50/23.50 **t.** 9.50 – 6.50 – **42 rm** 40.00/47.00 **t.**

Brook's, 6 Bradford Rd, HD6 1RW, ☎ (01484) 715284, *brooks@legend.co.uk Fax (01484) 712641* – AE VISA
closed 2 weeks January and 1 week August – **Meals** (dinner only and lunch in December) dinner 23.95 **t.** 12.50.

BRIGHTON AND HOVE *Brighton and Hove* 404 T 31 *Great Britain G. – pop. 192 453.*
See : *Town★★ - Royal Pavilion★★★ AC* CZ – *Seafront★★ – The Lanes★* BCZ – *St. Bartholomew's★ AC* CX **B** – *Art Gallery and Museum (20C decorative arts★)* CY **M.**
Env. : *Devil's Dyke (←★) NW : 5 m. by Dyke Rd (B 2121)* BY.
East Brighton, Roedean Rd ☎ (01273) 604838 CV – *The Dyke, Devil's Dyke, Dyke Rd ☎ (01273) 857296,* BV – *Hollingbury Park, Ditchling Rd ☎ (01273) 552010,* CV – *Waterhall, Waterhall Rd ☎ (01273) 508658,* AV.
Shoreham Airport : ☎ (01273) 296900, W : 8 m. by A 27 AV.
10 Bartholomew Sq ☎ (01273) 292599.
London 53 – Portsmouth 48 – Southampton 61.

Plans on following pages

Grand, Kings Rd, BN1 2FW, ✆ (01273) 224300, *reservations@grandbrighton.co.uk, Fax (01273) 224321*, ≤, Fа, ≘s, ◻ – |♦|, TV ✆ ♿ ⇔ – 🎭 800. MC AE ① VISA JCB BZ v
Meals a la carte 27.00/47.50 **t.** 🍷 17.00 – **195 rm** ⊐ 165.00/330.00 **st.**, 5 suites – SB.

Thistle Brighton, Kings Rd, BN1 2GS, ✆ (01273) 206700, *brighton@thistle.co.uk, Fax (01273) 820692*, ≤, Fа, ≘s, ◻ – |♦| ⇆ ▤ TV ✆ ♿ ⇔ – 🎭 300. MC AE ① VISA JCB CZ n
Promenade : Meals 6.95/18.50 **t.** 🍷 12.95 – ⊐ 12.00 – **204 rm** 215.00 **st.**, 4 suites – SB.

Hilton Brighton Metropole, Kings Rd, BN1 2FU, ✆ (01273) 775432, *reservations@brightonmet.stakis.co.uk, Fax (01273) 749632*, ≤, Fа, ≘s, ◻ – |♦|, ⇆ rm, ▤ rest, TV – 🎭 1500. MC AE ① VISA. ⚹ BZ s
Meals *(closed Saturday lunch)* 19.00 and a la carte 24.00/46.00 🍷 14.95 – ⊐ 13.50 – **323 rm** 210.00/260.00, 10 suites – SB.

Hilton Brighton West Pier, Kings Rd, BN1 2JF, ✆ (01273) 329744, *Fax (01273) 775877*, ≤ – |♦| ⇆, ▤ rest, TV ♿ ⇔ – 🎭 450. MC AE ① VISA BZ c
Meals *(closed Saturday lunch and Bank Holidays)* (carvery) 14.95/17.95 **t.** 🍷 14.95 – ⊐ 13.95 – **129 rm** 170.00/220.00 **t.**, 2 suites – SB.

Belgrave, 64 Kings Rd, BN1 1NA, ✆ (01273) 323221, *thebelgrave@cwc.net, Fax (01273) 312485*, ≤ – |♦|, ⇆ rm, ▤ rest, TV ✆ – 🎭 70. MC AE ① VISA. ⚹ BZ x
Meals 13.50 **t.** 🍷 9.50 – **59 rm** ⊐ 105.00/150.00 **t.**, 2 suites.

Topps without rest., 17 Regency Sq, BN1 2FG, ✆ (01273) 729334, *toppshotel@aol.com, Fax (01273) 203679* – |♦| TV. MC AE ① VISA JCB. ⚹ BZ a
14 rm ⊐ 69.00/129.00 **st.**

Blanch House, 17 Atlingworth St, BN2 1PL, ✆ (01273) 603504, *info@blanchhouse.co.uk, Fax (01273) 689813* – TV ✆. MC VISA CZ o
closed 23 December-7 January, minimum stay 2 nights at weekends – **Meals** *(closed Monday and lunch Tuesday-Thursday)* a la carte 23.00/38.00 **t.** 🍷 12.50 – **12 rm** ⊐ 80.00/230.00 **t.**

Nineteen without rest., 19 Broad St, BN2 1TJ, ✆ (01273) 675529, *info@hotelnineteen.co.uk, Fax (01273) 675531* – TV. MC VISA CZ z
minimum stay 2 nights at weekends – **7 rm** ⊐ 95.00/125.00 **st.**

Adelaide without rest., 51 Regency Sq, BN1 2FF, ✆ (01273) 205286, *adelaide@pavilion.co.uk, Fax (01273) 220904* – TV. MC AE ① VISA. ⚹ BZ z
closed 25 December – **12 rm** ⊐ 55.00/92.00 **t.**

Premier Lodge, 144 North St, BN1 1DN, ✆ (01273) 746833, *Fax (01273) 323878* – |♦| ⇆, ▤ rest, TV ♿ – 🎭 80. MC AE ① VISA CZ a
Meals (dinner only) a la carte approx. 12.45 **t.** 🍷 8.45 – **160 rm** 49.95 **t.**

Travelodge without rest., 165-167 Preston Rd, BN1 6AU, ✆ (01273) 550245, *Fax (01273) 554917* – |♦| ⇆ TV ♿ P. MC AE ① VISA JCB. ⚹ BV z
94 rm 59.95 **t.**

Allendale without rest., 3 New Steine, BN2 1PB, ✆ (01273) 675436, *Fax (01273) 602603* – ⇆ TV. MC VISA JCB CZ u
closed Christmas – **13 rm** ⊐ 35.00/80.00 **st.**

Arlanda without rest., 20 New Steine, BN2 1PD, ✆ (01273) 699300, *arlanda@brighton.co.uk, Fax (01273) 600930* – ⇆ TV. MC AE ① VISA JCB. ⚹ CZ x
closed 1 week Christmas – **14 rm** ⊐ 48.00/120.00 **t.**

Ainsley House without rest., 28 New Steine, BN2 1PD, ✆ (01273) 605310, *ahhotel@fastnet.co.uk, Fax (01273) 688604* – TV. MC AE ① VISA JCB. ⚹ CZ r
closed 1 week Christmas – **11 rm** ⊐ 33.00/80.00 **t.**

Amblecliff without rest., 35 Upper Rock Gdns, BN2 1QF, ✆ (01273) 681161, *amblecliff.brighton@virgin.net, Fax (01273) 676945* – ⇆ TV. MC AE VISA. ⚹ CZ s
8 rm ⊐ 50.00/80.00 **t.**

One Paston Place, 1 Paston Pl, Kemp Town, BN2 1HA, ✆ (01273) 606933, *Fax (01273) 675686* – ▤. MC AE ① VISA JCB CV a
closed first 2 weeks January, first 2 weeks August, Sunday and Monday – **Meals** 19.00 (lunch) and a la carte 38.50/43.00 **st.** 🍷 14.00.

Whytes, 33 Western St, BN1 2PG, ✆ (01273) 776618, *janthony@lineone.net* – ⇆. MC AE VISA JCB BZ u
closed 26-31 December, Sunday and Monday – **Meals** (booking essential) (dinner only) a la carte 21.95/24.00 **t.** 🍷 10.95.

La Marinade, 77 St Georges Rd, Kemp Town, BN2 1EF, ✆ (01273) 600992, *violavincent@yahoo.co.uk, Fax (01273) 600992* – ▤. MC AE ① VISA JCB CV c
closed 1 week in summer, 1 week in winter, Monday, Tuesday lunch and Sunday dinner – **Meals** - French - 13.00/21.00 **t.** 🍷 10.00.

BRIGHTON AND HOVE

Street	Grid	No.
Adelaide Crescent	AY	2
Brunswick Place	AY	3
Brunswick Square	AYZ	4
Carlton Terrace	AV	5
Chatham Place	BX	6
Churchill Square Shopping Centre	BYZ	
Denmark Road	BY	7
East Street	CZ	8
Eastern Road	CV	9
George Street	AV	10
Gladstone Terrace	CX	12
Gloucester Place	CY	13
Gloucester Road	CY	14
Goldsmid Road	BX	15
Grand Junction Road	CZ	16
Hollingbury Park Av	BV	17
Hollingdean Road	CV	18
Hove Street	AV	19
London Road	CX	
Market Place	CX	20
Marlborough Place	CY	21
Montpelier Place	BY	22
North Street	CZ	
Old Steine	CZ	23
Pavillon Parade	CZ	26
Richmond Place	CY	27
Richmond Terrace	CX	28
St. George's Place	CY	30
St. Peter's Place	CX	31
Terminus Road	BCX	32
Upper Lewes Road	CX	33
Warren Road	CV	37
Waterloo Place	CX	39
Wellington Road	AV	40
Western Road	ABY	
York Place	CY	42

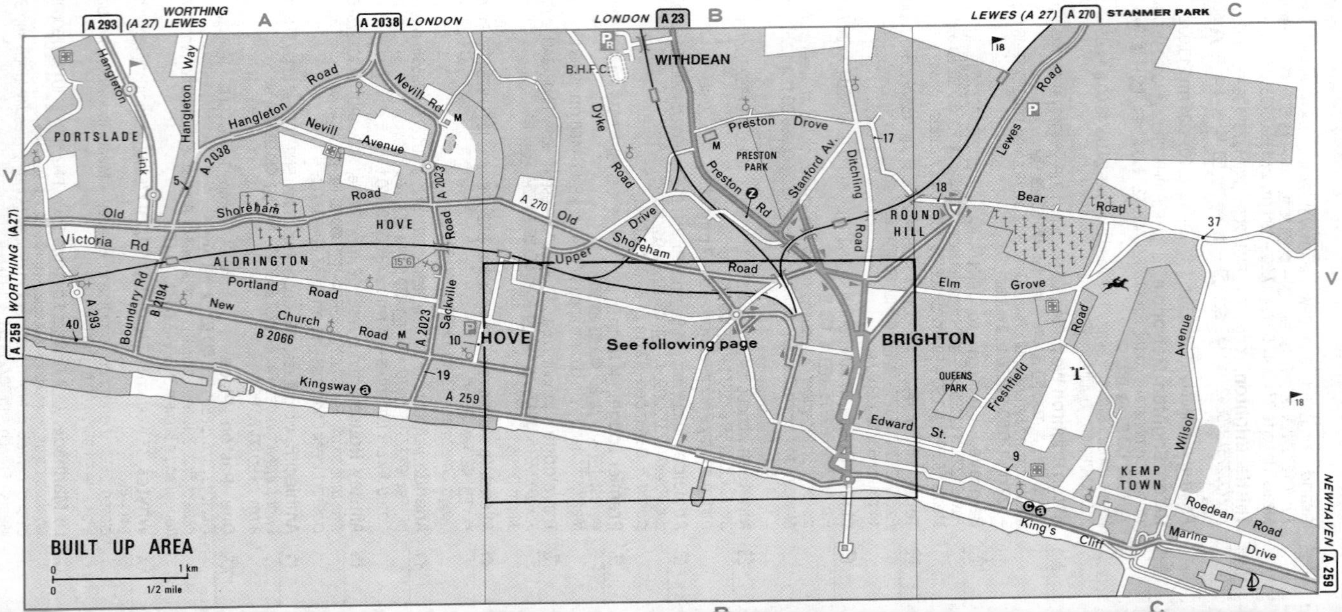

A 293 (A 27) WORTHING LEWES
A 2038 LONDON
LONDON A 23
LEWES (A 27) A 270 STANMER PARK
A B C
V
PORTSLADE
HOVE
ALDRINGTON
WITHDEAN
PRESTON PARK
ROUND HILL
BRIGHTON
QUEENS PARK
KEMP TOWN
B.H.F.C.
Hangleton Way
Hangleton Link
Hangleton Road
Nevill Rd
Nevill Avenue
Old Shoreham Road
Victoria Rd
Boundary Rd
Portland Road
New Church Road
B 2066
B 2194
A 2038
A 2023
A 293
A 270
Sackville Road
Kingsway
A 259
Dyke Road
Preston Drove
Preston Rd
Stanford Av.
Ditchling Road
Upper Shoreham Road
Drive
Lewes Road
Bear Road
Elm Grove
Freshfield Road
Wilson Avenue
Edward St.
King's Cliff
Roedean Road
Marine Drive
See following page
A 259 WORTHING (A27)
NEWHAVEN A 259
BUILT UP AREA
0 1 km
0 1/2 mile

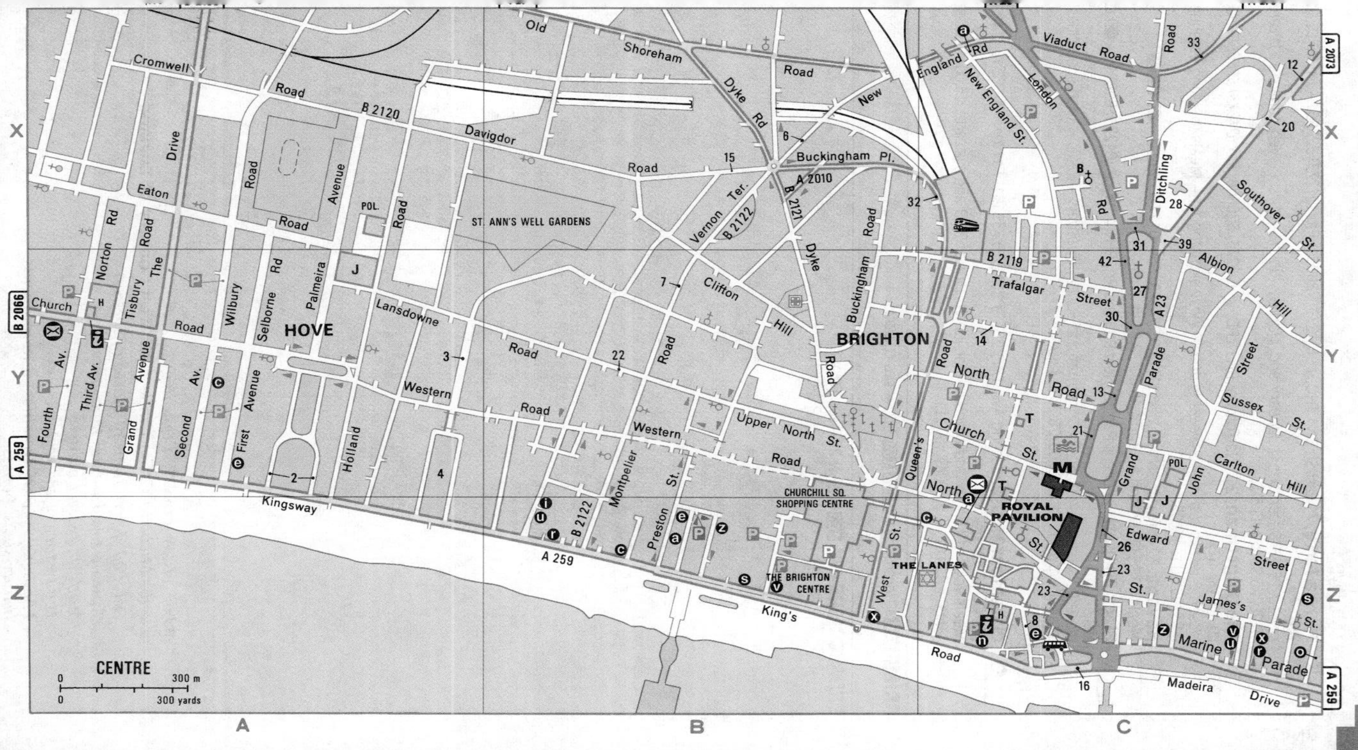

A 2073
A 259
B 2066
X
Y
Z
A
B
C
CENTRE
0 300 m
0 300 yards
BRIGHTON
HOVE
ROYAL PAVILION
THE LANES
CHURCHILL SQ. SHOPPING CENTRE
THE BRIGHTON CENTRE
ST. ANN'S WELL GARDENS
Kingsway
King's Road
Madeira Drive
Marine Parade
Grand Parade
James's St.
Edward Street
Carlton Hill
John St.
Sussex St.
Albion Hill
Southover St.
Ditchling Road
Viaduct Road
London Rd
New England St.
New England Rd
Trafalgar Street
North Road
Church St.
North St.
Queen's Road
West St.
Buckingham Road
Buckingham Pl.
Dyke Road
Dyke Rd
Clifton Hill
Vernon Ter.
Upper North St.
Western Road
Montpellier Road
Preston St.
Old Shoreham Road
Davigdor Road
Lansdowne Road
Holland Road
Palmeira Avenue
Selborne Rd
Wilbury Road
First Avenue
Second Av.
Grand Avenue
Third Av.
Fourth Av.
Cromwell Road
Eaton Road
The Drive
Tisbury Road
Norton Rd
Church Road
New Road
A 23
A 2010
B 2119
B 2121
B 2122
B 2120
POL.

Terre à Terre, 71 East St, BN1 1HQ, ✆ (01273) 729051, *Fax (01273) 327561* – ▤. MC AE ⓓ VISA JCB CZ
closed 25-26 December, 1 January and Monday lunch – **Meals** - Vegetarian - a la carte 19.20/26.90 **t.** 🍷 11.50.

The Gingerman, 21A Norfolk Sq, BN1 2PD, ✆ (01273) 326688, *Fax (01273) 326688* – MC AE ⓓ VISA JCB BZ
closed 2 weeks summer, 2 weeks winter, Sunday and Monday – **Meals** (booking essential) 9.95/23.50 **t.** 🍷 9.95.

Havana, 32 Duke St, BN1 1AG, ✆ (01273) 773388, *Fax (01273) 748923* – MC AE VISA CZ
Meals 19.95/29.95 and a la carte 16.40/38.95 **st.** 🍷 11.95.

Black Chapati, 12 Circus Par, off New England Rd, BN1 4GW, ✆ (01273) 699011 – MC AE VISA CX
closed 2 weeks July, 2 weeks Christmas and Sunday-Tuesday – **Meals** - Asian specialities - (dinner only) a la carte 22.05/28.25 **t.** 🍷 10.50.

at Hove.

Claremont House, Second Ave, BN3 2LL, ✆ (01273) 735161, *Fax (01273) 735161*, 🚗 - TV. MC AE ⓓ VISA AY
Meals *(closed Sunday and Monday)* (bar lunch)/dinner 9.50 and a la carte 13.00/18.50 **st.** 🍷 8.00 – **12 rm** ☕ 55.00/90.00 **st.**

BRIMFIELD *Herefordshire* 403 404 L 27 – *see Ludlow.*

BRIMSCOMBE *Glos.* 403 404 N 28 – *see Stroud.*

BRISTOL

403 404 M 29 *The West Country G.* – *pop. 407 992.*

London 121 – *Birmingham 91.*

TOURIST INFORMATION

St. Nicholas Church, St. Nicholas St. ☎ *(0117) 926 0767.*
Bristol Airport ☎ *(01275 47444).*

PRACTICAL INFORMATION

Mangotsfield, Carsons Rd ☎ *(0117) 956 5501,* **BV**.
Beggar Bush Lane, Failand, Clifton ☎ *(01275) 393117,* **AX**.
Knowle, Fairway, West Town Lane, Brislington ☎ *(0117) 977 6341,* **BX**.
Long Ashton, Clarken Coombe ☎ *(01275) 392229,* **AX**.
Stockwood Vale, Stockwood Lane, Keynsham ☎ *(0117) 986 6505,* **BX**.
Severn Bridge (toll).
Bristol Airport : ☎ *(01275) 474444, SW : 7 m. by A 38* **AX**.

SIGHTS

See : *City*★★ – *St. Mary Redcliffe*★★ **DZ** – *Brandon Hill*★★ **AX** – *Georgian House*★★ **AX K** – *Harbourside Industrial Museum*★★ **CZ M3** – *SS Great Britain*★★ *AC* **AX S2** – *The Old City*★ **CYZ** : *Theatre Royal*★★ **CZ T** – *Merchant Seamen's Almshouses*★ **CZ Q** – *St. Stephen's City*★ **CY S1** – *St. John the Baptist*★ **CY** – *College Green*★ **CYZ** *(Bristol Cathedral*★, *Lord Mayor's Chapel*★*)* – *City Museum and Art Gallery*★ **AX M1.**

Env. : *Clifton*★★ **AX** *(Suspension Bridge*★★ *(toll), R.C. Cathedral of St. Peter and St. Paul*★★ **F1**, *Bristol Zoological Gardens*★★ *AC, Village*★*)* – *Blaise Hamlet*★★ – *Blaise Castle House Museum*★, *NW : 5 m. by A 4018 and B 4057* **AV**.

Exc. : *Bath*★★★, *SE : 13 m. by A 4* **BX** – *Chew Magna*★ *(Stanton Drew Stone Circles*★ *AC) S : 8 m. by A 37* – **BX** – *and B 3130* – *Clevedon*★ *(Clevedon Court*★ *AC,* ≤★*) W : 11½ m. by A 370, B 3128* – **AX** – *and B 3130.*

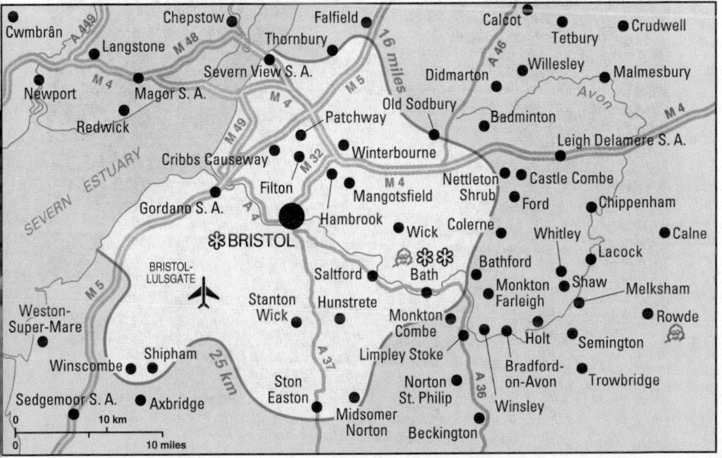

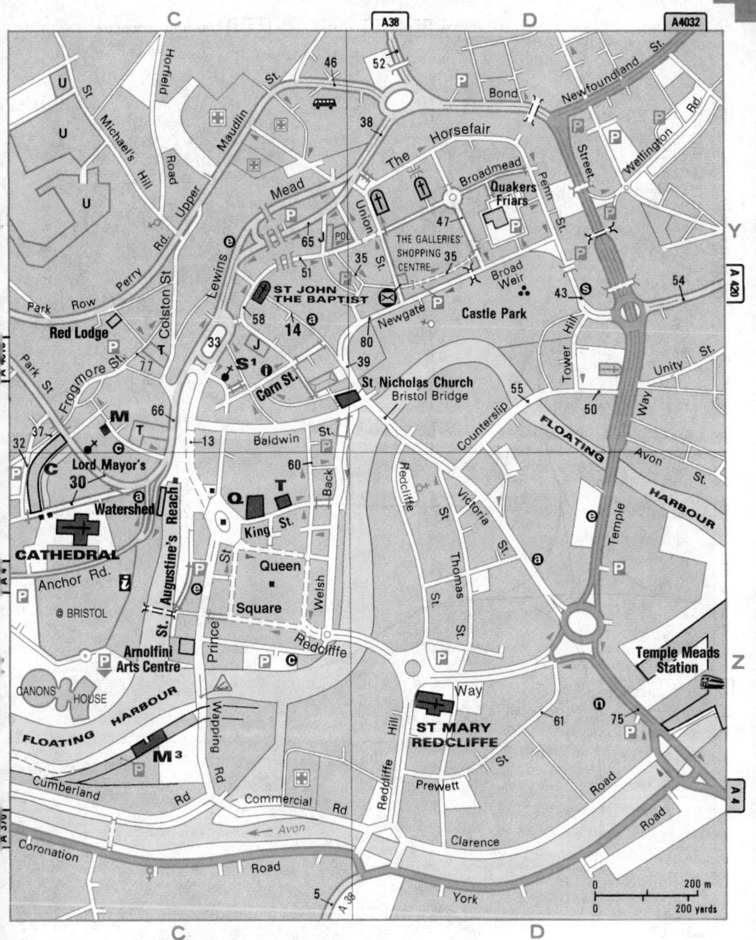

STREET INDEX TO BRISTOL TOWN PLANS

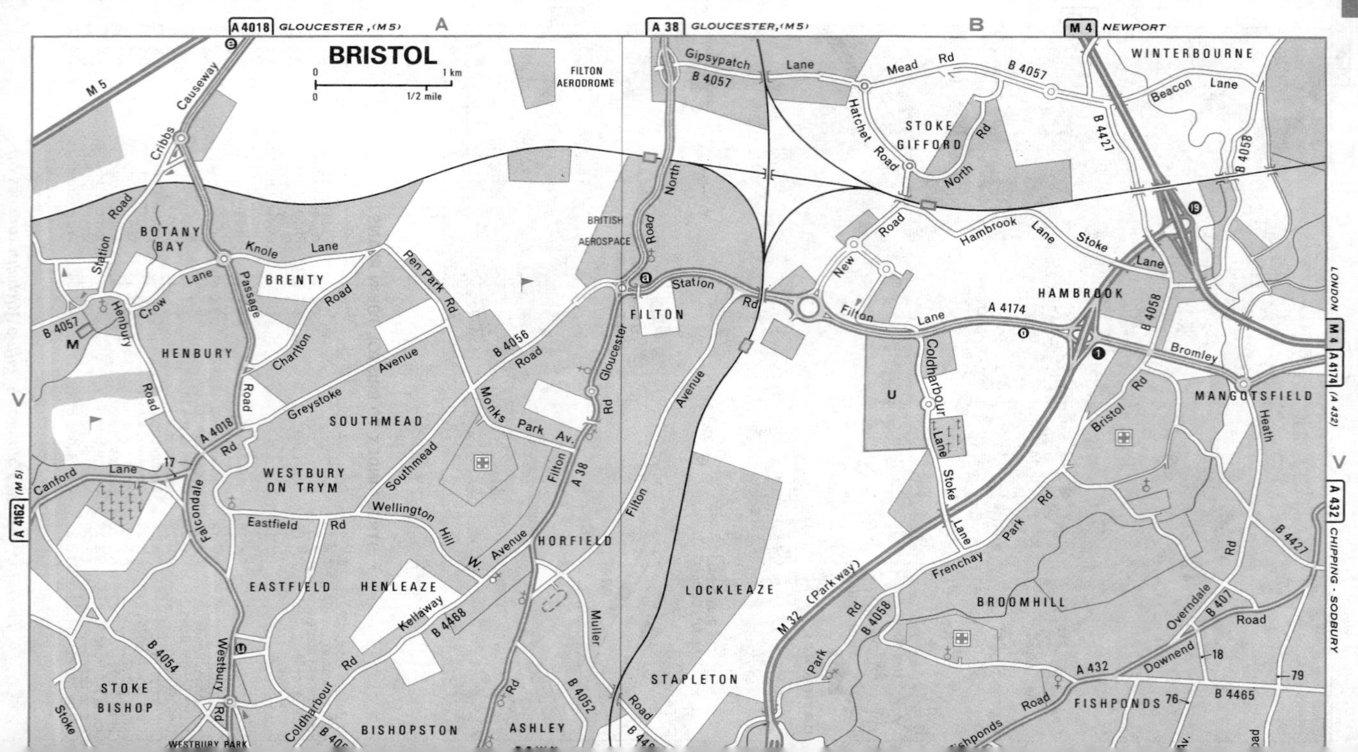

A 4018 GLOUCESTER, (M5)
A
A 38 GLOUCESTER, (M5)
B
M 4 NEWPORT
BRISTOL
0 1 km
0 1/2 mile
FILTON AERODROME
M 5
Cribbs Causeway
Station Road
BOTANY BAY
Knole Lane
Crow Lane
Passage Road
BRENTY
Henbury Road
B 4057
M
HENBURY
Charlton Road
Pen Park Rd
Greystoke Avenue
A 4018 Rd
SOUTHMEAD
Canford Lane
17
A 4162 (M 5)
Falcondale
WESTBURY ON TRYM
Southmead
Eastfield Rd
Wellington Hill
W. Avenue
EASTFIELD
HENLEAZE
Kellaway
B 4468
B 4054
Westbury Rd
STOKE BISHOP
Stoke
WESTBURY PARK
Coldharbour Rd
BISHOPSTON
ASHLEY
B 4052
Muller
Rd
HORFIELD
Filton A 38
Monks Park Av.
B 4056 Road
Gloucester Rd
BRITISH AEROSPACE
North Road
Gipsypatch Lane
B 4057
Station Rd
FILTON
Filton Avenue
LOCKLEAZE
STAPLETON
Road
Mead Rd
Hatchet Road
STOKE GIFFORD
North Rd
B 4427
WINTERBOURNE
Beacon Lane
B 4058
New Road
Hambrook Lane
Stoke Lane
Filton Lane
A 4174
HAMBROOK
B 4058
Bromley
U
Coldharbour Lane
Stoke Lane
Bristol Rd
MANGOTSFIELD
Heath
LONDON M 4 A 4174 (A 432)
A 432 CHIPPING - SODBURY
B 4427
Rd
Frenchay Park Rd
M 32 (Parkway)
Park Rd
B 4058
BROOMHILL
Overndale
B 407
Road
Downend
18
79
A 432
FISHPONDS
76
B 4465
Road
Fishponds

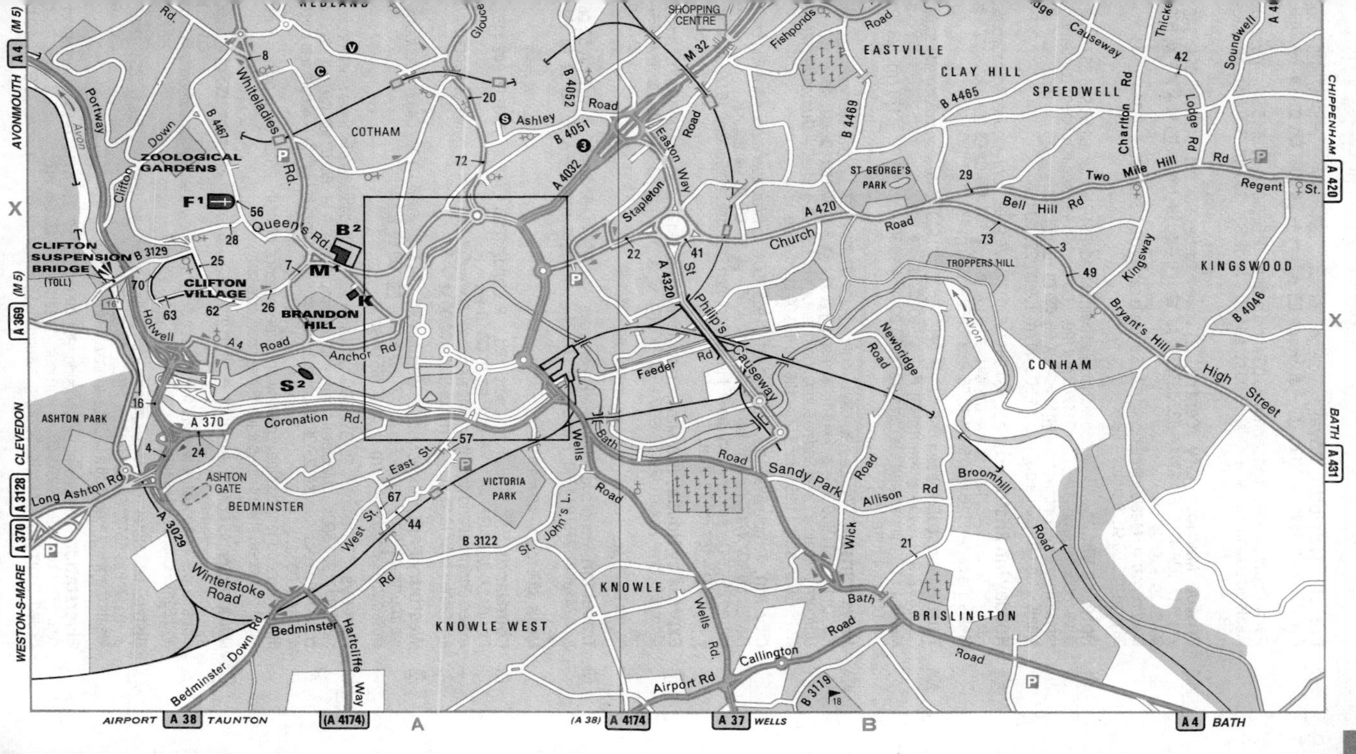

AVONMOUTH A 4 (M 5)
A 369 (M 5)
CLEVEDON A 3128
A 370 WESTON-S-MARE
CHIPPENHAM A 420
BATH A 431
AIRPORT A 38 TAUNTON
(A 4174)
A
(A 38) A 4174
A 37 WELLS
B
A 4 BATH
Portway
Avon
Clifton Down
B 4467
Whiteladies Rd.
COTHAM
ZOOLOGICAL GARDENS
F¹
Queen's Rd.
B²
M¹
K
CLIFTON SUSPENSION BRIDGE (TOLL)
B 3129
CLIFTON VILLAGE
BRANDON HILL
Hotwell
A 4 Road
Anchor Rd
S²
ASHTON PARK
A 370
Coronation Rd.
Long Ashton Rd
ASHTON GATE
BEDMINSTER
A 3029
Winterstoke Road
Bedminster Down Rd
Bedminster
Hartcliffe Way
East St.
West St.
Rd
VICTORIA PARK
B 3122
St. John's L.
KNOWLE WEST
KNOWLE
Wells Road
Wells Rd.
Airport Rd
Callington
Road
B 3119
Bath
BRISLINGTON
Wick Road
Sandy Park Road
Allison Rd
Broomhill Road
Newbridge Road
Avon
CONHAM
Feeder Rd
Philip's Causeway
A 4320
St
Stapleton Road
Easton Way
Road
B 4052
B 4051
A 4032
Ashley
Glouce
SHOPPING CENTRE
M 32
Fishponds Road
EASTVILLE
CLAY HILL
B 4469
B 4465
SPEEDWELL
Causeway
Charlton Rd
Lodge Rd
Soundwell
ST GEORGE'S PARK
A 420
Church Road
Bell Hill Rd
Two Mile Hill
Rd
Regent St.
TROPPERS HILL
Kingsway
KINGSWOOD
B 4046
Bryant's Hill
High Street

ENGLAND

Bristol Marriott Royal, College Green, BS1 5TA, (0117) 925 5100 *Fax (0117) 925 1515*, – 300.
CZ a
Palm Court : **Meals** (dinner only) 25.00 and a la carte 18.50/38.00 **st.** 13.50 – ***Terrace*** : **Meals** 20.00 and a la carte 20.00/35.00 **st.** 13.50 – 12.50 – **230 rm** 190.00 **st.**, 12 suites – SB.

Bristol Marriott City Centre, 2 Lower Castle St, Old Market, BS1 3AD, (0117) 929 4281, *Fax (0117) 922 5838*, rm, – 600.
DY s
Mediterrano : **Meals** (dinner only) 17.95 and a la carte 20.00/30.50 **st.** 13.50 – 13.00 – **281 rm** 125.00 **st.**, 8 suites – SB.

Hotel du Vin, The Sugar House, Narrow Lewins Mead, BS1 2NU, (0117) 925 5577, *info@bristol.hotelduvin.com, Fax (0117) 925 1199*, « Converted 18C sugar refinery, contemporary wine themed interior » – – 85. CY e
Meals – (see ***Bistro*** below) – 11.50 – **40 rm** 109.00/225.00 **t.**

Holiday Inn Bristol, Victoria St, BS1 6HY, (0117) 976 9988, *cbbhi@queensmoat.co.uk, Fax (0117) 925 5040*, – rm, rest, – 180. DZ a
Meals a la carte 17.95/26.75 **t.** 12.95 – 11.50 – **128 rm** 134.00/210.00 **st.**

Thistle Bristol, Broad St, BS1 2EL, (0117) 929 1645, *bristol@thistle.co.uk, Fax (0117) 922 7619* – rm, – 550. CY a
Meals 24.00 (dinner) and a la carte 22.00/33.00 **st.** 13.50 – 11.00 – **178 rm** 128.00/141.00 **st.**, 4 suites – SB.

Jurys Bristol, Prince St, BS1 4QF, (0117) 923 0333, *bristol@jurysdoyle.com, Fax (0117) 923 0300*, – rm, rest, – 300. CZ e
Unicorn : **Meals** *(closed Friday-Sunday)* (dinner only) 29.50 **st.** 11.95 – ***Quayside :*** **Meals** 12.95/20.95 **st.** 11.95 – 9.50 – **186 rm** 135.00 **st.**, 1 suite.

City Inn, Temple Way, BS1 6BF, (0117) 925 1001, *bristol.reservations@cityinn.com Fax (0117) 907 4116*, – rm, – 50. DZ e
closed 25-26 December – ***City Café :*** **Meals** (bar lunch Saturday and Sunday) 16.00/30.00 **st** – 10.50 – **167 rm** 79.00 **st.**

Express by Holiday Inn without rest., Templegate, BS1 6PL, (01179) 304800, *bristol@hmi.uk.com, Fax (01179) 304900* – – 30.
DZ n
96 rm 61.75 **st.**

Travel Inn, Hengrove Leisure Park, Hengrove Way, BS14 0HR, South : 4 m. by A 37 off A 4174 (01275) 834340, *Fax (01275) 834721* – rm, rest, .
Meals (grill rest.) – **40 rm** 41.95 **t.**

Courtlands, 1 Redland Court Rd, Redland, BS6 7EE, (0117) 942 4432, *Fax (0117) 923 2432*, – rest, . AX v
closed Christmas and New Year – **Meals** *(closed Friday-Sunday)* (dinner only) (residents only) a la carte 11.55/18.05 **st.** – **25 rm** 52.00/62.00 **st.**

Westbury Park without rest., 37 Westbury Rd, BS9 3AU, (0117) 962 0465, *reception@westburypark-hotel.co.uk, Fax (0117) 962 8607* – . AV u
closed 25 December – **8 rm** 45.00/55.00 **st.**

Harveys, 12 Denmark St, BS1 5DQ, (0117) 927 5034, *danielgalmiche@adswnet.com, Fax (0117) 927 5003*, « Medieval cellars and wine museum » – . CY c
closed 2 weeks August, 25-26 December, Sunday and Saturday lunch – **Meals** a la carte 40.00/53.00 **st.** 14.00
Spec. Sautéed langoustine, cauliflower purée, essence of crab. Roast farm pigeon with sauté potatoes, sherry vinegar jus. Bitter chocolate tart.

Markwicks, 43 Corn St, BS1 1HT, (0117) 926 2658, *Fax (0117) 926 2658* –
CY
closed 2 weeks August, 1 week Easter, 1 week Christmas-New Year, Sunday, Saturday lunch and Bank Holidays – **Meals** a la carte 26.75/33.20 **t.** 12.50.

Bistro (at Hotel du Vin), The Sugar House, Narrow Lewins Mead, BS1 2NU, (0117) 925 5577, *Fax (0117) 925 1199* – CY e
Meals (booking essential) a la carte approx. 28.25 **t.** 11.50.

Riverstation, The Grove, Harbourside, BS1 4RB, (0117) 914 4434, *relax@riverstation.co.uk, Fax (0117) 934 9990*, , « Harbourside setting » – CZ c
closed Christmas – **Meals** (booking essential) 13.75 (lunch) and a la carte 23.00/32.00 **t.** 10.50.

Bell's Diner, 1 York Rd, Montpelier, BS6 5QB, (0117) 924 0357, *info@bellsdiner.co.uk, Fax (0117) 924 4280* – . AE VISA JCB AX s
closed 24-30 December, Monday lunch and Sunday – **Meals** 16.95 and a la carte 21.50/29.50 **t.** 10.00.

Red Snapper, 1 Chandos Rd, Redland, BS6 6PG, (0117) 973 7999, *redsnapper@cix.co.uk, Fax (0117) 973 7999* – AE VISA JCB AX c
closed 25 December-3 January, Sunday dinner and Monday lunch – **Meals** 14.00 (lunch) and dinner a la carte 22.75/28.75 **t.** 9.50.

at Filton *North : 4½ m. on A 38 – Bristol.*

Premier Lodge, Shield Retail Park, Gloucester Road North, BS12 7AA, on A 4174 (eastbound carriageway) (0117) 979 1011, *Fax (0870) 700 1337* – rm, rest, TV P. AE VISA. BV a
Meals (grill rest.) a la carte approx. 17.00 **t.** 9.85 – **61 rm** 49.95 **t.**

at Patchway *(South Gloucestershire) North : 6½ m. on A 38* – BV – *Bristol.*

Aztec, Aztec West Business Park, BS12 4TS, North : 1 m. by A 38 (01454) 201090, *aztec@shireinns.co.uk, Fax (01454) 201593*, squash – rm, TV P – 200. AE VISA
Meals *(closed lunch Saturday and Sunday)* a la carte 27.75/35.00 **st.** 13.45 – **125 rm** 149.00/169.00 **st.**, 3 suites – SB.

Hilton Bristol, Woodlands Lane, BS32 4JF, North : 1 m. by A 38 (01454) 201144, *res.manager@bristol.stakis.co.uk, Fax (01454) 612022*, – rest, TV P – 200. AE VISA
Meals *(closed lunch Saturday and Bank Holidays)* (carvery) 15.95/17.95 and dinner a la carte 20.15/28.85 **t.** 12.30 – 11.95 – **141 rm** 170.00/180.00 **st.** – SB.

at Cribbs Causeway *North : 6¾ m. on A 4018 – Bristol.*

Travelodge without rest., BS10 7TL, on A 4018 (northbound carriageway) ¼ m. before junction 17 of M 4 (0117) 501530, *Fax (0117) 501530* – TV P. AE VISA JCB. AV e
56 rm 52.95 **t.**

at Hambrook *(South Gloucestershire) Northeast : 5½ m. by M 32 on A 4174 – Bristol.*

Holiday Inn Bristol North, Filton Rd, BS16 1QX, (0870) 400 9014, *Fax (0117) 956 9735*, – rm, rest, TV P – 250. AE VISA BV o
Meals *(closed Saturday lunch)* 12.95 (lunch) and a la carte 15.00/19.50 **st.** 11.95 – 11.95 – **194 rm** 127.00 **t.**, 4 suites – SB.

at Mangotsfield *Northeast : 5¾ m. by M 32 on A 4174* – BV – *Bristol.*

Travel Inn, 200-202 Westerleigh Rd, Emersons Green, BS16 7AN, East : ¾ m. off A 4174 (0117) 956 4755, *Fax (0117) 956 4644* – rm, TV P. AE VISA
Meals (grill rest.) – **40 rm** 41.95 **t.**

at Winterbourne *(South Gloucestershire) Northeast : 7½ m. by M 32 and A 4174 on B 4058* – BV – *Bristol.*

Grange H. & Country Club, Northwoods, BS36 1RP, Northwest : 2 m. by B 4057 on B 4427 (Rudgeway rd) (01454) 777333, *Fax (01454) 777447*, – TV P – 150. AE VISA
Meals *(closed Saturday lunch)* a la carte 17.25/28.75 **st.** 11.75 – 10.95 – **68 rm** 130.00/140.00 – SB.

at Wick *East : 7½ m. on A 420* – BX – *Bristol.*

Tracy Park Golf & Country Club, Bath Rd, BS30 5RN, Southeast : 1 m. on Lansdown rd (0117) 937 2251, *hotel@tracypark.com, Fax (0117) 937 4288*, « Part Georgian manor house », squash – TV P – 120. VISA.
Cavaliers Kitchen : **Meals** 15.95/17.95 and dinner a la carte 21.40/37.50 **st.** 9.95 – **18 rm** 55.00/110.00 **st.** – SB.

at Saltford *(Bath & North East Somerset) Southeast : 7½ m. on A 4* – BX – *Bristol.*

Brunel's Tunnel House, High St, BS31 3BQ, off Beech Rd (01225) 873873, *info@brunelstunnelhouse.com, Fax (01225) 874875*, – TV P. AE VISA JCB.
closed 1 week Christmas and New Year – **Meals** (by arrangement) (residents only) (dinner only) 16.50/18.00 **st.** 8.50 – **8 rm** 56.00/66.00 **st.**

at Hunstrete *(Bath & North East Somerset) Southeast : 10 m. by A 4 and A 37* – BX – *off A 368 – Bristol.*

Hunstrete House, BS39 4NS, (01761) 490490, *info@hunstretehouse.co.uk, Fax (01761) 490732*, « Late 17C country house, gardens and deer park », heated, – TV P – 40. AE VISA JCB.
Meals 15.95/19.95 (lunch) and a la carte 44.50/49.00 **t.** 14.95 – **20 rm** 135.00/195.00 **t.**, 2 suites – SB.

at Stanton Wick *(Bath & North East Somerset) South : 9 m. by A 37 – BX – and A 368 on Stanton Wick rd – ✉ Bristol.*

Carpenters Arms, BS39 4BX, ☎ (01761) 490202, *carpenters@dial.pipex.com, Fax (01761) 490763* – TV P. MC AE ① VISA. ✳
Meals a la carte 14.95/24.40 **t.** 9.55 – **12 rm** 62.00/84.50 **t.** – SB.

BRITWELL SALOME *Oxon. – pop. 187.*

London 75 – Oxford 21 – Reading 19.

The Goose, OX49 5LG, ☎ (01491) 612304, *Fax (01491) 614822,* – ✈ P. MC VISA
closed Monday and Sunday dinner – **Meals** 21.00/26.00 (dinner) and lunch a la carte 23.00/35.00 **t.** 11.50.

BRIXHAM *Devon* 403 J 32 *The West Country G. – pop. 15 865.*

Env. : *Berry Head* (≤***) NE : 1½ m.*
The Old Market House, The Quay ☎ (01803) 852861.
London 230 – Exeter 30 – Plymouth 32 – Torquay 8.

Berry Head ⛵, Berry Head Rd, TQ5 9AJ, ☎ (01803) 853225, *berryhd@aol.com, Fax (01803) 882084,* ≤ Torbay, ⬛, – ✈ rest, TV P – 300. MC AE VISA
Meals 12.00/21.00 and a la carte 16.00/26.50 **st.** 8.50 – **32 rm** 45.00/140.00 **st.** – SB.

Quayside, 41 King St, TQ5 9TJ, ☎ (01803) 855751, *quayside.hotel@virgin.net, Fax (01803) 882733,* ≤ – ✈ rest, TV P. MC AE ① VISA JCB
Meals (bar lunch)/dinner a la carte 14.00/22.50 **t.** 10.00 – **30 rm** 52.00/94.00 **t.** – SB.

BROAD CAMPDEN *Glos. – see Chipping Campden.*

BROADHEMBURY *Devon* 403 K 31 – *pop. 617* – ✉ *Honiton.*

London 191 – Exeter 17 – Honiton 5 – Taunton 23.

Drewe Arms, EX14 3NF, ☎ (01404) 841267, *drewe.arms@btinternet.com, Fax (01404) 841765,* « Part 13C thatched inn », – P. MC VISA
closed Sunday dinner – **Meals** - Seafood - 27.25 **t.** 11.50.

BROADWAY *Worcs.* 403 404 O 27 *Great Britain G. – pop. 2 328.*

See : *Town*.*
Env. : *Country Park (Broadway Tower ✳**), SE : 2 m. by A 44 – Snowshill Manor* (Terrace Garden*) AC, S : 2½ m.*
1 Cotswold Court ☎ (01386) 852937.
London 93 – Birmingham 36 – Cheltenham 15 – Worcester 22.

The Lygon Arms, High St, WR12 7DU, ☎ (01386) 852255, *info@the_lygon_arms.co.uk, Fax (01386) 858611,* , « Part 16C inn », ⬛, – ✈ rest, TV P – 80. MC AE ① VISA JCB
The Restaurant : **Meals** (bar lunch Monday to Friday)/dinner 39.50/42.50 and a la carte 39.00/51.25 **t.** 15.95 – (see also ***Oliver's*** below) – 16.50 – **65 rm** 135.00/229.00 **t.**, 4 suites – SB.

The Broadway, The Green, WR12 7AA, ☎ (01386) 852401, *bookings@cotswold-inns-hotels.co.uk, Fax (01386) 853879,* « Part 15C », – ✈ TV P. MC AE ① VISA JCB
Meals 12.50/21.95 **st.** 10.95 – **20 rm** 73.50/118.00 **st.** – SB.

Barn House without rest., 152 High St, WR12 7AJ, ☎ (01386) 858633, *Fax (01386) 858633,* « 17C », ⬛, – ✈ TV P
3 rm 35.00/75.00 **st.**, 1 suite.

Windrush House, Station Rd, WR12 7DE, ☎ (01386) 853577, *richard@broadway-windrush.co.uk,* – ✈ TV P
Meals 16.00 **st.** 10.00 **5 rm** 45.00/65.00 **st.**

Whiteacres without rest., Station Rd, WR12 7DE, ☎ (01386) 852320, *whiteacres@btinternet.com* – ✈ TV P. ✳
closed 25-26 December – **5 rm** 40.00/58.00 **st.**

The Olive Branch without rest., 78 High St, WR12 7AJ, ☎ (01386) 853440, *broadway@theolive-branch.co.uk, Fax (01386) 859070* – ✈ TV P. MC VISA JCB
8 rm 50.00/70.00 **st.**

Oliver's, High St, WR12 7DU, ☎ (01386) 854418, *info@the-lygon-arms.co.uk, Fax (01386) 858611,* « 16C » – ✈ P. MC AE ① VISA JCB
Meals (booking essential) a la carte 17.65/27.80 **t.** 12.50.

at Willersey Hill *(Glos.) East : 2 m. by A 44 – ✉ Broadway.*

Dormy House, WR12 7LF, ✆ (01386) 852711, *reservations@dormyhouse.co.uk, Fax (01386) 858636,* – rest, – 180. *closed 24-26 December* – ***Tapestries :*** **Meals** (dinner only and Sunday lunch)/dinner 32.50 and a la carte 34.00/41.00 **t.** 16.00 – ***Barn Owl :*** **Meals** a la carte 16.40/20.85 **t.** 12.95 – **45 rm** 113.00/162.00 **t.**, 3 suites – SB.

at Buckland *(Glos.) Southwest : 2 ¼ m. by B 4632 – ✉ Broadway.*

Buckland Manor, WR12 7LY, ✆ (01386) 852626, *buckland-manor-uk@msn.com, Fax (01386) 853557,* « Part 13C manor house in extensive gardens », heated, – rest,
Meals (booking essential to non-residents) 28.50/45.50 **t.** 15.50 – **13 rm** 205.00/350.00 **t.** – SB.

BROCKDISH *Norfolk* 404 X 26 – *see Diss.*

BROCKENHURST *Hants.* 403 404 P 31 *Great Britain G. – pop. 3 048.*

Env. : *New Forest★★ (Rhinefield Ornamental Drive★★, Bolderwood Ornamental Drive★★).*

Brockenhurst Manor, Sway Rd ✆ (01590) 623332.

London 99 – Bournemouth 17 – Southampton 14 – Winchester 27.

Rhinefield House, Rhinefield Rd, SO42 7QB, Northwest : 3 m. ✆ (01590) 622922, *rhinefield-house@arcadianhotels.co.uk, Fax (01590) 622800,* « Victorian country mansion, formal gardens », heated, – – 120. ***Armada :*** **Meals** 17.95/27.50 and dinner a la carte 36.50/41.00 **t.** 14.50 – **34 rm** 100.00/150.00 **t.** – SB.

New Park Manor, Lyndhurst Rd, SO42 7QH, North : 1 ½ m. on A 337 ✆ (01590) 623467, *enquiries@newparkmanorhotel.co.uk, Fax (01590) 622268,* heated, – – 150. ***Stag :*** **Meals** a la carte 14.00/31.00 **t.** 14.80 – **24 rm** 85.00/170.00 **t.**

Careys Manor, Lyndhurst Rd, SO42 7RH, on A 337 ✆ (01590) 623551, *careysmanorhotel@btinternet.com, Fax (01590) 622799,* – – 100. **Meals** 15.95/24.50 **t.** 12.95 – ***Blaireau's*** *(✆ (01590) 623032)* **: Meals** - French - 8.95/13.95 **t.** 10.25 – **78 rm** 89.00/179.00 **t.**, 1 suite – SB.

Whitley Ridge, Beaulieu Rd, SO42 7QL, East : 1 m. on B 3055 ✆ (01590) 622354, *whitleyridge@brockenhurst.co.uk, Fax (01590) 622856,* « Part Georgian », – rest, **Meals** (bar lunch Monday-Saturday)/dinner 24.50/26.00 and a la carte 27.50/30.50 **st.** 10.50 – **14 rm** 70.00/140.00 – SB.

Cloud, Meerut Rd, SO42 7TD, ✆ (01590) 622165, *enquiries@cloudhotel.co.uk, Fax (01590) 622818,* – rest, *closed 27 December-10 January* – **Meals** 8.25/22.00 **t.** 8.95 – **18 rm** 63.00/126.00 **t.** – SB.

The Cottage without rest., Sway Rd, SO42 7SH, ✆ (01590) 622296, *100604.22@compuserve.com, Fax (01590) 623014,* – *March-November* – **7 rm** 55.00/95.00 **st.**

Simply Poussin, The Courtyard, rear of 49-51 Brookley Rd, SO42 7RB, ✆ (01590) 623063, *sales@simplypoussin.co.uk, Fax (01590) 623144* – *closed 25-26 December, Sunday and Monday* – **Meals** (booking essential) 15.00/20.00 and a la carte 15.00/31.00 **t.** 9.95.

Thatched Cottage with rm, 16 Brookley Rd, SO42 7RR, ✆ (01590) 623090, *sales@thatchedcottage.co.uk, Fax (01590) 623479,* « 17C farmhouse » – rest, *closed 4 January-10 February* – **Meals** *(closed Sunday dinner and Monday)* (booking essential) (light lunch)/dinner 35.00 and a la carte 33.50/46.50 **t.** 15.00 – **5 rm** 90.00/170.00 **st.** – SB.

at Sway *Southwest : 3 m. by B 3055 – ✉ Lymington.*

String of Horses Country House, Mead End Rd, SO41 6EH, ✆ (01590) 682631, *relax@stringofhorses.co.uk, Fax (01590) 682911,* heated, – rest, **Meals** *(closed Sunday dinner)* (dinner only and Sunday lunch)/dinner 25.00 and a la carte 26.00/37.00 **t.** 13.00 – **8 rm** 73.00/124.00 **t.** – SB.

The Nurse's Cottage, Station Rd, SO41 6BA, ✆ (01590) 683402, *nurses.cottage@lineone.net, Fax (01590) 683402,* – *closed 2 weeks March and 3 weeks November* – **Meals** (dinner only and Sunday lunch)/dinner 20.65 **t.** 8.30 – **3 rm** 60.00/100.00 **t.** – SB.

BROCKWORTH *Glos.* 404 N 28 – *see Cheltenham.*

BROMBOROUGH *Mersey.* 402 403 L 24 – *pop. 14 518* – ✉ *Wirral.*
Raby Hall Rd ℘ (0151) 334 2155.
London 210 – Chester 14 – Liverpool 6 – Manchester 46.

The Village H. & Leisure Club, Pool Lane, CH62 4UE, on A 41 ℘ (0151) 643 1616, *village.bromborough@village-hotels.com, Fax (0151) 643 1420,* squash – rest, – 150. AE VISA
Meals a la carte 12.95/22.95 **s.** 7.75 – **93 rm** 94.00/109.00 **st.**

Travel Inn, High St, CH62 7HZ, ℘ (0151) 334 2917, *Fax (0151) 334 0443* – rm, – 70. AE VISA.
Meals (grill rest.) – **32 rm** 41.95 **t.**

BROME *Suffolk* 404 X 26 – *see Diss (Norfolk).*

BROMFIELD *Shrops.* 403 L 26 – *see Ludlow.*

BROMLEY CROSS *Gtr. Manchester* 402 404 M 23 – *see Bolton.*

BROMSGROVE *Worcs.* 403 404 N 26 – *pop. 26 366.*
Bromsgrove Museum, 26 Birmingham Rd ℘ (01527) 831809.
London 117 – Birmingham 14 – Bristol 71 – Worcester 13.

Hilton Bromsgrove, Birmingham Rd, B61 0JB, North : 2 ½ m. on A 38 ℘ (0121) 447 7888, *reservations@bromsgrove.stakis.co.uk, Fax (0121) 447 7273,* – rm, rest, – 250. AE VISA
Meals *(closed Saturday lunch)* (carvery lunch) 13.95 (lunch) and dinner a la carte 17.00/23.85 **st.** 14.30 – 12.50 – **146 rm** 110.00/130.00 **st.**, 2 suites – SB.

Hanover International H. & Club, 85 Kidderminster Rd, B61 9AB, West : 1 m. on A 448 ℘ (01527) 576600, *enquiries-hanover-bromsgrove@virgin.net, Fax (01527) 878981,* – rest, – 200. AE VISA
closed 27-30 December – **Meals** (closed Saturday lunch) 19.50 (dinner) and a la carte 14.70/29.70 **st.** 12.00 – 11.95 – **113 rm** 130.00/150.00 **t.**, 1 suite – SB.

Grafton Manor, Grafton Lane, B61 7HA, Southwest : 1 ¾ m. by Worcester Rd ℘ (01527) 579007, *steven@grafton.u-net.com, Fax (01527) 575221,* « 16C and 18C manor », – rest, AE VISA.
Meals *(closed Bank Holidays and Saturday lunch)* (lunch by arrangement) 20.50/27.85 **st.** 13.20 – **7 rm** 85.00/150.00 **st.**, 2 suites – SB.

Bromsgrove Country, 249 Worcester Rd, Stoke Heath, B61 7JA, Southwest : 2 m. ℘ (01527) 835522, *Fax (01527) 871257,* – VISA.
closed December – **Meals** (residents only) (dinner only) a la carte approx. 13.00 **st.** 12.00 – 7.00 – **7 rm** 49.00/55.00 **st.**

BROMYARD *Herefordshire* 403 404 M 27 – *pop. 3 117.*
T.I.C. & Heritage Centre, 1 Rowberry St ℘ (01432) 262082.
London 138 – Hereford 15 – Leominster 13 – Worcester 14.

Granary, Church House Farm, Collington, HR7 4NA, North : 4 ¼ m. by B 4214, Edvin Loach rd and Ripplewood rd ℘ (01885) 410345, *Fax (01885) 410555,* « Working farm », –
Meals (by arrangement) 18.75 **t.** 7.00 – **5 rm** 22.50/50.00 **t.**

at Acton Green *Southeast : 4 ¾ m. by A 44 on B 4220 – ✉ Bromyard.*

Hidelow House, Acton Beauchamp, WR6 5AH, South : ¼ m. ℘ (01886) 884547, *mg@hidelow.co.uk, Fax (01886) 884060,* – .
closed 25-26 December – **Meals** (by arrangement) (communal dining) 15.50 **st.** – **3 rm** 31.50/53.00 **st**

BROOK *Hants.* 403 404 P 31 – ✉ *Lyndhurst.*
London 92 – Bournemouth 24 – Southampton 14.

Bell Inn, SO43 7HE, ℘ (023) 8081 2214, *bell@bramshaw.co.uk, Fax (023) 8081 3958,* – – 40. AE VISA.
Meals (bar lunch Monday to Saturday)/dinner 26.50/32.50 **st.** 12.50 – **25 rm** 60.00/80.00 **st.** – SB.

BROUGHTON *Lancs.* 402 L 22 – *see Preston.*

BROXTED *Essex* 404 U 28 – *see Stansted Airport.*

BROXTON *Ches.* 402 403 L 24 – *pop. 417.*
London 197 – Birmingham 68 – Chester 12 – Manchester 44 – Stoke-on-Trent 29.

De Vere Carden Park, CH3 9DQ, West : 1 ½ m. on A 534 (01829) 731000, *reservations-carden@devere-hotels.com, Fax (01829) 731032*, 18, – rest, – 400. AE VISA.
Garden Restaurant : **Meals** (dinner only and Sunday lunch) 25.00/40.00 and a la carte 27.45/38.00 **st.** 14.00 – ***La Brasserie Renard :*** **Meals** 22.00/26.00 **t.** 14.00 – 12.50 – **179 rm** 130.00/150.00 **st.**, 13 suites – SB.

Broxton Hall Country House, Whitchurch Rd, CH3 9JS, on A 41 at junction with A 534 (01829) 782321, *reservation@broxtonhall.co.uk, Fax (01829) 782330*, « Part 17C timbered house, antiques », – AE VISA JCB
closed 25-26 December and 1 January – **Meals** 18.00/27.50 (dinner) and lunch a la carte 13.50/29.00 **t.** 13.50 – **10 rm** 70.00/140.00 **st.** – SB.

BRUTON *Somerset* 403 404 M 30 *The West Country G. – pop. 2 111.*
Exc. : *Stourhead*** AC, W : 8 m. by B 3081.*
London 118 – Bristol 27 – Bournemouth 44 – Salisbury 35 – Taunton 36.

XX **Truffles,** 95 High St, BA10 0AR, (01749) 812255, *trufflesbruton@tinyworld.co.uk, Fax (01749) 812255* – VISA
closed 2 weeks spring, 1 week autumn, Sunday and Monday – **Meals** (dinner only) 14.95/24.95 **st.** 11.95.

BRYHER *Cornwall* 403 ㉚ – *see Scilly (Isles of).*

BUCKDEN *Cambs.* 404 T 27 – *pop. 2 534* – ✉ *Huntingdon.*
London 65 – Bedford 15 – Cambridge 20 – Northampton 31.

Lion, High St, PE19 5XA, (01480) 810313, *Fax (01480) 811070*, « Part 15C inn » – rest, AE VISA
Meals 12.50/18.95 and a la carte 19.90/25.95 **t.** 8.95 – **15 rm** 65.00/90.00 **t.** – SB.

BUCKHURST HILL *Essex – pop. 11 243.*
London 12 – Brighton 82 – Cambridge 48 – Ipswich 73 – Oxford 68.
Plan : see Greater London (North-East) p. 11

Express by Holiday Inn, High Rd, IG9 5HT, on A 121 (020) 8504 4450, *Fax (020) 8498 0011* – rm, – 30. AE VISA HT e
Meals (grill rest.) – **49 rm** 59.00 **t.**

BUCKINGHAM *Bucks.* 403 404 Q 27 *Great Britain G. – pop. 10 168.*
Env. : *Stowe Gardens**, NW : 3 m. by minor rd.*
Exc. : *Claydon House* AC, S : 8 m. by A 413.*
18 *Silverstone, Silverstone Rd, Stowe (01280) 850005* – 18 *Tingewick Rd (01280) 813282.*
London 64 – Birmingham 61 – Northampton 20 – Oxford 25.

Villiers, 3 Castle St, MK18 1BS, (01280) 822444, *reception@villiers-hotels.co.uk, Fax (01280) 822113* – – 200. AE VISA.
Henrys : **Meals** (dinner only and Sunday lunch)/dinner 19.25/38.00 and a la carte 24.55/34.80 **st.** 12.25 – **42 rm** 115.00/135.00 **st.**, 4 suites – SB.

BUCKLAND *Glos.* 403 404 O 27 – *see Broadway (Worcs.).*

BUCKLAND *Oxon.* 403 404 P 28 – ✉ *Faringdon.*
London 78 – Oxford 16 – Swindon 15.

Lamb Inn with rm, Lamb Lane, SN7 8QN, (01367) 870484, *Fax (01367) 870675*, – rest, AE VISA.
closed 24-26 December and 1 January – **Meals** a la carte 19.15/33.50 **t.** 12.95 – **4 rm** 42.50/59.50 **t.**

BUCKLERS HARD *Hants.* 403 404 P 31 – *see Beaulieu.*

BUDE *Cornwall* 403 G 31 *The West Country G.* – *pop. 3 681.*

See : *The Breakwater*★★ – *Compass Point* (≤★).

Env. : *Poughill*★ *(church*★★*), N : 2 ½ m.* – *E : Tamar River*★★ – *Kilkhampton (Church*★*), NE : 5 ½ m. by A 39* – *Stratton (Church*★*), E : 1 ½ m.* – *Launcells (Church*★*), E : 3 m. by A 3072* – *Marhamchurch (St Morwenne's Church*★*), SE : 2 ½ m. by A 39* – *Poundstock*★ *(≤*★★*, church*★*, guildhouse*★*), S : 4½ m. by A 39.*

Exc. : *Morwenstow (cliffs*★★*, church*★*), N : 8 ½ m. by A 39 and minor roads* – *Jacobstow (Church*★*), S : 7 m. by A 39.*

Burn View ✆ *(01288) 352006.*

Bude Visitor Centre, The Crescent ✆ *(01288) 354240.*

London 252 – *Exeter 51* – *Plymouth 50* – *Truro 53.*

Falcon, Breakwater Rd, EX23 8SD, ✆ (01288) 352005, *reception@falconhotel.com, Fax (01288) 356359,* ≤, – rest, TV P – 60. VISA
closed 25 December – **Meals** (bar lunch Monday-Saturday)/dinner 17.50/19.50 and a la carte approx. 19.50 **st.** 7.50 – **26 rm** 44.00/88.00 **st.** – SB.

Hartland, HartlandTerr, EX23 8JY, ✆ (01288) 355661, *hartlandhotel@aol.com, Fax (01288) 355664,* ≤, heated – , rm, TV P. VISA
April-October – **Meals** (bar lunch)/dinner 19.00/21.00 **st.** 8.00 – **28 rm** 52.00/82.00 **t.**

Cliff, Crooklets Beach, EX23 8NG, ✆ (01288) 353110, *Fax (01288) 353110,* , , – rest, TV P. VISA JCB
March-October – **Meals** (bar lunch)/dinner 12.50 **st.** 7.45 – **15 rm** 35.40/67.00 **st.**

Camelot, Downs View, EX23 8RE, ✆ (01288) 352361, *stay@camelot-hotel.co.uk, Fax (01288) 355470* – TV P. VISA JCB.
closed Christmas-New Year – **Meals** (dinner only) 19.00 **st.** 9.50 – **24 rm** 41.00/82.00 **st.** – SB.

Bude Haven, Flexbury Ave, EX23 8NS, ✆ (01288) 352305, *enquiries@budehavenhotel.co.uk, Fax (01258) 352305* – TV P. VISA
Meals (bar lunch)/dinner a la carte 14.50/18.00 **st.** 7.50 – **10 rm** 35.00/70.00 **st.** – SB.

BUDLEIGH SALTERTON *Devon* 403 K 32 *The West Country G.* – *pop. 3 759.*

Env. : *East Budleigh (Church*★*), N : 2 ½ m. by A 376* – *Bicton*★ *(Gardens*★*) AC, N : 3 m. by A 376.*

East Devon, North View Rd ✆ *(01395) 442018.*

Fore St ✆ *(01395) 445275.*

London 182 – *Exeter 16* – *Plymouth 55.*

The Long Range, 5 Vales Rd, EX9 6HS, by Raleigh Rd ✆ (01395) 443321, *info@thelongrangehotel.co.uk, Fax (01395) 442132,* – TV P. VISA.
Meals (by arrangement) 17.50 **t.** 8.50 – **7 rm** 45.00/70.00 **t.** – SB.

BUDOCK WATER *Cornwall* – *see Falmouth.*

BUNBURY *Ches.* 402 403 404 M 24 – *see Tarporley.*

BURCHETT'S GREEN *Windsor & Maidenhead.*

London 35 – *Oxford 33* – *Maidenhead 6* – *Reading 12* – *Southampton 61.*

Burchett's Place Country House without rest., Burchett's Green Rd, SL6 6QZ, ✆ (01628) 825023, *Fax (01628) 826672,* – TV P.
5 rm 40.00/85.00 **s.**

BURFORD *Oxon.* 403 404 P 28 – *pop. 1 171.*

✆ *(01993) 822583.*

The Brewery, Sheep St ✆ *(01993) 823558.*

London 76 – *Birmingham 55* – *Gloucester 32* – *Oxford 20.*

Bay Tree, 12-14 Sheep St, OX18 4LW, ✆ (01993) 822791, *baytree.hotel@talk21.com, Fax (01993) 823008,* « 16C house, antique furnishings », – rest, TV P – 30. VISA
Meals 18.95/24.95 and dinner a la carte 25.75/35.40 **st.** 12.50 – **19 rm** 99.00/145.00 **st.**, 2 suites – SB.

Lamb Inn, Sheep St, OX18 4LR, (01993) 823155, *Fax (01993) 822228,* « Part 14C, antique furnishings », – rest, . VISA JCB
closed 25-26 December – **Meals** (bar lunch Monday-Saturday)/dinner 27.00 **t.** 10.00 – **15 rm** 70.00/115.00 **t.** – SB.

Burford House without rest., 99 High St, OX18 4QA, (01993) 823151, *stay@burfordhouse.co.uk, Fax (01993) 823240,* « Part 17C », – . AE VISA JCB.
closed 1 week February and 24-27 December – **7 rm** 75.00/115.00 **t.**

Golden Pheasant, 91 High St, OX18 4QA, (01993) 823223, *Fax (01993) 822621* – rest, . AE VISA
Meals (bar lunch Monday-Saturday)/dinner a la carte 17.40/29.70 **t.** 9.75 – **12 rm** 80.00/120.00 **t.**

Inn For All Seasons, The Barringtons, OX18 4TN, West : 3 ¼ m. on A 40 (01451) 844324, *sharp@innforallseasons.com, Fax (01451) 844375,* – – 35. AE VISA
Meals 15.75/21.50 (dinner) and a la carte 18.45/27.40 **st.** 9.95 – **10 rm** 51.50/115.00 **st.** – SB.

Travelodge, Bury Barn, OX8 4JS, on A 40 (Burford roundabout) (01993) 822699, *Fax (01993) 822699* – rm, . AE VISA JCB.
Meals (grill rest.) – **40 rm** 49.95 **t.**

Jonathan's at the Angel brasserie with rm, 14 Witney St, OX18 4SN, (01993) 822714, *jo@theangel-uk.com, Fax (01993) 822069,* , « 16C former coaching inn », – . VISA.
closed 13 January-8 February, 27 December, Sunday dinner except Bank Holidays, Monday and lunch Tuesday and Wednesday – **Meals** (booking essential) a la carte 18.80/28.05 **t.** 12.75 – **3 rm** 65.00/85.00 **t.**

BURGH-LE-MARSH *Lincs.* 402 404 U 24 – *pop. 2 718.*

London 110 – Boston 29 – Great Grimsby 38 – Lincoln 40.

Windmill, 46 High St, PE24 5JT, (01754) 810281, *Fax (01754) 811011* – . AE VISA
closed 1 week October, Sunday dinner and Monday – **Meals** (dinner only and Sunday lunch)/dinner a la carte 18.50/21.95 **st.** 9.95.

BURLEY *Hants.* 403 404 O 31 *Great Britain G.* – *pop. 1 438* – *Ringwood.*

Env. : *New Forest★★ (Rhinefield Ornamental Drive★★, Bolderwood Ornamental Drive★★).*
London 102 – Bournemouth 17 – Southampton 17 – Winchester 30.

The Burley Inn, The Cross, BH24 4AB, (01425) 403448, *Fax (01425) 402058* – . VISA.
Meals *(closed Sunday dinner)* a la carte 18.40/22.40 **t.** 12.50 – **9 rm** 55.00/95.00 **t.** – SB.

BURLEY IN WHARFEDALE *W. Yorks.* 402 O 22 – *pop. 5 528.*

London 218 – Bradford 14 – Harrogate 15 – Leeds 14 – Preston 52.

David Woolley's, 78 Main St, LS29 7BT, (01943) 864602, *david@davidwoolleysrestaurant.co.uk* – . VISA
closed Sunday and Bank Holidays – **Meals** (dinner only) 19.00 and a la carte approx. 28.50 **t.** 11.00.

BURNHAM *Bucks.* 404 S29 – *pop. 11 169.*

London 33 – Oxford 37 – Reading 17.

County H. Burnham Beeches, Grove Rd, SL1 8DP, Northwest : 1 m. by Britwell Rd (01628) 429955, *Fax (01628) 603994,* , , , , , – , rm, – 180. AE VISA.
Grays : **Meals** *(closed Saturday lunch and Bank Holidays)* 22.50/25.00 and a la carte 18.00/32.00 **t.** 15.50 – 12.50 – **80 rm** 140.00/180.00 **t.**, 2 suites – SB.

BURNHAM MARKET *Norfolk* 404 W 25 *Great Britain G. – pop. 898.*

Env. : Holkham Hall★★ AC, E : 3 m. by B 1155.

Lambourne, Dropmore Rd ☎ (01628) 666755.

London 128 – Cambridge 71 – Norwich 36.

Hoste Arms, The Green, PE31 8HD, ☎ (01328) 738777, *thehostearms@compuserve.com, Fax (01328) 730103,* « 17C inn », – TV P. MC VISA
Meals – (see ***The Restaurant*** below) – **28 rm** 66.00/108.00 **t.** – SB.

Railway Inn, Creake Rd, PE31 8EN, ☎ (01328) 730505, *thehostearms@compuserve.com, Fax (01328) 730103* – TV P. MC VISA
Meals – (see ***The Restaurant*** below) – **7 rm** 40.00/50.00 **t.** – SB.

The Restaurant (at Hoste Arms H.), The Green, PE31 8HD, ☎ (01328) 738777, *Fax (01328) 730103,* – P. MC VISA
Meals (booking essential) a la carte 19.75/30.85 **t.** 13.50.

BURNHAM-ON-CROUCH *Essex* 404 W 29 – *pop. 7 067.*

Burnham-on-Crouch, Ferry Rd, Creeksea ☎ (01621) 782282.

London 52 – Chelmsford 19 – Colchester 32 – Southend-on-Sea 25.

The Contented Sole, 80 High St, CM0 8AA, ☎ (01621) 782139 – . MC VISA
closed 2 weeks summer, 4 weeks winter, Sunday dinner and Monday – **Meals** (dinner only and Sunday lunch)/dinner 16.95 and a la carte 21.95/33.15 **t.** 12.95.

BURNLEY *Lancs.* 402 N 22 – *pop. 74 661.*

, Towneley, Towneley Park, Todmorden Rd ☎ (01282) 451636 – Glen View ☎ (01282) 421045.

Burnley Mechanics, Manchester Rd ☎ (01282) 664422.

London 236 – Bradford 32 – Leeds 37 – Liverpool 55 – Manchester 25 – Middlesbrough 104 – Preston 22 – Sheffield 68.

Oaks, Colne Rd, Reedley, BB10 2LF, Northeast : 2 ½ m. on A 56 ☎ (01282) 414141, *oaks@shireinns.co.uk, Fax (01282) 433401,* , , , – rm, TV P – 120. MC AE VISA
Quills : **Meals** (dinner only) a la carte 21.25/29.95 **st.** 13.45 – ***Archives Brasserie :*** **Meals** (lunch only Monday-Friday) a la carte approx. 9.95 **st.** 13.45 – **51 rm** 96.00/116.00 **st.** – SB.

Rosehill House, Rosehill Ave, Manchester Rd, BB11 2PW, South : 1 ¼ m. by A 56 ☎ (01282) 453931, *rhhotel@providel.co.uk, Fax (01282) 455628,* – rest, TV P. MC AE VISA.
Dugdales : **Meals** a la carte 14.50/21.50 **t.** 8.50 – ***El Nino's*** - Tapas - a la carte 9.00/18.50 **t.** 8.50 – **24 rm** 45.00/85.00 **st.**, 2 suites – SB.

Travel Inn, Queen Victoria Rd, BB10 3EF, Northeast : ¾ m. on A 6114 ☎ (01282) 450250, *Fax (01282) 452811* – rm, rest, TV P – 40. MC AE VISA.
Meals (grill rest.) – **40 rm** 41.95 **t.**

Travelodge, Cavalry Barracks, Barracks Rd, BB11 4AS, West : ½ m. at junction of A 671 with A 679 ☎ (01282) 416039, *Fax (01282) 416039* – rm, TV P. MC AE VISA JCB.
Meals (grill rest.) – **32 rm** 39.95 **t.**

BURNSALL *N. Yorks.* 402 O 21 – *pop. 108* – ✉ *Skipton.*

London 223 – Bradford 26 – Leeds 29.

Red Lion, BD23 6BU, ☎ (01756) 720204, *redlion@daelnet.co.uk, Fax (01756) 720292,* €, « Part 16C inn », – TV P. MC AE VISA JCB
Meals – (see ***The Restaurant*** below) – **11 rm** 85.00/130.00 **st.**

Devonshire Fell with rm, BD23 6BT, ☎ (01756) 729000, *sales@thedevonshirearms.co.uk, Fax (01756) 729009,* €, , – TV P – 50. MC AE VISA
Meals 15.95 (lunch) and a la carte 14.50/25.50 **st.** 9.95 – **10 rm** 70.00/110.00 **st.**, 2 suites – SB.

The Restaurant (at Red Lion H.), BD23 6BU, ☎ (01756) 720204, *Fax (01756) 720292,* « Part 16C inn » – P. MC AE VISA JCB
Meals (bar lunch Monday-Saturday)/dinner 25.95 and a la carte 16.15/27.95 **t.** 11.50.

BURNT YATES *N. Yorks.* – *see Ripley.*

BURPHAM *W. Sussex* 404 S 30 – *see Arundel.*

BURRINGTON *Devon* 403 I 31 – *pop. 533.*

London 260 – Barnstaple 14 – Exeter 28 – Taunton 50.

Northcote Manor, EX37 9LZ, Northwest : 2 m. on A 377 (01769) 560501, *rest@northcotemanor.co.uk, Fax (01769) 560770*, «, « 17C manor house », – TV P. MC AE VISA JCB
Meals (booking essential) (lunch by arrangement)/dinner 15.00/35.00 **t.** 13.95 – **10 rm** 90.00/200.00 **t.**, 1 suite – SB.

BURSLEM *Stoke-on-Trent* 402 403 404 N 24 – *see Stoke-on-Trent.*

BURTON-IN-KENDAL SERVICE AREA *Cumbria* 402 L 21 – *Carnforth.*

Travelodge without rest., LA6 1JF, on M 6 northbound carriageway between junctions 35 and 36 (01524) 784012, *Fax (01524) 784014* – TV P. MC AE VISA JCB.
47 rm 52.95 **t.**

BURTON-ON-THE-WOLDS *Leics.* 402 403 404 Q 25 – *see Loughborough.*

In this guide

a symbol or a character, printed in red or **black**, in **bold** or light type, does not have the same meaning.
Pay particular attention to the explanatory pages.

BURTON-UPON-TRENT *Staffs.* 402 403 404 O 25 – *pop. 60 525.*

18 Branston G. & C.C., Burton Rd (01283) 512211 – 18 Craythorne, Craythorne Rd, Stretton (01283) 564329.

183 High St (01283) 516609.

London 128 – Birmingham 29 – Leicester 27 – Nottingham 27 – Stafford 27.

Stanhope Arms, Ashby Road East, DE15 0PU, Southeast : 2 ½ m. on A 511 (01283) 217954, *info@stanhopearmshotel.com, Fax (01283) 550106*, – rest, TV P – 150. MC AE VISA.
Meals (grill rest.) a la carte 11.60/17.80 **st.** 8.00 – 5.95 – **24 rm** 49.50 **t.**

Express by Holiday Inn without rest., 2nd Ave, Centrum 100, DE14 2WF, Southwest : 2 m. by A 5121 (01283) 504300, *info@exhiburton.co.uk, Fax (01283) 504301* – TV P – 60. MC AE VISA JCB
82 rm 59.00 **st.**

Travelodge, DE13 8EH, Southwest : 4 ¾ m. by A 5121 on A 38 (southbound carriageway) (01283) 716784, *Fax (01283) 716784* – rm, TV P. MC AE VISA JCB.
Meals (grill rest.) – **40 rm** 39.95 **t.**

Travelodge, DE13 8EG, Southwest : 5 ¼ m. by A 5121 on A 38 (northbound carriageway) (01283) 716343, *Fax (01283) 716343* – rm, TV P. MC AE VISA JCB.
Meals (grill rest.) – **20 rm** 39.95 **t.**

at Stretton *North : 3½ m. by A 50 off A 5121 – Burton-upon-Trent.*

Dovecliff Hall with rm, Dovecliff Rd, DE13 0DJ, Northeast : 1 m. (01283) 531818, *Fax (01283) 516546*, «, « Restored Georgian house, gardens », – TV P. MC AE VISA JCB.
Meals *(closed Monday lunch and Sunday dinner)* 15.50/24.50 and a la carte 30.00/40.00 **t.** 14.00 – **7 rm** 65.00/130.00 **t.** – SB.

at Newton Solney *Northeast : 3 m. by A 50 on B 5008 – Burton-upon-Trent.*

Newton Park Ramada Jarvis, Newton Rd, DE15 0SS, (01283) 703568, *jnewtonpark.gm@jarvis.co.uk, Fax (01283) 703214*, – TV P – 100. MC AE VISA
Meals (bar lunch Monday-Saturday)/dinner 19.95 **st.** 12.95 – 12.95 – **50rm** 115.00/175.00 **st.** – SB.

at Barton-under-Needwood *Southwest : 6 m. by A 5121 on B 5016 – Burton-upon-Trent.*

Fairfield without rest., 55 Main St, DE13 8AB, (01283) 716396, *bookings@fairfield.f25.com, Fax (01283) 716396* – TV P. MC VISA.
closed 25 December and 1 January – **3 rm** 38.00/48.00 **s.**

ENGLAND

BURY *Gtr. Manchester* 402 N 23 403 ③ 404 N 23 – *pop. 62 633.*

Greenmount ☏ *(01204) 883712.*

The Mets Art Centre, Market St ☏ *(0161) 253 5111.*

London 211 – Leeds 45 – Liverpool 35 – Manchester 9.

Bolholt Country Park, Walshaw Rd, BL8 1PU, Northwest : 1 ½ m. by B 6214 ☏ (0161) 762 4000, *reservations@bolholt.co.uk, Fax (0161) 762 4100,* squash – P – 250. AE VISA.
Meals (bar lunch)/dinner 14.95 and a la carte 22.00/36.00 **st.** 12.00 – **65 rm** 69.00/94.00 **st.**

Est, Est, Est, 703 Manchester Rd, BL9 9SS, South : 2 m. on A 56 ☏ (0161) 766 4869, *Fax (0161) 796 5338* – P. AE VISA
closed 25-26 December – **Meals** - Italian - 10.95 and a la carte 16.70/21.80 **t.** 10.45.

at Walmersley *North : 1 ¾ m. on A 56 – ✉ Bury.*

Red Hall, Manchester Rd, BL9 5NA, North : 1 ¼ m. on A 56 ☏ (01706) 822476, *Fax (01706) 828086* – P – 40. AE VISA JCB.
closed 24 December-1 January – **Meals** (dinner only and Sunday lunch) 14.00 and a la carte 12.20/21.20 **t.** 9.60 – **20 rm** 53.00/66.00 **t.**

BURY ST. EDMUNDS *Suffolk* 404 W 27 *Great Britain G. – pop. 31 237.*

See : *Town★ – Abbey and Cathedral★.*

Env. : *Ickworth House★ AC, SW : 3 m. by A 143.*

Suffolk G. & C.C., St. John's Hill Plantation, The Street, Fornham All Saints ☏ *(01284) 706777.*

6 Angel Hill ☏ *(01284) 764667.*

London 79 – Cambridge 27 – Ipswich 26 – Norwich 41.

Angel, 3 Angel Hill, IP33 1LT, ☏ (01284) 714000, *sales@theangel.co.uk, Fax (01284) 714001* – P – 80. AE VISA JCB
Abbeygate : **Meals** 9.95/23.50 and a la carte 18.40/27.45 **st.** 10.85 – ***The Vaults :*** **Meals** a la carte 18.40/27.45 **st.** – **64 rm** 81.00/111.00 **st.**, 1 suite – SB.

Priory, Tollgate, IP32 6EH, North : 1 ¾ m. on A 1101 ☏ (01284) 766181, *reservations@prioryhotel.co.uk, Fax (01284) 767604,* – – P – 40. AE VISA
Meals *(closed Saturday lunch)* 19.95/23.95 and a la carte 26.85/33.85 **st.** 11.95 – **38 rm** 75.00/115.00 **st.** – SB.

Butterfly, Symonds Rd, IP32 7BW, Southeast : 1 ½ m. by A 1302 and A 134 at junction with A 14 ☏ (01284) 760884, *burybutterfly@lineone.net, Fax (01284) 755476* – rm, P – 60. AE VISA JCB
Meals 15.00/17.50 (dinner) and a la carte 15.95/26.95 **t.** 13.00 – 8.50 – **65 rm** 79.50 **t.** – SB.

Ounce House without rest., Northgate St, IP33 1HP, ☏ (01284) 761779, *pott@globalnet.co.uk, Fax (01284) 768315,* – P. AE VISA.
3 rm 65.00/100.00 **st.**

The Abbey without rest., 35 Southgate St, IP33 2AZ, ☏ (01284) 762020, *reception@theabbeyhotel.demon.co.uk, Fax (01284) 724770* – P. AE VISA JCB.
10 rm 65.00/75.00 **st.**, 2 suites.

Northgate House without rest., Northgate St, IP33 1HQ, ☏ (01284) 760469, *northgate_hse@hotmail.com, Fax (01284) 724008,* « Restored Georgian town house of Tudor origins », – P. AE VISA JCB.
closed 23 December-3 January – **3 rm** 60.00/110.00 **st.**

Maison Bleue, 30-31 Churchgate St, IP33 1RG, ☏ (01284) 760623, *info@maisonbleue.co.uk, Fax (01284) 761611* – . AE VISA JCB
closedJanuary, Sunday and Monday – **Meals** - Seafood - 14.95/19.95 and a la carte 18.85/29.65 **t.** 9.95.

42 Churchgate, 42 Churchgate St, IP33 1RG, ☏ (01284) 764179, *Fax (01284) 764179* – VISA
closed first 2 weeks January, first 2 weeks September, Sunday and Monday – **Meals** 12.75/25.95 **t.** 10.50.

at Ixworth *Northeast : 7 m. by A 143 – ✉ Bury St. Edmunds.*

Theobalds, 68 High St, IP31 2HJ, ☏ (01359) 231707, *Fax (01359) 231707,* , « Part 16C cottage » – VISA
closed 1 week summer, Saturday lunch, Sunday dinner and Monday – **Meals** 16.95 (lunch) and dinner a la carte 24.95/28.95 **t.** 11.25.

at Rougham Green *Southeast : 4 m. by A 1302 and A 134 off A 14 – Bury St. Edmunds.*

Ravenwood Hall, IP30 9JA, (01359) 270345, *reservations@ravenwood.co.uk, Fax (01359) 270788,* « 16C manor house », heated, – rm – 150. AE VISA
Meals a la carte 17.40/22.70 **t.** 14.50 – **14 rm** 71.00/129.00 **t.** – SB.

at Beyton *Southeast : 6 m. by A 1302 and A 134 off A 14 – Bury St. Edmunds.*

Manorhouse, The Green, IP30 9AF, (01359) 270960, *manorhouse@beyton.com,* « Part 15C Suffolk longhouse », – .
Meals (by arrangement) 16.00 **st.** – **4 rm** 45.00/56.00 **st.**

at Horringer *Southwest : 3 m. on A 143 – Bury St. Edmunds.*

Beehive, IP29 5SN, (01284) 735260, *Fax (01284) 830321,* – . VISA
closed Sunday dinner – **Meals** a la carte approx. 13.95 **t.** 9.50.

BUSHEY *Herts.* 404 S 29.

Bushey Hall, Bushey Hall Drive (01923) 222253, **BT** – *Bushey G. & C.C., High St (020) 8950 2283,* **BT.**
London 18 – Luton 21 – Watford 3.

Plan : see Greater London (North-West) p. 8

st James, 30 High St, WD2 3DN, (020) 8950 2480, *Fax (020) 8950 4107* – . AE VISA
closed Christmas and Sunday – **Meals** a la carte approx. 25.85 **t.** 11.95. **BT c**

BUTTERMERE *Cumbria* 402 K 20 – *pop. 139* – *Cockermouth.*
London 306 – Carlisle 35 – Kendal 43.

Bridge, CA13 9UZ, (017687) 70252, *enquiries@bridge-hotel.com, Fax (017687) 70215,* – . VISA
Meals (booking essential) (bar lunch)/dinner 21.00 and a la carte 7.25/15.45 **t.** 9.95 – **21 rm** (dinner included) 97.50/146.00 **t.** – SB.

Wood House , CA13 9XA, Northwest : ½ m. on B 5289 (017687) 70208, *(017687) 70241,* Crummock Water and Melbreak, « Lakeside setting », , – .
mid February-mid November – **Meals** (by arrangement) (communal dining) 19.50 **st.** 7.80 – **3 rm** 43.00/70.00 **st.**

BUXTON *Derbs.* 402 403 404 O24 – *pop. 19 854.*
Buxton and High Peak, Townend (01298) 23453.
The Crescent (01298) 25106.
London 172 – Derby 38 – Manchester 25 – Stoke-on-Trent 24.

Lee Wood, The Park, SK17 6TQ, on A 5004 (01298) 23002, *leewoodhotel@btinternet.com, Fax (01298) 23228,* , – , rm, – 100. AE VISA
Garden : **Meals** 20.95/25.25 (dinner) and a la carte 16.45/37.70 **st.** 11.95 – 12.00 – **40 rm** 72.00/105.00 **st.** – SB.

Grendon without rest., Bishops Lane, SK17 6UN, (01298) 78831, *parkerhl@talk21.com, Fax (01298) 79257,* – . VISA.
3 rm 40.00/66.00 **st.**

Coningsby without rest., 6 Macclesfield Rd, SK17 9AH, (01298) 26735, *coningsby@btinternet.com, Fax (01298) 26735,* – . VISA.
March-October – **3 rm** 52.50/70.00 **s.**

BYFORD *Herefordshire* 403 L 27 – *see Hereford.*

BYLAND ABBEY *N. Yorks.* 402 Q 21 – *see Helmsley.*

CADNAM *Hants.* 403 404 P 31 – *pop. 1 866.*
London 91 – Salisbury 16 – Southampton 8 – Winchester 19.

Walnut Cottage without rest., Old Romsey Rd, SO40 2NP, off A 3090 (023) 8081 2275, *Fax (023) 8081 2275,* – .
closed 24-27 December – **3 rm** 30.00/48.00.

CAISTOR ST EDMUND *Norfolk* 404 X 26 – *see Norwich.*

CALCOT *Glos.* – *see Tetbury.*

CALLINGTON *Cornwall* 403 H 32.
London 237 – Exeter 53 – Plymouth 15 – Truro 46.

XX **The Thyme and Plaice,** 3 Church St, PL17 7RE, ✆ (01579) 384933, *thethymeplaice@aol.com* – ⇔. MC VISA
closed Sunday-Wednesday – **Meals** (booking essential) (dinner only) 23.95 and a la carte 20.95/24.65 **t.** 8.95.

CALNE *Wilts.* 403 404 O 29 *The West Country G. – pop. 11 516.*
Env.: *Bowood House★ AC, (Library ←★) SW : 2 m. by A 4 – Avebury★★ (The Stones★, Church★) E : 6 m. by A 4.*
London 91 – Bristol 33 – Swindon 17.

Chilvester Hill House, SN11 0LP, West : ¾ m. by A 4 on Bremhill rd ✆ (01249) 813981, *gill.dilley@talk21.com, Fax (01249) 814217,* – ⇔ rest, TV P. MC AE VISA.
Meals (by arrangement) (communal dining) 18.00/25.00 **st.** 10.00 – **3 rm** 55.00/85.00 **st.**

CAMBERLEY *Surrey* 404 R 29 – *pop. 46 120 (inc. Frimley).*
Camberley Heath, Golf Drive ✆ (01276) 23258.
London 40 – Reading 13 – Southampton 48.

Frimley Hall, Lime Ave via Conifer Drive, GU15 2BG, East : ¾ m. off Portsmouth Rd (A 325) ✆ (0870) 400 8224, *heritagehotels-camberley.frimley-hall@forte-hotels.com, Fax (01276) 691253,* – ⇔ TV P – 60. MC AE VISA
Meals 7.50/9.50 (lunch) and dinner a la carte 23.50/34.50 **t.** 13.95 – 13.50 – **86 rm** 170.00/220.00 **st.**

Travel Inn, 221 Yorktown Rd, GU47 0RT, West : 2 m. by A 30 and A 321 on A 3095 ✆ (01276) 878181, *Fax (01276) 890648* – ⇔ rm, rest, TV P. MC AE VISA.
Meals (grill rest.) – **40 rm** 41.95 **t.**

Le Guide change, changez de ***guide Michelin*** *tous les ans.*

CAMBRIDGE *Cambs.* 404 U 27 *Great Britain G. – pop. 95 682.*
See : *Town★★★ – St John's College★★★ AC* Y – *King's College★★ (King's College Chapel★★★)* Z *The Backs★★* YZ – *Fitzwilliam Museum★★* Z **M1** – *Trinity College★★* Y – *Clare College★* Z B – *Kettle's Yard★* Y **M2** – *Queen's College★ AC* Z.
Exc. : *Audley End★★, S : 13 m. on Trumpington Rd, A 1309, A 1301 and B 1383 – Imperial War Museum★, Duxford, S : 9 m. on M 11.*
Cambridgeshire Moat House Hotel, Bar Hill ✆ (01954) 780555 X.
Cambridge Airport : ✆ (01223) 373737, E : 2 m. on A 1303 X.
Wheeler St ✆ (01223) 322640.
London 55 – Coventry 88 – Kingston-upon-Hull 137 – Ipswich 54 – Leicester 74 – Norwich 61 – Nottingham 88 – Oxford 100.

Plan opposite

Cambridge Garden House Moat House, Granta Pl, off Mill Lane, CB2 1RT, ✆ (01223) 259988, *cbcgh@queensmoat.co.uk, Fax (01223) 316605,* ←, « Riverside setting », – ⇔, rest, TV P – 180. MC AE VISA. Z n
Meals 13.00/22.00 and a la carte 18.00/27.00 **t.** 12.95 – 13.50 – **117 rm** 169.00/350.00 **t.** – SB.

Crowne Plaza, Downing St, CB2 3DT, ✆ (01223) 464466, *sales@cpcam.demon.co.uk, Fax (01223) 464440* – , ⇔ rm, TV P – 250. MC AE VISA JCB. Z a
Meals a la carte 18.00/30.00 – 13.95 – **200 rm** 175.00 **st.** – SB.

University Arms, Regent St, CB2 1AD, ✆ (01223) 351241, *dua.sales@devere-hotels.com, Fax (01223) 315256* – ⇔ TV P – 300. MC AE VISA JCB Z e
Meals (bar lunch Saturday) 14.95/24.50 and a la carte 24.40/31.85 **st.** 12.95 – 12.50 – **114 rm** 120.00/160.00 **st.**, 1 suite – SB.

Gonville, Gonville Pl, CB1 1LY, ✆ (01223) 366611, *info@gonvillehotel.co.uk, Fax (01223) 315470* – ⇔, rest, TV P – 200. MC AE VISA. Z r
Meals (bar lunch)/dinner 18.50 and a la carte 11.35/15.30 **t.** 9.95 – 9.50 – **64 rm** 99.50/120.00 **st.** – SB.

Arundel House, Chesterton Rd, CB4 3AN, ✆ (01223) 367701, *info@arundelhousehotels.co.uk, Fax (01223) 367721,* – ⇔, rest, TV P – 50. MC AE VISA. Y u
closed 25-26 December – ***Restaurant :*** **Meals** 19.75 and a la carte 17.75/27.75 **st.** 9.75 – ***Conservatory :*** **Meals** a la carte 11.45/19.15 **t.** 9.75 – 5.95 – **105 rm** 67.50/115.00 **st.** – SB.

CAMBRIDGE

Street	Ref.	Street	Ref.
Bridge Street	Y 2	Northampton St.	Y 22
Corn Exchange St.	Z 6	Parker Street	Z 23
Downing Street	Z 7	Peas Hill	Z 25
Free School Lane	Z 12	Pembroke Street	Z 26
Grafton Centre	Y	Petty Cury	Z 27
Hobson Street	Y 14	Rose Crescent	Y 28
King's Parade	Z 15	St. Andrew's St.	Z 30
Lion Yard Centre	Z	St. John's Street	Y 31
Madingley Rd	X, Y 16	Short Street	Y 32
Magdalene St.	Y 17	Sidney Street	Y 34
Market Hill	Z 18	Trinity Street	Y 36
Market Street	Y 19	Trumpington Road	Z 37
Milton Road	Y 20	Wheeler Street	Z 39
Newmarket Road	Y 21		

COLLEGES

College	Ref.	College	Ref.
CHRIST'S	Y A	NEW HALL	X D
CHURCHILL	X B	NEWNHAM	X E
CLARE	Z B	PEMBROKE	Z N
CLARE HALL	X N	PETERHOUSE	Z O
CORPUS CHRISTI	Z G	QUEENS'	Z
DARWIN	Z D	ROBINSON COLLEGE	X K
DOWNING	Z E	ST CATHARINE'S	Z R
EMMANUEL	Z F	ST EDMUNDS HOUSE	Y U
FITZWILLIAM	X G	ST JOHN'S	Y
GONVILLE AND CAIUS	Y G	SELWYN	X F
HUGHES HALL	Z K	SIDNEY SUSSEX	Y P
JESUS	Y K	TRINITY	Y
KING'S	Z	TRINITY HALL	Y V
LUCY CAVENDISH	Y O	WOLFSON	X U
MAGDALENE	Y N		

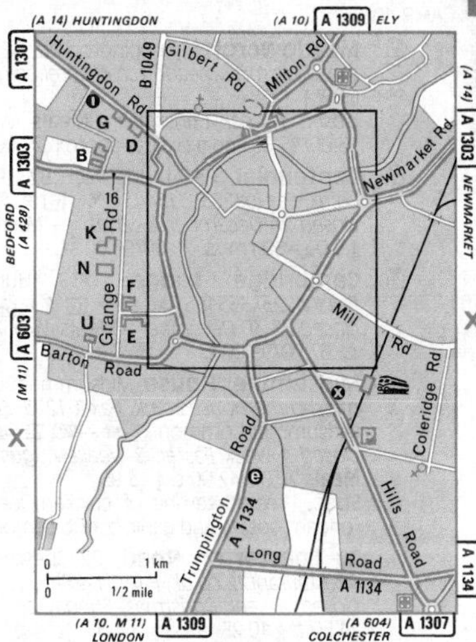

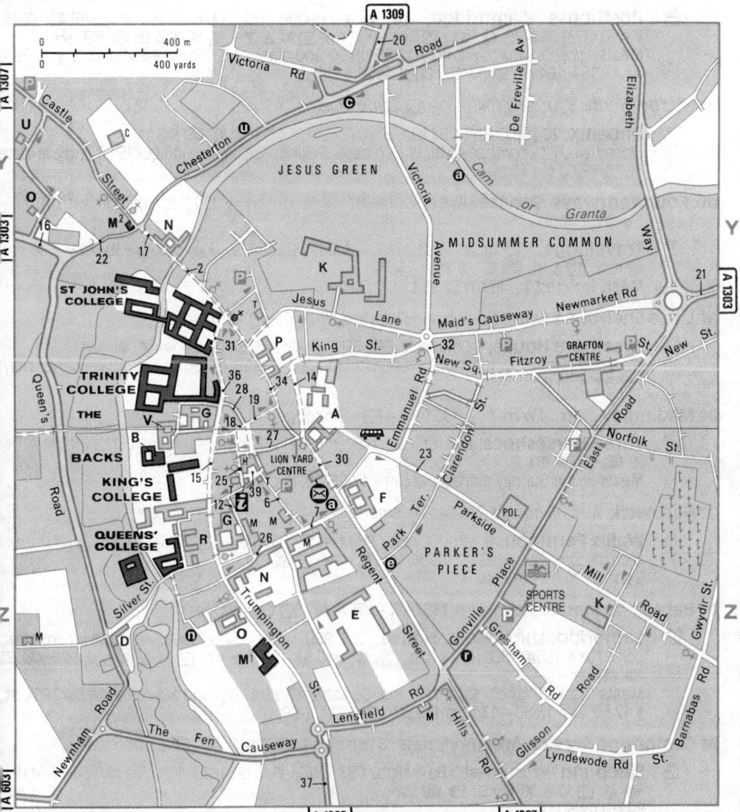

ENGLAND

Meadowcroft, Trumpington Rd, CB2 2EX, South : 1 ¼ m. on A 1134 ☎ (01223) 346120, *meadowcroft@meadowcrofthotel.co.uk, Fax (01223) 346138,* – rm, – 30. AE VISA X e
closed 1 week Christmas – **Meals** *(closed Sunday dinner, Monday and Tuesday lunch)* 15.00/25.00 and a la carte approx. 25.00 **t.** 15.00 – **12 rm** 95.00/150.00 **st.**

Centennial, 63-71 Hills Rd, CB2 1PG, ☎ (01223) 314652, *reception@centennialhotel.co.uk, Fax (01223) 315443* – . AE VISA. X x
closed 24 December-2 January – **Meals** (dinner only) 13.50 and a la carte 24.50/31.50 **st.** 9.00 – **39 rm** 70.00/96.00 **st.**

Cambridge Lodge, 139 Huntingdon Rd, CB3 0DQ, ☎ (01223) 352833, *Fax (01223) 355166,* – – 25. AE VISA. X
closed 25-30 December – **Meals** 15.95/20.95 and a la carte 20.65/29.20 **t.** 10.95 – **15 rm** 67.00/99.00 **t.**

Midsummer House, Midsummer Common, CB4 1HA, ☎ (01223) 369299, *reservations@midsummerhouse.co.uk, Fax (01223) 302672,* « Attractively situated beside River Cam, on Midsummer Common », – AE VISA Y a
closed 1 week Easter, 2 weeks August, 26 December-9 January, Sunday and Monday – **Meals** 20.00/42.00 **t.** 13.95
Spec. Pressed terrine of chicken, leeks and foie gras. Squab pigeon, Savoy cabbage, fondant potato and garlic confit. Lemon and lime tart, raspberry sorbet.

22 Chesterton Road, 22 Chesterton Rd, CB4 3AX, ☎ (01223) 351880, *davidcarter@restaurant22.co.uk, Fax (01223) 323814* – . AE VISA JCB Y c
closed 1 week Christmas, Sunday and Monday – **Meals** (booking essential) (dinner only) 24.50 **t.** 10.25.

at Impington *North : 2 m. on B 1049 at junction with A 14* – X – ✉ *Cambridge.*

Posthouse Cambridge, Lakeview, Bridge Rd, CB4 9PH, ☎ (0870) 400 9015, *Fax (01223) 233426,* , , , – rm, – 60. AE VISA JCB
Meals *(closed Saturday lunch)* 12.00/15.00 and dinner a la carte 19.35/29.15 **t.** 12.95 – 11.95 – **164 rm** 99.00/159.00 **st.** – SB.

at Histon *North : 3 m. on B 1049* – X – ✉ *Cambridge.*

Phoenix, 20 The Green, CB4 9JA, ☎ (01223) 233766 – . VISA
closed 24-27 December – **Meals** - Chinese (Peking, Szechuan) - 16.00/25.50 and a la carte 36.70/58.00 **t.** 10.00.

at Fourwentways Service Area *Southeast : 7 ½ m. on A 1307 at junction with A 11* – ✉ *Cambridge.*

Travelodge, Abington, CB1 6AP, ☎ (01223) 839479, *Fax (01223) 839479* – rm, rest, . AE VISA JCB.
Meals (grill rest.) – **40 rm** 52.95 **t.**

at Little Shelford *South : 5½ m. by A 1309* – X – *off A 10* – ✉ *Cambridge.*

Sycamore House, 1 Church St, CB2 5HG, ☎ (01223) 843396 – . VISA
closed Christmas-New Year, Sunday and Monday – **Meals** (booking essential) (dinner only) 23.50 **t.** 11.00.

at Madingley *West : 4½ m. by A 1303* – X – ✉ *Cambridge.*

Three Horseshoes, High St, CB3 8AB, ☎ (01954) 210221, *Fax (01954) 212043,* – . AE VISA
Meals (in bar Sunday dinner) a la carte 17.50/29.45 **t.** 13.00.

at Hardwick *West : 5 m. by A 1303* – ✉ *Cambridge.*

Wallis Farmhouse without rest., 98 Main St, CB3 7QU, ☎ (01954) 210347, *wallisfarm@mcmail.com, Fax (01954) 210988,* , –
5 rm 40.00/60.00 **st.**

at Bar Hill *Northwest : 5½ m. by A 1307* – X – *off A 14* – ✉ *Cambridge.*

Cambridgeshire Moat House, CB3 8EU, ☎ (01954) 249988, *recmb@queensmoat.com, Fax (01954) 780010,* , , , 18, , – , rm, – 200. AE VISA
Meals *(closed lunch Saturday and Sunday)* 12.95/17.95 and a la carte 14.85/26.70 **st.** 12.50 – 13.50 – **134 rm** 139.00/169.00 **st.** – SB.

at Cambridge Service Area *Northwest : 8½ m. by A 1307 on A 14* – ✉ *Cambridge.*

Sleep Inn without rest., Boxworth, CB3 8WG, ☎ (01954) 268400, *Fax (01954) 268419* – . AE VISA.
82 rm 49.50 **st.**

CANNINGTON *Somerset* 403 K 30 – *see Bridgwater.*

CANNOCK *Staffs.* 402 403 404 N 25 *Great Britain G. – pop. 60 106.*

Exc. : *Weston Park★★ AC, W : 11 m. by A 5.*

Cannock Park, Stafford Rd ✆ (01543) 578850.

London 135 – Birmingham 20 – Derby 36 – Leicester 51 – Shrewsbury 32 – Stoke-on-Trent 28.

Travel Inn, Watling St, WS11 1SJ, Southwest : 1 m. at junction of A 4601 with A 5 ✆ (01543) 572721, *Fax (01543) 466130* – rm, – 100. VISA.
Meals (grill rest.) – **60 rm** 41.95 **t.**

CANTERBURY *Kent* 404 X 30 *Great Britain G. – pop. 36 464.*

See : *City★★★ - Cathedral★★★* Y - *St Augustine's Abbey★★ AC* YZ **K** – *King's School★* Y **B** – *Mercery Lane★* Y **12** - *Christ Church Gate★* Y **A** – *Weavers★* Y **D** – *Hospital of St. Thomas the Martyr, Eastbridge★* Y **E** – *Poor Priests Hospital★ AC* Y **M1** – *St Martin's Church★* Y **N** – *West Gate★ AC* Y **R**.

34 St Margaret's St ✆ (01227) 766567.

London 59 – Brighton 76 – Dover 15 – Maidstone 28 – Margate 17.

Plan on next page

County, High St, CT1 2RX, ✆ (01227) 766266, *info@county.macdonald-hotels.co.uk, Fax (01227) 451512* – , rm, – 140. VISA Y n
Sullys : **Meals** a la carte 16.85/31.85 **t.** 14.95 – 10.50 – **72 rm** 92.00 **t.**, 1 suite – SB.

Falstaff, 8-10 St Dunstan's St, CT2 8AF, ✆ (01227) 462138, *Fax (01227) 463525*, « Part 15C coaching inn » – VISA Y a
Othello's : **Meals** a la carte 15.25/26.20 **t.** 9.95 – 10.50 – **46 rm** 95.00/105.00 **t.** – SB.

Thanington without rest., 140 Wincheap, CT1 3RY, ✆ (01227) 453227, *thanington@line one.net, Fax (01227) 453225*, , – VISA JCB Z s
closed Christmas – **15 rm** 65.00/78.00 **st.**

Ebury, 65-67 New Dover Rd, CT1 3DX, ✆ (01227) 768433, *info@ebury-hotel.co.uk, Fax (01227) 459187*, , – rest, VISA JCB Z r
closed 20 December-10 January – **Meals** *(closed Sunday)* (dinner only) 16.00/21.00 **st.** 9.50 – **15 rm** 50.00/79.00 **st.** – SB.

Magnolia House, 36 St Dunstan's Terr, CT2 8AX, ✆ (01227) 765121, *magnolia_house_canterbury@yahoo.com, Fax (01227) 765121*, – VISA. Y s
Meals (by arrangement (winter only)) 20.00 **st.** – **7 rm** 55.00/125.00 **st.** – SB.

Clare Ellen without rest., 9 Victoria Rd, CT1 3SG, ✆ (01227) 760205, *loraine.williams @clareellenguesthouse.co.uk, Fax (01227) 784482*, – VISA JCB. Z u
6 rm 30.00/54.00 **st.**

Zan Stel Lodge without rest., 140 Old Dover Rd, CT1 3NX, ✆ (01227) 453654, – . Z e
closed Christmas and New Year – **4 rm** 44.00/54.00 **st.**

Alexandra House without rest., 1 Roper Rd, CT2 7EH, ✆ (01227) 767011, *Fax (01227) 786617*, – . Y u
7 rm 28.00/55.00.

La Bonne Cuisine (at Canterbury H.), 71 New Dover Rd, CT1 3DZ, ✆ (01227) 450551, *canterbury.hotel@btinternet.com, Fax (01227) 780145* – VISA Z c
Meals - French - (dinner only) 22.50/30.00 **t.** 14.50.

Tuo e Mio, 16 The Borough, CT1 2DR, ✆ (01227) 761471, *james@greggio.freeserve.co.uk* – VISA JCB Y o
closed 2 weeks August, 10 days Christmas and New Year, Monday and Tuesday lunch – **Meals** - Italian - a la carte 16.50/25.00 **st.** 10.50.

Augustine's, 1-2 Longport, CT1 1PE, ✆ (01227) 453063 – . VISA JCB Z x
closed 25 December-8 January, Sunday dinner and Monday – **Meals** (booking essential) 9.95 (lunch) and dinner a la carte 22.50/30.50 **t.** 9.95.

at Chartham Hatch *West : 3¼ m. by A 28 – Z – ✉ Canterbury.*

Howfield Manor, Howfield Lane, CT4 7HQ, Southeast : 1 m. ✆ (01227) 738294, *@howfield.invictanet.co.uk, Fax (01227) 731535*, – – 100. VISA JCB.
Old Well : **Meals** 14.95/19.95 and a la carte 20.25/31.40 **st.** 10.95 – **15 rm** 79.50/100.00 **st.** – SB.

CANTERBURY

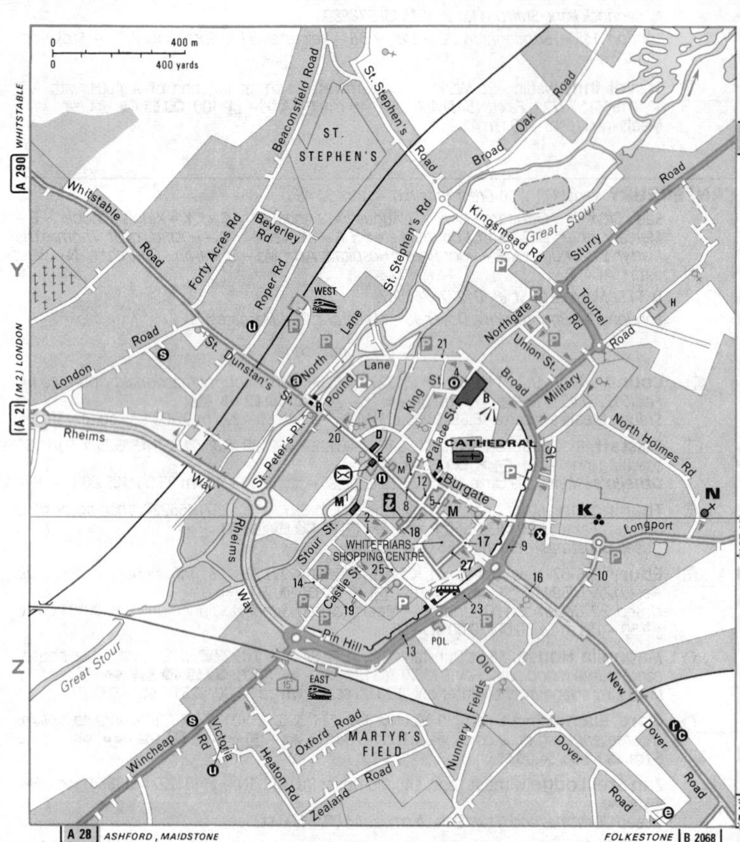

at Upper Harbledown Service Area *West : 4 m. on A 2 – Y – ✉ Canterbury.*

Express by Holiday Inn without rest., CT2 9HX, (eastbound carriageway) ✆ (01227) 865000, *canterbury@oriel-leisure.co.uk, Fax (01227) 865100* – 35. MC AE VISA JCB
89 rm 60.00 st.

at Gate Service Area *West : 4½ m. on A 2 – Y – ✉ Faversham.*

Travelodge, Dunkirk, ME13 9LN, (westbound carriageway) ✆ (01227) 752781 – rm, MC AE VISA JCB.
Meals (grill rest.) – **40 rm** 49.95 **t.**

This Guide is not a comprehensive list of all hotels and restaurants, nor even of all good hotels and restaurants in Great Britain and Ireland.
Since our aim is to be of service to all motorists, we must show establishments in all categories and so we have made a selection of some in each.

CANVEY ISLAND *Essex* 404 V 29 – *pop. 36 859.*

Castle Point, Waterside Farm, Somnes Ave (01268) 510830.

London 35 – Chelmsford 19 – Maidstone 44 – Southend-on-Sea 13.

Oysterfleet, Knightswick Rd, SS8 7UX, (01268) 510111, *Fax (01268) 511420,* – 200. VISA.
Meals *(closed Sunday dinner)* (grill rest.) (carvery lunch Sunday) a la carte 12.00/20.00 **st.** 8.50 – 4.50 – **40 rm** 39.50/50.00 **st.**

CAPEL ST. MARY *Suffolk* 404 X27 – *pop. 3 176 – Ipswich.*

London 78 – Cambridge 52 – Colchester 18 – Ipswich 3.

Travelodge, Bentley Services, IP9 2JP, East : ½ m. on A 12 (01473) 312157, *Fax (01473) 312157* – rm, VISA JCB.
Meals (grill rest.) – **32 rm** 42.95 **t.**

CARBIS BAY *Cornwall* 403 D 33 – *see St. Ives.*

CARCROFT *S. Yorks.* 402 403 404 Q 23 – *see Doncaster.*

CARLISLE *Cumbria* 401 402 L 19 *Great Britain G.* – *pop. 72 439.*

See : *Town*★ - *Cathedral*★ *(Painted Ceiling*★*)* AY **E** – *Tithe Barn*★ BY **A.**

Env. : *Hadrian's Wall*★★, *N : by A 7* AY.

Aglionby (01228) 513029 BY – *Stony Holme, St Aidan's Rd (01228) 625511* BY – *Dalston Hall, Dalston (01228) 710165,* AZ.

Carlisle Airport (01228) 573641, NW : 5½ m. by A 7 – BY – *and B 6264* – **Terminal :** *Bus Station, Lowther St.*

Carlisle Visitor Centre, Old Town Hall, Green Market (01228) 625600.

London 317 – Blackpool 95 – Edinburgh 101 – Glasgow 100 – Leeds 124 – Liverpool 127 – Manchester 122 – Newcastle upon Tyne 59.

Plan on next page

Cumbria Park, 32 Scotland Rd, CA3 9DG, North : 1 m. on A 7 (01228) 522887, *enquiries@cumbriaparkhotel.co.uk, Fax (01228) 514796,* – – 120. VISA JCB.
closed 25-26 December – **Meals** (bar lunch Sunday) 12.95/15.95 and a la carte 18.25/25.00 **t.** 10.10 – **47 rm** 74.00/120.00 **t.** – SB.

Premier Lodge, Kingstown Rd, CA3 0AT, North : 1 ¾ m. on A 7 (0870) 7001348, *Fax (0870) 7001349* – VISA.
Meals (grillrest.) a la carte approx. 12.50 **t.** 7.80 – **49 rm** 46.95 **t.**

Travel Inn, Warwick Rd, CA1 2WF, East : 1 ½ m. on A 69 (01228) 545290, *Fax (01228) 545354* – rm, VISA.
Meals (grill rest.) – **44 rm** 41.95 **t.**

Number Thirty One, 31 Howard Pl, CA1 1HR, (01228) 597080, *bestpep@aol.com, Fax (01228) 597080,* « Victorian town house » – VISA JCB. BY a
March-October – **Meals** (by arrangement) 20.00/25.00 12.00 – **3 rm** 65.00/95.00.

Fern Lee, 9 St Aidan's Rd, CA1 1LT, (01228) 511930, *Fax (01228) 511930* –
Meals (by arrangement) 10.00 **st.** – **8 rm** 30.00/45.00 **st.** BY e

Courtfield House without rest., 169 Warwick Rd, CA1 1LP, (01228) 522767, *mdawes @courtfield.fsnet.co.uk* – BY c
5 rm 25.00/40.00.

Langleigh House without rest., 6 Howard Pl, CA1 1HR, (01228) 530440, *Fax (01228) 530440* – BY s
closed 1 week Christmas – **4 rm** 25.00/40.00 **s.**

Magenta's, 18 Fisher St, CA3 8RH, (01228) 546363, *Fax (01228) 546363* – VISA JCB BY v
closed 1 week January, Sunday and Monday – **Meals** (dinner only) 19.00 and a la carte 19.50/25.20 **t.** 12.95.

No 10, 10 Eden Mount, Stanwix, CA3 9LY, North : ¾ m. on A 7. (01228) 524183, *Fax (01228) 524183* – VISA
closed February, 1 week late October, Sunday and Monday – **Meals** (booking essential) (dinner only) a la carte 17.50/26.60 **t.** 9.95.

CARLISLE

Annetwell Street .... AY 2
Botchergate.............. BZ
Bridge Street............ AY 3
Brunswick Street .... BZ 4
Castle Street............ BY 5
Cecil Street .... BZ 6
Charlotte Street .... AZ 7
Chiswick Street .... BY 8
Church Street .... AY 10
Eden Bridge .... BY 12
English Street............ BY 13
Lonsdale Street .... BY 14
Lowther Street............ BY 15
Port Road................. AY 16
St. Marys Gate............ BY 17
Scotch Street .... BY 19
Spencer Street .... BY 20
Tait Street .... BZ 21
The Lanes
Shopping Centre .... BY
Victoria Viaduct .... ABZ 24
West Tower Street .... BY 26
West Walls................ ABY 27
Wigton Road............... AZ 29

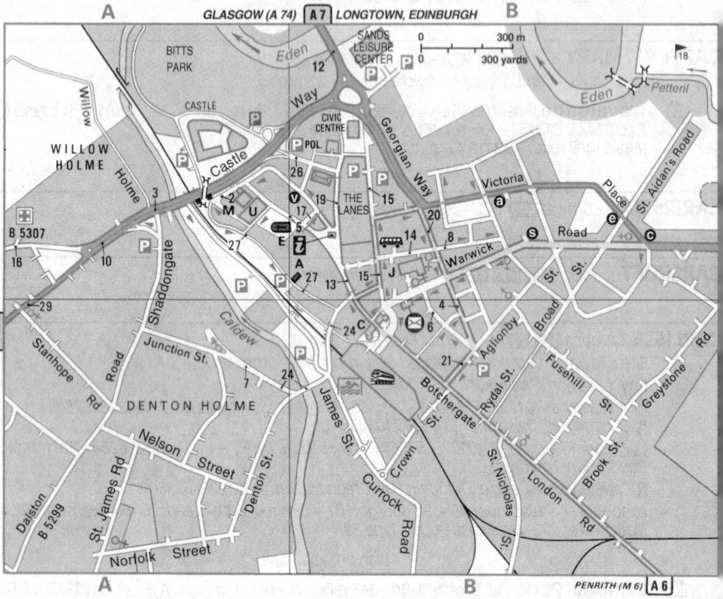

A
B
GLASGOW (A 74)
A 7
LONGTOWN, EDINBURGH
SANDS LEISURE CENTER
0
300 m
300 yards
BITTS PARK
Eden
CASTLE
CIVIC CENTRE
POL.
Way
Georgian Way
Y
WILLOW HOLME
Willow
Holme
Castle
Victoria
Place
St. Aidan's Road
Petteril
THE LANES
Road
Warwick
B 5307
COCKERMOUTH
A 595
Shaddongate
Caldew
Junction St.
Stanhope Rd
Road
Aglionby
Broad St.
Fusehill St.
Greystone Rd
Rydal St.
Botchergate St.
DENTON HOLME
James St.
Z
Nelson Street
Crown
Currock Road
St. James Rd
Denton St.
Dalston
B 5299
St. Nicholas St.
London Rd
Brook St.
Norfolk Street
PENRITH (M 6)
A 6

at Kingstown *North : 3 m. by A 7 – BY – ✉ Carlisle.*

Posthouse Carlisle, Park House Rd, CA3 0HR, at junction 44 of M 6 ✆ (0870) 400 9018, *Fax (01228) 543178,* Ls, ☰, ▢ – ⇔ rm, ▤ rest, TV ♿ P – 🏛 120. MC AE ⊙ VISA
Meals *(closed 31 December and Saturday lunch)* 15.00 (dinner) and a la carte 15.90/27.35 t. – 11.95 – ☕ 12.95 – **127 rm** 89.00 t.

at High Crosby *Northeast : 5 m. by A 7 and B 6264 – BY – off A 689 – ✉ Carlisle.*

Crosby Lodge Country House ⅋, CA6 4QZ, ✆ (01228) 573618, *crosbylodge@crosby_eden.demon.co.uk, Fax (01228) 573428,* ≤, « 18C country mansion », ⇔ – ⇔ rest, TV P. MC AE VISA
closed Christmas-mid January – **Meals** (Sunday dinner booking essential) a la carte 15.75/30.50 **t.** 12.50 – **11 rm** ☕ 85.00/150.00 **t.**

at Wetheral *East : 6¼ m. by A 69 – BZ – ✉ Carlisle.*

Crown, CA4 8ES, ✆ (01228) 561888, *info@crownhotelwetheral.co.uk, Fax (01228) 561637,* Ls, ☰, ▢, ⇔, squash – ⇔ TV ✆ ♿ P – 🏛 175. MC AE ⊙ VISA
Meals a la carte 26.00/36.00 **st.** – **49 rm** ☕ 102.00/122.00 **st.**, 2 suites – SB.

CARLTON-IN-COVERDALE *N. Yorks.* 402 O 21 – *see Middleham.*

CARLYON BAY *Cornwall* 403 F 33 – *see St. Austell.*

CARNFORTH *Lancs.* 402 L 21 – *see Lancaster.*

*Kataloge der **Michelin-Veröffentlichungen** erhalten Sie beim Buchhändler und direkt von **Michelin** (Karlsruhe).*

CARNON DOWNS *Cornwall* 403 E 33 – *see Truro.*

CARTERWAY HEADS *Northd.* 401 402 O 19 – ✉ *Shotley Bridge.*
London 272 – Carlisle 59 – Newcastle upon Tyne 21.

Manor House Inn with rm, DH8 9LX, on A 68 ✆ (01207) 255268, *manor@carterwayheads.com, Fax (01207) 255268* – TV P. MO AE VISA
closed dinner 25 December – **Meals** a la carte 15.70/24.15 **t.** 8.95 – **4 rm** ☕ 35.00/59.00 **t.**

CARTMEL *Cumbria* 402 L 21 – *see Grange-over-Sands.*

CARTMELL FELL *Cumbria* 402 L 21 – *see Newby Bridge.*

CASTERTON *Cumbria* 402 M 21 – *see Kirkby Lonsdale.*

CASTLE CARY *Somerset* 403 404 M 30 – *pop. 2 904.*
London 125 – Bristol 28 – Taunton 31 – Yeovil 13.

Bond's with rm, Ansford Hill, Ansford, BA7 7JL, North : ¾ m. by Ansford Rd on A 371 ✆ (01963) 350464, *bonds-bistro@faxvia.net, Fax (01963) 350464,* – TV P. MO VISA.
closed 1 week Christmas, Monday, Sunday dinner and Tuesday lunch – **Meals** (light lunch)/dinner a la carte 13.20/22.70 **st.** 10.50 – **7 rm** ☕ 58.00/69.50.

CASTLE COMBE *Wilts.* 403 404 N 29 *The West Country G.* – *pop. 347* – ✉ *Chippenham.*
See : *Village★★.*
London 110 – Bristol 23 – Chippenham 6.

Manor House H. and Golf Club, SN14 7HR, ✆ (01249) 782206, *enquiries@manorhouse.co.uk, Fax (01249) 782159,* « Part 14C manor house in park », , heated, 18, , , – rest, TV P – 50. MO AE VISA JCB.
The Bybrook : **Meals** 18.95/45.00 **st.** 19.75 – ☕ 15.00 – **44 rm** 145.00/350.00 **t.**, 2 suites – SB.

Castle Inn, SN14 7HN, ✆ (01249) 783030, *res@castle-inn.co.uk, Fax (01249) 782315,* « Part 12C » – rest, TV. MO AE VISA.
Meals a la carte 16.65/28.65 **s.** 14.75 – **11 rm** ☕ 69.50/95.00 **st.** – SB.

at Ford *South : 1 ¾ m. on A 420* – ✉ *Chippenham.*

White Hart Inn, SN14 8RP, ✆ (01249) 782213, *whitehart.ford@eldridge-pope.co.uk, Fax (01249) 783075* – TV P. MO AE VISA
*closed 25 December***Meals** *(closed dinner 26 December)* 13.95/15.95 (lunch) and dinner a la carte 14.10/28.50 **t.** 11.95 – **11 rm** ☕ 65.00/90.00 **t.**

at Nettleton Shrub *West : 2 m. by B 4039 on Nettleton rd (Fosse Way)* – ✉ *Chippenham.*

Fosse Farmhouse, SN14 7NJ, ✆ (01249) 782286, *caroncooper@compuserve.com, Fax (01249) 783066,* – rest, TV P. MO AE VISA JCB
Meals (by arrangement) 25.00 **t.** 14.00 – **6 rm** ☕ 65.00/125.00 **t.** – SB.

CASTLE DONINGTON *Leics.* 402 403 404 P 25 – *pop. 6 007* – ✉ *Derby.*
East Midlands Airport : ✆ (01332) 852852, S : by B 6540 and A 453.
London 123 – Birmingham 38 – Leicester 23 – Nottingham 13.

Priest House on the River, Kings Mills, DE74 2RR, West : 1 ¾ m. by Park Lane ✆ (01332) 810649, *priesthouse@arcadianhotels.co.uk, Fax (01332) 811141,* ←, « Riverside setting », , – rest, TV P – 130. MO AE VISA
Meals 18.00/42.00 and dinner a la carte 20.00/34.50 **st.** 13.50 – ☕ 12.95 – **43 rm** 140.00/185.00 **st.**, 2 suites – SB.

CASTLEFORD *W. Yorks.* 402 P/Q 22.
London 197 – Leeds 11 – Manchester 53 – Nottingham 70 – Sheffield 37 – York 29.

Premier Lodge, Commerce Park, Pioneer Way, WF10 5TG, Southwest : 2 m. by A 655 ✆ (01977) 665400, *Fax (01977) 667240* – , rest, TV P. MO AE VISA.
Meals (grill rest.) (dinner only) a la carte approx. 12.45 **t.** 8.45 – **62 rm** 46.95 **t.**

CASTOR *Peterborough* 404 S 26 – *see Peterborough.*

CATEL *Guernsey (Channel Islands)* 403 P 33 and 230 ⑨ – *see Channel Islands.*

CAUNTON *Notts.* 402 404 R 24 – *see Newark-on-Trent.*

CAXTON *Cambs.*

London 67 – Bedford 18 – Cambridge 12 – Huntingdon 7.

Church Farm, Gransden Rd, CB3 8PL, (01954) 719543, *churchfarm@aol.com, Fax (01954) 718999,* « Part 17C farmhouse », – P. MC AE VISA.
Meals (communal dining) 21.50 11.50 – **4 rm** 45.00/85.00 – SB.

CHADDESLEY CORBETT *Worcs.* 403 404 N 26 – *see Kidderminster.*

CHAGFORD *Devon* 403 I 31 *The West Country G. – pop. 1 417.*

Env. : *Dartmoor National Park*★★.

London 218 – Exeter 17 – Plymouth 27.

Gidleigh Park, TQ13 8HH, Northwest : 2 m. by Gidleigh Rd (01647) 432367, *gidleighpark@gidleigh.co.uk, Fax (01647) 432574,* ← Teign Valley, woodland and Meldon Hill, « Timbered country house, water garden », – rest, TV P. MC VISA JCB
Meals (booking essential) 33.00/72.50 **st.** 20.00 – **12 rm** (dinner included) 260.00/500.00 **st.**, 3 suites
Spec. Ravioli of lobster with cabbage and girolles. John Dory with aubergine galette, lemon thyme sauce. Poached cherries, cherry and kirsch ice cream.

Glendarah House without rest., Lower St, TQ13 8BZ, (01647) 433270, *enquiries@glendarah-house.co.uk,* ←, – TV P. MC VISA
closed 11 December-10 January – **7 rm** 35.00/58.00 **s.**

22 Mill Street with rm, 22 Mill St, TQ13 8AW, (01647) 432244, *Fax (01647) 433101* – rest, TV. MC VISA
closed 2 weeks January and 1 week May – **Meals** *(closed Sunday and lunch Monday and Tuesday)* 17.50/32.50 **st.** – 5.50 – **2 rm** 35.00/50.00 **st.**

at Easton *Northeast : 1½ m. on A 382 – ✉ Chagford.*

Easton Court, Easton Cross, TQ13 8JL, (01647) 433469, *stay@easton.co.uk, Fax (01647) 433654,* « Part 15C thatched house », – TV P. MC VISA
closed January – **Meals** (booking essential) (lunch by arrangement)/dinner 25.00 **t.** 10.95 – **8 rm** 57.00/95.00 **t.** – SB.

at Sandypark *Northeast : 2¼ m. on A 382 – ✉ Chagford.*

Mill End, TQ13 8JN, on A 382 (01647) 432282, *millendhotel@talk21.com, Fax (01647) 433106,* « Country house with water mill », – rest, TV P. MC AE VISA JCB
Meals (light lunch)/dinner 22.50/27.50 **t.** 12.00 – **16 rm** 80.00/120.00 – SB.

CHALGROVE *Oxon.* 403 404 Q 29 – *pop. 2 832.*

London 57 – Aylesbury 12 – Oxford 17 – Reading 32.

Red Lion Inn, 115 High St, OX44 7SS, (01865) 890625, *Fax (01865) 890795,* – . MC AE VISA JCB
closed 27 December and Sunday and Monday dinner – **Meals** (booking essential Christmas and New Year) (light lunch Monday and Tuesday) a la carte 12.70/23.45 **t.** 9.75.

CHANNEL ISLANDS 403 OPQ 33 and 230 ⑨ ⑩ ⑪ *The West Country G. – pop. 145 920.*

ALDERNEY

403 Q 33 and 230 ⑨ *The West Country G. – pop. 2 297.*

See : *Braye Bay★ – Mannez Garenne (≤★ from Quesnard Lighthouse) – Telegraph Bay★ Vallee des Trois Vaux★ – Clonque Bay★.*

(01481) 822886 - Booking Office : Aurigny Air Services (01481) 822888.

States Office, Queen Elizabeth II St (01481) 822811.

Braye.

First and Last, GY9 3TH, (01481) 823162, ≤ harbour – VISA
May-October – **Meals** *(closed Monday)* (dinner only) a la carte 18.45/30.00.

St Anne.

Belle Vue, The Butes, GY9 3UN, (01481) 822844, *bellevue@alderney.ne*
Fax (01481) 823601 – rest, TV. VISA JCB.
closed Christmas and New Year – **Meals** a la carte 12.30/25.45 6.25 – **17 rm** 50.0
100.00 – SB.

GUERNSEY

403 OP 33 and 230 ⑨ ⑩ *The West Country G. – pop. 58 867.*

See : *Island★ – Pezeries Point★★ – Icart Point★★ – Côbo Bay★★ – St Martin's Point★★ St. Apolline's Chapel★ – Vale Castle★ – Fort Doyle★ – La Gran'mere du Chimquiere★ Rocquaine Bay★ – Jerbourg Point★.*

Service Air (01481) 237682, Aurigny Air (01481) 37426.

from St Peter Port to France (St Malo) and Jersey (St Helier) (Emeraude Lines) – fro St Peter Port to Jersey (St Helier) and Weymouth (Condor Ferries Ltd).

– from St Peter Port to France (St Malo) and Jersey (St Helier) (Condor Ferries Ltd) weekly – from St Peter Port to France (Dielette) (Emeraude Lines) (summer only) (1 h 15 m – from St Peter Port to Herm (Herm Seaway) (25 mn) – from St Peter Port to Sark (Isle c Sark Shipping Co. Ltd) (45 mn) – from St Peter Port to Jersey (St Helier) (Emeraude Line (50 mn) – from St Peter Port to Jersey (St Helier) (Condor Ferries Ltd) daily except Sunday.

P.O. Box 23, North Esplanade (01481) 2723552 – Passenger Terminal, New Jet (01481) 715885 – The Airport, La Villiaze, Forest (01481) 237267.

Catel/Castel.

Hougue du Pommier, Hougue du Pommier Rd, GY5 7FQ, (01481) 256531, *hot @houguedupommier.guernsey.net, Fax (01481) 256260*, , , heated – TV
AE VISA
Meals *(closed January-12 February)* (dinner only) 17.25 and a la carte 21.00/28.50 **s.** 9.8
– **43 rm** 62.00/104.00 **s.** – SB.

Cobo Bay, Cobo Coast Rd, GY5 7HB, (01481) 257102, *Fax (01481) 254542*, ≤, –
rest, TV P. VISA.
closed 6 January-February – **Meals** (dinner only and Sunday lunch) 18.50 8.95 – **36 rr**
44.00/108.00 – SB.

Fermain Bay – *St. Peter Port.*

La Favorita, Fermain Bay, GY4 6SD, (01481) 235666, *info@favorita.con*
Fax (01481) 235413, ≤, , , , – TV P. AE VISA.
closed January, February and Christmas – **Meals** (bar lunch)/dinner 16.25 and a la cart
15.40/22.75 **s.** – **37 rm** 57.00/106.00 **s.** – SB.

Forest – *pop. 1 386.*

Maison Bel Air without rest., Le Chene, GY8 0AL, (01481) 238503, *juliette@maiso belair.com, Fax (01481) 239403*, – TV P. VISA.
6 rm 35.00/55.00.

Kings Mills.

Fleur du Jardin with rm, GY5 7JT, (01481) 257996, *info@fleurdujardin.guernsey.ne*
Fax (01481) 256834, , heated, – TV P. AE VISA JCB.
Meals (bar lunch)/dinner 14.95 and a la carte 16.40/22.95 **s.** 7.95 – **17 rm** 72.50
97.00 **s.** – SB.

St Martin – *pop. 6 082.*

St Peter Port 2.

Jerbourg, Jerbourg Point, GY4 6BJ, (01481) 238826, *hjerb8765@aol.com, Fax (01481) 238238,* sea and neighbouring Channel Islands, rest, P. VISA.
Meals 17.00 (dinner) and a la carte 15.50/27.50 **s.** 9.00 – **32 rm** 50.00/140.00 **s.**

Idlerocks, Jerbourg Point, GY4 6BJ, (01481) 237711, *info@idlerocks.com, Fax (01481) 235592,* sea and neighbouring Channel Islands, heated, P. AE VISA JCB
Meals (bar lunch Monday-Saturday)/dinner 17.00 9.90 – **28 rm** 43.00/86.00 – SB.

Bon Port, Moulin Huet Bay, GY4 6EW, (01481) 239249, *mail@bonport.com, Fax (01481) 239596,* Moulin Huet Bay and Jerbourg Point, rest, P. AE VISA.
Meals 12.50/18.50 and a la carte 11.50/25.50 10.00 – **15 rm** 61.00/130.00 – SB.

Green Acres, Les Hubits, GY4 6LS, (01481) 235711, *greenacres@guernsey.net, Fax (01481) 235978,* heated, rest, rest, P – 40. AE VISA.
24 March-20 October – **Meals** (bar lunch)/dinner 15.00 and a la carte 15.00/25.00 9.50 – **47 rm** 33.00/92.00.

Saints Bay, Icart, GY4 6JG, (01481) 238888, *info@saintsbayhotel.com, Fax (01481) 235558,* heated, rm, P. AE VISA JCB.
Meals (bar lunch)/dinner 17.50 and a la carte 16.35/26.95 12.40 – **36 rm** 68.00/114.00 – SB.

La Barbarie, Saints Bay, GY4 6ES, (01481) 235217, *barbarie@guernsey.net, Fax (01481) 235208,* heated, P. VISA.
closed 23-27 December – **Meals** (bar lunch Monday-Saturday)/dinner 15.95 and a la carte 14.65/24.95 8.95 – **22 rm** 54.50/85.00, 1 suite – SB.

Bella Luce, La Fosse, Moulin Huet, GY4 6EB, (01481) 238764, *info@bellalucehotel.guernsey.net, Fax (01481) 239561,* heated, rest, P. AE VISA
Meals (bar lunch Monday-Saturday)/dinner 16.00 and a la carte 15.00/22.50 **s.** 8.00 – **21 rm** 54.00/108.00.

La Michele, Les Hubits, GY4 6NB, (01481) 238065, *lamichelehotel@ukgateway.net, Fax (01481) 239492,* heated, rest, P. AE VISA.
Easter-16 October – **Meals** (residents only) (dinner only) 12.50 9.00 – **16 rm** (dinner included) 34.00/92.00 – SB.

The Auberge, Jerbourg Rd, GY4 6BH, (01481) 238485, *dixneuf@itl.net, Fax (01481) 710936,* Sea and neighbouring Channel Islands, P. AE VISA JCB
Meals a la carte 17.85/26.40 10.95.

St Peter in the Wood – *pop. 2 242* – *St Peters.*

Café du Moulin (Vincent), Rue de Quanteraine, GY7 9DP, (01481) 265944, *vincentfam@guernsey.net, Fax (01481) 267343,* « Converted granary », VISA
closed 2 weeks February, 2 weeks November, Monday, Tuesday lunch in summer and Sunday dinner in winter – **Meals** 14.50/24.00 and a la carte 21.00/32.50 **s.** 10.50
Spec. Roast scallops, asparagus fricassee, dill oil. Roast rack of lamb, crushed new potatoes. Raspberry sablé with clotted cream.

St Peter Port *The West Country G.* – *pop. 16 648.*

See : *Town*★★ – *St Peter's Church*★ Z – *Hauteville House*★ *AC* Z – *Castle Cornet*★ (★) *AC* Z.

Env. : *Saumarez Park*★ *(Guernsey Folk Museum*★*), W : 2 m. by road to Catel* Z – *Little Chapel*★, *SW : 2¼ m. by Mount Durand road* Z.

18 *Rohais, St Pierre Park* *(01481) 727039,* Z.

St Pierre Park, Rohais, GY1 1FD, West : 1 ½ m. by Grange Rd (01481) 728282, *enquiries@stpierrepark.co.uk, Fax (01481) 712041,* 9, rest, P – 200. AE VISA.
Café Renoir : **Meals** a la carte 18.15/25.70 9.50 – (see also ***Victor Hugo*** below) – **131 rm** 130.00/350.00 **s.** – SB.

Duke of Richmond, Cambridge Park, GY1 1UY, (01481) 726221, *duke@guernsey.net, Fax (01481) 728945,* heated – rm, – 100. AE VISA JCB Y c
Meals 10.00/16.50 and a la carte 14.00/22.00 **st.** 10.00 – **74 rm** 65.00/120.00 **st.**, 1 suite.

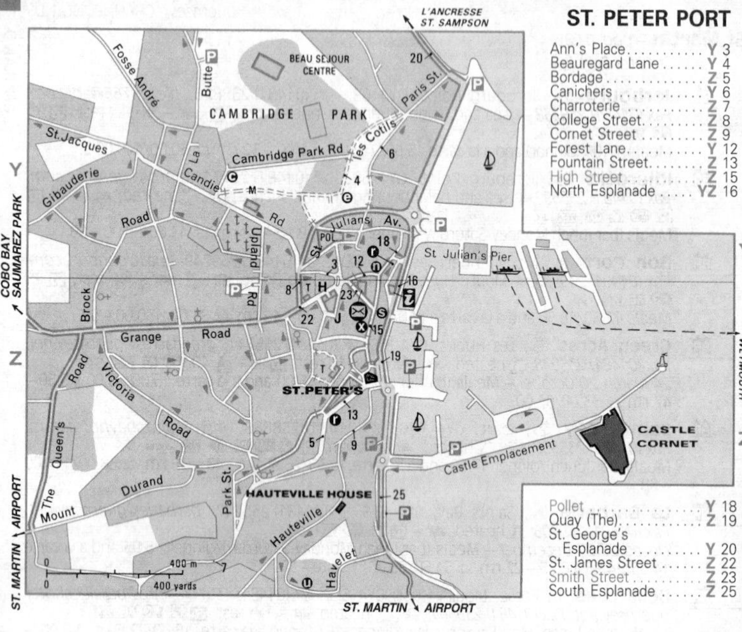

Les Rocquettes, Les Gravees, GY1 1RN, West : ¾ m. by Grange Rd ✆ (01481) 722146, *rocquettes@sarniahotels.com, Fax (01481) 7214543*, – TV P. MC AE VISA.
Meals (bar lunch)/dinner 14.75 and a la carte 10.50/28.00 10.00 – **51 rm** (dinner included) 67.00/134.00.

De Havelet, Havelet, GY1 1BA, ✆ (01481) 722199, *havelet@sarniahotels.com, Fax (01481) 714057*, – TV P. MC AE VISA. Z u
Wellington Boot : Meals (dinner only and Sunday lunch)/dinner 15.00 and a la carte 18.65/25.20 9.00 – ***Havelet Grill :*** Meals *(closed Sunday lunch and Monday dinner)* 10.00/17.50 and a la carte 17.00/32.00 **s.** 9.00 – **34 rm** 62.00/124.00 **s.**

Moore's Central, Le Pollet, GY1 1WH, ✆ (01481) 724452, *moores@sarniahotels.com, Fax (01481) 714037*, – TV. MC AE VISA. Y n
Conservatory : Meals 10.00/16.00 and a la carte 16.00/29.00 **s.** 9.25 – ***Library :*** Meals (carvery) a la carte 10.45/23.50 **s.** 9.25 – **49 rm** 56.00/172.00 – SB.

La Frégate, Les Cotils, GY1 1UT, ✆ (01481) 724624, *lafregate@guernsey.net, Fax (01481) 720443*, ⩤ town and harbour, – rest, TV P. MC AE VISA JCB. Y e
The Restaurant : Meals 14.50/22.50 and a la carte 23.15/32.85 **s.** 9.50 – **13 rm** 65.00/110.00.

Victor Hugo (at St Pierre Park H.), Rohais, GY1 1FD, West : 1 ½ m. by Grange Rd ✆ (01481) 728282, *Fax (01481) 712041* – P. MC AE VISA
closed lunch midweek May-October, Sunday dinner September-May and Saturday lunch – **Meals** - Seafood - 14.95/21.50 and dinner a la carte 32.00/56.00 12.50.

Le Nautique, Quay Steps, GY1 2LE, ✆ (01481) 721714, *Fax (01481) 721786*, ⩤ – MC AE VISA Z s
closed 1 week October, Saturday lunch and Sunday – **Meals** - Seafood specialities - 14.50 (lunch) and a la carte 16.00/31.00 9.50.

Merchant House, 38 High St, GY1 2JU, ✆ (01481) 728019, *dgmann@cinergy.co.uk, Fax (01481) 725875* – . MC VISA Z x
closed Sunday in winter – **Meals** 13.50/15.75 and a la carte 19.15/30.85 10.25.

The Absolute End, Longstore, GY1 2BG, North : ¾ m. by St George's Esplanade ✆ (01481) 723822, *Fax (01481) 729129* – MC AE VISA JCB
closed January, 25 and 31 December and Sunday – **Meals** - Seafood - 12.50 (lunch) and a la carte 16.25/34.00 9.90.

XX **Frogs,** 6 Tower Hill, GY1 1DF, ☎ (01481) 710088, *frenchrestaurant@gtonline.net, Fax (01481) 710878,* – . MO VISA Z r
closed Saturday lunch and Sunday – **Meals** - French - 9.45/11.45 (lunch) and a la carte 22.50/24.70 **s.** 9.50.

X **Christies (Restaurant),** Le Pollet, GY1 1WQ, ☎ (01481) 726624, *Fax (01481) 729138,* – . MO AE VISA Y r
Meals 9.50/17.95 and a la carte 23.25/27.65 9.75.

St Saviour – *pop. 2 419.*
St Peter Port 4.

L'Atlantique, Perelle Bay, GY7 9NA, ☎ (01481) 264056, *enquiries@perellebay.com, Fax (01481) 263800,* ≤, heated, – TV P. MO VISA.
March-October – **Meals** – (see ***L'Atlantique*** below) – **23 rm** 55.00/97.00 – SB.

XX **L'Atlantique** (at L'Atlantique H.), Perelle Bay, GY7 9NA, ☎ (01481) 264056, *Fax (01481) 263800,* – P. MO VISA
March-October – **Meals** (dinner only and Sunday lunch)/dinner 18.50 and a la carte 20.00/26.80 9.50.

Vale.

Bordeaux , Bordeaux Bay, GY3 5LX, ☎ (01481) 247461, *Fax (01481) 243669,* – TV P
April-October – **Meals** (by arrangement) 12.00 **s.** 6.80 – **8 rm** 31.00/56.00 **s.**

Vazon Bay – ✉ *Catel.*

La Grande Mare, Vazon Coast Rd, GY5 7LL, ☎ (01481) 256576, *Fax (01481) 256532,* ≤, , , heated, , 18, , – TV P – 30. MO AE VISA.
Meals 12.95/19.95 and a la carte 23.50/35.00 8.95 – **11 rm** 59.00/148.00, **13 suites** 178.00/218.00 – SB.

HERM

403 P 33 and 230 ⑩ *The West Country G.* – *pop. 97.*

See : *Le Grand Monceau*★.

to Guernsey (St. Peter Port) (Herm Seaway) (20 mn).

White House , GY1 3HR, ☎ (01481) 722159, *hotel@herm-island.com, Fax (01481) 710066,* « Private island setting ≤ Belle Greve Bay and Guernsey », heated, , , – rest. MO AE VISA JCB.
April-6 October – ***Conservatory :*** **Meals** (booking essential) 15.00/21.00 9.10 – ***Ship Inn :*** **Meals** *(closed winter)* (bar lunch)/dinner a la carte 12.00/18.00 9.10 – **39 rm** (dinner included) 71.00/142.00.

JERSEY

403 OP 33 and 230 ⑪ *The West Country G.* – *pop. 85 150.*

See : *Island*★★ – *Jersey Zoo*★★ *AC* – *Jersey Museum*★ – *Eric Young Orchid Foundation*★ – *St Catherine's Bay*★ (≤★★) – *Grosnez Point*★ – *Devil's Hole*★ – *St Matthews Church, Millbrook (glasswork*★*)* – *La Hougue Bie*★ *(Neolithic tomb*★ *AC)* – *Waterworks Valley - Hamptonne Country Life Museum*★ – *St. Catherine's Bay*★ (≤★★) – *Noirmont Point*★.

States of Jersey Airport : ☎ *(01534) 490999.*

from St Helier to France (St Malo) and Guernsey (St Peter Port) (Emeraude Lines) – from St Helier to France (Granville) (Emeraude Lines) (summer only) (1 h) – from St Helier to France (Dielette) (Emeraude Lines) (summer only) (1 h 10 mn) – from St Helier to France (Carteret) (Emeraude Lines) (summer only) (55 mn) – from St Helier to Sark (Emeraude Lines) (50 mn) – from St Helier to Guernsey (St Peter Port) and Weymouth (Condor Ferries Ltd).

from St Helier to France (Granville and St Malo) (Emeraude Lines and Condor Ferries Ltd) (summer only) – from St Helier to France (St Malo) (Condor Ferries Ltd) 3 weekly – from Gorey to France (Carteret) (Emeraude Lines) (summer only) (30-40 mn) – from St. Helier to Guernsey (St. Peter Port) (Condor Ferries Ltd) (50 mn) – from St. Helier to Guernsey (St. Peter Port) (Condor Ferries Ltd) daily except Sunday.

Liberation Sq, St Helier ☎ *(01534) 500777.*

Corbiere – ✉ *St. Brelade.*
St. Helier 8.

XXX **Sea Crest** with rm, Petit Port, JE3 8HH, ☎ (01534) 746353, *seacrest@super.net.uk, Fax (01534) 747316,* ≤, , , – rest, TV P. MO AE VISA.
closed late January-February – **Meals** *(closed Sunday dinner October-March and Monday)* a la carte 25.25/35.75 12.75 – **7 rm** 85.00/130.00.

ENGLAND

Gorey *The West Country G.* – ✉ *St. Martin.*

See : *Mont Orgueil Castle★ (≤★★) AC.*

St. Helier 4.

Old Court House, Gorey Village, JE3 9FS, ℘ (01534) 854444, *ochhotel@itl.ne* *Fax (01534) 853587*, heated, – TV P. VISA JCB.
mid April-mid October – **Meals** (bar lunch)/dinner 17.00 8.50 – **58 rm** (dinner include 65.00/130.00.

Moorings, Corey Pier, JE3 6EW, ℘ (01534) 853633, *casino@itl.net, Fax (01534) 857618* rest, TV. AE VISA
Meals 14.75/32.00 and a la carte 25.25/44.95 8.75 – **15 rm** 52.00/110.00 – SB.

Jersey Pottery (Garden Restaurant), Gorey Village, JE3 9EP, ℘ (01534) 85111 *jsypot@itl.net, Fax (01534) 856403*, « Working pottery », – P. AE VISA JCB
closed 23 December-26 January and Monday – **Meals** - Seafood - (lunch only) 15.00 and a carte 16.75/30.75 **s.** 11.95.

Suma's, Corey Hill, JE3 6ET, ℘ (01534) 853291, *Fax (01534) 851913*, ≤, – . AE VISA
closed 23 December-17 January – **Meals** (booking essential) 11.95/15.0 (lunch) and a la carte 20.00/34.00 **s.** 8.75.

Village Bistro (Cameron), Corey Village, JE3 9EP, ℘ (01534) 853429, *Fax (01534) 85342* – AE VISA JCB
closed Sunday dinner and Monday except Bank Holidays – **Meals** 13.50/14.9 (lunch) and a la carte 25.10/28.85 7.50
Spec. Terrine of foie gras with endive salad, orange and hazelnut oil. Roast salmon on warr potato, crab salad, tomato and cucumber dressing. Panna cotta, compôte of citrus fruit and shortbread fingers.

Green Island.

Green Island, St Clement, JE2 6LS, ℘ (01534) 857787, *amw@psilink.co.u* *Fax (01534) 619309*, « Beachside setting » – VISA
closed 2 weeks November, 23 December-2 January, Monday, Sunday dinner and Tuesda November-February – **Meals** - Seafood specialities - (booking essential) a la carte 21.50 25.00 10.25.

Grève De Lecq – ✉ *St. Ouen.*

Des Pierres, JE3 2DT, on B 65 ℘ (01534) 481858, *despierres@localdial.com* *Fax (01534) 485273* – TV P. VISA.
Meals (residents only) (dinner only) 10.85 9.00 – **16 rm** 34.00/68.00.

Grouville – *pop. 4 658.*

Lavender Villa, Rue a Don, JE3 9DX, on A 3 ℘ (01534) 854937, *Fax (01534) 856147*, – rest, TV P. VISA.
March-October – **Meals** (residents only) (dinner only) 10.00 4.70 – **21 rm** (dinne included) 37.00/74.00.

La Haule – ✉ *St. Brelade.*

La Place, Route du Coin, JE3 8BT, by B 25 on B 43 ℘ (01534) 744261, *hotlaplace@ac com, Fax (01534) 745164*, heated, – TV P – 100. AE VISA.
Knights : **Meals** (dinner only and Sunday lunch September to May)/dinner 27.0 and a la carte 24.50/33.00 12.75 – **42 rm** 116.00/224.00 **s.** – SB.

La Haule Manor, St Aubin's Bay, JE3 8BS, ℘ (01534) 741426, *Fax (01534) 74550* ≤ St Aubin's Fort and Bay, – rest, TV P. VISA.
Meals 10.00/14.00 and a la carte approx. 15.00 **s.** 9.00 – **14 rm** 85.00/156.00.

Au Caprice, Route de la Haule, JE3 8BA, on A 1 ℘ (01534) 722083, *aucaprice@jerseymai co.uk, Fax (01534) 280058* – TV. VISA.
April-October – **Meals** (by arrangement) 8.00 **s.** 7.00 – **12 rm** 39.00/56.00 **s.**

La Pulente – ✉ *St. Brelade.*

Les Mielles G. & C.C., St. Ouens Bay ℘ (01534) 482787.

St. Helier 7.

Atlantic, Le Mont de la Pulente, JE3 8HE, on B 35 ℘ (01534) 744101, *info@theatlanti hotel.com, Fax (01534) 744102*, ≤, heated, – rest, TV – 60. AE VISA.
closed January and February – **Meals** 17.50/30.00 and dinner a la carte 29.95/42.70 s 12.50 – **49 rm** 155.00/265.00 **s.**, 1 suite – SB.

La Rocque.
St. Helier 8.

XX **Borsalino Rocque,** JE3 9FF, ✆ (01534) 852111, *Fax (01534) 856404,* – P. MC AE VISA
closed 25-26 December and Tuesday – **Meals** - Seafood - 8.75/22.50 and a la carte 18.60/31.45 ₰ 10.75.

Rozel Bay – ✉ *St. Martin.*
St. Helier 6.

Chateau La Chaire ⛰, Rozel Valley, JE3 6AJ, ✆ (01534) 863354, *res@chateau-la-chaire.co.uk, Fax (01534) 865137,* , « Victorian country house », – rest, TV P. MC AE ① VISA JCB.
Meals 16.00 (lunch) and a la carte 28.50/35.20 ₰ 13.50 – **13 rm** 127.00/220.00 **s.**, 1 suite – SB.

Beau Couperon, JE3 6AN, ✆ (01534) 865522, *beaucouperon@southernhotels.com, Fax (01534) 865332,* ≤, heated – rest, TV P. MC AE VISA
22 March-28 October – **Meals** 12.90/17.50 and a la carte 13.00/24.00 ₰ 9.00 – **33 rm** 42.20/84.40 **s.**

XX **Frere de Mer,** Le Mont de Rozel, JE3 6AN, East : ½ m. on B 38 ✆ (01534) 861000, *Fax (01534) 864007,* ≤ Sea and French coastline, – P. MC AE VISA JCB
closed Monday – **Meals** - Seafood specialities - 10.50/14.50 and a la carte 20.50/34.50 ₰ 9.50.

St Aubin – ✉ *St Brelade.*
St Helier 4.

La Tour, High St, JE3 8BZ, ✆ (01534) 743770, *Fax (01534) 747143,* ≤ St. Aubin's Fort and Bay, – TV P. MC ① VISA
closed 2 January-16 March – ***Rooks :*** **Meals** (light lunch)/dinner 13.00 and a la carte 17.00/28.00 – **24 rm** 45.50/112.00 **s.**, 1 suite.

Somerville, Mont du Boulevard, JE3 8AD, South : ¾ m. via harbour ✆ (01534) 741226, *somerville@dolanhotels.com, Fax (01534) 746621,* ≤ St. Aubin's Bay, heated, – TV P. MC AE VISA.
Meals (livemusic and dancing Saturday) (bar lunch Monday to Saturday)/dinner 9.95/17.00 and dinner a la carte 14.50/22.50 **s.** ₰ 9.50 – **59 rm** 50.00/100.00 – SB.

Mont de La Roque, Mont de La Roque, JE3 8BQ, ✆ (01534) 742942, *mdlrq@supernet.uk, Fax (01534) 747841,* ≤ St. Aubin's Fort and Bay, – rest, TV P. MC AE VISA.
March-October – ***Le Mirage :*** **Meals** (dinner only and Sunday lunch)/dinner a la carte 18.40/29.85 **t.** ₰ 7.75 – **31 rm** 60.00/80.00 **t.**, 2 suites.

Panorama without rest., La Rue du Crocquet, JE3 8BZ, ✆ (01534) 742429, *Fax (01534) 745940,* ≤ St. Aubin's Fort and Bay, – TV. MC AE ① VISA JCB.
mid March-October – **16 rm** 41.00/94.00.

St Magloire, High St, JE3 8BZ, ✆ (01534) 741302, *Fax (01534) 744148* – rest, TV. MC VISA.
mid March-mid October – **Meals** (residents only) (dinner only) 8.50 ₰ 5.75 – **11 rm** 32.50/55.00.

Sabots d'or, High St, JE3 8BZ, ✆ (01534) 43732, *sandra.lecone@jerseymail.co.uk, Fax (01534) 490142* – rest, TV. MC AE ① VISA JCB
Meals (by arrangement) 8.50 **s.** ₰ 7.00 – **12 rm** 26.00/56.00 – SB.

Porthole Cottage without rest., La Route au Moestre (Market Hill), JE3 8AE, ✆ (01534) 745007, *portcott@itt.net, Fax (01534) 490336,* ≤, – TV P. MC AE VISA JCB.
10 March-28 October – **11 rm** 31.50/63.00 **s.**

Old Court House Inn with rm, St Aubin's Harbour, JE3 8AB, ✆ (01534) 746433, *ochstaubins@jerseymail.co.uk, Fax (01534) 745103,* ≤, – TV. MC AE ① VISA.
closed 25 December – **Meals** 12.95/17.95 and a la carte 21.95/34.95 ₰ 8.95 – **8 rm** 55.00/120.00, 1 suite – SB.

St Brelade's Bay *The West Country G.* – *pop. 9 560* – ✉ *St Brelade.*
See : *Fishermen's Chapel (frescoes★).*
St Helier 6.

L'Horizon, JE3 8EF, ✆ (01534) 743101, *hotellhorizon@jerseymail.co.uk, Fax (01534) 746269,* ≤ St. Brelade's Bay, , , , – TV P – 150. MC AE ① VISA.
Crystal Room : **Meals** (dinner only and Sunday lunch)/dinner 29.00 and a la carte 24.00/56.00 **t.** ₰ 12.50 – (see also ***The Grill*** below) – **104 rm** (dinner included) 115.00/230.00 **t.**, 3 suites – SB.

ENGLAND

St Brelade's Bay, Rue de la Baie, JE3 8EF, ✆ (01534) 746141, *info@stbreladesbayhote com, Fax (01534) 747278,* < St. Brelade's Bay, « Gardens », heated, – rest, P. VISA.
May-September – **Meals** 15.00/25.00 and a la carte 21.00/37.00 **t.** 9.00 – **71 rm** 101.00/202.00 **s.**, 1 suite.

Golden Sands, La Route de la Baie, JE3 8EF, ✆ (01534) 741241, *goldensands@dola hotels.com, Fax (01534) 499366,* < – , rest, . VISA.
April-October – **Meals** (bar lunch)/dinner a la carte 14.50/21.50 **s.** – **62 rm** 54.00 148.00 **s.**

Chateau Valeuse, Rue de la Valeuse, JE3 8EE, ✆ (01534) 746281, *chatval@itl.ne Fax (01534) 747110,* heated, – rest, P. VISA JCB.
April-October – **Meals** *(closed Sunday dinner)* 12.00/19.00 and dinner a la carte 18.50/27.1 7.50 – **34 rm** 40.00/122.00.

The Grill (at L'Horizon H.), JE3 8EF, ✆ (01534) 490082, *Fax (01534) 746269* – P. VISA
closed lunch Sunday and Monday – **Meals** 29.00 (dinner) and a la carte 26.00/32.50 t 12.50.

St Helier *The West Country G. – pop. 27 523.*

See : *Jersey Museum★ AC* Z – *Elizabeth Castle (<★) AC* Z – *Fort Regent (<★ AC)* Z.
Env. : *St Peter's Valley - German Underground Hospital★ AC, NW : 4 m. by A 1, A 1 St Peter's Valley rd and C 112.*

Plan opposite

De Vere Grand, Esplanade, JE4 8WD, ✆ (01534) 722301, *grand.jersey@devere-hotels com, Fax (01534) 737815,* <, , rest, – 180. VISA Y
Meals – (see ***Victoria's*** below) – **109 rm** 95.00/150.00, 5 suites – SB.

Hotel de France, St Saviours Rd, JE1 7XP, ✆ (01534) 614000, *enggen@defrance.co.u Fax (01534) 614299,* heated, , squash – P – 1000. VIS JCB. Y
closed Christmas and New Year – **Meals** (dinner only) 20.00/28.00 a la carte 24.00/31.00 st 9.95 – **297 rm** 99.00/160.00 **s.**, 8 suites.

Pomme d'Or, Liberation Sq, JE1 3UF, ✆ (01534) 880110, *pomme@seymour-hotels jersey.com, Fax (01534) 737781* – , rm, rest, – 180. VISA Z
Harbour Room : **Meals** (carvery) 15.50/17.50 and a la carte (approx.) 15.50 9.00 – (se also ***La Petite Pomme*** below) – **139 rm** 86.00/142.00 **s.**, 2 suites – SB.

Royal, David Pl, JE2 4TD, ✆ (01534) 726521, *royalhot@itl.net, Fax (01534) 724035* – 400. VISA Y
Meals *(bar lunch Monday-Saturday)/dinner* 16.95 and a la carte 25.75/33.75 9.95 – **88 rm** 79.50/170.00.

De la Plage, Havre des Pas, JE4 9NJ, ✆ (01534) 723474, *enquiries@delaplagehotel.com Fax (01534) 768642,* <, – P. VISA JCB Z
April-October – **Meals** (bar lunch)/dinner 17.50 and a la carte 17.50/24.50 9.00 – **77 rm** 47.00/122.00 – SB.

Queens, 14 Queens Rd, JE2 3GR, ✆ (01534) 722239, *queenshotel99@jahoo.com Fax (01534) 721930* – , rest, P. VISA. Y
closed 22 December-7 January – **Meals** (residents only) (dinner only) 12.95 7.60 – **37 rm** 40.00/108.00.

Laurels, La route du Fort, JE2 4PA, ✆ (01534) 736444, *reservations@seabird.co.je Fax (01534) 759904* – rest, P. VISA Z
March-October – **Meals** (residents only) (dinner only) 12.00 8.90 – **37 rm** 55.00/90.00 SB.

Brookfield, 24 Raleigh Ave, JE2 3ZG, ✆ (01534) 723168, *Fax (01534) 721543* – . VISA Y
March-October – **Meals** (residents only) (dinner only) 4.95 – **20 rm** (dinner included 32.00/72.00.

La Bonne Vie without rest., Roseville St, JE2 4PL, ✆ (01534) 735955, *labonneviegues house@yahoo.com, Fax (01534) 733357* – . VISA JCB. Z
10 rm 29.00/58.00 **st.**

Victoria's (at De Vere Grand H.), Peirson Rd, JE4 8WD, ✆ (01534) 872255 *Fax (01534) 737815* – . VISA Y
closed Bank Holidays – **Meals** (live music and dancing Friday and Saturday) (dinner only an Sunday lunch)/dinner 23.50 and a la carte 21.50/44.00 13.45.

La Petite Pomme (at Pomme d'Or H.), Liberation Sq, JE1 3UF, ✆ (01534) 76660 *Fax (01534) 737781* – . VISA JCB Z
closed Sunday – **Meals** (dinner only) 18.00/23.00 and a la carte 22.00/29.00 9.00.

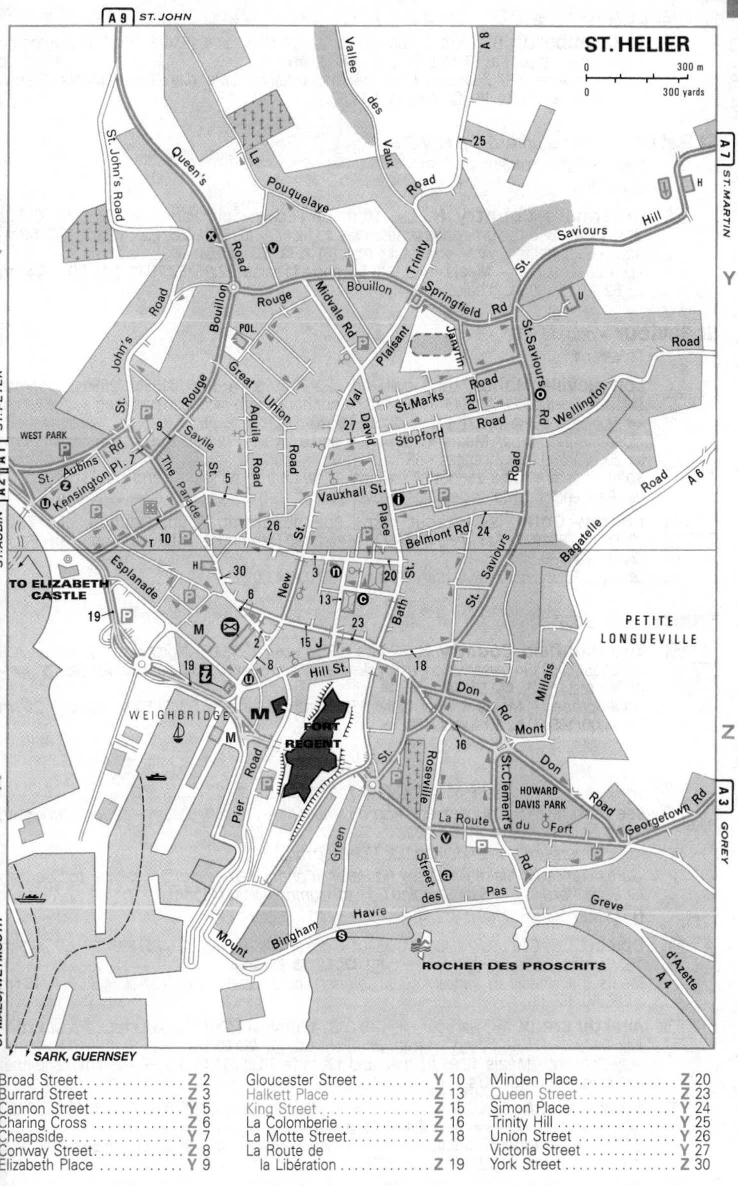

- Broad Street .... Z 2
- Burrard Street .... Z 3
- Cannon Street .... Y 5
- Charing Cross .... Z 6
- Cheapside .... Y 7
- Conway Street .... Z 8
- Elizabeth Place .... Y 9
- Gloucester Street .... Y 10
- Halkett Place .... Z 13
- King Street .... Z 15
- La Colomberie .... Z 16
- La Motte Street .... Z 18
- La Route de la Libération .... Z 19
- Minden Place .... Z 20
- Queen Street .... Z 23
- Simon Place .... Y 24
- Trinity Hill .... Y 25
- Union Street .... Y 26
- Victoria Street .... Y 27
- York Street .... Z 30

XXX **Le Chambertin Restaurant,** 1st floor, 20 Beresford St, JE2 4WN, ✆ (01534) 766678, *lechambertin@jerseymail.co.uk, Fax (01534) 877919* – MC AE VISA Z c
closed 24 December-7 January, Bank Holidays, Sunday and Monday dinner – **Meals** - French - 22.00/35.00 and a la carte 36.00/48.00 **s.** 11.50.

XX **La Capannina,** 65-67 Halkett Pl, JE2 4WG, ✆ (01534) 734602, *Fax (01534) 877628* – ▤. MC AE ① VISA Z n
closed 25 December-6 January and Sunday – **Meals** - Italian - a la carte 16.10/31.00 13.50.

Le Chambertin Bistrot, 20 Beresford St, JE2 4WN, ☎ (01534) 877912, *lechambertin@jerseymail.co.uk, Fax (01534) 877919* – MC AE VISA Z c
closed 24 December-7 January, Bank Holidays, Sunday and Monday dinner – **Meals** - French - 15.50 and a la carte 16.70/23.40 **st.** 11.50.

St Peter *The West Country G. – pop. 4 228.*

See : *Living Legend*★.

St Helier 5.

Greenhill's Country H., Mont de l'Ecole, Coin Varin, JE3 7EL, on C 112 ☎ (01534) 481042, *greenhills@messages.co.uk, Fax (01534) 485322,* « Part 17C farmhouse », heated, – rest, rest, TV P. MC AE VISA.
April-20 October – **Meals** 14.50/26.50 and a la carte 22.95/32.70 **t.** 12.00 – **24 rm** 62.00/124.00 **st.**, 1 suite – SB.

St Saviour – *pop. 12 680.*

St Helier 1.

Longueville Manor, Longueville Rd, JE2 7WF, on A 3 ☎ (01534) 725501, *longmar@itl.net, Fax (01534) 731613,* « Part 13C manor house with Jacobean panelling », heated, , – , rest, TV P. MC AE VISA
closed 3-17 January **Meals** 17.50/47.50 and a la carte 21.00/52.00 **s.** 14.00 – **28 rm** 200.00/300.00 **s.**, 2 suites – SB
Spec. Lobster risotto, ragoût of scallops. Pillow of smoked salmon and crab, yoghurt and dill. Best end of lamb, vegetables "provençale".

Champ Colin without rest., Rue du Champ Colin, Hougue, JE2 7UN ☎ (01534) 851877, *Fax (01534) 854902,* « Part 19C farmhouse, antiques », – TV P. MC AE VISA JCB.
closed 20 December-10 January – **3 rm** 35.00/54.00.

Trinity – *pop. 2 639.*

The Highfield Country H., Route d'Ebenezer, JE3 5DT, Northwest : ½ m. on A 8 ☎ (01534) 862194, *reservations@highfieldjersey.com, Fax (01534) 865342,* , , , – , rest, TV P. MC AE VISA JCB.
April-October – **Meals** (dinner only) 15.00 and a la carte 16.50/22.50 **s.** 8.00 – **28 rm** 56.00/100.00 **s.**, 10 suites – SB.

SARK

403 P 33 and 230 ⑩ *The West Country G. – pop. 550.*

See : *Island*★★ – *La Coupée*★★★ – *Port du Moulin*★★ – *Creux Harbour*★ – *La Seigneurie*★ AC – *Pilcher Monument*★ – *Hog's Back*★.

to Jersey (St Helier) (Emeraude Lines) (50 mn).

to France (St Malo) via Jersey (St Helier) (Condor Ferries Ltd) 3 weekly – to Guernsey (St Peter Port) (Isle of Sark Shipping Co. Ltd) (summer only) (45 mn).

Harbour Hill ☎ (01481) 832345.

Dixcart, GY9 0SD, ☎ (01481) 832015, *dixcart@ih.net, Fax (01481) 832164,* , « Part 16C farmhouse », , – rest, TV. MC AE VISA JCB
Meals (bar meals in winter) 16.00 (dinner) and a la carte 15.50/27.00 5.00 – **15 rm** 52.50/105.00.

Aval du Creux, Harbour Hill, GY9 0SB, ☎ (01481) 832036, *avalducreux@freeuk.com Fax (01481) 832368,* , heated, – rest, TV. MC AE VISA
May-October – **Meals** 18.95 (dinner) and a la carte 18.85/31.45 8.95 – **20 rm** (dinner included) 95.60/161.20 **s.**

Stocks Island, GY9 0SD, ☎ (01481) 832001, *stocks@sark.net, Fax (01481) 832130* , heated, – rest. MC AE VISA JCB
23 March-September – **Meals** 10.00/25.00 and a la carte 14.50/25.50 **st.** 9.50 – **19 rm** (dinner included) 60.00/150.00 **st.** – SB.

Petit Champ, GY9 0SF, ☎ (01481) 832046, *hpc@island_of_sark.co.uk Fax (01481) 832469,* ≤ coast, Herm, Jetou and Guernsey, , heated, – rest. MC AE VISA.
24 April-5 September – **Meals** 18.95 (dinner) and a la carte 11.50/22.25 7.95 – **16 rm** (dinner included) 60.00/116.00.

La Sablonnerie with rm, Little Sark, GY9 0SD, ☎ (01481) 832061, *Fax (01481) 832408* , « Part 16C farmhouse », – MC AE VISA.
Easter-mid October – **Meals** 23.80/25.80 and a la carte 21.60/28.80 5.50 – **22 rm** (dinner included) 59.50/149.50, 1 suite.

Founiais, Harbour Hill, GY9 0SB, ✆ (01481) 832626, *founais@gtonline.net, Fax (01481) 832642,* – MO VISA
April-October – **Meals** - Seafood specialities - *(closed Sunday)* a la carte 13.45/24.05 **s.** 7.95.

CHANNEL TUNNEL *Kent* 404 X 30 – *see Folkestone.*

CHAPELTOWN *N. Yorks.* 402 403 404 P 23 – *see Sheffield.*

CHARD *Somerset* 403 L 31 – *pop. 10 770.*
The Guildhall, Fore St ✆ (01460) 67463.
London 157 – Exeter 32 – Lyme Regis 12 – Taunton 18 – Yeovil 17.

Lordleaze, Henderson Drive, Forton Rd, TA20 2HW, Southeast : 1 ½ m. by A 358 off Forton rd ✆ (01460) 61066, *lordleaze@fsbdial.co.uk, Fax (01460) 66468* – TV P – 120. MO AE VISA
Meals a la carte 14.70/24.15 **t.** 8.50 – **16 rm** 55.00/85.00 **t.** – SB.

CHARINGWORTH *Glos. – see Chipping Campden.*

CHARLBURY *Oxon.* 403 404 P 28 – *pop. 2 694.*
London 72 – Birmingham 50 – Oxford 15.

Bull Inn with rm, Sheep St, OX7 3RR, ✆ (01608) 810689, « Part 17C inn » – TV P. MO VISA.
closed 25 and 31 December, 1 January and Monday – **Meals** *(closed Sunday dinner)* a la carte 15.40/26.95 **t.** 10.95 – 8.50 – **3 rm** 50.00/60.00 **t.**

CHARLECOTE *Warks.* 403 404 P 27 – *see Stratford-upon-Avon.*

CHARLESTOWN *Cornwall* 403 F 32 – *see St. Austell.*

CHARLTON *W. Sussex* 404 R 31 – *see Chichester.*

CHARMOUTH *Dorset* 403 L 31 – *pop. 1 497* – ✉ *Bridport.*
London 157 – Dorchester 22 – Exeter 31 – Taunton 27.

White House, 2 Hillside, The Street, DT6 6PJ, ✆ (01297) 560411, *whitehousehotel @excite.co.uk, Fax (01297) 560702* – TV P. MO VISA.
closed January – **Meals** (dinner only) 21.50 **t.** 12.00 – **8 rm** 49.50/79.00 **t.** – SB.

CHARTHAM HATCH *Kent* 404 X 30 – *see Canterbury.*

CHATTERIS *Cambs.* 402 404 U 26 – *pop. 7 261.*
London 85 – Cambridge 26 – Norwich 71.

Cross Keys, 12-16 Market Hill, PE16 6BA, ✆ (01354) 693036, *thefens@crosskeyshotel. fsnet.co.uk, Fax (01354) 694454,* « Part 16C inn » – TV P. MO VISA JCB.
Meals (bar meals Sunday dinner) a la carte approx. 15.75 **st.** 9.00 – **12 rm** 40.00/68.00 **st.** – SB.

CHEADLE *Ches.* 402 403 N 23.
London 200 – Manchester 7 – Stoke-on-Trent 33.

Village H. & Leisure Club, Cheadle Rd, SK8 1HW, South : ¾ m. by A 5149 ✆ (0161) 428 0404, *sharon.wilcock@village-hotels.com, Fax (0161) 428 1191,* , , squash – , rest, TV & P – 200. MO AE VISA JCB
Meals 14.95 and a la carte 13.65/23.95 **st.** 7.75 – **78 rm** 99.00/129.00 **st.**

Travel Inn, Royal Crescent, Cheadle Royal Retail Park, SK8 3FE, Southwest : 2 m. by A 560, A 34 off B 5358 ✆ (0161) 491 5884, *Fax (0161) 491 5886* – , rm, rest, TV & P – 30. MO AE VISA.
Meals (grill rest.) – **40 rm** 41.95 **t.**

CHEDDLETON *Staffs.* 402 403 404 N 24 – *pop. 3 534* – ✉ *Leek.*
London 125 – Birmingham 48 – Derby 33 – Manchester 42 – Stoke-on-Trent 11.

Choir Cottage without rest., Ostlers Lane, via Hollow Lane (opposite Red Lion on A 520), ST13 7HS, ☎ (01538) 360561, *enquiries@choircottage.co.uk*, – TV P.
2 rm 40.00/65.00 st.

CHELMSFORD *Essex* 404 V 28 – *pop. 97 451.*
County Hall, Market Rd ☎ (01245) 283400.
London 33 – Cambridge 46 – Ipswich 40 – Southend-on-Sea 19.

Atlantic, New St, CM1 1PP, ☎ (01245) 268168, *book@atlantichotel.co.uk Fax (01245) 268169,* – rm, TV P. VISA.
closed 27-30 December – ***New St Brasserie*** **:** **Meals** a la carte 17.75/21.95 **t.** 10.95 – 8.95 – **59 rm** 79.00/89.00 **st.**

Travel Inn, Chelmsford Service Area, Colchester Rd, Springfield, CM2 5PY, Northeast : at junction of A 12 with A 138 and A 130 ☎ (01245) 464008, *Fax (01245) 464010* – rm TV P. VISA.
Meals (grill rest.) – **61 rm** 41.95 **t.**

Vittorio, First Floor, Waterfront Pl, Wharf Rd, CM2 6LU, ☎ (01245) 252000, *info@waterfront-place.co.uk, Fax (01245) 252048,* « Canalside setting » – P. VISA
closed Sunday dinner – **Meals** (dinner only and Sunday lunch) a la carte 20.45/36.50 **st** 9.95.

Muddy Waters, Kings Head Walk, CM2 0HL, ☎ (01245) 348077, « Barge moored on River Cam » – VISA
closed 2 weeks summer, 2 weeks winter, Monday, Tuesday and Sunday dinner – **Meals** 18.00 and a la carte 21.50/28.15 **st.** 9.90.

at Great Baddow *Southeast : 3 m. by A 1114* – ✉ *Chelmsford.*

Pontlands Park, West Hanningfield Rd, CM2 8HR, ☎ (01245) 476444, *sales@pontlandsparkhotel.co.uk, Fax (01245) 478393,* heated, – TV P – 60. VISA.
closed 24 December-4 January – ***The Conservatory*** **:** **Meals** *(closed Saturday lunch)* a la carte 23.50/28.75 **t.** 9.95 – 11.00 – **35 rm** 110.00/180.00 **t.**, 1 suite.

CHELTENHAM *Glos.* 403 404 N 28 *Great Britain G.* – *pop. 91 301.*
See : *Town★* – *Pitville Pump Room★ AC A* **A.**
Exc. : *Sudeley Castle★ (Paintings★) AC, NE : 7 m. by B 4632* **A.**
Cleeve Hill ☎ (01242) 672025 **A** – *Cotswold Hills, Ullenwood ☎ (01242) 515317* **A.**
77 Promenade ☎ (01242) 522878.
London 99 – Birmingham 48 – Bristol 40 – Gloucester 9 – Oxford 43.

Plan opposite

Thistle Cheltenham, Gloucester Rd, GL51 0TS, West : 2 m. on A 40 ☎ (01242) 232691 *cheltenham@thistle.co.uk, Fax (01242) 221846,* – , rest, TV P – 400. VISA JCB
Burford Room **:** **Meals** *(closed Saturday lunch)* 23.00 (dinner) and a la carte 23.90/28.90 **st** 12.95 – 12.50 – **118 rm** 135.00/168.00 **st.**, 4 suites – SB.

The Queen's, Promenade, GL50 1NN, ☎ (0870) 4008107, *gm1050@forte_hotels.com Fax (01242) 224145,* – TV P – 80. VISA JCB B
Napier **:** **Meals** 12.50/30.00 and a la carte 13.00/22.00 **t.** 13.95 – 12.25 – **79 rm** 125.00/130.00 **st.** – SB.

Cheltenham Park, Cirencester Rd, Charlton Kings, GL53 8EA, ☎ (01242) 222021 *cheltenhampark@paramount.hotels.co.uk, Fax (01242) 226935,* – rest, TV P – 350. VISA. A
Meals 11.95/21.50 **st.** – **143 rm** 103.00/133.00 **st.**, 1 suite – SB.

On the Park, 38 Evesham Rd, GL52 2AH, ☎ (01242) 518898, *stay@hotelonthepark.co.uk Fax (01242) 511526,* « Regency town house », – TV. VISA. C
Meals – (see ***Bacchanalian*** below) – 8.50 – **12 rm** 80.50/162.50 **t.** – SB.

Kandinsky, Bayshill Rd, GL50 3AS, ☎ (01242) 527788, *info@hotelkandinsky.com Fax (01242) 226412,* – rest, TV P. VISA B
Café Paradiso **:** **Meals** a la carte 18.85/33.90 **t.** 11.95 – 10.95 – **46 rm** 75.00/89.00 **st** 2 suites.

White House, Gloucester Rd, GL51 0ST, West : 3 m. by A 40 on B 4063 ☎ (01452) 713226 *stay@white-house-hotel.co.uk, Fax (01452) 857590* – TV P – 180. VISA
Meals *(closed Saturday lunch)* 9.50/12.50 and dinner a la carte 17.50/30.40 **t.** 10.00 – **49 rm** 75.00/100.00 **t.** – SB.

CHELTENHAM

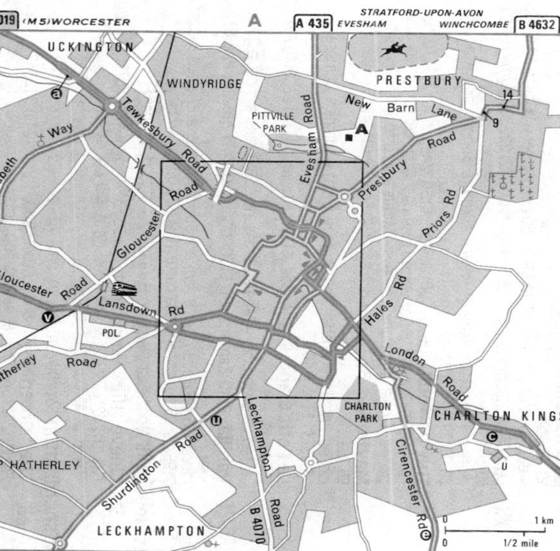

A 4019
(M5) WORCESTER
A 435
EVESHAM
STRATFORD-UPON-AVON
WINCHCOMBE
B 4632
UCKINGTON
WINDYRIDGE
PRESTBURY
PITTVILLE PARK
CHARLTON PARK
CHARLTON KINGS
UP HATHERLEY
LECKHAMPTON
OXFORD
A 40
SWINDON
STROUD
A 46
AIRPORT GLOUCESTER
B 4063
B 4070
POL.
1 km
1/2 mile

Lypiatt House without rest., Lypiatt Rd, GL50 2QW, ☎ (01242) 224994, *stay@lypiatt.co.uk, Fax (01242) 224996*, – TV P. MC AE VISA B c
10 rm 58.00/90.00 st.

Milton House without rest., 12 Royal Par, Bayshill Rd, GL50 3AY, ☎ (01242) 582601, *info@miltonhousehotel.co.uk, Fax (01242) 222326*, – TV P. MC AE VISA JCB. B e
closed 22 December-5 January – **8 rm** 54.00/92.00 **st.**

Beaumont House without rest., Shurdington Rd, GL53 0JE, ☎ (01242) 245986, *rocking.horse@virgin.net, Fax (01242) 520044*, – TV P. MC AE VISA JCB. A u
16 rm 52.00/86.00 **st.**

Wyastone, Parabola Rd, GL50 3BG, ☎ (01242) 245549, *reservations@wyastonehotel.co.uk, Fax (01242) 522659* – TV P. MC VISA JCB. B i
Meals (residents only) (dinner only) 19.00/23.00 **st.** 10.50 – **13 rm** 55.00/78.00 **st.**

Charlton Kings, London Rd, Charlton Kings, GL52 6UU, ☎ (01242) 231061, *enquiries@charltonkingshotel.co.uk, Fax (01242) 241900*, – TV P. MC AE VISA JCB A c
Meals (bar lunch Monday-Saturday)/dinner 18.95 **t.** 9.70 – **13 rm** 61.00/105.00 **t.** – SB.

Stretton Lodge, Western Rd, GL50 3RN, ☎ (01242) 570771, *info@strettonlodge.demon.co.uk, Fax (01242) 528724*, – TV P. MC AE VISA JCB B v
Meals (booking essential) (residents only) (lunch by arrangement)/dinner 21.25 **st.** 11.00 – **8 rm** 60.00/90.00 **st.**

Travel Inn, Tewkesbury Rd, Uckington, GL51 9SL, Northwest : 1 ¾ m. on A 4019 at junction with B 4634 ☎ (01242) 233847, *Fax (01242) 244887* – rm, rest, TV P. MC AE VISA. A a
Meals (grill rest.) – **40 rm** 41.95 **t.**

Travel Inn, 374 Gloucester Rd, GL51 7AY, ☎ (01242) 260103, *Fax (01242) 260042* – rm, rest, TV P. MC AE VISA. A v
Meals (grill rest.) – **42 rm** 41.95 **t.**

Georgian House without rest., 77 Montpellier Terr, GL50 1XA, ☎ (01242) 515577, *georgian-house@yahoo.com, Fax (01242) 545929* – TV P. MC AE VISA. B s
closed 21 December-3 January – **3 rm** 55.00/80.00 **st.**

Le Champignon Sauvage (Everitt-Matthias), 24-26 Suffolk Rd, GL50 2AQ, ☎ (01242) 573449, *Fax (01242) 254365* – MC AE VISA JCB B a
closed 3 weeks June, 10 days Christmas-New Year, Sunday and Monday – **Meals** 19.95/39.00 **t.** 10.95
Spec. Pan-fried foie gras with walnuts and quince, Banyuls sauce. Fillet of pork, chou farci and black pudding. Feuillantine of mango, Thai spiced cream and red wine syrup.

Bacchanalian (at On the Park H.), 38 Evesham Rd, GL52 2AH, ☎ (01242) 227713 – . MC AE VISA C r
Meals (booking essential) 16.95/22.50 and dinner a la carte 30.85/35.20 **t.** 13.95.

Lumière, Clarence Par, GL50 3PA, ☎ (01242) 222200, *lumiere@globalnet.co.uk* – . MC AE VISA BC z
closed 1 week January, 2 weeks autumn, Sunday and Monday – **Meals** (dinner only) 28.00/29.00 **t.** 13.75.

The Daffodil, 18-20 Suffolk Par, GL50 2AE, ☎ (01242) 700055, *daffodilrest@c5.com, Fax (01242) 700088*, « Converted cinema » – . MC AE VISA JCB B u
closed Sunday and Bank Holidays – **Meals** a la carte 14.90/25.95 **t.** 12.50.

Mayflower, 32-34 Clarence St, GL50 3NX, ☎ (01242) 522426, *Fax (01242) 251667* – . MC AE VISA B r
closed 24-26 December and Sunday lunch – **Meals** - Chinese - 6.95/18.50 and a la carte 16.50/31.50 **t.** 10.25.

Le Petit Blanc, Promenade, GL50 1NN, ☎ (01242) 266800, *Fax (01242) 266801* – . MC AE VISA B n
closed 25 December – **Meals** - Brasserie - 15.00 and a la carte 20.00/30.00 **t.** 11.00.

Vanilla, 9-10 Cambray Pl, GL50 1JS, ☎ (01242) 228228, *Fax (01242) 228228* – MC AE VISA JCB C e
closed 25-26 December, 1 January, Sunday dinner and lunch Saturday and Monday – **Meals** 7.95/12.95 (lunch) and a la carte 18.00/25.00 **t.** 10.50.

at Cleeve Hill *Northeast : 4 m. on B 4632* – **A** – ✉ *Cheltenham.*

Cleeve Hill without rest., GL52 3PR, ☎ (01242) 672052, *gbtoncleevehill@aol.com, Fax (01242) 679969*, ≤, – TV P. MC VISA.
10 rm 45.00/90.00 **t.**

at Shurdington *Southwest : 3 ¾ m. on A 46* – **A** – ✉ *Cheltenham.*

The Greenway, GL51 5UG, ☎ (01242) 862352, *greenway@btconnect.com, Fax (01242) 862780*, ≤, « Part 16C Cotswold country house, gardens », – TV P – 30. MC AE VISA.
closed first week January – **Meals** 21.00/38.50 and a la carte 38.50/44.00 **st.** 14.00 – **20 rm** 99.00/230.00 **t.** – SB.

at **Brockworth** *Southwest : 5½ m. on A 46 – A – ⊠ Cheltenham.*

Cheltenham and Gloucester Moat House, Shurdington Rd, GL3 4PB, on A 46 ✆ (01452) 519988, *cbcgl@queensmoat.co.uk, Fax (01452) 519977,* rest, – 340.
Meals *(closed Saturday lunch)* (carvery Sunday lunch) 15.50/19.50 and a la carte 16.00/27.95 **t.** 11.95 – 11.50 – **94 rm** 127.00/140.00 **st.**, 2 suites – SB.

CHENIES *Bucks.* 404 S 28 – *pop. 258* – ⊠ *Rickmansworth (Herts.).*
London 30 – Aylesbury 18 – Watford 7.

Bedford Arms, WD3 6EQ, ✆ (01923) 283301, *info@bedfordarms-hotel-chenies.com, Fax (01923) 284825,* – rm, .
Meals *(closed Sunday dinner)* (bar lunch Saturday) a la carte 24.75/35.00 **t.** 14.50 – 13.50 – **10 rm** 155.00 **t.** – SB.

CHERWELL VALLEY SERVICE AREA *Oxon.* 403 404 Q 28 – ⊠ *Bicester.*
Motorway Service Area, junction 10 M 40, Northampton Rd, Ardley, Bicester ✆ (01869) 345888.

Travelodge, Northampton Rd, Ardley, OX6 9RD, M 40, junction 10 ✆ (01869) 346060, *Fax (01869) 345030* – rm, rest, .
Meals (grill rest.) – **98 rms** 52.95 **t.**

CHESHUNT *Herts.* 404 T 28 – *pop. 51 998* – ⊠ *Broxbourne.*
Cheshunt, Park Lane ✆ (01992) 29777.
London 22 – Cambridge 40 – Ipswich 70 – Luton 34 – Southend-on-Sea 39.

Cheshunt Marriott, Halfhide Lane, Turnford, EN10 6NG, Northwest : 1 ¼ m. off B 176 ✆ (01992) 451245, *Fax (01992) 440120,* – – 120. .
Meals *(closed Sunday dinner)* 16.95 (lunch) and dinner a la carte 17.85/28.00 **t.** 13.95 – 12.50 – **131 rm** 119.00 **t.**, 12 suites.

CHESTER *Ches.* 402 403 L 24 *Great Britain G.* – *pop. 80 110.*
See : *City★★ - The Rows★★* B – *Cathedral★* B – *City Walls★* B.
Env. : *Chester Zoo★ AC, N : 3 m. by A 5116.*
Upton-by-Chester, Upton Lane ✆ (01244) 381183 A – *Curzon Park ✆ (01244) 675130* A.
Town Hall, Northgate St ✆ (01244) 402111 – Chester Visitor and Craft Centre, Vicars Lane ✆ (01244) 402111.
London 207 – Birkenhead 7 – Birmingham 91 – Liverpool 21 – Manchester 40 – Preston 52 – Sheffield 76 – Stoke-on-Trent 38.

Plans on following pages

Chester Grosvenor, Eastgate, CH1 1LT, ✆ (01244) 324024, *chesgrov@chestergrosvenor.co.uk, Fax (01244) 313246,* – – 250. B a
closed 25-26 December – **Meals** – (see ***Arkle*** and ***La Brasserie*** below) – 14.50 – **84 rm** 160.00/240.00 **t.**, 1 suite.

Crabwall Manor , Parkgate Rd, Mollington, CH1 6NE, Northwest : 2 ¼ m. on A 540 ✆ (01244) 851666, *crabwall@marstonhotels.com, Fax (01244) 851400,* « Part 16C manor », – rest, rest, – 100. . A d
The Restaurant : **Meals** 35.00 and a la carte approx. 40.00 **st.** 13.50 – **42 rm** 135.00/159.00 **st.**, 6 suites – SB.

Moat House Chester, Trinity St, CH1 2BD, ✆ (01244) 899988, *revchs@queensmoat.co.uk, Fax (01244) 316118,* – , rm, rest, – 600. B r
Meals 10.50/17.50 and a la carte 19.00/25.00 **t.** 14.50 – 11.50 – **158 rm** 135.00/158.00 **t.**, 2 suites – SB.

Mollington Banastre, Parkgate Rd, Mollington, CH1 6NN, Northwest : 2 ¼ m. on A 540 ✆ (01244) 851471, *events.mollington@arcadianhotels.co.uk, Fax (01244) 851165,* squash – , rest, – 250. A g
Meals *(closed lunch Saturday, Sunday and Bank Holidays)* (bar lunch Sunday) a la carte 24.25/32.50 **st.** 13.50 – 10.50 – **63 rm** 90.00/110.00 **st.** – SB.

The Queen, City Rd, CH1 3AH, ✆ (01244) 305000, *reservations.queens@principalhotels.co.uk, Fax (01244) 318483,* – – 220. B i
The Garden : **Meals** *(closed Saturday lunch)* 13.95/40.00 and a la carte 25.00/40.00 **st.** 14.95 – **127 rm** 95.00/130.00 **st.**, 1 suite – SB.

CHESTER BUILT UP AREA

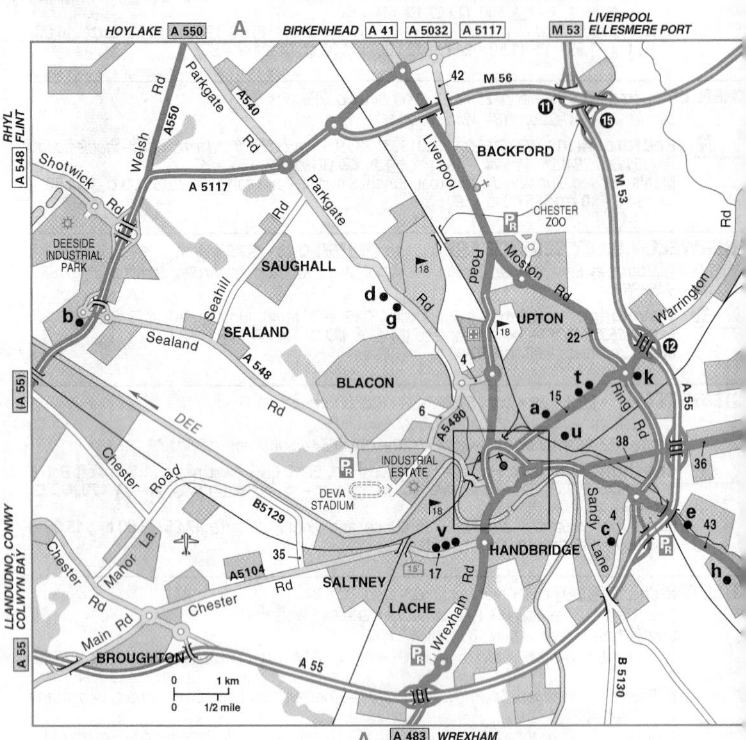

🏨 **Hoole Hall,** Warrington Rd, Hoole, CH2 3PD, Northeast : 2 m. on A 56 ✆ (01244) 408800 *hoolehall@corushotels.com, Fax (01244) 320251,* – |‡| ⇔ TV ✆ ♿ P – 🏛 150. MC AE ⓓ VISA JCB A
The Atrium : Meals *(closed Saturday lunch)* (buffet lunch Monday-Friday)/dinner 15.95/22.00 and a la carte 13.85/22.20 **st.** 🍷 10.50 – ☕ 12.95 – **97 rm** 86.00/96.00 SB.

🏨 **Blossoms,** St John St, CH1 1HL, ✆ (01244) 323186, *heritagehotels-chester.blossom @forte-hotels.com, Fax (01244) 346433* – |‡| ⇔ TV ✆ – 🏛 100. MC AE ⓓ VISA. ✗ B
Brookes : Meals 7.90 (lunch) and a la carte 16.50/21.50 **t.** – ☕ 13.00 – **63 rm** 136.00 144.00 **t.**, 1 suite – SB.

🏨 **Green Bough,** 60 Hoole Rd, CH2 3NL, on A 56 ✆ (01244) 326241, *greenboughhot @cwcom.net, Fax (01244) 326265* – ⇔ TV P. MC AE ⓓ VISA. ✗ A
Meals (lunch by arrangement)/dinner 19.50 and a la carte 23.50/27.00 **st.** 🍷 15.00 – **16 rm** ☕ 79.50/115.00 **t.**, 1 suite – SB.

🏨 **Redland** without rest., 64 Hough Green, CH4 8JY, Southwest : 1 m. by A 483 on A 510 ✆ (01244) 671024, *teresawhite@redlandhotelfsnet.co.uk., Fax (01244) 681309,* « Victorian mansion house », ≘s, – ⇔ TV P. MC VISA. ✗ A
closed 22 December-6 January – **12 rm** ☕ 45.00/80.00 **t.**

🏨 **Cavendish,** 42-44 Hough Green, CH4 8JQ, Southwest : 1 m. by A 483 on A 510 ✆ (01244) 675100, *cavendish@hotel_chester.com, Fax (01244) 678844,* – ⇔ rest, TV P. MC AE ⓓ VISA JCB. ✗ A
Meals (residents only) (dinner only) 18.95 **st.** 🍷 11.95 – **19 rm** ☕ 45.00/80.00 **st.** – SB.

CHESTER

Boughton . . . . **B** 2
Bridge Street . . . . **B** 3
Eastgate Street . . . . **B** 7
Frodsham Street . . . . **B** 9
Grosvenor Park Road . . . . **B** 10
Grosvenor Street . . . . **B** 12
Handbridge . . . . **B** 13
Little St. John Street . . . . **B** 19
Liverpool Road . . . . **B** 21
Lower Bridge Street . . . . **B** 23
Nicholas Street . . . . **B** 25
Northgate Street . . . . **B** 26
Parkgate Road . . . . **B** 28
Pepper Street . . . . **B** 30
St. John Street . . . . **B** 32
St. Martins Way . . . . **B** 33
Vicar's Lane . . . . **B** 40
Watergate Street . . . . **B**

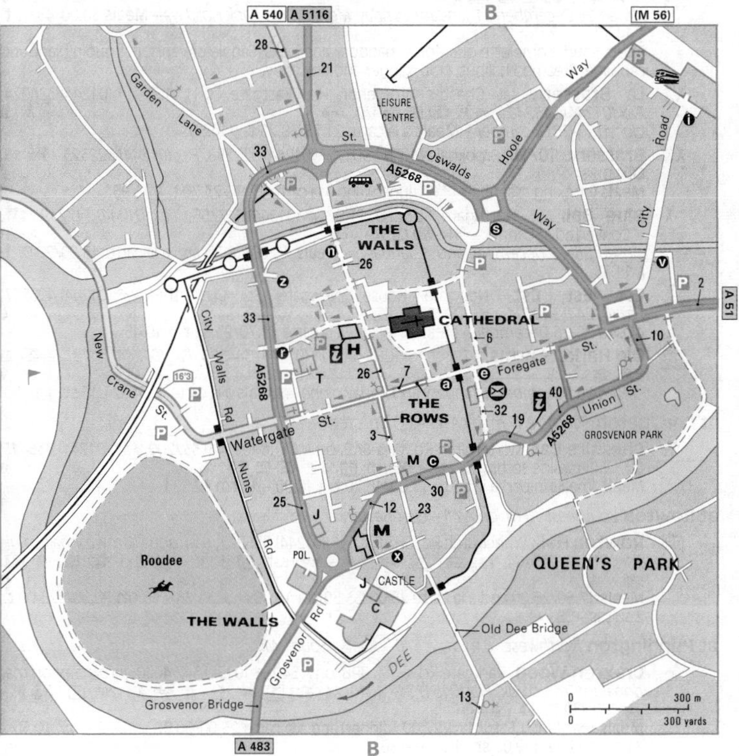

Alton Lodge, 78 Hoole Rd, CH2 3NT, on A 56 ☎ (01244) 310213, *enquiries@altonlodge.co.uk, Fax (01244) 319206* – TV P. MC VISA JCB. A t
closed Christmas and New Year – **Meals** *(closed Friday-Sunday)* (residents only) (dinner only) a la carte 10.70/19.95 7.95 – **17 rm** 55.00/70.00 **st.** – SB.

Travel Inn, Caldy Valley Rd, Broughton, CH3 5QJ, Southeast : 2 m. by A 51 off A 5115 ☎ (01244) 315766, *Fax (01244) 315061* – rm, rest, TV P – 25. MC AE VISA JCB. A c
Meals (grill rest.) – **74 rm** 41.95 **t.**

The Limes without rest., 12 Hoole Rd, CH2 3NJ, on A 56 ☎ (01244) 328239, *limeschester@btinternet.com, Fax (07968) 404105* – TV P. MC VISA JCB A a
closed 16 December-21 January – **7 rm** 40.00/74.00 **st.**

Mitchell's of Chester without rest., 28 Hough Green, CH4 8JQ, Southwest : 1 m. by A 483 on A 5104 ☎ (01244) 679004, *mitoches@dialstart.net, Fax (01244) 659567*, – TV P. MC VISA. A v
closed 19-26 December – **7 rm** 30.00/48.00.

Chester Town House without rest., 23 King St, CH1 2AH, ☎ (01244) 350021, *dbcth@aol.com, Fax (01244) 350021*, – TV P. MC VISA. B z
4 rm 45.00/60.00 **t.**

Castle House without rest., 23 Castle St, CH1 2DS, ☎ (01244) 350354, *Fax (01244) 350354*, « Part Elizabethan town house » – TV. MC VISA B x
5 rm 25.00/50.00.

ENGLAND

Stone Villa without rest., 3 Stone Pl, CH2 3NR, off A 56 (Hoole Rd) ☎ (01244) 345014 *stonevilla@hotmail.com, Fax (01244) 345015* – TV P. MC VISA JCB. A
closed Christmas – **9 rm** 30.00/60.00 **s.**

Arkle (at Chester Grosvenor H.), Eastgate, CH1 1LT, ☎ (01244) 324024, *Fax (01244) 31324* – P. MC AE VISA JCB B
closed 25 December-21 January, Sunday, Monday and Bank Holidays – **Meals** 30.00/48.00 **t** 14.50
Spec. Soufflé omelette of smoked haddock and leeks. Saddle of venison, boudin blanc and cabbage. Steamed halibut, crab, ginger and bok choy.

La Brasserie (at Chester Grosvenor H.), Eastgate, CH1 1LT, ☎ (01244) 324024 *Fax (01244) 313246* – P. MC AE VISA JCB B
closed 25-26 December – **Meals** a la carte 21.75/38.25 **t.** 14.50.

Brasserie 10/16, Brookdale Pl, CH1 3DY, ☎ (01244) 322288, *Fax (01244) 322325* – MC AE VISA B
Meals (booking essential) 13.90 (lunch) and a la carte 12.85/23.70 **t.** 11.95.

Blue Bell, 65 Northgate St, CH1 2HQ, ☎ (01244) 317758, *Fax (01244) 317759,* « Converted 15C inn » – . MC AE VISA JCB B
closed 25-26 December and 1 January – **Meals** 10.00/18.50 and a la carte 13.90/28.00 **t** 11.25.

Est, Est, Est, Newgate House, Newgate St, CH1 1DE, ☎ (01244) 400507 *Fax (01244) 320904* – . MC AE VISA B
closed 25-26 December – **Meals** - Italian - a la carte 11.70/23.35 **t.** 10.45.

Old Harkers Arms, 1 Russell St, CH3 5AL, ☎ (01244) 344525, *Fax (01244) 344812* – MC AE VISA. B
closed 26 December, 1 January and Friday dinner – **Meals** a la carte 12.75/21.15 **st.** 10.50

at Christleton *South : 2½ m. by A 41 – ✉ Chester.*

Cheshire Cat, Whitchurch Rd, CH3 6AE, on A 41 ☎ (01244) 332200, *Fax (01244) 336415* , « Canalside setting », – rm, TV P. MC AE VISA. A
Meals (meals in bar) a la carte 13.00/16.70 **t.** 10.00 – **14 rm** 52.50 **t.**

at Rowton *Southeast : 3 m. on A 41 – ✉ Chester.*

Rowton Hall, Whitchurch Rd, CH3 6AD, ☎ (01244) 335262, *rowtonhall@rowtonhall.co.uk Fax (01244) 335464,* , , , , – rest, TV P – 200. MC AE VISA A
Meals 17.50/25.00 and a la carte 25.00/33.50 **t.** 11.50 – 11.75 – **36 rm** 90.00/125.00 **t.** 2 suites – SB.

at Puddington *Northwest : 6 m. by A 540 –* **A** *– ✉ South Wirral.*

Craxton Wood, Parkgate Rd, CH66 9PB, on A 540 ☎ (0151) 347 4000, *info@craxton.macdonald-hotels.co.uk, Fax (0151) 347 4040,* , , , , – , rest, TV P – 400. MC AE VISA JCB
Meals (bar lunch Saturday) 27.00 (dinner) and a la carte 25.00/50.00 16.00 – 10.50 – **71 rm** 105.00/130.00 **st.**, 1 suite – SB.

CHESTERFIELD *Derbs.* 402 403 404 P 24 *Great Britain G. – pop. 71 945.*

Env. : *Bolsover Castle★ AC, E : 5 m. by A 632.*

18, 9 *Chesterfield Municipal, Murray House, Crow Lane ☎ (01246) 273887 –* 18 *Grassmoor, North Wingfield Rd ☎ (01246) 856044.*

Peacock Information Centre, Low Pavement ☎ (01246) 345777.

London 152 – Derby 24 – Nottingham 25 – Sheffield 12.

Ibis without rest., Lordsmill St, S41 7RW, at junction of A 619 and A 632 ☎ (01246) 221333 *h3160@accorhotels.com, Fax (01246) 221444* – TV P – 30. MC AE VISA
86 rm 49.50 **st.**

Travel Inn, Tapton Lock Hill, S41 7NJ, Northeast : 1 m. at junction of A 61 with A 619 ☎ (01246) 560700, *Fax (01246) 560707* – , rest, TV P. MC AE VISA JCB.
Meals (grill rest.) – **60 rm** 41.95 **t.**

CHESTER-LE-STREET *Durham* 401 402 P 19 *– pop. 35 123.*

18 *Lumley Park ☎ (0191) 388 3218 –* 18 *Roseberry Grange, Grange Villa ☎ (0191) 370 0670.*

London 275 – Durham 7 – Newcastle upon Tyne 8.

Lumley Castle, DH3 4NX, East : 1 m. on B 1284 ☎ (0191) 389 1111, *lumcastl@netcomuk.co.uk, Fax (0191) 389 1881,* « 14C », – rest, TV P – 120. MC AE VISA JCB.
closed 25-26 December and 1 January – ***Black Knight :*** **Meals** *(closed Saturday lunch)* 15.50/26.50 and a la carte 29.50/41.00 **st.** 13.95 – 12.50 – **58 rm** 79.50/185.00 **st.** 1 suite – SB.

CHESTER SERVICE AREA *Ches. – ✉ Chester.*

Travel Inn without rest., Elton, CH2 4QZ, at M 56 junction 14 ☎ (01928) 726192, *Fax (01928) 726721* – ⇔ TV & P – 🏛 25. MC AE ⓓ VISA. ✗
40 rm 41.95 **t.**

CHESTERTON *Oxon.* 404 Q 28 – *pop. 806* – ✉ *Bicester.*

Bicester ☎ (01869) 241204.
London 69 – Birmingham 65 – Northampton 36 – Oxford 15.

Bignell Park, OX26 1UE, on A 4095 ☎ (01869) 241444, *Fax (01869) 241444,* – TV ☎ & P – 🏛 25. MC AE VISA. ✗
Meals 19.00/25.00 and a la carte 26.00/31.50 **st.** 11.95 – **23 rm** 70.00/135.00 **st.** – SB.

CHETTLE *Dorset* – *see Blandford Forum.*

CHICHESTER *W. Sussex* 404 R 31 *Great Britain G.* – *pop. 26 572.*
See : *City* ★ – *Cathedral* ★ **BZ A** – *St. Mary's Hospital* ★ **BY D** – *Pallant House* ★ *AC* **BZ M.**
Env. : *Fishbourne Roman Palace (mosaics ★) AC* **AZ R.**
Exc. : *Weald and Downland Open Air Museum* ★ *AC, N : 6 m. by A 286* **AY.**
Goodwood, Kennel Hill ☎ (01243) 785012, **AY** – 18, 18, 9 *Chichester Golf Centre, Hunston Village ☎ (01243) 533833,* **AZ.**
29a South St ☎ (01243) 775888.
London 69 – Brighton 31 – Portsmouth 18 – Southampton 30.

CHICHESTER

Street	Grid	No.
Birdham Road	AZ	2
Bognor Road	AZ	3
Chapel Street	BY	6
Chichester Arundel Road	AY	7
East Pallant	BZ	9
East Street	BZ	
Florence Road	AZ	10
Hornet (The)	BZ	12
Kingsham Road	BZ	13
Lavant Road	AY	14
Little London	BY	15
Market Road	BZ	16
Northgate	BY	17
North Pallant	BZ	19
North Street	BYZ	
St. James's	AZ	21
St. John's Street	BZ	23
St. Martin's Square	BY	24
St. Pancras	BY	25
St. Paul's Road	BY	27
Sherborne Road	AZ	28
Southgate	BZ	29
South Pallant	BZ	31
South Street	BZ	
Spitalfield Lane	BY	32
Stockbridge Road	AZ	33
Tower Street	BY	35
Via Ravenna	AZ	37
Westhampnett Road	AYZ	38

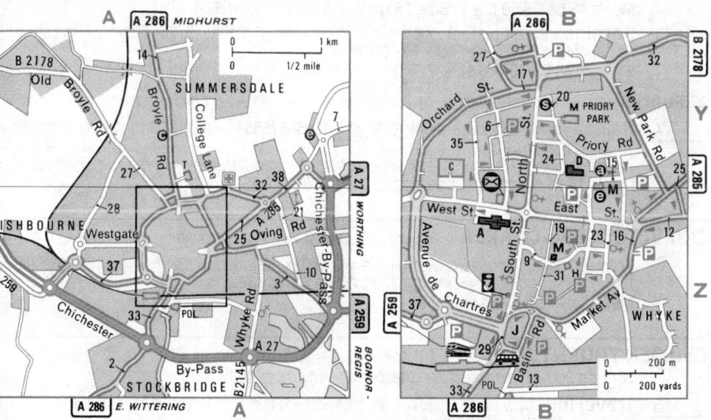

Jarvis Chichester, Westhampnett, PO19 4UL, ☎ (01243) 786351, *071gm@jarvis.co.uk, Fax (01243) 782371,* – ⇔, rest, TV & P – 🏛 300. MC AE ⓓ VISA **AY e**
Meals (bar lunch Monday-Saturday)/dinner 15.95/25.00 and a la carte 15.95/23.00 **st.** 12.50 – **76 rm** 79.00/150.00 **st.**, 1 suite – SB.

The Ship, North St, PO19 1NH, ☎ (01243) 778000, *bookings@shiphotel.com, Fax (01243) 788000* – ⇔ rest, TV ☎ P – 🏛 70. MC AE VISA **BY s**
Meals 16.95/19.95 and a la carte 22.00/28.00 **st.** 10.50 – **36 rm** 78.00/118.00 **st.** – SB.

Suffolk House, 3 East Row, PO19 1PD, ☎ (01243) 778899, *reservations@suffolkhshotel.demon.co.uk, Fax (01243) 787282,* – ⇔ rest, TV ☎. MC AE ⓓ VISA. ✗ **BY a**
Meals (dinner only and Sunday lunch)/dinner 19.95/29.95 **t.** 14.95 – **10 rm** 65.00/130.00 **t.** – SB.

Crouchers Bottom, Birdham Rd, Apuldram, PO20 7EH, Southwest : 2 ½ m. on A 28 (01243) 784995, *info@crouchersbottom.com, Fax (01243) 539797*, – rm, AE VISA
Meals *(closed Sunday)* (dinner only) a la carte 24.00/29.00 11.95 – **16 rm** 55.00/105.00 **t.** – SB.

Comme ça, 67 Broyle Rd, PO19 4BD, on A 286 (01243) 788724, *comme.ca@commeca.co.uk, Fax (01243) 530052*, , – AE VISA AY
closed 25 December, Monday and Sunday dinner – **Meals** - French - 15.95/17.95 (lunch) and a la carte approx. 22.00 **t.** 9.95.

at Charlton *North : 6 ¼ m. by A 286* – **AY** – *Chichester.*

Woodstock House, PO18 0HU, (01243) 811666, *Fax (01243) 811666*, – AE VISA.
closed 24-27 December – **Meals** *(closed Sunday-Monday)* (dinner only) 19.95 **t.** 9.95 – **11 rm** 48.50/120.00 – SB.

at Chilgrove *North : 6½ m. by A 286* – **AY** – *on B 2141* – *Chichester.*

Forge, PO18 9HX, (01243) 535333, *reservations@forgehotel.com, Fax (01243) 535363*, « Converted 17C forge », – rm, AE VISA JCB.
closed 10 days late October – **Meals** (by arrangement) (communal dining) 35.00 **st.** 12.50 – **5 rm** 45.00/100.00 **st.** – SB.

at Halnaker *Northeast : 3 ¼ m. on A 285* – **BY** – *Chichester.*

The Old Store without rest., Stane St, PO18 0QL, on A 285 (01243) 531977, *Fax (01243) 531977*, – VISA JCB.
7 rm 30.00/60.00.

at Goodwood *Northeast : 3½ m. by A 27* – **AY** – *on East Dean Rd* – *Chichester.*

Marriott Goodwood Park H. & Country Club, PO18 0QB, (01243) 775537, *Fax (01243) 520120*, , , , , , , – – 150. AE VISA.
Meals (bar lunch)/dinner 35.00 **st.** 14.00 – **93 rm** 99.00/109.00, 1 suite.

at Bosham *West : 4 m. by A 259* – **AZ** – *Chichester.*

Millstream, Bosham Lane, PO18 8HL, (01243) 573234, *info@millstream-hotel.co.uk, Fax (01243) 573459*, – , rest, AE VISA
Meals 15.50/23.50 **t.** 11.50 – **35 rm** 75.00/125.00 – SB.

Hatpins without rest., Bosham Lane, PO18 8HG, (01243) 572644, *mary@hatpins.co.uk, Fax (01243) 572644*, , – .
5 rm 45.00/100.00 **st.**

at Funtington *Northwest : 4 ¾ m. by B 2178 on B 2146* – **AY** – *Chichester.*

Hallidays, Watery Lane, PO18 9LF, (01243) 575331, « Part 13C thatched cottages » VISA JCB
closed 2 weeks March, 1 week September, Monday, Saturday lunch and Sunday dinner – **Meals** 13.75 (lunch) and a la carte 23.75/29.50 **t.** 9.95.

CHIEVELEY SERVICE AREA *Newbury* 403 404 Q 29 – *Thatcham.*

Travelodge, Oxford Rd, Hermitage, RG18 9XX, at junction 13 of M 4 (01635) 248024, *Fax (01635) 247886* – rm, AE VISA JCB.
Meals (grill rest.) – **64 rm** 59.95 **t.**

CHILDER THORNTON *Ches.* – *Wirral.*
London 200 – Birkenhead 7 – Chester 12 – Liverpool 10.

Travel Inn, New Chester Rd, CH66 1QW, on A 41 (0151) 339 8101, *Fax (0151) 347 1401* – rm, AE VISA.
Meals (grill rest.) – **31 rm** 41.95 **t.**

CHILGROVE *W. Sussex* 404 R 31 – *see Chichester.*

CHILLATON *Devon* 403 H 32 – *see Tavistock.*

CHILLINGTON *Devon* 403 I 33 – *see Kingsbridge.*

The Guide is updated annually so renew your Guide every year.

CHINLEY *Derbs.* 402 403 404 O 23 – ✉ *Stockport (Ches.).*
London 187 – Manchester 24 – Sheffield 25.

Ashen Clough , High Peak, SK23 6AH, North : 1 m. by Maynestone Rd ☎ (01663) 750311, ≤, « Gardens », – P.
Meals (by arrangement) (communal dining) 22.00 **s.** 9.00 – **3 rm** 45.00/70.00.

CHINNOR *Oxon.* 404 R 28 *The West Country G. – pop. 5 599.*
Exc. : *Ridgeway Path★★.*
London 45 – Oxford 19.

Cross Lanes Cottage without rest., West Lane, Bledlow, HP27 9PF, Northeast : 1 ½ m. on B 4009 ☎ (01844) 345339, *ronaldcou@aol.com, Fax (01844) 274165,* « Part 16C », – TV P.
3 rm 45.00/55.00 **st.**

at Sprig's Alley *Southeast : 2½ m. by Bledlow Ridge rd – ✉ Chinnor.*

Sir Charles Napier Inn, OX9 4BX, ☎ (01494) 483011, *Fax (01494) 485311,* – P. MC AE VISA
closed 25-26 December, Monday lunch and Sunday dinner – **Meals** a la carte 23.75/32.75 **t.** 13.50.

at Kingston Blount *Southwest : 1 ¾ m. on B 4009 – ✉ Chinnor.*

Town Farm Cottage without rest., Brook St, by Sydenham rd, ☎ (01844) 352152, *townfarmcottage@oxfree.com, Fax (01844) 352152,* « Working farm », – TV P. MC VISA.
3 rm 50.00/65.00.

CHIPPENHAM *Wilts.* 403 404 N 29 *The West Country G. – pop. 26 376.*
See : *Yelde Hall★.*
Env. : *Corsham Court★★ AC, SW : 4 m. by A 4 – Sheldon Manor★ AC, W : 1½ m. by A 420 – Biddestone★, W : 3½ m. – Bowood House★ AC (Library ≤★) SE : 5 m. by A 4 and A 342.*
Exc. : *Castle Combe★★, NW : 6 m. by A 420 and B 4039.*
Monkton Park (Par Three) ☎ (01249) 653928.
The Citadel, Bath Rd ☎ (01249) 706333.
London 106 – Bristol 27 – Southampton 64 – Swindon 21.

Crown Inn, Giddea Hall, Yatton Keynell, SN14 7ER, Northwest : 4 ½ m. on A 420 ☎ (01249) 782229, *Fax (01249) 782337* – TV P. MC AE VISA.
Meals a la carte 11.40/23.85 – **8 rm** 55.00/65.00 **t.**

at Stanton Saint Quintin *North : 5 m. by A 429 – ✉ Chippenham.*

Stanton Manor , SN14 6DQ, ☎ (01666) 837552, *reception@stantonmanor.co.uk, Fax (01666) 837022,* – TV P – 50. MC AE VISA JCB.
closed 24-31 December – **Meals** a la carte 15.70/27.75 **st.** 9.50 – **24 rm** 75.00/125.00 **st.** – SB.

CHIPPERFIELD *Herts.* 404 ㊷ – *pop. 1 680 – ✉ Kings Langley.*
London 27 – Hemel Hempstead 5 – Watford 6.

Two Brewers Inn, The Common, WD4 9BS, ☎ (01923) 265266, *Fax (01923) 261884* – rm, TV P. MC AE VISA.
Meals a la carte 13.95/23.15 – **20 rm** 99.50 **st.**

CHIPPING *Lancs.* 402 M 22 – *pop. 1 392 – ✉ Preston.*
London 233 – Lancaster 30 – Leeds 54 – Manchester 40 – Preston 12.

Gibbon Bridge , PR3 2TQ, East : 1 m. on Clitheroe rd ☎ (01995) 61456, *reception@gibbon-bridge.co.uk, Fax (01995) 61277,* ≤, « Gardens », – TV P – 120. MC AE VISA JCB.
Meals 14.00/25.00 and dinner a la carte 25.00/30.00 **t.** 13.00 – **11 rm** 70.00/100.00 **t.**, **18 suites** 130.00/230.00 **t.** – SB.

CHIPPING CAMPDEN *Glos.* 403 404 O 27 *Great Britain G. – pop. 1 741.*
See : *Town★.*
Env. : *Hidcote Manor Garden★★ AC, NE : 2½ m.*
Old Police Station ☎ (01386) 841206.
London 93 – Cheltenham 21 – Oxford 37 – Stratford-upon-Avon 12.

Cotswold House, The Square, GL55 6AN, ✆ (01386) 840330, *reception@cotswoldhouse.com, Fax (01386) 840310,* « Regency town house », – 30. MC AE VISA JCB
Garden Room : **Meals** (dinner only and Sunday lunch)/dinner 35.00 **st.** 14.00 – (see also *Hicks'* below) – **14 rm** 85.00/190.00 **st.** – SB.

Seymour House, High St, GL55 6AH, ✆ (01386) 840429, *enquiry@seymourhousehotel.com, Fax (01386) 840369,* « Part 17C mature grapevine in restaurant », – rest, – 65. MC AE VISA.
Meals 15.95 (lunch) and a la carte 16.75/28.45 **st.** 14.00 – **11 rm** 75.00/110.00 **st.**, 4 suites – SB.

Noel Arms, High St, GL55 6AT, ✆ (01386) 840317, *bookings@cotswold-inns-hotels.co.uk, Fax (01386) 841136,* « Part 14C » – rest, – 50. MC AE VISA JCB
Meals a la carte approx. 21.95 **st.** 10.95 – **26 rm** 85.00/115.00 **t.** – SB.

M'Dina Courtyard without rest., Park Rd, GL55 6EA, South by High St ✆ (01386) 841752, *chilver@globalnet.co.uk, Fax (01386) 840942* –
3 rm 48.00/75.00 **s.**, 1 suite.

Hicks' (at Cotswold House), The Square, GL55 6AN, ✆ (01386) 840330, *Fax (01386) 840310* – . MC AE VISA JCB
Meals (booking essential) a la carte approx. 21.50 **st.** 11.00.

Eight Bells Inn with rm, Church St, GL55 6JG, ✆ (01386) 840371, *Fax (01386) 841669,* « 14C inn » – . MC VISA
closed 25 December – **Meals** *(closed Sunday dinner)* a la carte 15.95/24.50 **st.** 10.00 – **5 rm** 40.00/70.00 **st.**

at Mickleton *North : 3 ¼ m. by B 4035 and B 4081 on B 4632 – ✉ Chipping Campden.*

Three Ways House, GL55 6SB, ✆ (01386) 438429, *threeways@puddingclub.com, Fax (01386) 438118,* – rest, rest, – 80. MC AE VISA
Meals (bar lunch Monday-Saturday)/dinner 24.50 and a la carte 24.50/33.00 **t.** 11.00 – **41 rm** 66.00/126.00 **st.** – SB.

Myrtle House, GL55 6SA, ✆ (01386) 430032, *kate@myrtlehouse.co.uk, Fax (01386) 438965,* – . MC VISA
Meals (by arrangement) 12.50 **s.** – **5 rm** 40.00/70.00 **s.**

at Charingworth *East : 3 m. by B 4035 – ✉ Chipping Campden.*

Charingworth Manor , GL55 6NS, on B 4035 ✆ (01386) 593555, *charingworthmanor@englishrosehotels.co.uk, Fax (01386) 593353,* ←, « Part early 14C manor house with Jacobean additions », , , , , , – – 50. MC AE VISA.
Meals 38.50 and a la carte 20.00/38.50 **st.** 18.00 – **26 rm** 115.00/275.00 **st.** – SB.

at Paxford *Southeast : 3 m. by B 4035 – ✉ Chipping Campden.*

Churchill Arms with rm, GL55 6XH, ✆ (01386) 594000, *churchill-arms@talk21.com, Fax (01386) 594005,* – rm, . MC VISA.
Meals (bookings not accepted) a la carte approx. 19.00 **t.** 9.95 – **4 rm** 40.00/70.00 **t.**

at Broad Campden *South : 1 ¼ m. by B 4081 – ✉ Chipping Campden.*

Malt House , GL55 6UU, ✆ (01386) 840295, *nick@the-malt-house.freeserve.co.uk, Fax (01386) 841334,* « 17C », – . MC AE VISA JCB
closed 24-26 December – **Meals** *(closed Tuesday-Wednesday)* (booking essential to non residents) (dinner only) 28.50/33.50 **t.** 18.00 – **7 rm** 59.50/118.50 **st.**, 1 suite.

Marnic House without rest., GL55 6UR, ✆ (01386) 841473, *marnic@zoom.co.uk, Fax (01386) 840441,* – .
closed 20 December-5 January – **3 rm** 38.00/55.00 **t.**

CHIPPING NORTON *Oxon.* 403 404 P 28 *Great Britain G. – pop. 5 386.*

Env. : *Chastleton House**, NW : 4 m. by A 44.*

Lyneham ✆ (01993) 831841 – Southcombe ✆ (01608) 642383.

London 77 – Birmingham 44 – Gloucester 36 – Oxford 21.

Chav Brasserie, 7 Horsefair, OX7 5AL, ✆ (01608) 645968, *chavignol@virginbiz.com, Fax (01608) 646794* – . MC VISA
closed 25 December, Sunday and Monday lunch – **Meals** a la carte 20.25/27.75 **t.** 9.50.

Masons Arms, Banbury Rd, Swerford, OX7 4AP, Northeast : 6 m. on A 361 ✆ (01608) 683212, *masonsarms@swerford.fsbusiness.co.uk, Fax (01608) 683105,* – MC VISA
Meals 12.95/24.95 and a la carte 14.35/24.85 **st.** 9.50.

CHISELDON *Wilts.* 403 404 O 29 – *see Swindon.*

CHITTLEHAMHOLT *Devon* 403 I 31 – *pop. 194* – ✉ *Umberleigh.*
London 216 – Barnstaple 14 – Exeter 28 – Taunton 45.

Highbullen ⛰, EX37 9HD, ☎ (01769) 540561, *info@highbullen.co.uk, Fax (01769) 540492*, ≤, ≘s, heated, ▢, 18, ⚹, ⚹, ⚹, ⚹indoor/outdoor, squash – ⚹ rest, TV P. MC ① VISA. ⚹
Meals (lunch by arrangement)/dinner 15.00/25.00 and a la carte 14.00/23.00 **st.** 12.00 – ⚹ 5.00 – **40 rm** (dinner included) 80.00/150.00 **st.** – SB.

CHOBHAM *Surrey* 404 S 29 – *pop. 3 411* – ✉ *Woking.*
London 35 – Reading 21 – Southampton 53.

Quails, 1 Bagshot Rd, GU24 8BP, ☎ (01276) 858491, *Fax (01276) 858491* – ▤. MC AE ① VISA
closed Saturday lunch, Sunday and Monday – **Meals** 15.95 (lunch) and a la carte 26.70/32.65 **t.** 10.95.

CHOLLERFORD *Northd.* 401 402 N 18 *Great Britain G.* – ✉ *Hexham.*
Env. : *Hadrian's Wall★★ – Chesters★ (Bath House★)* AC, *W : ½ m. by B 6318.*
London 303 – Carlisle 36 – Newcastle upon Tyne 21.

George, NE46 4EW, ☎ (01434) 681611, *chollerford.swallow@whitbread.com, Fax (01434) 681727*, ≤, « Riverside gardens », ⚹, ≘s, ▢, ⚹ – ⚹ TV ☎ ♿ P – 🔺 65. MC AE ① VISA
The Riverside **: Meals** 12.50/21.50 and a la carte 20.00/28.00 **st.** 13.50 – **47 rm** ⚹ 60.00/120.00 **st.** – SB.

CHOLLERTON *Northd.* 401 402 N 18 – *see Hexham.*

CHORLEY *Lancs.* 402 404 M 23 – *pop. 33 536.*
18 *Duxbury Park, Duxbury Hall Rd* ☎ *(01257) 265380* – 18 *Shaw Hill Hotel G. & C.C., Preston Rd, Whittle-le-Woods* ☎ *(01257) 269221.*
London 222 – Blackpool 30 – Liverpool 33 – Manchester 26.

Premier Lodge, Moss Lane, Whittle-le-Woods, PR6 8AB, Northeast : 1 ½ m. by A 6 and A 674 on B 6229 ☎ (0870) 7001354, *Fax (01257) 232 912*, ⚹ – |‡|, ⚹ rm, ▤ rest, TV ☎ ♿ P. MC AE VISA. ⚹
Meals a la carte approx. 16.95 **t.** 8.75 – **83 rm** 42.95 **t.**

at Whittle-le-Woods *North : 2 m. on A 6* – ✉ *Chorley.*

Shaw Hill H. Golf & Country Club, Preston Rd, PR6 7PP, ☎ (01257) 269221, *info@shaw-hill.co.uk, Fax (01257) 261223*, ⚹, ≘s, ▢, 18 – ⚹ rest, TV P – 🔺 200. MC AE ① VISA. ⚹
closed 26 December – ***Vardon*** **: Meals** *(closed dinner 25 December and Bank Holiday lunch)* (bar lunch Saturday) 14.50/18.00 and a la carte 20.00/30.00 **t.** 10.25 – **30 rm** ⚹ 78.00/130.00 **t.** – SB.

Parkville Country House, 174 Preston Rd, PR6 7HE, ☎ (01257) 261881, *Fax (01257) 273171*, ⚹ – TV P. MC AE ① VISA JCB. ⚹
Meals *(closed Sunday)* (dinner only) 13.95 and a la carte approx. 26.70 12.95 – **8 rm** ⚹ 70.00/80.00 **st.**

CHORLTON CUM HARDY *Gtr. Manchester* 402 403 404 N 23 – *see Manchester.*

CHRISTCHURCH *Dorset* 403 404 O 31 *The West Country G.* – *pop. 36 379.*
See : *Town★ – Priory★.*
Env. : *Hengistbury Head★ (≤★★) SW : 4½ m. by A 35 and B 3059.*
18 *Highcliffe Castle, 107 Lymington Rd, Highcliffe-on-Sea* ☎ *(01425) 272953* – 9 *Barrack Rd, Iford* ☎ *(01202) 473817.*
23 High St ☎ *(01202) 471780.*
London 111 – Bournemouth 6 – Salisbury 26 – Southampton 24 – Winchester 39.

Travel Inn, Barrack Rd, BH23 2BN, West : ¾ m. on A 35 ☎ (01202) 485215 – |‡|, ⚹ rm, TV ♿ P. MC AE ① VISA. ⚹
Meals (grill rest.) – **40 rm** 41.95 **t.**

Travel Inn, Somerford Rd, BH23 3QG, East : 2 m. on B 3059 ☎ (01202) 485376, *Fax (01202) 474939* – ⚹ rm, TV ♿ P. MC AE ① VISA. ⚹
Meals (grill rest.) – **70 rm** 41.95 **t.**

XX **Splinters,** 12 Church St, BH23 1BW, ✆ (01202) 483454, *eating@splinters.uk.com, Fax (01202) 480180* – MC AE DC VISA
closed 26-31 December, Sunday and Monday – **Meals** a la carte 24.50/32.00 **t.** 12.95.

X **Bistro on the Bridge,** 3-5 Bridge St, BH23 1DY, ✆ (01202) 482522, *bistro.bridge@virgin.net, Fax (01202) 470048* – ⇔ ▤. MC AE VISA
closed Monday and Tuesday – **Meals** 15.95 (dinner) and a la carte 16.95/29.90 **t.** 9.95.

at Mudeford *Southeast : 2 m.* – ✉ *Christchurch.*

Avonmouth, 95 Mudeford, BH23 3NT, ✆ (0870) 400 8120, *heritagehotels_mudeford_christchurch.avonmouth@forte-hotels.com, Fax (01202) 479004,* ≤, heated, – ⇔ TV P – 60. MC AE DC VISA JCB.
Meals (bar lunch Monday-Saturday)/dinner 23.95 and a la carte 21.30/27.85 **t.** 12.95 – 11.95 – **40 rm** 90.00/140.00 – SB.

Waterford Lodge, 87 Bure Lane, Friars Cliff, BH23 4DN, ✆ (01425) 272948, *waterford@bestwestern.co.uk, Fax (01425) 279130,* – ⇔ rest, TV P – 80. MC AE DC VISA
closed 27 December-3 January – **Meals** 14.50/25.50 **t.** 11.90 – 10.50 – **18 rm** 82.00/108.00 **t.** – SB.

CHRISTLETON *Ches.* 402 403 L 24 – *see Chester.*

CHURCHILL *Oxon.* 403 404 P 28 – *pop. 502* – ✉ *Chipping Norton.*
London 79 – Birmingham 46 – Cheltenham 29 – Oxford 23 – Swindon 31.

The Forge without rest., OX7 6NJ, ✆ (01608) 658173, *jon@theforge.co.uk, Fax (01608) 659262* – ⇔ TV P. MC VISA.
6 rm 45.00/65.00 **st.**

CHURCH STRETTON *Shrops.* 402 403 L 26 *Great Britain G.* – *pop. 3 435.*
Env. : *Wenlock Edge*★, *E : by B 4371.*
18 *Trevor Hill* ✆ *(01694) 722281.*
London 166 – Birmingham 46 – Hereford 39 – Shrewsbury 14.

Mynd House, Ludlow Rd, Little Stretton, SY6 6RB, Southwest : 1 ¼ m. on B 4370 ✆ (01694) 722212, *info@myndhouse.co.uk,* – ⇔ TV P. MC VISA JCB
Meals (booking essential) (dinner only and Sunday lunch) 17.50/20.00 **st.** 12.00 – **5 rm** 45.00/120.00 **st.**, 2 suites – SB.

Jinlye without rest., Castle Hill, All Stretton, SY6 6JP, North : 2 ¼ m. by B 4370 turning left beside telephone box in All Stretton ✆ (01694) 723243, *info@jinlye.co.uk, Fax (01694) 723243,* ≤, « 16C », – ⇔ TV P. MC VISA.
March-November – **8 rm** 42.00/70.00 **st.**

X **The Studio,** 59 High St, SY6 6BY, ✆ (01694) 722672, *Fax (01694) 722672,* – ⇔. MC VISA
closed 25-26 December, Sunday and Monday – **Meals** 7.50/12.50 (lunch) and a la carte 18.15/24.25 **t.** 8.95.

CIRENCESTER *Glos.* 403 404 O 28 *Great Britain G.* – *pop. 15 221.*
See : *Town*★ – *Church of St John the Baptist*★ – *Corinium Museum*★ *(Mosaic pavements*★*) AC.*
Env. : *Fairford : Church of St Mary*★ *(stained glass windows*★★*) E : 7 m. by A 417.*
18 *Cheltenham Rd, Bagendon* ✆ *(01285) 653939.*
Corn Hall, Market Pl ✆ *(01285) 654180.*
London 97 – Bristol 37 – Gloucester 19 – Oxford 37.

Stratton House, Gloucester Rd, Stratton, GL7 2LE, Northwest : 1 ¾ m. on A 417 ✆ (01285) 651761, *stratton.house@forestdale.com, Fax (01285) 640024,* – ⇔ TV P – 150. MC AE DC VISA
Meals (bar lunch Monday to Saturday)/dinner 10.45/18.95 and a la carte 17.45/26.45 **t.** 8.85 – **40 rm** 85.00/105.00 **t.** – SB.

Corinium, 12 Gloucester St, GL7 2DG, ✆ (01285) 659711, *info@coriniumhotel.co.uk, Fax (01285) 885807,* – ⇔ rest, TV P. MC AE VISA
closed 23-30 December – **Meals** a la carte 15.95/22.70 **st.** 9.50 – **15 rm** 65.00/85.00 **st.** – SB.

Wimborne House without rest., 91 Victoria Rd, GL7 1ES, ✆ (01285) 643653, *wimborneho@aol.com, Fax (01285) 653890,* – ⇔ TV P.
closed 24 December-1 January – **6 rm** 35.00/45.00 **s.**

Corner House without rest., 101A Victoria Rd, GL7 1EU, ✆ (01285) 641958, *thecornerhouse@virgin.net, Fax (01285) 640805,* – ⇔ TV P
5 rm 35.00/42.00 **st.**

The Ivy House without rest., 2 Victoria Rd, GL7 1EN, ✆ (01285) 656626, *info@ivyhousecotswolds.com* – ⇔ TV P. MC AE VISA JCB.
4 rm 35.00/45.00 **st.**

at Barnsley *Northeast : 4 m. by A 429 on B 4425 – ✉ Cirencester.*

Village Pub with rm, GL7 5EF, ☎ (01285) 740421, *reservations@thevillagepub.co.uk, Fax (01285) 740142,* « Part 17C » – rm, TV P. MO VISA
closed 25 December – **Meals** a la carte 17.20/24.15 **st.** 10.95 – **6 rm** 55.00/70.00 **st.**

at Ampney Crucis *East : 2 ¾ m. by A 417 – ✉ Cirencester.*

Crown of Crucis, GL7 5RS, on A 417 ☎ (01285) 851806, *Fax (01285) 851735,* – TV P – 90. MO AE VISA
closed 25 December – **Meals** (bar lunch)/dinner a la carte 11.20/20.75 **t.** 8.75 – **25 rm** 64.00/92.00 **t.** – SB.

at Ewen *Southwest : 3 ¼ m. by A 429 – ✉ Cirencester.*

Wild Duck Inn with rm, Drake's Island, GL7 6BY, ☎ (01285) 770310, *wduckinn@aol.com, Fax (01285) 770924,* « Part 16C former mill », – TV P. MO AE VISA
Meals a la carte 15.40/22.85 **t.** 9.95 – 6.50 – **11 rm** 60.00/80.00 **t.**

at Kemble *Southwest : 4 m. on A 429 – ✉ Cirencester.*

Smerrill Barns without rest., GL7 6BW, North : 1 ¼ m. on A 429 ☎ (01285) 770907, *gsopher@hotmail.com, Fax (01285) 770706,* « Converted 18C barn » – TV P. MO VISA JCB.
closed 23-28 December – **7 rm** 45.00/55.00.

at Sapperton *West : 5 m. by A 419 – ✉ Cirencester.*

The Bell, GL7 6LE, ☎ (01285) 760298, *Fax (01285) 760761,* – P. MO VISA
closed 25-26 and dinner 31 December – **Meals** a la carte 16.75/25.40 **t.** 11.95.

CLACKET LANE SERVICE AREA *Surrey* 404 U 30 – ✉ *Westerham.*
M 25 Motorway Services, junctions 5-6 (eastbound), Westerham ☎ (01959) 565063 – M 25 Motorway Services, junctions 5-6 (westbound), Westerham ☎ (01959) 565615.

Travel Inn Metro without rest., TN16 2ER, M 25 between junctions 5 and 6 (westbound carriageway) ☎ (01959) 565577, *Fax (01959) 561311* – TV P. MO AE VISA.
closed Christmas and New Year – **58 rm** 49.95 **t.**

CLACTON-ON-SEA *Essex* 404 X 28 – *pop. 45 065.*
18 West Rd ☎ (01255) 424331 – 23 Pier Ave ☎ (01255) 423400.
London 76 – Chelmsford 37 – Colchester 14 – Ipswich 28.

Chudleigh, 13 Agate Rd, Marine Parade West, CO15 1RA, ☎ (01255) 425407, *Fax (01255) 470280* – TV P. MO AE VISA JCB
Meals *(closed Christmas-end January)* (dinner only) (residents only) 16.00 **st.** 9.50 – **10 rm** 39.00/55.00 **st.** – SB.

CLANFIELD *Oxon.* 403 404 P 28 – *pop. 1 709 (inc. Shilton).*
London 75 – Oxford 24 – Swindon 16.

Plough at Clanfield, Bourton Rd, OX18 2RB, on A 4095 ☎ (01367) 810222, *ploughat clanfield@hotmail.com, Fax (01367) 810596,* « Elizabethan manor house », – TV P. MO AE VISA JCB.
closed 24 December-9 January – **Meals** *(closed Sunday dinner and Monday lunch)* 14.25/32.50 **t.** 12.50 – **12 rm** 82.25/125.00 **t.** – SB.

CLAPPERSGATE *Cumbria* – *see Ambleside.*

CLARE *Suffolk* 404 V 27 – *pop. 1 976* – ✉ *Sudbury.*
London 67 – Cambridge 27 – Colchester 24 – Ipswich 32 – Bury St.Edmunds 16.

Ship Stores, 22 Callis St, CO10 8PX, ☎ (01787) 277834, *shipclare@aol.co.uk* – rm, TV. MO VISA.
Meals (by arrangement) 8.50 – **6 rm** 45.00/50.00.

CLAVERING *Essex* 404 U 28 – *pop. 1 663* – ✉ *Saffron Walden.*
London 44 – Cambridge 25 – Colchester 44 – Luton 29.

Cricketers with rm, CB11 4QT, ☎ (01799) 550442, *cricketers@lineone.net, Fax (01799) 550882,* – TV P. MO AE VISA.
closed 25 and 26 December – **Meals** 25.00 (dinner) and a la carte 17.75/25.00 **t.** 9.00 – **8 rm** 65.00/90.00 **st.**

CLAYDON *Suffolk* 404 X 27 – *see Ipswich.*

CLAYGATE *Surrey* 404 ㊷ – *see Esher.*

CLAYTON-LE-DALE *Lancs.* – *see Blackburn.*

CLAYTON-LE-MOORS *Lancs.* 402 M 22 – *pop. 6 961* – ✉ *Accrington.*
London 232 – Blackburn 3.5 – Lancaster 37 – Leeds 44 – Preston 14.

Dunkenhalgh, Blackburn Rd, BB1 9JJ, Southwest : 1 ½ m. on A 678 ☎ (01254) 39802 *dunkenhalgh@macdonald-hotels.co.uk, Fax (01254) 872263,* – 400.
Cameo : **Meals** (bar lunch Saturday) 12.95/25.95 and a la carte **st.** 13.95 – 10.95
121 rm 95.00/115.00 **st.**, 1 suite – SB.

Sparth House, Whalley Rd, BB5 5RP, ☎ (01254) 872263, *Fax (01254) 872263,* – 100.
Meals a la carte 15.15/24.40 **st.** 9.50 – **16 rm** 57.50/99.00 **st.** – SB.

CLAYTON-LE-WOODS *Lancs.* 402 M 24 – *pop. 14 173* – ✉ *Chorley.*
London 220 – Liverpool 34 – Manchester 26 – Preston 5.5.

The Pines, 570 Preston Rd, PR6 7ED, on A 6 at junction with B 5256 ☎ (01772) 33855 *mail@thepines-hotel.co.uk, Fax (01772) 629002,* – rm, – 200.
closed 26 December – ***Haworths Bistro :*** **Meals** a la carte 10.00/28.20 **t.** 11.50 – **36 rm** 70.00/110.00 **t.**, 2 suites.

Travelodge, Preston Rd, PR6 7JB, on A 6 ☎ (01772) 311963, *Fax (01772) 311963* rm,
Meals (grill rest.) – **40 rm** 42.95 **t.**

CLAYTON WEST *W. Yorks.* 402 404 P 23 – *pop. 7 988 (inc. Skelmanthorpe)* – ✉ *Huddersfield.*
London 190 – Leeds 19 – Manchester 35 – Sheffield 24.

Bagden Hall, Wakefield Rd, Scissett, HD8 9LE, Southwest : 1 m. on A 63 ☎ (01484) 865330, *info@bagdenhall.demon.co.uk, Fax (01484) 861001,* 9, – rest – 70.
Meals 10.75/18.95 and dinner a la carte 17.70/26.40 **st.** 9.95 – **17 rm** 60.00/100.00 **st**

CLEARWELL *Glos.* – *see Coleford.*

CLEETHORPES *N.E. Lincs.* 402 404 U 23 – *pop. 32 719.*
Humberside Airport : ☎ (01652) 688456, W : 16 m. by A 46 and A 18 Y.
42-43 Alexandra Rd ☎ (01472) 323111.
London 171 – Boston 49 – Lincoln 38 – Sheffield 77.

Kingsway, Kingsway, DN35 0AE, ☎ (01472) 601122, *Fax (01472) 601381,* –
closed 25-26 December – **Meals** 14.30/18.95 and a la carte 23.65/29.45 **t.** 11.25 – **50 rm** 65.00/90.00 **t.** – SB.

CLEEVE HILL *Glos.* 403 404 N 28 – *see Cheltenham.*

CLEY NEXT THE SEA *Norfolk* 404 X 25 – *see Blakeney.*

CLIFFORD'S MESNE *Glos.* – *see Newent.*

CLIFTON HAMPDEN *Devon* 403 404 Q 29 – *see Abingdon.*

CLIMPING *W. Sussex* 404 S 31 – *see Littlehampton.*

CLIPSHAM *Rutland* – *see Stamford.*

CLITHEROE *Lancs.* 402 M 22 – *pop. 13 548.*
18 *Whalley Rd ☎ (01200) 422618* – *12-14 Market Pl ☎ (01200) 425566.*
London 64 – Blackpool 35 – Manchester 31.

Brooklyn, 32 Pimlico Rd, BB7 2AH, ☎ (01200) 428268 –
closed 24-26 December – **Meals** (by arrangement) 11.00 **s.** – **4 rm** 27.50/43.00 **s.**

Auctioneer, New Market St, BB7 2JW, ☎ (01200) 427153 –
closed Monday, Tuesday, Sunday dinner and lunch Wednesday and Thursday – **Meals** 11.95/19.75 and a la carte 17.50/33.95 **t.** 12.00.

at Waddington *North : 1 ¾ m. on B 6478* – ✉ *Clitheroe.*

Peter Barn without rest., Rabbit Lane, BB7 3JH, Northwest : 1 ½ m. by B 6478 o Cross Lane ☎ (01200) 428585, *jean@peterbarn.fsnet.co.uk,*
closed Christmas and New Year – **3 rm** 28.00/50.00.

CLOVELLY *Devon* 403 G 31 *The West Country G. – pop. 439 –* ✉ *Bideford.*

See : *Village*★★.

Env. : *SW : Tamar River*★★.

Exc. : *Hartland : Hartland Church*★ *– Hartland Quay*★ *(viewpoint*★★*) – Hartland Point* ≤★★★*, W : 6½ m. by B 3237 and B 3248 – Morwenstow (Church*★*, cliffs*★★*), SW : 11½ m. by A 39.*

to Lundy Island (Lundy Co. Ltd) (summer only) (1 h).

London 241 – Barnstaple 18 – Exeter 52 – Penzance 92.

Red Lion, The Quay, EX39 5TF, ☎ (01237) 431237, *redlion@clovelly.co.uk, Fax (01237) 431044,* ≤ – rest, TV P. MO AE VISA.
Meals 17.50/25.00 **st.** 10.00 – **11 rm** 45.50/91.00 **st.** – SB.

New Inn, High St, EX39 5TQ, ☎ (01237) 431303, *newinn@clovelly.co.uk, Fax (01237) 431636,* « 17C » – rest, TV. MO AE VISA.
Meals (bar lunch)/dinner 17.50/20.00 **st.** 10.00 – **8 rm** 39.75/79.50 **st.** – SB.

COATHAM MUNDEVILLE *Durham* 402 P 20 – *see Darlington.*

COBHAM *Surrey* 404 S 30 – *pop. 15 254 (inc. Oxshott).*

London 24 – Guildford 10.

Plan : see Greater London (South-West) p. 12

Hilton Cobham, Seven Hills Road South, KT11 1EW, West : 1 ½ m. by A 245 ☎ (01932) 864471, *gm_cobham@hilton.com, Fax (01932) 868017,* – rm, TV P – 300. MO AE VISA JCB
Meals (bar lunch Saturday) (dancing Saturday evening) a la carte 15.95/31.45 **t.** 12.50 – 13.95 – **152 rm** 160.00/170.00 **st.**, 3 suites.

Premier Lodge, Portsmouth Rd, Fairmile, KT11 1BW, Northeast : 1 m. on A 307 ☎ (01932) 868141, *Fax (01932) 866478,* – rm, TV P. MO AE VISA. AZ x
Meals (grill rest.) a la carte approx. 12.50 **t.** 7.80 – **48 rm** 54.95 **t.**

at Stoke D'Abernon *Southeast : 1½ m. on A 245 –* ✉ *Cobham.*

Woodlands Park, Woodlands Lane, KT11 3QB, on A 245 ☎ (01372) 843933, *info@woodlandspark.co.uk, Fax (01372) 842704,* – rm, TV P – 280. MO AE VISA.
Oak Room : **Meals** *(closed Sunday)* (dinner only and Sunday lunch) a la carte 32.50/45.00 **st.** 15.00 – ***Quotes Brasserie :*** **Meals** a la carte 16.00/24.00 **st.** 15.00 – 12.50 – **59 rm** 140.00/240.00 **st.** – SB.

COCKERMOUTH *Cumbria* 401 402 J 20 – *pop. 7 702.*

Embleton ☎ *(017687) 76223.*

Town Hall, Market St ☎ *(01900) 822603.*

London 306 – Carlisle 25 – Keswick 13.

Trout, Crown St, CA13 0EJ, ☎ (01900) 823591, *enquiries@trouthotel.co.uk, Fax (01900) 827514,* – TV P – 50. MO AE VISA
Meals 14.95/24.95 and a la carte 27.85/41.40 **t.** 9.95 – **29 rm** 59.95/150.00 **t.** – SB.

at Lorton *Southeast : 4¼ m. by B 5292 –* ✉ *Cockermouth.*

Winder Hall Country House, CA13 9UP, on B 5289 ☎ (01900) 85107, *stay@winderhall.com, Fax (01900) 85107,* ≤, « Part 17C manor house », TV P. MO VISA JCB.
Meals 18.00 **st.** 12.90 – **6 rm** (dinner included) 56.00/110.00 **st.** – SB.

New House Farm, CA13 9UU, South : 1 ¼ m. on B 5289 ☎ (01900) 85404, *hazel@newhouse-farm.co.uk, Fax (01900) 85404,* ≤, « Part 17C and 19C farmhouse », P. MO VISA
Meals 22.00 **st.** 10.00 – **5 rm** (dinner included) 66.00/132.00 **st.** – SB.

COGGESHALL *Essex* 404 W 28 – *pop. 3 927 –* ✉ *Colchester.*

London 49 – Braintree 6 – Chelmsford 16 – Colchester 9.

White Hart, Market End, CO6 1NH, ☎ (01376) 561654, *wharthotel@ndirect.co.uk, Fax (01376) 561789,* « Part 15C guildhall », – TV P. MO AE VISA JCB.
Meals - Italian - (in bar Sunday dinner) 15.00 and a la carte 21.50/31.00 **t.** 10.95 – **18 rm** 65.00/105.00 **st.** – SB.

Baumann's Brasserie, 4-6 Stoneham St, CO6 1TT, ☎ (01376) 561453, *food@baumanns.fsbusiness.co.uk, Fax (01376) 563762* – MO AE VISA JCB
closed first 2 weeks January, Monday and Tuesday – **Meals** 12.50/16.50 and a la carte 19.00/30.40 **t.** 9.95.

COLCHESTER *Essex* 404 W 28 *Great Britain G. – pop. 96 063.*

See : *Castle and Museum*★ *AC* BZ.

Birch Grove, Layer Rd ☎ *(01206) 734276.*

Visitor Information Centre, 1 Queen St ☎ *(01206) 282920.*

London 52 – Cambridge 48 – Ipswich 18 – Luton 76 – Southend-on-Sea 41.

George, 116 High St, CO1 1TD, ☎ (01206) 578494, *colcgeorge@aol.com, Fax (01206) 761732,* , « 15C former coaching inn » – rm, rest, TV P – 70. MC AE VISA JCB BZ b
Meals *(closed dinner 25 and 26 December)* 11.55/23.95 and a la carte 15.70/26.20 **t.** 9.80 – 8.95 – **47 rm** 75.95/99.95 **t.**

Rose and Crown, East St, Eastgates, CO1 2TZ, ☎ (01206) 866677, *info@rose-and-crown.com, Fax (01206) 866616,* « Part 15C inn » – rm, TV P – 100. MC AE VISA. CZ d
closed 27-30 December – **Meals** (in bar Sunday dinner) 18.50/27.95 **st.** 11.45 – 8.95 – **29 rm** 76.50/135.00 **st.**

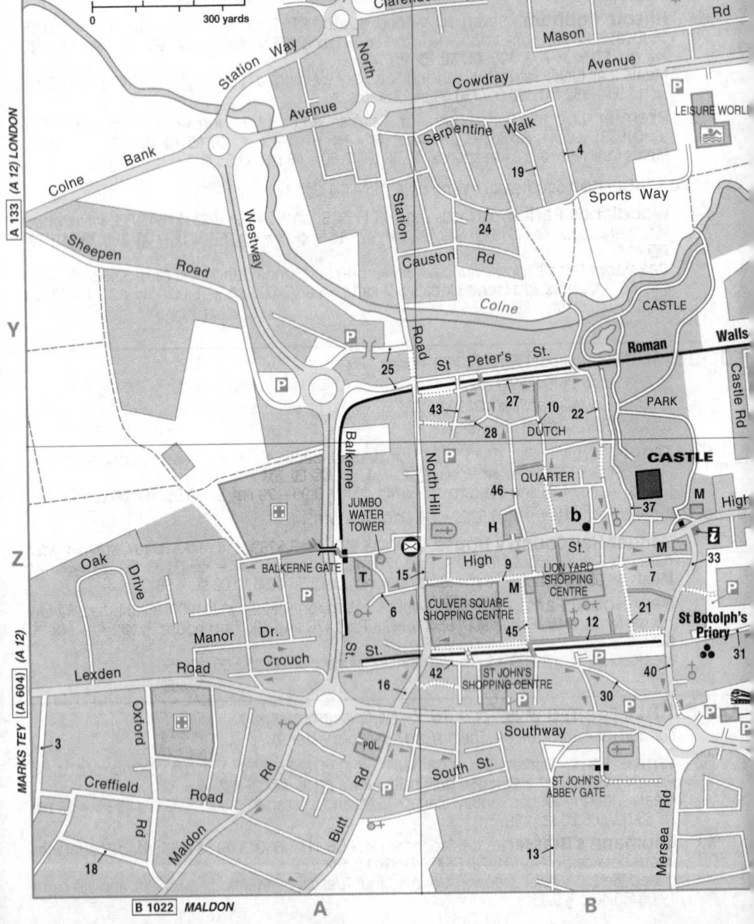

Butterfly, Old Ipswich Rd, CO7 7QY, Northeast : 4 ¼ m. by A 1232 at junction of A 12 with A 120 (via sliproad to A 120) ✆ (01206) 230900, *colbutterfly@lineone.net, Fax (01206) 231095* – [no smoking] rm, [TV] [phone] [wheelchair] [P] – [conference] 80. [MC] [AE] [DC] VISA JCB
Meals 15.00/17.50 (dinner) and a la carte 15.95/26.95 **t.** [wine] 13.00 – [breakfast] 8.50 – **50 rm** 75.00 **t.** – SB.

Travel Inn, Severalls Business Park, Ipswich Rd, CO4 4WP, Northeast : 3 ½ m. on A 1232 ✆ (01206) 855001, *Fax (01206) 211388* – [no smoking] rm, [no smoking] rest, [TV] [wheelchair] [P]. [MC] [AE] [DC] VISA
Meals (grill rest.) – **40 rm** 41.95 **t.**

at Eight Ash Green *West : 4 m. by A 1124 –* **AZ** *– ✉ Colchester.*

Posthouse Colchester, Abbotts Lane, CO6 3QL, at junction of A 1124 with A 12 ✆ (0870) 400 9020, *gm1064@forte-hotel.com, Fax (01206) 766577,* [gym], [sauna], [pool] – [no smoking] rm, [no smoking] rest, [TV] [wheelchair] [P] – [conference] 150. [MC] [AE] [DC] VISA
Meals 13.50/15.00 and a la carte 21.00/27.50 **st.** [wine] 13.00 – [breakfast] 15.95 – **110 rm** 89.00 **st.**

at Marks Tey *West : 5 m. by A 12 at junction with A 120 –* **AZ** *– ✉ Colchester.*

Marks Tey, London Rd, CO6 1DU, on B 1408 ✆ (01206) 210001, *info@markstyehotel.co.uk, Fax (01206) 212167,* [gym], [sauna], [pool], [tennis] – [no smoking] rm, [no smoking] rest, [TV] [P] – [conference] 200. [MC] [AE] [DC] VISA. [no dogs]
Meals 11.50/16.50 and a la carte 18.90/25.30 **st.** [wine] 8.00 – [breakfast] 8.95 – **109 rm** 79.00/85.00 **st.**, 1 suite – SB.

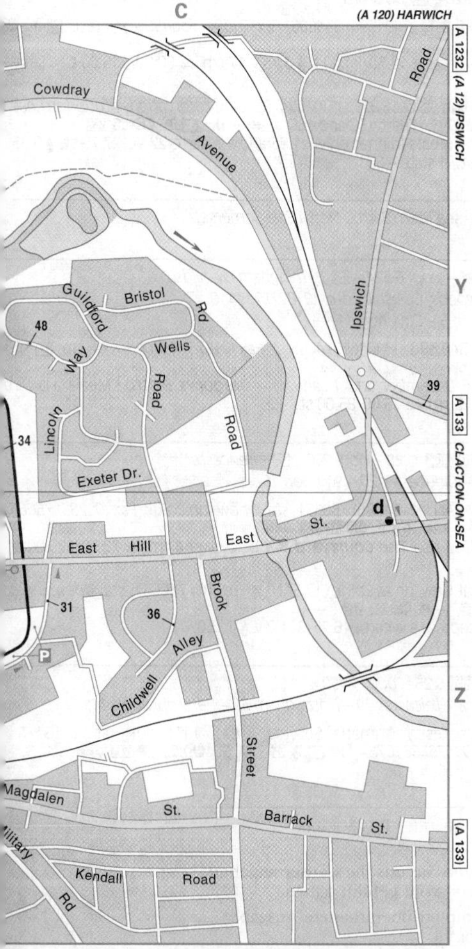

COLCHESTER

COLEFORD *Devon* 403 I 31 – ✉ *Crediton.*
London 214 – Barnstaple 29 – Exeter 14 – Plymouth 43 – Taunton 42.

New Inn with rm, EX17 5BZ, ✆ (01363) 84242, *new-inn@reallyreal-group.com Fax (01363) 85044,* « Part 13C thatched inn » – rm, TV P. MC AE VISA JCB. *closed 25-26 December* – **Meals** a la carte 15.20/21.90 **st.** 10.95 – **6 rm** 50.00/75.00 **st**

COLEFORD *Glos.* 403 404 M 28 *Great Britain G. – pop. 9 567.*
Env. : *W : Wye Valley★.*
Forest of Dean, Lords Hills ✆ (01594) 832583 – Forest Hills, Mile End Rd ✆ (01594) 810620.
High St ✆ (01594) 812388.
London 143 – Bristol 28 – Gloucester 19 – Newport 29.

Speech House, Forest of Dean, GL16 7EL, Northeast : 3 m. by B 4028 on B 4226 ✆ (01594) 822607, *relax@thespeechhouse.co.uk, Fax (01594) 823658,* – TV – 60. MC AE VISA
Meals (bar lunch)/dinner 21.95 **t.** – **32 rm** 49.75/101.50 **t.** – SB.

at Clearwell *South : 2 m. by B 4228* – ✉ *Coleford.*

Wyndham Arms, GL16 8JT, ✆ (01594) 833666, *Fax (01594) 836450* – rest, TV P. MC VISA JCB
Meals 13.75/21.25 and a la carte 19.50/24.00 **t.** 8.75 – **17 rm** 60.00/115.00 **t.**, 1 suite – SB.

Tudor Farmhouse, High St, GL16 8JS, ✆ (01594) 833046, *reservations@tudorfarmhse.-net.com, Fax (01594) 837093,* « Part 13C and 16C », – TV P. MC AE VISA
closed 24-27 December – **Meals** (dinner only) 21.95 and a la carte 22.90/27.70 **st.** 9.95 – **22 rm** 50.00/100.00 **st.**, 1 suite – SB.

COLERNE *Wilts.* 403 404 M 29 – *see Bath (Bath & North East Somerset).*

COLESHILL *Warks.* 403 404 O 26 – *pop. 6 324* – ✉ *Birmingham (W. Mids.).*
Atherstone, The Outwoods, Coleshill Rd ✆ (01827) 713110.
London 113 – Birmingham 8 – Coventry 11.

Coleshill, 152 High St, B46 3BG, ✆ (01675) 465527, *Fax (01675) 464013* – rm, TV – 150. MC AE VISA.
closed dinner 25 and 26 December and 1 January – ***Gregorys Bistro*** **:** **Meals** a la carte 10.65/20.20 **st.** 7.75 – **23 rm** 75.00/85.00 **st.** – SB.

COLN ST. ALDWYNS *Glos.* 403 404 O 28 – *pop. 260* – ✉ *Cirencester.*
London 101 – Bristol 53 – Gloucester 20 – Swindon 15.

New Inn At Coln, GL7 5AN, ✆ (01285) 750651, *stay@new-inn.co.uk, Fax (01285) 750657* « 16C coaching inn » – rest, TV P. MC AE VISA JCB
Meals 22.50/27.50 **t.** – (see also ***The Courtyard Bar*** below) – **14 rm** 72.00/125.00 **t.** – SB.

The Courtyard Bar (at New Inn at Coln), GL7 5AN, ✆ (01285) 750651, *stay@new_inn.co.uk, Fax (01285) 750657,* – P. MC AE VISA
Meals (bookings not accepted) a la carte 16.25/23.00 **t.** 11.50.

COLSTERWORTH *Lincs.* 402 404 S 25 – *pop. 1 452.*
London 105 – Grantham 8 – Leicester 29 – Nottingham 32 – Peterborough 14.

Travelodge without rest., Granada Service Area, NG33 5JR, at A 151/A ✆ (01476) 861077, *Fax (01476) 861078* – TV P – 30. MC AE VISA JCB.
36 rm 42.95 **t.**

Besonders angenehme Hotels oder Restaurants sind im Führer rot gekennzeichnet.
Sie können uns helfen, wenn Sie uns die Häuser angeben, in denen Sie sich besonders wohl gefühlt haben.
Jährlich erscheint eine komplett überarbeitete Ausgabe aller Roten Michelin-Führer.

COLSTON BASSETT *Notts.* 402 404 R 25 – *pop. 239* – ✉ *Nottingham.*
London 129 – Lincoln 40 – Nottingham 15 – Sheffield 51.

Martins Arms with rm, School Lane, NG12 3FD, ☎ (01949) 81361, *Fax (01949) 81309,* – P. MC VISA.
closed 25 December and Sunday dinner – **Meals** a la carte 19.85/32.40 **t.** 12.50 – **2 rm** 35.00/65.00 **t.**

COLTISHALL *Norfolk* 404 Y 25 *Great Britain G.* – *pop. 1 992* – ✉ *Norwich.*
Env. : *The Broads*★.
London 133 – Norwich 8.

Norfolk Mead, NR12 7DN, ☎ (01603) 737531, *info@norfolkmead.co.uk, Fax (01603) 737521,* heated, – TV P. MC AE VISA JCB
Meals *(closed Monday and Saturday lunch)* 12.00 (lunch) and dinner a la carte 19.00/30.75 **t.** 12.95 – **9 rm** 70.00/150.00 – SB.

Kings Head with rm, Wroxham Rd, NR12 7EA, ☎ (01603) 737426, *Fax (01603) 736542* – TV P. MC VISA.
Meals a la carte 18.00/24.25 **t.** 6.25 – **4 rm** 27.50/55.00 **t.** – SB.

COLWALL *Herefordshire* – *see Great Malvern.*

COLYFORD *Devon* 403 K 31 *Great Britain G.* – ✉ *Colyton.*
Env. : *Colyton*★ *(Church*★*), N : 1 m. on B 3161 – Axmouth (<*★*), S : 1 m. by A 3052 and B 3172.*
London 168 – Exeter 21 – Taunton 30 – Torquay 46 – Yeovil 32.

Swallows Eaves, EX24 6QJ, ☎ (01297) 553184, *Fax (01297) 553574,* – TV P. MC VISA.
Meals (dinner only) 23.00 11.75 – **8 rm** 45.00/90.00 – SB.

COMPTON ABBAS *Dorset* – *see Shaftesbury.*

CONGLETON *Ches.* 402 403 404 N 24 *Great Britain G.* – *pop. 24 897.*
Env. : *Little Moreton Hall*★★ *AC, SW : 3 m. by A 34.*
Biddulph Rd ☎ *(01260) 273540.*
Town Hall, High St ☎ *(01260) 271095.*
London 183 – Liverpool 50 – Manchester 25 – Sheffield 46 – Stoke-on-Trent 13.

Sandhole Farm without rest., Hulme Walfield, CW12 2JH, North : 2 ¼ m. on A 34 ☎ (01260) 224419, *veronica@sandholefarm.co.uk, Fax (01260) 224766,* « Converted farm buildings », – TV P. MC AE VISA.
17 rm 42.00/52.00.

CONISTON *Cumbria* 402 K 20 *Great Britain G.* – *pop. 1 304.*
Env. : *Coniston Water*★ – *Brantwood*★ *AC, SE : 2 m. on east side of Coniston Water.*
Exc. : *Hard Knott Pass*★★*, Wrynose Pass*★★*, NW : 10 m. by A 593 and minor road.*
Ruskin Ave ☎ *(015394) 41533.*
London 285 – Carlisle 55 – Kendal 22 – Lancaster 42.

Coniston Lodge, Station Rd, LA21 8HH, ☎ (015394) 41201, *robinson@conistonlodge.freeserve.co.uk, Fax (015394) 41201* – TV P. MC AE VISA.
closed December 23-29 and January – **Meals** *(closed Sunday and Monday)* (dinner only) 22.00 **st.** 12.50 – **6 rm** 47.50/83.00 **t.**

The Blackbull Inn with rm, 1 Yewdale Rd, LA21 8DU, ☎ (015394) 41335, *theblackbullconiston@easicom.com, Fax (015394) 41168,* « 16C coaching inn, home of Coniston brewery » – TV P. MC VISA
closed 25 December – **Meals** (dinner only) a la carte 13.65/21.85 **t.** 13.95 – **14 rm** 40.00/90.00 **t.**

at Water Yeat *South : 6½ m. by A 593 on A 5084* – ✉ *Ulverston.*

Water Yeat, LA12 8DJ, ☎ (01229) 885306, *Fax (01229) 885306,* <, « Part 17C », – P.
mid February-November – **Meals** (by arrangement) 20.00 **st.** 5.00 – **5 rm** 40.00/64.00 **st.**

at Torver *Southwest : 2 ¼ m. on A 593 – ✉ Coniston.*

Wheelgate Country House without rest., Little Arrow, LA21 8AU, Northeast : ¾ m. on A 593 ☎ (015394) 41418, *wheelgate@conistoncottages.co.uk, Fax (015394) 41114,* « Part 17C farmhouse », – TV P. MC VISA.
closed mid December – **5 rm** 30.00/70.00.

Old Rectory, LA21 8AX, Northeast : ¼ m. by A 593 ☎ (015394) 41353, *enquire@theoldrectoryhotel.com, Fax (015394) 41156,* ←, – TV P. MC VISA JCB
Meals (residents only) (dinner only) 18.00/22.50 **st.** 9.95 – **8 rm** (dinner included) 59.00/112.00 **st.** – SB.

Arrowfield Country without rest., Little Arrow, LA21 8AU, Northeast : ¾ m. on A 593 ☎ (015394) 41741, ←, – TV P.
March-November and New Year – **5 rm** 26.00/52.00 **st.**

CONISTON COLD *N. Yorks. – see Skipton.*

CONSTABLE BURTON *N. Yorks.* 402 O 21 – *see Leyburn.*

CONSTANTINE *Cornwall* 403 E 33 – ✉ *Falmouth.*
Env. : *Mawgan-in-Meneage (Church★), S : 3 m. by minor roads.*
London 303 – Falmouth 15 – Penzance 25 – Truro 24.

Trengilly Wartha Inn with rm, Nancenoy, TR11 5RP, South : 1 ½ m. by Fore St off Port Navas rd ☎ (01326) 340332, *trengilly@compuserve.com, Fax (01326) 340332,* – TV P. MC AE VISA JCB
Meals *(closed 25 December)* (bar lunch)/dinner 20.00/25.00 **t.** 9.50 – **8 rm** 48.00/88.00 **st.** – SB.

CONSTANTINE BAY *Cornwall* 403 E 32 – *see Padstow.*

COOKHAM *Windsor & Maidenhead* 404 R 29 *Great Britain G.* – *pop. 6 096* – ✉ *Maidenhead.*
See : *Stanley Spencer Gallery★ AC.*
to Marlow, Maidenhead and Windsor (Salter Bros. Ltd) (summer only).
London 32 – High Wycombe 7 – Reading 16.

Bel and the Dragon, High St, SL6 9SQ, ☎ (01628) 521263, *cookham@belandthedragon.co.uk, Fax (01628) 851008,* – MC AE VISA
Meals a la carte 20.40/32.40 **t.** 9.95.

COPTHORNE *W. Sussex* 404 T 30 – *see Crawley.*

CORBIERE *Jersey (Channel Islands)* 403 P 33 and 230 ⑩ ⑪ – *see Channel Islands.*

CORBRIDGE *Northd.* 401 402 N 19 *Great Britain G.* – *pop. 2 719.*
Env. : *Hadrian's Wall★★, N : 3 m. by A 68 – Corstopitum★ AC, NW : ½ m.*
Hill St ☎ (01434) 632815 (Easter-October).
London 300 – Hexham 3 – Newcastle upon Tyne 18.

Clive House without rest., Appletree Lane, NE45 5DN, off B 6321 (Princes St) ☎ (01434) 632617, *atclive@supanet.com* – TV.
closed Christmas and New Year – **4 rm** 36.00/56.00 **st.**

Riverside without rest., Main St, NE45 5LE, ☎ (01434) 632942, *riverside@ukonline.co.uk, Fax (01434) 633883,* – TV P. MC AE VISA JCB
closed Christmas-New Year – **10 rm** 38.00/60.00 **t.**

Town Barns without rest., off Trinity Terr, NE45 5HP, North : ¼ m. by A 68 off Hexham rd ☎ (01434) 633345, – TV P
March-October – **3 rm** 35.00/50.00 **s.**

Ramblers Country House, Farnley, NE45 5RN, Southeast : 1 m. on Riding Mill Rd ☎ (01434) 632424, *Fax (01434) 633656,* – P. MC AE VISA JCB
closed Sunday dinner and Monday – **Meals** (dinner only and Sunday lunch)/dinner 16.95/19.95 and a la carte 24.05/27.25 **t.** 9.85.

Valley, The Old Station House, Station Rd, NE45 5AY, South : ½ m. by Riding Mill rd ☎ (01434) 633434, *Fax (01434) 633923* – . MC AE VISA
closed 25 December and Sunday – **Meals** - Indian - (dinner only) a la carte 13.65/22.90 **t.** 9.50.

t Great Whittington *North : 5½ m. by A 68 off B 6318 – ✉ Corbridge.*

Queens Head Inn, NE19 2HP, ✆ (01434) 672267 – ⅍ P. MC VISA
closed Monday except Bank Holidays – **Meals** 8.95/13.95 (lunch) and a la carte 16.45/22.90 **t.** 9.95.

t Sandhoe *Northwest : 2 m. by A 68 – ✉ Corbridge.*

The Courtyard without rest., Mount Pleasant, NE46 4LX, Northeast : ¼ m. on Stagshaw rd ✆ (01434) 606850, *Fax (01434) 607962*, ⩽, – ⅍ TV P. ⅌
restricted opening in winter – **3 rm** 50.00/80.00 **s.**

ORBY *Northants.* 404 R 26 *Great Britain G. – pop. 49 053.*
Env. : *Boughton House*★★ *AC, S : 5½ m. by A 6116 and A 43.*
Priors Hall, Stamford Rd, Weldon ✆ (01536) 260756.
Festival Hall, George St ✆ (01536) 407507.
London 100 – Leicester 26 – Northampton 22 – Peterborough 24.

Hilton Corby, Geddington Rd, NN18 8ET, East : 2 ½ m. on A 6116 at junction with A 43 ✆ (01536) 401020, *reservations_corby@hilton.com*, *Fax (01536) 400767*, , , – ⅍ TV P – 200. MC AE VISA
Seasons : **Meals** *(closed Saturday lunch)* (live music and dancing Saturday evening) 15.00/21.50 **st.** 13.75 – ***Millers :*** **Meals** a la carte 18.50/20.00 **st.** 13.75 – 10.95 – **103 rm** 110.00/125.00 **t.**, 2 suites – SB.

Jährlich eine neue Ausgabe
Aktuellste Informationen, jährlich für Sie!

ORFE CASTLE *Dorset* 403 404 N 32 *The West Country G. – pop. 1 335 – ✉ Wareham.*
See : *Castle*★ *(⩽★★) AC.*
London 129 – Bournemouth 18 – Weymouth 23.

Mortons House, 45 East St, BH20 5EE, ✆ (01929) 480988, *stay@mortonshouse.co.uk*, *Fax (01929) 480820*, ⩽, « Part Elizabethan manor », – ⅍ rest, TV P. MC AE VISA. ⅌
Meals 16.00/26.00 and a la carte 20.00/37.00 **t.** 12.00 – **16 rm** 100.00/116.00 **t.**, 1 suite – SB.

ORNHILL-ON-TWEED *Northd.* 401 402 N 17 *Scotland G. – pop. 317.*
Env. : *Ladykirk (Kirk o'Steil*★*), NE : 6 m. by A 698 and B 6470.*
London 345 – Edinburgh 49 – Newcastle upon Tyne 59.

Tillmouth Park , TD12 4UU, Northeast : 2 ½ m. on A 698 ✆ (01890) 882255, *reception@tillmouthpark.f9.co.uk*, *Fax (01890) 882540*, ⩽, « 19C country house », , , – TV P. MC AE VISA JCB
Meals (bar lunch Monday to Saturday)/dinner 26.00 **st.** 11.50 – **15 rm** 90.00/170.00 **st.** – SB.

Coach House, Crookham, TD12 4TD, East : 4 m. on A 697 ✆ (01890) 820293, *stay@coachhousecrookham.com*, *Fax (01890) 820284*, – ⅍ rest, TV P. MC VISA
Easter-October – **Meals** (residents only) (dinner only) 17.50 **t.** 8.25 – **9 rm** 39.00/78.00 **t.** – SB.

ORSCOMBE *Dorset* 403 L 31 – ✉ *Dorchester.*
London 153 – Exeter 47 – Taunton 30 – Weymouth 24.

Fox Inn with rm, DT2 0NS, Northeast : ¾ m. on Halstock rd ✆ (01935) 891330, *dine@fox-inn.co.uk*, *Fax (01935) 891330*, « Thatched inn » – ⅍ rm, TV P. MC AE VISA. ⅌
closed 25 December – **Meals** a la carte 15.75/26.50 **t.** 9.95 – **3 rm** 55.00/90.00 **t.**

ORSE LAWN *Worcs. – see Tewkesbury (Glos.).*

OSHAM *Portsmouth* 403 404 Q 31 – *see Portsmouth and Southsea.*

OTEBROOK *Ches. – see Tarporley.*

OVENEY *Cambs. – see Ely.*

COVENTRY

Street	Grid	No.
Bayley Lane	AV	3
Bishop Street	AV	5
Broadgate	AV	6
Burges Cross	AV	7
Central Six Retail Park	AV	
Corporation Street	AV	
Earl Street	AV	10
Fairfax Street	AV	12
Far Gosford Street	AV	13
Gallagher Retail Park	BX	
Gosford Street	AV	15
Greyfriars Lane	AV	16
Hales Street	AV	17
Hearsall Lane	AY	21
High Street	AV	22
Ironmonger Road	AV	23
Jordan Well	AV	26
Leicester Row	AV	29
Light Lane	AV	30
Little Park Street	AV	31
Precincts Shopping	AV	
Primrose Hill Street	AV	34
Queen Victoria Road	AV	35
St. Johns (Ringway)	AV	38
St. Nicholas (Ringway)	AV	39
Swanswell (Ringway)	AV	40
Trinity Street	AV	41
Upper Well Street	AV	43
Vecqueray Street	AV	45
Victoria Street	AV	46
Warwick Road	AV	49
White Street	AV	51
Windsor Street	AV	52
White Friars (Ringway)	AV	54

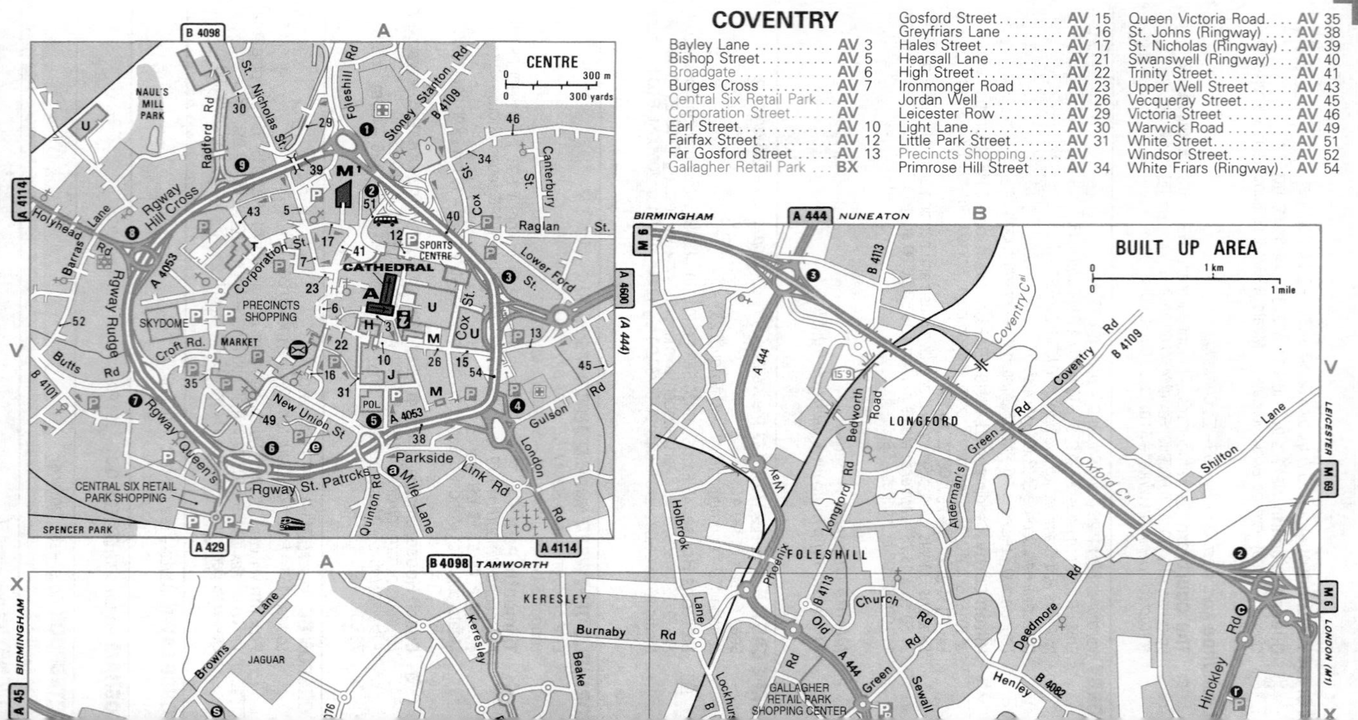

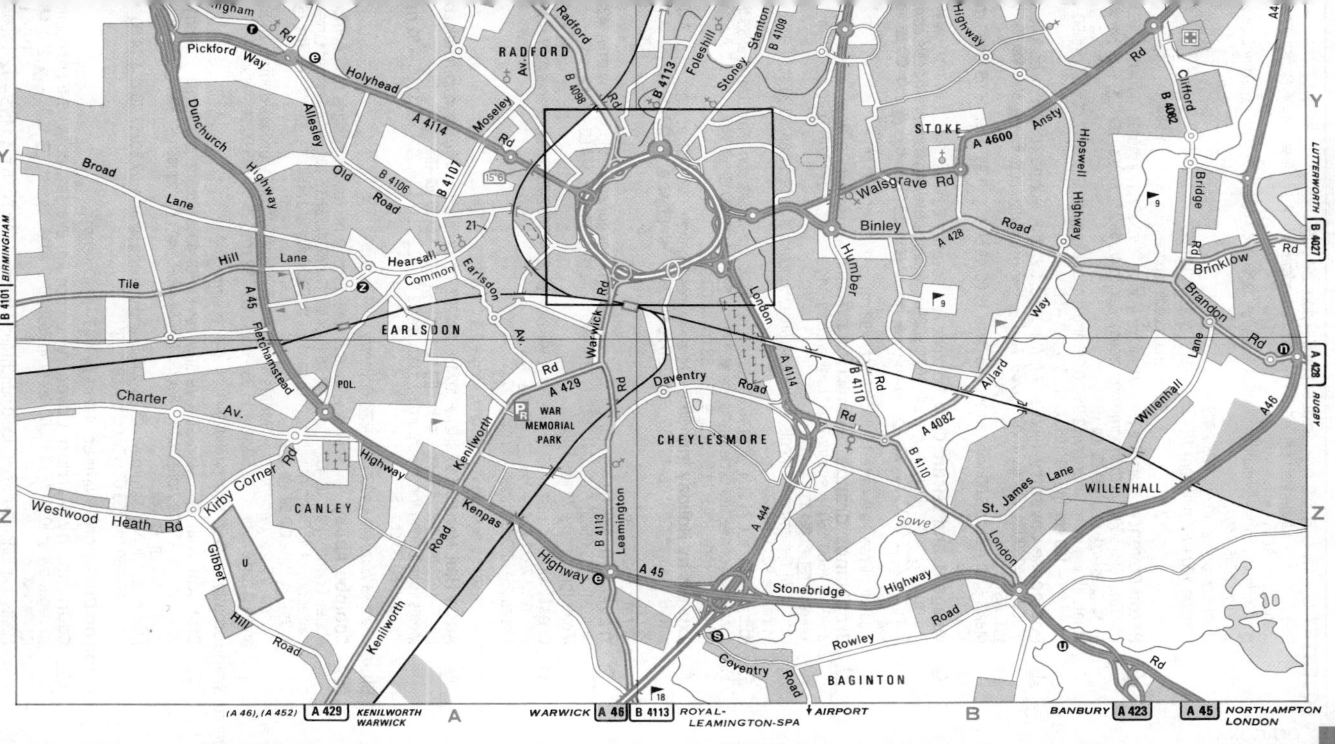
B 4101 BIRMINGHAM
LUTTERWORTH B 4027
A 428 RUGBY
(A 46), (A 452) A 429 KENILWORTH WARWICK
WARWICK A 46
B 4113 ROYAL-LEAMINGTON-SPA
AIRPORT
BANBURY A 423
A 45 NORTHAMPTON LONDON
RADFORD
STOKE
EARLSDON
CHEYLESMORE
WILLENHALL
CANLEY
BAGINTON
WAR MEMORIAL PARK
Pickford Way
Holyhead Rd
A 4114
Moseley Av.
Radford Rd
B 4098
B 4113
Foleshill
Stoney Stanton
B 4109
Highway
Clifford Bridge Rd
B 4082
Ansty Rd
A 4600
Hipswell Highway
Walsgrave Rd
Binley Road
A 428
Brinklow Rd
Brandon Rd
Dunchurch Highway
Allesley Old Road
B 4106
B 4107
Broad Lane
Tile Hill Lane
Hearsall Common
Earlsdon Av.
Warwick Rd
Humber Rd
London Road
A 4114
B 4110
Allard Way
A 4082
Willenhall Lane
A 46
A 45 Fletchamstead Highway
POL.
Charter Av.
Rd
A 429
Daventry Road
Kirby Corner Rd
Westwood Heath Rd
Gibbet Hill Road
Kenilworth Road
Kenpas Highway
B 4113
Leamington Rd
A 444
St. James Lane
Sowe
London Rd
Stonebridge Highway
Rowley Road
Coventry Road
Rd
Y
Z
A
B

COVENTRY *W. Mids.* 403 404 P 26 *Great Britain G. – pop. 299 316.*

See : *City*★ - *Cathedral*★★★ AC AV – *Old Cathedral*★ AV A – *Museum of British Roa Transport*★ AC AV M1.

18 *Windmill Village, Birmingham Rd, Allesley* ☎ *(024) 7640 4041* – 9 *Sphinx, Sphinx Driv* ☎ *(024) 7645 1361.*

Bayley Lane ☎ *(024) 7683 2303.*

London 100 – Birmingham 18 – Bristol 96 – Nottingham 52.

Plans on preceding pages

Hilton Coventry, Paradise Way, Walsgrave Triangle, CV2 2ST, Northeast : 4 m. by A 460 ☎ (024) 7660 3000, *cvthnhngm@hilton.com, Fax (024) 7660 3011,* – – 600. VISA BX
Meals (bar lunch Saturday) 9.95/20.95 and dinner a la carte 22.00/27.00 **st.** 11.50 – 11.95 – **169 rm** 143.00/163.00 **st.**, 3 suites – SB.

Posthouse Coventry, Hinckley Rd, Walsgrave, CV2 2HP, Northeast : 3 ½ m. on A 460 ☎ (0870) 4009021, *Fax (024) 7662 1736,* – rm, rest, – 300. VISA JCB BX
Meals (grill rest.) 15.00 (dinner) and a la carte 15.00/19.50 **t.** 11.95 – 13.95 – **160 rm** 129.00 – SB.

Village H. and Leisure Club, Dolomite Ave, Coventry Business Park, CV4 9GZ, West 2 m. by B 4101 ☎ (024) 7671 9000, *village.coventry@village-hotels.com Fax (024) 7671 9100,* squash – rest, – 250. VISA. AY
Meals (grill rest.) a la carte 11.45/22.65 **st.** – **98 rm** 95.00/108.00 **st.**

Brooklands Grange, Holyhead Rd, CV5 8HX, Northwest : 2 ½ m. on A 411 ☎ (024) 7660 1601, *enquiries@brooklands_grange.co.uk, Fax (024) 7660 1277,* rest, VISA. AY
closed 26 December – **Meals** *(closed Saturday lunch)* a la carte 22.85/30.85 **st.** 9.50 – **31 rm** 90.00/125.00 **st.**

Ibis, Mile Lane, CV1 2LN, ☎ (02476) 250500, *h2793@accor-hotels.com, Fax (02476) 553548* « Victorian converted cycle works » – rm, VISA AV
Meals a la carte 8.45/11.05 **st.** 9.25 – **88 rm** 42.00 **st.**

Express by Holiday Inn without rest., Kenpas Highway, CV3 6PB, at junction of A 45 with B 4113 ☎ (024) 7641 7555, *Fax (024) 7641 3388* – VISA JCB AZ
37 rm 52.50 **st.**

Travel Inn, Rugby Rd, Binley Woods, CV3 2TA, at junction of A 46 with A 428 ☎ (024) 7663 6585, *Fax (024) 7643 1178* – rm, rest, VISA. BZ
Meals (grill rest.) – **74 rm** 41.95 **t.**

Crest without rest., 39 Friars Rd, CV1 2LJ, ☎ (024) 7622 7822, *alanharve@aol.com Fax (024) 7622 7244* – VISA JCB AV
closed 25-26 December – **4 rm** 27.00/54.00.

at Ansty *Northeast : 5 ¾ m. by A 4600 on B 4065 – ✉ Coventry.*

Ansty Hall, Main Rd, CV7 9HZ, ☎ (02476) 612222, *events.anstyhall@macdonald-hotels.co uk, Fax (02476) 602155,* – – 200. VISA
Meals (bar lunch Monday-Saturday) a la carte 22.00/32.95 **st.** 14.90 – 11.95 – **62 rm** 150.00/180.00 **st.** – SB.

at Binley *East : 3½ m. on A 428 –* **BY** *– ✉ Coventry.*

Coombe Abbey , Brinklow Rd, CV3 2AB, East : 2 m. following signs for Coombe Abbey Country Park (B 4027) ☎ (024) 7645 0450, *Fax (024) 7663 5101,* « Former Cistercian abbey of 12C origins with formal gardens by Capability Brown », – rm, – 120. VISA
closed 25-26 December – **Meals** (bar lunch Monday to Saturday)/dinner 26.50 and a la carte approx. 37.50 **st.** 13.95 – 12.00 – **82 rm** 125.00/365.00 **st.**, 1 suite – SB.

at Brandon *(Warks.) East : 6 m. on A 428 –* **BZ** *– ✉ Coventry.*

Brandon Hall , Main St, CV8 3FW, ☎ (0870) 4008105, *heritagehotels-coventry brandon-hall@forte-hotels.com, Fax (024) 7654 4909,* squash – – 100. VISA
Meals (bar lunch Saturday) 12.95/24.95 and dinner a la carte 27.50/37.70 **t.** 14.00 – 12.95 – **60 rm** 120.00/160.00 **t.** – SB.

at Ryton on Dunsmore *Southeast : 4 ¾ m. by A 45 – ✉ Coventry.*

Courtyard by Marriott Coventry, London Rd, CV8 3DY, on A 45 (northbound carriageway) ☎ (024) 7630 1585, *Fax (024) 7630 1610* – rest, – 250. VISA. BZ
Meals (bar lunch Saturday) 12.50 (lunch) and a la carte 16.75/20.50 **t.** 11.75 – 10.00 – **47 rm** 89.00/95.00 **t.**, 2 suites.

t Baginton *(Warks.) South : 3 m. by A 4114 and A 444 off A 45 (off westbound carriageway and Howes Lane turning)* – ✉ *Coventry.*

Old Mill, Mill Hill, CV8 3AH, ✆ (024) 7630 2241, *oldmill.bag@btclick.com, Fax (024) 7630 7070,* « Converted corn mill » – ⇔ rm, ▤ rest, TV ⇔ P – 🏠 25. MC AE ◑ VISA. ✻ BZ s
Meals (grill rest.) a la carte 11.70/24.10 – ☕ 6.95 – **28 rm** 80.00 **t.**

t Berkswell *West : 6½ m. by B 4101 – AY –* ✉ *Coventry.*

Nailcote Hall, Nailcote Lane, CV7 7DE, South : 1 ½ m. on B 4101 ✆ (024) 7646 6174, *info @nailcotehall.co.uk, Fax (024) 7647 0720,* « Part 17C timbered house », Ls, ▣, ⛳9, ⛲, ✂ – TV P – 🏠 100. MC AE ◑ VISA JCB. ✻
Oak Room : Meals *(closed Saturday lunch, Sunday and dinner Bank Holiday Mondays)* (booking essential) 21.00/32.50 and a la carte 32.95/46.00 **st.** 🍷 14.00 – ***Rick's :*** Meals (booking essential) a la carte approx. 17.50 **st.** 🍷 14.00 – **38 rm** ☕ 145.00/265.00 **t.** – SB.

t Balsall Common *West : 6 ¾ m. by B 4101 – AY –* ✉ *Coventry.*

Haigs, 273 Kenilworth Rd, CV7 7EL, on A 452 ✆ (01676) 533004, *Fax (01676) 535132,* ⛲ – ⇔ TV ✆ ♿ P. MC AE VISA JCB. ✻
closed 25 December-5 January – ***Poppy's :*** Meals *(closed Sunday dinner)* (dinner only and Sunday lunch)/dinner 24.50 and a la carte 26.65/31.20 **t.** 🍷 10.95 – **23 rm** ☕ 70.00/105.00 **t.**

Travel Inn, Kenilworth Rd, CV7 7EX, Northwest : ½ m. on A 452 ✆ (01676) 533118, *Fax (01676) 535929* – ⇔ rm, TV ♿ P. MC AE ◑ VISA
Meals (grill rest.) – **42 rm** 41.95 **t.**

t Allesley *Northwest : 3 m. on A 4114 –* ✉ *Coventry.*

Allesley, Birmingham Rd, CV5 9GP, ✆ (024) 7640 3272, *sales@allesley-hotel.co.uk, Fax (024) 7640 5190* – |‡|, ⇔ rest, ▤ rest, TV P – 🏠 450. MC AE ◑ VISA AY r
Meals *(bar lunch Saturday)* 17.50/21.00 **st.** 🍷 11.50 – **90 rm** ☕ 95.00/110.00 **st.** – SB.

Brookfields without rest., 134 Butt Lane, CV5 9FE, ✆ (024) 7640 4866, *Fax (024) 7640 2022,* ⛲ – ⇔ P. ✻ AX s
– **4 rm** ☕ 30.00/60.00 **s.**

t Meriden *Northwest : 6 m. by A 45 on B 4104 – AX –* ✉ *Coventry.*

Marriott Forest of Arden H. & Country Club, Maxstoke Lane, CV7 7HR, Northwest : 2 ¾ m. on Maxstoke rd ✆ (01676) 522335, *Fax (01676) 523711,* Ls, ≘s, ▣, ⛳18, ⛵, 🎾, ✂ – |‡| ⇔, ▤ rest, TV ✆ ♿ P – 🏠 360. MC AE ◑ VISA
The Broadwater : Meals (dinner only and Sunday lunch)/dinner a la carte 26.50/31.50 **t.** 🍷 13.75 – ***The Long Weekend :*** Meals a la carte 17.45/22.85 🍷 12.75 – ☕ 12.95 – **214 rm** 132.00/179.00 **st.** – SB.

The Manor, Main Rd, CV7 7NH, ✆ (01676) 522735, *reservations@manorhotelmeriden.co. uk, Fax (01676) 522186,* ⛲ – ⇔, ▤ rest, TV ✆ ♿ P – 🏠 275. MC AE ◑ VISA
restricted opening 27-30 December – Meals *(closed Saturday lunch)* 21.00/22.00 and a la carte 23.40/33.85 **st.** 🍷 8.50 – **112 rm** ☕ 145.00/165.00 **st.**, 2 suites – SB.

COVERACK *Cornwall* 403 E 33.
London 300 – Penzance 25 – Truro 27.

Bay, North Corner, TR12 6TF, ✆ (01326) 280464, *enquiries@thebayhotel.co.uk, Fax (01326) 280464,* ≤, ⛲ – ⇔ rest, TV P. MC VISA
March-November and 2 weeks Christmas and New Year – Meals (bar lunch)/dinner 19.50 and a la carte approx. 29.50 **t.** 🍷 9.50 – **14 rm** ☕ (dinner included) 57.50/130.00 **t.**

COWAN BRIDGE *Cumbria* 402 M 21 – *see Kirkby Lonsdale.*

COWLEY *Oxon. – see Oxford.*

CRACKINGTON HAVEN *Cornwall* 403 G 31 *The West Country G.* – ✉ *Bude.*
Env. : *Poundstock★ (≤★★, church★, guildhouse★), NE : 5 ½ m. by A 39 – Jacobstow (Church★), E : 3½ m.*
London 262 – Bude 11 – Plymouth 44 – Truro 42.

Manor Farm 🐎, EX23 0JW, Southeast : 1 ¼ m. by Boscastle rd taking left turn onto Church Park Rd after 1.1 m. then taking first right onto unmarked lane ✆ (01840) 230304, ≤, « Part 11C manor », ⛲, 🎾 – ⇔ P. ✻
closed 25 December – Meals (by arrangement) (communal dining) 20.00 – **4 rm** ☕ 40.00/ 70.00 **s.**

Trevigue ⑤, EX23 0LQ, Southeast : 1 ¼ m. on High Cliff rd ☎ (01840) 23041
Fax (01840) 230418, « 16C farmhouse, working farm » – ⇔ P. MC VISA. ✗
closed 25 December – **Meals** (by arrangement) (communal dining) 18.00 ⅰ 7.95 – **3 r**
□ 40.00/72.00.

CRANBROOK *Kent* 404 V 30 *Great Britain G. – pop. 3 522.*

Env. : *Sissinghurst Castle* AC, NE : 2½ m. by A 229 and A 262.*
Vestry Hall, Stone St ☎ (01580) 712538 (summer only).
London 53 – Hastings 19 – Maidstone 15.

Kennel Holt ⑤, Goudhurst Rd, TN17 2PT, Northwest : 2 ¼ m. by A 229 on A 26
☎ (01580) 712032, *hotel@kennelholt.demon.co.uk, Fax (01580) 715495*, « Elizabetha
manor house with Edwardian additions, gardens » – ⇔ rest, TV P. MC VISA JCB. ✗
closed 2 weeks January – **Meals** *(closed Sunday to non-residents and Monday)* (dinner on
27.50/32.50 **t.** ⅰ 13.50 – **10 rm** □ 90.00/195.00 **st.**

Old Cloth Hall ⑤, TN17 3NR, East : 1 m. by Tenterden Rd ☎ (01580) 71222
Fax (01580) 712220, ←, « Tudor manor house, gardens », ⛱, ⛳ – ⇔ rm, TV P. ✗
closed 25 December – **Meals** (by arrangement) (communal dining) 22.00 – **3 rm** □ 45.0
110.00.

Soho South, 23 Stone St, TN17 3HF, ☎ (01580) 714666, *Fax (01580) 715653* – MC VISA
closed 1 week in spring, 1 week in autumn, 25-26 and 31 December, 1 January ar
Sunday-Tuesday – **Meals** a la carte 14.15/28.50 **t.** ⅰ 9.90.

at Sissinghurst *Northeast : 1 ¾ m. by B 2189 on A 262* – ✉ *Cranbrook.*

Rankins, The Street, TN17 2JH, on A 262 ☎ (01580) 713964 – MC VISA
closed Sunday dinner, Monday, Tuesday and Bank Holidays – **Meals** (dinner only and Sund
lunch)/dinner 24.50/28.50 **st.** ⅰ 9.50.

***En saison,** surtout dans les stations fréquentées,*
il est prudent de retenir à l'avance.
Cependant, si vous ne pouvez pas occuper la chambre
que vous avez retenue, prévenez immédiatement l'hôtelier.

Si vous écrivez à un hôtel à l'étranger, joignez à votre lettre
un coupon-réponse international (disponible dans les bureaux de poste).

CRANTOCK *Cornwall* 403 E 32 – *see Newquay.*

CRAVEN ARMS *Shrops.* 402 403 L 26 *Great Britain G. – pop. 1 892.*

Env. : *Wenlock Edge*, NE : by B 4368.*
London 170 – Birmingham 47 – Hereford 32 – Shrewsbury 21.

Old Rectory ⑤, Hopesay, SY7 8HD, West : 4 m. by B 4368 ☎ (01588) 660245, *romavill*
@onetel.net.uk, Fax (01588) 660502, ←, « Part 17C », 🚗 – ⇔ TV P. ✗
closed Christmas and New Year – **Meals** (by arrangement) (communal dining) 22.00 ⅰ 10.(
– **3 rm** □ 38.00/76.00.

CRAWLEY *W. Sussex* 404 T 30 – *pop. 88 203.*

18, 18 *Cottesmore, Buchan Hill, Pease Pottage ☎ (01293) 528256* – 18, 9 *Tilgate Fores*
Titmus Drive, Tilgate ☎ (01293) 530103 – 9 *Gatwick Manor, London Rd, Lowfield Hea*
☎ (01293) 538587 – 9 *Pease Pottage, Horsham Rd ☎ (01293) 521706.*
London 33 – Brighton 21 – Lewes 23 – Royal Tunbridge Wells 23.

Plan of enlarged Area : see Gatwick

Holiday Inn London Gatwick, Langley Drive, Tushmore Roundabout, RH11 7S
☎ (01293) 529991, *Fax (01293) 510653*, Fö, ≘s, ⊡ – |‡|, ⇔ rm, TV ✆ ♿ P – 🏛 275. MC
① VISA. ✗ BY
Colonnade : **Meals** *(closed Sunday dinner)* (dinner only and Sunday lunch)/dinner a la car
17.95/19.50 **t.** ⅰ 10.95 – ***La Brasserie :*** **Meals** a la carte approx. 16.85 **t.** ⅰ 10.95 – □ 12.50
219 rm 140.00/160.00 **t.**, 2 suites.

Premier Lodge, Goffs Park Rd, Southgate, RH11 8AX, ☎ (01293) 53544
Fax (01293) 542050, 🚗 – ⇔, ▤ rest, TV ✆ ♿ P – 🏛 150. MC AE ① VISA JCB. ✗ AZ
Meals (grill rest.) a la carte approx. 13.00 **t.** ⅰ 8.95 – **57 rm** 49.95 **t.** – SB.

Express by Holiday Inn without rest., The Squareabout, Haslett Ave East, RH10 1U
☎ (01293) 525523, *Fax (01293) 525529* – |‡| ⇔ TV ✆ ♿ P – 🏛 35. MC AE ① VIS
✗ on Gatwick town plan Z
74 rm 62.50 **t.**

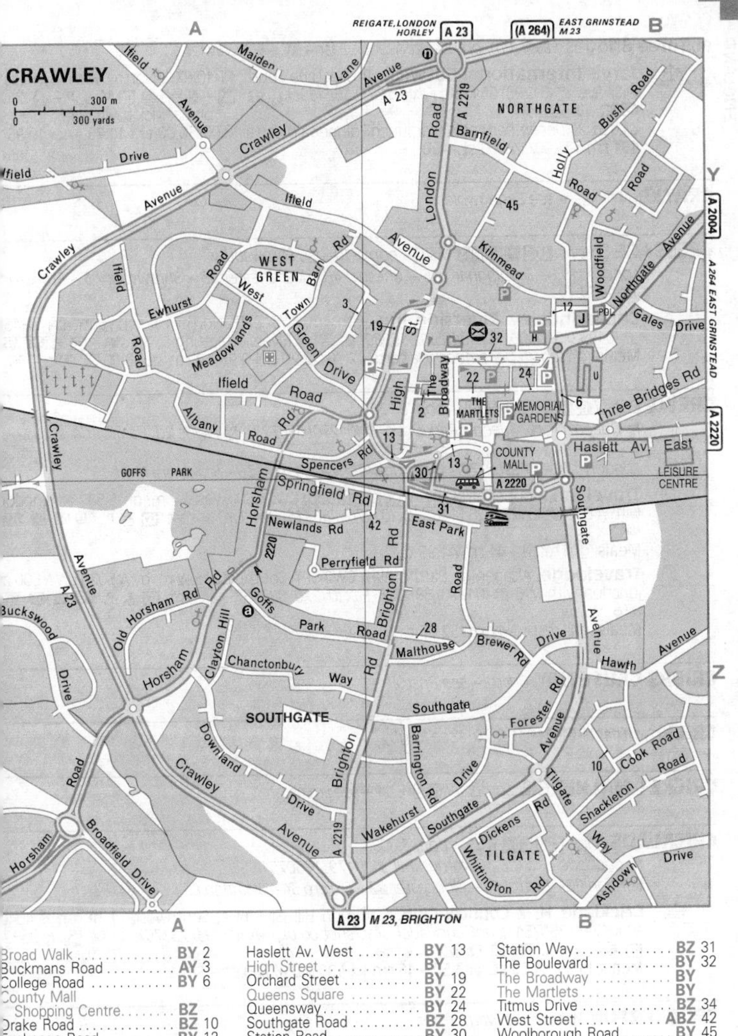

Broad Walk	BY 2	Haslett Av. West	BY 13	Station Way	BZ 31
Buckmans Road	AY 3	High Street	BY	The Boulevard	BY 32
College Road	BY 6	Orchard Street	BY 19	The Broadway	BY
County Mall Shopping Centre	BZ	Queens Square	BY 22	The Martlets	BY
Drake Road	BZ 10	Queensway	BY 24	Titmus Drive	BZ 34
Exchange Road	BY 12	Southgate Road	BZ 28	West Street	ABZ 42
		Station Road	BY 30	Woolborough Road	BY 45

at Copthorne *Northeast : 4½ m. on A 264* – **BY**.

Copthorne London Gatwick, Copthorne Way, RH10 3PG, ℘ (01342) 348800, *coplgw@mill-cop.com, Fax (01342) 348833*, squash – ⇔ rm, ▤ rest, 🅿 – 🅐 100. MC AE VISA JCB.
Lion D'Or **:** Meals 18.00/20.00 and a la carte 24.95/32.00 **st.** 13.50 – ***Brasserie*** **:** Meals (dinner only) 20.50 and a la carte 12.00/20.00 **st.** 13.50 – 13.50 – **227 rm** 139.00/199.00 **st.** – SB.

Copthorne Effingham Park, West Park Rd, RH10 3EU, on B 2028 ℘ (01342) 714994, *events.effingham@mill-cop.com, Fax (01342) 716039*, ▤ rest, 🅿 – 🅐 600. MC AE VISA
Meals (bar lunch)/dinner a la carte 27.00/39.00 **st.** – 13.95 – **119 rm** 145.00 **st.**, 3 suites.

ENGLAND

at Three Bridges *East : 1 m. on Haslett Avenue East* – **BY** – ✉ *Crawley.*

Jarvis International Gatwick, Tinsley Lane South, RH10 8XH, North : ½ m. by Hazelwick Ave ✆ (01293) 561186, *Fax (01293) 561169,* – – 21
MC AE VISA. on Gatwick town plan Y
closed 25 December **Meals** (bar lunch)/dinner a la carte 18.00/30.00 **t.** 11.75 – 10.95
151 rm 125.00/145.00 **st.** – SB.

CRAYKE *N. Yorks. – see Easingwold.*

CRESSAGE *Shrops.* 402 403 404 M 26 – *pop. 810* – ✉ *Shrewsbury.*
London 163 – Birmingham 46 – Chester 48 – Manchester 73 – Shrewsbury 6 – Stoke-on-Trent 34.

Cholmondeley Riverside Inn with rm, SY5 6AF, Northwest : 1 ½ m. on A 45 ✆ (01952) 510900, *Fax (01952) 510980,* « Riverside setting », – MC VISA
Meals *(closed 25 December)* a la carte 17.70/22.20 **t.** 9.95 – **7 rm** 50.00/90.00 **t.** – SB.

CREWE *Ches.* 402 403 404 M 24 – *pop. 63 351.*
Queen's Park, Queen's Park Drive ✆ (01270) 666724 – Fields Rd, Haslington ✆ (01270) 584227.
London 174 – Chester 24 – Liverpool 49 – Manchester 36 – Stoke-on-Trent 15.

Travel Inn, Coppenhall Lane, Woolstanwood, CW2 8SD, West : 2 m. on A 532 at junction with A 530 ✆ (01270) 251126, *Fax (01270) 256316* – rm, rest, MC AE VISA
Meals (grill rest.) – **41 rm** 41.95 **t.**

Travelodge, Alsager Rd, Barthomley, CW2 5PT, Southeast : 5 ½ m. by A 5020 on A 500 at junction with M 6 ✆ (01270) 883157, *Fax (01270) 883157* – rm, MC AE VISA JCB.
Meals (grill rest.) – **42 rm** 52.95 **t.**

CRIBBS CAUSEWAY *Bristol – see Bristol.*

CRICK *Northants.* 403 404 Q 26 – *see Rugby.*

CRICKET MALHERBIE *Somerset* 403 L 31 – *see Ilminster.*

CRICKLADE *Wilts.* 403 404 O 29 – *pop. 3 808.*
Cricklade H. & C.C., Common Hill ✆ (01793) 750751.
London 90 – Bristol 45 – Gloucester 27 – Oxford 34 – Swindon 6.

Cricklade H. & Country Club, Common Hill, SN6 6HA, Southwest : 1 m. on B 4040 ✆ (01793) 750751, *jane@crickladehotel.fsnet.co.uk, Fax (01793) 751767,* – 120. MC AE VISA JCB.
Meals 15.95/34.50 **st.** 13.50 – **46 rm** 100.00/165.00 **st.** – SB.

CROCKERTON *Wilts. – see Warminster.*

CROFT-ON-TEES *Durham* 402 P 20 – *see Darlington.*

CROMER *Norfolk* 404 X 25 – *pop. 7 267.*
Royal Cromer, Overstrand Rd ✆ (01263) 512884.
Prince of Wales Rd ✆ (01263) 512497.
London 132 – Norwich 23.

Morden House, 20 Cliff Ave, NR27 0AN, ✆ (01263) 513396, *rosemary@broadland.com*
restricted opening in winter – **Meals** 15.00 10.50 – **6 rm** 27.00/54.00 **st.** – SB.

at Overstrand *Southeast : 2½ m. by B 1159* – ✉ *Cromer.*

Sea Marge, High St, NR27 0AB, ✆ (01263) 579579, *reservations@mackenziehotels.com* *Fax (01263) 579524,* – MC VISA JCB
Meals a la carte 19.05/36.36 **t.** 10.95 – **18 rm** 65.00/90.00 **st.** – SB.

at **Northrepps** *Southeast : 3 m. by A 149 and Northrepps rd – ✉ Cromer.*

Shrublands Farm, NR27 0AA, ☎ (01263) 579297, *youngman@farming.co.uk, Fax (01263) 579297,* « Working farm », – TV P.
closed 1 week Christmas – **Meals** (by arrangement) (winter only) (communal dining) 15.00 **s.** – **3 rm** 30.00/50.00 **s.**

CRONDALL *Hants.* 404 R 30 – *pop. 6 113.*
London 56 – Reading 21 – Winchester 30.

The Chesa, Bowling Alley, GU10 5RJ, North : 1 m. ☎ (01252) 850328, *chesa@totalise.co.uk, Fax (01252) 850328* – P. MC VISA
closed 3 weeks November, 3 weeks January and Sunday-Tuesday – **Meals** (booking essential) (dinner only) a la carte approx. 35.00 12.00.

CROPTON *N. Yorks.* 402 R 21 – *see Pickering.*

CROSS HOUSES *Shrops.* 402 403 L 25 – *see Shrewsbury.*

CROSTHWAITE *Cumbria* 402 L 21 – *see Kendal.*

CROWTHORNE *Bracknell Forest* 404 R 29 – *pop. 21 500.*
London 42 – Reading 15.

Waterloo, Duke's Ride, RG45 6DW, on B 3348 ☎ (01344) 777711, *waterloohotel@corushotels.com, Fax (01344) 778913,* – rm, rest, TV P – 60. MC AE VISA JCB
closed 1 week Christmas – **Meals** *(closed Sunday dinner)* (bar lunch)/dinner 18.95 **t.** 9.95 – 10.50 – **58 rm** 120.00/145.00 **st.** – SB.

Beijing, 103 Old Wokingham Rd, RG45 6LH, Northeast : ¾ m. by A 3095 ☎ (01344) 778802 – P. MC AE VISA JCB
closed 25-26 December, 1 January and Sunday lunch – **Meals** - Chinese - 13.50/25.00 and a la carte 11.00/17.00 **t.** 8.50.

CROYDE *Devon* 403 H 30 – ✉ *Braunton.*
London 232 – Barnstaple 10 – Exeter 50 – Taunton 61.

Croyde Bay House, Moor Lane, Croyde Bay, EX33 1PA, Northwest : 1 m. by Baggy Point rd ☎ (01271) 890270, ≤ Croyde Bay, – rest, TV P. MC AE VISA JCB
March-mid November – **Meals** 22.00 **st.** 7.95 – **7 rm** (dinner included) 74.00/128.00 **st.**

Kittiwell House, St Mary's Rd, EX33 1PG, ☎ (01271) 890247, *relax@kittiwellhouse.co.uk, Fax (01271) 890469,* « 16C thatched Devon longhouse » – TV P. MC VISA
closed mid December-mid February – **Meals** (dinner only) 21.50 **st.** 5.50 – **12 rm** 51.00/90.00 **st.** – SB.

Whiteleaf, Hobbs Hill, EX33 1PN, ☎ (01271) 890266, – TV P. MC AE VISA JCB
*closed 25 December***Meals** (dinner only) 18.50 and a la carte 18.50/28.75 **t.** 9.75 – **5 rm** (dinner included) 58.00/100.00 **t.** – SB.

CRUDWELL *Wilts.* 403 404 N 29 – *see Malmesbury.*

CUCKFIELD *W. Sussex* 404 T 30 – *pop. 2 879.*
London 40 – Brighton 15.

Ockenden Manor, Ockenden Lane, RH17 5LD, ☎ (01444) 416111, *ockenden@hshotels.co.uk, Fax (01444) 415549,* « Part 16C manor house », – rest, TV P – 50. MC AE VISA.
Meals 12.95 (lunch) and a la carte 31.00/55.00 **t.** 16.50 – **19 rm** 99.00/210.00, 3 suites – SB.

CULLOMPTON *Devon* 403 J 31 *The West Country G.* – *pop. 5 676.*
See : *Town★ – St Andrew's Church★.*
Env. : *Uffculme (Coldharbour Mill★★ AC) NE : 5½ m. by B 3181 and B 3391.*
Exc. : *Killerton★★, SW : 6½ m. by B 3181 and B 3185.*
Padbrook Park ☎ (01884) 38286.
London 197 – Exeter 15 – Taunton 29.

Manor, 2-4 Fore St, EX15 1JL, ☎ (01884) 32281, *Fax (01884) 38344* – TV P. MC VISA
Meals (bar lunch)/dinner a la carte 7.00/12.00 **st.** 8.50 – **10 rm** 46.50/59.50 **st.**

CURDWORTH *W. Mids.* 402 ⑩ 403 ㉛ 404 ⑳ – *see Sutton Coldfield.*

DALTON *N. Yorks.* 402 O 20 – *see Richmond.*

DALTON-IN-FURNESS *Cumbria* 402 K 21 – *pop. 7 550.*

The Dunnerholme, Duddon Rd, Askham-in-Furness (01229) 462675.
London 283 – Barrow-in-Furness 3.5 – Kendal 30 – Lancaster 41.

Clarence House Country, Skelgate, LA15 8BQ, Northwest : ½ m. on Askam r (01229) 462508, *vba1761186@aol.com, Fax (01229) 467177,* – P. VISA JCB
closed 25-26 December – **Meals** 19.25/21.95 and a la carte 18.40/26.70 **t.** 8.95 – **17 rm** 69.00/105.00 **t.**

DARESBURY *Warrington* 402 403 404 M 23 – *pop. 1 579* – ✉ *Warrington.*
London 197 – Chester 16 – Liverpool 23 – Manchester 25.

Daresbury Park, Chester Rd, WA4 4BB, Southwest : 1 ½ m. by A 56 (01925) 267331 *daresburyparksales@devere-hotels.com, Fax (01925) 601496,* , squash – rm, rest, P – 400. VISA JCB
Cheshire Room : **Meals** *(closed Sunday)* (dinner only) a la carte 14.75/20.70 **st.** 4.60
The Looking Glass : **Meals** *(closed Saturday lunch)* (carving lunch Sunday) a la carte 14.75/20.70 4.60 – 9.95 – **167 rm** 130.00 **st.,** 14 suites – SB.

DARGATE *Kent* – *see Faversham.*

DARLEY ABBEY *Derbs.* 402 403 404 P 25 – *see Derby.*

DARLINGTON *Darlington* 402 P 20 – *pop. 86 767.*

Blackwell Grange, Briar Close (01325) 464464 – Stressholme, Snipe Lane (01325) 461002.
Teesside Airport : (01325) 332811, E : 6 m. by A 67.
13 Horsemarket (01325) 388666.
London 251 – Leeds 61 – Middlesbrough 14 – Newcastle upon Tyne 35.

New Grange, Southend Ave, DL3 7HZ, Southwest : ¾ m. by A 167 (01325) 365859 *Fax (01325) 487111,* – , rest, P – 100. VISA.
Maxine's : **Meals** 11.95 (lunch) and dinner a la carte 16.50/24.15 **st.** – **24 rm** 70.00/115.00 **st.** – SB.

Balmoral without rest., 63 Woodland Rd, DL3 7BQ, (01325) 461908 *Fax (01325) 461908* – .
closed 24-31 December – **9 rm** 28.00/46.00.

at Coatham Mundeville *North : 4 m. on A 167* – ✉ *Darlington.*

Hall Garth Golf & Country Club, DL1 3LU, East : ¼ m. on Brafferton rd (01325) 300400, *Fax (01325) 310083,* – P – 250. VISA
Hugo's : **Meals** (dinner only) a la carte 19.90/31.00 **t.** 12.00 – ***Stables :*** **Meals** *(closed Sunday dinner)* a la carte 12.80/19.70 **t.** 11.00 – 11.00 – **38 rm** 90.00/110.00 **t.,** 3 suites – SB.

at Aycliffe *North : 5½ m. on A 167* – ✉ *Darlington.*

The County, 13 The Green, DL5 6LX, (01325) 312273, *Fax (01325)308780* – P. VISA
closed Sunday dinner – **Meals** (booking essential) a la carte 13.90/23.50 **t.** 10.95.

at Croft-on-Tees *South : 3½ m. on A 167* – ✉ *Darlington.*

Clow Beck House , Monk End Farm, DL2 2SW, West : ¾ m. by A 167 off Barton rd (01325) 721075, *heather@clowbeckhouse.co.uk, Fax (01325) 720419,* – P. VISA.
– **Meals** (residents only) (dinner only) a la carte 16.00/25.00 **st.** 10.00 – **13 rm** 47.00/75.00 **st.**

t Headlam *Northwest : 6 m. by A 67 – ✉ Gainford.*

Headlam Hall, DL2 3HA, ☎ (01325) 730238, *admin@headlamhall.co.uk, Fax (01325) 730790*, ←, « Part Jacobean and part Georgian manor house, gardens », – 150. MC AE VISA JCB
closed 25 and 26 December – ***The Pannelled Restaurant :*** Meals 12.50/25.00 (lunch) and a la carte 22.00/25.50 **st.** 9.75 – **35 rm** 69.00/99.00 **st.**, 1 suite – SB.

t Heighington *Northwest : 6 m. by A 68 off A 6072 – ✉ Darlington.*

Eldon House without rest., East Green, DL5 6PP, ☎ (01325) 312270, *kbartram @btinternet.com, Fax (01325) 315580*, « Part 17C », –
3 rm 35.00/55.00.

t Redworth *Northwest : 7 m. by A 68 on A 6072 – ✉ Bishop Auckland.*

Redworth Hall H. & Country Club, DL5 6NL, ☎ (01388) 772442, *redworthhall @paramount-hotels.co.uk, Fax (01388) 775112*, « Part 18C and 19C manor house of Elizabethan origins », – rm, – 250. MC AE VISA.
Conservatory : Meals 14.50/23.50 **t.** 12.50 – (see also ***The Blue Room*** below) – **96 rm** 110.00/145.00 **st.**, 4 suites – SB.

The Blue Room (at Redworth Hall H. & Country Club), DL5 6NL, ☎ (01388) 772442, *Fax (01388) 775112*, « Part 18C and 19C manor house of Elizabethan origins », – MC AE VISA
closed December, Sunday and Bank Holidays Mondays – **Meals** (dinner only) 23.50 **t.** 12.50.

ARTFORD *Kent* 404 U 29 – *pop. 59 411.*
Dartford Tunnel and Bridge (toll).
London 20 – Hastings 51 – Maidstone 22.

Hilton Dartford Bridge, Masthead Close, Crossways Business Park, DA2 6QF, Northeast : 2 ½ m. by A 226, Cotton Lane and Crossways Boulevard ☎ (01322) 284444, *Fax (01322) 288225*, – rm, – 240. MC AE VISA
Meals *(closed lunch Saturday)* 16.95/19.95 and a la carte 23.30/34.85 **st.** 12.30 – 11.95 – **171 rm** 110.00/120.00 **st.**, 4 suites – SB.

Express by Holiday Inn Dartford Bridge without rest., University Way, DA1 5PA, Northeast : 3 m. by A 226 and Cotton Lane on A 206 (westbound carriageway) ☎ (01322) 290333, *dartford@khl.co.uk, Fax (01322) 290444* – – 35. MC AE VISA JCB.
126 rm 66.00 **st.**

ARTMOUTH *Devon* 403 J 32 *The West Country G.* – *pop. 5 676.*
See : *Town★★ (←★) – Old Town - Butterwalk★ - Dartmouth Castle (←★★★) AC.*
Exc. : *Start Point (←★) S : 13 m. (including 1 m. on foot).*
The Engine House, Mayor's Ave ☎ (01803) 834224.
London 236 – Exeter 36 – Plymouth 35.

Royal Castle, 11 The Quay, TQ6 9PS, ☎ (01803) 833033, *enquiry@royalcastle.co.uk, Fax (01803) 835445*, ← – rest, MC AE VISA
Meals 8.00/18.50 and a la carte 21.85/25.40 **st.** 11.95 – **25 rm** 68.95/149.90 – SB.

Dart Marina, Sandquay, TQ6 9PH, ☎ (0870) 4008134, *heritagehotels-dartmouth.dart_marina@forte-hotels.com, Fax (01803) 835040*, ← Dart Marina – , rest, MC AE VISA.
Meals 23.95 12.95 – 12.00 – **50 rm** 80.00/135.00 **t.**

Ford House, 44 Victoria Rd, TQ6 9DX, ☎ (01803) 834047, *richard@ford-house-freeserve.co.uk, Fax (01803) 834047*, – MC AE VISA
May-October – **Meals** (residents only) (communal dining) (dinner only) (unlicensed) 32.00 – **4 rm** 55.00/75.00 **st.** – SB.

The Gunfield, Castle Rd, TQ6 0JN, ☎ (01803) 834571, *enquiry@gunfield.co.uk, Fax (01803) 834772*, ← Dart Estuary and Kingswear, – MC AE VISA
closed January and 25 December – **Meals** *(closed Sunday, Monday and Tuesday dinner in winter)* (lunch by arrangement except summer and weekends)/dinner a la carte 21.15/25.70 **t.** 10.00 – **10 rm** 62.50/105.00 **t.**

The Little Admiral, 27-29 Victoria Rd, TQ6 9RT, ☎ (01803) 832572, *info@little-admiral.co.uk, Fax (01803) 835815*, « Georgian town house » – rm, MC VISA
restricted opening in winter – **Meals** *(closed Monday, Tuesday and Sunday dinner)* a la carte 16.40/22.45 **t.** 9.95 – **10 rm** 60.00/130.00 **t.**

ENGLAND

Wadstray House without rest., Blackawton, TQ9 7DE, West : 4 ½ m. on A 312 (01803) 712539, *Fax (01803) 712539*, « Georgian country house », – TV P. *closed 25 December* – **3 rm** 50.00/70.00 **st.**

Hedley House without rest., Newcomen Rd, TQ6 9BN, (01803) 832885, *hedleyhou @yahoo.com*, Dart Estuary and Kingswear – TV. **3 rm** 50.00/70.00 **s.**

Woodside Cottage without rest., Blackawton, TQ9 7BL, West : 5 ½ m. by A 3122 c Blackawton rd (01803) 712375, *woodside-cottage@lineone.net*, *Fax (01803) 712375*, – TV P. *closed Christmas, New Year and January* – **3 rm** 50.00 **s.**

The Carved Angel, 2 South Embankment, TQ6 9BH, (01803) 832465, *enquirie @thecarvedangel.com*, *Fax (01803) 835141*, Dart Estuary – . MO AE VISA *closed 24-26 December, Monday lunch and Sunday dinner* – **Meals** 26.00/39.50 and dinner a la carte 32.25/38.50 **t.** 14.75.

Hooked, 5 Higher St, TQ6 9RB, (01803) 832022, *hookedthefish@hotmail.com* – MO VIS *closed January, Christmas, New Year, Sunday and lunch Monday* – **Meals** - Seafood 15.00/40.00 **t.** 12.00.

at Kingswear *East : via lower ferry taking first right onto Church Hill before Steam Packet Inn ✉ Dartmouth.*

Nonsuch House, Church Hill, TQ6 0BX, (01803) 752829, *enquiries@nonsuch-house.c .uk*, *Fax (01803) 752357*, Dartmouth Castle and Warfleet, – TV. MO VISA. **Meals** *(closed first 2 weeks in January, Tuesday and Wednesday)* (residents only) (dinne only) (set menu only) (unlicensed) 23.00 **st.** – **5 rm** 60.00/80.00 **st.** – SB.

at Stoke Fleming *Southwest : 3 m. on A 379 – ✉ Dartmouth.*

Stoke Lodge, Cinders Lane, TQ6 0RA, (01803) 770523, *mail@stokelodge.co.u Fax (01803) 770851*, , heated, , , – rest, TV P. MO AE VISA **Meals** 11.95/20.00 and a la carte 16.20/25.00 **t.** 9.75 – **24 rm** 55.00/102.00 **t.** – SB.

DARWEN *Blackburn* **402** **404** M 22.

Winterhill (01254) 701287.

London 222 – Manchester 24 – Blackburn 5 – Blackpool 34 – Leeds 59 – Liverpool 43.

Astley Bank, Bolton Rd, BB3 2QB, South : ¾ m. on A 666 (01254) 777700, *sales@astle bank.co.uk*, *Fax (01254) 777707*, – TV P – 70. MO AE VISA JCB. **Meals** 14.50/24.00 and a la carte 19.10/31.70 **t.** 10.95 – **37 rm** 78.00/118.00 **t.** – SB.

DAVENTRY *Northants.* **404** Q 27 – *pop. 18 099.*

Norton Rd (01327) 702829 – , Hellidon Lakes H. & C.C., Hellidon (01327) 62550
Staverton Park, Staverton (01327) 302000.
Moot Hall, Market Sq (01327) 300277.
London 79 – Coventry 23 – Northampton 13 – Oxford 46.

Fawsley Hall , Fawsley, NN11 3BA, South : 6 ½ m. by A 45 off A 36 (01327) 892000, *reservations@fawsleyhall.com*, *Fax (01327) 892001*, , « Tudor manc house with Georgian and Victorian additions », , , , – TV P – 100. MO AE VISA JCB **Meals** 15.00/31.00 and a la carte 23.50/44.50 **t.** 17.50 – **28 rm** 125.00/155.00 **st** 2 suites – SB.

Hanover International, Sedgemoor Way, off Ashby Rd, NN11 5SG, North : 2 m. o A 361 (01327) 307000, *reservations@hanoverdaventry.ndo.co.uk*, *Fax (01327) 70631*, , , – , rest, TV P – 600. MO AE VISA *closed 24-31 December* **Meals** *(closed lunch Saturday)* 12.95/19.95 and dinner a la carte s 12.00 – 11.95 – **136 rm** 110.00 **st.**, 2 suites – SB.

at Flore *East : 6 m. on A 45 – ✉ Northampton.*

Courtyard by Marriott Daventry, High St, NN7 4LP, East : ½ m. on A 4 (01327) 349022, *reservations.davenrty@whitbread.com*, *Fax (01327) 349017*, rm, rest, TV P – 80. MO AE VISA JCB **Meals** a la carte 16.40/25.20 **st.** 11.75 – **53 rm** 82.00/89.00 **st.** – SB.

at Staverton *Southwest : 2 ¾ m. by A 45 off A 425 – ✉ Daventry.*

Colledges House, Oakham Lane, NN11 6JQ, off Glebe Lane (01327) 702737 *Fax (01327) 300851*, « Part 17C », – rm, TV P. MO VISA. *closed 25 December* – **Meals** (by arrangement) (communal dining) 25.00 – **4 rm** 47.50 75.00 **s.**

DAWLISH *Devon* 403 J 32 – *pop. 9 648.*

Warren ☎ (01626) 862255.

The Lawn ☎ (01626) 863589.

London 215 – Exeter 13 – Plymouth 40 – Torquay 11.

Langstone Cliff, Dawlish Warren, EX7 0NA, North : 2 m. by A 379 ☎ (01626) 868000, *reception@langstone-hotel.co.uk, Fax (01626) 868006,* heated, – rest, – 400.
Meals (bar lunch Monday to Saturday) 15.50 **st.** 9.60 – **68 rm** 56.00/138.00 **st.** – SB.

DEAL *Kent* 404 Y 30 – *pop. 28 504.*

Walmer & Kingsdown, The Leas, Kingsdown ☎ (01304) 373256.

Town Hall, High St ☎ (01304) 369576.

London 78 – Canterbury 19 – Dover 8.5 – Margate 16.

Royal, Beach St, CT14 6JD, ☎ (01304) 375555, *royalhotel@theroyalhotel.com, Fax (01304) 372270,* – rm,
closed 26 December-1 January – ***The Boathouse Brasserie*** : **Meals** 16.95/18.75 and a la carte 20.85/27.95 **t.** 10.50 – **22 rm** 45.00/150.00 **t.** – SB.

Dunkerley's, 19 Beach St, CT14 7AH, ☎ (01304) 375016, *dunkerleysofdeal@btinternet.com, Fax (01304) 380187,* –
Meals – (see ***Restaurant*** below) – **16 rm** 55.00/90.00 **t.** – SB.

Sutherland House, 186 London Rd, CT14 9PT, ☎ (01304) 362853, *Fax (01304) 381146,* – rm,
Meals (by arrangement) 21.00 **st.** 9.95 – **5 rm** 45.00/60.00 **st.** – SB.

Restaurant (at Dunkerley's H.), 19 Beach St, CT14 7AH, ☎ (01304) 375016, *Fax (01304) 380187* –
closed Monday – **Meals** 8.95/22.50 and dinner a la carte 24.40/34.85 **t.** 9.95.

La guida cambia, cambiate la guida ogni anno.

DEDDINGTON *Oxon.* 403 404 Q 28 – *pop. 2 319.*

London 72 – Birmingham 46 – Coventry 33 – Oxford 18.

Holcombe, High St, OX15 0SL, ☎ (01869) 338274, *reception@holcombehotel.freeserve.co.uk, Fax (01869) 337167,* – rest,
closed 24-30 December – **Meals** 14.95/30.00 and a la carte 23.95/31.95 **t.** – **16 rm** 75.00/112.00 – SB.

Deddington Arms, Horsefair, OX15 0SH, ☎ (01869) 338364, *deddarms@aol.com, Fax (01869) 337010* – rest, – 30.
Meals 7.50 (lunch) and a la carte 20.00/25.00 **t.** 18.00 – **27 rm** 80.00/110.00 **t.** – SB.

Dexter's, Market Pl, OX15 0SA, ☎ (01869) 338813, *dexteruk@globalnet.co.uk, Fax (01869) 338813* –
closed 24 December-2 January, Sunday and Monday – **Meals** 19.00/23.50 and a la carte 24.50/34.00 **st.** 12.00.

DEDHAM *Essex* 404 W 28 *Great Britain G.* – *pop. 1 847* – ✉ *Colchester.*

Env. : *Stour Valley★ – Flatford Mill★, E : 6 m. by B 1029, A 12 and B 1070.*

London 63 – Chelmsford 30 – Colchester 8 – Ipswich 12.

Maison Talbooth, Stratford Rd, CO7 6HN, West : ½ m. ☎ (01206) 322367, *mtreception@talbooth.co.uk, Fax (01206) 322752,* –
Meals – (see ***Le Talbooth*** below) – 7.50 – **9 rm** 120.00/210.00 **t.**, 1 suite – SB.

Milsoms, Stratford Rd, CO7 6HW, West : ¾ m. ☎ (01206) 322795, *milsoms@talbooth.co.uk, Fax (01206) 323689,* –
Meals (bookings not accepted) a la carte 14.75/23.70 **t.** 10.95 – 10.00 – **14 rm** 80.00/120.00 **t.**

Le Talbooth, Gun Hill, CO7 6HP, West : 1 m. ☎ (01206) 323150, *ltreception@talbooth.co.uk, Fax (01206) 322309,* « Part Tudor house in riverside setting », –
closed Sunday dinner September-May – **Meals** 21.00/28.00 and a la carte 30.00/42.50 **t.** 13.50.

Fountain House & Dedham Hall with rm, Brook St, CO7 6AD, ☎ (01206) 323027, *sarton@dedhamhall.demon.co.uk, Fax (01206) 323293,* – rest,
closed 25-26 December and 2 weeks February – **Meals** *(closed Sunday and Monday)* (dinner only) 23.00 **t.** 12.00 – **6 rm** 45.00/75.00 **t.** – SB.

ENGLAND

DENMEAD *Hants.* 403 Q 31 – *pop. 5 626.*
London 70 – Portsmouth 11 – Southampton 27.

XX **Barnard's,** Hambledon Rd, PO7 6NU, ℘ (023) 9225 7788, *Fax (023) 9225 7788*, – MC AE VISA JCB
closed 25-26 December, Saturday lunch, Sunday and Monday – **Meals** (light lunch)/dinne a la carte 18.00/26.95 **t.** 10.00.

DENTON *Gtr. Manchester* 402 404 N 23 – *pop. 37 785.*
Denton, Manchester Rd ℘ (0161) 336 3218.
London 196 – Chesterfield 41 – Manchester 6.

Old Rectory, Meadow Lane, Haughton Green, M34 7GD, South : 2 m. by A 6017, Two Trees Lane and Haughton Green Rd, ℘ (0161) 336 7516, *reservations@oldrectoryhote manchester.co.uk, Fax (0161) 320 3212*, – rest, – 100. MC AE VISA
Meals (bar lunch Saturday) 8.95/16.95 and a la carte 20.95/26.80 **st.** 12.00 – 9.50 – **36 rm** 49.50/89.50 **st.**

Travel Inn, Manchester Road South, M34 3SH, West : 1 m. by A 57 at junction of M 60 and M 67 ℘ (0161) 320 1116, *Fax (0161) 337 9652* – rm, rest, . MC AE VISA
Meals (grill rest.) – **40 rm** 41.95 **t.**

DERBY *Derby* 402 403 404 P 25 *Great Britain G.* – *pop. 223 836.*
See : *City★ – Museum and Art Gallery★ (Collection of Derby Porcelain★)* **YZ M1** – *Royal Crown Derby Museum★ AC* **Z M2.**
Env. : *Kedleston Hall★★ AC, NW : 4½ m. by Kedleston Rd* **X.**
Wilmore Rd, Sinfin ℘ (01332) 766323 – Mickleover, Uttoxeter Rd ℘ (01332) 513339 – Kedleston Park, Kedlston, Quardon ℘ (01332) 840035 – , Marriott Breadsall Prior H. & C.C., Moor Rd, Morley ℘ (01332) 832235 – Allestree Park, Allestree Hall, Allestree ℘ (01332) 550616.
East Midlands Airport, Castle Donington : ℘ (01332) 852852, SE : 12 m. by A 6 **X.**
Assembly Rooms, Market Pl ℘ (01332) 255802.
London 132 – Birmingham 40 – Coventry 49 – Leicester 29 – Manchester 62 – Nottingham 16 – Sheffield 47 – Stoke-on-Trent 35.

Plan opposite

Midland, Midland Rd, DE1 2SQ, ℘ (01332) 345894, *sales@midland-derby.co.uk Fax (01332) 293522*, – , rm, – 150. MC AE VISA JCB. Z
Meals *(closed lunch Saturday and Bank Holidays)* 22.50/33.00 **t.** 12.50 – 12.00 – **99 rm** 108.00/115.00, 1 suite – SB.

Premier Lodge, Foresters Leisure Park, Osmaston Park Rd, DE23 8AG ℘ (01332) 270027, *Fax (01332) 270528* – rm, – 40. MC AE VISA. X
Meals (grill rest.) a la carte approx. 13.00 **t.** 8.95 – **26 rm** 46.95 **t.**

Express by Holiday Inn without rest., Roundhouse Rd, Pride Park, DE24 8HX ℘ (01332) 388000, *Fax (01332) 388038* – . MC AE VISA JCB X
103 rm 55.00 **st.**

European Inn without rest., Midland Rd, DE1 2SL, ℘ (01332) 292000, *admin@euro_derby.co.uk, Fax (01332) 293940* – – 120. MC AE VISA. Z
6.75 – **88 rm** 48.00 **t.**

Travel Inn, Wyvern Business Park, DE21 6BF, ℘ (01332) 667826, *Fax (01332) 667827* – rm, rest, . MC AE VISA. X
Meals (grill rest.) – **82 rm** 41.95 **t.**

XX **Zest,** 16D George St, DE1 1EH, ℘ (01332) 381101, *Fax (01332) 381101* – MC AE VISA Y
closed Sunday and Monday – **Meals** 8.50 (lunch) and a la carte 15.15/25.35 **t.** 8.95.

at Darley Abbey *North : 2½ m. off A 6* – **X** – ✉ *Derby.*

XX **Darleys,** Darley Abbey Mill, DE22 1DZ, ℘ (01332) 364987, *davidpinchbeck@darleys.com Fax (01332) 364987*, « Converted cotton mill in attractive riverside setting » – . MC AE VISA JCB
closed Sunday dinner and Bank Holiday Mondays – **Meals** 17.50 (lunch) and a la carte 28.45/33.45 **t.** 14.00.

at Breadsall *Northeast : 4 m. by A 52 off A 61* – **X** – ✉ *Derby.*

Marriott Breadsall Priory H. & Country Club , Moor Rd, Morley, DE7 6DL Northeast : 1 ¼ m. by Rectory Lane ℘ (01332) 832235, *Fax (01332) 833509*, ←, , , , , , – , rest, – 140. MC AE VISA
***Priory* :** **Meals** (dinner only and Sunday lunch) a la carte 22.50/29.50 **st.** 12.75 – ***Long Weekend* :** **Meals** a la carte 13.00/23.15 **st.** 12.75 – 12.95 – **107 rm** 130.00 **st.** 5 suites – SB.

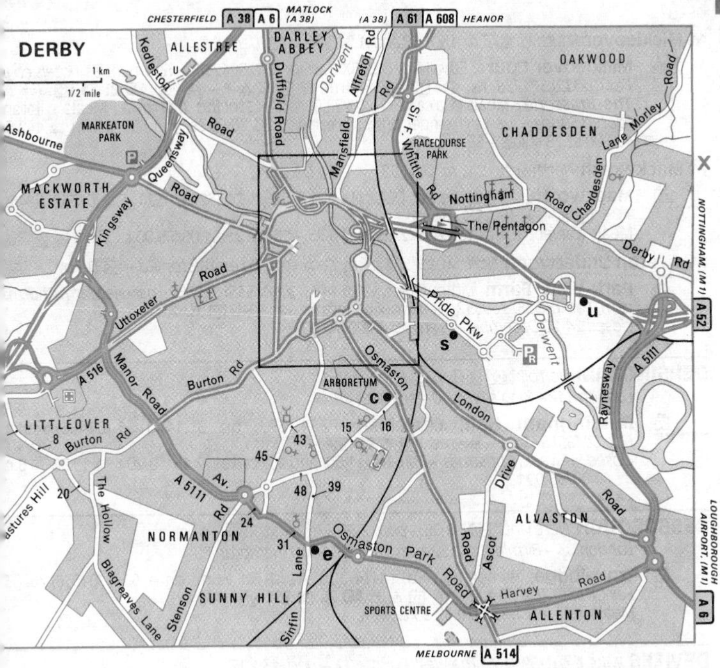

DERBY
CHESTERFIELD A 38 A 6 MATLOCK (A 38)
(A 38) A 61 A 608 HEANOR
1 km
1/2 mile
ALLESTREE
DARLEY ABBEY
OAKWOOD
Kedleston Road
Duffield Road
Derwent
Alfreton Rd
Sir F. Whittle Rd
Mansfield Rd
MARKEATON PARK
Ashbourne Road
Queensway
CHADDESDEN
RACECOURSE PARK
Morley Lane
Chaddesden Lane
Road
MACKWORTH ESTATE
Kingsway
Nottingham Road
The Pentagon
Derby Rd
NOTTINGHAM (M 1)
A 52
Uttoxeter Road
Pride Pkw
Derwent
A 516
Manor Road
Burton Rd
A 5111
Raynesway
ARBORETUM
Osmaston
London Road
LITTLEOVER
Burton Rd
Pastures Hill
The Hollow
A 5111
Av.
Rd
Drive
NORMANTON
ALVASTON
Osmaston Park Road
Ascot
Road
LOUGHBOROUGH AIRPORT (M 1)
A 6
Blagreaves Lane
Stenson
SUNNY HILL
Lane
Sinfin
SPORTS CENTRE
Harvey Road
ALLENTON
MELBOURNE A 514

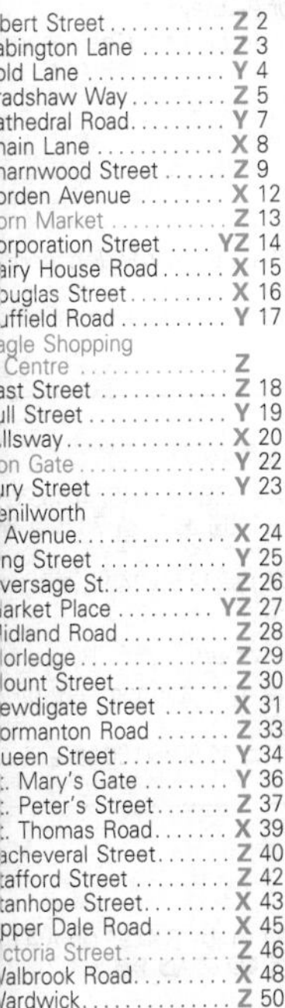

bert Street . . . . Z 2
abington Lane . . . . Z 3
old Lane . . . . Y 4
radshaw Way . . . . Z 5
athedral Road . . . . Y 7
hain Lane . . . . X 8
harnwood Street . . . . . . Z 9
orden Avenue . . . . X 12
orn Market . . . . Z 13
orporation Street . . . . YZ 14
airy House Road . . . . . . X 15
ouglas Street . . . . X 16
uffield Road . . . . Y 17
agle Shopping
Centre . . . . Z
ast Street . . . . Z 18
ull Street . . . . Y 19
llsway . . . . X 20
on Gate . . . . Y 22
ury Street . . . . Y 23
enilworth
Avenue . . . . X 24
ng Street . . . . Y 25
versage St. . . . . Z 26
arket Place . . . . YZ 27
idland Road . . . . Z 28
orledge . . . . Z 29
ount Street . . . . Z 30
ewdigate Street . . . . . . X 31
ormanton Road . . . . Z 33
ueen Street . . . . Y 34
. Mary's Gate . . . . Y 36
. Peter's Street . . . . Z 37
. Thomas Road . . . . X 39
acheveral Street . . . . . . Z 40
tafford Street . . . . Z 42
tanhope Street . . . . X 43
pper Dale Road . . . . X 45
ctoria Street . . . . Z 46
Valbrook Road . . . . X 48
Vardwick . . . . Z 50

A 6
A 61
CENTRE
200 m
200 yards
Derwent
Mansfield Road
Sir F. Whittle Road
Garden St.
Lodge La.
Fox Street
Stores Road
Alkmund's
Saint
Way
Nottingham Road
LEISURE CENTRE
Eastgate
A 52
Ford St.
Friar Gate
Derwent St.
A 516
Curzon St.
The Cock Pitt
MARKET
Station App.
Macklin St.
EAGLE CENTRE
Siddals Rd
Street
Gerard Street
Green La.
Osmaston
Traffic St.
Railway Ter.
Canal St.
Abbey
Rd
London Road
Leopold St.
MIDLAND
Burton
Lane
Litchurch St.
Road
Mill Hill
A 5250 (A 38)
A 514
A 6

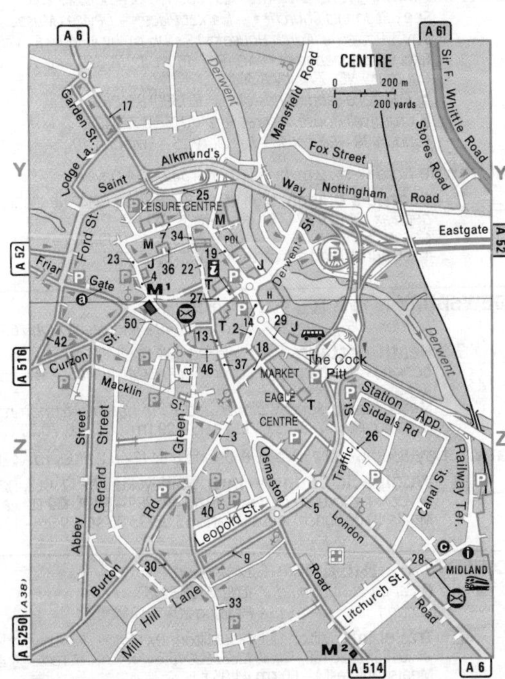

at Mickleover *Southwest : 3 m. by A 38 and A 516 – X – ✉ Derby.*

Mickleover Court, Etwall Rd, DE3 5XX, ☎ (01332) 521234, *info@menzies-hotels.co.*
Fax (01332) 521238, – rm, – 200. VISA JCB
The Brasserie : **Meals** a la carte 11.70/22.00 **st.** – ***Stelline Trattoria :*** **Meals** - Italian *(closed Sunday-Tuesday)* (dinner only) a la carte 15.20/28.50 **st.** 11.35 – **91 rm** 142.5 190.00 **st.,** 8 suites – SB.

at Mackworth *Northwest : 2 ¾ m. by A 52 – X – ✉ Derby.*

Mackworth, Ashbourne Rd, DE22 4LY, on A 52 ☎ (01332) 824324, *Fax (01332) 8246*
– – 160. VISA.
Meals (carvery) a la carte 12.15/22.80 **t.** 8.95 – **13 rm** 51.00/65.00 **t.**

at Weston Underwood *Northwest : 5½ m. by Kedleston Rd on Weston Rd – ✉ Derby.*

Park View Farm without rest., DE6 4PA, ☎ (01335) 360352, *parkviewfarm@hotm.*
com, Fax (01335) 360352, ≤, « Working farm », – .
closed 24-25 December – **3 rm** 40.00/70.00.

DERSINGHAM *Norfolk* 402 404 V 25 – *pop. 3 961.*
London 112 – King's Lynn 10 – Norwich 48.

Dersingham Hall, Chapel Rd, PE31 6PJ, on B 1440 ☎ (01485) 54351
Fax (01485) 543433 – rest, . VISA
closed 1 week Christmas – **Meals** 11.50 and a la carte 12.15/18.20 **t.** 10.50 – **5 r** 40.00/55.00 **t.**

DESBOROUGH *Northants.* 404 R 26 – *pop. 7 351.*
London 83 – Birmingham 52 – Leicester 20 – Northampton 20.

Travelodge, Harborough Rd, NN14 2UG, North : 1 ½ m. on A 6 ☎ (01536) 76203
Fax (01536) 762034 – rm, . VISA JCB.
Meals (grill rest.) – **32 rm** 39.95 **t.**

DEVIZES *Wilts.* 403 404 O 29 *The West Country G.* – *pop. 13 205.*
See : *St John's Church*★★ – *Market Place*★ – *Devizes Museum*★ *AC.*
Env. : *Potterne (Porch House*★★*) S : 2½ m. by A 360 – E : Vale of Pewsey*★.
Exc. : *Stonehenge*★★★ *AC, SE : 16 m. by A 360 and A 344 – Avebury*★★ *(The Stones Church*★*) NE : 7 m. by A 361.*
Erlestoke Sands, Erlestoke ☎ (01380) 831069.
Cromwell House, Market Sq ☎ (01380) 729408.
London 98 – Bristol 38 – Salisbury 25 – Swindon 19.

at Rowde *Northwest : 2 m. by A 361 on A 342 – ✉ Devizes.*

George & Dragon, High St, SN10 2PN, on A 342 ☎ (01380) 723053, *gd-rowde@lineor.*
net, Fax (01380) 724738, – . VISA
closed 25 December, 1 January, Sunday and Monday – **Meals** - Seafood - (booking essenti 12.50 (lunch) and a la carte 18.00/30.50 **t.** 9.50.

DEWSBURY *W. Yorks.* 402 P 22 – *pop. 50 168.*
London 205 – Leeds 9 – Manchester 40 – Middlesbrough 76 – Sheffield 31.

Heath Cottage, Wakefield Rd, WF12 8ET, East : ¾ m. on A 638 ☎ (01924) 46539
bookings@heathcottage.co.uk, Fax (01924) 459405 – , rest, – 70. VI JCB.
Meals *(closed Sunday dinner and Bank Holidays to non-residents)* 12.50/14.95 and dinner a la carte 14.95/23.00 **t.** 9.95 – **29 rm** 52.00/70.00 **t.** – SB.

at Whitley *Southwest : 4 m. by B 6409 and B 6117 on Whitley rd – ✉ Dewsbury.*

Woolpack Country Inn, Whitley Rd, WF12 0LZ, ☎ (01924) 499999, *enquiri @woolpackhotel.co.uk, Fax (01924) 495289* – . VISA
Meals 10.00 (lunch) and a la carte 15.95/23.95 **st.** 9.95 – **12 rm** 44.50/60.00 **st.** – SB.

DIDCOT *Oxon.* 403 404 Q 29 – ✉ *Abingdon.*
Car park, Station Rd ☎ (01235) 813243.
London 58 – Oxford 15 – Reading 20 – Swindon 31.

Travel Inn, Milton Heights, Milton, OX14 4DP, Northwest : 3 ¼ m. by B 4493 on A 413
☎ (01235) 835168, *Fax (01235) 820465* – rm, rest, . VISA.
Meals (grill rest.) – **60 rm** 41.95 **t.**

ENGLAND

DDLEBURY *Shrops.* 402 403 L 26 *Great Britain G. – pop. 911 – ✉ Craven Arms.*
Env. : *NW : Wenlock Edge★.*
London 169 – Birmingham 46.

Delbury Hall ⓢ, SY7 9DH, entrance on B 4368 beside lodge, opposite 40 mph sign ✆ (01584) 841267, *wrigley@delbury.com, Fax (01584) 841441*, ≤, « Georgian mansion », ... – TV P. MC VISA JCB. ✱
closed Christmas – **Meals** (booking essential) (residents only) (communal dining) (dinner only) 34.00 **st.** 11.50 – **4 rm** 60.00/120.00 **st.**

IDMARTON *Glos.* 403 404 N 29 – *pop. 429* – ✉ *Tetbury.*
London 120 – Bristol 20 – Gloucester 27 – Swindon 33.

Old Rectory without rest., GL9 1DS, on A 433 ✆ (01454) 238233, *Fax (01454) 238909*, – TV P. ✱
closed Christmas and New Year – **3 rm** 35.00/50.00.

Kings Arms with rm, The Street, GL9 1DT, on A 433 ✆ (01454) 238245, *kingsarm@kingsarm.freeserve.co.uk, Fax (01454) 238249*, – rm, TV P – 25. MC VISA. ✱
closed 25 December – **Meals** (in bar dinner Sunday) a la carte 15.40/27.85 **t.** 10.50 – **4 rm** 45.00/80.00 **t.**

IDSBURY *Gtr. Manchester* 402 403 404 N 23 – *see Manchester.*

Les prix — Pour toutes précisions sur les prix indiqués dans ce guide, reportez-vous aux pages de l'introduction.

ISLEY *Ches.* 402 403 404 N 23 – *pop. 3 743* – ✉ *Stockport.*
London 187 – Chesterfield 35 – Manchester 12.

Hilton Moorside Grange ⓢ, Mudhurst Lane, Higher Disley, SK12 2AP, Southeast : 2 m. by Higher Disley rd ✆ (01663) 764151, *fo.manager@moorside.stakis.co.uk, Fax (01663) 762794*, ≤, ..., squash – TV P – 300. MC AE VISA JCB
Meals (bar lunch Saturday) 12.00/39.50 and dinner a la carte 13.85/36.00 **st.** 12.50 – **99 rm** 120.00/170.00 **st.** – SB.

ISS *Norfolk* 404 X 26 – *pop. 6 538.*
Meres Mouth, Mere St ✆ (01379) 650523.
London 98 – Ipswich 25 – Norwich 21 – Thetford 17.

Weavers, Market Hill, IP22 4JZ, ✆ (01379) 642411, « Part 15C weaver's cottage » – MC AE VISA JCB
closed 2 weeks Christmas, Sunday and lunch Saturday and Monday – **Meals** 12.75/15.95 and dinner a la carte 15.95/24.95 **st.** 10.95.

at Brockdish *East : 7 m. by A 1066, A 140 and A 143* – ✉ *Diss.*

Grove Thorpe ⓢ without rest., Grove Rd, IP21 4JR, North : ¾ m. ✆ (01379) 668305, *b-b@grovethorpe.freeserve.co.uk, Fax (01379) 668305*, « 17C bailiffs house », – P. ✱
3 rm 45.00/70.00 **s.**

at Brome *(Suffolk) Southeast : 2 ¾ m. by A 1066 on B 1077* – ✉ *Eye.*

The Cornwallis ⓢ, IP23 8AJ, ✆ (01379) 870326, *info@thecornwallis.com, Fax (01379) 870051*, « Part 16C dower house, topiary gardens », – TV P – 30. MC VISA
Meals 23.00 **t.** 11.00 – **16 rm** 79.50/135.00 **t.** – SB.

at Wingfield *Southeast : 7 m. by A 1066, A 140 and B 1118.*

De La Pole Arms, Church Rd, IP21 5RA, ✆ (01379) 384545, *Fax (01379) 384377*, « Part 17C inn » – P. MC VISA JCB
closed Monday lunch – **Meals** a la carte 15.90/20.95 **t.** 9.50.

at Fersfield *Northwest : 7 m. by A 1066* – ✉ *Diss.*

Strenneth ⓢ without rest., Airfield Rd, IP22 2BP, ✆ (01379) 688182, *ken@strenneth.co.uk, Fax (01379) 688260*, « Part 17C farmhouse », – TV P. MC VISA
8 rm 28.00/70.00 **s.**

ODDISCOMBSLEIGH *Devon* 403 J 31 – *see Exeter.*

DONCASTER *S. Yorks.* 402 403 404 Q 23 – *pop. 71 595.*

Doncaster Town Moor, Bawtry Rd, Belle Vue ☎ (01302) 533778, B – *Crookhill Pa Conisborough ☎ (01709) 862979 – Wheatley, Amthorpe Rd ☎ (01302) 831665,* B – *Owston Park, Owston Hall, Owston ☎ (01302) 330821.*

Central Library, Waterdale ☎ (01302) 734309.

London 173 – Kingston-upon-Hull 46 – Leeds 30 – Nottingham 46 – Sheffield 19.

DONCASTER

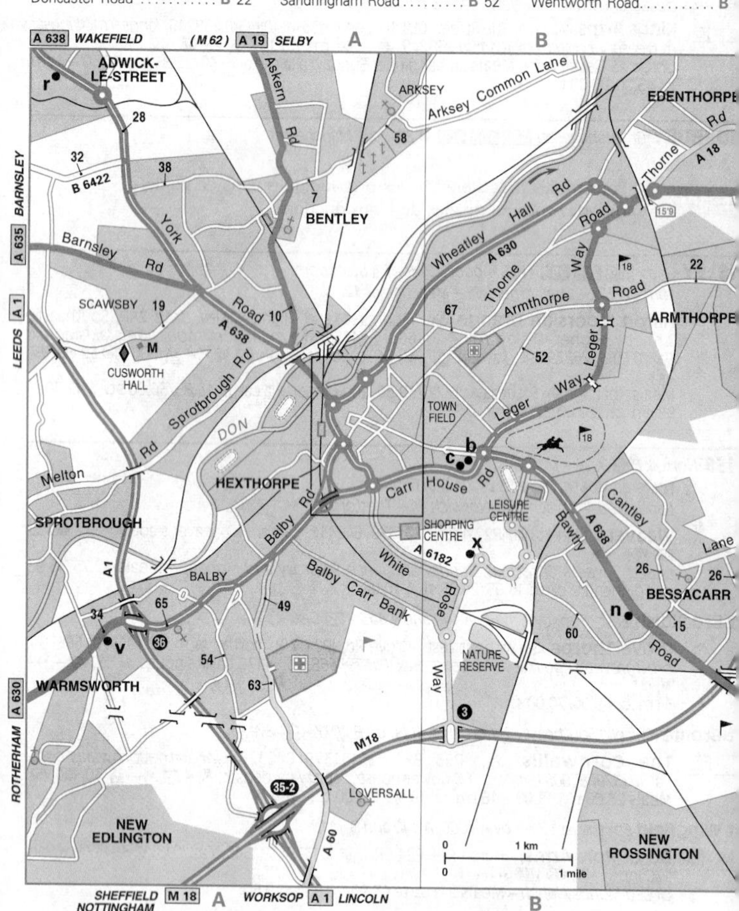

Doncaster Moat House, Warmsworth, DN4 9UX, Southwest : 2 ¾ m. on A 63
☎ (01302) 799988, *cbdan@queensmoat.co.uk, Fax (01302) 310197*, Ls, ≘s, – , rm rest, TV & P – 400. AE VISA A
Meals (bar lunch Monday-Saturday)/dinner 16.95/30.00 and a la carte 16.95/30.00 st
12.95 – 10.50 – **100 rm** 105.00/120.00 **st.**, 2 suites – SB.

DONCASTER

lbion Place . . . . C 3
pley Road . . . . C 5
alby Road . . . . C 8
roxholme Lane C
arr House Road C
hequer Avenue . . . . C 12
hequer Road. C
hrist Church Road C
hurch Way C
leveland Street. C
olonnades Shopping Centre C
unningham Road . . . . . . C 17
ast Laith Gate. . . . . C 24
renchgate Schopping Centre C
rey Friars Road C
all Gate C
igh Street . . . . C 36
ighfield Road C
Ailton Walk. . . . . C 40
ether hall Road . . . . C 43
orth Bridge Road. . . . . . C 44
ueen's Road. . . . . C 46
t James's Bridge . . . . . . C 48
t James's Street C
lver Street C
outh Parade C
horne Road C
rafford Way C
Vaterdale C
Vaterdale Shopping Centre C
Vhite Rose Way . . . . C 70
Vood Street C

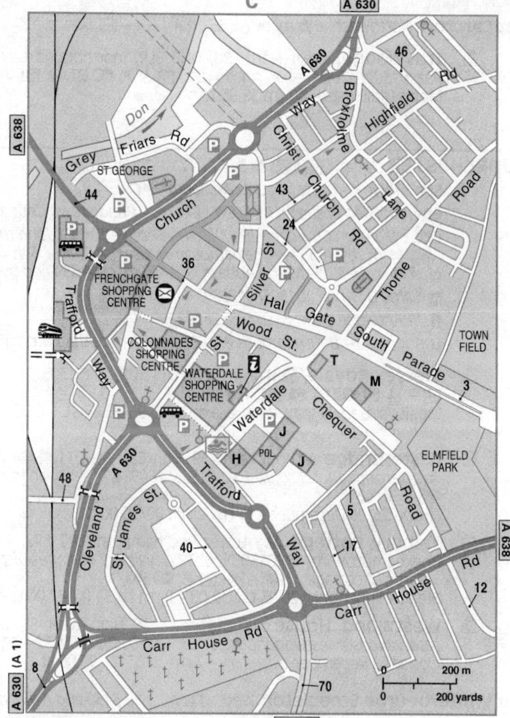

Mount Pleasant, Great North Rd, DN11 0HP, Southeast : 6 m. on A 638 ☎ (01302) 868219, *mountpleasant@fax.co.uk, Fax (01302) 865130,* – TV P – 100. MC AE VISA.
closed 25 December – **Meals** a la carte 20.50/27.05 **t.** 12.50 – **38 rm** 62.00/103.00 **t.**, 2 suites.

Grand St Leger, Racecourse Roundabout, Bennetthorpe, DN2 6AX, Southeast : 1 ½ m. on A 638 ☎ (01302) 364111, *grandstleger.hotel@virgin.net, Fax (01302) 329865* – TV P – 80. MC AE VISA. B b
Meals a la carte 17.50/25.45 **t.** 9.50 – **20 rm** 55.00/90.00 **t.**

Travel Inn, South Entry Drive, White Rose Way, DN4 5JH, South : 1 ½ m. by A 6182 ☎ (01302) 361134, *Fax (01302) 364811* – rm, rest, TV P. MC AE VISA B x
Meals (grill rest.) – **42 rm** 41.95 **t.**

Travelodge, at junction 5, DN8 5GS, Northeast : 8 ½ m. by A 630 and M 18 ☎ (01302) 847700 – rm, TV P. MC AE VISA JCB.
Meals (grill rest.) – **39 rm** 39.95 **t.**

Hamilton's with rm, Carr House Rd, DN4 5HP, Southeast : 2 m. on A 638 ☎ (01302) 760770, *frenchysbrasserie@yahoo.com, Fax (01302) 768101,* « Victorian town house » – TV P – 30. MC AE VISA JCB. B c
Meals a la carte 15.85/25.15 **st.** 7.75 – **4 rm** 70.00/210.00 **st.**

Aagrah, Great North Rd, Woodlands, DN6 7RA, Northwest : 4 m. on A 638 ☎ (01302) 728888 – P. MC AE VISA JCB A r
closed 25 December – **Meals** - Indian (Kashmiri) - (booking essential) (dinner only) a la carte 13.30/17.25 **t.** 9.95.

t Bawtry *Southeast : 9 m. by A 638 – ✉ Doncaster.*

Chimneys, Great North Rd, DN10 6DF, North : 1 ½ m. on A 638 ☎ (01302) 714426, *Fax (01302) 714427,* – P. MC AE VISA
closed first 2 weeks August and first week November – **Meals** (booking essential) (dinner only Wednesday-Saturday) 32.00 **st.** 11.95.

ENGLAND

at Carcroft *Northwest : 6½ m. by A 638 on A 1 – A – ✉ Doncaster.*

Travelodge, Great North Rd, DN6 8LR, (northbound carriageway) ☎ (01302) 3308… *Fax (01302) 330841* – ⇆ rm, ▤ rest, TV ♿ P. MC AE DC VISA JCB. ✂
Meals (grill rest.) – **40 rm** 39.95 **t.**

DORCHESTER *Dorset* 403 404 M 31 *The West Country G. – pop. 15 037.*

See : *Town★ - Dorset County Museum★ AC.*

Env. : *Maiden Castle★★ (≤★) SW : 2½ m. – Puddletown Church★, NE : 5½ m. by A 35.*

Exc. : *Moreton Church★★, E : 7½ m. – Bere Regis★ (St John the Baptist Church★ - Roof★ NE : 11 m. by A 35 – Athelhampton House★ AC, NE : 6½ m. by A 35 - Cerne Abbas N : 7 m. by A 352 – Milton Abbas★, NE : 12 m. on A 354 and by-road.*

Came Down ☎ (01305) 812531.

11 Antelope Walk ☎ (01305) 267992.

London 135 – Bournemouth 27 – Exeter 53 – Southampton 53.

Wessex Royale, 32 High West St, DT1 1UP, ☎ (01305) 262660, *Fax (01305) 251941* – … TV – 🎤 80. MC AE DC VISA JCB
Meals *(closed Sunday lunch)* a la carte 16.95/25.85 **st.** 🍷 9.95 – **27 rm** ☕ 59.00/129.00 **st** SB.

Casterbridge without rest., 49 High East St, DT1 1HU, ☎ (01305) 264043, *recepti… @casterbridgehotel.co.uk, Fax (01305) 260884,* « Georgian town house » – TV ☎. MC AE … VISA JCB. ✂
closed 25-26 December – **15 rm** ☕ 45.00/90.00 **t.**

Yalbury Cottage 🐦, Lower Bockhampton, DT2 8PZ, East : 2 ¼ m. by B 3150 a… Bockhampton rd ☎ (01305) 262382, *yalbury.cottage@virgin.net, Fax (01305) 2664…* « Part 17C cottage », 🌳 – ⇆ TV P. MC VISA
Meals (dinner only) 28.95 **t.** 🍷 12.00 – **8 rm** ☕ 53.00/82.00 **t.** – SB.

Westwood House without rest., 29 High West St, DT1 1UP, ☎ (01305) 2680… *reservations@westwoodhouse.co.uk, Fax (01305) 250282* – TV. MC AE VISA JCB
closed 28 December-6 January – **7 rm** ☕ 55.00/90.00 **st.**

at Winterbourne Steepleton *West : 4¾ m. by B 3150 and A 35 on B 3159 – ✉ Dorchester.*

Old Rectory without rest., DT2 9LG, ☎ (01305) 889468, *trees@eurobell.co.u… Fax (01305) 889737,* 🌳 – ⇆ TV P. ✂
closed Christmas and New Year – **4 rm** ☕ 45.00/110.00 **st.**

DORCHESTER *Oxon.* 403 404 Q 29 *Great Britain G. – pop. 2 256.*

See : *Town★.*

Exc. : *Ridgeway Path★★.*

London 51 – Abingdon 6 – Oxford 8 – Reading 17.

George, 25 High St, OX10 7HH, ☎ (01865) 340404, *Fax (01865) 341620,* « Part 1… coaching inn », 🌳 – ⇆ TV P – 🎤 40. MC AE DC VISA
closed 10 days Christmas – **Meals** a la carte 20.00/30.50 **t.** 🍷 9.10 – **18 rm** 65.00/85.00 – S…

White Hart, 26 High St, OX10 7HN, ☎ (01865) 340074, *whitehartdorches@aol.co… Fax (01865) 341082,* « 17C coaching inn » – TV P – 🎤 40. MC AE DC VISA
Meals a la carte 18.50/29.50 **st.** 🍷 10.95 – **19 rm** ☕ 79.50/95.00 **st.**, 4 suites – SB.

ENGLAND

ORKING Surrey 404 T 30 – *pop. 15 658.*

Betchworth Park, Reigate Rd (01306) 882052.

London 26 – Brighton 39 – Guildford 12 – Worthing 33.

Burford Bridge, Box Hill, RH5 6BX, North : 1 ½ m. on A 24 (0870) 400 8283, *gb1071 forte-hotels.com, Fax (01306) 880386,* heated, – – 300. VISA
Meals 10.00/25.00 **t.** 15.00 – 13.50 – **57 rm** 170.00/185.00 **st.** – SB.

White Horse, High St, RH4 1BE, (0870) 4008282, *heritagehotels-dorking.white-horse @forte-hotels.com, Fax (01306) 887241* – – 50. VISA
Meals 7.50/17.50 and a la carte 13.45/31.90 **t.** 13.00 – 12.50 – **78 rm** 135.00/165.00 **t.** – SB.

Travelodge, Reigate Rd, RH4 1QB, East : ½ m. on A 25 (01306) 740361, *Fax (01306) 740361* – , rest, . VISA JCB.
Meals (grill rest.) – **54 rm** 59.95 **t.**

at Abinger Common *Southwest : 4½ m. by A 25 – Dorking.*

The Stephan Langton Inn, Friday St, RH5 6JR, East : ½ m. by Friday Street Rd, taking first turn on the right before duck pond (01306) 730775, *cyraja@tinyworld.co.uk* – VISA
closed 2 weeks January and 1 week August – **Meals** *(closed Monday and Sunday dinner)* a la carte 10.00/18.00 **t.** 10.75.

ORRINGTON *Shrops.* 402 403 L 26 – *see Shrewsbury.*

OUGLAS *Isle of Man* 402 G 21 – *see Man (Isle of).*

Se cercate un albergo tranquillo,
oltre a consultare le carte dell'introduzione,
rintracciate nell'elenco degli esercizi quelli con il simbolo o .

OVER *Kent* 404 Y 30 *Great Britain G.* – *pop. 34 179.*

See : *Castle★★ AC* Y.

to France (Calais) (P & O Stena Line) frequent services daily (1 h 15 mn) – to France (Calais) (SeaFrance S.A.) frequent services daily (1 h 30 mn) – to France (Calais) (Hoverspeed Ltd) frequent services daily (35 mn) – to Belgium (Ostend) (Hoverspeed Ltd) 5 daily (2 h).

Townwall St (01304) 205108.

London 76 – Brighton 84.

Plan on next page

Churchill, Dover Waterfront, CT17 9BP, (01304) 203633, *enquiries@churchill-hotel. com, Fax (01304) 216320,* <, , – – 120. VISA JCB. Z a
Meals a la carte 16.75/22.50 **st.** 10.95 – 9.00 – **66 rm** 59.00/79.00 **t.** – SB.

Travel Inn, Jubilee Way, Guston Wood, CT15 5FD, Northeast : 2 m. by A 258 at junction with A 2 (01304) 204660, *Fax (01304) 215273* – rm, . VISA. Z r
Meals (grill rest.) – **40 rm** 41.95 **t.**

Travel Inn, Folkestone Rd, CT15 7AB, Southwest : 2 ½ m. on B 2011 (01304) 213339, *Fax (01304) 214504* – rm, . VISA.
Meals (grill rest.) – **62 rm** 41.95 **t.**

Old Vicarage without rest., Chilverton Elms, Hougham, CT15 7AS, West : 2 ¾ m. by B 2011 and Elms Vale Rd on West Hougham rd (01304) 210668, *vicarage@csi.com, Fax (01304) 225118,* <, – . VISA.
closed Christmas – **3 rm** 80.00 **s.**

East Lee without rest., 108 Maison Dieu Rd, CT16 1RT, (01304) 210176, *eastlee@eclipse .co.uk, Fax (01304) 206705* – . VISA. Y o
4 rm 40.00/50.00 **st.**

at St Margaret's at Cliffe *Northeast : 4 m. by A 258 – Z – Dover.*

Wallett's Court, West Cliffe, CT15 6EW, Northwest : ¾ m. on Dover rd (01304) 852424, *wc@wallettscourt.com, Fax (01304) 853430,* « Part 17C manor house », , , , , – . VISA JCB.
Meals – (see ***The Restaurant*** below) – **16 rm** 75.00/150.00 **t.** – SB.

The Restaurant (at Wallett's Court H.), West Cliffe, CT15 6EW, Northwest : ¾ m. on Dover rd (01304) 852424, *Fax (01304) 853430,* – . VISA JCB
Meals 13.50/35.00 and a la carte 17.50/35.00 **t.** 12.00.

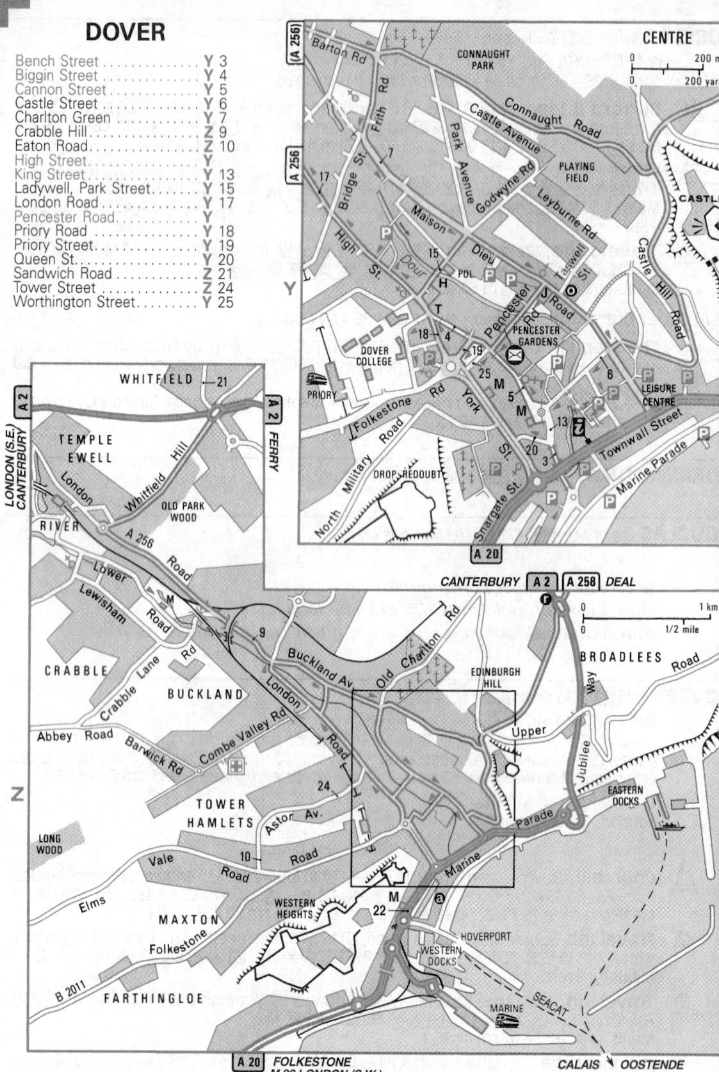

Pour visiter une ville ou une région : utilisez les Guides Verts Michelin.

DRIFT *Cornwall – see Penzance.*

DRIGHLINGTON *W. Yorks.* 402 P 22 – *see Leeds.*

DROITWICH SPA *Worcs.* 403 404 N 27 – *pop. 20 966.*

Ombersley, Bishopswood Rd ☎ (01905) 620747 – Droitwich G. & C.C., Ford Lan ☎ (01905) 770129.

St Richard's House, Victoria Sq ☎ (01905) 774312.

London 129 – Birmingham 20 – Bristol 66 – Worcester 6.

Travelodge, Rashwood Hill, WR9 8DA, Northeast : 1 ½ m. on A 38 ☎ (01527) 861545 – ⇔ rm, [TV] ♿ [P]. MC AE DC VISA JCB. ✗
Meals (grill rest.) – **32 rm** 52.95 **t.**

XX **Rossini,** 6 Worcester Rd, WR9 8AB, ☎ (01905) 794799, *Fax (01905) 775175* – ▤ [P]. MC AE VISA
closed Sunday and Bank Holidays – **Meals** - Italian - 8.50/17.95 and a la carte 19.40/31.20 **st.** 🍷 12.95.

t Oddingley *Southeast : 3 m. by B 4090 – ✉ Worcester.*

Church Farm House without rest., WR9 7NE, Southeast : ¼ m. on Netherwood rd ☎ (01905) 772387, *Fax (01905) 772387*, ⛫, 🐴, 🎾 – ⇔ [TV] [P]. ✗
3 rm ☕ 40.00/59.00 **st.**

t Smite *South : 3 ¾ m. by B 4090 and A 38 off A 4538 – ✉ Worcester.*

Pear Tree, WR3 8SY, ☎ (01905) 756565, *thepeartreeuk@aol.com, Fax (01905) 756777* – ⇔ rm, [TV] ♿ [P] – 🎤 300. MC AE DC VISA. ✗
accommodation closed 25 December – **Meals** (carvery lunch Sunday) a la carte 15.85/21.85 **t.** 🍷 10.95 – **21 rm** ☕ 75.00/120.00 **t.**, 3 suites.

t Hadley Heath *Southwest : 4 m. by Ombersley Way, A 4133 and Ladywood rd – ✉ Droitwich Spa.*

Hadley Bowling Green Inn, WR9 0AR, ☎ (01905) 620294, *hadleybowlinggreen@freeserve.co.uk, Fax (01905) 620771* – [TV] ☏ [P]. MC AE DC VISA. ✗
Meals a la carte 16.00/25.00 **st.** – **14 rm** ☕ 58.00/69.00 **st.** – SB.

Old Farmhouse without rest., WR9 0AR, ☎ (01905) 620837, *judylambe@ombersley.demon.co.uk, Fax (01905) 621722*, ⛫, 🎾 – ⇔ [TV] [P]
5 rm ☕ 30.00/60.00 **s.**

RONFIELD *Derbs.* 402 403 404 P 24 – *pop. 22 985* – ✉ *Sheffield (S. Yorks.).*
London 158 – Derby 30 – Nottingham 31 – Sheffield 6.

XX **Manor House** with rm, 10-15 High St, Old Dronfield, S18 1PY, ☎ (01246) 413971, *manorhouse@barrelsandbottles.co.uk, Fax (01246) 412104* – ⇔ [TV] [P]. MC AE DC VISA JCB
closed 25-26 December – **Meals** *(closed Sunday dinner)* (light lunch)/dinner 21.95/35.00 and a la carte 24.50/52.50 **st.** 🍷 11.95 – **8 rm** ☕ 59.50/79.50 **st.**, 2 suites – SB.

UDLEY *W. Mids.* 402 403 404 N 26 *Great Britain G.* – *pop. 304 615.*
See : *Black Country Museum★.*
ℹ *39 Churchill Centre ☎ (01384) 812830.*
London 132 – Birmingham 10 – Wolverhampton 6.

Plan : see Birmingham p. 4

Copthorne Merry Hill, The Waterfront, Level St, Brierley Hill, DY5 1UR, Southwest : 2 ¼ m. by A 461 ☎ (01384) 482882, *Fax (01384) 482773*, 🏋, ♨, 🏊 – 🛗, ⇔ rm, ▤ rest, [TV] ☏ ♿ [P] – 🎤 570. MC AE DC VISA AU z
Meals (bar lunch Saturday) 6.95/18.00 and a la carte 19.95/34.20 **st.** – ☕ 13.50 – **129 rm** 140.00/150.00 **st.**, 9 suites – SB.

Ward Arms, Birmingham Rd, DY1 4RN, Northeast : ¾ m. on A 461 ☎ (01384) 458070, *wardarms@corushotels.com, Fax (01384) 457502* – ⇔ rm, [TV] ♿ [P] – 🎤 150. MC AE DC VISA JCB BT a
Meals *(closed Saturday lunch)* (carvery) 8.95/17.95 and a la carte 14.70/22.70 **st.** 🍷 8.95 – ☕ 10.50 – **72 rm** 65.00 **t.** – SB.

Travel Inn, Dudley Rd, Kingswinford, DY6 8WT, West : 3 m. on A 4101 ☎ (01384) 291290, *Fax (01384) 277593* – 🛗, ⇔ rm, ▤ rest, [TV] ♿ [P] – 🎤 35. MC AE DC VISA. ✗ AU e
Meals (grill rest.) – **43 rm** 41.95 **t.**

Travelodge without rest., Dudley Rd, Brierley Hill, DY5 1LQ, Southwest : 2 m. on A 461 ☎ (01384) 481579 – ⇔ [TV] ♿ [P]. MC AE DC VISA JCB. ✗ AU c
32 rm 42.95 **t.**

ULVERTON *Somerset* 403 J 30 *The West Country G.* – *pop. 1 870 (inc. Brushford).*
See : *Village★.*
Env. : *Exmoor National Park★★ – Tarr Steps★★, NW : 6 m. by B 3223.*
London 198 – Barnstaple 27 – Exeter 26 – Minehead 18 – Taunton 27.

Ashwick House 🐦, TA22 9QD, Northwest : 4 ¼ m. by B 3223 turning left after second cattle grid ☎ (01398) 323868, *ashwickhouse@talk21.com, Fax (01398) 323868*, ≤, 🌳, « Edwardian country house in extensive gardens » – ⇔ rest, [TV] [P]. ✗
Meals (booking essential to non-residents) (set menu only) (light lunch Monday to Saturday residents only)/dinner 14.95/21.00 **t.** 🍷 10.50 – **6 rm** ☕ (dinner included) 79.00/138.00 **t.** – SB.

Highercombe, TA22 9PT, Northwest : 2 ½ m. on B 3223 ☎ (01398) 323451, *highcombe@btconnect.co.uk, Fax (01398) 323451,* « Georgian house of 14C origin », rm, TV P. MC AE VISA
Meals (by arrangement) (communal dining) 15.00 – **2 rm** 30.00/60.00, 1 suite.

DUNSLEY *N. Yorks. – see Whitby.*

DUNSTABLE *Beds.* 404 S 28 – *pop. 49 666.*
Tilsworth, Dunstable Rd ☎ (01525) 210721.
The Library, Vernon Pl ☎ (01582) 471012.
London 40 – Bedford 24 – Luton 4.5 – Northampton 35.

Hanover International, Church St, LU5 4RT, ☎ (01582) 662201, *Fax (01582) 696422*, rest, TV P – 40. MC AE VISA
closed 26, 28 and 29 December – **Meals** (bar lunch Saturday) 9.95/35.00 and a la carte 22.50/35.00 **t.** 12.95 – 11.95 – **68 rm** 105.00/145.00 **st.** – SB.

Travel Inn, 350 Luton Rd, LU5 4LL, Northeast : 1 ¾ m. on A 505 ☎ (01582) 60993 *Fax (01582) 664114* – rm, rest, TV P. MC AE VISA
Meals (grill rest.) – **42 rm** 41.95 **t.**

Travel Inn, Watling St, Kensworth, LU6 3QP, Southeast : 2 ½ m. on A 5 ☎ (01582) 84050 *Fax (01582) 842811* – rm, TV P. MC AE VISA.
Meals (grill rest.) – **40 rm** 41.95 **t.**

at Hockliffe *Northwest : 3 ¼ m. on A 5 – ✉ Dunstable.*

Travelodge, LU7 9LZ, Southeast : ¾ m. on A 5 ☎ (01525) 211177, *Fax (01525) 211177* rm, TV P. MC AE VISA JCB.
Meals (grill rest.) – **28 rm** 49.95 **t.**

DURHAM *Durham* 401 402 P 19 *Great Britain G. – pop. 36 937.*
See : *City★★★ - Cathedral★★★ (Nave★★★, Chapel of the Nine Altars★★★, Sanctuary Knocker★)* **B** *– Oriental Museum★★* **AC** *(at Durham University by A 167)* **B** *– City and Riverside (Prebends' Bridge ≤★★★* **A** *, Framwellgate Bridge ≤★★* **B**) *– Monastic Buildings (Cathedral Treasury★, Central Tower≤★)* **B** *– Castle★ (Norman chapel★)* **AC B.**
Exc. : *Hartlepool Historic Quay★, SE : 14 m. by A 181, A 19 and A 179.*
Mount Oswald, South Rd ☎ (0191) 386 7527.
Market Pl ☎ (0191) 384 3720.
London 267 – Leeds 77 – Middlesbrough 23 – Sunderland 12.

Plan opposite

Durham Marriott H. Royal County, Old Elvet, DH1 3JN, ☎ (0191) 386 6821, *durhamroyal@marriotthotels.co.uk, Fax (0191) 386 0704,* – rest, TV P 120. MC AE VISA JCB **B**
County : **Meals** 18.00/35.00 and a la carte 22.25/34.00 **st.** 13.75 – ***Bowes :*** **Meals** a la carte 14.70/22.00 **st.** 13.75 – 15.00 – **134 rm** 119.00/144.00 **st.**, 4 suites – SB.

Ramside Hall, Carrville, DH1 1TD, Northeast : 3 m. on A 690 ☎ (0191) 386 5282, *ramsidehall@ukonline.co.uk, Fax (0191) 386 0399,* 18, 9, – TV P – 400. MC AE VISA
The Restaurant : **Meals** 25.00/28.50 (dinner) and a la carte 14.10/25.00 **t.** 10.50 – **78 rm** 115.00/150.00 **t.**, 2 suites – SB.

Kingslodge, Flass Vale, DH1 4BG, ☎ (0191) 370 9977, *kingslodge@kingslodge-leisure.co.uk, Fax (0191) 370 9988,* – rest, TV P. MC AE VISA. **A**
Knights : **Meals** (music at dinner) 15.00/20.00 and a la carte 20.00/40.00 **t.** 5.95 – **20 rm** 67.00/110.00 **t.**, 1 suite – SB.

Swallow Three Tuns, New Elvet, DH1 3AQ, ☎ (0191) 386 4326, *threetuns.reservation@btinternet, Fax (0191) 386 1406* – TV P – 350. MC AE VISA JCB **B**
Browns : **Meals** (bar lunch Monday-Saturday)/dinner 22.50/28.00 and a la carte 18.45/27.25 **st.** 13.50 – **48 rm** 102.00/150.00 **st.**, 2 suites – SB.

Waterside without rest., Elvet Waterside, DH1 3BW, ☎ (0191) 384 6660, *watersidedurham@breathe.mail.net, Fax (0191) 384 6996,* « Riverside setting » – TV P. MC VISA JCB **B**
closed 2 weeks Christmas and New Year – **11 rm** 55.00/80.00 **t.**

Farnley Tower without rest., The Avenue, DH1 4DX, ☎ (0191) 375 0011, *enquiries@farnleytower.freeservenet.co.uk, Fax (0191) 383 9694,* – TV P **A**
closed 25-26 December – **12 rm** 50.00/80.00 **st.**

Travel Inn, Arnison Retail Centre, DH1 5GB, North : 3 m. by A 691 off A 16 ☎ (0191) 383 9140, *Fax (0191) 383 1166* – rm, rest, TV P. MC AE VISA
Meals (grill rest.) – **60 rm** 41.95 **t.**

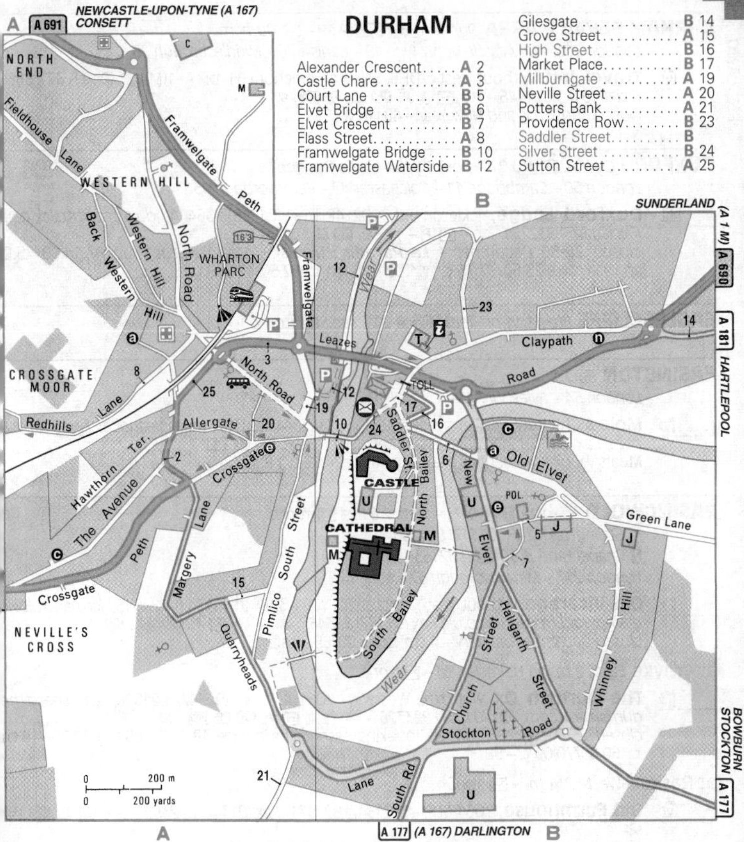

⌂ **Castle View** without rest., 4 Crossgate, DH1 4PS, ✆ (0191) 386 8852, *castle_view@hotmail.com, Fax (0191) 386 8852* – ⇔ TV. MC AE VISA JCB — A e
closed 3 weeks Christmas and New Year – **6 rm** ☕ 45.00/58.00.

⌂ **Cathedral View Guest House** without rest., 212 Gilesgate, DH1 1QN, ✆ (0191) 386 9566, *cathedralview@hotmail,com*, – ⇔ TV. MC VISA. — B n
6 rm ☕ 40.00/60.00 **st.**

✕ **Bistro 21,** Aykley Heads House, Aykley Heads, DH1 5TS, Northwest : 1 ½ m. by A 691 and B 6532 ✆ (0191) 384 4354, *Fax (0191) 384 1149*, , « Part 17C Mediterranean style villa » – ⇔ P. MC AE VISA
closed Christmas, Bank Holidays and Sunday – **Meals** 12.00/14.50 (lunch) and a la carte 16.50/36.00 **t.** 10.50.

at Shincliffe *Southeast : 2 m. on A 177* – ✉ *Durham.*

Bracken, Shincliffe, DH1 2PD, on A 177 ✆ (0191) 386 2966, *Fax (0191) 384 5423* – ⇔ TV P. MC VISA.
Meals *(closed Sunday)* (residents only) (dinner only) a la carte 18.50/23.50 **st.** 8.95 – **13 rm** ☕ 45.00/90.00 **st.**

The Seven Stars Inn with rm, High Street North, DH1 2NU, ✆ (0191) 384 8454, *enquiries@sevenstarsinn.co.uk, Fax (0191) 386 0640* – ⇔ TV. MC VISA
Meals a la carte 17.00/20.50 **st.** 9.50 – **8 rm** ☕ 40.00/65.00 **st.**

Les prix — Pour toutes précisions sur les prix indiqués dans ce guide, reportez-vous aux pages de l'introduction.

DURHAM SERVICE AREA *Durham* 401 402 P 19 – ✉ *Durham.*
London 280 – Newcastle upon Tyne 19 – Carlisle 76 – Middlesbrough 25.

Travel Inn without rest., DH6 5NP, at junction 61 of A 1(M) ✆ (0191) 377 366(
Fax (0191) 377 1448 – ✈ TV ♿ P. MO AE ⓓ VISA. ✂
closed Christmas and New Year – **40 rm** 41.95 **t.**

DUXFORD *Cambs.* 404 U 27 – *pop. 1 848* – ✉ *Cambridge.*
London 50 – Cambridge 11 – Colchester 45 – Peterborough 45.

Duxford Lodge, Ickleton Rd, CB2 4RU, ✆ (01223) 836444, *duxford@btclick.con*
Fax (01223) 832271, ⛲ – TV P – 🎤 30. MO AE ⓓ VISA
closed 26-30 December – ***Le Paradis :*** **Meals** *(closed Saturday lunch)* 14.00/25.0
and a la carte 25.50/37.75 **t.** 🍷 11.00 – **15 rm** ☕ 82.50/120.00 **t.**

EAGLESCLIFFE *Stockton-on-Tees* 402 P 20 – *see Stockton-on-Tees.*

EASINGTON *Bucks.*
London 54 – Aylesbury 13 – Oxford 18.

Mole & Chicken, The Terrace, HP18 9EY, ✆ (01844) 208387, *themoleandchicken@hotma*
com, Fax (01844) 208250, « Characterful inn » – P. MO AE VISA
Meals (booking essential) a la carte 16.40/24.85 **t.** 🍷 9.35.

EASINGWOLD *N. Yorks.* 402 Q 21 – *pop. 2 816* – ✉ *York.*
⛳18 *Stillington Rd* ✆ *(01347) 821486.*
ℹ *Chapel Lane* ✆ *(01347) 821530.*
London 217 – Middlesbrough 37 – York 14.

Old Vicarage without rest., Market Pl, YO61 3AL, ✆ (01347) 821015, *kirman@oldvic*
easingwold.freeserve.co.uk, Fax (01347) 823465, ⛲ – ✈ TV P. MO VISA. ✂
closed December-January – **4 rm** ☕ 45.00/65.00 **st.**

at Crayke *East : 2 m. on Helmsley Rd* – ✉ *York.*

The Durham Ox with rm, Westway, YO61 4TE, ✆ (01347) 821506, *enquiries@the*
durham-ox.com, Fax (01347) 823326 – ✈ rest, TV P. MO AE VISA. ✂
closed 25 December – **Meals** (booking essential) a la carte 18.40/31.85 **t.** 🍷 10.50 – **6 rn**
☕ 60.00/70.00 **t.** – SB.

at Raskelf *West : 2 ¾ m.* – ✉ *York.*

Old Farmhouse, YO61 3LF, ✆ (01347) 821971, *Fax (01347) 822392* – ✈ TV P. MO VISA
✂
closed January – **Meals** (dinner only) 21.50 **t.** 🍷 9.50 – **10 rm** ☕ (dinner included) 60.00
100.00 **t.** – SB.

EASTBOURNE *E. Sussex* 404 U 31 *Great Britain G.* – *pop. 94 793.*
See : *Seafront*★.
Env. : *Beachy Head*★★★, *SW : 3 m. by B 2103* Z.
⛳18, ⛳9 *Royal Eastbourne, Paradise Drive* ✆ *(01323) 729738* Z – ⛳18 *Eastbourne Downs, Eas*
Dean Rd ✆ *(01323) 720827* – ⛳9 *Eastbourne Golfing Park, Lottbridge Drove* ✆ *(01323*
520400.
ℹ *Cornfield Rd* ✆ *(01323) 411400.*
London 68 – Brighton 25 – Dover 61 – Maidstone 49.

Plan opposite

Grand, King Edward's Par, BN21 4EQ, ✆ (01323) 412345, *reservations@grandeastbourne*
co.uk, Fax (01323) 412233, ≤, 🏋, ♨, 🏊 heated, 🏊, ⛲ – 🛗, ✈ rest, ▤ rest, TV ✆ P
🎤 300. MO AE ⓓ VISA JCB Z
Garden Restaurant : **Meals** 15.50/32.00 and a la carte 35.00/49.00 **st.** 🍷 16.50 – (see also
Mirabelle below) – **128 rm** ☕ 130.00/280.00 **st.**, 24 suites – SB.

Lansdowne, King Edward's Par, BN21 4EE, ✆ (01323) 725174, *the.lansdowne@btinte*
net.com, Fax (01323) 739721, ≤ – 🛗, ✈ rest, TV ✆ 🚗 – 🎤 120. MO AE ⓓ VISA JCB Z
closed 1-17 January – **Meals** (bar lunch Monday to Saturday)/dinner 17.95 **t.** 🍷 11.25 –
112 rm ☕ 65.00/134.00 **st.** – SB.

Chatsworth, Grand Par, BN21 3YR, ✆ (01323) 411016, *stay@chatsworth-hotel.con*
Fax (01323) 643270, ≤ – 🛗 ✈ TV – 🎤 100. MO AE ⓓ VISA X
Meals (bar lunch)/dinner 18.50 and a la carte 21.25/38.50 **st.** 🍷 10.50 – **46 rm** ☕ 53.00
93.00 **st.**, 1 suite – SB.

EASTBOURNE

rndale Centre V
shford Road . . . . V 2
edfordwell Road. . . . . V 3
hurch Street . . . . Z 4
ornfield Road . . . . V 5
evonshire Place . . . . X 6
ildredge Road. . . . . V 7
rove Road V
ailsham Road . . . . Y 8
igh Street. . . . . Z 9
ewes Road . . . . Y 13
smore Road . . . . V 14
orth Street . . . . V 15
olegate By-Pass . . . . Y 18
t. Anthony's
Avenue . . . . Y 21
Seaside Rd. V
South Street. V
Station Road. . . . . Y 24
Susan's Road. . . . . V 25
Terminus Road V
The Goffs . . . . Z 26
Trinity Trees. . . . . V 27
Upperton Road. . . . . V, Z 28

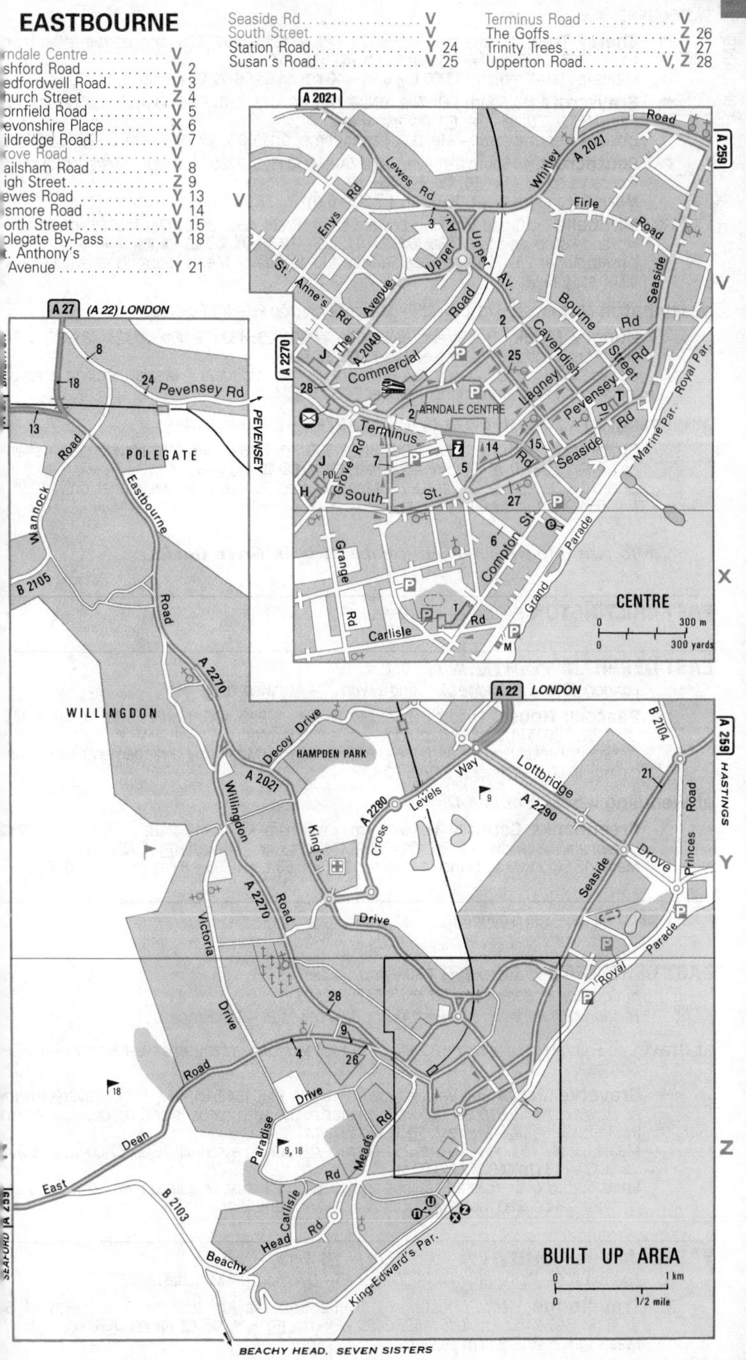

Cherry Tree, 15 Silverdale Rd, BN20 7AJ, ☎ (01323) 722406, *anncherrytree@aol.com, Fax (01323) 648838* – ⇔ TV. MC AE ⓓ VISA JCB. ✗ Z
Meals (by arrangement) 13.00 **t.** 8.95 – **10 rm** 33.00/72.00 **t.** – SB.

Brayscroft, 13 South Cliff Ave, BN20 7AH, ☎ (01323) 647005, *braycroft@hotmail.com, Fax (01323) 720705* – ⇔ TV. MC VISA JCB Z
closed 2 weeks autumn – **Meals** (by arrangement) 12.00 **s.** 7.00 – **5 rm** 29.50/59.00 **s**

Southcroft, 15 South Cliff Ave, BN20 7AH, ☎ (01323) 729071, *southcroft@eastbourne34.freeserve.co.uk* – ⇔ TV. MC VISA JCB. ✗ Z
Meals (by arrangement) 10.00 **st.** 7.50 – **6 rm** 27.00/54.00 **st.** – SB.

XXXX **Mirabelle** (at Grand H.), King Edward's Par, BN21 4EQ, ☎ (01323) 435066, *reservations@grandeastbourne.co.uk, Fax (01323) 412233* – ⇔ ▤ P. MC AE ⓓ VISA JCB Z
closed dinner 25, 26 December, Sunday and Monday – **Meals** (booking essential) 19.00/49.00 **st.** 16.50.

at Jevington *Northwest : 6 m. by A 259 – Z – on Jevington Rd – ✉ Polegate.*

XX **Hungry Monk,** The Street, BN26 5QF, ☎ (01323) 482178, *Fax (01323) 483989*, « Part Elizabethan cottages », 🌳 – ⇔ ▤ P. MC AE VISA
closed 24-26 and 31 December and Bank Holiday Mondays – **Meals** (booking essential) (dinner only and Sunday lunch)/dinner 26.50 **t.** 14.00.

at Wilmington *Northwest : 6½ m. by A 22 on A 27 – Y – ✉ Eastbourne.*

XX **Crossways** with rm, Lewes Rd, BN26 5SG, ☎ (01323) 482455, *stay@crosswayshotel.co.uk, Fax (01323) 487811*, 🌳 – ⇔ rest, TV P. MC AE VISA JCB. ✗
closed 23 December-23 January – **Meals** *(closed Sunday-Monday)* (dinner only) 30.95 **t.** 11.95 – **7 rm** 52.00/82.00 **st.** – SB.

*To visit a town or region: use the **Michelin Green Guides.***

EAST CHILTINGTON *E. Sussex – see Lewes.*

EAST DEREHAM *Norfolk* 404 W 25 – *pop. 12 974.*
London 109 – Cambridge 57 – King's Lynn 27 – Norwich 16.

Peacock House, Peacock Lane, Old Beetley, NR20 4DG, North : 3 ½ m. on B 1110 ☎ (01362) 860371, *peackh@aol.com*, « Part 17C farmhouse », 🌳 – ⇔ P
closed 2 weeks January and 1 week November – **Meals** (by arrangement) (communal dining) 14.00 – **3 rm** 27.00/45.00 **s.**

at Wendling *West : 5½ m. by A 47.*

X **Greenbanks Country H.** with rm, Swaffham Rd, NR19 2AB, ☎ (01362) 687742, *greenbanks@skynow.net, Fax (01362) 687742*, ⛆, 🌳 – ⇔ rest, TV P. MC VISA
Meals 18.00/21.00 and lunch a la carte 12.50/30.50 **t.** 10.95 – **8 rm** 48.00/90.00 **t.**

EAST END *Hants. – see Lymington.*

EAST GRINSTEAD *W. Sussex* 404 T 30 – *pop. 24 383.*
18 Copthorne, Borers Arm Rd ☎ (01342) 712508.
London 48 – Brighton 30 – Eastbourne 32 – Lewes 21 – Maidstone 37.

at Gravetye *Southwest : 4½ m. by B 2110 taking second turn left towards West Hoathly – ✉ East Grinstead.*

Gravetye Manor ⛰, Vowels Lane, RH19 4LJ, ☎ (01342) 810567, *info@gravetyemanor.co.uk, Fax (01342) 810080*, ←, « 16C manor house with gardens and grounds by William Robinson », ⛆, 🌲 – ⇔ rest, TV P. MC VISA. ✗
✿ **Meals** *(closed to non-residents 25 December)* (booking essential) 26.00/57.00 **st.** 16.00 – ⊒ 16.00 – **18 rm** 160.00/330.00 **st.**
Spec. Spiced crab, roasted scallops and gazpacho. Breast of guinea fowl, strawberry and tarragon sauce. Red mullet with carrot and vanilla emulsion.

EASTHAM *Mersey.* 402 403 L 24 – *pop. 15 011* – ✉ *Wirral.*
London 209 – Birmingham 45 – Chester 13 – Liverpool 8 – Manchester 45.

Travelodge, New Chester Rd, CH62 9AQ, at junction of A 41 with M 53 ☎ (0151) 327 2489, *Fax (0151) 327 2489* – ⇔ rm, TV ♿ P. MC AE ⓓ VISA JCB. ✗
Meals (grill rest.) – **31 rm** 39.95 **t.**

ENGLAND

EAST HOATHLY E. Sussex 404 U 31 – pop. 1 206.

London 60 – Brighton 16 – Eastbourne 13 – Hastings 25 – Maidstone 32.

Old Whyly, Halland Rd, BN8 6EL, West : ½ m., turning right after post box on right, taking centre gravel drive after approx. 400 metres ☎ (01825) 840216, *Fax (01825) 840738*, ≤, « Georgian manor house, antiques », heated, – rm, P.
Meals (by arrangement) (communal dining) 22.00 – **3 rm** 67.50/90.00.

EAST HORNDON Essex.

London 21 – Chelmsford 13 – Southend-on-Sea 17.

Travelodge, CM13 3LL, on A 127 (eastbound carriageway) ☎ (01277) 810819, *Fax (01277) 810819* – rm, TV P. MC AE VISA JCB.
Meals (grill rest.) – **22 rm** 59.95 **t.**

EASTLEIGH Hants. 403 P 31 – pop. 49 934.

Fleming Park, Magpie Lane ☎ (023) 8061 2797.

Southampton (Eastleigh) Airport : ☎ (023) 8062 0021.

The Point, Leigh Rd ☎ (023) 8064 1261.

London 74 – Winchester 8 – Southampton 4.

Holiday Inn, Leigh Rd, SO50 9PG, West : ¼ m. on A 335 ☎ (0870) 4009075, *Fax (023) 8064 3945*, – rm, rest, TV P – 200. MC AE VISA JCB.
Meals (bar lunch Saturday) a la carte 17.85/27.85 **t.** – 13.95 – **120 rm** 105.00 **t.** – SB.

Travel Inn, Leigh Rd, SO50 9YX, West : ½ m. on A 335 ☎ (023) 8065 0541, *Fax (023) 8065 0531* – rm, TV P. MC AE VISA
Meals (grill rest.) – **60 rm** 41.95 **t.**

Travelodge, Twyford Rd, SO50 4LF, North : 1 m. on A 335 ☎ (023) 8061 6813 – rm, TV P. MC AE VISA JCB.
Meals (grill rest.) – **32 rm** 52.95 **t.**

EASTLING Kent 404 W 30 – see Faversham.

EAST MIDLANDS AIRPORT Leics. 402 403 404 P/Q 25 – ✉ Derby.

London 125 – Nottingham 15 – Derby 13 – Birmingham 40 – Leicester 24.

Hilton East Midlands Airport, Derby Rd, Lockington, DE74 2YW, Northeast : 2 ¾ m. by A 453 on A 50 at junction 24 of M 1 ☎ (01509) 674000, *Fax (01509) 672412*, – rm, TV P – 300. MC AE VISA
Meals *(closed Saturday lunch)* (carvery lunch) 12.95/23.95 and dinner a la carte approx. 19.00 **st.** 13.75 – 12.95 – **150 rm** 140.00/160.00 **st.**, 2 suites.

Thistle East Midlands Airport, DE74 2SH, ☎ (01332) 850700, *east.midlandsairport @thistle.co.uk, Fax (01332) 850823*, – TV P – 220. MC AE VISA
Meals (bar lunch Saturday and Bank Holidays) 13.95/19.95 and a la carte 22.20/39.95 **st.** 12.95 – 12.00 – **164 rm** 150.00/170.00 **st.** – SB.

Travelodge, Donington Park, DE74 2TN, East : ½ m. by A 453 at junction with A 42 and 23a of M 1 ☎ (01509) 670900, *Fax (01509) 686316* – rm, rest, TV P. MC AE VISA JCB
Meals (grill rest.) – **80 rm** 42.95 **t.**

EASTON Devon 403 I 31 – see Chagford.

EASTON Somerset – see Wells.

EAST TYTHERLEY Hants. – see Romsey.

EAST WITTERING W. Sussex 404 R 31 – pop. 4 630 – ✉ Chichester.

London 74 – Brighton 37 – Portsmouth 25.

Clifford's Cottage, Bracklesham Lane, Bracklesham Bay, PO20 8JA, East : 1 m. by B 2179 on B 2198 ☎ (01243) 670250 – P. MC AE VISA.
closed 2 weeks November, 1 week spring, Monday, Tuesday and Sunday dinner – **Meals** (dinner only and Sunday lunch)/dinner 19.50 and a la carte 17.95/27.70 **t.** 10.50.

EAST WITTON *N. Yorks.* 402 O 21 – *pop. 153* – ✉ *Leyburn.*
London 238 – Leeds 45 – Middlesbrough 30 – York 39.

Blue Lion with rm, DL8 4SN, ✆ (01969) 624273, *bluelion@breathemail.ne* *Fax (01969) 624189*, « Part 18C former coaching inn », – TV P. MC VISA
The Restaurant : **Meals** (dinner only and Sunday lunch)/dinner a la carte 21.15/31.85 10.50 – (see also ***The Bar*** below) – **12 rm** 53.00/89.00 **t.**

The Bar (at Blue Lion), DL8 4SN, ✆ (01969) 624273, *Fax (10969) 624189*, , « Part 18 former coaching inn », – P. MC VISA
Meals (booking essential) a la carte 16.15/31.95 **t.** 10.50.

EBCHESTER *Durham* 401 402 O 19 – ✉ *Consett.*
Consett and District, Elmfield Rd, Consett ✆ (01207) 502186.
London 275 – Carlisle 64 – Newcastle upon Tyne 16.

Raven Country H., Broomhill, DH8 6RY, Southeast : ¾ m. on B 6309 ✆ (01207) 56256 *enquiries@ravenhotel.co.uk, Fax (01207) 560262*, ← – rest, TV P – 120. MC AE VISA.
The Conservatory : **Meals** a la carte 10.00/24.00 **st.** 8.95 – **28 rm** 55.00/70.00 **st** 1 suite – SB.

ECCLES *Gtr. Manchester* 402 403 404 M 23 – *see Manchester.*

Les prix

Pour toutes précisions sur les prix indiqués dans ce guide, reportez-vous aux pages de l'introduction.

ECCLESHALL *Staffs.* 403 404 N 25 – *pop. 5 892.*
London 154 – Birmingham 37 – Stoke-on-Trent 13.

Julians, 21 High St, ST21 6BW, ✆ (01785) 851200, *Fax (01785) 859097* – . MC AE VISA
Meals 11.95 (lunch) and a la carte 18.10/28.15 **t.**

ECCLESTON *Lancs.* 402 L 23 – *pop. 5 003 (inc. Heskin).*
London 219 – Liverpool 29 – Birmingham 103 – Preston 11.

Parr Hall Farm without rest., Parr Lane, PR7 5SL, ✆ (01257) 451917, *parrhall@talk2 com, Fax (01257) 453749*, « Part 18C », , – TV P. MC VISA.
4 rm 30.00/50.00 **st.**

EDENBRIDGE *Kent* 404 U 30 *Great Britain G.* – *pop. 7 196.*
Env. : *Hever Castle* AC, E : 2½ m. – Chartwell* AC, N : 3 m. by B 2026.*
18, 18, 9 *Edenbridge G & C.C., Crouch House Rd ✆ (01732) 867381.*
London 35 – Brighton 36 – Maidstone 29.

Honours Mill, 87 High St, TN8 5AU, ✆ (01732) 866757, , « Renovated 18C mill » – MC VISA
closed 2 weeks Christmas, Monday, Sunday dinner and Saturday lunch – **Meals** 15.50 32.75 **t.** 10.15.

Haxted Mill, Haxted Rd, TN8 6PU, West : 2 ¼ m. on Haxted Rd ✆ (01732) 862914, *david haxtedmill.co.uk, Fax (01732) 865705*, , « Converted 17C stables, riverside setting », – P. MC VISA
closed 24 December-9 January, Monday, Tuesday and Sunday dinner – **Meals** a la cart 27.90/35.95 **t.** 13.40.

at Four Elms *Northeast : 2½ m. on B 2027* – ✉ *Edenbridge.*

Oak House Barn without rest., Mapleton Rd, TN8 6PL, Northwest : 1 m. off B 26 ✆ (01732) 700725, « Converted part 16C barn », – TV P.
closed December and New Year – **3 rm** 45.00/60.00 **t.**

EDGWORTH *Gtr. Manchester* 402 404 M 23 – *see Bolton.*

EGERTON *Gtr. Manchester* 402 ㉑ 403 ② 404 ⑨ – *see Bolton.*

EGGLESTON *Durham* 402 N/O 20 – *see Barnard Castle.*

EGHAM *Surrey* 404 S 29 – *pop. 23 816.*
London 29 – Reading 21.

Runnymede, Windsor Rd, TW20 0AG, on A 308 ☎ (01784) 436171, *info@runnymedehotel.com, Fax (01784) 436340,* « Riverside setting », – rm, P – 350. VISA
Meals – (see ***Left Bank*** below) – 13.95 – **177 rm** 162.00/225.00 **st.**, 3 suites – SB.

Great Fosters, Stroude Rd, TW20 9UR, South : 1 ¼ m. by B 388 ☎ (01784) 433822, *enquiries@greatfosters.co.uk, Fax (01784) 472455,* « Elizabethan mansion, gardens », heated, – rest, P – 100. VISA
Meals 22.50/30.00 and a la carte 34.45/47.70 **t.** 13.50 – 12.50 – **38 rm** 115.00/295.00 **t.**, 3 suites.

Left Bank (at Runnymede H.), Windsor Rd, TW20 0AG, on A 308 ☎ (01784) 437400, « Riverside setting », – P. VISA JCB
closed Saturday lunch and Sunday dinner – **Meals** 19.95/26.75 and a la carte 26.00/32.25 **t.** 9.50.

EGLINGHAM *Northd.* 401 402 O 17 – *see Alnwick.*

EIGHT ASH GREEN *Essex* 404 W 28 – *see Colchester.*

ELLAND *W. Yorks.* 402 O 22 – *pop. 10 931* – ✉ *Halifax.*
Hammerstones Leach Lane, Hullen Edge ☎ (01422) 372505.
London 204 – Bradford 12 – Burnley 29 – Leeds 17 – Manchester 30.

La Cachette, 31 Huddersfield Rd, HX5 9AN, ☎ (01422) 378833, *Fax (01422) 327567* – .
VISA
closed last 2 weeks July, 10 days Christmas and New Year, Sunday and Bank Holiday Mondays – **Meals** 14.95 (dinner) and a la carte 16.40/24.40 **st.** 8.95.

ELLESMERE PORT *Mersey.* 402 403 L 24 – *pop. 64 504.*
London 211 – Birkenhead 9 – Chester 9 – Liverpool 12 – Manchester 44.

Holiday Inn Ellesmere Port Chester, Centre Island, Waterways, Lower Mersey St, CH65 2AL, Northeast : 1 ½ m. by A 5032 (M 53 junction 9) ☎ (0151) 356 8111, *hiepsales@aol.com, Fax (0151) 356 8444,* ←, « Marina setting overlooking Boat Museum », – rm, rest, P – 120. VISA JCB
Waterways : Meals a la carte 16.50/26.50 **st.** 9.95 – 10.00 – **83 rm** 100.00/110.00.

ELSING *Norfolk* 404 X 25 – *pop. 261* – ✉ *East Dereham.*
London 118 – Cambridge 66 – King's Lynn 33 – Norwich 15.

Bartles Lodge without rest., Church St, NR20 3EA, ☎ (01362) 637177, – P. VISA
7 rm 27.00/46.00 **st.**

ELSLACK *N. Yorks.* 402 N 22 – *see Skipton.*

ELSTED *W. Sussex* 404 R 31 – *see Midhurst.*

ELSTOW *Beds.* 404 S 27 – *see Bedford.*

ELSTREE *Herts.* 404 T 29 – *pop. 2 196.*
Watling St. ☎ (020) 8953 6115.
London 10 – Luton 22.

Plan : see Greater London (North West) pp. 8 and 9

Edgwarebury, Barnet Lane, WD6 3RE, ☎ (020) 8953 8227, *edgwarebury@corushotels.com, Fax (020) 8207 3668,* – P – 80. VISA CT e
The Cavendish : Meals *(closed Saturday lunch)* a la carte 26.00/43.00 **st.** 13.50 – 12.75 – **47 rm** 130.00/215.00 **st.** – SB.

ELTERWATER *Cumbria* – *see Ambleside.*

ENGLAND

ELY Cambs. 404 U 26 *Great Britain G. – pop. 10 329.*

See : Cathedral★★ AC.
Exc. : Wicken Fen★, SE : 9 m. by A 10 and A 1123.
107 Cambridge Rd (01353) 662751.
Oliver Cromwell's House, 29 St Mary's St (01353) 662062.
London 74 – Cambridge 16 – Norwich 60.

Lamb, 2 Lynn Rd, CB7 4EJ, (01353) 663574, *Fax (01353) 662023* – rest, – 30
Meals 11.95/16.95 and a la carte 18.85/27.85 **t.** 10.00 – **32 rm** 70.00/95.00 **t.** – SB.

Travelodge, Witchford Rd, CB6 3NN, West : 1 m. on A 10/A 142 roundabout, Ely bypass (01353) 668499, *Fax (01353) 668499* – rm, . VISA JCB.
Meals (grill rest.) – **39 rm** 52.95 **t.**

at Littleport *North : 5 ¾ m. on A 10 – Ely.*

Fen House, 2 Lynn Rd, CB6 1QG, (01353) 860645 – . VISA
closed 1 week Christmas and Sunday-Tuesday – **Meals** (booking essential) (dinner only) 28.75 12.50.

at Little Thetford *South : 2 ¾ m. off A 10 – Ely.*

Springfields without rest., CB6 3HJ, North : ½ m. on A 10 (01353) 663637 *Fax (01353) 663130,* – .
closed Christmas – **3 rm** 40.00/50.00 **s.**

at Witchford *West : 3 m. by A 142 – Ely.*

Rosendale Lodge, 223 Main St, CB6 2HT, (01353) 667700, *Fax (01353) 667799,* VISA.
Meals (by arrangement) (communal dinning) 10.00 – **4 rm** 35.00/59.00 **st.**

at Sutton Gault *West : 8 m. by A 142 off B 1381 – Ely.*

Anchor Inn with rm, CB6 2BD, (01353) 778537, *anchorinnsg@aol.com Fax (01353) 776180,* , « Part 17C inn » – . VISA.
closed 25-26 December – **Meals** a la carte 19.00/25.95 **t.** 11.95 – **1 rm** 50.00/66.50 **t** 1 suite.

at Coveney *Northwest : 4 m. by West Fen rd – Ely.*

Hill House Farm without rest., 9 Main St, CB6 2DJ, (01353) 778369 *Fax (01353) 778369,* – . VISA.
closed Christmas – **3 rm** 30.00/50.00.

EMSWORTH *Hants.* 404 R 31 – *pop. 18 310 (inc. Southbourne).*

London 75 – Brighton 37 – Portsmouth 10.

Brookfield, 93-95 Havant Rd, PO10 7LF, East : 1 m. on A 259 (01243) 373363, *booking @brookfieldhotel.co.uk, Fax (01243) 376342,* – rm, rest, – 50. VISA.
closed 24 December-2 January – ***Hermitage :*** **Meals** 13.95/25.00 **t.** 12.00 – **40 rm** 60.00/150.00 **t.** – SB.

Travelodge, PO10 7RB, Northeast : 1 ½ m. on A 27 (eastbound carriageway) (01243) 370877 – rm, . VISA JCB.
Meals (grill rest.) – **36 rm** 52.95 **t.**

36 on the Quay (Farthing), 47 South St, The Quay, PO10 7EG, (01243) 375592 *Fax (01243) 375593,* – . VISA JCB
closed 1-20 January, last week October, Sunday, Bank Holidays and lunch Saturday and Monday – **Meals** (booking essential) 16.95/20.95 (lunch) and a la carte 35.95/43.95 **t.** 13.50
Spec. Sea bass with mussel cream sauce. Roast and braised guinea fowl with grilled figs. Chocolate délice with walnut cream.

Spencers, 36 North St, PO10 7DG, (01243) 372744, *Fax (01243) 372744* – . VISA
closed 24-26 December, Sunday and Bank Holiday Mondays – **Meals** (dinner only) a la carte 15.05/25.95 **t.** 11.00.

Fat Olives, 30 South St, PO10 7EH, (01243) 377914, *fatolives@lcmjm.fsnet.co.uk,* . VISA
closed 2 weeks Christmas and New Year, Sunday, Monday and Tuesday after Bank Holidays – **Meals** 14.50 (lunch) and a la carte 18.20/25.65 **t.** 10.95.

*Pour visiter une ville ou une région : utilisez les **Guides Verts Michelin.***

ENSTONE *Oxon.* 403 404 P 28 – *pop. 1 523* – ✉ *Chipping Norton.*
London 73 – Birmingham 48 – Gloucester 32 – Oxford 18.

Swan Lodge without rest., OX7 4NE, on A 44 ☏ (01608) 678736, *Fax (01608) 677963*, – TV P.
3 rm ☐ 40.00/50.00.

EPSOM *Surrey* 404 ㉚ – *pop. 64 405 (inc. Ewell).*
Longdown Lane South, Epsom Downs ☏ (01372) 721666 – Horton Park C.C., Hook Rd ☏ (020) 8393 8400.
London 17 – Guildford 16.

Chalk Lane, Chalk Lane, KT18 7BB, Southwest : ½ m. by A 24 and Woodcote Rd ☏ (01372) 721179, *chalklane@compuserve.com, Fax (01372) 727878* – TV P – 150. MC AE VISA
Meals *(closed Saturday lunch and Sunday dinner)* 12.50 (lunch) and a la carte 21.50/31.00 **t.** 13.50 – **22 rm** ☐ 85.00/150.00 **t.**

Travel Inn Metro, 2-4 St Margarets Drive, KT18 7LB, Southwest : ½ m. on A 24 ☏ (01372) 739786, *Fax (01372) 739761* – rm, rest, TV P – 40. MC AE VISA
Meals (grill rest.) – **40 rm** 49.95 **t.**

Le Raj, 211 Fir Tree Rd, Epsom Downs, KT19 3LB, Southeast : 2 ¼ m. by B 289 and B 284 on B 291 ☏ (01737) 371371, *booking@leraj.com, Fax (01737) 211903* – . MC AE VISA
closed 25 and 26 December – **Meals** - Indian - 20.00/30.00 and a la carte 19.95/35.45 **t.**

Per visitare una città o una regione : utilizzate le guide verdi Michelin.

ERPINGHAM *Norfolk* 404 X 25 – *pop. 1 871.*
London 123 – Cromer 8 – King's Lynn 46 – Norwich 16.

The Ark with rm, The Street, NR11 7QB, ☏ (01263) 761535, – TV P.
closed 2 weeks January, 3 weeks October and 25-26 December – **Meals** *(closed Sunday dinner and Monday)* (dinner only and Sunday lunch)/dinner 23.00/30.00 **t.** 11.75 – **3 rm** ☐ (dinner included) 75.00/140.00 **t.**

Saracen's Head with rm, Wolterton, NR11 7LX, West : 1 ½ m. ☏ (01263) 768909, *Fax (01263) 768993*, – rm, P. MC AE VISA
closed 25 December – **Meals** a la carte 16.45/21.50 **t.** 9.25 – **4 rm** ☐ 30.00/60.00 **t.** – SB.

ESCRICK *N. Yorks.* 402 Q 22 – *see York.*

ESHER *Surrey* 404 S 29 – *pop. 46 599 (inc. Molesey).*
Thames Ditton & Esher, Portsmouth Rd ☏ (020) 8398 1551 BZ – *Moore Place, Portsmouth Rd ☏ (01372) 463533* BZ – , *Sandown Park, More Lane ☏ (01372) 461234* BZ.
London 20 – Portsmouth 58.

Plan : see Greater London (South-West) p. 12

Good Earth, 14-18 High St, KT10 9RT, ☏ (01372) 462489, *Fax (01372) 460668* – . MC AE VISA BZ e
closed 23-30 December – **Meals** - Chinese - 12.00/28.50 and a la carte 7.50.

at Claygate *Southeast : 1 m. by A 244* – ✉ *Esher.*

Le Petit Pierrot, 4 The Parade, KT10 0NU, ☏ (01372) 465105, *Fax (01372) 467642* – MC AE VISA BZ r
closed 1 week Christmas, Saturday lunch, Sunday and Bank Holidays – **Meals** - French - 14.15/24.50 **t.** 11.50.

ESHOTT *Northd.* – *see Morpeth.*

EVERSHOT *Dorset* 403 404 M 31 – *pop. 225* – ✉ *Dorchester.*
London 149 – Bournemouth 39 – Dorchester 12 – Salisbury 53 – Taunton 30 – Yeovil 10.

Summer Lodge , Summer Lane, DT2 0JR, ☏ (01935) 83424, *reservations@summerlodgehotel.com, Fax (01935) 83005*, , « Part Georgian dower house », heated, , – rest, TV P. MC AE VISA JCB
Meals 15.50/39.50 and a la carte 36.25/42.75 12.75 – **17 rm** ☐ 135.00/285.00 **st.**, 1 suite – SB.

EVESHAM *Worcs.* 403 404 O 27 – *pop. 17 823.*

The Almonry, Abbey Gate (01386) 446944.

London 99 – Birmingham 30 – Cheltenham 16 – Coventry 32.

Wood Norton Hall, WR11 4YB, Northwest : 2 ¼ m. on A 4538 (01386) 420007, *woodnortonhall@bbc.co.uk, Fax (01386) 420190,* « Victorian country house », squash – rest. 70. VISA.
Duc's : Meals *(closed Saturday lunch)* (booking essential) 19.50/45.00 **st.** 15.50 – **44 rm** 125.00/170.00 **st.**, 1 suite – SB.

Evesham, Coopers Lane, WR11 6DA, off Waterside (01386) 765566, Reservations (Freephone) 0800 716969, *reception@eveshamhotel.com, Fax (01386) 765443,* – VISA
closed 25-26 December – **Meals** a la carte 17.00/22.50 **st.** 11.00 – **40 rm** 68.00/124.00 **st.** – SB.

Waterside, 56-59 Waterside, WR11 1JZ, (01386) 442420, *Fax (01386) 446272,* VISA
Meals (grill rest.) a la carte 12.20/20.55 **t.** 7.65 – **14 rm** 66.90/86.70 **t.** – SB.

Riverside, The Parks, Offenham Rd, WR11 5JP, Northeast : 2 m. by Waterside and B 4035 off B 4510 (01386) 446200, *riversidehotel@theparksoffenham.freeserve.co.uk, Fax (01386) 40021,* – rest, VISA.
closed 2 weeks January and 25 December – **Meals** *(closed Sunday dinner and Monday)* 19.95/29.95 and lunch a la carte 17.95/26.35 **st.** 12.95 – **7 rm** 65.00/95.00 **st.** – SB.

at Harvington *Northeast : 4½ m. by A 4184 and B 4088 off Bidford rd – Evesham.*

Mill at Harvington , Anchor Lane, WR11 5NR, Southeast : 1 ½ m. (01386) 870688, *millatharvington@aol.com, Fax (01386) 870688,* « 18C mill with riverside garden », heated, – rest, VISA.
closed 24-31 December – **Meals** 12.95/34.95 and a la carte 15.95/25.95 **t.** 11.95 – **21 rm** 66.00/129.00 **t.** – SB.

at Abbot's Salford *(Warks.) Northeast : 5 m. by A 4184 and B 4088 on Bidford rd – Evesham.*

Salford Hall, WR11 5UT, (01386) 871300, *reception@salfordhall.co.uk, Fax (01386) 871301,* « Tudor mansion with early 17C extension and gatehouse », – rest, – 50. VISA JCB.
closed 24-30 December – ***Stanford Room :*** **Meals** *(closed Saturday lunch)* 15.95/32.50 **t.** 12.95 – **34 rm** 85.00/140.00 **t.** – SB.

EWELL *Surrey* 404 T 29 – *pop. 4 862.*

London 13 – Crawley 26 – Guildford 22.

Plan : see Greater London (South-West) p. 13

Premier Lodge, 272 Kingston Rd, KT19 0SH, (020) 8393 2666, *Fax (020) 8394 1780* – rm, VISA. CZ
Meals (grill rest.) 11.75 and a la carte approx. 11.95 **t.** 8.95 – **29 rm** 54.95 **t.**

EWEN *Glos.* 403 404 O 28 – *see Cirencester.*

EXETER *Devon* 403 J 31 *The West Country G.* – *pop. 94 717.*

See : *City★★ - Cathedral★★* Z – *Royal Albert Memorial Museum★* Y.

Exc. : *Killerton★★* ***AC****, NE : 7 m. by B 3181* V – *Ottery St Mary★ (St Mary's★) E : 12 m. by B 3183* – Y – *A 30 and B 3174 – Crediton (Holy Cross Church★), NW : 9 m. by A 377.*

Downes Crediton, Hookway (01363) 773991.

Exeter Airport : (01392) 367433, E : 5 m. by A 30 V – **Terminal :** *St. David's and Central Stations.*

Civic Centre, Paris St (01392) 265700.

London 201 – Bournemouth 83 – Bristol 83 – Plymouth 46 – Southampton 110.

Plans on following pages

Southgate, Southernhay East, EX1 1QF, (0870) 4008333, *sales.southgate@heritage-hotels.com, Fax (01392) 413549,* – – 150. VISA Z
Meals *(closed Saturday lunch)* 22.00 (dinner) and a la carte 20.90/31.70 13.00 – 12.95 – **109 rm** 115.00 **st.**, 1 suite – SB.

Thistle Exeter, Queen St, EX4 3SP, (01392) 254982, *iain.mcguigan@thistle.co.uk, Fax (01392) 420928* – , rm, rest, – 300. VISA Y
Meals (bar lunch)/dinner 19.50 and a la carte 16.25/26.20 **st.** 12.50 – 9.50 – **88 rm** 109.00/119.00 **st.**, 2 suites – SB.

EXETER

BUILT UP AREA

ʼlackboy Road .... V 8
ʼuddle Lane .... X 9
ʼutts Road................. X 12
ast Wonford Hill.......... X 17
ʼeavitree Road .... VX 20
Hill Lane..................... V 21
Marsh Barton Road .... X 25
Mount Pleasant Road ...... V 29
North Street
HEAVITREE .... X 32
Old Tiverton Road.......... V 35
Polsloe Road .... V 39
Prince Charles Road........ V 41
Prince of Wales Road ...... V 42
St. Andrew's Road.......... V 48
Summer Lane .... V 51
Sweetbriar Lane .... VX 52
Trusham Road.............. X 53
Union Road .... V 54
Whipton Lane .... X 55
Wonford Road............... X 57
Wonford Street............. X 58
Woodwater Lane .... X 60

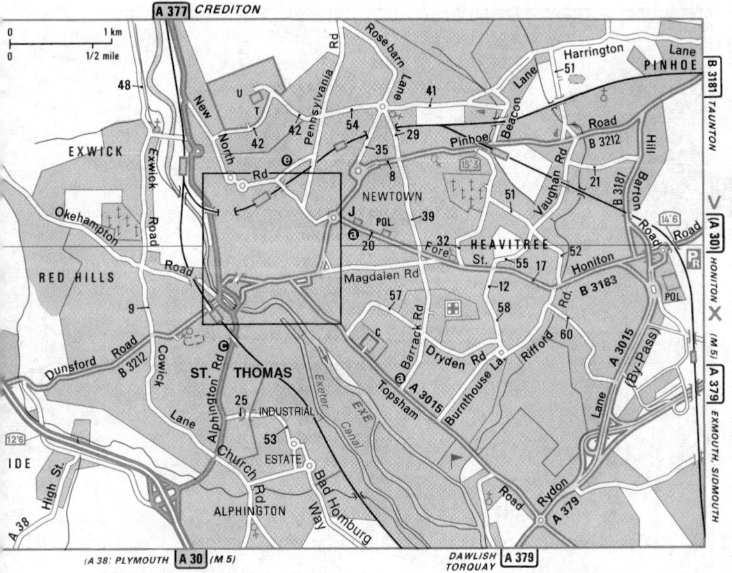

Barcelona, Magdalen St, EX2 4HY, ✆ (01392) 281000, *info@hotelbarcelona-uk.com, Fax (01392) 281001,* « Contemporary interior » – lift, ⇔ rest, TV ✆ P – 35. MC AE ① VISA Z s
Café Paradiso : **Meals** a la carte 16.00/28.40 **t.** 10.50 – ☐ 10.50 – **46 rm** 70.00/90.00 **t.** – SB.

Royal Clarence, Cathedral Yard, EX1 1HD, ✆ (01392) 319955, *Fax (01392) 439423* – lift ⇔ TV – 120. MC AE ① VISA Y z
St Martin's Cafe Bar : **Meals** 18.00/20.00 (lunch) and a la carte 21.95/30.70 **t.** 13.50 – (see also ***Michael Caines*** below) – ☐ 9.95 – **56 rm** 105.00/130.00 **st.**, 1 suite – SB.

Buckerell Lodge, Topsham Rd, EX2 4SQ, ✆ (01392) 221111, *Fax (01392) 491111,* – ⇔ TV & P – 80. MC AE ① VISA JCB X a
Meals *(closed lunch Saturday and Sunday)* 9.95/19.95 and dinner a la carte 15.65/23.25 **t.** 11.95 – ☐ 10.50 – **53 rm** 84.00/116.00 **t.** – SB.

The Queens Court, Bystock Terr, EX4 4HY, ✆ (01392) 272709, *office@queenscourt-hotel.co.uk, Fax (01392) 491390,* – lift ⇔ TV P – 50. MC AE ① VISA Y n
Olive Tree : **Meals** - Mediterranean - *(closed lunch Sunday and Bank Holidays)* a la carte 15.50/28.00 **t.** 10.00 – ☐ 6.00 – **18 rm** 59.00/69.00 **t.** – SB.

Gipsy Hill , Gipsy Hill Lane, via Pinn Lane, EX1 3RN, East : 2 m. by Honiton Rd (A 30) off Gipsy Hill rd (junction 29 M 5) ✆ (01392) 465252, *gipsyhill@bestwestern.co.uk, Fax (01392) 464302,* – ⇔ rest, TV P – 120. MC AE ① VISA JCB
closed 24-30 December – **Meals** 9.00/17.50 and a la carte **st.** 10.25 – **37 rm** ☐ 80.00/103.00 **st.** – SB.

St Olaves, Mary Arches St, EX4 3AZ, ✆ (01392) 217736, *info@olaves.co.uk, Fax (01392) 413054,* – TV P. MC AE VISA Z e
Meals – (see ***The Restaurant*** below) – ☐ 8.00 – **13 rm** 95.00/145.00 **t.**, 2 suites – SB.

Devon, Matford, EX2 8XU, South : 3 m. by A 377 on A 379 ✆ (01392) 259268, *info@devonhotel.co.uk, Fax (01392) 413142* – ⇔ rest, TV P – 160. MC AE ① VISA
Meals 12.00/19.50 and a la carte 20.00/25.00 **st.** 10.00 – ☐ 10.00 – **41 rm** 49.00/69.00 **st.** – SB.

EXETER CENTRE

Alphington Rd . . . . Z 2
Barnfield Rd . . . . Z 3
Bedford St. . . . . Y 4
Castle St. . . . . Y 13
Cathedral Close Walk . . . . . YZ 14
Cowick St. . . . . Z 15
Edmund St. . . . . Z 18
Fore St. . . . . Z
Guildhall Shopping Centre . . . Y
Harlequins Shopping Centre . Y
High St. . . . . Y
King St. . . . . Z 22
Mary Arches St. . . . . Z 26
Mint (The) . . . . Z 28
New Bridge St. . . . . Z 3
Palace Gate . . . . Z 3
Paul St. . . . . Y 3
Preston St. . . . . Z 4
Princesshay . . . . Y 4
Quay Hill . . . . Z 4
Queen's Terrace . . . . Y 4
St. Martin's Lane . . . . Y 4
Stepcote Hill. . . . . Z 5

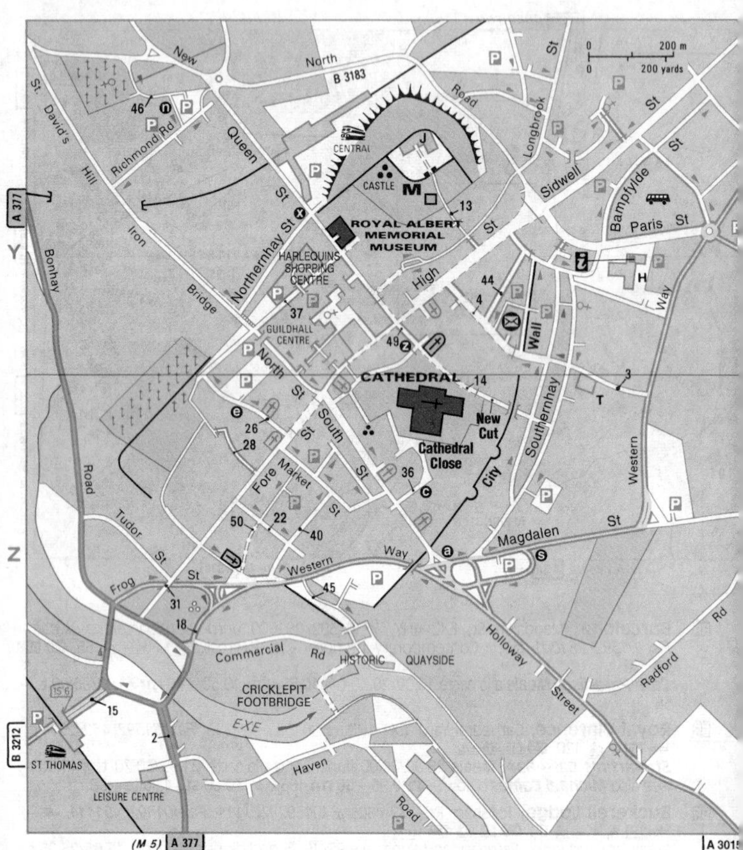

St Andrews, 28 Alphington Rd, EX2 8HN, ✆ (01392) 276784, *Fax (01392) 250249* X
rest, TV, P. *closed 23 December-3 January* – **Meals** (booking essential Friday-Sunday) (dinner only) a la carte 13.05/22.25 t. – **17 rm** 45.00/65.00 t.

Express by Holiday Inn without rest., Exeter Business Park, EX1 3PE, East : 2 ¾ m. on Honiton Rd (A 30) (junction 29 M 5) ✆ (01392) 261000, *Fax (01392) 261061* – TV, P. – 30.
122 rm 54.00 t.

The Edwardian without rest., 30-32 Heavitree Rd, EX1 2LQ, ✆ (01392) 276102 V
edwardex@globalnet.co.uk, Fax (01392) 253393 – TV.
closed 25-26 December – **12 rm** 36.00/58.00 st.

The Grange without rest., Stoke Hill, EX4 7JH, North : 1 ¾ m. by Old Tiverton R
✆ (01392) 259723, *dudleythegrange@aol.com*, heated, – TV P.
3 rm 28.00/42.00 t.

Raffles, 11 Blackall Rd, EX4 4HD, ☎ (01392) 270200, *raffleshtl@btinternet.com, Fax (01392) 270200* – TV. MC AE VISA JCB V e
Meals (by arrangement) 16.00 **st.** 8.50 **7 rm** 34.00/50.00 **st.** – SB.

Michael Caines (at Royal Clarence H.), Cathedral Yard, EX1 1HD, ☎ (01392) 310031, *tables@michaelcaines.com, Fax (01392) 310032* – . MC AE VISA Y z
Meals 18.00 (lunch) and a la carte 22.00/30.00 13.50.

The Restaurant (at St Olaves H.), Mary Arches St, EX4 3AZ, ☎ (01392) 217736, *info@olaves.co.uk, Fax (01392) 413054,* – P. MC AE VISA Z e
Meals 23.00 and a la carte 16.40/26.50 **t.**

Brazz, 10-12 Palace Gate, EX1 1JA, ☎ (01392) 252525, *Fax (01392) 253045* – . MC AE VISA Z c
closed 25 December – **Meals** 14.95 (dinner) and a la carte 15.40/27.40 **t.** 10.50.

at Stoke Canon *North : 5 m. by A 377 off A 396 – V – ✉ Exeter.*

Barton Cross, Huxham, EX5 4EJ, East : ½ m. on Huxham rd ☎ (01392) 841245, *bartonxhuxham@aol.com, Fax (01392) 841942,* « Part 17C thatched cottages », – rest, TV P. MC AE VISA JCB
Meals (dinner only) 16.50/25.00 and a la carte 20.00/29.50 **t.** 9.50 – **8 rm** 65.50/120.00 **t.** – SB.

at Whimple *Northeast : 9 m. by A 30 – V – ✉ Exeter.*

Woodhayes without rest., EX5 2TD, ☎ (01404) 822237, *res@woodhayes-hotel.co.uk, Fax (01404) 822337,* « Georgian country house », – TV P. MC AE VISA JCB.
March-November – **6 rm** 55.00/90.00 **t.**

at Kennford *South : 5 m. on A 30 off A 38 – X – ✉ Exeter.*

Fairwinds, EX6 7UD, ☎ (01392) 832911, *Fax (01392) 832911* – TV P. MC VISA.
closed November-mid January – **Meals** (residents only) (dinner only) a la carte 13.95/16.20 8.50 – **6 rm** 37.00/58.00 – SB.

at Doddiscombsleigh *Southwest : 10 m. by B 3212 off B 3193 – X – ✉ Exeter.*

Nobody Inn, EX6 7PS, ☎ (01647) 252394, *inn-nobody@virgin.net, Fax (01647) 252978,* « Part 16C », – P. MC AE VISA
closed 25-26 December – **Meals** a la carte 15.30/18.70 8.00.

EXETER SERVICE AREA *Devon* 403 J 31 – ✉ *Exeter.*

Travelodge, Moor Lane, Sandygate, EX2 7HF, M 5 junction 30 ☎ (01392) 274044, *Fax (01392) 410406* – rm, TV P – 30. MC AE VISA JCB.
Meals (grill rest.) – **74 rm** 59.95 **t.**

EXFORD *Somerset* 403 J 30 *The West Country G.*
See : *Church*★.
Env. : *Exmoor National Park*★★.
London 193 – Exeter 41 – Minehead 14 – Taunton 33.

Crown, TA24 7PP, ☎ (01643) 831554, *Fax (01643) 831665,* « Attractively furnished country inn, water garden », – TV P. MC AE VISA
Meals (in bar) a la carte 13.00/16.00 **t.** 11.95 – (see also ***The Restaurant*** below) – **17 rm** 55.00/110.00 **t.** – SB.

The Restaurant (at Crown H.), TA24 7PP, ☎ (01643) 831554, *Fax (01643) 831665* – P. MC AE VISA
Meals (dinner only and Sunday lunch)/dinner 25.00 and a la carte 25.00/32.95 **t.** 11.95.

EXMOUTH *Devon* 403 J 32 *The West Country G. – pop. 30 386.*
Env. : *A la Ronde*★ *AC, N : 2 m. by B 3180.*
Alexandra Terr ☎ (01395) 222299.
London 210 – Exeter 11.

Barn, Foxholes Hill, EX8 2DF, East : 1 m. via Esplanade and Queens Drive ☎ (01395) 224411, *info@barnhotel.co.uk, Fax (01395) 225445,* heated, – TV P – 100. MC AE VISA.
closed 23 December-7 January – **Meals** (dinner only and Sunday lunch)/dinner 16.00 **st.** 10.50 – **11 rm** 37.00/74.00 **st.**

The Seafood, 9 Tower St, EX8 1NT, ☎ (01395) 269459, *seafoodexmouth@aol.com* – MC VISA
closed Sunday-Monday – **Meals** - Seafood - (dinner only) a la carte 22.40/25.55 **t.** 9.95.

EYNSHAM *Oxon.* 403 404 P 28 – *pop. 4 764.*
London 65 – Gloucester 40 – Oxford 8.

XX **Off the Square,** 4 Lombard St, OX8 1HT, ☎ (01865) 881888, *christiano.butler@virgin.ne*
Fax (01865) 883537 – ⊁ P. MC VISA
closed Sunday dinner and Monday – **Meals** a la carte 18.00/26.95 **t.** 11.95.

FADMOOR *N. Yorks. – see Kirkbymoorside.*

FAKENHAM *Norfolk* 404 W 25 – *pop. 6 471.*
Fakenham, The Racecourse ☎ (01328) 862867.
Red Lion House, Market Pl ☎ (01328) 851981.
London 111 – Cambridge 64 – Norwich 27.

Sculthorpe Mill ⑤, Lynn Rd, Sculthorpe, NR21 9QG, West : 2 ½ m. by A 14 ☎ (01328) 856161, *Fax (01328) 856651*, ≤, « Converted late 18C watermill », – ⊁ P. MC AE ① VISA
Meals a la carte 12.90/22.90 **t.** 9.75 – **6 rm** 55.00/70.00 **t.**

FALFIELD *South Gloucestershire* 403 404 M 29.
London 132 – Bristol 16 – Gloucester 22.

Gables, Bristol Rd, GL12 8DL, North : ½ m. on A 38 ☎ (01454) 260502, *Fax (01454) 26182*
Fö, ≘s – ⊁ rest, TV ☏ & P – 150. MC AE ① VISA. ⊁
Meals *(closed Sunday dinner)* (bar lunch Monday-Saturday)/dinner 16.50 and a la cart 19.50/25.00 **st.** 9.25 – 7.75 – **46 rm** 72.50 **st.**

FALMOUTH *Cornwall* 403 E 33 *The West Country G. – pop. 19 217.*
See : *Town★ – Pendennis Castle★ (≤★★) AC* B.
Env. : *Glendurgan Garden★★ AC – Trebah Garden★, SW : 4 ½ m. by Swanpool Rd* A *Mawnan Parish Church★ (≤★★) S : 4 m. by Swanpool Rd* A *– Cruise along Helford River★.*
Exc. : *Trelissick★★ (≤★★) NW : 13 m. by A 39 and B 3289* A *– Carn Brea (≤★★) NW : 10 m. b A 393* A *– Gweek (Setting★, Seal Sanctuary★) SW : 8 m. by A 39 and Treverva rd – Wendro (Poldark Mine★) AC, SW : 12½ m. by A 39 –* A *– and A 394.*
Swanpool Rd ☎ (01326) 311262 A *– Budock Vean Hotel, Mawnan Smith ☎ (0132 250892.*
28 Killigrew St ☎ (01326) 312300.
London 308 – Penzance 26 – Plymouth 65 – Truro 11.

Plan opposite

Royal Duchy, Cliff Rd, TR11 4NX, ☎ (01326) 313042, *info@royalduchy.co.u Fax (01326) 319420*, ≤, ≘s, , – TV P. MC AE ① VISA. ⊁ B
Meals 11.50/24.00 and a la carte 30.00/41.00 **st.** 9.00 – **42 rm** 75.00/200.00 **st.**, 1 suit – SB.

Greenbank, Harbourside, TR11 2SR, ☎ (01326) 312440, *thegreenbankhotel@btinterne com, Fax (01326) 211362*, ≤ harbour – ⊁ TV ☏ P. MC AE ① VISA A
Harbourside : **Meals** 10.00/12.00 (lunch) and a la carte 18.25/24.25 **st.** 12.50 – **60 rr** 57.00/145.00 **st.**, 1 suite – SB.

Penmere Manor ⑤, Mongleath Rd, TR11 4PN, ☎ (01326) 211411, *reservatior @penmere.co.uk, Fax (01326) 317588*, ≘s, heated, , – ⊁ TV P – 60. MC AE ① VISA A
closed 24 to 27 December – ***Bolitho's :*** **Meals** (bar lunch)/dinner 17.50/23.00 **st.** 9.00 **37 rm** 64.00/130.00 **st.** – SB.

Prospect House without rest., 1 Church Rd, Penryn, TR10 8DA, Northwest : 2 m. b A 39 on B 3292 ☎ (01326) 373198, *bbudd@freeuk.com, Fax (01326) 373198*, – P. MC VIS **3 rm** 30.00/60.00 **s.**

Rosemullion without rest., Gyllyngvase Hill, TR11 4DF, ☎ (01326) 314690, *gail@ros mullionhotel.demon.co.uk, Fax (01326) 210098* – ⊁ TV P. ⊁ B
closed Christmas – **13 rm** 26.50/52.00 **t.**

Melvill House, 52 Melvill Rd, TR11 4DQ, ☎ (01326) 316645, *enquiries@melvill-house falmouth.co.uk, Fax (01326) 211608* – ⊁ TV P. MC VISA JCB. ⊁ B
closed Christmas **Meals** (by arrangement) 10.50 **st.** 7.50 – **7 rm** 25.00/50.00 **st.**

Dolvean without rest., 50 Melvill Rd, TR11 4DQ, ☎ (01326) 313658, *reservations@dolvear freeserve.co.uk, Fax (01326) 313995* – ⊁ TV P. MC AE VISA JCB. ⊁ B
– **10 rm** 35.00/80.00 **st.**

Chelsea House, 2 Emslie Rd, TR11 4BG, ☎ (01326) 212230, *info@chelseahousehote com, Fax (01326) 212230*, ≤, – ⊁ TV P. MC VISA. ⊁ B
March-October – **Meals** (by arrangement) 10.00 **st.** 5.95 – **7 rm** 25.00/56.00 **st.** – SB.

FALMOUTH

Arwenack Street . . . . B 2
Avenue Road . . . . B 3
Beacon Road . . . . A 4
Belmont Road . . . . A 7
Berkeley Vale . . . . A 8
Boscawen Road . . . . A 9
Budock Terrace . . . . A 13
Church Street . . . . B
Conway Road . . . . A 14
Emslie Road . . . . B 18
Fenwick Road . . . . A 19
Glasney Road . . . . A 20
Grovehill Crescent . . . . . B 23
Gyllyngvase Hill . . . . . . B 24
Gyllyngvase Road . . . . . B 25
High Street . . . . A
Kimberley Place . . . . . . A 28
Langton Road . . . . A 29
Madeira Walk . . . . A 30
Market Street . . . . A 33
Crescent . . . . A 34
Park Terrace . . . . A 35
Pendennis Road . . . . B 38
Swanpool Road . . . . A 39
Symons Hill . . . . A 40
Tredova Crescent . . . . . . A 43
Trescobeas Road . . . . . . A 44
Wellington Terrace . . . . . A 45
Windsor Terrace . . . . . . A 48
Wodehouse Terrace . . . . . A 49

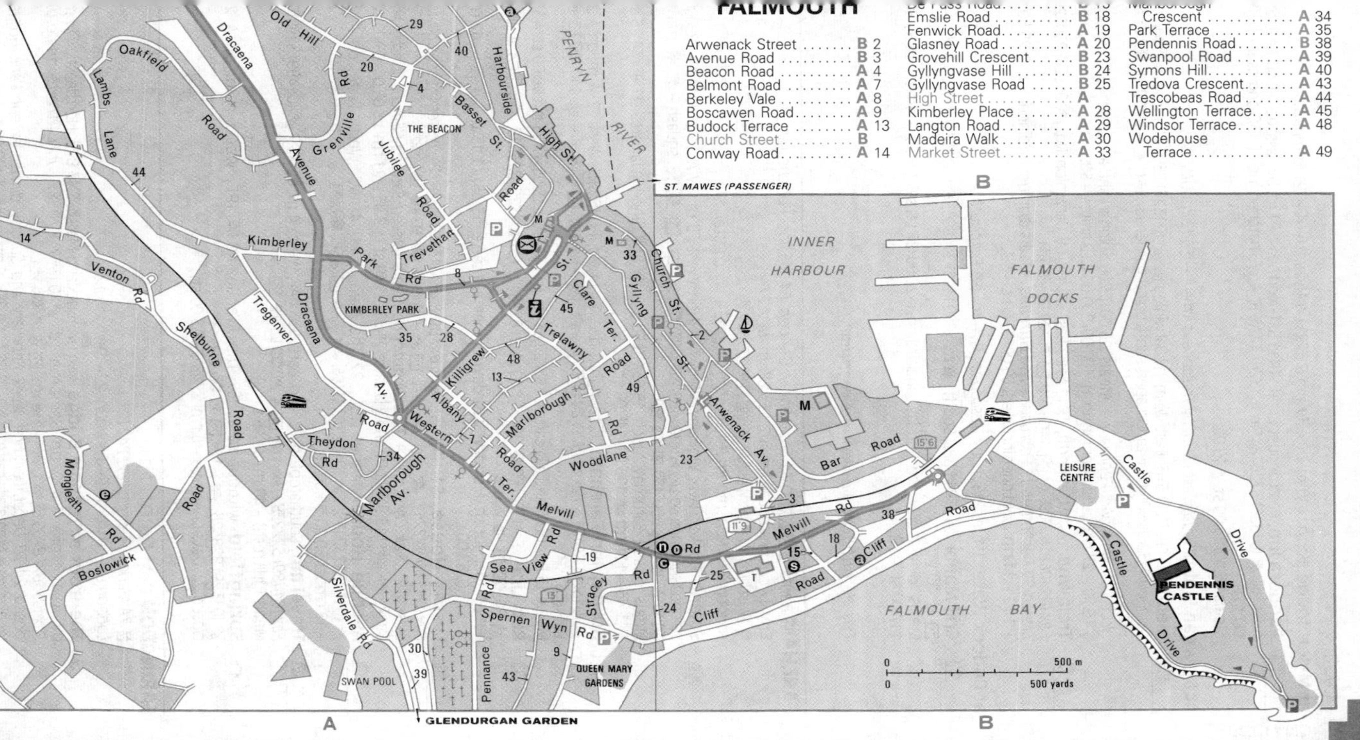

at Mylor Bridge *North : 4½ m. by A 39 and B 3292 on Mylor rd* – **A** – ✉ *Falmouth.*

Pandora Inn, Restronguet Creek, TR11 5ST, Northeast : 1 m. by Passage Hill off Restronguet Hill ✆ (01326) 372678, *Fax (01326) 372678*, ←, « Thatched inn of 13C origins » – VISA
Meals 15.00/25.00 **st.** 10.00.

at Mawnan Smith *Southwest : 5 m. by Trescobeas Rd* – **A** – ✉ *Falmouth.*

Meudon, TR11 5HT, East : ½ m. by Carwinion Rd ✆ (01326) 250541, *info@meudon.co.uk, Fax (01326) 250543*, « Landscaped sub-tropical gardens », – TV P. AE VISA
closed 2 January-1 February – **Meals** 25.00/33.00 (dinner) and a la carte 15.00/33.00 13.00 – **27 rm** (dinner included) 100.00/200.00 **t.**, 2 suites – SB.

Trelawne, Maenporth, TR11 5HS, East : ¾ m. by Carwinion Rd ✆ (01326) 25022 *Fax (01326) 250909*, ←, – TV P. AE VISA
closed 22 December-11 February – ***The Hutches :*** **Meals** (bar lunch)/dinner 19.50/25.50 9.90 – **14 rm** (dinner included) 69.00/85.00 **t.** – SB.

at Budock Water *West : 2¼ m. by Trescobeas Rd* – **A** – ✉ *Falmouth.*

Crill Manor, TR11 5BL, South : ¾ m. ✆ (01326) 211880, *Fax (01326) 211229*, – TV P. VISA.
Meals (dinner only and Sunday lunch)/dinner 20.00/22.00 **st.** 9.75 – **14 rm** 58.50 117.00 **st.** – SB.

Pas de publicité payée dans ce guide.

FAREHAM *Hants.* 403 404 Q 31 *Great Britain G. – pop. 54 866 (inc. Portchester).*
Env. : *Portchester castle* AC, SE : 2½ m. by A 27.*
Westbury Manor, West St ✆ (01329) 221342.
London 77 – Portsmouth 9 – Southampton 13 – Winchester 19.

Solent, Rookery Ave, Whiteley, PO15 7AJ, Northwest : 5 m. by A 27 ✆ (01489) 88000 *solent@shireinns.co.uk, Fax (01489) 880007*, squash – rm, TV – 250. AE VISA
Meals closed Saturday lunch 16.95/19.50 (lunch) and dinner a la carte 27.95/34.25 **s** 13.45 – **111 rm** 125.00/145.00 **st.** – SB.

Holiday Inn Fareham, Cartwright Drive, Titchfield, PO15 5RJ, West : 2 ¾ m. on A 2 ✆ (01329) 844012, *Fax (01329) 844666*, – rm, TV P – 140. AE VISA JCB.
Meals 13.50/15.00 and a la carte 20.65/28.65 **st.** 11.95 – 13.95 – **125 rm** 98.00 **st.** – S

Red Lion, East St, PO16 0BP, ✆ (01329) 822640, *Fax (01329) 823579*, – TV P 80. AE VISA.
Meals (bar lunch Monday-Saturday)/dinner a la carte 13.35/21.15 **t.** 8.95 – **42 r** 64.50/87.00 **t.**

Lysses House, 51 High St, PO16 7BQ, ✆ (01329) 822622, *lysses@lysses.co.u* *Fax (01329) 822762*, – rest, TV P – 100. AE VISA.
closed 1 week Christmas – ***The Richmond :*** **Meals** *(closed Saturday lunch, Sunday ar Bank Holidays)* 13.95/21.00 and a la carte 21.35/23.40 **st.** 9.95 – **21 rm** 68.00/85.00 **st**

Avenue House without rest., 22 The Avenue, PO14 1NS, West : ½ m. on A 2 ✆ (01329) 232175, *Fax (01329) 232196*, – TV P. VISA
– **19 rm** 50.00/55.00 **st.**

Travel Inn, Southampton Rd, Park Gate, SO3 6AF, West : 4 m. by A 27 ✆ (01489) 57985 *Fax (01489) 577238* – rm, TV P. AE VISA.
Meals (grill rest.) – **40 rm** 41.95 **t.**

Springfield without rest., 67 The Avenue, PO14 1PE, West : 1 m. on A 2 ✆ (01329) 828325, – TV P. VISA.
closed 2 weeks Christmas – **6 rm** 45.00/55.00 **st.**

FARINGDON *Oxon.* 403 404 P 29.
7A Market Pl ✆ (01367) 242191.
London 81 – Oxford 19 – Newbury 29 – Swindon 12.

The Trout at Tadpole Bridge with rm, Buckland Marsh, SN7 8RF, Northeast : 4 ½ m by A 417 off A 420 on Bampton rd ✆ (01367) 870382, *info@trout-inn.co.u* *Fax (01367) 870515*, – rm, TV P. VISA
closed 24-30 December, first week February and Sunday dinner except Bank Holida weekends – **Meals** a la carte 15.50/25.65 **t.** 9.25 – **6 rm** 55.00/80.00 **t.**

at Littleworth *Northeast : 3 m. by A 417 off A 420 – ✉ Faringdon.*

The Snooty Fox Inn, SN7 8PW, on A 420 ☎ (01367) 240549, – P. VISA
closed 25-26 December – **Meals** a la carte 15.95/22.40 **t.** 11.00.

FARNBOROUGH *Hants.* 404 R 30 – *pop. 52 535.*

Southwood, Ively Rd ☎ (01252) 548700.
London 41 – Reading 17 – Southampton 44 – Winchester 33.

Posthouse Farnborough, Lynchford Rd, GU14 6AZ, South : 1 ½ m. on A 325 ☎ (0870) 400 9029, *Fax (01252) 377210,* – rm, rest, P – 110. AE VISA.
Meals *(closed Saturday lunch)* 15.00 (lunch) and a la carte approx. 17.50 10.00 – 13.95 – **143 rm** 139.00 **st.** – SB.

Falcon, 68 Farnborough Rd, GU14 6TH, South : ¾ m. on A 325 ☎ (01252) 545378, *falcon@meridianleisure.com, Fax (01252) 522539* – P. AE VISA JCB.
Meals *(closed lunch Saturday and Sunday)* closed 24 December-1 January 14.95/20.00 and a la carte 14.45/20.75 **st.** 9.75 – **30 rm** 86.00/99.00 **st.**

Travel Inn, Ively Rd, Southwood, GU14 0JP, Southwest : 2 m. by A 325 on A 327 ☎ (01252) 546654, *Fax (01252) 546427* – rm, P. AE VISA JCB.
Meals (grill rest.) – **40 rm** 41.95 **t.**

Wings Cottage, 32 Alexandra Rd, GU14 6DA, South : 1 ¼ m. by A 325 off Boundary Rd ☎ (01252) 544141, *Fax (01252) 519071* – . AE VISA JCB
closed lunch Saturday and Sunday – **Meals** - Chinese - 20.00/25.00 and a la carte 26.00/32.00 **st.** 9.95.

FARNHAM *Dorset* 403 N 31 – *see Blandford Forum.*

FARNHAM *Surrey* 404 R 30 – *pop. 36 178.*

Farnham Park (Par Three) ☎ (01252) 715216.
Council Offices, South St ☎ (01252) 715109.
London 45 – Reading 22 – Southampton 39 – Winchester 28.

Bishop's Table, 27 West St, GU9 7DR, ☎ (01252) 710222, *welcome@bishopstable.com, Fax (01252) 733494,* – rest, . AE VISA.
closed 25 December-5 January – **Meals** *(closed lunch Monday)* 10.50/16.50 and a la carte 26.45/35.95 **t.** 10.95 – **17 rm** 95.00/165.00 **t.** – SB.

FAR SAWREY *Cumbria* 402 L 20 – *see Hawkshead.*

FAVERSHAM *Kent* 404 W 30 – *pop. 17 070.*

Fleur de Lis Heritage Centre, 13 Preston St ☎ (01795) 534542.
London 52 – Dover 26 – Maidstone 21 – Margate 25.

Preston Lea without rest., Canterbury Rd, ME13 8XA, East : 1 m. on A 2 ☎ (01795) 535266, *preston.lea@which.net, Fax (01795) 533388,* « Late 19C neo-Gothic house », – P. VISA JCB.
3 rm 40.00/60.00 **st.**

Read's (Pitchford) with rm, Macknade Manor, Canterbury Rd, ME13 8XE, East : 1 m. on A 2 ☎ (01795) 535344, *enquiries@reads.com, Fax (01795) 591200,* « Georgian house », – P. AE VISA JCB.
closed Sunday and Monday – **Meals** 18.50/38.00 **t.** 16.00 – **6 rm** 95.00/150.00 **t.**
Spec. Smoked eel with baby beetroot and chives. Prime cuts of Kentish lamb. "Harvey Wallbanger" soufflé.

at Dargate *East : 6 m. by A 2 off A 299 – ✉ Faversham.*

Dove Inn, Plum Pudding Lane, ME13 9HB, ☎ (01227) 751360, *Fax (01227) 751360,* – P. VISA JCB
closed Monday and dinner Sunday and Tuesday – **Meals** (booking essential) a la carte 19.50/25.00 **st.** 10.00.

at Boughton *Southeast : 3 m. by A 2 – ✉ Faversham.*

The Garden, 167-169 The Street, ME13 9BH, ☎ (01227) 751411, *garden-hotel@lineone.net, Fax (01227) 751801,* – rest, P. AE VISA
closed 27-31 December – **Meals** *(closed Sunday dinner)* 14.95 and a la carte 18.50/34.00 **t.** 11.25 – **10 rm** 60.00/80.00 **t.** – SB.

ENGLAND

at Eastling *Southwest : 5 m. by A 2 – ✉ Faversham.*

Frith Farm House , Otterden, ME13 0DD, Southwest : 2 m. by Otterden rd o Newnham rd ☎ (01795) 890701, *enquiries@frithfarmhouse.co.uk, Fax (01795) 890009,* – ▣ P. VISA.
Meals (by arrangement) (communal dining) 17.50 – **3 rm** 38.00/64.00 **st.** – SB.

FAWKHAM GREEN *Kent* 404 ㊹ *– see Brands Hatch.*

FEERING *Essex* 404 W 28.
London 56 – Braintree 10 – Chelmsford 23 – Colchester 14.

Travelodge, London Rd, CO5 9EL, on A 12 (northbound carriageway) ☎ (01376) 57284[illegible] *Fax (01376) 572848* – rm, ▣ & P. AE VISA JCB.
Meals (grill rest.) – **39 rm** 49.95 **t.**

FELIXSTOWE *Suffolk* 404 Y 28 – *pop. 28 606.*
18, 9 Felixstowe Ferry, Ferry Rd ☎ (01394) 283060.
The Seafront, Undercliff Road West ☎ (01394) 276770.
London 84 – Ipswich 11.

Orwell, Hamilton Rd, IP11 7DX, ☎ (01394) 285511, *welcome@orwellhotel.co.u[illegible] Fax (01394) 670687,* – , rest, ▣ P – 250. AE VISA.
Meals 16.50/18.50 and a la carte 24.00/34.00 **st.** 12.00 – 9.50 – **57 rm** 65.00/80.00 **t** 1 suite – SB.

FELTON *Herefordshire* 403 404 M 27 – *pop. 93.*
London 130 – Birmingham 54 – Hereford 14 – Shrewsbury 50 – Worcester 27.

Felton House without rest., HR1 3PH, ☎ (01432) 820366, *bandb@ereal.ne[illegible] Fax (01432) 820366,* – P
– **4 rm** 25.00/50.00 **s.**

FERMAIN BAY *Guernsey (Channel Islands)* 403 P 33 and 230 ⑩ *– see Channel Islands.*

FERNDOWN *Dorset* 403 404 O 31 – *pop. 25 177.*
18 Ferndown Forest, Forest Links Rd ☎ (01202) 876096.
London 108 – Bournemouth 6 – Dorchester 27 – Salisbury 23.

The Dormy, New Rd, BH22 8ES, on A 347 ☎ (01202) 872121, *devere.dormy@airtim[illegible] co.uk, Fax (01202) 895388,* , , , 18, , , squash – , ▣ & P – 250. AE VISA
Hennessys : **Meals** *(closed lunch Saturday, Sunday and Monday)* (dancing Saturda[illegible] evening) 12.50/30.00 and a la carte 28.90/37.45 – ***Garden :*** **Meals** (carvery) 19.50/25.00 **s[illegible]** 11.00 – ***Pavilion Brasserie :*** **Meals** *(closed 25 December)* a la carte 15.00/18.00 **s[illegible]** 11.00 – **110 rm** 110.00/145.00 **st.**, 5 suites – SB.

Travel Inn, Ringwood Rd, Tricketts Cross, BH22 9BB, Northeast : 1 m. on A 34[illegible] ☎ (01202) 874210, *Fax (01202) 897794* – rm, ▣ & P. AE VISA.
Meals (grill rest.) – **32 rm** 41.95 **t.**

FERNHURST *W. Sussex* 404 R 30.
London 50 – Southampton 46 – Brighton 40.

King's Arms, Midhurst Rd, GU27 3HA, South : 1 m. on A 286 ☎ (01428) 652005, – P VISA
closed Sunday dinner – **Meals** a la carte 19.25/23.00 **st.** 10.25.

FERRENSBY *N. Yorks. – see Knaresborough.*

FERRYBRIDGE SERVICE AREA *W. Yorks.* 402 Q 22 – ✉ *Leeds.*
London 178 – Leeds 14 – Doncaster 14 – Rotherham 28 – York 28.

Travelodge, WF11 0AF, at junction 33 of M 62 with A 1 ☎ (01977) 672767 *Fax (01977) 622509* – ▣ & P. AE VISA JCB.
Meals (grill rest.) – **36 rm** 49.95 **t.**

FERSFIELD *Norfolk – see Diss.*

FILEY *N. Yorks.* 402 T 21 – *pop. 6 619.*
London 238 – Kingston-upon-Hull 42 – Leeds 68 – Middlesbrough 58.

White Lodge, The Crescent, YO14 9JX, ☎ (01723) 514771, *white.lodge@lineone.net, Fax (01723) 516590,* ← – |‡| TV P. MC VISA
Meals (bar lunch Monday-Saturday)/dinner 16.50 and a la carte 15.00/25.15 **st.** 9.50 – **20 rm** 46.00/100.00 **st.** – SB.

Downcliffe House, The Beach, YO14 9LA, ☎ (01723) 513310, *downcliff@filey.net, Fax (01723) 513773,* ← – ⇔ rest, TV P. MC ⓓ VISA. ✻
closed 18 December-1 February – **Meals** 17.00/19.00 (dinner) and a la carte 18.00/24.00 **t.** 9.00 – **10 rm** 45.00/100.00 **t.**

FILTON *Bristol* 403 404 M 29 – *see Bristol.*

FINDON *W. Sussex* 404 S 31 – *pop. 1 776* – ✉ *Worthing.*
London 49 – Brighton 13 – Southampton 50 – Worthing 4.

Findon Manor, High St, BN14 0TA, off A 24 ☎ (01903) 872733, *findon@dircon.co.uk, Fax (01903) 877473,* « Part 16C stone and flint house », ← – ⇔ rest, TV ☏ P – 40. MC AE ⓓ VISA JCB. ✻
Meals *closed Sunday dinner* 19.50/24.50 and a la carte 14.00/26.45 **t.** 12.00 – **11 rm** 58.00/120.00 **t.** – SB.

FINEDON *Northants.* 404 S 26 – *see Wellingborough.*

FLAMSTEAD *Herts.* 404 S 28 – *pop. 1 399* – ✉ *St. Albans.*
London 32 – Luton 5.

Hertfordshire Moat House, London Rd, AL3 8HH, on A 5 ☎ (01582) 449988, *cbhfd @queensmoat.co.uk, Fax (01582) 449041,* Ⅰ6, ≘s, ⊠ – |‡|, ⇔ rm, ▤ rest, TV ♿ P – 180. MC AE ⓓ VISA JCB
Meals 14.95/17.95 and a la carte 18.95/24.70 **t.** 13.95 – 11.50 – **140 rm** 115.00/130.00 **st.** – SB.

Express by Holiday Inn, London Rd, AL3 8HT, Northeast : 1 m. on A 5 at junction 9 of M 1 ☎ (01582) 841332, *express@luton-hemel.fsbusiness.co.uk, Fax (01582) 846482* – ⇔ rm, ▤ rest, TV ☏ ♿ P – 30. MC AE ⓓ VISA JCB. ✻
Meals (grill rest.) a la carte 11.45/16.95 **t.** 8.95 – **75 rm** 62.50 **st.**

FLEET *Hants.* 404 R 30 – *pop. 30 391.*
18 North Hants, Minley Rd ☎ (01252) 616443.
The Harlington Centre, 236 Fleet Rd ☎ (01252) 811151.
London 40 – Basingstoke 11 – Reading 17.

Lismoyne, Church Rd, GU13 8NA, ☎ (01252) 628555, *lismoyne@lismoyne.f9.co.uk, Fax (01252) 811761,* ← – ⇔ rest, ▤ rest, TV P – 100. MC AE ⓓ VISA
Meals *(closed Sunday dinner and Bank Holidays)* 14.95/18.95 and a la carte 16.75/28.00 **st.** 11.95 – 9.95 – **44 rm** 81.00/117.00 **st.**

FLEET SERVICE AREA *Hants.* 404 R 30 – ✉ *Basingstoke.*

Days Inn (without rest.), Hartley Witney, RG27 8BN, M 3 between junctions 4a and 5 (southbound carriageway) ☎ (01252) 815587, Reservations (Freephone) 0800 0280400, *Fax (01252) 815587* – TV ♿ P. MC AE ⓓ VISA JCB
– **58 rm** 55.00/60.00 **t.**

FLEETWOOD *Lancs.* 402 K 22 – *pop. 27 227.*

Fleetwood, Golf House, Princes Way ℘ (01253) 873114.

to Northern Ireland (Larne) (P & O Irish Sea) daily (8 h).

Old Ferry Office, The Esplanade ℘ (01253) 773953.

London 245 – Blackpool 10 – Lancaster 28 – Manchester 53.

North Euston, The Esplanade, FY7 6BN, ℘ (01253) 876525, *reception@northeustor hotel.co.uk, Fax (01253) 777842,* ≤ Wyre estuary and Lake District hills, « Victorian former musketry » – |‡| ⇔ TV P – 200. MC AE VISA.
Meals (bar lunch Saturday) 9.75/19.95 dinner and a la carte 18.75/28.70 **t.** 11.00 – **53 rm** 57.50/87.00 **t.** – SB.

FLETCHING *E. Sussex* 404 U 30/31 – *pop. 1 722.*

London 45 – Brighton 20 – Eastbourne 24 – Maidstone 20.

The Griffin Inn with rm, TN22 3SS, ℘ (01825) 722890, *Fax (01825) 722810,* , « 16C coaching inn », – ⇔ rm, TV P. MC AE VISA.
closed 25 December – **Meals** (meals in bar Sunday dinner in winter) a la carte 17.50/22.95 **t** 9.80 – **8 rm** 70.00/85.00 **st.**

FLITWICK *Beds.* 404 S 27 – *pop. 11 063.*

London 45 – Bedford 13 – Luton 12 – Northampton 28.

Flitwick Manor , Church Rd, MK45 1AE, off Dunstable Rd ℘ (01525) 712242, *info @menzies-hotels.co.uk, Fax (01525) 718753,* ≤, « 18C manor house », , , – ⇔ TV P. MC AE VISA JCB
Meals 24.50/38.00 **st.** 19.50 – 16.50 – **17 rm** 120.00/145.00 **st.** – SB.

FLORE *Northants.* 403 404 Q 27 – *see Daventry.*

FOLKESTONE *Kent* 404 X 30 *Great Britain G.* – *pop. 45 587.*

See : *The Leas★ (≤★) Z.*

Channel Tunnel : Eurotunnel information and reservations ℘ (08705) 353535.

Harbour St ℘ (01303) 258594.

London 76 – Brighton 76 – Dover 8 – Maidstone 33.

Plan opposite

Clifton, The Leas, CT20 2EB, ℘ (01303) 851231, *reservations@thecliftonhotel.com Fax (01303) 223949,* ≤, – |‡| TV – 80. MC AE VISA JCB Z
Meals 12.50/19.50 and a la carte 22.20/30.20 **t.** 8.75 – 8.50 – **80 rm** 53.00/185.00 **t.** – SB.

Travel Inn, Cherry Garden Lane, CT19 4AP, Northwest : 1 ¼ m. by A 259 at junction 13 of M 20 ℘ (01303) 273620, *Fax (01303) 273641* – ⇔ rm, TV P. MC AE VISA. X b
Meals (grill rest.) – **40 rm** 41.95 **t.**

Harbourside without rest., 13-14 Wear Bay Rd, CT19 6AT, ℘ (01303) 256528, *joy@ harboursidehotel.com, Fax (01303) 241299,* ≤, , – ⇔ TV. MC AE VISA. X e
14 rm 35.00/100.00 **st.**

La Tavernetta, Leaside Court, Clifton Gdns, CT20 2ED, ℘ (01303) 254955 *Fax (01303) 244732* – MC AE VISA JCB Z n
closed 25 December, Sunday and Bank Holidays – **Meals** - Italian - 9.80 (lunch) and a la carte 18.90/33.30 **t.** 9.80.

at Sandgate *West : 1 ¾ m. on A 259 – ✉ Folkestone.*

Sandgate, The Esplanade, CT20 3DY, West : ½ m. ℘ (01303) 220444, *Fax (01303) 220496,* ≤ – |‡| TV. MC AE VISA. X a
closed January and 10 days October – **Meals** – (see ***La Terrasse*** below) – **14 rm** 45.00/78.00 **t.**

La Terrasse (Gicqueau) (at Sandgate H.), The Esplanade, CT20 3DY, West : ½ m. ℘ (01303) 220444, *Fax (01303) 220496,* ≤ – ⇔. MC AE VISA X a
closed January, 10 days October, Monday, Sunday dinner and Tuesday lunch – **Meals** - French - (booking essential) 24.50/34.00 and a la carte 38.00/44.50 **t.** 14.00
Spec. Pan-fried scallops with black truffle. Poached turbot with bean mousseline in a bacon jus. Valhrona chocolate dessert with almond cream and coffee ice cream.

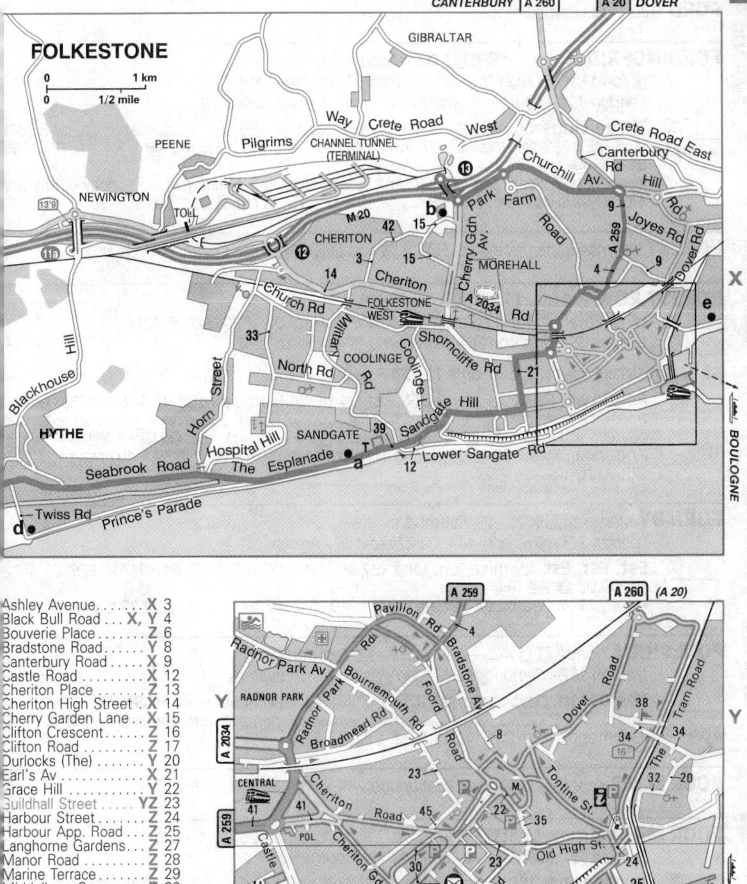

The Guide is updated annually so renew your Guide every year.

FONTWELL *W. Sussex* **404** S 31 – ✉ *Arundel.*

Little Chef Complex ☎ (01243) 543269.

London 60 – Chichester 6 – Worthing 15.

Travelodge, BN18 0SB, at A 27/A 29 roundabout ☎ (01243) 543973, *Fax (01243) 543973* – ⇔ rm, TV ♿ P. MC AE ◑ VISA JCB. ✻
Meals (grill rest.) – **62 rm** 49.95 **t.**

FORD *Wilts. – see Castle Combe.*

FORDINGBRIDGE *Hants.* 403 404 O 31 – *pop. 4 301.*

Town Hall, 63 High St ☎ (01425) 654560 (summer only).

London 101 – Bournemouth 17 – Salisbury 11 – Winchester 30.

Three Lions with rm, Stuckton Rd, Stuckton, SP6 2HF, Southeast : 1 m. by B 3078 ☎ (01425) 652489, *the3lions@btinternet.com, Fax (01425) 656144,* – rm, TV P. MC AE VISA JCB.
closed last 2 weeks January and first week February – **Meals** *(closed Sunday dinner and Monday)* a la carte 24.25/31.25 **t.** 16.50 – 5.75 – **3 rm** 75.00/85.00 **st.** – SB.

FOREST *Guernsey (Channel Islands)* 403 P 33 and 230 ⑨ ⑩ – *see Channel Islands.*

FOREST ROW *E. Sussex* 404 U 30 – *pop. 3 508.*

18, 18 *Royal Ashdown Forest, Chapel Lane, Forest Row ☎ (01342) 822018.*

London 35 – Brighton 26 – Eastbourne 30 – Maidstone 32.

at Wych Cross *South : 2½ m. on A 22 – ✉ Forest Row.*

Ashdown Park, RH18 5JR, East : ¾ m. on Hartfield rd ☎ (01342) 824988, *reservations@ashdownpark.com, Fax (01342) 826206,* ≤, « Part 19C manor house in extensive gardens », 18, – rest, TV P – 150. MC AE VISA.
Anderida : **Meals** 23.00/35.00 and a la carte 31.25/50.45 **st.** 16.50 – **102 rm** 130.00/175.00 **st.**, 5 suites – SB.

FORMBY *Mersey.* 402 K 23 – ✉ *Southport.*

London 213 – Liverpool 14 – Manchester 46 – Preston 27.

Est, Est, Est, 29 Three Tuns Lane, L37 4FB, ☎ (01704) 833775, *Fax (01704) 879168,* – . MC AE VISA JCB
closed 25-26 December – **Meals** - Italian - 10.00 and a la carte 11.70/21.75 **t.** 10.45.

FOULSHAM *Norfolk* 404 X 25 – *pop. 1 379 – ✉ East Dereham.*

London 121 – Cambridge 69 – King's Lynn 31 – Norwich 18.

The Gamp, Claypit Lane, NR20 5RW, ☎ (01362) 684114, – P. MC VISA
closed first 2 weeks January, Monday, Sunday dinner and Tuesday lunch – **Meals** 12.50 (lunch) and a la carte 17.40/26.30 **st.** 8.95.

FOUR ELMS *Kent* 404 U 30 – *see Edenbridge.*

FOUR MARKS *Hants.* 403 404 Q 30 – *pop. 3 843 (inc. Medstead) – ✉ Alton.*

London 58 – Guildford 24 – Reading 29 – Southampton 24.

Travelodge, 156 Winchester Rd, GU34 5HZ, on A 31 ☎ (01420) 562659 – TV P. MC AE VISA JCB.
Meals (grill rest.) – **31 rm** 49.95 **t.**

at Lower Wield *Northwest : 4 m. taking Wield rd through Medstead – ✉ Four Marks.*

Yew Tree, SO24 9RX, ☎ (01256) 389224, *yewtreerestaurant@tinyworld.co.uk, Fax (01256) 389224,* – P. MC VISA
closed two weeks Christmas and New Year – **Meals** (booking essential) 16.95/22.95 and a la carte 25.00/34.40 **t.** 11.50.

FOURWENTWAYS SERVICE AREA *Cambs. – see Cambridge.*

FOWEY *Cornwall* 403 G 32 *The West Country G. – pop. 2 123.*

See : *Town★★.*

Env. : *Gribbin Head★★ (≤★★) 6 m. rtn on foot – Bodinnick (≤★★) - Lanteglos Church★, E : 5 m. by ferry – Polruan (≤★★) SE : 6 m. by ferry – Polkerris★, W : 2 m. by A 3082.*

4 Custom House Hill ☎ (01726) 833616.

London 277 – Newquay 24 – Plymouth 34 – Truro 22.

Fowey Hall, Hanson Drive, PL23 1ET, West : ½ m. off A 3082 ☎ (01726) 833866, *Fax (01726) 834100,* ≤, « Part Victorian country house », heated, – rest, TV P – 40. MC AE VISA
Meals (light lunch Monday-Saturday)/dinner 29.50 and a la carte 29.00/42.50 **t.** 12.00 – **17 rm** 155.00/205.00 **t.**, 8 suites – SB.

Marina, 17 The Esplanade, PL23 1HY, (01726) 833315, *marina.hotel@dial.pipex.com*, *Fax (01726) 832779*, < Fowey river and harbour, – rest, . VISA
Meals (bar lunch)/dinner 23.50 and a la carte 18.00/45.00 **st.** 11.95 – **13 rm** (dinner included) 85.00/172.00 **st.** – SB.

Carnethic House, Lambs Barn, PL23 1HQ, Northwest : 3/4 m. on A 3082 (01726) 833336, *carnethic@btinternet.com*, *Fax (01726) 833296*, heated, , – rest, VISA
closed mid December-mid January – **Meals** (bar lunch)/dinner 18.00 **st.** 9.00 – **8 rm** 50.00/80.00 **st.** – SB.

XX **Food for Thought,** The Quay, PL23 1AT, (01726) 832221, *Fax (01726) 832077*, « 17C converted coastguard's cottage on quayside » – VISA
closed Christmas, January and Sunday – **Meals** (booking essential in winter) (dinner only) 14.95 and a la carte 18.45/32.00 **t.**

t Golant *North : 3 m. by B 3269 – Fowey.*

Cormorant, PL23 1LL, (01726) 833426, *relax@cormoranthotels.co.uk*, *Fax (01726) 833574*, < River Fowey, , – rest, VISA
Meals (light lunch)/dinner 20.00/25.00 and a la carte 26.70/29.95 **t.** 10.50 – **11 rm** 96.00/110.00 **t.** – SB.

OWNHOPE *Herefordshire* 403 404 M 27 – *pop. 900* – *Hereford.*
London 132 – Cardiff 46 – Hereford 6 – Gloucester 27.

Green Man Inn, HR1 4PE, (01432) 860243, *Fax (01432) 860207*, , , , , – rest, VISA
Meals (bar lunch Monday-Saturday)/dinner 12.50/17.50 a la carte 16.45/20.70 **st.** 10.50 – **20 rm** 39.50/70.00 **st.** – SB.

RADDON *Cornwall* 403 F 32 – *St. Columbus Major.*
London 264 – Exeter 77 – Penzance 35 – Newquay 7 – Plymouth 44 – Truro 12.

Travel Inn, Penhale, TR9 6NA, on A 30 (eastbound carriageway) (01726) 861148, *Fax (01726) 861336* – rm, rest, VISA.
Meals (grill rest.) – **40 rm** 41.95 **t.**

RAMLINGHAM *Suffolk* 404 Y 27 – *pop. 2 697* – *Woodbridge.*
London 92 – Ipswich 19 – Norwich 42.

Colston Hall without rest., Badingham, IP13 8LB, Northeast : 4 m. by B 1120 offf A 1120 (01728) 638375, *lizjohn@colstonhall.com*, *Fax (01728) 638084*, « Working farm », , , – VISA.
6 rm 33.00/55.00.

RANKLEY SERVICE AREA *W. Mids.* 403 404 ⑲ – *Birmingham.*
Plan : see Birmingham p. 4

Travelodge, B32 4AR, M 5 between junctions 3 and 4 (0121) 550 3131, *Fax (0121) 501 2880* – VISA JCB. BU a
Meals (grill rest.) – **62 rm** 52.95 **t.**

RANT *E. Sussex* 404 U 30 – *see Royal Tunbridge Wells.*

RESHWATER BAY *I.O.W.* 403 404 P 31 – *see Wight (Isle of).*

RITHSDEN *Herts.* – *see Hemel Hempstead.*

RODSHAM *Ches.* 402 403 404 L 24 – *pop. 8 903* – *Warrington.*
18 *Frodsham, Simons Lane (01928) 732159.*
London 203 – Chester 11 – Liverpool 21 – Manchester 29 – Stoke-on-Trent 42.

Old Hall, Main St, WA6 7AB, (01928) 732052, *theoldhall@lineone.net*, *Fax (01928) 739046*, – – 30. VISA JCB
Meals 12.75/21.75 and a la carte 20.65/33.40 **t.** 9.50 – **25 rm** 67.50/82.50 **t.**, 1 suite – SB.

FROME *Somerset* 403 404 M/N 30.
London 118 – Bristol 24 – Southampton 52 – Swindon 44.

Babington House, Babington, BA11 3RW, Northwest : 6 ½ m. by A 362 on Vobst rd ☎ (01373) 812266, *babingtonhouse@babhouse.co.uk, Fax (01373) 812112,* « Georgian manor house, contemporary interior and informal atmosphere », heated, – – 45.
The Log Room : **Meals** (dinner only) (residents only) a la carte 26.50/34.00 **st.** 13.00 – 10.50 – **22 rm** 265.00 **t.**, 5 suites – SB.

FULLER STREET *Essex – Chelmsford.*
London 45 – Cambridge 46 – Colchester 24 – Southend-on-Sea 30.

Square & Compasses, CM3 2BB, ☎ (01245) 361477, –
Meals a la carte 14.00/25.00 **t.** 9.50.

FUNTINGTON *W. Sussex* 404 R 31 – *see Chichester.*

GALMPTON *Devon* 403 J 32 – *Brixham.*
London 229 – Plymouth 32 – Torquay 6.

Maypool Park, Maypool, TQ5 0ET, Southwest : 1 m. by Greenway R ☎ (01803) 842442, *peacock@maypoolpark.co.uk, Fax (01803) 845782,* –
Meals (dinner only and Sunday lunch)/dinner 18.50/21.50 **t.** 9.25 – **10 rm** 48.0 80.00 **t.** – SB.

GARFORTH *W. Yorks.* 402 P 22 – *see Leeds.*

GARSTANG *Lancs.* 402 L 22 – *pop. 5 697.*
Discovery Centre, Council Offices, High St ☎ (01995) 602125.
London 233 – Blackpool 13 – Manchester 41.

Garstang Country H. and Golf Club, Bowgreave, PR3 1YE, South : 1 ¼ m. on B 643 ☎ (01995) 600100, *reception@garstanghotelandgolf.co.uk, Fax (01995) 600950,* – – 250.
Meals 10.95/12.95 and a la carte 15.65/21.15 **t.** 8.45 – **32 rm** 60.00/80.00 **t.** – SB.

Crofters, Cabus, PR3 1PH, West : ¾ m. on A 6 ☎ (01995) 604128, *Fax (01995) 601646* – – 200.
Meals (dancing Saturday evening) (bar lunch Monday-Saturday)/dinner a la carte 14.1 21.15 **t.** 8.95 – **19 rm** 46.00/64.00 **st.**

at Bilsborrow *South : 3 ¾ m. by B 6430 on A 6 – Preston.*

Guy's Thatched Hamlet, Canalside, St Michaels Rd, PR3 0RS, off A 6 ☎ (01995) 64001 *guyshamlet@aol.com, Fax (01995) 640141,* « Thatched village, canalside setting » – 50.
closed 25 December – **Meals** 6.00/15.00 and a la carte 14.00/25.00 **st.** 9.50 – 6.00 **53 rm** 42.50/52.00 **st.** – SB.

Premier Lodge, Garstang Rd, PR3 0RN, ☎ (0870) 7001516, *Fax (0870) 7001517* – rr
Meals (grill rest.) a la carte approx. 16.95 **t.** 8.75 – **40 rm** 42.95 **t.**

Olde Duncombe House without rest., Garstang Rd, PR3 0RE, ☎ (01995) 64033 *Fax (01995) 640336,* –
9 rm 35.00/49.50.

GATEFORTH *N. Yorks. – pop. 176.*
London 203 – Leeds 22 – Manchester 70 – York 16.

XXX **Martel**, Gateforth Hall, YO8 9LJ, West : ½ m. ☎ (01757) 228225, *martel@uk.packardb .org, Fax (01757) 228189,* « Early 19C former hunting lodge », –
closed 26-29 December, 1 week January, Saturday lunch, Sunday dinner and Monday
Meals 17.00/25.00 and a la carte 31.50/45.00 **t.** 12.75.

GATE SERVICE AREA *Kent* 404 X 30 – *see Canterbury.*

GATESHEAD *Tyne and Wear* 401 402 P 19 *Great Britain G. – pop. 83 159.*

Exc. : *Beamish : North of England Open Air Museum*** AC, *SW : 6 m. by A 692 and A 6076* BX.

Ravensworth, Moss Heaps, Wrekenton (0191) 487 6014 – Heworth, Gingling Gate (0191) 469 9832 BX.

Tyne Tunnel (toll).

Central Library, Prince Consort Rd (0191) 477 3478 BX – *Metrocentre, Portcullis, 7 The Arcade (0191) 460 6345* AX.

London 282 – Durham 16 – Middlesbrough 38 – Newcastle upon Tyne 1 – Sunderland 11.

Plan : see Newcastle upon Tyne

Newcastle Marriott, Cameron Park, Metro Centre, NE11 9XF, (0191) 493 2233, *reservations.newcastle@marriotthotels.co.uk, Fax (0191) 493 2030,* – rm, – 450. VISA JCB AX e
Meals (bar lunch)/dinner a la carte 19.45/27.40 **st.** – **148 rm** 109.00/119.00 **st.**

Express by Holiday Inn without rest., Riverside Way, Derenthaugh, NE16 3BE, (01207) 541100, *gateshead@premierhotels.co.uk, Fax (0191) 414 6967* – – 25. VISA JCB AX a
100 rm 59.50 **st.**

Travel Inn, Derwenthaugh Rd, NE16 3BL, (0191) 414 6308, *Fax (0191) 414 5032* – , rest, . VISA AX c
Meals (grill rest.) – **40 rm** 41.95 **t.**

at Low Fell *South : 2 m. by A 167* – BX – *Gateshead.*

Eslington Villa, 8 Station Rd, NE9 6DR, West : ¾ m. by Belle Vue Bank, turning left at T junction, right at roundabout then taking first turn right (0191) 487 6017, *admin@eslingtonvilla.fsnet.co.uk, Fax (0191) 420 0667,* – – 35. VISA.
closed 25 December and Bank Holidays – **Meals** – (see ***The Restaurant*** below) – **17 rm** 59.50/75.00 **t.**

The Restaurant (at Eslington Villa), 8 Station Rd, NE9 6DR, West : ¾ by Belle Vue Bank, turning left at T junction, right at roundabout then taking first turn right (0191) 487 6017, *Fax (0191) 420 0667,* – . VISA
closed Saturday lunch and Sunday dinner to non-residents – **Meals** 11.50/18.50 and a la carte 22.85/29.00 **t.** 11.50.

at Whickham *West : 4 m. by B 601, A 692 on B 6317* – *Gateshead.*

Gibside, Front St, NE16 4JG, (0191) 488 9292, *reception@gibside-hotel.co.uk, Fax (0191) 488 8000* – rm, rest, – 120. VISA AX s
Meals (bar lunch Monday to Saturday)/dinner 15.95/19.95 and a la carte 15.45/29.90 **st.** 10.50 – – 8.95 – **45 rm** 57.50/69.00 **st.**

GATWICK AIRPORT *W. Sussex* 404 T 30 – *Crawley.*

Gatwick Airport : (01293) 535353.

London 29 – Brighton 28.

Plan on next page

Hilton London Gatwick Airport, South Terminal, RH6 0LL, (01293) 518080, *gathitwsal@hilton.com, Fax (01293) 528980,* – rm, – 500. VISA JCB. Y u
Meals a la carte approx. 37.00 **t.** 15.00 – 14.95 – **565 rm** 190.00/340.00.

Le Meridien London Gatwick, Gatwick Airport (North Terminal), RH6 0PH, (0870) 400 8494, *sales.gatwick@lemeridien-hotels.com, Fax (01293) 567739,* – rm, – 300. VISA JCB. Y e
Gatwick Oriental : **Meals** - Asian - 17.00/27.00 and a la carte 15.30/29.90 **t.** 16.00 – ***Brasserie :*** **Meals** *(closed lunch Saturday and Sunday)* (buffet lunch) 19.95 and a la carte 28.95/38.50 **t.** 16.00 – 13.95 – **488 rm** 179.00 **st.**, 6 suites.

Renaissance London Gatwick, Povey Cross Rd, RH6 0BE, (01293) 820169, *alex.holmes@renaissancehotels.com, Fax (01293) 820259,* squash – rm, – 180. VISA Y a
Meals *(closed Sunday lunch)* 16.50/18.50 and a la carte 19.00/29.00 **t.** 12.95 – 12.50 – **253 rm** 135.00/150.00 **st.**, 2 suites – SB.

Holiday Inn Gatwick, Povey Cross Rd, RH6 0BA, (0870) 400 9030, *gm1090@forte-hotels.com, Fax (01293) 771054* – rm, rest, – 300. VISA JCB Y c
Meals *(closed Saturday and Sunday lunch)* 14.75/15.00-28.45 and a la carte 14.75/28.45 **t.** 11.95 – 13.95 – **210 rm** 120.00 **st.** – SB.

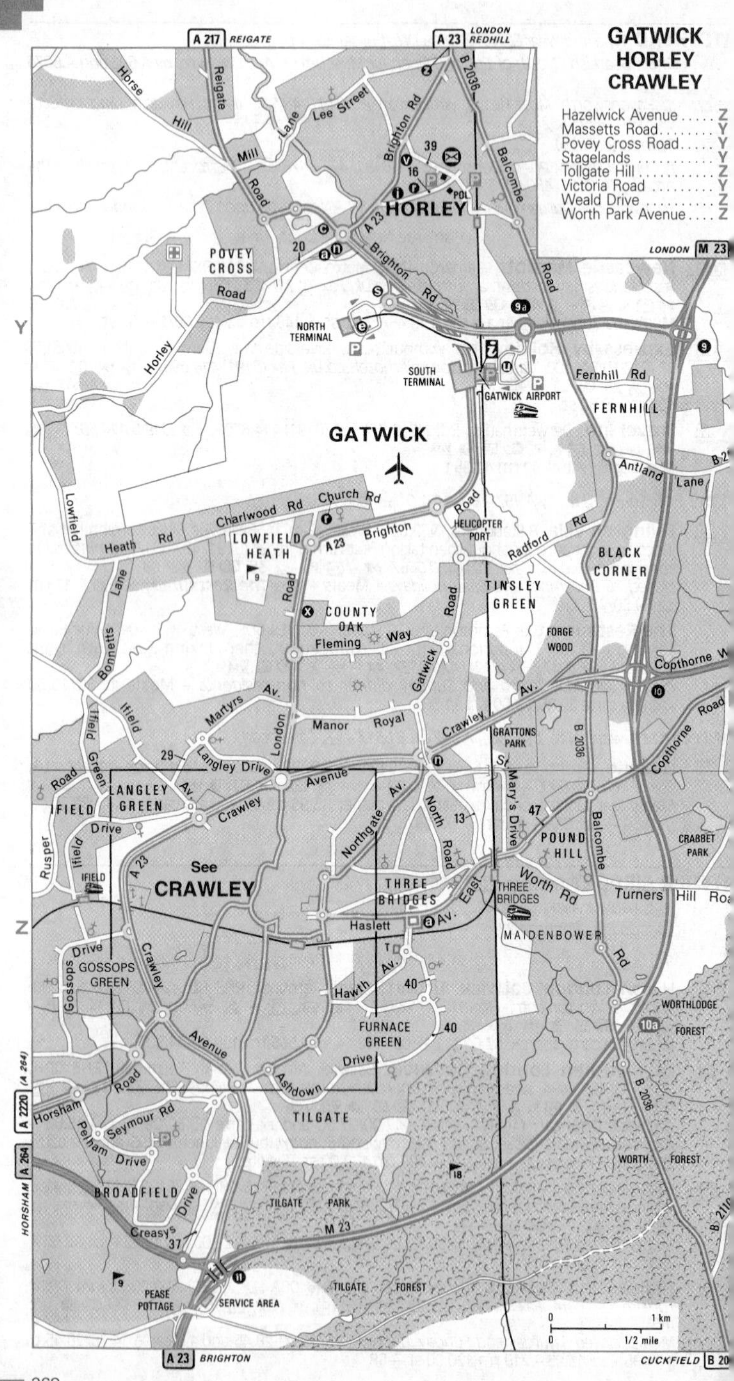

GATWICK
HORLEY
CRAWLEY
Hazelwick Avenue . . . . . Z
Massetts Road. . . . . Y
Povey Cross Road. . . . . Y
Stagelands . . . . Y
Tollgate Hill . . . . Z
Victoria Road . . . . Y
Weald Drive . . . . Z
Worth Park Avenue . . . . Z
A 217 REIGATE
A 23 LONDON REDHILL
LONDON M 23
HORLEY
POVEY CROSS
NORTH TERMINAL
SOUTH TERMINAL
GATWICK AIRPORT
GATWICK
FERNHILL
LOWFIELD HEATH
HELICOPTER PORT
BLACK CORNER
TINSLEY GREEN
COUNTY OAK
FORGE WOOD
GRATTONS PARK
LANGLEY GREEN
IFIELD
See CRAWLEY
THREE BRIDGES
POUND HILL
CRABBET PARK
MAIDENBOWER
GOSSOPS GREEN
FURNACE GREEN
WORTHLODGE FOREST
TILGATE
BROADFIELD
TILGATE PARK
WORTH FOREST
PEASE POTTAGE
SERVICE AREA
TILGATE FOREST
A 23 BRIGHTON
CUCKFIELD B 20
HORSHAM A 264
A 2220
(A 264)
1 km
1/2 mile
Y
Z

Gatwick Moat House, Longbridge Roundabout, Povey Cross Rd, RH6 0AB, ✆ (01293) 899988, *revgat@queensmoat.co.uk, Fax (01293) 785991,* – rm, – 150. VISA JCB Y n
Meals (bar lunch)/dinner a la carte 16.60/28.00 11.95 – 10.50 – **124 rm** 99.00/119.00.

Travel Inn Metro, Longbridge Way, Gatwick Airport (North Terminal), RH6 0NX, ✆ (01293) 568158, *Fax (01293) 568278* – , rm, rest, . VISA. Y s
Meals (grill rest.) (dinner only) – **219 rm** 49.95 **t.**

Premier Lodge, London Rd, Lowfield Heath, RH10 2ST, ✆ (0870) 7001388, *Fax (0870) 7001389,* « Part 15C manor house », – , rm, – 220. VISA. Y x
Meals a la carte approx. 16.95 **t.** 8.75 – **100 rm** 49.95 **t.**

Travelodge, Church Rd, Lowfield Heath, RH11 0PQ, ✆ (01293) 533441, *Fax (01293) 535369* – , rm, rest, – 40. VISA JCB. Y r
Meals (grill rest.) – **186 rm** 49.95 **t.**

GERRARDS CROSS *Bucks.* 404 S 29 – *pop. 19 523 (inc. Chalfont St. Peter).*

London 22 – Aylesbury 22 – Oxford 36.

Bull, Oxford Rd, SL9 7PA, on A 40 ✆ (01753) 885995, *bull@sarova.co.uk, Fax (01753) 885504,* – – 200. VISA JCB.
Meals *(closed Saturday lunch)* 19.95/23.50 **t.** 12.95 – 10.95 – **109 rm** 160.00/180.00 **t.**, 2 suites – SB.

Les prix — Pour toutes précisions sur les prix indiqués dans ce guide, reportez-vous aux pages de l'introduction.

GILLAN *Cornwall* 403 E 33 – ✉ *Helston.*

London 301 – Falmouth 23 – Penzance 25 – Truro 26.

Tregildry , TR12 6HG, ✆ (01326) 231378, *trgildry@globalnet.co.uk, Fax (01326) 231561,* , – . VISA JCB
March-October – **Herra :** Meals (dinner only) 23.00 **st.** 11.25 – **10 rm** (dinner included) 80.00/170.00 **st.** – SB.

GILLINGHAM *Dorset* 403 404 N 30 *The West Country G.* – *pop. 6 404.*

Exc. : *Stourhead★★★ AC, N : 9 m. by B 3092, B 3095 and B 3092.*

London 116 – Bournemouth 34 – Bristol 46 – Southampton 52.

Stock Hill Country House , Stock Hill, SP8 5NR, West : 1 ½ m. on B 3081 ✆ (01747) 823626, *reception@stockhillhouse.co.uk, Fax (01747) 825628,* « Victorian country house, antiques and gardens », , , , – rest, . VISA.
Meals *(closed Monday lunch)* (booking essential) 22.00-25.00/35.00 **t.** 15.95 – **8 rm** (dinner included) 120.00/300.00 **t.** – SB.

GITTISHAM *Devon* 403 K 31 – *pop. 602* – ✉ *Honiton.*

London 168 – Exeter 18 – Southampton 95 – Taunton 21.

Combe House , EX14 3AD, ✆ (01404) 540400, *stay@thishotel.com, Fax (01404) 46004,* , « Elizabethan mansion », , , – – 60. VISA
Meals (booking essential to non-residents) 16.00/28.50 **st.** 15.50 – **14 rm** 99.00/190.00 **st.**, 1 suite – SB.

GLENRIDDING *Cumbria* 402 L 20 – *see Ullswater.*

GLEWSTONE *Herefordshire* – *see Ross-on-Wye.*

GLOSSOP *Derbs.* 402 403 404 O 23 – *pop. 30 771 (inc. Hollingworth).*

Sheffield Rd ✆ (01457) 865247.

The Gatehouse, Victoria St ✆ (01457) 855920.

London 194 – Manchester 18 – Sheffield 25.

The Wind in the Willows , Hurst Rd, Derbyshire Level, SK13 7PT, East : 1 m. by A 57 ✆ (01457) 868001, *info@windinthewillows.co.uk, Fax (01457) 853354,* – rest, . VISA JCB.
Meals (dinner only) 25.00 **st.** 12.00 – **12 rm** 75.00/121.00 **st.**

GLOUCESTER

Barnwood By-Pass ...... Z 3
Black Dog Way .... Y 5
Commercial Road .... Y 6
Cotteswold Road .... Z 8
Derby Road .... Z 9
Eastgate Shopping Centre ... Y
Eastgate Street .... Y 10
Great Western Road .... Y 12
Heathville Road .... Y 13
King Edward's Avenue .. Z 14
Lower Westgate Street ..... Y 15
Northgate Street ...... Y 16
Parkend Road .... Z 17
Parliament Street ..... Y 18
Pitt Street .... Y 19
Quay Street .... Y 20
Royal Oak Road .... Y 21
St. Aldate Street ..... Y 22
St. Johns Lane .... Y 23
Southern Avenue .... Z 24
Southgate Street ...... Y
Spa Road .... Y 26
Stroud Road .... Z 28
Tredworth Road .... Z 30
Worcester Street ...... Y 31

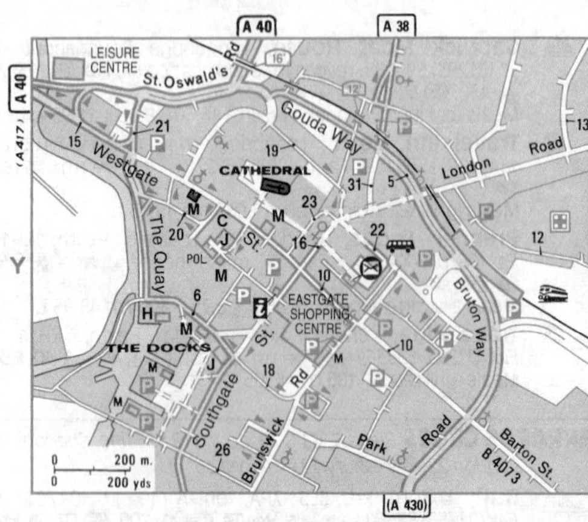

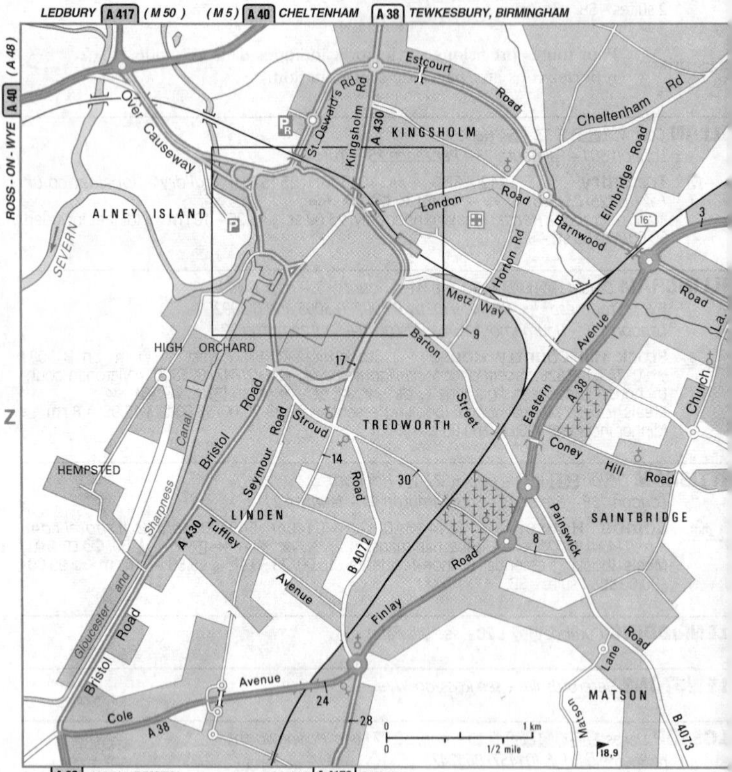

GLOUCESTER *Glos.* 403 404 N 28 *Great Britain G. – pop. 114 003.*

See : *City★ - Cathedral★★* Y – *The Docks★* Y – *Bishop Hooper's Lodging★* AC Y M.
18, 9 *Gloucester Hotel, Matson Lane ☎ (01452) 525653.*
28 Southgate St ☎ (01452) 421188.
London 106 – Birmingham 52 – Bristol 38 – Cardiff 66 – Coventry 57 – Northampton 83 – Oxford 48 – Southampton 98 – Swansea 92 – Swindon 35.

Plans opposite

Express by Holiday Inn without rest., Waterwells Business Park, Nr Quedgeley, GL2 4SA, Southwest : 3 m. on A 38 ☎ (01452) 726400, *gloucester@oriel-leisure.co.uk, Fax (01452) 722922* – 25. VISA JCB
106 rm 55.00 st.

Premier Lodge, Tewkesbury Rd, Twigworth, GL2 9PG, Northeast : 2 ½ m. on A 38 ☎ (0870) 7001404, *Fax (0870) 7001405* – rm, rest, – 60. VISA.
Meals (grill rest.) a la carte approx. 12.50 **t.** 7.80 – **52 rm** 42.95 **t.**

Travel Inn, Tewkesbury Rd, Longford, GL2 9BE, North : 1 ¼ m. on A 38 ☎ (01452) 523519, *Fax (01452) 300924* – rm, – 40. VISA.
Meals (grill rest.) – **60 rm** 41.95 **t.**

at Upton St. Leonards *Southeast : 3½ m. by B 4073 – Z – ✉ Gloucester.*

Hatton Court, Upton Hill, GL4 8DE, South : ¾ m. on B 4073 ☎ (01452) 617412, *res@hatton-court.co.uk, Fax (01452) 612945*, <, rm, rest, – 60. VISA.
Carringtons : **Meals** 14.50/26.25 and a la carte 22.50/34.00 **t.** 14.00 – **45 rm** 93.50/190.00 **t.** – SB.

Jarvis Bowden Hall , Bondend Lane, GL4 8ED, East : 1 m. by Bondend rd ☎ (01452) 614121, *Fax (01452) 611885*, <, – – 85. VISA.
Meals (bar lunch Monday-Saturday) (carving lunch Sunday)/dinner a la carte 20.75/28.95 **t.** 11.95 – 10.95 – **71 rm** 109.20/129.00 **st.**, 1 suite – SB.

Bullens Manor Farm without rest., High St, GL4 8DL, Southeast : ½ m. ☎ (01452) 616463, <, « Working farm », – .
closed Christmas and New Year – **3 rm** 23.00/45.00.

at Witcombe *Southeast : 7 m. by A 40 and A 417 – Z – off A 46 – ✉ Gloucester.*

Travel Inn, GL3 4SS, ☎ (01452) 862521, *Fax (01452) 864926* – rm, rest, . VISA.
Meals (grill rest.) – **39 rm** 41.95 **t.**

GOATHLAND *N. Yorks.* 402 R 20 – *pop. 444 – ✉ Whitby.*

London 248 – Middlesbrough 36 – York 38.

Mallyan Spout , The Common, YO22 5AN, ☎ (01947) 896486, *mallyan@ukgateway.net, Fax (01947) 896327*, <, – . VISA
closed 1 week Christmas – **Meals** (bar lunch Monday-Saturday)/dinner 20.50 **st.** 10.00 – **26 rm** 55.00/130.00 **st.** – SB.

Heatherdene , The Old Vicarage, The Common, YO22 5AN, ☎ (01947) 896334, *info@heatherdenehotel.co.uk*, <, – rest, . VISA.
closed 1 week Christmas – **Meals** (booking essential) 12.50/15.00 **s.** 10.50 **6 rm** 35.00/70.00 **s.**

GODALMING *Surrey* 404 S 30 – *pop. 20 630.*

18 *West Surrey, Enton Green ☎ (01483) 421275* – 9 *Shillinglee Park, Chiddingfold ☎ (01428) 653237.*
London 39 – Guildford 5 – Southampton 48.

Bel and the Dragon, Bridge St, GU7 3DU, ☎ (01483) 527333, *Fax (01483) 427833*, , « Converted church » – VISA
Meals a la carte 20.40/30.50 **t.** 9.95.

GODSTONE *Surrey* 404 T 30 – *pop. 2 399.*

London 22 – Brighton 36 – Maidstone 28.

XXX **Tutu L'Auberge,** Tilburstow Hill, South Godstone, RH9 8JY, South : 2 ¼ m. ☎ (01342) 892318, *hr36@dial.pipex.com, Fax (01342) 893435*, – – 100. VISA
closed 26 to 30 December, Sunday dinner and Monday – **Meals** - French - 15.00/19.50 and a la carte 25.50/32.50 **st.** 13.00.

GOLANT *Cornwall* 403 G 32 – *see Fowey.*

GOLCAR *W. Yorks. – see Huddersfield.*

GOMERSAL *W. Yorks.* 402 O 22 – *see Bradford.*

GOODWOOD *W. Sussex* 404 R 31 – *see Chichester.*

GOOSNARGH *Lancs.* 402 L 22 – *pop. 1 087 – ✉ Preston.*
London 238 – Blackpool 18 – Preston 6.

Solo, Goosnargh Lane, PR3 2BN, ✆ (01772) 865206, *Fax (01772) 865206* – P. MC AE JCB
closed 26 December and Monday – **Meals** (dinner only and Sunday lunch)/dinner a la car 20.10/28.30 **st.** 11.90.

Ye Horns Inn with rm, Horns Lane, PR3 2FJ, Northeast : 2 ½ m. by B 52 ✆ (01772) 865230, *enquiries@yehornsinn.co.uk, Fax (01772) 864299,* « Part 18C », rest, TV P. MC AE VISA JCB.
Meals *(closed Monday lunch)* 12.95/17.95 and a la carte 14.95/19.20 **t.** 9.95 – **6 r** 55.00/75.00 **t.** – SB.

Jährlich eine neue Ausgabe
Aktuellste Informationen, jährlich für Sie!

GORDANO SERVICE AREA *North Somerset – ✉ Bristol.*
Severn Bridge (toll).

Days Inn without rest., BS20 9XG, M 5 junction 19 ✆ 460275) 373709, Reservations (Fre phone) 0800 0280400, *Fax (01275) 374104* – rm, TV P. MC AE VISA
7.45 **60 rm** 49.00 **st.**

GOREY *Jersey (Channel Islands)* 403 P 33 and 230 ⑪ – *see Channel Islands.*

GORING *Oxon.* 403 404 Q 29 *The West Country G. – pop. 4 193 (inc. Streatley).*
Exc. : *Ridgeway Path★★.*
London 56 – Oxford 16 – Reading 12.

Leatherne Bottel, RG8 0HS, North : 1 ½ m. by B 4009 ✆ (01491) 872667, *leather bottel@aol.com, Fax (01491) 875308,* ←, « Thames-side setting » – P. MC AE VISA
closed 25 December and Sunday dinner – **Meals** (booking essential) 19.50 (lunch) a la ca 28.20/34.60 **st.** 14.50.

at South Stoke *North : 2 m. by B 4009 – ✉ Goring.*

Perch and Pike with rm, RG8 0JS, ✆ (01491) 872415, *forallthatalesthee@excite.co Fax (01491) 875852,* « Part 17C inn » – P. MC VISA JCB.
Meals (booking essential) a la carte 20.85/28.85 **t.** 10.00 – **4 rm** 70.00 **st.** – SB.

GORLESTON-ON-SEA *Norfolk* 404 Z 26 – *see Great Yarmouth.*

GOSFORTH *Tyne and Wear* 401 402 P 18 – *see Newcastle upon Tyne.*

GOUDHURST *Kent* 404 V 30 – *pop. 2 498.*
London 50 – Hastings 25 – Maidstone 17.

West Winchet without rest., Winchet Hill, TN17 1JX, North : 2 ½ m. on B 20 ✆ (01580) 212024, *annieparker@jpaltd.co.uk, Fax (01580) 212250,* – TV P
closed 1 week Christmas – **3 rm** 35.00/55.00 **s.**

GRAMPOUND *Cornwall* 403 F 33 *The West Country G. – ✉ Truro.*
Env. : *Trewithen★★★ AC, W : 2 m. by A 390 – Probus★ (tower★, Country Demonstrati Garden★ AC) W : 2½ m. by A 390.*
London 287 – Newquay 16 – Plymouth 44 – Truro 8.

Creed House without rest., Creed, TR2 4SL, South : 1 m. by Creed rd turning left just past the church (01872) 530372, <, « Georgian rectory, gardens » – P.
closed Christmas and New Year – **4 rm** 55.00/70.00 **st.**

Eastern Promise, 1 Moor View, TR2 4RT, (01726) 883033 – P. MC AE VISA JCB
closed Wednesday – **Meals** - Chinese - (booking essential) (dinner only) 20.00 and a la carte 20.00/25.00 **t.** 8.50.

ENGLAND

RANGE-IN-BORROWDALE *Cumbria* 402 K 20 – *see Keswick.*

RANGE-OVER-SANDS *Cumbria* 402 L 21 *Great Britain G.* – *pop. 4 473.*

Env. : *Cartmel Priory★, NW : 3 m.*

18 Meathop Rd (015395) 33180 – 9 Grange Fell, Fell Rd (015395) 32536.

Victoria Hall, Main St (015395) 34026.

London 268 – Kendal 13 – Lancaster 24.

Netherwood, Lindale Rd, LA11 6ET, (015395) 32552, *blawith@aol.com, Fax (015395) 34121,* < Morecambe Bay, « Victorian country house, gardens », – , rest, TV – 150. MC VISA
Meals 12.00/27.00 **t.** 10.50 – **28 rm** 60.00/140.00 **t.** – SB.

Graythwaite Manor , Fernhill Rd, LA11 7JE, (015395) 32001, *sales@graythwaite manor.co.uk, Fax (015395) 35549,* <, « Extensive flowered gardens », , – , rest, TV P. MC AE VISA JCB.
Meals 12.00/25.00 and a la carte 11.25/20.95 **t.** 7.50 – **21 rm** 68.00/147.00 **t.** – SB.

Mount Eden , Eden Mount, LA11 6BZ, (015395) 34794, – TV P.
April-October – **Meals** (by arrangement) 12.50 **st.** – **3 rm** 25.00/50.00 **t.**

t Lindale *Northeast : 2 m. on B 5277 – Grange-over-Sands.*

Greenacres, LA11 6LP, (015395) 34578, *Fax (015395) 34578* – TV P. MC VISA JCB.
closed Christmas and New Year – **Meals** (by arrangement) 14.00 6.50 – **4 rm** 30.00/60.00 **s.**

t Witherslack *Northeast : 5 m. by B 5277 off A 590.*

Old Vicarage , Church Rd, LA11 6RS, Northwest : 3/4 m. (015395) 52381, *hotel@old vicarage.com, Fax (015395) 52373,* « Part Georgian country house », , – rest, TV P. MC AE VISA JCB
Meals (dinner only and Sunday lunch)/dinner a la carte 26.50/31.50 **t.** – **14 rm** 90.00/220.00 **t.** – SB.

t Cartmel *Northwest : 3 m.*

Aynsome Manor , LA11 6HH, North : 3/4 m. by Cartmel Priory rd on Wood Broughton rd (015395) 36653, *info@aynsomemanorhotel.co.uk, Fax (015395) 36016,* – rest, TV P. MC AE VISA JCB
closed January – **Meals** *(closed Sunday dinner to non-residents)* (dinner only and Sunday lunch)/dinner 19.50 **t.** 11.65 – **12 rm** (dinner included) 74.00/129.00 **t.** – SB.

Uplands , Haggs Lane, LA11 6HD, East : 1 m. (015395) 36248, *uplands@kencomp. net, Fax (015395) 36848,* <, – rest, TV P. MC AE VISA JCB
closed January and February – **Meals** *(closed Monday and lunch Tuesday and Wednesday)* (booking essential) 15.50/28.50 **t.** 11.50 – **5 rm** (dinner included) 89.00/160.00 **t.**

RANTHAM *Lincs.* 402 404 S 25 *Great Britain G.* – *pop. 33 243.*

See : *St. Wulfram's Church★.*

Env. : *Belton House★ AC, N : 2½ m. by A 607.*

Exc. : *Belvoir Castle★★ AC, W : 6 m. by A 607.*

9, 9, 9 Belton Park, Belton Lane, Londonthorpe Rd (01476) 567399 – 18, 18, 9 Belton Woods H. (01476) 593200.

The Guildhall Centre, St Peter's Hill (01476) 406166.

London 113 – Leicester 31 – Lincoln 29 – Nottingham 24.

Belton Woods, Belton, NG32 2LN, North : 2 m. on A 607 (01476) 593200, *devere. belton@airtime.co.uk, Fax (01476) 574547,* , , , , 18, 9, , , , squash – , rest, TV P – 245. MC AE VISA JCB
Manor : **Meals** (dinner only) a la carte 19.70/31.10 **t.** 9.50 – ***Plus Fours :*** **Meals** 16.00/18.50 **t.** 12.50 – **132 rm** 129.00/149.00, 4 suites – SB.

Grantham Marriott, Swingbridge Rd, NG31 7XT, South : 1 ¼ m. at junction of A 607 with A 1 southbound sliproad (01476) 593000, *deborah.wright@whitbread.com, Fax (01476) 592592,* , , , – , rest, TV P – 200. MC AE VISA
Tapestry : **Meals** 13.00/20.50 a la carte 19.50/35.00 **st.** 12.95 – 13.00 – **89 rm** 79.00 **st.**, 1 suite – SB.

at Great Gonerby *Northwest : 2 m. on B 1174 – Grantham.*

Harry's Place (Hallam), 17 High St, NG31 8JS, (01476) 561780 – P. VISA
closed 25-26 December, 1 January, Sunday and Monday – **Meals** (booking essenti
a la carte 39.50/50.00 **t.** 20.00
Spec. Lobster salad, truffle oil dressing. Roast Lincolnshire pigeon with bacon and sag
Apricot soufflé.

at Grantham Service Area *Northwest : 3 m on B 1174 at junction with A 1 – Grantham.*

Travelodge, NG32 2AB, (01476) 577500, *Fax (01476) 577500* – rm, P.
VISA JCB.
Meals (grill rest.) – **40 rm** 42.95 **t.**

at Woolsthorpe-by-Belvoir *Southwest : 7½ m. by A 607 – Grantham.*

The Chequers with rm, NG32 1LU, (01476) 870701, *Fax (01476) 870085*, , –
P. VISA.
closed Sunday dinner–**Meals** a la carte 18.50/32.70 **t.** 11.00 – 5.00 – **4 rm** 40.00/50.00

GRASMERE *Cumbria* 402 K 20 *Great Britain G.* – *Ambleside.*
See : *Dove Cottage★ AC* **AY A.**
Env. : *Lake Windermere★★, SE : by A 591* **AZ.**
Redbank Rd (015394) 35245 (summer only) **BZ.**
London 282 – Carlisle 43 – Kendal 18.

Plans : see Ambleside

Michaels Nook, LA22 9RP, Northeast : ½ m. off A 591, turning by Swan
(015394) 35496, *m-nook@wordsworth-grasmere.co.uk, Fax (015394) 35645*, mou
tains and countryside, « Victorian country house extensively furnished with antique
landscaped gardens », – rest, P. VISA. **AY**
Meals (booking essential) 34.50/58.00 **t.** 21.00 – **12 rm** (dinner included) 137.5
275.00 **t.**, 2 suites – SB
Spec. Assiette of duckling and foie gras. Nage of lobster and langoustine, scented wi
truffle. Feuillantine of pineapple parfait.

Wordsworth, Stock Lane, LA22 9SW, (015394) 35592, *enquiry@wordsworth.grasme
.co.uk, Fax (015394) 35765*, , , , – , rest, rest, P. – 130.
VISA. **BZ**
Prelude : **Meals** 19.50/30.00 13.50 – **35 rm** (dinner included) 120.00/230.00
2 suites – SB.

Gold Rill, Red Bank Rd, LA22 9PU, (015394) 35486, *enquiries@gold-rill.co
Fax (015394) 35486*, , – rest, rest, P. VISA JCB. **BZ**
closed 9-22 December and 5-17 January – **Meals** (bar lunch)/dinner 20.00 and a la car
25.00 **st.** – **24 rm** (dinner included) 67.00/134.00 **st.**, 1 suite – SB.

Swan, LA22 9RF, on A 591 (0870) 400 8132, *heritagehotels-grasmere.swan@fort
hotels.com, Fax (015394) 35741*, , – P. VISA JCB **AY**
Meals 12.00/25.00 **t.** 15.00 – **38 rm** (dinner included) 95.00/250.00 **st.** – SB.

Red Lion, Red Lion Sq, LA22 9SS, (015394) 35456, *enquiries@hotelgrasmere.uk.co
Fax (015394) 35579*, , – , rest, P. – 60. VISA **BZ**
Meals (bar lunch)/dinner 16.25 and a la carte 6.45/19.85 **st.** 11.00 – **46 rm** 42.0
84.00 **st.**, 1 suite – SB.

Thistle Grasmere, Keswick Rd, LA22 9PR, on A 591 (015394) 35666, *grasmere@thist
.co.uk, Fax (015394) 35565*, , « Lakeside setting », , – P. – 100.
VISA. **AY**
Meals (bar lunch)/dinner 21.50 and a la carte 21.50 **st.** 11.95 – 8.50 – **72 rm** 135.0
151.00 **st.** – SB.

White Moss House, Rydal Water, LA22 9SE, South : 1½ m. on A 591 (015394) 3529
sue@whitemoss.com, Fax (015394) 35516, , – rest, P. VISA. **BY**
closed January and December – **Meals** *(closed Sunday)* (booking essential) (dinner only) (s
menu only) 29.50 **t.** 10.95 – **6 rm** (dinner included) 89.00/178.00 **st.**, 1 suite – SB.

Bridge House, Stock Lane, LA22 9SN, (015394) 35425, *enquiries@bridgehou
grasmere.co.uk, Fax (015394) 35523*, – P. VISA JCB. **BZ**
– **Meals** (dinner only) a la carte 14.50/18.00 **st.** 10.50 – **18 rm** (dinner included) 90.0
110.00 **st.** – SB.

Oak Bank, Broadgate, LA22 9TA, (015394) 35217, *grasmereoakbank@btinternet.co
Fax (015394) 35685*, – P. VISA **BZ**
closed 23-26 December – **Meals** (bar lunch)/dinner 10.95/19.95 **t.** 9.95 – **15 rm** (dinn
included) 52.00/94.00 **t.** – SB.

Grasmere, Broadgate, LA22 9TA, ✆ (015394) 35277, *enquiries@grasmerehotel.co.uk, Fax (015394) 35277,* – rest, VISA JCB BZ r
closed 2 January-12 February – **Meals** (dinner only) 18.50/22.50 11.00 – **12 rm** (dinner included) 45.00/100.00 **st.** – SB.

Lancrigg Vegetarian Country House, Easedale Rd, LA22 9QN, West : ½ m. on Easedale Rd ✆ (015394) 35317, *info@lancrigg.co.uk, Fax (015394) 35058,* ≤ Easedale Valley, – rest, VISA AY u
Meals (lunch by arrangement)/dinner 25.00 **t.** 12.45 – **12 rm** (dinner included) 65.00/198.00 **t.** – SB.

Woodland Crag without rest., How Head Lane, LA22 9SG, Southeast : ¾ m. by B 5287 ✆ (015394) 35351, *woodlandcrag@aol.com, Fax (01539) 435351,* ≤, – VISA JCB. AY s
closed 25-26 December – **5 rm** 22.50/70.00 **t.**

Banerigg without rest., Lake Rd, LA22 9PW, South : ¾ m. on A 591 ✆ (015394) 35204, *banerigg2001@hotmail.com,* ≤, – AY a
closed 25-27 December – **6 rm** 28.00/56.00 **st.**

RASSENDALE *Mersey.* 402 403 L 23 – *see Liverpool.*

RASSINGTON *N. Yorks.* 402 O 21 – *pop. 1 102* – ✉ *Skipton.*
National Park Centre, Colvend, Hebden Rd ✆ (01756) 752774.
London 240 – Bradford 30 – Burnley 28 – Leeds 37.

Ashfield House, Summers Fold, BD23 5AE, ✆ (01756) 752584, *info@ashfieldhouse.co.uk, Fax (01756) 752584,* « Part 17C », – VISA.
– **Meals** (by arrangement) 16.50 **st.** 8.00 – **7 rm** 58.00/68.00 **st.** – SB.

Grassington Lodge without rest., 8 Wood Lane, BD23 5LU, ✆ (01756) 752518, *grassington.lodge@totalise.co.uk, Fax (01756) 752518* –
closed 2 weeks November and 26-26 December – **7 rm** 35.00.

RAVESEND *Kent* 404 V 29 – *pop. 51 435.*
to Tilbury (White Horse Fast Ferries) frequent services daily (approx. 8 mn).
18a St George's Sq ✆ (01474) 337600.
London 25 – Dover 54 – Maidstone 16 – Margate 53.

Manor, Hever Court Rd, Singlewell, DA12 5UQ, Southeast : 2 ½ m. by A 227 off A 2 (eastbound carriageway) ✆ (01474) 353100, *manorhotel@clara.net, Fax (01474) 354978,* , , – , rest, – 200. VISA.
Meals *(closed Saturday and Sunday)* (bar lunch)/dinner 18.00 and a la carte 20.95/32.00 **st.** 11.75 – **52 rm** 78.00/150.00 **st.**

Overcliffe, 15-16 Overcliffe, DA11 0EF, on A 226 (Dartford rd) ✆ (01474) 322131, *Fax (01474) 536737,* – VISA
Meals (dinner only) a la carte 18.50/25.00 **t.** 9.50 – **29 rm** 75.00/85.00 **t.**

Travel Inn, Wrotham Rd, DA11 7LF, South : 1 m. on A 227 ✆ (01474) 533556, *Fax (01474) 323776* – rm, VISA JCB
Meals (grill rest.) – **36 rm** 41.95 **t.**

RAVETYE *W. Sussex* – *see East Grinstead.*

RAZELEY GREEN *Wokingham* – *see Reading.*

REAT BADDOW *Essex* 404 V 28 – *see Chelmsford.*

REAT BARR *W. Mids.* 403 404 O 26 – *see Birmingham.*

REAT BROUGHTON *N. Yorks.* 402 Q 20 – *pop. 937 (inc. Little Broughton)* – ✉ *Middlesbrough.*
London 241 – Leeds 61 – Middlesbrough 10 – York 54.

Wainstones, 31 High St, TS9 7EW, ✆ (01642) 712268, *wstones@netcomuk.co.uk, Fax (01642) 711560* – – 120. VISA JCB.
Meals a la carte 17.15/20.75 **t.** – **24 rm** 62.50/82.50 **t.** – SB.

GREAT DUNMOW *Essex* 404 V 28 – *pop. 4 907.*
London 42 – Cambridge 27 – Chelmsford 13 – Colchester 24.

XXX **The Starr** with rm, Market Pl, CM6 1AX, ✆ (01371) 874321, *starrestaurant@btintern com, Fax (01371) 876337* – ⇔ TV P – 35. MC AE D VISA
closed 1-4 January – **Meals** *(closed Sunday dinner)* 23.00/35.00 **st.** 12.50 – **8 rm** 70.0 130.00 **st.**

GREAT GONERBY *Lincs.* 402 404 S 25 – *see Grantham.*

GREAT GRIMSBY *N.E. Lincs.* 402 404 T 23.
London 173 – Boston 51 – Kingston-upon-Hull 33 – Lincoln 37 – Sheffield 73.

Travel Inn, Europa Park, off Gilbey Rd, DN31 2UT, ✆ (01472) 242630, *Fax (01472) 2502* – ⇔ rm, ▤ rest, TV ♿ P. MC AE D VISA. ✻
Meals (grill rest.) – **40 rm** 41.95 **t.**

GREAT LONGSTONE *Derbs.* 402 403 404 O 24 – *see Bakewell.*

Es ist empfehlenswert, ***in der Hauptsaison*** *und vor allem in Urlaubsorten, Hotelzimmer im voraus zu bestellen. Benachrichtigen Sie sofort das Hotel, wenn Sie ein bestelltes Zimmer nicht belegen können.*

Wenn Sie an ein Hotel im Ausland schreiben, fügen Sie Ihrem Brief einen internationalen Antwortschein bei (im Postamt erhältlich).

GREAT MALVERN *Worcs.* 403 404 N 27 – *pop. 31 537.*
21 Church St ✆ (01684) 892289 B.
London 127 – Birmingham 34 – Cardiff 66 – Gloucester 24.

Plan opposite

Red Gate without rest., 32 Avenue Rd, WR14 3BJ, ✆ (01684) 565013, *red_gate@lineo net, Fax (01684) 565013,* – ⇔ TV P. MC VISA. ✻ B
closed 25 December – **7 rm** 36.00/70.00.

Pembridge, 114 Graham Rd, WR14 2HX, ✆ (01684) 574813, *pembridgehotel@aol.co Fax (01684) 566885,* – ⇔ TV P. MC AE VISA. ✻ B
closed 22 December-5 January – **Meals** *(closed Sunday)* 13.50/17.50 and a la carte 15.50 8.95 – **8 rm** 48.00/68.00 **t.** – SB.

Cowleigh Park Farm without rest., Cowleigh Rd, WR13 5HJ, Northwest : 1 ½ m. B 4232 on B 4219 ✆ (01684) 566750, *cowleighparkfarm@talk21.com, Fax (01684) 5667* « Part 17C farmhouse », – ⇔ TV P A
closed 1 week Christmas – **3 rm** 38.00/58.00 **st.**

at Welland *Southeast : 4½ m. by A 449 on A 4104 – ✉ Great Malvern.*

Holdfast Cottage ⊗, Marlbank Rd, WR13 6NA, West : ¾ m. on A 41 ✆ (01684) 310288, *holdcothot@aol.com, Fax (01684) 311117,* « 17C country cottage », – ⇔ TV P. MC VISA A
closed 2 weeks January and New Year – **Meals** (booking essential) (dinner only) 26.00 **st** **8 rm** 50.00/92.00 **st.** – SB.

at Malvern Wells *South : 2 m. on A 449 – ✉ Malvern.*

Cottage in the Wood ⊗, Holywell Rd, WR14 4LG, ✆ (01684) 575859, *proprie @cottageinthewood.co.uk, Fax (01684) 560662,* ← Severn and Evesham Vales, ⇔ rest, ▤ rest, TV P. MC AE VISA JCB A
Meals 15.95 (lunch) and dinner a la carte 31.75/37.00 **st.** 13.95 – **20 rm** 77.0 150.00 **st.** – SB.

XX ✿ **Croque-en-Bouche** (Marion Jones), 221 Wells Rd, WR14 4HF, ✆ (01684) 565612, *ma croque-en-bouche.co.uk, Fax (0870) 7066232* – ⇔. MC VISA A
closed 1 week May, 1 week July, 1 week September, Christmas-New Year and Sunday Wednesday – **Meals** (booking essential) (dinner only) 29.00/35.00 **st.** 7.50
Spec. Crab and lobster croustade with bouillabaisse sauce. Japanese style selections. Sala and herbs from the garden.

X **Planters,** 191-193 Wells Rd, WR14 4HE, ✆ (01684) 575065 – MC VISA A
closed 25 26 December, January, Sunday, Monday and Tuesday – **Meals** - South East Asia (booking essential) (dinner only) 17.50/28.50 and a la carte 20.75/23.90 **t.** 9.50.

Street	Map	Ref
Albert Road South	B	3
Blackmore Park Road	A	5
Church Street	B	
Clerkenwell Crescent	B	6
Cockshot Road	B	8
Court Road	B	12
Croft Bank	A	13
Happy Valley off St. Ann's Road	B	15
Imperial Road	B	16
Jubilee Drive	A	17
Lygon Bank	B	18
Madresfield Road	B	20
Moorlands Road	B	22
North Malvern Road	B	23
Orchard Road	B	24
Richmond Road	B	25
Townsend Way	A	26
Upper Welland Road	A	27
Walwyn Road	A	29
Wells Road	B	
Wells Road	A	30
Zetland Road	B	31

Town plans
roads most used by traffic and those on which guide listed hotels and restaurants stand are fully drawn; the beginning only of lesser roads is indicated.

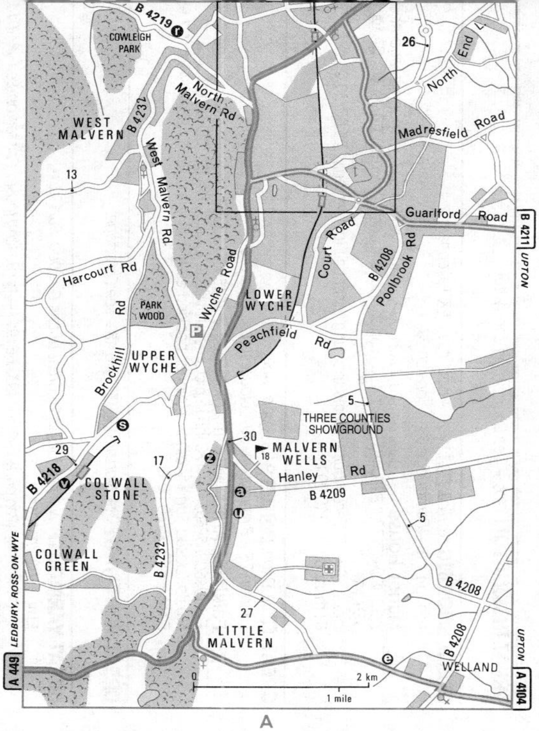

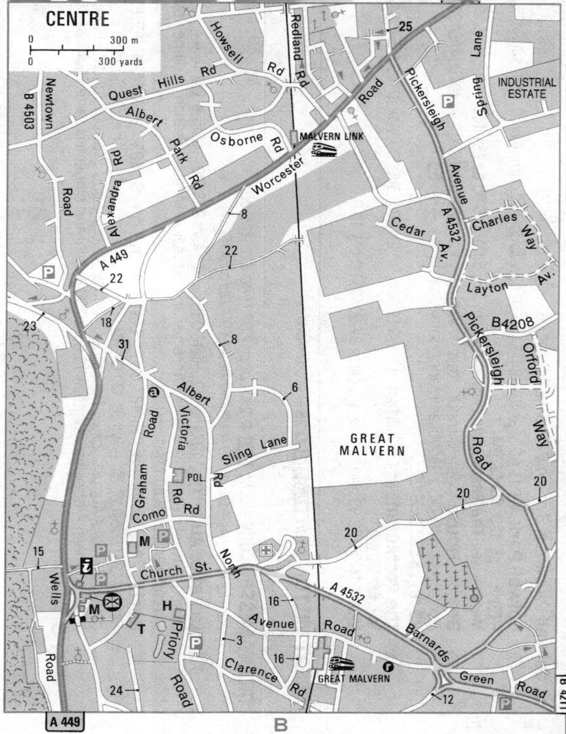

ENGLAND

at Colwall *Southwest : 3 m. on B 4218 – ✉ Great Malvern.*

Colwall Park, WR13 6QG, ✆ (01684) 540000, *hotel@colwall.com, Fax (01684) 540847,* – TV P – 120. MC AE VISA A
Meals – (see ***The Restaurant*** below) – **20 rm** 65.00/120.00 **t.**, 2 suites – SB.

Brook House without rest., Walwyn Rd, WR13 6QX, ✆ (01684) 5406(
Fax (01684) 540604, « Jacobean manor house, gardens » – TV P. A
– **3 rm** 39.50/59.00.

The Restaurant (at Colwall Park H.), WR13 6QG, ✆ (01684) 540000, *Fax (01684) 54084.*
. MC AE VISA A
Meals 14.95/22.95 and dinner a la carte 27.20/35.80 **t.** 10.95.

GREAT MILTON *Oxon.* 403 404 Q 28 – *see Oxford.*

GREAT MISSENDEN *Bucks.* 404 R 28 – *pop. 7 980 (inc. Prestwood).*
London 34 – Aylesbury 10 – Maidenhead 19 – Oxford 35.

La Petite Auberge, 107 High St, HP16 0BB, ✆ (01494) 865370 – MC VISA JCB
closed 2 weeks Easter, 2 weeks Christmas and Sunday – **Meals** - French - (dinner or
a la carte 24.20/29.60 **t.** 12.60.

Berts, Chesham Rd, HP16 0QT, East : 1 m. on B 485 ✆ (01494) 8656
Fax (01494) 866406, – P. MC AE VISA
closed 2 weeks August, 25-26 December, Sunday, Monday, and Saturday lunch – **Meal**
Mediterranean - (booking essential) 15.00/20.00 (lunch) and dinner a la carte 20.40/31.35
10.95.

There is no paid advertising in this Guide.

GREAT RISSINGTON *Glos. – see Bourton-on-the-Water.*

GREAT SNORING *Norfolk* 404 W 25 – *pop. 191 – ✉ Fakenham.*
London 115 – Cambridge 68 – Norwich 28.

Manor House , Barsham Rd, NR21 0HP, ✆ (01328) 820597, *gtsnoringmanorho@
com, Fax (01328) 820048,* « Part 15C manor house », – rest, TV P. MC AE
JCB.
closed 24-27 December – **Meals** (booking essential) (dinner only) 25.00/30.00 **t.** 9.5(
6 rm 80.00/110.00 **t.**

GREAT TEW *Oxon.* 403 404 P 28 – *pop. 145.*
London 75 – Birmingham 50 – Gloucester 42 – Oxford 21.

Falkland Arms with rm, OX7 4DB, ✆ (01608) 683653, *sjcourage@btconnect.co
Fax (01608) 683656,* « 17C inn in picturesque village », – TV. MC AE VISA JCB.
Meals *(closed Sunday dinner)* (dinner booking essential) a la carte 12.95/20.45 **t.** 7.9
5 rm 50.00/80.00 **t.**

GREAT WHITTINGTON *Northd.* 401 402 O 18 – *see Corbridge.*

GREAT YARMOUTH *Norfolk* 404 Z 26 *Great Britain G. – pop. 56 190.*
Env. : *The Broads★.*
*18 Gorleston, Warren Rd ✆ (01493) 661911 – 18 Beach House, Caister-on-Sea ✆ (014
728699.*
Town Hall ✆ (01493) 846221.
London 126 – Cambridge 81 – Ipswich 53 – Norwich 20.

Elizabeth, Marine Par, NR30 3AG, ✆ (01493) 855551, *enquiries@hotelelizabeth.co.
Fax (01493) 853338* – TV – 150. MC AE VISA.
Meals 11.95/17.95 (dinner) and a la carte 13.85/26.85 **st.** 8.95 – **47 rm** 50.00/90.00
3 suites – SB.

Imperial, North Drive, NR30 1EQ, ✆ (01493) 842000, *imperial@scs_datacom.co.
Fax (01493) 852229* – , rm, rest, TV P – 140. MC AE VISA
Rambouillet : **Meals** *(closed lunch Saturday and Bank Holiday Monday)* 12.50/21
and a la carte 16.25/26.25 **t.** 12.50 – **39 rm** 69.00/86.00 **t.** – SB.

at **Gorleston-on-Sea** *South : 3 m. on A 12 – ✉ Great Yarmouth.*

Cliff, Cliff Hill, NR31 6DH, ✆ (01493) 662179, *cliffhotel@aol.com, Fax (01493) 653617,* – rest, TV P – 170. MC AE D VISA JCB
Meals 13.95/17.95 and (dinner) a la carte 19.95/26.40 **t.** 10.25 – **38 rm** 75.00/95.00 **st.**, 1 suite – SB.

GREAT YELDHAM *Essex* 404 V 27 – *pop. 1 513* – ✉ *Colchester.*
London 58 – Cambridge 29 – Chelmsford 24 – Colchester 21 – Ipswich 37.

White Hart, Poole St, CO9 4HJ, ✆ (01787) 237250, *whitehartyeldham@hotmail.com, Fax (01787) 238044,* , « 16C inn », – P. MC AE D VISA
Meals a la carte 14.45/23.95 **st.** 10.00.

GREEN ISLAND *Jersey (Channel Islands) – see Channel Islands.*

GRENOSIDE *S. Yorks.* 402 403 404 P 23 – *see Sheffield.*

GRETA BRIDGE *Durham* 402 O 20 – *see Barnard Castle.*

GREVE DE LECQ *Jersey (Channel Islands)* 403 P 33 and 230 ⑪ – *see Channel Islands.*

GRIMSBY *N.E Lincs.* 402 404 T 23 – *see Great Grimsby.*

GRIMSTHORPE *Lincs.* 402 404 S 25 – ✉ *Bourne.*
London 114 – Leicester 38 – Peterborough 22 – Lincoln 38.

Black Horse Inn with rm, PE10 0LY, on A 151 ✆ (01778) 591247, *dine@blackhorseinn.co.uk, Fax (01778) 591373,* – rest, TV P. MC AE D VISA JCB.
Meals *(closed dinner Sunday and Monday)* a la carte 17.00/25.00 10.00 – **5 rm** 50.00/79.00 **t.**, 1 suite.

GRIMSTON *Norfolk* 404 V 25 – *see King's Lynn.*

GRINDLEFORD *Derbs.* 402 403 404 P 24 – ✉ *Sheffield (S. Yorks.).*
London 165 – Derby 31 – Manchester 34 – Sheffield 10.

Maynard Arms, Main Rd, S32 2HE, on B 6521 ✆ (01433) 630321, *info@maynardarms.co.uk, Fax (01433) 630445,* ≤, – rest, TV P – 130. MC AE VISA
Padley : **Meals** *(closed Saturday lunch)* a la carte approx. 23.40 **t.** 10.25 – **8 rm** 69.00/79.00 **t.**, 2 suites – SB.

GRIZEDALE *Cumbria* 402 K 20 – *see Hawkshead.*

GROUVILLE *Jersey (Channel Islands)* 403 P 33 and 230 ⑪ – *see Channel Islands.*

GUERNSEY 403 OP 33 and 230 ⑨ ⑩ – *see Channel Islands.*

GUILDFORD *Surrey* 404 S 30 – *pop. 65 998.*
ℹ *14 Tunsgate* ✆ *(01483) 444333* Y.
London 33 – Brighton 43 – Reading 27 – Southampton 49.

Plan on next page

Angel Posting House and Livery, High St, GU1 3DP, ✆ (01483) 564555, *angelhotel@hotmail.com, Fax (01483) 533770,* « 16C coaching inn with 13C vaulted cellar restaurant » – , rest, rest, TV – 70. MC AE D VISA JCB. Y e
No 1 Angel Gate : **Meals** 18.50/32.00 and a la carte **st.** 11.50 – 13.50 – **14 rm** 140.00 **st.**, 7 suites – SB.

Holiday Inn, Egerton Rd, GU2 7XZ, ✆ (0870) 400 9036, *Fax (01483) 302960,* , , , – rm, TV P – 200. MC AE D VISA JCB Z v
Meals *(closed Saturday lunch)* 10.00/15.00 a la carte 18.85/28.85 **t.** 11.95 – 14.95 – **163 rm** 165.00 **t.**, 4 suites.

GUILDFORD

Bedford Road . . . . Y 2
Bridge Street. . . . . Y 3
Castle Street . . . . Y 5
Chertsey Street . . . . Y 6
Commercial Road. . . . . Y 8
Eastgate Gardens. . . . . Y 9
Friary Bridge . . . . Y 12
Friary Centre . . . . Y
High Street . . . . Y
Ladymead . . . . Z 13
Leapale Lane. . . . . Y 15
Leapale Road . . . . Y 16
Leas Road . . . . Y 17
Market Street . . . . Y 18
Mary Road. . . . . Y 19
Midleton Road . . . . Z 20
Millbrook . . . . Y 21
New Inn Lane . . . . Z 22
North Street . . . . Y
One Tree Hill Road. . . . . Z 24
Onslow Street . . . . Y 25
Park Street . . . . Y 27
Quarry Street . . . . Y 28
Stoughton Road . . . . Z 30
Trood's Lane . . . . Z 31
Tunsgate Shopping Centre . . . . . . Y
Tungsgate . . . . Y 33
Warwick's Bench . . . . Y 34
Woodbridge Road . . . . Z 37

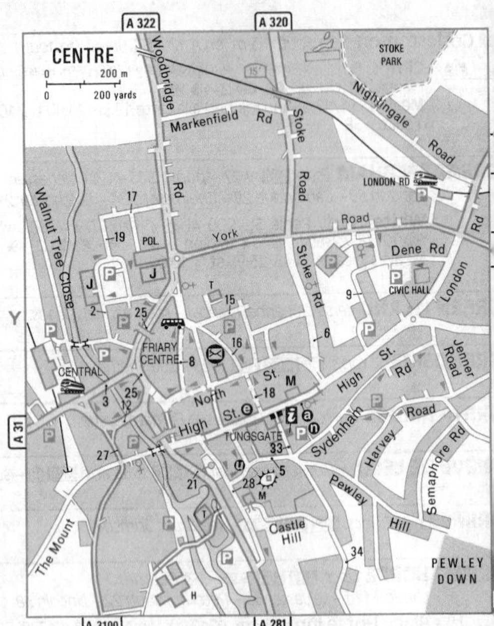

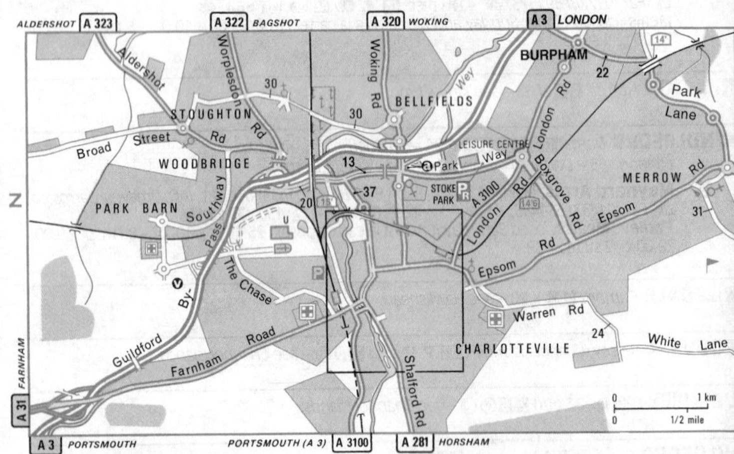

Travel Inn, Parkway, GU1 1UP, North : 1 ½ m. by A 320 on A 25 ✆ (01483) 30493 Z
Fax (01483) 304935 – |♦|, ⇔ rm, ▤ rest, TV & P – 45. MC AE ◑ VISA. ✕
Meals (grill rest.) – **87 rm** 41.95 **t.**

Café de Paris, 35 Castle St, GU1 3UQ, ✆ (01483) 534896, *Fax (01483) 300411* – MC VISA Y
closed Sunday – **Meals** - French - 16.50 (lunch) and a la carte 15.50/29.00 **t.**

Fish, Rooftop, Sydenham Road Car Park, GU1 3RT, ✆ (020) 7234 3333, *fish@bgr.plc.* Y
Fax (020) 7234 3343, ←, « Rooftop terrace » – ▤. MC AE ◑ VISA
closed 31 August and Sunday dinner – **Meals** - Seafood - a la carte 22.00/34.00 **t.** 10.00

The Gate, No 3 Milkhouse Gate, GU1 3EZ, ✆ (01483) 576300 – ⇔. MC AE ◑ VISA Y
closed Sunday – **Meals** 14.00/17.00 (lunch) and a la carte 26.70/33.95 **t.** 14.00.

Shere *East : 6 ¾ m. by A 246 off A 25 – Z – ✉ Guildford.*

🍴🍴 **Kinghams,** Gomshall Lane, GU5 9HE, ✆ (01483) 202168, *Fax (01483) 202168,* « 17C cottage » – P. MC AE ① VISA JCB
closed 25 December-2 January, Sunday dinner and Monday – **Meals** (booking essential) a la carte 26.85/29.98 **t.** 11.95.

JITING POWER *Glos.* 403 404 O 28 – ✉ *Cheltenham.*
London 95 – Birmingham 47 – Gloucester 30 – Oxford 39.

Guiting Guest House, Post Office Lane, GL54 5TZ, ✆ (01451) 850470, *guiting.guesthouse@virgin.net, Fax (01451) 850034,* « 16C farmhouse » – TV. MC VISA JCB
closed 2 weeks spring and 3 days Christmas – **Meals** (by arrangement) 20.00 – **5 rm** 38.00/60.00 **st.**

JLWORTHY CROSS *Devon* 403 H 32 – *see Tavistock.*

JNTHORPE *Notts.* 402 403 404 R 25 – *pop. 646.*
London 132 – Lincoln 32 – Nottingham 12 – Sheffield 40.

Unicorn, Gunthorpe Bridge, NG14 7FB, Southeast : 1 ½ m. by A 6097 and Gunthorpe (riverside) rd ✆ (0115) 966 3612, *Fax (0115) 966 4801,* ←, – ⚓, rest, TV P. MC AE VISA.
Meals (grill rest.) (bar lunch Monday-Saturday)/dinner a la carte 10.05/19.85 **t.** 7.45 – **15 rm** 51.00/62.00 **t.**

JNWALLOE *Cornwall* 403 E 33 – *see Helston.*

ACKNESS *N. Yorks.* 402 S 21 – *see Scarborough.*

ADDENHAM *Bucks.* 404 R 28 – *pop. 4 906.*
London 54 – Aylesbury 8 – Oxford 21.

Green Dragon, Churchway, HP17 8AA, ✆ (01844) 291403, *the.greendragon@virgin.net, Fax (01844) 299532,* – P. MC AE VISA
Meals (booking essential) a la carte 18.00/22.00 **t.** 10.95.

ADLEIGH *Suffolk* 404 W 27 – *pop. 6 595.*
Hadleigh Library, 29 High St ✆ (01473) 823778.
London 72 – Cambridge 49 – Colchester 17 – Ipswich 10.

Edge Hall, 2 High St, IP7 5AP, ✆ (01473) 822458, *Fax (01473) 827751,* – TV P.
Meals 25.00 **st.** 8.00 **9 rm** 40.00/80.00 **st.** – SB.

ADLEY HEATH *Worcs. – see Droitwich Spa.*

AILEY *Oxon.* 403 404 P 28 – *see Witney.*

AILSHAM *E. Sussex* 404 U 31 – *pop. 18 426.*
Wellshurst G. & C.C., North St., Hellingly ✆ (01435) 813636.
London 57 – Brighton 23 – Eastbourne 7 – Hastings 20.

Travelodge, Boship Roundabout, Lower Dicker, BN27 4DT, Northwest : 3 m. by A 295 and A 22 on A 267 ✆ (01323) 844556, *Fax (01323) 844556* – rm, rest, TV & P. MC AE ① VISA JCB.
Meals (grill rest.) – **58 rm** 49.95 **t.**

Magham Down *Northeast : 2 m. by A 295 on A 271 – ✉ Hailsham.*

Olde Forge, BN27 1PN, ✆ (01323) 842893, *theoldeforgehotelandrestaurant@tesco.net, Fax (01323) 842893* – TV P. MC VISA
Meals (dinner only) 23.50 **t.** 10.50 – **7 rm** 45.00/65.00 **st.** – SB.

ALE *Gtr. Manchester* 402 403 404 M 23 – *see Altrincham.*

ALEBARNS *Gtr. Manchester* 402 ㉝ 403 ③ 404 ⑨ – *see Altrincham.*

HALFWAY BRIDGE *W. Sussex* 404 R 31 – *see Petworth.*

HALIFAX *W. Yorks.* 402 O 22 – *pop. 91 069.*

Halifax Bradley Hall, Holywell Green (01422) 374108 – Halifax West End, Paddc Lane, Highroad Well (01422) 353608, Union Lane, Ogden (01422) 244171 – Ryburn, Norland, Sowerby Bridge (01422) 831355 – Lightcliffe, Knowle Top (01422) 202459.

Piece Hall (01422) 368725.

London 205 – Bradford 8 – Burnley 21 – Leeds 15 – Manchester 28.

Holdsworth House, Holmfield, HX2 9TG, North : 3 m. by A 629 and Shay La (01422) 240024, *info@holdsworthhouse.co.uk, Fax (01422) 245174,* « Part 17C mar house », – – 150. VISA
closed 26 to 30 December – **Meals** *(closed lunch Saturday and Sunday)* 13. (lunch) and a la carte 25.00/35.20 **t.** 12.50 – 8.25 – **36 rm** 90.00/110.00 **t.**, 4 suites – S

Imperial Crown, 42-46 Horton St, HX1 1QE, (01422) 342342, *Fax (01422) 34986*
rm, – 150. VISA
Meals (bar lunch Monday to Friday)/dinner a la carte 15.25/28.05 **st.** 14.95 – 10.7
39 rm 85.00/99.00 **st.**, 2 suites – SB.

Travelodge without rest., Dean Clough (Gate 9), HX3 5AH, (01422) 3622
Fax (01422) 362151 – , rm, . VISA JCB.
52 rm 42.95 **t.**

Design House (Restaurant), Dean Clough (Gate 5), HX3 5AX, (01422) 3832
enquiries@designhouserestaurant.co.uk, Fax (01422) 322732 – . VISA
closed 25-26 December, 1 January, Sunday and Saturday lunch – **Meals** - Italian influence 15.95 (dinner) and a la carte 23.90/29.40 **st.** 12.00.

Les prix — Pour toutes précisions sur les prix indiqués dans ce guide, reportez-vous aux pages de l'introduction.

HALLAND *E. Sussex* 404 U 31 – *Lewes.*

London 59 – Brighton 17 – Eastbourne 15 – Maidstone 35.

Shortgate Manor Farm without rest., BN8 6PJ, Southwest : 1 m. on B 21 (01825) 840320, *ewalt@shortgate.co.uk, Fax (01825) 840320,* – .
3 rm 40.00/65.00.

HALL GREEN *W. Mids.* 402 403 404 O 26 – *see Birmingham.*

HALNAKER *W. Sussex* – *see Chichester.*

HALTWHISTLE *Northd.* 401 402 M 19 *Great Britain G.* – *pop. 3 773.*

Env. : *Hadrian's Wall★★, N : 4½ m. by A 6079 – Housesteads★★ AC, NE : 6 m. by B 631 Roman Army Museum★ AC, NW : 5 m. by A 69 and B 6318 – Vindolanda (Museum★) A NE : 5 m. by A 69 – Steel Rig (≤★) NE : 5½ m. by B 6318.*

Wallend Farm, Greenhead (01697) 747367.

Railway Station, Station Rd (01434) 322002.

London 335 – Carlisle 22 – Newcastle upon Tyne 37.

Centre of Britain, Main St, NE49 0BH, (01434) 322422, *enquiries@centre-of-brita org.uk, Fax (01434) 322655* – . VISA
Meals 10.00/16.95 and a la carte 10.00/18.95 **t.** 8.95 – **10 rm** 39.00/96.00 **t.** – SB.

Ashcroft without rest., Lantys Lonnen, NE49 0DA, (01434) 320213, *enquiries@ashcr guesthouse.freeserve.co.uk, Fax (01434) 321641,* « Gardens » – . VISA.
closed 1 week October and 25 December – **7 rm** 25.00/56.00 **st.**

Broomshaw Hill Farm without rest., Willia Rd, NE49 9NP, North : ¾ m. by Aes Rd (off High St) on Willia Rd, follow signs for Hadrians Wall and Bun Gor (01434) 320866, *stay@broomshaw.com, Fax (01434) 320866,* – .
March-October – **3 rm** 48.00 **st.**

HAMBLETON *Rutland* – *see Oakham.*

HAMBROOK *South Gloucestershire* 403 404 M 29 – *see Bristol.*

HAMSTERLEY *Durham* 401 402 O 19 – *pop. 397* – ✉ *Bishop Auckland.*
London 260 – Carlisle 75 – Middlesbrough 30 – Newcastle upon Tyne 22.

Grove House, Hamsterley Forest, DL13 3NL, West : 3 ½ m. by Woodland rd on Hamsterley Forest Drive ☎ (01388) 488203, *x0v47@dial.pipex.com, Fax (01388) 488174,* « Former shooting lodge », – P.
closed Christmas and New Year – **Meals** (by arrangement) 22.50 **s.** – **3 rm** 26.00/65.00.

HANDFORTH *Ches.* 402 403 404 N 23 – *see Wilmslow.*

HANWOOD *Shrops.* 402 403 L 25 – *see Shrewsbury.*

HARDWICK *Cambs.* – *see Cambridge.*

HAREWOOD *W. Yorks.* 402 P 22 – *pop. 3 222* – ✉ *Leeds.*
London 214 – Harrogate 9 – Leeds 10 – York 20.

Harewood Arms, Harrogate Rd, LS17 9LH, on A 61 ☎ (0113) 288 6566, *unwind@the-harewood-arms-hotel.co.uk, Fax (0113) 288 6064,* – rest, P. MC AE VISA
Meals (bar lunch Monday-Saturday)/dinner 17.50/21.50 **t.** – **24 rm** 70.00/84.00 **t.**

Keine bezahlte Reklame im ***Michelin-Führer.***

HARLOW *Essex* 404 U 28 – *pop. 74 629.*
18 *Nazeing, Middle St ☎ (01992) 893798.*
London 22 – Cambridge 37 – Ipswich 60.

Swallow Churchgate, Churchgate St, Old Harlow, CM17 0JT, East : 3 ¼ m. by A 414 and B 183 ☎ (01279) 420246, *gillian.crichton@whitbread.com, Fax (01279) 437720,* , , , – P – 170. MC AE VISA JCB
closed 24-29 December – **Meals** (bar lunch Saturday) 21.95 (dinner) and a la carte 23.40/29.20 **st.** 12.95 – 11.00 – **82 rm** 99.00/132.00 **t.**, 3 suites – SB.

Harlow/Stansted Moat House, Southern Way, CM18 7BA, Southeast : 2 ¼ m. by A 1025 on A 414 ☎ (01279) 829988, *revhar@queensmoat.co.uk, Fax (01279) 635094,* , , , – , rest, P – 200. MC AE VISA JCB.
Meals (bar lunch Saturday) 15.95/17.95 and a la carte 11.70/29.10 13.75 – 11.50 – **119 rm** 120.00/140.00 **t.** – SB.

Green Man, Mulberry Green, Old Harlow, CM17 0ET, East : 2 ¼ m. by A 414 and B 183 ☎ (01279) 442521, *reservations@corushotels.com, Fax (01279) 626113,* – rm, P – 60. MC AE VISA
Meals (bar lunch Monday-Saturday)/dinner 16.85 and a la carte 16.85/23.85 **st.** 9.95 – 10.95 – **55 rm** 95.00/105.00 **st.**

Travel Inn, Cambridge Rd, Old Harlow, CM20 2EP, Northeast : 3 ¼ m. by A 414 on A 1184 ☎ (01279) 442545, *Fax (01279) 452169* – rm, P. MC AE VISA.
Meals (grill rest.) – **62 rm** 41.95 **t.**

at North Weald *Southeast : 6 ¼ m. by A 1025 on A 414* – ✉ *Harlow.*

Travelodge, CM16 1BJ, ☎ (01992) 523726, *Fax (01992) 523726* – rm, rest, P. MC AE VISA JCB.
Meals (grill rest.) – **60 rm** 59.95 **t.**

HARNHAM *Wilts.* 403 404 O 30 – *see Salisbury.*

HAROME *N. Yorks.* – *see Helmsley.*

HARPENDEN *Herts.* 404 S 28 – *pop. 28 097.*
18 *Harpenden Common, East Commmon ☎ (01582) 712856* – 18 *Hammonds End, ☎ (01582) 712580.*
London 32 – Luton 6.

Hanover International, 1 Luton Rd, AL5 2PX, ☎ (01582) 760271, *david.hunter9@virgin.net, Fax (01582) 460819,* – , rm, rest, P – 150. MC AE VISA JCB
closed 25-30 December – ***Sheldons Brasserie :*** **Meals** a la carte 21.00/25.00 **t.** 12.00 – 11.95 – **58 rm** 102.50/160.00 **st.**, 2 suites – SB.

HARROGATE *N. Yorks.* **402** P 22 *Great Britain G.* – *pop. 66 178.*

See : *Town*★ – **Exc.** : *Fountains Abbey*★★★ **AC** :- *Studley Royal*★★ **AC** (≤★ *from Anne Boleyn's Seat) - Fountains Hall (Façade*★), *N* : *13 m. by A 61 and B 6265* **AY** – *Harewood House*★★ *(The Gallery*★) **AC**, *S* : *7½ m. by A 61* **BZ**.

Forest Lane Head ℘ *(01423) 863158* – *Follifoot Rd, Pannal* ℘ *(01423) 871641* – *Oakdale* ℘ *(01423) 567162* – *Crimple Valley, Hookstone Wood Rd* ℘ *(01423) 883485.*

Royal Baths Assembly Rooms, Crescent Rd ℘ *(01423) 537300.*

London 211 – Bradford 18 – Leeds 15 – Newcastle upon Tyne 76 – York 22.

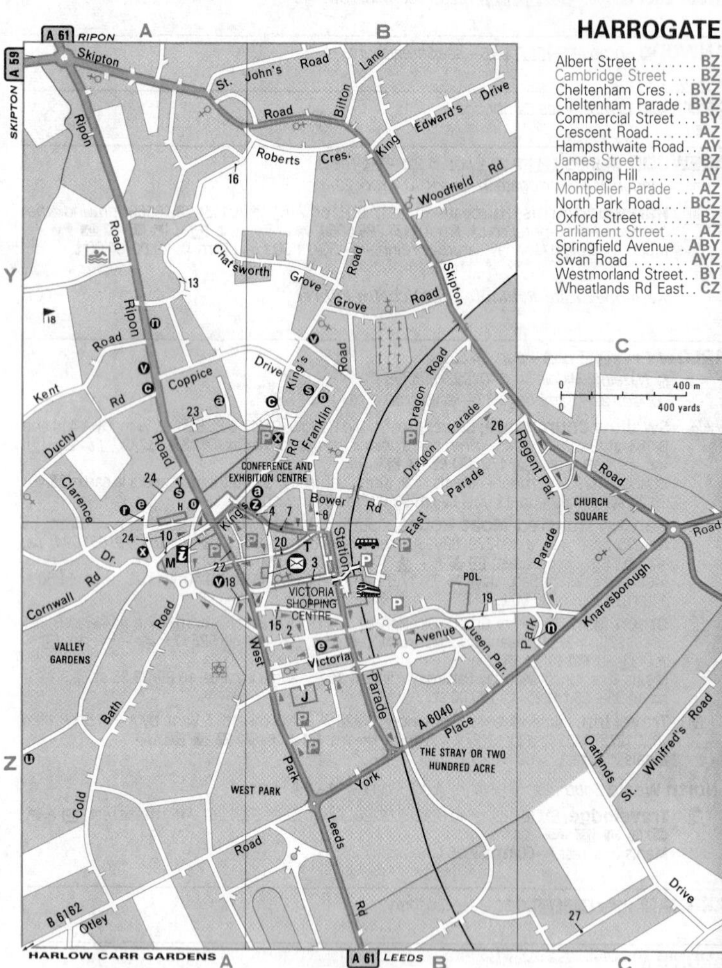

Rudding Park, Rudding Park, Follifoot, HG3 1JH, Southeast : 3 ¾ m. by A 6… ℘ (01423) 871350, *sales@rudding-park.com, Fax (01423) 872286*, – rm, rest, – 300. **VISA**.

The Clocktower **:** Meals 15.95/24.50 **t.** 11.50 – **48 rm** 115.00/165.00 **st.**, 2 suites – …

Cedar Court, Queen Building, Park Par, HG1 5AH, ℘ (01423) 858585, *cedarcourt@b… western.co.uk, Fax (01423) 504950*, – , rm, rest, – 325. **VISA**.
CZ

Queens **:** Meals *(closed Saturday lunch)* 12.50/23.50 **t.** 10.95 – **100 rm** 120.0… 195.00 **st.** – SB.

Harrogate Moat House, Kings Rd, HG1 1XX, ✆ (01423) 849988, *cbhgt@queensmoat.co.uk, Fax (01423) 524435,* ← – |‡|, ⇔ rm, ▤ rest, TV ♿ P – 🎤 400. MC AE ⓓ VISA JCB BY x
Abbey : Meals (carvery) (dinner only) 18.50 **st.** 🍷 11.95 – ***Boulevard :*** Meals (dinner only) a la carte 16.60/28.80 **st.** 🍷 11.95 – ☕ 11.50 – **205 rm** 122.00/144.00 **st.**, 9 suites – SB.

Swallow St George, 1 Ripon Rd, HG1 2SY, ✆ (01423) 561431, *info@swallowhotels.com, Fax (01423) 530037,* 🏋, ≘s, 🏊 – |‡| ⇔ TV 📞 P – 🎤 120. MC AE ⓓ VISA JCB. ✗ AY o
Meals (bar lunch)/dinner 19.95 **st.** 🍷 12.50 – **89 rm** ☕ 105.00/130.00 **st.**, 1 suite – SB.

Old Swan, Swan Rd, HG1 2SR, ✆ (01423) 500055, *gm.oldswan@macdonald-hotels.co.uk, Fax (01423) 500055,* 🌳 – |‡| ⇔ TV P – 🎤 400. MC AE ⓓ VISA JCB. ✗ AY e
Wedgewood Room : Meals (dinner only and Sunday lunch)/dinner 22.50 and a la carte 18.75/29.95 **st.** 🍷 13.50 – ***Library :*** Meals *(closed Sunday)* (dinner only) a la carte 18.75/29.95 **st.** 🍷 13.50 – ☕ 10.95 – **127 rm** 105.00/135.00 **st.**, 9 suites – SB.

The Balmoral, Franklin Mount, HG1 5EJ, ✆ (01423) 508208, *info@balmoralhotel.co.uk, Fax (01423) 530652,* « Antique furnishings », 🌳 – TV P. MC AE VISA JCB BY v
Meals – (see ***Villu Toots*** below) – **18 rm** ☕ 872.00/184.00 **t.**, 4 suites.

Grants, Swan Rd, HG1 2SS, ✆ (01423) 560666, *enquiries@grantshotel-harrogate.com, Fax (01423) 502550* – |‡|, ⇔ rest, ▤ rest, TV P – 🎤 70. MC AE ⓓ VISA JCB AY s
Chimney Pots Bistro : Meals a la carte 9.00/24.40 **t.** 🍷 11.50 – **41 rm** ☕ 114.00/160.00 **t.**, 1 suite – SB.

Studley, 28 Swan Rd, HG1 2SE, ✆ (01423) 560425, *studley@hotels.activebooking.com, Fax (01423) 530967* – |‡| TV P. MC AE ⓓ VISA AZ x
Le Breton : Meals *(closed Saturday lunch)* a la carte 15.75/23.25 **st.** 🍷 11.00 – **34 rm** ☕ 68.00/88.00 **t.**, 2 suites – SB.

Quality Kimberley without rest., 11-19 Kings Rd, HG1 5JY, ✆ (01423) 505613, *info@kimberley.scotnet.co.uk, Fax (01423) 530276* – |‡| TV P – 🎤 40. MC AE ⓓ VISA. ✗ BY c
closed 20 December-5 January – ☕ 8.50 – **48 rm** 79.50/109.50 **st.**

Ruskin, 1 Swan Rd, HG1 2SS, ✆ (01423) 502045, *ruskin.hotel@virgin.net, Fax (01423) 506131,* 🌳 – ⇔ TV P. MC AE VISA AY s
Meals (residents only) (dinner only) 24.50 **st.** 🍷 6.75 – **7 rm** ☕ 75.00/135.00 **st.** – SB.

Britannia Lodge without rest., 16 Swan Rd, HG1 2SA, ✆ (01423) 508482, *britlodge3@aol.com, Fax (01423) 526840,* 🌳 – ⇔ TV P. MC AE ⓓ VISA. ✗ AYZ r
closed 24 December-2 January – **5 rm** ☕ 70.00/95.00 **st.**

Alexa House, 26 Ripon Rd, HG1 2JJ, ✆ (01423) 501988, *alexahouse@msn.com, Fax (01423) 504086* – ⇔ TV P. MC AE ⓓ VISA. ✗ AY n
Meals (booking essential) (dinner only) 14.50 **st.** 🍷 9.00 – **13 rm** ☕ 53.00/70.00 **st.** – SB.

The Delaine without rest., 17 Ripon Rd, HG1 2JL, ✆ (01423) 567974, *Fax (01423) 561723,* 🌳 – ⇔ TV P. MC ⓓ VISA JCB AY c
10 rm ☕ 40.00/62.00 **st.**

Alexandra Court without rest., 8 Alexandra Rd, HG1 5JS, ✆ (01423) 502764, *janette@alexandracourt.co.uk, Fax (01423) 523151* – ⇔ TV P. MC AE ⓓ VISA BY o
13 rm ☕ 42.00/69.00 **st.**

Acacia Lodge without rest., 21 Ripon Rd, HG1 2JL, ✆ (01423) 560752, *Fax (01423) 503725* – ⇔ TV P. ✗ AY v
6 rm ☕ 58.00/75.00 **st.**

Brookfield House without rest., 5 Alexandra Rd, HG1 5JS, ✆ (01423) 506646, *brookfieldhouse@hotmail.com, Fax (01423) 850383* – ⇔ TV P. MC AE ⓓ VISA. ✗ BY s
closed Christmas and New Year – **7 rm** ☕ 45.00/65.00 **st.**

Ashwood House without rest., 7 Spring Grove, HG1 2HS, ✆ (01423) 560081, *ashwoodhouse@aol.com, Fax (01423) 527928* – ⇔ TV P. ✗ AY a
closed 16 December-2 January – **9 rm** ☕ 37.00/58.00 **st.**

Knox Mill House 🐌 without rest., Knox Mill Lane, HG3 2AE, North : 1 ½ m. by A 61 ✆ (01423) 560650, *Fax (01423) 560650,* ← – ⇔ P. ✗
closed 25 December – **3 rm** ☕ 40.00/45.00.

Garden House without rest., 14 Harlow Moor Drive, HG2 0JX, ✆ (01423) 503059, *gardenhouse@hotels.harrogate.com, Fax (01423) 503059* – TV. MC AE. ✗ AZ u
closed 25-31 December – **7 rm** ☕ 26.00/55.00 **st.**

XX **Villu Toots** (at The Balmoral H.), Franklin Mount, HG1 5EJ, ☎ (01423)705805, *inf balmoralhotel.co.uk, Fax (01423) 530652* – ▤ P. MO AE VISA BY
closed Saturday lunch – **Meals** 18.00/24.00 and a la carte 15.15/24.85 **t.** 13.00.

XX **Spice Box,** 24 Kings Rd, HG1 5JW, ☎ (01423) 568600 – ⚡ BY
closed 26 December-2 January, Sunday and lunch Monday – **Meals** 8.50/16 and a la carte 19.65/25.65 **t.** 10.75.

X **Courtyard,** 1 Montpellier Mews, HG1 2TQ, ☎ (01423) 530708, *Fax (01423) 530708,* ⚡. MO VISA JCB AZ
closed Sunday and Monday – **Meals** 12.95 a la carte 13.90/25.65 10.45.

X **Sasso,** 8-10 Princes Sq, HG1 1LX, ☎ (01423) 508838, *Fax (01423) 508838* – MO VISA BZ
closed first week January, 1 week September, 25-26 December, Sunday, Monday lunch a Bank Holidays – **Meals** - Italian - a la carte 18.00/25.50 **t.** 9.95.

X **Est, Est, Est,** 16 Cheltenham Cres, HD1 1DL, ☎ (01423) 566453, *Fax (01423) 521737* – MO AE ① VISA JCB BY
closed 25 and 26 December – **Meals** - Italian - a la carte 16.30/22.65 **t.**

at Kettlesing *West : 6½ m. by A 59 – AY – ✉ Harrogate.*

⌂ **Knabbs Ash** without rest., Skipton Rd, HG3 2LT, South : 2 m. on A 59 ☎ (01423) 7710 *colin+sheila@knabbsash.freeserve.co.uk, Fax (01423) 771515,* ≤, ⚘, ♞ – ⚡ TV ✗
closed 25-26 December – **3 rm** ☐ 35.00/50.00.

HARTFIELD *E. Sussex* 404 U 30 – *pop. 2 026.*

London 47 – Brighton 28 – Maidstone 25.

⌂ **Bolebroke Mill** ⚘ without rest., Edenbridge Rd, TN7 4JP, North : 1 ¼ m. by B 20 turning right onto unmarked rd ☎ (01892) 770425, *etb@bolebrokemill.demon.co. Fax (01892) 770425,* « Part early 17C cornmill, original features », ⚘ – ⚡ TV P. MO AE JCB. ✗
closed 20 December-10 February – **5 rm** ☐ 60.00/79.00 **t.**

HARTINGTON *Derbs.* 402 403 404 O 24 – *pop. 1 604 (inc. Dovedale)* – ✉ *Buxton.*

London 168 – Derby 36 – Manchester 40 – Sheffield 34 – Stoke-on-Trent 22.

🏠 **Biggin Hall** ⚘, Biggin, SK17 0DH, Southeast : 2 m. by B 5054 ☎ (01298) 84451, *big hall@compuserve.com, Fax (01298) 84681,* ≤, « Part 17C », ⚘ – ⚡ TV P. MO AE VISA
Meals (booking essential to non-residents) (dinner only) 15.50 **st.** 5.50 – ☐ 3.50 – 19 55.00/90.00 – SB.

HARTLEBURY *Worcs.* 403 N 26 – *pop. 2 253.*

London 135 – Birmingham 20 – Worcester 11.

🏠 **Travelodge,** Crossway Green, DY13 9SH, South : 2 ½ m. by B 4193 on A 449 (southbou carriageway) ☎ (01299) 250553, *Fax (01299) 251774* – ⚡ rm, TV ♿ P. MO AE ① VISA J ✗
Meals (grill rest.) – **32 rm** 49.95 **t.**

HARTLEPOOL *Hartlepool* 402 Q 19 – *pop. 87 310.*

Seaton Carew, Tees Rd ☎ (01429) 266249 – Castle Eden & Peterlee ☎ (014 836220 – Hart Warren ☎ (01429) 274398.

Teesside Airport : ☎ (0870) 000 2468, SW : 20 m. by A 689, A 1027, A 135 and A 67.

Hartlepool Art Gallery Information Centre, Church Sq ☎ (01429) 869706.

London 263 – Durham 19 – Middlesbrough 9 – Sunderland 21.

🏨 **Grand,** Swainson St, TS24 8AA, ☎ (01429) 266345, *Fax (01429) 265217* – ⧖ TV P – 🏛 1 MO AE ① VISA. ✗
Pippers : **Meals** (bar lunch)/dinner a la carte approx. 20.00 **st.** 10.95 – **46 rm** ☐ 54. 100.00 **st.** – SB.

🏠 **Travel Inn,** Old West Quay, Maritime Ave, The Marina, TS24 0XZ, ☎ (01429) 8901 *Fax (01429) 233105,* ≤, « Marina setting » – ⚡, ▤ rest, TV ♿ P. MO AE ① VISA. ✗
Meals (grill rest.) – **40 rm** 41.95 **t.**

X **Krimo's,** Neptune House, The Marina, TS24 0BY, ☎ (01429) 266120, *krimo@krimos.co. Fax (01429) 222111,* « Marina setting » – ⚡ ▤ P. MO VISA
closed 24-25 December, 1 January, Sunday and Monday – **Meals** 11.90 (lunch) and a la ca 17.20/25.40 **st.** 9.50.

Seaton Carew *Southeast : 2 m. on A 178.*

Staincliffe, The Cliff, TS25 1AB, ✆ (01429) 264301, *Fax (01429) 421366*, ≤, – rm, TV P – 200. MC AE VISA JCB
The Brasserie : **Meals** a la carte 14.75/26.25 **t.** 9.50 – **20 rm** 48.00/88.00 **st.** – SB.

ARTSHEAD MOOR SERVICE AREA *W. Yorks.* 402 O 22 – ✉ *Brighouse.*
London 213 – Bradford 8 – Burnley 31 – Manchester 35 – Sheffield 39.

Days Inn without rest., Clifton, HD6 4JX, M 62 between junctions 25 and 26 (eastbound carriageway) ✆ (01274) 851706, Reservations (Freephone) 0800 0280400, *Fax (01274) 855169* – TV P. MC AE VISA JCB
38 rm 45.00/55.00 **t.**

ARVINGTON *Worcs.* 403 404 O27 – *see Evesham.*

ARWELL *Oxon.* 403 404 Q 29 – *pop. 2 236.*
London 64 – Oxford 16 – Reading 18 – Swindon 22.

Kingswell, Reading Rd, OX11 0LZ, South : ¾ m. on A 417 ✆ (01235) 833043, *kingswell@breathemail.net, Fax (01235) 833193* – TV P – 30. MC AE VISA.
– **Meals** 17.50/22.50 and a la carte 14.40/33.00 **t.** 10.00 – **19 rm** 90.00/110.00 **t.** – SB.

ARWICH and DOVERCOURT *Essex* 404 X 28 – *pop. 18 436 (Harwich).*
Station Rd, Parkeston ✆ (01255) 503616.
to Germany (Hamburg) (DFDS Seaways A/S) daily (19 h 30 mn) – to Denmark (Esbjerg) (DFDS Seaways A/S) 1-3 daily (21 h) – to The Netherlands (Hook of Holland) (Stena Line) 2 daily (3 h 30 mn).
Iconfield Park, Parkeston ✆ (01255) 506139.
London 78 – Chelmsford 41 – Colchester 20 – Ipswich 23.

Pier at Harwich, The Quay, CO12 3HH, ✆ (01206) 241212, *lesley@pieratharwich.co.uk, Fax (01206) 551922*, ≤ – TV P. MC AE VISA.
Harbourside : **Meals** - Seafood - 12.00/19.00 and a la carte 20.00/42.70 **t.** 11.95 – 5.50 – **14 rm** 62.50/150.00 **st.** – SB.

ASLEMERE *Surrey* 404 R 30 – *pop. 12 218.*
London 47 – Brighton 46 – Southampton 44.

Lythe Hill, Petworth Rd, GU27 3BQ, East : 1 ½ m. on B 2131 ✆ (01428) 651251, *lythe@lythehill.co.uk, Fax (01428) 644131*, ≤, , , , – rest, TV P – 100. MC AE VISA
Meals *(closed Saturday and Sunday)* (lunch only) a la carte 34.50/43.00 **st.** 12.50 – ***Auberge de France :*** **Meals** - French - (dinner only and Saturday and Sunday lunch)/dinner a la carte 32.50/46.00 **t.** 12.50 – 12.00 – **29 rm** 98.00/125.00 **st.**, 12 suites – SB.

Georgian House, High St, GU27 2JY, ✆ (01428) 656644, *mail@georgianhousehotel.com, Fax (01428) 645600*, – TV P – 120. MC AE VISA.
Meals a la carte 19.00/28.00 **st.** 10.00 – 8.50 – **49 rm** 75.00 **st.**

ASTINGS and ST LEONARDS *E. Sussex* 404 V 31 – *pop. 81 139 (Hastings).*
18 *Beauport Park, Battle Rd, St Leonards-on-Sea ✆ (01424) 852977.*
Town Hall, Queen's Sq, Priory Meadow ✆ (01424) 781111 – Old Town Hall ✆ (01424) 781111.
London 65 – Brighton 37 – Folkestone 37 – Maidstone 34.

Plan on next page

Beauport Park , Battle Rd, TN38 8EA, Northwest : 3 ½ m. at junction of A 2100 with B 2159 ✆ (01424) 851222, *reservations@beauportprkhotel.demon.co.uk, Fax (01424) 852465*, ≤, « Formal garden », heated, 18, , – , rest, TV P – 60. MC AE VISA JCB
Meals 18.00/25.00 and a la carte 28.40/31.50 **st.** 11.00 – ***Brasserie :*** **Meals** a la carte 16.75/19.85 **st.** 11.00 – **26 rm** 90.00/150.00 **t.** – SB.

Cinque Ports, Summerfields, Bohemia Rd, TN34 1ET, ✆ (01424) 439222, *enquiries@cinqueports.co.uk, Fax (01424) 437277* – TV P – 200. MC AE VISA JCB. AZ a
Meals (bar lunch Monday-Saturday) 14.95/20.00 9.95 – **40 rm** 65.00/85.00 **st.** – SB.

HASTINGS AND ST. LEONARDS

A 21 LONDON
B 2093 (A 21), BATTLE
HOLLINGTON
ST HELEN'S WOOD
ST-HELEN'S
SILVERHILL
ALEXANDRA PARK
HASTINGS
OLD TOWN
ST. CLEMENT'S CAVES
ST.LEONARDS
BRIGHTON
A 259
Sedlescombe Rd
North
St. Helen's
A 2101
Amherst Rd
Gillsmans Hill
Bohemia Road
The Green
London
Dane Rd
Marina
Filsham
Harley Shute Rd
B 2092
Ironlatch Av.
Blackman Av.
B 2159 Battle Road
Downs Rd
Elphinstone Road
Mt Pleasant Rd
Priory Road
Old London Road
Harold Rd
Frederick Rd
The Ridge
Rock Lane
Saxon Road
0 1 km

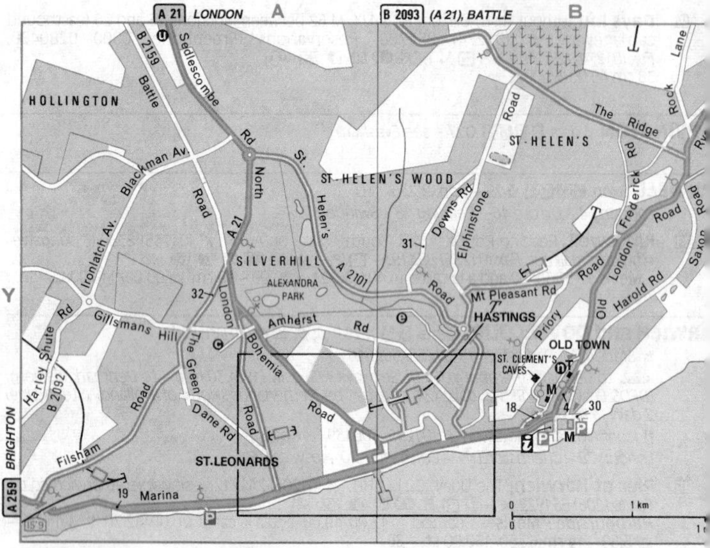

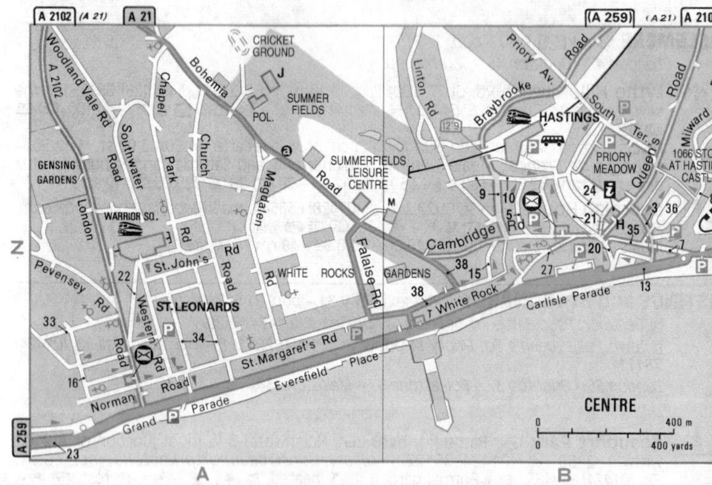

Dieser Führer ist kein vollständiges Hotel- und Restaurantverzeichnis.
Um den Ansprüchen aller Touristen gerecht zu werden,
haben wir uns auf eine Auswahl in jeder Kategorie beschränkt.

Tower House, 26-28 Tower Road West, TN38 0RG, ✆ (01424) 427217, *towerhot@dial.pipex.com, Fax (01424) 427217,* – TV. MC AE VISA. AY c
closed Christmas **Meals** (residents only) (dinner only) 17.50/20.00 **st.** 8.50 – **10 rm** 45.00/65.00 **st.** – SB.

Travel Inn, 1 John Macadam Way, TN37 7DB, ✆ (01424) 754070, *Fax (01424) 753139* – rm, TV P. MC AE VISA. AY u
Meals (grill rest.) – **44 rm** 41.95 **t.**

Parkside House without rest., 59 Lower Park Rd, TN34 2LD, ✆ (01424) 433096, *Fax (01424) 421431,* – TV. MC VISA. BY e
5 rm 30.00/60.00.

Lionsdown House without rest., 116 High St, Old Town, TN34 3ET, ✆ (01424) 420802, *sharonlionsdown@aol.com, Fax (01424) 420802,* « Medieval Wealden hall house with Georgian facade » – TV. MC VISA JCB. BY n
closed 25 and 26 December – **3 rm** 30.00/46.00 **st.**

ATCH BEAUCHAMP *Somerset* 403 K 30 – *see Taunton.*

ATFIELD *Herts.* 404 T 28 *Great Britain G.* – *pop. 31 104.*
See : *Hatfield House*★★ *AC.*
18 *Hatfield London C.C., Bedwell Park, Essendon ✆ (01707) 642624.*
London 27 – Bedford 38 – Cambridge 39.

Jarvis International Hatfield, 301 St Albans Rd West, AL10 9RH, West : 1 m. by B 6426 on A 1057 at junction with A 1001 ✆ (01707) 265411, *Fax (01707) 264019,* – rm, TV P – 120. MC AE VISA
Meals (buffet lunch)/dinner 11.95/12.95 and dinner a la carte 22.05/29.25 **t.** 12.75 – 10.95 – **128 rm** 115.00/130.00 **st.** – SB.

Quality Hatfield, Roehyde Way, AL10 9AF, South : 2 m. by B 6426 on A 1001 ✆ (01707) 275701, *admin@gb059.u-net.com, Fax (01707) 266033* – , rest, TV P – 120. MC AE VISA
Meals (closed Saturday lunch) 17.50 and a la carte 10.25/14.95 11.95 – 10.75 – **76 rm** 105.00/115.00 **t.** – SB.

Travel Inn, Lemsford Rd, Comet Way, AL10 0DA, Northwest : 1 m. by B 197 at junction with A 1001 ✆ (01707) 268990, *Fax (01707) 268293* – rm, rest, TV P. MC AE VISA.
Meals (grill rest.) – **40 rm** 41.95 **t.**

ATFIELD HEATH *Essex* 404 U 28 – *see Bishop's Stortford (Herts.).*

ATHERSAGE *Derbs.* 402 403 404 P 24 – *pop. 2 858* – ✉ *Sheffield (S. Yorks.).*
18 *Sickleholme, Bamford ✆ (01433) 651306.*
London 177 – Derby 39 – Manchester 34 – Sheffield 11 – Stoke-on-Trent 44.

George, S32 1BB, ✆ (01433) 650436, *info@george-hotel.net, Fax (01433) 650099* – rest, TV P – 70. MC AE VISA
George's : **Meals** a la carte 17.00/35.25 **t.** 12.50 – **19 rm** 59.50/99.50 **t.** – SB.

Highlow Hall without rest., Hope Valley, S32 1AX, South : 2 m. by B 6001 on Abney rd ✆ (01433) 650393, *Fax (01433) 659505,* ≤, « Part 16C manor house », – P. MC VISA.
closed Christmas and New Year – **3 rm** 40.00/65.00.

ATTON *Warks.* – *see Warwick.*

AVANT *Hants.* 404 R 31.
1 Park Rd South ✆ (023) 9248 0024.
London 75 – Southampton 24 – Brighton 39 – Portsmouth 12.

Travel Inn, 65 Bedhampton Hill, Bedhampton, PO9 3JN, West : 1 ½ m. by B 2177 at junction with A 3 (M) ✆ (023) 9247 2619, *Fax (023) 9245 3471* – rm, TV P. MC AE VISA.
Meals (grill rest.) – **36 rm** 41.95 **t.**

Benachrichtigen Sie sofort das Hotel, wenn Sie ein bestelltes Zimmer nicht belegen können.

ENGLAND

HAWES *N. Yorks.* 402 N 21 – *pop. 1 117.*

Dales Countryside Museum, Station Yard ☎ (01969) 667450.
London 253 – Kendal 27 – Leeds 72 – York 65.

Simonstone Hall, Simonstone, DL8 3LY, North : 1 ½ m. on Muker ☎ (01969) 667255, *simonstone@demon.co.uk, Fax (01969) 667741,* «, « Part 18C cour house », – rest, TV P. MC AE VISA
Meals (bar lunch Monday to Saturday)/dinner a la carte 20.15/27.65 **t.** 12.00 – **19** 60.00/170.00 **t.**, 2 suites – SB.

Stone House, Sedbusk, DL8 3PT, North : 1 m. by Muker rd ☎ (01969) 667571, *da hotel@aol.com, Fax (01969) 667720,* «, – TV P. MC VISA
– **Meals** (dinner only) 20.50 **t.** 11.95 – **22 rm** 39.50/92.00 **t.** – SB.

Cockett's, Market Pl, DL8 3RD, ☎ (01969) 667312, *enquiries@cocketts.co. Fax (01969) 667162,* – TV. MC VISA.
Meals *(closed Tuesday and lunch Monday, Friday and Saturday)* 15.95 (dinner) and a la ca 9.45/24.15 **t.** 11.50 – **8 rm** 45.00/69.00 **st.** – SB.

Herriot's, Main St, DL8 3QW, ☎ (01969) 667536, *herriotshotel@aol.cc Fax (01969) 667810* – TV. MC VISA JCB
weekends only November-March and closed January – **Meals** (dinner only and lunch summer) a la carte 16.15/20.15 **st.** 8.95 – **7 rm** 23.00/55.00 **st.** – SB.

Rookhurst Georgian Country House, Gayle, DL8 3RT, South : ½ m. by Gayle ☎ (01969) 667454, *rookhurst@lineone.net, Fax (01969) 667128,* – TV P. MC VISA.
closed first 3 weeks January – **Meals** (booking essential) (residents only) (dinner or 18.00/22.00 **st.** 13.00 – **5 rm** 90.00/120.00 **st.** – SB.

Brandymires, DL8 3PR, North : ¼ m. on Muker rd ☎ (01969) 667482 – P
mid February-October – **Meals** (by arrangement) 14.00 **st.** 5.95 – **4 rm** 29.00/42.00

HAWKHURST *Kent* 404 V 30 – *pop. 4 217.*

London 55 – Folkestone 37 – Hastings 18 – Maidstone 18.

The Wren's Nest without rest., Hastings Rd, TN18 4RT, South : 1 ½ m. by A 229 B 2244 ☎ (01580) 754919, *Fax (01580) 754919,* – TV P.
closed 2 weeks Christmas and New Year – **3 rm** 45.00/59.00 **s.**

HAWKSHEAD *Cumbria* 402 L 20 *Great Britain G.* – *pop. 570* – ✉ *Ambleside.*

See : *Village*★.
Env. : *Lake Windermere*★★ – *Coniston Water*★ *(Brantwood*★, *on east side), SW : by B 528*
Main Car Park ☎ (015394) 36525 (summer only).
London 283 – Carlisle 52 – Kendal 19.

Highfield House Country H., Hawkshead Hill, LA22 0PN, West : ¾ m. on B 52 (Coniston rd) ☎ (015394) 36344, *rooms@highfield-hawkshead.com, Fax (015394) 367* « Kirkstone Pass and Fells, – rest, TV P. MC AE VISA
closed January and 23 to 27 December – **Meals** (bar lunch)/dinner 20.00/25.00 **t.** 11.5 **11 rm** (dinner included) 60.00/160.00 **t.** – SB.

Rough Close Country House, LA22 0QF, South : 1 ½ m. on Newby Bridge ☎ (015394) 36370, *rclosehawkshead@aol.com, Fax (015394) 36002,* – TV P. VISA.
April-October and restricted opening in March and November – **Meals** (booking essent (residents only) (dinner only) (set menu only) 13.00 **t.** 7.50 – **5 rm** (dinner includ 55.00/90.00 **t.**

Ivy House, Main St, LA22 0NS, ☎ (015394) 36204, *ivyhousehotel@btinternet.com,* rest, TV P. MC VISA JCB
March-October – **Meals** (by arrangement) 12.50 4.00 – **11 rm** 34.00/68.00 **st.** – SB.

Bracken Fell without rest., Barngates Rd, Outgate, LA22 0NH, North : 1 ¼ m. B 5286 on Barngates rd ☎ (015394) 36289, *hart.brackenfell@virgin.net,* – TV P.
7 rm 30.00/56.00 **st.**

at Near Sawrey *Southeast : 2 m. on B 5285* – ✉ *Ambleside.*

Sawrey House Country H., LA22 0LF, ☎ (015394) 36387, *enquiries@sawrey-ho .com, Fax (015394) 36010,* « Esthwaite Water and Grizedale Forest, – TV P. VISA
closed January and early December – **Meals** (booking essential) (dinner only) 30.0 11.95 – **11 rm** (dinner included) 65.00/130.00 **t.** – SB.

Ees Wyke Country House, LA22 0JZ, ☎ (015394) 36393, *eeswke@aol.co Fax (015394) 36393,* « Esthwaite Water and Grizedale Forest, – rest, TV P. AE
March-November – **Meals** (booking essential) (dinner only) 24.00 **t.** 6.50 – **8 rm** (dinr included) 65.00/130.00 **t.**

Far Sawrey *Southeast : 2½ m. on B 5285 – ✉ Ambleside.*

West Vale, LA22 0LQ, ✆ (015394) 42817, *enquiries@westvalecountryhouse.co.uk, Fax (015394) 45302,* ≤ – ⇌ P. MC AE VISA JCB. ✻
closed 2 weeks February and 25 December – **Meals** (by arrangement) 22.00 **st.** 8.00 – **6 rm** 40.00/66.00 **st.** – SB.

Grizedale *Southwest : 2 ¾ m. – ✉ Ambleside.*

Grizedale Lodge without rest., LA22 0QL, ✆ (015394) 36532, *enquiries@grizedale-lodge.com, Fax (015394) 36572,* ≤ – ⇌ TV P. MC AE VISA JCB
February-November – **9 rm** 42.50/90.00 **t.**

HAWNBY *N. Yorks.* 402 Q 21 – ✉ *Helmsley.*
London 245 – Newcastle upon Tyne 69 – Middlesbrough 27 – York 30.

Hawnby, YO62 5QS, ✆ (01439) 798202, *info@hawnbyhotel.co.uk, Fax (01439) 798344,* ≤, ⇌ rm, TV P. MC VISA JCB. ✻
Meals a la carte 10.20/18.30 **t.** 9.95 – **6 rm** 49.00/69.00 **t.** – SB.

Laskill *Northeast : 1½ m. by B 1257 – ✉ Hawnby.*

Laskill Farm, Easterside, YO62 5BN, ✆ (01439) 798268, *Fax (01439) 798498,* « Working farm », – ⇌ TV P. MC VISA
Meals (by arrangement) (communal dining) 13.50 **st.** 12.50 – **6 rm** 30.00/63.00 **st.**

Questa Guida non contiene pubblicità a pagamento.

HAWORTH *W. Yorks.* 402 O 22 *Great Britain G. – pop. 4 956 –* ✉ *Keighley.*
See : *Town*★.
2-4 West Lane ✆ (01535) 642329.
London 213 – Burnley 22 – Leeds 22 – Manchester 34.

Ashmount without rest, Mytholmes Lane, BD22 8EZ, ✆ (01535) 645726, *ashmount haworth@aol.com, Fax (01535) 645726,* ≤, « Victorian country house », – ⇌ TV P. MC VISA
closed 1 week spring, 1 week autumn and 2 days at Christmas – **6 rm** 29.00/43.00 **s.**

Weaver's with rm, 15 West Lane, BD22 8DU, ✆ (01535) 643822, *weavers@amserve.net, Fax (01535) 644832,* « Former weavers cottages » – ⇌ rest, TV. MC AE VISA JCB. ✻
closed 2 weeks Christmas and New Year – **Meals** *(closed Sunday and Monday)* (dinner only) a la carte 14.00/26.95 **t.** 10.50 – **3 rm** 55.00/80.00 **t.** – SB.

HAYDOCK *Mersey.* 402 403 404 M 23 *– pop. 16 705 –* ✉ *St. Helens.*
London 198 – Liverpool 19 – Manchester 18.

Thistle Haydock, Penny Lane, WA11 9SG, Northeast : ½ m. on A 599 ✆ (01942) 272000, *haydock@thistle.co.uk, Fax (01942) 711092,* – ⇌, rest, TV P – 300. MC AE VISA JCB
Beecher's : **Meals** *(closed Saturday lunch)* 10.50/21.00 and a la carte 19.40/23.85 **st.** 12.95 – 11.50 – **134 rm** 125.00/141.00 **t.**, 4 suites – SB.

Posthouse Haydock, Lodge Lane, Newton-le-Willows, WA12 0JG, Northeast : 1 m. on A 49 ✆ (0870) 400 9039, *gmmail1117@forte-hotels.com, Fax (01942) 718419,* – ⇌ rm, TV P – 180. MC AE VISA
Meals 10.00/17.95 and a la carte 16.85/27.85 **t.** 11.95 – 12.95 – **138 rm** 89.00/129.00 **st.** – SB.

Travel Inn, Yew Tree Way, Golborne, WA3 3JD, East : 2 ½ m. by A 580 ✆ (01942) 273422, *Fax (01942) 296100* – ⇌ rm, rest, TV P. MC AE VISA JCB. ✻
Meals (grill rest.) – **60 rm** 41.95 **t.**

Travelodge, Piele Rd, WA11 9TL, on A 580 (westbound carriageway) ✆ (01942) 272055, *Fax (01942) 272067* – ⇌ rm, rest, TV P. MC AE VISA JCB. ✻
Meals (grill rest.) – **62 rm** 39.95 **t.**

HAYDON BRIDGE *Northd.* 401 402 N 19.
London 324 – Newcastle upon Tyne 29 – Carlisle 31 – Leeds 124.

General Havelock Inn, 9 Ratcliffe Rd, NE47 6ER, on A 69 ✆ (01434) 684376, *general havelock@aol.com, Fax (01434) 684283,* « Riverside setting » – ⇌. MC VISA
closed Sunday dinner, Monday, Tuesday in November, January and February – **Meals** 13.00/17.00 **t.** 10.50.

HAYLE *Cornwall* 403 D 33.
London 288 – Penzance 9 – Truro 20.

Travel Inn, Loggans Moor, Carwin Rise, TR27 4PN, North : 1 m. by B 3301 off A
☏ (01736) 755025, *Fax (01736) 757029* – ⇔ rm, ▤ rest, TV & P. MC AE ⓓ VISA. ✻
Meals (grill rest.) – **40 rm** 41.95 **t.**

HAYLING ISLAND *Hants.* 404 R 31 – *pop. 14 054.*
Links Lane ☏ (023) 9246 3712.
Beachlands, Seafront ☏ (023) 9246 7111 (summer only).
London 77 – Brighton 45 – Southampton 28.

Cockle Warren Cottage without rest., 36 Seafront, PO11 9HL, ☏ (023) 9246 49
Fax (023) 9246 4838, heated, – ⇔ TV P. MC VISA JCB
5 rm ☐ 40.00/65.00 **st.**

HAYTOR *Devon – see Bovey Tracey.*

HAYTOR VALE *Devon – see Bovey Tracey.*

HAYWARDS HEATH *W. Sussex* 404 T 31 – *pop. 28 923.*
Paxhill Park, East Mascalls Lane, Lindfield ☏ (01444) 484467.
London 41 – Brighton 16.

Birch, Lewes Rd, RH17 7SF, East : ¾ m. on A 272 ☏ (01444) 451565, *info@birch-hot co.uk, Fax (01444) 440109* – ⇔ rest, TV & P – 60. MC AE VISA. ✻
closed 25-30 December – **Meals** *(closed Sunday dinner)* 12.95/17.50 **st.** 10.95 – **51 r**
☐ 88.00/98.00 **st.**

Jeremy's at Borde Hill, Borde Hill Gdns, RH16 1XP, North : 1 ¾ m. by B 2028
Balcombe Rd ☏ (01444) 441102, *jeremys.bordehill@btinternet.com., Fax (01494) 4439*
, « Converted 19C stables ≤ Victorian walled garden » – ⇔ P. MC AE ⓓ VISA
closed 1 week January, Sunday dinner and Monday – **Meals** 20.50 and a la carte 22.7
35.00 **t.** 11.00.

Dining Room 2, 65 The Broadway, RH16 3AS, ☏ (01444) 417755, *Fax (01444) 41775*
▤. MC AE ⓓ VISA
closed 1 week Christmas, 1 week Easter, first 2 weeks August, Sunday, and Saturday lunc
Meals 16.50/21.90 **t.** 11.95.

HEADLAM *Durham* 402 O 20 – *see Darlington.*

HEATHROW AIRPORT *Middx.* 404 S 29 – *see Hillingdon (Greater London).*

HEBDEN BRIDGE *W. Yorks.* 402 N 22 – *pop. 3 681* – ✉ *Halifax.*
Great Mount, Wadsworth ☏ (01422) 842896.
1 Bridge Gate ☏ (01422) 843831.
London 223 – Burnley 13 – Leeds 24 – Manchester 25.

Carlton, Albert St, HX7 8ES, ☏ (01422) 844400, *ctonhotel@aol.com, Fax (01422) 84311*
, ⇔ rest, TV – 150. MC AE ⓓ VISA JCB
Meals 9.00/14.95 and dinner a la carte 23.85/29.40 **st.** 9.95 – **16 rm** ☐ 56.00/75.00 **st.**

The White Lion, Bridge Gate, HX7 8EX, ☏ (01422) 842197, *Fax (01422) 846619,* « P
17C inn » – ⇔ rm, TV P. MC VISA JCB. ✻
closed 25 December – **Meals** (in bar Sunday to Thursday) a la carte 9.15/19.15 **st.** 5.75
10 rm ☐ 35.00/65.00 **st.**

Redacre Mill, Mytholmroyd, HX7 5DQ, Southeast : 1 ½ m. by A646 off Westfield Te
☏ (01422) 881569, *peters@redacremill.freeserve.co.uk, Fax (01422) 885563,* « Convert
canalside warehouse », – ⇔ TV P. MC VISA. ✻
Meals (by arrangement) (communal dining) 21.00 **st.** 14.50 – ☐ 39.00/59.00 **st.**

HEIGHINGTON *Durham* 402 P20 – *see Darlington.*

Les prix — Pour toutes précisions sur les prix indiqués dans ce guide, reportez-vous aux pages de l'introduction.

ELMSLEY *N. Yorks.* 402 Q 21 *Great Britain G. – pop. 1 833.*

Env. : *Rievaulx Abbey*★★ *AC, NW : 2½ m. by B 1257.*

Ampleforth College, Court Cottage, Cawton, York ℘ *(01653) 628555.*

Town Hall, Market Pl ℘ *(01439) 770173.*

London 239 – Middlesbrough 28 – York 24.

The Black Swan, Market Pl, YO62 5BJ, ℘ (01439) 770466, *heritagehotels-helmsley.black swan@forte-hotels.com, Fax (01439) 770174,* « Part 16C inn », – rest, TV P. MC AE VISA

The Rutland Room : **Meals** 26.50/37.00 (dinner) and a la carte 26.50/37.75 **t.** 15.00 – 12.50 – **45 rm** 120.00/145.00 **st.** – SB.

Feversham Arms, YO62 6AG, on B 1257 ℘ (01439) 770766, *fevershamarms@hotmail. com, Fax (01439) 770346,* , , heated, , – TV P. MC AE VISA

Brasserie at the Fev : **Meals** a la carte 19.50/25.00 **t.** 10.00 – **13 rm** 70.00/140.00 – SB.

Carlton Lodge, Bondgate, YO62 5EY, ℘ (01439) 770557, *Fax (01439) 770623,* – rest, TV P – 130. MC VISA

The Stirrings : **Meals** *(closed Sunday)* (dinner only) a la carte 12.65/23.70 **t.** 10.00 – **11 rm** 39.50/75.00 **st.** – SB.

The Feathers, Market Pl, YO62 5BH, ℘ (01439) 770275, *feathers@aol.com, Fax (01439) 771101,* – rest, TV P. MC VISA.

Meals a la carte 12.50/19.00 **t.** – **14 rm** 45.00/60.00 **t.**

at Nawton *East : 3¼ m. on A 170 – York.*

Plumpton Court, High St, YO62 7TT, ℘ (01439) 771223, *chrisand sarah@plumptoncourt.com, Fax (01439) 771223,* – TV P.

Meals (by arrangement) 14.50 **st.** 8.00 – **7 rm** 34.00/52.00 **st.**

at Harome *Southeast : 2¾ m. by A 170 – York.*

The Pheasant, YO62 5JG, ℘ (01439) 771241, *Fax (01439) 771744,* , – rest, TV P. MC AE VISA JCB.

mid March-November – **Meals** (bar lunch)/dinner 22.00 **t.** 6.90 – **10 rm** (dinner included) 65.00/130.50 **t.**, 2 suites.

The Star Inn (Pern) with rm, YO62 5JE, ℘ (01439) 770397, *Fax (01439) 771833,* , « Part 14C thatched inn », – TV P. MC VISA.

closed 1 week November, 3 weeks January, 25 December, Monday, Sunday dinner and Bank Holidays – **Meals** (booking essential) a la carte 20.00/27.40 **t.** 11.00 – **3 rm** 45.00/ 90.00 **st.**

Spec. Terrine of chicken livers, marjoram and gooseberry relish. Roast fillet of cod with bubble and squeak rösti. "Pimms No.1" jelly, spearmint water ice.

at Nunnington *Southeast : 6¼ m. by A 170 off B 1257 – Helmsley.*

Ryedale Country Lodge with rm, YO62 5XB, West : 1 m. ℘ (01439) 748246, *ryecountrylodge@amserve.com, Fax (01439) 748346,* « Converted railway station », , – TV P. MC VISA.

closed Monday and Tuesday to non-residents – **Meals** a la carte 16.50/21.50 **st.** – **7 rm** 45.00/87.00 – SB.

at Wass *Southwest : 6 m. by A 170 – Helmsley.*

Wombwell Arms, YO61 4BE, ℘ (01347) 868280, *Fax (01347) 868039* – P. MC VISA

Meals a la carte 15.95/23.95 11.40.

at Byland Abbey *Southwest : 6½ m. by A 170 – Helmsley.*

Abbey Inn with rm, YO61 4BD, ℘ (01347) 868204, *jane@bylandabbeyinn.com, Fax (01347) 868678,* <, , – rest, TV P. MC AE VISA.

Meals *(closed Sunday dinner and Monday lunch)* a la carte 19.00/27.50 **t.** 11.50 – **3 rm** 100.00 **st.**

at Scawton *West : 4½ m. by B 1257 – Helmsley.*

The Hare Inn, YO7 2HG, ℘ (01845) 597289, *grahamatthehare@aol.com, Fax (01845) 597289,* « Part 17C » – P. MC VISA JCB

closed Monday lunch – **Meals** a la carte 12.95/22.95 **t.** 10.95.

ELSTON *Cornwall* 403 E 33 *The West Country G. – pop. 8 505.*

See : *The Flora Day Furry Dance*★★.

Env. : *Lizard Peninsula*★ *– Gunwalloe Fishing Cove*★*, S : 4 m. by A 3083 and minor rd – Culdrose (Flambards Village Theme Park*★*), SE : 1 m. – Wendron (Poldark Mine*★*), NE : 2½ m. by B 3297 – Gweek (Seal Sanctuary*★ *– setting*★*), E : 4 m. by A 394 and minor rd.*

London 306 – Falmouth 13 – Penzance 14 – Truro 17.

Nansloe Manor, Meneage Rd, TR13 0SB, (01326) 574691, *info@nansloe-manor.uk, Fax (01326) 564680*, – rest, P. VISA JCB.
Meals (bar lunch Monday-Saturday)/dinner 24.95/26.95 **t.** 11.50 – **7 rm** 59.0 140.00 **t.**

at Gunwalloe *South : 5 m. by A 394 off A 3083 – Helston.*

The Halzephron Inn with rm, TR12 7QB, (01326) 240406, *halzephroninn@ban cornwall.net, Fax (01326) 241442*, – rest, P. AE VISA.
closed 25 December – **Meals** a la carte 18.00/24.50 **t.** 5.50 – **2 rm** 40.00/70.00 **t.**

HEMEL HEMPSTEAD *Herts.* 404 S 28 – *pop. 79 235.*

Little Hay Golf Complex, Box Lane, Bovingdon (01442) 833798 – Boxmoor, 18 B Lane (01442) 242434.

Dacorum Information Centre, Marlowes (01442) 234222.

London 30 – Aylesbury 16 – Luton 10 – Northampton 46.

Holiday Inn, Breakspear Way, HP2 4UA, East : 2 ½ m. on A 414 (0870) 400 904 *Fax (01442) 211812*, rm, P – 55. AE VISA JCB
Meals *(closed lunch Saturday and Bank Holidays)* (buffet lunch)/dinner 12.00/15. and a la carte 22.00/26.00 **t.** 12.95 – 14.95 – **145 rm** 154.00 **st.** – SB.

Boxmoor Lodge, London Rd, HP1 2RA, West : 1 m. on A 4251 (01442) 23077 *boxmoorlodge@compuserve.com, Fax (01442) 252230*, – P – 25. VISA JCB
closed 25 December-7 January – **Meals** *(closed Sunday and lunch Saturday and Mond* 12.00 (lunch) and a la carte 26.50/32.00 **st.** 12.00 – **25 rm** 100.00/120.00 **t.** – SB.

Travelodge without rest., Wolsey House, Wolsey Rd, HP2 4TU, (01442) 24445 *Fax (01442) 266887* – rm, P. AE VISA JCB.
53 rm 69.95 **t.**

Travel Inn, Stoney Lane, Bourne End, HP1 2SB, West : 3 ½ m. by A 4251 off A (01442) 879149, *Fax (01442) 879147* – rm, rest, P. AE VISA.
Meals (grill rest.) (dinner only) – **61 rm** 41.95 **t.**

at Frithsden *Northwest : 4½ m. by A 4146 – Hemel Hempstead.*

The Alford Arms, HP1 3DD, (01442) 864480, *Fax (01442) 876893*, – P. AE V JCB
closed 25-26 December – **Meals** a la carte 16.00/23.75 **t.** 9.75.

HENFIELD *W. Sussex* 404 T 31 – *pop. 4 111.*

London 47 – Brighton 10 – Worthing 11.

Tottington Manor, Edburton, BN5 9LJ, Southeast : 3 ½ m. by A 2037 on Fulking (01903) 815757, *tottingtonmanor@compuserve.com, Fax (01903) 879331*, rest, P. AE VISA JCB.
closed 1-15 January and 2 weeks October – **Meals** *(closed Saturday lunch and Sund dinner)* 17.00/30.00 and a la carte approx. 26.25 **t.** 11.75 – **6 rm** 55.00/90.00 **t.** – SB.

at Wineham *Northeast : 3½ m. by A 281, B 2116 and Wineham Lane – Henfield.*

Frylands without rest., BN5 9BP, West : ¼ m. taking left turn at telephone b (01403) 710214, *b+b@frylands.co.uk, Fax (01403) 711449*, « Part Elizabethan farr house », heated, – P.
closed 20 December-1 January – **3 rm** 25.00/45.00 **s.**

HENLADE *Somerset – see Taunton.*

HENLEY-IN-ARDEN *Warks.* 403 404 O 27 – *pop. 2 803.*

London 104 – Birmingham 15 – Stratford-upon-Avon 8 – Warwick 8.5.

Ardencote Manor H. & Country Club, Lye Green Rd, Claverdon, CV35 8LS, Eas 3 ¾ m. by A 4189 on Shrewley rd (01926) 843111, *hotel@ardencote.co Fax (01926) 842646*, squash – rm, P – 22 AE VISA.
Oak Room : **Meals** (booking essential) (dinner only and Sunday lunch)/dinner a la car 20.95/29.95 **st.** 10.95 – ***The Lodge :*** **Meals** a la carte 15.00/25.00 **st.** – **75 rm** 95.0 225.00 **st.** – SB.

India India, 148 High St, B95 5BS, (01564) 795080, *indiaindia@hotmail.co Fax (01564) 793089* – VISA
closed Sunday, 25 December and 1 January – **Meals** - Indian - (dinner only) a la car 18.00/31.00 **t.** 10.95.

Crabmill, Preston Bagot, Claverdon, B95 5DR, East : 1 m. on A 4189 (01926) 843342, *Fax (01926) 843989,* – P. MC AE VISA JCB
closed Sunday dinner – **Meals** (booking essential) a la carte 20.00/32.00 **t.** 12.00.

ENLEY-ON-THAMES *Oxon.* 404 R 29 – *pop. 10 558.*

Huntercombe, Nuffield (01491) 641207.
to Reading (Salter Bros. Ltd) (summer only) – to Marlow (Salter Bros. Ltd) (summer only).
Kings Arms Barn, Kings Rd (01491) 578034.
London 40 – Oxford 23 – Reading 9.

Red Lion, RG9 2AR, (01491) 572161, *reservations@redlionhenley.co.uk, Fax (01491) 410039* – TV P – 30. MC AE VISA JCB.
Meals 16.00 and a la carte 22.00/33.00 **t.** 13.00 – 12.50 – **26 rm** 99.00/165.00 **t.** – SB.

Thamesmead House without rest., Remenham Lane, RG9 2LR, (01491) 574745, *thamesmead@supanet.com, Fax (01491) 579944,* « Contemporary interior » – TV P. MC AE.
closed Christmas – **6 rm** 105.00/125.00 **st.**

The Rise without rest., Rotherfield Rd, RG9 1NR, (01491) 579360, *Fax (01491) 578691,* – TV P
3 rm 50.00/65.00 **s.**

Lenwade without rest., 3 Western Rd, RG9 1JL, (01491) 573468, *lenwadeuk@compuserve.com, Fax (01491) 573468,* – TV P.
3 rm 45.00/60.00 **s.**

Alftrudis without rest., 8 Norman Ave, RG9 1SG, (01491) 573099, *etb@alftrudis.fsnet.co.uk, Fax (01491) 411747* – TV.
3 rm 40.00/60.00.

Villa Marina, 18 Thameside, RG9 1BH, (01491) 575262, *Fax (01491) 411394* – . MC AE VISA
Meals - Italian - 6.00/15.00 (dinner) and a la carte approx. 23.00 **t.** 10.00.

Stonor *North : 4 m. by A 4130 on B 480 – Henley-on-Thames.*

Stonor Arms, RG9 6HE, (01491) 638866, *stonorarms.hotel@virgin.net, Fax (01491) 638863,* , – rest, TV P. MC AE VISA
Meals *closed Sunday dinner* 17.45/25.00 and dinner a la carte 25.95/38.20 **t.** 12.50 – **10 rm** 120.00/175.00 **t.**

Binfield Heath *Southwest : 4 m. by A 4155 – Henley-on-Thames.*

Holmwood without rest., Shiplake Row, RG9 4DP, (0118) 947 8747, *Fax (0118) 947 8637,* « Part Georgian country house », , , – TV P. MC VISA.
5 rm 40.00/60.00 **s.**

EREFORD *Herefordshire* 403 L 27 *Great Britain G. – pop. 54 326.*

See : *City★ - Cathedral★★ (Mappa Mundi★)* A A – *Old House★* A B.
Exc. : *Kilpeck (Church of SS. Mary and David★★) SW : 8 m. by A 465* B.
Raven's Causeway, Wormsley (01432) 830219 – Belmont Lodge, Belmont (01432) 352666 – Burghill Valley, Tillington Rd, Burghill (01432) 760456 – Hereford Municipal, Holmer Rd (01432) 344376 B.
1 King St (01432) 268430.
London 133 – Birmingham 51 – Cardiff 56.

Plan on next page

Castle House, Castle St, HR1 2NW, (01432) 356321, *info@castlehse.co.uk, Fax (01432) 365909,* « Georgian mansion, contemporary interior », – , rest, TV P. MC AE VISA A e
La Rive : **Meals** - French - *(closed Sunday dinner and Monday lunch)* 14.00/42.00 **t.** 19.00 – 19.00 – **15 rm** 90.00/210.00 **st.** – SB.

Three Counties, Belmont Rd, HR2 7BP, Southwest : 1 ½ m. on A 465 (01432) 299955, *enquiries@threecountieshotel.co.uk, Fax (01432) 275114* – rm, TV P – 350. MC AE VISA B c
Meals (bar lunch)/dinner 17.50/23.00 **st.** 9.75 – **60 rm** 61.50/79.50 **st.** – SB.

Aylestone Court, Aylestone Hill, HR1 1HS, (01432) 341891, *ayleshotel@aol.com, Fax (01432) 267691,* – rest, TV P – 40. MC AE VISA JCB. B a
Meals (residents only) (dinner only) 15.50/26.50 and dinner a la carte 22.50/26.50 **st.** 11.95 – **9 rm** 55.00/95.00 **t.**

Travel Inn, Holmer Rd, Holmer, HR4 9RS, North : 1 ¾ m. on A 49 (01432) 274853, *Fax (01432) 343003* – rm, TV P. MC AE VISA.
Meals (grill rest.) – **42 rm** 41.95 **t.**

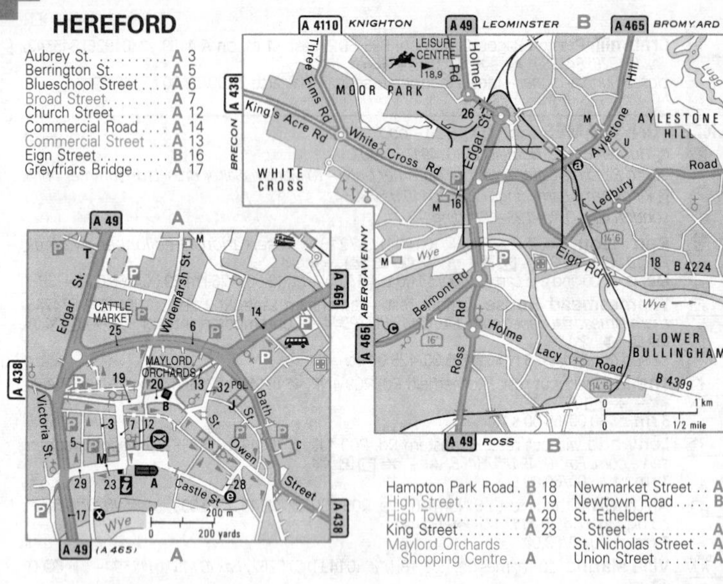

⌂ **Grafton Villa Farm** without rest., Grafton, HR2 8ED, South : 2 ¼ m. on A
℘ (01432) 268689, *jennielayton@real.net, Fax (01432) 268689,* « Working farm »,
closed December – **3 rm** 30.00/46.00 **st.**

✗ **Floodgates Brasserie,** Left Bank Village, Bridge St, HR4 9DG, ℘ (01432) 349008, *i @leftbank.co.uk, Fax (01432) 349012,* « River-side setting » – P. MC AE VISA A
Meals a la carte 15.95/23.45 **t.** 10.85.

at Marden *North : 5 ¾ m. by A 49 –* **B** *– ✉ Hereford.*

⌂ **The Vauld Farm**, HR1 3HA, Northeast : 1 ½ m. by Litmarsh rd ℘ (01568) 7978
« 16C timbered farmhouse », – rest, TV P.
Meals (by arrangement) (communal dining) 20.00 – **3 rm** 35.00/70.00, 1 suite.

at Madley *West : 6 m. by A 465 on B 4352 –* **B** *– ✉ Hereford.*

Comet Inn, Storrey St, HR2 9NJ, ℘ (01981) 250600, *enquiriesatthecometinn@btop world.com, Fax (01981) 250643* – P. MC VISA
Meals a la carte 14.00/22.00 **st.** 8.95.

at Ruckhall *West : 5 m. by A 49 off A 465 –* **B** *– ✉ Eaton Bishop.*

Ancient Camp Inn with rm, HR2 9QX, ℘ (01981) 250449, *ancientcampinn@cwef ham.worldonline.co.uk, Fax (01981) 251581,* ≤ River Wye and countryside, – TV MC VISA.
Meals (booking essential) (residents only) (dinner only) 19.50 **t.** 8.95 – **4 rm** 50.0 60.00 **t.**, 1 suite.

at Byford *West : 7½ m. by A 438 –* **B** *– ✉ Hereford.*

⌂ **Old Rectory,** HR4 7LD, ℘ (01981) 590218, *info@-ltd.com, Fax (01981) 590499,* – TV P.
March-November – **Meals** (by arrangement) 15.00 – **3 rm** 25.00/48.00 **s.**

HERM 403 P 33 and 230 ⑩ – *see Channel Islands.*

HERMITAGE *Dorset – see Sherborne.*

Si vous cherchez un hôtel tranquille,
consultez d'abord les cartes de l'introduction
ou repérez dans le texte les établissements indiqués avec le signe ou

HERSTMONCEUX *E. Sussex* 404 U 31 – *pop. 3 898.*

London 63 – Eastbourne 12 – Hastings 14 – Lewes 16.

XX **Sundial,** Gardner St, BN27 4LA, ℘ (01323) 832217, *sundialrestaurant@hotmail.com, Fax (01323) 832909,* « Converted 16C cottage », – P. MC AE VISA JCB
closed 2 weeks October, Sunday dinner and Monday – **Meals** - French - 19.50/25.50 and a la carte 29.50/50.35 **t.** 13.25.

at Wartling *Southeast : 3 ¾ m. by A 271 and Wartling rd – ✉ Herstmonceux.*

Wartling Place without rest., BN27 1RY, ℘ (01323) 832590, *accom@wartlingplace.prestel.co.uk, Fax (01323) 831558,* « Part Georgian », – TV P. MC AE VISA JCB.
4 rm 55.00/95.00 **s.**

HESSLE *Kingston-upon-Hull* 402 S 22 – *see Kingston-upon-Hull.*

HESWALL *Mersey.* 402 403 K 24 – *pop. 16 569.*

London 212 – Birkenhead 12 – Chester 14 – Liverpool 11.

Travel Inn, Chester Rd, Gayton, CH60 3FD, Southeast : ½ m. on A 540 ℘ (0151) 342 1982, *Fax (0151) 342 8983* – rm, TV P. MC AE VISA.
Meals (grill rest.) – **37 rm** 41.95 **t.**

XX **Gem,** 1 Milner Rd, CH60 5RT, ℘ (0151) 342 4811, *enquiries@gem-restaurant.co.uk, Fax (0151) 342 4811* – MC VISA
closed Monday – **Meals** (booking essential) (dinner only) 12.95 and a la carte 19.25/25.90 **t.** 9.50.

X **Est, Est, Est,** 146-148 Telegraph Rd, CH60 0AH, ℘ (0151) 342 9550, *Fax (0151) 342 9905* – . MC AE VISA
closed 25-26 December – **Meals** - Italian - a la carte 12.40/23.20 **t.**

HETHERSETT *Norfolk* 404 X 26 – *see Norwich.*

HETTON *N. Yorks.* 402 N 21 – *see Skipton.*

HEXHAM *Northd.* 401 402 N 19 *Great Britain G.* – *pop. 11 008.*

See : *Abbey*★ *(Saxon Crypt*★★*, Leschman chantry*★*).*

Env. : *Hadrian's Wall*★★*, N : 4½ m. by A 6079.*

Exc. : *Housesteads*★★*, NW : 12½ m. by A 6079 and B 6318.*

18 *Spital Park* ℘ *(01434) 602057* – 18 *Slaley Hall G. & C.C., Slaley* ℘ *(01434) 673350* – 9 *Tynedale, Tyne Green* ℘ *(01434) 608154.*

Wentworth Car Park ℘ *(01434) 652220.*

London 304 – Carlisle 37 – Newcastle upon Tyne 21.

Beaumont, Beaumont St, NE46 3LT, ℘ (01434) 602331, *beaumont.hotel@btinternet.com, Fax (01434) 606184* – TV – 100. MC AE VISA JCB.
The Park : Meals 11.50/18.75 **t.** 10.50 – 6.50 – **25 rm** 65.00/85.00 **t.** – SB.

West Close House without rest., Hextol Terr, NE46 2AD, by Allendale Rd ℘ (01434) 603307, – P.
4 rm 21.00/52.00.

East Peterel Field Farm, NE46 2JT, South : 2 m. by B 6306 off Whiteley Chapel rd ℘ (01434) 607209, *ben@petfield.demon.uk, Fax (01434) 601753,* ←, , – TV P
Meals (by arrangement) (communal dining) 20.00 **st.** – **4 rm** 40.00/65.00 **st.**

Dene House without rest., Juniper, NE46 1SJ, South : 3 ¾ m. by B 6306 following signs for Dye House ℘ (01434) 673413, *margaret@denehouse-hexam.co.uk, Fax (01434) 673413,* – P. MC AE VISA
3 rm 22.50/45.00.

XX **Valley Connection 301,** Market Pl, NE46 3NX, ℘ (01434) 601234, *Fax (01434) 606629* – . MC AE VISA JCB
closed Monday – **Meals** - Indian - (dinner only) a la carte 12.00/23.95 **t.** 9.50.

at Chollerton *North : 6 m. on A 6079 – ✉ Hexham.*

The Hermitage, NE48 4DG, North : 1 m. on A 6079 ℘ (01434) 681248, *stewart@thehermitagenow.freeserve.co.uk, Fax (01434) 681110,* , , – P.
closed December-January – **Meals** (by arrangement) (communal dining) 20.00 **st.** – **3 rm** 45.00/70.00 **st.**

ENGLAND

at Slaley *Southeast : 5½ m. by B 6306 – ✉ Hexham.*

Slaley Hall, NE47 0BY, Southeast : 2 ¼ m. ☎ (01434) 673350, *slaley.hall@devere-hotels.com, Fax (01434) 673962*, ≤, 🏋, ≘s, 🏊, 🏌18, 🌲, 🎾 – 🛗 ⋟ ▤ 📺 📞 ♿ 🅿 – 🎪 400. 🆎 AE ⓓ VISA
The Restaurant : Meals (dinner only and Sunday lunch) 24.95 and a la carte 27.95/39.90 ♦ – 🍷 13.95 – **129 rm** ☕ 130.00/170.00 **st.**, 10 suites – SB.

The Strothers ⟋ without rest., NE47 0AA, South : 1 m. on B 6306 ☎ (01434) 67341 *ednahardy@the-strothers.co.uk, Fax (01434) 673417*, ≤, 🌲 – ⋟ 📺 🅿
3 rm ☕ 25.00/50.00 **st.**

The Travellers Rest with rm, NE46 1TT, Northwest : 1 m. on B 6306 ☎ (01434) 67323 *enq@travellersrest.sagehost.co.uk, Fax (01434) 673906*, ≤, 🍽, 🌲 – ⋟ rm, 📺 🅿. 🆎 VISA JCB
Meals *(closed Sunday dinner)* a la carte 12.35/22.35 **t.** 🍷 9.50 – **3 rm** ☕ 35.00/50.00 **t.**

HEYTESBURY *Wilts.* **403** **404** N 30 – *see Warminster.*

HICKSTEAD *W. Sussex.*
London 40 – Brighton 8.

Travelodge, Jobs Lane, RH17 5NX, off A 23 ☎ (01444) 881377, *Fax (01444) 881377* ⋟ rm, ▤ rest, 📺 ♿ 🅿. 🆎 AE ⓓ VISA JCB. ⋟
Meals (grill rest.) – **55 rm** 59.95 **t.**

Le Grand Londres (GREATER LONDON) est composé de la City et de 32 arrondissements administratifs (Borough) eux-mêmes divisés en quartiers ou en villages ayant conservé leur caractère propre (Area).

HIGHCLIFFE *Dorset* **403** **404** O 31.
London 112 – Bournemouth 10 – Salisbury 21 – Southampton 26 – Winchester 37.

Lord Bute, Lymington Rd, BH23 4JS, ☎ (01425) 278884, *mail@lordbute.co.uk Fax (01425) 279258* – ⋟ rest, ▤ 📺 📞 🅿 – 🎪 30. 🆎 AE VISA
Meals *(closed Saturday lunch, Sunday dinner and Monday)* 13.95/24.95 and a la carte 22.65/31.95 **t.** 🍷 11.95 – ☕ 7.00 – **10 rm** 65.00/95.00 **t.** – SB.

HIGH CROSBY *Cumbria* **401** **402** L 19 – *see Carlisle.*

HIGH WYCOMBE *Bucks.* **404** R 29 *Great Britain G. – pop. 71 718.*
Env. : *Chiltern Hills★.*
🏌18 *Hazlemere G & C.C., Penn Rd, Hazlemere ☎ (01494) 714722 –* 🏌18, 🏌18 *Wycombe Heights, Rayners Ave, Loudwater ☎ (01494) 816686.*
🅸 *Paul's Row ☎ (01494) 421892.*
London 34 – Aylesbury 17 – Oxford 26 – Reading 18.

Posthouse High Wycombe, Handycross, HP11 1TL, Southwest : 1 ½ m. by A 404 junction 4 of M 40 ☎ (0870) 400 9042, *Fax (01494) 439071* – ⋟ rm, ▤ rest, 📺 ♿ 🅿 – 🎪 200. 🆎 AE ⓓ VISA
Meals *closed Saturday lunch* a la carte 16.00/24.00 **st.** – ☕ 11.95 – **113 rm** 139.00 **st.** – S

Alexandra, Queen Alexandra Rd, HP11 2JX, ☎ (01494) 463494, *reservations@alexandra-hotel.co.uk, Fax (01494) 463560* – ⋟ 📺 ♿ 🅿. 🆎 AE VISA JCB. ⋟
closed 1 week Christmas – **Meals** *(closed Friday-Sunday)* (dinner only) a la carte 15.0 24.95 **st.** 🍷 13.00 – ☕ 8.90 – **28 rm** 81.00/110.00 **st.**

Travel Inn, London Rd, HP10 9YL, Southeast : 3 m. on A 40 ☎ (01494) 53708 *Fax (01494) 446855* – ⋟ rm, ▤ rest, 📺 ♿ 🅿. 🆎 AE ⓓ VISA. ⋟
Meals (grill rest.) – **81 rm** 41.95 **t.**

HILTON PARK SERVICE AREA *W. Mids. – ✉ Wolverhampton.*

Travelodge, WV11 2AT, M 6 between junctions 10A and 11 (southbound carriageway) ☎ (01922) 701997, *Fax (01922) 701967* – ⋟ 📺 ♿ 🅿. 🆎 AE ⓓ VISA JCB. ⋟
Meals (grill rest.) – **64 rm** 49.95 **t.**

HINCKLEY *Leics.* 402 403 404 P 26 – *pop. 40 608.*
Hinckley Library, Lancaster Rd ✆ (01455) 635106.
London 103 – Birmingham 31 – Coventry 12 – Leicester 14.

Sketchley Grange, Sketchley Lane, LE10 3HU, South : 1 ½ m. by B 4109 (Rugby Rd) ✆ (01455) 251133, *sketchleygrange@btinternet.com, Fax (01455) 631384,* – rest, – 280. VISA
The Willow : **Meals** (dinner only) 22.95 **st.** 10.95 – ***The Terrace Bistro :*** **Meals** a la carte 15.00/25.00 **st.** 10.95 – 10.95 – **54 rm** 99.00 **st.**, 1 suite – SB.

Hanover International H. & Club, Watling St, LE10 3JA, Southeast : 2 ½ m. by B 4019 on A 5 ✆ (01455) 631122, *Fax (01455) 634536,* – – 400. VISA.
closed 24-30 December – ***The Conservatory :*** **Meals** (dinner only) 18.95 and a la carte 23.95/32.45 **st.** 12.50 – ***Brasserie 209 :*** **Meals** 18.95 and a la carte approx. 18.95 **s.** 12.50 – 12.50 – **345 rm** 105.00 **st.**, 5 suites.

HINDON *Wilts.* 403 404 N 30 – *pop. 493* – ✉ *Salisbury.*
London 107 – Exeter 71 – Salisbury 21 – Taunton 47.

Grosvenor Arms with rm, SP3 6DJ, ✆ (01747) 820696, *Fax (01747) 820869,* – VISA
Meals *(closed Sunday dinner)* a la carte 20.40/29.40 **t.** 10.00 – **7 rm** 45.00/95.00 **t.**

HINTLESHAM *Suffolk* 404 X 27 – *see Ipswich.*

Pour un bon usage des plans de ville, voir les signes conventionnels.

HISTON *Cambs.* 404 U 27 – *see Cambridge.*

HITCHIN *Herts.* 404 T 28 – *pop. 32 221.*
London 40 – Bedford 14 – Cambridge 26 – Luton 9.

Just 32, 32 Sun St, SG5 1AH, ✆ (01462) 455666 – VISA JCB
closed 26 December, Sunday and Monday – **Meals** a la carte 20.65/33.75 **t.** 9.75.

HOCKLEY HEATH *W. Mids.* 403 404 O 26 – *pop. 14 538* – ✉ *Solihull.*
London 117 – Birmingham 11 – Coventry 17.

Nuthurst Grange Country House, Nuthurst Grange Lane, B94 5NL, South : ¾ m. by A 3400 ✆ (01564) 783972, *info@nuthurst-grange.co.uk, Fax (01564) 783919,* – – 80. VISA
Meals – (see ***The Restaurant*** below) – **15 rm** 135.00/185.00 **t.** – SB.

Travel Inn, Stratford Rd, B94 6NX, on A 3400 ✆ (01564) 782144, *Fax (01564) 783197* – rm, – 35. VISA.
Meals (grill rest.) – **40 rm** 41.95 **t.**

The Restaurant (at Nuthurst Grange Country House), Nuthurst Grange Lane, B94 5NL, South : ¾ m. by A 3400 ✆ (01564) 783972, *Fax (01564) 783919,* – VISA
closed Saturday lunch – **Meals** 25.00/45.00 **t.** 14.50.

at Lapworth *Southeast : 2 m. on B 4439* – ✉ *Warwick.*

The Boot, Old Warwick Rd, B94 6JU, on B 4439 ✆ (01564) 782464, *Fax (01564) 784989,* , – VISA
closed 25 December and 1 January – **Meals** (booking essential) a la carte 16.40/27.40 **t.** 10.95.

HOCKLIFFE *Beds.* 404 S 28 – *see Dunstable.*

HOLBEACH *Lincs.* 402 404 U 25 – *pop. 5 318.*
London 117 – Kingston-upon-Hull 81 – Norwich 62 – Nottingham 60 – Peterborough 25.

Pipwell Manor without rest., Washway Rd, Saracen's Head, PE12 8AL, Northeast : 1 ½ m. by A 17 ✆ (01406) 423119, *Fax (01406) 423119,* « Georgian manor house », –
closed 24 December-2 January – **4 rm** 33.00/46.00 **st.**

HOLBROOK *Suffolk* 404 X 28 – *see Ipswich.*

HOLFORD *Somerset* 403 K 30 *Great Britain G. – pop. 307 –* ✉ *Bridgwater.*
Env. : *Stogursey Priory Church★★, W : 4½ m.*
London 171 – Bristol 48 – Minehead 15 – Taunton 22.

Combe House ⛰, TA5 1RZ, Southwest : 1 m., turning off A 39 at Elf petrol station
✆ (01278) 741382, *enquiries@combehouse.co.uk, Fax (01278) 741322,* ⛱, 🎾 – ⇎ rest
TV P. MC AE VISA JCB
closed mid November-mid February except Christmas and New Year – **Meals** (bar lunch)/
dinner 20.00 **st.** 7.95 – **15 rm** ☕ 41.00/93.00 **st.**, 1 suite – SB.

HOLMES CHAPEL *Ches.* 402 403 404 M 24 – *pop. 5 465.*
London 181 – Chester 25 – Liverpool 41 – Manchester 24 – Stoke-on-Trent 20.

Holly Lodge, 70 London Rd, CW4 7AS, on A 50 ✆ (01477) 537033, *sales@hollylodgehotel.co.uk, Fax (01477) 535823* – ⇎ TV ♿ P – 🏛 120. MC AE ⓓ VISA
Meals (bar lunch Monday to Saturday)/dinner a la carte 18.40/24.40 **t.** 8.95 – **42 rm**
☕ 79.00/92.00 **t.** – SB.

Old Vicarage, Knutsford Rd, Cranage, CW4 8EF, Northwest : ½ m. on A 50
✆ (01477) 532041, *oldvichotel@aol.com, Fax (01477) 535728* – ⇎ TV ♿ P – 🏛 30. MC AE
ⓓ VISA. ✂
The Vicarage : **Meals** a la carte 14.65/23.05 **st.** 9.95 – **29 rm** ☕ 73.50/86.50 **st.** – SB.

Cottage Rest. and Lodge, London Rd, Allostock, WA16 9LU, North : 3 m. on A 50
✆ (01565) 722470, *Fax (01565) 722749* – ⇎ TV P – 🏛 60. MC AE VISA. ✂
Meals *(closed Sunday dinner)* 12.95 and a la carte 19.15/30.10 **t.** 10.25 – **12 rm** ☕ 70.00/
80.00 **t.**

HOLNE *Devon* 403 I 32 – *see Ashburton.*

HOLT *Norfolk* 404 X 25 – *pop. 2 972.*
London 124 – King's Lynn 34 – Norwich 22.

Yetman's, 37 Norwich Rd, NR25 6SA, ✆ (01263) 713320 – ⇎. MC AE VISA
closed 3 weeks October-November, 25, 26 and 31 December and Sunday-Tuesday – **Meals**
(dinner only and Sunday lunch)/dinner 30.00 **t.** 16.75.

HOLT *Wilts.* 403 404 N 29 – *see Trowbridge.*

HOLYWELL *Cambs.* 404 T 27 – *see St. Ives.*

HOLYSTONE *Tyne and Wear – see Newcastle upon Tyne.*

HONILEY *Warks. – see Warwick*

HONITON *Devon* 403 K 31 *The West Country G. – pop. 9 008.*
See : *All Hallows Museum★ AC.*
Env. : *Ottery St Mary★ (St Mary's★) SW : 5 m. by A 30 and B 3177.*
Exc. : *Faraway Countryside Park (⇐★) AC, SE : 6½ m. by A 375 and B 3174.*
Lace Walk Car Park ✆ (01404) 43716.
London 186 – Exeter 17 – Southampton 93 – Taunton 18.

Deer Park ⛰, Buckerell Village, Weston, EX14 3PG, West : 2 ½ m. by A 30
✆ (01404) 41266, *admin@deerparkcountryhotel.com, Fax (01404) 46598,* ⇐, heated
, ⛱, , 🎾, squash – TV P – 🏛 70. MC AE ⓓ VISA. ✂
Meals 15.00/25.00 and a la carte 24.00/40.50 **st.** 12.00 – **21 rm** ☕ 55.00/140.00 **st.** – SB.

at Yarcombe *Northeast : 8 m. on A 30 –* ✉ *Honiton.*

Belfry Country H., EX14 9BD, on A 30 ✆ (01404) 861234, *Fax (01404) 861579,* ⇐ – ⇎
TV P. MC AE VISA
*closed Christmas and New Year***Meals** (dinner only) 22.00 **st.** 10.50 – **6 rm** ☕ 45.00/
72.00 **st.** – SB.

at Wilmington *East : 3 m. on A 35 –* ✉ *Honiton.*

Home Farm, EX14 9JR, on A 35 ✆ (01404) 831278, *homefarmhotel@breathemail.net,
Fax (01404) 831411,* « Part 16C thatched farmhouse », ⛱ – ⇎ rest, TV P. MC VISA
Meals 16.75/25.00 and a la carte 17.45/25.20 **t.** 9.95 – **12 rm** ☕ 39.50/85.00 **t.** – SB.

t Payhembury *Northwest : 7 m. by A 373 – ✉ Honiton.*

Cokesputt House ⊗, EX14 3HD, West : ¼ m. on Tale rd ☎ (01404) 841289, *Fax (0870) 1642511*, ≤, « Part 17C and 18C, gardens » – ⊁ P. MC AE VISA. ⊁
– **Meals** (booking essential) (communal dining) 22.50 **s.** – **3 rm** ☐ 34.00/68.00 **st.**

OO GREEN *Ches. – see Knutsford.*

OOK *Hants.* 404 R 30 – *pop. 6 471* – ✉ *Basingstoke.*
London 47 – Reading 13 – Southampton 35.

Hanover International H. & Club, Scures Hill, Nately Scures, RG27 9JS, West : 1 m. on A 30 ☎ (01256) 764161, *Fax (01256) 768341*, Lδ, ≘s, ☐, ⛱ – |‡|, ⊁ rm, ☐ rest, TV ☎ ♿ P – 🎪 240. MC AE ◑ VISA. ⊁
closed 25 December-2 January **Meals** *(closed Sunday dinner and lunch Saturday and Bank Holidays)* a la carte 19.70/28.15 **t.** 🍷 14.25 – ☐ 12.25 – **100 rm** 130.00/190.00 **st.** – SB.

Hook House, London Rd, RG27 9EQ, East : ½ m. on A 30 ☎ (01256) 762630, *Fax (01256) 760232*, « Part Georgian house », ⛱ – ⊁ TV ☎ P. MC AE ◑ VISA. ⊁
closed 21 December-2 January – **Meals** *(closed Saturday, Sunday and Bank Holidays)* (residents only) (dinner only) a la carte 15.00/21.00 **t.** 🍷 10.95 – **17 rm** ☐ 72.50/84.50 **st.**

t Rotherwick *North : 2 m. by A 30 and B 3349 on Rotherwick rd – ✉ Basingstoke.*

Tylney Hall ⊗, RG27 9AZ, South : 1 ½ m. by Newnham rd on Ridge Lane ☎ (01256) 764881, *sales@tylneyhall.com, Fax (01256) 768141*, « 19C mansion in extensive gardens by Gertrude Jekyll », Lδ, ≘s, ⛲ heated, ☐, 🎾, ⁂ – ⊁ rm, TV ☎ P – 🎪 120. MC AE ◑ VISA JCB. ⊁
Meals 23.00/35.00 and a la carte 38.00/50.50 **st.** 🍷 16.50 – **101 rm** ☐ 130.00/220.00 **st.**, 9 suites – SB.

In this guide

a symbol or a character, printed in red or **black**, in **bold** or light type, does not have the same meaning.
Pay particular attention to the explanatory pages.

OOK *Wilts. – see Swindon.*

OPE *Derbs.* 402 403 404 O 23 – ✉ *Sheffield.*
London 180 – Derby 50 – Manchester 31 – Sheffield 15 – Stoke-on-Trent 40.

Underleigh House ⊗ without rest., Hope Valley, S33 6RF, North : 1 m. by Edale rd ☎ (01433) 621372, *underleigh.house@btinternet.com, Fax (01433) 621324*, ≤, ⛱ – ⊁ TV P. MC VISA. ⊁
closed Christmas and New Year – **5 rm** ☐ 46.00/80.00 **st.**, 1 suite.

OPE COVE *Devon* 403 I 33 – *see Salcombe.*

OPTON WAFERS *Shrops.* 403 404 M 26 – *pop. 609* – ✉ *Kidderminster.*
London 150 – Birmingham 32 – Shrewsbury 38.

The Crown Inn with rm, DY14 0NB, on A 4117 ☎ (01299) 270372, *desk@crownathopton.co.uk, Fax (01299) 271127*, ⛱ – ⊁ rm, TV P. MC AE VISA JCB. ⊁
closed 25 December and 2-9 January – **Meals** *(closed Sunday dinner and Monday)* 14.95/21.95 and lunch a la carte 17.20/24.95 **t.** 🍷 11.95 – **8 rm** ☐ 48.00/75.00 **t.** – SB.

OPWAS *Staffs.* 402 ⑩ 403 ㉒ 404 ⑩ – *see Tamworth.*

OPWOOD *W. Mids.* 402 ⑨ 403 ㉒ 404 ⑳ – ✉ *Birmingham.*
London 131 – Birmingham 8.

Westmead, Redditch Rd, B48 7AL, on A 441 ☎ (0121) 445 1202, *reservations@corushotels.com, Fax (0121) 445 6163* – ⊁, ☐ rest, TV ☎ P – 🎪 250. MC AE ◑ VISA JCB
– **Meals** closed lunch Saturday a la carte 17.95/25.00 **st.** 🍷 9.95 – ☐ 11.50 – **56 rm** 98.00/108.00 **st.**, 2 suites – SB.

HORLEY *Surrey* 404 T 30 – *pop. 19 267.*

London 27 – Brighton 26 – Royal Tunbridge Wells 22.

Plan : see Gatwick

Langshott Manor, Langshott, RH6 9LN, North : by A 23 turning right at Thistle Gatwic H. onto Ladbroke Rd ℘ (01293) 786680, *admin@langshottmanor.com, Fax (01293) 78390*, « Part Elizabethan manor house, gardens » – ⋟ TV P. MC AE D VISA JCB
***Mulberry* :** **Meals** (booking essential) 25.00/37.50 and a la carte 31.00/52.00 **st.** 17.00
14 rm ☐ 165.00/245.00 **st.**, 1 suite – SB.

Thistle Gatwick, Brighton Rd, RH6 8PH, on A 23 ℘ (0870) 333 9134, *gatwick@thistle.c uk, Fax (0870) 333 9234* – ⋟, ▤ rest, TV P – 60. MC AE D VISA JCB Y
Meals (bar lunch Saturday) 15.95/21.50 **t.** 11.95 – ☐ 12.50 – **78 rm** 119.00/152.00 **s.** – S

Lawn without rest., 30 Massetts Rd, RH6 7DE, ℘ (01293) 775751, *info@lawnguesthous co.uk, Fax (01293) 821803*, – ⋟ TV P. MC AE VISA JCB Y
12 rm ☐ 40.00/55.00 **st.**

The Turret without rest., 48 Massetts Rd, RH6 7DS, ℘ (01293) 782490, *theturret@tesc net, Fax (01293) 431492* – ⋟ TV P. MC VISA. Y
11 rm ☐ 39.00/55.00 **st.**

Rosemead without rest., 19 Church Rd, RH6 7EY, ℘ (01293) 784965, *rosemead@glob net.co.uk, Fax (01293) 430547* – ⋟ TV P. MC AE VISA JCB Y
6 rm ☐ 34.00/50.00 **st.**

HORNCASTLE *Lincs.* 402 404 T 24 – *pop. 4 994.*

The Trinity Centre, 52 East St ℘ (01507) 526636.
London 140 – Boston 19 – Great Grimsby 31 – Lincoln 21.

XX **The Magpies,** 71-75 East St, LN9 6AA, ℘ (01507) 527004, *magpies@fsbdial.co.u Fax (01507) 524064* – ⋟. MC VISA
closed 3 weeks August, Monday, Tuesday, Sunday dinner and restricted opening Januar February – **Meals** (dinner only and Sunday lunch)/dinner 20.00/24.00 **t.** 11.00.

HORNDON-ON-THE-HILL *Essex* 404 V 29.

London 25 – Chelmsford 22 – Maidstone 34 – Southend-on-Sea 16.

Bell Inn with rm, High Rd, SS17 8LD, ℘ (01375) 642463, *bell-inn@fdn.co.u Fax (01375) 361611*, « 16C coaching inn » – ⋟ TV P. MC AE VISA JCB
Meals *(closed 25-26 December and Bank Holiday Mondays)* 17.95 (lunch) and a la car 15.45/25.95 **t.** 10.00 – ☐ 7.50 – **5 rm** 50.00/85.00 **t.**

HORNS CROSS *Devon* 403 H 31 *The West Country G.* – ✉ *Bideford.*

Exc. : *Clovelly★★, NW : 7 m. by A 39 and B 3237.*
London 237 – Barnstaple 15 – Exeter 48.

Lower Waytown without rest., EX39 5DN, Northeast : 1 ¼ m. on A 3 ℘ (01237) 451787, *aircp@penny26.freeserve.com, Fax (01237) 451787*, « Part 17 thatched cottage », – ⋟ TV P.
3 rm ☐ 41.00/60.00 **st.**

HORRINGER *Suffolk* 404 W 27 – *see Bury St. Edmunds.*

HORSFORTH *W. Yorks.* 402 P 22 – *see Leeds.*

HORSHAM *W. Sussex* 404 T 30 – *pop. 42 552.*

18, 18 *Fullers, Hammerpond Rd, Mannings Heath ℘ (01403) 210228.*
9 Causeway ℘ (01403) 211661.
London 39 – Brighton 23 – Guildford 20 – Lewes 25 – Worthing 20.

South Lodge, Brighton Rd, Lower Beeding, RH13 6PS, Southeast : 5 m. on A 2 ℘ (01403) 891711, *enquiries@southlodgehotel.co.uk, Fax (01403) 891766*, <, « Victori mansion, gardens », 18, – ⋟ rest, TV P – 80. MC AE D VISA JCB
Meals 24.00/37.50 and dinner a la carte 42.50/49.50 **t.** 20.00 – ☐ 15.00 – **37 rm** 170.0 370.00 **t.**, 4 suites – SB.

Travel Inn, The Station, 57 North St, RH12 1RB, ℘ (01403) 250141, *Fax (01403) 270797* ⋟ rm, ▤ rest, TV P. MC AE D VISA.
Meals (grill rest.) – **40 rm** 41.95 **t.**

at Southwater *South : 3 m. by B 2237* – ✉ *Horsham.*

XX **Cole's,** Worthing Rd, RH13 7BS, ℘ (01403) 730456, *coles@colesrest.fsnet.co.u Fax (01403) 891540* – ⋟ P. MC AE D VISA JCB
closed 2 weeks in summer, 1 week Christmas-New Year, Saturday lunch, Sunday dinner a Monday – **Meals** 12.95/15.00 (lunch) and a la carte 23.75/30.65 **t.** 11.95.

t Slinfold *West : 4 m. by A 281 off A 264 – ✉ Horsham.*

Random Hall without rest., Stane St, RH13 7QX, West : ½ m. on A 29 ☎ (01403) 790558, *nigel@randomhall.fsnet.co.uk, Fax (01403) 791046,* « Part 16C farmhouse » – TV P. MC VISA.
closed 2 weeks Christmas and New Year – **13 rm** 70.00/80.00 **st.**

ORTON-CUM-STUDLEY *Oxon.* 403 404 Q 28 – *pop. 453* – ✉ *Oxford.*
London 57 – Aylesbury 23 – Oxford 7.

Studley Priory, OX33 1AZ, ☎ (01865) 351203, *res@studley-priory.co.uk, Fax (01865) 351613,* ←, « Elizabethan manor house in park », 18, , – TV P – 50. MC AE VISA.
Meals (booking essential to non-residents) a la carte 34.15/39.40 **st.** – 9.00 – **17 rm** 110.00/250.00 **st.**, 1 suite – SB.

ORWICH *Lancs.* 402 404 M 23 – ✉ *Bolton.*
London 217 – Liverpool 35 – Manchester 21 – Preston 16.

Whites, The Reebok Stadium, (Car Park A), De Havilland Way, BL6 6SF, Southeast : 2 ½ m. by A 673 on A 6027 ☎ (01204) 667788, *whites@devere-hotel.com, Fax (01204) 673721,* « Within Bolton Wanderers Football Club », , , – , rest, TV P – 550. MC AE VISA JCB.
Reflections : **Meals** *(closed Sunday)* (dinner only) 28.50 and a la carte 27.85/38.40 **st.** 16.65 – ***Brasserie at Whites :*** **Meals** *(closed lunch Saturday)* 14.50/18.50 and a la carte 18.15/32.40 **st.** 12.95 – **119 rm** 130.00/145.00 **st.**, 6 suites – SB.

Express by Holiday Inn without rest., 3 Arena Approach, BL6 6LB, Southeast : 2 ½ m. by A 673 on A 6027 ☎ (01204) 469111, *Fax (01204) 469222* – TV P – 25. MC AE VISA JCB.
74 rm 52.50 **st.**

OTHFIELD *Kent* 404 W 30 – *see Ashford.*

OUGHTON CONQUEST *Beds.* 404 S 27 – *see Bedford.*

OVE *Brighton and Hove* 404 T 31 – *see Brighton and Hove.*

OVINGHAM *N. Yorks.* 402 R 21 – *pop. 322* – ✉ *York.*
London 235 – Middlesbrough 36 – York 25.

Worsley Arms, YO62 4LA, ☎ (01653) 628234, *worsleyarms@aol.com, Fax (01653) 628130,* « Part 19C coaching inn », – TV P – 25. MC AE VISA JCB
Meals a la carte 25.00/35.00 **st.** 12.95 – ***Cricketer's Bistro :*** **Meals** 12.50/35.00 and a la carte 25.00/35.00 **st.** 12.95 – **19 rm** 60.00/90.00 **st.** – SB.

UDDERSFIELD *W. Yorks.* 402 404 O 23 – *pop. 143 726.*

18, 9 Bradley Park, Bradley Rd ☎ (01484) 223772 – 18 Woodsome Hall, Fenay Bridge ☎ (01484) 602971 – 18 Outlane, Slack Lane ☎ (01422) 374762 **A** *– 18 Meltham, Thick Hollins Hall ☎ (01484) 850227 – 18 Fixby Hall, Lightridge Rd ☎ (01484) 420110* **B** *– 18 Crosland Heath, Felks Stile Rd ☎ (01484) 653216* **A**.

3 Albion St ☎ (01484) 223200.
London 191 – Bradford 11 – Leeds 15 – Manchester 25 – Sheffield 26.

Plans on following pages

Cedar Court, Ainley Top, HD3 3RH, Northwest : 3 m. at junction of A 629 with A 643 ☎ (01422) 375431, *Fax (01422) 310067,* , , – TV P – 400. MC AE VISA
A e
Meals *(closed Saturday lunch)* 12.95/19.95 11.25 – 12.95 – **113 rm** 95.00/115.00 **st.**, 1 suite – SB.

George, St George's Sq, HD1 1JA, ☎ (01484) 515444, *Fax (01484) 435056* – TV P – 200. MC AE VISA JCB
C a
Meals (bar lunch Saturday) 9.95 (lunch) and dinner a la carte 15.65/23.45 **t.** 10.95 – 10.00 – **59 rm** 80.00/100.00 **st.**, 1 suite – SB.

HUDDERSFIELD

Acre Street . . . . AB 3
Armitage Road . . . . B 4
Ashes Lane . . . . B 6
Balmoral Avenue . . . . B 7
Bolstermoor Road . . . . A 12
Brighouse Road . . . . AB 15
Butternab Road . . . . B 16
Church Lane . . . . B 19
Clough Road . . . . A 24
Crosland Factory Lane . . . . . A 27
Dog Kennel Bank . . . . B 28
East Street . . . . A 31
Edgerton Road . . . . B 33
Fartown Green Road . . . . . . B 36
Gillroyd Lane . . . . A 40
Glead Road . . . . A 42
Gleholt Road . . . . B 43
Grimescar Road . . . . B 46
Haeton Road . . . . B 48
Halifax Old Road . . . . B 49
Halifax Road . . . . B 51
Helme Lane . . . . A 54
Hey Lane . . . . B 55
Huddersfield Road . . . . B 58
Kaye Lane . . . . B 61
King's Mill In . . . . B 64
Knowl Road . . . . A 66
Leymoor Road . . . . A 72
Lindley Moor . . . . A 73
Lockwood Road . . . . B 75
Lockwood Scar . . . . B 76
Longwood Gate . . . . A 78
Manchester Road . . . . B 84
New Mill Road . . . . B 97
Norttgate . . . . B 106
Pack Road . . . . B 1
Pike Low Road . . . . A 1
Quarmby Road . . . . A 1
Reinwood Road . . . . A 1
Rochdale Road . . . . A 1
St. John's Road . . . . B 1
St. Thomas Road . . . . B 1
Scar Lane . . . . A 1
Scotgate Road . . . . B 1
Slades Lane . . . . A 1
Station Road . . . . A 1
Swallow Lane . . . . A 1
Udget Street . . . . A 1
Vicarage Road . . . . A 1
Waingate . . . . B 1
Walpde Road . . . . B 1
West Bourne Road . . . . B 1
Whitehead Lane . . . . B 1
Woodhead Road . . . . B 1

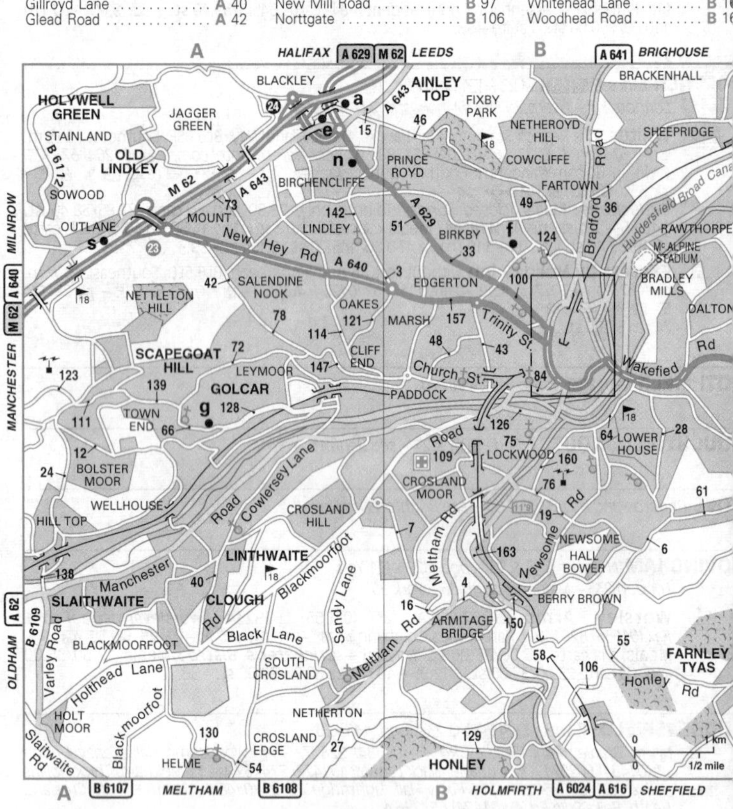

Briar Court, Halifax Rd, Birchencliffe, HD3 3NT, Northwest : 2 m. on A 6 ℘ (01484) 519902, *info@briarcourthotel.com, Fax (01484) 431812* – rm, 150. VISA JCB. A
closed 1 week Christmas, 4 days Easter and Bank Holidays – ***Da Sandro :*** **Meals** - Italiar a la carte 14.40/24.85 **t.** 9.95 – **47 rm** 65.00/75.00 **st.**, 1 suite.

The Lodge, 48 Birkby Lodge Rd, Birkby, HD2 2BG, North : 1 ½ m. by A 629 and Blacker ℘ (01484) 431001, *Fax (01484) 421590,* – 30. VISA. B
closed 26-27 December and 1 January – **Meals** *(closed Saturday lunch)* (residents or Sunday dinner) 14.95/23.95 **t.** 10.95 – **12 rm** 60.00/100.00 **t.**

Travelodge, Leeds Rd, WF14 0BY, Northeast : 4 ½ m. on A 62 ℘ (01924) 48992 *Fax (01924) 479917* – rm, VISA JCB.
Meals (grill rest.) – **27 rm** 49.95 **t.**

HUDDERSFIELD

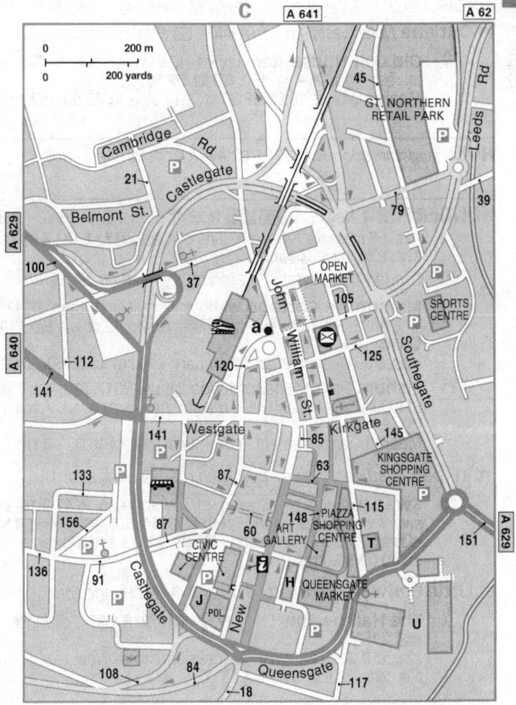

*Great Britain and Ireland is now covered by an **Atlas** at a scale of 1 inch to 4.75 miles.*

Three easy to use versions: Paperback, Spiralbound and Hardback.

Premier Lodge, New Hey Rd, Fixby, HD2 2EA, Northwest : 3 ½ m. by A 629 off A 643 (Brighouse rd) ✆ (0870) 7001408, *Fax (0870) 7001409* – TV P. VISA. **Meals** (carving rest.) 11.75 and a la carte approx. 11.95 **t.** 8.95 – **40 rm** 42.95 **t.** A a

at Almondbury *Southeast : 1 ¾ m. by A 629 on Almondbury rd –* **B** *– ✉ Huddersfield.*

XX **Thorpe Grange Manor,** Thorpe Lane, HD5 8TA, ✆ (01484) 425115, *admin@thorpegrangemanor.com, Fax (01484) 425115,* – P. VISA JCB *closed 19 May-5 June, 1-14 January, Saturday lunch, Sunday dinner and Monday –* **Meals** 14.95 and a la carte 23.70/30.95 **st.** 10.95.

at Shelley *Southeast : 6 ¼ m. by A 629 on B 6116 –* **B** *– ✉ Huddersfield.*

Three Acres Inn, Roydhouse, HD8 8LR, Northeast : 1 ½ m. on Flockton rd ✆ (01484) 602606, *3acres@globalnet.co.uk, Fax (01484) 608411* – TV P. VISA. *closed 25 December and 1 January –* **Meals** – (see ***The Restaurant*** below) – **20 rm** 55.00/75.00 **t.**

XX **The Restaurant** (at Three Acres Inn H.), Roydhouse, HD8 8LR, Northeast : 1 ½ m. on Flockton rd ✆ (01484) 602606, *3acres@globalnet.co.uk, Fax (01484) 608411* – P. VISA *– closed 25 December, 1 January and Saturday lunch –* **Meals** 17.95 (lunch) and a la carte 21.05/37.90 **t.** 6.95.

at Lockwood *Southwest : 1 m. by A 616 –* **B** *– ✉ Huddersfield.*

X **Ciao!,** 2 Water St, HD4 6EJ, ✆ (01484) 534444, *Fax (01484) 536655* – P. VISA *closed 25-26 December, 1 January, Saturday lunch and Monday –* **Meals** - Italian - (booking essential) a la carte 18.95/22.50 **t.** 9.50.

at Golcar *West : 3 ½ m. by A 62 on B 6111 – ✉ Huddersfield.*

XXX **The Weaver's Shed** with rm, Knowl Rd, via Scar Lane, HD7 4AN, ✆ (01484) 654284, *info@weaversshed.demon.co.uk, Fax (01484) 650980,* « Part 18C woollen mill » – TV P. VISA A g *closed Christmas and New Year –* **Meals** *(closed Sunday, Monday and lunch Saturday and Good Friday)* 9.95/13.95 (lunch) and a la carte 17.95/32.85 **t.** 10.95 – **5 rm** 55.00/70.00 **t.** – SB.

ENGLAND

at Outlane *Northwest : 4 m. on A 640 – ✉ Huddersfield.*

Old Golf House, New Hey Rd, HD3 3YP, ☎ (01422) 379311, *Fax (01422) 372694,* – rest, – 100. VISA A
Meals a la carte 16.85/28.80 **st.** 11.95 – 10.50 – **52 rm** 59.50/69.50 **st.** – SB.

HULL *Kingston-upon-Hull* 402 S 22 – *see Kingston-upon-Hull.*

HUNGERFORD *Newbury* 403 404 P 29 *The West Country G. – pop. 5 046.*

Exc. : *Savernake Forest★★ (Grand Avenue★★★), W : 7 m. by A 4 – Crofton Beam Engines SW : 8 m. by A 338 and minor roads.*

London 74 – Bristol 57 – Oxford 28 – Reading 26 – Southampton 46.

Marshgate Cottage without rest., Marsh Lane, RG17 0QX, West : ¾ m. by Church ☎ (01488) 682307, *reservations@marshgate.co.uk, Fax (01488) 685475,* ←, – VISA JCB
closed 25 December and 1 January – **10 rm** 36.50/60.00 **st.**

Fishers Farm, Shefford Woodlands, RG17 7AB, Northeast : 4 m. by A 4 and A 338 c B 4000 ☎ (01488) 648466, *mail@fishersfarm.co.uk, Fax (01488) 648706,* « Working farm », –
Meals (by arrangement) (communal dining) 18.00 – **3 rm** 35.00/60.00 **st.**

at Inkpen *Southeast : 3½ m. by Inkpen rd – ✉ Hungerford.*

Swan Inn with rm, Craven Rd, Lower Green, RG17 9DX, ☎ (01488) 668326, *enquiries@th swaninn-organics.co.uk, Fax (01488) 668306,* – VISA.
closed 25-26 December – **Meals** 21.00 and a la carte 15.45/24.50 **st.** 11.50 – **10 r** 40.00/90.00 **st.**

at Little Bedwyn *Southwest : 3 m. by A 4 – ✉ Hungerford.*

The Harrow Inn, SN8 3JP, ☎ (01672) 870871, *dining@harrowinn.co.uk,* – VISA
closed 2 weeks August, 2 weeks Christmas-New Year, Sunday dinner and Monday – **Mea** a la carte 28.95/39.45 **t.** 13.00.

HUNSTANTON *Norfolk* 402 404 V 25 – *pop. 4 634.*

Golf Course Rd ☎ (01485) 532811.

Town Hall, The Green ☎ (01485) 532610.

London 120 – Cambridge 60 – Norwich 45.

Le Strange Arms, Golf Course Rd, Old Hunstanton, PE36 6JJ, North : 1 m. by A 14 ☎ (01485) 534411, *reception@lestrangearms.co.uk, Fax (01485) 534724,* ←, – res – 150. VISA JCB
Meals (bar lunch Monday-Saturday)/dinner 19.00 and a la carte 13.50/22.00 **t.** 10.00 **33 rm** 57.50/103.00, 3 suites – SB.

Oriel Lodge without rest., 24 Homefields Rd, PE36 5HJ, ☎ (01485) 532368, *info@or lodge.co.uk, Fax (01485) 532388,* –
5 rm 35.00/58.00.

Claremont without rest., 35 Greevegate, PE36 6AF, ☎ (01485) 533171 –
closed Christmas and New Year – **7 rm** 24.00/48.00.

HUNSTRETE *Bath & North East Somerset* 403 404 M 29 – *see Bristol.*

HUNTINGDON *Cambs.* 404 T 26 – *pop. 15 575 – Hemingford Abbots, New Farm Lodg Cambridge Rd ☎ (01480) 495000.*

The Library, Princes St ☎ (01480) 388588.

London 69 – Bedford 21 – Cambridge 16.

Huntingdon Marriott, Kingfisher Way, Hinchingbrooke Business Park, PE29 6FL, West 1 ½ m. by A 141 at junction with A 14 ☎ (01480) 446000, *huntingdon@marriotthote co.uk, Fax Fax (01480) 451111,* – 260. VISA
Meals a la carte 17.65/29.50 **st.** 12.75 – 13.00 – **146 rm** 110.00 **st.**, 4 suites – SB.

Old Bridge, 1 High St, PE29 3TQ, ☎ (01480) 424300, *oldbridge@huntsbridge.co.u Fax (01480) 411017,* – , rm, – 50. VISA
Meals – (see ***The Restaurant and Terrace*** below) – **24 rm** 80.00/100.00 **st.**

Travelodge, PE18 9JF, Southeast : 5 ½ m. on A 14 (eastbound carriageway) ℘ (01954) 230919, *Fax (01954) 230919* – rm, rest, TV P. MC AE VISA JCB.
Meals (grill rest.) – **40 rm** 52.95 **t.**

The Restaurant and Terrace (at Old Bridge H.), 1 High St, PE29 3TQ, ℘ (01480) 424300, *Fax (01480) 411017*, – P. MC AE VISA
Meals 19.00 (lunch) and a la carte 21.50/30.00 **st.** 11.50.

UNTON *Kent – pop. 603 – ✉ Maidstone.*
London 37 – Canterbury 28 – Folkestone 34 – Hastings 35 – Maidstone 5.

The Woolhouse without rest., Grove Lane, ME15 0SE, ℘ (01622) 820778, *Fax (01622) 820645*, « Converted 17C barn », – P
closed Christmas and New Year – **4 rm** 30.00/60.00 **s.**

URLEY-ON-THAMES *Windsor & Maidenhead* 404 R 29 – *pop. 1 712 – ✉ Maidenhead.*
London 38 – Oxford 26 – Reading 12.

Ye Olde Bell H. Ramada Jarvis, High St, SL6 5LX, ℘ (01628) 825881, *sales.yeolde@ramadajarvis.co.uk, Fax (01628) 825939*, « Part 12C inn », – TV P – 130. MC AE VISA
Meals 17.95/30.00 14.95 – 11.95 – **45 rm** 175.00/195.00 **st.**, 1 suite – SB.

URST *Berks.* 403 404 Q 29 – *see Reading.*

Halten Sie beim Betreten des Hotels oder des Restaurants den Führer in der Hand.
Sie zeigen damit, daß Sie aufgrund dieser Empfehlung gekommen sind.

URSTBOURNE TARRANT *Hants.* 403 404 P 30 – *pop. 700 – ✉ Andover.*
London 77 – Bristol 77 – Oxford 38 – Southampton 33.

Esseborne Manor , SP11 0ER, Northeast : 1 ½ m. on A 343 ℘ (01264) 736444, *essebornemanor@cs.com, Fax (01264) 736725*, – TV P – 40. MC AE VISA
Meals 15.00/20.00 (lunch) and dinner a la carte 25.00/35.00 **st.** 13.50 – **15 rm** 95.00/150.00 **st.** – SB.

URST GREEN *Lancs.* 402 M 22 – ✉ *Clitheroe.*
London 236 – Blackburn 12 – Burnley 13 – Preston 12.

Shireburn Arms, Whalley Rd, BB7 9QJ, on B 6243 ℘ (01254) 826518, *steven@shireburnarms.fsnet.co.uk, Fax (01254) 826208*, – TV P. MC AE VISA JCB
Meals 12.50/13.95 and a la carte 13.00/21.50 **t.** 11.95 – **18 rm** 45.00/65.00 **t.** – SB.

UTTON-LE-HOLE *N. Yorks.* 402 R 21 – *pop. 162.*
London 244 – Scarborough 27 – York 33.

Hammer and Hand, YO62 6UA, ℘ (01751) 417300, *info@hammerandhandhouse.com, Fax (01751) 417711*, « 18C former beer house », – TV P. MC VISA
Meals (by arrangement) 15.00 **s.** 9.00 – **3 rm** 27.00/50.00 **s.**

Quaker Cottage, YO62 6UA, ℘ (01751) 417300, *info@hammerandhandhouse.com, Fax (01751) 417711*, « 17C Yorkshire longhouse », – TV P. MC VISA
Meals (by arrangement) 15.00 9.00 – **4 rm** 28.00/52.00 **st.**

UYTON *Mersey.* 402 403 L 23 – *see Liverpool.*

YDE *Gtr. Manchester* 402 403 404 N 23 – *pop. 30 666.*
London 202 – Manchester 10.

Village, Captain Clarke Rd, Dukinfield, SK14 4QG, Northwest : 1 ¼ m. by A 627 ℘ (0161) 368 1456, *jillkays@village-hotels.com, Fax (0161) 367 8343*, , , , squash – TV P – 180. MC AE VISA
Meals a la carte 12.65/23.25 **st.** 7.95 – **89 rm** 80.00/107.00 **st.**

Premier Lodge, Stockport Rd, SK14 3AU, East : 2 m. by A 57 ℘ (0870) 7001478, *Fax (0870) 7001479* – , rm, rest, TV P. MC AE VISA.
Meals (grill rest.) a la carte approx. 14.20 **t.** 8.75 – **83 rm** 42.95 **t.**

HYTHE *Kent* 404 X 30 – *pop. 14 569.*

Sene Valley, Sene, Folkestone ✆ (01303) 268513.

En Route Travel, Red Lion Sq ✆ (01303) 267799.

London 68 – Folkestone 6 – Hastings 33 – Maidstone 31.

Plan : see Folkestone

Hythe Imperial, Prince's Par, CT21 6AE, ✆ (01303) 267441, *hytheimperial@marstc hotels.com, Fax (01303) 264610,* ←, squash – P – 250. VISA.

Meals *(closed Saturday lunch)* 19.50/27.00 and a la carte approx. 35.00 **st.** 12.95 – ***Th Terrace :*** **Meals** (light lunch)/dinner a la carte 17.00/27.50 **st.** 12.95 – 11.00 – **97 r** 99.00/149.00, 3 suites – SB.

Stade Court, West Par, CT21 6DT, ✆ (01303) 268263, *stadecourt@marstonhotels.cor Fax (01303) 261803,* ← – rest, P – 35. VISA

Meals (bar lunch Monday to Saturday)/dinner 22.00 **st.** 12.95 – **42 rm** 69.50/99.00 **s** – SB.

IFFLEY *Oxon. – see Oxford.*

ILCHESTER *Somerset* 403 L 30 – *pop. 1 733.*

London 138 – Bridgwater 21 – Exeter 48 – Taunton 24 – Yeovil 5.

Ilchester Arms, The Square, BA22 8LN, ✆ (01935) 840220, *Fax (01935) 841353,* – P. VISA JCB.

Meals *(closed Sunday dinner)* (bar lunch)/dinner 14.95/17.95 and a la carte 16.70/24.65 8.75 – **8 rm** 60.00/95.00 **st.** – SB.

Ask your bookshop for the catalogue of ***Michelin Publications.***

ILKLEY *W. Yorks.* 402 O 22 – *pop. 13 530.*

Myddleton ✆ (01943) 607277.

Station Rd ✆ (01943) 436200.

London 210 – Bradford 13 – Harrogate 17 – Leeds 16 – Preston 46.

Rombalds, 11 West View, Wells Rd, LS29 9JG, ✆ (01943) 603201, *reception@rombalc demon.co.uk, Fax (01943) 816586,* « Georgian town house » – P – 70. VISA JCB

Meals 9.95 (lunch) and a la carte 14.15/24.45 **t.** 9.95 – **11 rm** 69.50/104.00 **t.**, 4 suites SB.

The Crescent, Brook St, LS29 8DG, ✆ (01943) 600012, *creshot@dialstart.ne Fax (01943) 601513* – rm, P – 100. VISA.

Meals (bar lunch and Sunday dinner)/dinner a la carte 15.00/20.00 **st.** – **20 rm** 62.5(82.00 **st.** – SB.

Cow and Calf, Hangingstone Rd, LS29 8BT, Southeast : 1 ¼ m. by Cowpasture R ✆ (01943) 607335, *Fax (01943) 604712,* ←, – rm, P – 25. VISA.

Meals (in bar) a la carte 10.35/16.95 **t.** 8.25 – **16 rm** 52.50 **st.**

The Grove without rest., 66 The Grove, LS29 9PA, ✆ (01943) 600298, *info@grovehote org, Fax (0870) 706 5587* – P. VISA.

6 rm 47.00/69.00 **t.**

Box Tree, 37 Church St, LS29 9DR, on A 65 ✆ (01943) 608484, *info@theboxtree.co.u Fax (01943) 607186,* « 18C stone farmhouse, collection of paintings and objets d'art » VISA JCB

closed 2 weeks January, Christmas-New Year and Monday dinner – **Meals** a la carte 35.5(51.00 **st.** 11.50

Spec. Foie gras with braised lettuce and lentils. Poached brill, shallot purée, red wir fumet. Tarte Tatin, vanilla ice cream.

ILLOGAN *Cornwall* 403 E 33 *The West Country G.* – *pop. 13 095* – ✉ *Redruth.*

Env. : *Portreath★, NW : 2 m. by B 3300 – Hell's Mouth★, SW : 5 m. by B 3301.*

London 305 – Falmouth 14 – Penzance 17 – Truro 11.

Aviary Court , Mary's Well, TR16 4QZ, Northwest : ¾ m. by Alexandra R ✆ (01209) 842256, *aviarycourt@connexions.co.uk, Fax (01209) 843744,* – rest, P. VISA.

Meals *(closed Sunday dinner to non-residents)* (dinner only and Sunday lunch)/dinne 14.00 and a la carte 16.95/21.20 **t.** 10.00 – **6 rm** 45.00/65.00 **t.**

LMINSTER *Somerset* 403 L 31 *The West Country G. – pop. 4 162.*
See : *Town★ – Minster★★.*
Env. : *Barrington Court Gardens★* AC, *NE : 3½ m. by B 3168 – Chard (Museum★), S : 6 m. by B 3168 and A 358.*
London 145 – Taunton 12 – Yeovil 17.

Travelodge, Southfield Roundabout, Horton Cross, TA19 9PT, Northwest : 1 ½ m. at junction of A 303 with A 358 ☎ (01460) 53748 – rm, TV ♿ P. MC AE VISA JCB. ✻
Meals (grill rest.) – **32 rm** 52.95 **t.**

t Cricket Malherbie *South : 2½ m. by Chard rd – ✉ Ilminster.*

Old Rectory, TA19 0PW, ☎ (01460) 54364, *theoldrectory@malherbie.freeserve.co.uk, Fax (01460) 57374,* – TV P. MC VISA JCB. ✻
closed 25 December – **Meals** (by arrangement) (communal dining) 19.50 **st.** 10.00 – **5 rm** 48.00/85.00 **st.**

MPINGTON *Cambs. – see Cambridge.*

NGLEBY GREENHOW *N. Yorks.* 402 Q 20 – *pop. 391.*
London 262 – Darlington 28 – Leeds 62 – Middlesbrough 12 – Scarborough 50 – York 49.

Manor House Farm, TS9 6RB, South : 1 m. via lane to manor, next to church ☎ (01642) 722384, *mbloom@globalnet.co.uk,* ≤, « Working farm », – P. MC VISA JCB. ✻
closed December – **Meals** 7.50 – **3 rm** (dinner included) 50.00/95.00 **st.**

NGLETON *N. Yorks.* 402 M 21 – *pop. 1 979* – ✉ *Carnforth (Lancs.).*
The Community Centre ☎ (015242) 41049.
London 266 – Kendal 21 – Lancaster 18 – Leeds 53.

Pines Country House, Kendal Rd, LA6 3HN, Northwest : ¼ m. on A 65 ☎ (015242) 41252, *pineshotel@aol.com, Fax (015242) 41252,* – TV P. MC AE VISA
closed November-December – **Meals** (booking essential) (residents only) (dinner only) 12.50 **st.** 8.80 – **8 rm** 34.00/56.00 **st.** – SB.

Ferncliffe Country Guest House, 55 Main St, LA6 3HJ, ☎ (015242) 42405, *ferncliffe@hotmail.com* – TV P. MC VISA
closed 25-26 December – **Meals** (by arrangement) 13.95 **s.** – **5 rm** 30.00/48.00 **s.**

Riverside Lodge, 24 Main St, LA6 3HJ, ☎ (015242) 41359, *info@riversideingleton.co.uk,* ≤, – TV P. MC VISA. ✻
Meals (by arrangement) 12.00 **st.** 9.95 – **8 rm** 30.00/48.00 **st.** – SB.

NKBERROW *Worcs.* 403 404 O 27 – ✉ *Worcester.*
London 116 – Birmingham 21 – Cheltenham 25 – Stratford-upon-Avon 12.

The Old Windmill, Withybed Lane, off Stonepit Lane, WR7 4JL, ☎ (01386) 792801, *sheila@theoldwindmill.co.uk, Fax (01386) 793762,* ≤, – TV P. MC VISA. ✻
Meals (by arrangement) (communal dining) 22.50 **s.** – **3 rm** 60.00/90.00 **s.**

NKPEN *Newbury* 403 404 P 29 – *see Hungerford.*

NSTOW *Devon* 403 H 30 – *see Bideford.*

PSWICH *Suffolk* 404 X 27 *Great Britain G. – pop. 130 157.*
See : *Christchurch Mansion (collection of paintings★)* X **B.**
Rushmere, Rushmere Heath ☎ (01473) 727109 – Purdis Heath, Bucklesham Rd ☎ (01473) 727474 – Fynn Valley, Witnesham ☎ (01473) 785267.
St Stephens Church, St Stephens Lane ☎ (01473) 258070.
London 76 – Norwich 43.

Plan on next page

Swallow Belstead Brook, Belstead Rd, IP2 9HB, Southwest : 2 ½ m. ☎ (01473) 684241, *sales@belsteadbrook.co.uk, Fax (01473) 681249,* – TV ♿ P. – 200. MC AE VISA Z u
Meals *(closed Saturday lunch)* 20.50 and a la carte 21.45/39.85 **st.** 13.95 – **86 rm** 99.00/108.75 **st.**, 2 suites – SB.

IPSWICH

Argyle Street .... X 2
Back Hamlet .... Z 3
Birkfield Drive .... Z 5
Bond Street .... X 6
Bridgwater Road .... Z 7
Buttermarket Centre .... X 9
Carr Street .... X 10
Chevallier Street ...... Y 13
College Street .... X 15
Corn Hill .... X 16
Dogs Head Street ...... X 18
Ellenbrook Road .... Z 19
Falcon Street .... X 21
Fore Hamlet .... Z 22
Franciscan Way .... X 24
Friars Street .... X 25
Grey Friars Road ...... X 26
Grove Lane .... YZ 28
Handford Road ...... X, Y 30
Lloyds Avenue .... X 31
Lower Orwell Street .... X 32
Northgate Street .... X 33
Orwell Place .... X 34
Quadling Street .... X 35
Queen Street .... X 37
St. Helen's Street ... X, Y 39
St. Margarets Street .... X 40
St. Nicholas Street ..... X 41
St. Peter's Street ...... X 42
Salthouse Street .... X 43
Silent Street .... X 46
Tavern Street X
Tower Ramparts Centre . X 47
Upper Orwell Street .... X 49
Waterworks Street ...... X 51
Westgate Street .... X 52
Wolsey Street .... X 53
Yarmouth Road .... Y 54

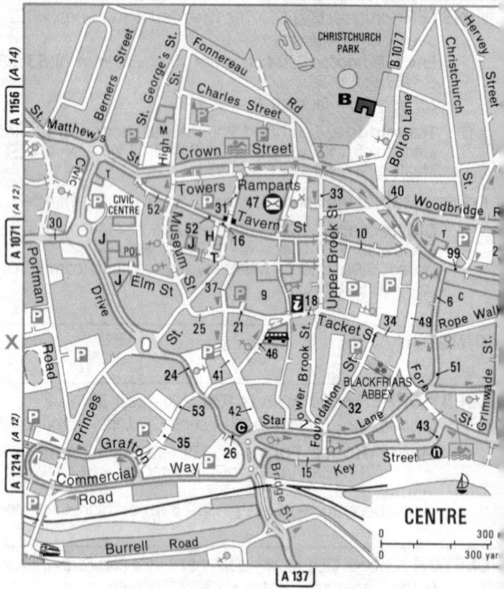

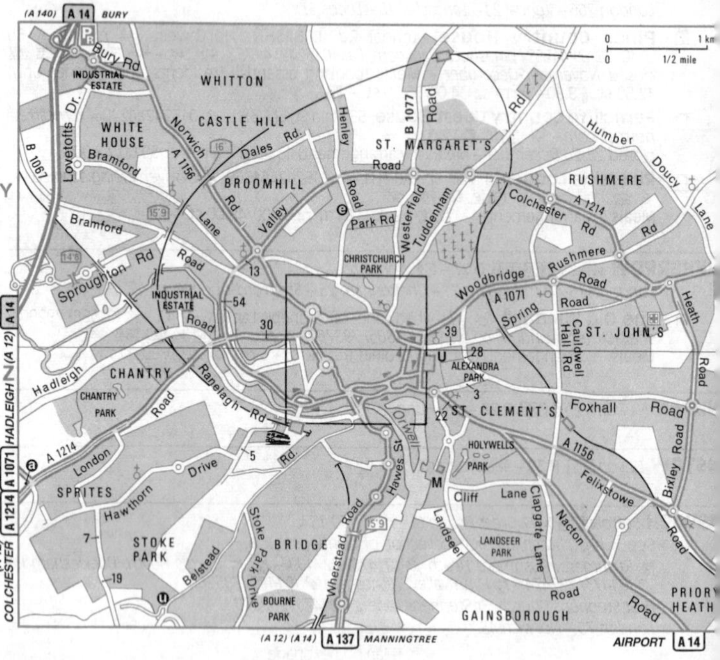

Europe

If the name of the hotel
is not in bold type,
on arrival ask the hotelier his prices.

Courtyard by Marriott Ipswich, The Havens, Ransomes Europark, IP3 9SJ, Southeast : 3 ½ m. by A 1156 and Nacton Rd at junction with A 14 (01473) 272244, *Fax (01473) 272484*, – , rm, rest, – 180. VISA.
Meals a la carte 15.75/23.15 st. 11.75 – **60 rm** 99.00/125.00 st. – SB.

Holiday Inn Ipswich, London Rd, IP2 0UA, Southwest : 2 ¼ m. by A 1214 on A 1071 (0870) 400 9045, *Fax (01473) 680412*, , , , – rm, – 100. VISA. Z a
Meals *(closed Saturday lunch)* 10.00/15.00 and a la carte approx. 21.00 t. 9.95 – **110 rm** 99.00 st. – SB.

Marlborough, Henley Rd, IP1 3SP, (01473) 257677, *reception@themarlborough.co.uk, Fax (01473) 226927*, , – rest, – 50. VISA Y e
Meals 16.95/24.95 and a la carte 32.40/39.40 t. – 11.15 – **21 rm** 69.00/91.00 t., 1 suite – SB.

Novotel, Greyfriars Rd, IP1 1UP, (01473) 232400, *ho995@accor-hotels.com, Fax (01473) 232414* – , rm, – 180. VISA JCB X c
Meals 15.00 and a la carte 13.75/24.15 t. 9.95 – 11.00 – **100 rm** 79.00 t. – SB.

Express by Holiday Inn without rest., Old Hadleigh Rd, Sproughton, IP8 3AR, West : 2 ½ m. by A 1214 and A 1071 on B 1113 (01473) 222279, *Fax (01473) 222297*, – – 30. VISA JCB
49 rm 55.00 t.

Travel Inn, Bourne Hill, Wherstead, IP2 8ND, South : 1 ¾ m. by A 137 (Wherstead Rd) (01473) 692372, *Fax (01473) 692283* – rm, . VISA
Meals (grill rest.) – **40 rm** 41.95 t.

Mortimer's, Wherry Quay, IP4 1AS, (01473) 230225, *Fax (01473) 230225* – VISA X n
closed 2 weeks Christmas, Saturday lunch and Sunday – **Meals** - Seafood - a la carte 11.20/29.70 t. 9.95.

at Woolverstone *South : 5½ m. by A 137 – Z – on B 1456 – Ipswich.*

Woolverstone House , Mannings Lane, IP9 1AN, (01473) 780940, *cooks@enterprise.net, Fax (01473) 780959*, « Lutyens house, Gertrude Jekyll gardens », – .
closed mid December-mid January – **Meals** (by arrangement) (communal dining) 17.50 s. – **3 rm** 45.00/90.00 s. – SB.

at Holbrook *South : 5 ¾ m. by A 137 – Z – and B 1456 on B 1080 – Ipswich.*

Highfield without rest., Harkstead Rd, IP9 2RA, East : ½ m. by Fishponds Lane (01473) 328250, *Fax (01473) 328250*, , – .
closed Christmas and New Year – **3 rm** 32.00/48.00 st.

at Hintlesham *West : 5 m. by A 1214 on A 1071 – Y – Ipswich.*

Hintlesham Hall , IP8 3NS, (01473) 652334, *reservations@hintleshamhall.com, Fax (01473) 652463*, , « Georgian country house of 16C origins », , , heated, , , , – rest, – 80. VISA
Meals *(closed Saturday lunch)* 21.00/40.00 st. 12.95 – 7.50 – **29 rm** 98.00/235.00 st., 4 suites – SB.

at Claydon *Northwest : 4½ m. by A 1156 off A 14 – Y – Ipswich.*

Claydon Country House, 16-18 Ipswich Rd, IP6 0AR, (01473) 830382, *kayshotel@aol.com, Fax (01473) 832476*, – . VISA.
Meals *(closed Sunday dinner)* 15.00/29.50 and a la carte 18.55/26.45 st. 10.95 – **14 rm** 64.00/74.00 st. – SB.

Travel Inn, Paper Mill Lane, IP6 0AP, Southwest : ½ m. off A 14 roundabout (01473) 833125, *Fax (01473) 833127* – , rm, . VISA
Meals (grill rest.) (dinner only) – **59 rm** 41.95 t.

IREBY *Cumbria* 401 402 K 19 – *see Bassenthwaite.*

IRONBRIDGE *Wrekin* 403 404 M 26 *Great Britain G.* – *pop. 2 184.*
See : *Ironbridge Gorge Museum*★★ *AC (The Iron Bridge*★★, *Coalport China Museum*★★, *Blists Hill Open Air Museum*★★, *Museum of the River and visitors centre*★*).*
The Wharfage (01952) 432166.
London 135 – Birmingham 36 – Shrewsbury 18.

Severn Lodge without rest., New Rd, TF8 7AS, (01952) 432148, *enquiries@severnlodge.com, Fax (01952) 432062*, – .
closed Christmas and New Year – **3 rm** 45.00/59.00 s.

Bridge House without rest., Buildwas, TF8 7BN, West : 2 m. on B 438 ℘ (01952) 432105, *janethedges@talk21.com, Fax (01952) 432105,* « 17C cottage », P.
closed Christmas and January – **4 rm** 40.00/60.00.

The Library House without rest., 11 Severn Bank, TF8 7AN, ℘ (01952) 432299, *libhous @enta.net, Fax (01952) 433967,*
closed 25-26 December and January – **4 rm** 45.00/60.00 **st.**

da Vinci's, 26 High St, TF8 7AD, ℘ (01952) 432250, *nlord43303@aol.com Fax (01952) 433039* – . VISA
closed 3 weeks January, Sunday and Monday – **Meals** - Italian - (booking essential) (dinner only) a la carte 16.20/24.65 **t.** 9.95.

ISLE OF MAN 402 FG 21 – *see Man (Isle of).*

IVY HATCH *Kent* – *see Sevenoaks.*

IXWORTH *Suffolk* 404 W 27 – *see Bury St. Edmunds.*

JERSEY 403 OP 33 and 230 ⑩ ⑪ – *see Channel Islands.*

JEVINGTON *E. Sussex* 404 U 31 – *see Eastbourne.*

KEIGHLEY *W. Yorks.* 402 O 22 – *pop. 49 567.*
Branshaw, Branshaw Moor, Oakworth ℘ (01535) 643235 – *Riddlesden, Howden Roug ℘ (01535) 602148.*
London 200 – Bradford 10 – Burnley 20.

Dalesgate, 406 Skipton Rd, Utley, BD20 6HP, Northwest : 1 ¼ m. on B 6265 (Utley r ℘ (01535) 664930, *stephen.e.atha@btinternet.com, Fax (01535) 611253* – P. AE VISA
closed 1 week Christmas – **Meals** *(closed Sunday)* (dinner only) 13.95 and a la carte 15.7 20.25 **st.** 7.50 – **20 rm** 40.00/60.00 **st.** – SB.

KELLING *Norfolk* 404 X 25 – *pop. 161* – ✉ *Holt.*
London 125 – King's Lynn 39 – Norwich 30.

The Pheasant, Coast Rd, NR25 7EG, on A 149 ℘ (01263) 588382, *enquiries@pheasa hotelnorfolk.co.uk, Fax (01263) 588101,* P. VISA JCB.
Meals (bar lunch)/dinner 17.95 **t.** 8.15 – **30 rm** 49.00/78.00 **t.** – SB.

KELSALE *Suffolk* 404 Y 27 – *pop. 1 309* – ✉ *Saxmundham.*
London 103 – Cambridge 68 – Ipswich 23 – Norwich 37.

Mile Hill Barn, North Green, IP17 2RG, North : 1 ½ m. on (main) A 12 ℘ (01728) 66851 *richard@milehillbarn.freeserve.co.uk,* « Converted 16C barn », P.
Meals (by arrangement) 17.00 **st.** – **3 rm** 55.00/70.00 **st.** – SB.

Harrisons, IP17 2RF, North : 1 m. on (main) A 12 ℘ (01728) 604444, *mel@harriso restaurant.com, Fax (01728) 604444,* « 17C thatched house », P. VISA JCB
closed 25 December-21 January, Sunday dinner and Monday – **Meals** 12.5 (lunch) and a la carte 16.45/22.85 **t.** 9.95.

KEMBLE *Glos.* 403 404 N 28 – *see Cirencester.*

KENDAL *Cumbria* 402 L 21 *Great Britain G.* – *pop. 25 461.*
Env. : *Levens Hall and Garden★ AC, S : 4½ m. by A 591, A 590 and A 6.*
Exc. : *Lake Windermere★★, NW : 8 m. by A 5284 and A 591.*
The Heights ℘ (01539) 723499.
Town Hall, Highgate ℘ (01539) 725758.
London 270 – Bradford 64 – Burnley 63 – Carlisle 49 – Lancaster 22 – Leeds 72 Middlesbrough 77 – Newcastle upon Tyne 104 – Preston 44 – Sunderland 88.

Stonecross Manor, Milnthorpe Rd, LA9 5HP, South : 1 ½ m. on A 6 ☎ (01539) 733559, *info@stonecrossmanor.co.uk, Fax (01539) 736386,* – rest, – 180.
Meals 15.00 12.20 – 9.95 – **30 rm** 42.00/59.00 **t.** – SB.

Burrow Hall without rest., Plantation Bridge, LA8 9JR, Northwest : 3 ¼ m. by A 5284 on A 591 ☎ (01539) 821711, *Fax (01539) 821711,* – .
3 rm 30.00/50.00.

The Moon, 129 Highgate, LA9 4EN, ☎ (01539) 729254, *moon@129highgate.freeserve.co.uk, Fax (01539) 729254* – .
closed Christmas, Monday, Tuesday and Bank Holidays – **Meals** (dinner only) a la carte 16.65/22.75 **st.** 8.95.

at Selside *North : 6 m. on A 6 – ✉ Kendal.*

Low Jock Scar , LA8 9LE, North : 1 ½ m. by A 6 ☎ (01539) 823259, *philip@low-jock-scar.freeserve.co.uk, Fax (01539) 823259,* – .
mid March-October – **Meals** (by arrangement) 17.00 **st.** 9.00 – **5 rm** 33.50/58.00 **st.**

at Crosthwaite *West : 5 ¼ m. by All Hallows Lane – ✉ Kendal.*

Crosthwaite House, LA8 8BP, ☎ (015395) 68264, *bookings@crosthwaitehouse.co.uk, Fax (015395) 68264,* – rest, .
closed January and December – **Meals** (by arrangement) 15.00 **st.** 8.50 – **6 rm** 25.00/50.00 **st.** – SB.

Punch Bowl Inn with rm, LA8 8HR, ☎ (015395) 68237, *enquiries@punchbowl.fsnet.co.uk, Fax (015395) 68875,* , « Part 17C inn » – .
closed 25 December, Sunday dinner and Monday – **Meals** (booking essential) a la carte 17.20/23.75 **t.** 9.50 – **3 rm** 40.00/60.00 **t.**

KENILWORTH *Warks.* 403 404 P 26 *Great Britain G. – pop. 21 623.*
See : *Castle★ AC.*
The Library, 11 Smalley Pl ☎ (01926) 852595.
London 102 – Birmingham 19 – Coventry 5 – Warwick 5.

Chesford Grange, Chesford Bridge, CV8 2LD, Southeast : 1 ¾ m. by A 452 on B 4115 ☎ (01926) 859331, *samantha.brown@principlehotels.co.uk, Fax (01926) 859075,* – – 860.
Meals *(closed Saturday lunch)* 14.50/18.95 and dinner a la carte 25.65/35.85 **t.** 12.50 – **218 rm** 130.00/165.00 **st.** – SB.

Victoria Lodge without rest., 180 Warwick Rd, CV8 1HU, ☎ (01926) 512020, *info@victorialodgehotel.co.uk, Fax (01926) 858703,* – .
closed 23 December-1 January – **9 rm** 40.00/75.00 **t.**

Castle Laurels without rest., 22 Castle Rd, CV8 1NG, North : ½ m. on Stonebridge rd ☎ (01926) 856179, *moore22@aol.com, Fax (01926) 854954* – .
closed 1 week Christmas – **11 rm** 39.00/59.00 **t.**

Simpson's (Antona), 101-103 Warwick Rd, CV8 1HL, ☎ (01926) 864567, *Fax (01926) 864510* – .
closed last 2 weeks August, 24-28 December, Sunday, Monday and Bank Holidays – **Meals** 20.00/33.75 and a la carte 32.75/41.50 **t.** 12.50
Spec. Roast squab pigeon with braised cabbage and wild mushrooms. Tranche of salmon with potato scales and spinach. Turrón parfait with chocolate brownie.

Bosquet, 97a Warwick Rd, CV8 1HP, ☎ (01926) 852463, *restaurantbosquet@aol.com, Fax (01926) 852463* – .
closed 3 weeks August, 1 week Christmas, Sunday and Monday – **Meals** - French - (lunch by arrangement) a la carte 30.00/32.00 **t.** 13.00.

KENNFORD *Devon* 403 J 32 – *see Exeter.*

KERNE BRIDGE *Herefordshire* 403 404 M 28 – *see Ross-on-Wye.*

KESWICK *Cumbria* 402 K 20 *Great Britain G. – pop. 4 836.*
Env. : *Derwentwater★* **X** – *Thirlmere (Castlerigg Stone Circle★), E : 1½ m.* **X A.**
Threlkeld Hall ☎ (017687) 79010.
Moot Hall, Market Sq. ☎ (017687) 72645 – at Seatoller, Seatoller Barn, Borrowdale ☎ (017687) 77294.
London 294 – Carlisle 31 – Kendal 30.

KESWICK

Bank Street . . . . . . Z 2
Borrowdale Road . . Z 3
Brackenrigg Drive . . Z 5
Brundholme Road . X 6
Chestnut Hill . . . . . . X 8
Church Street . . . . . Z 10
Crosthwaite Road. . X 12
Derwent Street . . . . Z 13
High Hill . . . . Z 14
Main Street . . . . Z
Manor Brow . . . . . . X 17
Market Square. . . . . Z 18
Museum Square . . . Z 19
Otley Road. . . . . Z 20
Pack Horse Yard . . . Z 21
Police Station
Court . . . . Z 22
Ratcliffe Place . . . . . Z 23
St. Herbert
Street . . . . Z 24
Standish Street . . . . Z 25
Station Street . . . . . Z 26
The Crescent. . . . . . Z 27
The Hawthorns . . . . Y 29
The Headlands . . . . Z 31
Tithebarn Street . . . Z 32

North is at the top on all town plans.

Les plans de villes sont disposés le Nord en haut.

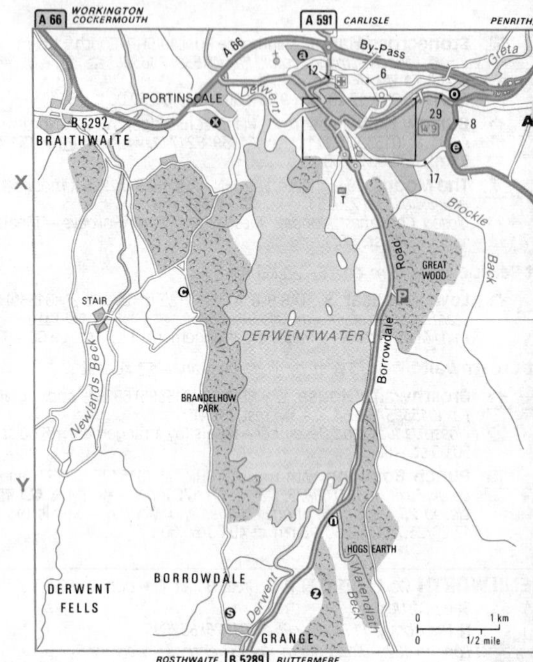

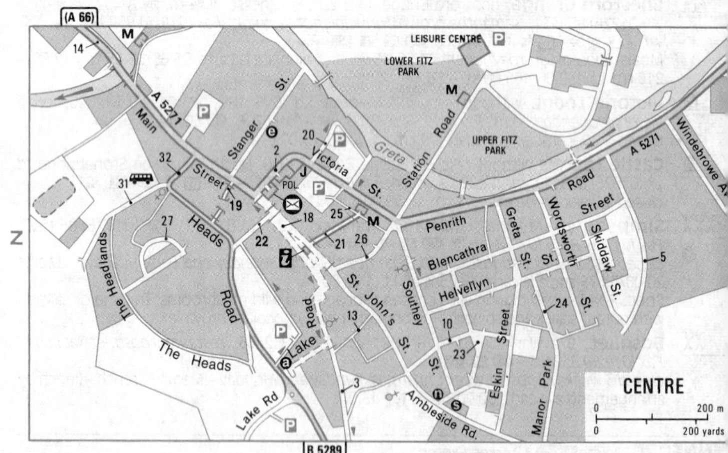

Underscar Manor ⑤, Applethwaite, CA12 4PH, North : 1 ¾ m. by A 591 on Underscar rd ☎ (017687) 75000, *Fax (017687) 74904*, < Derwent Water and Fells, « Victorian Italianate country house », ⊮, ⊜, ☒, ⊼, ⊻ – ▣ ℗. ⊙ ⊡ VISA. ⊛
closed 2-4 January – **Meals** – (see ***The Restaurant*** below) – **11 rm** ⊏ (dinner included) 125.00/250.00 **t.**

Lyzzick Hall ⑤, Underskiddaw, CA12 4PY, Northwest : 2 ½ m. on A 591 ☎ (017687) 72277, *lyzzickhall@netscapeonline.co.uk, Fax (017687) 72278*, <, ⊜, ☒, ⊼, ⊁ rest, ▣ ℗ – ⊻ 25. ⊙ ⊡ VISA JCB. ⊛
closed mid January-mid February and 24-26 December – **Meals** 23.00/25.00 (dinner) and a la carte 12.50/28.95 **t.** ⅰ 7.50 – **29 rm** ⊏ 46.00/92.00 **t.**

ENGLAND

Dale Head Hall Lakeside, Thirlmere, CA12 4TN, Southeast : 5 ¾ m. on A 591 ℘ (017687) 72478, *onthelakeside@dale-head-hall.co.uk, Fax (017687) 71070*, ← Lake Thirlmere, « Lakeside setting », – rest, P. VISA JCB.
closed January – **Meals** (dinner only) 32.50 **st.** 15.00 – **13 rm** 67.50/105.00 **st.**, 1 suite – SB.

Applethwaite Country House, Applethwaite, CA12 4PL, Northwest : 1 ¾ m. by A 591 on Underscar rd ℘ (017687) 72413, *ryan@applethwaite.com, Fax (017687) 75706*, ←, – TV P. VISA.
mid February-mid November – **Meals** (dinner only) 17.50 **st.** 7.95 – **12 rm** 39.00/78.00 **st.** – SB.

Lairbeck, Vicarage Hill, CA12 5QB, ℘ (017687) 73373, *mg@lairbeckhotel-keswick.co.uk, Fax (017687) 73144*, – TV P. VISA JCB. X a
mid March-November – **Meals** (dinner only) 16.50 **t.** 9.65 – **14 rm** 38.50/77.00 **t.**

Brackenrigg Country House without rest., Thirlmere, CA12 4TF, Southeast : 3 m. on A 591 ℘ (017687) 72258, *Fax (017687) 72258*, – TV P.
Easter-October – **6 rm** 37.50/55.00.

Abacourt House without rest., 26 Stanger St, CA12 5JU, ℘ (017687) 72967, *abacourt@btinternet.com* – TV P. Z e
closed Christmas and Bank Holidays – **5 rm** 30.00/44.00 **s.**

Greystones without rest., Ambleside Rd, CA12 4DP, ℘ (017687) 73108, *greystones@keslakes.freeserve.co.uk* – TV P. VISA. Z n
restricted opening January and December – **8 rm** 24.00/48.00 **st.**

Craglands, Penrith Rd, CA12 4LJ, ℘ (017687) 74406, *keswick@craglands.freeserve.co.uk* – TV P. X o
Meals (by arrangement) 13.00 – **5 rm** 30.00/50.00 **st.**

Acorn House without rest., Ambleside Rd, CA12 4DL, ℘ (017687) 72553, *info@acornhousehotel.co.uk, Fax (017687) 75332* – TV P. VISA. Z s
closed January and December – **10 rm** 28.00/64.00 **t.**

Claremont House without rest., Chestnut Hill, CA12 4LT, ℘ (017687) 72089, *claremonthouse@btinternet.com, Fax (017687) 72089*, ←, – TV P. X e
Easter-December – **4 rm** 35.00/55.00 **st.**

XXX **The Restaurant** (at Underscar Manor H.), Applethwaite, CA12 4PH, North : 1 ¾ m. by A 591 on Underscar rd ℘ (017687) 75000, *Fax (017687) 74904*, ← Derwent Water and Fells, « Victorian Italianate country house », – P. VISA
Meals 28.00/30.00 and a la carte 34.50/41.50 **t.** 16.00.

X **Morrel's** with rm, 34 Lake Rd, CA12 5DQ, ℘ (017687) 72666, *bex@lakedistricthotel.co.uk, Fax (017687) 74879* – TV P. VISA Z a
closed 1 week January and 24-26 December – **Meals** (dinner only) a la carte 19.00/26.00 **t.** 9.75 – **14 rm** 31.00/62.00 **st.**

at Threlkeld *East : 4 m. by A 66* – X – ✉ *Keswick.*

Scales Farm without rest., CA12 4SY, Northeast : 1 ½ m. off A 66 ℘ (017687) 79660, *scales@scalesfarm.com, Fax (017687) 79660*, « Part 17C », – TV P. VISA
closed 25-26 December – **6 rm** 31.00/56.00.

at Borrowdale *South : on B 5289* – ✉ *Keswick.*

Hilton Keswick Lodore, CA12 5UX, ℘ (017687) 77285, *robert_duncan@hilton.com, Fax (017687) 77343*, ←, heated, squash – rest, TV P – 120. VISA JCB Y n
Meals (bar lunch Monday-Saturday)/dinner 23.00 **st.** 13.50 – **70 rm** 89.00/198.00 **st.**, 1 suite – SB.

Greenbank Country House, CA12 5UY, ℘ (017687) 77215, *jeanwood@lineone.net, Fax (017687) 77215*, ←, – P. VISA. Y z
closed January – **Meals** (dinner only) (set menu only) 15.00 **st.** 7.95 – **10 rm** (dinner included) 35.00/100.00 **st.**

at Grange-in-Borrowdale *South : 4 ¾ m. by B 5289* – ✉ *Keswick.*

Borrowdale Gates Country House, CA12 5UQ, ℘ (017687) 77204, *hotel@borrowdale-gates.com, Fax (017687) 77254*, ← Borrowdale Valley, – rest, TV P. VISA. Y s
closed January – **Meals** (light lunch)/dinner 32.50/35.00 and a la carte 16.75/39.50 **t.** 14.00 – **29 rm** (dinner included) 92.50/175.00 **t.** – SB.

at Rosthwaite *South : 6 m. on B 5289* – Y – ✉ *Keswick.*

Hazel Bank, CA12 5XB, ℘ (017687) 77248, *enquiries@hazelbankhotel.co.uk, Fax (017687) 77373*, ←, – TV P. VISA JCB.
Meals (dinner only) (set menu only) 19.95 **t.** 8.95 – **7 rm** (dinner included) 64.50/129.00 **t.**, 1 suite – SB.

at Portinscale *West : 1½ m. by A 66 – ✉ Keswick.*

Swinside Lodge ⛰, Newlands, CA12 5UE, South : 1 ½ m. on Grange R... ☏ (017687) 72948, *info@swinsidelodge-hotel.co.uk, Fax (017687) 72948,* ← Catbells an... Causey Pike, 🌳 – ⇆ TV P. MC VISA. ✱ X
Meals (set menu only) (booking essential) (dinner only) 25.00 **t.** 9.50 – **7 rm** (dinne... included) 75.00/179.00 **t.** – SB.

Derwent Cottage ⛰, CA12 5RF, ☏ (017687) 74838, 🌳 – ⇆ TV P. MC VISA JCB ✱ X
March-October – **Meals** (by arrangement) 15.00 **s.** 7.50 – **5 rm** 63.00/110.00 **s.** – SB.

at Thornthwaite *Northwest : 3½ m. by A 66 – X – ✉ Keswick.*

Thwaite Howe ⛰, CA12 5SA, ☏ (017687) 78281, *info@thwaitehouse.co.u...* *Fax (017687) 78529,* ← Skiddaw and Derwent Valley, 🌳 – ⇆ TV P. MC VISA
closed January – **Meals** (residents only) (dinner only) (set menu only) 17.00 **st.** 10.95 **8 rm** 45.00/70.00 **st.** – SB.

KETTERING *Northants.* 404 R 26 – *pop. 47 186.*

The Coach House, Sheep St ☏ (01536) 410266.
London 88 – Birmingham 54 – Leicester 16 – Northampton 24.

Kettering Park, Kettering Parkway, NN15 6XT, South : 2 ¼ m. by A 509 (Wellingboroug... rd) at junction with A 14 ☏ (01536) 416666, *kpark@shireinns.co.uk, Fax (01536) 416171,* ..., 🏊, 🌳, squash – 🛗 ⇆, ▤ rm, TV ♿ P – 🎤 250. MC AE ◑ VISA
***Langberrys :* Meals** (bar lunch Saturday and Sunday) a la carte 21.50/32.00 **st.** 13.45 **119 rm** 125.00/145.00 **st.** – SB.

Travel Inn, Rothwell Rd, NN16 8XF, West : 1 ¼ m. at junction of A 14 with A 4... ☏ (01536) 310082, *Fax (01536) 310104* – ⇆ rm, ▤ rest, TV ♿ P. MC AE ◑ VISA. ✱
Meals (grill rest.) – **39 rm** 41.95 **t.**

KETTLESING *N. Yorks.* 402 P 21 – *see Harrogate.*

KEYSTON *Cambs.* 404 S 26 – *pop. 257 (inc. Bythorn) – ✉ Huntingdon.*

London 75 – Cambridge 29 – Northampton 24.

Pheasant, Village Loop Rd, PE18 0RE, ☏ (01832) 710241, *Fax (01832) 710340,* ... « Characterful thatched inn » – ⇆ P. MC AE ◑ VISA
Meals (booking essential) 12.95 (lunch) and a la carte 17.50/26.50 **st.** 11.50.

KIBWORTH BEAUCHAMP *Leics. – pop. 3 550 – ✉ Leicester.*

London 85 – Birmingham 49 – Leicester 16 – Northampton 17.

XX **Firenze,** 9 Station St, LE8 0LN, ☏ (0116) 279 6260, *poli.firenze@virgin.ne...* *Fax (0116) 279 3646* – MC VISA
closed 2 weeks August, 1 week Christmas, 1 week Easter Saturday lunch, Sunday ar... Monday – **Meals** - Italian - a la carte 15.50/28.50 **st.** 11.50.

KIDDERMINSTER *Worcestershire* 403 404 N 26 – *pop. 54 644.*

Severn Valley Railway Station, Comberton Hill ☏ (01562) 829400 (summer only).
London 139 – Birmingham 17 – Shrewsbury 34 – Worcester 15.

Stone Manor, Stone, DY10 4PJ, Southeast : 2 ½ m. on A 448 ☏ (01562) 77755... *enquiries@stonemanorhotel.co.uk, Fax (01562) 777834,* 🏊, 🌳, 🎾, ✂ – ⇆ TV P – 🎤 15... MC AE ◑ VISA
***Fields :* Meals** 13.50/21.00 and a la carte 21.50/37.50 **t.** 10.50 – 8.75 – **56 rm** 90.0... 135.00 **t.**, 1 suite – SB.

at Chaddesley Corbett *Southeast : 4½ m. by A 448 – ✉ Kidderminster.*

Brockencote Hall ⛰, DY10 4PY, on A 448 ☏ (01562) 777876, *info@brockencoteha... com, Fax (01562) 777872,* ←, « Part 19C mansion in park », 🌳 – TV ♿ P – 🎤 25. MC AE ◑ VISA. ✱
Meals – (see ***The Restaurant*** below) – **17 rm** 110.00/170.00 **st.** – SB.

XXX **The Restaurant** (at Brockencote Hall), DY10 4PY, on A 448 ☏ (01562) 77787... *Fax (01562) 777872* – ⇆. MC AE ◑ VISA
closed Saturday lunch – **Meals** - French 12.00/27.50 and a la carte 24.30/44.50 **st.** 12.80

at Bewdley *Northeast : 1 m. by A 190 – ✉ Kidderminster.*

Ramada H. and Resort, Habberley Rd, DY12 1LJ, Northeast : 1 m. by A 190 ☎ (01299) 406400, *Fax (01299) 400921*, – 650. VISA
Meals *(closed Saturday lunch)* (buffet lunch)/dinner 15.95 and a la carte 17.95/26.00 **t.** 11.25 – **44 rm** 92.00/149.00 **t.** – SB.

KILLINGTON LAKE SERVICE AREA *Cumbria* 402 M 21 – ✉ *Kendal.*

Killington Lake Services, M 6 south, near Kendal ☎ (015396) 20138.

Travel Inn without rest., LA8 0NW, M 6 between junctions 36 and 37 (southbound carriageway) ☎ (01539) 621666, *Fax (01539) 621660* – VISA.
closed Christmas and New Year – **36 rm** 41.95 **t.**

KIMBOLTON *Herefordshire* 403 L 27 – *see Leominster.*

KINGHAM *Oxon.* 403 404 P 28 – *pop. 1 434.*

London 81 – Gloucester 32 – Oxford 25.

Mill House , OX7 6UH, ☎ (01608) 658188, *stay@millhousehotel.co.uk*, *Fax (01608) 658492*, – rest, – 70. VISA JCB
Meals (bar lunch)/dinner 23.75 and a la carte 23.75/35.00 **t.** 12.75 – **23 rm** (dinner included) 90.00/175.50 **st.** – SB.

KINGSBRIDGE *Devon* 403 I 33 *The West Country G.* – *pop. 5 258.*

See : *Town★ – Boat Trip to Salcombe★★ AC.*

Exc. : *Prawle Point (≤★★★) SE : 10 m. around coast by A 379.*

18 *Thurlestone ☎ (01548) 560405.*

The Quay ☎ (01548) 853195.

London 236 – Exeter 36 – Plymouth 24 – Torquay 21.

Buckland-Tout-Saints , Goveton, TQ7 2DS, Northeast : 2 ½ m. by A 381 ☎ (01548) 853055, *buckland@tout-saints.co.uk, Fax (01548) 856261*, ≤, « Queen Anne mansion », – rest, – 100. VISA
closed 3 weeks January – **Meals** 14.00/25.00 and a la carte 25.00/33.50 **st.** 10.00 – **8 rm** 65.00/170.00 **st.**, 2 suites – SB.

Ship to Shore with rm, 45 Church St, TQ7 1BT, ☎ (01548) 854076, *ship-to-shore @hotmail.com, Fax (01548) 857890* – VISA JCB.
closed Monday and Sunday except August – **Meals** (dinner only) a la carte 17.70/29.00 **st.** 9.95 – **3 rm** 25.00/50.00 **st.**

at Chillington *East : 5 m. on A 379 – ✉ Kingsbridge.*

White House, TQ7 2JX, ☎ (01548) 580580, *tina.whthse@cs.com, Fax (01548) 581124*, – VISA.
closed 3 weeks January – **Meals** *closed Tuesday and Sunday* (dinner only) 16.00/18.95 **t.** 8.50 – **7 rm** 56.00/92.00 **t.**

at Thurlestone *West : 4 m. by A 381 – ✉ Kingsbridge.*

Thurlestone , TQ7 3NN, ☎ (01548) 560382, *enquires@thurlestone.co.uk*, *Fax (01548) 561069*, ≤, heated, 9, squash – rest, rest, – 100. VISA
– ***Margaret Amelia :*** **Meals** (lunch by arrangement)/dinner 30.00 **t.** 15.00 – ***Terrace :*** **Meals** *(closed 3-15 January)* (lunch only except Sunday) a la carte approx. 17.25 **t.** 10.95 – **62 rm** 64.00/128.00 **t.**, 5 suites – SB.

at Bantham *West : 5 m. by A 379 – ✉ Kingsbridge.*

Sloop Inn with rm, TQ7 3AJ, ☎ (01548) 560489, *Fax (01548) 561940* –
Meals a la carte 14.85/18.75 **t.** 8.95 – **5 rm** 34.00/68.00 **t.** – SB.

KING'S CLIFFE *Northants.* 404 S 26 – ✉ *Peterborough.*

London 93 – Leicester 21 – Northampton 19 – Peterborough 7.

King's Cliffe House, 31 West St, PE8 6XB, ☎ (01780) 470172, *kchr@onetel.net.uk*, *Fax (0870) 1268588*,
closed 2 weeks spring, 2 weeks autumn, 25-26 December, 1 January and Sunday-Tuesday – **Meals** (booking essential) (dinner only) a la carte 18.45/28.60 **st.** 9.95.

KINGSKERSWELL *Devon* 403 J 32 – *pop. 3 672* – ✉ *Torquay.*
London 219 – Exeter 21 – Plymouth 33 – Torquay 4.

XX **Pitt House,** 2 Church End Rd, TQ12 5DS, ✆ (01803) 873374, « 15C thatched dower house », – P. VISA
closed Sunday and Monday – **Meals** (dinner only) 21.00/25.00 **t.** 12.95.

KINGS LANGLEY *Herts.* 404 S 28 – *pop. 8 144.*
London 26 – Luton 14.

Premier Lodge, Hempstead Rd, WD4 8BR, ✆ (0870) 7001568, *Fax (0870) 7001569* – rm, rest, TV P. VISA.
Meals (grill rest.) a la carte approx. 11.00 **t.** 7.95 – **60 rm** 49.95 **t.**

KING'S LYNN *Norfolk* 402 404 V 25 *Great Britain G.* – *pop. 41 281.*
Exc. : *Houghton Hall*★★ *AC, NE : 14 ½ m. by A 148 – Four Fenland Churches*★ *(Terrington St Clement, Walpole St Peter, West Walton, Walsoken) SW : by A 47.*
Eagles, School Rd, Tilney All Saints ✆ (01553) 827147.
The Custom House, Purfleet Quay ✆ (01553) 763044.
London 103 – Cambridge 45 – Leicester 75 – Norwich 44.

Knights Hill, Knights Hill Village, South Wootton, PE30 3HQ, Northeast : 4 ½ m. on A 148 at junction with A 149 ✆ (01553) 675566, *reception@knightshill.co.uk, Fax (01553) 675568* – TV P – 300. VISA.
Garden : **Meals** (dinner only and Sunday lunch)/dinner 20.00 and a la carte 19.80/25.15 **st** 12.95 – ***Farmers Arms :*** **Meals** (carvery) a la carte 13.55/17.05 **st.** 7.95 – 9.85 – **61 rm** 55.00/98.00 **st.** – SB.

Butterfly, Beveridge Way, PE30 4NB, Southeast : 2 ¼ m. by Hardwick Rd at junction of A 10 with A 47 ✆ (01553) 771707, *kingsbutterfly@lineone.net, Fax (01553) 768027* – rm TV P – 40. VISA JCB
Meals 16.00/17.50 (dinner) and a la carte 15.95/26.95 **t.** 13.00 – 8.50 – **50 rm** 75.00 **t.** – SB.

Travel Inn, Freebridge Farm, Clenchwarten Rd, PE34 3LJ, Southwest : 3 ¼ m. by Hardwick Rd at junction of A 47 with A 17 ✆ (01485) 772221, *Fax (01485) 775827* – rm, rest, TV P. VISA.
Meals (grill rest.) – **40 rm** 41.95 **t.**

Old Rectory without rest., 33 Goodwins Rd, PE30 5QX, ✆ (01553) 768544, *clive@theoldrectory-kingslynn.com,* « Restored Georgian style Victorian residence », – TV P. VISA
4 rm 32.00/42.00.

Fairlight Lodge without rest., 79 Goodwins Rd, PE30 5PE, ✆ (01553) 762234, *joel@nash42.freeserve.co.uk, Fax (01553) 770280,* – TV P
closed 24 December-2 January – **7 rm** 20.00/42.00.

at Grimston *East : 6 ¼ m. by A 148* – ✉ *King's Lynn.*

Congham Hall, Lynn Rd, PE32 1AH, ✆ (01485) 600250, *reception@conghamhallhotel.co.uk, Fax (01485) 601191,* ←, « Part Georgian manor house, herb garden », heated – TV P – 30. VISA JCB.
Orangery : **Meals** 15.50/34.00 **t.** 15.50 – **12 rm** 85.00/175.00 **st.**, 2 suites – SB.

KINGS MILLS *Guernsey (Channel Islands)* – *see Channel Islands.*

KINGSTON BAGPUIZE *Oxon.* 403 404 P 28 – *see Oxford.*

KINGSTON BLOUNT *Oxon.* – *see Chinnor.*

KINGSTON-UPON-HULL *Kingston-upon-Hull* 402 S 22 *Great Britain G.* – *pop. 310 636.*
Exc. : *Burton Constable*★ *AC, NE : 9 m. by A 165 and B 1238 Z.*
Springhead Park, Willerby Rd ✆ (01482) 656309 – Sutton Park, Salthouse Rd ✆ (01482) 374242.
Humber Bridge (toll).
Humberside Airport : ✆ (01652) 688456, S : 19 m. by A 63 – **Terminal :** *Coach Service*
to The Netherlands (Rotterdam) (P & O North Sea Ferries) daily (12 h 30 mn) – Belgium (Zeebrugge) (P & O North Sea Ferries) daily (12 h 45 mn).
1 Paragon St ✆ (01482) 223559 – King George Dock, Hedon Rd ✆ (01482) 702118.
London 183 – Leeds 61 – Nottingham 94 – Sheffield 68.

KINGSTON-UPON-HULL

nd Street	X	3
rr Lane	Y	
mmercial Road	Y	8
unty Road North	Z	9
ck Office Row	X	10
ck Street	X	12
rfax Avenue	Z	13
rensway	XY	14
orge Street	X	
msston Street	X	15
mber Dock Street	Y	16
meson Street	Y	17
ratt Street	X	18
g Edward Street	Y	19
gston Retail Park	Y	
wgate	Y	23
arket Place	Y	24
aybury Road	Z	25
ragon Street	Y	29
nce's Avenue	Z	31
nce's Dock Street	Y	32
nces Quay Shopping Centre	Y	
ospect Shopping Centre	X	
ospect Street	X	
een's Road	Z	33
een Street	Y	35
een's Dock Avenue	X	36
form Street	X	37
ulcoates Bridge	X	42
uthcoates Avenue	Z	43
uthcoates Lane	Z	44
aterhouse Lane	Y	47
hitefriargate	Y	49
lberforce Drive	X	50
orship Street	X	52

A 1079
Beverley Road
Waterloo St.
Barmston Street
Wincolmlee
Lockwood St.
B 1237
Cleveland Street
42
Jenning St.
St. Mark St.
Cannon St.
Caroline St.
Scott St.
Liddell St.
Norfolk St.
Charles St.
37
Lime Street
Freetown Way
B 1428
Prospect St.
Albion St.
52
Witham
Great Union St.
A 165
18
15
George
POL.
10
14
PROSPECT CENTRE
3
50
36
12
Guildhall Road
U
23
H
17
19
J
St.
29
Alfred Gelder
M
Carr La.
High St.
Hull
A 1105
Anlaby Rd
St
49
Osborne
14
PRINCES QUAY
47
32
24
Garrison Rd
A 63
Castle St.
TIDAL SURGE BARRIER
35
Hessle Road
8
16
Humber St.
KINGSTON RETAIL PARK
DOCKS
THE DEEP
HULL ARENA
English Street
HUMBER
CENTRE
0
400 m
400 yards
X
Y

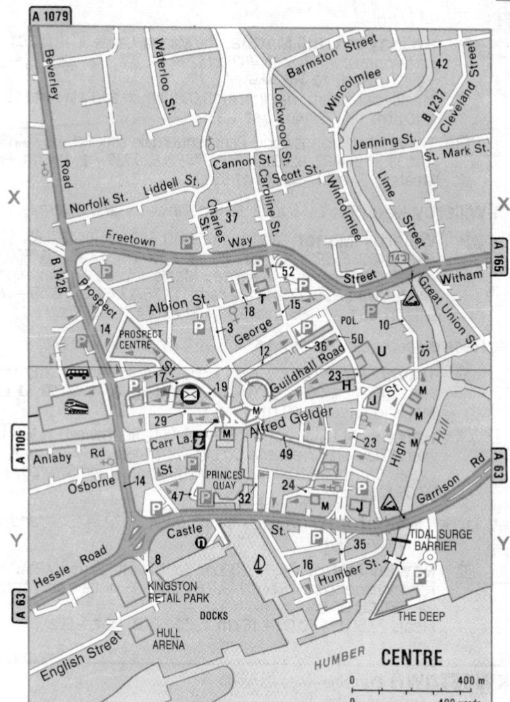

BEVERLEY, YORK
A 1079
A 1033
(A 1079)
SUTTON-ON-HULL
BRIDLINGTON HORNSEA
Greenwood Av.
ENNERDALE LEISURE CENTRE
Sutton Road
A 165
Endike Lane
Hall Road
Beverley Road
INDUSTRIAL ESTATE
Hull
A 1033
Leads Road
B 1237
Saltshouse Road
Sutton Road
SUTTON INGS
Ings Rd
Road
Cottingham Rd
U
B 1233
Clough Road
STONEFERRY
Stoneferry Rd
Reckitt Avenue
POL.
13
Chanterlands Avenue
EAST PARK
25
Z
Bricknell Av.
SCULCOATES
James
SUMMERGANGS
31
33
Holderness Road
43
Preston Rd
Lane
44
44
Marfleet
WITHERNSEA HEDON
West Spring Bank
Spring Bank
Walton St.
WEST PARK
Junction 12/02
Hedon Road
A 1033
Anlaby Road
ALEXANDRA DOCK
KING GEORGE DOCK
A 63
Garrisson Rd
ZEEBRUGGE ROTTERDAM
Boulevard
Road
Hessle
HUMBER
INDUSTRIAL ESTATES
BUILT UP AREA
0
2 km
1 mile
ER BRIDGE LEEDS
A 63

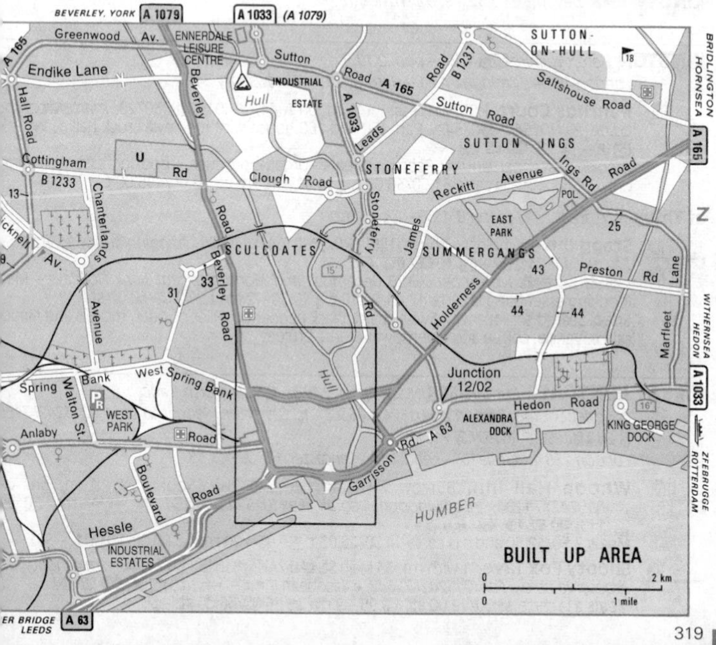

Holiday Inn Hull Marina, The Marina, Castle St, HU1 2BX, (0870) 400 9043, *gm1710@forte-hotel.com, Fax (01482) 213299,* <, , , , – , rm, rest, – 120.
Meals *(closed Saturday lunch)* 15.00 (dinner) and a la carte 19.85/28.85 **t.** 12.95 – 12.95 – **101 rm** 120.00/140.00 **st.** – SB.

Travel Inn, Kingswood Park, Ennerdale Link Rd, HU7 4HS, North : 5 m. by A 1079 on A 1033 (01482) 820225, *Fax (01482) 820300* – , rm, rest, VISA
Meals (grill rest.) – **42 rm** 41.95 **t.**

at Willerby *West : 5 m. by A 1079, Spring Bank – Z – and Willerby Rd – Kingston-upon-Hull.*

Willerby Manor, Well Lane, HU10 6ER, (01482) 652616, *info@willerbymanor.co.uk Fax (01482) 653901,* , , , – rm, – 500. VISA.
closed 25 December – ***Lafite :*** **Meals** *(closed Sunday dinner)* (dinner only and Sunday lunch)/dinner 20.00 and a la carte 17.75/27.40 **t.** 6.15 – ***Everglades :*** **Meals** a la carte 9.85/17.55 **t.** 10.95 – 9.50 – **51 rm** 74.50/90.00 **t.**

at Hessle *Southwest : 6 m. by A 63 – Z – Kingston-upon-Hull.*

Travel Inn, Ferriby Rd, HU13 0JA, West : 1 m. off A 164 (01482) 645285 *Fax (01482) 645299* – , rm, rest, VISA.
Meals (grill rest.) – **40 rm** 41.95 **t.**

Harry's, 14 Livingstone Rd, HU13 0EG, Southwest : 1 ½ m. off A 63 (01482) 646400 *harry@harrysbar.freeserve.co.uk, Fax (01482) 646469* – VISA
closed Christmas, 1 January, Sunday, Monday and Saturday lunch – **Meals** a la carte 18.00/27.00 **t.** 10.00.

at Little Weighton *Northwest : 9 m. by A 1079 – Z – and B 1233 via Skidby Village – Cottingham.*

Rowley Manor , HU20 3XR, Southwest : ½ m. by Rowley Rd (01482) 848248, *info@rowleymanor.com, Fax (01482) 849900,* <, « Georgian manor house », – 100. VISA
Meals 22.50 **t.** 10.00 – **16 rm** 55.00/90.00 **t.** – SB.

KINGSTOWN *Cumbria – see Carlisle.*

KINGSWEAR *Devon* 403 J 32 – *see Dartmouth.*

KINGTON *Herefordshire* 403 K 27 – *pop. 2 197.*
London 152 – Birmingham 61 – Hereford 19 – Shrewsbury 54.

Penrhos Court, HR5 3LH, East : 1 ½ m. on A 44, (01544) 230720, *martin@penrhos.co.uk, Fax (01544) 230754,* « Part 15C and 16C house with medieval cruck hall », – – 25. VISA.
(booking essential January-February) **Meals** - Organic produce - (booking essential) (dinner only) 31.50 and a la carte 31.50/36.00 **t.** 15.50 – **19 rm** 72.00/115.00 **t.**

at Titley *Northeast : 3½ m. on B 4355 – Kington.*

Stagg Inn (Reynolds) with rm, HR5 3RL, (01544) 230221, *stagginn@titley.kc3ltd.co.uk Fax (01544) 231390* – VISA
closed 2 weeks November 25-26 December, and Monday except Bank Holidays – **Meals** (booking essential) a la carte 17.40/24.10 **t.** 10.50 – **2 rm** 40.00/60.00 **st.**
Spec. Seared scallops with Swiss chard, black pepper oil. Fillet of beef, morels and Madeira sauce. Vanilla, coffee and elderflower crème brûlées.

KIRKBY LONSDALE *Cumbria* 402 M 21 – *pop. 2 076 – Carnforth (Lancs.).*
Scaleber Lane, Barbon (015242) 76365 – Casterton, Sedbergh Rd (015242) 7159
24 Main St (015242) 71437.
London 259 – Carlisle 62 – Kendal 13 – Lancaster 17 – Leeds 58.

Whoop Hall Inn, Burrow with Burrow, LA6 2HP, Southeast : 1 m. on A (015242) 71284, *info@whoophall.co.uk, Fax (015242) 72154,* – rm, 140. VISA
Meals 7.50/12.50 and a la carte 14.50/26.00 **t.** 9.95 – **20 rm** 60.00/90.00 **t.** – SB.

Snooty Fox Tavern with rm, 33 Main St, LA6 2AH, (015242) 71308, *kim@snootyfox.freeserve.co.uk, Fax (015242) 72642,* « Jacobean inn » – rm, VISA
Meals a la carte 13.50/19.00 **st.** 9.95 – **9 rm** 36.00/56.00 **st.** – SB.

t Casterton *Northeast : 1 ¼ m. by A 65 on A 683 – ✉ Carnforth (Lancs.).*

Pheasant Inn with rm, LA6 2RX, ☎ (015242) 71230, *pheasant.casterton@eggconnect.net, Fax (015242) 71230,* – rest, TV P. VISA JCB
closed 25-26 December, Monday and Sunday November-March **Meals** a la carte 13.20/24.70 **t.** 10.35 – **10 rm** 40.00/76.00 **t.**

t Cowan Bridge *(Lancs.) Southeast : 2 m. on A 65 – ✉ Carnforth (Lancs.).*

Hipping Hall, LA6 2JJ, Southeast : ½ m. on A 65 ☎ (015242) 71187, *hippinghal@aol.com, Fax (015242) 72452,* « 15C former hamlet », – TV P. AE VISA
Meals (dinner only) a la carte 18.95/24.50 **t.** 12.00 – **5 rm** 74.00/96.00 **st.**, 2 suites – SB.

IRKBY MALHAM *N. Yorks.* 402 N 21 – *pop. 70 – ✉ Skipton.*
London 235 – Bradford 25 – Burnley 30 – Carlisle 97 – Harrogate 25 – York 47.

Holgate Head, BD23 4BJ, ☎ (01729) 830376, *holgate@nildram.co.uk, Fax (01729) 830576,* <, « Part 17C », – TV P. VISA JCB.
mid March-mid October – **Meals** (communal dining) 22.00 **st.** 8.75 – **3 rm** 52.50/75.00 **st.**

IRKBYMOORSIDE *N. Yorks.* 402 R 21 – *pop. 2 650.*
Manor Vale ☎ (01751) 431525.
London 244 – Scarborough 26 – York 33.

George and Dragon, 17 Market Pl, YO62 6AA, ☎ (01751) 433334, *Fax (01751) 432933,* « Part 17C coaching inn », – rest, TV P. VISA JCB
Meals (bar lunch Monday to Saturday)/dinner a la carte 15.95/24.40 **t.** 10.80 – **18 rm** 49.00/79.00 **t.** – SB.

t Fadmoor *Northwest : 2 ¼ m. – ✉ Kirbymoorside.*

The Plough Inn, YO62 7HY, ☎ (01751) 431515, – P. VISA
closed 2 weeks November, 25 December and Tuesday – **Meals** (booking essential) a la carte 14.95/26.85 **t.** 11.60.

IRKBY STEPHEN *Cumbria* 402 M 20 – *pop. 2 209.*
London 296 – Carlisle 46 – Darlington 37 – Kendal 28.

Augill Castle, CA17 4DE, Northeast : 4 ½ m. by A 685 ☎ (01768) 341937, *enquiries@augillcastle.co.uk, Fax (01768) 341936,* <, « Victorian Gothic mansion house », , – TV P. VISA.
Meals (dinner only) (set menu only) (communal dining) 22.50 **st.** 16.00 – **6 rm** 40.00/80.00 **st.**

IRKCAMBECK *Cumbria* 401 402 L 18 – *see Brampton.*

IRKHAM *Lancs.* 402 L 22 – *pop. 9 038 – ✉ Preston.*
London 240 – Blackpool 9 – Preston 7.

Cromwellian, 16 Poulton St, PR4 2AB, ☎ (01772) 685680, *Fax (01772) 685680* – AE VISA
closed 1 week May, 2 weeks September, Sunday and Monday – **Meals** (dinner only) 19.50/26.50 **s.** 10.50.

t Wrea Green *Southwest : 3 m. on B 5259 – ✉ Kirkham.*

The Villa, Moss Side Lane, PR4 2PE, Southwest : ½ m. on B 5259 ☎ (01772) 684347, *Fax (01772) 687647,* – , rm, rm, TV P. – 25. AE VISA JCB.
Meals 10.00 (lunch) and a la carte 15.00/23.00 **st.** 9.50 – **25 rm** 65.00/80.00 **t.** – SB.

IRKWHELPINGTON *Northd.* 401 402 N/O 18 *Great Britain G. – pop. 353 – ✉ Morpeth.*
Env. : *Wallington House* AC, E : 3½ m. by A 696 and B 6342.*
London 305 – Carlisle 46 – Newcastle upon Tyne 20.

Shieldhall, Wallington, NE61 4AQ, Southeast : 2 ½ m. by A 696 on B 6342 ☎ (01830) 540387, *robinson.gay@btinternet.com, Fax (01830) 540387,* – TV P. VISA.
March-November – **Meals** (by arrangement) 20.00 **st.** 10.00 – **4 rm** 40.00/60.00.

KNARESBOROUGH *N. Yorks.* 402 P 21 – *pop. 13 380.*

Boroughbridge Rd ☎ (01423) 863219.

9 Castle Courtyard, Market Pl ☎ (01423) 866886 (summer only).

London 217 – Bradford 21 – Harrogate 3 – Leeds 18 – York 18.

Dower House, Bond End, HG5 9AL, ☎ (01423) 863302, *enquiries@bwdowerhouse.co.u* *Fax (01423) 867665,* – 65. VISA
Meals (bar lunch Monday to Saturday)/dinner 20.00 **t.** 11.95 – **30 rm** 60.00/106.00 **t** 1 suite – SB.

at Ferrensby *Northeast : 3 m. on A 6055.*

The General Tarleton Inn with rm, Boroughbridge Rd, HG5 0QB, ☎ (01423) 34028 *gti@generaltarleton.co.uk, Fax (01423) 340288* – – 40. VISA
closed 25 December – ***The Dining Room :*** **Meals** *(closed Sunday dinner)* (dinner only ar Sunday lunch)/dinner 25.00 and a la carte approx. 25.45 **t.** 10.95 – (see also below) **14 rm** (dinner included) 99.95/134.90 **t.** – SB.

The General Tarleton Inn, Boroughbridge Rd, HG5 0QB, ☎ (01423) 340284, *gti generaltarleton.co.uk, Fax (01423) 340288,* « Characterful 18C inn » – VISA
closed 25 December – ***Bar/Brasserie :*** **Meals** (bookings not accepted) a la carte 14.45 25.20 **t.** 10.95.

KNIGHTWICK *Worcs.* 403 404 M 27 – *pop. 87* – ✉ *Worcester.*

London 132 – Hereford 20 – Leominster 18 – Worcester 8.

Talbot with rm, WR6 5PH, on B 4197 ☎ (01886) 821235, *admin@the-talbot.co.u* *Fax (01886) 821060,* – VISA.
closed dinner 25 December – **Meals** 9.95/22.95 **t.** 9.75 – **10 rm** 38.00/69.50 **t.** – SB.

When looking for a quiet hotel
use the maps found in the introduction
or look for establishments with the sign or .

KNOWLE *W. Mids.* 403 404 O 26 – *pop. 17 588* – ✉ *Solihull.*

London 108 – Birmingham 9 – Coventry 10 – Warwick 11.

Greswolde Arms, 1657 High St, B93 0LL, ☎ (01564) 772711, *Fax (01564) 770354* rm, – 150. VISA JCB.
Meals a la carte approx. 16.20 **st.** 8.95 – **36 rm** 75.00 **st.**

KNOWL HILL *Windsor & Maidenhead* 404 R 29 – ✉ *Twyford.*

Hennerton, Crazies Hill Rd, Wargrave ☎ (0118) 940 1000.

London 38 – Maidenhead 5 – Reading 8.

Bird in Hand, Bath Rd, RG10 9UP, ☎ (01628) 826622, *Fax (01628) 826748,* , – VISA
accommodation closed 1 week Christmas – **Meals** 12.50/18.50 and a la carte 22.40/26.95 10.00 – **15 rm** 110.00/120.00 **st.** – SB.

KNOWSLEY INDUSTRIAL PARK *Mersey.* – *see Liverpool.*

KNUTSFORD *Ches.* 402 403 404 M 24 – *pop. 13 352.*

Council Offices, Toft Rd ☎ (01565) 632611.

London 187 – Chester 25 – Liverpool 33 – Manchester 18 – Stoke-on-Trent 30.

Cottons, Manchester Rd, WA16 0SU, Northwest : 1 ½ m. on A 50 ☎ (01565) 65033 *cottons@shireinns.co.uk, Fax (01565) 755351,* , squash – 200. VISA
Magnolia : **Meals** *(closed Saturday lunch)* a la carte 26.45/34.75 **st.** 13.45 – **108 r** 125.00/145.00 **st.** – SB.

Longview, 55 Manchester Rd, WA16 0LX, on A 50 ☎ (01565) 632119, *enquiries@longvie hotel.com, Fax (01565) 652402* – rest, VISA
closed 24 December-7 January – **Meals** *(closed Sunday and Bank Holidays)* (bar lunch dinner a la carte 15.00/27.70 **t.** 10.25 – **24 rm** 69.50/99.00 **t.**, 2 suites.

Travelodge, Chester Rd, Tabley, WA16 0PP, Northwest : 2 ¾ m. by A 5033 on A 5 ☎ (01565) 652187, *Fax (01565) 652187* – rm, rest, VISA JCB.
Meals (grill rest.) – **32 rm** 49.95 **t.**

Belle Epoque Brasserie with rm, 60 King St, WA16 6DT, ☎ (01565) 633060, *info@thebelleepoque.com, Fax (01565) 634150*, « Art Nouveau », – 60.
closed 25-26 December and Bank Holidays – **Meals** *(closed Saturday and Monday lunch and Sunday dinner)* a la carte 19.00/26.00 **t.** 9.95 – 7.95 – **6 rm** 60.00 **st.**

Est, Est, Est, 81 King St, WA16 6DX, ☎ (01565) 755487, *estestest@ccruk.com, Fax (01565) 633186* –
closed 25-26 December – **Meals** - Italian - a la carte 13.55/22.90 **t.** 10.45.

at Mobberley *Northeast : 2½ m. by A 537 on B 5085 – ✉ Knutsford.*

Hinton, Town Lane, WA16 7HH, on B 5085 ☎ (01565) 873484, *Fax (01565) 873484*,
Meals (by arrangement) 14.50 – **6 rm** 44.00/58.00 **t.**

Laburnum Cottage, Knutsford Rd, WA16 7PU, West : ¾ m. on B 5085 ☎ (01565) 872464, *Fax (01565) 872464*,
Meals 15.00 **t.** – **6 rm** 44.00/58.00 **t.**

at Hoo Green *Northwest : 3½ m. on A 50 – ✉ Knutsford.*

Mere Court, Warrington Rd, WA16 0RW, Northwest : 1 m. on A 50 ☎ (01565) 831000, *sales@merecourt.co.uk, Fax (01565) 831001*, « Part Edwardian manor house, gardens » – 75.
Meals *(closed Saturday lunch)* 14.95/24.95 and a la carte approx. 25.35 **t.** 14.95 – **34 rm** 125.00/170.00 **t.**

KYNASTON *Herefordshire – see Ledbury.*

LACOCK *Wilts.* 403 404 N 29 *The West Country G.* – *pop. 1 068* – ✉ *Chippenham.*
See : *Village★★ - Lacock Abbey★* AC – *High St★, St Cyriac★, Fox Talbot Museum of Photography★* AC.
London 109 – Bath 16 – Bristol 30 – Chippenham 3.

Sign of the Angel, 6 Church St, SN15 2LB, ☎ (01249) 730230, *angel@lacock.co.uk, Fax (01249) 730527*, « Part 14C and 15C former wool merchant's house in National Trust village »,
closed 1 week Christmas – **Meals** - English - *(closed Monday lunch except Bank Holidays)* a la carte 17.85/31.85 **t.** 11.00 – **10 rm** 65.00/137.50 **t.**

LADOCK *Cornwall* 403 F 33.
London 268 – Exeter 84 – Penzance 37 – Newquay 12 – Plymouth 51 – Truro 13.

Bissick Old Mill, TR2 4PG, ☎ (01726) 882557, *sonia.v@bissickoldmill.ndo.co.uk, Fax (01726) 884057* –
closed January and December **Meals** (by arrangement) 19.50 **s.** 9.60 – **4 rm** 42.50/69.00 **s.**

LANCASTER *Lancs.* 402 L 21 *Great Britain G.* – *pop. 44 497.*
See : *Castle★* AC.
18 *Ashton Hall, Ashton-with-Stodday ☎ (01524) 752090* – 9 *Lansil, Caton Rd ☎ (01524) 39269.*
29 Castle Hill ☎ (01524) 32878.
London 252 – Blackpool 26 – Bradford 62 – Burnley 44 – Leeds 71 – Middlesbrough 97 – Preston 26.

Lancaster House, Green Lane, Ellel, LA1 4GJ, South : 3 ¼ m. by A 6 ☎ (01524) 844822, *info@elh.co.uk, Fax (01524) 844766*, rest, – 120.
The Gressingham : **Meals** 20.95 and a la carte 20.95/28.95 12.50 – 9.95 – **80 rm** 99.00 **st.** – SB.

Holiday Inn, Waterside Park, Caton Rd, LA1 3RA, Northeast : 1 ½ m. on A 683 at junction 34 of M 6 ☎ (0870) 4009047, *Fax (01524) 841265*, rm, – 120.
Meals 15.00 and a la carte 20.00/30.00 11.95 – 12.95 – **157 rm** 98.00 **st.** – SB.

Royal Kings Arms, Market St, LA1 1HP, ☎ (01524) 32451, *info@menzies-hotels.co.uk, Fax (01524) 841698* – – 80.
Meals 9.25 (lunch) and a la carte 13.65/18.75 **st.** – 9.95 – **55 rm** 69.50/89.50 – SB.

Edenbreck House without rest., Sunnyside Lane, off Ashfield Ave, LA1 5ED, by Westbourne Rd, near the station ☎ (01524) 32464,
closed 25 December – **3 rm** 30.00/55.00.

ENGLAND

at Carnforth *North : 6 ¼ m. on A 6.*

New Capernwray Farm ⛰, Capernwray, LA6 1AD, Northeast : 3 m. by B 625 ✆ (01524) 734284, *newcapfarm@aol.com, Fax (01524) 734284,* ←, « 17C former farmhouse », – ⊁ TV P. MO VISA JCB
March-October – **Meals** (by arrangement) (communal dining) 19.50 – **3 rm** 48.00/78.00 **s.**

LANCASTER SERVICE AREA *Lancs.* 402 L 22 – ✉ *Forton.*

(M 6) Service Area, White Carr Lane, Bay Horse ✆ (01524) 792181.

Travelodge, LA2 9DU, on M 6 between junctions 32 and 33 (northbound carriageway) ✆ (01524) 792227, *Fax (01524) 791703* – ⊁ TV ♿ P. MO AE ⓓ VISA JCB.
Meals (grill rest.) – **53 rm** 52.95 **t.**

LANCING *W. Sussex* 404 S 31 – *pop. 29 575 (inc. Sompting).*
London 59 – Brighton 4 – Southampton 53.

Sussex Pad, Old Shoreham Rd, BN15 0RH, East : 1 m. off A 27 ✆ (01273) 45464 *reception@sussexpadhotel.co.uk, Fax (01273) 453010,* – ⊁ rest, TV P. MO AE ⓓ VISA
closed Christmas **Meals** 18.00/22.00 **t.** 11.50 – **18 rm** 65.00/80.00 **t.**

LANGAR *Notts..*
London 132 – Leicester 25 – Boston 45 – Lincoln 37 – Nottingham 14.

Langar Hall ⛰, NG13 9HG, ✆ (01949) 860559, *langarhall-hotel@ndirect.co.uk, Fax (01949) 861045,* ←, « Georgian manor house, antiques », – ⊁ rm, TV P. AE ⓓ VISA
Meals 12.50/35.00 and dinner a la carte 27.00/40.00 **t.** 11.00 – **12 rm** 65.00/185.00 **t.**

LANGHO *Lancs.* 402 M 22 – *see Blackburn.*

LANGTON GREEN *Kent – see Royal Tunbridge Wells.*

LAPWORTH *Warks. – see Hockley Heath.*

LARKFIELD *Kent* 404 V 30 – *see Maidstone.*

LASKILL *N. Yorks. – see Helmsley.*

LASTINGHAM *N. Yorks.* 402 R 21 – *pop. 87* – ✉ *York.*
London 244 – Scarborough 26 – York 32.

Lastingham Grange ⛰, YO62 6TH, ✆ (01751) 417345, *reservations@lastingham grange.com, Fax (01751) 417358,* « Part 17C farmhouse, gardens », – ⊁ rest, TV P. AE ⓓ VISA JCB
March-November – **Meals** (light lunch Monday to Saturday)/dinner 32.75 **t.** 7.75 – **12 rm** 92.00/175.00 **t.** – SB.

LAUNCESTON *Cornwall* 403 G32.
Trethorne, Kennards House ✆ (01566) 86324.
London 228 – Bude 23 – Exeter 47 – Plymouth 27.

Springer Spaniel, Treburley, PL15 9NS, South : 4 ½ m. on A 388 ✆ (01579) 37042 *Fax (01579) 370113* – P. MO VISA
closed 25 December – **Meals** a la carte 14.00/22.75 **t.** 9.25.

LAVENHAM *Suffolk* 404 W 27 *Great Britain G. – pop. 1 231* – ✉ *Sudbury.*
See : *Town*★★ – *Church of St. Peter and St. Paul*★.
Lady St ✆ (01787) 248207.
London 66 – Cambridge 39 – Colchester 22 – Ipswich 19.

Swan, High St, CO10 9QA, ✆ (01787) 247477, *heritagehotels_lavenham.swan@forte hotels.com, Fax (01787) 248286,* « Part 14C timbered inn », – ⊁ TV P – 45. AE ⓓ VISA
Meals 13.95/27.95 and dinner a la carte **t.** 14.95 – **49 rm** 109.00 **st.**, 2 suites – SB.

Lavenham Priory without rest., Water St, CO10 9RW, (01787) 247404, *mail@lavenhampriory.co.uk, Fax (01787) 248472,* « Part 13C timbered former priory », – P. VISA JCB.
closed Christmas-New Year – **6 rm** 59.00/108.00 **t.**

Great House with rm, Market Pl, CO10 9QZ, (01787) 247431, *info@greathouse.co.uk, Fax (01787) 248007,* , « Part 14C timbered house » – . AE VISA JCB
closed 3 weeks January – **Meals** - French - *(closed Sunday dinner and Monday)* 15.95/22.95 and a la carte 16.50/33.20 **t.** 11.50 – **3 rm** 65.00/80.00 **t.**, 2 suites 90.00 **t.** – SB.

Angel with rm, Market Pl, CO10 9QZ, (01787) 247388, *angellav@aol.com, Fax (01787) 248344,* « 15C inn », – P. AE VISA
closed 25-26 December – **Meals** a la carte 14.95/20.00 **t.** 9.95 – **8 rm** 45.00/70.00 **t.** – SB.

EA *Lancs. – see Preston.*

EAMINGTON SPA *Warks.* 403 404 P 27 – *see Royal Leamington Spa.*

EDBURY *Herefordshire* 403 404 M 27 – *pop. 6 216.*
3 The Homend (01531) 636147.
London 119 – Hereford 14 – Newport 46 – Worcester 16.

The Feathers, High St, HR8 1DS, (01531) 635266, *mary@feathers-ledbury.co.uk, Fax (01531) 638955,* « Timbered 16C inn », , – P – 120. AE VISA
Quills : **Meals** a la carte 17.00/30.00 **t.** 10.95 – ***Fuggles :*** **Meals** a la carte 20.00/28.25 **t.** 10.95 – **19 rm** 71.50/145.00 **t.** – SB.

The Barn House without rest., New St, HR8 2DX, (01531) 632825, *barnhouseledbury@lineone.net,* « Part 17C », – P – 60. VISA.
closed 25 and 26 December – **3 rm** 48.00/65.00.

The Malthouse, Church Lane, HR8 1DW, (01531) 634443, *jtlipton@aol.com, Fax (01531) 634664,* – . VISA JCB
closed 22 December-2 January, Sunday and Monday – **Meals** (booking essential) (dinner only and Saturday lunch)/dinner a la carte 17.00/25.45 **t.** 9.95.

t Kynaston *Southwest : 6½ m. by A 449, A 4172, Aylton Rd, on Fownhope Rd – Ledbury.*

Hallend , HR8 2PD, (01531) 670225, *Fax (01531) 670747,* , « Working farm », – P. VISA.
closed Christmas and New Year – **Meals** (booking essential) (communal dining) (by arrangement) 22.50 **st.** – **2 rm** 47.50/75.00 **st.**, 1 suite.

LEEDS

W. Yorks. **402** **P 22** *Great Britain G. – pop. 424 194.*

London 204 – Liverpool 75 – Manchester 43 – Newcastle upon Tyne 95 – Nottingham 74.

TOURIST INFORMATION

The Arcade, City Station ☎ (0113) 242 5242.

PRACTICAL INFORMATION

18, 18 *Temple Newsam, Temple Newsam Rd, Halton ☎ (0113) 264 5624,* **CT**.
18 *Gotts Park, Armley Ridge Rd, Armley ☎ (0113) 234 2019,* **BT**.
18 *Middleton Park, Ring Rd, Beeston Park, Middleton ☎ (0113) 270 9506,* **CU**.
18, 9 *Moor Allerton, Coal Rd, Wike ☎ (0113) 266 1154.*
18 *Howley Hall, Scotchman Lane, Morley ☎ (01924) 472432.*
9 *Roundhay, Park Lane ☎ (0113) 266 2695* **CT**.
Leeds – Bradford Airport : ☎ (0113) 250 9696, NW : 8 m. by A 65 and A 658 **BT**.

SIGHTS

See : *City★ - Royal Armouries Museum★★★ – City Art Gallery★* **AC GY M.**

Env. : *Kirkstall Abbey★* **AC**, *NW : 3 m. by A 65* **GY** *– Temple Newsam★ (decorative arts★)* **AC**, *E : 5 m. by A 64 and A 63* **CU D.**

Exc. : *Harewood House★★ (The Gallery★)* **AC**, *N : 8 m. by A 61* **CT** *– Nostell Priory★, SE : 18 m. by A 61 and A 638 – Yorkshire Sculpture Park★, S : 20 m. by M 1 to junction 38 and 1 m. north off A 637 – Brodsworth Hall★, SE : 25 m. by M 1 to junction 40, A 638 and minor rd (right) in Upton.*

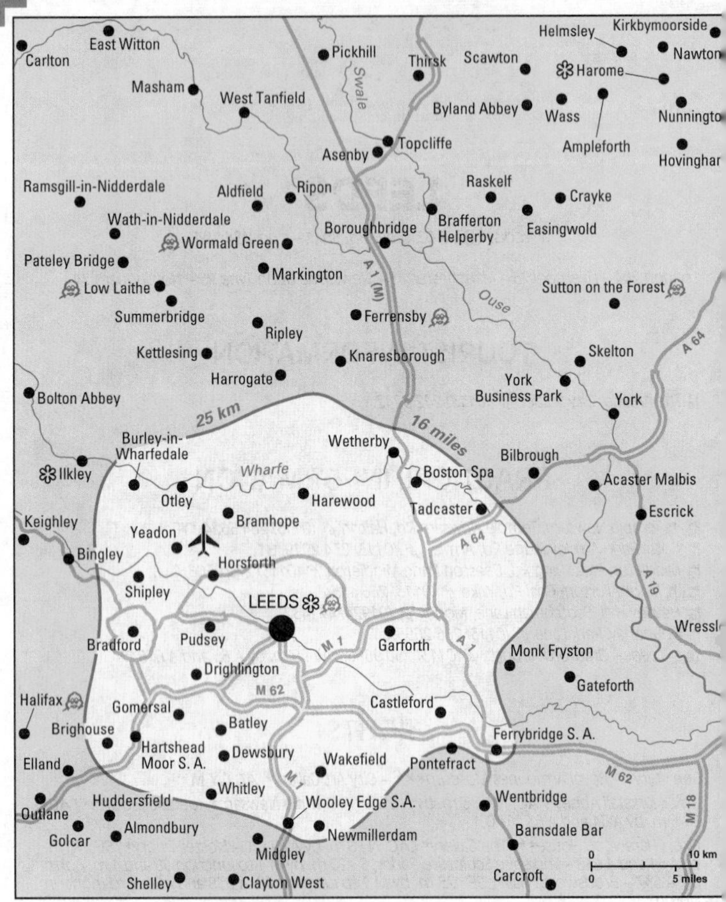

Devere Oulton Hall, Rothwell Lane, Oulton, LS26 8HN, Southeast : 5 ½ m. by A 61 a
A 639 on A 654 ☎ (0113) 282 1000, *oulton.hall@devere-hotels.com, Fax (0113) 282 8066,*
« Part Victorian mansion », ⅙, ≘s, ⌂, 18, 9, – ⎮, ⥇, ▤ rest, TV ♿ P – 🏠 33
MC AE ⓓ VISA
CU

Bronte : Meals *(closed Saturday lunch)* 13.50 (lunch) and a la carte 23.00/55.00 **st.** 14.
– **150 rm** ⊐ 150.00/170.00 **st.**, 2 suites.

Leeds Marriott, 4 Trevelyan Sq, Boar Lane, LS1 6ET, ☎ (0113) 236 636
Fax (0113) 236 6367, ⅙, ≘s, ⌂ – ⎮, ⥇ rm, ▤ TV ✆ ♿ – 🏠 280. MC AE ⓓ VI
GZ

John T's : Meals *(closed lunch Saturday and Sunday)* 24.00 and a la carte 18.25/32.00
12.25 – ⊐ 13.00 – **243 rm** 114.00 **st.**, 1 suite.

Crowne Plaza Leeds, Wellington St, LS1 4DL, ☎ (0113) 244 2200, *Fax (0113) 244 04*
⅙, ≘s, ⌂ – ⎮, ⥇ rm, ▤ TV ✆ ♿ P – 🏠 200. MC AE ⓓ VISA
FZ

Meals 18.00 and a la carte 16.00/26.00 **st.** 12.95 – ⊐ 12.95 – **130 rm** 140.00 **st.**, 5 suite
SB.

42 The Calls, 42 The Calls, LS2 7EW, ☎ (0113) 244 0099, *hotel@42thecalls.co.*
Fax (0113) 234 4100, ≤, « Converted riverside grain mill » – ⎮ TV ✆ ♿ – 🏠 85. MC
ⓓ VISA JCB
GZ

closed Christmas – **Meals** – (see ***Pool Court at 42*** below) – (see also ***Brasserie Forty Fo***
below) – ⊐ 12.50 – **38 rm** 105.00/160.00 **t.**, 3 suites.

Le Meridien Queen's, City Sq, LS1 1PL, (0113) 243 1323, *queens.reservations@forte-hotels.com, Fax (0113) 242 5154* – rm, – 600. GZ u
No. 1 City Square : **Meals** (carvery lunch) 16.50 lunch and dinner a la carte 19.95/28.20 **t.** 14.50 – 12.75 – **194 rm** 125.00/160.00 **t.**, 5 suites – SB.

Village H. and Leisure Club, 186 Otley Rd, Headingley, LS16 5PR, Northwest : 3 ½ m. on A 660 (0113) 278 1000, *village.l@cybase.co.uk, Fax (0113) 278 1111*, squash – rest, – 220. BT s
Meals (grill rest.) a la carte approx. 21.00 **st.** 8.50 – **94 rm** 98.00/129.00 **st.**

Weetwood Hall, Otley Rd, LS16 5PS, Northwest : 4 m. on A 660 (0113) 230 6000, *sales@weetwood.co.uk, Fax (0113) 230 6095*, – – 150. BT c
Meals (bar lunch Monday-Saturday)/dinner 16.25/30.00 **st.** 11.95 – 10.75 – **108 rm** 96.00/167.00 **st.** – SB.

Hilton Leeds City, Neville St, LS1 4BX, (0113) 244 2000, *leehnhngm@hilton.com, Fax (0113) 243 3577*, – rm, rm, – 400. GZ r
Meals *(closed lunch Saturday and Sunday)* (bar lunch)/dinner 13.50/18.95 and dinner a la carte 19.85/25.65 **t.** 12.30 – 12.95 – **186 rm** 135.00/145.00 **st.**, 20 suites – SB.

Malmaison, Sovereign Quay, LS1 1DQ, (0113) 398 1000, *leeds@malmaison.com, Fax (0113) 398 1002*, « Riverside setting, contemporary interior », – rm, – 40. GZ n
Meals 11.95/12.95 and a la carte 22.40/24.40 **st.** 13.95 – 10.75 – **99 rm** 95.00/120.00 **st.**, 1 suite – SB.

Haley's, Shire Oak Rd, Headingley, LS6 2DE, Northwest : 2 m. by A 660 (0113) 278 4446, *info@haleys.co.uk, Fax (0113) 275 3342* – – 25. DV s
closed 26-30 December – **Meals** *(closed Sunday dinner to non-residents)* (dinner only and Sunday lunch)/dinner 24.95 and a la carte 24.95/31.00 **st.** 13.95 – **29 rm** 95.00/230.00 **st.** – SB.

Metropole, King St, LS1 2HQ, (0113) 245 0841, *Fax (0113) 242 5156* – – 250. FZ e
Meals 18.00 (dinner) and a la carte approx. 26.00 **st.** 12.50 – 12.95 – **117 rm** 105.00/125.00 **st.**, 1 suite – SB.

Merrion, Merrion Centre, 17 Wade Lane, LS2 8NH, (0113) 243 9191, *info@merrion-hotel-leeds.com, Fax (0113) 242 3527* – rm, – 80. GY e
Meals a la carte 19.45/24.40 **st.** 8.95 – 11.75 – **109 rm** 99.00/170.00 **st.**

Golden Lion, 2 Lower Briggate, LS1 4AE, (0113) 243 6454, *info@goldenlion-hotel-leeds.com, Fax (0113) 242 9327* – rm, – 120. GZ v
Meals (bar lunch)/dinner a la carte 16.40/22.40 **st.** 9.25 – **89 rm** 99.00/120.00 **st.** – SB.

Premier Lodge, City West One Office Park, Gelderd Rd, LS12 6SN, Southwest : 3 ½ m. by A 62 (0870) 7001414, *Fax (0870) 7001415* – rest, CU n
Meals (grill rest.) (dinner only) a la carte approx. 12.45 **t.** 8.45 – **126 rm** 46.95 **t.**

Travel Inn Metro, Citygate, Wellington St, LS3 1LH, (0113) 242 8104, *Fax (0113) 242 8105* – rm, rest, FZ v
Meals (grill rest.) – **140 rm** 49.95 **t.**

Express by Holiday Inn without rest., Cavendish St (off Kirkstall Rd), LS3 1LY, (0113) 242 6200, *leeds@khl.uk.com, Fax (0113) 242 6300* – – 40. FY e
112 rm 66.00 **t.**

Express by Holiday Inn without rest., Aberford Rd, Oulton, LS26 8EJ, Southeast : 5 ½ m. by A 61 on A 639 (0113) 282 6201, *Fax (0113) 288 7210* – – 40. CU e
77 rm 55.00 **st.**

Travelodge without rest., Blayds Court, Swinegate, LS1 4AG, (0113) 244 5793, *Fax (0113) 246 0076* – GZ v
100 rm 52.95 **t.**

Pinewood, 78 Potternewton Lane, LS7 3LW, (0113) 262 2561, *Fax (0113) 262 2561*, – rest, DV a
closed Christmas-New Year – **Meals** (by arrangement) 12.95 **st.** 7.00 – **10 rm** 39.00/50.00 **t.**

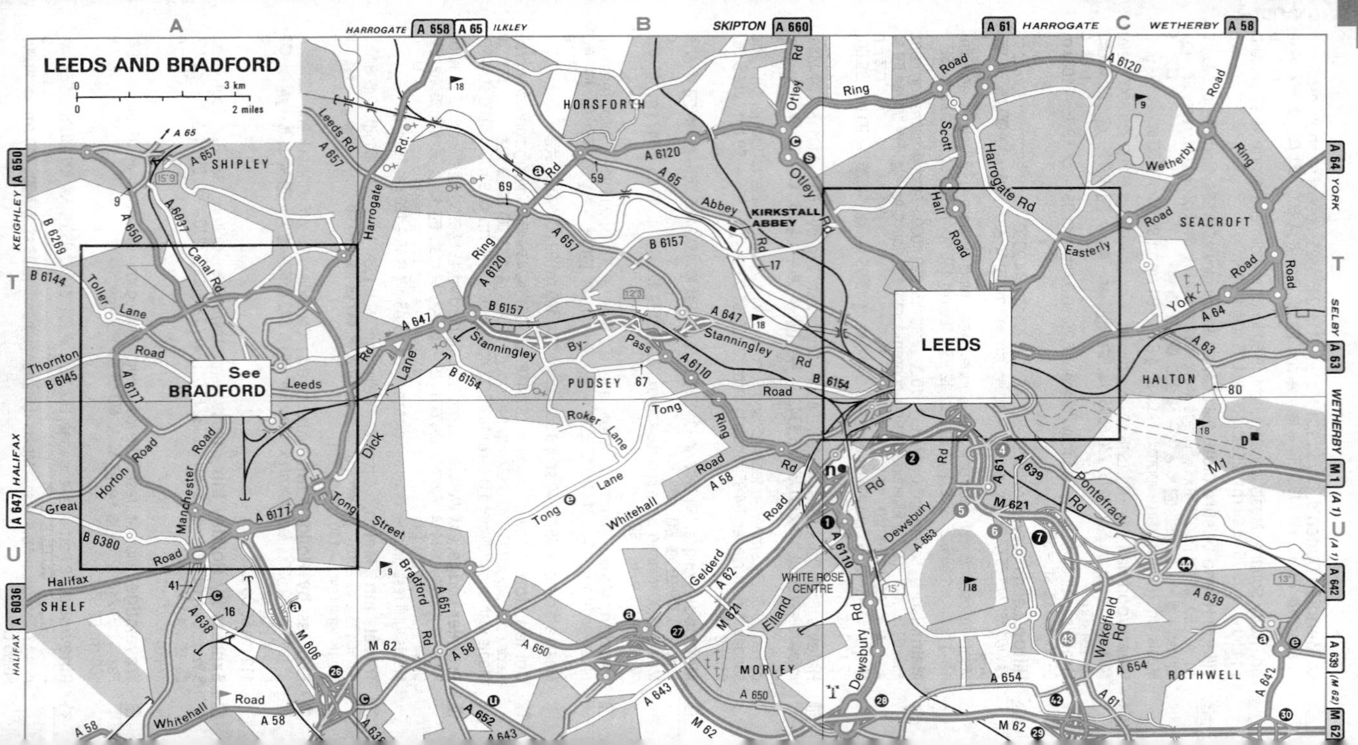
LEEDS AND BRADFORD
0 3 km
0 2 miles
A B C
T U
HARROGATE A 658 A 65 ILKLEY
SKIPTON A 660
A 61 HARROGATE
WETHERBY A 58
A 64 YORK
SELBY A 63
WETHERBY M 1 (A 1)
(A 1) A 642
A 639 (M 62) M 62
KEIGHLEY A 650
HALIFAX A 647
HALIFAX A 6036
LEEDS
See BRADFORD
SHIPLEY
HORSFORTH
KIRKSTALL ABBEY
SEACROFT
HALTON
PUDSEY
MORLEY
ROTHWELL
SHELF
WHITE ROSE CENTRE
Ring Road
Otley Rd
Scott Hall Road
Harrogate Rd
Wetherby Road
Easterly Road
York Road
Stanningley By-Pass
Stanningley Rd
Dick Lane
Tong Lane
Roker Lane
Tong Street
Bradford Rd
Whitehall Road
Dewsbury Rd
Elland Road
Gelderd Rd
Pontefract Rd
Wakefield Rd
Leeds Rd
Harrogate Rd.
Abbey Rd
Canal Rd
Toller Lane
Thornton Road
Leeds Road
Manchester Road
Horton Road
Great Horton Road
Halifax Road
Leeds Road
Whitehall Road
A 6120
A 657
A 65
A 6037
A 650
A 6177
A 647
A 6110
A 58
A 62
A 653
A 61
A 639
A 654
A 651
A 652
A 643
A 638
A 642
M 621
M 606
M 62
M1
B 6157
B 6154
B 6144
B 6145
B 6269
B 6380

LEEDS

Bradford Road . . . . . . **AT** 9
Cambridge Road . . . **DV** 14
Cleckheaton Road . . **AU** 16
Commercial Road . . **BT** 17
Domestic Street . . . . **DX** 23
East Park Parade . . . **EX** 28
Gelderd Road . . . . . . **DX** 32
Harrogate Road . . . . **DV** 40
Huddersfield Road . . . . **AU** 41
Hyde Park Road . . . . **AV** 43
Ivy Street . . . . **EX** 45
Lupton Avenue . . . . . **EX** 51
New Road Side . . . . . **BT** 59
Oakwood Lane . . . . . **EV** 63
Pudsey Road . . . . **BT** 67
Rodley Lane . . . . **BV** 69
Roseville Road . . . . **EVX** 70
Shaw Lane . . . . **DV** 74
South Accommodation Road . . . . **EX** 77
Stainbeck Road . . . . **DV** 79
Templenewsam Road **CT** 80
White Rose Centre . **CU**

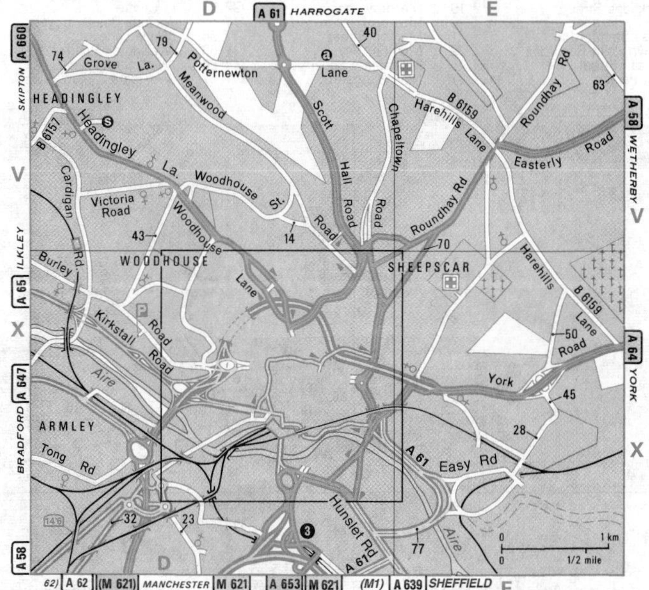

XXX ✿ **gueller,** 3 York Pl, LS1 2DR, ☏ (0113) 245 9922, *dine@guellers.com, Fax (0113) 245 9965* – ▤. MO AE VISA FZ e
closed Christmas, Sunday and Monday – **Meals** 16.50/24.50 **t.** 🍷 9.95
Spec. Roast scallops, celeriac purée, truffle vinaigrette. Braised pig's trotter stuffed with ham hock and morels. Chocolate mousse with red berries.

XXX ✿ **Pool Court at 42** (at 42 The Calls H.), 44 The Calls, LS2 7EW, ☏ (0113) 244 4242, *poolcourt@onetel.net.uk, Fax (0113) 234 3332*, ⛱, « Riverside setting » – ⊁ ▤. MO AE ① VISA GZ z
closed Saturday lunch, Sunday and Bank Holidays – **Meals** 30.00/37.50 **t.** 🍷 17.50
Spec. Marinière of mussels and salted cod, artichoke, leeks and saffron. Fillet of beef, oxtail risotto and parsnip crisps. Apricot and almond frangipane.

XX **Rascasse,** Canal Wharf, Water Lane, LS11 5BB, ☏ (0113) 244 6611, *Fax (0113) 244 0736*, ≤, « Converted grain warehouse, canalside setting » – ▤. MO AE ① VISA FZ c
closed 25 December-3 January, Sunday, Saturday lunch and Bank Holiday Mondays – **Meals** 18.00 (lunch) and a la carte 22.00/32.50 **t.** 🍷 12.00.

XX **Leodis,** Victoria Mill, Sovereign St, LS1 4BJ, ☏ (0113) 242 1010, *Fax (0113) 243 0432*, ⛱, « Converted riverside warehouse » – MO AE ① VISA GZ b
closed Sunday, lunch Saturday, 26 December and 1 January and Bank Holidays – **Meals** a la carte 21.60/31.20 **t.** 🍷 13.95.

XX **Brasserie Forty Four** (at 42 The Calls H.), 44 The Calls, LS2 7EW, ☏ (0113) 234 3232, *brasserie44@onetel.net.uk, Fax (0113) 234 3332*, « Riverside setting » – ▤. MO AE ① VISA GZ z
closed Sunday, Saturday lunch and Bank Holidays – **Meals** a la carte 20.35/26.40 **t.** 🍷 13.95.

XX **Fourth Floor** (at Harvey Nichols), 107-111 Briggate, LS1 6AZ, ☏ (0113) 204 8000, *Fax (0113) 204 8080*, ⛱ – ▤. MO AE ① VISA JCB GZ s
closed 25-26 December, 1 January, and dinner Sunday-Wednesday – **Meals** (lunch bookings not accepted) 16.00 (lunch) and a la carte 27.00/31.00 **t.** 🍷 12.50.

LEEDS

Street	Grid	No.
Aire Street	FZ	2
Albion Street	GZ	3
Bond Street	GZ	8
Bridge Street	GY	10
Briggate	GZ	
City Square	GZ	15
Commercial Street	GZ	18
Cookridge Street	GY	19
County Arcade	GZ	20
Cross Stamford St.	GY	21
Crown Point Road	GZ	22
Duncan Street	GZ	25
East Parade	FGZ	27
Eastgate	GZ	31
Hanover Way	FY	38
Headrow (The)	GY	
Headrow Centre	GZ	39
Infirmary Street	GZ	44
King Street	FZ	46
Kirkgate	GZ	48
Lands Lane	GZ	49
Leeds Shopping Plaza	GZ	50
Marsh Lane	GZ	52
Meadow Lane	GZ	53
Merrion Centre	GY	
Merrion Street	GY	54
Merrion Way	GY	55
Millennium Square	GY	56
New Briggate	GY	57
New York Road	GY	
Park Lane	FY	
Queen Street	FZ	
St. John's Centre	GY	
St. Paul's Street	FZ	
St. Peter's Street	GZ	
Sheepscar St. South	GY	
Skinner Lane	GY	
South Parade	FGZ	
Trinity St. Shopping Centre	GZ	
Victoria Road	GZ	
Wade Lane	GY	
Wellington Road	FZ	
West Street	FZ	
Westgate	FZ	

XX **Maxi's,** 6 Bingley St, LS3 1LX, off Kirkstall Rd ✆ (0113) 244 0552, *info@maxi-s.co.*
Fax (0113) 234 3902, « Pagoda, ornate decor » – ▤ 🅿. MC AE ⓓ VISA JCB FY
closed 25-26 December – **Meals** - Chinese (Canton, Peking) - 17.80/24.90 and a la ca
16.70/20.50 **t.** 🍾 9.90.

X **The Calls Grill,** Calls Landing, 38 The Calls, LS2 7EW, ✆ (0113) 245 38
Fax (0113) 243 9035, « Converted riverside warehouse » – ▤. MC AE ⓓ VISA GZ
closed 22 December-3 January – **Meals** 11.95/17.50 and a la carte 16.70/26.25 **t.** 🍾 9.95.

X **Fish!,** 159 Headrow, LS1 3RG, ✆ (0113) 247 0177, *Fax (0113) 245 3064* – ▤. MC AE ⓓ VI
closed 25 December – **Meals** - Seafood - a la carte 18.05/30.15 **st.** 🍾 9.90. FGY

at Garforth *East : 7 m. by A 63 – CT –* ✉ *Leeds.*

XX **Aagrah,** Aberford Rd, LS25 1BA, on A 642 (Garforth rd) ✆ (0113) 287 6606 – ▤ 🅿. MC
VISA JCB
closed 25 December – **Meals** - Indian (Kashmiri) - (booking essential) (dinner only) a la ca
13.30/17.25 **t.** 🍾 9.95.

at Drighlington *Southwest : 6 m. by A 62 and A 650 on B 6135 – ✉ Leeds.*

Travel Inn, The Old Brickworks, Wakefield Rd, BD11 1EA, ✆ (0113) 287 9132, *Fax (0113) 287 9115,* – rm, rest, P. *VISA*. BU a
Meals (grill rest.) – **42 rm** 41.95 **t.**

at Pudsey *West : 5 ¾ m. by A 647 – ✉ Leeds.*

Aagrah, 483 Bradford Rd, LS28 8ED, on A 647 ✆ (01274) 668818, *Fax (01274) 669803* – P. *VISA* JCB BT e
closed 25 December – **Meals** - Indian (Kashmiri) - (booking essential) (dinner only) a la carte 13.30/17.25 **t.** 9.95.

at Horsforth *Northwest : 5 m. by A 65 off A 6120 – ✉ Leeds.*

Paris, Calverley Bridge, Calverley Lane, Rodley, LS13 1NP, Southwest : 1 m. by A 6120 ✆ (0113) 258 1885, *Fax (0113) 239 0651* – P. *VISA* JCB BT a
closed 26-28 December, 1-3 January and Saturday lunch – **Meals** 13.95/15.95 and a la carte 15.90/26.70 **t.** 10.95.

at Bramhope *Northwest : 8 m. on A 660 –* **BT** *– ✉ Leeds.*

Posthouse Leeds/Bradford, Leeds Rd, LS16 9JJ, ✆ (0870) 400 9049, *gm1123@forte-hotels.com, Fax (0113) 284 3451,* <, – – P – 160. *VISA*
Meals 9.95/12.95 and a la carte 17.00/20.00 **t.** 12.95 – 12.50 – **130 rm** 99.00 **st.**, 1 suite – SB.

The Cottages without rest., Moor Rd, LS16 9HH, South : ¼ m. on Cookridge rd ✆ (0113) 284 2754, *Fax (0113) 203 7496,* – P.
closed Christmas – **5 rm** 35.00/48.00.

at Yeadon *Northwest : 8 m. by A 65 on A 658 –* **BT** *– ✉ Leeds.*

Travel Inn, Victoria Av, LS19 7AW, on A 658 ✆ (0113) 250 4284, *Fax (0113) 250 5838* – rm, rest, P. *VISA*.
Meals (grill rest.) – **40 rm** 41.95 **t.**

When looking for a quiet hotel
use the maps found in the introduction
or look for establishments with the sign or .

LEEK *Staffs.* 402 403 404 N 24 – *pop. 18 167.*

Westwood, Newcastle Rd, Wallbridge ✆ (01538) 398385.

1 Market Pl. ✆ (01538) 483741.

London 122 – Derby 30 – Manchester 39 – Stoke-on-Trent 12.

Country Cottage , Back Lane Farm, Winkhill, ST13 7XZ, Southeast : 5 ½ m. by A 523, turning left opposite Little Chef (Ford rd) ✆ (01538) 308273, *mjb6435@netscapeonline.co.uk, Fax (01538) 308098,* <, , – P.
Meals (by arrangement) 13.50 **st.** – **4 rm** 22.50/43.00 **st.**

LEEMING BAR *N. Yorks.* 402 P 21 – *pop. 1 824 – ✉ Northallerton.*

Great North Rd, Bedale ✆ (01677) 424262.

London 235 – Leeds 44 – Middlesbrough 30 – Newcastle upon Tyne 52 – York 37.

Little Holtby, DL7 9LH, Northwest : 2 m. on A 1 (northbound carriageway) ✆ (01609) 748762, *littleholtby@yahoo.co.uk, Fax (01609) 748822,* <, – P.
Meals (by arrangement) (communal dining) 12.50 **s.** – **3 rm** 30.00/50.00 – SB.

LEICESTER *Leicester* 402 403 404 Q 26 *Great Britain G. – pop. 318 518.*

See : *Guildhall★* **BY B** – *Museum and Art Gallery★* **CY M2** – *St. Mary de Castro Church★* **BY A.**

Leicestershire, Evington Lane ✆ (0116) 273 8825 **AY** – *Western Park, Scudamore Rd ✆ (0116) 287 6158* – *Humberstone Heights, Gipsy Lane ✆ (0116) 299 5570* **AX** – *Oadby, Leicester Road Racecourse ✆ (0116) 270 0215* **AY** – *Lutterworth Rd, Blaby ✆ (0116) 278 4804.*

East Midlands Airport, Castle Donington : ✆ (01332) 852852 NW : 22 m. by A 50 – **AX** *– and M1.*

7-9 Every St, Town Hall Sq ✆ (0116) 299 8888.

London 107 – Birmingham 43 – Coventry 24 – Nottingham 26.

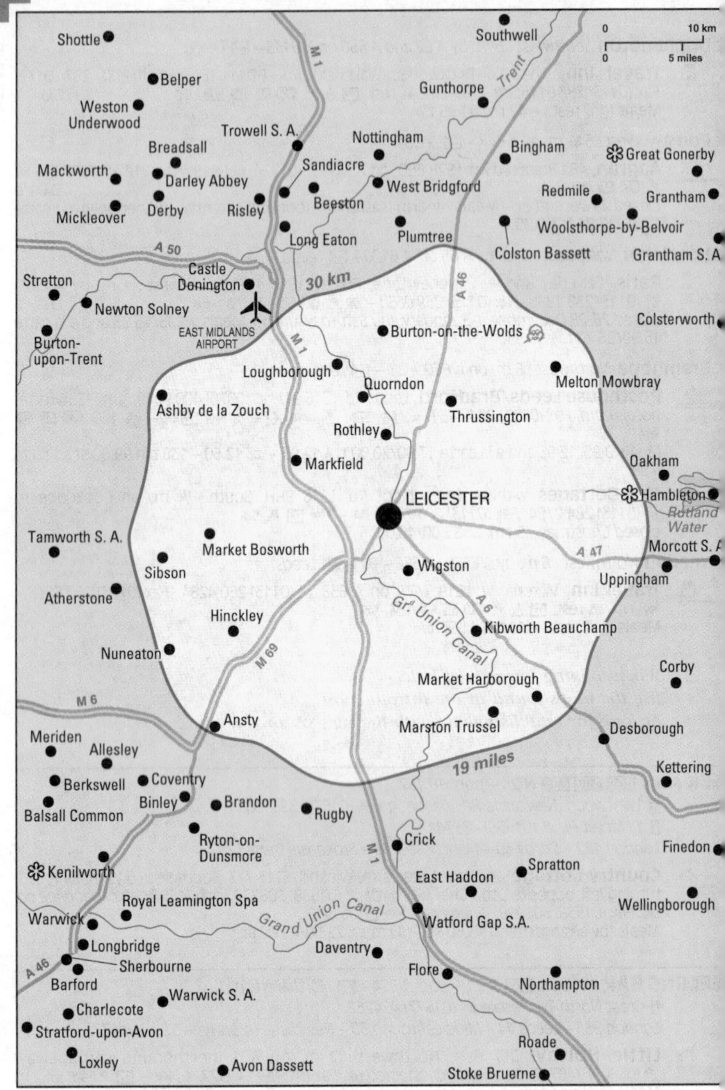

Ramada Jarvis Leicester, 73 Granby St, LE1 6ES, ✆ (0116) 255 559
Fax (0116) 254 4736 – |◙|, ⇔ rm, ▣ ✆ 🅿 – 🏛 500. MC AE VISA CY
Meals (bar lunch Monday-Saturday)/dinner 18.50 and a la carte approx. 18.50 **st.** 🍷 11.75
☕ 9.45 – **103 rm** 115.00/125.00 **st.**, 1 suite – SB.

Holiday Inn Leicester, 129 St Nicholas Circle, LE1 5LX, ✆ (0116) 253 1161, *leicest @basshotel-uknorth.co.uk, Fax (0116) 251 3169,* 🏋, ≘s, 🏊 – |◙|, ⇔ rm, ▤ ▣ ✆ ♿ 🅿
🏛 250. MC AE ⓓ VISA JCB BY
Vermont : **Meals** (buffet lunch)/dinner 12.95/18.95 and a la carte 16.50/26.75 **st.** 🍷 11.00
☕ 13.50 – **187 rm** 145.00/155.00 **st.**, 1 suite.

LEICESTER
BUILT UP AREA

quith Way .... AY 2
lgrave Road .... AX 4
aunstone Avenue .... AY 10
aunstone Lane East .... AY 13
aunstone Way .... AY 14
Checketts Road .... AX 17
Fosse Road North .... AX 21
Fullhurst Avenue .... AY 23
Glenfrith Way .... AX 24
Henley Road .... AX 29
Humberstone Road .... AX 34
King Richards Road .... AY 37
Knighton Road .... AY 38
Loughborough Road .... AX 40
Marfitt Street .... AX 41
Middleton Street .... AY 44
Raw Dykes Road .... AY 62
Stoughton Road .... AY 66
Upperton Road .... AY 68
Walnut Street .... AY 69
Wigston Lane .... AY 75
Woodville Road .... AY 76
Wyngate Drive .... AY 78

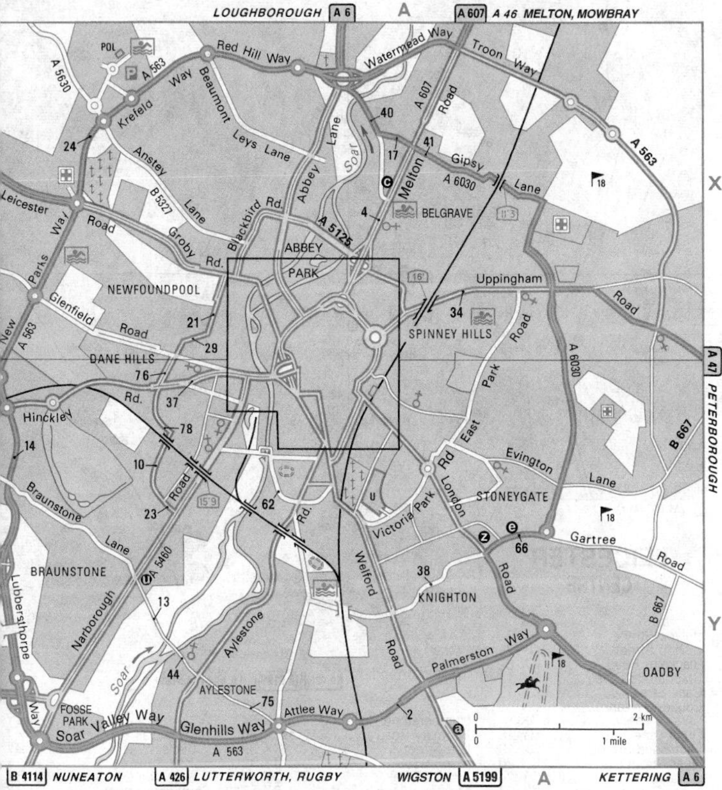

Belmont House, De Montfort St, LE1 7GR, (0116) 254 4773, *info@belmonthotel.co.uk, Fax (0116) 247 0804* – rm, P – 160. VISA JCB CY c
closed 25-26 December – ***Cherry's*:** Meals *(closed lunch Saturday and Bank Holidays)* a la carte 20.65/30.45 **t.** 11.95 – 9.50 – **78 rm** 95.00/120.00 **st.** – SB.

Holiday Inn Leicester West, Braunstone Lane East, LE3 2FW, Southwest : 2 m. on A 5460 (0870) 400 9051, *gm1124@forte-hotels.com, Fax (0116) 282 3623* – rest, TV P – 80. VISA AY u
Meals (bar lunch Saturday) 10.00/12.00 (lunch) and dinner a la carte 17.35/28.35 **t.** – 12.95 – **172 rm** 110.00 **st.** – SB.

The Regency, 360 London Rd, LE2 2PL, Southeast : 2 m. on A 6 (0116) 270 9634, *info@the-regency-hotel.com, Fax (0116) 270 1375* – rest, TV P. VISA AY z
Meals *(closed Saturday lunch)* 10.95/14.95 and a la carte 12.95/22.75 **t.** 8.95 – **32 rm** 46.00/67.00 **t.**

Comfort, 23-25 Loughborough Rd, LE4 5LJ, (0116) 268 2626, *reservations@comforthotelleicester.com, Fax (0116) 268 2641* – TV P – 90. VISA JCB AX c
Meals – (see ***Kabalou's*** below) – **22 rm** 75.00/110.00 **st.** – SB.

Premier Lodge, Glen Rise, Oadby, LE2 4RG, Southeast : 5 ¾ m. on A 6 (0870) 7001418, *Fax (0870) 7001419* – rm, TV P. VISA.
Meals (grill rest.) a la carte approx. 12.50 **t.** 7.80 – **30 rm** 46.95 **t.**

(A 6)
B
A 6
C
A 607
300 m
300 yards
ABBEY PARK
Dysart Way
A 5125
Wood Gate
A 50
Frog Island
N. Gate St.
St. Margaret's Way
Belgrave Rd
Montreal Rd
Way
Burleys
Abbey St.
Gate
Wharf St.
St. Matthew's Way
A 594
Sanvey Gate
Vaughan Way
Church Gate
Belgrave Gate
Charles
Highcross
St. Peter's L
THE SHIRES
High Street
Tudor
Road
A 47
X
Y
St. George's Way
Street
POL St.
Granby St.
LONDON ROAD
A 5460
Newarke
St.
Oxford St.
Welford
New Walk
Conduit Street
London Road
The Gateway
Street
Regent
Way
St.
Montfort
De
Road
Waterloo
Jarrom
Rd
(M 69) (M 1)
A 426
A 5199
A 594
(A 5199)

LEICESTER
CENTRE

Belgrave Road .... **CX**
Belvoir Street .... **CY** 5
Bishop Street .... **CY** 7
Blackbird Road .... **BX** 8
Braunstone Gate .... **BY** 12
Cank Street .... **BCY** 15
Causeway Lane .... **BX** 16
Church Gate .... **BCX**
Duns Lane .... **BY** 18
East Bond Street ..... **BCX** 19
Fleet Street .... **CX** 20
Gallowtree Gate .... **CY** 24
Great Central Street .... **BX** 27
Hinckley Road .... **BY** 30
High Street .... **BXY**
Horsefair Street .... **CY** 31
Humberstone Gate ..... **CX** 33
Humberstone Road .... **CX** 34
Infirmary Road .... **BCY** 36
Lee Street .... **CX** 39
Market Street .... **CY** 42
Market (The) .... **CY** 43
Millstone Lane .... **BY** 45
Narborough Road North .... **BY** 46
Newarke (The) .... **BY** 47
Peacock Lane .... **BY** 50
St. Augustine Road .... **BY** 51
St. Martin's .... **BY**
St. Nicholas Circle .... **BY**
Shires (The) Shopping Centre .... **BX**
Southgate Street .... **BY**
Sparkenhoe Street .... **CY**
Swain Street .... **CY**
Welford Place .... **CY**
Western Boulevard .... **BY**

Premier Lodge, Leicester Rd, Glenfield, LE3 8HB, Northwest : 3 ½ m. on A ☎ (0870) 7001416, *Fax (0870) 7001417*, – rm, 𝐏. MO AE VISA. **AX**
Meals (grill rest.) a la carte approx. 12.50 **t.** 7.80 – **43 rm** 46.95 **t.**

Travel Inn, Meridian Business Park, Meridian Way, Braunstone, LE3 2LW, Southwes 3 ¾ m. by A 47 off A 563 ☎ (0116) 289 0945, *Fax (0116) 282 7486*, – rm, rest, 𝐏. MO AE VISA **AY**
Meals (grill rest.) – **51 rm** 41.95 **t.**

Watsons, 5-9 Upper Brown St, LE1 5TE, ☎ (0116) 222 7770, *Fax (0116) 222 77.* « Converted Victorian cotton mill » – MO AE VISA **BY**
closed 24 December-5 January, Sunday and Bank Holidays – **Meals** 11. (lunch) and a la carte 16.75/25.00 **t.** 9.00.

Kabalou's (at Comfort H.), 23-25 Loughborough Rd, LE4 5LJ, ☎ (0116) 268 262 *Fax (0116) 268 2641* – 𝐏. MO AE VISA JCB **AX**
Meals - Indian - 12.00/25.00 and a la carte 11.85/19.30 **st.** 9.50.

XX **The Tiffin,** 1 De Montfort St, LE1 7GE, ✆ (0116) 247 0420, *pravin@the-tiffin.co.uk, Fax (0116) 255 3737* – ▤. MC AE ◑ VISA CY r
Meals - Indian - (booking essential) 7.00/18.50 and a la carte 17.95/27.45 **t.** 15.00.

XX **The Opera House,** 10-12 Guildhall Lane, LE1 5FQ, ✆ (0116) 223 6666, *Fax (0116) 223 4704,* « 17C » – MC VISA BY a
closed 25 December, 1 January and Sunday – **Meals** 11.25 (lunch) and a la carte 22.50/27.75 **t.** 10.95.

XX **The Case,** 4-6 Hotel St, St Martin's, LE1 5AW, ✆ (0116) 251 7675, *Fax (0116) 251 7675* – MC AE ◑ VISA JCB BY n
closed 24-27 December, Sunday and Bank Holidays – **Meals** a la carte 12.15/26.70 **t.** 8.95.

X **Truffles,** 13 Allandale Rd, Stoneygate, LE2 2DA, ✆ (0116) 244 8235, *andrew@trufflesuk.com, Fax (0116) 274 5516* – MC AE VISA AY e
closed Sunday-Monday – **Meals** 13.95/15.00 and a la carte 20.50/24.00 **t.** 11.00.

Rothley *North : 5 m. by A 6* – **AX** – *on B 5328* – ✉ *Leicester.*

Limes, 35 Mountsorrel Lane, LE7 7PS, ✆ (0116) 230 2531 – ⇔ rest, ▤ TV P. MC AE ◑ VISA JCB. ⚘
closed 23 December-2 January – **Meals** (residents only) (dinner only) 11.00/17.00 and a la carte approx. 11.50 **st.** – **11 rm** ☕ 42.50/55.00 **st.**

Wigston *Southeast : 3¼ m. on A 50* – ✉ *Leicester.*

Leicester Stage H., 299 Leicester Rd, LE18 1JW, ✆ (0116) 288 6161, *sales@stagehotel.co.uk, Fax (0116) 281 1874,* Ꮇ, ≘s, ▢ – ⇔ rm, ▤ rest, TV P – 🏰 500. MC AE ◑ VISA. ⚘ AY a
Meals 9.95/17.95 and a la carte 22.00/30.00 **st.** 11.95 – **75 rm** ☕ 85.00/105.00 **st.** – SB.

Blaby *South : 4¼ m. on A 426* – **AY** – ✉ *Leicester.*

Time Out, Enderby Rd, LE8 4GD, ✆ (01162) 787898, *reservations@corushotels.com, Fax (01162) 781974,* Ꮇ, ≘s, ▢ – ⇔ rm, ▤ rest, TV ✆ & P – 🏰 70. MC AE ◑ VISA JCB
Meals *(closed Saturday lunch)* 11.95/19.95 and a la carte 21.50/25.50 **st.** 11.50 – ☕ 11.50 – **48 rm** 99.00/130.00 **st.** – SB.

Leicester Forest East *West : 3½ m. on A 47* – **AY** – ✉ *Leicester.*

Red Cow, Hinckley Rd, LE3 3PG, ✆ (0116) 238 7878, *alanjudd@msn.com, Fax (0116) 238 6539* – ⇔ rm, TV & P. MC AE ◑ VISA. ⚘
Meals (grill rest.) a la carte 13.90/21.95 **t.** 6.95 – ☕ 4.95 – **31 rm** 39.50 **t.**

Travel Inn, Hinckley Rd, LE3 3GD, ✆ (0116) 239 4677, *Fax (0116) 239 3429* – ⇔, ▤ rest, TV & P. MC AE ◑ VISA. ⚘
Meals (grill rest.) – **40 rm** 41.95 **t.**

EICESTER FOREST EAST *Leics.* 402 403 404 Q 26 – *see Leicester.*

EIGH *Dorset* 403 404 M 31 – *see Sherborne.*

EIGH DELAMERE SERVICE AREA *Wilts.* 403 404 N 29 – ✉ *Chippenham.*

Travelodge, SN14 6LB, M 4 between junctions 18 and 17 (eastbound carriageway) ✆ (01666) 837691, *Fax (01666) 837112* – ⇔ rm, TV & P. MC AE ◑ VISA JCB. ⚘
Meals (grill rest.) – **70 rm** 49.95 **t.**

EIGH-ON-SEA *Essex* 404 W 29.

London 37 – Brighton 85 – Dover 86 – Ipswich 57.

XX **Boatyard,** 8-13 High St, SS9 2EN, ✆ (01702) 475588, *Fax (01702) 475588,* ≤, 🏛, « Harbourside setting » – ⚓ ▤ P. MC VISA
closed 4 days Christmas, Monday and dinner Sunday – **Meals** 14.95/19.95 (lunch) and dinner a la carte 26.00/45.00 **t.** 10.00.

EINTWARDINE *Shrops.* 403 L 26 – ✉ *Craven Arms.*

London 156 – Birmingham 55 – Hereford 24 – Worcester 40.

Upper Buckton Farm ⛰, Buckton, SY7 0JU, West : 2 m. by A 4113 and Buckton rd ✆ (01547) 540634, *Fax (01547) 540634,* ≤, « Working farm », 🌳, 🐑 – ⇔ P. ⚘
Meals (by arrangement) 20.00 **s.** 9.00 – **3 rm** ☕ 40.00/70.00.

The Guide is updated annually so renew your Guide every year.

LENHAM *Kent* 404 W 30 – *pop. 2 167* – ✉ *Maidstone.*
London 45 – Folkestone 28 – Maidstone 9.

Chilston Park, Sandway, ME17 2BE, South : 1 ¾ m. off Broughton Malherbe ✆ (01622) 859803, *chilstonpark@arcadianhotels.co.uk, Fax (01622) 858588,* ≤, « Part 1 mansion, antiques », – 110.
Meals *(closed Saturday lunch)* 21.00/34.95 and a la carte 48.00/52.00 **t.** 18.00 – 12.9
49 rm 115.00/165.00 **t.**, 4 suites – SB.

Lime Tree, 8-10 The Limes, The Square, ME17 2PQ, ✆ (01622) 859509, *Fax (01622) 850*
Meals 18.95/27.50 and a la carte 32.95/40.75 **t.** 14.00.

LEOMINSTER *Herefordshire* 403 L 27 *Great Britain G.* – *pop. 9 543.*
Env. : *Berrington Hall★ AC, N : 3 m. by A 49.*
Ford Bridge ✆ (01568) 612863.
1 Corn Sq ✆ (01568) 616460.
London 141 – Birmingham 47 – Hereford 13 – Worcester 26.

at Kimbolton *Northeast : 3 m. by A 49 on A 4112.*

Lower Bache House, HR6 0ER, East : 1 ¾ m. by A 4112 ✆ (01568) 750304, *les wiles@care4free.net,* « 17C farmhouse »,
Meals (by arrangement) 21.50 **st.** 8.80 – **4 rm** 39.50/59.00 **st.** – SB.

at Leysters *Northeast : 5 m. by A 49 on A 4112* – ✉ *Leominster.*

The Hills Farm, HR6 0HP, ✆ (01568) 750205, *conolly@bigwig.n Fax (01568) 750306,* ≤, « Working farm »,
March-October except 3 weeks June – **Meals** (by arrangement) 19.00 **s.** – **5 rm** 48.0 62.00.

Le Grand Londres (GREATER LONDON) est composé de la City et de 32 arrondissements administratifs (Borough) eux-mêmes divisés en quartiers ou en villages ayant conservé leur caractère propre (Area).

LEWDOWN *Devon* 403 H 32 *The West Country G.*
Env. : *Lydford★★, E : 4 m.*
Exc. : *Launceston★ - Castle★ (≤★) St Mary Magdalene★, W : 8 m. by A 30 and A 388.*
London 238 – Exeter 37 – Plymouth 29.

Lewtrenchard Manor, EX20 4PN, South : ¾ m. by Lewtrenchard ✆ (01566) 783256, *etj@lewtrenchard.co.uk, Fax (01566) 783332,* ≤, « 17C manor hou and gardens », – rest, – 50.
Meals (booking essential to non-residents) 32.00 **t.** 12.00 – **9 rm** 95.00/180.00 **t.** – S

LEWES *E. Sussex* 404 U 31 *Great Britain G.* – *pop. 15 376.*
See : *Town★ (High St.★, Keere St.★) – Castle (≤★) AC.*
Exc. : *Sheffield Park Garden★ AC, N : 9½ m. by A 275.*
Chapel Hill ✆ (01273) 473245.
187 High St ✆ (01273) 483448.
London 53 – Brighton 8 – Hastings 29 – Maidstone 43.

Shelleys, High St, BN7 1XS, ✆ (01273) 472361, *info@shelleys-hotel-lewes.co Fax (01273) 483152,* « Part Georgian former inn, antiques », – 50.
Meals 28.50 (dinner) and a la carte 20.00/35.00 **t.** 14.50 – 13.50 – **18 rm** 130.0 170.00 **t.**, 1 suite – SB.

Millers without rest., 134 High St, BN7 1XS, ✆ (01273) 475631, *millers134@aol.co Fax (01273) 486226,*
closed 4-5 November and 20 December-5 January – **3 rm** 54.00/60.00 **s.**

at East Chiltington *Northwest : 5½ m. by A 275 and B 2116 off Novington Lane* – ✉ *Lewes.*

Jolly Sportsman, Chapel Lane, BN7 3BA, ✆ (01273) 890400, *jollysportsman@mistral. uk, Fax (01273) 890400,*
closed 25-28 December, Sunday dinner and Monday except lunch Bank Holidays – **Me** a la carte 18.60/26.25 **t.** 9.85.

EYBURN *N. Yorks.* 402 O 21 – *pop. 2 074.*

4 Central Chambers, Market Pl ☎ (01969) 623069.

London 251 – Darlington 25 – Kendal 43 – Leeds 53 – York 49.

Greenhills without rest., 5 Middleham Rd, DL8 5EY, ☎ (01969) 623859, *val.pringle@freenet.co.uk* – TV P.
closed Christmas and New Year – **3 rm** 25.00/45.00.

Sandpiper Inn, Market Pl, DL8 5AT, ☎ (01969) 622206, *hsandpiper.99@aol.com, Fax (01969) 625367,* « Part 16C », – P. MC VISA
closed Monday except Bank Holidays – **Meals** (restricted lunch) a la carte 15.85/24.00 **t.** 9.50.

Constable Burton *East : 3½ m. on A 684 – ✉ Leyburn.*

Park Gate House, Constable Burton, DL8 5RG, East : 3½ m. on A 684 ☎ (01677) 450466, *Fax (01677) 450466,* – TV P. MC VISA.
Meals (by arrangement) 12.50 **st.** 9.00 – **4 rm** 35.00/65.00 **st.** – SB.

Wyvill Arms with rm, DL8 5LH, ☎ (01677) 450581 – TV P. MC AE VISA
Meals - Steak specialities - a la carte 14.85/26.85 **st.** 14.95 – **3 rm** 34.00/56.00 **st.** – SB.

EYSTERS *Herefordshire* 403 404 M 27 – *see Leominster.*

CHFIELD *Staffs.* 402 403 404 O 25 *Great Britain G.* – *pop. 28 666.*

See : *City★ - Cathedral★★ AC.*

18, 9 *Seedy Mill, Elmhurst ☎ (01543) 417333.*

Donegal House, Bore St ☎ (01543) 252109.

London 128 – Birmingham 16 – Derby 23 – Stoke-on-Trent 30.

Little Barrow, Beacon St, WS13 7AR, ☎ (01543) 414500, *hinecjp@netscape.online.co.uk, Fax (01543) 415734* – TV P – 80. MC AE VISA JCB.
closed 24-27 December – **Meals** 8.00/17.00 and a la carte 14.45/25.50 **st.** 8.15 – **24 rm** 65.00/80.00 **st.** – SB.

Chandlers Grande Brasserie, Corn Exchange, Conduit St, WS13 6JU, ☎ (01543) 416688, *Fax (01543) 417887* – MC AE VISA JCB
Meals 11.50/13.50 and a la carte 16.35/21.85 **st.** 9.95.

Olive Tree, 34 Tamworth St, WS13 6JJ, ☎ (01543) 263363, *Fax (0121) 353 5009* – MC AE VISA
closed 25 December, Sunday and lunch Monday-Wednesday – **Meals** 11.95 (dinner) and a la carte 14.40/20.95 **t.** 9.95.

Thrales, 40-44 Tamworth St, WS13 6JJ, (corner of Backcester Lane) ☎ (01543) 255091, *Fax (01543) 415352* – MC AE VISA
closed 26 December-2 January, Sunday dinner and Bank Holiday Mondays – **Meals** 10.95/13.50 and a la carte 16.75/28.25 **t.** 10.95.

CKFOLD *W. Sussex – see Petworth.*

FTON *Devon* 403 H 32 *The West Country G.* – *pop. 964.*

Env. : *Launceston★ – Castle★ (≤★) St Mary Magdalene★, W : 4½ m. by A 30 and A 388.*

London 238 – Bude 24 – Exeter 37 – Launceston 4 – Plymouth 26.

Arundell Arms, Fore St, PL16 0AA, ☎ (01566) 784666, *reservations@arundellarms.com, Fax (01566) 784494,* – rest, TV P – 100. MC AE VISA
closed 3 days Christmas – **Meals** – (see ***The Restaurant*** below) – **27 rm** 48.00/150.00 **st.** – SB.

The Restaurant (at Arundell Arms H.), Fore St, PL16 0AA, ☎ (01566) 784666, *arundellarms@btinternet.com, Fax (01566) 784494* – P. MC AE VISA
Meals 23.00/37.00 **st.** 15.00.

MPLEY STOKE (LOWER) *Bath & North East Somerset* 403 404 N 29 – *see Bath.*

Bitte beachten Sie die Geschwindigkeitsbeschränkungen in Großbritannien
- 60 mph (= 96 km/h) außerhalb geschlossener Ortschaften
- 70 mph (= 112 km/h) auf Straßen mit getrennten Fahrbahnen und Autobahnen.

ENGLAND

LINCOLN *Lincs.* **402** **404** S 24 *Great Britain G. – pop. 80 281.*

See : *City★★ – Cathedral and Precincts★★★* **AC Y** *– High Bridge★★* **Z 9** *– Usher Gallery★* **YZ M1** *– Jew's House★* **Y** *– Castle★* **AC Y.**

Env. : *Doddington Hall★* **AC**, *W : 6 m. by B 1003 –* **Z** *– and B 1190.*

Exc. : *Gainsborough Old Hall★* **AC**, *NW : 19 m. by A 57 –* **Z** *– and A 156.*

18 *Carholme, Carholme Rd ☎ (01522) 523725.*

Humberside Airport : ☎ (01652) 688456, N : 32 m. by A 15 – **Y** *– M 180 and A 18.*

9 Castle Sq ☎ (01522) 529828.

London 140 – Bradford 81 – Cambridge 94 – Kingston-upon-Hull 44 – Leeds 73 – Leices 53 – Norwich 104 – Nottingham 38 – Sheffield 48 – York 82.

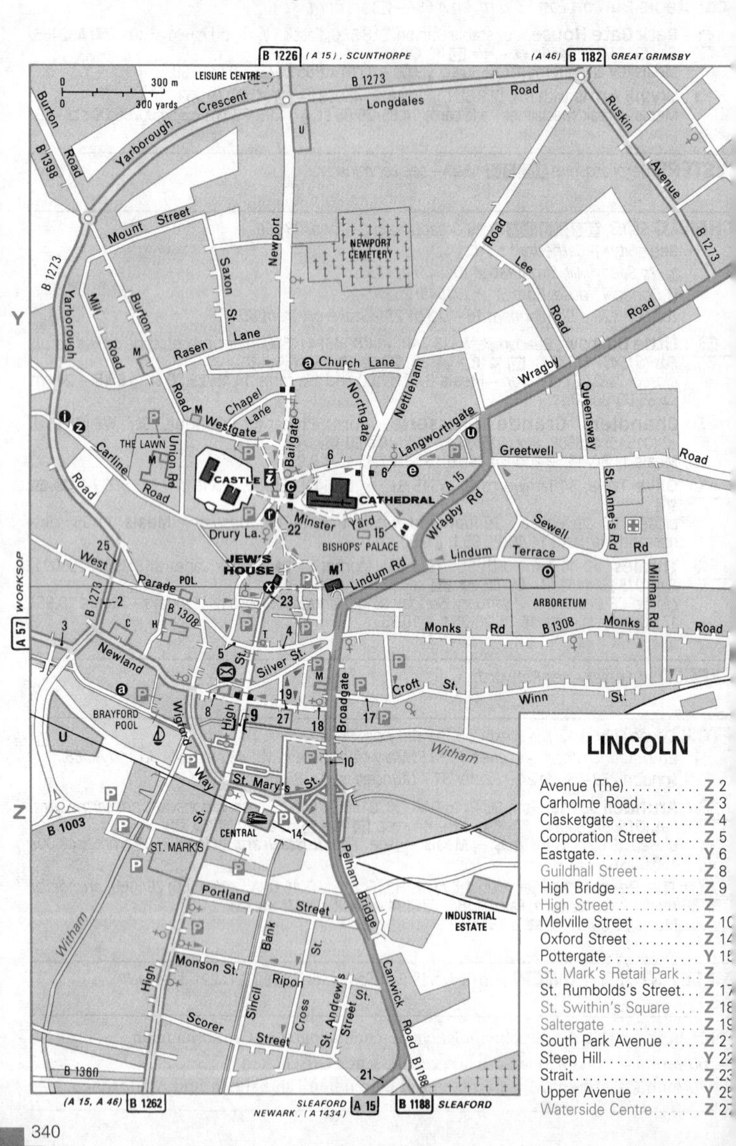

White Hart, Bailgate, LN1 3AR, ☎ (01522) 526222, *heritagehotels-lincoln.thewhitehart @fortehotels.com, Fax (01522) 531798,* « Antique furniture » – ⛅, ⚓ ▢ ⇔ – 🏨 70. MC AE ⓓ VISA JCB Y c
Orangery Bistro : **Meals** a la carte 21.10/30.35 **t.** 10.25 – ⊡ 11.25 – **39 rm** 115.00/136.00 **t.**, 9 suites – SB.

Courtyard by Marriott, Brayford Wharf North, LN1 1YW, ☎ (01522) 544244, *Fax (01522) 560805,* – ⛅, ⚓ rm, ▤ ▢ ✆ ♿ P – 🏨 30. MC AE ⓓ VISA. ✂ Z a
Meals a la carte 14.20/23.15 **t.** – ⊡ 10.00 – **95 rm** 69.00 **t.** – SB.

Bentley, Newark Rd, South Hykeham, LN6 9NH, Southwest : 5 ¾ m. by A 15 on B 1434 at junction with A 46 ☎ (01522) 878000, *info@thebentleyhotel.uk.com, Fax (01522) 878001,* – ⛅ ⚓, ▤ rest, ▢ ✆ ♿ P – 🏨 325. MC AE ⓓ VISA. ✂
Meals (carvery lunch)/dinner 7.95/16.25 and dinner a la carte 18.25/33.45 **st.** 7.95 – **53 rm** ⊡ 65.00/100.00 **st.** – SB.

Hillcrest, 15 Lindum Terr, LN2 5RT, ☎ (01522) 510182, *reservations@hillcrest-hotel.com, Fax (01522) 510182,* ≤, – ⚓ ▢ P. MC AE VISA JCB Y o
closed 23 December-6 January – **Meals** *(closed Sunday)* (bar lunch)/dinner 17.00 and a la carte 18.90/23.20 **t.** 10.50 – **15 rm** ⊡ 54.00/81.00 **t.** – SB.

D'Isney Place without rest., Eastgate, LN2 4AA, ☎ (01522) 538881, *info@disneyplace hotel.co.uk, Fax (01522) 511321,* – ⚓ ▢. MC AE ⓓ VISA JCB Y e
17 rm ⊡ 63.50/83.00 **t.**

Ibis without rest., off Whisby Rd, LN6 3QZ, Southwest : 6 m. by A 15, A 1434 and B 1190 on A 46 ☎ (01522) 698333, *h3161@accor-hotels.com, Fax (01522) 698444* – ⛅ ⚓ ▢ ✆ ♿ P – 🏨 25. MC AE ⓓ VISA
86 rm 39.95 **st.**

Damons Motel, 997 Doddington Rd, LN6 3SE, Southwest : 4 ¼ m. by A 15 and A 1434 on B 1190 at junction with A 46 ☎ (01522) 887733, *Fax (01522) 887734,* – ⚓ rm, ▢ ♿ P. MC AE ⓓ VISA. ✂
Meals (grill rest.) (booking essential) a la carte 12.85/21.10 **t.** – ⊡ 5.75 – **47 rm** 43.50/46.50 **t.**

Travel Inn, Lincoln Rd, Canwick Hill, LN4 2RF, Southeast : 1 ¾ m. by B 1188 on B 1131 ☎ (01522) 525216, *Fax (01522) 542521,* – ⚓ rm, ▢ ♿ P. MC AE ⓓ VISA. ✂
Meals (grill rest.) – **40 rm** 41.95 **t.**

Travelodge, Thorpe on the Hill, LN6 9AJ, Southwest : 6 m. by A 15 and A 1434 at junction with A 46 ☎ (01522) 697213, *Fax (01522) 697213* – ⚓ rm, ▢ ♿ P. MC AE ⓓ VISA. ✂
Meals (grill rest.) – **32 rm** 42.95 **t.**

Minster Lodge without rest., 3 Church Lane, LN2 1QJ, ☎ (01522) 513220, *minsterlodge @cs.com, Fax (01522) 513220* – ⚓ ▢ P. MC AE VISA. ✂ Y a
6 rm ⊡ 65.00/85.00 **st.**

St Clements Lodge without rest., 21 Langworthgate, LN2 2AD, ☎ (01522) 521532, *Fax (01522) 521532* – ⚓ ▢ P Y u
3 rm ⊡ 35.00/50.00.

Carline without rest., 1-3 Carline Rd, LN1 1HL, ☎ (01522) 530422, *Fax (01522) 530422* – ⚓ ▢ P. ✂ Y i
closed Christmas and New Year – **8 rm** ⊡ 30.00/44.00 **t.**

Tennyson without rest., 7 South Park, LN5 8EN, South : 1 ¼ m. on A 15 ☎ (01522) 521624, *tennyson.hotel@virgin.net, Fax (01522) 521355* – ▢ P. MC VISA. ✂
closed 24-27 December – **8 rm** ⊡ 33.00/45.00 **st.**

Abbottsford House without rest., 5 Yarborough Terr, LN1 1HN, ☎ (01522) 826696, *Fax (01522) 826696* – ⚓ ▢ P. ✂ Y z
Easter-20 December – **3 rm** ⊡ 30.00/44.00.

Jew's House, Jew's House, 15 The Strait, LN2 1JD, ☎ (01522) 524851, *Fax (01522) 520084,* « 12C town house » – ⚓. MC AE ⓓ VISA YZ x
closed Sunday dinner – **Meals** 9.00/32.50 and a la carte approx. 15.70 **st.** 10.50.

Wig and Mitre, First Floor, 30-32 Steep Hill, LN2 1TL, ☎ (01522) 523705, *reservations @wigandmitre.co.uk, Fax (01522) 532402,* « Part 14C » – MC AE ⓓ VISA JCB Y r
Meals 12.00 (lunch) and a la carte 17.75/25.70 **st.** 14.80.

t Washingborough *East : 3 m. by B 1188 – Z – on B 1190 – ✉ Lincoln.*

Washingborough Hall ⛰, Church Hill, LN4 1BE, ☎ (01522) 790340, *washingborough. hall@btinternet.com, Fax (01522) 792936,* « Georgian manor house », heated, – ⚓ ▢ P – 🏨 40. MC AE VISA JCB
Wedgewood : **Meals** 11.75/18.50 **t.** 10.95 – **14 rm** ⊡ 65.00/99.50 **t.** – SB.

INDALE *Cumbria* 402 L 21 – *see Grange-over-Sands.*

LIPHOOK *Hants.* 404 R 30.
London 51 – Brighton 48 – Guildford 16 – Portsmouth 30 – Southampton 41 – Winchester 30.

Travelodge, GU30 7TT, Southwest : 2 m. by B 2131 on A 3 (northbound carriagewa
(01428) 727619, *Fax (01428) 727619* – rm, rest, TV P. MC AE VISA JCB.
Meals (grill rest.) – **40 rm** 52.95 **t.**

LISKEARD *Cornwall* 403 G 32 *The West Country G. – pop. 7 044.*
See : *Church*★.
Exc. : *Lanhydrock*★★*, W : 11½ m. by A 38 and A 390 – NW : Bodmin Moor*★★ *- St Endellic Church*★★ *- Altarnun Church*★ *- St Breward Church*★ *- Blisland*★ *(church*★*) - Camelford*★ *Cardinham Church*★ *- Michaelstow Church*★ *- St Kew*★ *(church*★*) - St Mabyn Church*★ *– Neot*★ *(Parish Church*★★*) - St Sidwell's, Laneast*★ *- St Teath Church*★ *- St Tudy*★ *– Launceston*★ *– Castle*★ *(<*★*) St Mary Magdalene*★*, NE : 19 m. by A 390 and A 388.*
London 261 – Exeter 59 – Plymouth 19 – Truro 37.

The Well House, St Keyne, PL14 4RN, South : 3 ½ m. by B 3254 on St Keyne Well
(01579) 342001, *enquiries@wellhouse.co.uk, Fax (01579) 343891,* <, « Victorian count house », heated, – rest, TV P. MC VISA JCB
Meals (booking essential to non-residents) 32.50 **t.** – **9 rm** 75.00/160.00 **t.**

Pencubitt Country House, Station Rd, PL14 4EB, South : ½ m. by B 3254 c Lamellion rd (01579) 342694, *claire@penc.co.uk, Fax (01579) 342694,* – rest, P. MC VISA
Meals (booking essential) (dinner only) 25.00 **st.** 12.00 – **5 rm** 39.00/80.00 **st.** – SB.

LITTLE BEDWYN *Newbury* 403 404 P 29 – *see Hungerford.*

LITTLEBOROUGH *Lancs.* 402 404 N 23.
London 225 – Manchester 17 – Huddersfield 17 – Leeds 30 – Liverpool 48.

Hollingworth Lake without rest., 164 Smithybridge Rd, OL15 0DB, Southwest : 1 ½ r on B 6225 (01706) 376583, *karen@hollingworth.masterflash.co.uk,* – TV P. VISA JCB
5 rm 30.00/45.00 **st.**

LITTLEHAMPTON *W. Sussex* 404 S 31 – *pop. 50 408.*
Visitors Centre, Windmill Complex, Coastguard Rd (01903) 713480.
London 64 – Brighton 18 – Portsmouth 31.

Bailiffscourt, Climping St, Climping, BN17 5RW, West : 2 ¾ m. by A 25
(01903) 723511, *bailiffscourt@h.s.hotels.co.uk, Fax (01903) 723107,* « Reconstructed "medieval" house », heated, – rest, TV P – 35. MC AE VISA JCB
Meals 21.50/45.00 and dinner a la carte 28.50/44.00 **t.** 15.50 – **31 rm** 150.00/315.00 – SB.

Travelodge, Worthing Rd, Rustington, BN17 6JN, East : 1 ¼ m. on B 218
(01903) 733150, *Fax (01903) 733150* – rm, TV P. MC AE VISA JCB.
Meals (grill rest.) – **36 rm** 49.95 **t.**

Amberley Court without rest., Crookthorn Lane, Climping, BN17 5SN, West : 1 ¾ m. b B 2187 off A 259 (01903) 725131, *Fax (01903) 732264,* – TV P.
closed 24-26 December – **3 rm** 35.00/60.00 **s.**

LITTLE LANGDALE *Cumbria* 402 K 20 – *see Ambleside.*

LITTLE LANGFORD *Wilts.* – *see Salisbury.*

LITTLE PETHERICK *Cornwall* 403 F 32 – *see Padstow.*

LITTLEPORT *Cambs.* 404 U 26 – *see Ely.*

LITTLE SHELFORD *Cambs.* 404 U 27 – *see Cambridge.*

LITTLE SINGLETON *Lancs.* – *see Blackpool.*

TTLE THETFORD *Cambs. – see Ely.*

TTLE THORNTON *Lancs.* 402 L 22 – *see Blackpool.*

TTLE WALSINGHAM *Norfolk* 404 W 25 – ✉ *Walsingham.*
London 117 – Cambridge 67 – Cromer 21 – Norwich 32.

XX **Old Bakehouse** with rm, 33-35 High St, NR22 6BZ, ✆ (01328) 820454, *chris@cpadley.freeserve.co.uk* – ⇆ TV. MC VISA. ✂
closed 2 weeks January-February, 1 week June and 2 weeks November – **Meals** (Sunday-Thursday set menu only, residents only) (dinner only) 14.45 and a la carte approx. 24.85 ⌂ 10.50 – **3 rm** ☐ 37.00/50.00.

TTLE WEIGHTON *East Riding* 402 S 22 – *see Kingston-upon-Hull.*

TTLEWORTH *Oxon.* 403 404 P 28 – *see Faringdon.*

This Guide is not a comprehensive list of all hotels and restaurants, nor even of all good hotels and restaurants in Great Britain and Ireland.
Since our aim is to be of service to all motorists, we must show establishments in all categories and so we have made a selection of some in each.

LIVERPOOL

Mersey. 402 403 L 23 *Great Britain G. – pop. 481 786.*

London 219 – Birmingham 103 – Leeds 75 – Manchester 35.

TOURIST INFORMATION

Merseyside Welcome Centre, Queens Sq, Roe St ☎ (0151) 709 3285 – Atlantic Pavilion, Albert Dock ☎ (0151) 708 8854.

PRACTICAL INFORMATION

18, 9 Allerton Municipal, Allerton Rd ☎ (0151) 428 1046 – 18 Liverpool Municipal, Ingoe Lane, Kirkby ☎ (0151) 546 5435, BV *– 9 Bowring, Bowring Park, Roby Rd ☎ (0151) 489 1901.*
Mersey Tunnels (toll) AX.

Liverpool Airport : ☎ (0151) 288 4000, SE : 6 m. by A 561 BX – **Terminal** : *Pier Head.*
to Isle of Man (Douglas) (Isle of Man Steam Packet Co. Ltd) (2 h 30 mn/4 h) – to Northern Ireland (Belfast) (Norse Irish Ferries Ltd) 1-2 daily (8 h 30 mn) – to Dublin (Merchant Ferries Ltd) 2 daily (approx. 7 h 45 mn) – to Dublin (P & O Irish Sea) daily (8 h) – to Dublin (Sea Containers Ferries Scotland Ltd) daily (3 h 45 mn).
to Birkenhead and Wallasey (Mersey Ferries) frequent services daily.

SIGHTS

City★ – *Walker Art Gallery★★* DY **M3** – *Liverpool Cathedral★★ (Lady Chapel★)* EZ – *Metropolitan Cathedral of Christ the King★★* EY – *Albert Dock★* CZ *(Merseyside Maritime Museum★ AC* **M2** *- Tate Liverpool★).*

Env. : *Claverton (American Museum★★ AC, Claverton Pumping Station★ AC) E : 3 m. by A 36* Y.

Exc. : *Speke Hall★ AC, SE : 8 m. by A 561* BX.

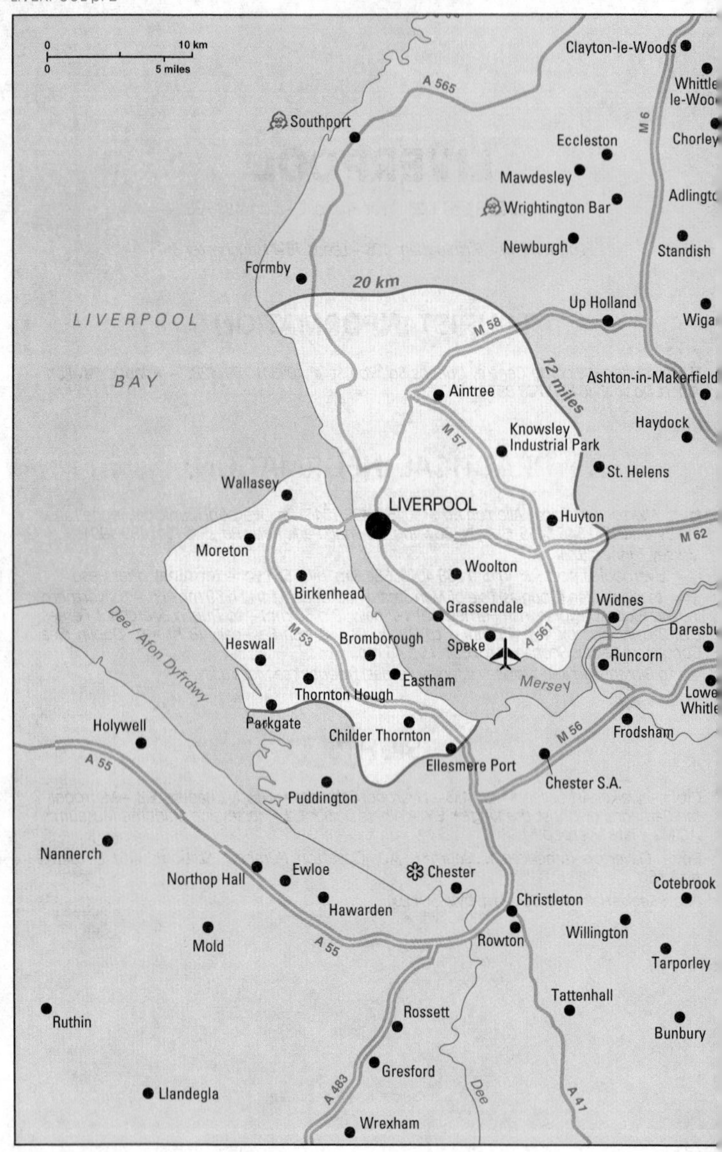

Particularly pleasant hotels and restaurants are shown in the Guide by a red symbol.

Please send us the names of anywhere you have enjoyed your stay.

Your **Michelin Guide** will be even better.

Town plans : Liverpool pp. 4-7

Liverpool Marriott, One Queen Sq, L1 1RH, ☎ (0151) 476 8000, *Fax (0151) 474 5000*, – rm, – 250. MC AE VISA JCB DY e
Olivier's : **Meals** *(closed Saturday lunch and Bank Holidays)* (buffet lunch)/dinner 24.00 and a la carte 16.70/24.00 **st.** 12.95 – 14.45 – **143 rm** 109.00 **st.**, 3 suites – SB.

Crowne Plaza Liverpool, St Nicholas Pl, Princes Dock, Pier Head, L3 1QN, ☎ (0151) 243 8000, *sales@crowneplaza-liverpool.co.uk, Fax (0151) 243 8111*, – rm, – 700. MC AE VISA. CY a
closed 24-26 December – **Meals** *(closed lunch Saturday, Sunday and Bank Holidays)* 12.95/15.95 and a la carte 6.95 – 12.95 – **155 rm** 125.00 **st.**, 4 suites – SB.

Holiday Inn, Lime St, L1 1NQ, ☎ (0151) 709 7090, *sales@holidayinn-liverpool.co.uk, Fax (0151) 709 0137*, – rm, – 500. MC AE VISA. DY z
Signals : **Meals** *(closed Saturday and Sunday lunch)* 9.50/12.95 and a la carte 17.90/26.40 **t.** 10.95 – **138 rm** 90.00/110.00 **t.**, 1 suite.

Liverpool Moat House, Paradise St, L1 8GT, ☎ (0151) 471 9988, *gmliv@queensmoat house.co.uk, Fax (0151) 709 2706*, – rm, – 500. MC AE VISA DZ n
Meals 9.50/16.50 and dinner a la carte 18.15/27.05 **st.** 12.50 – 11.50 – **261 rm** 120.00/140.00 **st.**, 2 suites – SB.

Thistle Liverpool, 30 Chapel St, L3 9RE, ☎ (0151) 227 4444, *liverpool@thistle.co.uk, Fax (0151) 236 3973*, – rm, – 100. MC AE VISA. CY r
Meals *(closed Bank Holidays)* 14.00/19.00 and a la carte 14.90/25.90 **st.** – 10.25 – **223 rm** 136.00/147.00 **st.**, 3 suites – SB.

Devonshire House, 293-297 Edge Lane, L7 9LD, East : 2 ¼ m. on A 5047 ☎ (0151) 264 6600, *Fax (0151) 263 2109*, – rm, – 300. MC AE VISA. BX a
Meals a la carte approx. 18.95 **st.** – **54 rm** 75.00/85.00 **t.** – SB.

Express by Holiday Inn without rest., Britannia Pavilion, Albert Dock, L3 4AD, ☎ (0151) 709 1133, *liverpool@premierhotels.co.uk, Fax (0151) 709 1144*, « Victorian former cotton mill » – – 25. MC AE VISA. CZ r
closed 24-27 December and 31 December-2 January – **117 rm** 65.00 **t.**

Travel Inn, Northern Perimeter Rd, L30 7PT, North : 6 m. by A 59 on A 5036 ☎ (0151) 531 1497, *Fax (0151) 520 1842* – rm, rest, – 50. MC AE VISA.
Meals (grill rest.) – **63 rm** 41.95 **t.**

Travel Inn, Queens Drive, West Derby, L13 0DL, East : 4 m. on A 5058 (Ringroad) ☎ (0151) 228 4724, *Fax (0151) 220 7610* – rm, rest, . MC AE VISA. BV a
Meals (grill rest.) – **84 rm** 41.95 **t.**

60 Hope Street, 60 Hope St, L1 9BZ, ☎ (0151) 707 6060, *info@60hopestreet.com, Fax (0151) 707 6016* – . MC VISA EZ x
closed 25-26 December, Saturday lunch, Sunday and Bank Holidays – **Meals** 10.95/13.95 (lunch) and a la carte 24.95/30.95 **t.** 13.95.

Becher's Brook, 29a Hope St, L1 9BQ, ☎ (0151) 707 0005, *Fax (0151) 708 7011* – . MC AE VISA EZ a
closed 24 December-2 January, Sunday, Saturday lunch and Bank Holidays – **Meals** a la carte 12.90/50.00 **t.** 12.95.

Simply Heathcotes, Beetham Plaza, 25 The Strand, L2 0XL, ☎ (0151) 236 3536, *liverpool @simplyheathcotes.co.uk, Fax (0151) 236 3534* – . MC AE VISA CY s
closed 25-26 December and Bank Holiday Mondays – **Meals** 15.50 (lunch) and a la carte 20.50/26.50 **t.** 11.50.

Ziba, 15-19 Berry St, L1 9DF, ☎ (0151) 708 8870, *Fax (0151) 707 9926* – MC AE VISA EZ s
closed 25-26 and 31 December, 1 January, Sunday, lunch Saturday and Bank Holidays – **Meals** 13.00/16.50 and a la carte 16.50/29.50 **t.** 11.00.

Mister M's, 6 Atlantic Pavilion, Albert Dock, L3 4AA, ☎ (0151) 707 2202, *mikemcdonald@ misterms.freeserve.co.uk, Fax (0151) 708 8769*, – MC AE VISA JCB CZ c
closed lunch Monday and Sunday, first 2 weeks January and 25 December – **Meals** - Seafood - 9.95/14.95 (lunch) and a la carte 25.85/53.90 **st.** 9.95.

at Aintree *North : 6 m. by A 59* – **BV** – ✉ *Liverpool.*

Travel Inn, 1 Ormskirk Rd, L9 5AS, on A 59 ☎ (0151) 524 2885, *Fax (0151) 525 8696* – rm, rest, . MC AE VISA JCB. BV e
Meals (grill rest.) – **40 rm** 41.95 **t.**

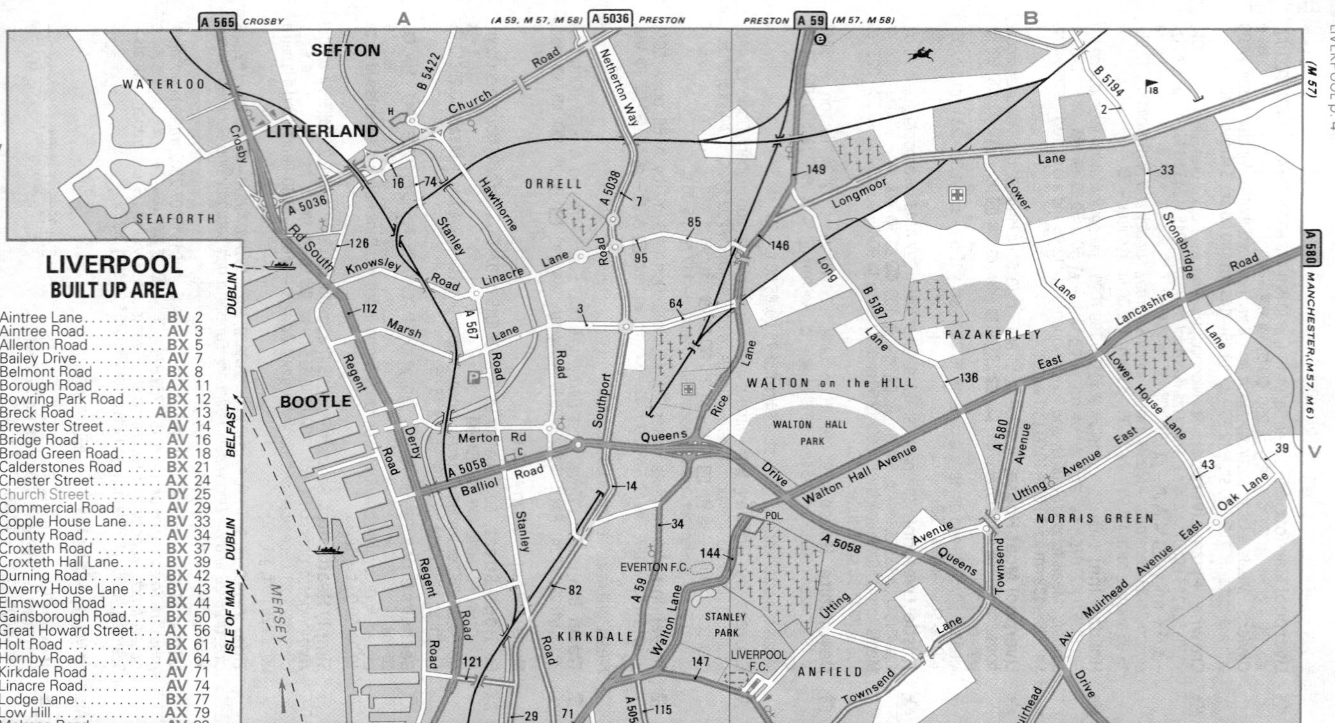

LIVERPOOL
BUILT UP AREA

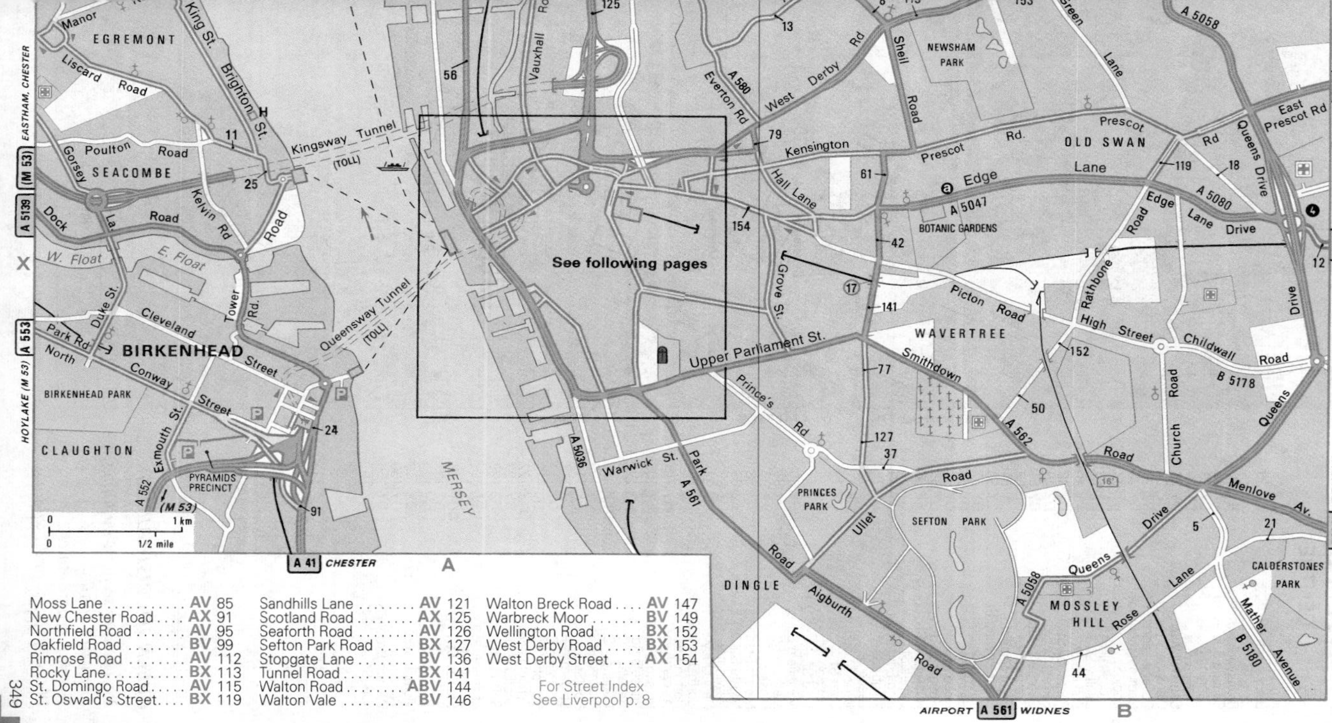

Moss Lane	AV	85
New Chester Road	AX	91
Northfield Road	AV	95
Oakfield Road	BV	99
Rimrose Road	AV	112
Rocky Lane	BX	113
St. Domingo Road	AV	115
St. Oswald's Street	BX	119
Sandhills Lane	AV	121
Scotland Road	AX	125
Seaforth Road	AV	126
Sefton Park Road	BX	127
Stopgate Lane	BV	136
Tunnel Road	BX	141
Walton Road	ABV	144
Walton Vale	BV	146
Walton Breck Road	AV	147
Warbreck Moor	BV	149
Wellington Road	BX	152
West Derby Road	BX	153
West Derby Street	AX	154

For Street Index
See Liverpool p. 8

LIVERPOOL
CENTRE

Argyle St. . . . . DZ 6
Blackburne Pl. . . . . EZ 10
Bold St. DZ
Brunswick Rd. . . . . EY 19
Canada Boulevard . . . . CYZ 22
Canning Pl. . . . . CZ 23
Church St. . . . . DY
Churchill Way. . . . . DY 26
Clarence St. . . . . EYZ 27
College Lane . . . . DZ 28
Commutation Row . . . . DY 30
Cook St. . . . . CY 32
Crosshall St. . . . . DY 36
Daulby St. . . . . EY 40
Erskine St. . . . . EY 45
Fontenoy St. . . . . DY 48
Forrest St. . . . . DZ 49
George's Dock Gate . . . . CY 51
Grafton St. . . . . DZ 53
Great Charlotte St. . . . . DY 54
Great Howard St. . . . . CY 56
Hatton Garden . . . . DY 57
Haymarket . . . . DY 58
Hood St. . . . . DY 62
Houghton St. . . . . DY 65
Huskisson St. . . . . EZ 66
James St. . . . . CY 68
King Edward St. . . . . CY 69
Knight St. . . . . EZ 72
Leece St. . . . . EZ 73
Lime St. . . . . DY
Liver St. . . . . CZ 76
London Rd. . . . . DEY
Lord St. . . . . CDY
Mansfield St. . . . . DEY 80
Mathew St. . . . . CDY 81
Moss St. . . . . EY 86
Mount St. . . . . EZ 88
Myrtle St. . . . . EZ 89
Newington . . . . DZ 92
New Quay . . . . CY 93
North John St. . . . . CY 96
Norton St. . . . . EY 97
Parker St. . . . . DY 103
Prescot St. . . . . EY 105
Prince's Rd . . . . EZ 107
Ranelagh St. . . . . DY 108
Renshaw St. . . . . DEZ
Richmond St. . . . . DY 109
Roe St. DY 114
St. James Pl. . . . . EZ 117
St. Johns Centre . . . . DY
St. John's Lane . . . . DY 118
School Lane. . . . . DYZ 122
Scotland Pl. . . . . DY 123
Sefton St. . . . . DZ 129
Seymour St. . . . . EY 130
Skelhorne St. . . . . DY 133
Stanley St. . . . . CDY 135
Suffolk St. . . . . DZ 137
Tarleton St. . . . . DY 139
Victoria St. . . . . DY 143
Water St. . . . . CY 150
William Brown St. . . . . DY 156
York St. . . . . DZ 157

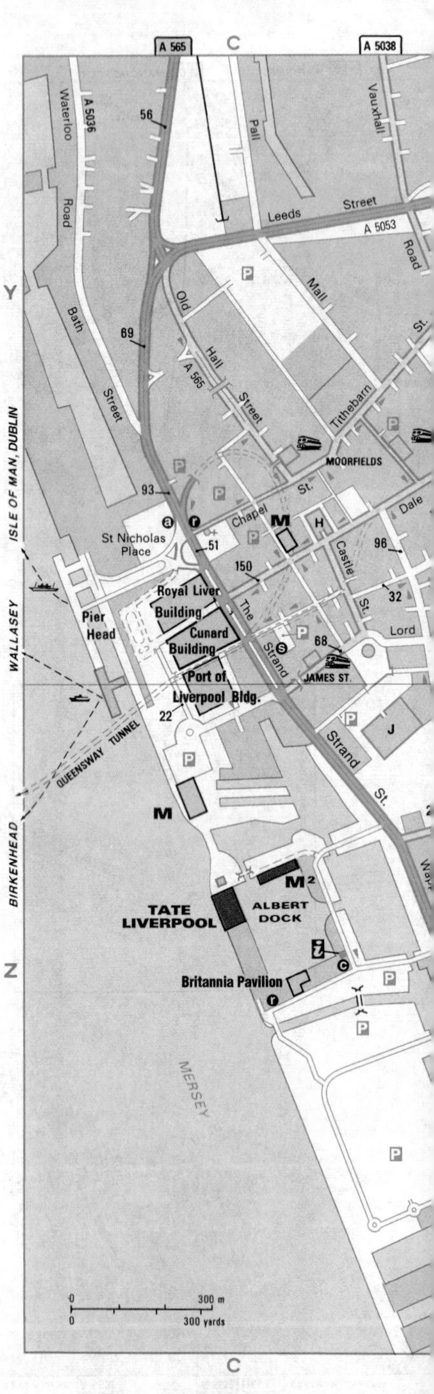

GREEN TOURIST GUIDES

Picturesque scenery, buildings
Attractive routes
Touring programmes
Plans of towns and buildings.

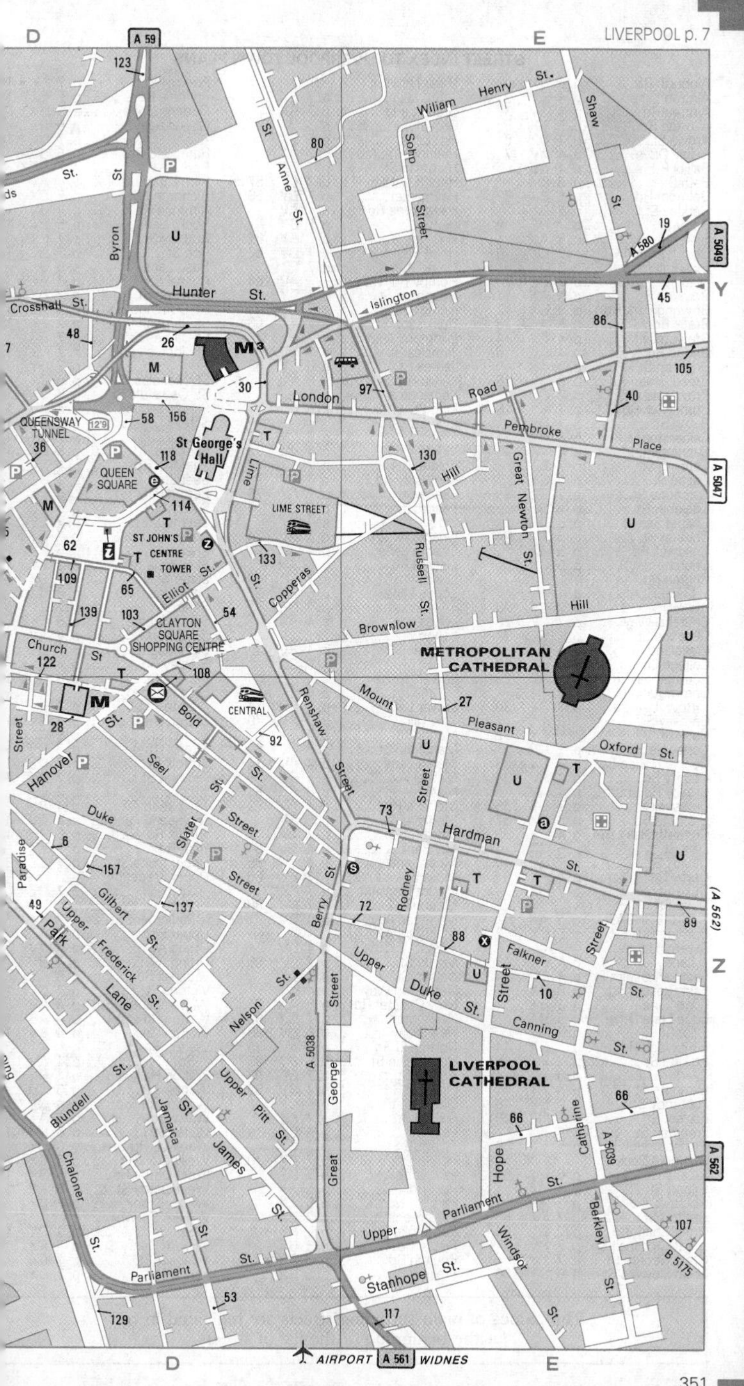
D
E
A 59
METROPOLITAN CATHEDRAL
LIVERPOOL CATHEDRAL
St George's Hall
LIME STREET
CENTRAL
QUEEN SQUARE
QUEENSWAY TUNNEL
ST JOHN'S CENTRE
TOWER
CLAYTON SQUARE SHOPPING CENTRE
Hunter St.
Islington
London Road
Pembroke Place
Brownlow Hill
Mount Pleasant
Oxford St.
Hardman St.
Falkner St.
Upper Duke St.
Canning St.
Upper Parliament St.
Great George Street
Hope Street
Rodney Street
Renshaw Street
Berry St.
Bold St.
Seel St.
Duke Street
Hanover St.
Church St.
Lime St.
Russell St.
Great Newton St.
Copperas Hill
Elliot St.
Crosshall St.
Byron St.
St Anne St.
Shaw St.
William Henry St.
Sohp Street
Slater St.
Gilbert St.
Upper Frederick St.
Park Lane
Paradise Street
Nelson St.
Upper Pitt St.
St James St.
Jamaica St.
Blundell St.
Chaloner St.
Parliament St.
Stanhope St.
Windsor St.
Berkley St.
Catharine Street
A 580
A 5049
A 5047
A 562
A 5038
A 5039
B 5175
Y
Z
AIRPORT A 561 WIDNES

STREET INDEX TO LIVERPOOL TOWN PLANS

Street	Page	Grid	No.
Aigburth Rd.	p. 5	BX	
Aintree Lane	p. 4	BV	2
Aintree Rd.	p. 4	AV	3
Allerton Rd	p. 5	BX	5
Argyle St.	p. 7	DZ	6
Bailey Drive	p. 4	AV	7
Balliol Rd	p. 4	AV	
Bath St.	p. 6	CY	
Belmont Rd.	p. 5	BX	8
Berkley St.	p. 7	EZ	
Berry St.	p. 7	DZ	
Birkenhead Rd	p. 5	AX	
Blackburne Pl.	p. 7	EZ	10
Blundell St.	p. 7	DZ	
Bold St.	p. 7	DZ	
Borough Rd.	p. 5	AX	11
Bowring Park Rd	p. 5	BX	12
Breck Rd	p. 5	ABX	13
Brewster St.	p. 4	AV	14
Bridge Rd	p. 4	AV	16
Brighton St.	p. 5	AX	
Broad Green Rd	p. 5	BX	18
Brownlow Hill	p. 7	DEY	
Brunswick Rd	p. 7	EY	19
Byron St.	p. 7	DY	
Calderstones Rd	p. 5	BX	21
Canning Pl.	p. 6	CZ	23
Canning St.	p. 7	EZ	
Castle St.	p. 6	CY	
Catharine St.	p. 7	EZ	
Chaloner St.	p. 7	DZ	
Chapel St.	p. 6	CY	
Chester St.	p. 5	AX	24
Childwall Rd	p. 5	BX	
Church Rd	p. 5	BX	
Church Rd LITHERLAND	p. 4	AV	
Church St.	p. 7	DY	25
Churchill Way	p. 7	DY	26
Clarence St.	p. 7	EYZ	27
Cleveland St.	p. 5	AX	
College Lane	p. 7	DZ	28
Commercial Rd	p. 4	AV	29
Commutation Row	p. 7	DY	30
Conway St.	p. 5	AX	
Cook St.	p. 6	CY	32
Copperas Hill	p. 7	DE	
Copple House La.	p. 4	BV	33
County Rd	p. 4	AV	34
Crosby Rd South	p. 4	AV	
Crosshall St.	p. 7	DY	36
Croxteth Rd	p. 5	BX	37
Croxteth Hall Lane	p. 4	BV	39
Dale St.	p. 6	CDY	
Daulby St.	p. 7	EY	40
Derby Rd	p. 4	AV	
Duke St.	p. 7	DZ	
Duke St. BIRKENHEAD	p. 5	AX	
Durning Rd	p. 5	BX	42
Dwerry House Lane	p. 4	BV	43
East Lancashire Rd	p. 4	BV	
East Prescot Rd	p. 5	BX	
Edge Lane	p. 5	BX	
Edge Lane Drive	p. 5	BX	
Elliot St.	p. 7	DY	
Elmswood Rd.	p. 5	BX	44
Erskine St.	p. 7	EY	45
Everton Rd.	p. 5	AX	
Exmouth St.	p. 5	AX	
Fontenoy St.	p. 7	DY	48
Forrest St.	p. 7	DZ	49
Freeman St.	p. 5	AX	
Gainsborough Rd	p. 5	BX	50
George's Dock Lane	p. 6	CY	51
Gilbert St.	p. 7	DZ	
Gorsey Lane	p. 5	AX	
Grafton St.	p. 7	DZ	53
Great Charlotte St.	p. 7	DY	54
Great Crosshall St.	p. 7	DY	
Great George St.	p. 7	DY	
Great Howard St.	p. 6	CY	56
Great Newton St.	p. 7	EY	
Green Lane	p. 5	BX	
Grove St.	p. 5	BX	
Hall Lane	p. 5	BX	
Hannover St.	p. 7	DZ	
Hardman St.	p. 7	EZ	
Hatton Garden	p. 7	DY	57
Haymarket	p. 7	DY	58
Hawthorne Rd	p. 4	AV	
High St.	p. 5	BX	
Holt Rd.	p. 5	BX	61
Hood St.	p. 7	DY	62
Hope St.	p. 7	EZ	
Hornby Rd	p. 4	AV	64
Houghton St.	p. 7	DY	65
Hunter St.	p. 7	DY	
Huskisson St.	p. 7	EZ	66
Islington	p. 7	EY	
Jamaica St.	p. 7	DZ	
James St.	p. 6	CY	68
Kelvin Rd	p. 5	AX	
Kensington	p. 5	BX	
King St.	p. 5	AX	
King Edward St.	p. 6	CY	69
Kirkdale Rd	p. 4	AV	71
Knight St.	p. 7	EZ	72
Knowsley Rd.	p. 4	AV	
Leece St.	p. 7	EZ	73
Leeds St.	p. 6	CY	
Lime St.	p. 7	DY	
Linacre Rd	p. 4	AV	74
Linacre Lane	p. 4	AV	
Liscard Rd	p. 5	AX	
Liver St.	p. 7	CZ	76
Lodge Lane	p. 5	BX	77
London Rd.	p. 7	DEY	
Long Lane	p. 4	BV	
Longmoor Lane	p. 4	BV	
Lord St.	p. 6	CDY	
Lower House Lane	p. 4	BV	
Lower Lane	p. 4	BV	
Low Hill	p. 5	ABX	79
Manor Rd.	p. 4	AX	
Mansfield St.	p. 7	DEY	80
Marsh Lane	p. 4	AV	
Mather Av.	p. 5	BX	
Mathew St.	p. 6	CDY	81
Melrose Rd	p. 4	AV	82
Menlove Av.	p. 5	BV	
Merton Rd	p. 4	AV	
Mill Bank	p. 4	BV	84
Moss Lane	p. 4	AV	85
Moss St.	p. 7	EY	86
Mount Pleasant	p. 7	EZ	
Mount St.	p. 7	EZ	88
Muirhead Av.	p. 4	BV	
Muirhead Av. East	p. 4	BV	
Myrtle St.	p. 7	EZ	89
Nelson St.	p. 7	DZ	
Netherton Way	p. 4	AV	
New Chester Rd.	p. 5	AX	91
Newington	p. 7	DZ	92
New Quay	p. 6	CY	93
Northfield Rd.	p. 4	AV	95
North John St.	p. 6	CY	96
Norton St.	p. 7	EY	97
Oakfield Rd	p. 4	BV	99
Old Hall St.	p. 6	CY	
Oxford St.	p. 7	EZ	
Pall Mall	p. 6	CY	
Paradise St.	p. 7	DZ	
Parker St.	p. 7	DY	103
Park Lane	p. 7	DZ	
Park Rd	p. 5	AX	
Park Rd North	p. 5	AX	
Parliament St.	p. 7	DZ	
Pembroke Pl.	p. 7	EY	
Picton Rd	p. 5	BX	
Poulton Rd.	p. 5	AX	
Prescot Rd.	p. 5	BX	
Prescot St.	p. 7	EY	1
Prince's Rd	p. 7	EZ	1
Queens Drive	p. 5	BX	
Queensway	p. 5	AX	
Ranelagh St.	p. 7	DY	1
Rathbone Rd.	p. 5	BX	
Renshaw St.	p. 7	DEZ	
Rice Lane	p. 4	AV	
Richmond St.	p. 7	DY	1
Rimrose Rd	p. 4	AV	1
Rocky Lane	p. 5	BX	1
Rodney St.	p. 7	EZ	
Roe St.	p. 7	DY	1
Rose Lane	p. 5	BX	
Russel St.	p. 7	EY	
St. Anne St.	p. 7	DY	
St. Domingo Rd	p. 4	AV	1
St. James Pl.	p. 7	EZ	1
St. James St.	p. 7	DZ	
St. John's Lane	p. 7	DY	1
St. Johns Centre	p. 7	DY	
St. Nicholas Pl.	p. 6	CY	
St. Oswald's St.	p. 5	BX	1
Sandhills Lane	p. 4	AV	1
School Lane	p. 7	DYZ	1
Scotland Pl.	p. 7	DY	1
Scotland Rd.	p. 5	AX	1
Seaforth Rd	p. 4	AV	1
Seel St.	p. 7	DZ	
Sefton Park Rd	p. 5	BX	1
Sefton St.	p. 5	DZ	1
Seymour St.	p. 7	EY	1
Shaw St.	p. 7	EY	
Sheil Rd	p. 5	BX	
Skelhorne St.	p. 7	EY	1
Slater St.	p. 7	DZ	
Smithdown Rd	p. 5	BX	
Soho St.	p. 7	EY	
South John St.	p. 6	CYZ	
Southport Rd.	p. 4	AV	
Stanhope St.	p. 7	DZ	
Stanley Rd	p. 4	AV	
Stanley St.	p. 6	CDY	1
Stonebridge Lane	p. 4	BV	
Stopgate Lane	p. 4	BV	1
Strand St.	p. 6	CZ	
Strand (The)	p. 6	CY	
Suffolk St.	p. 7	DZ	1
Tarleton St.	p. 7	DY	1
Tithebarn St.	p. 6	CY	
Townsend Av.	p. 4	BV	
Townsend Lane	p. 4	BV	
Tunnel Rd	p. 5	BX	1
Ullet Rd	p. 5	BX	
Upper Duke St.	p. 7	EZ	
Upper Frederick St.	p. 7	DZ	
Upper Parliament St.	p. 7	EZ	
Upper Pitt	p. 7	DZ	
Utting Av.	p. 4	AV	
Utting Av. East	p. 4	BV	
Vauxhall Rd	p. 6	CY	
Victoria St.	p. 7	DY	1
Walton Lane	p. 4	AV	
Walton Rd	p. 4	ABV	1
Walton Vale	p. 4	BV	1
Walton Breck Rd	p. 4	AV	1
Walton Hall Av.	p. 4	BV	
Wapping	p. 6	CDZ	
Warbreck Moor	p. 4	BV	1
Warwick	p. 5	AX	
Water St.	p. 6	CY	1
Waterloo Rd	p. 6	CY	
Wellington Rd	p. 5	BX	1
West Derby Rd	p. 5	BX	1
West Derby St.	p. 5	AX	1
Whitechapel	p. 7	DY	
William Brown St.	p. 7	DY	1
William Henry St.	p. 7	EY	
Windsor St.	p. 7	EZ	
York St.	p. 7	DZ	1

The names of main shopping streets are indicated in red at the beginning of the list of streets.

ENGLAND

at Knowsley Industrial Park *Northeast : 8 m. by A 580 – BV – ✉ Liverpool.*

Suites H., Ribblers Lane, L34 9HA, ☎ (0151) 549 2222, *enquiries@suiteshotelgroup.com, Fax (0151) 549 1116,* – rm, – 300. VISA.
Meals *(closed Saturday and Sunday lunch)* a la carte 14.85/25.00 **st.** 9.95 –, **80 suites** 120.00/130.00 **st.**

Howard Johnson without rest., Ribblers Lane, Knowsley, L34 9HA, ☎ (0151) 549 2700, *knowsley@howardjohnson.co.uk, Fax (0151) 549 2800* – – 40. VISA
86 rm 49.95 **t.**

at Huyton *East : 8¼ m. by A 5047 and A 5080 – BX – on B 5199 – ✉ Liverpool.*

Village H. and Leisure Club, Fallows Way, L35 1RZ, Southeast : 3 ¼ m. by A 5080 off Whiston rd ☎ (0151) 449 2341, *village.whiston@village-hotels.com, Fax (0151) 449 3832,* squash – rm, – 230. VISA JCB.
Meals *(closed Saturday lunch and Sunday dinner)* a la carte 17.00/25.25 **st.** 9.95 – **62 rm** 95.00/108.00 **st.**

Premier Lodge, Roby Rd, L36 4HD, Southwest : 1 m. on A 5080 ☎ (0870) 7001426, *Fax (0870) 7001427,* – rm, rest, – 35. VISA.
Meals (grill rest.) a la carte approx. 13.00 **t.** 8.95 – **53 rm** 46.95 **t.**

Travel Inn, Wilson Rd, Tarbock, L36 6AD, Southeast : 2 ¼ m. on A 5080 ☎ (0151) 480 9614, *Fax (0151) 480 9361* – rm, rest, VISA.
Meals (grill rest.) – **41 rm** 41.95 **t.**

at Grassendale *Southeast : 4½ m. on A 561 – BX – ✉ Liverpool.*

Gulshan, 544-548 Aigburth Rd, L19 3QG, on A 561 ☎ (0151) 427 2273, *Fax (0151) 427 2111* – VISA
Meals - Indian - (dinner only) a la carte 19.05/23.45 **t.** 8.95.

at Woolton *Southeast : 6 m. by A 562 – BX – ✉ Liverpool.*

Woolton Redbourne, Acrefield Rd, L25 5JN, ☎ (0151) 421 1500, *wooltonredbourne @cwcom.net, Fax (0151) 421 1501,* « Victorian house, antiques », – rest, VISA JCB
Meals (residents only) (dinner only) 25.50 11.95 – **18 rm** 68.00/99.00 **t.**, 1 suite.

at Speke *Southeast : 8 ¾ m. by A 561 – BX – ✉ Liverpool.*

Liverpool Marriott H. South, Speke Aerodrome, Speke Rd, L24 8QD, West : 1 ¾ m. on A 561 ☎ (0151) 494 5000, *reservations.liverpoolsouth@marriotthotels.co.uk, Fax (0151) 494 5051,* « Converted Art Deco former airport terminal building », squash – – 250. VISA.
Starways : **Meals** a la carte 17.40/25.95 **st.** 12.95 – 13.00 – **163 rm** 115.00 **st.**, 1 suite – SB.

LIZARD *Cornwall* 403 E 34 *The West Country G.*

Env. : *Lizard Peninsula★ - Mullion Cove★★ (Church★) - Kynance Cove★★ - Cadgwith★ - Coverack★ – Cury★ (Church★) - Gunwalloe Fishing Cove★ - St Keverne (Church★) - Landewednack★ (Church★) – Mawgan-in-Meneage (Church★) - Ruan Minor (Church★) - St Anthony-in-Meneage★.*

London 326 – Penzance 24 – Truro 29.

Housel Bay , Housel Bay, TR12 7PG, ☎ (01326) 290417, *info@houselbay.com, Fax (01326) 290359,* ≤ Housel Cove, – rest, VISA JCB.
Meals (barlunch Monday-Saturday)/dinner 15.00/21.00 **st.** 9.50 – **21 rm** 38.00/110.00 **t.** – SB.

Landewednack House , Church Cove, TR12 7PQ, East : 1 m. by A 3083 ☎ (01326) 290909, *landewednack.house@virgin.net, Fax (01326) 290192,* « Part 17C, antique furnished, former rectory overlooking Church Cove », heated, – VISA.
closed 25-26 December – **Meals** (by arrangement) (communal dining) 26.00 **st.** 10.50 – **3 rm** 49.00/92.00 **st.**

Tregullas House without rest., Housel Bay, TR12 7PF, ☎ (01326) 290351, *judy.hendy @tinyworld.co.uk,* ≤, –
closed 1 week Christmas – **3 rm** 35.00/46.00.

Si vous cherchez un hôtel tranquille,
consultez d'abord les cartes de l'introduction
ou repérez dans le texte les établissements indiqués avec le signe ou .

LOCKINGTON *East Riding* 402 S 22.
London 211 – Kingston-upon-Hull 16 – Leeds 64 – York 38.

XX **Rockingham** with rm, 52 Front St, YO25 9SH, ☎ (01430) 810607, *Fax (01430) 81073* ⇔ rm, TV P. MC AE VISA. ✻
closed 2 weeks Christmas-New Year and Bank Holidays – **Meals** *(closed Sunday-Tuesd* (dinner only) 29.00 t. 13.95 – **3 rm** 85.00/110.00 **t.**

LOCKWOOD *W. Yorks. – see Huddersfield.*

LOFTUS *Redcar & Cleveland* 402 R 20 – *pop. 5 931* – ✉ *Saltburn-by-the-Sea.*
London 264 – Leeds 73 – Middlesbrough 17 – Scarborough 36.

Grinkle Park ⛰, Easington, TS13 4UB, Southeast : 3 ½ m. by A 174 on Grinkle ☎ (01287) 640515, *grinkle.parkhotel@sixcretail.com, Fax (01287) 641278,* <, ⛳, ✱ TV P. MC AE ⊕ VISA. ✻
Meals 12.00/23.00 and dinner a la carte approx. 26.00 10.00 – **20 rm** 83.00/110.00 t SB.

LONDON

404 folds ㊷ to ㊹ – *London G.* – *pop. 6 679 699*

SIGHTS

HISTORIC BUILDINGS AND MONUMENTS

*Palace of Westminster*** : House of Lords**, Westminster Hall** (hammerbeam roof***), Robing Room*, Central Lobby*, House of Commons*, Big Ben*, Victoria Tower* p. 30* LY – *Tower of London*** (Crown Jewels***, White Tower or Keep***, St. John's Chapel**, Beauchamp Tower* Tower Hill Pageant*) p. 31* PVX – *British Airways London Eye (views***).*

*Banqueting House** p. 30* LX – *Buckingham Palace** (Changing of the Guard**, Royal Mews**) p. 36* BVX – *Kensington Palace** p. 28* FX – *Lincoln's Inn** p. 37* EV – *London Bridge* p. 31* PVX – *Royal Hospital Chelsea** p. 35* FU – *St. James's Palace** p. 33* EP – *Somerset House** p. 37* EXY – *South Bank Arts Centre** (Royal Festival Hall*, National Theatre*, County Hall*) p. 30* MX – *The Temple** (Middle Temple Hall*) p. 26* MV – *Tower Bridge** p. 31* PX.

Albert Memorial p. 34* CQ – *Apsley House* p. 32* BP – *Burlington House* p. 33* EM – *Charterhouse* p. 27* NOU – *George Inn*, Southwark p. 31* PX – *Gray's Inn* p. 26* MU – *Guildhall* (Lord Mayor's Show**) p. 27* OU – *International Shakespeare Globe Centre* p. 31* OX **T** – *Dr Johnson's House* p. 27* NUV **A** – *Lancaster House* p. 33* EP – *Leighton House* p. 28* EY – *Linley Sambourne House* p. 28* EY – *Lloyds Building** p. 27* PV – *Mansion House* (plate and insignia**) p. 27* PV **P** – *The Monument* (✻*) p. 27* PV **G** – *Old Admiralty* p. 30* KLX – *Royal Albert Hall* p. 34* CQ – *Royal Exchange* p. 27* PV **V** – *Royal Opera Arcade* (New Zealand House) p. 33* FGN – *Royal Opera House* (Covent Garden) p. 37* DX – *Spencer House** p. 33* DP – *Staple Inn* p. 26* MU **Y** – *Theatre Royal* (Haymarket) p. 33* GM – *Westminster Bridge* p. 30* LY.

CHURCHES

The City Churches

St. Paul's Cathedral★★★ (Dome ≤★★★) p. 27 NOV.

St. Bartholomew the Great★★ (choir★) p. 27 OU **K** – *St. Dunstan-in-the-East★★* p. 27 PV **F** – *St. Mary-at-Hill★★ (woodwork★★, plan★)* p. 27 PV **B** – *Temple Church★★* p. 26 MV.

All Hallows-by-the-Tower (font cover★★ brasses★) p. 27 PV **Y** – *Christ Church★* p. 25 OU **E** – *St. Andrew Undershaft (monuments★)* p. 27 PV **A** – *St. Bride★ (steeple★★)* p. 27 NV **Y** – *St. Clement Eastcheap (panelled interior★★)* p. 27 PV **E** – *St. Edmund the King and Martyr (tower and spire★)* p. 27 PV **D** – *St-Giles Cripplegate★* p. 27 OU **N** – *St. Helen Bishopsgate★ (monuments★★)* p. 27 PUV **R** – *St. James Garlickhythe (tower and spire★, sword rests★)* p. 27 OV **R** – *St. Magnus the Martyr (tower★, sword rest★)* p. 27 PV **K** – *St. Margaret Lothbury★ (tower and spire★, woodwork★, screen★, font★)* p. 27 PU **S** – *St. Margaret Pattens (spire★, woodwork★)* p. 27 PV **N** – *St. Martin-within-Ludgate (tower and spire★, door cases★)* p. 27 NOV **B** – *St. Mary Abchurch★ (reredos★★, tower and spire★, dome★)* p. 27 PV **X** – *St. Mary-le-Bow (tower and steeple★★)* p. 27 OV **G** – *St. Michael Paternoster Royal (tower and spire★)* p. 27 OV **D** – *St. Nicholas Cole Abbey (tower and spire★)* p. 27 OV **F** – *St. Olave★* p. 27 PV **S** – *St. Peter upon Cornhill (screen★)* p. 27 PV **L** – *St. Stephen Walbrook★ (tower and steeple★, dome★)*, p. 27 PV **Z** – *St. Vedast (tower and spire★, ceiling★)*, p. 27 OU **E**.

Other Churches

Westminster Abbey★★★ (Henry VII Chapel★★★, Chapel of Edward the Confessor★★, Chapter House★★, Poets' Corner★) p. 30 LY.

Southwark Cathedral★★ p. 31 PX.

Queen's Chapel★ p. 33 EP – *St. Clement Danes★* p. 37 EX – *St. James's★* p. 33 EM – *St. Margaret's★* p. 30 LY **A** – *St. Martin-in-the-Fields★* p. 37 DY – *St. Paul's★ (Covent Garden)* p. 37 DX – *Westminster Roman Catholic Cathedral★* p. 30 KY **B**.

PARKS

Regent's Park★★★ p. 25 HI *(terraces★★), Zoo★★*.

Hyde Park – Kensington Gardens★★ (Orangery★) pp. 28 and 29 – St. James's Park★★ p. 30 KXY.

STREETS AND SQUARES

The City★★★ p. 27 NV.

Bedford Square★★ p. 26 KLU – *Belgrave Square★★* p. 36 AVX – *Burlington Arcade★★* p. 33 DM – *Covent Garden★★ (The Piazza★★)* p. 37 DX – *The Mall★★* p. 33 FP – *Piccadilly★* p. 33 EM – *The Thames★★* pp. 29-31 – *Trafalgar Square★★* p. 37 DY – *Whitehall★★ (Horse Guards★)* p. 30 LX.

Barbican★ p. 27 OU – *Bond Street★* pp. 32-33 CK-DM – *Canonbury Square★* p. 27 NS – *Carlton House Terrace★* p. 33 GN – *Cheyne Walk★* p. 29 GHZ – *Fitzroy Square★* p. 26 KU – *Jermyn Street★* p. 33 EN – Leicester Square★ p. 33 GM – *Merrick Square★* p. 31 OY – *Montpelier Square★* p. 35 EQ – *Neal's Yard★* p. 37 DV – *Piccadilly Arcade★* p. 33 DEN – *Portman Square★* p. 32 AJ – *Queen Anne's Gate★* p. 30 KY – Regent Street★ p. 33 EM – *Piccadilly Circus★* p. 33 FM – *St. James's Square★* p. 33 FN – *St. James's Street★* p. 33 EN – *Shepherd Market★* p. 32 CN – *Soho★* p. 33 – *Trinity Church Square★* p. 31 OY – *Victoria Embankment gardens★* p. 37 DEXY – *Waterloo Place★* p. 33 FN.

MUSEUMS

British Museum★★★ p. 26 LU – *National Gallery★★★* p. 33 GM – *Science Museum★★★* p. 34 CR – *Tate Britain★★★* p. 30 LZ – *Victoria and Albert Museum★★★* p. 35 DR – *Wallace Collection★★★* p. 32 AH.

Courtauld Institute Galleries★★ (Somerset House) p. 37 EXY – *Gilbert Collection★★ (Somerset House)* p. 37 EX Y – *Museum of London★★* p. 27 OU **M** – *National Portrait Gallery★★* p. 33 GM – *Natural History Museum★★* p. 34 CS – *Sir John Soane's Museum★★* p. 26 MU **M** – *Tate Modern★★ (views★★★ from top floors)* p. 31 OX **M**.

Clock Museum★ (Guildhall) p. 26 OU – *Imperial War Museum★* p. 31 NY – *London's Transport Museum★* p. 37 DX – *Madame Tussaud's★* p. 25 IU **M** – *Museum of Mankind★* p. 33 DM – *National Army Museum★* p. 35 FU – *Percival David Foundation of Chinese Art★* p. 26 KLT **M** – *Planetarium★* p. 25 IU **M** – *Wellington Museum★ (Apsley House)* p. 32 BP.

OUTER LONDON

Blackheath p. 15 HX *terraces and houses★, Eltham Palace★* **A**
Brentford p. 12 BX *Syon Park★★, gardens★*
Bromley p. 14 GY *The Crystal Palace Park★*
Chiswick p. 13 CV *Chiswick Mall★★, Chiswick House★* **D,** *Hogarth's House★* **E**
Dulwich p. 14 *Picture Gallery★* FX **X**
Greenwich pp. 14 and 15 : *Cutty Sark★★* GV **F,** *Footway Tunnel(≤ ★★) – Fan Museum★* p. 10 GV **A,** – *National Maritime Museum★★ (Queen's House★★)* GV **M,** *Royal Naval College★★ (Painted Hall★, the Chapel★)* GV **G,** *The Park and Old Royal Observatory★ (Meridian Building : collection★★)* HV **K,** *Ranger's House★* GX **N**
Hampstead *Kenwood House★★ (Adam Library★★, paintings★★)* p. 9 EU **P,** *Fenton House★★,* p. 24 ES
Hampton Court p. 12 BY *(The Palace★★★, gardens★★★, Fountain Court★, The Great Vine★)*
Kew p. 13 CX *Royal Botanic Gardens★★★ : Palm House★★, Temperate House★, Kew Palace or Dutch House★★, Orangery★, Pagoda★, Japanese Gateway★*
Hendon★ p. 9, *Royal Air Force Museum★★* CT **M**
Hounslow p. 12 BV *Osterley Park★★*
Lewisham p. 14 GX *Horniman Museum★* **M**
Richmond pp. 12 and 13 : *Richmond Park★★, ✻★★★* CX, *Richmond Hill✻★★* CX, *Richmond Bridge★★* BX **R,** *Richmond Green★★* BX **S** *(Maids of Honour Row★★, Trumpeter's House★), Asgill House★* BX **B,** *Ham House★★* BX **V**
Shoreditch p. 10 FU *Geffrye Museum★* **M**
Tower Hamlets p. 10 GV *Canary Wharf★★* B, *Isle of Dogs★ St. Katharine Dock★* **Y**
Twickenham p. 12 BX *Marble Hill House★* **Z,** *Strawberry Hill★* **A** .

PRACTICAL INFORMATION

Britain Visitor Centre, 1 Regent St, W1

Airports

Heathrow ☎ 08700 000123 p. 12 **AX** - *Terminal: Airbus (A1) from Victoria, Airbus (A2) from Paddington - Underground (Piccadilly line) frequent service daily.*
Gatwick ☎ 08700 002468 p. 13: *by A23* **EZ** *and M23* - Terminal: *Coach service from Victoria Coach Station (Flightline 777, hourly service) - Railink (Gatwick Express) from Victoria (24 h service).*
London City Airport ☎ (020) 7646 0000 p. 11 **HV**
Stansted, at Bishop's Stortford ☎ 08700 000303, NE: 34m p. 11 *by M11* **JT** *and A120.*
British Airways, Victoria Air Terminal: 115 Buckingham Palace Rd, SW1 ☎ (020) 7707 4750 p. 36 **BX**

Banks

Open, generally 9.30 am to 4.30 pm weekdays (except public holidays). Most have cash dispensers. You need ID (passport) for cashing cheques. Banks levy smaller commissions than hotels.
Many 'Bureaux de Change' around Piccadilly open 7 days.

Medical Emergencies

To contact a doctor for first aid, emergency medical advice and chemists night service: 07000 372255.
Accident & Emergency: dial 999 for Ambulance, Police or Fire Services.

Post Offices

Open Monday to Friday 9 am to 5.30 pm. Late collections made from Leicester Square.

Shopping

Most stores are found in Oxford Street (Selfridges, M & S), Regent Street (Hamleys, Libertys) and Knightsbridge (Harrods, Harvey Nichols). Open usually Monday to Saturday *9 am to 6 pm. Some open later (8 pm) once a week; Knightsbridge* Wednesday, *Oxford Street and Regent Street* Thursday. *Other areas worth visiting include Jermyn Street and Savile Row (mens outfitters), Bond Street (jewellers and haute couture).*

Theatres

The "West End" has many major theatre performances and can generally be found around Shafte bury Avenue. Most daily newspapers give details of performances. A half-price ticket booth is locat in Leicester Square and is open Monday-Saturday 1 - 6.30 pm, Sunday and matinée days 12 noor 6.30 pm. Restrictions apply.

Tipping

When a service charge is included in a bill it is not necessary to tip extra. If service is not include discretionary 10% is normal.

Travel

As driving in London is difficult, it is advisable to take the Underground, a bus or taxi. Taxis can hailed when the amber light is illuminated.

Localities outside the Greater London limits are listed alphabetically throughout the guide.

Les localités situées en dehors des limites de Greater London se trouvent à leur place alphabetique dans le guide.

Alle Städte und Gemeinden außerhalb von Greater London sind in alphabetischer Reihenfolge aufgelistet.

Le località situate al di fuori dei confini della Greater London sono ordinate alfabeticamente all'interno della Guida.

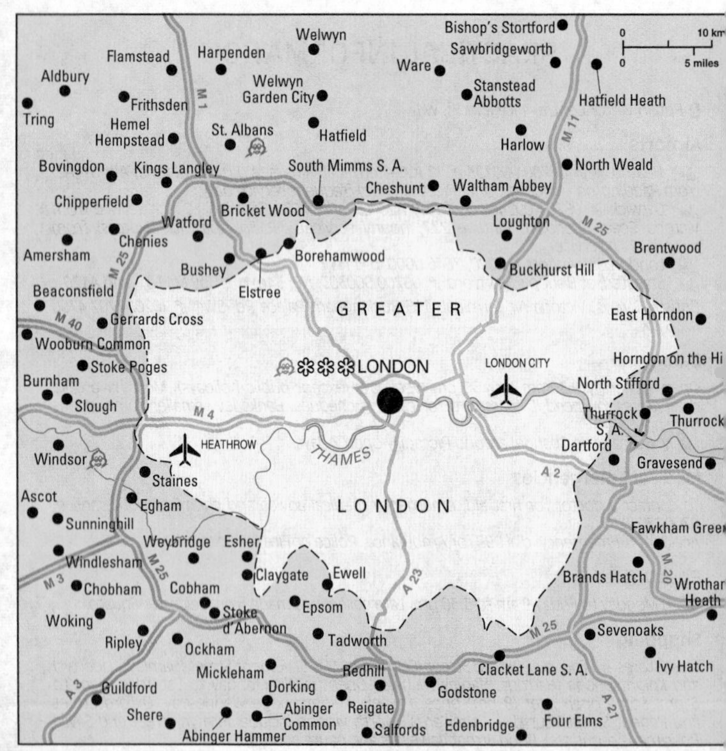

Key to lines
Bakerloo
Central
Circle
District †
East London
peak hours and Sunday mornings
Hammersmith & City †
Jubilee
Metropolitan
Northern
Piccadilly †
Victoria
Waterloo & City †
Docklands Light Railway
National Rail
Harrow & Wealdstone
Amersham
Chesham
Uxbridge
Watford
Stanmore
Edgware
Hampstead Heath
Gospel Oak
High Barnet
Mill Hill East
Cockfosters
Walthamstow Central
Harlesden
Willesden Green
Kilburn
Willesden Junction
Brondesbury Park
Brondesbury
Kensal Rise
West Hampstead
Finchley Road & Frognal
Finchley Road
Belsize Park
Chalk Farm
Kentish Town West
Kentish Town
Camden Road
† Camden Town
Arsenal
Finsbury Park
Holloway Road
Caledonian Road
Hackney Central
Canonbury
North Woolwich
Kensal Green
Queen's Park
Swiss Cottage
Mornington Crescent
Dalston Kingsland
Highbury & Islington
Caledonian Road & Barnsbury
St. John's Wood
King's Cross St. Pancras
Kilburn Park
Maida Vale
Edgware Road
Marylebone
Warwick Avenue
Baker Street
Great Portland Street
Euston
Angel
West Ruislip
Uxbridge
Sudbury Town
Hanger Lane
Alperton
Royal Oak
Westbourne Park
Paddington
Edgware Road
Warren Street
Euston Square
Euston
Farringdon
Barbican
Old Street
Liverpool Street
Bethnal Green
Mile End
Epping
Hainault
Shoreditch †
Barking
Upminster
Bow Road
Ladbroke Grove
Latimer Road
Park Royal
Bayswater
Regent's Park
Goodge Street
Russell Square
Moorgate
North Ealing
North Acton
White City
Holland Park
Marble Arch
Queensway
Oxford Circus
Holborn
Ealing Broadway
West Acton
East Acton
Shepherd's Bush
Notting Hill Gate
Lancaster Gate
Bond Street
Tottenham Court Road
Chancery Lane
St. Paul's
Aldgate East
Stepney Green
Whitechapel
Acton Central
Shepherd's Bush
Kensington (Olympia)
High Street Kensington
Green Park
Covent Garden
Bank
Aldgate
Cannon Street
Limehouse
Beckton
Lewisham
Ealing Common
Goldhawk Road
Hyde Park Corner
Leicester Square
Mansion House
Monument
Tower Hill
Fenchurch Street
Shadwell
Westferry
Knightsbridge
Piccadilly Circus
Tower Gateway
Acton Town
South Acton
Hammersmith
Barons Court
Gloucester Road
Charing Cross
Wapping
South Ealing
Blackfriars
River Thames
Northfields
Sloane Square
St. James's Park
Temple
Boston Manor
Chiswick Park
Turnham Green
Stamford Brook
Ravenscourt Park
West Kensington
Earl's Court
South Kensington
Victoria
Westminster
Embankment
Charing Cross
London Bridge
Rotherhithe
Osterley
Bermondsey
Canada Water
Stratford
Hounslow East
West Brompton
New Cross
New Cross Gate
Gunnersbury
Waterloo
Southwark
Waterloo East
Heathrow Terminals 1, 2, 3
Hounslow Central
Fulham Broadway
UNDERGROUND
Hounslow West
Kew Gardens
Hatton Cross
Parsons Green
Pimlico
Lambeth North
Borough
Putney Bridge
Heathrow Terminal 4 †
River Thames
Richmond
East Putney
Vauxhall
Elephant & Castle
Interchange stations
Connections with National Rail
Connections with National Rail within walking distance
Airport interchange
Connection with riverboat services
Closed Sundays
Served by Piccadilly line trains early morning and late evening
† For opening times see poster journey planners. Certain stations are closed on public holidays.
London Travel Information
020 7222 1234
24 hours
Textphone
020 7918 3015
© Transport Trading Limited
Wimbledon
Brixton
Morden
LTM CD(b) 7.00
Reg. user No. 02/3600

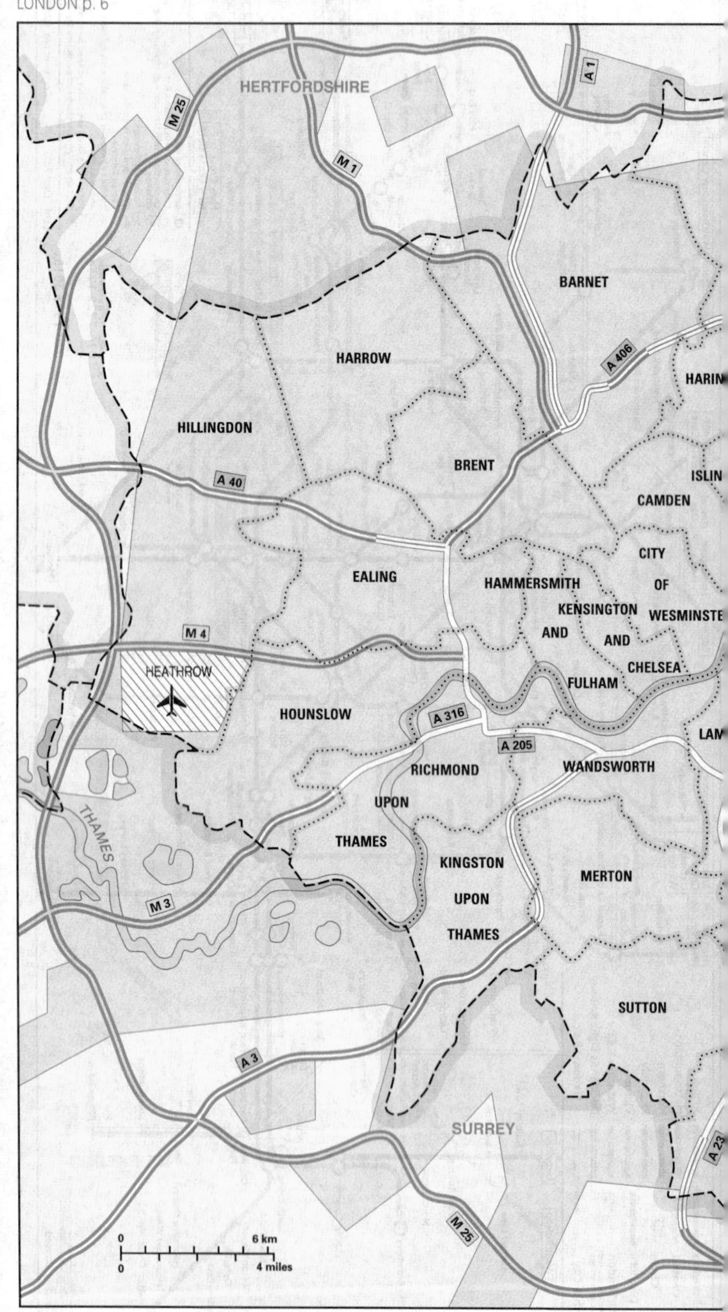

HERTFORDSHIRE
M 25
M 1
A 1
BARNET
HARROW
A 406
HARIN
HILLINGDON
BRENT
A 40
ISLIN
CAMDEN
CITY
OF
WESMINSTE
EALING
HAMMERSMITH
AND
FULHAM
KENSINGTON
AND
CHELSEA
M 4
HEATHROW
HOUNSLOW
A 316
A 205
LAM
RICHMOND
UPON
THAMES
WANDSWORTH
THAMES
KINGSTON
UPON
THAMES
MERTON
M 3
SUTTON
A 3
SURREY
A 23
M 25
0
6 km
0
4 miles

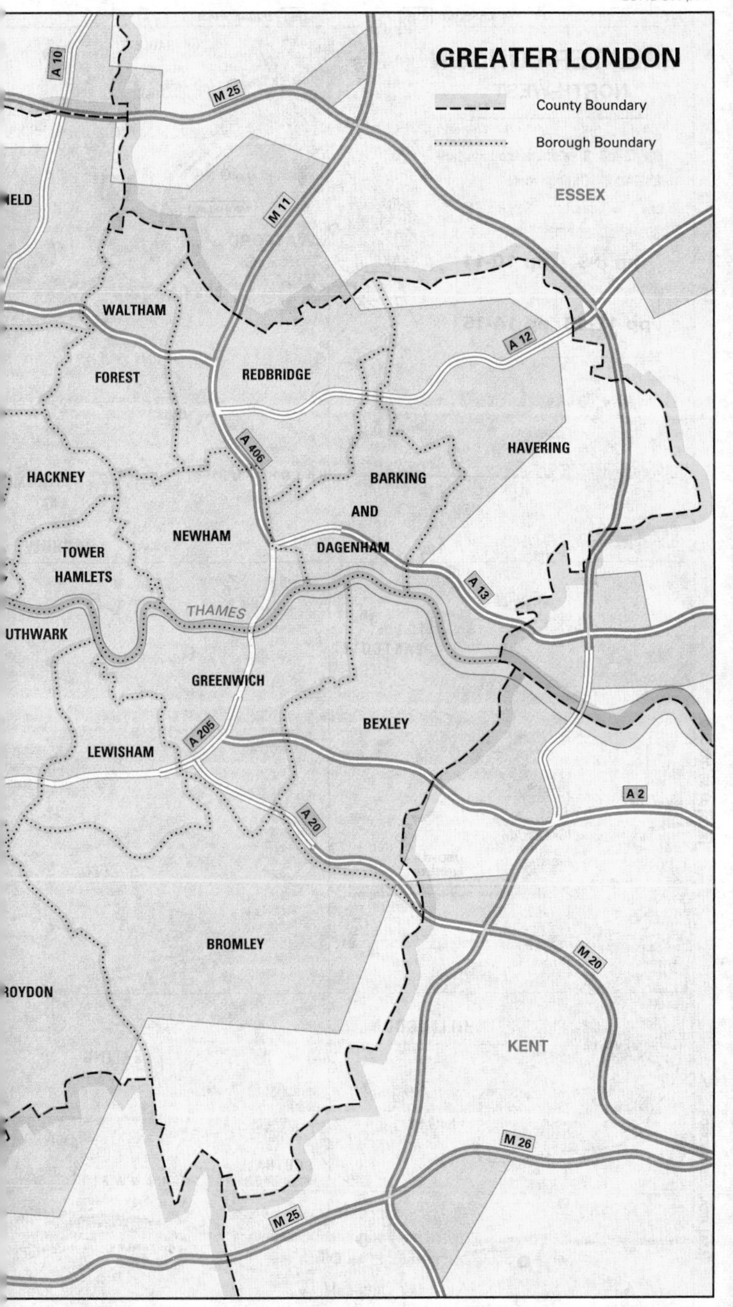
GREATER LONDON
County Boundary
Borough Boundary
ESSEX
A 10
M 25
M 11
A 12
A 406
A 13
A 205
A 20
A 2
M 20
M 26
M 25
IELD
WALTHAM
FOREST
REDBRIDGE
HAVERING
HACKNEY
BARKING
AND
DAGENHAM
NEWHAM
TOWER
HAMLETS
THAMES
UTHWARK
GREENWICH
BEXLEY
LEWISHAM
BROMLEY
ROYDON
KENT

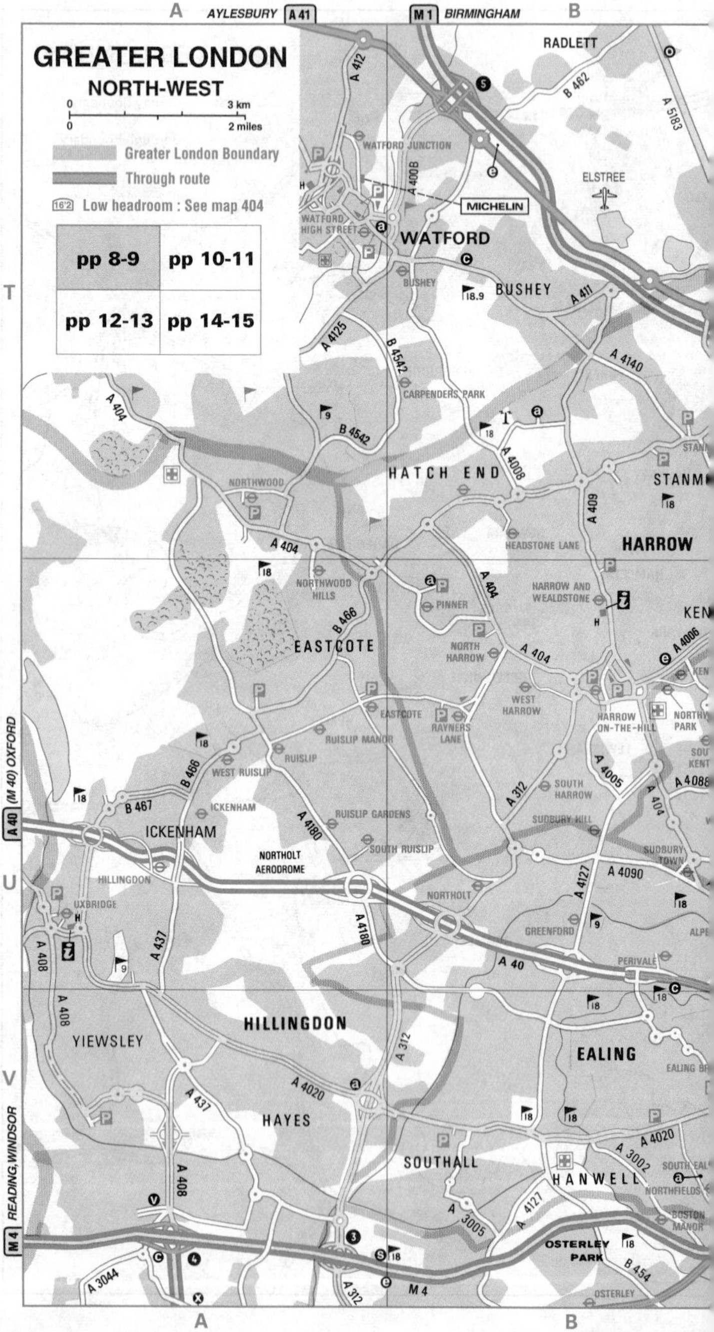

A AYLESBURY A 41 M 1 BIRMINGHAM B

GREATER LONDON
NORTH-WEST

0 3 km
0 2 miles

Greater London Boundary
Through route
16'2 Low headroom : See map 404

pp 8-9	pp 10-11
pp 12-13	pp 14-15

RADLETT
B 462
A 5183
A 412
WATFORD JUNCTION
A 400B
ELSTREE
MICHELIN
WATFORD HIGH STREET
WATFORD
BUSHEY
BUSHEY
A 411
T
A 4125
B 4542
A 4140
A 404
CARPENDERS PARK
B 4542
A 4008
HATCH END
NORTHWOOD
STANMORE
A 409
HEADSTONE LANE
HARROW
A 404
NORTHWOOD HILLS
PINNER
HARROW AND WEALDSTONE
B 466
EASTCOTE
NORTH HARROW
A 404
A 4006
EASTCOTE
RAYNERS LANE
WEST HARROW
HARROW ON-THE-HILL
NORTHWICK PARK
RUISLIP MANOR
RUISLIP
WEST RUISLIP
B 466
A 4005
SOUTH KENTON
A 4088
A 40 (M 40) OXFORD
B 467
ICKENHAM
ICKENHAM
A 4180
RUISLIP GARDENS
A 312
SOUTH HARROW
A 404
SUDBURY HILL
SOUTH RUISLIP
SUDBURY TOWN
NORTHOLT AERODROME
HILLINGDON
A 4127
A 4090
U
UXBRIDGE
NORTHOLT
A 437
A 4180
GREENFORD
ALPERTON
A 408
A 40
PERIVALE
A 408
HILLINGDON
YIEWSLEY
A 312
EALING
V
A 4020
EALING BROADWAY
A 437
HAYES
A 4020
A 3002
M 4 READING, WINDSOR
A 408
SOUTHALL
HANWELL
SOUTH EALING
NORTHFIELDS
A 3005
A 4127
BOSTON MANOR
OSTERLEY PARK
B 454
A 3044
A 312
M 4
OSTERLEY
A B

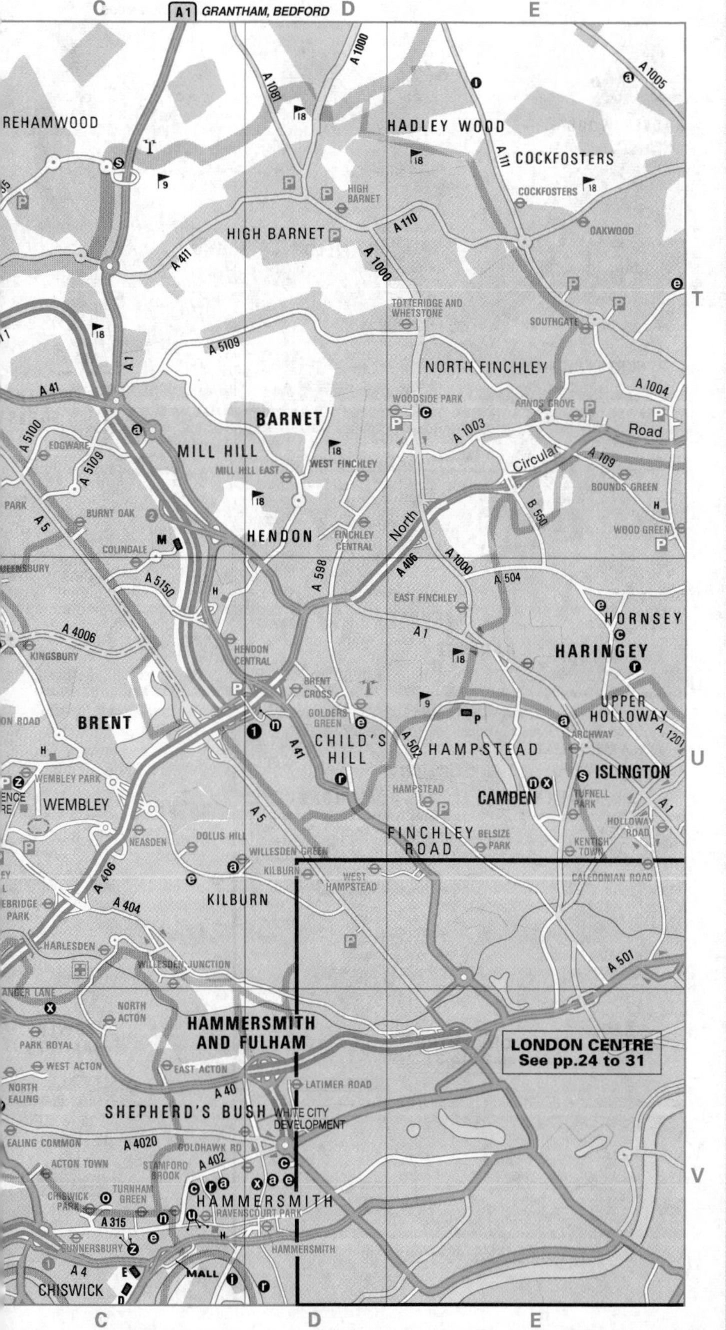
A1 GRANTHAM, BEDFORD
REHAMWOOD
HADLEY WOOD
COCKFOSTERS
HIGH BARNET
OAKWOOD
TOTTERIDGE AND WHETSTONE
SOUTHGATE
NORTH FINCHLEY
WOODSIDE PARK
ARNOS GROVE
BARNET
MILL HILL
EDGWARE
MILL HILL EAST
WEST FINCHLEY
North Circular Road
BOUNDS GREEN
BURNT OAK
HENDON
FINCHLEY CENTRAL
WOOD GREEN
COLINDALE
EAST FINCHLEY
HORNSEY
KINGSBURY
HARINGEY
HENDON CENTRAL
BRENT CROSS
BRENT
GOLDERS GREEN
UPPER HOLLOWAY
CHILD'S HILL
HAMPSTEAD
ARCHWAY
ISLINGTON
WEMBLEY PARK
CAMDEN
TUFNELL PARK
WEMBLEY
NEASDEN
DOLLIS HILL
FINCHLEY ROAD
BELSIZE PARK
HOLLOWAY ROAD
KENTISH TOWN
WILLESDEN GREEN
KILBURN
WEST HAMPSTEAD
CALEDONIAN ROAD
HARLESDEN
WILLESDEN JUNCTION
NORTH ACTON
HAMMERSMITH AND FULHAM
LONDON CENTRE
See pp.24 to 31
PARK ROYAL
WEST ACTON
EAST ACTON
LATIMER ROAD
NORTH EALING
SHEPHERD'S BUSH
WHITE CITY DEVELOPMENT
EALING COMMON
GOLDHAWK RD
ACTON TOWN
STAMFORD BROOK
TURNHAM GREEN
CHISWICK PARK
HAMMERSMITH
RAVENSCOURT PARK
GUNNERSBURY
MALL
CHISWICK
C
D
E
T
U
V

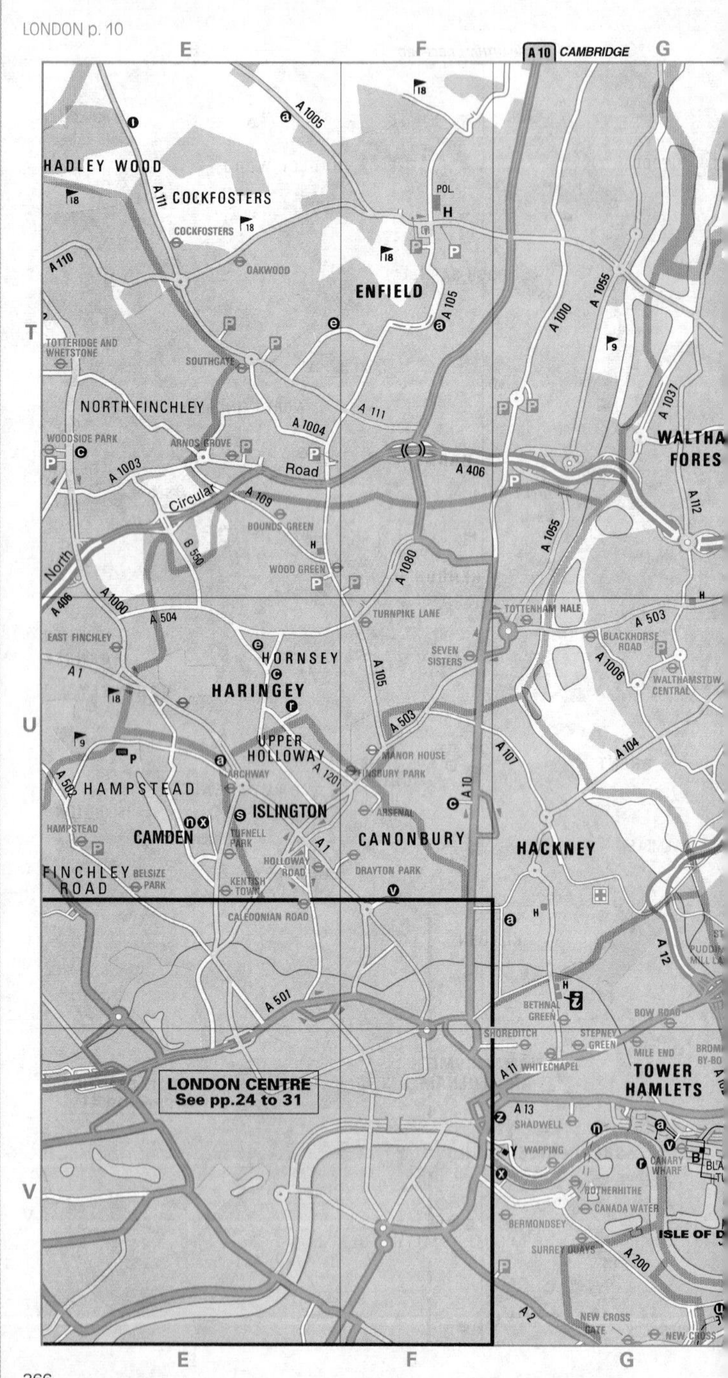
E
F
G
A 10 CAMBRIDGE
HADLEY WOOD
COCKFOSTERS
A 111
A 1005
POL.
ENFIELD
A 110
OAKWOOD
A 105
A 1010
A 1055
TOTTERIDGE AND WHETSTONE
SOUTHGATE
NORTH FINCHLEY
A 111
A 1004
A 1037
WOODSIDE PARK
ARNOS GROVE
A 1003
Road
A 406
WALTHA
FORES
Circular
A 109
BOUNDS GREEN
A 112
B 550
North
A 1055
WOOD GREEN
A 1080
A 406
A 1000
A 504
TURNPIKE LANE
TOTTENHAM HALE
A 503
EAST FINCHLEY
HORNSEY
BLACKHORSE ROAD
SEVEN SISTERS
A 1006
A 1
HARINGEY
A 105
WALTHAMSTOW CENTRAL
A 503
UPPER HOLLOWAY
MANOR HOUSE
A 104
A 502
HAMPSTEAD
ARCHWAY
A 1201
FINSBURY PARK
A 107
ISLINGTON
A 10
ARSENAL
HAMPSTEAD
CAMDEN
TUFNELL PARK
A 1
CANONBURY
HACKNEY
HOLLOWAY ROAD
FINCHLEY ROAD
BELSIZE PARK
KENTISH TOWN
DRAYTON PARK
CALEDONIAN ROAD
A 12
A 501
BETHNAL GREEN
BOW ROAD
SHOREDITCH
STEPNEY GREEN
MILE END
A 11
WHITECHAPEL
TOWER HAMLETS
LONDON CENTRE See pp.24 to 31
A 13
SHADWELL
WAPPING
CANARY WHARF
ROTHERHITHE
CANADA WATER
BERMONDSEY
ISLE OF D
SURREY QUAYS
A 200
A 2
NEW CROSS GATE
NEW CROSS
T
U
V

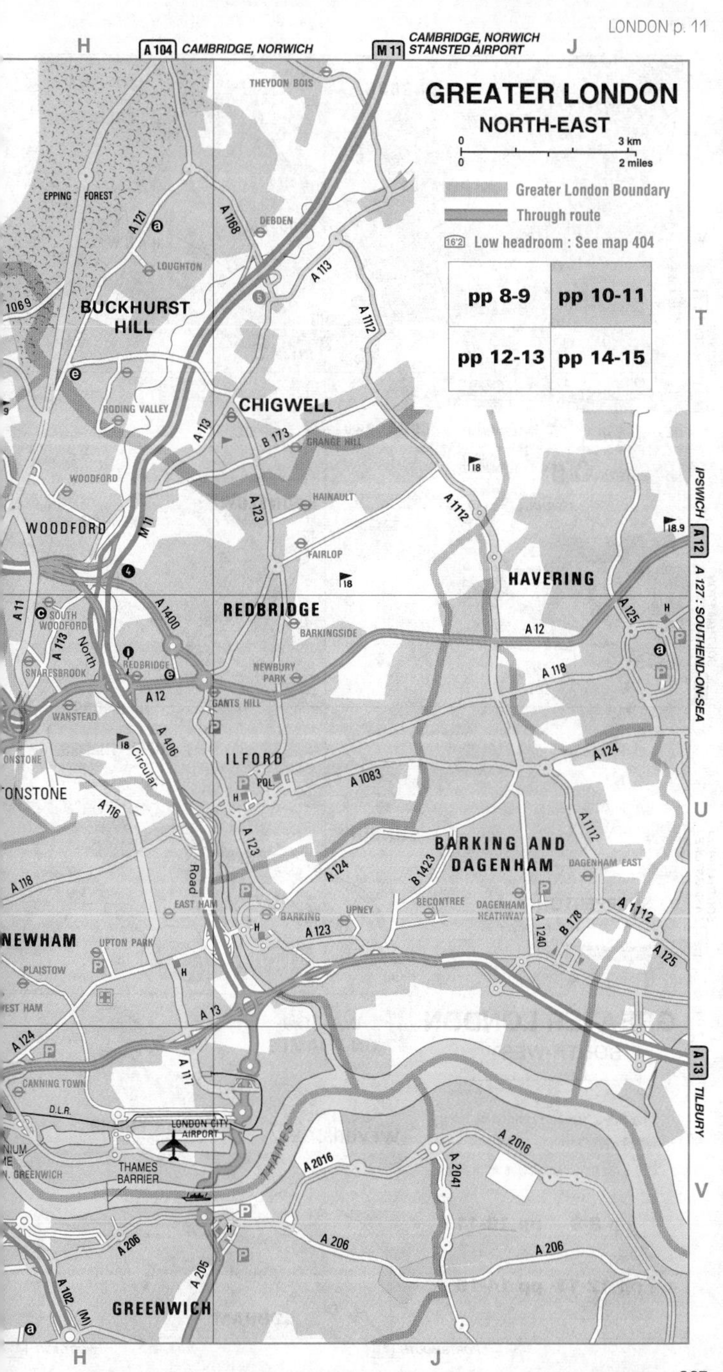
A 104 CAMBRIDGE, NORWICH
M 11 CAMBRIDGE, NORWICH STANSTED AIRPORT
GREATER LONDON
NORTH-EAST
3 km
2 miles
Greater London Boundary
Through route
Low headroom : See map 404
pp 8-9
pp 10-11
pp 12-13
pp 14-15
BUCKHURST HILL
CHIGWELL
WOODFORD
REDBRIDGE
HAVERING
ILFORD
BARKING AND DAGENHAM
NEWHAM
GREENWICH
EPPING FOREST
THEYDON BOIS
DEBDEN
LOUGHTON
RODING VALLEY
GRANGE HILL
HAINAULT
FAIRLOP
BARKINGSIDE
NEWBURY PARK
GANTS HILL
SOUTH WOODFORD
SNARESBROOK
WANSTEAD
North Circular Road
EAST HAM
BARKING
UPNEY
BECONTREE
DAGENHAM HEATHWAY
DAGENHAM EAST
UPTON PARK
PLAISTOW
CANNING TOWN
D.L.R.
LONDON CITY AIRPORT
THAMES BARRIER
THAMES
IPSWICH A 12
A 127 : SOUTHEND-ON-SEA
A 13 TILBURY

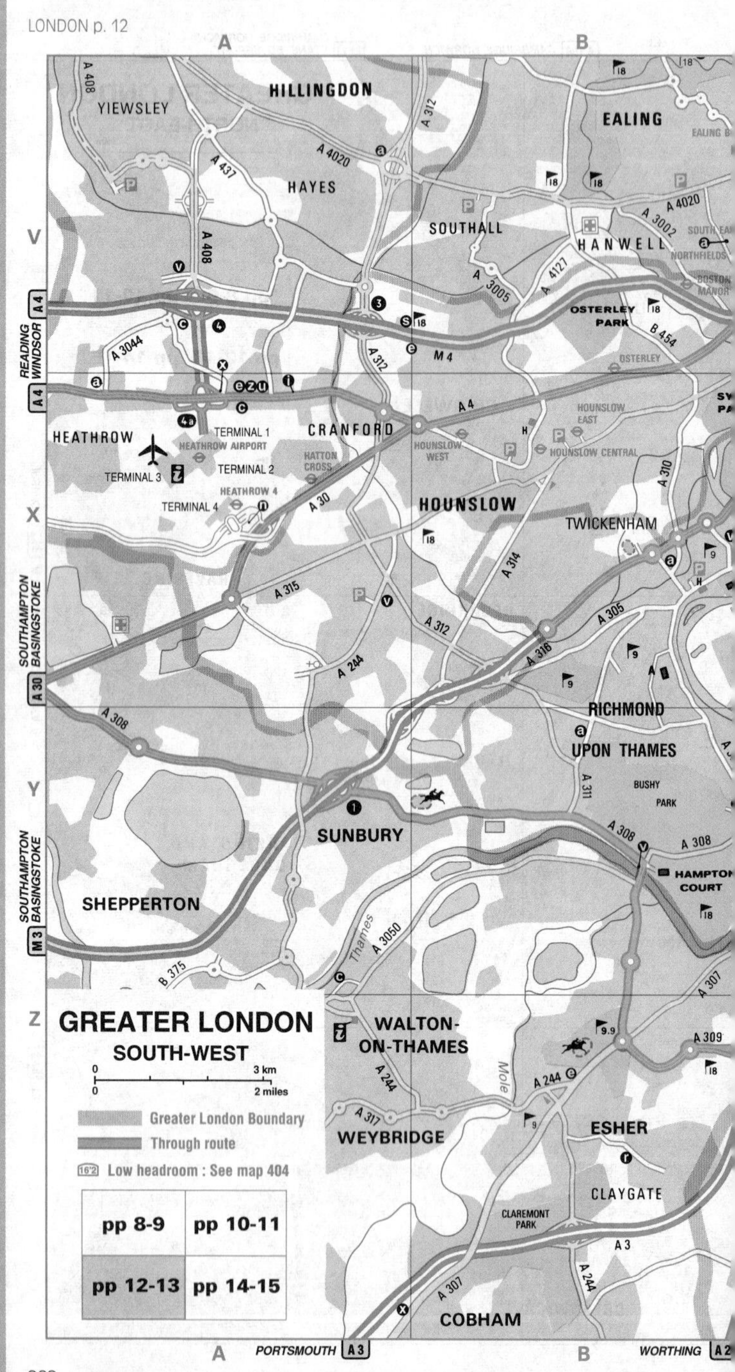
A
B
HILLINGDON
YIEWSLEY
EALING
HAYES
SOUTHALL
HANWELL
OSTERLEY PARK
CRANFORD
HEATHROW
TERMINAL 1
HEATHROW AIRPORT
TERMINAL 2
TERMINAL 3
TERMINAL 4
HOUNSLOW
TWICKENHAM
RICHMOND UPON THAMES
BUSHY PARK
SUNBURY
SHEPPERTON
HAMPTON COURT
WALTON-ON-THAMES
WEYBRIDGE
ESHER
CLAYGATE
CLAREMONT PARK
COBHAM
V
X
Y
Z
READING WINDSOR A4
SOUTHAMPTON BASINGSTOKE A30
SOUTHAMPTON BASINGSTOKE M3
PORTSMOUTH A3
WORTHING A2
GREATER LONDON
SOUTH-WEST
0 3 km
0 2 miles
Greater London Boundary
Through route
Low headroom : See map 404
pp 8-9
pp 10-11
pp 12-13
pp 14-15

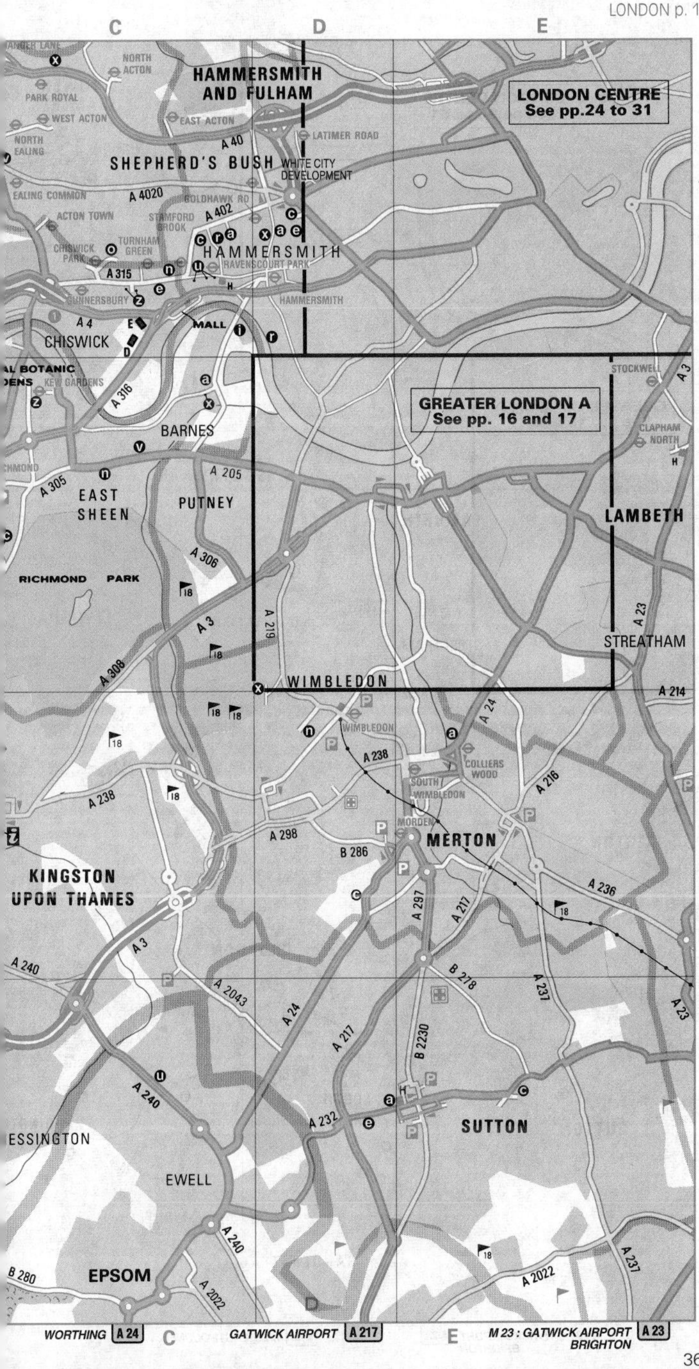

C D E

HANGER LANE
NORTH ACTON
PARK ROYAL
WEST ACTON
EAST ACTON
NORTH EALING
HAMMERSMITH AND FULHAM

LONDON CENTRE
See pp.24 to 31

LATIMER ROAD
A 40
SHEPHERD'S BUSH
WHITE CITY DEVELOPMENT
EALING COMMON
A 4020
GOLDHAWK RD
V
ACTON TOWN
STAMFORD BROOK
A 402
TURNHAM GREEN
CHISWICK PARK
HAMMERSMITH
RAVENSCOURT PARK
A 315
GUNNERSBURY
HAMMERSMITH
A 4
MALL
CHISWICK
ROYAL BOTANIC GARDENS
KEW GARDENS
A 316
STOCKWELL
A 3

GREATER LONDON A
See pp. 16 and 17

BARNES
CLAPHAM NORTH
RICHMOND
A 205
A 305
EAST SHEEN
PUTNEY
LAMBETH
X
A 306
RICHMOND PARK
A 3
A 219
A 23
STREATHAM
A 308
WIMBLEDON
A 214
WIMBLEDON
A 24
A 238
COLLIERS WOOD
SOUTH WIMBLEDON
A 216
A 238
MORDEN
A 298
MERTON
Y
B 286
KINGSTON UPON THAMES
A 297
A 217
A 236
A 3
A 240
B 278
A 2043
A 237
A 24
A 23
A 217
B 2230
A 240
A 232
SUTTON
CHESSINGTON
Z
EWELL
A 240
A 237
B 280
EPSOM
A 2022
A 2022
D

WORTHING A 24 C GATWICK AIRPORT A 217 E M 23 : GATWICK AIRPORT BRIGHTON A 23

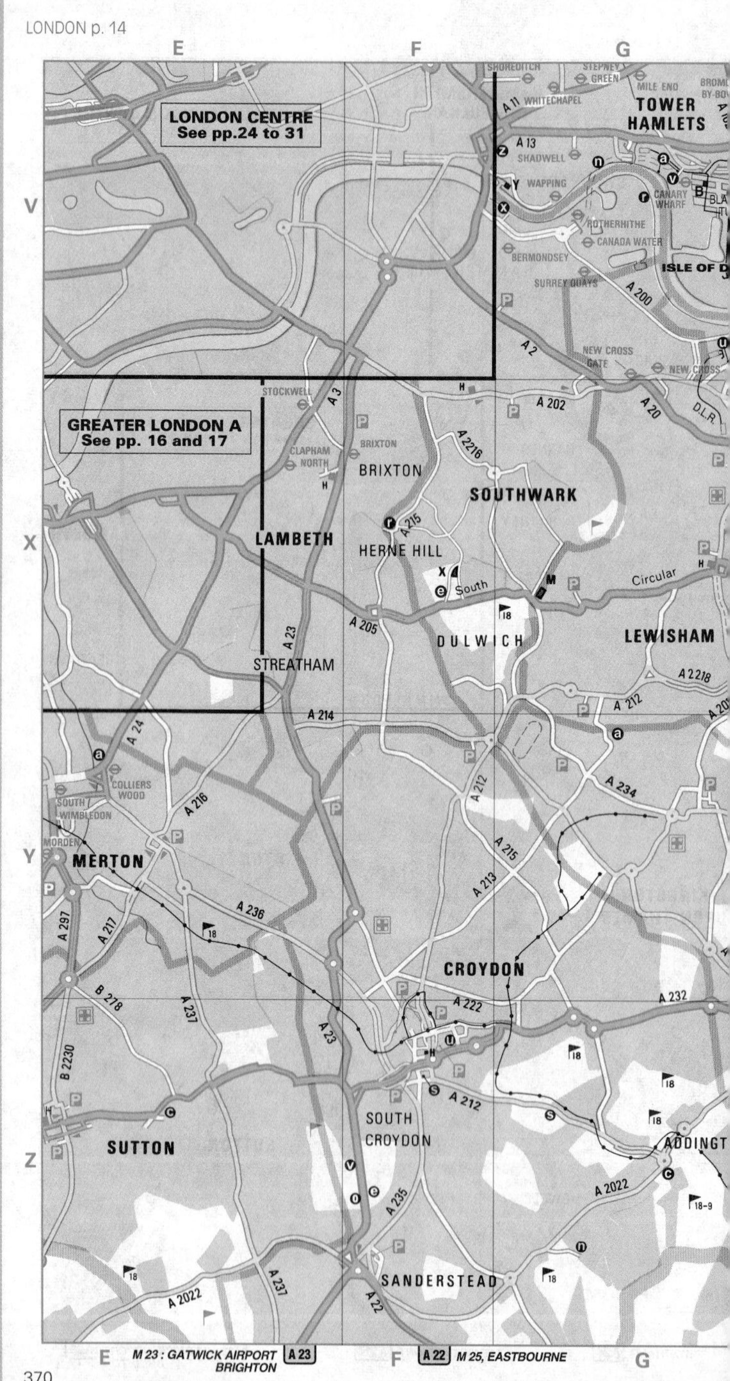
E
F
G
SHOREDITCH
STEPNEY GREEN
MILE END
TOWER HAMLETS
WHITECHAPEL
A 11
A 13
SHADWELL
WAPPING
CANARY WHARF
ROTHERHITHE
CANADA WATER
BERMONDSEY
SURREY QUAYS
ISLE OF D
A 200
A 2
NEW CROSS GATE
NEW CROSS
A 20
D.L.R.
LONDON CENTRE
See pp.24 to 31
V
GREATER LONDON A
See pp. 16 and 17
STOCKWELL
A 3
A 202
A 2216
CLAPHAM NORTH
BRIXTON
SOUTHWARK
A 215
LAMBETH
X
HERNE HILL
South
Circular
A 205
DULWICH
LEWISHAM
A 23
STREATHAM
A 2218
A 212
A 214
A 24
COLLIERS WOOD
SOUTH WIMBLEDON
A 216
A 234
MORDEN
Y
MERTON
A 215
A 213
A 297
A 217
A 236
CROYDON
B 278
A 237
A 23
A 222
A 232
B 2230
A 212
SOUTH CROYDON
SUTTON
ADDINGT
Z
A 2022
A 235
SANDERSTEAD
A 237
A 22
A 2022
E
M 23 : GATWICK AIRPORT BRIGHTON
A 23
F
A 22
M 25, EASTBOURNE
G

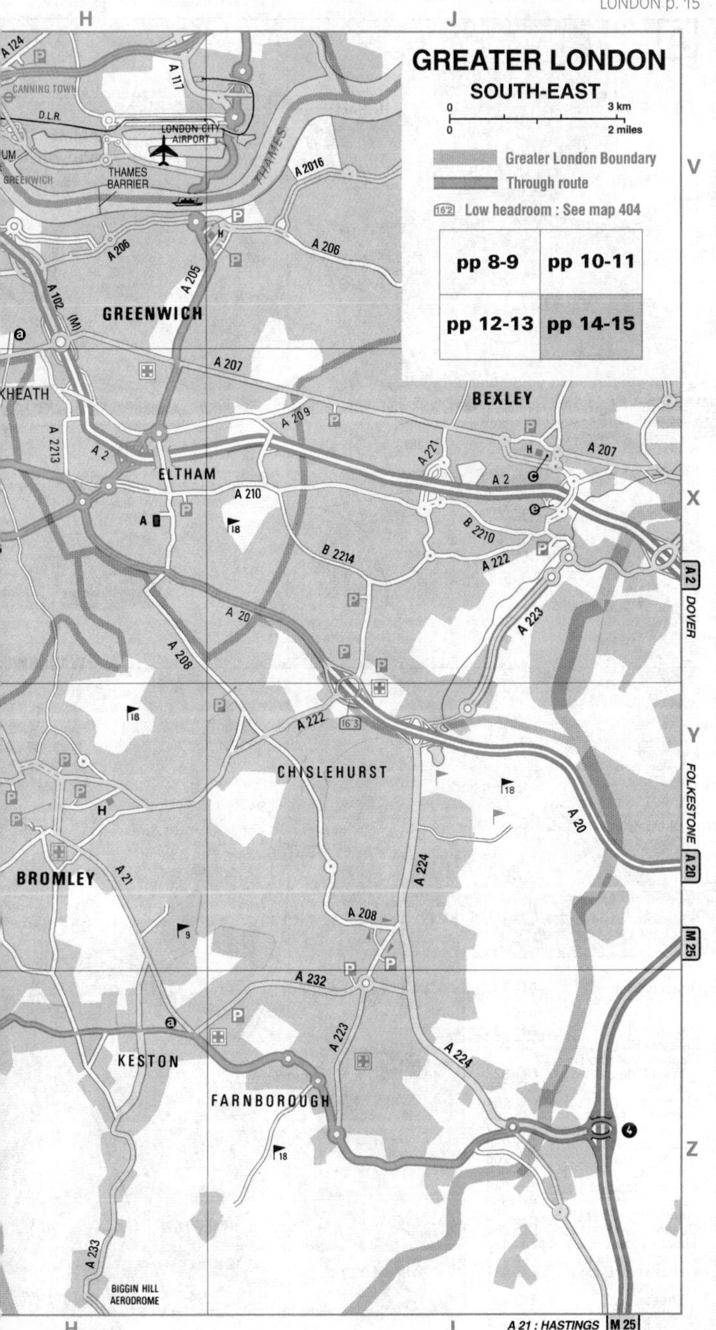
GREATER LONDON
SOUTH-EAST
0 3 km
0 2 miles
Greater London Boundary
Through route
Low headroom : See map 404
pp 8-9
pp 10-11
pp 12-13
pp 14-15
H
J
V
X
Y
Z
CANNING TOWN
D.L.R.
LONDON CITY AIRPORT
THAMES
THAMES BARRIER
GREENWICH
BEXLEY
ELTHAM
CHISLEHURST
BROMLEY
KESTON
FARNBOROUGH
BIGGIN HILL AERODROME
A 124
A 117
A 2016
A 206
A 205
A 102 (M)
A 207
A 209
A 2213
A 2
A 210
A 221
B 2210
B 2214
A 222
A 20
A 208
A 223
A 224
A 21
A 232
A 233
A 2 DOVER
FOLKESTONE A 20
M 25
A 21 : HASTINGS M 25

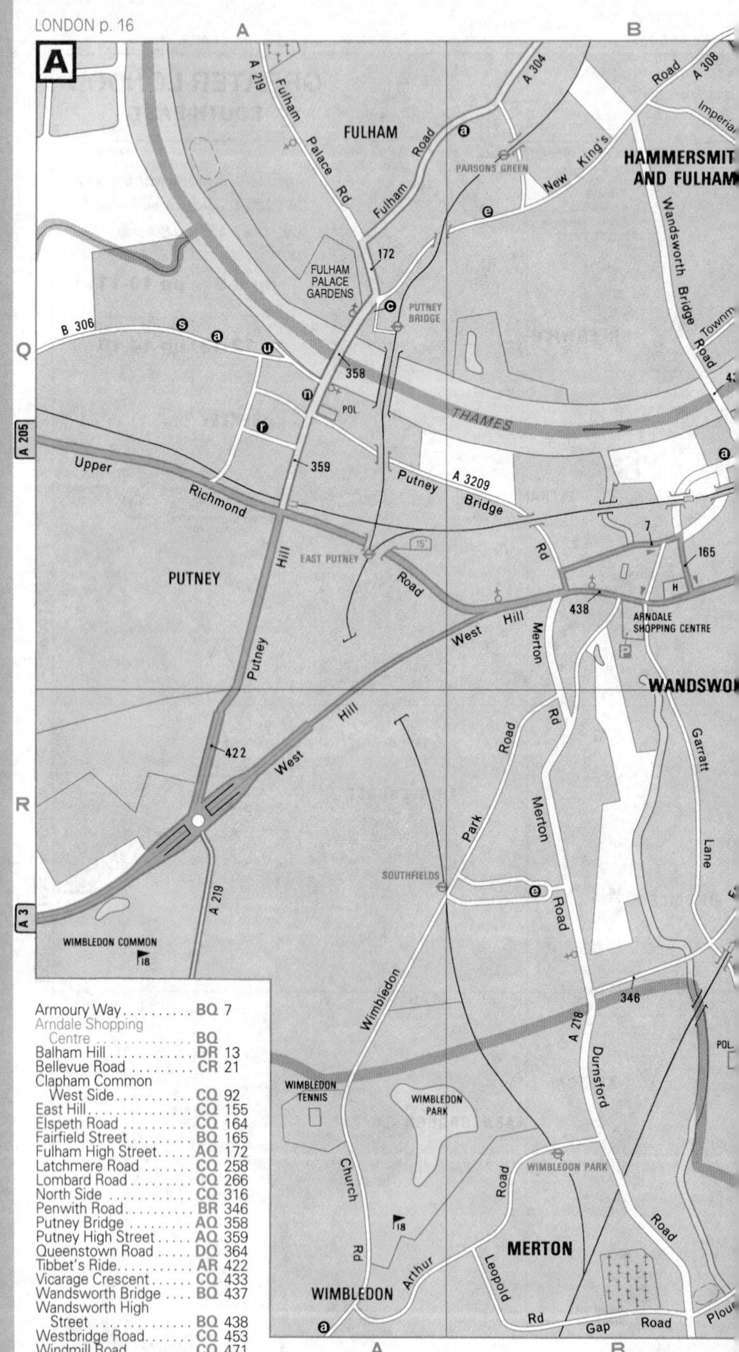
A
B
FULHAM
HAMMERSMITH AND FULHAM
PUTNEY
WANDSWORTH
MERTON
WIMBLEDON
THAMES
Fulham Palace Rd
Fulham Road
New King's
Wandsworth Bridge Road
Putney Bridge
Upper Richmond
Putney Hill
East Hill
West Hill
Merton Rd
Garratt Lane
Park Road
Merton Road
Durnsford Road
Wimbledon Park
Church Rd
Arthur Road
Leopold Rd
Gap Road
FULHAM PALACE GARDENS
PUTNEY BRIDGE
PARSONS GREEN
EAST PUTNEY
SOUTHFIELDS
WIMBLEDON PARK
WIMBLEDON COMMON
WIMBLEDON TENNIS
ARNDALE SHOPPING CENTRE
POL.
A 219
A 304
A 308
A 3209
A 205
A 3
A 218
B 306
Q
R

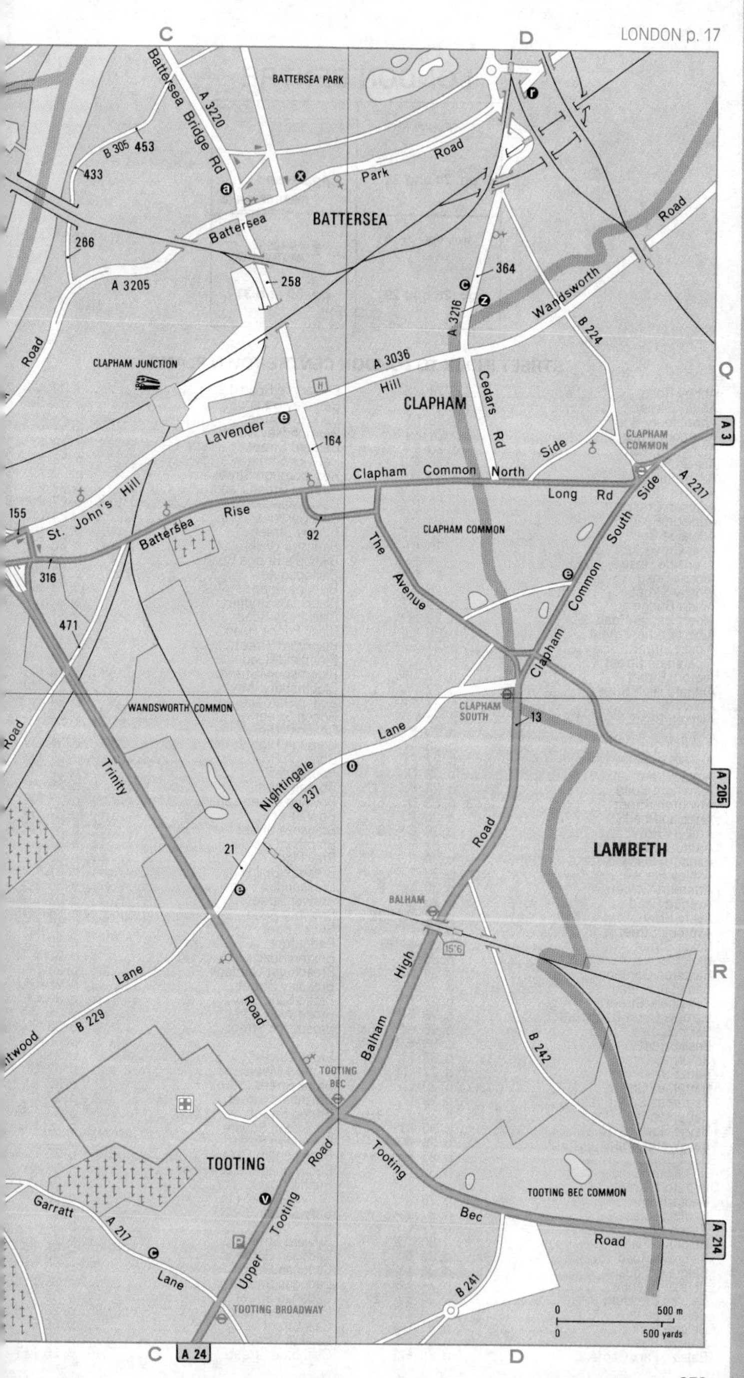

C
D
BATTERSEA PARK
Battersea Bridge Rd
A 3220
B 305
453
433
Park
Road
BATTERSEA
Battersea
266
258
A 3205
Road
364
A 3216
Wandsworth
Road
B 224
CLAPHAM JUNCTION
A 3036
Hill
CLAPHAM
Cedars
Rd
Lavender
164
Side
CLAPHAM COMMON
A 3
Clapham Common North
Long Rd
A 2217
155
St. John's Hill
Battersea
Rise
92
CLAPHAM COMMON
The Avenue
South Side
Common
316
471
Clapham
WANDSWORTH COMMON
CLAPHAM SOUTH
13
Lane
Road
Trinity
Nightingale
B 237
A 205
Road
LAMBETH
21
BALHAM
15'6
R
Lane
High
B 229
Road
B 242
ttwood
Balham
TOOTING BEC
TOOTING
Road
Tooting
TOOTING BEC COMMON
Garratt
Upper Tooting
Bec
A 217
Road
A 214
Lane
B 241
TOOTING BROADWAY
0
500 m
0
500 yards
C
A 24
D
Q

LONDON CENTRE

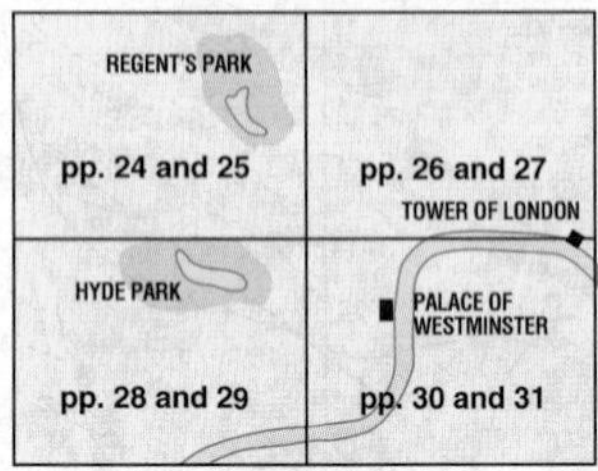

STREET INDEX TO LONDON CENTRE TOWN PLANS

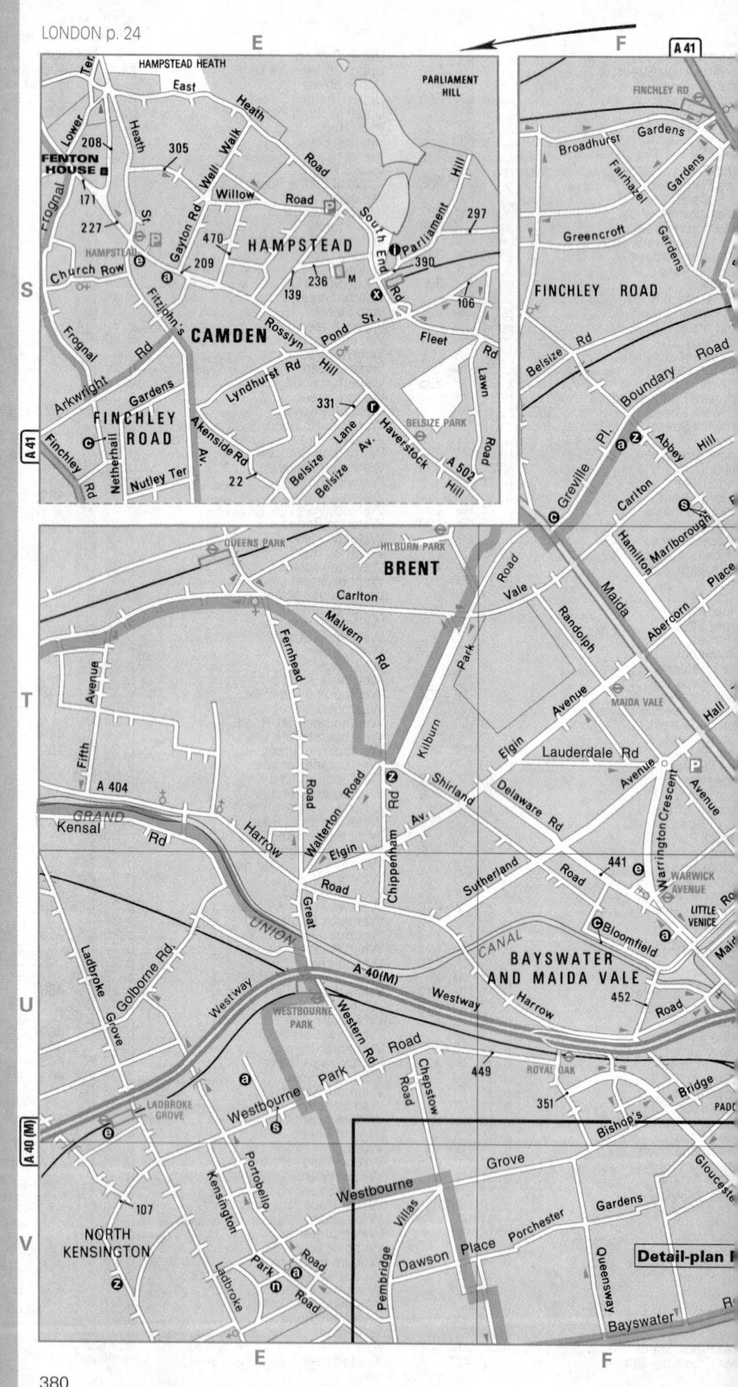
E
F
A 41
HAMPSTEAD HEATH
PARLIAMENT HILL
FENTON HOUSE
HAMPSTEAD
CAMDEN
FINCHLEY ROAD
BELSIZE PARK
BRENT
QUEENS PARK
KILBURN PARK
MAIDA VALE
WARWICK AVENUE
LITTLE VENICE
BAYSWATER AND MAIDA VALE
GRAND UNION CANAL
A 40(M)
Westway
WESTBOURNE PARK
LADBROKE GROVE
ROYAL OAK
NORTH KENSINGTON
Detail-plan
S
T
U
V
A 404
A 502
A 40 (M)
Church Row
Frognal
Arkwright Rd
Fitzjohn's
Rosslyn Hill
Pond St.
Fleet Rd
Lyndhurst Rd
Haverstock Hill
Belsize Lane
Belsize Av.
Akenside Rd
Nutley Ter
Netherhall
Finchley Rd
Heath St.
Gayton Rd
Well Walk
Willow Road
East Heath Road
South End Rd
Parliament Hill
Lawn Road
Lower Ter.
Broadhurst Gardens
Fairhazel Gardens
Greencroft Gardens
Belsize Rd
Boundary Road
Greville Pl.
Abbey Hill
Carlton
Hamilton
Marlborough
Maida
Abercorn Place
Hall
Carlton Vale
Kilburn Park Road
Randolph Avenue
Malvern Rd
Fernhead Road
Fifth Avenue
Elgin Avenue
Lauderdale Rd
Warrington Crescent
Shirland Road
Delaware Rd
Walterton Road
Chippenham Rd
Elgin Av.
Kensal Rd
Harrow Road
Great Western Rd
Sutherland Avenue
Bloomfield
Ladbroke Grove
Golborne Rd.
Westbourne Park Road
Chepstow Road
Bishop's Bridge
Westbourne Grove
Gloucester
Porchester Gardens
Pembridge Villas
Dawson Place
Queensway
Bayswater
Kensington Park Road
Portobello
Ladbroke
208
305
171
227
209
470
236
139
390
297
106
331
22
441
452
449
351
107

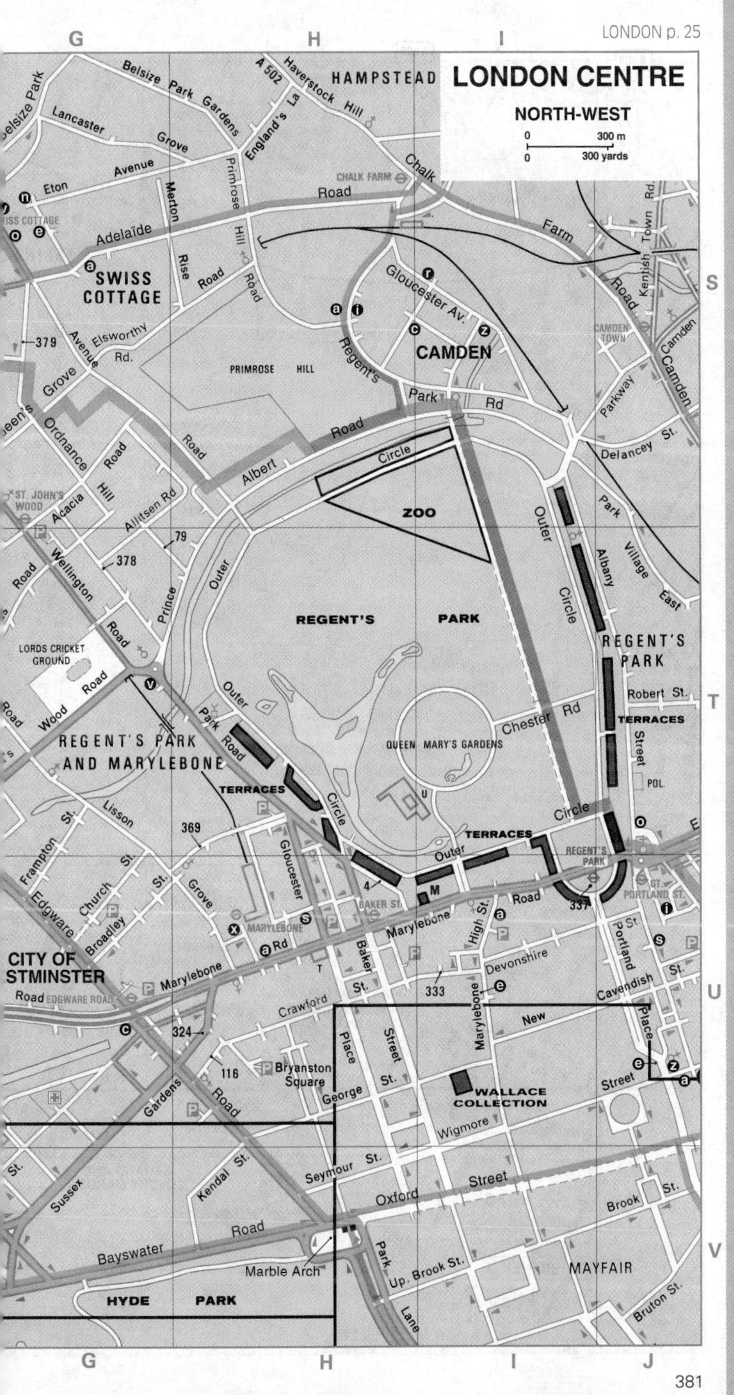
LONDON CENTRE
NORTH-WEST
0 300 m
0 300 yards
G
H
I
J
S
T
U
V
HAMPSTEAD
SWISS COTTAGE
CAMDEN
PRIMROSE HILL
ZOO
REGENT'S PARK
QUEEN MARY'S GARDENS
REGENT'S PARK TERRACES
REGENT'S PARK AND MARYLEBONE
TERRACES
LORDS CRICKET GROUND
CITY OF WESTMINSTER
WALLACE COLLECTION
HYDE PARK
MAYFAIR
Marble Arch
Belsize Park Gardens
Haverstock Hill
England's La
A 502
Lancaster Grove
Eton Avenue
Adelaïde Road
Chalk Farm Road
Primrose Hill Road
Merton Rise
Elsworthy Rd.
Avenue Road
Gloucester Av.
Regent's Park Rd
Albert Road
Parkway
Camden
Kentish Town Rd.
Delancey St.
Park Village East
Albany Street
Outer Circle
Chester Rd
Robert St.
Ordnance Hill
Acacia Road
Allitsen Rd
Prince Albert Road
Wellington Road
Grove End Road
St. John's Wood Road
Park Road
Lisson Grove
Frampton St.
Church St.
Broadley St.
Edgware Road
Gloucester Place
Baker St.
Marylebone Road
Marylebone High St.
Devonshire St.
Portland Place
Cavendish Place
New Cavendish Street
Crawford Street
Bryanston Square
George St.
Wigmore St.
Seymour St.
Oxford Street
Brook St.
Up. Brook St.
Park Lane
Bayswater Road
Sussex Gardens
Kendal St.
Bruton St.
CHALK FARM
CAMDEN TOWN
SWISS COTTAGE
ST. JOHN'S WOOD
BAKER ST.
MARYLEBONE
EDGWARE ROAD
REGENT'S PARK
GT. PORTLAND ST.
POL.
379
378
79
369
337
333
324
116
4

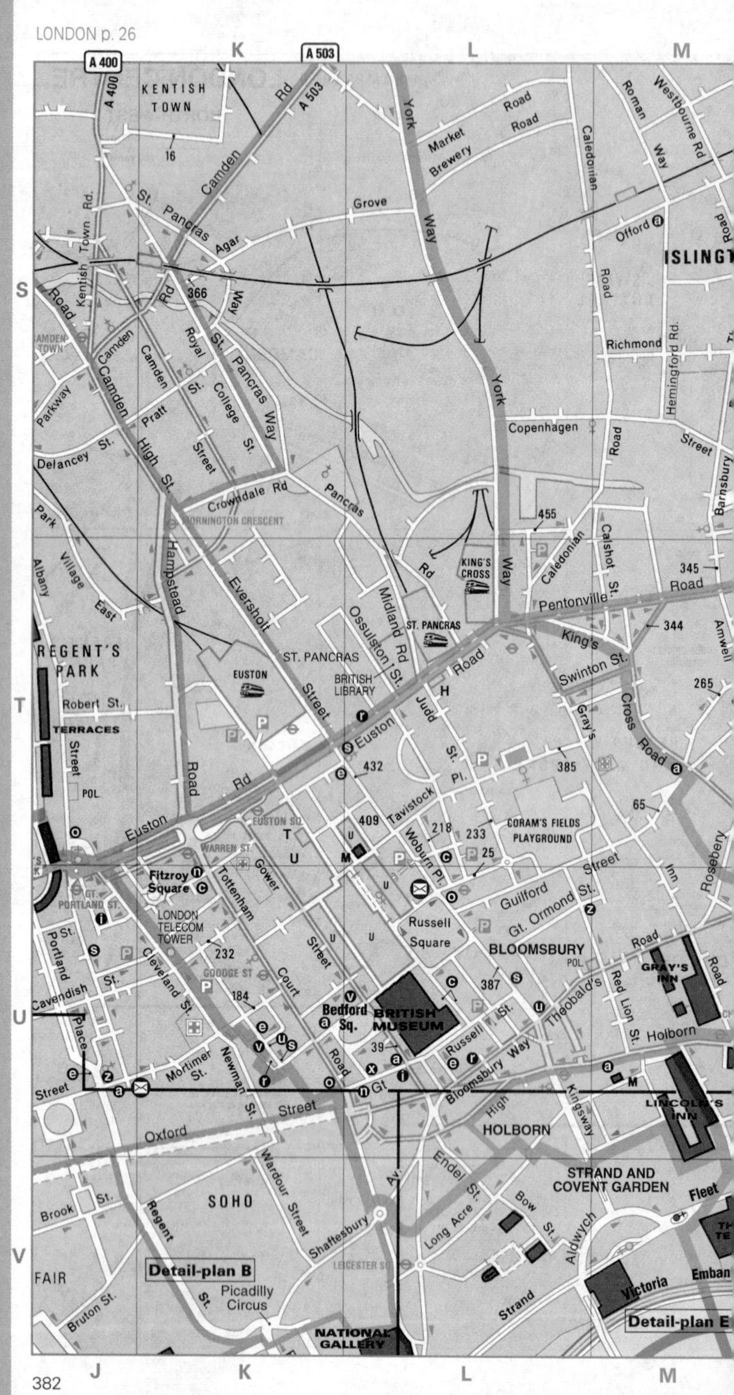
K
L
M
A 400
A 503
KENTISH TOWN
Camden Rd
York Way
Market Road
Brewery Road
Caledonian Road
Roman Way
Westbourne Rd
St. Pancras
Agar Grove
Offord
ISLINGT
Kentish Town Rd.
366
Royal College St.
St. Pancras Way
Camden High St.
Camden St.
Pratt St.
Parkway
Delancey St.
Richmond
Hemingford Rd.
Copenhagen Street
Barnsbury
Crowndale Rd
MORNINGTON CRESCENT
Pancras Rd
455
Calshot St.
345
Pentonville Road
KING'S CROSS
ST. PANCRAS
King's Cross Road
344
Swinton St.
Amwell
Albany
Park Village East
Hampstead Road
Eversholt Street
Midland Rd
Ossulston St.
REGENT'S PARK
EUSTON
BRITISH LIBRARY
Judd St.
265
Robert St.
TERRACES
Euston Road
Gray's Inn Road
385
432
Tavistock Pl.
POL.
Euston Rd
409
218
233
CORAM'S FIELDS PLAYGROUND
65
EUSTON SQ.
WARREN ST.
Woburn Pl.
25
Rosebery
Fitzroy Square
Gower Street
Guilford Street
GT. PORTLAND ST.
Tottenham Court
LONDON TELECOM TOWER
Russell Square
Gt. Ormond St.
Portland Pl.
232
BLOOMSBURY
GRAY'S INN
Cleveland St.
GOODGE ST
387
Theobald's Road
Red Lion St.
Cavendish Place
184
Bedford Sq.
BRITISH MUSEUM
Holborn
39
Russell St.
Mortimer St.
Newman St.
Bloomsbury Way
Kingsway
Street
Gt. Russell
Oxford Street
High Holborn
HOLBORN
LINCOLN'S INN
Wardour Street
Endell St.
STRAND AND COVENT GARDEN
Brook St.
Regent St.
SOHO
Bow St.
Fleet
Shaftesbury Av.
Long Acre
FAIR
Detail-plan B
LEICESTER SQ
Aldwych
Victoria Embankment
Bruton St.
Picadilly Circus
Strand
Detail-plan E
NATIONAL GALLERY
S
T
U
V
J
K
L
M

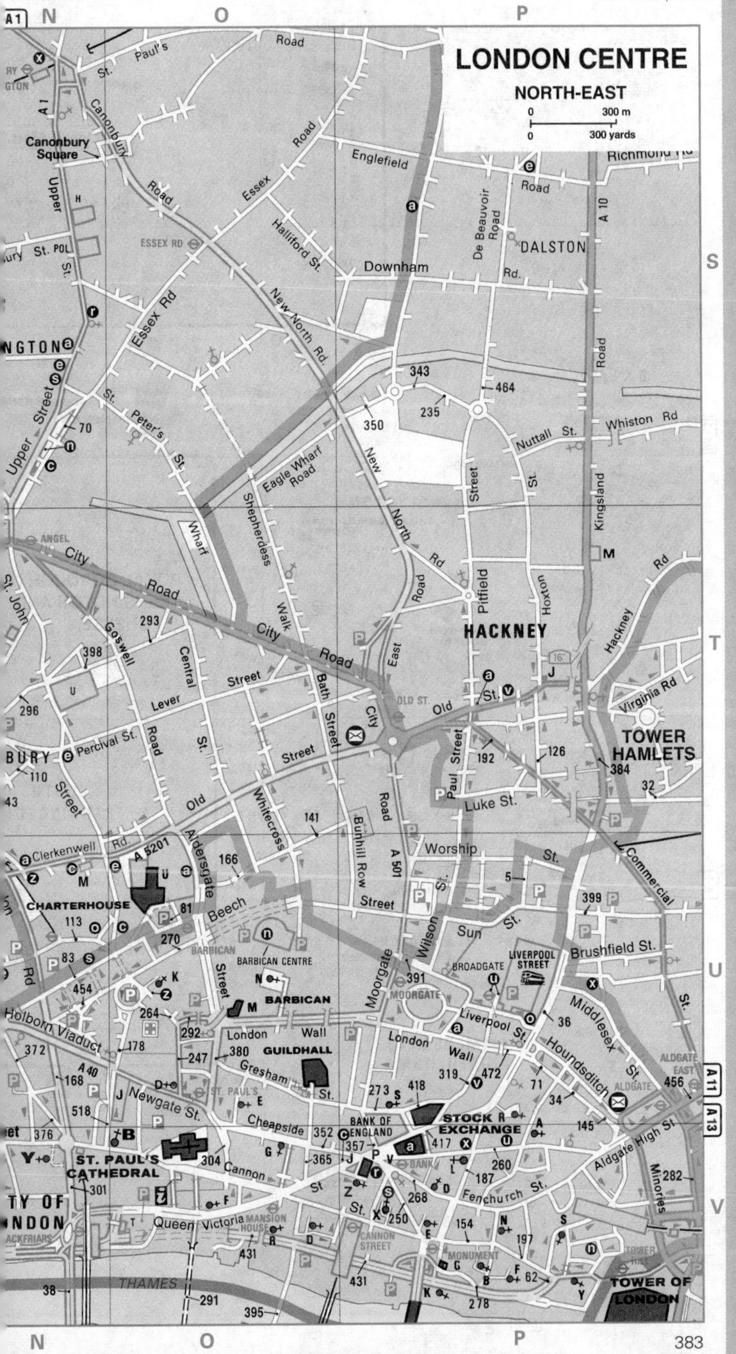
LONDON CENTRE
NORTH-EAST
0 300 m
0 300 yards
DALSTON
HACKNEY
TOWER HAMLETS
CHARTERHOUSE
BARBICAN CENTRE
BARBICAN
GUILDHALL
ST. PAUL'S CATHEDRAL
BANK OF ENGLAND
STOCK EXCHANGE
LIVERPOOL STREET
BROADGATE
MOORGATE
TOWER OF LONDON
Canonbury Square
City Road
Old Street
Kingsland Road
Hackney Rd
Commercial St.
Middlesex St.
Houndsditch
Aldgate High St.
Minories
Fenchurch St.
Cannon St.
Queen Victoria St.
Cheapside
Newgate St.
Holborn Viaduct
London Wall
Moorgate
Aldersgate Street
Goswell Road
Englefield Road
Essex Road
Downham Rd.
New North Rd.
Whiston Rd
Nuttall St.
Virginia Rd
Luke St.
Worship St.
Sun St.
Brushfield St.
Liverpool St.
Gresham St.
Bunhill Row
Whitecross Street
Bath Street
Shepherdess Walk
Eagle Wharf Road
Wharf Road
Central Street
Lever Street
Percival St.
Clerkenwell Rd.
Beech Street
THAMES

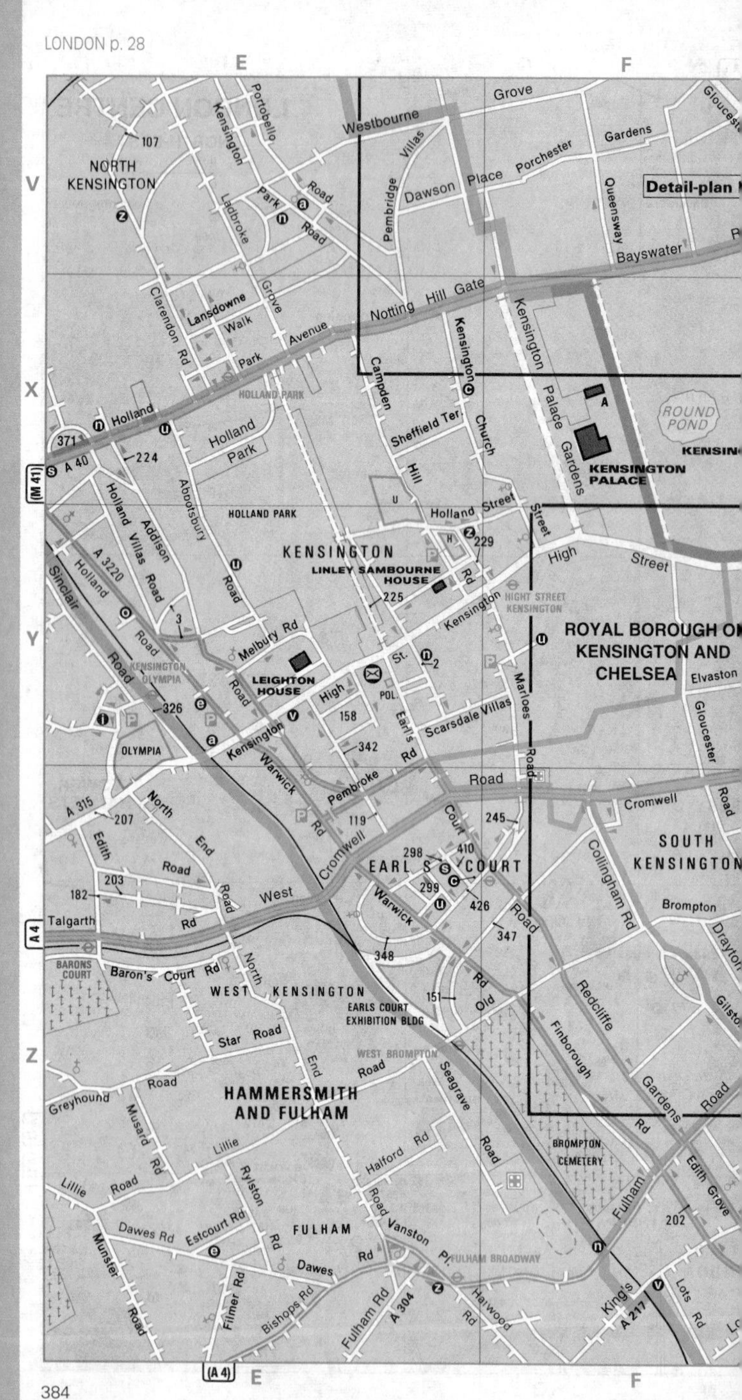
E
F
V
X
Y
Z
NORTH KENSINGTON
Detail-plan
KENSINGTON PALACE
ROUND POND
HOLLAND PARK
KENSINGTON
LINLEY SAMBOURNE HOUSE
HIGHT STREET KENSINGTON
ROYAL BOROUGH OF KENSINGTON AND CHELSEA
LEIGHTON HOUSE
KENSINGTON OLYMPIA
OLYMPIA
EARL'S COURT
SOUTH KENSINGTON
BARONS COURT
WEST KENSINGTON
EARLS COURT EXHIBITION BLDG
WEST BROMPTON
HAMMERSMITH AND FULHAM
BROMPTON CEMETERY
FULHAM
FULHAM BROADWAY
Westbourne
Grove
Gardens
Porchester
Dawson Place
Pembridge Villas
Queensway
Bayswater
Notting Hill Gate
Kensington Church
Kensington Palace Gardens
Campden Hill
Sheffield Ter.
Holland Street
High Street
Kensington High St.
Lansdowne Walk
Clarendon Rd
Holland Park Avenue
Holland Park
Abbotsbury Road
Holland Villas Road
Addison Road
Melbury Rd
Earl's Court Rd
Scarsdale Villas
Marloes Road
Cromwell Road
Pembroke Road
Warwick Rd
West Cromwell Rd
Talgarth Rd
North End Road
Edith Road
Baron's Court Rd
Star Road
Old Brompton Road
Seagrave Road
Redcliffe Gardens
Finborough Rd
Collingham Rd
Gloucester Road
Greyhound Road
Musard Rd
Lillie Road
Rylston Rd
Dawes Rd
Estcourt Rd
Munster Road
Filmer Rd
Bishops Rd
Fulham Rd
Vanston Pl.
Halford Rd
Harwood Rd
King's Road
Lots Rd
Edith Grove
Fulham Road
Elvaston
Brompton
A 40
M 41
A 3220
A 315
A 4
A 304
A 217
107
371
224
229
225
3
326
158
342
207
203
182
119
245
298
410
299
426
347
348
151
202

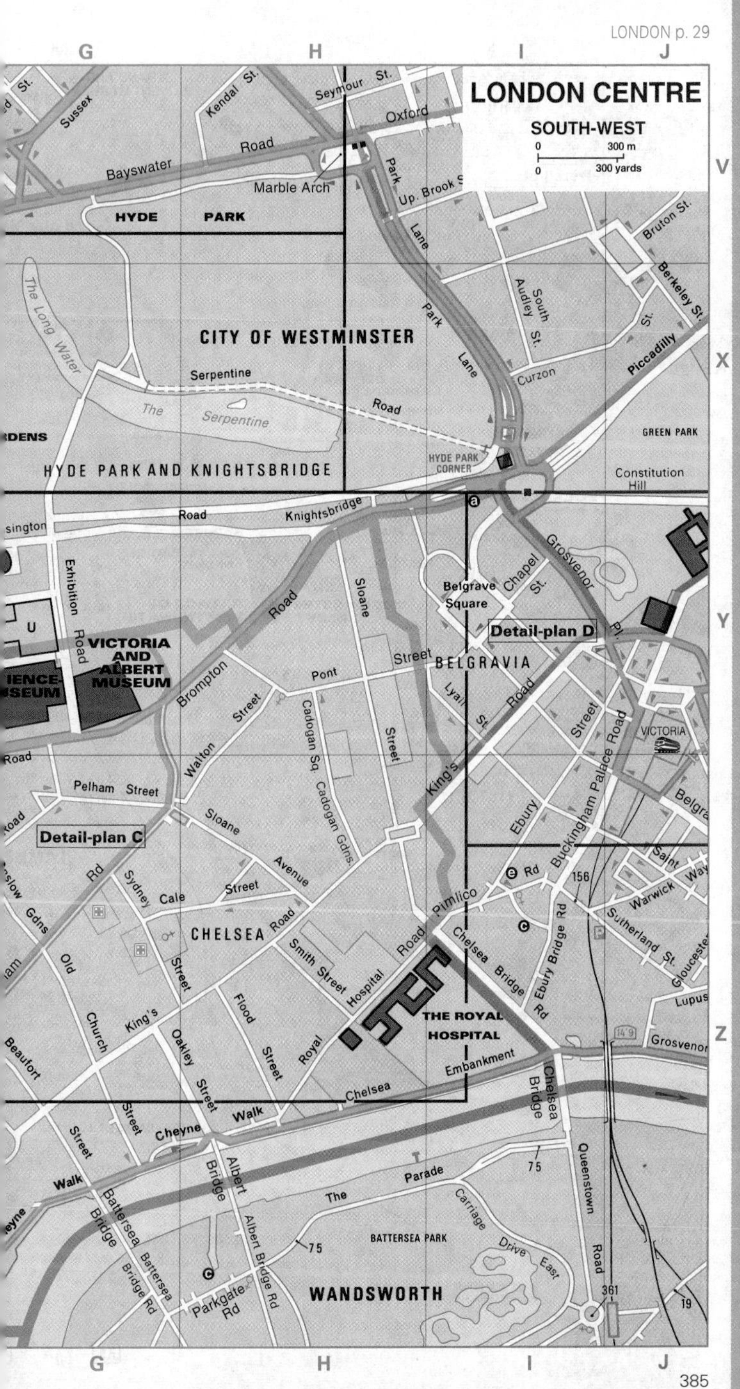
LONDON CENTRE
SOUTH-WEST
0 300 m
0 300 yards
G
H
I
J
V
X
Y
Z
Sussex
Kendal St.
Seymour St.
Oxford
Bayswater Road
Marble Arch
Park Lane
Up. Brook St.
HYDE PARK
The Long Water
CITY OF WESTMINSTER
South Audley St.
Bruton St.
Berkeley St.
Piccadilly
Curzon
Serpentine Road
The Serpentine
HYDE PARK CORNER
GREEN PARK
Constitution Hill
HYDE PARK AND KNIGHTSBRIDGE
Road
Knightsbridge
Exhibition Road
VICTORIA AND ALBERT MUSEUM
Brompton Road
Sloane Street
Belgrave Square
Chapel St.
Grosvenor Pl.
Detail-plan D
BELGRAVIA
Pont Street
Cadogan Sq.
Cadogan Gdns.
Lyall St.
Road
Street
Buckingham Palace Road
VICTORIA
Walton Street
Pelham Street
Sloane Avenue
King's Road
Ebury
Detail-plan C
Sydney Cale Street
CHELSEA
Smith Street
Royal Hospital Road
Pimlico Rd
Chelsea Bridge Rd
Ebury Bridge Rd
Warwick Way
Sutherland St.
Saint
Gloucester
Lupus
156
Old Church Street
King's
Flood Street
Oakley Street
THE ROYAL HOSPITAL
Embankment
Chelsea
Grosvenor
Chelsea Bridge
Beaufort
Cheyne Walk
Albert Bridge
Battersea Bridge
Queenstown Road
The Parade
Carriage Drive East
BATTERSEA PARK
75
Albert Bridge Rd
Battersea Bridge Rd
Parkgate Rd
WANDSWORTH
361
19

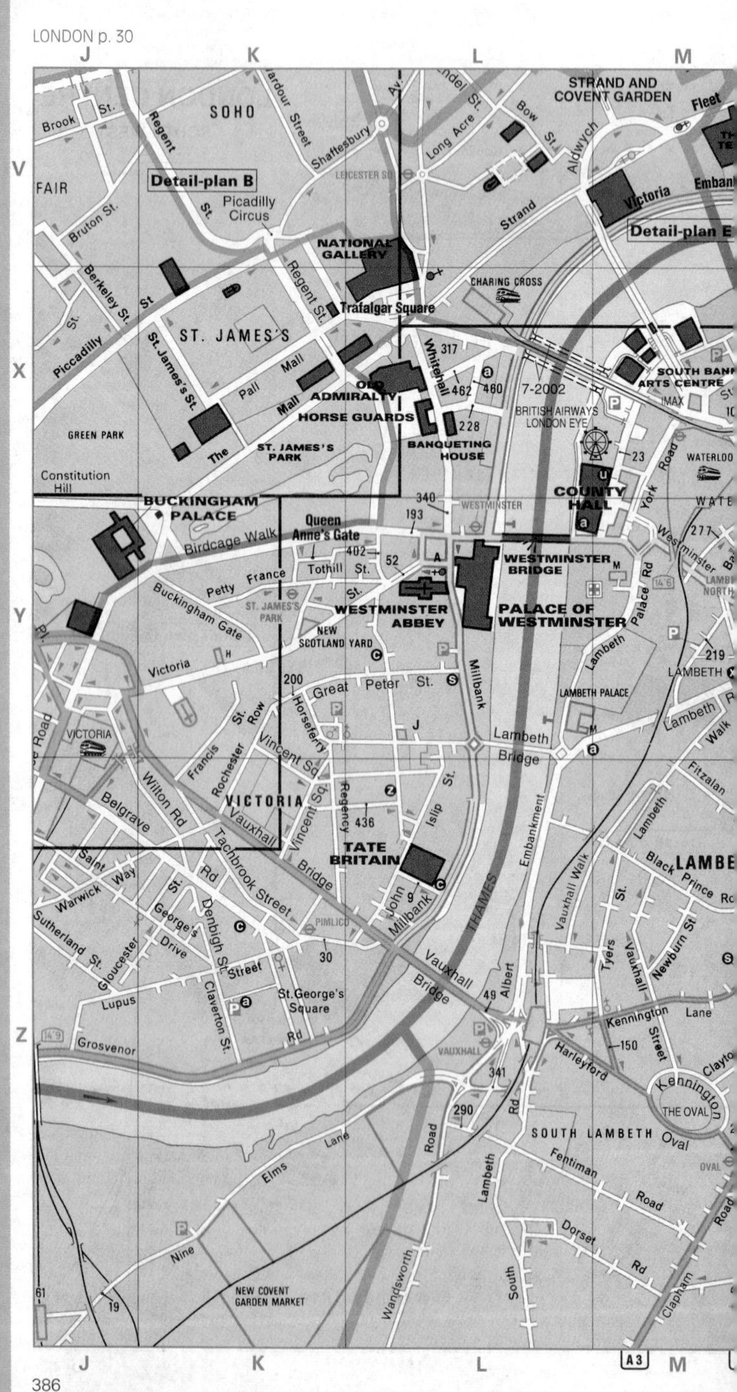
J
K
L
M
V
X
Y
Z
SOHO
STRAND AND COVENT GARDEN
Brook St.
Regent St.
Wardour Street
Shaftesbury Av.
Long Acre
Bow St.
Aldwych
Fleet
FAIR
Detail-plan B
Picadilly Circus
LEICESTER SQ.
Strand
Victoria
Embankment
Detail-plan E
Bruton St.
Berkeley St.
NATIONAL GALLERY
Trafalgar Square
CHARING CROSS
Piccadilly
St. James's St.
ST. JAMES'S
Pall Mall
The Mall
Whitehall
317
462
460
7-2002
OLD ADMIRALTY
HORSE GUARDS
228
BANQUETING HOUSE
BRITISH AIRWAYS LONDON EYE
SOUTH BANK ARTS CENTRE
IMAX
23
WATERLOO
York Road
COUNTY HALL
GREEN PARK
ST. JAMES'S PARK
Constitution Hill
BUCKINGHAM PALACE
340
193
WESTMINSTER
Queen Anne's Gate
Birdcage Walk
402
52
Tothill St.
Petty France
WESTMINSTER BRIDGE
Westminster Bridge Rd
277
Buckingham Gate
ST. JAMES'S PARK
WESTMINSTER ABBEY
PALACE OF WESTMINSTER
Lambeth Palace Rd
NEW SCOTLAND YARD
219
LAMBETH
Victoria St.
200
Great Peter St.
Millbank
LAMBETH PALACE
Horseferry
St. Row
Rochester
Francis
Vincent Sq.
Lambeth Bridge
Lambeth Walk
VICTORIA
Wilton Rd
Belgrave
Regency
436
Islip St.
Fitzalan
Vauxhall Bridge
TATE BRITAIN
Embankment
Vauxhall Walk
Black Prince Rd
LAMBE
Saint Way
Warwick
Tachbrook Street
Denbigh St.
St. George's Drive
John Islip
Millbank
9
THAMES
Sutherland St.
Gloucester
PIMLICO
30
Newburn St.
Tyers
Vauxhall Street
Lupus
Claverton St.
Street
St.George's Square
Rd
49
Albert
Kennington Lane
Grosvenor
150
VAUXHALL
Harleyford
Clayton
341
Kennington Oval
THE OVAL
290
Rd
SOUTH LAMBETH
Lane
Road
Elms
Lambeth
Fentiman Road
OVAL
Dorset Rd
Nine Elms
NEW COVENT GARDEN MARKET
Wandsworth
South Lambeth
Clapham Road
61
19
A3

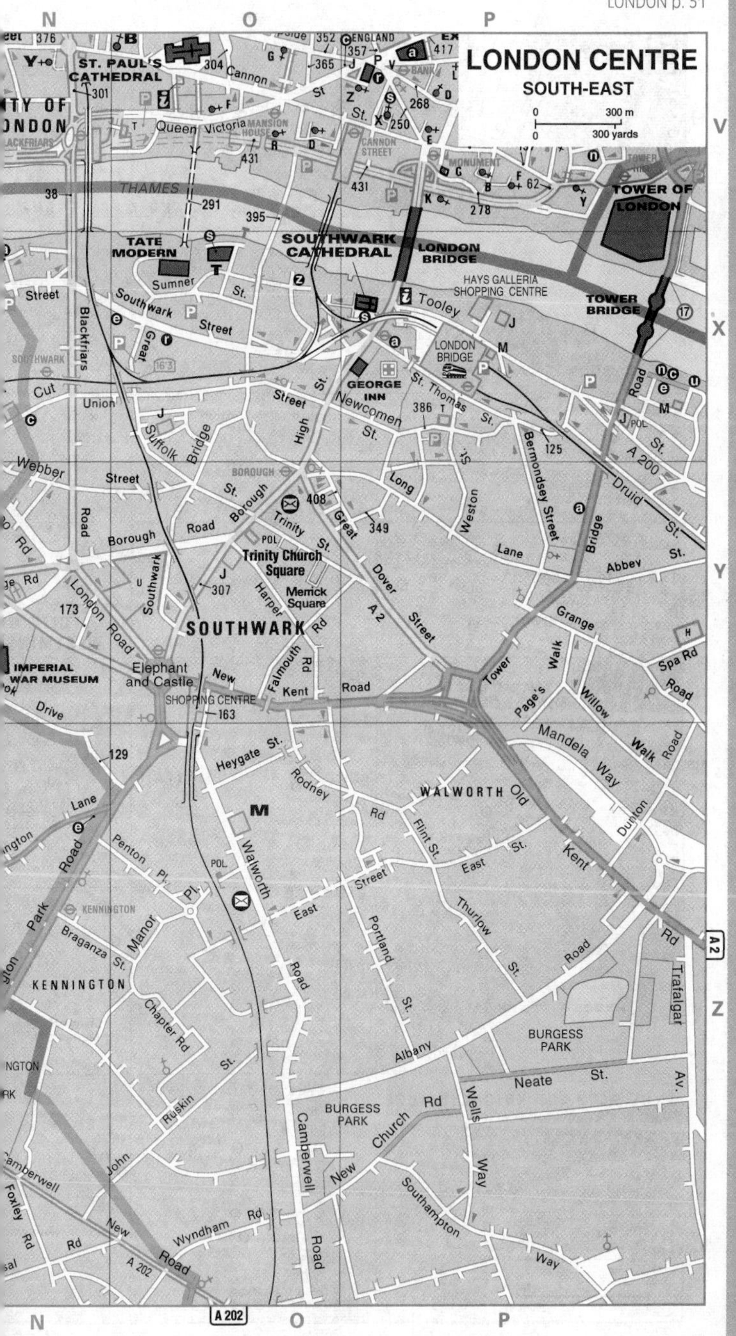
LONDON CENTRE
SOUTH-EAST
300 m
300 yards
ST. PAUL'S CATHEDRAL
TATE MODERN
SOUTHWARK CATHEDRAL
LONDON BRIDGE
TOWER OF LONDON
TOWER BRIDGE
HAYS GALLERIA SHOPPING CENTRE
GEORGE INN
Trinity Church Square
Merrick Square
SOUTHWARK
IMPERIAL WAR MUSEUM
Elephant and Castle
SHOPPING CENTRE
WALWORTH
KENNINGTON
BURGESS PARK
THAMES
Queen Victoria
Cannon St.
Southwark Street
Tooley
Borough High St.
Great Dover Street
New Kent Road
Old Kent Rd
Walworth Road
Albany Road
Camberwell Road
Bermondsey Street
Tower Bridge Road
Mandela Way
East Street
N
O
P
V
X
Y
Z
A 2
A 202
A 200

B
A
B
C
H
J
K
L
M
N
P
WALLACE COLLECTION
REGENT'S PARK AND MARYLEBONE
Portman Square
MARBLE ARCH
Grosvenor Square
CITY OF WESTMINS
MAYFAIR
Berkeley Square
HYDE PARK
HYDE PARK AND KNIGHTSBRIDGE
Shepherd Market
GREEN PARK
APSLEY HOUSE WELLINGTON MUSEUM
Oxford Street
Piccadilly
Park Lane
Serpentine Road
Cavendish Sq.
0 200 m
0 200 yards

Oxford Street is closed to private traffic, Mondays to Saturdays : from 7 am to 9 pm between Portman Street and St. Giles Circus

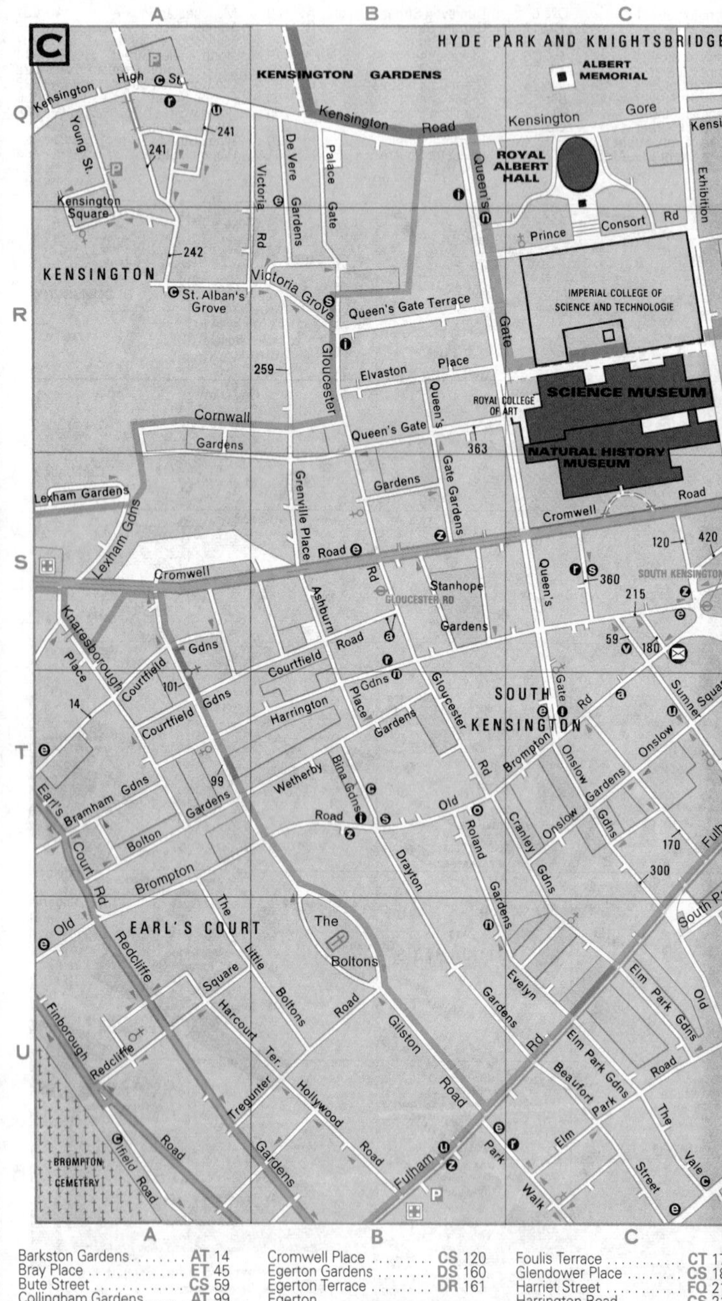
C
HYDE PARK AND KNIGHTSBRIDGE
KENSINGTON GARDENS
ALBERT MEMORIAL
ROYAL ALBERT HALL
IMPERIAL COLLEGE OF SCIENCE AND TECHNOLOGIE
SCIENCE MUSEUM
ROYAL COLLEGE OF ART
NATURAL HISTORY MUSEUM
KENSINGTON
SOUTH KENSINGTON
EARL'S COURT
BROMPTON CEMETERY
GLOUCESTER RD
SOUTH KENSINGTON
The Boltons
Kensington High St.
Kensington Road
Kensington Gore
Prince Consort Rd
Exhibition
Young St.
Kensington Square
St. Alban's Grove
Victoria Rd
De Vere Gardens
Palace Gate
Queen's Gate
Victoria Grove
Queen's Gate Terrace
Gloucester Rd
Elvaston Place
Cornwall Gardens
Queen's Gate Gardens
Lexham Gardens
Lexham Gdns
Grenville Place
Cromwell Road
Stanhope Gardens
Queen's Gate
Kynance Place
Ashburn Gdns
Courtfield Road
Courtfield Gdns
Harrington Gardens
Bina Gdns
Wetherby Gardens
Old Brompton Road
Roland Gardens
Cranley Gdns
Onslow Gardens
Onslow Gdns
Onslow Sq.
Sumner Place
Drayton Gardens
Bramham Gdns
Bolton Gardens
Earl's Court Rd
Redcliffe Gardens
Redcliffe Square
The Little Boltons
Harcourt Ter.
Boltons Road
Gilston Road
Tregunter Road
Hollywood Road
Finborough Road
Redcliffe Road
Ifield Road
Fulham Road
Park Walk
Elm Park Gdns
Elm Park Road
Beaufort Street
Elm Park Gdns
The Vale
Old Church Street
South Parade
Evelyn Gardens
Fulham Rd
241
242
259
363
120
420
360
215
59
180
101
14
99
170
300
A
B
C
Q
R
S
T
U

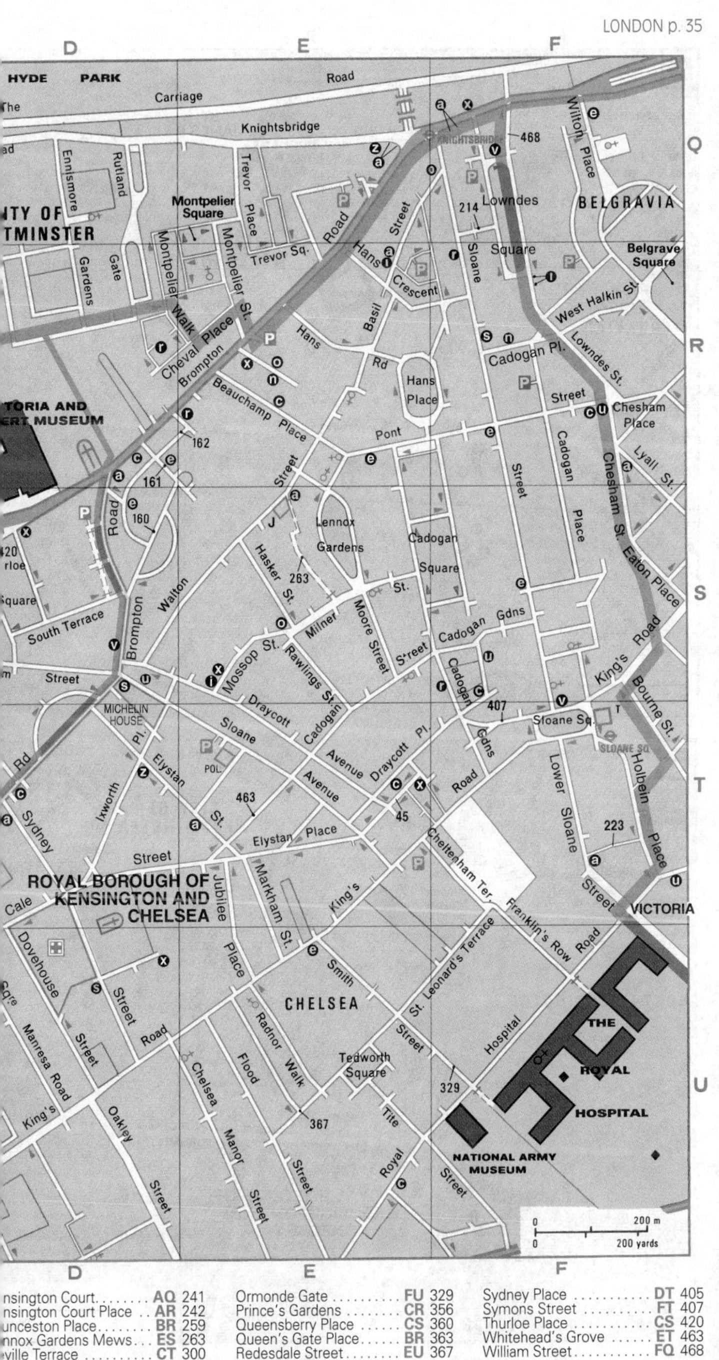
D
E
F
Q
R
S
T
U
HYDE PARK
The
Carriage
Road
Knightsbridge
KNIGHTSBRIDGE
468
Wilton Place
BELGRAVIA
Ennismore
Rutland
Gate
Gardens
CITY OF
WESTMINSTER
Montpelier Square
Montpelier Walk
Montpelier St.
Trevor Place
Trevor Sq.
Brompton Road
Hans Crescent
Basil Street
Sloane Street
Lowndes Square
214
Belgrave Square
West Halkin St.
Cheval Place
Brompton
Hans Rd
Hans Place
Beauchamp Place
Cadogan Pl.
Lowndes St.
Chesham Street
Chesham Place
Lyall St.
Chesham St.
Eaton Place
VICTORIA AND ALBERT MUSEUM
162
161
160
Pont Street
Cadogan Place
Lennox Gardens
Cadogan Square
Hasker St.
263
Milner St.
Moore Street
Walton Street
South Terrace
Brompton Road
Mossop St.
Rawlings St.
Cadogan Street
Cadogan Gdns
Cadogan Gdns
King's Road
Bourne St.
Street
MICHELIN HOUSE
Sloane Avenue
Draycott Avenue
Draycott Pl.
Cadogan Gdns
407
Sloane Sq.
SLOANE SQ.
Holbein Place
Pl.
Elystan St.
POL.
463
Elystan Place
45
Road
Lower Sloane Street
223
Ixworth
Sydney Street
Street
Cheltenham Ter.
Franklin's Row
VICTORIA
ROYAL BOROUGH OF KENSINGTON AND CHELSEA
Jubilee Place
Markham St.
King's Road
Cale
Dovehouse Street
Smith Street
St. Leonard's Terrace
Road
CHELSEA
Hospital
Radnor Walk
THE ROYAL HOSPITAL
Manresa Road
Flood Street
Tedworth Square
329
Chelsea Manor Street
367
Tite Street
King's
Oakley Street
Royal
NATIONAL ARMY MUSEUM
0
200 m
0
200 yards

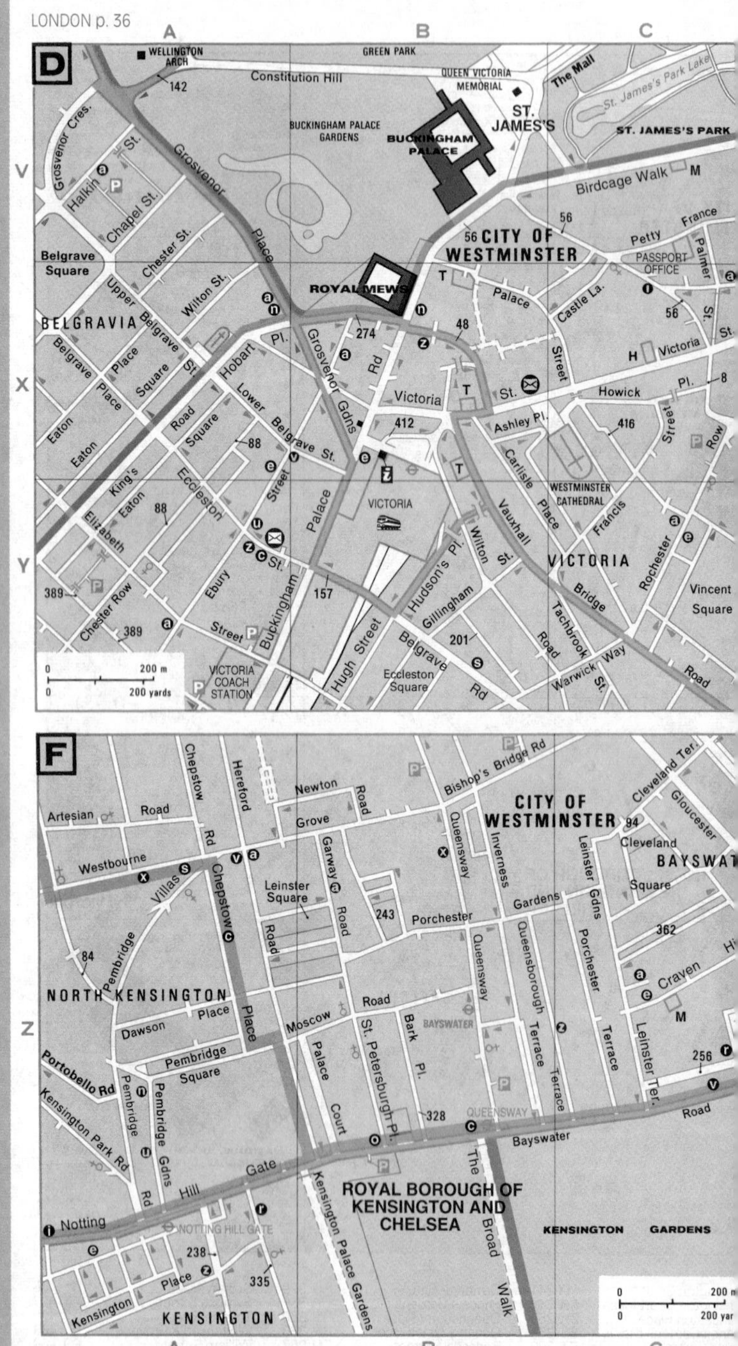

D
A
B
C
WELLINGTON ARCH
GREEN PARK
Constitution Hill
142
QUEEN VICTORIA MEMORIAL
The Mall
St. James's Park Lake
ST. JAMES'S
ST. JAMES'S PARK
BUCKINGHAM PALACE GARDENS
BUCKINGHAM PALACE
Grosvenor Cres.
Halkin St.
Chapel St.
Grosvenor Place
Birdcage Walk
M
56
France
Petty
Palmer St.
CITY OF WESTMINSTER
PASSPORT OFFICE
Belgrave Square
Chester St.
Upper Belgrave St.
Wilton St.
ROYAL MEWS
Palace
Castle La.
BELGRAVIA
274
48
Belgrave Place
Eaton Place
Eaton Square
Hobart Pl.
Grosvenor Gdns
Rd
Street
Victoria St.
H
Howick Pl.
8
Lower Belgrave St.
Road
Square
88
Ashley Pl.
412
416
King's
Eccleston
Street
Palace
VICTORIA
Carlisle Place
WESTMINSTER CATHEDRAL
Francis
Row
Elizabeth
88
Hudson's Pl.
Wilton St.
Vauxhall
Rochester
VICTORIA
Bridge
Vincent Square
389
Chester Row
Ebury
157
Buckingham
Gillingham
Tachbrook
Road
389
Street
Hugh Street
Belgrave
201
Warwick Way
St.
Road
VICTORIA COACH STATION
Eccleston Square
Rd
0 200 m
0 200 yards
V
X
Y
F
Chepstow Rd
Hereford
Newton Road
Bishop's Bridge Rd
Cleveland Ter.
Gloucester
Artesian Road
Grove
CITY OF WESTMINSTER
94
Westbourne
Garway Road
Queensway
Inverness
Leinster Gdns
Cleveland Square
BAYSWAT
Villas
Chepstow Place
Leinster Square
Road
243
Porchester
Gardens
Queensway
Queensborough Terrace
Porchester Terrace
362
84
Pembridge
Craven
NORTH KENSINGTON
Road
M
Dawson Place
Moscow
St. Petersburgh Pl.
Bark Pl.
BAYSWATER
Z
Pembridge Square
Palace Court
Leinster Ter.
256
Portobello Rd
Pembridge Rd
Pembridge Gdns
Kensington Park Rd
328
QUEENSWAY
Bayswater
Road
Gate
The Broad Walk
Hill
Notting
NOTTING HILL GATE
Kensington Palace Gardens
ROYAL BOROUGH OF KENSINGTON AND CHELSEA
KENSINGTON GARDENS
238
335
Place
Kensington
KENSINGTON
0 200 m
0 200 yar
A
B
C

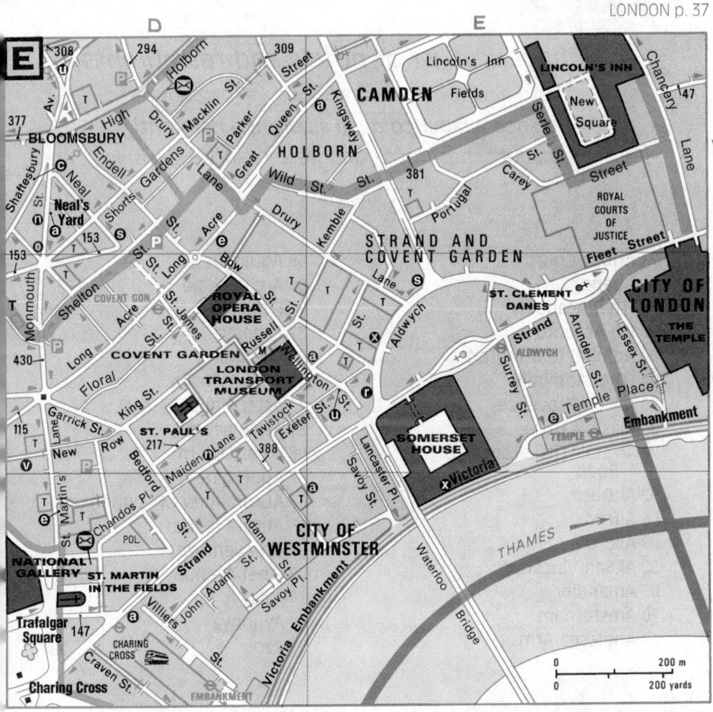

D E
E
CAMDEN
Lincoln's Inn Fields
LINCOLN'S INN
New Square
BLOOMSBURY
HOLBORN
Neal's Yard
STRAND AND COVENT GARDEN
ROYAL COURTS OF JUSTICE
Fleet Street
CITY OF LONDON
THE TEMPLE
ST. CLEMENT DANES
ROYAL OPERA HOUSE
COVENT GARDEN
LONDON TRANSPORT MUSEUM
ST. PAUL'S
SOMERSET HOUSE
Victoria Embankment
CITY OF WESTMINSTER
THAMES
Waterloo Bridge
NATIONAL GALLERY
ST. MARTIN IN THE FIELDS
Trafalgar Square
CHARING CROSS
Charing Cross
Strand
Embankment
0 200 m
0 200 yards
V X Y

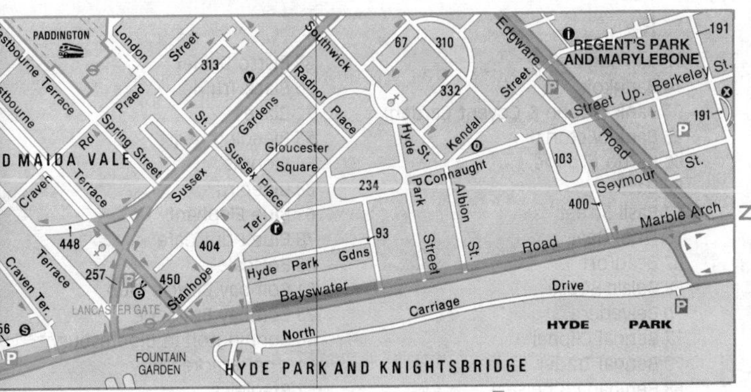

Alphabetical list of hotels and restaurants

Liste alphabétique des hôtels et restaurants

Elenco alfabetico degli alberghi e ristoranti

Alphabetisches Hotel- und Restaurantverzeichnis

A

B

C

D

E

F

G

H

I

N

O

P

Q

R

S

T

U - V - W

X - Y - Z

Starred establishments in London

Les établissements à étoiles de Londres
Gli esercizi con stelle a Londra
Die Stern-Restaurants in London

✿✿✿

67 *Chelsea* XXXX Gordon Ramsay

66 *Chelsea* — Capital
90 *Regent's Park & Marylebone* XXXXX John Burton-Race
86 *Mayfair* XXXX Le Gavroche
83 *Belgravia* XXXX La Tante Clair
86 *Mayfair* XXX The Square

Mayfair		Connaught
Belgravia		Nahm
Mayfair	XXXXX	Cheznico
Mayfair	XXXXX	The Oak Room Marco Pierre White
Chelsea	XXX	Aubergine
Farnborough	XXX	Chapter One
City of London	XXX	City Rhodes
Soho	XXX	L'Escargot
Hyde Park & Knightsbridge	XXX	Foliage
Mayfair	XXX	Mirabelle
City of London	XXX	1 Lombard Street (Restaurant)
St James's	XXX	L'Oranger
Regent's Park & Marylebone	XXX	Orrery
91 *St James's*	XXX	Pétrus
80 *Putney*	XXX	Putney Bridge
95 *Victoria*	XXX	Rhodes in the Square
81 *Wandsworth*	XX	Chez Bruce
58 *City of London*	XX	Club Gascon
76 *Kew*	XX	The Glasshouse
76 *Hampton Hill*	XX	Monsieur Max
87 *Mayfair*	XX	Nobu
54 *Bloomsbury*	XX	Pied à Terre
92 *Soho*	XX	Richard Corrigan at Lindsay House
61 *Hammersmith*	XX	River Café
96 *Victoria*	XX	Roussillon
86 *Mayfair*	XX	Tamarind
83 *Belgravia*	XX	Zafferano
71 *Kensington*	XX	Zaika

Good food at moderate prices

Repas soignés à prix modérés
Pasti accurati a prezzi contenuti
Sorgfältig zubereitete, preiswerte Mahlzeiten

 "Bib Gourmand"

Whitechapel	XX	Cafe Spice Namaste
Greenwich	XX	Chapter Two
Islington	XX	Metrogusto
Bayswater & Maida Vale	X	L'Accento
St. James's	X	Al Duca
Southwark	X	Cantina Vinopolis (Brasserie)
Chelsea	X	(I) Cardi
Regent's Park and Marylebone	X	Chada Chada
93 *Soho*	X	Il Forno
75 *Wimbledon*	X	Light House
71 *Kensington*	X	Malabar
80 *Battersea*	X	Metrogusto
64 *Archway*	X	The Parsee
80 *Putney*	X	The Phoenix
53 *Brent*	X	Sabras
81 *Southfields*	X	Sarkhel's
82 *Bayswater & Maida Vale*	X	The Vale

Particularly pleasant hotels and restaurants

Hôtels et restaurants agréables

Alberghi e ristoranti ameni

Angenehme Hotels und Restaurants

83 *Belgravia* The Berkeley
84 *Mayfair* Claridge's
84 *Mayfair* Dorchester
83 *Hyde Park & Knightsbridge* Mandarin Oriental Hyde Park
91 *St James's* Ritz
93 *Strand & Covent Garden* Savoy

84 *Mayfair* Connaught

72 *South Kensington* Blakes
66 *Chelsea* Capital
88 *Regent's Park & Marylebone* Charlotte Street
66 *Chelsea* Cliveden Town House
54 *Bloomsbury* Covent Garden
66 *Chelsea* Durley House
95 *Victoria* The Goring
83 *Belgravia* The Halkin
70 *Kensington* The Milestone
94 *Strand & Covent Garden* One Aldwych
72 *South Kensington* The Pelham

91 *St. James's* 22 Jermyn Street

XXXXX

91 *St. James's* The Restaurant (at Ritz H.)

XXXX

86 *Mayfair* Grill Room

XXX

90 *Regent's Park & Marylebone* Orrery
78 *Southwark* Oxo Tower
77 *Bermondsey* Le Pont de la Tour

XX

94 *Strand & Covent Garden* J. Sheekey
92 *St. James's* Quaglino's
94 *Strand & Covent Garden* Rules

Restaurants classified according to type

Restaurants classés suivant leur genre

Ristoranti classificati secondo il loro genere

Restaurants nach Art und Einrichtung geordnet

Bangladeshi

2 *Bayswater & Maida Vale*	X	Ginger

Chinese

6 *Mayfair*	XXXX	The Oriental
7 *Mayfair*	XXX	Kai
1 *St James's*	XXX	Orient
7 *Richmond*	XX	Four Regions
2 *Mill Hill*	XX	Good Earth
9 *Chelsea*	XX	Good Earth
5 *Bloomsbury*	XX	Hakkasan
5 *South Woodford*	XX	Ho-Ho
3 *City of London*	XX	Imperial City
6 *Victoria*	XX	Ken Lo's Memories of China
68 *Chelsea*	XX	Mao Tai
61 *Fulham*	XX	Mao Tai
59 *Ealing*	XX	Maxim
71 *Kensington*	XX	Memories of China
84 *Hyde Park & Knightsbridge*	XX	Mr Chow
82 *Bayswater & Maida Vale*	XX	Poons
53 *Orpington*	XX	Xian
56 *Hampstead*	XX	ZeNW3
92 *St James's*	X	China House
93 *Soho*	X	Fung Shing
59 *Croydon*	X	Tai Tung

Danish

3 *South Kensington*	XX	Lundum's

Eastern Mediterranean

0 *Regent's Park & Marylebone*	XX	Levant

English

6 *Mayfair*	XXXX	Grill Room (at Dorchester H.)
6 *Victoria*	XXX	Shepherd's
94 *Strand & Covent Garden*	XX	Rules

Filipino

5 *Bloomsbury*	X	Josephine's

French

0 *Regent's Park & Marylebone*	XXXXX	✿✿ John Burton-Race
6 *Mayfair*	XXXX	✿✿ (Le) Gavroche
3 *Belgravia*	XXXX	✿✿ (La) Tante Claire
1 *North Kensington*	XXX	Chez Moi
4 *Strand & Covent Garden*	XX	(The) Admiralty
82 *Bayswater and Maida Vale*	XX	Amandier
62 *Crouch End*	XX	(Les) Associés
90 *Regent's Park & Marylebone*	XX	L'Aventure
68 *Chelsea*	XX	Brasserie St. Quentin
58 *City of London*	XX	✿ Club Gascon
69 *Chelsea*	XX	(Le) Colombier
74 *Kingston*	XX	Gravier's

55 *Bloomsbury*	XX	Mon Plaisir
76 *Hampton Hill*	XX	✿ Monsieur Max
68 *Chelsea*	XX	Parisienne Chophouse
68 *Chelsea*	XX	Poissonnerie de l'Avenue
83 *Belgravia*	XX	Vong (French Thai)
83 *Bayswater and Maida Vale*	X	Bistro Daniel
74 *Surbiton*	X	(The) French Table
74 *Kennington*	X	Lobster Pot
96 *Victoria*	X	(La) Poule au Pot
60 *Dalston*	X	Soulard

Greek

61 *Hoxton*	X	Real Greek

Indian

77 *Bermondsey*	XXX	Bengal Clipper
73 *South Kensington*	XXX	Bombay Brasserie
68 *Chelsea*	XXX	Chutney Mary (Anglo-Indian)
95 *Victoria*	XXX	(The) Cinnamon Club
86 *Mayfair*	XXX	✿ Tamarind
95 *Victoria*	XXX	Quilon
79 *Spitalfields*	XX	Bengal Trader
92 *Soho*	XX	Café Lazeez
73 *South Kensington*	XX	Café Lazeez
80 *Battersea*	XX	Cafe Spice Namaste
79 *Whitechapel*	XX	☺ Cafe Spice Namaste
87 *Mayfair*	XX	Chor Bizarre
73 *South Kensington*	XX	Khan's of Kensington
55 *Bloomsbury*	XX	Malabar Junction
73 *South Kensington*	XX	Memories of India
58 *Addington*	XX	Planet Spice
90 *Regent's Park & Marylebone*	XX	(La) Porte des Indes
61 *Hammersmith*	XX	Rafique
90 *Regent's Park & Marylebone*	XX	Rasa Samudra
81 *Southfields*	XX	☺ Sarkhel's
74 *Herne Hill*	XX	3 Monkeys
69 *Chelsea*	XX	Vama
87 *Mayfair*	XX	Yatra
71 *Kensington*	XX	✿ Zaika
81 *Wandsworth*	X	Bombay Bicycle Club
65 *Finsbury*	X	Café Lazeez City
81 *Tooting*	X	Kastoori (Vegetarian)
71 *Kensington*	X	☺ Malabar
64 *Archway*	X	☺ (The) Parsee
53 *Willesden Green*	X	☺ Sabras (Vegetarian)
73 *South Kensington*	X	Star of India
88 *Mayfair*	X	Veeraswamy
69 *Chelsea*	X	Zaika Bazaar

Italian

86 *Mayfair*	XXX	Cecconi's
68 *Chelsea*	XXX	Floriana
95 *Victoria*	XXX	(L') Incontro
84 *Hyde Park & Knightsbridge*	XXX	Isola
96 *Victoria*	XXX	Santini
86 *Mayfair*	XXX	Sartoria
68 *Chelsea*	XXX	Toto's
87 *Mayfair*	XX	Alloro
82 *Bayswater & Maida Vale*	XX	Al San Vincenzo
71 *Kensington*	XX	(The) Ark
90 *Regent's Park & Marylebone*	XX	Bertorelli's
90 *Regent's Park & Marylebone*	XX	Caldesi
68 *Chelsea*	XX	Caraffini
96 *Victoria*	XX	(Il) Convivio
80 *Putney*	XX	Enoteca Turi
66 *Islington*	XX	☺ Metrogusto
68 *Belgravia*	XX	Montes
55 *Bloomsbury*	XX	Neal Street
68 *Chelsea*	XX	Pellicano
59 *Bedford Park*	XX	Riso
61 *Hammersmith*	XX	✿ River Café
90 *Regent's Park & Marylebone*	XX	Rosmarino
87 *Mayfair*	XX	Teca
77 *Bermondsey*	XX	Tentazioni
79 *Carshalton*	XX	(La) Veranda
52 *Golders Green*	XX	(The) Villa
83 *Belgravia*	XX	✿ Zafferano
82 *Bayswater & Maida Vale*	X	☺ (L') Accento

	St. James's	X ☺	Al Duca
	Bayswater & Maida Vale	X	Assaggi
	Soho	X	Bertorelli
	Primrose Hill	X	Black Truffle
	Bermondsey	X	Cantina Del Ponte
	Chelsea	X ☺	(I) Cardi
	Kensington	X	Cibo
	Crouch End	X	Florians
	Soho	X ☺	(Il) Forno
	Bayswater & Maida Vale	X	Green Olive
90	*Regent's Park & Marylebone*	X	Ibla
76	*Barnes*	X	Lemon Thyme
59	*Croydon*	X	Mario
80	*Battersea*	X ☺	Metrogusto
96	*Victoria*	X	Olivo
55	*Bloomsbury*	X	Passione
90	*Regent's Park & Marylebone*	X	Purple Sage
76	*Barnes*	X	Riva
93	*Soho*	X	Vasco and Piero's Pavillion

panese

	St. James's	XXX	Suntory
	City of London	XXX	Tatsuso
	Chelsea	XX	Benihana
	Swiss Cottage	XX	Benihana
	St James's	XX	Matsuri
	Mayfair	XX ✿	Nobu
	Mayfair	XX	Shogun
79	*Canary Wharf*	XX	Ubon by Nobu
55	*Bloomsbury*	X	Abeno
69	*Chelsea*	X	itsu
93	*Soho*	X	itsu
62	*Shepherd's Bush*	X	Onami
53	*Willesden Green*	X	Sushi-Say

orean

	Highbury	X	Bu-San

ebanese

	Belgravia	XX	Noura Brasserie
71	*Kensington*	XX	Phoenicia

oroccan

	Mayfair	XX	Momo
73	*South Kensington*	XX	Pasha

orth African

	Hammersmith & Fulham	X	Azou

olish

	Kensington	X	Wódka

ubs

	Chelsea	Admiral Codrington
	Hammersmith	Anglesea Arms
	Clerkenwell	(The) Bear
	Chelsea	Builders Arms
	Dartmouth Park	Bull & Last
	Canonbury	Centuria
	Chelsea	Chelsea Ram
	Bayswater & Maida Vale	(The) Chepstow
	Putney	Coat and Badge
	Islington	(The) Crown
	Battersea	Duke of Cambridge
	Primrose Hill	(The) Engineer
	Wimbledon	(The) Fire Stables
	Shepherds Bush	Havelock Tavern
60	*Winchmore Hill*	(The) Kings Head
56	*Primrose Hill*	(The) Lansdowne
60	*Dalston*	LMNT
55	*Dartmouth Park*	Lord Palmerston
56	*Hampstead*	(The) Magdala
66	*Islington*	(The) Northgate
65	*Finsbury*	(The) Peasant
56	*Primrose Hill*	(The) Queens
64	*Archway*	St John's
61	*Fulham*	(The) Salisbury Tavern
89	*Regents Park & Marylebone*	(The) Salt House
69	*Chelsea*	Swag and Tails
61	*Hammersmith*	Thatched House

Russian

86 *Mayfair* XXX Firebird

Scottish

96 *Victoria* XX Boisdale

Seafood

68 *Chelsea* XXX One-O-One
86 *Mayfair* XXX Scotts
87 *Mayfair* XX Bentley's
74 *Kingston* XX Gravier's (French)
82 *Bayswater & Maida Vale* XX Jason's
94 *Strand & Covent Garden* XX J. Sheekey
68 *Chelsea* XX Poissonnerie de l'Avenue (French)
90 *Regent's Park and Marylebone* XX Rasa Samudra (Indian)
73 *South Kensington* XX (The) Restaurant at One Ninety
69 *Chelsea* X Bibendum Oyster Bar
74 *South Kensington* X Catch
80 *Battersea* X Fish!
79 *Canary Wharf* X Fish!
78 *Southwark* X Fish!
74 *Kennington* X Lobster Pot (French)
72 *North Kensington* X Livebait
78 *Southwark* X Livebait
94 *Strand & Covent Garden* X Livebait

South African

64 *Chiswick* X Springbok Grill

South East Asian

87 *Mayfair* XX Cassia Oriental
58 *City of London* XX Pacific Oriental

Spanish

65 *Clerkenwell* XX Gaudi
73 *South Kensington* XX Cambio De Tercio
55 *Bloomsbury* X Cigala

Thai

83 *Belgravia* Nahm
61 *Fulham* XX Blue Elephant
80 *Battersea* XX Chada
83 *Belgravia* XX Mango Tree
82 *Bayswater & Maida Vale* XX Nipa
58 *City of London* XX Sri Siam City
83 *Belgravia* XX Vong (French Thai)
74 *Kingston* X Ayudhya
74 *South Kensington* X Bangkok
91 *Regent's Park & Marylebone* X Chada Chada
81 *Tooting* X Oh Boy
93 *Soho* X Sri Siam

Turkish

90 *Regent's Park & Marylebone* XX Ozer

Vegetarian

90 *Regent's Park & Marylebone* XX Rasa Samudra (Indian)
81 *Tooting* XX Kastoori (Indian)
53 *Willesden Green* X Sabras (Indian)

Vietnamese

93 *Soho* X Saigon

Boroughs and areas

Greater London *is divided, for administrative purposes, into 32 boroughs plus the City: the sub-divide naturally into minor areas, usually grouped around former villages or quarters, whi often maintain a distinctive character.*

BARNET.

Brent Cross – ✉ *NW2.*

Holiday Inn London Brent Cross, Tilling Rd, NW2 1LP, ✆ (020) 8201 8686, *joanr fielding@basshotels.com, Fax (020) 8455 4660* – , rm, – 50. VISA JCB p. 9 **DU**
Meals (bar lunch)/dinner 18.95 and a la carte 18.00/27.50 **st.** 10.50 – 12.50 – **153 r** 155.00 **st.**

Child's Hill – ✉ *NW2.*

Quincy's, 675 Finchley Rd, NW2 2JP, ✆ (020) 7794 8499, *aaronanita@quincys.freeserv co.uk* – . VISA JCB p. 9 **DU**
closed New Year, 26 December, Sunday and Monday – **Meals** (booking essential) (dinn only) 25.00 **t.** 10.00.

Golders Green – ✉ *NW11.*

The Villa, 38 North End Rd, NW11 7PT, ✆ (020) 8458 6344, *Fax (020) 8458 6344* – . VISA p. 9 **DU**
closed 1 January and Monday – **Meals** - Italian - 14.50/18.00 and a la carte 20.80/27.70 10.90.

Mill Hill – ✉ *NW7.*

100 Barnet Way, Mill Hill ✆ (020) 8959 2282 **CT.**

Good Earth, 143 The Broadway, NW7 4RN, ✆ (020) 8959 7011, *Fax (020) 8959 1464* – VISA JCB p. 9 **CT**
closed 23-30 December – **Meals** - Chinese - a la carte 21.80/29.80.

BEXLEY.

Bexley – ✉ *Kent.*

Holiday Inn, Black Prince Interchange, Southwold Rd, DA5 1ND, on A ✆ (0870) 400 9006, *Fax (01322) 526113* – , rm, – 70. VISA p. 15 **JX**
Meals *(closed Saturday lunch)* 13.50/15.00 **t.** 11.95 – 11.95 – **108 rm** 89.00 **t.** – SB.

Bexleyheath – ✉ *Kent.*

Bexleyheath Marriott, 1 Broadway, DA6 7JZ, ✆ (020) 8298 1000, *bexleyhea @swallow-hotels.co.uk, Fax (020) 8298 1234,* , – , rm, – 250. VISA. p. 15 **JX**
Copper: **Meals** (carvery rest.) 19.75 (dinner) and a la carte 20.00/33.00 **st.** 12.00 13.00 – **138 rm** 95.00/180.00 **st.** – SB.

BRENT.

Kingsbury – ✉ *NW9.*

Kingsland without rest., Kingsbury Circle, NW9 9RR, ✆ (020) 8206 0666, *hemang@talk .com, Fax (020) 8206 0555* – . VISA. p. 9 **CU**
26 rm 55.00/65.00 **st.**

embley – Middx.

Premier Lodge, 151 Wembley Park Drive, HA9 8HQ, (0870) 7001446, *wembleypremier lodge@snr.co.uk, Fax (0870) 7001447* – p. 9 **CU z**
Meals (grill rest.) (dinner only) a la carte approx. 12.45 **t.** 8.45 – **153 rm** 54.95 **t.**

illesden Green – Middx.

Sabras, 263 High Rd, NW10 2RX, (020) 8459 0340, *Fax (020) 8459 0541* – p. 9 **CU e**
closed Monday – **Meals** - Indian Vegetarian - (dinner only) a la carte 15.95/22.95.

Sushi-Say, 33B Walm Lane, NW2 5SH, (020) 8459 2971, *Fax (020) 8907 3229.* p. 9 **CU a**
closed 25-26 December, 1 January, Easter, 1 week August and Monday – **Meals** - Japanese - (dinner only and lunch Saturday and Sunday)/dinner 18.30/28.70 and a la carte 12.95/35.65 **t.** 9.80.

ROMLEY.

18, 9 Cray Valley, Sandy Lane, St. Paul's Cray, Orpington (01689) 837909 **JY**.

omley – Kent.

9 Magpie Hall Lane (020) 8462 7014 **HY**.

Bromley Court, Bromley Hill, BR1 4JD, (020) 8464 5011, *bromleyhotel@btinternet.com, Fax (020) 8460 0899,* – rm, rest, – 150. p. 15 **HY z**
Meals *(closed Saturday lunch)* 15.50/16.95 (dinner) and a la carte 13.35/25.40 **st.** 6.25 – **113 rm** 102.00/115.00 **st.**, 2 suites.

rnborough – Kent.

Chapter One, Farnborough Common, Locksbottom, BR6 8NF, (01689) 854848, *pennyatch1@aol.com, Fax (01689) 858439* – p. 15 **HZ a**
closed 1-3 January – **Meals** 19.50/23.95 **t.** 13.50
Spec. Carpaccio of smoked goose with apple, walnut and raspberry salad. Pan-fried halibut, lobster and celeriac rémoulade. Braised oxtail with smoked bacon and parsnip purée.

pington – Kent.

18 High Elms, High Elms Rd, Downe, Orpington (01689) 858175.

Xian, 324 High St, BR6 0NG, (01689) 871881 – p. 15 **JY a**
closed 1 week August, Christmas and Sunday lunch – **Meals** - Chinese (Peking, Szechuan) - 7.50/22.00 and a la carte 12.30/15.60 **t.** 8.80.

nge – SE20.

Melrose House without rest., 89 Lennard Rd, SE20 7LY, (020) 8776 8884, *melrose.hotel@virgin.net, Fax (020) 8325 7636,* – p. 14 **GY a**
closed Christmas – **6 rm** 35.00/55.00 **st.**

AMDEN.

oomsbury – NW1/W1/WC1.

Russell, Russell Sq, WC1B 5BE, (020) 7837 6470, *reservations.russell@principalhotels.co.uk, Fax (020) 7837 2857* – rm, – 400.
Fitzroy Doll's: **Meals** 15.95 **st.** 15.95 – ***Virginia Woolf's:*** **Meals** a la carte approx. 18.00 **st.** 15.95 – 15.00 – **378 rm** 190.00/205.00 **st.**, 2 suites. p. 26 **LU o**

Holiday Inn Kings Cross, 1 Kings Cross Rd, WC1X 9HX, (020) 7833 3900, *sales@holidayinnlondon.demon.co.uk, Fax (020) 7917 6163,* – rm, – 220. p. 26 **MT a**
Simply Spice: **Meals** - Indian - *(closed Saturday lunch)* a la carte 10.00/23.00 – ***Carriages:*** **Meals** a la carte 10.00/25.00 – 12.50 – **403 rm** 190.00 **st.**, 2 suites.

Marlborough, 9-14 Bloomsbury St, WC1B 3QD, (020) 7636 5601, *resmarl@radisson.com, Fax (020) 7240 0532* – rm, rest, – 200. p. 26 **LU i**
Glass: **Meals** 19.50 and a la carte 17.00/27.50 **st.** 15.75 – 15.00 – **171 rm** 195.00/222.00 **s.**, 2 suites.

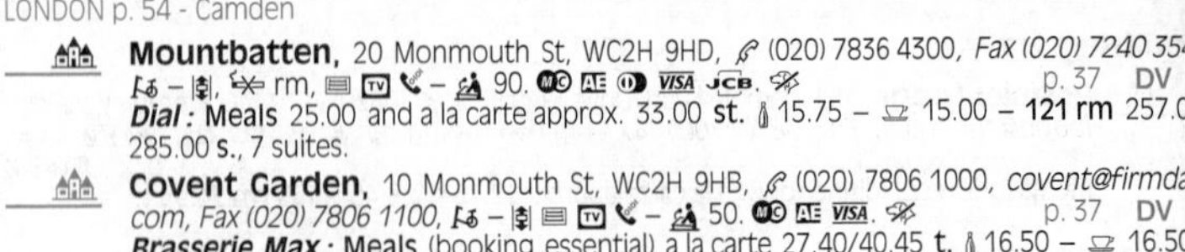

Mountbatten, 20 Monmouth St, WC2H 9HD, ☎ (020) 7836 4300, *Fax (020) 7240 354(* – ▮, ⇔ rm, ▤ TV ☎ – 🔗 90. MC AE ① VISA JCB. ✂ p. 37 **DV**
Dial : Meals 25.00 and a la carte approx. 33.00 **st.** 15.75 – 15.00 – **121 rm** 257.0C 285.00 **s.**, 7 suites.

Covent Garden, 10 Monmouth St, WC2H 9HB, ☎ (020) 7806 1000, *covent@firmdal com, Fax (020) 7806 1100,* – ▮ ▤ TV ☎ – 50. MC AE VISA. ✂ p. 37 **DV**
Brasserie Max : **Meals** (booking essential) a la carte 27.40/40.45 **t.** 16.50 – 16.50 **56 rm** 190.00/325.00, 2 suites.

Grafton, 130 Tottenham Court Rd, W1P 9HP, ☎ (020) 7388 4131, *resgraf@radisson.con Fax (020) 7387 7394,* – ▮, ⇔ rm, ▤ rest, TV ☎ – 100. MC AE ① VISA JC ✂ p. 26 **KU**
Aston's : **Meals** 19.95 and a la carte approx. 22.00 **st.** 14.00 – 12.00 – **320 rm** 172.0C 199.00 **s.**, 4 suites.

Kenilworth, 97 Great Russell St, WC1B 3LB, ☎ (020) 7637 3477, *resmarl@radisson.cor Fax (020) 7631 3133* – ▮, ⇔ rm, ▤ TV ♿ – 65. MC AE ① VISA JC ✂ p. 26 **LU**
Meals 19.50/35.00 **st.** 13.75 – 12.00 – **187 rm** 195.00/222.00 **s.**

Grange Holborn, 50-60 Southampton Row, WC1B 4AR, ☎ (020) 7242 1800, *holbor @grangehotels.co.uk, Fax (020) 7404 1641,* – ▮ ⇔ ▤ TV ☎ ♿ – 180. AE ① VISA JCB. ✂ p. 26 **LU**
Constellations : **Meals** *(closed Saturday, Sunday and Bank Holidays)* (dinner only) 26.5 and a la carte 26.85/35.45 **st.** – ***Koto :*** **Meals** - Sushi - 10.50/15.50 and a la carte 11.5(20.50 **st.** 12.15 – 16.50 – **200 rm** 280.00/400.00 **st.**

Jurys Gt Russell St, 16-22 Gt Russell St, WC1B 3NN, ☎ (020) 7347 100 *Fax (020) 7347 1001* – ▮, ⇔ rm, ▤ TV ☎ ♿ – 220. MC AE ① VISA JCB. ✂
Lutyens : **Meals** (bar lunch)/dinner 23.50 and a la carte 20.00/31.00 **st.** 14.00 – 16.00 **168 rm** 215.00 **st.**, 1 suite – SB. p. 26 **LU**

Montague, 15 Montague St, WC1B 5BJ, ☎ (020) 7637 1001, *bookmt@rchmail.cor Fax (020) 7637 2516,* – ▮, ⇔ rm, ▤ TV ☎ ♿ – 120. MC AE ① VISA JC ✂ p. 26 **LU**
Blue Door Bistro : **Meals** a la carte 23.15/29.40 **t.** 15.50 – 11.50 – **98 rm** 165.0(190.00 **s.**, 6 suites.

Thistle Bloomsbury, Bloomsbury Way, WC1A 2SD, ☎ (020) 7242 5881, *bloomsbu @thistle.co.uk, Fax (020) 7831 0225* – ▮, ⇔ rm, ▤ rest, TV ♿ – 100. MC AE ① VISA JC ✂ p. 26 **LU**
Meals *(closed lunch Saturday, Sunday and Bank Holidays)* 16.50 and a la carte 18.5 29.25 **st.** 12.50 – 11.95 – **138 rm** 167.00/312.00 **st.**

Holiday Inn London Bloomsbury, Coram St, WC1N 1HT, ☎ (0870) 400922 *reservations-bloomsbury@6c.com, Fax (020) 7837 5374* – ▮, ⇔ rm, ▤ TV ☎ ♿ – 30 MC AE ① VISA JCB. ✂ p. 26 **LT**
Meals *(closed Saturday and Sunday dinner and Bank Holiday lunch)* 13.00/15.00 and di ner a la carte 22.65/29.00 **st.** 12.95 – 14.95 – **312 rm** 179.00 **st.** – SB.

Blooms, 7 Montague St, WC1B 5BP, ☎ (020) 7323 1717, *blooms@mermaid.co.u Fax (020) 7636 6498,* – ▮ TV ☎. MC AE ① VISA JCB p. 26 **LU**
Meals a la carte 19.50/26.50 **st.** 15.00 – 10.00 – **27 rm** 135.00/205.00 **st.** – SB.

Myhotel, 11-13 Bayley St, Bedford Sq, WC1B 3HD, ☎ (020) 7667 6000, *guest-servic @myhotels.co.uk, Fax (020) 7667 6001,* « Contemporary interior », – ▮ ⇔ ▤ TV ☎ 40. MC AE ① VISA p. 26 **KU**
Yo! Sushi : **Meals** - Japanese - a la carte 16.00/24.40 **t.** 12.50 – 16.00 – **76 rm** 170.0 355.00 **s.**

Bonnington in Bloomsbury, 92 Southampton Row, WC1B 4BH, ☎ (020) 7242 282 *sales@bonnington.com, Fax (020) 7831 9170* – ▮, ⇔ rm, ▤ TV ☎ ♿ – 250. MC AE VISA p. 26 **LU**
Meals *(closed Sunday and Bank Holiday Mondays)* (bar lunch)/dinner 19.75 **t.** 12.00 **215 rm** 117.00/149.00 **t.** – SB.

The Academy without rest., 21 Gower St, WC1E 6HG, ☎ (020) 7631 4115, *res_academ etontownhouse.com, Fax (020) 7636 3442,* – ⇔ ▤ TV ☎. MC AE ① VISA JCB
closed 23-27 December – **49 rm** 136.00/225.00 **s.** p. 26 **KLU**

XXX **Conrad Gallagher Shaftesbury Avenue,** 179 Shaftesbury Ave, W1D 7E ☎ (020) 7836 3111, *info@conradgallagher.co.uk, Fax (020) 7836 3888* – ▤. MC AE VISA p. 37 **DV**
closed 25 December – **Meals** 18.75/23.75 (lunch) and a la carte 33.50/50.00 **t.** 20.00.

XX **Pied à Terre,** 34 Charlotte St, W1P 1HJ, ☎ (020) 7636 1178, *p-a-t@dircon.co. Fax (020) 7916 1171* – ▤. MC AE ① VISA JCB p. 26 **KU**
✿ *closed 2 weeks Christmas-New Year, Saturday lunch and Sunday* – **Meals** 23.00/65.0C 18.00
Spec. Scallop ceviche, avocado and crème fraîche. Poached foie gras, Sauterr consommé. Venison fillet, juniper boudin, celeriac purée.

XXX **Incognico,** 117 Shaftesbury Ave, WC2H 8AD, ☎ (020) 7836 8866, *Fax (020) 7240 9525* – ▤. MC AE ⓓ VISA p. 33 **GK** a
closed 4 days Easter, 10 days Christmas, Sunday and Bank Holidays – **Meals** 12.50 (lunch) and a la carte 27.50/41.50 **t.** ⅰ 12.50.

XX **Neal Street,** 26 Neal St, WC2H 9QW, ☎ (020) 7836 8368, *Fax (020) 7240 3964* – MC AE ⓓ VISA p. 37 **DV** s
closed 1 week Christmas-New Year, Sunday and Bank Holidays – **Meals** - Italian - a la carte 30.00/45.00 **t.** ⅰ 15.00.

XX **Hakkasan,** 8 Hanway Pl, W1P 9DH, ☎ (020) 7927 7000, *mail@hakkasan.com, Fax (020) 7907 1889* – ▤. MC AE VISA p. 26 **KU** o
closed 24-26 December – **Meals** - Chinese (Canton) - a la carte 18.70/57.90 **t.** ⅰ 18.50.

XX **Mon Plaisir,** 21 Monmouth St, WC2H 9DD, ☎ (020) 7836 7243, *eatafrog@mail.com, Fax (020) 7240 4774* – MC AE ⓓ VISA JCB p. 37 **DV** a
closed Christmas-New Year, Saturday lunch, Sunday and Bank Holidays – **Meals** - French - 13.95/15.95 (lunch) and a la carte 21.70/34.50 **t.** ⅰ 10.50.

XX **Archipelago,** 110 Whitfield St, W1T 5EA, ☎ (020) 7383 3346, *Fax (020) 7383 7181* – MC AE VISA p. 26 **KU** c
closed Christmas-New Year, Saturday lunch and Sunday – **Meals** 20.50/38.50 **t.** ⅰ 18.50.

XX **Malabar Junction,** 107 Great Russell St, WC1B 3NA, ☎ (020) 7580 5230, *Fax (020) 7436 9942* – ▤. MC AE VISA p. 26 **LU** x
closed 25-26 December – **Meals** - South Indian - a la carte 25.00/30.00 **t.**

X **Passione,** 10 Charlotte St, W1P 1HE, ☎ (020) 7636 2833, *lizprzybylski@lineone.net, Fax (020) 7636 2889* – MC AE ⓓ VISA JCB p. 26 **KU** u
closed Christmas-New Year, Saturday lunch, Sunday and Bank Holidays – **Meals** - Italian - (booking essential) a la carte 22.80/31.50 **t.** ⅰ 11.50.

X **Alfred,** 245 Shaftesbury Ave, WC2H 8EH, ☎ (020) 7240 2566, *Fax (020) 7497 0672*, ⛱ – ▤. MC AE ⓓ VISA JCB p. 37 **DV** u
closed Saturday lunch, Sunday and Bank Holidays – **Meals** 13.90/17.00 and a la carte 20.45/25.45 **t.** ⅰ 12.65.

X **Cigala,** 54 Lamb's Conduit St, WC1N 3LW, ☎ (020) 7405 1717, *Fax (020) 7242 9949* – MC AE ⓓ VISA p. 26 **LU** z
closed Christmas, New Year, Sunday dinner and Bank Holidays – **Meals** - Spanish - 18.00 (lunch) and a la carte 20.00/36.00 **t.** ⅰ 12.00.

X **Josephine's,** 4 Charlotte St, W1T 2LP, ☎ (020) 7580 6551, *jones4@aol.com, Fax (020) 7580 1514* – MC AE ⓓ VISA p. 26 **KU** s
closed 25 December, 1 January and Sunday lunch – **Meals** - Filipino - a la carte 11.90/17.15 **t.** ⅰ 10.95.

X **Abeno,** 47 Museum St, WC1A 1LY, ☎ (020) 7405 3211, *okonomi@abeno.co.uk, Fax (020) 7405 3212* – ▤. MC AE VISA JCB p. 26 **LU** e
closed 25-26 and 31 December and 1 January – **Meals** - Japanese (Okonomi-Yaki) - 6.50/16.00 (lunch) and a la carte 10.70/26.60 **t.** ⅰ 12.75.

artmouth Park – ✉ *NW5.*

🍺 **Bull & Last,** 168 Highgate Rd, NW5 1QS, ☎ (020) 7267 3641, *Fax (020) 7482 6366* – MC VISA p. 24 **EU** n
closed 25 December – **Meals** a la carte 15.00/22.00 **t.** ⅰ 10.00.

🍺 **Lord Palmerston,** 33 Dartmouth Park Hill, NW5 1HU, ☎ (020) 7485 1578 – MC VISA p. 24 **EU** x
Meals (bookings not accepted) a la carte approx. 17.00 ⅰ 8.90.

uston – ✉ *WC1.*

🏨 **Shaw Park Plaza,** 100-110 Euston Rd, NW1 2AJ, ☎ (020) 7666 9000, *sppres@parkplaza hotels.co.uk, Fax (020) 7666 9100*, Fö, ≘s – |♦|, ⇔ rm, ▤ TV ☎ ♿ – 🏛 450. MC AE ⓓ VISA JCB. ✂ p. 26 **LT** r
Meals 23.95 and a la carte 26.00/33.00 **t.** ⅰ 17.00 – ☕ 14.50 – **312 rm** 180.00 **st.**

🏨 **Euston Plaza,** 17-18 Upper Woburn Pl, WC1H 0HT, ☎ (020) 7943 4500, *eustonplaza @euston-plaza-hotel.co.uk, Fax (020) 7943 4501*, Fö, ≘s – |♦|, ⇔ rm, ▤ TV ☎ ♿ – 🏛 150. MC AE ⓓ VISA JCB. ✂ p. 26 **KLT** e
Three Crowns : **Meals** 18.95/19.95 and dinner a la carte 28.85/33.90 **t.** ⅰ 13.95 – ***Terrace :*** **Meals** *(closed Saturday lunch and Sunday dinner)* a la carte 14.60/16.85 **t.** ⅰ 13.95 – ☕ 12.95 – **150 rm** 179.00/199.00 **st.**

🏨 **London Euston Travel Inn Capital,** 141 Euston Rd, NW1 2AU, ☎ (020) 7554 3400, *Fax (020) 7554 3419* – |♦|, ⇔ rm, ▤ rest, TV ♿. MC AE ⓓ VISA. ✂ p. 26 **LT** s
Meals (grill rest.) (dinner only) – **220 rm** 74.95 **t.**

Hampstead – ✉ NW3.

Winnington Rd, Hampstead ✆ (020) 8455 0203.

Posthouse Hampstead, 215 Haverstock Hill, NW3 4RB, ✆ (0870) 400 90
Fax (020) 7435 5586 – 30. p. 24 ES
Meals – (see ***MPW Brasserie*** below) – 13.95 – **140 rm** 99.00/159.00 – SB.

Langorf without rest., 20 Frognal, NW3 6AG, ✆ (020) 7794 4483, *langorf@aol.co*
Fax (020) 7435 9055 – p. 24 ES
31 rm 82.00/98.00 **st.**, 5 suites.

ZeNW3, 83-84 Hampstead High St, NW3 1RE, ✆ (020) 7794 7863, *Fax (020) 7794 695*
p. 24 ES
closed 24-25 December – **Meals** - Chinese - 13.80/33.50 and a la carte 22.40/34.2
12.50.

MPW Brasserie (at Posthouse Hampstead H.), 215 Haverstock Hill, NW3 4
✆ (020) 7435 6080, *Fax (020) 7435 5586*, – p. 24 ES
Meals 13.50 and a la carte **st.** 12.95.

Cucina, 45a South End Rd, NW3 2QB, ✆ (020) 7435 7814, *enquiries@cucina.uk.co*
Fax (020) 7435 7815 – p. 24 ES
closed 4 days Christmas and Sunday dinner – **Meals** a la carte 20.00/24.00 **t.** 11.95.

Base, 71 Hampstead High St, NW3 1QP, ✆ (020) 7431 2224, *Fax (020) 7433 1262* –
p. 24 ES
Meals - North African specialities - a la carte 12.00/21.00 **t.**

The Magdala, 2A South Hill Park, NW3 2SB, ✆ (020) 7435 2503, *Fax (020) 7435 6167* –
p. 24 ES
closed 25 December – **Meals** a la carte 17.50/24.95 **t.** 9.95.

Hatton Garden – ✉ EC1.

Bleeding Heart, Bleeding Heart Yard, EC1N 8SJ, off Greville St ✆ (020) 7242 20
bookings@bleedingheart.co.uk, *Fax (020) 7831 1402*, –
p. 27 NU
closed Christmas-New Year, Saturday, Sunday and Bank Holidays – **Meals** a la carte 21.
32.15 **t.** 12.95.

Holborn – ✉ WC2.

Renaissance London Chancery Court, 252 High Holborn, WC1V 7
✆ (020) 7829 9888, *sales.chancerycourt@renaissancehotels.com, Fax (020) 7829 9889,*
rm, – 450. p. 26 MU
QC : Meals a la carte 23.70/47.90 **st.** 21.00 – 16.95 – **357 rm** 275.00/395.00 **s.**

Kingsway Hall, Great Queen St, WC2B 5BX, ✆ (020) 7309 0909, *kingswayhall@com*
serve.com, Fax (020) 7309 9696, – rm, – 150.
p. 37 EV
Harlequin : Meals 18.50/22.00 and a la carte 27.75/36.25 **t.** 13.50 – 15.25 – **168**
180.00/190.00 **st.**, 2 suites.

Primrose Hill – ✉ NW1.

Odette's, 130 Regent's Park Rd, NW1 8XL, ✆ (020) 7586 5486, *Fax (020) 7586 2575* –
p. 25 HS
closed 1 week Christmas and Sunday dinner – **Meals** 12.50 (lunch) and a la carte 25.
33.50 **t.** 12.50 – (see also ***Odette's Wine Bar*** below).

Black Truffle, 40 Chalcot Rd, NW1 8LS, ✆ (020) 7483 0077, *Fax (020) 7483 0088* –
p. 25 HIS
closed Sunday – **Meals** - Italian - (dinner only) 15.00/19.00 and a la carte 18.00/27.5
11.50.

Odette's Wine Bar (at Odette's), 130 Regent's Park Rd, NW1 8XL, ✆ (020) 7586 54
Fax (020) 7586 2575 – p. 25 HS
closed 1 week Christmas and Sunday dinner – **Meals** (booking essential) 12.
(lunch) and a la carte 16.50/22.00 **t.** 12.50.

The Queens, 49 Regent's Park Rd, NW1 8XD, ✆ (020) 7586 0408, *Fax (020) 7586 56*
– p. 25 HS
Meals a la carte 14.85/22.35 **t.** 9.90.

The Engineer, 65 Gloucester Ave, NW1 8JH, ✆ (020) 7722 0950, *info@the-eng.co*
Fax (020) 7483 0592, – p. 25 IS
closed 25-26 December – **Meals** a la carte 23.50/30.50 **t.** 11.50.

The Lansdowne, 90 Gloucester Ave, NW1 8HX, ✆ (020) 7483 0409, *Fax (020) 7586 1*
– p. 25 IS
closed Monday – **Meals** (dinner only and Sunday lunch) a la carte 16.50/22.50 **t.**

gent's Park – ✉ NW1.

Meliá White House, Albany St, NW1 3UP, ☎ (020) 7387 1200, *melia.whitehouse@solmelia.com, Fax (020) 7388 0091,* – rm, rest, – 120. VISA. p. 25 JT o
The Restaurant : Meals *(closed Sunday and Bank Holidays)* 19.50/24.50 and dinner a la carte 27.95/37.00 **t.** 15.00 – ***Garden Cafe :*** Meals 12.95/14.95 and a la carte 22.50/29.00 **t.** 14.95 – 16.95 – **580 rm** 243.00 **st.**, 2 suites.

wiss Cottage – ✉ NW3.

Marriott Regents Park, 128 King Henry's Rd, NW3 3ST, ☎ (020) 7722 7711, *Fax (020) 7586 5822,* – rm, – 300. VISA. p. 25 GS a
Meals *(closed Saturday lunch)* 18.95 (lunch) and a la carte 19.00/30.50 **st.** 13.75 – 16.45 – **298 rm** 175.00 **s.**, 5 suites.

Swiss Cottage without rest., 4 Adamson Rd, NW3 3HP, ☎ (020) 7722 2281, *reservations@swisscottagehotel.co.uk, Fax (020) 7483 4588* – – 35. VISA JCB. p. 25 GS n
53 rm 97.50/115.00 **st.**, 6 suites.

Bradley's, 25 Winchester Rd, NW3 3NR, ☎ (020) 7722 3457, *Fax (020) 7435 1392* – . VISA JCB p. 25 GS e
closed 1 week Christmas-New Year, Saturday lunch and Bank Holidays – **Meals** 14.00/27.00 **t.**

Benihana, 100 Avenue Rd, NW3 3HF, ☎ (020) 7586 9508, *benihana@dircon.co.uk, Fax (020) 7586 6740* – . VISA JCB p. 25 GS o
closed 25 December – **Meals** - Japanese (Teppan-Yaki) - 10.00/60.00 and a la carte 24.00/40.00 **t.** 12.00.

Globe, 100 Avenue Rd, NW3 3HF, ☎ (020) 7722 7200, *globerella@aol.com, Fax (020) 7722 2772* – . VISA p. 25 GS v
closed Saturday lunch and Monday – **Meals** a la carte 22.00/28.00 **t.**

TY OF LONDON.

Great Eastern, Liverpool St, EC2M 7QN, ☎ (020) 7618 5000, *sales@great-eastern-hotel.co.uk, Fax (020) 7618 5011,* – rm, – 250. VISA p. 27 PU o
Fishmarket : Meals - Seafood - *(closed Saturday lunch and Sunday)* a la carte 27.00/53.00 **t.** – ***Miyabi :*** Meals - Japanese - *(closed Saturday, Sunday and Bank Holidays)* a la carte 20.50/42.50 **t.** 12.95 – (see also ***Aurora*** below) – 19.00 – **264 rm** 225.00/285.00, 3 suites – SB.

Novotel London Tower Bridge, 10 Pepys St, EC3N 2NR, ☎ (020) 7265 6000, *h3107@accor-hotels.com, Fax (020) 7265 6060,* – rm, rest, – 80. VISA p. 27 PV n
The Garden Brasserie : Meals 12.00 (lunch) and a la carte 13.50/24.00 **st.** 12.50 – 12.00 – **199 rm** 155.00/175.00 **st.**, 4 suites.

Travelodge without rest., 1 Harrow Pl, E1 7DB, ☎ (020) 7626 1142, *Fax (020) 7626 1105* – . VISA JCB. p. 27 PU s
142 rm 79.95 **t.**

Aurora (at Great Eastern H.), Liverpool St, EC2M 7QN, ☎ (020) 7618 7000, *restaurants@great-eastern-hotel.co.uk, Fax (020) 7618 7001* – . VISA p. 27 PU o
closed Saturday, Sunday and Bank Holidays – **Meals** a la carte 40.00/48.50 **t.** 19.95.

City Rhodes, 1 New Street Sq, EC4A 3BF, ☎ (020) 7583 1313, *Fax (020) 7353 1662* – . VISA p. 27 NU u
closed 25 and 31 December, 1 January, Saturday, Sunday and Bank Holidays – **Meals** a la carte 33.00/52.50 **t.** 16.50
Spec. Steamed langoustine salad, truffle dressing. Rack of lamb with artichoke and coriander barigoule. Bread and butter pudding.

Coq d'Argent, No 1 Poultry, EC2R 8EJ, ☎ (020) 7395 5000, *Fax (020) 7395 5050,* « Rooftop terrace » – . VISA JCB p. 27 PV c
closed 25 December, Saturday lunch, Sunday dinner and Bank Holidays – **Meals** (booking essential) a la carte 32.50/41.00 **t.** 13.50.

Twentyfour, 24th floor, Tower 42, 25 Old Broad St, EC2N 1HQ, ☎ (020) 7877 2424, *Fax (020) 7877 7788,* London – . VISA JCB p. 27 PU v
closed Saturday, Sunday and Bank Holidays – **Meals** (booking essential) 28.00 (lunch) and a la carte 32.50/44.20 **t.** 13.95.

XXX **Tatsuso,** 32 Broadgate Circle, EC2M 2QS, ☎ (020) 7638 5863, *Fax (020) 7638 5864* – ▤. AE ⓓ VISA JCB p. 27 PU
closed 25 December, Saturday, Sunday and Bank Holidays – **Meals** - Japanese - (book essential) 28.00/36.00 and a la carte approx. 40.00 **t.** 14.50.

XXX ✿ **1 Lombard Street (Restaurant),** 1 Lombard St, EC2V 9AA, ☎ (020) 7929 66 *hb@1lombardstreet.com, Fax (020) 7929 6622* – ▤. MC AE ⓓ VISA JCB p. 27 PV
closed 1 week Christmas, Saturday, Sunday and Bank Holidays – **Meals** (lunch book essential) 28.00/38.00 and a la carte 40.00/56.00 **t.** – (see also ***1 Lombard Str (Brasserie)*** below)
Spec. Feuilleté of smoked haddock with quail eggs, mustard sauce. Suprême and fricas of chicken with young leeks. Chocolate, whisky and coffee praline "Lombardo".

XXX **Prism,** 147 Leadenhall, EC3V 4QT, ☎ (020) 7256 3875, *Fax (020) 7256 3876* – ▤. MC AE VISA JCB p. 27 PV
closed 25-26 December, Saturday, Sunday and Bank Holidays – **Meals** a la carte 35. 61.00 **t.** 13.80.

XX ✿ **Club Gascon** (Aussignac), 57 West Smithfield, EC1A 9DS, ☎ (020) 7796 06 *Fax (020) 7796 0601* – ▤. MC AE VISA p. 27 OU
closed 21 December-6 January, Sunday, Saturday lunch and Bank Holidays – **Meals** - Fre (Gascony specialities) - (booking essential) 30.00/50.00 and a la carte 20.60/40.50 **t.** 12.
Spec. Tatin of foie gras, truffle and turnips. Crispy veal fillet, sorrel and courgette. Pr and Armagnac parfait.

XX **Searcy's at The Barbican,** Level 2, The Barbican, Silk St, EC2Y 8DS, ☎ (020) 7588 30 *searcys@barbican.org.uk, Fax (028) 7382 7247* – ▤. MC AE ⓓ VISA p. 27 OU
closed 24-25 December, Saturday lunch and Sunday – **Meals** 22.50 and a la carte appr 37.50 **t.** 15.40.

XX **The Don,** The Courtyard, 20 St Swithins Lane, EC4N 8AD, ☎ (020) 7626 2606, *booki @thedonrestaurant.co.uk, Fax (020) 7626 2616* – ▤. MC AE ⓓ VISA p. 27 PV
closed 23 December-2 January, Saturday, Sunday and Bank Holidays – **Meals** (lunch book essential) 14.95/17.95 (dinner) and a la carte 23.10/32.95 **t.** 14.25.

XX **1 Lombard Street (Brasserie),** 1 Lombard St, EC2V 9AA, ☎ (020) 7929 66 *Fax (020) 7929 6622* – ▤. MC AE ⓓ VISA JCB p. 27 PV
closed Saturday, Sunday and Bank Holidays – **Meals** (lunch booking essential) a la ca 26.50/35.80 **t.** 15.00.

XX **Brasserie Rocque,** 37 Broadgate Circle, EC2M 2QS, ☎ (020) 7638 79 *Fax (020) 7628 5899,* 🏠 – ▤. MC AE VISA p. 27 PU
closed Saturday, Sunday and Bank Holidays – **Meals** (booking essential) (lunch o a la carte 21.65/36.35 **t.** 10.50.

XX **Pacific Oriental,** first floor, 1 Bishopsgate, EC2N 3AB, ☎ (020) 7621 9988, *enquiries@ plc.co.uk, Fax (020) 7621 9911* – ▤. MC AE ⓓ VISA p. 27 PV
closed 25-26 December, 1 January, Saturday, Sunday and Bank Holidays – **Meals** - South E Asian influences - a la carte 25.75/37.75 **t.** 15.00.

XX **Imperial City,** Royal Exchange, Cornhill, EC3V 3LL, ☎ (020) 7626 3437, *enquiries@org co.uk, Fax (020) 7338 0125* – ▤. MC AE ⓓ VISA p. 27 PV
closed 25-26 December, Saturday, Sunday and Bank Holidays – **Meals** - Chinese - 20. 40.00 and a la carte 16.50/32.80 **t.** 12.50.

XX **Sri Siam City,** 85 London Wall, EC2M 7AD, ☎ (020) 7628 5772, *enquiries@cvgplc.co. Fax (020) 7628 3395* – ▤. MC AE ⓓ VISA p. 27 PU
closed 25-26 December, 1 January, Saturday, Sunday and Bank Holidays – **Meals** - Th (booking essential) 16.95/27.95 and a la carte approx. 20.25 **t.** 16.50.

CROYDON.

Addington – ✉ *Surrey.*

18, 18, 9 *Addington Court, Featherbed Lane* ☎ *(020) 8657 0281* GZ – 18 *The Addington, Shirley Church Rd* ☎ *(020) 8777 1055* GZ.

XX **Planet Spice,** 88 Selsdon Park Rd, CR2 8JT, ☎ (020) 8651 3300, *Fax (020) 8651 4400* – P. MC AE ⓓ VISA p. 14 GZ
closed 25-26 December – **Meals** - Indian - a la carte 14.00/15.45 **t.** 7.95.

Coulsdon – ✉ *Surrey.*

Coulsdon Manor ⛰, Coulsdon Court Rd, via Stoats Nest Rd, CR5 2 ☎ (020) 8668 0414, *coulsdonmanor@marstonhotel.com, Fax (020) 8668 3118,* <, Fб, 18, squash – ▤ ⇔ TV P – 180. MC AE ⓓ VISA.
Manor House : **Meals** *(closed Saturday lunch)* 19.50/27.00 and dinner a la carte appr 38.00 **st.** 12.60 – ☕ 11.00 – **35 rm** 105.00/149.00 **st.** – SB.

Croydon – ✉ *Surrey.*

Croydon Clocktower, Katharine St ✆ (020) 8253 1009.

Hilton Croydon, Waddon Way, Purley Way, CR9 4HH, ✆ (020) 8680 3000, *Fax (020) 8681 6171,* ... – 400. MC AE ① VISA JCB. p. 14 FZ e
Meals a la carte 16.95/21.95 **st.** 13.95 – 14.00 – **168 rm** 140.00/180.00 **st.**

Croydon Park, 7 Altyre Rd, CR9 5AA, ✆ (020) 8680 9200, *reservations@croydonparkhotel.co.uk, Fax (020) 8760 0426,* ..., squash – ..., rm, ... – 300. MC AE ① VISA. p. 14 FZ u
Oscars : **Meals** 15.95/20.95 and a la carte 24.45/41.50 **st.** 12.50 – **211 rm** 112.00/150.00 **st.** – SB.

Posthouse Croydon, Purley Way, CR9 4LT, ✆ (0870) 400 9022, *Fax (020) 8681 6438,* ... – ..., rest, ... – 120. MC AE ① VISA JCB p. 14 FZ o
Meals a la carte 15.00/25.00 11.95 – 12.95 – **83 rm** 119.00/139.00 **st.** – SB.

Travel Inn Metro, 104 Coombe Rd, CR0 5RB, on A 212 ✆ (020) 8686 2030, *Fax (020) 8686 6435,* ... – rm, ... MC AE ① VISA. p. 14 GZ s
Meals (grill rest.) – **39 rm** 49.95 **t.**

Premier Lodge, 619 Purley Way, CR0 4RJ, ✆ (020) 8225 1909, *Fax (020) 8680 9109* – ... MC AE ① VISA. p. 14 FZ e
Meals (grill rest.) a la carte approx. 17.00 **t.** 9.85 – **82 rm** 54.95 **t.**

Mario, 299 High St, CR0 1QL, ✆ (020) 8686 5624 – MC AE VISA p. 14 FZ s
closed 25-26 December, last 2 weeks August, Sunday, Monday, Saturday lunch and Bank Holidays – **Meals** - Italian - 15.00 (lunch) and a la carte 21.15/33.50 **t.** 10.50.

Tai Tung, Unit 1A, Wing Yip Centre, 550 Purley Way, CR0 4RF, ✆ (020) 8688 3668, *Fax (020) 8688 0116* – ... MC AE VISA JCB p. 14 FZ v
closed 24 to 26 December – **Meals** - Chinese (Canton) - 12.00/15.80 and a la carte 10.00/16.30 **t.** 8.60.

Sanderstead – ✉ *Surrey.*

Selsdon Park Hotel, Addington Rd, Sanderstead ✆ (020) 8657 8811 **GZ.**

Selsdon Park, Addington Rd, CR2 8YA, ✆ (020) 8657 8811, *sales.selsdonpark@principalhotels.co.uk, Fax (020) 8651 6171,* ..., heated, ..., squash – ..., rest, ... – 150. MC AE ① VISA. p. 14 GZ n
Meals (dancing Saturday evening) (buffet lunch Monday-Saturday) 19.95/25.50 and dinner a la carte approx. 39.95 **st.** 15.95 – 12.95 – **200 rm** 125.00/160.00 **st.**, 4 suites – SB.

EALING.

Bedford Park – ✉ *W4.*

Riso, 76 South Par, W4 5LF, ✆ (020) 8742 2121, *Fax (020) 8742 2121* – MC VISA JCB
Meals - Italian - (dinner only) a la carte 19.50/23.50 **t.** 12.00. p. 13 CV o

Ealing – ✉ *W5.*

West Middlesex, Greenford Rd, Southall ✆ (020) 8574 3450 **BV** – *Horsenden Hill, Woodland Rise, Greenford ✆ (020) 8902 4555* **BU.**

Ramada Jarvis London West, Ealing Common, W5 3HN, ✆ (020) 8896 8400, *jiealing.rs@jarvis.co.uk, Fax (020) 8992 7082* – ..., rm, rest, ... – 250. MC AE ① VISA JCB. p. 9 CV v
Meals (buffet lunch Monday-Friday) (bar lunch Saturday) a la carte 18.15/23.85 **t.** 14.20 – 11.50 – **189 rm** 140.00.160.00 **st.** – SB.

Travel Inn Metro, Western Ave, Greenford, UB6 8TR, off A 40 ✆ (020) 8998 8820, *Fax (020) 8998 8823* – rm, rest, ... MC AE ① VISA JCB. p. 8 BU c
Meals (grill rest.) – **39 rm** 49.95 **t.**

Travelodge without rest., Western Ave, W3 0TE, ✆ (020) 8752 1072, *Fax (020) 8752 1134* – ... MC AE ① VISA. p. 13 CV x
64 rm 69.95 **t.**

Parade, 18-19 The Mall, W5 2PJ, ✆ (020) 8810 0202, *Fax (020) 8810 0303* – ... MC AE VISA p. 13 CV s
closed 25-26 December, Sunday dinner and Bank Holidays – **Meals** 15.00 (lunch) and a la carte 23.00/29.00 **t.** 10.50.

Maxim, 153-155 Northfield Ave, W13 9QT, ✆ (020) 8567 1719, *maximrest@hotmail.com, Fax (020) 8932 0717* – ... MC AE VISA JCB p. 8 BV a
closed 25 to 28 December and Sunday lunch – **Meals** - Chinese (Peking) - 12.90/27.90 and a la carte 15.00/29.00 **t.** 9.90.

ENFIELD.

Lee Valley Leisure, Picketts Lock Lane, Edmonton (020) 8803 3611 GT.

Enfield – Middx.

Whitewebbs, Beggars Hollow, Clay Hill (020) 8363 2951, N : 1 m. FT.

Royal Chace, The Ridgeway, EN2 8AR, (020) 8884 8181, *royal.chace@dial.pipex.co Fax (020) 8884 8150,* heated, – – 270. p. 10 ET
closed 25-26 December – **Meals** *(closed Sunday dinner)* (bar lunch Monday to Saturda dinner a la carte approx. 26.00 **t.** – **92 rm** 110.00/125.00 **st.**

Oak Lodge, 80 Village Rd, Bush Hill Park, EN1 2EU, (020) 8360 7082, *oaklodge@fsm net,* , – . p. 10 FT
Meals (dinner only) a la carte 17.40/26.80 **t.** 13.00 – **6 rm** 94.00/130.00 **st.**

Hadley Wood – Herts.

West Lodge Park, off Cockfosters Rd, EN4 0PY, (020) 8216 3900, *info@w lodgepark.com, Fax (020) 8216 3937,* , , , – , rest, – 80. p. 10 ET
The Cedar : **Meals** 22.00/32.25 **t.** 13.90 – 13.50 – **55 rm** 105.00/125.00 **t.** – SB.

Winchmore Hill – N21.

The Kings Head, 1 The Green, N21 1BB, (020) 8886 1988, *geronimo@geronimoin co.uk, Fax (020) 8882 3881* – . p. 10 FT
closed Sunday dinner – **Meals** a la carte 16.50/20.00 **t.** 9.80.

***Le Grand Londres** (GREATER LONDON) est composé de la City et de 32 arrondissements administratifs (Borough) eux-mêmes divisés en quartiers ou en villages ayant conservé leur caractère propre (Area).*

GREENWICH.

Blackheath – SE3.

Bardon Lodge, 15 Stratheden Rd, SE3 7TH, (020) 8853 7000, *bardonlodge@btcl com, Fax (020) 8858 7387,* – rest, – 30. p. 15 HV
Lamplight : **Meals** (dinner only) a la carte approx. 25.00 **t.** 11.00 – **28 rm** 85.(130.00 **t.**

Chapter Two, 43-45 Montpelier Vale, SE3 0TJ, (020) 8333 2666, *fiona.chapter2@talk .com, Fax (020) 8355 8399* – . p. 15 HX
closed 1-4 January – **Meals** 14.50/22.50 **t.** 13.50.

Greenwich – SE10.

Pepys House, Old Royal Naval College, King William Walk (0870) 6082000.

Spread Eagle, 1-2 Stockwell St, SE10 9JN, (020) 8853 2333, *goodfood@spreadeag org, Fax (020) 8305 0447* – . p. 14 GV
closed 25 to 27 December, Sunday dinner and Bank Holiday Monday – **Meals** 13.50/16. (lunch) and a la carte 23.00/29.75 **t.** 10.75.

North Pole, 131 Greenwich High Rd, SE10 8JA, (020) 8853 3020, *Fax (020) 8853 350* p. 14 GV
Meals 17.00 (dinner) and a la carte 20.00/29.00 **t.** 11.00.

Time, 7a College Approach, SE10 8SS, (020) 8305 9767, *andrea.time@virgin.n Fax (020) 8293 3888* – p. 14 GV
Meals 25.00 and a la carte 18.00/33.00 **t.** 11.50.

HACKNEY.

Dalston – N1.

Soulard, 113 Mortimer Rd, N1 4JY, (020) 7254 1314, *Fax (020) 7254 1314* – p. 27 PS
closed 3 weeks August-September, between Christmas-New Year, Sunday and Monda **Meals** - French - (dinner only and lunch December) 21.00 **t.** 10.40.

LMNT, 316 Queensbridge Rd, E8 3NH, (020) 7249 6727, *lmnt.gastrobar@virgin.n Fax (020) 7249 6538* – . p. 10 GU
closed 25-26 December – **Meals** 12.50 (lunch) and a la carte approx. 21.03 **t.** 10.90.

oxton – ✉ *N1.*

Express by Holiday Inn, 275 Old St, EC1V 9LN, ✆ (020) 7300 4300, *reservationsfc@holidayinnlondon.com, Fax (020) 7300 4400* – lift, ⇔ rm, ▤ rest, TV ✆ ♿ – 80. MC AE DC VISA JCB. ✗ p. 27 PT a
Meals (dinner only) a la carte approx. 20.90 **t.** 15.50 – **224 rm** 105.00 **st.** – SB.

Real Greek, 15 Hoxton Market, N1 6HG, ✆ (020) 7739 8212, *admin@therealgreek.co.uk, Fax (020) 7739 4910* – MC VISA p. 27 PT v
closed Sunday and Bank Holidays – **Meals** - Greek - a la carte 27.40/33.90 **t.** 12.50.

:oke Newington – ✉ *N16.*

Mesclun, 24 Stoke Newington Church St, N16 0LU, ✆ (020) 7249 5029, *Fax (020) 7275 8448* – MC VISA JCB p. 10 FU c
Meals (dinner only) a la carte 20.90/23.40 **t.** 10.95.

AMMERSMITH and FULHAM.

ulham – ✉ *SW6.*

London Putney Bridge Travel Inn Capital, 3 Putney Bridge Approach, SW6 3JD, ✆ (020) 7471 8300, *Fax (020) 7471 8315* – lift, ⇔ rm, ▤ rest, TV ♿. MC AE DC VISA. ✗ p. 16 AQ c
Meals (grill rest.) (dinner only) – **154 rm** 74.95 **t.**

Le Potiron Sauvage, 755 Fulham Rd, SW6 5UU, ✆ (020) 7371 0755, *Fax (020) 7371 0695* – MC AE VISA JCB p. 16 BQ a
closed 25-29 December, 1-7 January, Sunday dinner and Monday – **Meals** (dinner only and Sunday lunch except August)/dinner 26.00 **t.** 15.00.

Blue Elephant, 4-6 Fulham Broadway, SW6 1AA, ✆ (020) 7385 6595, *london@blueelephant.com, Fax (020) 7386 7665* – ▤. MC AE DC VISA p. 28 EZ z
closed Christmas and Saturday lunch – **Meals** - Thai - (booking essential) 10.00/36.00 and a la carte 18.50/32.00 **t.** 14.00.

Mao Tai, 58 New Kings Rd, Parsons Green, SW6 4LS, ✆ (020) 7225 2500, *mbmaotai@aol.com, Fax (020) 7471 8992* – ▤. MC AE DC VISA p. 16 BQ e
closed 25-26 December – **Meals** - Chinese (Szechuan) - 24.70 and a la carte 27.70/36.00 **t.** 14.50.

The Salisbury Tavern, 21 Sherbrooke Rd, SW6 7HX, ✆ (020) 7381 4005, *longshot@dial.pipex.com, Fax (020) 7381 1002* – ▤. MC AE VISA p. 28 EZ e
closed 25-26 December – **Meals** (live jazz Monday evening) a la carte 19.15/25.90 **t.** 11.00.

ammersmith – ✉ *W6/W12/W14.*

River Café (Ruth Rogers/Rose Gray), Thames Wharf, Rainville Rd, W6 9HA, ✆ (020) 7386 4200, *info@rivercafe.co.uk, Fax (020) 7386 4201,* ☂ – MC AE DC VISA p. 13 DV r
closed Christmas-New Year, Sunday dinner and Bank Holidays – **Meals** - Italian - (booking essential) a la carte 42.00/48.00 **t.** 10.50
Spec. Chargrilled squid with red chilli and rocket. Bollito misto. "Chocolate nemesis".

Rafique, 291 King St, W6 9NH, ✆ (020) 8748 7345, *Fax (020) 8563 9679* – ▤. MC AE DC VISA JCB p. 13 CV u
closed Monday lunch – **Meals** - Indian - 9.50 (lunch) and a la carte 18.95/23.85.

Snows on the Green, 166 Shepherd's Bush Rd, Brook Green, W6 7PB, ✆ (020) 7603 2142, *Fax (020) 7602 7553* – ▤. MC AE DC VISA p. 13 DV x
closed 1 week Christmas, Saturday lunch and Sunday dinner – **Meals** 13.50/16.00 (lunch) and a la carte 22.50/28.50 **t.** 11.00.

The Brackenbury, 129-131 Brackenbury Rd, W6 0BQ, ✆ (020) 8748 0107, *Fax (020) 8741 0905,* ☂ – MC AE DC VISA p. 13 CV a
closed 24-26 December, Saturday lunch and Sunday dinner – **Meals** 12.50 (lunch) and a la carte 19.50/29.30 **t.** 11.00.

Azou, 375 King St, W6 9NJ, ✆ (020) 8536 7266, *Fax (020) 8748 1009* – ▤. MC DC VISA p. 13 CV u
closed 25 December and 1 January – **Meals** - North African - (lunch booking essential) a la carte 14.85/21.75 **t.** 9.70.

Thatched House, 115 Dalling Rd, W6 0ET, ✆ (020) 8748 6174, *thatchedhouse@establishment.co.uk, Fax (020) 8563 2735* – MC VISA JCB p. 13 CV r
closed 25 December – **Meals** a la carte 15.85/22.85 **t.** 10.95.

Anglesea Arms, 35 Wingate Rd, W6 0UR, ✆ (020) 8749 1291, *fievans@aol.com, Fax (020) 8749 1254* – MC VISA p. 13 CV c
closed 24-31 December – **Meals** (bookings not accepted) a la carte 18.45/20.65 **t.** 10.25.

Olympia – ✉ *W14.*

XX **Cotto,** 44 Blythe Rd, W14 0HA, ☏ (020) 7602 9333, *bookings@cottorestaurant.co.u*
Fax (020) 7602 5003 – ▤. MC AE VISA JCB p. 28 **EZ**
closed 1 week Christmas, Saturday lunch, Sunday and Bank Holidays – **Meals** 15.50/18.0 (lunch) and a la carte 22.25/31.70 **t.** 🍷 12.50.

Shepherd's Bush – ✉ *W12/W14.*

XX **Chinon,** 23 Richmond Way, W14 0AS, ☏ (020) 7602 5968, *johnchinon@hotmail.con*
Fax (020) 7602 4082 – ▤. MC AE ⓓ VISA JCB p. 13 **DV**
closed Christmas, Easter and Sunday – **Meals** (dinner only) 25.00 **t.** 🍷 16.00.

X **Onami,** 236 Blythe Rd, W14 0HJ, ☏ (020) 7603 7267 p. 13 **DV**
Meals - Japanese - a la carte approx. 15.00 **t.** 🍷 10.50.

Havelock Tavern, 57 Masbro Rd, W14 0LS, ☏ (020) 7603 5374, *Fax (020) 7602 1163*, – ▤ p. 13 **DV**
closed 23-26 December – **Meals** (bookings not accepted) a la carte 18.50/24.00 **st.** 🍷 9.50

HARINGEY.

Crouch End – ✉ *N8.*

Mountview without rest., 31 Mount View Rd, N4 4SS, ☏ (020) 8340 9222, *mountviewb@aol.com, Fax (020) 8342 8494*, – ⊭ TV. MC VISA. p. 10 **EU**
3 rm ☕ 40.00/70.00 **st.**

XX **Les Associés,** 172 Park Rd, N8 8JT, ☏ (020) 8348 8944 – MC VISA p. 10 **EU**
closed 20 August-5 September, 1 January, Sunday dinner and Monday – **Meals** - French (dinner only and Sunday lunch)/dinner 13.50/16.50 a la carte 19.40/25.50 **t.** 🍷 11.40.

X **Florians,** 4 Topsfield Par, Middle Lane, N8 8RP, ☏ (020) 8348 8348, *Fax (020) 8292 209*
– ▤. VISA p. 10 **EU**
closed 25-26 December and 1 January – **Meals** - Italian - a la carte 19.00/24.00 **t.** 🍷 9.95.

Prices — For notes on the prices quoted in this Guide, see the introduction.

HARROW.

Harrow Weald – ✉ *Middx.*

Grim's Dyke, Old Redding, HA3 6SH, ☏ (020) 8385 3100, *enquiries@grimsdyke.cor*
Fax (020) 8954 4560, – ⊭ rm, TV P – 70. MC AE ⓓ VISA JCB p. 8 **BT**
Meals *(closed Saturday lunch)* 23.00 and a la carte 27.45/49.00 **t.** 🍷 16.00 – **44 r** ☕ 125.00/170.00 **t.** – SB.

Kenton – ✉ *Middx.*

Travel Inn Metro, Kenton Rd, HA3 8AT, ☏ (020) 8907 4069, *Fax (020) 8909 1604* –
⊭ rm, TV ♿ P. MC AE ⓓ VISA. p. 8 **BU**
Meals (grill rest.) – **70 rm** 49.95 **t.**

Pinner – ✉ *Middx.*

XX **Friends,** 11 High St, HA5 5PJ, ☏ (020) 8866 0286, *info@friendsrestaurant.co.u*
Fax (020) 8866 0286 – ⊭. MC AE ⓓ VISA p. 8 **BU**
closed 2 weeks August, 25-26 December, Sunday dinner, Monday and Bank Holidays
Meals 16.50/25.00 and a la carte 27.25/31.15 **t.** 🍷 12.00.

HAVERING.

Romford – ✉ *Essex.*

18, 9 *Risebridge, Risebridge Chase, Lower Bedfords Rd* ☏ *(01708) 741429*, **JT**.

Travel Inn Metro, Mercury Gdns, RM1 3EN, ☏ (01708) 760548, *Fax (01708) 760456* –
⊭ rm, TV ♿ P. MC AE ⓓ VISA p. 11 **JU**
Meals (grill rest.) – **40 rm** 49.95 **t.**

HILLINGDON.

18 *Haste Hill, The Drive, Northwood* ☏ *(01923) 825224* **AU**.

ayes – ✉ *Middx.*

Travel Inn Metro, 362 Uxbridge Rd, UB4 0HF, ✆ (020) 8573 7479, *Fax (020) 8569 1204* – ⇔ rm, ▤ rest, TV ♿ P. MC AE D VISA. ✻ p. 8 AV a
Meals (grill rest.) – **62 rm** 49.95 **t.**

eathrow Airport – ✉ *Middx.*

Radisson Edwardian, 140 Bath Rd, Hayes, UB3 5AW, ✆ (020) 8759 6311, *busctr@radissonedwardian.com, Fax (020) 8759 4559,* Fö, ≘s, ⊠ – |‡|, ⇔ rm, ▤ TV ✆ P – 🏛 550. MC AE D VISA JCB. ✻ p. 12 AX e
Henleys : Meals 25.00 and a la carte 33.00/43.00 **st.** 🌢 15.25 – ***Brasserie :*** Meals a la carte approx. 24.00 **st.** 🌢 15.25 – ☕ 15.00 – **442 rm** 199.00/219.00 **s.**, 17 suites.

Crowne Plaza London Heathrow, Stockley Rd, West Drayton, UB7 9NA, ✆ (01895) 445555, *cpsales3@netscape.co.uk, Fax (01895) 445122,* Fö, ≘s, ⊠, ⛳9 – |‡|, ⇔ rm, ▤ TV ✆ ♿ P – 🏛 200. MC AE D VISA JCB. ✻ p. 8 AV v
Concha Grill : Meals 18.50/23.50 and a la carte 21.95/43.95 **t.** 🌢 11.95 – (see also ***Simply Nico Heathrow*** below) – ☕ 16.50 – **457 rm** 195.00 **st.**, 1 suite.

Sheraton Skyline, Bath Rd, Hayes, UB3 5BP, ✆ (020) 8759 2535, *res268_skyline@sheraton.com, Fax (020) 8750 9150,* Fö, ⊠ – |‡|, ⇔ rm, ▤ TV ✆ P – 🏛 500. MC AE D VISA JCB. ✻ p. 12 AX u
Sage : Meals (dinner only) a la carte 22.00/39.00 🌢 18.50 – ☕ 17.00 – **349 rm** 174.00 **st.**, 3 suites.

Hilton London Heathrow Airport, Terminal 4, TW6 3AF, ✆ (020) 8759 7755, *gm_heathrow@hilton.com, Fax (020) 8759 7579,* Fö, ≘s, ⊠ – |‡|, ⇔ rm, ▤ TV ✆ ♿ P – 🏛 240. MC AE D VISA JCB p. 12 AX n
Brasserie : Meals 23.50/29.50 and a la carte 13.40/28.50 **st.** 🌢 15.90 – ***Zen Oriental :*** Meals - Chinese - 28.80/38.50 and a la carte 25.50/30.00 **t.** 🌢 28.00 – ☕ 17.50 – **390 rm** 148.00/195.00 **s.**, 5 suites – SB.

London Heathrow Marriott, Bath Rd, Hayes, UB3 5AN, ✆ (020) 8990 1100, *Fax (020) 8990 1110,* Fö, ≘s, ⊠ – |‡|, ⇔ rm, ▤ TV ✆ ♿ P – 🏛 540. MC AE D VISA JCB. ✻ p. 12 AX z
Tuscany : Meals - Italian - *(closed Sunday)* (dinner only) a la carte 24.50/37.00 **t.** 🌢 20.00 – ***Allie's grille :*** Meals a la carte 21.25/31.20 **t.** 🌢 13.95 – ☕ 16.45 – **388 rm** 190.00/215.00 **st.**, 2 suites.

Le Méridien Heathrow, Bath Rd, West Drayton, UB7 0DU, ✆ (020) 8759 6611, *excelsior@lemeridien.co.uk, Fax (020) 8759 3421,* Fö, ≘s, ⊠ – |‡|, ⇔ rm, ▤ TV ♿ P – 🏛 700. MC AE D VISA JCB. ✻ p. 12 AX x
Meals *(closed Saturday lunch)* (carvery) 22.95 **t.** 🌢 17.95 – ***Snappers :*** Meals *(closed Saturday and Sunday lunch and Bank Holidays)* 15.50/39.50 and a la carte 36.10/53.40 **t.** 🌢 17.95 – ☕ 14.95 – **525 rm** 125.00 **s.**, 10 suites – SB.

Holiday Inn London Heathrow, Sipson Rd, West Drayton, UB7 0JU, ✆ (0870) 400 8595, *Fax (020) 8897 8659* – |‡|, ⇔ rm, ▤ TV ♿ P – 🏛 140. MC AE D VISA JCB. ✻ p. 8 AV c
Sampans : Meals - Chinese - (dinner only) 18.95/29.95 and a la carte 18.35/27.95 **t.** 🌢 12.55 – ***Rotisserie :*** Meals *(closed Saturday lunch)* 19.50 and a la carte 20.35/30.15 **st.** 🌢 11.95 – ☕ 14.95 – **604 rm** 169.00, 6 suites – SB.

Renaissance London Heathrow, Bath Rd, TW6 2AQ, ✆ (020) 8897 6363, *106047.3556@compuserve.com, Fax (020) 8897 1113,* Fö, ≘s – |‡|, ⇔ rm, ▤ TV ✆ ♿ P – 🏛 550. MC AE D VISA JCB. ✻ p. 12 AX c
Meals 18.50/21.50 and a la carte 18.00/37.25 **st.** 🌢 18.00 – ☕ 13.95 – **643 rm** 189.00 **st.**, 5 suites.

Sheraton Heathrow, Colnbrook bypass, West Drayton, UB7 0HJ, ✆ (020) 8759 2424, *res29_heathrow@sheraton.com, Fax (020) 8759 2091,* Fö – |‡|, ⇔ rm, ▤ TV ✆ P – 🏛 70. MC AE D VISA JCB. ✻ p. 12 AVX a
Meals 21.50 and a la carte 21.75/33.95 **st.** 🌢 24.00 – ☕ 14.25 – **426 rm** 199.00/225.00 **st.**, 5 suites.

Posthouse Heathrow, 118 Bath Rd, Hayes, UB3 5AJ, ✆ (0870) 400 9040, *reservations-heathrow@posthouse-hotels.com, Fax (020) 8564 9265* – |‡|, ⇔ rm, ▤ rest, TV P – 🏛 55. MC AE D VISA JCB p. 12 AX i
Meals *(closed Saturday lunch)* (bar lunch Saturday) (buffet lunch) 13.95 (lunch) and a la carte 23.00/28.00 **t.** 🌢 13.00 – ☕ 13.95 – **186 rm** 109.00/189.00 **st.** – SB.

Travelodge, Sipson Rd, West Drayton, UB7 0UD, ✆ (020) 8897 7775, *Fax (020) 8897 6381* – |‡| ⇔ ▤ TV ♿ P. MC AE D VISA JCB. ✻ p. 12 AX x
Meals (grill rest.) – **289 rm** 69.95 **t.**

XX **Simply Nico Heathrow** (at Crowne Plaza London Heathrow H.), Stockley Rd, West Drayton, UB7 9NA, ✆ (01895) 437564, *heathrow@simplynico.co.uk, Fax (01895) 437565* – ▤ P. MC AE ⓓ VISA p. 12 AV
closed 25-26 December, Saturday lunch, Sunday and Bank Holidays – **Meals** 10.00/12. (lunch) and a la carte 26.00/36.50 **t.** 13.00.

HOUNSLOW.

Wyke Green, Syon Lane, Isleworth ✆ (020) 8560 8777 BV – *Airlinks, Southall La. ✆ (020) 8561 1418* ABV – *Hounslow Heath, Staines Rd ✆ (020) 8570 5271* BX.
24 The Treaty Centre, High St ✆ (020) 8572 8279 (closed Sunday).

Chiswick – ✉ *W4.*

XX **La Trompette,** 5-7 Devonshire Rd, W4 2EU, ✆ (020) 8747 1836, *Fax (020) 8995 8097,* – ▤. MC AE VISA p. 13 CV
closed Christmas – **Meals** 19.50/25.00 **t.** 14.50.

X **The Chiswick,** 131 Chiswick High Rd, W4 2ED, ✆ (020) 8994 6887, *thechiswick@talk.com, Fax (020) 8994 5504* – MC AE VISA p. 13 CV
closed 25-26 December, Saturday lunch, Sunday dinner and Bank Holidays – **Meals** 12.9 15.50 (lunch) and a la carte 18.50/29.00 **t.** 11.50.

X **Springbok Grill,** 42 Devonshire Rd, W4 2HD, ✆ (020) 8742 3149, *springbokgrill@hotm.com, Fax (020) 8742 8541* – MC ⓓ VISA p. 13 CV
closed 21 December-3 January and Sunday – **Meals** - South African - (dinner only) a la car 14.50/31.25 **t.** 12.50.

X **Pug,** 68 Chiswick High Rd, W4 1SY, ✆ (020) 8987 9988, *Fax (020) 8987 9911,* – ▤. MC VISA p. 13 CV
Meals 14.50 (dinner) and a la carte 20.95/27.20 **t.** 11.95.

Feltham – ✉ *Middx.*

St Giles, Hounslow Rd, TW14 9AD, ✆ (020) 8817 7000, *Fax (020) 8817 7001,* ≤, Fб – ⇔ rm, ▤ TV ♿ P. – 🏛 120. MC AE ⓓ VISA. ✂ p. 12 AX
*closed 25-26 December***Meals** - Italian - *(closed lunch Saturday and Sunday)* a la ca 20.00/28.00 **st.** 11.95 – ☕ 10.50 – **292 rm** 115.00/125.00 **st.**, 8 suites.

Heston Service Area – ✉ *Middx.*

Travelodge without rest., TW5 9NB, on M 4 (between junctions 2 and 3 westbou carriageway) ✆ (020) 8580 2000, *Fax (020) 8580 2006* – ⇔ TV ♿ P. MC AE ⓓ VISA JCB. ✂ p. 12 ABV
145 rm 69.95 **t.**

Travelodge, TW5 9NA, on M 4 (between junctions 3 and 2 on eastbound carriagew ✆ (020) 8580 2122, *Fax (020) 8580 2128* – ⇔ rm, TV ♿ P. MC AE ⓓ VISA JCB. ✂ p. 12 AV
Meals (grill rest.) – **66 rm** 69.95 **t.**

ISLINGTON.

Archway – ✉ *N19.*

X **The Parsee,** 34 Highgate Hill, N19 5NL, ✆ (020) 7272 9091, *dining@theparsee.co. Fax (020) 7687 1139* – ▤. MC AE VISA p. 10 EU
closed 25 December, Good Friday and Monday – **Meals** - Indian (Parsee) - (dinner only a Sunday lunch) 20.00/30.00 and a la carte 14.70/23.95 **t.** 11.90.

St John's, 91 Junction Rd, N19 5QU, ✆ (020) 7272 1587, *stjohnsarchway@virgin.r Fax (020) 7272 8023* – MC VISA p. 10 EU
closed Monday lunch – **Meals** a la carte 16.50/24.50 **t.** 11.00.

Barnsbury – ✉ *N1.*

X **The Dining Room,** 169 Hemingford Rd, N1 1DA, ✆ (020) 7609 3009 p. 26 MS
closed 25-26 December, Sunday dinner and Monday – **Meals** (dinner only and Sun lunch) a la carte 16.00/25.00 **t.** 10.00.

Canonbury – ✉ *N1.*

Centuria, 100 St Paul's Rd, N1 2QP, ✆ (020) 7704 2345 – MC VISA p. 10 FU
closed lunch Monday-Friday – **Meals** a la carte 15.70/22.70 **t.** 11.70.

Clerkenwell – ✉ *EC1.*

The Rookery without rest., 12 Peters Lane, Cowcross St, EC1M 6DS, ✆ (020) 7336 0931, *reservations@rookery.co.uk, Fax (020) 7336 0932,* « Georgian town houses » – TV. MC AE DC VISA p. 27 NU o
closed 24-25 December – **32 rm** 183.00/205.00 **s.**, 1 suite.

Maison Novelli, 29 Clerkenwell Green, EC1R 0DU, ✆ (020) 7251 6606, *jcnovelli@wslrestaurants.co.uk, Fax (020) 7490 1083* – . MC AE DC VISA p. 27 NU a
closed Sunday, Saturday lunch and Bank Holidays – **Meals** a la carte 29.95/48.95 **t.** 14.95.

Smiths of Smithfield, Top Floor, 67-77 Charterhouse St, EC1M 6HJ, ✆ (020) 7236 6666, *smiths@smithfield.co.uk, Fax (020) 7236 5666,* ≤, – . MC AE DC VISA p. 27 NU s
closed 25-26 December and Saturday lunch – **Meals** a la carte 27.50/37.50 **t.** 10.00 – ***The Dining Room :*** Meals *(closed Sunday)* a la carte 19.25/20.25 **t.** 10.00.

Gaudi, 63 Clerkenwell Rd, EC1M 5PT, ✆ (020) 7608 3220, *gaudi@turnmills.co.uk, Fax (020) 7250 1057* – . MC AE DC VISA JCB p. 27 NU z
closed 24 December-3 January, Good Friday, Saturday lunch, Sunday and Bank Holiday Monday – **Meals** - Spanish - 15.00 (lunch) and a la carte 32.50/36.50 **t.** 11.50.

St John, 26 St John St, EC1M 4AY, ✆ (020) 7251 0848, *reservations@stjohnrestaurant.co.uk, Fax (020) 7251 4090,* « 19C converted former smokehouse » – . MC AE DC VISA JCB p. 27 OU c
closed Christmas-New Year, Easter weekend, Saturday lunch and Sunday – **Meals** a la carte 21.50/31.10 **t.** 11.50.

The Bear, No 2 St Johns Sq, EC1M 4DE, ✆ (020) 7608 2117, *Fax (020) 7608 2116* – . MC AE VISA p. 27 NU c
closed 25-26 December, Saturday, Sunday and Bank Holidays – **Meals** a la carte 11.90/17.40 **t.** 9.80.

Finsbury – ✉ *WC1/EC1/EC2.*

Simply Nico, 7 Goswell Rd, EC1M 7AH, ✆ (020) 7336 7677, *barbican@simplynico.co.uk, Fax (020) 7336 7690* – . MC AE DC VISA JCB p. 27 OUT a
closed 22 December-6 January, Sunday and Saturday lunch – **Meals** 12.50 and a la carte 19.50/29.60 **t.** 12.95.

Café Lazeez City, 88 St John St, EC1M 4EH, ✆ (020) 7253 2224, *lazclerkwell@cs.com, Fax (020) 7253 2112* – . MC AE DC VISA JCB p. 27 OU e
closed 22 December-1 January, Saturday lunch, Sunday and Bank Holidays – **Meals** - North Indian - 12.95/25.00 and a la carte 15.50/27.75 **t.** 9.95.

Quality Chop House, 94 Farringdon Rd, EC1R 3EA, ✆ (020) 7837 5093, *qualitychophouse@clara.net, Fax (020) 7833 8748* – . MC VISA p. 26 MT n
closed 23 December-3 January and Saturday lunch – **Meals** a la carte 19.00/34.00 **t.** 11.00.

Moro, 34-36 Exmouth Market, EC1R 4QE, ✆ (020) 7833 8336, *info@moro.co.uk, Fax (020) 7833 9338* – . MC AE DC VISA p. 27 NT a
closed 23 December-1 January, Saturday lunch, Sunday and Bank Holidays – **Meals** a la carte 19.00/28.50 **t.** 10.50.

The Peasant, 240 St John St, EC1V 4PH, ✆ (020) 7336 7726, *Fax (020) 7490 1089* – MC AE DC VISA p. 27 NT e
closed 24 December-2 January, Saturday lunch and Sunday – **Meals** a la carte 10.70/22.10 **t.** 10.50.

Highbury – ✉ *N7.*

Bu-San, 41-43 Holloway Rd, N7 8JP, ✆ (020) 7607 8264, *Fax (020) 7700 0961* – P. MC VISA p. 27 NS x
closed 25-26 December, lunch Saturday and Sunday and Bank Holiday Mondays – **Meals** - Korean - a la carte 11.40/30.60 **t.**

Islington – ✉ *N1.*

Hilton London Islington, 53 Upper St, N1 0UY, ✆ (020) 7354 7700, *Fax (020) 7354 7711,* , , – , rm, TV – 35. MC AE DC VISA JCB. p. 27 NS s
Meals 17.50/22.50 and dinner a la carte 18.00/28.50 **t.** 15.90 – 16.00 – **178 rm** 144.00 **s.**, 6 suites – SB.

Jurys Inn London, 60 Pentonville Rd, N1 9LA, ✆ (020) 7282 5500, *jurysinnlondon@jurysdoyle.com, Fax (020) 7282 5511* – , rm, TV – 40. MC AE VISA p. 26 MT e
closed 24-26 December – **Meals** (bar lunch)/dinner a la carte 16.00 **st.** 9.95 – 9.00 – **229 rm** 94.00 **st.**

XX **Frederick's,** Camden Passage, N1 8EG, ✆ (020) 7359 2888, *eat@fredericks.co. Fax (020) 7359 5173,* – . MO AE VISA JCB p. 27 NS
closed Christmas, Sunday and Bank Holidays – **Meals** 15.50 (lunch) and a la carte 20. 36.00 10.95.

XX **Lola's,** Mall Building, 359 Upper St, N1 0PD, ✆ (020) 7359 1932, *lolasreatuk@btinterr com, Fax (020) 7359 2209,* « Converted tram shed » – . MO AE VISA p. 27 NS
closed lunch Bank Holidays – **Meals** 15.00 (lunch) and a la carte 25.00/28.75 **t.** 10.75.

XX **La Margherita,** 297 Upper St, N1 2TU, ✆ (020) 7359 3533, *Fax (020) 7359 3533* – . AE VISA JCB p. 27 NS
Meals (dinner only and lunch Saturday and Sunday)/dinner a la carte 16.50/24.50 **t.** 10.

XX **Metrogusto,** 13 Theberton St, N1 0RY, ✆ (020) 7226 9400, *Fax (020) 7226 9400* – . VISA JCB p. 27 NS
closed 2 weeks August, 12 days Christmas, New Year and Monday – **Meals** - Italia a la carte 21.00/26.75 **t.** 12.50.

X **Granita,** 127 Upper St, N1 1PQ, ✆ (020) 7226 3222, *Fax (020) 7226 4833* – . VISA p. 27 NS
closed 1 weeks August, 1 week Easter, 10 days Christmas, Monday and lunch Tuesda **Meals** 14.95/16.95 (lunch) and dinner a la carte approx. 26.40 **t.** 10.95.

The Crown, 116 Cloudesley Rd, N1 0EB, ✆ (020) 7837 7107, *thecrown@fullers.co. Fax (020) 7833 1084,* – MO AE VISA p. 27 NS
closed Sunday dinner – **Meals** a la carte 12.50/23.80 **st.** 11.00.

The Northgate, 113 Southgate Rd, N1 3JS, ✆ (020) 7359 7392, *Fax (020) 7359 7393,* – MO VISA JCB p. 27 PS
closed 24-26 December and 1 January – **Meals** (dinner only and lunch Saturday and Sund a la carte 19.00/23.50 **t.** 11.00.

KENSINGTON and CHELSEA *(Royal Borough of).*

Chelsea – ✉ *SW1/SW3/SW10.*

Carlton Tower, Cadogan Pl, SW1X 9PY, ✆ (020) 7235 1234, *reservations@ london.co.uk, Fax (020) 7235 9129,* ←, , , , , – , rm, 400. MO AE VISA JCB. p. 35 FR
Rib Room : **Meals** 23.00/33.00 and a la carte 30.00/62.00 **t.** 18.00 – ***Grissini :*** **Meal** Italian - *(closed Saturday lunch and Sunday dinner)* 16.00/21.00 (lunch) and a la carte 20.(37.00 **t.** 18.00 – 19.50 – **191 rm** 295.00/360.00, 29 suites – SB.

Conrad London, Chelsea Harbour, SW10 0XG, ✆ (020) 7823 3000, *lonch-rm@hilton.cc Fax (020) 7351 6525,* ←, , , – , rm, – 200. MO AE JCB p. 17 CQ
Meals – (see ***Aquasia*** below) – 18.50, **160 suites** 350.00/410.00.

Sheraton Park Tower, 101 Knightsbridge, SW1X 7RN, ✆ (020) 7235 8050, *reservatic _central_london@sheraton.com, Fax (020) 7235 8231,* ← – , rm, 100. MO AE VISA JCB. p. 35 FQ
Meals – (see ***One-O-One*** below) – 20.75 – **258 rm** 335.00/355.00, 22 suites.

Capital, 22-24 Basil St, SW3 1AT, ✆ (020) 7589 5171, *reservations@capitalhotel.co. Fax (020) 7225 0011* – – 25. MO AE VISA. p. 35 ER
Meals (booking essential) 26.50/53.00 **t.** 14.50 – 16.50 – **49 rm** 190.00/315.00
Spec. Sautéed scallops and boudin noir. Saddle of rabbit with calamari "à la provençal Coconut and passion fruit fusion.

The Cadogan, 75 Sloane St, SW1X 9SG, ✆ (020) 7235 7141, *info@cadogan.co Fax (020) 7245 0994,* , – , rm, rest, – 40. MO AE VISA p. 35 FR
Meals *(closed Saturday lunch)* 15.90/28.50 and a la carte 35.00/48.00 **st.** 14.00 – 16 – **61 rm** 190.00/240.00 **s.**, 4 suites.

Chelsea Village, Fulham Rd, SW6 1HS, ✆ (020) 7565 1400, *reservations@chelseavilla com, Fax (020) 7565 1450,* « Adjacent to Chelsea Football Club » – , rm, – 300. MO AE VISA. p. 28 FZ
Arkles : **Meals** - Irish - *(closed Monday and dinner Sunday)* a la carte 23.25/31.75 **t.** 13. – ***Kings brasserie :*** **Meals** a la carte 17.00/29.00 **t.** 13.95 – ***Fishnets :*** **Meals** - Seafoo *(closed Sunday and lunch Monday)* (live music Friday evening) a la carte 17.75/25.25 13.95 – 14.00 – **288 rm** 155.00/175.00 **st.**, 3 suites.

Durley House, 115 Sloane St, SW1X 9PJ, ✆ (020) 7235 5537, *durley@firmdale.co Fax (020) 7259 6977,* « Georgian town house », , – . MO AE VISA. p. 35 FS
Meals (room service only) – 18.50, **11 suites** 295.00/550.00.

Cliveden Town House, 26 Cadogan Gdns, SW3 2RP, ✆ (020) 7730 6466, *reservation clivedentownhouse.co.uk, Fax (020) 7730 0236,* – , rm, rm, . MO AE VISA p. 35 FS
Meals (room service only) – 18.50 – **31 rm** 160.00/310.00 **s.**, 4 suites.

Millennium Knightsbridge, 17-25 Sloane St, SW1X 9NU, ☎ (020) 7235 4377, *sales-knightsbridge@mill-cop.com, Fax (020) 7235 3705* – 120. p. 35 FR r
Mju : **Meals** - French-Japanese - *(closed Saturday, Sunday dinner and Bank Holidays)* (set menu only) 50.00 **st.** 15.00 – **218 rm** 230.00/260.00 **s.**, 4 suites.

Franklin, 22-28 Egerton Gdns, SW3 2DB, ☎ (020) 7584 5533, *bookings@franklinhotel.co.uk, Fax (020) 7584 5449,* « Tastefully furnished Victorian town house », p. 35 DS e
Meals (room service only) a la carte 23.50/31.00 **t.** – 16.00 – **47 rm** 160.00/325.00.

Basil Street, 8 Basil St, SW3 1AH, ☎ (020) 7581 3311, *info@thebasil.com, Fax (020) 7581 3693* – rm, – 30. p. 35 FQ o
Meals 15.50/25.00 **t.** 14.50 – 15.00 – **80 rm** 138.00/198.00 **t.**

The London Outpost of the Carnegie Club without rest., 69 Cadogan Gdns, SW3 2RB, ☎ (020) 7589 7333, *londonoutpost@dial.pipex.com, Fax (020) 7581 4958,* p. 35 FS r
closed 24-28 December – 16.95 – **11 rm** 160.00/270.00 **s.**

The Sloane, 29 Draycott Pl, SW3 2SH, ☎ (020) 7581 5757, *reservations@sloanehotel.com, Fax (020) 7584 1348,* « Victorian town house, antiques » – p. 35 ET c
Meals (room service) – 12.00 – **22 rm** 150.00/240.00 **s.**

Eleven Cadogan Gardens, 11 Cadogan Gdns, SW3 2RJ, ☎ (020) 7730 7000, *reservations@number-eleven.co.uk, Fax (020) 7730 5217,* p. 35 FS u
Meals (room service) – 13.00 – **56 rm** 165.00/295.00 **t.**, 4 suites.

Egerton House, 17-19 Egerton Terr, SW3 2BX, ☎ (020) 7589 2412, *bookings@egertonhousehotel.co.uk, Fax (020) 7584 6540,* « Tastefully furnished Victorian town house » – p. 35 DR e
Meals (room service only) – 16.00 – **29 rm** 160.00/250.00 **s.**

Sydney without rest., 9-11 Sydney St, SW3 6PU, ☎ (020) 7376 7711, *sh@zoohotels.com, Fax (020) 7376 4233* – p. 35 DT a
5.00 – **21 rm** 175.00/270.00 **s.**

Chelsea Green without rest., 35 Ixworth Pl, SW3 3QX, ☎ (020) 7225 7500, *cghotel@dircon.co.uk, Fax (020) 7225 7555* – 80.
12.00 – **42 rm** 176.00/212.00 **st.**, 4 suites. p. 35 DT z

Beaufort without rest., 33 Beaufort Gdns, SW3 1PP, ☎ (020) 7584 5252, *enquiries@thebeaufort.co.uk, Fax (020) 7589 2834,* « English floral watercolour collection » – p. 35 ER n
28 rm 155.00/295.00 **s.**

Parkes without rest., 41 Beaufort Gdns, SW3 1PW, ☎ (020) 7581 9944, *reception@parkeshotel.com, Fax (020) 7581 1999* – p. 35 ER x
10.00 – **19 rm** 195.00/290.00 **s.**, 14 suites 325.00/415.00 **s.**

57 Pont Street without rest., 57 Pont St, SW1X 0BD, ☎ (020) 7590 1090, *sgregory@no57.com, Fax (020) 7590 1099* – p. 35 ER e
15.00 – **22 rm** 125.00/350.00 **s.**

L'Hotel, 28 Basil St, SW3 1AS, ☎ (020) 7589 6286, *reservations@lhotel.co.uk, Fax (020) 7823 7826* – rest, p. 35 ER i
closed Christmas – ***Le Metro :*** **Meals** *(closed 25 December, Sunday and Bank Holidays)* a la carte approx. 17.75 **t.** 12.95 – **12 rm** 135.00/155.00 **s.**

Sloane Square Moat House, Sloane Sq, SW1W 8EG, ☎ (020) 7896 9988, *reservations@queensmoat.co.uk, Fax (020) 7824 8381* – – 40. p. 35 FST v
Meals – (see ***Simply Nico*** below) – 8.50 – **105 rm** 163.00/236.00 **st.**

Claverley without rest., 13-14 Beaufort Gdns, SW3 1PS, ☎ (020) 7589 8541, *reservations@claverleyhotel.co.uk, Fax (020) 7584 3410* – p. 35 ER o
30 rm 110.00/195.00 **t.**

XXX **Gordon Ramsay,** 68-69 Royal Hospital Rd, SW3 4HP, ☎ (020) 7352 4441, *Fax (020) 7352 3334* – p. 35 EU c
closed 1 week Christmas, Saturday, Sunday and Bank Holidays – **Meals** (booking essential) 35.00/80.00 18.00
Spec. Carpaccio of pigeon with creamed truffle sauce. Fillet of sea bass wrapped in basil, crème fraîche and caviar sauce. Pineapple ravioli with summer fruits.

XXX **Aubergine,** 11 Park Walk, SW10 0AJ, ☎ (020) 7352 3449, *Fax (020) 7351 1770* – p. 34 CU r
closed 2 weeks August, 2 weeks Christmas, Saturday lunch, Sunday and Bank Holidays – **Meals** (booking essential) 25.00/65.00 **t.** 20.00
Spec. Warm salad of quail, foie gras and sweetbreads. Roast sea bass with baby artichokes and sweet pepper sauce. Roasted peaches with almond ice cream.

XXX **Drones,** 1 Pont St, SW1X 9EJ, ℘ (020) 7235 9555, *Fax (020) 7235 9566* – ▤. MC AE ⓓ
Meals a la carte 28.50/52.50 **t.** ⅓ 16.50. p. 35 FR

XXX **Bibendum,** Michelin House, 81 Fulham Rd, SW3 6RD, ℘ (020) 7581 5817, *manag bibendum.co.uk, Fax (020) 7823 7925* – ▤. MC AE ⓓ VISA p. 35 DS
closed 25-26 December – **Meals** 27.00 (lunch) and dinner a la carte 40.00/50.00 **t.**

XXX **Floriana,** 15 Beauchamp Pl, SW3 1NQ, ℘ (020) 7838 1500, *Fax (020) 7584 1464* – ▤. AE ⓓ VISA JCB p. 35 ER
Meals - Italian - 15.50/19.50 (lunch) and a la carte approx. 44.50 **t.** ⅓ 19.00.

XXX **The Fifth Floor** (at Harvey Nichols), Knightsbridge, SW1X 7RJ, ℘ (020) 7235 52 *Fax (020) 7823 2207* – |♦| ▤. MC AE ⓓ VISA JCB p. 35 FQ
closed 25-26 December and Sunday dinner – **Meals** 18.50 (lunch) and dinner a la ca 36.00/50.00 **t.** ⅓ 13.50.

XXX **One-O-One** (at Sheraton Park Tower H.), William St, SW1X 7RN, ℘ (020) 7290 71 *Fax (020) 7235 6196* – ▤. MC AE ⓓ VISA JCB p. 35 FQ
Meals - Seafood - 19.50 (lunch) and a la carte 35.00/51.00 **t.** ⅓ 23.00.

XXX **Toto's,** Walton House, Walton St, SW3 2JH, ℘ (020) 7589 0075, *Fax (020) 7581 9668,* ☂ MC AE ⓓ VISA JCB p. 35 ES
closed 25-27 December – **Meals** - Italian - 20.50 (lunch) and a la carte 30.00/42.00 ⅓ 17.00.

XXX **Chutney Mary,** 535 King's Rd, SW10 0SZ, ℘ (020) 7351 3113, *action@realindianfo com, Fax (020) 7351 7694* – ▤. MC AE ⓓ VISA JCB p. 28 FZ
closed dinner 25 December – **Meals** - Indian - 14.00 (lunch) and a la carte 21.50/28.5 ⅓ 11.75.

XX **Montes,** 164 Sloane St, SW1X 9QB, ℘ (020) 7245 0896, *Fax (020) 7235 3456* – ▤. MC AE VISA p. 35 FR
closed Sunday and Bank Holidays – **Meals** - Italian - (booking essential) (lunch only) 23 and a la carte 30.00/40.00 **t.** ⅓ 19.00.

XX **Aquasia** (at Conrad London H.), Chelsea Harbour, SW10 0XG, ℘ (020) 7300 84 *Fax (020) 7351 6525,* ≤, ☂, « Harbourside setting » – ▤ P. MC AE ⓓ VISA JCB
Meals 12.00/21.00 and a la carte 24.00/33.00 **t.** ⅓ 13.00. p. 17 CQ

XX **Bluebird,** 350 King's Rd, SW3 5UU, ℘ (020) 7559 1000, *Fax (020) 7559 1111* – |♦| ▤. MC ⓓ VISA JCB p. 34 CU
Meals 16.50 (lunch) and dinner a la carte 28.00/39.50 **t.** ⅓ 12.75.

XX **Poissonnerie de l'Avenue,** 82 Sloane Ave, SW3 3DZ, ℘ (020) 7589 2457, *inf poissonnerie.co.uk, Fax (020) 7581 3360* – ▤. MC AE ⓓ VISA JCB p. 35 DS
closed 24 December-3 January, Sunday and Bank Holidays – **Meals** - French Seafood - 18 (lunch) and a la carte 31.50/43.50 **t.** ⅓ 14.00.

XX **English Garden,** 10 Lincoln St, SW3 2TS, ℘ (020) 7584 7272, *english.garden@ukgatev net, Fax (020) 7584 1961* – ▤. MC AE ⓓ VISA JCB p. 35 ET
closed 2 weeks August, Christmas and Monday lunch – **Meals** 19.50/27.50 **t.** ⅓ 14.50.

XX **Mao Tai,** 96 Draycott Ave, SW3 3AD, ℘ (020) 7225 2500, *mbmaotai@aol.cc Fax (020) 7471 8992* – ▤. MC AE ⓓ VISA p. 35 ES
closed 25-26 December – **Meals** - Chinese (Szechuan) - 24.70 and a la carte 20.50/43.0 ⅓ 14.50.

XX **The House,** 3 Milner St, SW3 2QA, ℘ (020) 7584 3002, *Fax (020) 7581 2848* – MC AE ⓓ JCB p. 35 ES
closed last 2 weeks August, Saturday lunch and Sunday – **Meals** 14.50/27.00 **st.** ⅓ 13.50.

XX **Parisienne Chophouse,** 3 Yeoman's Row, SW3 3AL, ℘ (020) 7590 9999, *sales@wl starline.org.uk, Fax (020) 7590 9900* – ▤. MC AE ⓓ VISA p. 35 ER
Meals - French - 12.95 and a la carte 18.00/33.00 **t.** ⅓ 12.50.

XX **Pellicano,** 19-21 Elystan St, SW3 3NT, ℘ (020) 7589 3718, *Fax (020) 7584 1789,* ☂ – MC AE VISA p. 35 ET
closed 23 December-2 January – **Meals** - Italian - 13.50 (lunch) and a la carte 18.50/29.5 ⅓ 12.00.

XX **Brasserie St Quentin,** 243 Brompton Rd, SW3 2EP, ℘ (020) 7589 80 *Fax (020) 7584 6064* – ▤. MC AE ⓓ VISA p. 35 DR
closed 25 December – **Meals** - French - a la carte 13.90/24.85 **st.** ⅓ 10.00.

XX **Benihana,** 77 King's Rd, SW3 4NX, ℘ (020) 7376 7799, *benihana@dircon.co Fax (020) 7376 7377* – ▤. MC AE ⓓ VISA JCB p. 35 EU
closed 25 December – **Meals** - Japanese (Teppan-Yaki) - 8.50/14.00 and a la carte appr 40.00 **t.**

XX **Caraffini,** 61-63 Lower Sloane St, SW1W 8DH, ℘ (020) 7259 0235, *info@caraffini.co. Fax (020) 7259 0236,* ☂ – ▤. MC AE VISA p. 35 FT
closed Sunday and Bank Holidays – **Meals** - Italian - a la carte 19.65/32.25 **t.** ⅓ 10.25.

XX **Vama,** 438 King's Rd, SW10 0LJ, ✆ (020) 7351 4118, *vamaoffice@aol.com, Fax (020) 7565 8501* – MC AE D VISA p. 29 GZ e
Meals - Indian - (booking essential) 7.95/9.95 (lunch) and a la carte 16.50/31.25 **t.** 12.95.

XX **Le Colombier,** 145 Dovehouse St, SW3 6LB, ✆ (020) 7351 1155, *colombier@compuserve.com, Fax (020) 7351 0077,* – MC AE D VISA p. 35 DT e
Meals - French - 16.90 (lunch) and a la carte 20.80/36.30 **t.** 12.90.

XX **The Collection,** 264 Brompton Rd, SW3 2AS, ✆ (020) 7225 1212, *collection.office@belgo-restaurants.co.uk, Fax (020) 7225 1050* – . MC AE D VISA JCB p. 35 DS v
closed 25-26 December, 1 January and Bank Holidays – **Meals** (dinner only) a la carte 28.00/39.25 **t.** 12.95.

XX **Good Earth,** 233 Brompton Rd, SW3 2EP, ✆ (020) 7584 3658, *goodearthgroup@aol.com, Fax (020) 7823 8769* – . MC AE VISA JCB p. 35 DR c
closed 22-30 December – **Meals** - Chinese - 7.95/29.50 and a la carte 14.60/23.30 **t.**

XX **Dan's,** 119 Sydney St, SW3 6NR, ✆ (020) 7352 2718, *Fax (020) 7352 3265,* – MC AE VISA JCB p. 35 DU s
closed 24 December-New Year, Easter, Saturday lunch, Sunday and Bank Holidays – **Meals** 17.50 (lunch) and a la carte 24.00/30.50 **t.** 12.50.

X **Simply Nico** (at Sloane Square Moat House H.), Sloane Sq, SW1W 8CG, ✆ (020) 7896 9909, *sloanesquare@simplynico.co.uk, Fax (020) 7896 9908* – . MC AE D VISA JCB p. 35 FST v
closed 25-26 December and Bank Holidays – **Meals** a la carte 22.25/27.00 **t.** 12.95.

X **Thierry's,** 342 King's Rd, SW3 5UR, ✆ (020) 7352 3365, *thierrys@trpplc.com, Fax (020) 7352 3365* – . MC AE D VISA p. 34 CU c
closed 24 December-3 January, sunday dinner and Bank Holidays – **Meals** 9.50/14.45 (lunch) and a la carte 17.45/34.95 **t.** 13.50.

X **I Cardi,** 351 Fulham Rd, SW10 9TW, ✆ (020) 7351 2939, *Fax (020) 7376 4619* – . MC AE VISA p. 34 BU z
Meals - Italian - a la carte 15.00/25.00 12.50.

X **Zaika Bazaar,** 2a Pond Pl, SW3 6QU, ✆ (020) 7584 6655, *info@zaika-bazaar.co.uk, Fax (020) 7584 6755* – . MC AE VISA p. 35 DT c
closed Sunday, Saturday lunch and Bank Holidays – **Meals** - Indian - a la carte 20.85/27.00 **t.**

X **Bibendum Oyster Bar,** Michelin House, 81 Fulham Rd, SW3 6RD, ✆ (020) 7589 1480, *manager@bibendum.co.uk, Fax (020) 7823 7148* – MC AE D VISA p. 35 DS s
closed 25 and 26 December – **Meals** - Seafood specialities - (bookings not accepted) a la carte 20.25/29.00 **t.** 13.50.

X **itsu,** 118 Draycott Ave, SW3 3AE, ✆ (020) 7590 2401, *cebsanetcomuk.co.uk, Fax (020) 7590 2403* – . MC AE VISA p. 35 DS a
closed 23 December-2 January – **Meals** - Japanese - (bookings not accepted) a la carte 18.00/25.00 **t.** 14.95.

Admiral Codrington, 17 Mossop St, SW3 2LY, ✆ (020) 7581 0005, *londshot@dial.pipex.com, Fax (020) 7589 2452* – MC AE VISA p. 35 ES x
closed 25-26 December – **Meals** a la carte 20.95/28.45 **t.** 11.00.

Chelsea Ram, 32 Burnaby St, SW10 0PL, ✆ (020) 7351 4008, *pint@chelsearam.com, Fax (020) 7349 0885* – MC AE VISA p. 28 FZ r
closed 25 December – **Meals** (bookings not accepted) a la carte 14.35/22.85 **t.** 9.95.

Swag and Tails, 10-11 Fairholt St, SW7 1EG, ✆ (020) 7584 6926, *swagandtails@mway.com, Fax (020) 7581 9935* – MC AE VISA JCB p. 35 DR r
closed Christmas, Saturday, Sunday and Bank Holidays – **Meals** a la carte 16.20/23.20 **t.** 10.95.

Builders Arms, 13 Britten St, SW3 3TY, ✆ (020) 7349 9040, *Fax (020) 7357 3181* – . MC AE D VISA p. 35 DU x
closed 25 December – **Meals** (bookings not accepted) a la carte 15.35/22.85 **s.** 9.80.

rl's Court – ✉ *SW5/SW10.*

K + K George, 1-15 Templeton Pl, SW5 9NB, ✆ (020) 7598 8700, *hotelgeorge@kkhotels.co.uk, Fax (020) 7370 2285,* – – 30. MC AE D VISA JCB p. 28 EZ s
Meals (in bar) a la carte 13.50/19.50 **st.** 10.50 – **154 rm** 165.00/195.00 **st.**

Twenty Nevern Square, Nevern Sq, SW5 9PD, ✆ (020) 7565 9555, *hotel@twentynevernsquare.co.uk, Fax (020) 7565 9444* – . MC AE D VISA JCB.
Meals *(closed Sunday and Monday)* (residents only) (dinner only) a la carte 26.00/40.00 11.70 – 9.00 – **19 rm** 140.00/275.00 **st.** – SB. p. 28 EZ u

Henley House without rest., 30 Barkston Gdns, SW5 0EN, ✆ (020) 7370 4111, *reservations@henleyhousehotel.com, Fax (020) 7370 0026* – . MC AE D VISA JCB.
3.40 – **20 rm** 72.00/91.00 **st.** p. 34 AT e

Amsterdam without rest., 7 and 9 Trebovir Rd, SW5 9LS, (020) 7370 2814, *reservatic @amsterdam-hotel.com, Fax (020) 7244 7608,* – . AE VISA J
p. 28 EZ
2.75 – **19 rm** 78.00/87.00 **st.**, 8 suites.

Rushmore without rest., 11 Trebovir Rd, SW5 9LS, (020) 7370 3839, *rushmore-rese tions@london.com, Fax (020) 7370 0274* – . AE VISA JCB. p. 28 EZ
22 rm 59.00/79.00 **t.**

Langan's Coq d'Or, 254-260 Old Brompton Rd, SW5 9HR, (020) 7259 2599, *admi langansrestaurant.co.uk, Fax (020) 7370 7735,* – . AE VISA JCB p. 34 AU
closed Monday and Bank Holidays – **Meals** 16.50 (lunch) and a la carte 19.50/26.0 12.50.

Chezmax, 168 Ifield Rd, SW10 9AF, (020) 7835 0874, *chezmaxl@aol.co Fax (020) 7244 0618* – AE VISA p. 34 AU
closed Christmas, Sunday and Bank Holidays – **Meals** (dinner only and Saturday lunc dinner 12.50 and a la carte 24.90/47.50 **t.** 13.50.

Kensington – *SW7/W8/W11/W14.*

Royal Garden, 2-24 Kensington High St, W8 4PT, (020) 7937 8000, *sales@royalgard co.uk, Fax (020) 7361 1991,* – rm, – 600. AE JCB. p. 34 AQ
Park Terrace*:** **Meals** 9.50/14.75 (lunch) and a la carte 24.15/32.75 **st.** – (see a ***The Tenth below) – 18.00 – **381 rm** 235.00/295.00 **st.**, 15 suites – SB.

Copthorne Tara, Scarsdale Pl, W8 5SR, (020) 7937 7211, *sales.tara@mill-cop.co Fax (020) 7872 7100* – , rm, – 400. AE VISA J p. 28 FY
***Jerome K. Jerome*:** **Meals** a la carte 17.90/32.00 **t.** 19.00 – ***Brasserie*:** **Meals** 19 and a la carte approx. 26.00 **t.** 19.00 – 15.00 – **827 rm** 215.00 **st.**, 7 suites.

Halcyon, 81 Holland Park, W11 3RZ, (020) 7727 7288, *reservations@thehalcyon.co Fax (020) 7229 8516* – . AE VISA JCB p. 28 EX
Meals – (see ***Aix en Provence*** below) – 17.95 – **39 rm** 173.00/213.00 **t.**, 3 suites – SB

Hilton London Kensington, 179-199 Holland Park Ave, W11 4UL, (020) 7603 33 *sales_kensington@hilton.com, Fax (020) 7602 9397* – , rm, – 300. AE VISA JCB. p. 28 EX
***Market*:** **Meals** *(closed lunch Saturday and Sunday)* 22.00 **t.** 16.50 – ***Hiroko*:** **Mea** Japanese - 16.00/35.00 and a la carte 21.00/39.00 **t.** 16.50 – 15.00 – **603 rm** 149.00 SB.

Hilton London Olympia, 380 Kensington High St, W14 8NL, (020) 7603 33 *rm_olympia@hilton.com, Fax (020) 7603 4846* – , rm, – 250. VISA JCB p. 28 EY
Meals a la carte 18.00/29.00 **st.** 18.00 – 16.50 – **395 rm** 179.00/209.00, 10 suites.

Thistle Kensington Park, 16-32 De Vere Gdns, W8 5AG, (020) 7937 8080, *sa kensington@thistle.co.uk, Fax (020) 7937 7616* – , rm, – 120. AE VISA JCB. p. 34 BQ
Meals (dinner only) a la carte 19.90/27.95 **st.** 13.95 – 13.95 – **346 rm** 165. 245.00 **st.**, 6 suites.

The Milestone, 1-2 Kensington Court, W8 5DL, (020) 7917 1000, *reservatior milestone.redcarnationhotels.com, Fax (020) 7917 1010,* – , rm, . AE VISA p. 34 AQ
Meals a la carte 36.50/50.50 **t.** 18.50 – 17.50 – **52 rm** 250.00/400.00 **s.**, 5 suites.

Holland Court without rest., 31-33 Holland Rd, W14 8HJ, (020) 7371 1133, *rese tions@hollandcourt.com, Fax (020) 7602 9114,* – . AE VISA.
22 rm 100.00/130.00 **st.** p. 28 EY

The Tenth (at Royal Garden H.), 2-24 Kensington High St, W8 4PT, (020) 7361 19 *Fax (020) 7361 1921,* Kensington Palace and Gardens – . AE JCB p. 34 AQ
closed Sunday and lunch Saturday – **Meals** (live music Saturday) 21.00 (lunch) and a la ca 30.25/41.75 **st.** 25.00.

Belvedere, Holland House, off Abbotsbury Rd, W8 6LU, (020) 7602 1238, *sales@w starline.org.uk, Fax (020) 7610 4382,* , « 19C orangery in Holland Park » – . AE VISA p. 28 EY
Meals 17.95/42.50 and a la carte 30.50/48.00 **t.** 20.00.

Clarke's, 124 Kensington Church St, W8 4BH, (020) 7221 9225, *restaurant@sallycla com, Fax (020) 7229 4564* – . AE VISA JCB p. 28 EX
closed 2 weeks August, 10 days Christmas-New Year, Saturday and Sunday – **Meals** menu only at dinner) 28.50/44.00 **st.** 14.00.

Aix en Provence (at Halcyon H.), 129 Holland Park Ave, W11 3UT, (020) 7727 7 *Fax (020) 7229 8516,* – . AE VISA JCB p. 28 EX
Meals 15.00 (lunch) and a la carte 33.00/38.75 **t.** 17.95.

XX **Launceston Place,** 1a Launceston Pl, W8 5RL, ☎ (020) 7937 6912, *Fax (020) 7938 2412* – ▤. MC AE Ⓓ VISA p. 34 BR a
closed 25-26 December, Easter, Saturday lunch, Sunday dinner and Bank Holidays – **Meals** 18.50 (lunch) and a la carte 28.50/36.50 **st.** 14.50.

XX **Zaika,** 1 Kensington High St, W8 5NP, ☎ (020) 7351 7823, *info@zaika-restaurant.co.uk, Fax (020) 7376 4971* – ▤. MC AE VISA p. 34 AQ r
✿ *closed Christmas-New Year, Saturday lunch and Bank Holidays* – **Meals** - Indian - 14.95 (lunch) and a la carte 21.90/40.85 **t.** 14.50
Spec. Dhungar machli tikka (tandoori smoked salmon). Gilafi dum biryani (lamb cooked with aromatic spices). Chocolate samosas.

XX **Memories of China,** 353 Kensington High St, W8 6NW, ☎ (020) 7603 6951, *Fax (020) 7603 0848* – ▤. MC AE Ⓓ VISA JCB p. 28 EY v
closed Christmas and Sunday lunch – **Meals** - Chinese - (booking essential) 14.50/32.50 and a la carte 19.25/28.40 **t.** 13.50.

XX **The Terrace,** 33c Holland St, W8 4LX, ☎ (020) 7937 3224, *Fax (020) 7937 3323*, 余 – ▤. MC AE Ⓓ VISA JCB p. 28 EY z
closed 24 December-3 January and Sunday dinner – **Meals** (booking essential) 14.50/17.50 (lunch) and a la carte 28.50/36.00 **t.** 11.50.

XX **The Ark,** 122 Palace Gardens Terr, W8 4RT, ☎ (020) 7229 4024, *Fax (020) 7792 8787*, 余 – ▤. MC AE VISA JCB p. 36 AZ r
closed 25-26 December, Sunday dinner and Monday lunch – **Meals** - Italian - 12.50 (lunch) and a la carte 25.00/30.00 **t.** 12.50.

XX **Phoenicia,** 11-13 Abingdon Rd, W8 6AH, ☎ (020) 7937 0120, *Fax (020) 7937 7668* – ▤. MC AE Ⓓ VISA JCB p. 28 EY n
closed 25-26 December – **Meals** - Lebanese - 11.95/30.95 and a la carte 20.65/26.80 **t.** 10.90.

X **Kensington Place,** 201 Kensington Church St, W8 7LX, ☎ (020) 7727 3184, *kpr@placerestaurants.co.uk, Fax (020) 7229 2025* – ▤. MC AE Ⓓ VISA p. 36 AZ z
closed 24-26 December and 1 January – **Meals** (booking essential) a la carte 24.50/36.00 **t.** 14.50.

X **Cibo,** 3 Russell Gdns, W14 8EZ, ☎ (020) 7371 6271, *Fax (020) 7602 1371* – MC AE Ⓓ VISA JCB p. 28 EY o
closed 24 December-2 January, Saturday lunch and Sunday dinner – **Meals** - Italian - a la carte 18.50/40.25 **t.** 11.50.

X **Malabar,** 27 Uxbridge St, W8 7TQ, ☎ (020) 7727 8800, *feedback@malabar-restaurant.co.uk* – MC VISA p. 36 AZ e
Meals - Indian - (booking essential) (buffet lunch Sunday) a la carte 16.45/24.95 **st.** 9.25.

X **Wódka,** 12 St Albans Grove, W8 5PN, ☎ (020) 7937 6513, *john@wodka.demon.co.uk, Fax (020) 7937 8621* – MC AE Ⓓ VISA p. 34 AR c
closed 25-26 December, 1 January and lunch Saturday and Sunday – **Meals** - Polish - 10.90/13.50 (lunch) and a la carte 21.00/40.90 **t.** 10.50.

rth Kensington – ✉ W2/W10/W11.

Westbourne without rest., 165 Westbourne Grove, W11 2RS, ☎ (020) 7243 6008, *wh@zoohotels.com, Fax (020) 7229 7201* – ⇔ ▤ TV ☏. MC AE VISA JCB. ✈ p. 36 AZ s
☕ 5.00 **20 rm** 175.00 **st.**

Pembridge Court without rest., 34 Pembridge Gdns, W2 4DX, ☎ (020) 7229 9977, *reservations@pemct.co.uk, Fax (020) 7727 4982*, « Collection of antique clothing » – ▯ ▤ TV ☏. MC AE Ⓓ VISA p. 36 AZ n
20 rm ☕ 130.00/200.00 **st.**

Abbey Court without rest., 20 Pembridge Gdns, W2 4DU, ☎ (020) 7221 7518, *info@abbeycourthotel.co.uk, Fax (020) 7792 0858*, « Victorian town house » – ⇔ TV. MC AE Ⓓ VISA JCB. ✈ p. 36 AZ u
22 rm 105.00/210.00 **st.**

Portobello, 22 Stanley Gdns, W11 2NG, ☎ (020) 7727 2777, *info@portobello-hotel.co.uk, Fax (020) 7792 9641*, « Attractive town house in Victorian terrace » – ▯ TV ☏. MC AE VISA p. 28 EV n
closed 23 December-2 January – **Meals** a la carte approx. 26.00 **t.** – ☕ 8.50 – **24 rm** 150.00/280.00 **st.**

XXX **Chez Moi,** 1 Addison Ave, Holland Park, W11 4QS, ☎ (020) 7603 8267, *chezmoi_res@hotmail.com, Fax (020) 7603 3898* – ▤. MC AE Ⓓ VISA p. 28 EX n
closed Sunday, Saturday and Monday lunch and Bank Holidays – **Meals** - French - 15.00 (lunch) and a la carte 26.75/34.50 **t.** 10.75.

XX **Pharmacy,** 150 Notting Hill Gate, W11 3QG, ☎ (020) 7221 2442, *mail@pharmacylondon.com, Fax (020) 7243 2345* – ▤. MC AE Ⓓ VISA p. 36 AZ a
closed 25-26 December – **Meals** 17.00 (lunch) and a la carte 23.00/35.50 **t.** 14.00.

XX **Notting Hill Brasserie,** 92 Kensington Park Rd, W11 2PN, ✆ (020) 7229 4481, *no hill@firmdale.com, Fax (020) 7221 1246* – ▤. MC AE VISA p. 28 EV
closed 24-25 December – **Meals** 14.00/19.95 (lunch) and a la carte 25.00/33.00 **t.** 15.(

X **Manor,** 6-8 All Saints Rd, W11 1HH, ✆ (020) 7243 6363, *mail@manorw11. Fax (020) 7243 6360* – ▤. MC AE VISA p. 24 EU
Meals (dinner only and lunch Saturday and Sunday) a la carte 21.50/33.00 **t.** 12.50.

X **Bali Sugar,** 33a All Saints Rd, W11 1HE, ✆ (020) 7221 4477, *Fax (020) 7221 9955,* AE VISA p. 24 EU
closed 25-26 December, 1 January and August Bank Holiday – **Meals** 1 (lunch) and a la carte 25.20/31.20 **t.** 12.60.

X **Alastair Little Lancaster Road,** 136a Lancaster Rd, W11 1TP, ✆ (020) 7243 2 *Fax (020) 7792 4535* – ▤. MC AE VISA JCB p. 24 EU
closed Sunday dinner and Bank Holidays – **Meals** (booking essential) 1 (lunch) and a la carte 22.50/32.00 **t.** 14.00.

X **Wiz,** 123A Clarendon Rd, W11 4JG, ✆ (020) 7229 1500, *awtwiz@hotmail.c Fax (020) 7229 8889,* – MC AE VISA JCB p. 24 EV
closed 4 days Christmas, Sunday dinner, Monday lunch and August Bank Holiday – **M** a la carte 22.50/30.50 **t.** 10.95.

X **Livebait,** 175 Westbourne Grove, W11 2SB, ✆ (020) 7727 4321, *Fax (020) 7792 3655* - MC AE VISA p. 36 AZ
closed 25 December and Monday – **Meals** - Seafood - 15.50 (lunch) and a la carte 22 34.65 **st.** 12.25.

South Kensington – ✉ *SW5/SW7/W8.*

Millennium Gloucester, 4-18 Harrington Gdns, SW7 4LH, ✆ (020) 7373 6 *gloucester@mill-cop.com, Fax (020) 7373 0409,* – ▤, rm, ▤ TV ♿ P – 650 AE VISA JCB p. 34 BS
SW7: **Meals** - Italian - *(closed Sunday)* (dinner only) a la carte approx. 19.45 – ***Bugis Str*** **Meals** - Singaporean - a la carte 7.50/15.97 – 15.00 – **604 rm** 250.00 **t.**, 6 suites – SB

The Pelham, 15 Cromwell Pl, SW7 2LA, ✆ (020) 7589 8288, *pelham@firmdale.c Fax (020) 7584 8444,* « Tastefully furnished Victorian town house » – , rm, ▤ MC AE VISA. p. 34 CS
Kemps: **Meals** *(closed lunch Saturday and Sunday)* 15.00/20.00 and a la carte 25 33.20 **t.** 13.00 – 15.50 – **48 rm** 150.00/250.00, 3 suites.

Blakes, 33 Roland Gdns, SW7 3PF, ✆ (020) 7370 6701, *blakes@easynet.cc Fax (020) 7373 0442,* , « Antique oriental furnishings » – , ▤ rest, TV . MC AE JCB. p. 34 BU
Meals a la carte 51.00/65.00 **t.** 21.50 – 23.00 – **40 rm** 165.00/325.00, 5 suites.

Vanderbilt, 68-86 Cromwell Rd, SW7 5BT, ✆ (020) 7761 9000, *resvand@radisson.c Fax (020) 7761 9003* – , rm, ▤ TV – 120. MC AE VISA JCB. p. 34 BS
Meals 19.50 and a la carte approx. 21.00 **st.** 15.50 – 12.00 – **215 rm** 183.00/222.00

Harrington Hall, 5-25 Harrington Gdns, SW7 4JW, ✆ (020) 7396 9696, *harringtonsa compuserve.com, Fax (020) 7396 9090,* – , rm, ▤ TV – 260. MC AE JCB. p. 34 BST
Wetherby's: **Meals** a la carte 23.95/32.20 **st.** 16.00 – 14.50 – **200 rm** 185 215.00 **st.**

Millennium Bailey's, 140 Gloucester Rd, SW7 4QH, ✆ (020) 7373 6000, *baileys@mill .com, Fax (020) 7370 3760* – , rm, ▤ TV – 460. MC AE VISA JCB.
Olives: **Meals** (bar lunch)/dinner a la carte 20.95/30.70 **t.** 14.75 – 13.00 – **212** 125.00/723.00 **t.** p. 34 BS

Rembrandt, 11 Thurloe Pl, SW7 2RS, ✆ (020) 7589 8100, *rembrandt@sarova.co Fax (020) 7225 3476,* , , – , rm, ▤ rest, TV – 200. MC AE VISA p. 35 DS
Meals (carving lunch)/dinner a la carte 17.85/25.85 **st.** 15.00 – 14.95 – **195 rm** 195 240.00 **st.**

Jurys Kensington, 109-113 Queen's Gate, SW7 5LR, ✆ (020) 7589 6300, *kensing @jurydoyle.com, Fax (020) 7581 1492* – , rm, ▤ TV – 80. MC AE p. 34 CT
closed 24-26 December – **Meals** (bar lunch)/dinner 17.50 **st.** 12.50 – 15.00 – **173** 200.00 **st.**

Regency, 100 Queen's Gate, SW7 5AG, ✆ (020) 7373 7878, *info@regency-london.co Fax (020) 7370 5555,* , – , rm, ▤ TV – 100. MC AE VISA p. 34 CT
Meals *(closed lunch Saturday and Sunday)* (carvery lunch) a la carte 15.00/26.00 **st.** 12 – 13.00 – **204 rm** 160.00 **s.**, 6 suites.

Holiday Inn Kensington, 100 Cromwell Rd, SW7 4ER, (020) 7373 2222, *info@hik.co.uk, Fax (020) 7373 0559,* – , rm, – 200. p. 34 **BS** e
Meals *(closed dinner 25 December and Sunday lunch)* a la carte 16.40/30.00 **t.** 11.95 – 12.75 – **143 rm** 205.00/225.00 **t.**, 19 suites.

Gore, 189 Queen's Gate, SW7 5EX, (020) 7584 6601, *sales@gorehotel.co.uk, Fax (020) 7589 8127,* « Antiques » – , rm, . p. 34 **BR** n
Bistrot 190 : **Meals** *(closed 24-25 December)* (booking essential) a la carte 19.45/25.20 **t.** 13.50 – (see also ***The Restaurant at One Ninety*** below) – 9.50 – **53 rm** 147.00/278.00 **s.**

John Howard, 4 Queen's Gate, SW7 5EH, (020) 7808 8400, *info@johnhowardhotel.co.uk, Fax (020) 7808 8402* – . p. 34 **BQ** i
Meals *(closed Sunday)* (dinner only) 15.00 and a la carte 15.25/19.50 **st.** 6.00 – 12.50 – **45 rm** 129.00/159.00 **st.**, 7 suites.

The Cranley, 10-12 Bina Gdns, SW5 0LA, (020) 7373 0123, *info@thecranley.com, Fax (020) 7373 9497,* « Antiques » – . p. 34 **BT** c
Meals (room service only) – 9.95 – **35 rm** 170.00/242.00 **s.**, 3 suites.

The Gallery without rest., 8-10 Queensberry Pl, SW7 2EA, (020) 7915 0000, *gallery@eeh.co.uk, Fax (020) 7915 4400* – . p. 34 **CS** r
36 rm 120.00/250.00 **s.**

The Gainsborough without rest., 7-11 Queensberry Pl, SW7 2DL, (020) 7957 0000, *gainsborough@eeh.co.uk, Fax (020) 7957 0001* – .
46 rm 67.00/145.00 **s.**, 3 suites. p. 34 **CS** s

Five Sumner Place without rest., 5 Sumner Pl, SW7 3EE, (020) 7584 7586, *reservations@sumnerplace.com, Fax (020) 7823 9962* – .
13 rm 99.00/152.00 **t.** p. 34 **CT** u

Aster House without rest., 3 Sumner Pl, SW7 3EE, (020) 7581 5888, *asterhouse@btinternet.com, Fax (020) 7584 4925,* – . p. 34 **CT** u
14 rm 99.00/180.00 **st.**

Bombay Brasserie, Courtfield Rd, SW7 4QH, (020) 7370 4040, *bombaybrasserie@aol.com, Fax (020) 7835 1669,* « Raj-style decor, conservatory » – . p. 34 **BS** a
closed 25-26 December – **Meals** - Indian - (buffet lunch) 16.95 and a la carte 26.50/31.00 **t.** 13.25.

The Restaurant at One Ninety (at Gore H.), 190 Queen's Gate, SW7 5EU, (020) 7581 5666, *Fax (020) 7581 8172* – . p. 34 **BR** n
closed 24-25 December, Sunday and Monday – **Meals** - Seafood - (booking essential) (dinner only) a la carte 22.85/26.15 **t.** 13.50.

Chives, 204 Fulham Rd, SW10 9PG, (020) 7351 4747, *Fax (020) 7351 7646,* – p. 34 **BU** u
Meals (dinner only) a la carte 24.00/27.50 **t.** 13.50.

Lundum's, 119 Old Brompton Rd, SW7 3RN, (020) 7373 7774, *Fax (020) 7373 4472,* – . p. 34 **BT** o
closed 23 December-4 January, last 2 weeks August and Sunday dinner – **Meals** - Danish - 15.50/21.50 and a la carte 14.00/33.00 **t.**

Café Lazeez, First Floor, 93-95 Old Brompton Rd, SW7 3LD, (020) 7581 9993, *cafelazeez@compuserve.com.uk, Fax (020) 7581 8200* – . p. 34 **CT** a
Meals - North Indian - a la carte 18.75/35.40 **t.** 9.95.

Khan's of Kensington, 3 Harrington Rd, SW7 3ES, (020) 7581 2900, *Fax (020) 7581 2900* – . p. 34 **CS** e
Meals - Indian - 8.95/18.50 and a la carte 13.95/22.35 8.50.

Cambio de Tercio, 163 Old Brompton Rd, SW5 0LJ, (020) 7244 8970, *Fax (020) 7373 8817* – p. 34 **BT** z
closed 2 weeks Christmas – **Meals** - Spanish - a la carte 24.40/32.00 **t.** 14.50.

Pasha, 1 Gloucester Rd, SW7 4PP, (020) 7589 7969, *Fax (020) 7581 9996* – . p. 34 **BR** i
closed 24-26 December, and Sunday lunch – **Meals** - Moroccan - a la carte 23.25/31.25 **t.** 13.50.

Memories of India, 18 Gloucester Rd, SW7 4RB, (020) 7589 6450, *Fax (020) 7584 4438* – . p. 34 **BR** s
closed 25 December – **Meals** - Indian - a la carte 13.70/15.85 **t.** 9.95.

Star of India, 154 Old Brompton Rd, SW5 0BE, (020) 7373 2901, *info@starofindia.co.uk, Fax (020) 7373 5664* – . p. 34 **BT** s
closed 25-26 December, 1 January and Bank Holidays – **Meals** - Indian - a la carte 25.45/33.95 **st.**

Bangkok, 9 Bute St, SW7 3EY, ✆ (020) 7584 8529 – ▤. MO VISA p. 34 CS
closed Christmas-New Year, Sunday and Bank Holidays – **Meals** - Thai Bistro - a la car 18.30/30.45 **t.** 14.00.

Catch, 158 Old Brompton Rd, SW5 0BA, ✆ (020) 7370 3300, *Fax (020) 7370 3377* – ▤. AE VISA JCB p. 34 BT
closed 24 December-7 January and Sunday – **Meals** - Seafood - (booking essential) (dinn only) a la carte 24.50/33.50 **t.**

KINGSTON UPON THAMES.

Home Park, Hampton Wick ✆ (020) 8977 6645, BY.

Travel Inn Metro, Leatherhead Rd, KT9 2NE, on A 243 ✆ (01372) 7440 *Fax (01372) 720889* – rm, P. MO AE VISA. p. 12 BZ
Meals (grill rest.) – **42 rm** 49.95 **t.**

Kingston – ✉ *Surrey.*

Kingston Lodge, Kingston Hill, KT2 7NP, ✆ (020) 8541 4481, *heritagehotels-kingsto upon-thames.kingston-lodge@forte-hotels.com, Fax (020) 8547 1013,* – r ▤ rest, P – 60. MO AE VISA JCB. p. 13 CY
The Burnt Orange : **Meals** 16.95 and a la carte 22.45/34.20 **st.** 13.50 – 11.50 – **62** 150.00/170.00 **st.** – SB.

Gravier's, 9 Station Rd, Norbiton, KT2 7AA, ✆ (020) 8549 5557 – MO AE JCB p. 13 CY
closed 1 week Easter, 1 week Christmas, 2 weeks August, Saturday and Monday lun Sunday and Bank Holidays – **Meals** - French Seafood - a la carte 21.40/28.05 **t.** 13.50.

Ayudhya, 14 Kingston Hill, KT2 6NH, ✆ (020) 8549 5984, *Fax (020) 8546 5878* – MO AE VISA p. 13 CY
closed 25 December, 1 January and Monday – **Meals** - Thai - a la carte 18.00/25.00 **s.** 5.0

Surbiton – ✉ *Surrey.*

The French Table, 85 Maple Rd, KT6 4AW, ✆ (020) 8399 2365, *Fax (020) 8390 5353* – MO VISA p. 13 CY
closed 25-26 December, 1-8 January, Sunday dinner and Monday – **Meals** - French-Medit ranean - a la carte 23.50/27.20 **t.** 11.75.

LAMBETH.

Clapham Common – ✉ *SW4.*

Windmill on the Common, Clapham Common South Side, SW4 9D ✆ (020) 8673 4578, *Fax (020) 8675 1486* – rm, ▤ P. MO AE VISA
Meals a la carte 13.70/18.40 **st.** 11.50 – **29 rm** 96.00/130.00 **st.** p. 17 DQ

Herne Hill – ✉ *SE24.*

3 Monkeys, 136-140 Herne Hill, SE24 9QH, ✆ (020) 7738 5500, *jan@3monkeysrestaura com, Fax (020) 7738 5505* – ▤. MO AE VISA p. 14 FX
closed 25-26 December – **Meals** - Indian - (dinner only and Sunday lunch) 10.95/15 and a la carte 16.85/22.85 **t.** 13.95.

Kennington – ✉ *SE11.*

Kennington Lane, 205-209 Kennington Lane, SE11 5QS, ✆ (020) 7793 83 *Fax (020) 7793 8323,* – ▤. MO AE VISA JCB p. 30 MZ
Meals 14.75 and a la carte 20.00/25.00 **st.** 14.00.

Lobster Pot, 3 Kennington Lane, SE11 4RG, ✆ (020) 7582 5556 – ▤. MO AE JCB p. 31 NZ
closed 24 December-first week January, Sunday and Monday – **Meals** - French Seafoo 13.50/39.50 and a la carte 27.30/39.10 **t.** 10.50.

Lambeth – ✉ *SE1.*

Novotel London Waterloo, 113 Lambeth Rd, SE1 7LS, ✆ (020) 7793 1010, *h178 accor-hotels.com, Fax (020) 7793 0202,* – rm, ▤ – 40. MO VISA p. 30 LMY
Meals (bar lunch Saturday and Sunday) 19.95 and a la carte 22.00/34.50 **st.** 11.25 12.00 – **185 rm** 135.00/155.00 **s.**, 2 suites – SB.

terloo – ✉ *SE1.*

Channel Tunnel : Eurostar information and reservations ✆ *(08705) 186186.*

London Marriott H. County Hall, SE1 7PB, ✆ (020) 7928 5200, *salesadmin.countyhall@marriotthotels.co.uk, Fax (020) 7928 5300*, <, Ⅰ, ≘, Ⅰ – |¢|, ⇐ rm, ▤ Ⓣ ✆ & – 🏛 70. Ⓜ AE ⓓ VISA JCB. ✗ p. 30 **LY** a

County Hall : **Meals** 23.50 (lunch) and a la carte 33.75/37.50 **st.** 🍷 18.00 – ☕ 18.95 – **195 rm** 255.00/385.00 **s.**, 5 suites – SB.

London County Hall Travel Inn Capital, Belvedere Rd, SE1 7PB, ✆ (020) 7902 1600, *Fax (020) 7902 1619* – |¢| ⇐, ▤ rest, Ⓣ &. Ⓜ AE ⓓ VISA. ✗ p. 30 **MX** u

Meals (grill rest.) (dinner only) – **313 rm** 74.95 **t.**

Days Inn without rest., 54 Kennington Rd, SE1 7BJ, ✆ (020) 7922 1331, Reservations (Freephone) 0800 0280400, *waterloo@daysinn.co.uk, Fax (020) 7922 1441* – |¢| ⇐ Ⓣ ✆ & – 🏛 35. Ⓜ AE ⓓ VISA JCB. ✗ p. 30 **MY** x

162 rm 85.00.

NDON HEATHROW AIRPORT – *see Hillingdon, London p. 61.*

RTON.

lliers Wood – ✉ *SW19.*

Express by Holiday Inn without rest., 200 High St, SW19 2BH, on A 24 ✆ (020) 8545 7300, *Fax (020) 8545 7301* – |¢| ⇐ Ⓣ ✆ & 🚗 – 🏛 50. Ⓜ AE ⓓ VISA p. 14 **EY** a

83 rm 89.00/92.00 **st.**

rden – ✉ *Morden.*

Travelodge without rest., Epsom Rd, SM4 5PH, Southwest : on A 24 ✆ (020) 8640 8227, *Fax (020) 8640 8227* – ⇐ Ⓣ & Ⓟ. Ⓜ AE ⓓ VISA JCB. ✗ p. 13 **DY** c

32 rm 69.95 **t.**

mbledon – ✉ *SW19.*

Cannizaro House ♨, West Side, Wimbledon Common, SW19 4UE, ✆ (020) 8879 1464, *cannizaro.house@thistle.co.uk, Fax (0870) 3339224*, <, « Part 18C country house in Cannizaro Park », ⛱ – |¢|, ⇐ rm, Ⓣ ✆ Ⓟ – 🏛 60. Ⓜ AE ⓓ VISA. ✗ p. 13 **DXY** x

Meals 27.75/32.75 and a la carte 36.20/48.25 **st.** 🍷 16.00 – ☕ 15.00 – **43 rm** 200.00/290.00 **st.**, 2 suites – SB.

Light House, 75-77 Ridgway, SW19 4ST, ✆ (020) 8944 6338, *lightrest@aol.com, Fax (020) 8946 4440* – Ⓜ AE VISA p. 13 **DY** n

closed Easter and 25-26 December – **Meals** - Italian influences - a la carte 21.45/31.75 **t.** 🍷 11.50.

The Fire Stables, 27-29 Church Rd, SW19 5DQ, ✆ (020) 8946 3197, *thefirestables@punchgroup.co.uk, Fax (020) 8946 1101* – ▤. Ⓜ AE ⓓ VISA JCB p. 16 **AR** a

closed 25 December – **Meals** a la carte 19.50/25.50 **t.** 🍷 11.00.

DBRIDGE.

Town Hall, 128-142 High Rd ✆ *(020) 8478 3020.*

ord – ✉ *Essex.*

Wanstead Park Rd ✆ *(020) 8554 2930,* **HU** – 18, 9 *Fairlop Waters, Forest Rd, Barkingside* ✆ *(020) 8500 9911* **JT**.

Travelodge, Beehive Lane, IG4 5DR, ✆ (020) 8550 4248, *Fax (020) 8550 4248* – ⇐ rm, Ⓣ & Ⓟ. Ⓜ AE ⓓ VISA JCB. ✗ p. 11 **HU** e

Meals (grill rest.) – **32 rm** 59.95 **t.**

Travel Inn Metro, Redbridge Lane East, IG4 5BG, ✆ (020) 8550 7909, *Fax (020) 8550 6214* – |¢|, ⇐ rm, ▤ rest, Ⓣ & Ⓟ – 🏛 40. Ⓜ AE ⓓ VISA. ✗

Meals (grill rest.) – **44 rm** 49.95 **t.** p. 11 **HU** i

uth Woodford – ✉ *Essex.*

Ho-Ho, 20 High Rd, E18 2QL, ✆ (020) 8989 1041 – ▤. Ⓜ AE ⓓ VISA p. 11 **HU** c

closed 25-27 December and Saturday lunch – **Meals** - Chinese (Peking, Szechuan) - 16.50/27.50 and a la carte 32.10/43.80 **st.** 🍷 9.50.

Woodford – ✉ *Essex.*

⛳9 2 Sunset Av., Woodford Green ✆ (020) 8504 0553.

London 13 – Brentwood 16 – Harlow 16.

County H. Epping Forest, 30 Oak Hill, Woodford Green, IG8 9NY, ✆ (020) 8787 9 *Fax (020) 8506 0941* – , rest, – 150. MC AE VISA JCB p. 11 HT
Meals *(closed Saturday lunch)* 15.95 (dinner) and a la carte 18.40/24.95 **st.** 10.9 – 11.75 – **99 rm** 95.00/115.00 **st.** – SB.

RICHMOND-UPON-THAMES.

Barnes – ✉ *SW13.*

XX **Sonny's,** 94 Church Rd, SW13 0DQ, ✆ (020) 8748 0393, *Fax (020) 8748 2698* – . MC VISA p. 13 CX
closed 24-26 December, Sunday dinner and Bank Holidays – **Meals** 16.00/18 (lunch) and a la carte 19.45/30.50 **t.** 10.50.

X **Riva,** 169 Church Rd, SW13 9HR, ✆ (020) 8748 0434, *Fax (020) 8748 0434* – MC AE JCB
closed last 2 weeks August, 10 days Christmas-New Year, 4 days Easter, Saturday lunch Bank Holidays – **Meals** - Italian - a la carte 23.00/34.00 **t.** 11.50. p. 13 CX

X **Lemon Thyme,** 190 Castelnau, SW13 9DH, ✆ (020) 8748 3437, *Fax (020) 8748 3966* – MC AE VISA p. 13 CV
closed Monday – **Meals** - Italian - (dinner only and Sunday lunch)/dinner 9.50/12 and a la carte 11.50/21.50 **t.** 10.50.

East Sheen – ✉ *SW14.*

XX **Redmond's,** 170 Upper Richmond Road West, SW14 8AW, ✆ (020) 8878 1922, *pippa ward@btconnect.com, Fax (020) 8878 1133* – . MC AE VISA p. 13 CX
closed first week January, Saturday lunch, Sunday dinner and Bank Holidays – **Me** 19.50/27.00 **t.** 13.50.

XX **Crowther's,** 481 Upper Richmond Rd West, SW14 7PU, ✆ (020) 8876 63 *Fax (020) 8876 6372* – . MC VISA JCB p. 13 CX
closed 2 weeks August, 25-31 December, Sunday and Monday – **Meals** (booking essen (lunch by arrangement)/dinner 24.75 **t.** 11.50.

Hampton Court – ✉ *Surrey.*

Carlton Mitre, Hampton Court Rd, KT8 9BN, ✆ (020) 8979 9988, *gmmitre@carltonho .co.uk, Fax (020) 8979 9777,* ≤, , « Thames-side setting » – – 25. MC VISA. p. 12 BY
Rivers Edge : **Meals** a la carte 21.00/29.50 **st.** 12.95 – 12.00 – **35 rm** 175.00 **st.**, 1 su – SB.

Hampton Hill – ✉ *Middx.*

XX ✿ **Monsieur Max,** 133 High St, TW12 1NJ, ✆ (020) 8979 5546, *monsmax@aol.co Fax (020) 8979 3747* – . MC AE VISA p. 12 BY
closed Christmas and Saturday lunch – **Meals** - French - 25.00/45.00 **t.** 14.50
Spec. Rack of Welsh lamb, beignet of sweetbreads. Roast poulet de Bresse "en de services". Mandarin and passion fruit soufflé.

Hampton Wick – ✉ *Surrey.*

Chase Lodge, 10 Park Rd, KT1 4AS, ✆ (020) 8943 1862, *info@chaselodgehotel.co Fax (020) 8943 9363* – . MC AE VISA JCB p. 12 BY
Meals (lunch by arrangement) 12.00/20.00 **st.** 9.95 – **13 rm** 65.00/150.00 **t.** – SB.

Kew – ✉ *Surrey.*

XX ✿ **The Glasshouse,** 14 Station Par, TW9 3PZ, ✆ (020) 8940 6777, *Fax (020) 8940 3833* – MC AE VISA p. 13 CX
closed 4 days at Christmas – **Meals** 19.50/27.50 **t.** 13.50
Spec. Salad of wood pigeon and truffled egg. Fillet of cod, bubble and squeak, pea pur Strawberry and Champagne trifle.

chmond – ✉ *Surrey.*

Richmond Park, Roehampton Gate ✆ *(020) 8876 3205* **CX** – *Sudbrook Park* ✆ *(020) 8940 1463* **CX**.

Old Town Hall, Whittaker Av. ✆ *(020) 8940 9125.*

Petersham, Nightingale Lane, TW10 6UZ, ✆ (020) 8940 7471, *enq@petershamhotel.co.uk, Fax (020) 8939 1002,* ≤, « Working cellars », – 50. p. 13 CX c
closed 25 December – **Meals** – (see ***Nightingales*** below) – **60 rm** 135.00/170.00 **st.**, 1 suite – SB.

Richmond Gate, 158 Richmond Hill, TW10 6RP, ✆ (020) 8940 0061, *richmondgate@corushotels.com, Fax (020) 8332 0354,* – 45. p. 13 CX c
Gates On The Park **:** **Meals** *(closed lunch Saturday and Bank Holidays)* 17.25/31.00 and dinner a la carte 25.25/37.50 **t.** 14.95 – **67 rm** 150.00/198.00 **st.**, 1 suite.

Richmond Hill, Richmond Hill, TW10 6RW, ✆ (020) 8940 2247, *richmondhill@corushotels.com, Fax (020) 8940 5424,* rm, rest, – 200. p. 13 CX c
Pembrokes **:** **Meals** (dancing Saturday evening) (carving lunch Sunday) 16.00 (lunch) and a la carte 24.95/32.85 **st.** 13.50 – **133 rm** 135.00/155.00 **st.**, 5 suites – SB.

Doughty Cottage without rest., 142A Richmond Hill, TW10 6RN, ✆ (020) 8332 9434, *deniseoneill425@netscapeonline.co.uk, Fax (020) 8332 9434,* « 18C terrace house, Italianate walled garden » – p. 13 CX c
closed 24-26 December – **3 rm** 70.00/98.00.

Nightingales (at Petersham H.), Nightingale Lane, TW10 6UZ, ✆ (020) 8939 1084, *Fax (020) 8939 1002,* ≤, p. 13 CX c
Meals (residents only Sunday dinner) 20.00 (lunch) and a la carte 26.00/40.00 **st.** 17.50.

Four Regions, 102-104 Kew Rd, TW9 2PQ, ✆ (020) 8940 9044, *Fax (020) 8332 6130,* p. 13 CX e
Meals - Chinese - 18.00/30.00 and a la carte 20.00/35.00 **st.** 10.00.

ickenham – ✉ *Middx.*

McClements, 2 Whitton Rd, TW1 1BJ, ✆ (020) 8744 9610, *johnmac21@aol.com, Fax (020) 8744 9598* – p. 12 BX a
Meals 18.00/34.00 **t.**

Brula, 43 Crown Rd, St Margarets, TW1 3EJ, ✆ (020) 8892 0602, *Fax (020) 8892 0602*
closed 23-30 December, Sunday and Bank Holidays – **Meals** (booking essential) 10.00 (lunch) and dinner a la carte 17.50/25.00 **t.** 10.00. p. 12 BX v

---

UTHWARK.

London Bridge, 6 Tooley St. ✆ *(020) 7403 8299.*

rmondsey – ✉ *SE1.*

London Bridge, 8-18 London Bridge St, SE1 9SG, ✆ (020) 7855 2200, *sales@london-bridge-hotel.co.uk, Fax (020) 7855 2233,* rm, – 85. p. 31 PX a
Meals – (see ***Simply Nico*** below) – 13.95 – **138 rm** 185.00/195.00 **st.**, 3 suites.

London Tower Bridge Travel Inn Capital, 159 Tower Bridge Rd, SE1 3LP, ✆ (020) 7940 3700, *Fax (020) 7940 3719* – rest, p. 31 PY a
Meals (grill rest.) (dinner only) – **195 rm** 74.95 **t.**

Le Pont de la Tour, 36d Shad Thames, Butlers Wharf, SE1 2YE, ✆ (020) 7403 8403, *Fax (020) 7403 0267,* ≤, « Thames-side setting » – p. 31 PX c
closed 25 December and Saturday lunch – **Meals** 28.50 (lunch) and dinner a la carte approx. 57.75 **t.** 12.95.

Bengal Clipper, Cardamom Building, Shad Thames, Butlers Wharf, SE1 2YR, ✆ (020) 7357 9001, *clipper@bengalrestaurants.co.uk, Fax (020) 7357 9002* – p. 31 PX e
closed Christmas – **Meals** - Indian - a la carte 19.10/28.45.

Tentazioni, 2 Mill St, Lloyds Wharf, SE1 2BD, ✆ (020) 7237 1100, *tentazioni@aol.com, Fax (020) 7237 1100* – p. 14 GV x
closed first week January, last week August, Sunday and lunch Saturday and Monday and Bank Holidays – **Meals** - Italian - 15.00/19.00 (lunch) and a la carte 25.00/35.00 **t.** 12.50.

Simply Nico (at London Bridge H.), 8-18 London Bridge St, SE1 9SG, ✆ (020) 7407 4536, *simplynico@trpplc.com, Fax (020) 7407 4554* – p. 31 PX a
closed Christmas-New Year, lunch Saturday and Sunday and Bank Holidays – **Meals** 14.95 and a la carte 24.00/29.00 **t.** 12.95.

X **Blue Print Café,** Design Museum, Shad Thames, Butlers Wharf, SE1 2
(020) 7378 7031, *Fax (020) 7357 8810,* , « Thames-side setting, < Tower Bridge »
MC AE VISA JCB p. 31 PX
closed 25 December and Sunday dinner – **Meals** 22.50 (lunch) and dinner a la carte 25.0
36.50 **t.** 15.00.

X **Butlers Wharf Chop House,** 36e Shad Thames, Butlers Wharf, SE1 2
(020) 7403 3403, *Fax (020) 7403 3414,* , « Thames-side setting, < Tower Bridge »
MC AE VISA JCB p. 31 PX
closed Sunday dinner and Saturday lunch – **Meals** 23.75 (lunch) and dinner a la carte 25.2
55.50 **t.**

X **Cantina Del Ponte,** 36c Shad Thames, Butlers Wharf, SE1 2YE, (020) 7403 54
Fax (020) 7403 4432, <, , « Thames-side setting » – MC AE VISA JCB p. 31 PX
closed 25 December – **Meals** - Italian - 12.50 (lunch) and a la carte 20.65/31.10 **t.** 13.95

Dulwich – SE19.

XX **Belair House,** Gallery Rd, Dulwich Village, SE21 7AB, (020) 8299 97
Fax (020) 8299 6793, , « Georgian summer house », – P. MC AE VISA JCB
closed Monday and dinner Sunday – **Meals** 21.95/29.95 **t.** 16.00. p. 14 FX

Rotherhithe – SE16.

Hilton London Nelson Dock, 265 Rotherhithe St, Nelson Dock, SE16 5H
(020) 7231 1001, *Fax (020) 7231 0599,* <, , « Thames-side setting », , , –
rm, rest, TV & P – 350. MC AE VISA. p. 14 GV
closed 21-30 December – ***Three Crowns :*** **Meals** (dinner only) a la carte 27.95/33.75
13.95 – ***Columbia's :*** **Meals** - Chinese - *(closed Sunday)* (dinner only) a la carte appr
16.95 **st.** 13.95 – 13.00 – **364 rm** 165.00 **st.**, 4 suites.

Southwark – SE1.

Mercure, 75-79 Southwark St, SE1 0JA, (020) 7902 0800, *h2814@accor-hotels.co*
Fax (020) 7902 0810, – TV & – 35. MC AE VISA JCB p. 31 OX
The Loft : **Meals** 18.00/21.00 and a la carte 25.00/28.50 **st.** 13.00 – 12.00 – **144**
140.00/170.00 **st.** – SB.

Express by Holiday Inn without rest., 103-109 Southwark St, SE1 0
(020) 7401 2525, *stay@expresssouthwark.co.uk, Fax (020) 7401 3322* – TV &
MC AE VISA. p. 31 OX
88 **rm** 99.00 **st.**

XXX **Neat (Restaurant),** (2nd Floor), Oxo Tower Wharf, Barge House St, SE1 9F
(020) 7928 5533, *eat@neatrestaurant.co.uk, Fax (020) 7928 8644* – . MC AE
VISA p. 31 NX
closed 11-25 August, 2 weeks Christmas-New Year, Saturday lunch, Sunday and Ba
Holidays – **Meals** 29.00/49.00 **t.** 19.95.

XXX **Oxo Tower,** (8th floor), Oxo Tower Wharf, Barge House St, SE1 9PH, (020) 7803 38
oxo.reservations@harveynichols.co.uk, Fax (020) 7803 3838, < London skyline and Riv
Thames, – . MC AE VISA JCB p. 31 NX
closed 25-26 December and lunch Saturday – **Meals** 28.50 (lunch) and a la carte 25.5
50.00 **t.** 13.50 – (see also ***Oxo Tower Brasserie*** below).

XX **Neat Brasserie,** (2nd Floor), Oxo Tower Wharf, Barge House St, SE1 9F
(020) 7928 4433, *eat@neatrestaurant.co.uk, Fax (020) 7928 8644* – MC
VISA p. 31 NX
closed Easter Sunday and Monday, 25-26 December and 1 January – **Meals** 16.
(lunch) and a la carte approx. 29.50 **t.** 13.45.

X **Oxo Tower Brasserie,** (8th floor), Oxo Tower Wharf, Barge House St, SE1 9F
(020) 7803 3888, *Fax (020) 7803 3838,* < London skyline and River Thames, –
MC AE VISA JCB p. 31 NX
closed 25-26 December – **Meals** 25.00 (lunch) and a la carte 27.50/36.00 **t.** 13.50.

X **Cantina Vinopolis (Brasserie),** No 1 Bank End, SE1 9BU, (020) 7940 8333, *cantin*
vinopolis.co.uk, Fax (020) 7940 8334 – MC AE VISA p. 31 OX
closed Sunday dinner and Bank Holidays – **Meals** 26.50 and a la carte 16.85/28.25 **t.** 14.

X **Livebait,** 43 The Cut, SE1 8LF, (020) 7928 7211, *Fax (020) 7928 2279* – MC AE
VISA p. 31 NX
closed 25 December – **Meals** - Seafood - 15.50 (lunch) and a la carte 22.45/34.65 **st.**

X **Fish!,** Cathedral St, Borough Market, SE1 9AL, (020) 7234 3333, *info@fish.plc.*
Fax (020) 7234 3343, – . MC AE VISA p. 31 PX
closed 25-26 and 31 December and 1 January – **Meals** - Seafood - a la carte 14.45/26.8
9.90.

X **Tate Cafe (7th Floor),** Tate Modern, Bankside, SE1 9TE, ☎ (020) 7401 5020, *Fax (020) 7401 5171,* ≤ London skyline and River Thames – ⋟. MC AE ① VISA
closed 24-26 December – **Meals** (lunch only and dinner Friday-Saturday) a la carte 15.10/21.50 **t.** 🍷 11.95. p. 31 **OX** s

UTTON.

Carshalton – ✉ *Surrey.*

XX **La Veranda,** 18-19 Beynon Rd, SM5 3RL, ☎ (020) 8647 4370 – ▤. MC AE ① VISA p. 13 **EZ** c
closed Sunday and Bank Holidays – **Meals** - Italian - a la carte 21.70/30.00 **t.** 🍷 9.80.

Sutton – ✉ *Surrey.*

18, 9 *Oak Sports Centre, Woodmansterne Rd, Carshalton* ☎ *(020) 8643 8363.*

Holiday Inn, Gibson Rd, SM1 2RF, ☎ (020) 8770 1311, *Fax (020) 8770 1539,* Ls, ≘s, ⊠ – |‡|, ⋟ rm, ▤ TV ✆ ♿ P – 🏛 180. MC AE ① VISA JCB. ⋟ p. 13 **DZ** a
Meals 16.00 and a la carte 19.80/25.30 **st.** 🍷 11.95 – ☕ 14.95 – **115 rm** 165.00 **st.**, 1 suite.

Thatched House, 135-141 Cheam Rd, SM1 2BN, ☎ (020) 8642 3131, *Fax (020) 8770 0684,* ⌂ – ⋟ rest, TV P – 🏛 50. MC ① VISA JCB. ⋟ p. 13 **DZ** e
Meals *(closed dinner Saturday and Sunday and Bank Holidays)* 13.50 and a la carte 14.00/22.25 **t.** 🍷 8.95 – **34 rm** ☕ 75.00/90.00 **t.**

TOWER HAMLETS.

Blackwall – ✉ *E14.*

Ibis without rest., 1 Baffin Way, E14 9PE, ☎ (020) 7517 1100, *h2177@accor-hotels.com, Fax (020) 7987 5916* – |‡|, ⋟ rm, ▤ TV ✆ ♿. MC AE ① VISA p. 15 **HV** c
87 rm 64.95 **st.**

Canary Wharf – ✉ *E14.*

Four Seasons, Westferry Circus, E14 8RS, ☎ (020) 7510 1999, *caw.reservations@fourseasons.com, Fax (020) 7510 1998,* ≤, ⛱, Ls, ≘s, ⊠ – |‡|, ⋟ rm, ▤ TV ✆ ♿ 🚗 – 🏛 200. MC AE ① VISA JCB p. 10 **GV** v
Quadrato **:** Meals - Italian - 22.50/35.00 and a la carte **t.** – ☕ 18.50 – **128 rm** 260.00/310.00 **s.**, 14 suites.

Circus Apartments without rest., 39 Westferry Circus, E14 8RW, ☎ (020) 7719 7000, *res@circusapartments.co.uk, Fax (020) 7719 7001,* Ls, ≘s, ⊠ – |‡| ⋟ ▤ TV ✆ 🚗. MC AE ① VISA. ⋟ p. 14 **GV** a
49 suites 240.00/290.00 **s.**

XX **Ubon by Nobu,** 34 Westferry Circus, E14 8RR, ☎ (020) 7719 7800, *Fax (020) 7719 7801,* ≤ River Thames and city skyline – |‡| ▤ P. MC AE ① VISA JCB p. 14 **GV** a
closed Christmas-New Year, Bank Holidays, Sunday and Saturday lunch – **Meals** - New style Japanese - 19.50/100.00 and a la carte **t.**

X **Fish!,** Hanover House, 33 West Circus, E14 8RR, ☎ (020) 7234 3333, *info@fish.plc.uk, Fax (020) 7234 3343,* ⛱, « Thames-side setting » – ▤. MC AE ① VISA JCB p. 10 **GV** v
closed 25-26 and 31 December and 1 January – **Meals** - Seafood - a la carte 14.45/26.85 **t.** 🍷 9.90.

East India Docks – ✉ *E14.*

Travelodge, A 13 Coriander Ave, off East India Dock Rd, E14 2AA, off East India Dock Rd ☎ (020) 7531 9705, *Fax (020) 7515 9178,* ≤ – |‡|, ⋟ rm, ▤ rest, TV ♿ P. MC AE ① VISA. ⋟ p. 14 **GV** s
Meals (grill rest.) – **232 rm** 79.95 **t.**

Spitalfields – ✉ *E1.*

XX **Bengal Trader,** 44 Artillery Lane, E1 7NA, ☎ (020) 7375 0072, *trader@bengalrestaurant.com, Fax (020) 7247 1002* – ▤. MC AE ① VISA p. 27 **PU** x
closed Saturday, Sunday and Bank Holidays – **Meals** - Indian - a la carte 14.25/26.50 **t.** 🍷 8.95.

Whitechapel – ✉ *E1.*

XX **Cafe Spice Namaste,** 16 Prescot St, E1 8AZ, ☎ (020) 7488 9242, *Fax (020) 7481 0508* – ▤. MC AE ① VISA JCB p. 14 **GV** z
closed 1 week Christmas, Sunday, Saturday lunch and Bank Holidays – **Meals** - Indian - 22.00 and a la carte 21.95/28.45 **t.** 🍷 11.90.

Wapping – ✉ E1.

Wapping Food, Wapping Wall, E1W 3ST, ✆ (020) 7680 2080, *wappingfood@wappin wpt.com, Fax (020) 7680 2081,* « Converted hydraulic power station » – P. MC AE VISA p. 14 GV
closed 25-26 December, Good Friday and Sunday dinner – **Meals** a la carte 21.50/27. 14.00.

WANDSWORTH.

Battersea – ✉ SW8/SW11.

Express by Holiday Inn without rest., Smugglers Way, SW18 1EG, ✆ (020) 8877 595 *wandsworth@premierhotels.co.uk, Fax (020) 8877 0631* – TV P – 35. AE VISA JCB. p. 16 BQ
148 rm 85.00 st.

Travelodge without rest., 200 York Rd, SW11 3SA, ✆ (020) 7228 550 *Fax (020) 7978 5898* – TV P. MC AE VISA JCB. p. 17 CQ
87 rm 69.95 t.

Cafe Spice Namaste, 247 Lavender Hill, SW11 1JW, ✆ (020) 7738 171 *Fax (020) 7738 1666* – rest. MC AE VISA JCB p. 17 CQ
closed 25-26 December, 1 January, Monday and Bank Holidays – **Meals** - Indian - (dinn only and buffet Sunday lunch)/dinner 18.00/25.00 and a la carte 19.25/26.25 **t.** 11.90.

Chada, 208-210 Battersea Park Rd, SW11 4ND, ✆ (020) 7622 2209, *Fax (020) 7924 2178* . MC AE VISA JCB p. 17 CQ
closed Sunday and Bank Holidays – **Meals** - Thai - (dinner only) a la carte 11.55/24.00 11.95.

Metrogusto, 153 Battersea Park Rd, SW8 4BX, ✆ (020) 7720 0204, *Fax (020) 7720 0888* MC VISA JCB p. 17 DQ
closed 4 days Christmas, Sunday dinner and Bank Holidays – **Meals** - Italian - 19. (lunch) and a la carte 22.50/27.00 **t.** 12.50.

The Stepping Stone, 123 Queenstown Rd, SW8 3RH, ✆ (020) 7622 0555, *thesteppi stone@aol.com, Fax (020) 7622 4230* – . MC VISA p. 17 DQ
closed 5 days Christmas, Saturday lunch, Sunday dinner and Bank Holidays – **Meals** 12. (lunch) and a la carte 19.00/27.50 **t.** 11.50.

Ransome's Dock, 35-37 Parkgate Rd, SW11 4NP, ✆ (020) 7223 1611, *chef@ransom dock.co.uk, Fax (020) 7924 2614,* – MC AE VISA JCB p. 29 HZ
closed Christmas, August Bank Holiday and Sunday dinner – **Meals** a la carte 23.50/34.00 14.00.

Fish!, 41a Queenstown Rd, SW8 3RE, ✆ (020) 7234 3333, *info@fish.plc.u Fax (020) 7234 3343* – . MC AE VISA JCB p. 17 DQ
closed 25, 26 and 31 December and 1 January – **Meals** - Seafood - a la carte 14.45/26.85 9.90.

Duke of Cambridge, 228 Battersea Bridge Rd, SW11 3AA, ✆ (020) 7223 566 *Fax (020) 7801 9684,* – MC VISA p. 17 CQ
Meals a la carte 14.85/22.35 **t.** 9.90.

Putney – ✉ SW15.

Putney Bridge, Lower Richmond Rd, SW15 1LB, ✆ (020) 8780 18 *Fax (020) 8780 1211,* ←, « Thames-side setting » – . MC VISA JCB p. 16 AQ
closed Christmas-New Year, Sunday dinner, Monday and Bank Holidays – **Meals** 22.5 45.00 **t.**
Spec. Trelough duck with turnips, confit of leg and young leaf salad. Scottish lobs roasted with spices and squid ink polenta. Chocolate moelleux.

Enoteca Turi, 28 Putney High St, SW15 1SQ, ✆ (020) 8785 4449, *Fax (020) 8785 444* . MC AE VISA p. 16 AQ
closed 25-26 December, 1 January, Sunday and lunch Monday and Bank Holidays – **Meal** Italian - a la carte 20.95/26.95 **t.** 12.50.

The Phoenix, Pentlow St, SW15 1LY, ✆ (020) 8780 3131, *Fax (020) 8780 1114,* – MC AE VISA p. 16 AQ
closed Bank Holidays – **Meals** 12.00/18.50 (lunch) and a la carte 20.50/29.50 **t.** 10.95.

The Cookhouse, 56 Lower Richmond Rd, SW15 1JT, ✆ (020) 8785 2300, *info@the_co house.com* – . MC AE VISA p. 16 AQ
closed Sunday and Monday – **Meals** (dinner only and lunch Saturday and Sunday) a la ca 19.00/25.50.

Coat and Badge, 8 Lacy Rd, SW15 1NL, ✆ (020) 8788 4900, *Fax (020) 8780 5733,* MC VISA p. 16 AQ
Meals (bookings not accepted) a la carte 13.85/18.85 **t.** 9.80.

outhfields – ✉ SW18.

XX **Sarkhel's,** 199 Replingham Rd, SW18 5LY, ✆ (020) 8870 1483, *veronica@sarkhels.co.uk, Fax (020) 8874 6603* – ▤. MC AE VISA p. 16 **BR** e
closed 25-26 December and Monday – **Meals** - Indian - 9.95 (lunch) and a la carte 18.35/ 25.90 **t.** 10.90.

ooting – ✉ SW17.

X **Kastoori,** 188 Upper Tooting Rd, SW17 7EJ, ✆ (020) 8767 7027 – ▤. MC VISA
closed 25 December, 1 week mid January and lunch Monday and Tuesday – **Meals** - Indian Vegetarian - a la carte 10.50/11.50 **t.** 7.75. p. 17 **CR** v

X **Oh Boy,** 843 Garratt Lane, SW17 0PG, ✆ (020) 8947 9760 – ▤. MC AE ① VISA JCB p. 17 **CR** c
closed Monday – **Meals** - Thai - (dinner only) a la carte 18.20/25.60 **t.** 8.95.

andsworth – ✉ SW12/SW17/SW18.

X **Chez Bruce** (Poole), 2 Bellevue Rd, SW17 7EG, ✆ (020) 8672 0114, *Fax (020) 8767 6648* – ▤. MC AE ① VISA JCB p. 17 **CR** e
closed 24-26 December and Sunday dinner – **Meals** (booking essential) 21.50/30.00 **t.**
Spec. Salad paysanne with deep-fried calves brains. Pot-roast rabbit with pappardelle and creamed wild mushrooms. Glazed plum and almond tart, Jersey cream.

X **Bombay Bicycle Club,** 95 Nightingale Lane, SW12 8NX, ✆ (020) 8673 6217, *Fax (020) 8673 9100* – MC AE ① VISA p. 17 **DR** o
closed 1 week Christmas and Sunday – **Meals** - Indian - (dinner only) a la carte 22.00/ 28.50 **t.** 11.00.

X **Ditto,** 55-57 East Hill, SW18 2QE, ✆ (020) 8877 0110, *christian-gilles@ditto1.fsnet.co.uk, Fax (020) 8875 0110* – MC VISA JCB p. 16 **BQ** n
closed 25-26 December, 1 January and Saturday lunch – **Meals** 14.50/18.50 and a la carte 19.00/28.45 **t.**

ESTMINSTER (City of).

ayswater and Maida Vale – ✉ W2/W9.

Royal Lancaster, Lancaster Terr, W2 2TY, ✆ (020) 7262 6737, *sales@royallancaster.com, Fax (020) 7724 3191,* ≤ – |‡|, ⇹ rm, ▤ TV ✆ ♿ P – 🔺 1400. MC AE ① VISA JCB. ✂ p. 37 **DZ** e
Park : **Meals** *(closed Sunday, Saturday lunch and Bank Holidays)* 25.90 **t.** 20.00 – ***Pavement Cafe :*** **Meals** a la carte 20.15/18.10 **t.** 11.90 – (see also ***Nipa*** below) – ☕ 15.00 – **394 rm** 230.00/305.00 **s.**, 22 suites.

Hilton London Metropole, Edgware Rd, W2 1JU, ✆ (020) 7402 4141, *Fax (020) 7724 8866,* ≤, Fá, ≘s, ▣ – |‡|, ⇹ rm, ▤ TV ✆ P – 🔺 2000. MC AE ① VISA JCB. ✂ p. 25 **GU** c
Meals a la carte 20.00/30.00 **t.** 16.50 – (see also ***Aspects*** below) – ☕ 17.95 – **1033 rm** 220.00/240.00 **s.**, 25 suites – SB.

Marriott, Plaza Parade, NW6 5RP, ✆ (020) 7543 6000, *marriottmaidavale@btinternet.com, Fax (020) 7543 2100,* Fá, ≘s, ▣ – |‡|, ⇹ rm, ▤ TV ✆ ♿ 🚗 – 🔺 200. MC AE ① VISA p. 24 **FS** c
Fratelli : **Meals** - Italian - (dinner only) a la carte 17.00/32.00 **st.** 15.00 – ☕ 13.50 – **207 rm** 99.00/145.00 **st.**, 16 suites.

The Hempel ⛭, 31-35 Craven Hill Gdns, W2 3EA, ✆ (020) 7298 9000, *hotel@the-hempel.co.uk, Fax (020) 7402 4666,* « Minimalist », ⛱ – |‡| ▤ TV ✆ ♿. MC AE ① VISA JCB. ✂
I-Thai : **Meals** - Thai-Italian - 22.50/45.00 and dinner a la carte 43.00/53.00 **t.** 18.00 – ☕ 15.00 – **41 rm** 265.00/305.00 **s.**, 6 suites. p. 36 **CZ** a

Thistle Hyde Park, Bayswater Rd, 90-92 Lancaster Gate, W2 3NR, ✆ (020) 7262 2711, *Fax (020) 7262 2147* – |‡| ⇹ ▤ TV ✆ P – 🔺 30. MC AE ① VISA JCB. ✂ p. 36 **CZ** v
Meals (bar lunch Saturday) a la carte 18.95/30.95 **t.** 15.95 – ☕ 14.95 – **52 rm** 160.00/ 210.00 **st.**, 2 suites – SB.

Hilton London Hyde Park, 129 Bayswater Rd, W2 4RJ, ✆ (020) 7221 2217, *Fax (020) 7229 0557* – |‡| ⇹, ▤ rest, TV ✆ – 🔺 100. MC AE ① VISA JCB. ✂ p. 36 **BZ** c
Meals (bar lunch)/dinner 19.95 and a la carte approx. 25.00 **st.** – ☕ 12.95 – **128 rm** 130.00/ 150.00 **s.**, 1 suite – SB.

Ramada Jarvis Hyde Park, 150 Bayswater Rd, W2 4RT, ✆ (020) 7229 1212, *jihydepark@jarvis.co.uk, Fax (020) 7229 2623* – |‡|, ⇹ rm, TV ✆ P – 🔺 100. MC AE ① VISA p. 36 **BZ** o
Meals a la carte 17.65/26.50 **t.** 12.95 – ☕ 10.50 – **212 rm** 155.00/175.00 **st.**, 1 suite – SB.

Mornington without rest., 12 Lancaster Gate, W2 3LG, ✆ (020) 7262 7361, *london@mornington.co.uk, Fax (020) 7706 1028* – |‡| ⇹ TV. MC AE ① VISA JCB. ✂ p. 37 **DZ** s
closed 23-27 December – **66 rm** ☕ 120.00/160.00 **st.**

Colonnade Town House without rest., 2 Warrington Cres, W9 1E (020) 7286 1052, *res_colonnade@etontownhouse.com, Fax (020) 7286 1057,* « Victoria town house » – rm, AE VISA JCB p. 24 FU
closed 23-27 December – **40 rm** 147.00/179.00 **s.**, 3 suites.

Commodore, 50 Lancaster Gate, W2 3NA, (020) 7402 5291, *reservations@commodo -hotel.com, Fax (020) 7262 1088* – rm, AE VISA JCB. p. 36 CZ
Meals a la carte 16.50/24.00 **st.** 9.00 – 12.50 – **76 rm** 115.00/150.00 **st.**, 3 suites.

Miller's without rest., 111A Westbourne Grove, W2 4UW, (020) 7243 1024, *enquiries millersuk.com, Fax (020) 7243 1064,* « Antique furnishings » – AE VISA JC p. 36 AZ
12.50 **6 rm** 160.00/188.00 **s.**

Byron without rest., 36-38 Queensborough Terr, W2 3SH, (020) 7243 0987, *byron capricornhotels.co.uk, Fax (020) 7792 1957* – AE VISA JCB. p. 36 CZ
44 rm 78.00/120.00 **st.**, 1 suite.

Delmere, 130 Sussex Gdns, W2 1UB, (020) 7706 3344, *delmerehotel@compuserv com, Fax (020) 7262 1863* – rm, AE VISA JCB. p. 37 DZ
Meals *(closed Sunday and Bank Holidays)* (dinner only) 19.00 **t.** 9.00 – 6.00 – **36 r** 86.00/107.00 **st.**

Comfort Inn without rest., 18-19 Craven Hill Gdns, W2 3EE, (020) 7262 6644, *comf inn_hydepark@compuserve.com, Fax (020) 7262 0673* – AE VI p. 36 CZ
4.50 – **67 rm** 82.00/104.00 **st.**

Aspects (at Hilton London Metropole H.), Edgware Rd, W2 1JU, (020) 7402 414 *Fax (020) 7724 8866,* London – AE VISA JCB p. 25 GU
closed Sunday dinner – **Meals** a la carte 30.00/50.00 **t.**

Amandier, 26 Sussex Pl, W2 2TH, (020) 7262 6073, *Fax (020) 7723 8395* – AE VISA JCB p. 37 DZ
closed 26 December-3 January, Sunday, Saturday lunch and Bank Holidays – **Meals** - Fren - 25.50/31.50 **t.** 12.95 – (see also ***Bistro Daniel*** below).

Nipa (at Royal Lancaster H.), Lancaster Terr, W2 2TY, (020) 7262 67 *Fax (020) 7724 3191* – AE VISA JCB p. 37 DZ
Meals - Thai - 24.50/27.70 and a la carte 23.80/36.10 **t.** 20.00.

Al San Vincenzo, 30 Connaught St, W2 2AF, (020) 7262 9623 – VISA
closed Saturday lunch and Sunday – **Meals** - Italian - (booking essential) 27.50/33.50 15.00. p. 37 EZ

Poons, Unit 205, Whiteleys, Queensway, W2 4YN, (020) 7792 2884, *Fax (020) 8458 09* – AE VISA JCB p. 36 BZ
closed 24-26 December – **Meals** - Chinese - 16.00/22.00 and a la carte 22.00/43.00 11.00.

Jason's, Blomfield Rd, Little Venice, W9 2PD, (020) 7286 6752, *enquiries@jasons.co. Fax (020) 7266 4332,* « Canalside setting » – AE VISA JCB p. 24 FU
closed 25 December-1 January and Sunday dinner – **Meals** - Seafood - 21.50 and a la ca 24.15/50.45 **t.** 11.50.

Green Olive, 5 Warwick Pl, W9 2PX, (020) 7289 2469, *Fax (020) 7289 4178* – VISA JCB p. 24 FU
closed 25-26 December, Saturday lunch and Bank Holidays – **Meals** - Italian - (booki essential) 9.50/24.50 **t.** 13.50.

Assaggi, 39 Chepstow Pl, (above Chepstow pub), W2 4TS, (020) 7792 5501 – AE VISA JCB p. 36 AZ
closed 2 weeks Christmas, Sunday and Bank Holidays – **Meals** - Italian - a la carte 29. 35.65 **t.** 10.95.

The Vale, 99 Chippenham Rd, W9 2AB, (020) 7266 0990, *Fax (020) 7286 7224* – VISA JCB p. 24 ET
closed Christmas and lunch Monday and Saturday – **Meals** 12.00/15.00 and a la carte 19. 23.00 **t.** 10.50.

Ginger, 115 Westbourne Grove, W2 4UP, (020) 7908 1990, *info@gingerrestaura co.uk, Fax (020) 7908 1991* – AE VISA JCB p. 36 AZ
closed 25-26 December – **Meals** - Bangladeshi - a la carte 18.50/22.50 **t.** 12.00.

L'Accento, 16 Garway Rd, W2 4NH, (020) 7243 2201, *laccentorest@aol.co Fax (020) 7243 2201,* – AE VISA JCB p. 36 BZ
closed 25 December and lunch Sunday – **Meals** - Italian - 12.50 and a la carte 21.50/28.0 10.50.

Bistro Daniel (at Amandier), 26 Sussex Pl, W2 2TH, (020) 7262 6073, *Fax (020) 7723 8395* – MC AE VISA JCB p. 37 **DZ** r
closed 26 December-3 January, Sunday, Saturday lunch and Bank Holidays – **Meals** - French - 12.95 (lunch) and a la carte 17.35/24.45 **t.** 9.95.

The Chepstow, 39 Chepstow Pl, W2 4TS, (020) 7229 0323, *Fax (020) 7229 0323* – MC VISA p. 36 **AZ** c
Meals a la carte 25.25/31.45 **st.** 11.50.

Belgravia – SW1.

The Lanesborough, Hyde Park Corner, SW1X 7TA, (020) 7259 5599, *reservations@lanesborough.co.uk, Fax (020) 7259 5606,* – rm, – 90. MC AE VISA JCB. p. 29 **IY** a
***The Conservatory*:** **Meals** 15.00/44.00 and a la carte 39.50/59.50 **st.** 19.50 – 23.50 – **86 rm** 275.00/460.00 **s.**, 9 suites.

The Berkeley, Wilton Pl, SW1X 7RL, (020) 7235 6000, *info@the-berkeley.co.uk, Fax (020) 7235 4330,* « Rooftop », – rm, – 220. MC AE VISA JCB. p. 35 **FQ** e
Meals – (see ***La Tante Claire*** and ***Vong*** below) – 21.50 – **140 rm** 320.00/540.00 **st.**, 28 suites.

The Halkin, 5 Halkin St, SW1X 7DJ, (020) 7333 1000, *res@halkin.co.uk, Fax (020) 7333 1100,* « Contemporary interior design » – rm, . MC AE VISA JCB. p. 36 **AV** a
***Nahm*:** **Meals** - Thai - *(closed lunch Saturday and Sunday)* (booking essential) 25.00/55.00 **t.** 18.00 – 18.00 – **37 rm** 295.00 **s.**, 4 suites
Spec. Geng jeut gradtai (rabbit and mushroom soup). Pla ling wua tort (lemon sole). Geng gari bpet (duck curry).

Sheraton Belgravia, 20 Chesham Pl, SW1X 8HQ, (020) 7235 6040, *reservations_central_london@sheraton.com, Fax (020) 7201 1926* – rm, – 25. MC AE VISA JCB. p. 35 **FR** u
***The Mulberry*:** **Meals** 15.00/25.00 and a la carte 27.95/36.00 **t.** 18.00 – 17.50 – **82 rm** 280.00/300.00 **s.**, 7 suites.

The Lowndes, 21 Lowndes St, SW1X 9ES, (020) 7823 1234, *lowndes@hyattintl.com, Fax (020) 7235 1154,* – rm, – 25. MC AE VISA JCB. p. 35 **FR** i
***Brasserie 21*:** **Meals** 16.50/20.00 and a la carte 25.00/39.00 **st.** 17.50 – 16.50 – **77 rm** 250.00/280.00 **s.**, 1 suite.

Diplomat without rest., 2 Chesham St, SW1X 8DT, (020) 7235 1544, *diplomat.hotel@btinternet.co.uk, Fax (020) 7259 6153* – . MC AE VISA JCB. p. 35 **FR** a
26 rm 95.00/170.00 **st.**

La Tante Claire (Koffmann) (at The Berkeley H.), Wilton Pl, SW1X 7RL, (020) 7823 2003, *Fax (020) 7823 2001* – . MC AE VISA JCB p. 35 **FQ** e
closed 22 December-6 January, Saturday lunch, Sunday and Bank Holidays – **Meals** - French - (booking essential) 28.00 (lunch) and a la carte 62.00/77.00 **t.** 21.00
Spec. Foie gras poêlé, sauce cappuccino. Pied de cochon. Soufflé à la pistache.

Zafferano, 15 Lowndes St, SW1X 9EY, (020) 7235 5800, *Fax (020) 7235 1971* – . MC AE VISA p. 35 **FR** i
Meals - Italian - 21.50/35.50 **t.** 12.50
Spec. Pan-fried sea bass with sun-dried tomato crust. Rabbit with polenta and Parma ham. Pasta ribbons with broad beans and rocket.

Vong (at The Berkeley H.), Wilton Pl, SW1X 7RL, (020) 7235 1010, *Fax (020) 7235 1011* – . MC AE VISA JCB p. 35 **FQ** e
closed Christmas and Bank Holidays – **Meals** - French-Thai - (booking essential) 20.00 (lunch) and a la carte 20.00/70.00 **t.**

Mango Tree, 46 Grosvenor Pl, SW1X 7EQ, (020) 7823 1888, *Fax (020) 7838 9275* – . MC AE VISA p. 36 **AX** a
closed 25-26 December and Saturday lunch – **Meals** - Thai - 28.00/38.00 and a la carte 26.00/34.00 **t.** 15.00.

Noura Brasserie, 16 Hobart Pl, SW1W 0HH, (020) 7235 9444, *Fax (020) 7235 9244* – . MC AE VISA p. 36 **AX** n
Meals - Lebanese - 12.50/28.50 and a la carte 20.50/26.25 **t.**

Hyde Park and Knightsbridge – SW1/SW7.

Mandarin Oriental Hyde Park, 66 Knightsbridge, SW1X 7LA, (020) 7235 2000, *Fax (020) 7235 4552,* – rm, – 220. MC AE VISA JCB. p. 35 **FQ** x
The Park*:** **Meals** 19.00 (lunch) and a la carte 25.00/42.50 **t.** 18.50 – (see also ***Foliage below) – 19.00 – **175 rm** 255.00/495.00, 25 suites – SB.

Knightsbridge Green without rest., 159 Knightsbridge, SW1X 7PD, ✆ (020) 7584 62 *thekghotel@aol.com, Fax (020) 7225 1635* – VISA. p. 35 EQ
10.50 – **16 rm** 110.00/145.00 **st.**, 12 suites 170.00 **st.**

Foliage (at Mandarin Oriental Hyde Park H.), 66 Knightsbridge, SW1X 7 ✆ (020) 7201 3723, *Fax (020) 7235 4552* – VISA p. 35 FQ
Meals 24.00/42.50 **t.** 17.50
Spec. Poached lobster, crab vinaigrette and caviar dressing. Bresse pigeon, braised c bage, celeriac bouillon. Iced coconut parfait, bitter chocolate sorbet.

Isola, 145 Knightsbridge, SW1X 7PA, ✆ (020) 7838 1044, *Fax (020) 7838 1099* – VISA p. 35 EQ
Meals - Italian - 19.50 (lunch) and a la carte 29.00/39.00 **t.** 13.50.

Mr Chow, 151 Knightsbridge, SW1X 7PA, ✆ (020) 7589 7347, *Fax (020) 7584 5780* – VISA JCB p. 35 EQ
closed 24-26 December, 1 January and Easter Monday – **Meals** - Chinese - 15 (lunch) and a la carte 34.00/40.00 **t.** 13.50.

Mayfair – ✉ *W1.*

Dorchester, Park Lane, W1A 2HJ, ✆ (020) 7629 8888, *reservations@dorchesterho com, Fax (020) 7409 0114,* rm, – 550. VISA p. 32 BN
Meals – (see ***The Oriental*** and ***Grill Room*** below) – 23.00 – **201 rm** 305.00/375.00 49 suites – SB.

Claridge's, Brook St, W1A 2JQ, ✆ (020) 7629 8860, *info@claridges.co. Fax (020) 7499 2210,* « Art Deco », rm, – 200. VISA p. 32 BL
Gordon Ramsay at Claridge's *(✆ (020) 7499 0099)* **: Meals** (booking essential) 21.0 38.00 **t.** – **143 rm** 345.00/420.00, 60 suites.

Le Meridien Piccadilly, 21 Piccadilly, W1V 0BH, ✆ (0870) 400 8400, *lmpiccres meridien-hotels.com, Fax (020) 7437 3574,* squash – rm, 250. VISA JCB p. 33 EM
Meals – (see ***The Oak Room Marco Pierre White*** and ***Terrace*** below) – 18.50 – **248** 295.00/315.00, 18 suites.

Le Meridien Grosvenor House, Park Lane, W1A 3AA, ✆ (020) 7499 6363, *grosven reservations@forte-hotels.com, Fax (020) 7493 3341,* – rm, – 1500. VISA JCB. p. 32 AM
La Terrazza : **Meals** - Italian influences - a la carte 34.00/45.50 **t.** 18.50 – (see a ***cheznico*** below) – 18.50 – **373 rm** 396.00/417.00 **s.**, 74 suites.

Four Seasons, Hamilton Pl, Park Lane, W1A 1AZ, ✆ (020) 7499 0888, *fsn.london@fo seasons.com, Fax (020) 7493 1895,* – rm, – 500. JCB. p. 32 BP
Lanes : **Meals** 36.00/33.50 and a la carte 33.75/49.75 **st.** 16.00 – 21.00 – **185** 285.00/340.00 **s.**, 35 suites.

London Hilton, 22 Park Lane, W1Y 4BE, ✆ (020) 7493 8000, *reservations@hilton.co Fax (020) 7208 4146,* « Panoramic ≤ of London », rm, 1000. VISA JCB. p. 32 BP
Trader Vics *(✆ (020) 7208 4113)* **: Meals** (dinner only) 30.00 and a la carte 24.50/45.50 21.00 – ***Park Brasserie :*** **Meals** 23.50/26.50 and a la carte 25.00/44.50 **t.** 17.50 – (s also ***Windows*** below) – 24.50 – **396 rm** 325.00 **s.**, 53 suites – SB.

Connaught, Carlos Pl, W1K 2AL, ✆ (020) 7499 7070, *info@theconnaught.co. Fax (020) 7495 3262,* – VISA. p. 32 BM
The Restaurant : **Meals** (booking essential) 28.50/58.00 and a la carte 45.00/80.00 23.00 – ***Grill Room :*** **Meals** *(closed Sunday and Monday)* (booking essential) 28.50/58 and a la carte 45.00/80.00 **t.** – 23.00 – **68 rm** 345.00/425.00 **s.**, 23 suites – SB
Spec. Terrine Connaught. Homard d'Ecosse, "Reine Elizabeth". Sole jubilee.

Brown's, Albemarle St, W1S 4BP, ✆ (020) 7493 6020, *brownshotel@brownshotel.co Fax (020) 7493 9381,* – rm, – 70. VISA JCB.
Meals – (see ***1837*** below) – 20.00 – **112 rm** 290.00/320.00, 6 suites. p. 33 DM

Inter-Continental, 1 Hamilton Pl, Hyde Park Corner, W1J 7QY, ✆ (020) 7409 31 *london@interconti.com, Fax (020) 7493 3476,* ≤, – rm, 1000. VISA JCB. p. 32 BP
Meals 25.10/29.50 and a la carte 13.00 – (see also ***Le Soufflé*** below) – 22.00 – **418** 370.00 **s.**, 40 suites.

Millennium Mayfair, Grosvenor Sq, W1K 2HP, ✆ (020) 7629 9400, *sales.mayfair@n cop.com, Fax (020) 7629 7736,* – rm, – 770. VISA p. 32 BM
Meals *(closed Saturday lunch)* 18.50/21.50 and a la carte 28.50/39.50 **t.** 24.50 – (see a ***Shogun*** below) – 17.50 – **342 rm** 190.00/275.00 **s.**, 6 suites.

May Fair Inter-Continental, Stratton St, W1A 2AN, ☎ (020) 7629 7777, *mayfair@interconti.com, Fax (020) 7629 1459,* – rm, – 300. VISA JCB. p. 33 DN z
Opus 70*: Meals** *(closed lunch August, Saturday and Bank Holidays)* 20.00 (lunch) and a la carte 24.00/38.50 **t.** 18.00 – ***May Fair Café *(☎ (020) 7915 2842)* **: Meals** (lunch only) 17.00 and a la carte 17.50/20.50 **t.** 17.00 – 19.50 – **278 rm** 315.00/375.00, 12 suites – SB.

Park Lane, Piccadilly, W1Y 8BX, ☎ (020) 7499 6321, *reservations_central_london@sheraton.com, Fax (020) 7499 1965,* – rm, – 300. VISA JCB. p. 32 CP x
Citrus *(☎ (020) 7290 7364)* **: Meals** 15.00/24.00 and a la carte 22.75/29.00 **st.** 15.00 – 19.95 – **287 rm** 260.00/280.00 **s.**, 20 suites.

47 Park Street, 47 Park St, W1K 7EB, ☎ (020) 7491 7282, *reservations@47parkstreet.com, Fax (020) 7491 7281* – . VISA JCB. p. 32 AM c
Meals (room service) – (see also ***Le Gavroche*** below) – 24.50, **52 suites** 300.00/655.00 **s.**

Westbury, Bond St, W1S 2YF, ☎ (020) 7629 7755, *westburyhotel@compuserve.com, Fax (020) 7495 1163* – rm, – 120. VISA JCB.
Meals 16.50/21.50 and a la carte **st.** 16.00 – 16.75 – **233 rm** 225.00/290.00 **s.**, 21 suites – SB. p. 33 DM a

The Metropolitan, Old Park Lane, W1Y 4LB, ☎ (020) 7447 1000, *sales@metropolitan.co.uk, Fax (020) 7447 1100,* « Contemporary interior design », – rm, . VISA JCB. p. 32 BP c
Meals – (see ***Nobu*** below) – 20.00 – **152 rm** 240.00/545.00 **s.**, 3 suites.

Athenaeum, 116 Piccadilly, W15 7BS, ☎ (020) 7499 3464, *foxs@athenaeumhotel.com, Fax (020) 7493 1860,* – rm, – 55. VISA. p. 32 CP s
***Bulloch's at 116*: Meals** *(closed lunch Saturday and Sunday)* 17.00 (lunch) and a la carte approx. 33.40 **st.** 17.00 – 18.50 – **124 rm** 265.00/340.00 **s.**, 33 suites.

London Marriott Grosvenor Square, Duke St, Grosvenor Sq, W1K 6JP, ☎ (020) 7493 1232, *reservations@londonmarriott.co.uk, Fax (020) 7491 3201,* – rm, – 600. VISA JCB. p. 32 BL a
***Diplomat*: Meals** *(closed lunch Saturday and Bank Holidays)* a la carte 23.10/32.00 **st.** 17.50 – 15.95 – **209 rm** 180.00/230.00, 12 suites.

Washington Mayfair, 5-7 Curzon St, W1J 5HE, ☎ (020) 7499 7000, *sales@washington-mayfair.co.uk, Fax (020) 7495 6172* – rm, – 90. VISA JCB. p. 32 CN s
Meals 14.95 and a la carte 22.90/40.85 12.95 – 13.95 – **168 rm** 195.00/220.00 **s.**, 5 suites.

Chesterfield, 35 Charles St, W1J 5EB, ☎ (020) 7491 2622, *reservations@chesterfield.redcarnationhotels.com, Fax (020) 7491 4793* – rm, – 110. VISA JCB p. 32 CN c
Meals *(closed Saturday lunch)* 15.50 and a la carte 25.90/37.95 **t.** 15.50 – 16.50 – **106 rm** 195.00/250.00 **s.**, 4 suites.

Holiday Inn Mayfair, 3 Berkeley St, W1J 8NE, ☎ (020) 7493 8282, *himayfair@holidayinnmayfair.co.uk, Fax (020) 7629 2827,* – rm, – 60. VISA JCB. p. 33 DN r
Meals a la carte 23.00/37.75 **st.** 12.95 – 14.95 – **184 rm** 249.00 **st.**, 2 suites.

Flemings, Half Moon St, W1J 7BB, ☎ (020) 7499 2964, *reservations@flemings-mayfair.co.uk, Fax (020) 7629 4063* – rm, – 55. VISA JCB.
Meals 15.00/26.50 and a la carte 22.50/31.50 **st.** 18.00 – 17.00 – **120 rm** 169.00/199.00 **s.**, 10 suites. p. 32 CN z

No 5 Maddox St without rest., 5 Maddox St, W1S 2QD, ☎ (020) 7647 0200, *no5maddoxst@living-rooms.co.uk, Fax (020) 7647 0300,* « Contemporary interior » – . VISA JCB. p. 33 DK a
12.00 **s.**, **12 suites** 230.00/575.00.

Hilton London Green Park, Half Moon St, W1Y 8BP, ☎ (020) 7629 7522, *greenparkhotel@btinternet.com, Fax (020) 7491 8971* – , rest, – 130. VISA JCB. p. 32 CN a
Meals *(closed Sunday lunch)* a la carte 30.95/38.25 **st.** 15.90 – 16.50 – **161 rm** 160.00/210.00 **s.** – SB.

Hilton London Mews, 2 Stanhope Row, W1Y 7HE, ☎ (020) 7493 7222, *lonmwtw@hilton.com, Fax (020) 7629 9423* – – 50. VISA p. 32 BP u
Meals (dinner only) a la carte 21.70/25.40 **st.** 15.90 – 14.00 – **71 rm** 155.00/175.00 **s.** – SB.

XXXXX ✿ **The Oak Room Marco Pierre White** (at Le Meridien Piccadilly H.), 21 Piccadilly, W1 0BH, ✆ (020) 7437 0202, *Fax (020) 7851 3141* – ▤. MC AE D VISA JCB p. 33 EM
closed Christmas-New Year, Saturday lunch and Sunday – **Meals** (booking essential) 15.00/75.00 **t.** 20.00
Spec. Panaché of langoustine and pork belly. Grilled sea bass on the bone with beurre noisette. Feuillantine of raspberries.

XXXXX ✿ **cheznico** (at Le Meridien Grosvenor House H.), 90 Park Lane, W1K 7TN, ✆ (020) 7409 1290, *cheznico@globalnet.co.uk, Fax (020) 7355 4877* – ▤. MC AE D VISA p. 32 AM
closed 10 days Christmas, 4 days Easter, Sunday, Saturday lunch and Bank Holidays – **Meals** (booking essential) 43.00/70.00 **t.** 20.00
Spec. Seared foie gras with brioche and oranges. John Dory with provençal vegetables. Chocolate tart with pistachio sauce.

XXXX ✿✿ **Le Gavroche** (Roux), 43 Upper Brook St, W1K 7QR, ✆ (020) 7408 0881, *gavroche@cwcom.net, Fax (020) 7409 0939* – ▤. MC AE D VISA JCB p. 32 AM
closed Christmas-New Year, Sunday, Saturday lunch and Bank Holidays – **Meals** - French (booking essential) 40.00 (lunch) and a la carte 56.50/94.20 **t.** 25.00
Spec. Foie gras chaud et pastilla de canard à la cannelle. Râble de lapin et galette au parmesan. Le palet au chocolat amer et praline croustillant.

XXXX **The Oriental** (at Dorchester H.), Park Lane, W1A 2HJ, ✆ (020) 7317 632..., *Fax (020) 7317 6464* – ▤. MC AE D VISA JCB p. 32 BN
closed August, 25 December, Saturday lunch and Sunday – **Meals** - Chinese (Canton) - 25.00/43.00 and a la carte 43.50/66.00 **st.** 23.50.

XXXX **Grill Room** (at Dorchester H.), Park Lane, W1A 2HJ, ✆ (020) 7317 633..., *Fax (020) 7317 6464* – ▤. MC AE D VISA JCB p. 32 BN
Meals - English - 29.50/39.50 and a la carte 41.00/62.00 **st.** 23.50.

XXXX **1837** (at Brown's H.), Albemarle St, W1S 4BP, ✆ (020) 7408 1837, *brownshotel@ukbusiness.com, Fax (020) 7493 9381* – ▤. MC AE D VISA JCB p. 33 DM
closed Saturday lunch and Sunday – **Meals** 25.00/37.00 and a la carte 35.50/50.50 19.00.

XXXX **Windows** (at London Hilton H.), 22 Park Lane, W1Y 4BE, ✆ (020) 7208 402..., *Fax (020) 7208 4147,* « Panoramic ≤ of London » – ▤. MC AE D VISA JCB p. 32 BP
closed Saturday lunch and Sunday dinner – **Meals** 42.50 (lunch) and dinner a la carte 43.00/64.00 **t.** 21.00.

XXX ✿✿ **The Square** (Howard), 6-10 Bruton St, W1J 6PU, ✆ (020) 7495 7100, *squarethe@aol.com, Fax (020) 7495 7150* – ▤. MC AE D VISA JCB p. 32 CM
closed 25-26 December, 1 January, lunch Saturday, Sunday and Bank Holidays – **Meals** 25.00/50.00 **t.** 18.50
Spec. Lasagne of crab with langoustine cappuccino. Herb crusted saddle of lamb, shallot purée and rosemary. Roast foie gras, endive and Muscat grape tart.

XXX ✿ **Mirabelle,** 56 Curzon St, W1J 8PA, ✆ (020) 7499 4636, *sales@whitestarline.org.uk, Fax (020) 7499 5449,* ☂ – ▤. MC AE D VISA p. 32 CN
Meals 19.95 (lunch) and a la carte 33.40/53.40 **t.** 20.00
Spec. Grilled scallops with chives and ginger. Bresse pigeon with foie gras en chou vert. Raspberry soufflé "Mirabelle".

XXX **Terrace** (at Le Meridien Piccadilly H.), 21 Piccadilly, W1V 0BH, ✆ (020) 7851 308..., *Fax (020) 7851 3090,* ☂ – ▤. MC AE D VISA JCB p. 33 EM
Meals a la carte 24.50/42.00 21.00.

XXX **Cecconi's,** 5a Burlington Gdns, W1X 1LE, ✆ (020) 7434 1500, *Fax (020) 7434 2440* – ▤. MC AE D VISA p. 33 DM
closed 25 December – **Meals** - Italian - a la carte 27.00/37.00 **t.**

XXX ✿ **Tamarind,** 20 Queen St, W1X 7PJ, ✆ (020) 7629 3561, *tamarind.restaurant@virgin.net, Fax (020) 7499 5034* – ▤. MC AE VISA p. 32 CN
closed 25-26 December, lunch Saturday and Bank Holidays – **Meals** - Indian - 14... (lunch) and a la carte 24.50/30.00 **t.** 14.50
Spec. Murg kaleji masala (chicken livers). Changezi champen (lamb cutlets). Hara cholia paneer (cottage cheese with ginger).

XXX **Sartoria,** 20 Savile Row, W1X 1AE, ✆ (020) 7534 7000, *sartoriareservations@conran-restaurants.co.uk, Fax (020) 7534 7070* – ▤. MC AE D VISA JCB p. 33 DL
closed 25-26 December, and Sunday lunch – **Meals** - Italian - a la carte 28.50/33.50 15.00.

XXX **Firebird,** 23 Conduit St, W1S 2XS, ✆ (020) 7493 7000, *sales@firebirdrestaurants.co.uk, Fax (020) 7493 7088* – ▤. MC AE D VISA p. 33 DL
closed Easter Sunday, 25 December, 1 January, Saturday lunch, Sunday and Bank Holidays – **Meals** - Tsarist Russian - 19.95 (lunch) and a la carte 36.00/144.00 **t.** 19.50.

XXX **Scotts,** 20 Mount St, W1Y 6HE, ✆ (020) 7629 5248, *Fax (020) 7499 8246* – ▤. MC AE VISA p. 32 BM
closed 25 December – **Meals** - Seafood - 26.50 (lunch) and a la carte 26.50/34.50 12.50.

XXX **Greenhouse,** 27a Hay's Mews, W1X 7RJ, ✆ (020) 7499 3331, *reservations@greenhouse restaurant.co.uk, Fax (020) 7499 5368* – ▤. MC AE ⓓ VISA JCB p. 32 **BN** e
closed 25 December and Saturday lunch – **Meals** 25.00 (lunch) and a la carte approx. 43.50 **t.** ₫ 14.00.

XXX **Morton's - The Restaurant,** 28 Berkeley Sq, W1X 5HA, ✆ (020) 7493 7171, *reception@mortonsclub.co.uk, Fax (020) 7495 3160* – MC AE ⓓ VISA p. 32 **CM** a
closed 1 week Christmas, Sunday and Saturday lunch – **Meals** a la carte 28.75/40.50 **st.** ₫ 15.00.

XXX **Le Soufflé** (at Inter-Continental H.), 1 Hamilton Pl, Hyde Park Corner, W1V 0QY, ✆ (020) 7318 8577, *Fax (020) 7409 7460* – ▤ 🚗. MC AE ⓓ VISA p. 32 **BP** o
closed Monday, Saturday lunch and Sunday dinner – **Meals** (dancing Saturday dinner) a la carte 30.50/41.00 ₫ 13.00.

XXX **Kaspia,** 18-18A Bruton Pl, W1X 7AA, ✆ (020) 7493 2612, *Fax (020) 7408 1627* – ▤. MC AE ⓓ VISA p. 32 **CM** i
closed Sunday and Bank Holidays – **Meals** - Caviar specialities - 39.90 and a la carte 32.50/46.70 **st.** ₫ 16.00.

XXX **Kai,** 65 South Audley St, W1Y 5FD, ✆ (020) 7493 8988, *kai@kaimayfair.co.uk, Fax (020) 7493 1456* – ▤. MC AE ⓓ VISA JCB p. 32 **BM** c
closed 25-26 December and 1 January – **Meals** - Chinese - a la carte 27.00/50.00 **t.** ₫ 19.00.

XX **Cassia Oriental,** 12 Berkeley Sq, W1X 5HG, ✆ (020) 7629 8886, *Fax (020) 7491 8883* – ▤. MC AE ⓓ VISA p. 32 **CM** z
closed 25-26 December, 1 January, Sunday and Bank Holidays – **Meals** - South East Asian - 23.80 (dinner) and a la carte 18.50/28.50.

XX **Noble Rot,** 3-5 Mill St, W1R 9TF, ✆ (020) 7629 8877, *noble@noblerot.com, Fax (020) 7629 8878* – ▤. MC AE ⓓ VISA JCB p. 33 **DL** r
closed 25-26 December, 1 January, Saturday lunch and Sunday – **Meals** a la carte 24.00/43.00 **t.** ₫ 14.50.

XX **Alloro,** 19-20 Dover St, W1S 4LU, ✆ (020) 7495 4768, *Fax (020) 7629 5348* – ▤. MC AE ⓓ VISA p. 33 **DM** r
closed 23 December-2 January, Sunday and Bank Holidays – **Meals** - Italian - 23.00/28.00 **t.** ₫ 16.50.

XX ✿ **Nobu** (at The Metropolitan H.), 19 Old Park Lane, W1Y 4LB, ✆ (020) 7447 4747, *Fax (020) 7447 4749,* ⋞ – ▤. MC AE ⓓ VISA JCB p. 32 **BP** c
closed 25-26 December and Saturday and Sunday lunch – **Meals** - New style Japanese with South American influences - (booking essential) 24.50 (lunch) and a la carte 55.00/85.00 **t.** ₫ 18.00
Spec. Tiradito. Black cod with miso. Chocolate bento box.

XX **Chor Bizarre,** 16 Albemarle St, W1S 4HW, ✆ (020) 7629 9802, *chorbizarrelondon@oldworldhosptials.com, Fax (020) 7493 7756,* « Authentic Indian decor and furnishings » – ▤. MC AE ⓓ VISA JCB p. 33 **DM** s
Meals - Indian - a la carte 27.00/29.50 **t.** ₫ 14.50.

XX **Yatra,** 34 Dover St, W1S 4NG, ✆ (020) 7493 0200, *yatra@lineone.net, Fax (020) 7493 4228* – ▤. MC AE VISA p. 33 **DM** o
closed 25 December, Sunday, Saturday lunch and Bank Holidays – **Meals** - Indian - 17.50 (lunch) and a la carte 22.75/27.75 **t.** ₫ 14.00.

XX **L'Odéon,** 65 Regent St, W1R 7HH, ✆ (020) 7287 1400, *Fax (020) 7287 1300* – ▤. MC AE ⓓ VISA p. 33 **EM** r
closed Christmas, Sunday and Bank Holidays – **Meals** 18.50 and a la carte 23.50/37.00 **t.** ₫ 12.50.

XX **Bentley's,** 11-15 Swallow St, W1B 4DG, ✆ (020) 7734 4756, *Fax (020) 7287 2972* – ▤. MC AE ⓓ VISA JCB p. 33 **EM** i
closed 25-26 December – **Meals** - Seafood - a la carte 21.40/38.45 **t.** ₫ 18.95.

XX **Langan's Brasserie,** Stratton St, W1J 8LB, ✆ (020) 7491 8822, *admin@langans restaurants.co.uk, Fax (020) 7493 8309* – ▤. MC AE ⓓ VISA JCB p. 33 **DN** e
closed Christmas, Easter, Sunday, Saturday lunch and Bank Holidays – **Meals** a la carte 23.00/32.95 **t.** ₫ 13.00.

XX **Teca,** 54 Brooks Mews, W1Y 2NY, ✆ (020) 7495 4774, *Fax (020) 7491 3545* – MC AE VISA p. 32 **CL** a
closed 23 December-3 January, Sunday, Saturday lunch and Bank Holidays – **Meals** - Italian - 24.50/29.50 **t.** ₫ 15.00.

XX **Hush,** 8 Lancashire Court, Brook St, W1S 1EY, ✆ (020) 7659 1500, *steamroller@hush.co.u*
Fax (020) 7659 1501 – |‡|, ▤. MC AE VISA JCB p. 32 CL
closed Sunday and Bank Holidays – ***hush down*** : **Meals** a la carte 24.50/38.50 **t.** ↓ 13.5
– ***hush up***: **Meals** *(closed Saturday lunch and Sunday)* (booking essential) 26.5
(lunch) and dinner a la carte 33.50/47.50 **t.** ↓ 13.50.

XX **Shogun** (at Millennium Mayfair H.), Adams Row, W1Y 5DF, ✆ (020) 7493 1255, *britann*
res@mill_cop, Fax (020) 7493 1255 – ▤. MC AE ⓓ VISA JCB p. 32 BM
closed 10 days summer, 10 days December and Monday – **Meals** - Japanese - (dinner on
42.00 **t.** ↓ 12.50.

XX **Momo,** 25 Heddon St, W1B 4BH, ✆ (020) 7434 4040, *momoresto@aol.co*
Fax (020) 7287 0404 – ▤. MC AE ⓓ VISA p. 33 EM
Meals - Moroccan - 17.00 (lunch) and a la carte 25.00/42.00 **t.** ↓ 12.00.

XX **Nicole's** (at Nicole Farhi), 158 New Bond St, W1Y 9PA, ✆ (020) 7499 840
Fax (020) 7409 0381 – ▤. MC AE ⓓ VISA JCB p. 33 DM
closed 25 December, Saturday dinner, Sunday and Bank Holidays – **Meals** (booking esse
tial) a la carte 26.20/36.40 **t.** ↓ 12.50.

X **Veeraswamy,** Victory House, 99 Regent St, W1B 4RS, entrance on Swallow
✆ (020) 7734 1401, *Fax (020) 7439 8434* – ▤. MC AE ⓓ VISA JCB p. 33 EM
Meals - Indian - 14.00 (lunch) and a la carte 19.25/27.50 **t.** ↓ 12.50.

X **The Cafe** (at Sotheby's), 34-35 New Bond St, W1A 2AA, ✆ (020) 7293 507
Fax (020) 7293 5920 – ⚡. MC AE ⓓ VISA p. 33 DL
closed 23 December-2 January, last 2 weeks August, Saturday and Sunday – **Meals** (bookir
essential) (lunch only) a la carte 26.00/29.15 **st.**

X **Zinc Bar & Grill,** 21 Heddon St, W1R 7LF, ✆ (020) 7255 8899, *Fax (020) 7255 8888* – MC
ⓓ VISA JCB p. 33 EM
closed 25-26 December, Sunday and Bank Holidays – **Meals** 14.00 (lunch) and a la car
22.20/27.50 **t.** ↓ 13.00.

X **Truc Vert,** 42 North Audley St, W1K 6ZR, ✆ (020) 7491 9988, *Fax (020) 7491 7717* – ⚡ ▤
MC AE VISA p. 32 AL
closed 25-26 December, Sunday dinner and Bank Holidays – **Meals** (booking essenti
a la carte 20.00/28.00 **t.** ↓ 10.00.

Regent's Park and Marylebone – ✉ *NW1/NW6/NW8/W1.*

Landmark London, 222 Marylebone Rd, NW1 6JQ, ✆ (020) 7631 8000, *reservatio*
@thelandmark.co.uk, Fax (020) 7631 8080, « Victorian Gothic architecture, atrium and wi
ter garden », Lб, ≘, ▢ – |‡|, ⚡ rm, ▤ TV ✆ ♿ ⇔ – 🔺 350. MC AE ⓓ VIS
✂ p. 25 HU
Winter Garden*:** **Meals** 23.00 and a la carte 30.00/41.00 **t.** ↓ 19.50 – (see also ***Joh
Burton-Race below) – ☐ 18.50 – **290 rm** 305.00/330.00, 9 suites – SB.

Langham Hilton, 1c Portland Pl, Regent St, W1N 4JA, ✆ (020) 7636 1000, *langha*
@hilton.com, Fax (020) 7323 2340, Lб, ≘s, ▢ – |‡|, ⚡ rm, ▤ TV ✆ ♿ – 🔺 250. MC AE
VISA JCB. ✂ p. 25 JU
***Memories*:** **Meals** 24.50 (lunch) and a la carte 29.50/53.75 **t.** ↓ 19.00 – ***Tsar's*:** **Mea**
(closed 1 week Easter and Sunday) a la carte 24.00/31.00 **t.** ↓ 19.00 – ☐ 21.50 – **419 r**
250.00 **s.**, 20 suites.

Churchill Inter-Continental London, 30 Portman Sq, W1A 4ZX, ✆ (020) 7486 580
churchill@interconti.com, Fax (020) 7486 1255, Lб, ≘s, 🎾 – |‡|, ⚡ rm, ▤ TV ✆ ♿
🔺 300. MC AE ⓓ VISA JCB. ✂ p. 32 AJ
***Terrace on Portman Square*:** **Meals** 26.50 (lunch) and a la carte 33.15/39.70 **t.** ↓ 17.50
☐ 20.75 – **405 rm** 340.00, 40 suites.

Selfridge Thistle, Orchard St, W1H 6JS, ✆ (020) 7408 2080, *selfridge@thistle.co.u*
Fax (020) 7409 2295 – |‡|, ⚡ rm, ▤ TV – 🔺 250. MC AE ⓓ VISA JCB. ✂ p. 32 AK
Fletchers*:** **Meals** (dinner only) 19.00 and a la carte 25.20/32.00 **t.** ↓ 12.10 – ***Orcha
***Terrace*:** **Meals** (lunch only) 14.50 **t.** ↓ 13.50 – ☐ 15.95 – **290 rm** 202.00/247.00 **t.**, 4 suit
– SB.

Charlotte Street, 15 Charlotte St, W1P 1HB, ✆ (020) 7806 2000, *charlotte@firmda*
com, Fax (020) 7806 2002, « Modern English interior », Lб – |‡| ▤ TV ✆ ♿ – 🔺 65. MC
VISA. ✂ p. 26 KU
Meals – (see ***Oscar*** below) – ☐ 16.50 – **44 rm** 175.00/280.00, 8 suites.

Sanderson, 50 Berners St, W1P 3NG, ✆ (020) 7300 1400, *sanderson@ianschragerhote*
com, Fax (020) 7300 1401, 🏠, « Contemporary interior », Lб – |‡|, ⚡ rm, ▤ TV ✆. MC
ⓓ VISA. ✂ p. 33 EJ
***Spoon+*:** **Meals** 25.00 (lunch) and a la carte 45.00/70.00 **t.** ↓ 30.00 – ☐ 19.00 – **150 r**
340.00/365.00.

The Leonard, 15 Seymour St, W1H 7JW, ☎ (020) 7935 2010, *theleonard@dial.pipex.com, Fax (020) 7935 6700,* « Attractively furnished Georgian town houses », – ▮ ▤ TV ☎. MC AE ① VISA JCB. ✻ p. 32 AK n
Meals (room service only) – ▭ 18.50 – **9 rm** 200.00/220.00 **s.**, **20 suites** 280.00/550.00 **s.**

Radisson SAS Portman, 22 Portman Sq, W1H 7BG, ☎ (020) 7208 6000, *sales@lonza.rd sas.com, Fax (020) 7208 6001,* – ▮, ⇔ rm, ▤ TV ☎ – 650. MC AE ① VISA JCB. ✻ p. 32 AJ o
Portman Corner : Meals (buffet lunch)/dinner a la carte 23.00/35.00 **t.** 16.00 – ▭ 17.50 – **265 rm** 195.00/205.00 **s.**, 7 suites.

Montcalm, Great Cumberland Pl, W1A 2LF, ☎ (020) 7402 4288, *montcalm@montcalm.co .uk, Fax (020) 7724 9180* – ▮, ⇔ rm, ▤ TV ☎ – 80. MC AE ① VISA JCB p. 37 EZ x
Meals – (see ***The Crescent*** below) – ▭ 17.95 – **110 rm** 230.00/250.00, 10 suites – SB.

Ramada Plaza London, 18 Lodge Rd, NW8 7JT, ☎ (020) 7722 7722, *regentspark@jarvis .co.uk, Fax (020) 7483 2408* – ▮, ⇔ rm, ▤ TV P – 150. MC AE ① VISA JCB. ✻ p. 25 GT v
Minsky's : Meals 19.50/20.95 and a la carte 24.05/32.20 **t.** 14.95 – ***Kashinoki :*** Meals - Japanese - *(closed Sunday and Monday)* 18.00/32.00 and a la carte 19.60/37.80 **t.** 11.00 – ▭ 15.50 – **376 rm** 209.00 **st.**, 1 suite.

Jurys Clifton Ford, 47 Welbeck St, W1M 8DN, ☎ (020) 7486 6600, *clifton@jurysdoyle. com, Fax (020) 7486 7492,* – ▮ ▤ TV ☎ ♿ – 230. MC AE ① VISA. ✻ p. 32 BH a
closed 25-26 December – **Meals** *(closed lunch Saturday and Sunday)* a la carte approx. 25.00 **st.** 15.00 – ▭ 16.00 – **253 rm** 200.00 **st.**, 2 suites.

Berners, 10 Berners St, W1A 3BE, ☎ (020) 7666 2000, *berners@berners.co.uk, Fax (020) 7666 2001* – ▮, ⇔ rm, ▤ rest, TV ☎ ♿ – 160. MC AE ① VISA JCB. ✻ p. 33 EJ r
Meals (carving lunch) 16.95 (lunch) and a la carte 22.00/27.50 **t.** 14.50 – ▭ 15.95 – **213 rm** 190.00/260.00 **st.**, 3 suites.

Holiday Inn Regent's Park, Carburton St, W1W 5EE, ☎ (0870) 400 9111, *Fax (020) 7387 2806* – ▮, ⇔ rm, ▤ rest, TV ☎ – 350. MC AE ① VISA JCB. ✻ p. 25 JU i
Meals a la carte 21.85/29.15 **t.** 12.95 – ▭ 13.95 – **333 rm** 179.00 **st.** – SB.

London Marriott Marble Arch, 134 George St, W1H 6DN, ☎ (020) 7723 1277, *sales admin.marblearch@marriott.co.uk, Fax (020) 7402 0666,* – ▮, ⇔ rm, ▤ TV ☎ ♿ P – 150. MC AE ① VISA JCB. ✻ p. 37 EZ i
Meals *(closed lunch Saturday)* a la carte 17.20/26.65 **st.** – ▭ 18.95 – **240 rm** 215.00 **s.**

Berkshire, 350 Oxford St, W1N 0BY, ☎ (020) 7629 7474, *resberk@radisson.com, Fax (020) 7629 8156* – ▮, ⇔ rm, ▤ TV ☎ – 40. MC AE ① VISA JCB. ✻ p. 32 BK n
Ascots : Meals 25.00 **st.** 15.25 – ▭ 15.00 – **145 rm** 247.00/285.00 **s.**, 2 suites.

Durrants, 26-32 George St, W1H 5BJ, ☎ (020) 7935 8131, *enquiries@durrantshotel.co.uk, Fax (020) 7487 3510,* « Converted Georgian houses with Regency façade » – ▮, ▤ rest, TV ☎ – 55. MC AE VISA. ✻ p. 32 AH e
Meals 19.50 and a la carte 24.95/41.95 **t.** 14.50 – ▭ 13.50 – **88 rm** 110.00/165.00, 4 suites.

Dorset Square, 39-40 Dorset Sq, NW1 6QN, ☎ (020) 7723 7874, *dorset@firmdale.com, Fax (020) 7724 3328,* « Attractively furnished Regency town houses », – ▮ ▤ TV ☎. MC AE VISA. ✻ p. 25 HU s
The Potting Shed : Meals *(closed Sunday)* (booking essential) (live jazz Tuesday and Saturday dinner) 17.95/23.50 and a la carte 24.45/28.30 **t.** 13.95 – ▭ 14.00 – **38 rm** 98.00/240.00.

10 Manchester Street without rest., 10 Manchester St, W1U 4DG, ☎ (020) 7486 6669, *stay@10manchesterstreet.fsnet.co.uk, Fax (020) 7224 0348* – ▮ TV. MC AE VISA. ✻ p. 32 AH c
▭ 4.00 **37 rm** 120.00/150.00 **st.**, 9 suites.

Ramada Jarvis Marylebone, Harewood Row, NW1 6SE, ☎ (020) 7262 2707, *107gm @jarvis.co.uk, Fax (020) 7262 2975* – ▮, ⇔ rm, ▤ rest, TV ☎. MC AE ① VISA. ✻
Meals *(closed Saturday and Sunday lunch)* 9.00 and a la carte approx. 18.90 **st.** 11.95 – ▭ 11.95 – **92 rm** 125.00/165.00 **st.** p. 25 HU x

Hart House without rest., 51 Gloucester Pl, W1U 8JF, ☎ (020) 7935 2288, *reservations @harthouse.co.uk, Fax (020) 7935 8516* – TV. MC AE VISA. ✻ p. 32 AH a
15 rm ▭ 70.00/105.00 **st.**

XXXXX ✿✿ **John Burton-Race** (at Landmark London H.), 222 Marylebone Rd, NW1 6J
☎ (020) 7723 7800, *jbrthelandmark@btconnect.co.uk, Fax (020) 7723 4700* – ▤ 🚗. MC VISA
p. 25 HU
closed first week January, Saturday lunch, Sunday and Bank Holidays – **Meals** - French 29.50/70.00 **t.** 15.00
Spec. Ravioli of langoustine, truffle scented potato, Madeira jus. Roast poussin with fo gras, baby spinach and Sauternes sauce. Plate of chocolate desserts.

XXX ✿ **Orrery,** 55 Marylebone High St, W1M 3AE, ☎ (020) 7616 8000, *Fax (020) 7616 808*
« Converted 19C stables, contemporary interior » – |$|. MC AE VISA JCB p. 25 IU
closed 1-3 January and 25 December – **Meals** (booking essential) 23.5 (lunch) and a la carte 31.50/50.50 **t.** 12.00
Spec. Cannelloni of Dorset crab. Fillet of beef, foie gras, spinach and Madeira jus. Chocola fondant, iced crème fraîche.

XX **Oscar** (at Charlotte Street H.), 15 Charlotte St, W1T 1RJ, ☎ (020) 7907 4005, *charlot @firmdale.com, Fax (020) 7806 2002* – ▤. MC AE VISA p. 26 KU
closed Sunday – **Meals** (booking essential) a la carte 31.00/39.00 **t.** 16.50.

XX **The Crescent** (at Montcalm H.), Great Cumberland Pl, W1A 2LF, ☎ (020) 7402 4288, *res vations@montcalm.co.uk, Fax (020) 7724 9180* – ▤. MC AE VISA JCB p. 37 EZ
closed lunch Saturday, Sunday and Bank Holidays – **Meals** 25.00 **t.** 17.00.

XX **The Providores,** 109 Marylebone High St, W1U 4RX, ☎ (020) 7431 3319, *anyone@t providores.co.uk, Fax (020) 7431 6877* – ⇎. MC AE VISA p. 32 BH
Meals a la carte 23.60/33.60 **t.**

XX **Ozer,** 4-5 Langham Pl, Regent St, W1B 3DG, ☎ (020) 7323 0505, *info@sofra.co.u Fax (020) 7323 0111* – ▤. MC AE VISA JCB p. 25 JU
Meals - Turkish - 13.95 and a la carte 16.40/32.50 **t.** 12.50.

XX **Rasa Samudra,** 5 Charlotte St, W1P 1HD, ☎ (020) 7637 0222, *Fax (020) 7637 0224* – ⇎
MC AE VISA JCB p. 26 KU
closed 24-31 December – **Meals** - Indian Seafood and Vegetarian - a la carte 12.75/23. 10.50.

XX **La Porte des Indes,** 32 Bryanston St, W1H 7EG, ☎ (020) 7224 0055, *pilondon@aol.co Fax (020) 7224 1144* – ▤. MC AE VISA JCB p. 32 AK
closed 25-26 December, 1 January and Saturday lunch – **Meals** - Indian - 30.00/34. and a la carte 22.30/45.10 **t.** 6.25.

XX **Rosmarino,** 1 Blenheim Terr, NW8 0EH, ☎ (020) 7328 5014, *Fax (020) 7625 2639*,
▤. MC AE VISA p. 24 FS
closed 23 December-3 January and Bank Holidays – **Meals** - Italian - 27.00 (di ner) and lunch a la carte 19.00/24.00 **t.** 16.50.

XX **Levant,** Jason Court, 76 Wigmore St, W1H 9DQ, ☎ (020) 7224 1111, *Fax (020) 7486 121*
▤. MC AE VISA p. 32 BJ
closed lunch Saturday and Sunday – **Meals** - Eastern Mediterranean - 8.50/19. and a la carte 22.70/28.75 **t.** 13.50.

XX **Caldesi,** 15-17 Marylebone Lane, W1V 2NE, ☎ (020) 7935 9226, *Fax (020) 7935 9228* –
MC AE VISA JCB p. 32 BJ
closed 25 December, Saturday lunch, Sunday and Bank Holidays – **Meals** - Italian - a la ca 19.50/29.50 **t.** 13.50.

XX **Bertorelli's,** (First Floor), 19-23 Charlotte St, W1P 1HP, ☎ (020) 7636 41 *Fax (020) 7467 8902* – ▤. MC AE VISA p. 26 KU
closed 25 December – **Meals** - Italian - a la carte 17.85/23.95 **t.** 10.00.

XX **L'Aventure,** 3 Blenheim Terr, NW8 0EH, ☎ (020) 7624 6232, *Fax (020) 7625 5548*, –
AE VISA – *closed 1-15 January, Easter, Sunday, Saturday lunch and Bank Holidays* – **Meal** French - 18.50/28.50 **t.** 15.25. p. 24 FS

X **Mash,** 19-21 Great Portland St, W1N 5DB, ☎ (020) 7637 5555, *Fax (020) 7637 7333* – ▤.
AE VISA – *closed Sunday and Bank Holidays* – **Meals** (booking essential) a la carte 17.5 27.00 **t.** 13.00. p. 33 DJ

X **Purple Sage,** 92 Wigmore St, WIU 3RE, ☎ (020) 7486 1912, *Fax (020) 7486 1913* – ▤.
AE VISA JCB – **Meals** - Italian - 12.50/15.50. p. 32 BJ

X **Ibla,** 89 Marylebone High St, W1U 4QY, ☎ (020) 7224 3799, *ibla@ibla.co. Fax (020) 7486 1370* – MC AE VISA JCB p. 25 IU
closed Bank Holidays, Monday and Saturday lunch – **Meals** - Italian - 15.00/35 and a la carte approx. 30.00 **t.** 16.00.

X **Villandry,** 170 Great Portland St, W1N 5TB, ☎ (020) 7631 3131, *Fax (020) 7631 3030* –
▤. MC AE VISA p. 25 JU
closed 25 December, 1 January and Sunday dinner – **Meals** a la carte 20.00/32.00 **t.**

X **Union Café,** 96 Marylebone Lane, W1M 5FP, ☎ (020) 7486 4860, *Fax (020) 7486 486*
MC AE VISA – *closed Christmas, New Year, Sunday and Bank Holidays* – **Meals** a la ca 19.50/27.00 **t.** 7.00. p. 32 BH

Chada Chada, 16-17 Picton Pl, W1M 5DE, (020) 7935 8212, *Fax (020) 7924 2178* – ▤. MC AE VISA JCB p. 32 BJ i
closed Sunday and Bank Holidays – **Meals** - Thai - a la carte 10.75/23.20 **t.** 11.95.

Stanleys, 6 Little Portland St, W1N 5NG, (020) 7462 0099, *info@stanleysausages.com, Fax (020) 7462 0088* – ▤. MC AE VISA p. 25 JU a
closed 24 December-3 January and Sunday – **Meals** - specialising in sausages - a la carte 17.70/21.15 **t.** 11.95.

The Salt House, 63 Abbey Rd, NW8 0AE, (020) 7328 6626, *enquiries@thesalthouse.fsnet.co.uk, Fax (020) 7625 9168,* – ▤. MC AE VISA p. 24 FS z
Meals (booking essential) 11.95 (lunch) and a la carte 21.50/27.50 **t.**

St James's – ✉ *W1/SW1/WC2.*

Ritz, 150 Piccadilly, W1J 9BR, (020) 7493 8181, *enquire@theritzlondon.com, Fax (020) 7493 2687,* – ▤, rm, ▤ TV – 50. MC AE VISA JCB. p. 33 DN a
Meals – (see ***The Restaurant*** below) – 23.50 – **116 rm** 305.00/425.00, 17 suites – SB.

Dukes, 35 St James's Pl, SW1A 1NY, (020) 7491 4840, *enquiries@dukeshotel.co.uk, Fax (020) 7493 1264,* – ▤, rest, ▤ TV – 50. MC AE VISA JCB.
Meals *(closed Saturday lunch and Bank Holidays)* (residents only) 20.00/40.00 and a la carte 24.00/43.00 **t.** 26.00 – 14.75 – **82 rm** 195.00/260.00, 7 suites. p. 33 EP x

The Trafalgar, 2 Spring Gdns, SW1A 2TS, (020) 7870 2900, *lontshirm@hilton.com, Fax (020) 7870 2911* – ▤, rm, ▤ TV – 50. MC AE VISA JCB.
Jago : **Meals** 19.50 (lunch) and a la carte 25.50/32.00 **t.** 16.00 – 18.50 – **127 rm** 270.00 **s.**, 2 suites. p. 33 GN a

Stafford, 16-18 St James's Pl, SW1A 1NJ, (020) 7493 0111, *info@thestaffordhotel.co.uk, Fax (020) 7493 7121* – ▤ ▤ TV – 40. MC AE VISA p. 33 DN u
Meals *(closed Saturday lunch)* 27.00/32.50 and a la carte 42.50/54.50 **st.** 19.50 – 16.00 – **75 rm** 220.00/290.00 **s.**, 6 suites.

Cavendish, 81 Jermyn St, SW1Y 6JF, (020) 7930 2111, *cavendish.reservations@devere-hotels.com, Fax (020) 7839 2125* – ▤, rm, ▤ rest, TV – 80. MC AE VISA JCB. p. 33 EN i
Meals *(closed lunch Saturday, Sunday and Bnak Holidays)* 24.50 and a la carte 24.50/36.50 **t.** 13.50 – 16.95 – **249 rm** 235.00/265.00 **st.**, 2 suites – SB.

22 Jermyn Street, 22 Jermyn St, SW1Y 6HL, (020) 7734 2353, *office@22jermyn.com, Fax (020) 7734 0750* – ▤ ▤ TV. MC AE VISA JCB. p. 33 FM e
Meals (room service only) – 17.00 – **5 rm** 210.00 **s.**, **13 suites** 295.00/335.00 **s.**

Thistle Piccadilly without rest., 39 Coventry St, W1V 7FH, (020) 7930 4033, *piccadilly@thistle.co.uk, Fax (020) 7925 2586* – ▤ ▤ TV. MC AE VISA. p. 33 FGM a
14.50 – **92 rm** 181.00/295.00 **st.**

Thistle Trafalgar Square, Whitcomb St, WC2H 7HG, (020) 7930 4477, *trafalgarsquare@thistle.co.uk, Fax (020) 7925 2149* – ▤, rm, ▤ rest, TV. MC AE VISA. p. 33 GM r
Meals 14.50/20.50 and a la carte 12.80/31.00 **t.** 11.50 – 14.50 – **116 rm** 152.00/185.00 **s.** – SB.

The Restaurant (at Ritz H.), 150 Piccadilly, W1V 9DG, (020) 7493 8181, *Fax (020) 7493 2687,* , « Elegant restaurant in Louis XVI style » – ▤. MC AE VISA JCB p. 33 DN a
Meals (dancing Friday and Saturday evenings) 35.00/59.00 and a la carte 41.50/65.00 **st.** 22.00.

Pétrus, 33 St James's St, SW1A 1HD, (020) 7930 4272, *Fax (020) 7930 9702* – ▤. MC AE VISA JCB p. 33 EN v
closed 1 week Christmas, Sunday, Saturday lunch and Bank Holidays – **Meals** (booking essential) 26.00/60.00 **t.** 18.00
Spec. Fricassée of frog's legs, ceps, spinach and foie gras. Braised turbot with oyster ravioli, morels and white asparagus. Prune and vanilla soufflé, prune and Armagnac ice cream.

L'Oranger, 5 St James's St, SW1A 1EF, (020) 7839 3774, *Fax (020) 7839 4330* – ▤. MC AE VISA p. 33 EP a
closed Christmas, 2 weeks August, Saturday lunch and Sunday – **Meals** 23.50/39.50 **t.** 26.00
Spec. Pot-au-feu of pork belly and black truffle. Braised calves cheeks, mozzarella cheese. Chocolate fondant, vanilla and nougatine ice cream.

Orient, 160 Piccadilly (1st floor), W1V 9DF, (020) 7499 6888, *Fax (020) 7659 9300* – ▤ ▤. MC AE VISA p. 33 DN i
closed Saturday lunch and Sunday – **Meals** - Chinese - a la carte 30.00/65.00.

Suntory, 72-73 St James's St, SW1A 1PH, (020) 7409 0201, *Fax (020) 7499 0208* – ▤. MC AE VISA JCB p. 33 EP z
closed Easter, Christmas-New Year and Sunday lunch – **Meals** - Japanese - 17.00/53.00 and a la carte 38.00/87.00 **st.** 19.00.

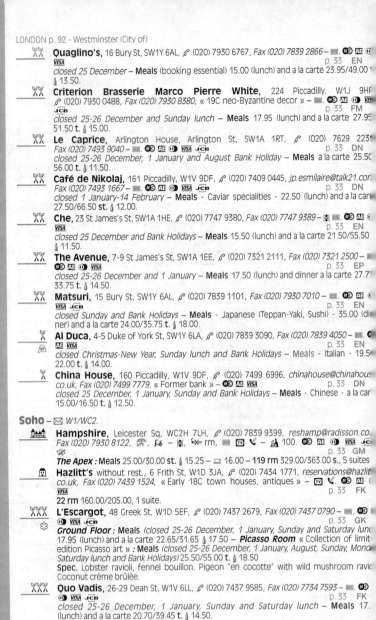

XX **Quaglino's,** 16 Bury St, SW1Y 6AL, ☎ (020) 7930 6767, *Fax (020) 7839 2866* – ▤. MC AE ① VISA p. 33 EN
closed 25 December – **Meals** (booking essential) 15.00 (lunch) and a la carte 23.95/49.00 t. 13.50.

XX **Criterion Brasserie Marco Pierre White,** 224 Piccadilly, W1J 9HP ☎ (020) 7930 0488, *Fax (020) 7930 8380*, « 19C neo-Byzantine decor » – ▤. MC AE ① VISA JCB p. 33 FM
closed 25-26 December and Sunday lunch – **Meals** 17.95 (lunch) and a la carte 27.95/51.50 **t.** 15.00.

XX **Le Caprice,** Arlington House, Arlington St, SW1A 1RT, ☎ (020) 7629 2239 *Fax (020) 7493 9040* – ▤. MC AE ① VISA JCB p. 33 DN
closed 25-26 December, 1 January and August Bank Holiday – **Meals** a la carte 25.50/56.00 **t.** 11.50.

XX **Café de Nikolaj,** 161 Piccadilly, W1V 9DF, ☎ (020) 7409 0445, *jp.esmilaire@talk21.com Fax (020) 7493 1667* – ▤. MC AE ① VISA JCB p. 33 DN
closed 1 January-14 February – **Meals** - Caviar specialities - 22.50 (lunch) and a la carte 27.50/66.50 **st.** 12.00.

XX **Che,** 23 St James's St, SW1A 1HE, ☎ (020) 7747 9380, *Fax (020) 7747 9389* – ▤. MC AE ① VISA p. 33 EN
closed 25 December and Bank Holidays – **Meals** 15.50 (lunch) and a la carte 21.50/55.50 11.50.

XX **The Avenue,** 7-9 St James's St, SW1A 1EE, ☎ (020) 7321 2111, *Fax (020) 7321 2500* – ▤. MC AE ① VISA p. 33 EP
closed 25-26 December and 1 January – **Meals** 17.50 (lunch) and dinner a la carte 27.75/33.75 **t.** 14.50.

XX **Matsuri,** 15 Bury St, SW1Y 6AL, ☎ (020) 7839 1101, *Fax (020) 7930 7010* – ▤. MC AE ① VISA JCB p. 33 EN
closed Sunday and Bank Holidays – **Meals** - Japanese (Teppan-Yaki, Sushi) - 35.00 (dinner) and a la carte 24.00/35.75 **t.** 18.00.

X **Al Duca,** 4-5 Duke of York St, SW1Y 6LA, ☎ (020) 7839 3090, *Fax (020) 7839 4050* – ▤. MC AE VISA p. 33 EN
closed Christmas-New Year, Sunday lunch and Bank Holidays – **Meals** - Italian - 19.50/22.00 **t.** 14.00.

X **China House,** 160 Piccadilly, W1V 9DF, ☎ (020) 7499 6996, *chinahouse@chinahouse.co.uk, Fax (020) 7499 7779*, « Former bank » – MC AE VISA p. 33 DN
closed 25 December, 1 January, Sunday and Bank Holidays – **Meals** - Chinese - a la carte 15.00/16.50 **t.** 12.50.

Soho – ✉ *W1/WC2.*

Hampshire, Leicester Sq, WC2H 7LH, ☎ (020) 7839 9399, *reshamp@radisson.com Fax (020) 7930 8122*, – ▤, ⇔ rm, ▤ TV – 100. MC AE ① VISA JCB p. 33 GM
The Apex : **Meals** 25.00/30.00 **st.** 15.25 – 16.00 – **119 rm** 329.00/363.00 **s.**, 5 suites.

Hazlitt's without rest., 6 Frith St, W1D 3JA, ☎ (020) 7434 1771, *reservations@hazlitts.co.uk, Fax (020) 7439 1524*, « Early 18C town houses, antiques » – TV. MC AE ① VISA p. 33 FK
22 rm 160.00/205.00, 1 suite.

XXX **L'Escargot,** 48 Greek St, W1D 5EF, ☎ (020) 7437 2679, *Fax (020) 7437 0790* – ▤. MC ① VISA JCB p. 33 GK
Ground Floor : **Meals** *(closed 25-26 December, 1 January, Sunday and Saturday lunch)* 17.95 (lunch) and a la carte 22.65/31.65 17.50 – ***Picasso Room*** « Collection of limited edition Picasso art » **: Meals** *(closed 25-26 December, 1 January, August, Sunday, Monday, Saturday lunch and Bank Holidays)* 25.50/55.00 **t.** 18.50
Spec. Lobster ravioli, fennel bouillon. Pigeon "en cocotte" with wild mushroom ravioli. Coconut crème brûlée.

XXX **Quo Vadis,** 26-29 Dean St, W1V 6LL, ☎ (020) 7437 9585, *Fax (020) 7734 7593* – ▤. MC ① VISA JCB p. 33 FK
closed 25-26 December, 1 January, Sunday and Saturday lunch – **Meals** 17. (lunch) and a la carte 20.70/39.45 **t.** 14.50.

XX **Richard Corrigan at Lindsay House,** 21 Romilly St, W1V 5TG, ☎ (020) 7439 04 *Fax (020) 7437 7349* – ▤. MC AE ① VISA JCB p. 33 GL
closed 1 week Christmas, last week August, first week September, Sunday and Saturday lunch – **Meals** 23.00/44.00 **t.** 17.00
Spec. Sardines with salt cod, langoustine and tomato butter. Red mullet, barigoule cream, artichoke vinaigrette. Rhubarb compote, vanilla cream.

XX **Café Lazeez,** 21 Dean St, W1V 5AH, ☎ (020) 7434 9393, *soho@cafelazeez.co Fax (020) 7434 0022* – ▤. MC AE ① VISA JCB p. 33 FJ
closed Saturday lunch and Sunday – **Meals** - North Indian - a la carte 18.75/35.40 **t.** 9.9

XX **Teatro,** 93-107 Shaftesbury Ave, W1D 5DY, ✆ (020) 7494 3040, *Fax (020) 7494 3050* – ▤. MC AE ◐ VISA JCB p. 33 **GL** e
closed 25-31 December, Sunday, Saturday lunch and Bank Holidays – **Meals** 14.00 (lunch) and a la carte 29.50/42.50 **t.** 13.50.

XX **The Sugar Club,** 21 Warwick St, W1R 5RB, ✆ (020) 7437 7776, *Fax (020) 7437 7778* – ⇹. MC AE ◐ VISA p. 33 **EL** r
closed 25-26 December – **Meals** a la carte 26.80/31.70 **t.** 24.00.

XX **Circus,** 1 Upper James St, W1F 4DF, ✆ (020) 7534 4000, *circus@egami.co.uk, Fax (020) 7534 4010* – ▤. MC AE ◐ VISA p. 33 **EL** e
closed 24-26 December, 1-2 January, Sunday and lunch Saturday – **Meals** 19.50 (lunch) and dinner a la carte 20.50/32.40 **t.** 14.50.

XX **Mezzo,** Lower Ground Floor, 100 Wardour St, W1F 0TN, ✆ (020) 7314 4000, *Fax (020) 7314 4040* – ▤. MC AE ◐ VISA JCB p. 33 **FK** a
closed 24-25 December and lunch Monday, Tuesday and Saturday – **Meals** 12.50 (lunch) and a la carte 22.50/49.50 **t.** 13.50.

X **Bertorelli,** First Floor, 11-13 Frith St, W1D 4RB, ✆ (020) 7494 3491, *Fax (020) 7437 3091*, 余 – ▤. MC AE ◐ VISA p. 33 **FK** s
closed 25 December – **Meals** - Italian - a la carte 17.85/23.95 **t.** 10.00.

X **Il Forno,** 63-64 Frith St, W1V 5TA, ✆ (020) 7734 4545, *info@ilforno-restaurant.co.uk, Fax (020) 7287 8624* – ▤. MC AE VISA JCB p. 33 **FJK** n
closed lunch Saturday and Sunday and Bank Holidays – **Meals** - Italian - a la carte 15.25/29.75 **t.** 12.50.

X **Alastair Little,** 49 Frith St, W1D 5SG, ✆ (020) 7734 5183, *Fax (020) 7734 5206* – ▤. MC AE ◐ VISA JCB p. 33 **FK** o
closed Sunday, Saturday lunch and Bank Holidays – **Meals** (booking essential) 27.00/35.00 **t.** 14.00.

X **Vasco and Piero's Pavilion,** 15 Poland St, W1V 3DE, ✆ (020) 7437 8774, *Fax (020) 7437 0467* – ▤. MC AE ◐ VISA JCB p. 33 **EJK** i
closed Sunday, Saturday lunch and Bank Holidays – **Meals** - Italian - (lunch booking essential) 18.50 (dinner) and lunch a la carte 28.00/32.00 **t.** 11.50.

X **itsu,** 103 Wardour St, W1V 3TD, ✆ (020) 7479 4794, *glenn.edwards@itsu.co.uk, Fax (020) 7479 4795* – ▤. MC AE VISA JCB p. 33 **FK** c
closed 25 December-3 January – **Meals** - Japanese - (bookings not accepted) a la carte 10.00/20.00 **t.** 10.50.

X **Sri Siam Soho,** 16 Old Compton St, W1V 5PE, ✆ (020) 7434 3544, *Fax (020) 7287 1311* – ▤. MC AE ◐ VISA p. 33 **GK** r
closed 25-26 December, 1 January and Sunday lunch – **Meals** - Thai - 14.95 and a la carte 30.00/50.00 **t.** 10.95.

X **Aurora,** 49 Lexington St, W1F 9AP, ✆ (020) 7494 0514, *aurora-restaurant@yahoo.co.uk, Fax (020) 7494 4357*, 余 – MC VISA p. 33 **EK** e
closed 25 December-3 January, Sunday and Bank Holidays – **Meals** (booking essential) a la carte 19.20/25.40 **t.**

X **Soho Spice,** 124-126 Wardour St, W1V 3LA, ✆ (020) 7434 0808, *info@sohospice.co.uk, Fax (020) 7434 0799* – ⇹ ▤. MC AE ◐ VISA JCB p. 33 **FJ** e
Meals - Indian - (bookings not accepted) 16.95/27.95 and a la carte 15.45/25.70 **t.**

X **Fung Shing,** 15 Lisle St, WC2H 7BE, ✆ (020) 7437 1539, *Fax (020) 7734 0284* – ▤. MC AE ◐ VISA p. 33 **GL** a
closed 24-26 December and lunch Bank Holidays – **Meals** - Chinese (Canton) - a la carte 19.70/25.65 **t.** 13.50.

X **Saigon,** 45 Frith St, W1V 5TE, ✆ (020) 7437 7109, *Fax (020) 7734 1668* – ▤. MC AE ◐ VISA p. 33 **FGK** x
closed Easter, 25-26 December, Sunday and Bank Holidays – **Meals** - Vietnamese - a la carte approx. 16.25 **t.** 10.90.

Strand and Covent Garden – ✉ *WC2.*

Savoy, Strand, WC2R 0EU, ✆ (020) 7836 4343, *info@the-savoy.co.uk, Fax (020) 7240 6040*, Ls, ≘s, ▣ – |¢|, ⇹ rm, ▤ TV ✆ ⇔ – 🔏 500. MC AE ◐ VISA. ✂ p. 37 **DEY** a
River: Meals 29.75/44.50 and a la carte 44.00/63.00 **t.** 20.50 – ***Grill:*** Meals *(closed August, Sunday, Saturday lunch and Bank Holidays)* a la carte 37.50/62.00 **t.** 24.50 – ☐ 23.50 – **159 rm** 290.00/370.00 **s.**, 48 suites.

Le Meridien Waldorf, Aldwych, WC2B 4DD, ✆ (0870) 400 8484, *etb.waldorf@lemeridien-hotels.com, Fax (020) 7836 7244*, Ls, ≘s, ▣ – |¢|, ⇹ rm, ▤ rm, TV ✆ – 🔏 200. MC AE ◐ VISA JCB. ✂ p. 37 **EX** x
Palm Court: Meals *(closed Saturday lunch)* 18.50 and a la carte 27.70/37.00 **t.** 21.00 – ***Matinée:*** Meals a la carte 15.50/24.20 **t.** 21.00 – ☐ 18.00 – **286 rm** 280.00/290.00, 6 suites.

Swissôtel London, The Howard, Temple Pl, WC2R 2PR, ☎ (020) 7836 3555, *reser tions.london@swissotel.com, Fax (020) 7379 4547,* ←, – |‡|, ⇔ rm, ▤ TV ☎ – 150. MC AE ① VISA JCB. ✗ p. 37 EX
The Restaurant : Meals *(closed Saturday lunch)* 23.00/29.00 and a la carte 37.00/44.00 s 21.00 – ☐ 23.50 – **148 rm** 295.00 **s.**, 8 suites.

One Aldwych, 1 Aldwych, WC2B 4RH, ☎ (020) 7300 1000, *reservations@onealdwych.c uk, Fax (020) 7300 1001,* « Contemporary interior », Fб, ≘s, ☐ – |‡|, ⇔ rm, ▤ TV ☎ & 50. MC AE ① VISA JCB. ✗ p. 37 EX
Indigo : Meals a la carte 30.00/35.00 **t.** 19.50 – (see also ***Axis*** below) – ☐ 18.75 – **96 r** 280.00/375.00 **s.**, 9 suites.

St Martins Lane, 45 St Martin's Lane, WC2N 4HX, ☎ (020) 7300 5500, *sml@ianschrag hotels.com, Fax (020) 7300 5501,* « Contemporary interior », Fб – |‡|, ⇔ rm, ▤ TV – 40. MC AE ① VISA. ✗ p. 37 DY
Asia de Cuba : Meals - Asian - 22.50/37.50 and a la carte 50.00/100.00 **t.** 30.00 – ***Tusca Steak :*** Meals *(closed Sunday dinner)* 22.50/37.50 and a la carte 50.00/75.00 **t.** 25.00 – 18.50 – **200 rm** 265.00/285.00, 4 suites.

Thistle Charing Cross, Strand, WC2N 5HX, ☎ (020) 7839 7282, *charingcross@thistle.c uk, Fax (020) 7839 3933* – |‡|, ⇔ rm, ▤ TV ☎ & – 140. MC AE ① VISA JC ✗ p. 37 DY
The Strand Terrace : Meals 22.95 **t.** 14.95 – ☐ 16.50 – **238 rm** 223.00 **s.** – SB.

Ivy, 1 West St, WC2H 9NG, ☎ (020) 7836 4751, *Fax (020) 7240 9333* – ▤. MC AE ① VISA JC *closed dinner 24-26 and 31 December, 1 January and August Bank Holiday* – **Mea** a la carte 23.25/64.25 **t.** 11.50. p. 33 GK

Axis, 1 Aldwych, WC2B 4BZ, ☎ (020) 7300 0300, *sales@onealdwych.co.u Fax (020) 7300 0301* – ▤. MC AE ① VISA JCB p. 37 EX
closed Sunday and Saturday lunch – **Meals** 24.75 (lunch) and a la carte 30.90/34.80 19.95.

J.Sheekey, 28-32 St Martin's Court, WC2N 4AL, ☎ (020) 7240 2565, *Fax (020) 7240 8114* ▤. MC AE ① VISA JCB p. 37 DX
closed dinner 24 December-2 January and Bank Holidays – **Meals** - Seafood - (bookir essential) a la carte 21.25/53.25 **t.** 11.50.

Rules, 35 Maiden Lane, WC2E 7LB, ☎ (020) 7836 5314, *info@rules.co.u Fax (020) 7497 1081,* « London's oldest restaurant with collection of antique cartoor drawings and paintings » – ⇔ ▤. MC AE ① VISA JCB p. 37 DX
closed 5 days Christmas – **Meals** - English - (booking essential) a la carte 30.65/37.65 13.95.

The Admiralty, Somerset House, The Strand, WC2R 1LA, ☎ (020) 7845 464 *Fax (020) 7845 4647,* « Sited within magnificent 18C palace, former Naval headquarters » ⇔. MC AE ① VISA p. 37 EY
closed Sunday dinner – **Meals** 28.00 (lunch) and a la carte 34.50/47.50 **t.** 12.90.

Bank, 1 Kingsway, Aldwych, WC2B 6XF, ☎ (020) 7379 9797, *aldres@bankrestaurants.co Fax (020) 7379 5070* – ▤. MC AE ① VISA p. 37 EX
closed 25 December, 1 January and Bank Holidays – **Meals** a la carte 27.45/38.50 **t.** 12.9

Le Deuxième, 65a Long Acre, WC2E 9JH, ☎ (020) 7379 0033, *Fax (020) 7379 0066* – ▤ MC AE ① VISA p. 37 DV
closed 24-25 December – **Meals** 13.50 (lunch) and a la carte 21.00/28.00 **t.** 11.00.

Le Café du Jardin, 28 Wellington St, WC2E 7BD, ☎ (020) 7836 8769, *Fax (020) 7836 41* – ▤. MC AE ① VISA p. 37 EX
closed 24-25 December – **Meals** 13.50 (lunch) and a la carte 21.00/28.00 **t.** 9.75.

Livebait, 21 Wellington St, WC2E 7DN, ☎ (020) 7836 7161, *Fax (020) 7836 7141* – MC ① VISA p. 37 EX
closed 25 December – **Meals** - Seafood - 15.50 (lunch) and a la carte 22.45/34.65 **st.**

Victoria – ✉ *SW1.*

ℹ *Victoria Station Forecourt.*

Royal Horseguards, 2 Whitehall Court, SW1A 2EJ, ☎ (020) 7839 3400, *royal.hor guards@thistle.co.uk, Fax (020) 7925 2263,* Fб – |‡| ⇔ ▤ TV ☎ – 200. MC AE ① JCB. ✗ p. 30 LX
One Twenty One Two : Meals *(closed Saturday and Sunday lunch)* 19.50/24.50 and d ner a la carte **st.** 18.50 – ☐ 16.50 – **276 rm** 277.00/300.00 **st.**, 4 suites – SB.

Crowne Plaza London St James, 45 Buckingham Gate, SW1E 6A ☎ (020) 7834 6655, *sales@cplonsj.co.uk, Fax (020) 7630 7587,* Fб, ≘s – |‡|, ⇔ rm, ▤ TV – 180. MC AE ① VISA JCB. ✗ p. 36 CX
Café Mediterranée : Meals *(closed Sunday)* a la carte 20.00/32.50 **t.** 12.00 – (see al ***Quilon*** and ***Bank*** below) – ☐ 16.00 – **323 rm** 245.00/295.00 **s.**, 19 suites.

51 Buckingham Gate, 51 Buckingham Gate, SW1E 6AF, ☎ (020) 7769 7766, *info@51-buckinghamgate.co.uk, Fax (020) 7828 5909,* – ■ ■ TV ✆. MC AE ⓓ VISA JCB
Meals 20.00 (lunch) and a la carte 33.00/40.00 **t.** 16.50 – ☐ 17.50 –, **82 suites** 358.00/511.00 **st.** p. 36 **CX** i

The Goring, 15 Beeston Pl, Grosvenor Gdns, SW1W 0JW, ☎ (020) 7396 9000, *reception @goringhotel.co.uk, Fax (020) 7834 4393,* – ■ ■ TV ✆ – 50. MC AE ⓓ VISA. p. 36 **BX** a
Meals 25.00/40.00 **st.** 10.50 – ☐ 16.50 – **68 rm** 195.00/240.00 **s.**, 6 suites.

41, 41 Buckingham Palace Rd, SW1W 0PS, ☎ (020) 7300 0041, *book41@rchmail.com, Fax (020) 7300 0141* – ■ ■ TV ✆ ♿. MC AE ⓓ VISA JCB p. 36 **BX** n
Meals (residents only) – **16 rm** (fully inclusive) 295.00 **s.**, 4 suites.

The Rubens at The Palace, 39 Buckingham Palace Rd, SW1W 0PS, ☎ (020) 7834 6600, *reservations@rubens.redcarnationhotels.com, Fax (020) 7828 5401* – ■, rm, ■ TV ✆ – 75. MC AE ⓓ VISA. p. 36 **BX** n
Meals *(closed lunch Saturday, Sunday and Bank Holidays)* (carving lunch) 16.95 (lunch) and a la carte approx. 18.00 **t.** 14.50 – ***The Library :*** **Meals** (dinner only) a la carte 31.00/47.00 **t.** 14.50 – ☐ 15.00 – **171 rm** 180.00/210.00 **s.**, 2 suites.

Dolphin Square, Dolphin Sq, Chichester St, SW1V 3LX, ☎ (020) 7834 3800, *reservations @dolphinsquarehotel.co.uk, Fax (020) 7798 8735,* , , , , , squash – ■ , ■ rest, TV – 50. MC AE ⓓ VISA. p. 30 **KZ** a
The Brasserie : **Meals** 14.50 and a la carte approx. 18.65 **st.** 11.00 – (see also ***Rhodes in the Square*** below) – ☐ 12.95 – **48 rm** 155.00/190.00 **st.**, **117 suites** 190.00/400.00 **st** – SB.

Jolly St Ermin's, Caxton St, SW1H 0QW, ☎ (020) 7222 7888, *Fax (020) 7222 6914* – ■, rm, TV ✆ – 110. MC AE ⓓ VISA JCB. p. 36 **CX** a
Cloisters Brasserie : **Meals** (buffet lunch) 19.75 and a la carte 20.00/35.00 **t.** 14.50 – ☐ 15.95 – **283 rm** 175.00/215.00 **s.**, 8 suites – SB.

Thistle Victoria, 101 Buckingham Palace Rd, SW1W 0SJ, ☎ (020) 7834 9494, *victoria @thistle.co.uk, Fax (020) 7630 1978* – ■, rm, TV ✆ – 200. MC AE ⓓ VISA. p. 36 **BX** e
Meals – (see ***Christopher's*** below) – ☐ 13.95 – **361 rm** 176.00/247.00 **st.**, 3 suites – SB.

Thistle Westminster, 49 Buckingham Palace Rd, SW1W 0QT, ☎ (020) 7834 1821, *westminster@thistle.co.uk, Fax (020) 7931 7542* – ■, rm, ■ TV ✆ – 150. MC AE ⓓ VISA. p. 36 **BX** z
Meals 14.75 and a la carte approx. 23.35 11.95 – ☐ 10.95 – **134 rm** 215.00/242.00 **s.** – SB.

Grange Rochester, 69 Vincent Sq, SW1P 2PA, ☎ (020) 7828 6611, *rochester@grange hotels.co.uk, Fax (020) 7233 6724* – ■ , ■ rest, TV – 70. MC AE ⓓ VISA JCB. p. 36 **CY** e
The Pavilion : **Meals** (bar lunch Saturday, Sunday and Bank Holidays) 24.50 and a la carte 17.55/27.85 **st.** 12.15 – ☐ 15.00 – **76 rm** 170.00/190.00 **st.**

Tophams Belgravia, 28 Ebury St, SW1W 0LU, ☎ (020) 7730 8147, *tophams_belgravia @compuserve.com, Fax (020) 7823 5966* – ■ TV – 30. MC AE ⓓ VISA JCB.
closed Christmas-New Year – **Meals** *(closed Sunday, Saturday lunch and Bank Holidays)* a la carte 17.00/23.50 **st.** 10.50 – **39 rm** ☐ 115.00/170.00 **st.** p. 36 **AX** e

Winchester without rest., 17 Belgrave Rd, SW1V 1RB, ☎ (020) 7828 2972, *Fax (020) 7828 5191* – TV. p. 36 **BY** s
closed 24-27 December – **18 rm** ☐ 85.00/120.00.

Express by Holiday Inn without rest., 106-110 Belgrave Rd, SW1V 2BS, ☎ (020) 7630 8888, *ligatom@expressvictoria.co.uk, Fax (020) 7828 0441* – ■ TV ✆ ♿. MC AE ⓓ VISA p. 30 **KZ** c
52 rm 97.00 **t.**

Rhodes in the Square (at Dolphin Square H.), Dolphin Sq, Chichester St, SW1V 3LX, ☎ (020) 7798 6767, *Fax (020) 7798 5685* – ■. MC AE ⓓ VISA p. 30 **KZ** a
closed Saturday lunch, Sunday and Monday – **Meals** 19.80/36.50 **st.** 16.50
Spec. Lobster omelette thermidor. Milk-poached pork, broad beans and sage cream. Grand Marnier baba, compote of kumquats.

The Cinnamon Club, Great Smith St, SW1P 3BU, ☎ (020) 7222 2555, *info@cinnamon club.com, Fax (020) 7222 1333,* « Former public library » – ■ P. MC AE ⓓ VISA. p. 30 **LY** c
closed Saturday lunch and Sunday dinner – **Meals** - Indian - 18.00 (lunch) and a la carte 23.50/32.50 **t.** 13.00.

Quilon (at Crowne Plaza London St James H.), 45 Buckingham Gate, SW1 6AF, ☎ (020) 7821 1899, *Fax (020) 7828 5802* – ■. MC AE ⓓ VISA p. 36 **CX** i
closed Sunday and Saturday lunch – **Meals** - Indian - 12.95/15.95 (lunch) and dinner a la carte 21.00/28.00.

L'Incontro, 87 Pimlico Rd, SW1W 8PH, ☎ (020) 7730 6327, *Fax (020) 7730 5062* – ■. MC AE ⓓ VISA JCB p. 35 **FT** u
closed Easter, 25-26 December and lunch Saturday and Sunday – **Meals** - Italian - 19.50 (lunch) and a la carte 29.50/49.00 **t.** 15.75.

XXX **Santini,** 29 Ebury St, SW1W 0NZ, ✆ (020) 7730 4094, *Fax (020) 7730 0544* – ▤. MC AE VISA JCB p. 36 ABX
closed Easter Sunday, 25-26 December and lunch Saturday and Sunday – **Meals** - Italian 19.75 (lunch) and a la carte 26.50/43.00 **t.** 11.00.

XXX **Shepherd's,** Marsham Court, Marsham St, SW1P 4LA, ✆ (020) 7834 9552, *admin@langa restaurants.co.uk, Fax (020) 7233 6047* – ▤. MC AE ◑ VISA JCB p. 30 LZ
closed Saturday, Sunday and Bank Holidays – **Meals** - English - (booking essential) 27.00 13.00.

XX ✿ **Roussillon,** 16 St Barnabas St, SW1W 8PB, ✆ (020) 7730 5550, *alexis@roussillon.co.u Fax (020) 7824 8617* – ▤. MC AE VISA JCB p. 29 IZ
closed last 2 weeks August, Sunday, Saturday lunch and Bank Holidays – **Meals** 18.0 50.00 **t.** 13.50
Spec. Blue Bembridge lobster salad. Fricassée of chicken and crayfish with morels a chervil. Spicy goose egg soufflé, maple infusion and gingerbread fingers.

XX **Il Convivio,** 143 Ebury St, SW1W 9QN, ✆ (020) 7730 4099, *Fax (020) 7730 4103,* 佘 – ▤ MC AE ◑ VISA JCB p. 36 AY
closed 1 week Christmas, Sunday and Bank Holidays – **Meals** - Italian - 20.00/35.50 14.50.

XX **Simply Nico,** 48a Rochester Row, SW1P 1JU, ✆ (020) 7630 8061, *Fax (020) 7828 8541* ▤. MC AE ◑ VISA JCB p. 36 CY
closed Easter, 25-26 December, Saturday lunch, Sunday and Bank Holidays – **Meals** (bookin essential) a la carte 21.90/33.95 **t.** 12.95.

XX **Bank,** 45 Buckingham Gate, SW1E 6BS, ✆ (020) 7379 9797, *westres@bankrestauran co.uk, Fax (020) 7379 5070,* 佘 – ▤. MC AE ◑ VISA p. 36 CX
closed 25-26 December – **Meals** 15.50 (lunch) and a la carte 23.80/36.25 **t.** 12.90.

XX **Boisdale,** 15 Eccleston St, SW1W 9LX, ✆ (020) 7730 6922, *katarina@boisdale.co.u Fax (020) 7730 0548,* 佘 – ▤. MC AE ◑ VISA p. 36 AY
closed 25 December-1 January, Bank Holidays, Sunday and Saturday lunch – **Meals** Scottish - (live jazz at dinner) 17.45 and a la carte 22.45/47.40 **t.** 14.00.

XX **Christopher's,** 101 Buckingham Palace Rd, SW1W 0SJ, ✆ (020) 7976 5522, *info christophers.uk.net, Fax (020) 7976 5521* – ▤. MC AE ◑ VISA p. 36 BX
Meals - American Grill - 16.50 (lunch) and a la carte 30.00 **t.** 15.50.

XX **Tate Britain,** Tate Gallery, Millbank, SW1P 4RG, ✆ (020) 7887 8825, *tate.restaurant@tat org.uk, Fax (020) 7887 8902,* « Rex Whistler murals » – ▤. MC AE ◑ VISA p. 30 LZ
Meals (booking essential) (lunch only) 16.75/19.50 and a la carte 20.95/31.50 **t.** 20.00.

XX **Ken Lo's Memories of China,** 67-69 Ebury St, SW1W 0NZ, ✆ (020) 7730 773 *Fax (020) 7730 2992* – ▤. MC AE ◑ VISA p. 36 AY
closed 24 December-1 January, Easter Sunday-Monday, Sunday lunch and Bank Holidays **Meals** - Chinese - 19.00/28.50 and a la carte 22.00/36.70 **t.** 13.50.

XX **The Atrium,** 4 Millbank (lower ground floor), SW1P 3JA, ✆ (020) 7233 003 *Fax (020) 7233 0010* – ▤. MC AE ◑ VISA JCB p. 30 LY
closed Christmas, Saturday, Sunday and Bank Holidays – **Meals** a la carte 20.25/27.70 **t.**

X **Olivo,** 21 Eccleston St, SW1W 9LX, ✆ (020) 7730 2505 – ▤. MC AE VISA
closed lunch Saturday and Sunday and Bank Holidays – **Meals** - Italian - 17.00 (lunc and dinner a la carte 24.50/32.50 **t.** 13.50. p. 36 AY

X **La Poule au Pot,** 231 Ebury St, SW1W 8UT, ✆ (020) 7730 7763, *Fax (020) 7259 9651,* 佘 – ▤. MC AE ◑ VISA JCB p. 29 IZ
Meals - French - 14.50 (lunch) and a la carte 24.75/36.75 **t.** 11.50.

ONGBRIDGE *Warks. – see Warwick.*

ONG CRENDON *Bucks.* 403 404 R 28 – *pop. 2 505* – ✉ *Aylesbury.*
London 50 – Aylesbury 11 – Oxford 15.

✕ **Angel Inn** with rm, Bicester Rd, HP18 9EE, ✆ (01844) 208268, *Fax (01844) 202497*, « Part 16C » – ⇸ rm, TV P. MC VISA.
Meals *(closed Sunday dinner)* 14.50 (lunch) and a la carte 17.95/32.20 **t.** 13.50 – 5.00 – **3 rm** 55.00/65.00 **t.**

ONGHORSLEY *Northd.* 401 402 O 18 – *see Morpeth.*

ONG MELFORD *Suffolk* 404 W 27 *Great Britain G. – pop. 2 808.*
See : *Melford Hall★ AC.*
London 62 – Cambridge 34 – Colchester 18 – Ipswich 24.

Bull, Hall St, CO10 9JG, ✆ (01787) 378494, *Fax (01787) 880307*, « Part 15C coaching inn » – ⇸ TV P – 60. MC AE VISA JCB.
Meals 12.95/22.95 and dinner a la carte 24.00/32.00 **st.** 10.95 – **25 rm** 75.00/160.00 **st.** – SB.

Black Lion, The Green, CO10 9DN, ✆ (01787) 312356, *Fax (01787) 374557*, – ⇸ rest, TV P. MC AE VISA
Meals 26.95 **st.** – **9 rm** 71.00/118.50 **t.**, 1 suite – SB.

✕✕✕ **Chimneys,** Hall St, CO10 9JR, ✆ (01787) 379806, *Fax (01787) 312294*, « Part 16C timbered house », – MC VISA
closed Sunday and Bank Holidays – **Meals** (lunch booking essential) 18.50 and a la carte 29.65/34.65 **t.** 12.50.

✕ **Scutchers,** Westgate St, CO10 9DP, on A 1092 ✆ (07000) 728824, *Fax (07000) 785443*, « Former medieval hall house » – . MC AE VISA
closed 24-25 December, 1-10 January, 2 weeks August-September, Sunday, Monday and Bank Holidays – **Meals** a la carte 18.90/31.30 **t.** 11.50.

at Shimpling *North : 4½ m. by A 1092 and A 134* – ✉ *Bury St. Edmunds.*

Gannocks House without rest., Old Rectory Lane, IP29 4HG, ✆ (01284) 830499, *gannocks-house@lineone.net, Fax (01284) 830499*, – ⇸ TV P. MC VISA JCB.
3 rm 30.00/50.00.

ONGRIDGE *Lancs.* 402 M 22 – *pop. 7 351.*
London 241 – Blackburn 12 – Burnley 18.

✕✕✕ **Paul Heathcote's,** 104-106 Higher Rd, PR3 3SY, Northeast : ½ m. by B 5269 following signs for Jeffrey Hill ✆ (01772) 784969, *longridge@heathcotes.co.uk, Fax (01772) 785713* – ⇸. MC AE VISA JCB
closed 1-3 January, Monday, Tuesday and Saturday lunch – **Meals** 16.50 (lunch) and dinner a la carte 34.50/49.75 **t.** 13.50
Spec. Ravioli of crab, vanilla jus. Local suckling pig, hash brown of black pudding. Assiette of seven desserts.

ONG SUTTON *Lincs.* 404 U 25 – *pop. 4 185.*
London 100 – Lincoln 51 – Leicester 67 – Norwich 54.

Travelodge, Wisbech Rd, PE12 9AG, Southeast : 1 m. at junction of A 17 with B 1359 ✆ (01406) 362230 – ⇸ rm, TV P. MC AE VISA JCB.
Meals (grill rest.) – **40 rm** 42.95 **t.**

ONGTOWN *Cumbria* 401 402 L 18.
74 Swan St ✆ (01228) 792835.
London 326 – Carlisle 9 – Newcastle upon Tyne 61.

Bessiestown Farm, Catlowdy, CA6 5QP, Northeast : 8 m. by Netherby St. on B 6318 ✆ (01228) 577219, *bestbb2000@cs.com, Fax (01228) 577019*, « Working farm », – ⇸ TV P. MC VISA.
Meals (by arrangement) 12.50 5.00 – **4 rm** 35.00/65.00.

The Guide is updated annually so renew your Guide every year.

LOOE *Cornwall* 403 G 32 *The West Country G. – pop. 5 022.*

See : *Town★ – Monkey Sanctuary★ AC.*

Bin Down ℘ (01503) 240239 – Whitsand Bay Hotel, Portwrinkle, Torpoint ℘ (0150 230470.

The Guildhall, Fore St ℘ (01503) 262072.

London 264 – Plymouth 23 – Truro 39.

Klymiarven, Barbican Hill, East Looe, PL13 1BH, East : 2 m. by A 387 off B 3253 access from town on foot ℘ (01503) 262333, *klymiarven@cwcom.net, Fax (01503) 26233* ≤ Looe and harbour, – ... VISA JCB
closed January – **Meals** 10.95/15.95 and dinner a la carte 19.50/26.00 **t.** 10.95 – **14 r** 59.00/98.00 **t.** – SB.

Bucklawren Farm, St Martin-by-Looe, PL13 1NZ, Northeast : 3 ½ m. by A 387 ar B 3253 turning right onto single track road signposted to monkey sanctua ℘ (01503) 240738, *bucklawren@compuserve.com, Fax (01503) 240481*, ≤, « Workir farm », – ... AE VISA.
closed December and January – **Meals** (by arrangement) 13.50 **t.** 9.50 – **6 rm** 30.0 50.00 **st.** – SB.

Coombe Farm, Widegates, PL13 1QN, Northeast : 3 ½ m. on B 325 ℘ (01503) 240223, *coombe_farm@hotmail.com, Fax (01503) 240895*, ≤ countrysid heated, – ... AE VISA
March-October – **Meals** (by arrangement) 18.00 **t.** – **10 rm** 39.00/78.00 **t.** – SB.

St Aubyn's without rest., Marine Drive, Hannafore, West Looe, PL13 2DH, by Quay R ℘ (01503) 264351, *welcome@staubyns.co.uk, Fax (01503) 263670*, ≤, – ... VISA JCB
April-October – **8 rm** 28.00/70.00 **s.**

Trawlers, Buller Quay, East Looe, PL13 1AH, ℘ (01503) 263593 – ... AE VISA
closed 24-26 December, Tuesday-Wednesday in winter and Monday – **Meals** (dinner onl 21.00 and a la carte 21.50/29.75 **t.** 9.75.

at Talland Bay *Southwest : 4 m. by A 387 – Looe.*

Talland Bay, PL13 2JB, ℘ (01503) 272667, *tallandbay@aol.com, Fax (01503) 27294* ≤, « Country house atmosphere », heated, – rest, ... AE VISA
closed January-mid February – **Meals** 12.50/23.00 and dinner a la carte 23.00/39.50 11.00 – **20 rm** (dinner included) 79.00/188.00 **t.**, 1 suite – SB.

at Pelynt *Northwest : 4 m. by A 387 on B 3359 – Looe.*

Jubilee Inn, Pelynt, PL13 2JZ, ℘ (01503) 220312, *Fax (01503) 220920*, « Part 16C » – ... VISA JCB
Meals a la carte 12.30/23.00 **t.** 7.25 – **11 rm** 38.50/70.00 **t.**

LORTON *Cumbria* 402 K 20 – *see Cockermouth.*

LOUGHBOROUGH *Leics.* 402 403 404 Q 25 – *pop. 46 867.*

Lingdale, Joe Moore's Lane, Woodhouse Eaves ℘ (01509) 890703.

Town Hall, Market Pl ℘ (01509) 218113.

London 117 – Birmingham 41 – Leicester 11 – Nottingham 15.

Quality, New Ashby Rd, LE11 0EX, West : 2 m. on A 512 ℘ (01509) 211800, *admin@gb61 u_net.com, Fax (01509) 211868*, – rm, rest, – 225. AE VISA
Meals (dinner only and Sunday lunch) 14.50 and a la carte 14.95/24.25 **t.** 11.95 – 11. – **94 rm** 120.00 **t.** – SB.

Charnwood Lodge, 136 Leicester Rd, LE11 2AQ, Southeast : ¾ m. on A ℘ (01509) 211120, *charnwoodlodge@charwat.freeserve.co.uk, Fax (01509) 211121* rm, ... VISA.
Meals (by arrangement) a la carte 9.45/14.85 **st.** 6.95 – **8 rm** 35.00/55.00 **st.**

The Old Manor with rm, 11-14 Sparrow Hill, LE11 1BT, off Baxter Gate ℘ (01509) 2112 *bookings@oldmanor.com, Fax (01509) 211128*, « Part 15C » – ... AE VISA.
closed 25-26 December – **Meals** (dinner only) 32.50 **st.** – 12.00 – **8 rm** 88.0 115.00 **st.**

at Burton-on-the-Wolds *East : 3 ¾ m. by A 60 on B 676 – Loughborough.*

Lang's, Horse Leys Farm, LE12 5TQ, East : 1 m. on B 676 ℘ (01509) 880980, *langsrestaura @amserve.net, Fax (01509) 880980* – ... AE VISA
closed lunch Monday and Saturday – **Meals** (restricted lunch) 12.95 (lunch) and di ner a la carte 22.55/26.50 **st.** 12.75.

Quorndon *Southeast : 3 m. by A 6 – ✉ Loughborough.*

Quorn Country H., 66 Leicester Rd, LE12 8BB, ☎ (01509) 415050, *Fax (01509) 415557*, – ⇔ rm, ▤ rm, TV ☎ P – 🏛 120. MC AE ⊙ VISA JCB
Shires : Meals *(closed Saturday lunch)* 22.50 and a la carte 27.40/38.40 **t.** 🍷 12.95 – ***Orangery :*** Meals *(closed Saturday lunch)* 22.50 and a la carte 27.40/38.40 **t.** 🍷 12.95 – ☕ 8.95 – **21 rm** 102.00/115.00 **t.**, 2 suites – SB.

Quorn Grange, 88 Wood Lane, LE12 8DB, Southeast : ¾ m. ☎ (01509) 412167, *Fax (01509) 415621*, – ⇔ TV ☎ ♿ P – 🏛 100. MC AE VISA. ⛔
closed 25-26 and 31 December – **Meals** *(closed Saturday lunch)* 13.50/17.50 and a la carte **st.** 🍷 10.20 – **38 rm** ☕ 83.00/103.00 **st.**

LOUGHTON *Essex* 404 U 29.
⛳9 *Loughton, Clays Lane, Debden Green ☎ (020) 8502 2923.*
London 15 – Cambridge 44 – Ipswich 66 – Luton 30 – Southend-on-Sea 35.

Plan : see Greater London (North-East) p. 11

Ne'als Brasserie, 241 High Rd, IG10 1AD, ☎ (020) 8508 3443 – ▤. MC ⊙ VISA JCB HT a
closed 1 week Christmas, Sunday dinner and Monday – **Meals** 12.95 (lunch) and a la carte 23.50/29.50 **t.** 🍷 9.95.

LOUTH *Lincs.* 402 404 U 23 – *pop. 14 248.*
ℹ *The New Market Hall, off Cornmarket ☎ (01507) 609289.*
London 156 – Boston 34 – Great Grimsby 17 – Lincoln 26.

Kenwick Park 🐎, LN11 8NR, Southeast : 2 ¼ m. by B 1520 on A 157 ☎ (01507) 608806, *enquiries@kenwick-park.co.uk, Fax (01507) 608027*, ≤, 🏋, ≘s, 🏊, ⛳18, 🌳, 🎾, squash – ⇔ TV ♿ P – 🏛 30. MC AE ⊙ VISA. ⛔
Meals 18.50/21.95 and a la carte 15.85/28.10 **st.** 🍷 10.95 – **34 rm** ☕ 98.00/135.00 **st.** – SB.

Brackenborough Arms, Cordeaux Corner, Brackenborough, LN11 0SZ, North : 2 m. by A 16 ☎ (01507) 609169, *info@brackenborough.co.uk, Fax (01507) 609413* – ⇔ rm, TV P – 🏛 35. MC AE ⊙ VISA JCB. ⛔
closed 25-26 December – ***The Brackens :*** Meals *closed Sunday dinner and Monday lunch* a la carte 15.00/20.00 **t.** – **24 rm** ☕ 62.00/105.00 **t.** – SB.

The Beaumont, 66 Victoria Rd, LN11 0BX, by Eastgate off Ramsgate Rd ☎ (01507) 605005, *enquiries@thebeaumont.freeserve.co.uk, Fax (01507) 607768* – 🛗 TV P. MC AE VISA
Meals *(closed Sunday)* 14.95 and a la carte 14.95/27.40 **t.** 🍷 9.95 – **16 rm** ☕ 45.00/70.00 **t.**

LOWER ODDINGTON *Glos.* 403 404 P 28 – *see Stow-on-the-Wold.*

LOWER SLAUGHTER *Glos.* 403 404 O 28 – *see Bourton-on-the-Water.*

LOWER SWELL *Glos. – see Stow-on-the-Wold.*

LOWER WHITLEY *Ches..*
London 199 – Liverpool 25 – Manchester 24 – Warrington 7.

Chetwode Arms, Street Lane, WA4 4EN, ☎ (01925) 730203, « 17C coaching inn », – P. MC VISA
Meals a la carte 21.00/31.00 **t.** 🍷 10.95.

LOWER WIELD *Hants. – see Four Marks.*

LOWESTOFT *Suffolk* 404 Z 26 *Great Britain G. – pop. 62 907.*
Env. : *The Broads*★.
⛳18, ⛳9 *Rookery Park, Carlton Colville ☎ (01502) 560380.*
ℹ *East Point Pavillion, Royal Plain ☎ (01502) 523000.*
London 116 – Ipswich 43 – Norwich 30.

Travel Inn, 249 Yarmouth Rd, NR32 4AA, North : 2 ½ m. on A 12 ☎ (01502) 572441 – ⇔ rm, TV ♿ P. MC AE VISA. ⛔
Meals (grill rest.) – **41 rm** 41.95 **t.**

ENGLAND

at Oulton Broad *West : 2 m. by A 146 – ✉ Lowestoft.*

Ivy House Farm ⛔, Ivy Lane, NR33 8HY, Southwest : 1 ½ m. by A 1
(01502) 501353, *admin@ivyhousefarm.co.uk, Fax (01502) 501539,* – TV P
50. VISA JCB
closed 23 December-2 January – **Meals** – (see ***The Crooked Barn*** below) – **19 r**
75.00/130.00 **st.** – SB.

The Crooked Barn (at Ivy House Farm), Ivy Lane, NR33 8HY, Southwest : 1 ½ m. by A 1
(01502) 501353, *admin@ivyhousefarm.co.uk, Fax (01502) 501539,* « Part 1
thatched converted barn » – P. VISA
closed 23 December-2 January – **Meals** a la carte 17.85/31.85 **st.** 10.75.

LOW FELL *Tyne and Wear – see Gateshead.*

LOW LAITHE *N. Yorks. – see Pateley Bridge.*

LOXLEY *Warks. – see Statford-upon-Avon.*

LUDLOW *Shrops.* 403 L 26 *Great Britain G. – pop. 9 040.*

See : *Town★ – Castle★ AC – Feathers Hotel★ – St Laurence's Parish Church (Misericords★).*

Exc. : *Stokesay Castle★ AC, NW : 6½ m. by A 49.*

Castle St (01584) 875053.

London 162 – Birmingham 39 – Hereford 24 – Shrewsbury 29.

Plan opposite

Dinham Hall, Dinham, SY8 1EJ, (01584) 876464, *info@dinhamhall.co.u*
Fax (01584) 876019, – rest, TV P. VISA Z
Meals - French - 14.50/28.50 **t.** 15.50 – **14 rm** 70.00/180.00 **t.** – SB.

Overton Grange, Hereford Rd, SY8 4AD, South : 1 ¾ m. by B 4361 (01584) 87350
Fax (01584) 873524, ←, – rest, TV P – 100. VISA.
closed 2 weeks Christmas – ***Les Marches :*** Meals *(closed lunch Friday and Saturda* (booking essential for non-residents) 22.50/32.50 **st.** 16.00 – **12 rm** 65.00/125.00 **s**
2 suites – SB.

Cliffe ⛔, Dinham, SY8 2JE, West : ½ m. via Dinham Bridge (01584) 872063, *cliffho*
@lineone.net, Fax (01584) 873991, – TV P. VISA Z
closed 3 days Christmas – **Meals** (booking essential) (bar lunch Monday to Saturday)/dinn
14.95 8.95 – **9 rm** 35.00/70.00 **t.**

Number Twenty Eight without rest., 28 Lower Broad St, SY8 1PQ, (01584) 8769
ross.no28@btinternet.com, Fax (01584) 876860, – TV. VISA. Z
6 rm 80.00/95.00 **st.**

Hibiscus (Bosi), 17 Corve St, SY8 1DA, (01584) 872325, *Fax (01584) 874024* – P.
VISA JCB Y
closed 2 Weeks January, 1 week August, Sunday and lunch Monday and Tuesday – **Mea**
(booking essential) 19.50/42.50 **t.** 14.00
Spec. Sautéed langoustine tails, peanut butter and roast peach. Bresse chicken wi
crayfish, tagliatelle and tarragon. Strawberries in hibiscus and black pepper trifle.

Mr Underhill's at Dinham Weir (Bradley) with rm, Dinham Bridge, SY8 1E
(01584) 874431, *Fax (01584) 874431,* ←, « Riverside setting », – TV P.
VISA. Z
closed 1 week January and 1 week Christmas – **Meals** *(closed Tuesday dinner)* (set me
only) (booking essential) (lunch by arrangement) 29.00 **t.** 13.00 – **6 rm** 70.00/100.00
– SB
Spec. Pavé of turbot with cardamom and lemon. Breast of duck, haricot and broad be
purées. Prune and Armagnac tart, clementine cream.

Merchant House (Hill), Lower Corve St, SY8 1DU, (01584) 875438, *Fax (01584) 8769*
« Jacobean house » – . VISA JCB Y
closed 1 week spring, 1 week Christmas, Sunday and Monday – **Meals** (dinner only a
lunch Friday and Saturday) 27.50/32.50 **st.** 13.50
Spec. Monkfish with mustard and cucumber sauce. Squab pigeon with saffron and he
risotto. Apricot tart, amaretto ice cream.

Courtyard, 2 Quality Sq, SY8 1AR, (01584) 878080 – Z
closed 25-26 December, 1 January, 6 May and Sunday – **Meals** (booking essential) 10.7
16.15 **t.** 9.50.

Koo, 127 Old St, SY8 1NU, (01584) 878462 – VISA Z
closed Sunday and Monday – **Meals** - Japanese - (light lunch) 13.95/15.95 and a la carte
9.00.

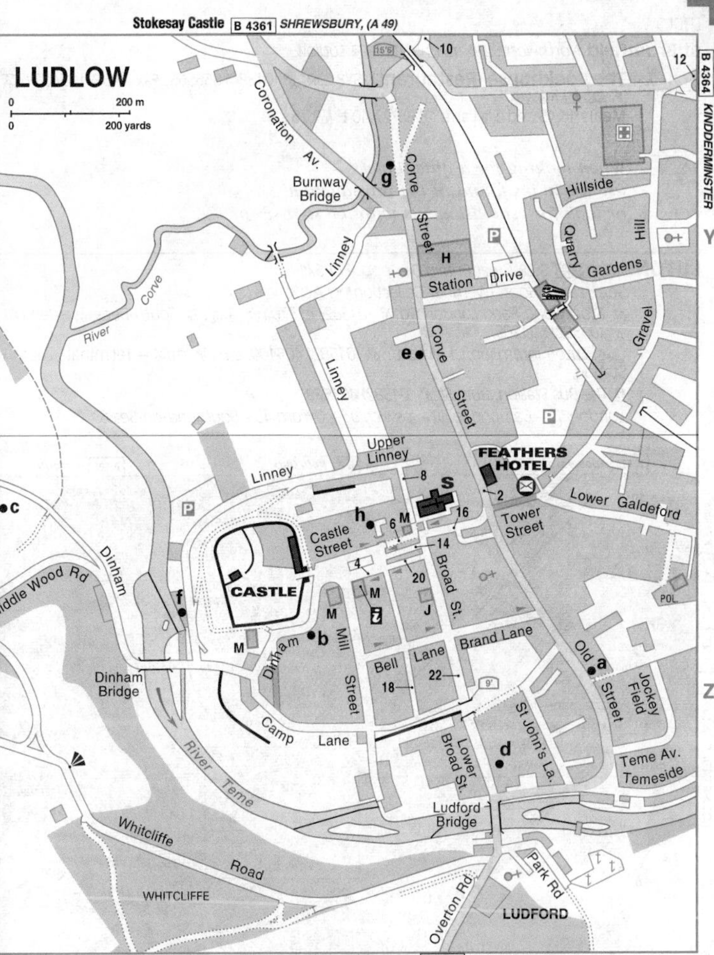

ll Ring	Z 2	Fishmore Road	Y 10	Lower Raven Lane	Z 18
stle Square	Z 4	Henley Road	Y 12	Market Street	Z 20
urch Street	Z 6	Hight Street	Z 14	Silk Mill	Z 22
llege Street	Z 8	King Street	Z 16		

Woofferton *South : 4 m. by B 4361 and A 49 –* **Z** *– ✉ Ludlow.*

Travelodge, SY8 4AL, ✆ (01584) 711695, *Fax (01584) 711695* – ⇔ rm, TV ♿ P. MC AE O VISA JCB. ✗
Meals (grill rest.) – **32 rm** 39.95 **t.**

Brimfield *South : 4½ m. by B 4361 and A 49 –* **Z** *– ✉ Ludlow.*

The Marcle, SY8 4NE, ✆ (01584) 711459, *marcle@supanet.com, Fax (01584) 711459,* « 16C cottage », ⚘ – ⇔ TV P. ✗
March-November – **Meals** (by arrangement) 19.50 – **3 rm** ☕ 45.00/65.00.

Roebuck Inn with rm, SY8 4NE, ✆ (01584) 711230, *Fax (01584) 711654,* ⚘ – TV P. MC VISA JCB
closed 25 December – **Meals** 20.00/23.50 **t.** 🍷 10.00 – **3 rm** ☕ 45.00/70.00 **t.**

at Bromfield *Northwest : 2½ m. on A 49 – ✉ Ludlow.*

X **The Cookhouse (Restaurant),** SY8 2JR, ☏ (01584) 856565, *Fax (01584) 856661,* ⛱ P. MC AE ⓓ VISA
Meals 14.45 and a la carte 18.85/27.40 **t.** 🍷 9.75.

When looking for a quiet hotel
use the maps found in the introduction
or look for establishments with the sign 🐎 *or* 🐎.

LUTON *Luton* 404 S 28 *Great Britain G. – pop. 171 671.*
See : *Luton Hoo★ (Wernher Collection★★)* **AC X.**
⛳18 *Stockwood Park, London Rd* ☏ *(01582) 413704,* X – ⛳18, ⛳9 *South Beds, Warden Hill* ☏ *(01582) 591209.*
✈ *Luton International Airport :* ☏ *(01582) 405100, E : 1½ m.* X – **Terminal :** Luton B Station.
ℹ *The Bus Station, Bute St* ☏ *(01582) 401579.*
London 35 – Cambridge 36 – Ipswich 93 – Oxford 45 – Southend-on-Sea 63.

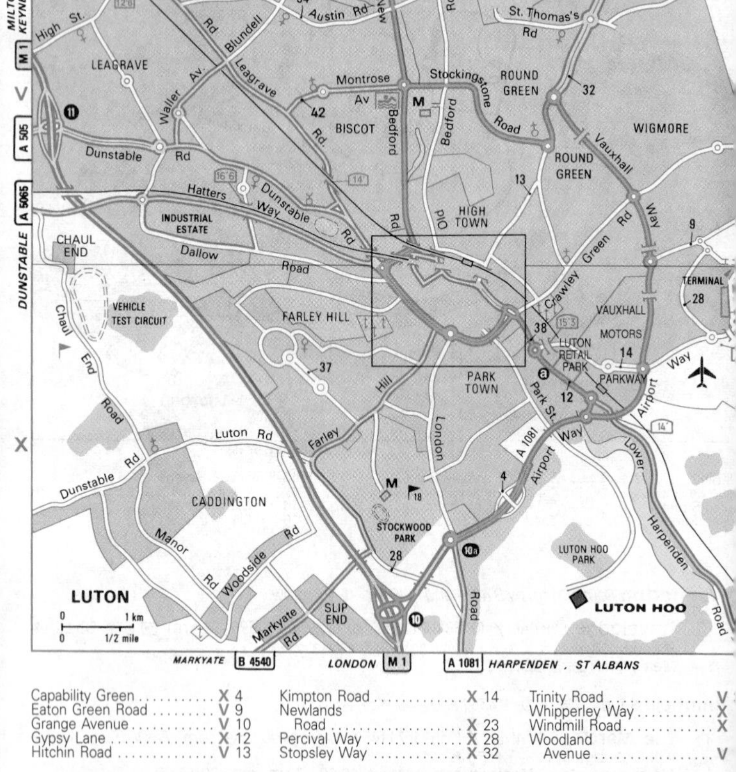

Capability Green	X 4	Kimpton Road	X 14	Trinity Road	V
Eaton Green Road	V 9	Newlands Road	X 23	Whipperley Way	X
Grange Avenue	V 10	Percival Way	X 28	Windmill Road	X
Gypsy Lane	X 12	Stopsley Way	X 32	Woodland Avenue	V
Hitchin Road	V 13				

🏠 **Travel Inn,** Osborne Rd, LU1 3HJ, Southeast : ½ m. on A 505 ☏ (01582) 41765 *Fax (01582) 421900* – 🛗, ⇹ rm, ▤ rest, TV ♿ P. – 🎤 40. MC AE ⓓ VISA JCB. ✗ X
Meals (grill rest.) – **129 rm** 41.95 **t.**

LUTON

ndale Centre . . . . YZ
te Street . . . . Y 3
urch Street . . . . Y 5
llow Road . . . . Y 7
Dunstable Road. . . . . Y 8
George St. . . . . Z
King Street . . . . Z 16
Liverpool Road . . . . Y 17
Manchester Street . . . . Y 19
Market Hill . . . . Z 20
Mill Street . . . . Y 21
Old Bedford Road. . . . . Y 24
Park Square . . . . Z 26
Park Street West . . . . Z 27
Silver Street . . . . Y 30
Upper George Street. . . . . Z 36
Windmill Road . . . . Z 38

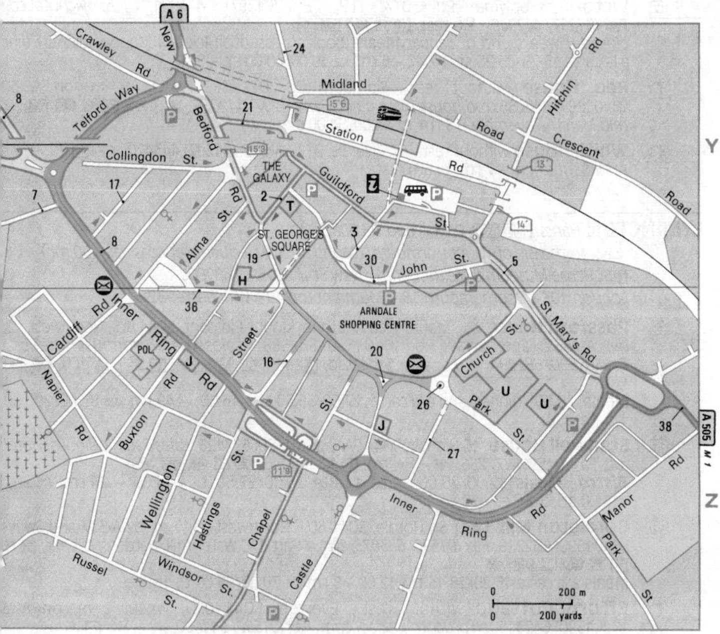

UXBOROUGH *Somerset* 403 J 30 – *pop. 201* – ✉ *Watchet.*
London 205 – Exeter 42 – Minehead 9 – Taunton 25.

Royal Oak of Luxborough with rm, Exmoor National Park, TA23 0SH, ℘ (01984) 640319, *royaloakof.luxborough@virgin.net*, « Part 14C inn », – P. VISA
Meals a la carte 14.65/20.95 **t.** 8.95 – **13 rm** 45.00/75.00 **st.**

DFORD *Devon* 403 H 32 *The West Country G.* – *pop. 1 734* – ✉ *Okehampton.*
See : *Village*★★.
Env. : *Dartmoor National Park*★★.
London 234 – Exeter 33 – Plymouth 25.

Moor View House, Vale Down, EX20 4BB, Northeast : 1 ½ m. on A 386 ℘ (01822) 820220, *Fax (01822) 820220*, – TV P
Meals (by arrangement) (communal dining) 20.00 **st.** 8.50 – **4 rm** 50.00/70.00 – SB.

Dartmoor Inn, EX20 4AY, East : 1 m. on A 386 ℘ (01822) 820221, *Fax (01822) 820494* – P. VISA
closed 4-11 February, Monday and Sunday dinner – **Meals** 15.00/21.50 (lunch) and a la carte 16.25/26.75 **t.** 9.75.

ME REGIS *Dorset* 403 L 31 *The West Country G.* – *pop. 3 566.*
See : *Town*★ – *The Cobb*★.
18 *Timber Hill* ℘ *(01297) 442963.*
Guildhall Cottage, Church St ℘ *(01297) 442138.*
London 160 – Dorchester 25 – Exeter 31 – Taunton 27.

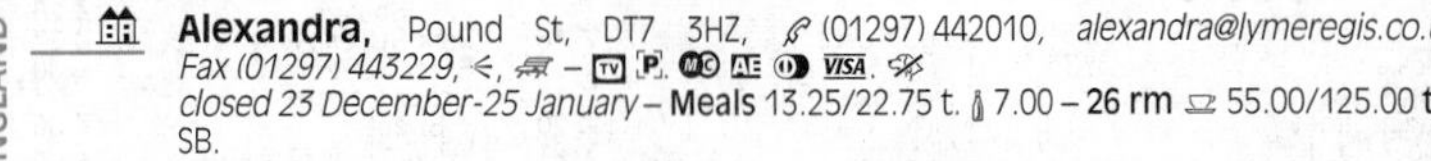

Alexandra, Pound St, DT7 3HZ, ✆ (01297) 442010, *alexandra@lymeregis.co.*
Fax (01297) 443229, ≤, – TV P. MC AE ① VISA.
closed 23 December-25 January – **Meals** 13.25/22.75 t. 7.00 – **26 rm** 55.00/125.00 t
SB.

Victoria, Uplyme Rd, DT7 3LP, ✆ (01297) 444801, *info@vichotel.co.*
Fax (01297) 442949 – rest, TV P. MC VISA.
*closed 2 weeks end of January***Meals** (booking essential) (closed Monday dinner)/dinr
a la carte 13.75/23.25 **st.** 7.40 – **6 rm** 30.00/60.00 **st.** – SB.

Red House without rest., Sidmouth Rd, DT7 3ES, West : ¾ m. on A 30
✆ (01297) 442055, *red.house@virgin.net, Fax (01297) 442055*, – TV P. MC VISA.
mid March-November – **3 rm** 33.00/54.00 **s.**

White House without rest., 47 Silver St, DT7 3HR, ✆ (01297) 443420, ≤ – TV P
April-September – **7 rm** 50.00 **st.**

LYMINGTON *Hants.* 403 404 P 31 – *pop. 13 508.*

to the Isle of Wight (Yarmouth) (Wightlink Ltd) frequent services daily (30 mn).

St Barbe Museum & Visitor Centre, New St ✆ (01590) 689000.

London 103 – Bournemouth 18 – Southampton 19 – Winchester 32.

Passford House , Mount Pleasant Lane, Mount Pleasant, SO41 8LS, Northwest : 2
by A 337 and Sway Rd ✆ (01590) 682398, *sales@passfordhousehotel.co.*
Fax (01590) 683494, ≤, , , heated, , , , – TV P – 100. MC AE
VISA
Meals 28.50 (dinner) and a la carte 27.50/36.50 **t.** 16.50 – **49 rm** 85.00/200.00
1 suite – SB.

Stanwell House, 15 High St, SO41 9AA, ✆ (01590) 677123, *sales@stanwellhousehotel*
.uk, Fax (01590) 677756, – rm, TV – 40. MC AE ① VISA JCB
Bistro : **Meals** 12.00/25.00 and a la carte 25.00/27.50 **t.** 15.00 – **24 rm** 90.0
115.00 **st.**, 5 suites – SB.

Gordleton Mill, Silver St, Hordle, SO41 6DJ, Northwest : 3 ½ m. by A 337 and Sway
✆ (01590) 682219, *Fax (01590) 683073*, , « Part 17C water mill, gardens » – , re
TV P. MC AE VISA.
Meals a la carte 15.25/28.15 **t.** 12.00 – **8 rm** 70.00/85.00 **t.**, 1 suite.

Efford Cottage without rest., Everton, SO41 0JD, West : 2 m. on A 3
✆ (01590) 642315, *effordcottage@aol.com, Fax (01590) 641030*, – TV P
3 rm 60.00/65.00.

Limpets, 9 Gosport St, SO41 9BG, ✆ (01590) 675595, *Fax (01590) 674186* – MC VISA
closed last 2 weeks January-first 2 weeks February, 25-26 December, Tuesday and Saturc
lunch – **Meals** 10.95/14.95 (lunch) and a la carte 18.95/23.10 **t.** 10.95.

at East End *Northeast : 4 ¼ m. by B 3054 off South Baddesley rd – ✉ Lymington.*

East End Arms, Main Rd, SO41 5SY, ✆ (01590) 626223, *jennie@eastendarms.co.*
Fax (01590) 626223, – MC VISA JCB
closed 1 January, Sunday dinner and Monday lunch – **Meals** a la carte 14.00/20.0
11.00.

LYNDHURST *Hants.* 403 404 P 31 *Great Britain G.* – *pop. 2 381.*

Env. : *New Forest★★ (Bolderwood Ornamental Drive★★, Rhinefield Ornamental Drive★★*

18, 9 *Dibden Golf Centre, Main Rd ✆ (023) 8084 5596* – 18 *New Forest, Southampton*
✆ (023) 8028 2752.

New Forest Museum & Visitor Centre, Main Car Park ✆ (01590) 689000.

London 95 – Bournemouth 20 – Southampton 10 – Winchester 23.

Crown, 9 High St, SO43 7NF, ✆ (023) 8028 2922, *reception@crownhotel.lyndhurst.co.*
Fax (023) 8028 2751, – , rest, TV P – 70. MC AE ① VISA.
Meals (bar lunch Monday to Saturday)/dinner 21.00 **t.** 11.95 – **38 rm** 85.00/130.00
1 suite – SB.

Beaulieu, Beaulieu Rd, SO42 7YQ, Southeast : 3 ½ m. on B 3056 ✆ (023) 8029 3344, *inf*
carehotels.co.uk, Fax (023) 8029 2729, , – rest, TV P – 40. MC AE VISA
Meals (dinner only) 21.50 **t.** 11.95 – **17 rm** 72.50/130.00 **st.**, 1 suite – SB.

Ormonde House, Southampton Rd, SO43 7BT, ✆ (023) 8028 2806, *info@ormor*
house.co.uk, Fax (023) 8028 2004, – TV P. MC AE VISA JCB
closed 1 week Christmas – **Meals** (by arrangement) (residents only) (dinner only) 18.0
19 rm 35.00/100.00 **st.** – SB.

Whitemoor House, Southampton Rd, SO43 7BU, (023) 8028 2186, *Fax (023) 8028 2186* – VISA JCB
closed 25-26 December and 1 January – **Meals** (by arrangement) 12.50 **st.** 9.50 – **8 rm** 45.00/65.00 **st.** – SB.

Le Poussin at Parkhill (Aitken) with rm, Beaulieu Rd, SO43 7FZ, Southeast : 1 1/4 m. on B 3056 (023) 8028 2944, *sales@lepoussinatparkhill.co.uk, Fax (023) 8028 3268*, « Tastefully furnished country house », heated, – 50. VISA.
Meals 15.00/37.00 and a la carte 30.50/43.00 **t.** 12.00 – 5.00 – **18 rm** 55.00/125.00 **t.**, 2 suites – SB
Spec. Terrine of roast poussin, foie gras and prunes. Roast turbot on the bone, honey-glazed marrow bone. Passion fruit soufflé.

LYNMOUTH *Devon* 403 I 30 – *see Lynton.*

LYNTON *Devon* 403 I 30 *The West Country G. – pop. 1 870 (inc. Lynmouth).*
See : *Town★ (≤★).*
Env. : *Valley of the Rocks★, W : 1 m. – Watersmeet★, E : 1½ m. by A 39.*
Exc. : *Exmoor National Park★★ – Doone Valley★, SE : 7½ m. by A 39 (access from Oare on foot).*
Town Hall, Lee Rd (01598) 752225.
London 206 – Exeter 59 – Taunton 44.

Lynton Cottage, North Walk Hill, EX35 6ED, (01598) 752342, *enquiries@lynton-cottage.co.uk, Fax (01598) 752597*, bay and Countisbury Hill, – rest, VISA JCB.
Meals 19.95 (dinner) and a la carte 19.15/29.85 **st.** 10.95 – **17 rm** 49.00/85.00 **st.** – SB.

Hewitt's, North Walk, EX35 6HJ, (01598) 752293, *hewitts.hotel@talk21.com, Fax (01598) 752489*, bay and Countisbury Hill, « Victorian house in wooded cliffside setting », – VISA JCB
closed 15 December-15 January – **Meals** *(closed Tuesday)* (booking essential) 16.50/25.00 and a la carte 20.00/28.50 **st.** 13.50 – **10 rm** 50.00/140.00 **st.** – SB.

Victoria Lodge, 30-31 Lee Rd, EX35 6BS, (01598) 753203, *info@victorialodge.co.uk, Fax (01598) 753203*, – VISA.
April-October – **Meals** *(closed Monday to Wednesday)* (dinner only) 19.50 – **9 rm** 40.00/86.00 **st.** – SB.

Highcliffe House, Sinai Hill, EX35 6AR, (01598) 752235, *highcliffe.hotel@excite.co.uk, Fax (01598) 752235*, bay and Countisbury Hill, « Victorian residence, antiques », – VISA.
closed mid December-mid January – **Meals** (residents only) (dinner only) 19.50 8.75 – **6 rm** 52.00/70.00 **t.** – SB.

Seawood, North Walk, EX35 6HJ, (01598) 752272, *Fax (01598) 752272*, bay and headland – rest,
April-October – **Meals** (dinner only) 16.00 **st.** – **12 rm** 30.00/64.00 **st.** – SB.

Rockvale, Lee Rd, EX35 6HW, off Lee Rd (01598) 752279, *judithwoodland@rockvale.fsbusiness.co.uk*, – VISA JCB.
March-October – **Meals** (by arrangement) 17.00 **st.** 8.25 – **8 rm** 24.00/52.00 **st.** – SB.

at Lynmouth.

Tors, EX35 6NA, (01598) 753236, *torshotel@torslynmouth.co.uk, Fax (01598) 752544*, Lynmouth and bay, heated, – rest, – 80. VISA
closed 3 January-March – **Meals** 25.00 (dinner) and a la carte 19.95/31.95 **st.** 9.00 – **33 rm** 35.00/110.00 **st.** – SB.

Rising Sun, Harbourside, EX35 6EQ, (01598) 753223, *risingsunlynmouth@easynet.co.uk, Fax (01598) 753480*, « Part 14C thatched inn », – VISA JCB.
Meals – (see ***The Restaurant*** below) – **15 rm** 63.00/138.00 **t.**, 1 suite – SB.

Heatherville, Tors Park, EX35 6NB, by Tors Rd (01598) 752327, *Fax (01598) 752634*, – VISA JCB
closed December and January – **Meals** (by arrangement) 18.50 6.95 – **7 rm** 25.00/64.00 **st.**

The Restaurant (at Rising Sun H.), Harbourside, EX35 6EQ, (01598) 753223, *Fax (01598) 753480*, « Part 14C thatched inn », – VISA JCB
Meals (booking essential) 14.50/27.50 t. 10.95.

ENGLAND

at Martinhoe *West : 4 ¼ m. via Coast rd (toll) – ✉ Barnstaple.*

Old Rectory, EX31 4QT, ✆ (01598) 763368, *reception@oldrectoryhotel.co.* *Fax (01598) 763567*, – – VISA JCB, *March-November* – **Meals** (booking essential) (dinner only) 27.00 **st.** 9.50 – **8 r** 60.00/98.00 – SB.

LYTHAM ST. ANNE'S *Lancs.* 402 L 22 – *pop. 40 866.*

Fairhaven, Lytham Hall Park, Ansdell ✆ (01253) 736741 – St Annes Old Links, Highbu Rd ✆ (01253) 723597.

290 Clifton Drive South ✆ (01253) 725610.

London 237 – Blackpool 7 – Liverpool 44 – Preston 13.

at Lytham.

Clifton Arms, West Beach, FY8 5QJ, ✆ (01253) 739898, *welcome@cliftonarms.co.* *Fax (01253) 730657*, – – 150. VISA
Meals 14.50/19.50 and a la carte 12.50 – **46 rm** 91.00/115.00 **t.**, 2 suites – SB.

9 Clifton Street, 9 Clifton St, FY8 5EP, ✆ (01253) 794000, *Fax (01253) 795255* – VISA JCB
closed 26 December and Sunday – **Meals** 12.95/15.95 and a la carte 9.50.

Pleasant Street Brasserie, 2 Pleasant St, FY8 5JA, ✆ (01253) 7338(*Fax (01253) 733800* – VISA JCB
closed Sunday – **Meals** 9.95/13.00 and a la carte 13.05/23.75 **t.** 9.95.

at St Anne's.

Dalmeny, 19-33 South Promenade, FY8 1LX, ✆ (01253) 712236, *info@dalmenyhot com, Fax (01253) 724447*, , , , , squash – – 200. VISA.
closed 24-26 December – **Meals** – (see ***Atrium*** below) – **139 rm** 80.00/116.00 **t.** – SB.

The Grand, South Promenade, FY8 1NB, ✆ (01253) 721288, *book@the-grand.co.* *Fax (01253) 714459*, – , rm, – 140. VISA.
closed 25 to 26 December – ***The Bay :*** **Meals** (bar lunch Monday to Saturday)/dinner 21. and a la carte 20.00/31.70 **t.** 11.50 – **40 rm** 72.00/144.00 **t.** – SB.

Glendower, North Promenade, FY8 2NQ, ✆ (01253) 723241, *glendower@bestweste co.uk, Fax (01253) 640069*, , , – , rest, – 150. VISA JCB
Meals (bar lunch)/dinner 17.50 **st.** 9.95 – **62 rm** 57.00/110.00 **st.** – SB.

Bedford, 307-311 Clifton Drive South, FY8 1HN, ✆ (01253) 724636, *reservation bedfordhotel.com, Fax (01253) 729244*, , – , rest, – 120. JCB.
Meals 8.95/17.95 and a la carte 12.60/22.00 **t.** 7.95 – **35 rm** 42.00/75.00 **t.** – SB.

Atrium (at Dalmeny H.), 19-33 South Promenade, FY8 1LX, ✆ (01253) 7160(*Fax (01253) 724447* – VISA
closed 24-26 December and Sunday dinner – **Meals** (dinner only and Sunday lun a la carte 22.40/30.50 **t.**

MACCLESFIELD *Ches.* 402 403 404 N 24 – *pop. 50 270.*

The Tytherington Club ✆ (01625) 506000 – Shrigley Hall, Shrigley Park, Pott Shrig ✆ (01625) 575757.

Town Hall ✆ (01625) 504114.

London 186 – Chester 38 – Manchester 18 – Stoke-on-Trent 21.

Chadwick House, 55 Beech Lane, SK10 2DS, North : ¼ m. on A 538 ✆ (01625) 6155 *Fax (01625) 610265* – VISA JCB.
Meals (booking essential) (dinner only) (residents only) 8.95 **st.** 7.50 – **13 rm** 25.0 55.00 **st.**

Travel Inn, Tytherington Business Park, Springwood Way, SK10 2XA, Northeast : 2 ½ m. A 523 ✆ (01625) 427809, *Fax (01625) 422874* – rm, rest, VISA
Meals (grill rest.) – **40 rm** 41.95 **t.**

Premier Lodge, Congleton Rd, Gawsworth, SK11 7XD, Southwest : 2 m. by A 537 A 536 ✆ (0870) 7001466, *Fax (0870) 7001467* – rm, rest, VISA.
Meals (grill rest.) a la carte approx. 12.50 **t.** 7.80 – **28 rm** 46.95 **t.**

at Adlington *North : 5 m. on A 523 – ✉ Macclesfield.*

Travelodge, London Road South, SK12 4NA, on A 523 ✆ (01625) 8752(*Fax (01625) 875292* – rm, rest, VISA JCB.
Meals (grill rest.) – **32 rm** 49.95 **t.**

at Bollington *Northeast : 3½ m. by A 523 on B 5090 – ✉ Macclesfield.*

Beasdales, 22 Old Market Pl, High St, SK10 5PH, ☎ (01625) 575058 – ⅔. MC VISA
closed 2 weeks August and Sunday-Tuesday – **Meals** - Bistro - (dinner only) a la carte 15.85/22.40 **t.** 10.00.

at Pott Shrigley *Northeast : 4¾ m. by A 523 on B 5090 – ✉ Macclesfield.*

Shrigley Hall, Shrigley Park, SK10 5SB, North : ¼ m. ☎ (01625) 575757, *shrigleyhotel @paramount-hotels.co.uk, Fax (01625) 573323,* « Part 19C country house in park », – 250. MC AE VISA
Oakridge : **Meals** (dinner only) 24.00 and a la carte 31.85/38.70 **t.** 19.95 – **150 rm** 125.00/155.00 **st.** – SB.

MACKWORTH *Derbs.* 402 403 404 P 25 – *see Derby.*

MADINGLEY *Cambs.* 404 U 27 – *see Cambridge.*

MADLEY *Herefordshire* 403 L 27 – *see Hereford.*

MAGHAM DOWN *E. Sussex – see Hailsham.*

MAIDENCOMBE *Devon* 403 J 32 – *see Torquay.*

MAIDENHEAD *Windsor & Maidenhead* 404 R 29 – *pop. 59 605.*

Bird Hills, Drift Rd, Hawthorn Hill ☎ (01628) 771030 – Shoppenhangers Rd ☎ (01628) 624693 X.

to Marlow, Cookham and Windsor (Salter Bros. Ltd) (summer only).

The Library, St Ives Rd ☎ (01628) 781110.

London 33 – Oxford 32 – Reading 13.

Plan on next page

Holiday Inn Maidenhead, Manor Lane, SL6 2RA, off Shoppenhangers Rd ☎ (01628) 506000, *Fax (01628) 506001,* squash – rest, – 400. MC AE VISA JCB X n
The Dining Room : **Meals** (carving rest.) 21.50 **st.** 10.95 – ***Borders Brasserie :*** **Meals** *closed Sunday and Bank Holidays* (lunch booking essential) a la carte 20.85/29.75 **st.** 10.95 – 13.95 – **187 rm** 185.00/205.00 **st.**, 2 suites.

Fredrick's, Shoppenhangers Rd, SL6 2PZ, ☎ (01628) 581000, *reservations@fredricks-hotel.co.uk, Fax (01628) 771054,* – 150. MC AE VISA JCB. X c
closed Christmas and New Year – **Meals** – (see ***Fredrick's*** below) – **36 rm** 195.00/260.00 **t.**, 1 suite – SB.

Walton Cottage, Marlow Rd, SL6 7LT, ☎ (01628) 624394, *res@waltoncottagehotel.co.uk, Fax (01628) 773851* – rest, – 60. MC AE VISA JCB. Y e
closed 23 December-2 January – **Meals** *(closed Friday-Sunday and Bank Holidays)* (lunch booking essential)/dinner 17.75 **t.** 9.00 – **66 rm** 113.00/150.00 **st.**, 3 suites.

Fredrick's (at Fredrick's H.), Shoppenhangers Rd, SL6 2PZ, ☎ (01628) 581000, *reservations@fredricks-hotel.co.uk, Fax (01628) 771054,* – MC AE VISA JCB X c
closed Christmas, New Year and Saturday lunch – **Meals** (booking essential for non-residents) 27.50/38.50 and a la carte 44.00/61.50 **t.** 17.50.

MAIDENHEAD

Bad Godesberg Way ..... Y 2
Belmont Park Avenue .... V 3
Blackamoor Lane .... V 5
Boyn Hill Avenue .... Z 6
Braywick Road .... Z 7
Bridge Street............. Y 9
College Road............. V 13
Cookham Road .... Y 14
Crescent (The) .... Y 15
Ferry Road.............. X 17
Frascati Way............ YZ 18
Furze Platt Road.......... V 20
Grenfell Place .... Z 21
Gringer Hill .... V 22
Harrow Lane .... V 24
High Street .... Y
High Street
BRAY-ON-THAMES .... X 25
King's Grove .... Z 27
Linden Avenue .... V 28
Lower Cookham
Road.................. V 29
Manor Lane............. X 31
Market Street .... Y 32
Nicholson's Walk
Shopping Centre ..... YZ
Norreys Drive .... X 35
Oldfield Road .... V 36
Ray Street .... V 38
Ray Mill Rd West......... V 39
St. Ives Road .... Y 41
St. Mark Road .... V 42
Stafferton Way .... Z 43
Upper Bray Road .... X 45

For business or tourist interest:
MICHELIN Red Guide EUROPE.

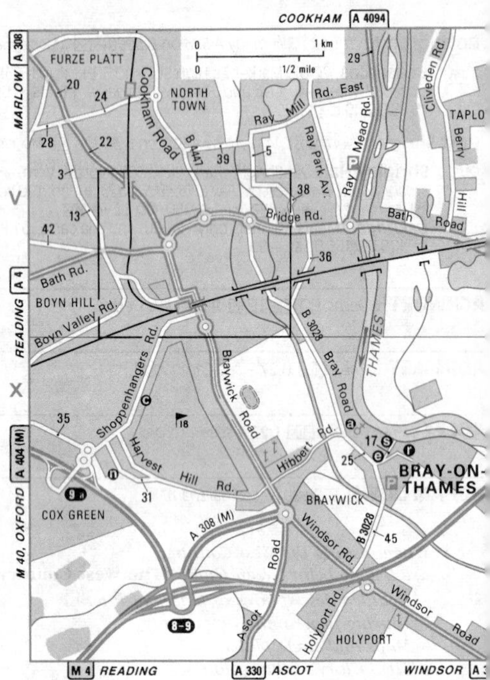

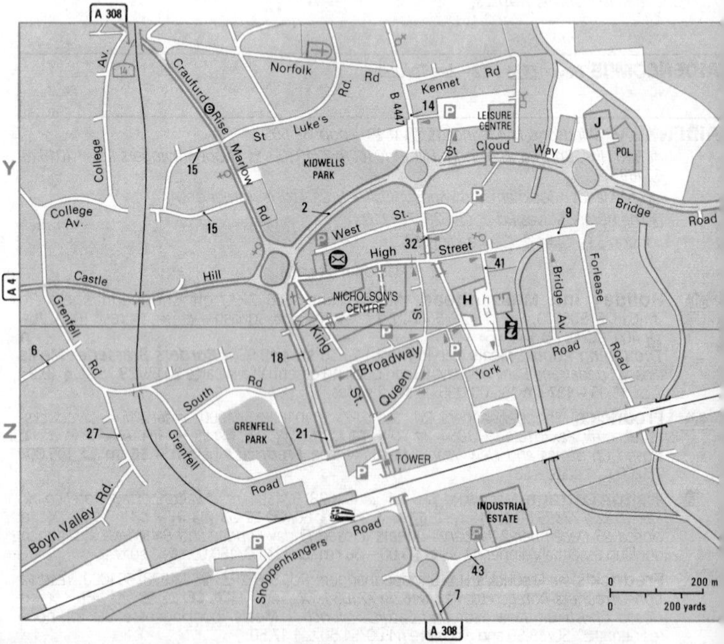

ENGLAND

AIDEN NEWTON *Dorset* 403 404 M 31.
London 144 – Exeter 55 – Taunton 37 – Weymouth 16.

Le Petit Canard, Dorchester Rd, DT2 0BE, (01300) 320536, *craigs@le-petit-canard.freeserve.co.uk, Fax (01300) 321286* – . MC AE VISA
closed Sunday and Monday – **Meals** (dinner only) 26.00/28.00 **t.** 12.50.

AIDSTONE *Kent* 404 V 30 *Great Britain G. – pop. 90 878.*
Env. : *Leeds Castle* ★ *AC, SE : 4½ m. by A 20 and B 2163.*
Tudor Park Hotel, Ashford Rd, Bearsted (01622) 734334 – Cobtree Manor Park, Chatham Rd, Boxley (01622) 753276.
The Gatehouse, Palace Gdns, Mill St (01622) 602169 – Motorway Service Area, junction 8, M 20, Hollingbourne (01622) 739029.
London 36 – Brighton 64 – Cambridge 84 – Colchester 72 – Croydon 36 – Dover 45 – Southend-on-Sea 49.

Hilton Maidstone, Bearsted Rd, ME14 5AA, Northeast : 1 ½ m. by A 249 (01622) 734322, *reservations@hilton.com, Fax (01622) 734600,* , , , – , rest, – 200. MC AE VISA
Meals *(closed Saturday lunch)* 14.95/19.95 and dinner a la carte approx. 28.65 **st.** 11.80 – 10.50 – **145 rm** 125.00 **st.**, 1 suite – SB.

Travel Inn, Allington Lock, Sandling, ME14 3AS, North : 2 ¼ m. by A 229 off Aylesford rd (01622) 717251, *Fax (01622) 715159,* – rm, rest, . MC AE VISA.
Meals (grill rest.) – **40 rm** 41.95 **t.**

Travel Inn, London Rd, ME16 0HG, Northwest : 2 m. on A 20 (01622) 752515, *Fax (01622) 672469* – rm, . MC AE VISA.
Meals (grill rest.) – **40 rm** 41.95 **t.**

at Bearsted *East : 3 m. by A 249 off A 20 – Maidstone.*

Marriott Tudor Park H. & Country Club, Ashford Rd, ME14 4NQ, on A 20 (01622) 734334, *Fax (01622) 735360,* <, , , , , , , – – 250. MC AE VISA.
Fairviews **: Meals** (dinner only) a la carte 25.00/40.00 **t.** 12.75 – ***LongWeekend*** **: Meals** a la carte 16.50/29.50 **t.** 12.75 – 14.00 – **119 rm** 105.00/109.00 **t.**, 1 suite.

Soufflé Restaurant on the Green, The Green, ME14 4DN, (01622) 737065, *Fax (01622) 737065,* – . MC AE VISA JCB
closed Saturday lunch, Sunday dinner and Monday – **Meals** 13.50/22.50 and a la carte 31.00/33.00 **t.** 12.50.

at Wateringbury *Southwest : 4½ m. on A 26 – Maidstone.*

Premier Lodge, Tonbridge Rd, ME18 5NS, (0870) 7001560, *Fax (0870) 7001561,* – rm, – 25. MC AE VISA.
Meals (grill rest.) a la carte approx. 16.95 **t.** 8.75 – **38 rm** 49.95 **t.**

at Larkfield *Northwest : 3¼ m. on A 20 – Maidstone.*

Larkfield Priory, London Rd, ME20 6HJ, (01732) 846858, *larkfieldpriory@corushotels.com, Fax (01732) 846786* – – 80. MC AE VISA.
Meals (bar lunch Monday to Saturday)/dinner a la carte 16.40/23.30 **st.** 11.95 – 10.75 – **52 rm** 80.00/90.00 **st.** – SB.

MAIDSTONE SERVICE AREA *Kent* 404 V 30 – *Maidstone.*

Travel Inn without rest., Hollingbourne, ME17 1SS, at junction 8 of M 20 (01622) 631100, *Fax (01622) 739535* – . MC AE VISA.
closed Christmas and New Year – **58 rm** 41.95.

MALDON *Essex* 404 W 28 – *pop. 15 841.*
Forrester Park, Beckingham Rd, Great Totham (01621) 891406 – , Bunsay Downs, Little Baddow Rd, Woodham Walter (01245) 412648.
Coach Lane (01621) 856503.
London 42 – Chelmsford 9 – Colchester 17.

Five Lakes H. Golf Country Club & Spa, Colchester Rd, Tolleshunt Knights, CM9 8HX, Northeast : 8 ¼ m. by B 1026 (01621) 868888, *enquiries@fivelakes.co.uk, Fax (01621) 869696,* , , , , , , , squash – – 400. MC AE VISA.
Camelot **: Meals** *(closed Sunday and Monday)* (dinner only) 24.50 and a la carte 22.40/30.40 **t.** 13.00 – ***Bejerano's Brasserie*** **: Meals** 17.85/18.50 and a la carte 13.00 – 9.50 – **110 rm** 105.00/148.00 **st.**, 4 suites – SB.

MALMESBURY *Wilts.* 403 404 N 29 *The West Country G. – pop. 4 218.*
See : *Town★ – Market Cross★★ – Abbey★.*
Town Hall, Market Lane *(01666) 823748.*
London 108 – Bristol 28 – Gloucester 24 – Swindon 19.

Old Bell, Abbey Row, SN16 0AG, (01666) 822344, *info@oldbellhotel.com*, *Fax (01666) 825145*, « Part 13C former abbots hostel », – – 35. VISA
Meals – (see ***The Restaurant*** below) – **29 rm** 75.00/100.00 **t.**, 2 suites – SB.

Knoll House, Swindon Rd, SN16 9LU, on B 4042 (01666) 823114, *knollhotel@malmesbury64.freeserve.co.uk*, *Fax (01666) 823897*, heated, – VISA
closed 27-29 December – **Meals** (dinner only) a la carte 14.00/25.00 **t.** 10.00 – **22 rm** 50.00/90.00 **t.** – SB.

XXX **The Restaurant** (at Old Bell H.), Abbey Row, SN16 0AG, (01666) 822344, *Fax (01666) 825145*, – VISA JCB
Meals (booking essential) 11.75/21.75 and a la carte 21.75/28.00 **t.** 15.75.

at Crudwell *North : 4 m. on A 429 – Malmesbury.*

Mayfield House, SN16 9EW, on A 429 (01666) 577409, *mayfield@callnetuk.com*, *Fax (01666) 577977*, – rest, – 30. VISA JCB
Meals (bar lunch Monday-Saturday)/dinner 18.50 **t.** 8.95 – **24 rm** 60.00/80.00 **t.** – SB.

MALPAS *Ches.* 402 403 L 24 – *pop. 3 684.*
London 177 – Birmingham 60 – Chester 15 – Shrewsbury 26 – Stoke-on-Trent 30.

Tilston Lodge without rest., Tilston, SY14 7DR, Northwest : 3 m. on Tilston R (01829) 250223, *Fax (01829) 250223*, « Rare breed farm animals », , –
3 rm 45.00/74.00 **st.**

MALVERN *Worcs.* 403 404 N 27 – *see Great Malvern.*

MALVERN WELLS *Worcs.* 403 404 N 27 – *see Great Malvern.*

MAN (Isle of)

402 FG 21 *Great Britain G.* – *pop. 71 714.*

PRACTICAL INFORMATION

⛴ *from Douglas to Belfast (Isle of Man Steam Packet Co. Ltd) (summer only) (2 h 45 mn) – from Douglas to Republic of Ireland (Dublin) (Isle of Man Steam Packet Co. Ltd) (2 h 45 mn) – from Douglas to Heysham (Isle of Man Steam Packet Co.) (3 h 30 mn) – from Douglas to Liverpool (Isle of Man Steam Packet Co. Ltd) (2 h 30 mn/4 h).*

SIGHTS

See : *Laxey Wheel★★ – Snaefell★ (✳★★★) – Cregneash Folk Museum★.*

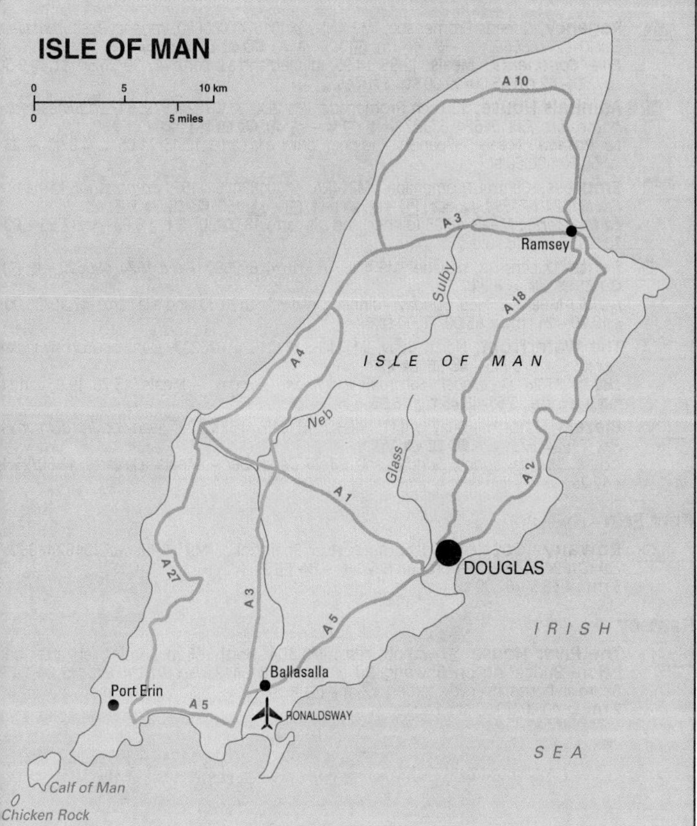

llasalla.

XX **Haworths,** Main Rd, IM9 2DA, ℘ (01624) 822940 – MO VISA
Meals 15.00/30.00 and dinner a la carte 25.00/28.00 **t.** 10.00.

uglas – *pop. 23 487.*

Douglas Municipal, Pulrose Park ℘ (01624) 675952 – King Edward Bay, Groudle Rd, Onchan ℘ (01624) 620430.

Ronaldsway Airport : ℘ (01624) 821600, SW : 7 m. – **Terminal** : *Coach service from Lord St.*

Sea Terminal Building ℘ (01624) 686766.

Sefton, Harris Promenade, IM1 2RW, ℘ (01624) 645500, *info@seftonhotel.co.inn, Fax (01624) 676004,* – rm, – 80. MO AE VISA.
The Gallery : **Meals** a la carte 16.00/23.00 **t.** 9.00 – **96 rm** 81.00/99.00 **st.**, 4 suites – SB.

Mount Murray H. & Country Club, Santon, IM4 2HT, Southwest : 4 ¾ m. by A 5 ℘ (01624) 661111, *hotel@mountmurray.com, Fax (01624) 611116,* squash – rm, – 300. MO AE VISA.
Murray's : **Meals** (dinner only and Sunday lunch)/dinner 18.95 and a la carte approx. 26.85 **st.** 10.95 – ***Charlotte's Bistro :*** **Meals** *(closed Sunday lunch)* a la carte 11.95/16.85 **st.** 10.95 – **90 rm** 85.00/105.00 **st.**

Regency, Queens Promenade, IM2 4NN, ℘ (01624) 680680, *regency@securemail-l.*
Fax (01624) 680690, ≤ – |‡|, ⇌ rm, TV ✆ – 🏛 70. MC AE Diners VISA JCB. ✂
Five Continents: **Meals** 12.95/14.95 (dinner) and a la carte 17.90/26.50 **st.** 🍷 9.5
☐ 7.50 – **42 rm** 65.00/90.00 **st.**, 3 suites.

Admirals House, 12 Loch Promenade, IM1 2LX, ℘ (01624) 629551, *enquiries@adm*
house.com, Fax (01624) 675021 – |‡| TV ✆ – 🏛 40. MC AE VISA. ✂
La Posada: **Meals** - Spanish - (dinner only) a la carte 16.43/21.05 **t.** 🍷 9.50 – **23**
☐ 60.00/120.00 **st.**

Empress, Central Promenade, IM2 4RA, ℘ (01624) 661155, *empresshotel@manx.*
Fax (01624) 673554, Lб, ≘s, ☐ – |‡|, ▤ rest, TV – 🏛 150. MC AE Diners VISA. ✂
La Brasserie: **Meals** 16.95 (dinner) and a la carte 18.00/20.75 **t.** 🍷 6.95 – ☐ 7.95 – **99**
70.00/75.00 **t.**, 3 suites.

Penta, Queens Promenade, IM9 4NE, ℘ (01624) 680680, *Fax (01624) 680690* – |‡| TV
MC AE Diners VISA JCB. ✂
Ivaldi: **Meals** *(closed Sunday)* (dinner only) 13.50/20.00 and a la carte 17.15/26.00
🍷 10.00 – **21 rm** ☐ 65.00/73.00 **st.**

The Waterfront, North Quay, IM1 4LH, ℘ (01624) 673222, *jeanwoodford@manx.*
Fax (01624) 673145 – MC AE Diners VISA
closed 25-26 December, Saturday lunch and Sunday – **Meals** 15.75/19.95 and
ner a la carte 26.65/48.45 **t.** 🍷 15.95.

Blazers, North Quay, IM1 4LH, ℘ (01624) 673222, *jeanwoodford@manx.*
Fax (01624) 673145 – MC AE Diners VISA
closed Saturday lunch, Sunday and 25-26 December – **Meals** a la carte 12.60/23.1
🍷 12.25.

Port Erin – *pop. 3 218.*

Rowany Cottier without rest., Spaldrick, IM9 6PE, ℘ (01624) 8322
Fax (01624) 835685, ≤ Port Erin Bay, 🌳 – ⇌ TV P. ✂
5 rm ☐ 38.50/62.00 **t.**

Ramsey – *pop. 6 874.*

The River House 🐦 without rest., IM8 3DA, North : ¼ m. turning left after bri
before Bridge Inn on Bowring Rd ℘ (01624) 816412, *Fax (01624) 816412,* ≤, «
Georgian house, riverside setting », 🌳 – TV P. ✂
2 rm ☐ 40.00/70.00 **st.**, 1 suite.

Questa guida non è un repertorio di tutti gli alberghi e ristoranti,
nè comprende tutti i buoni alberghi e ristoranti di Gran Bretagna ed Irlanda.
Nell'intento di tornare utili a tutti i turisti,
siamo indotti ad indicare esercizi
di tutte le classi ed a citarne soltanto un certo numero di ognuna.

MANCHESTER

Gtr. Manchester 402 403 404 N 23 *Great Britain G. – pop. 402 889*

London 202 – Birmingham 86 – Glasgow 221 – Leeds 43 – Liverpool 35 – Nottingham 72.

TOURIST INFORMATION

Manchester Visitor Centre, Town Hall Extension, Lloyd St. ☎ (0161) 234 3157.

Manchester Airport, International Arrivals Hall, Terminal 1 ☎ (0161) 436 3344 – Manchester Airport, International Arrivals Hall, Terminal 2 ☎ (061) 489 6412.

PRACTICAL INFORMATION

18 *Heaton Park, Prestwich ☎ (0161) 654 9899,* ABV.

18 *Houldsworth Park, Houldsworth St., Reddish, Stockport ☎ (0161) 442 9611.*

18 *Chorlton-cum-Hardy, Barlow Hall, Barlow Hall Rd ☎ (0161) 881 3139.*

18 *William Wroe, Pennybridge Lane, Flixton ☎ (0161) 748 8680.*

Manchester International Airport : ☎ (0161) 489 3000, S : 10 m. by A 5103 – AX – and M 56 – **Terminal** : *Coach service from Victoria Station.*

SIGHTS

See : *City★ - Castlefield Heritage Park★* CZ – *Town Hall★* CZ – *City Art Gallery★* CZ **M2** – *Cathedral★ (stalls and canopies★)* CY – *Museum of Science and Industry★* CZ M.

Env. : *Whitworth Art Gallery★, S* : *1½ m.*

Exc. : *Quarry Bank Mill★, S : 10 m. off B 5166, exit 5 from M 56.*

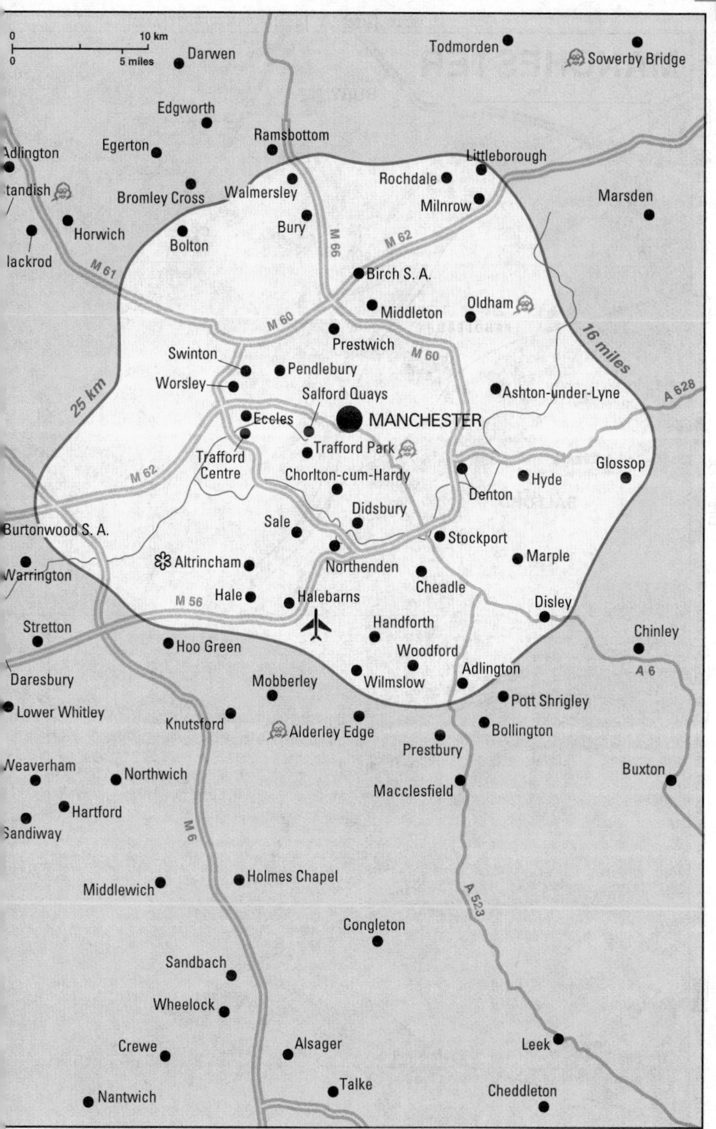

__En saison,__ surtout dans les stations fréquentées,
il est prudent de retenir à l'avance.
Cependant, si vous ne pouvez pas occuper la chambre
que vous avez retenue, prévenez immédiatement l'hôtelier.

Si vous écrivez à un hôtel à l'étranger, joignez à votre lettre
un coupon-réponse international (disponible dans les bureaux de poste).

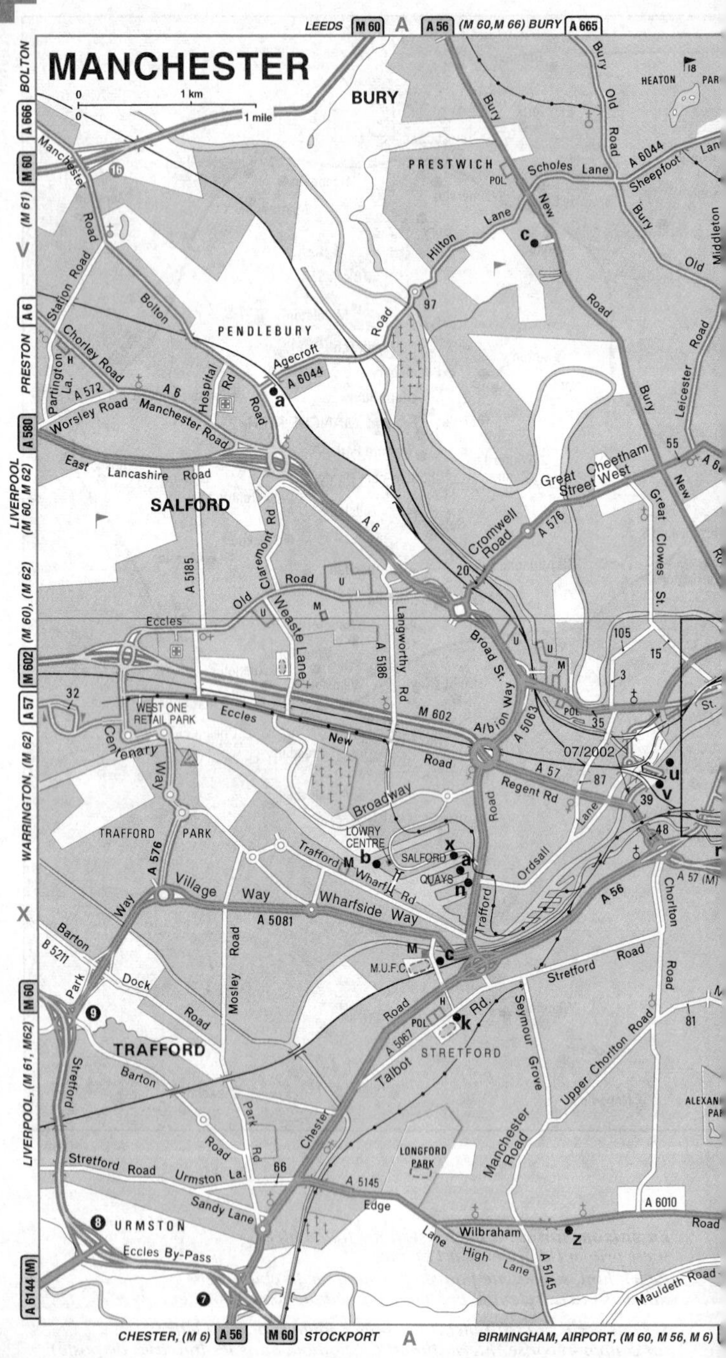

MANCHESTER
0 1 km
0 1 mile
LEEDS M 60 A A 56 (M 60, M 66) BURY A 665
BOLTON A 666 M 60 (M 61) V A 6 PRESTON A 580 LIVERPOOL (M 60, M 62) (M 60), (M 62) M 602 A 57 WARRINGTON, (M 62) X M 60 LIVERPOOL, (M 61, M62) A 6144 (M)
CHESTER, (M 6) A 56 M 60 STOCKPORT A BIRMINGHAM, AIRPORT, (M 60, M 56, M 6)
BURY
PRESTWICH
PENDLEBURY
SALFORD
TRAFFORD PARK
TRAFFORD
URMSTON
STRETFORD
HEATON PARK
LOWRY CENTRE
SALFORD QUAYS
WEST ONE RETAIL PARK
M.U.F.C.
LONGFORD PARK
Manchester Road
Bolton Road
Station Road
Chorley Road
Partington La.
Worsley Road
Manchester Road
Hospital Rd
Agecroft Road
East Lancashire Road
Hilton Lane
Scholes Lane
Bury Old Road
Bury New Road
Sheepfoot Lane
Leicester Road
Great Cheetham Street West
Cromwell Road
Great Clowes St.
Old Road
Claremont Rd
Weaste Lane
Langworthy Rd
Broad St.
Albion Way
Eccles New Road
Regent Rd
Ordsall Lane
Centenary Way
Broadway
Trafford Wharf Rd
Village Way
Wharfside Way
Trafford Road
Chorlton Road
Barton Dock Road
Mosley Road
Park Road
Stretford Road
Talbot Rd.
Chester Road
Seymour Grove
Upper Chorlton Road
Manchester Road
Barton Road
Park Rd
Stretford Road
Urmston La.
Sandy Lane
Edge Lane
Wilbraham Road
High Lane
Mauldeth Road
Eccles By-Pass
A 6044 A 572 A 6 A 5185 A 576 A 5186 A 5063 A 57 A 56 A 5081 B 5211 A 5067 A 5145 A 6010
M 602
07/2002
POL

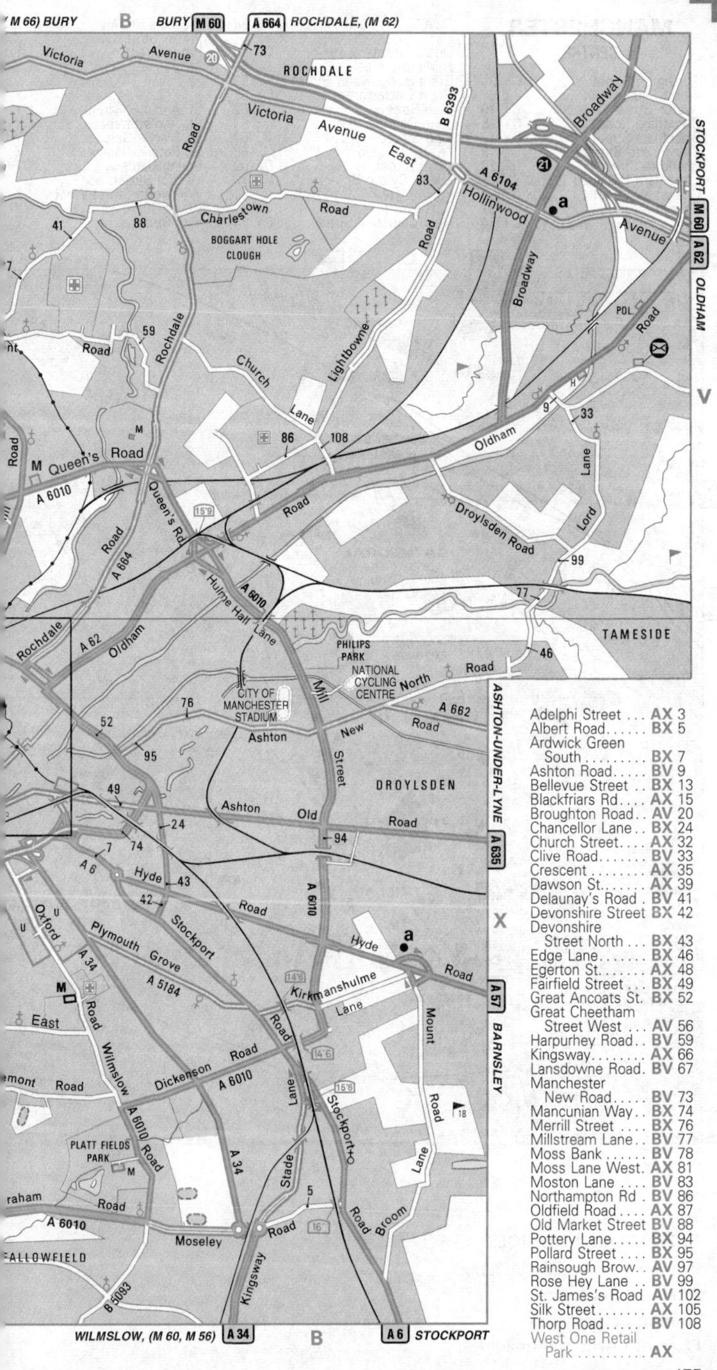
(M 66) BURY
B
BURY M 60
A 664 ROCHDALE, (M 62)
Victoria Avenue
ROCHDALE
Victoria Avenue East
B 6393
A 6104
Hollinwood Avenue
Broadway
STOCKPORT
M 60
A 62
OLDHAM
Charlestown Road
BOGGART HOLE CLOUGH
Rochdale Road
Church Lane
Lightbowne Road
Moston Lane
POL
Road
V
Oldham Road
Lord Lane
Droylsden Road
M Queen's Road
A 6010
Queen's Rd
A 664
Hulme Hall Lane
A 6010
TAMESIDE
Rochdale
A 62
Oldham
PHILIPS PARK
NATIONAL CYCLING CENTRE
North Road
CITY OF MANCHESTER STADIUM
Ashton New Road
A 662
Mill Street
DROYLSDEN
Ashton Old Road
ASHTON-UNDER-LYNE
A 635
A 6
Hyde Road
Stockport
A 6010
X
Oxford Road
Plymouth Grove
A 34
A 5184
Kirkmanshulme Lane
A 57
BARNSLEY
Mount Road
East
Wilmslow Road
Dickenson Road
A 6010
Stockport Road
PLATT FIELDS PARK
Road
A 6010
Moseley Road
Stade
Kingsway
Broom Lane
FALLOWFIELD
B 5093
WILMSLOW, (M 60, M 56) A 34
B
A 6 STOCKPORT

MANCHESTER
CENTRE

Addington Street .... CY 2
Albert Square .... CZ 6
Aytoun Street .... CZ 10
Blackfriars Road .... CY 15
Blackfriars Street .... CY 17
Brazennose Street .... CZ 18
Charlotte Street .... CZ 25
Cheetham Hill Road .... CY 27
Chepstow Street .... CZ 28
Church Street .... CY 31
Corn Exchange .... CY 34
Dale Street .... CZ 38
Deansgate .... CYZ
Ducie Street .... CZ 45
Fairfield Street .... CZ 49
Great Bridgewater Street .. CZ 53
Great Ducie Street .... CY 57
High Street .... CY 62
John Dalton Street .... CZ 63
King Street .... CZ 64
Liverpool Road .... CZ 68
Lloyd Street .... CZ 69
Lower Byrom St. .... CZ 70
Lower Mosley Street ...... CZ 71
Mosley Street .... CZ
New Cathedral Street ..... CY 84
Nicholas Street .... CZ 85
Parker Street .... CZ 91
Peter Street .... CZ 92
Princess Street .... CZ
Shambles (The) Shopping Centre .... CY
St. Ann's Square .... CY 1
St. Ann's Street .... CY 1
St. Mary's Gate .... CY 1
St. Peter's Square .... CZ 1
Spring Gardens .... CZ 1
Viaduct Street .... CY 1
Whitworth Street West .. CZ 1
Withy Grove .... CY 1
York Street .... CZ 1

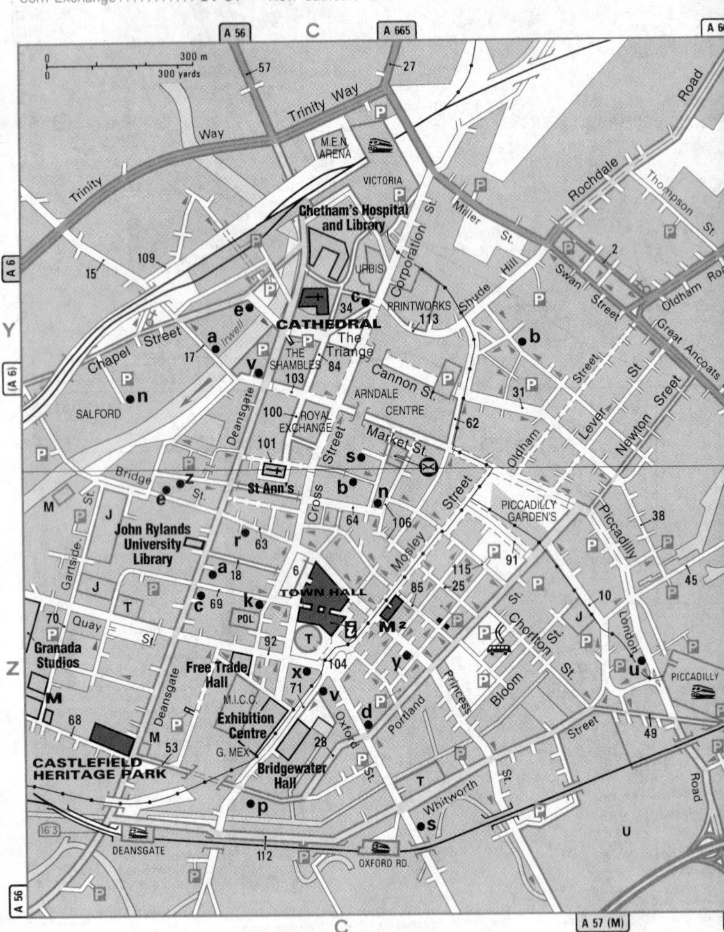

GREEN TOURIST GUIDES
Picturesque scenery, buildings
Attractive routes
Touring programmes
Plans of towns and buildings.

The Lowry, 50 Dearmans Pl, Chapel Wharf, Salford, M3 5LH, (0161) 827 4000, *enquiries@thelowryhotel.com, Fax (0161) 827 4001,* – rm, – 400. VISA CY n
Meals – (see ***River Room Marco Pierre White*** below) – 15.50 – **157 rm** 185.00, 7 suites.

Crowne Plaza Manchester-The Midland, Peter St, M60 2DS, (0161) 236 3333, *sales@basshotels-uknorth.co.uk, Fax (0161) 932 4100,* , , squash – , rm, – 500. VISA CZ x
Trafford Room : Meals *(closed Monday and Tuesday dinner and Saturday lunch)* (carving rest.) 16.95/26.95 **st.** 13.95 – (see also ***The French Restaurant*** and ***Nico Central*** below) – 14.50 – **289 rm** 160.00 **t.**, 14 suites.

Le Meridien Victoria and Albert, Water St, M3 4JQ, (0161) 832 1188, *gm1452@forte-hotels.com, Fax (0161) 834 2484,* « 19C converted warehouse, television themed interior » – , rm, – 300. VISA. AX u
1844 : Meals 18.44 (dinner) and a la carte 16.70/35.00 **st.** – 15.00 – **154 rm** 170.00/190.00 **st.**, 4 suites.

Renaissance, Blackfriars St, Deansgate, M3 2EQ, (0161) 835 2555, *manchester.sales@renaissancehotels.com, Fax (0161) 835 3077* – – 400. VISA. CY v
Meals 12.50/15.50 and dinner a la carte 17.00/24.50 **st.** 14.00 – 12.50 – **196 rm** 110.00/145.00 **st.**, 4 suites – SB.

Palace, Oxford St, M60 7HA, (0161) 288 1111, *Fax (0161) 288 2222,* « Victorian Gothic architecture, former Refuge Assurance building » – – 700. VISA. CZ s
Waterhouses : Meals (carving lunch) 19.00/39.50 and dinner a la carte 19.00/39.00 13.50 – 13.50 – **241 rm** 154.00/174.00 **st.**, 11 suites – SB.

Malmaison, Piccadilly, M1 3AQ, (0161) 278 1000, *manchester@malmaison.com, Fax (0161) 278 1002,* « Contemporary interior », , – , rm, – 75. VISA JCB. CZ u
Brasserie : Meals 11.95/12.95 and a la carte 21.35/26.80 **t.** 13.95 – 10.75 – **154 rm** 120.00 **s.**, 13 suites.

Castlefield, Liverpool Rd, M3 4JR, (0161) 832 7073, *info@castlefield-hotel.co.uk, Fax (0161) 837 3534,* , , – , rest, – 60. VISA JCB. AX v
Meals *(closed Sunday dinner)* (bar lunch)/dinner a la carte 12.35/21.00 **st.** 8.45 – **48 rm** 81.00/87.00 **st.** – SB.

Jurys Inn, 56 Great Bridgewater St, M1 5LE, (0161) 953 8888, *jurysinnmanchester@jurysdoyle.com, Fax (0161) 953 9090* – , rm, – 50. VISA. CZ p
Meals (bar lunch)/dinner 16.95 **st.** 10.00 – **265 rm** 67.00 **st.**

Premier Lodge, North Tower, Victoria Bridge St, Salford, M3 5AS, (0870) 7001488, *mpremierlodge1@snr.co.uk, Fax (0870) 7001489* – , rm, rest, . VISA. CY e
Meals (grill rest.) (dinner only) a la carte approx. 12.45 **t.** 8.45 – **170 rm** 49.95 **t.**

Premier Lodge, Gaythorne, River St, M15 5JF, (0870) 7001490, *Fax (0870) 7001491* – , rm, . VISA AX r
closed 24-29 December – **Meals** (grill rest.) (dinner only) a la carte approx. 12.45 **t.** 8.45 – **200 rm** 49.95 **t.**

Express by Holiday Inn without rest., Debdale Park, Hyde Rd, M18 7LJ, Southeast : 4 m. by A 6 off A 57 (0161) 231 9900, *Fax (0161) 220 8555* – – 45. VISA JCB BX a
97 rm 57.00 **st.**

Travel Inn Metro, 112-114 Portland St, M1 4WB, (0870) 2383315, *Fax (0161) 233 5299* – , rest, . VISA JCB. CZ d
Meals (grill rest.) – **226 rm** 49.95 **t.**

Travelodge, Townbury House, Blackfriars St, Salford, M3 5AB, (0161) 834 9476, *Fax (0161) 839 5181* – , rm, rest, . VISA. CY a
Meals (cafe bar) – **181 rm** 49.95 **t.**

Premier Lodge, 7-11 Lower Mosley St, M2 3DW, (0870) 7001476, *Fax (0870) 7001477* – , rm, rest, – 50. VISA CZ v
Meals (grill rest.) – **147 rm** 49.95 **t.**

ENGLAND

XXXX **The French** (at Crowne Plaza Manchester-The Midland H.), Peter St, M60 2
(0161) 236 3333 – P. MC AE VISA CZ
Meals (dinner only) 29.00 and a la carte 34.70/48.85 **st.** 13.95.

XXX **River Room Marco Pierre White** (at The Lowry H.), 50 Dearmans Pl, Chapel Wh
Salford, M3 5LH, (0161) 827 4003, *enquiries@thelowryhotel.com, Fax (0161) 827 40(*
P. MC AE VISA CY
Meals 12.00/22.00 and a la carte 23.50/35.50 **t.** 10.50.

XXX **The Lincoln,** 1 Lincoln Sq, M2 5LN, (0161) 834 9000, *Fax (0161) 834 9555* – . MC
VISA JCB CZ
closed 1 week Christmas, Saturday lunch, Sunday dinner and Bank Holidays – **Meals** 16
(lunch) and a la carte 19.40/28.85 **t.** 11.00.

XX **Simply Heathcotes,** Jackson Row, M2 5WD, (0161) 835 3536, *manchester@sin*
heathcotes.co.uk, Fax (0161) 835 3534 – . MC AE VISA CZ
closed Bank Holidays – **Meals** 15.50 (lunch) and a la carte 23.50/31.00 **t.** 11.50.

XX **Nico Central** (at Crowne Plaza Manchester-The Midland H.), 2 Mount St, M60 2
(0161) 236 6488, *manchester@nicocentral.co.uk, Fax (0161) 236 8897* – . MC AE
JCB – *closed lunch Saturday and Sunday and Bank Holidays* – **Meals** 12.95 (lur
and a la carte 19.25/27.95 **t.** 12.95. CZ

XX **Stock,** The Stock Exchange, 4 Norfolk St, M2 1DW, (0161) 839 6644, *stockrestauran*
ol.com, Fax (0161) 839 6655, « Edwardian, former stock exchange trading floor » – MC
VISA – *closed 25-26 December, first week January and Sunday* – **Meals** - Italian - 12
(lunch) and a la carte 17.45/31.00 **t.** 12.50. CY

XX **Reform,** King St, Spring Gdns, M2 4ST, (0161) 839 9966, *Fax (0161) 839 0404* – . MC
VISA JCB CZ
closed lunch Saturday and Sunday – **Meals** 16.95 (lunch) and a la carte 23.90/36.9
16.00.

XX **Yang Sing,** 34 Princess St, M1 4JY, (0161) 236 2200, *info@yang.sing.co*
Fax (0161) 236 5934 – . MC AE VISA CZ
closed 25 December – **Meals** - Chinese - a la carte 14.70/21.80 **st.** 10.95.

XX **Koreana,** Kings House, 40a King St West, M3 2WY, (0161) 832 4330, *113036.17*
compuserve.com, Fax (0161) 832 2293 – MC AE VISA CZ
closed 25-26 December, 1 January, Sunday and lunch Saturday and Bank Holidays – **Mea**
Korean - 12.40 and a la carte 12.50/27.00 **t.** 7.95.

X **Shimla Pinks,** Dolefield Crown Sq, M3 3EN, (0161) 839 7099, *Fax (0161) 832 2202* –
MC AE VISA JCB CZ
closed 25 December, 1 January, Sunday and Saturday lunch – **Meals** - Indian - 15.95/19
and a la carte **t.** 10.50.

X **Le Petit Blanc,** 55 King St, M2 4LQ, (0161) 832 1000, *manchester@lepetitblanc.co*
Fax (0161) 832 1001 – . MC AE VISA CZ
closed 25 December – **Meals** 15.00 (lunch) and a la carte 19.45/29.00 **t.** 11.00.

X **The Restaurant Bar and Grill,** 14 John Dalton St, M2 6JR, (0161) 839 19
Fax (0161) 835 1886 – . MC AE VISA JCB CZ
Meals a la carte 20.00/30.00 **t.** 10.95.

X **Livebait,** 22 Lloyd St, Albert Sq, M2 5WH, (0161) 817 4110, *Fax (0161) 817 4111* – .
AE VISA CZ
closed 25 December – **Meals** - Seafood - a la carte 22.45/34.65 **st.**

X **Zinc Bar & Grill,** The Triangle, Hanging Ditch, M4 3ES, (0870) 3334333, *zinc@conr*
restaurants.co.uk, Fax (0161) 827 4212, – MC AE VISA CY
closed 25-26 December – **Meals** a la carte 17.00/35.00 **st.** 10.50.

X **Market,** 104 High St, M4 1HQ, (0161) 834 3743, *marketrestaurant@btinternet.co*
Fax (0161) 834 3743 – MC AE VISA JCB CY
closed August, 1 week Easter, 1 week Christmas and Sunday-Tuesday – **Meals** (dinner o
a la carte 19.15/26.35 **t.** 9.95.

at Northenden *South : 5¼ m. by A 5103* – **AX** – *Manchester.*

Posthouse Manchester, Palatine Rd, M22 4FH, (0870) 400 90
Fax (0161) 946 0139 – , rm, rest, P – 150. MC AE VISA
Meals (bar lunch Saturday) 15.00 and a la carte approx. 20.00 **st.** – 11.50 – **190**
79.00 **st.** – SB.

at Didsbury *South : 5½ m. by 5103* – **AX** – *on A 5145* – *Manchester.*

Eleven Didsbury Park without rest., 11 Didsbury Park, M20 5LH, (0161) 448 77
enquiries@elevendidsburypark.com, Fax (0161) 448 8282, « Contemporary interior »,
P. MC AE VISA JCB,
10.50 **14 rm** 99.50/125.50 **st.**

Manchester Airport *South : 9 m. by A 5103 – AX – off M 56 – ✉ Manchester.*

Radisson SAS Manchester Airport, Chicago Ave, M90 3RA, ✆ (0161) 490 5000, *sales airport.manchester@radissonsas.com, Fax (0161) 490 5100,* <, Ls, ≘s, ▢ – |‡|, ✈ rm, ▤ TV ✆ & P – 🏛 350. MC AE ① VISA JCB. ✂
Phileas Fogg : **Meals** (buffet lunch)/dinner a la carte 26.00/40.50 **t.** 18.00 – ***Runway Café :*** **Meals** a la carte 14.75/23.15 **t.** 18.00 – ☕ 13.00 – **354 rm** 140.00/195.00 **st.**, 6 suites.

Hilton Manchester Airport, Outwood Lane (Terminal One), M90 4WP, ✆ (0161) 435 3000, *manhitw@hilton.com, Fax (0161) 435 3040,* Ls, ≘s, ▢ – |‡|, ✈ rm, ▤ TV ✆ & P – 🏛 300. MC AE VISA
Meals 21.00 and a la carte 3.95 – ***Portico :*** **Meals** *(closed Sunday)* (dinner only) 22.50/35.00 **t.** 13.50 – ***Lowry's :*** **Meals** *(closed Saturday lunch)* 21.00/25.00 and dinner a la carte 20.70/29.85 **t.** 13.50 – ☕ 16.50 – **224 rm** 150.00/185.00 **st.**, 1 suite – SB.

Posthouse Manchester Airport, Outwood Lane (Terminal One), M90 3NS, ✆ (0161) 437 5811, *Fax (0161) 436 2340,* Ls, ≘s, ▢ – |‡|, ✈ rm, ▤ TV & P – 🏛 30. MC AE ① VISA JCB. ✂
Meals (bar lunch Saturday) 15.00 and a la carte 22.85/27.95 **st.** 11.95 – ***Sampans*** *(✆ (0161) 448 4074) :* **Meals** - South East Asian - *(closed Sunday)* (dinner only) 17.95/24.95 and a la carte approx. 25.00 **t.** 12.45 – ☕ 13.95 – **295 rm** 109.00 **st.** – SB.

Etrop Grange, Thorley Lane, M90 4EG, ✆ (0161) 499 0500, *etropgrange@corushotels.com, Fax (0161) 499 0790* – ✈ TV ✆ P – 🏛 40. MC AE ① VISA JCB
Meals *(closed Saturday lunch)* 18.50/25.00 **st.** 14.00 – ☕ 12.50 – **62 rm** 125.00/145.00 **st.**, 2 suites – SB.

Holiday Inn Garden Court, Outwood Lane, (Terminal One), M90 4HL, ✆ (0161) 498 0333, *reservations@mchap.co.uk, Fax (0161) 498 0222* – |‡|, ✈ rm, ▤ rest, TV ✆ & P – 🏛 90. MC AE ① VISA JCB. ✂
Meals (bar lunch)/dinner 15.95 and a la carte 15.70/29.70 **t.** 10.75 – ☕ 9.95 – **226 rm** 72.50/99.00 **st.**

Travel Inn, Finney Lane, Heald Green, SK8 2QH, East : 2 m. by B 5166 ✆ (0161) 499 1944, *Fax (0161) 437 4910* – ✈ rm, ▤ rest, TV & P – 🏛 70. MC AE ① VISA. ✂
Meals (grill rest.) – **60 rm** 41.95 **t.**

XXX **Moss Nook,** Ringway Rd, Moss Nook, M22 5WD, East : 1 ¼ m. on Cheadle rd ✆ (0161) 437 4778, *Fax (0161) 498 8089* – P. MC AE VISA
closed 2 weeks Christmas-New Year, Saturday lunch, Sunday and Monday – **Meals** 18.50/31.50 and a la carte 32.50/49.50 **t.** 12.00.

Trafford Park *Southwest : 2 m. by A 56 and A 5081 – ✉ Manchester.*

Golden Tulip, Waters Reach, M17 1WS, ✆ (0161) 873 8899, *info@qualitymanchester.co.uk, Fax (0161) 872 6556* – |‡| ✈ TV ✆ & P – 🏛 250. MC AE ① VISA. ✂ AX c
closed 24 December-1 January – **Meals** – (see ***Rhodes & Co.*** below) – ☕ 10.00 – **111 rm** 85.00/99.50 **st.**

Old Trafford Lodge without rest., Lancashire County Cricket Club, Talbot Rd, Old Trafford, M16 0PX, ✆ (0161) 874 3333, *lodge@lccc.co.uk,* <, « Within Lancashire County Cricket Club » – |‡| ✈ TV ✆ P. MC AE VISA. ✂ AX k
68 rm 59.00 **t.**

XX **Rhodes & Co.,** Waters Reach, M17 1WS, ✆ (0161) 868 1900, *Fax (0161) 868 1901* – ▤ P. MC AE ① VISA AX c
closed 1 week Christmas, Saturday, Sunday and lunch Bank Holidays – **Meals** 12.50 (lunch) and a la carte 18.70/30.15 **t.** 12.50.

Salford Quays *Southwest : 2¼ m. by A 56 – AX – off A 5063 – ✉ Manchester.*

Copthorne Manchester, Clippers Quay, M5 2XP, ✆ (0161) 873 7321, *manchester@mill-cop.com, Fax (0161) 873 7318,* Ls, ≘s – |‡|, ✈ rm, ▤ rest, TV ✆ & P – 🏛 150. MC AE ① VISA. ✂ AX n
Chandlers : **Meals** (dinner only) 31.50 **st.** 16.25 – ***Clippers :*** **Meals** (carving rest.) (bar lunch Saturday and Sunday) 21.00 **st.** 16.25 – ☕ 13.95 – **166 rm** 150.00/185.00 **st.**

Express by Holiday Inn without rest., Waterfront Quay, M5 2XW, ✆ (0161) 868 1000, *Fax (0161) 868 1068,* < – |‡| ✈ TV ✆ & P – 🏛 25. MC AE ① VISA. ✂ AX a
120 rm 65.00 **st.**

Travel Inn, Basin 8, The Quays, M5 4SQ, ✆ (0161) 872 4026, *Fax (0161) 876 0094,* < – |‡|, ✈ rm, ▤ rest, TV & P. MC AE ① VISA. ✂ AX x
Meals (grill rest.) – **52 rm** 41.95 **t.**

XX **The Lowry,** Pier 8, M5 2AZ, ✆ (0161) 876 2121, *Fax (0161) 876 2021* – ✈ ▤. MC AE ① VISA AX b
closed 25 December – **Meals** (booking essential Sunday and Monday dinner) a la carte 17.15/25.90 **t.** 11.95.

ENGLAND

at Chorlton-Cum-Hardy *Southwest : 5 m. by A 5103 on A 6010 – ✉ Manchester.*

Abbey Lodge without rest., 501 Wilbraham Rd, M21 0UJ, ✆ (0161) 862 92 *Fax (0161) 862 9266,* – TV P. AX
☕ 5.00 – **4 rm** 40.00/50.00.

at Trafford Centre *Southwest : 5¼ m. by A 56 –* **AX** *– and A 5081 – ✉ Manchester.*

Travel Inn, Wilderspool Wood, M17 8WW, ✆ (0161) 747 8850, *Fax (0161) 747 4763 –* rm, rest, TV P. MO AE VISA.
Meals (grill rest.) – **59 rm** 41.95 **t.**

at Eccles *West : 4 m. by M 602 –* **AX** *– ✉ Manchester.*

Highbury without rest., 113 Monton Rd, M30 9HQ, Northwest : 1 ¼ m. by A 576 B 5229 ✆ (0161) 787 8545, *enquiries@highbury-hotel.co.uk, Fax (0161) 787 9023 –* TV MO AE VISA
16 rm ☕ 38.00/49.50 **st.**

at Worsley *West : 7¼ m. by M 602 –* **AV** *– and M 60 (eastbound) on A 572 – ✉ Manchester.*

Marriott Worsley Park Hotel & Country Club, Worsley Park, M28 2QT, on A ✆ (0161) 975 2000, *salesadmin.worsleypark@marriotthotels.co.uk, Fax (0161) 799 63* , Lδ, ≘s, , 18, – , rm, rest, TV P – 250. MO AE VISA JCB
Brindley's : **Meals** *(closed Saturday lunch)* 15.00/29.00 and dinner a la carte 24.00/31 13.50 – ☕ 13.00 – **153 rm** 114.00, 5 suites.

Novotel Manchester West, Worsley Brow, M28 2YA, at junction 13 of M ✆ (0161) 799 3535, *Fax (0161) 703 8207,* heated – , rm, TV P – 220. MO VISA JCB
Meals 13.00/17.00 and a la carte 17.15/22.00 **t.** 11.25 – ☕ 9.50 – **119 rm** 72.00 **t.**

at Pendlebury *Northwest : 4 m. by A 6 on A 666 – ✉ Manchester.*

Premier Lodge, 219 Bolton Rd, M27 8TG, ✆ (0870) 7001470, *Fax (0870) 700147* rm, rest, TV P. MO AE VISA. AV
Meals (grill rest.) a la carte approx. 13.00 **t.** 8.95 – **31 rm** 46.95 **t.**

at Swinton *Northwest : 4 m. by A 580 –* **AV** *– and A 572 on B 5231 – ✉ Manchester.*

Premier Lodge, East Lancs Rd, M27 0AA, Southwest : ½ m. on A 580 ✆ (0870) 70014 *Fax (0870) 7001473 –* rm, rest, TV P. MO AE VISA.
Meals (grill rest.) a la carte approx. 12.50 **t.** 7.80 – **27 rm** 46.95 **t.**

MANCHESTER AIRPORT *Gtr. Manchester* 402 403 404 N 23 – *see Manchester.*

MANGOTSFIELD *Bristol* 403 404 M 29 – *see Bristol.*

MANNINGTREE *Essex* 404 X 28 – *pop. 5 043 – ✉ Colchester.*
London 67 – Colchester 10 – Ipswich 12.

Stour Bay Café, 39-43 High St, CO11 1AH, ✆ (01206) 396687, *Fax (01206) 395462 –* VISA
closed first 2 weeks January, Monday, Tuesday and Sunday dinner – **Meals** 10 (lunch) and a la carte 14.00/28.00 11.00.

MANSFIELD *Notts.* 402 403 404 Q 24.
18 *Sherwood Forest, Eakring Rd ✆ (01623) 626689.*
London 145 – Derby 24 – Nottingham 16 – Sheffield 30.

Stoneleigh, Crow Hill Drive, NG19 7AE, off A 617 ✆ (01623) 650692, *stoneleigh.mansf @ntlworld.com,* « Victorian Gothic house », – TV P.
closed 1 week spring, 2 weeks autumn, 25 December and 1 January – **Meals** (by arran ment) 25.00 **st.** – **3 rm** ☕ 37.50/70.00 **st.** – SB.

MARAZION *Cornwall* 403 D 33 *The West Country G. – pop. 1 381 – ✉ Penzance.*
Env. : *St Michael's Mount★★ (≤★★) – Ludgvan★ (Church★) N : 2 m. by A 30 – Chysaus Village★, N : 2 m. by A 30 – Gulval★ (Church★) W : 2½ m – Prussia Cove★, SE : 5½ m. by A and minor rd.*
9 *Praa Sands, Penzance ✆ (01736) 763445.*
London 318 – Penzance 3 – Truro 26.

Ennys without rest., Trewhella Lane, St Hilary, TR20 9BZ, East : 2 ½ m. by Turnpike Rd, on B 3280 (01736) 740262, *ennys@zetnet.co.uk, Fax (01736) 740055,* « 17C manor house, working farm », heated, VISA. *13 February-October* – **5 rm** 45.00/80.00 **st.**

Perranuthnoe *Southeast : 1 ¾ m. by A 394 – Penzance.*

Ednovean Farm without rest., TR20 9LZ, (01736) 711883, *info@ednoveanfarm.co.uk, Fax (01736) 710480,* « Converted 17C barn », VISA. *closed25-26 December* – **3 rm** 50.00/70.00 **s.**

ARDEN *Herefordshire – see Hereford.*

ARGATE *Kent* 404 Y 29.

22 High St (01843) 220241.

London 74 – Canterbury 17 – Dover 21 – Maidstone 43.

Travel Inn, Station Green, Station Rd, CT9 5AF, (01843) 299280, *Fax (01843) 221453* – rm, rest, VISA.
Meals (grill rest.) – **44 rm** 41.95 **t.**

ARKET BOSWORTH *Leics.* 402 403 404 P 26 – *pop. 2 019* – *Nuneaton.*

London 109 – Birmingham 30 – Coventry 23 – Leicester 22.

Softleys, Market Pl, CV13 0JS, (01455) 290464, *Fax (01455) 290464* – VISA.
closed 25 December – **Meals** *(closed Monday lunch and Sunday)* a la carte 15.00/22.70 **t.** 10.75 – **3 rm** 50.00/65.00 **t.**

ARKET HARBOROUGH *Leics.* 404 R 26 – *pop. 16 563.*

Great Oxendon Rd (01858) 463684.

Council Offices, Adam and Eve St (01858) 821270.

London 88 – Birmingham 47 – Leicester 15 – Northampton 17.

The Angel, High St, LE16 7NL, (01858) 462702, *angel@menzies_hotels.co.uk, Fax (01858) 410464* – rest, – 25. VISA JCB
The Brasserie : **Meals** 8.50 (lunch) and dinner a la carte 13.75/24.20 **st.** 9.95 – **37 rm** 65.00/95.00 **st.** – SB.

Marston Trussell *(Northants.) West : 3 ½ m. by A 4304 – Market Harborough.*

The Sun Inn, Main St, LE16 9TY, (01858) 465531, *manager@suninn.com, Fax (01858) 433155* – 80. VISA.
closed 24 December-7 January – **Meals** (bar lunch)/dinner a la carte 18.00/26.00 **t.** 10.00 – **20 rm** 69.00 **t.**

ARKET RASEN *Lincs.* 402 404 T 23 – *pop. 2 948.*

London 156 – Boston 41 – Great Grimsby 19 – Lincoln 16.

Bleasby House without rest., Legsby, LN8 3QN, Southeast : 4 ¼ m. by B 1202 (01673) 842383, *Fax (01673) 844808,* « Working farm »,
closed 2 week Christmas – **3 rm** 22.00/42.00 **st.**

ARKFIELD *Leics.* 402 403 404 Q 25 – *pop. 3 897.*

London 113 – Birmingham 45 – Leicester 6 – Nottingham 24.

Field Head, Markfield Lane, LE67 9PS, on B 5327 (01530) 245454, *fieldhead.hotel@virgin.net, Fax (01530) 243740* – 50. VISA.
*accommodation closed 24-26 December***Meals** a la carte approx. 15.00 **st.** 7.75 – **28 rm** 75.00/95.00 **st.**

Travelodge, Littleshaw Lane, LE67 0PP, Northwest : 1 m. on A 50 at junction 22 of M 1 (01530) 244777, *Fax (01530) 244580* – VISA JCB.
Meals (grill rest.) – **40 rm** 49.95 **t.**

ARKHAM MOOR *Notts.* 403 – *Retford.*

London 143 – Lincoln 18 – Nottingham 28 – Sheffield 27.

Travelodge, DN22 0QU, on A 1 (northbound carriageway) (01777) 838091, *Fax (01777) 838091* – rm, rest, VISA JCB.
Meals (grill rest.) – **40 rm** 42.95 **t.**

MARKINGTON *N. Yorks.* 402 P 21 – *see Ripon.*

MARKS TEY *Essex* 404 W 28 – *see Colchester.*

MARLBOROUGH *Wilts.* 403 404 O 29 *The West Country G.* – *pop. 6 788.*

See : *Town*★.

Env. : *Savernake Forest*★★ *(Grand Avenue*★★★*), SE : 2 m. by A 4 – Whitehorse (≤★), N*
5 m – West Kennett Long Barrow★*, Silbury Hill*★*, W : 6 m. by A 4.*

Exc. : *Ridgeway Path*★★ *– Avebury*★★ *(The Stones*★*, Church*★*), W : 7 m. by A 4 – Crof*
Beam Engines★ **AC**, *SE : 9 m. by A 346 – Wilton Windmill*★ **AC**, *SE : 9 m. by A 346, A 338*
minor rd.

The Common ℘ (01672) 512147.

George Lane Car Park ℘ (01672) 513989.

London 84 – Bristol 47 – Southampton 40 – Swindon 12.

Ivy House, High St, SN8 1HJ, ℘ (01672) 515333, *ivy.house@btconnect.cc*
Fax (01672) 515338 – ⇔ rest, TV P – 50. MC AE VISA.
Scotts : **Meals** 18.00 (dinner) and a la carte 22.50/25.00 **t.** 9.00 – **30 rm** 75.
110.00 **t.** – SB.

Coles, 27 Kingsbury Hill, SN8 1JA, ℘ (01672) 515004, *Fax (01672) 841504* – MC VISA
closed 25-26 December and Bank Holidays – **Meals** a la carte 19.75/28.25 **t.** 9.75.

MARLOW *Bucks.* 404 R 29 – *pop. 17 771.*

to Henley-on-Thames (Salter Bros. Ltd) (summer only) – to Maidenhead, Cookham
Windsor (Salter Bros. Ltd) (summer only).

31 High St ℘ (01628) 483597.

London 35 – Aylesbury 22 – Oxford 29 – Reading 14.

Danesfield House, Henley Rd, SL7 2EY, Southwest : 2 ½ m. on A 41
℘ (01628) 891010, *sales@danesfieldhouse.co.uk, Fax (01628) 890408,* « Italian Ren
sance style mansion ≤ terraced gardens and River Thames », –
⇔ rest, rest, TV P – 100. MC AE VISA JCB.
Oak Room : **Meals** 24.50/39.50 and a la carte 40.75/51.00 **st.** 19.50 – ***Orangery :*** **Me**
a la carte 23.45/27.00 **st.** 19.50 – **86 rm** 185.00/225.00 **st.**, 1 suite – SB.

Compleat Angler, Marlow Bridge, Bisham Rd, SL7 1RG, ℘ (0870) 4008100, *herit*
hotels-marlow.compleat-angler@forte-hotels.com, Fax (01628)486388, ≤ River Tham
, « Riverside setting », – , ⇔ rm, TV P – 120. MC AE VISA JCB
Riverside : **Meals** 23.50/34.50 and a la carte 44.50/55.00 **t.** 18.50 – ***Waltons brasse***
Meals a la carte 17.00/47.50 **t.** 15.00 – 15.50 – **61 rm** 215.00/270.00, 3 suites – SB.

Country House without rest., Bisham Rd, SL7 1RP, ℘ (01628) 890606, *countryhouse*
rlow@btinternet.com, Fax (01628) 890983, – TV P. MC AE VISA JCB
11 rm 80.00/109.00 **t.**

Holly Tree House without rest., Burford Close, Marlow Bottom, SL7 3NE, North : 2 m
A 4155 and Wycombe Rd, off Marlow Bottom ℘ (01628) 891110, *hollytreeaccommoda*
@yahoo.co.uk, Fax (01628) 481278, heated, – ⇔ TV P. MC AE VISA JCB.
5 rm 69.50/89.50 **st.**

Royal Oak, Frieth Rd, Bovingdon Green, SL7 2JF, West : 1 ¼ m. by A 4
℘ (01628) 488611, *Fax (01628) 478680,* , – P. MC AE VISA
closed 25-26 December – **Meals** a la carte 16.00/24.00 **t.** 9.75.

MARPLE *Gtr. Manchester* 402 403 404 N 23 – *pop. 19 829.*

London 190 – Chesterfield 35 – Manchester 11.

Springfield without rest., 99 Station Rd, SK6 6PA, ℘ (0161) 449 07
Fax (0161) 449 0766, – ⇔ TV P. MC AE VISA.
8 rm 45.00/65.00 **st.**

MARSDEN *W. Yorks.* 402 404 O 23 – *pop. 3 873* – ✉ *Huddersfield.*

London 195 – Leeds 22 – Manchester 18 – Sheffield 30.

Olive Branch with rm, Manchester Rd, HD7 6LU, Northeast : 1 m. on A
℘ (01484) 844487, *reservations@olivebranch.uk.com, Fax (01484) 841549* – TV P. MC VI
closed 2 weeks January and 1 week August – **Meals** *(closed Monday and lunch Tuesday*
Saturday) 14.95 (lunch) and a la carte 23.85/29.80 **t.** 10.95 – 5.50 – **3 rm** 45.00/60.0

MARSH BENHAM *West Berks.* – *see Newbury.*

ARSTON MORETAINE *Beds.* 404 S 27 – *see Bedford.*

ARSTON TRUSSELL *Northants.* 404 R 26 – *see Market Harborough.*

ARTINHOE *Devon – see Lynton.*

ARTOCK *Somerset* 403 L 31 *The West Country G. – pop. 4 051.*

See : *Village★ – All Saints★★.*

Env. : *Montacute House★★ AC, SE : 4 m. – Muchelney★★ (Parish Church★★), NW : 4½ m. by B 3165 – Ham Hill (≤★★), S : 2 m. by minor roads.*

Exc. : *Martock★ – Barrington Court★ AC, SW : 7½ m. by B 3165 and A 303.*

London 148 – Taunton 19 – Yeovil 6.

Hollies, Bower Hinton, TA12 6LG, South : 1 m. on B 3165 ☎ (01935) 822232, *theholliés hotel@ukonline.co, Fax (01935) 822249,* – TV ☎ & P – 175. MC AE VISA JCB.
Meals *(closed Sunday)* (dinner only) a la carte 18.45/22.45 **st.** 10.25 – **30 rm** 68.00/ 88.00 **st.**, 2 suites.

ARTON *Lincs.* 402 404 R 24 – *pop. 508.*

London 155 – Doncaster 27 – Lincoln 14 – Nottingham 40.

Black Swan without rest., 21 High St, DN21 5AH, ☎ (01427) 718878, *info/reservations @blackswan-marton.co.uk, Fax (01427) 718878,* – TV & P. MC VISA.
8 rm 30.00/60.00 **s.**

ARYPORT *Cumbria* 401 402 J 19 – *pop. 11 572.*

London 324 – Carlisle 28 – Keswick 20.

The Lifeboat Inn & Harbour Restaurant, Shipping Brow, Senhouse St, CA15 6AB, ☎ (01900) 810906, *Fax (01900) 810907* –
closed Monday and Tuesday – **Meals** - Seafood specialities - a la carte 13.50/23.00 **t.** 8.95.

ASHAM *N. Yorks.* 402 P 21 – *pop. 1 171 – ✉ Ripon.*

London 231 – Leeds 38 – Middlesbrough 37 – York 32.

Swinton Park, Swinton, HG4 4JH, Southwest : 2 m ☎ (01765) 680900, *enquiries @swintonpark.com, Fax (01765) 680901,* ≤, « 17C castle with Georgian and Victorian additions », – TV ☎ & P – 120. MC AE VISA
***Samuels* :** **Meals** 16.00/22.00 and dinner a la carte 23.50/35.00 **t.** 11.00 – **17 rm** 95.00/275.00 **t.**, 3 suites – SB.

King's Head, Market Pl, HG4 4EF, ☎ (01765) 689295, *Fax (01765) 689070,* « 18C » – TV ☎. MC AE VISA JCB.
Meals a la carte 13.35/24.40 **st.** 10.25 – 6.95 – **10 rm** 55.00/70.00 **st.**

Floodlite, 7 Silver St, HG4 4DX, ☎ (01765) 689000 – MC AE VISA
closed 1 week February, 1 week October, Monday, Sunday dinner and lunch Tuesday-Thursday – **Meals** 12.50/15.00 and a la carte 16.00/27.70 **t.** 9.50.

ATFEN *Northd.* 401 402 O 18 – *pop. 500.*

London 309 – Carlisle 42 – Newcastle upon Tyne 24.

Matfen Hall, NE20 0RH, ☎ (01661) 886500, *info@matfenhall.com, Fax (01661) 886055,* ≤, « Early 19C country mansion in extensive parkland », 18, – TV & P – 100. MC AE VISA
***Library* :** **Meals** (dinner only and Sunday lunch) 22.50 **st.** 14.45 – ***The Conservatory* :** **Meals** a la carte 17.25/24.50 **st.** 14.45 – **31 rm** 110.00/235.00 **st.** – SB.

ATFIELD *Kent – see Royal Tunbridge Wells.*

ATLOCK *Derbs.* 402 403 404 P 24 *Great Britain G. – pop. 14 680.*

Exc. : *Hardwick Hall★★ AC, E : 12½ m. by A 615 and B 6014.*

The Pavilion, Matlock Bath ☎ (01629) 55082 – Crown Sq ☎ (01629) 583388.

London 153 – Derby 17 – Manchester 46 – Nottingham 24 – Sheffield 24.

Riber Hall, Riber Village, DE4 5JU, Southeast : 3 m. by A 615 ☎ (01629) 582795, *info @riber-hall.co.uk, Fax (01629) 580475,* « Part Elizabethan manor house », – TV P. MC AE VISA JCB
Meals 16.00/34.00 **t.** 14.95 – 8.00 – **14 rm** 97.00/127.00 **t.** – SB.

MAWDESLEY *Lancs.* 402 L 23 – *pop. 1 750* – ✉ *Ormskirk.*
London 217 – Liverpool 26 – Manchester 28 – Preston 15.

Mawdsley Eating House and H., Hall Lane, L40 2QZ, Northeast : ½
✆ (01704) 822552, *mawdsley@aol.com, Fax (01704) 822096,* – –
MC AE VISA.
closed 25 and 26 December – **Meals** 11.00 and dinner a la carte 15.00/20.75 **t.** 10.00
56 rm 45.00/65.00 **t.** – SB.

MAWNAN SMITH *Cornwall* 403 E 33 – *see Falmouth.*

MEADOW HEAD *S. Yorks.* – *see Sheffield.*

MEDWAY SERVICE AREA *Medway* 404 V 29/30 – ✉ *Gillingham.*
London 39 – Canterbury 22 – Maidstone 11.

Travelodge without rest., ME8 8PQ, on M 2 between junctions 4 and 5 (westbou
carriageway) ✆ (01634) 236903, *Fax (01634) 263187* – MC AE VISA JCB.
58 rm 59.95 **t.**

MELBOURN *Cambs.* 404 U 27 – *pop. 4 006* – ✉ *Royston (Herts.).*
London 44 – Cambridge 10.

MelbournBury, Royston Rd, SG8 6DE, Southwest : ¾ m. ✆ (01763) 2611
melbournbury@biztobiz.co.uk, Fax (01763) 262375, ≤, « Country house of Tudor origin
– MC AE VISA.
closed Easter, 2 weeks in summer and Christmas-2 January – **Meals** (by arrangeme
(communal dining) 20.00 **st.** 9.50 – **3 rm** 65.00/100.00 **st.**

Chiswick House without rest., 3 Chiswick End, Meldreth, SG8 6LZ, Northwest : 1 m.
Meldreth rd, off Whitecroft Rd ✆ (01763) 260242, « Part 14C timbered former far
house », –
March-October – **6 rm** 40.00/48.00.

Pink Geranium, 25 Station Rd, SG8 6DX, ✆ (01763) 260215, *lawrence@pinkgeranium.
uk, Fax (01763) 262110,* – MC AE VISA JCB
closed Sunday dinner and Monday – **Meals** 18.00/19.50 (lunch) and a la carte 33.50/47.50
11.95.

Sheene Mill with rm, Station Rd, SG8 6DX, ✆ (01763) 261393, *reservations@stevensau
ers.co.uk, Fax (01763) 261376,* ≤, « Restored 17C water mill », – rm, rest,
MC AE VISA.
closed 26 December and 1 January – **Meals** *(closed Sunday dinner)* 14.00/19.
and a la carte 27.95/37.50 10.95 – **9 rm** 75.00/110.00 **t.**

MELKSHAM *Wilts.* 403 404 N 29 *The West Country G.* – *pop. 13 074.*
Env. : *Corsham Court*★★ *AC, NW : 4½ m. by A 365 and B 3353 – Lacock*★★ *(Lacock Abbe
AC, High Street*★*, St Cyriac*★*, Fox Talbot Museum of Photography*★ *AC) N : 3 ½
by A 350.*
Church St ✆ *(01225) 707424.*
London 113 – Bristol 25 – Salisbury 35 – Swindon 28.

Beechfield House, Beanacre, SN12 7PU, North : 1 m. on A 350 ✆ (01225) 7037
Fax (01225) 790118, ≤, « Late Victorian country house, gardens », heated, –
– 50. MC AE VISA.
closed 26 December-1 January – **Meals** *closed Sunday dinner* 13.95 (lunch) and a la ca
19.50/28.15 **t.** 11.95 – **21 rm** 80.00/175.00 **t.** – SB.

Shurnhold House without rest., Shurnhold, SN12 8DG, Northwest : 1 m. on A 3
✆ (01225) 790555, *susan.tanir@shurnholdhouse.com, Fax (01225) 793147,* « Jacobe
manor house, gardens » – MC AE VISA.
closed 1 week Christmas – – 7.50 – **4 rm** 45.00/98.00 **s.**

at Whitley *Northwest : 2 m. by A 365 on B 3353* – ✉ *Melksham.*

Pear Tree Inn, Top Lane, SN12 8QX, by First Lane ✆ (01225) 709131, *Fax (01225) 7022*
– MC VISA
Meals (booking essential) 12.25 (lunch) and a la carte 18.25/28.45 **t.** 10.50.

MELLOR *Lancs.* – *see Blackburn.*

ELTON MOWBRAY *Leics.* 402 404 R 25 – *pop. 24 348.*
Waltham Rd, Thorpe Arnold ✆ (01664) 562118.
Melton Carnegie Museum, Thorpe End ✆ (01664) 480992.
London 113 – Leicester 15 – Northampton 45 – Nottingham 18.

Stapleford Park, LE14 2EF, East : 5 m. by B 676 on Stapleford rd ✆ (01572) 787522, *reservations@stapleford.co.uk, Fax (01572) 787651,* ≤, « Part 16C and 19C mansion in park », – 200. VISA
Meals (booking essential to non-residents) (light lunch Monday-Saturday)/dinner 44.00 **t.** 22.00 – **49 rm** 175.00/265.00, 2 suites – SB.

Quorn Lodge, 46 Asfordby Rd, LE13 0HR, West : ½ m. on A 6006 ✆ (01664) 566660, *quornlodge@aol.com, Fax (01664) 480660* – – 80. VISA JCB.
Meals *(closed Sunday dinner)* 15.75/19.75 and a la carte **t.** 9.95 – **19 rm** 53.50/75.00 **t.** – SB.

EMBURY *Devon – see Axminster.*

EMBURY SERVICE AREA *Newbury* 403 404 P 29 – ✉ *Newbury.*

Days Inn, Membury, Lambourn Woodlands, RG17 7TZ, M 4 between junctions 14 and 15 (westbound carriageway) ✆ (01488) 72336, Reservations (Freephone) 0800 0280400, *Fax (01488) 72336* – rm, VISA JCB
Meals (grill rest.) a la carte approx. 9.00 **st.** – 5.00 – **38 rm** 49.00 **st.**

ENDLESHAM GREEN *Suffolk* 404 W 27 – *see Stowmarket.*

ERIDEN *W. Mids.* 403 404 P 26 – *see Coventry.*

EVAGISSEY *Cornwall* 403 F 33 *The West Country G.* – *pop. 2 272.*
See : *Town*★★.
Env. : *NW : Lost Gardens of Heligan*★.
London 287 – Newquay 21 – Plymouth 44 – Truro 20.

Kerryanna without rest., Treleaven Farm, PL26 6RZ, ✆ (01726) 843558, *linda.hennah@talk21.com, Fax (01726) 843558,* heated, – VISA.
March-October – – **6 rm** 48.00/56.00 **st.**

EYSEY HAMPTON *Glos.* 403 404 O 28 – ✉ *Cirencester.*
London 101 – Bristol 44 – Gloucester 26 – Oxford 29.

Masons Arms with rm, High St, GL7 5JT, ✆ (01285) 850164, *jane@themasonsarms.freeserve.co.uk, Fax (01285) 850164,* « Part 17C inn » – rest, VISA JCB.
Meals *(closed Sunday dinner November-April)* a la carte 12.90/18.35 **t.** 9.95 – **9 rm** 40.00/64.00 **t.**

ICHAELWOOD SERVICE AREA *Glos.* 403 M29 – ✉ *Dursley.*

Days Inn without rest., Lower Wick, GL11 6DD, M 5 between junctions 13 and 14 (northbound carriageway) ✆ (01454) 261513, Reservations (Freephone) 0800 0280400, *michaelwood.hotel@welcomebreak.co.uk, Fax (01454) 261513* – VISA JCB
7.45 – **38 rm** 45.00 **t.**

ICKLEHAM *Surrey* 404 (42) – *pop. 484.*
London 21 – Brighton 32 – Guildford 14 – Worthing 34.

The King William IV, Byttom Hill, RH5 6EL, North : ½ m. by A 24 ✆ (01372) 372590, – VISA
closed 25 December and dinner 31 January – **Meals** a la carte 14.50/20.00 **t.** 8.95.

CKLEOVER *Derbs.* 402 403 404 P 25 – *see Derby.*

CKLETON *Glos.* 403 404 O 27 – *see Chipping Campden.*

DDLEHAM *N. Yorks.* 402 O 21 – *pop. 754.*
London 233 – Kendal 45 – Leeds 47 – York 45.

Carlton-in-Coverdale *Southwest : 4½ m. on Coverdale Rd* – ✉ *Leyburn.*

Abbots Thorn, DL8 4AY, ✆ (01969) 640620, *abbots.thorn@virgin.net, Fax (01969) 640304,* ≤ –
Meals (by arrangement) (communal dining) 14.00 **st.** – **3 rm** 32.00/54.00.

MIDDLESBROUGH *Middlesbrough* **402** Q 20 – *pop. 147 430.*

Middlesbrough Municipal, Ladgate Lane ✆ (01642) 315533 – Brass Castle Lane, Mart ✆ (01642) 311515.

Cleveland Transporter Bridge (toll) **BY**.

Teesside Airport : ✆ (01325) 332811, SW : 13 m. by A 66 – **AZ** *– and A 19 on A 67.*

51 Corporation Rd ✆ (01642) 243425.

London 246 – Kingston-upon-Hull 89 – Leeds 66 – Newcastle upon Tyne 41.

MIDDLESBROUGH

Albert Road . . . . **BY** 2
Ayresome Green Lane . . . . **AZ** 3
Bridge Street West . . . . **AY** 4
Bright Street . . . . **BY** 5
Clairville Road . . . . **BZ** 6
Cleveland Centre . . . . **ABY**
Cleveland Street . . . . **BY** 7
Corporation Road . . . . **BY** 8
Devonshire Road . . . . **AZ** 10
Dundas Street . . . . **ABY** 12
Eastbourne Road . . . . **AZ** 14
Ferry Road . . . . **BY** 15
Finsbury Street . . . . **AZ** 16
Grange Road . . . . **ABY** 17
Gresham Road . . . . **AZ** 18
Hartington Road . . . . **AY** 19
Hill Street Centre . . . . **AY**
Linthorpe Road . . . . **AY**
Longford Street . . . . **AZ** 22
Newport Road . . . . **AY**
Ormesby Road . . . . **BZ** 24
Princes Road . . . . **AZ** 26
St. Barnabas Road . . . . **AZ** 27
Saltersgill Avenue . . . . **BZ** 28
Sussex Street . . . . **AY** 30
Tees Bridge Approach Road . . . . **AZ**
West Terrace . . . . **BZ**
Westbourne Grove . . . . **BZ**
Wilson Street . . . . **AY**
Woodlands Road . . . . **BZ**
Zetland Street . . . . **ABY**

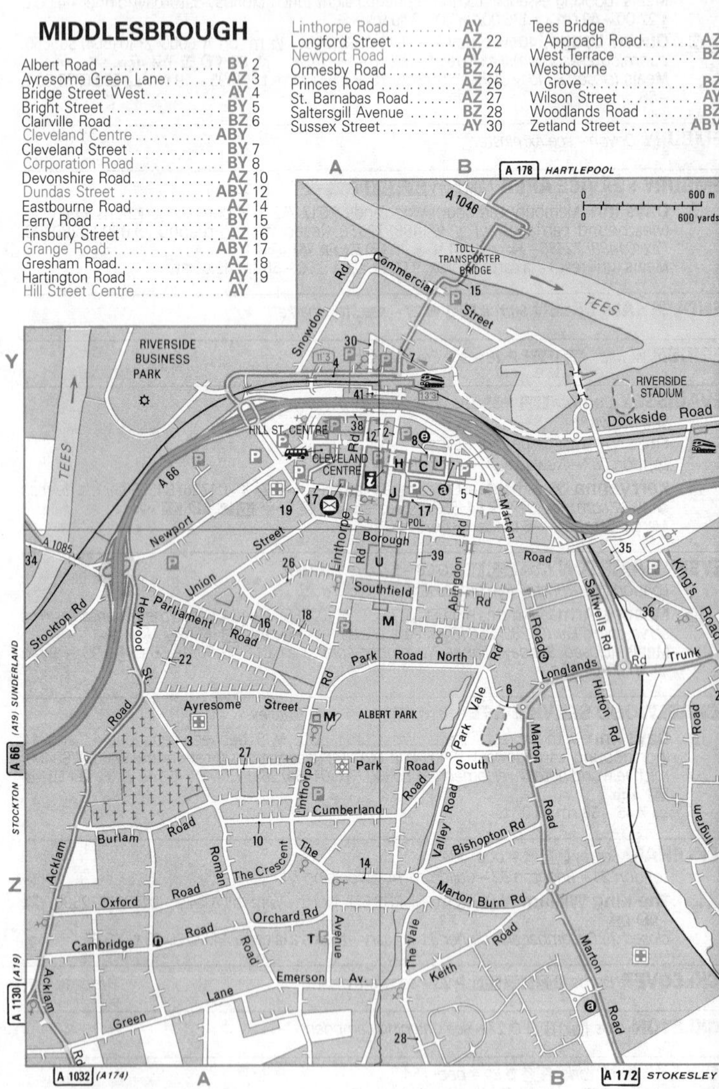

Thistle, Fry St, TS1 1JH, ✆ (0870) 3339141, *Fax (0870) 3339241*, – rest, 350. **BY**
Gengis : Meals a la carte 13.95/22.50 **st.** 11.75 – 11.00 – **132 rm** 103.00/134.00 st, SB.

Express by Holiday Inn without rest., Marton Rd, TS4 3BS, ☎ (01642) 814444, *Fax (01642) 829999* – lift, ⇔ TV ☎ & P – 30. MC AE VISA BZ a
74 rm 49.95 t.

Grey House without rest., 79 Cambridge Rd, TS5 5NL, ☎ (01642) 817485, *Fax (01642) 817485*, – ⇔ TV P. MC VISA AZ n
9 rm 40.00/60.00 s.

The Purple Onion, 80 Corporation Rd, TS1 2RF, ☎ (01642) 222250, *Fax (01642) 248088* – ▤. MC AE VISA BY a
closed 25 December, 1 January and Sunday dinner – **Meals** - Brasserie - (booking essential) a la carte 15.50/30.00 **t.** 10.95.

IDDLETON *Gtr. Manchester* 402 403 404 N 23 – *pop. 45 729.*
London 210 – Manchester 6 – Leeds 38 – Liverpool 35.

Travel Inn, Middleton Rd, Crumpsall, M8 6NB, Southwest : 1 ¼ m. on A 576 ☎ (0161) 720 6171, *Fax (0161) 740 9142* – lift, ⇔ rm, ▤ rest, TV & P. MC AE VISA JCB. on Manchester town plan AV e
Meals (grill rest.) – **45 rm** 41.95 **t.**

Premier Lodge, 818 Manchester Old Rd, Rhodes, M24 4RF, ☎ (0870) 7001474, *Fax (0870) 7001475* – ⇔ rm, ▤ rest, TV ☎ & P – 60. MC AE VISA.
Meals (grill rest.) a la carte approx. 13.00 **t.** 8.95 – **42 rm** 42.95 **t.**

IDDLETON *N.Yorks. – see Pickering.*

IDDLETON-IN-TEESDALE *Durham* 402 N 20 – *pop. 1 143.*
London 447 – Newcastle upon Tyne 65 – Carlisle 91 – Leeds 124 – Middlesbrough 70.

Grove Lodge, Hucle, DL12 0QW, Northwest : ½ m. on B 6277 ☎ (01833) 640798, ≤, « Victorian former shooting lodge », – ⇔ TV P
Meals a la carte 14.70/22.20 **st.** 8.25 – **3 rm** 29.50/49.00 **st.**

IDDLETON STONEY *Oxon.* 403 404 Q 28 – *pop. 304.*
London 66 – Northampton 30 – Oxford 12.

Jersey Arms, OX6 8SE, ☎ (01869) 343234, *jerseyarms@bestwestern.co.uk*, *Fax (01869) 343565*, – ⇔ rest, TV P. MC AE VISA.
Meals a la carte 16.50/27.70 **t.** 9.75 – **17 rm** 81.00/95.00 **st.**, 3 suites – SB.

IDDLE WALLOP *Hants.* 403 404 P 30 – ✉ *Stockbridge.*
London 80 – Salisbury 11 – Southampton 21.

Fifehead Manor, SO20 8EG, on A 343 ☎ (01264) 781565, *Fax (01264) 781400*, « Part 16C manor house », – ⇔ rest, TV P – 30. MC AE VISA
Meals 9.95/12.95 (lunch) and a la carte 23.45/37.75 **t.** 10.25 – **16 rm** 80.00/150.00 **t.** – SB.

IDDLEWICH *Ches.* 402 403 404 M 24.
London 180 – Manchester 29 – Chester 21 – Liverpool 21 – Stoke-on-Trent 58.

Travelodge, Holmes Chapel Rd, CW10 0NZ, East : ½ m. on A 54 ☎ (01606) 738229, *Fax (01606) 738229* – ⇔ rm, TV & P. MC AE VISA JCB
Meals (grill rest.) – **32 rm** 49.95 **t.**

IDDLE WINTERSLOW *Wilts. – see Salisbury.*

IDGLEY *W. Yorks.* 402 P 22 – *see Wakefield.*

MIDHURST *W. Sussex* 404 R 31 – *pop. 6 451.*

North St (01730) 817322.

London 57 – Brighton 38 – Chichester 12 – Southampton 41.

Spread Eagle, South St, GU29 9NH, (01730) 816911, *spreadeagle@hshot* *Fax (01730) 815668,* « 15C hostelry, antique furnishings », – rest, 50. VISA
Meals 18.50/35.00 and a la carte 35.00/44.50 **t.** 17.50 – **37 rm** 80.00/195.00 **t.**, 2 su – SB.

Angel, North St, GU29 9DN, (01730) 812421, *angel@hshotels.co.uk, Fax (01730) 815* « 16C coaching inn », – – 60. VISA.
Brasserie : **Meals** (lunch booking essential) a la carte 15.25/29.25 **t.** 12.60 – **28** 80.00/150.00 **t.** – SB.

Maxine's, Red Lion St, GU29 9PB, (01730) 816271, *maxines@lineone.net,* « 15C t bered cottage » – . VISA
closed 2 weeks January, 2 weeks October, Monday, Tuesday and Sunday dinner – **Me** 16.95 and a la carte 20.85/28.85 **st.** 11.50.

at Bepton *Southwest : 2½ m. by A 286 on Bepton rd – Midhurst.*

Park House , Bepton, GU29 0JB, (01730) 812880, *reservations@parkhouse.c* *Fax (01730) 815643,* heated, , – rest, – 70. VISA
Meals (booking essential) 15.00/26.00 **t.** 7.90 – **18 rm** 65.00/180.00 **t.**, 1 suite – SB.

at Stedham *West : 2 m. by A 272 – Midhurst.*

Nava Thai at Hamilton Arms, School Lane, GU29 0NZ, (01730) 812555, *hamil arms@hotmail.com, Fax (01730) 817459* – . VISA JCB
closed Monday except Bank Holidays – **Meals** - Thai - 19.50 (dinner) and a la carte 15. 20.95 **t.**

at Trotton *West : 3¼ m. on A 272 – Petersfield (Hants.).*

Southdowns Country , GU31 5JN, South : 1 m. (01730) 821521, *receptic southdownhotel.freeserve.co.uk, Fax (01730) 821790,* , , , – , rest, 100. VISA
Meals 13.50/25.00 and a la carte 13.95/25.00 **t.** 11.95 – **20 rm** 80.00/120.00 **t.** – SB

at Elsted *Southwest : 5 m. by A 272 on Elsted rd – Midhurst.*

Three Horseshoes, GU29 0JY, (01730) 825746, « 16C drovers inn » – . VISA
Meals *(closed Sunday dinner in winter)* a la carte approx. 18.85 **t.** 9.95.

MIDSOMER NORTON *Bath & North East Somerset* 403 M 30 – *Bath.*

Fosseway C.C., Charlton Lane (01761) 412214.

London 129 – Bath 10 – Bristol 15 – Wells 8.

Centurion, Charlton Lane, BA3 4BD, Southeast : 1 m. by B 3355, Charlton Rd a Fosseway (01761) 417711, *enquiries@centurionhotel.co.uk, Fax (01761) 418357,* , , , , – rest, – 180. VISA.
closed 24-27 December – **Meals** *(closed Saturday lunch)* 15.00/16.95 **t.** 9.00 – **44** 65.00/85.00 **t.** – SB.

MILBORNE PORT *Dorset* 403 404 M 31 – *see Sherborne.*

MILDENHALL *Suffolk* 404 V 26 – *pop. 12 827.*

London 72 – Cambridge 24 – Ipswich 37 – Norwich 45.

Riverside, Mill St, IP28 7DP, (01638) 717274, *bookings@riverside-hotel.r* *Fax (01638) 715997,* , – – 60. VISA
Meals 20.50 and a la carte 23.35/29.90 **t.** 12.50 – **29 rm** 69.50/95.00 **t.** – SB.

Remember the speed limits that apply in the United Kingdom, unless otherwise signposted.

- 60 mph on single carriageway roads
- 70 mph on dual carriageway roads and motorways

MILFORD-ON-SEA *Hants.* 403 404 P 31 – *pop. 4 434* – ✉ *Lymington.*
London 109 – Bournemouth 15 – Southampton 24 – Winchester 37.

Westover Hall, Park Lane, SO41 0PT, ✆ (01590) 643044, *westoverhallhotel@barclays.net, Fax (01590) 644490,* ≤ Christchurch Bay, Isle of Wight and The Needles, « Victorian mansion built by Arnold Mitchell », – rm, TV P. MC AE VISA JCB
Meals 21.50/29.50 and a la carte 25.00/30.00 **t.** 12.95 – **13 rm** 70.00/160.00 **t.** – SB.

South Lawn, Lymington Rd, SO41 0RF, ✆ (01590) 643911, *enquiries@southlawn.co.uk, Fax (01590) 644820,* – TV P. MC VISA.
closed late December-late January – **Meals** *(closed Monday lunch)* 12.50/22.00 and a la carte 20.00/25.50 **t.** 13.50 – **24 rm** 65.00/130.00 **t.** – SB.

Rouille, 69-71 High St, SO41 0QG, ✆ (01590) 642340, *rouille@ukonline.co.uk, Fax (01590) 642340* – ▤. MC AE VISA JCB
closed Sunday and Monday – **Meals** (lunch booking essential) 14.95/25.95 **t.** 13.50.

MILNROW *Gtr. Manchester* 402 404 N 23 – *see Rochdale.*

MILTON COMMON *Oxon.* – *see Thame.*

MILTON ERNEST *Beds.* 404 S 27 – *see Bedford.*

In questa guida
uno stesso simbolo, uno stesso carattere
stampati in rosso o in **nero**, in magro o in **grassetto**
hanno un significato diverso.
Leggete attentamente le pagine esplicative.

MILTON KEYNES *Milton Keynes* 404 R 27 – *pop. 156 148.*
Abbey Hill, Monks Way, Two Mile Ash ✆ (01908) 563845 **AV** – *Windmill Hill, Tattenhoe Lane, Bletchley ✆ (01908) 648149* **BX** – *Wavendon Golf Centre, Lower End Rd, Wavendon ✆ (01908) 281811* **CV**.
890 Midsummer Boulevard ✆ (01908) 558300 **FY**.
London 56 – Birmingham 72 – Bedford 16 – Northampton 18 – Oxford 37.

Plans on following pages

Posthouse Milton Keynes, 500 Saxon Gate West, Central Milton Keynes, MK9 2HQ, ✆ (0870) 400 9057, *gm1748@forte-hotels.com, Fax (01908) 674714,* – rm, TV P – 150. MC AE VISA **EYZ a**
Meals 13.50/15.00 and a la carte 18.75/24.95 **t.** 11.95 – 13.50 – **155 rm** 150.00 **st.**, 2 suites – SB.

Hilton Milton Keynes, Timbold Drive, Kents Hill Park, MK7 6HL, Southeast : 4 m. by B 4034 and A 421 off Brickhill St. (V10) ✆ (01908) 694433, *Fax (01908) 695533,* – , ▤ rest, TV P – 300. MC AE VISA. **CVX d**
Britisserie : **Meals** 12.50 (lunch) and dinner a la carte 18.35/30.65 **st.** 12.30 – 11.50 – **138 rm** 155.00/225.00 **st.** – SB.

Courtyard by Marriott Milton Keynes, London Rd, MK16 0JA, Northeast : 4 ¼ m. on A 509 ✆ (01908) 613688, *Fax (01908) 617335,* – , ▤ rest, TV P – 200. MC AE VISA JCB. **CV r**
Meals a la carte 14.00/22.00 **st.** 11.50 – 10.50 – **49 rm** 104.00/150.00 **st.**

Premier Lodge, Shirwell Cres, Furzton, MK4 1GA, South : 3 m. by A 509 and Portway (H 5) off Watling St (V 4) ✆ (0870) 7001494, *Fax (0870) 7001495* – rm, ▤ rest, TV P. MC AE VISA. **BX g**
Meals (grill rest.) a la carte approx. 13.00 **t.** 8.95 – **120 rm** 49.95 **t.**

Premier Lodge, Bletcham Way (H10), MK7 8HP, Southeast : 5 ½ m. by A 509 and A 5, taking 2nd junction left signposted Milton Keynes (South and East) ✆ (01908) 366188, *Fax (01908) 366603,* « Windmill feature, lakeside setting » – rm, TV P. MC AE VISA. **CX h**
Meals (grill rest.) (in bar) a la carte approx. 12.50 **t.** 7.80 – **40 rm** 49.95 **t.**

Express by Holiday Inn without rest., Eastlake Park, Tongwell St, Fox Milne, MK15 0YA, ✆ (01908) 681000, *exhimiltonkeynes@aol.com, Fax (01908) 609429* – ▤ TV P – 60. MC AE VISA. **CV a**
119 rm 69.50.

MILTON KEYNES

Buckingham Road . . . . BX
London Road . . . . CUV
Manor Road CX
Marsh End Road . . . . CU
Newport Road . . . . BV
Northampton Road . . . . AU
Stoke Road CX
Stratford Road . . . . AV
Whaddon Way . . . . BX
Wolverton Road . . . . BU

« VERTICAL » ROADS

V1 Snelshall Street . . . . BX
V2 Tattenhoe Street . . . . ABX
V3 Fulmer Street . . . . ABX
V4 Watling Street . . . . AV, BX
V5 Great Monks Street . . . . AV
V6 Grafton Street . . . . BVX
V7 Saxon Street . . . . BVX
V8 Marlborough Street . . . . BV, CX
V9 Overstreet . . . . BV
V10 Brickhill Street . . . . BU, CX
V11 Tongwell Street CVX

« HORIZONTAL » ROADS

H1 Ridgeway . . . . AV
H2 Millers Way . . . . AV
H3 Monks Way . . . . ABV
H4 Dansteed Way . . . . ABV
H5 Portway . . . . BCV
H6 Childs Way . . . . BX, CV
H7 Chaffron Way . . . . BX, CV
H8 Standing Way . . . . BX, CV
H9 Groveway CVX
H10 Bletcham Way CX

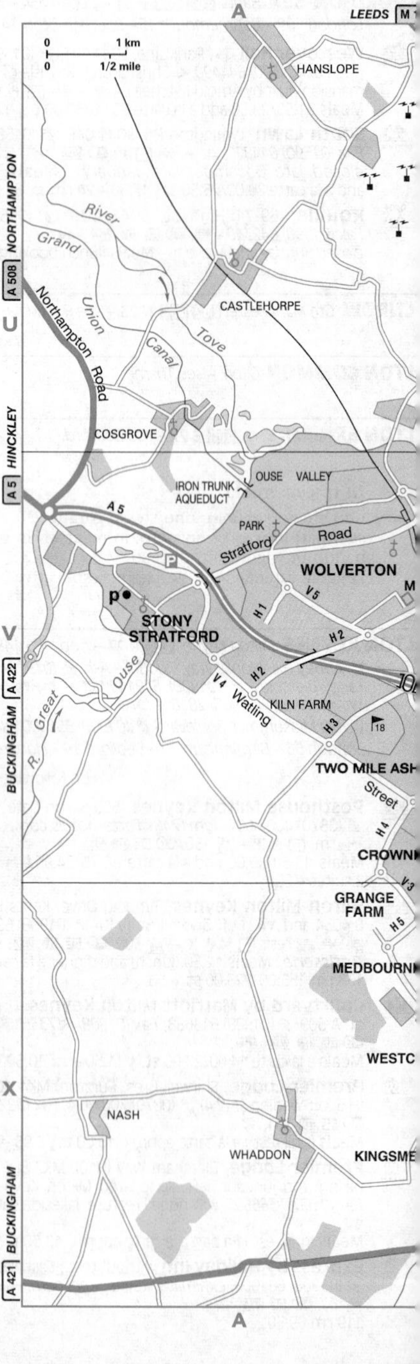

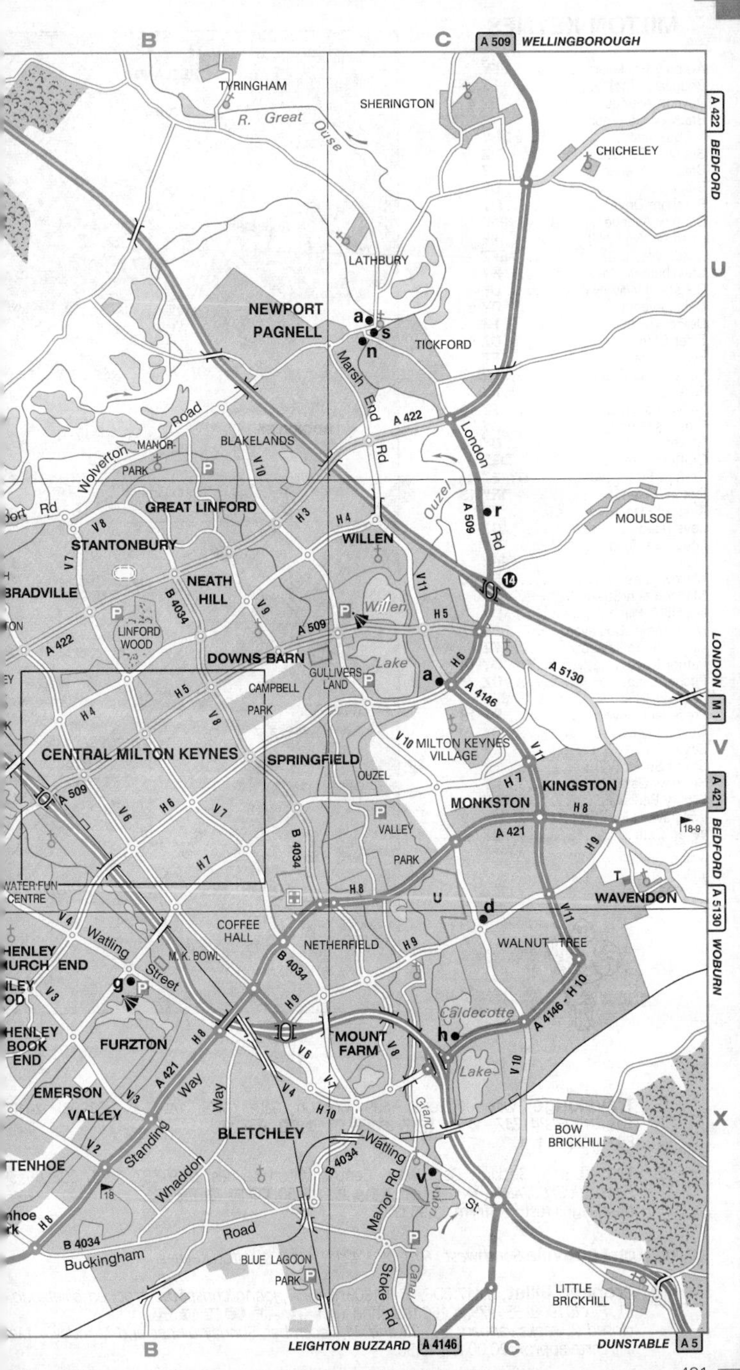

B
C
A 509 WELLINGBOROUGH
A 422 BEDFORD
U
V
X
LONDON M 1
A 421 BEDFORD
A 5130 WOBURN
LEIGHTON BUZZARD A 4146
DUNSTABLE A 5
TYRINGHAM
SHERINGTON
R. Great Ouse
CHICHELEY
LATHBURY
NEWPORT PAGNELL
TICKFORD
Marsh End Rd
A 422
London Rd
A 509
Wolverton Road
MANOR PARK
BLAKELANDS
GREAT LINFORD
STANTONBURY
WILLEN
MOULSOE
BRADVILLE
NEATH HILL
Willen Lake
LINFORD WOOD
DOWNS BARN
GULLIVERS LAND
CAMPBELL PARK
A 5130
A 4146
CENTRAL MILTON KEYNES
SPRINGFIELD
MILTON KEYNES VILLAGE
OUZEL
MONKSTON
KINGSTON
VALLEY PARK
WAVENDON
WATER-FUN CENTRE
COFFEE HALL
NETHERFIELD
WALNUT TREE
Watling Street
M.K. BOWL
A 4146 - H 10
Caldecotte Lake
MOUNT FARM
FURZTON
EMERSON VALLEY
BLETCHLEY
BOW BRICKHILL
Standing Way
Whaddon Way
Watling St.
Manor Rd
Grand Union Canal
Buckingham Road
B 4034
BLUE LAGOON PARK
Stoke Rd
LITTLE BRICKHILL

MILTON KEYNES

Avebury Boulevard . . . . EFY
Boundary (The). . . . . FZ 3
Boycott Avenue . . . . EZ 4
Bradwell Common
  Boulevard. . . . . DEY
Bradwell Road . . . . DZ
Brearley Avenue . . . . EFZ
Brill Place . . . . DY
Burnham Drive . . . . DY
Century Avenue. . . . . EFZ
Chaffron Way (H7). . . . . FZ
Childs Way (H6) . . . . EFZ
Conniburrow Boulevard . . . . EY
Dansteed Way (H4) . . . . DY
Deltic Avenue . . . . DY 6
Dexter Avenue . . . . FZ 7
Elder Gate . . . . DZ 9
Evans Gate . . . . EZ
Fishermead Boulevard . . . . FZ
Food Centre . . . . FY
Fulwoods Drive . . . . FZ 10
Gibsons Green. . . . . DY
Glovers Lane . . . . DY 12
Grafton Gate . . . . DEZ
Grafton Street (V6) . . . . DY, EZ
Ibstone Avenue . . . . DEY 13
Kirkstall Place . . . . EZ
Leys Road . . . . DZ
Loughton Road . . . . DY
Main Shopping Centre. . . . . EFY
Mallow Gate. . . . . EY 15
Marlborough Street (V8) . . . . . . FY
Mayditch Place . . . . DY
Midsummer Boulevard . . . . . . EFY
Oldbrook Boulevard . . . . EFZ
Patriot Drive. . . . . DY 16
Pitcher Lane. . . . . DZ
Portway (H5) . . . . EFY
Precedent Drive . . . . DY 18
Quinton Drive . . . . DY
Saxon Gate (V7) . . . . EY
Saxon Street (V7). . . . . EY, FZ
Secklow Gate. . . . . FY
Silbury Boulevard . . . . EFY
Walgrave Drive . . . . DY 19
Witan Gate . . . . EZ

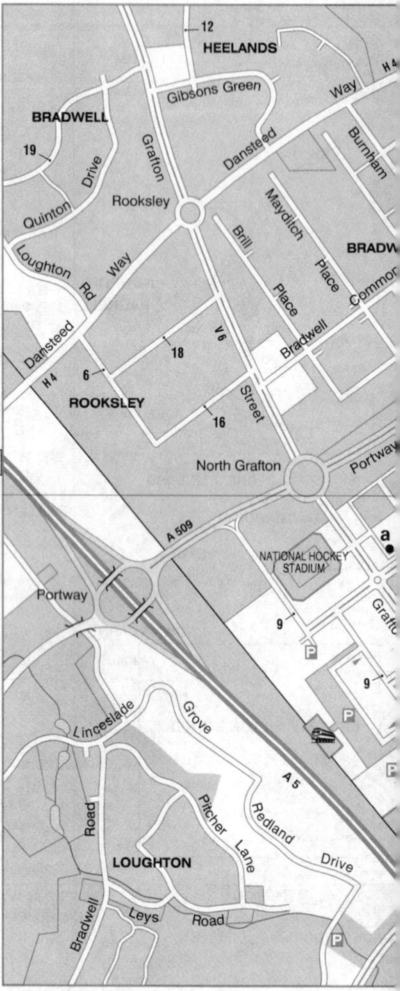

Travelodge without rest., 199 Grafton Gate, MK9 1AL, ☎ (01908) 2410
Fax (01908) 241737 – ⬍ ⇹ TV ♿ P. MO AE ① VISA JCB. ✻ DZ
80 rm 59.95 **t.**

Travel Inn, Secklow Gate West, Central Milton Keynes, MK9 3BZ, ☎ (01908) 6633
Fax (01908) 607481 – ⇹, ▤ rest, TV ♿ P – 🏟 50. MO AE ① VISA. ✻ FY
Meals (grill rest.) – **38 rm** 41.95 **t.**

at Newton Longville *Southwest : 6 m. by A 421* – **AX** – ✉ *Milton Keynes.*

Crooked Billet, MK17 0DF, ☎ (01908) 373936, *johngilchrist@the-crooked-billet-pub.uk, Fax (01908) 631979,* « 16C thatched inn », 🍽 – P. MO AE ① VISA
closed 2 weeks January, 25, 26 and 31 December, Sunday dinner and Monday – **Me**
a la carte approx. 20.00 **t.** 🍷 13.50.

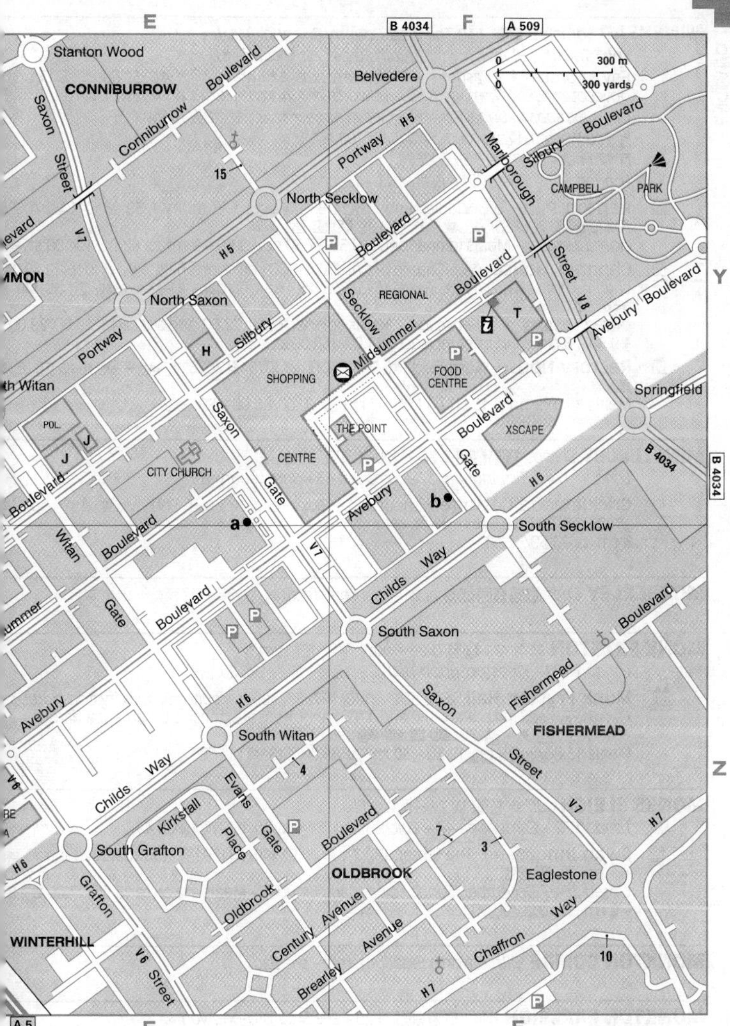

ILTON-UNDER-WYCHWOOD *Oxon. – pop. 2 030.*

London 83 – Birmingham 52 – Gloucester 35 – Oxford 27.

Hillborough House without rest., The Green, OX7 6JH, ✆ (01993) 830501, *wendy@hillboroughhouse.co.uk, Fax (01993) 832005,* ⇌ – TV P. MC VISA
4 rm ⊐ 30.00/50.00 **s.**

INCHINHAMPTON *Glos.* 403 404 N 28 – *pop. 3 201.*

London 115 – Bristol 26 – Gloucester 11 – Oxford 51.

Hunters Lodge without rest., Dr Brown's Rd, GL6 9BT, Northwest : ½ m. by West End ✆ (01453) 883588, *Fax (01453) 731449,* ≤, « Cotswold stone house on Minchinhampton common », ⇌ – ⇸ TV P. ⇸
closed Christmas – **3 rm** ⊐ 30.00/50.00 **s.**

MINEHEAD *Somerset* 403 J 30 *The West Country G. – pop. 9 904.*

See : *Town★ - Higher Town (Church Steps★, St Michael's★).*
Env. : *Dunster★★ - Castle★★* **AC** *(upper rooms ≤★) Water Mill★* **AC**, *St George's Church★ Dovecote★, SE : 2½ m. by A 39 – Selworthy★ (Church★, ≤★★) W : 4½ m. by A 39.*
Exc. : *Exmoor National Park★★ – Cleeve Abbey★★* **AC**, *SE : 6½ m. by A 39.*
The Warren, Warren Rd ℘ (01643) 702057.
17 Friday St ℘ (01643) 702624.
London 187 – Bristol 64 – Exeter 43 – Taunton 25.

Periton Park, Middlecombe, TA24 8SN, West : 1 ½ m. by A 39 ℘ (01643) 70688 *Fax (01643) 706885*, ≤, – rest, TV P. MC AE VISA JCB
closed January – **Meals** (dinner only) 19.50/27.50 **st.** 9.50 – **8 rm** 62.00/104.00 **st.** – S

Channel House, Church Path, TA24 5QG, off Northfield Rd ℘ (01643) 70322 *channel.house@virgin.net, Fax (01643) 708925*, ≤, « Gardens » – rest, TV P. MC V JCB.
closed January and February – **Meals** (dinner only) 22.00 and a la carte 19.00/29.00 s 9.90 – **8 rm** (dinner included) 84.00/138.00 **st.** – SB.

Rectory House, Northfield Rd, TA24 5QH, ℘ (01643) 702611, – rest, TV P. VISA
Meals (dinner only) 19.50 11.00 – **7 rm** 30.00/60.00 – SB.

MINSTERLEY *Shrops.* 402 403 L 26 – *pop. 1 397.*
London 174 – Birmingham 57 – Hereford 55 – Shrewsbury 10.

Cricklewood Cottage without rest., Plox Green, SY5 0HT, Southwest : 1 m. on A 4 ℘ (01743) 791229, – P.
3 rm 23.50/52.00.

MOBBERLEY *Ches.* 402 403 404 N 24 – *see Knutsford.*

MONK FRYSTON *N. Yorks.* 402 Q 22 – *pop. 722* – ✉ *Lumby.*
London 190 – Kingston-upon-Hull 42 – Leeds 13 – York 20.

Monk Fryston Hall, LS25 5DU, ℘ (01977) 682369, *reception@monkfryston-hotel.co Fax (01977) 683544*, « Part 16C and 17C manor house, extensive ornamental gardens », – rest, TV P – 70. MC AE VISA
Meals 13.80/24.25 **t.** 12.50 – **30 rm** 85.00/115.00 **t.** – SB.

MONKS ELEIGH *Suffolk* 404 W 27 – *pop. 460.*
London 72 – Cambridge 47 – Colchester 17 – Ipswich 16 – Norwich 49.

Swan Inn with rm, The Street, IP7 7AU, ℘ (01449) 741391, « 16C thatched inn », rm, P. MC VISA
closed 25-27 December, Sunday dinner and Monday – **Meals** a la carte 13.50/27.00 **t.** 8. – **2 rm** 40.00/60.00 **t.**

MONKTON COMBE *Bath & North East Somerset – see Bath.*

MONKTON FARLEIGH *Wilts.* 403 404 N 29 – *see Bradford-on-Avon.*

MORCOTT SERVICE AREA *Rutland – see Uppingham.*

MORETON *Mersey.* 402 403 K 23 – *pop. 12 053.*
London 225 – Birkenhead 4 – Liverpool 6.

Lee Ho, 304-308 Hoylake Rd, L46 6DE, West : ¼ m. on A 553 ℘ (0151) 677 6440 – MC VISA JCB
closed 3 weeks summer, 25-26 December, Sunday, Monday and Bank Holidays – **Meal** Chinese - (dinner only) 18.50/26.50 and a la carte 12.20/36.50 **st.** 9.90.

Dieser Führer ist kein vollständiges Hotel- und Restaurantverzeichnis.
Um den Ansprüchen aller Touristen gerecht zu werden,
haben wir uns auf eine Auswahl in jeder Kategorie beschränkt.

MORETONHAMPSTEAD *Devon* 403 I 32 *The West Country G.* – *pop. 1 380* – ✉ *Newton Abbot.*

Env. : *Dartmoor National Park*★★.

Manor House Hotel ☎ *(01647) 440998.*

London 213 – Exeter 13 – Plymouth *30.*

Manor House ⟡, TQ13 8RE, Southwest : 2 m. on B 3212 ☎ (01647) 440355, *reception. manorhouse@principalhotels.co.uk, Fax (01647) 440961,* ←, « Part 19C », – – 120. MC AE VISA.
Meals 12.50/25.00 and dinner a la carte – **86 rm** 90.00/116.00 **st.** – SB.

Great Slocombe Farm ⟡, TQ13 8QF, Northwest : 1 ½ m. by A 382 ☎ (01647) 440595, *hmerchant@slocombe.freeserve.co.uk, Fax (01647) 440595,* « Working farm », – TV P
Meals (by arrangement) 13.00 – **3 rm** 30.00/48.00 **st.** – SB.

Moorcote without rest., TQ13 8LS, Northwest : ¼ m. on A 382 ☎ (01647) 440966, *moorcote@smartone.co.uk,* – TV P.
March-October – **5 rm** 25.00/42.00 **t.**

MORETON-IN-MARSH *Glos.* 403 404 O28 *Great Britain G.* – *pop. 1 895.*

Env. : *Chastleton House*★★, *SE : 5 m. by A 44.*

London 86 – Birmingham 40 – Gloucester 31 – Oxford *29.*

Manor House, High St, GL56 0LJ, ☎ (01608) 650501, *Fax (01608) 651481,* « Part 16C manor house », , – , rest, TV P – 90. MC AE VISA JCB.
Mulberry **:** Meals 12.50/30.00 **st.** 12.50 – **36 rm** 99.00/115.00 **st.**, 2 suites – SB.

Treetops without rest., London Rd, GL56 0HE, on A 44 (Oxford rd) ☎ (01608) 651036, *treetops1@talk21.com, Fax (01608) 651036,* – TV P. MC VISA JCB
6 rm 35.00/50.00.

Marsh Goose, High St, GL56 0AX, ☎ (01608) 653500, *manager@marshgoose.com, Fax (01608) 653510* – . MC AE VISA JCB
closed Tuesday lunch, Sunday dinner and Monday – **Meals** 15.50 (lunch) and dinner a la carte 19.50/36.00 **st.** 12.50.

Annies, 3 Oxford St, GL56 0LA, ☎ (01608) 651981, *anniesrest@easicom.com, Fax (01608) 651981* – MC AE VISA JCB
closed Sunday – **Meals** (dinner only) a la carte 23.30/32.25 **st.** 12.95.

MORPETH *Northd.* 401 402 O 18 – *pop. 14 393.*

The Common ☎ *(01670) 504942.*

The Chantry, Bridge St ☎ *(01670) 511323.*

London 301 – Edinburgh 93 – Newcastle upon Tyne *15.*

at Eshott *North : 6 m. by A 1 –* ✉ *Morpeth.*

Eshott Hall ⟡, NE65 9EP, ☎ (01670) 787777, *thehall@eshott.com, Fax (01670) 787999,* « Georgian mansion, Victorian fernery », – P – 120. MC AE VISA JCB
closed Christmas and New Year – **Meals** (by arrangement) (communal dining) 17.50/30.00 **st.** 4.50 – **5 rm** 48.00/96.00 **st.**

at Longhorsley *Northwest : 6½ m. by A 192 on A 697 –* ✉ *Morpeth.*

Linden Hall ⟡, NE65 8XF, North : 1 m. on A 697 ☎ (01670) 500000, *stay@lindenhall.co.uk, Fax (01670) 500001,* ←, « Georgian country house in extensive grounds », , , , – , rest, TV P – 400. MC AE VISA JCB
Dobson **:** Meals 15.50/24.50 **t.** 13.50 – **50 rm** 73.00/104.00 **t.** – SB.

Thistleyhaugh Farm ⟡, NE65 8RG, Northwest : 3 ¾ m. by A 697 and Todburn rd taking first right turn ☎ (01665) 570629, *Fax (01665) 570629,* « Working farm », – TV P.
closed 2 weeks Christmas-New Year – **Meals** (by arrangement) (communal dining) 14.00 **t.** 5.00 – **5 rm** 35.00/50.00 **st.**

MORSTON *Norfolk – see Blakeney.*

MORTEHOE *Devon* 403 H 30 – *see Woolacombe.*

MOTCOMBE *Dorset* 403 404 N 30 – *see Shaftesbury.*

MOULSFORD *Oxon.* 403 404 Q 29 *The West Country G. – pop. 491.*
Exc. : *Ridgeway Path*★★.
London 58 – Oxford 17 – Reading 13 – Swindon 37.

XXX **Beetle and Wedge** with rm, Ferry Lane, OX10 9JF, ✆ (01491) 6513
Fax (01491) 651376, ≤, « Thames-side setting », – ⚓ ⇹ TV P. MC AE ⓘ VISA JC
The Dining Room : **Meals** *(closed Sunday dinner and Monday)* (booking essential) a la ca
28.75/35.75 **t.** 15.00 – (see also ***The Boathouse*** below) – **10 rm** 95.00/165.00 **t.** – S

X **The Boathouse** (at Beetle and Wedge), Ferry Lane, OX10 9JF, ✆ (01491) 6513
Fax (01491) 651376, ≤, « Thames-side setting », – ⚓ P. MC AE ⓘ VISA JCB
Meals (bookingessential) a la carte 23.75/30.50 **t.** 15.00.

MOULTON *N. Yorks.* 402 P 20 – *pop. 197* – ✉ *Richmond.*
London 243 – Leeds 53 – Middlesbrough 25 – Newcastle upon Tyne 43.

XX **Black Bull Inn,** DL10 6QJ, ✆ (01325) 377289, *sarah@blackbullinn.demon.co.*
Fax (01325) 377422, « Brighton Belle Pullman coach » – P. MC AE ⓘ VISA JCB
closed 24-26 December, Sunday and Saturday lunch – **Meals** - Seafood specialities - 15
(lunch) and a la carte 23.75/33.70 **st.** 9.95.

MOUSEHOLE *Cornwall* 403 D 33 *The West Country G.* – ✉ *Penzance.*
See : *Village*★.
Env. : *Penwith*★★ – *Lamorna (The Merry Maidens and The Pipers Standing Stone*★*) SW : 3 by B 3315.*
Exc. : *Land's End*★ *(cliff scenery*★★★*) W : 9 m. by B 3315.*
London 321 – Penzance 3 – Truro 29.

The Old Coastguard, The Parade, TR18 6PR, ✆ (01736) 731222, *bookings@oldcc guardhotel.co.uk, Fax (01736) 731720*, ≤, – ⇹ TV P. MC AE VISA
closed 25 December – **Meals** a la carte 13.00/21.00 **st.** 9.00 – **22 rm** 35.00/90.00 **st** SB.

X **Cornish Range** with rm, 6 Chapel St, TR19 6SB, ✆ (01736) 731488, *Fax (01736) 73217*
⇹ rm, TV. MC VISA JCB
closed Monday-Wednesday November-Easter except December – **Meals** - Seafood- (boo ing essential) (dinner only and Sunday lunch November-Easter) a la carte 21.50/25.0
10.50 – **3 rm** 57.00/65.00 **t.** – SB.

MUCH WENLOCK *Shrops.* 402 403 M26 *Great Britain G. – pop. 1 921.*
See : *Priory*★ *AC.*
Env. : *Ironbridge Gorge Museum*★★ *AC (The Iron Bridge*★★ *- Coalport China Museum*★ *Blists Hill Open Air Museum*★★ *– Museum of the River and Visitor Centre*★*) NE : 4½ m. A 4169 and B 4380.*
The Museum, High St ✆ (01952) 727679 (summer only).
London 154 – Birmingham 34 – Shrewsbury 12 – Worcester 37.

Raven, Barrow St, TF13 6EN, ✆ (01952) 727251, *Fax (01952) 728416*, – ⇹ rest, TV
MC AE ⓘ VISA JCB.
closed 25 December – **Meals** 15.00/19.50 **t.** 12.00 – **15 rm** 65.00/115.00 **t.** – SB.

MUDEFORD *Dorset* 403 404 O 31 – *see Christchurch.*

MULLION *Cornwall* 403 E 33 *The West Country G. – pop. 2 040* – ✉ *Helston.*
See : *Mullion Cove*★★ *(Church*★*) – Lizard Peninsula*★.
Env. : *Kynance Cove*★★*, S : 5 m. – Cury*★ *(Church*★*), N : 2 m. by minor roads.*
Exc. : *Helston (The Flora Day Furry Dance*★★*) (May), N : 7 ½ m. by A 3083 – Culdr (Flambards Village Theme Park*★*) AC, N : 6 m. by A 3083 – Wendron (Poldark Mine*★*), 9½ m. by A 3083 and B 3297.*
London 323 – Falmouth 21 – Penzance 21 – Truro 26.

Polurrian, TR12 7EN, Southwest : ½ m. ✆ (01326) 240421, *polurotel@aol.cc Fax (01326) 240083*, ≤ Mount's Bay, heated, squash – ⇹ rest, P – 150. MC AE ⓘ VISA JCB
Meals (bar lunch Monday-Saturday)/dinner 22.50 and a la carte 15.40/30.95 **t.** 12.4
38 rm (dinner included) 105.00/220.00 **t.**, 1 suite – SB.

Mullion Cove, TR12 7EP, Southwest : 1 m. by B 3296 ☎ (01326) 240328, *mullioncove@btinternet.com, Fax (01326) 240998,* ≤ Mullion Cove and Mount's Bay, ≘s, ⛱, 🌳 – ⇎ rest, TV P. MC AE VISA JCB
Meals (bar lunch)/dinner 19.50 and a la carte 14.40/18.50 **st.** 9.25 – **32 rm** ☕ (dinner included) 75.00/170.00 **st.** – SB.

MUNGRISDALE *Cumbria* 401 402 L 19 20 – *pop. 330* – ✉ *Penrith.*

London 301 – Carlisle 33 – Keswick 8.5 – Penrith 13.

Mosedale House 🐦, Mosedale, CA11 0XQ, North : 1 m. by Mosedale rd ☎ (017687) 79371, *mosedale@northlakes.co.uk* – ⚓ ⇎ TV ♿ P. MC ⊕ VISA JCB
closed 24-26 December – **Meals** (by arrangement) 14.00 **st.** 8.40 – **7 rm** ☕ (dinner included) 41.50/92.00 **s.** – SB.

MYLOR BRIDGE *Cornwall* 403 E 33 – *see Falmouth.*

NAILSWORTH *Glos.* 403 404 N 28 – *pop. 5 242.*

London 120 – Bristol 30 – Swindon 41.

Egypt Mill, GL6 0AE, ☎ (01453) 833449, *ch@egypt-mill.co.uk, Fax (01453) 836098,* 🏠, « Part 16C converted riverside mill », 🌳 – TV P – 🎓 100. MC AE ⊕ VISA. ✂
Restaurant : Meals a la carte 12.75/25.50 **st.** 9.90 – ***Cellar Bistro :*** Meals a la carte 12.75/25.50 **t.** 9.90 – **18 rm** ☕ 49.50/95.00 **t.** – SB.

NANTWICH *Ches.* 402 403 404 M 24 – *pop. 11 695.*

Alvaston Hall, Middlewich Rd ☎ (01270) 624321.

Church House, Church Walk ☎ (01270) 610983.

London 176 – Chester 20 – Liverpool 45 – Stoke-on-Trent 17.

Rookery Hall 🐦, Worleston, CW5 6DQ, North : 2 ½ m. by A 51 on B 5074 ☎ (01270) 610016, *rookery@arcadianhotels.co.uk, Fax (01270) 626027,* ≤, « Part 19C country house », 🐟, 🌳, 🎾, ✂ – |‡|, ⇎ rest, TV ♿ P – 🎓 70. MC AE ⊕ VISA JCB
Meals *(closed Saturday lunch)* (booking essential) 15.00/37.50 **t.** 14.00 – **43 rm** ☕ 95.00/130.00 **t.**, 2 suites – SB.

Oakland House without rest., 252 Newcastle Rd, Blakelow, Shavington, CW5 7ET, East : 2 ½ m. by A 51 on A 500 ☎ (01270) 567134, *Fax (01270) 651752,* 🌳 – ⇎ TV P. MC VISA JCB
9 rm ☕ 34.00/45.00 **st.**

The Limes without rest., 5 Park Rd, CW5 7AQ, on A 530 (Whitchurch rd) ☎ (01270) 624081, *Fax (01270) 624081,* « Victorian house built in Queen Anne style », 🌳 – ⇎ TV P
closed Christmas-6 January and 2 weeks June – **3 rm** ☕ 50.00/60.00.

NATIONAL EXHIBITION CENTRE *W. Mids.* 403 404 O 26 – *see Birmingham.*

NAWTON *N. Yorks.* – *see Helmsley.*

NAYLAND *Suffolk* 404 W 28.

London 64 – Bury St. Edmunds 24 – Cambridge 54 – Colchester 6 – Ipswich 19.

Gladwins Farm 🐦, Harpers Hill, CO6 4NU, Northwest : ½ m. on A 134 ☎ (01206) 262261, *gladwinsfarm@compuserve.com, Fax (01206) 263001,* ≤, ≘s, 🏊, 🐟, 🌳, 🎾, ✂ – ⇎ TV P. MC VISA. ✂
closed Christmas-New Year – **Meals** (by arrangement) 20.00 – **3 rm** ☕ 25.00/65.00 **st.**

White Hart Inn with rm, High St, CO6 4JF, ☎ (01206) 263382, *nayhart@aol.com, Fax (01206) 263638,* 🏠, « Part 15C former coaching inn » – ⇎ rm, TV ☎ P. MC AE ⊕ VISA JCB. ✂
closed 26 December-8 January – **Meals** *(closed Monday except Bank Holidays)* (booking essential) 13.50/20.50 and a la carte 18.50/28.30 **t.** 11.00 – **6 rm** ☕ 66.00/76.50 **st.** – SB.

NEAR SAWREY *Cumbria* 402 L20 – *see Hawkshead.*

NEEDHAM MARKET *Suffolk* 404 X 27 – *pop. 4 312.*

London 77 – Cambridge 47 – Ipswich 8.5 – Norwich 38.

Travelodge, Beacon Hill Service Area, IP6 8NY, Southeast : 1 ¾ m. by B 1078, at junctio of A 14 with A 140 (01449) 721640, *Fax (01449) 721640* – rm, TV P. MC AE VISA JCB.
Meals (grill rest.) – **40 rm** 42.95 **t.**

Pipps Ford, Norwich Rd roundabout, IP6 8LJ, Southeast : 1 ¾ m. by B 1078 at junctio of A 14 with A 140 (01449) 760208, *b&b@pippsford.co.uk, Fax (01449) 76056* « Elizabethan farmhouse », – P. MC AE VISA.
closed Christmas-New Year – **Meals** (by arrangement) (communal dining) 19.50 8.95 **7 rm** 46.00/72.00.

NETHER WASDALE *Cumbria* – *pop. 105.*

London 309 – Ambleside 24 – Blackpool 85 – Carlisle 52 – Whitehaven 17.

Low Wood Hall with rm, CA20 1ET, (019467) 26100, *reservations@lowwoodhall.co.u Fax (019467) 26111,* « Victorian country house », – TV P. MC AE VISA JC
closed Sunday and Monday – **Meals** (dinner only) 15.95/18.95 **st.** 12.95 – **6 rm** 55.0(100.00 **st.** – SB.

NETTLETON SHRUB *Wilts.* 403 404 N 29 – *see Castle Combe.*

GRÜNE REISEFÜHRER
Landschaften, Baudenkmäler
Sehenswürdigkeiten
Touristenstraßen
Tourenvorschläge
Stadtpläne und Übersichtskarten

NEWARK-ON-TRENT *Notts.* 402 404 R 24 *Great Britain G.* – *pop. 35 129.*

See : *St Mary Magdalene*★.
18 *Kelwick, Coddington (01636) 626241.*
London 127 – Lincoln 16 – Nottingham 20 – Sheffield 42.

Grange, 73 London Rd, NG24 1RZ, South : ½ m. on Grantham rd (B 632 (01636) 703399, *info@grangenewark.co.uk, Fax (01636) 702328,* – TV P. MC VISA.
closed Christmas-New Year – **Meals** (dinner only and Sunday lunch) 17.95/25.00 **t.** 9.95 **15 rm** 49.00/80.00 **t.** – SB.

Travel Inn, Lincoln Rd, NG24 2DB, Northwest : 1 ½ m. at A1/A46 roundabo (01636) 640690, *Fax (01636) 605135* – rm, TV P. MC AE VISA.
Meals (grill rest.) – **40 rm** 41.95 **t.**

at North Muskham *North : 4½ m. by A 46 and A 1 – Newark-on-Trent.*

Travelodge, NG23 6HT, North : ½ m. on A 1 (southbound carriagewa (01636) 703635, *Fax (01636) 703635* – rm, TV P. MC AE VISA JCB.
Meals (grill rest.) – **30 rm** 42.95 **t.**

at Caunton *Northwest : 4½ m. by A 616 – Newark-on-Trent.*

Caunton Beck, Main St, NG23 6AB, (01636) 636793, *Fax (01636) 636828,* – MC AE VISA JCB
Meals 12.00 (lunch) and a la carte 15.45/25.20 **st.** 11.45.

NEWBURGH *Lancs.* 402 L 23.

London 217 – Liverpool 23 – Manchester 39 – Preston 20 – Southport 13.

Red Lion, 9 Ash Brow, WN8 7NG, on A 5209 (01257) 462336, *Fax (01257) 462827* – TV – 45. MC AE VISA
Meals (in bar) a la carte 9.85/18.15 **t.** 5.95 – 5.95 – **13 rm** 37.50 **st.**

EWBURY *Newbury* 403 404 Q 29 – *pop. 33 273.*

Newbury and Crookham, Bury's Bank Rd, Greenham Common ✆ (01635) 40035 **AX** – *Donnington Valley, Old Oxford Rd ✆ (01635) 32488* **AV**.

The Wharf ✆ (01635) 30267.

London 67 – Bristol 66 – Oxford 28 – Reading 17 – Southampton 38.

NEWBURY

ere is no paid vertising in this Guide.

Donnington Valley H. & Golf Course, Old Oxford Rd, Donnington, RG14 3AG, North : 1 ¾ m. by A 4 off B 4494 ✆ (01635) 551199, *general@donningtonvalley.co.uk, Fax (01635) 551123,* – 140. **AV a**
Winepress : Meals 18.00/25.00 **t.** 11.50 – 13.50 – **58 rm** 146.00/210.00 **t.** – SB.

Vineyard, Stockcross, RG20 8JU, Northwest : 2 m. by A 4 on B 4000 ✆ (01635) 528770, *reservations@the-vineyard.co.uk, Fax (01635) 528398,* – rm, – 125. **AV b**
Meals 24.00/49.00 and a la carte 37.50/54.50 **t.** 12.00 – **16 rm** 190.00/266.00 **t.**, 15 suites 340.00/636.00 **t.** – SB
Spec. Black pudding beignet with potato purée, chervil salad. Duckling with foie gras, spinach and boulangère potatoes. Dark chocolate torte, passion fruit sorbet.

Newbury Manor, London Rd, RG14 2BY, ✆ (01635) 528838, *enquires@newbury-manorhotel.co.uk, Fax (01635) 523406,* « Gardens and river » – , rest, – 70. **AV n**
Meals *(closed Sunday dinner)* 16.00/36.00 and dinner a la carte 25.00/43.00 **st.** 16.50 – **32 rm** 165.00/175.00 **st.**, 1 suite.

NEWBURY

Andover Road . . . . **AX**
Bath Road . . . . **AV** 7
Benham Hill . . . . **AV** 9
Burys Bank Road. . . . . **AX**
Bussok Hill . . . . **AV** 12
Coombesbury Lane . . . . **AV** 21
Cope Halle Lane . . . . **AX** 22
Curridge Road. . . . . **AV**
Enborne Road. . . . . **AV**
Enborne Street. . . . . **AX**
Ermin Street . . . . **AV**
Essex Street. . . . . **AX** 28
Fir Tree Lane. . . . . **AV** 30
Gravel Hill . . . . **AV**
Greenham Road . . . . **AVX** 34
Grove Road. . . . . **AV**
Hambridge Road . . . . **AV** 37
Lambourn Road . . . . **AV**
London Road . . . . **AV**
Long Lane. . . . . **AV**
Lower Way . . . . **AV** 42
Monks Lane . . . . **AX**
Newtown Road . . . . **AVX**
Oxford Road . . . . **AV**
Pinchington Lane. . . . . **AX**
Sandleford Link . . . . **AVX**
Skinners Green Lane . . . . . **AX**
Station Road. . . . . **AX**
Stoney Lane . . . . **AV**
Tile Barn Row. . . . . **AX**
Turnpike Road. . . . . **AV**
Vanner's Lane . . . . **AX**
Wantage Road . . . . **AV**
Wash Water . . . . **AX**
Wheatlands Lane. . . . . **AX**
Winterbourne Road . . . . **AV**

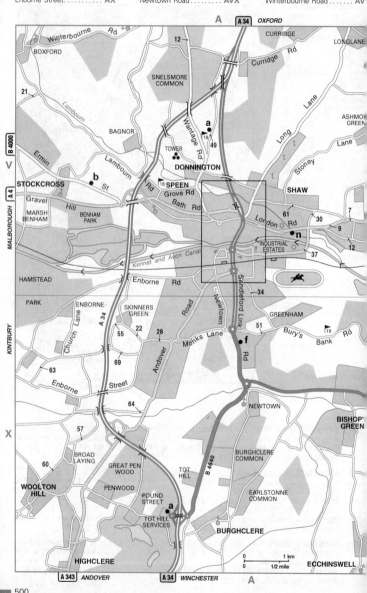

Hilton Newbury Centre, Pinchington Lane, RG14 7HL, South : 2 m. by A 339 ☎ (01635) 529000, *gm-newbury@hilton.com, Fax (01635) 529337*, – 200. AX f
Meals (bar lunch Saturday) 12.25/18.20 and dinner a la carte 16.80/21.75 **st.** 11.75 – 11.25 – **109 rm** 147.00/190.00 **st.** – SB.

Ramada H. Elcot Park, RG20 8NJ, West : 5 m. by A 4 ☎ (01488) 658100, *Fax (01488) 658288*, – 110.
Meals *(closed Saturday lunch)* a la carte 21.90/27.70 **st.** 12.50 – 10.95 – **72 rm** 130.00/175.00 **st.** – SB.

Hilton Newbury North, Oxford Rd, RG20 8XY, North : 3 ¼ m. on A 34 at junction 13 of M 4 ☎ (01635) 247010, *Fax (01635) 247077*, – rest, – 90.
closed 2-5 January **Meals** *(bar lunch)/dinner* a la carte 18.45/25.00 **t.** 11.95 – 12.95 – **109 rm** 145.00/165.00 **t.** – SB.

Travelodge, Tot Hill Service Area, RG20 9ED, South : 5 m. by A 339 and B 4640 at junction with A 34 ☎ (01635) 278169, *Fax (01635) 278169* – rm, rest, AX a
Meals (grill rest.) – **40 rm** 59.95 **t.**

at Marsh Benham *West : 3½ m. by A 4 – AV – ✉ Newbury.*

The Red House, RG20 8LY, ☎ (01635) 582017, *Fax (01635) 581621*, « Thatched inn »,
closed Christmas, Sunday dinner and Monday – **Meals** a la carte 23.50/31.00 11.00.

NEWBY BRIDGE *Cumbria* 402 L 21 *Great Britain G. – ✉ Ulverston.*

Env. : *Lake Windermere★★.*
London 270 – Kendal 16 – Lancaster 27.

Lakeside, Lakeside, LA12 8AT, Northeast : 1 m. on Hawkshead rd ☎ (015395) 31207, *sales@lakesidehotel.co.uk, Fax (015395) 31699*, « Lakeside setting », – 100.
Lakeview : **Meals** (dinner only and Sunday lunch) 35.00 **st.** 15.00 – ***John Ruskins Brasserie :*** **Meals** (dinner only and Sunday lunch) 20.90 **st.** – **73 rm** 140.00/205.00 **st.**, 3 suites – SB.

Swan, LA12 8NB, ☎ (015395) 31681, *swanhotel@aol.com, Fax (015395) 31917*, – 140.
Revells : **Meals** (dinner only and Sunday lunch) 26.95 **t.** 10.00 – ***Mail Coach Brasserie :*** **Meals** a la carte 13.25/20.75 **t.** 10.00 – **55 rm** 80.00/160.00 **t.** – SB.

Whitewater, The Lakeland Village, LA12 8PX, Southwest : 1 ½ m. by A 590 ☎ (015395) 31133, *enquiries@whitewater-hotel.co.uk, Fax (015395) 31881*, squash – rest, – 70.
closed 7-10 January – **Meals** (bar lunch Monday-Saturday)/dinner 21.00/24.50 and a la carte 22.40/25.45 **st.** 11.00 – **35 rm** 85.00/140.00 **st.** – SB.

at Cartmell Fell *Northeast : 3 ¼ m. by A 590 off A 592 – ✉ Grange-over-Sands.*

Lightwood Farmhouse LA11 6NP, ☎ (015395) 31454, *Fax (015395) 31454*, « 17C »,
closed Christmas – **Meals** (by arrangement) 15.00 12.00 – **6 rm** 37.00/52.00 **s.** – SB.

NEWBY WISKE *N. Yorks.* 402 P 21 – *see Northallerton.*

NEWCASTLE AIRPORT *Tyne and Wear* 401 402 O 19 – *see Newcastle upon Tyne.*

Dans le guide Vert Michelin **"Londres"**
(édition en français) vous trouverez :

- des descriptions détaillées des principales curiosités
- de nombreux renseignements pratiques
- des itinéraires de visite dans les secteurs sélectionnés
- des plans de quartiers et de monuments.

NEWCASTLE-UNDER-LYME *Staffs.* 402 403 404 N24 *Great Britain G. – pop. 73 731.*

Exc. : *Wedgwood Visitor's Centre★ AC, SE : 6½ m. by A 34 Z.*

Keele Golf Centre, Keele Rd ℘ (01782) 717417.

Newcastle Library, Ironmarket ℘ (01782) 297313.

London 161 – Birmingham 46 – Liverpool 56 – Manchester 43.

Plan of Built up Area : see Stoke-on-Trent

NEWCASTLE-UNDER-LYME (CENTRE)

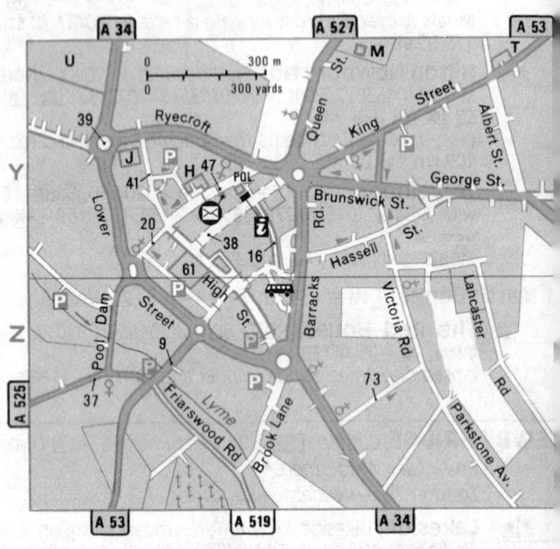

Posthouse Stoke-on-Trent, Clayton Rd, Clayton, ST5 4DL, South : 2 m. on A 51 ℘ (0870) 400 9077, *Fax (01782) 717138*, – ✻ rm, P – 70. VISA
on Stoke-on-Trent town plan V

Meals *(closed Sunday lunch)* 10.00/25.00 and dinner a la carte 20.85/33.00 **t.** 11.45 – 11.95 – **119 rm** 89.00/129.00 **t.** – SB.

Bauhinia, Parklands, ST4 6NW, ℘ (01782) 719709 – P. VISA JCB
closed 25-26 December, lunch Sunday and Bank Holidays – **Meals** - Chinese - 5.95/18.4 and a la carte 12.25/28.40 **t.** 9.45.
on Stoke-on-Trent town plan V

NEWCASTLE UPON TYNE

Tyne and Wear 401 402 O 19 *Great Britain G. – pop. 189 150.*

London 276 – Edinburgh 105 – Leeds 95.

TOURIST INFORMATION

Main Concourse, Central Station ☎ (0191) 230 0030.
132 Grainger St. ☎ (0191) 277 8000.
Newcastle International Airport ☎ (0191) 214 280.

PRACTICAL INFORMATION

Broadway East, Gosforth ☎ (0191) 285 6710, BV.
City of Newcastle, Three Mile Bridge, Gosforth ☎ (0191) 285 1775.
Wallsend, Rheydt Av., Bigges Main ☎ (0191) 262 1973, NE : by A 1058 BV.
Whickham, Hollinside Park Fellside Rd ☎ (0191) 488 7309.
Tyne Tunnel (toll).

Newcastle Airport : ☎ (0191) 286 0966, NW : 5 m. by A 696 AV.

Terminal : *Bus Assembly : Central Station Forecourt.*

to Norway (Bergen, Haugesund and Stavanger) (Fjord Line) (26 h) – to Sweden (Gothenburg) (via Kristiansand, Norway) (Scandinavian Seaways) weekly (22 h) – to The Netherlands (Amsterdam) (Scandinavian Seaways) daily (14 h).

SIGHTS

See : *City★★ – Grey Street★* CZ *– Quayside★* CZ *: Composition★, All Saints Church★ (interior★) – Castle Keep★ AC* CZ *– Laing Art Gallery and Museum★ AC* CY **M1** *– Museum of Antiquities★* CY **M2.**

Env. : *Hadrian's Wall★★, W : by A 69* AV.

Exc. : *Beamish : North of England Open-Air Museum★★ AC, SW : 7 m. by A 692 and A 6076* AX *– Seaton Delaval Hall★ AC, NE : 11 m. by A 189 –* BV *– and A 190.*

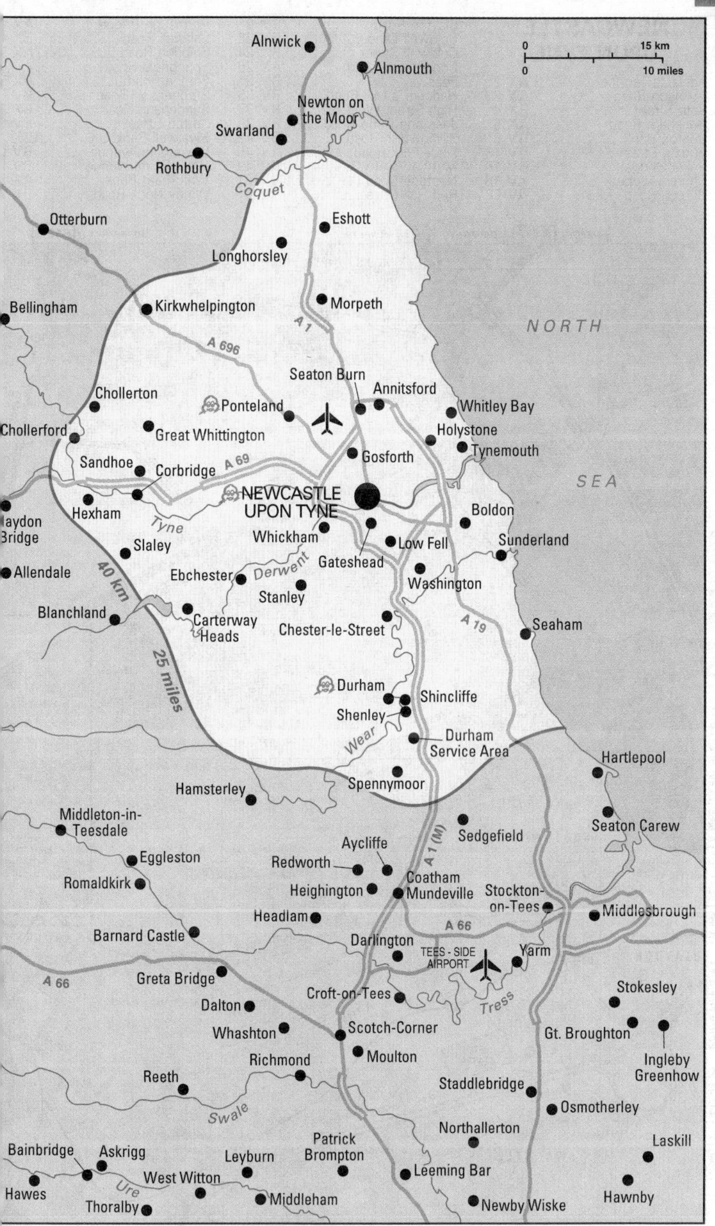

Wenn Sie ein ruhiges Hotel suchen,
benutzen Sie zuerst die Karte in der Einleitung
oder wählen Sie im Text ein Hotel mit dem Zeichen ⛬ *oder* ⛬.

NEWCASTLE UPON TYNE

Adelaide Terrace .... **AX** 2
Atkinson Road .... **AX** 3
Bath Street .... **BX** 4
Bensham Road .... **AX** 6
Benton Bank .... **BV** 8
Buddle Street .... **BV** 13
Byker Bridge .... **BV** 15
Church Avenue .... **AV** 16
Church Road .... **AV** 18
Clayton Road .... **BV** 21
Coldwell Lane .... **BX** 22
Coldwell Street .... **BX** 24
Condercum Road .... **AX** 26
Fossway .... **BV** 31
Haddrick's Mill Road .... **BV** 36
High Street West .... **BV** 37
Jesmond Dene Road .... **BV** 39
Killingworth Road .... **BV** 42
Lobley Hill Road .... **AX** 45
Matthew Bank .... **BV** 49
Neptune Road .... **BV** 51
Red Hall Drive .... **BV** 61
Redheugh Bridge .... **AX** 6
Saltwell Road .... **BX**
Shipdon Road .... **AX**
Springfield Road .... **AV**
Station Road .... **BX**
Stephenson Road .... **BV**
Sunderland Road .... **BX**
Sutton Street .... **BV**
Swalwell Bank .... **ABX**
Waverdale Avenue .... **BV**
West Farm Avenue .... **BV**
Whickham Bank .... **AX**
Windy Nook Road .... **BX**

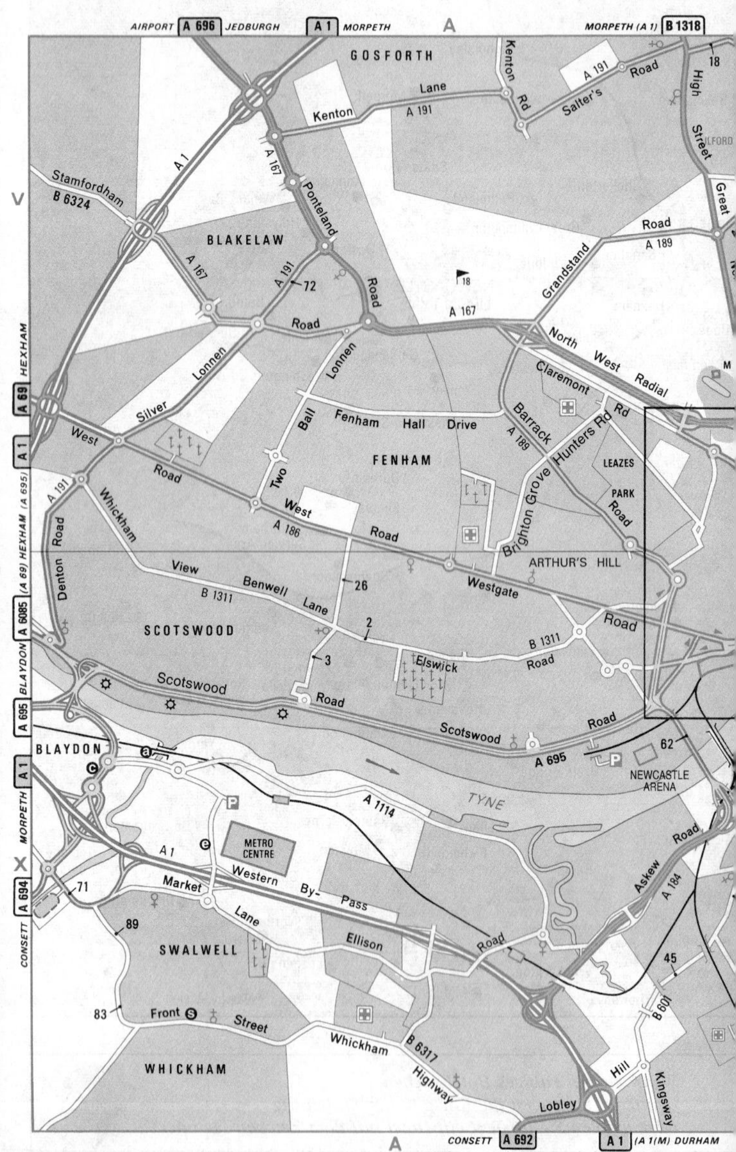

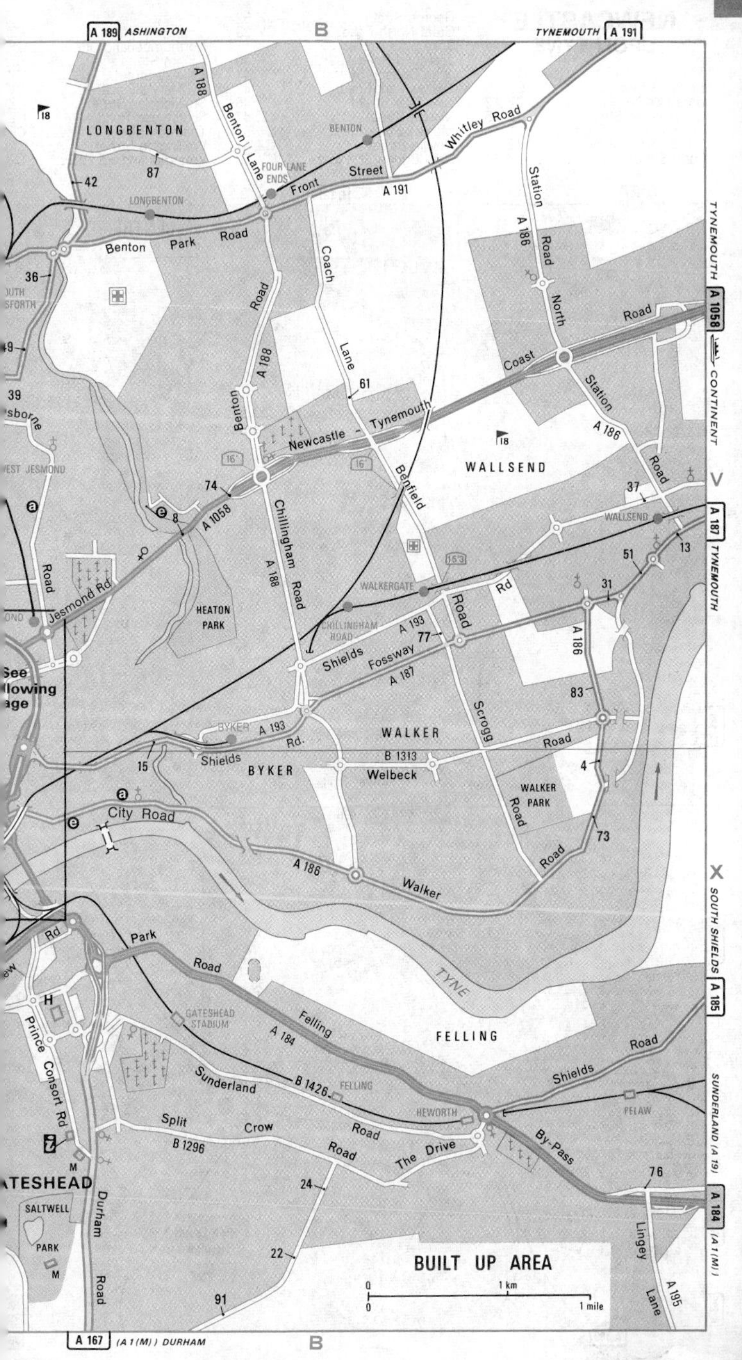
A 189 ASHINGTON
B
TYNEMOUTH A 191
LONGBENTON
A 188
Benton Lane
BENTON
FOUR LANE ENDS
Front Street
A 191
Whitley Road
Station Road
A 186
North
87
42
LONGBENTON
Benton Park Road
36
Coach Lane
Road
A 188
Benton
61
Newcastle - Tynemouth
Coast Road
Station
A 186
Road
WALLSEND
39
WEST JESMOND
74
8
A 1058
Jesmond Rd
Chillingham Road
A 188
Benfield
Road
HEATON PARK
WALLSEND
37
13
51
31
Rd
WALKERGATE
CHILLINGHAM ROAD
A 193
77
Shields
Fossway
A 187
A 186
83
See following page
BYKER
A 193
Rd.
Shields
15
BYKER
WALKER
B 1313
Welbeck
Scrogg Road
Road
4
WALKER PARK
Road
73
City Road
A 186
Walker
Road
Rd
Park
Road
TYNE
GATESHEAD STADIUM
Felling
A 184
FELLING
H
Prince Consort Rd
Sunderland
B 1426
FELLING
Road
HEWORTH
Shields
Road
PELAW
Split
Crow
B 1296
Road
The Drive
By-Pass
76
GATESHEAD
24
SALTWELL PARK
Durham Road
22
91
BUILT UP AREA
0 1 km
0 1 mile
Lingey Lane
A 195
A 167 (A 1(M)) DURHAM
B
TYNEMOUTH
A 1058
CONTINENT
V
A 187 TYNEMOUTH
X
SOUTH SHIELDS A 185
SUNDERLAND (A 19)
A 184 (A 1(M))

NEWCASTLE UPON TYNE

Blackett Street . . . . CY
Bridge Street . . . . CZ 10
Broad Chare . . . . CZ 12
Collingwood Street . . . . CZ 25
Eldon Square
Shopping Centre . . . . . . CYZ
Forth Street . . . . CZ 30
George Street . . . . CZ 32
Great North Road . . . . CY 33
Grey Street . . . . CZ
Jesmond Road . . . . CY 40
John Dobson Street . . . . . . CY 41
Leazes Park Road . . . . CY 43
Low Friar Street . . . . CZ 46
Market Street . . . . CZ 47
Mosley Street . . . . CZ 50
Neville Street . . . . CZ 52
New Bridge St. West . . . . . CY 53
Newgate
Street . . . . CZ
Northumberland Street . . . . CY
Pilgrim Street . . . . CZ
Railway Street . . . . CZ
St. Mary's Place . . . . CY
St. Nicholas Street . . . . CZ
Scotswood Road . . . . CZ
Thornton Street . . . . CZ
Wellington Street . . . . CY
Westmorland Rd . . . . CZ

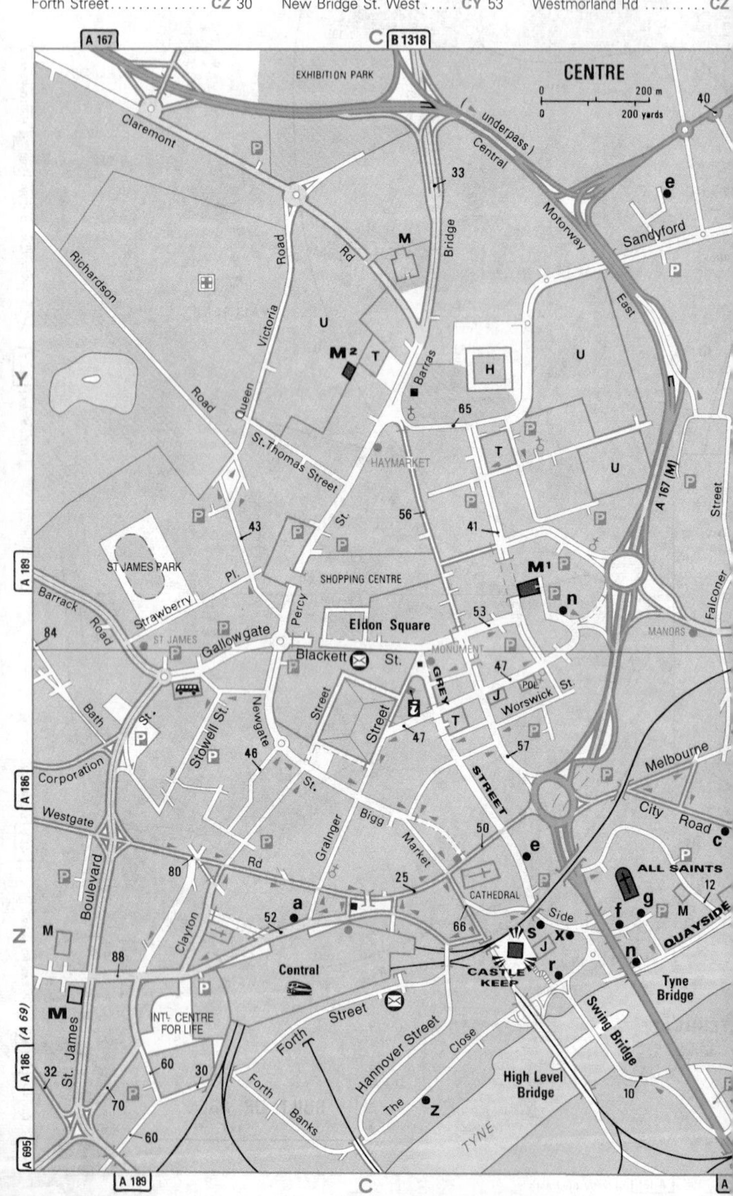

Copthorne H. Newcastle, The Close, Quayside, NE1 3RT, (0191) 222 0333, *sales.newcastle@mill-cop.com, Fax (0191) 230 1111,* « Riverside setting », rest, – 175. CZ z
Le Rivage : **Meals** (dinner only) 30.00 **t.** 14.95 – ***Harry's :*** **Meals** *(closed Saturday lunch)* 8.50/15.95 and a la carte 16.00/29.40 **t.** 14.75 – 13.50 – **156 rm** 165.00/250.00 **st.** – SB.

Malmaison, Quayside, NE1 3DX, (0191) 245 5000, *jjohnson@malmaison.com, Fax (0191) 245 4545,* « Contemporary interior », – rest, – 50. BX e
Brasserie : **Meals** a la carte 19.00/24.00 **t.** 13.95 – 11.75 – **112 rm** 120.00 **st.**, 4 suites.

Vermont, Castle Garth (off St Nicholas St), NE1 1RQ, (0191) 233 1010, *info@vermont.co.uk, Fax (0191) 233 1234,* – rm, – 200. CZ s
The Bridge : **Meals** 15.50/18.50 and a la carte 15.10/28.75 **st.** 11.50 – ***Blue Room :*** **Meals** *(closed Sunday and Monday)* (dinner only) a la carte 28.50/38.00 **st.** 16.50 – 13.50 – **95 rm** 145.00/165.00 **st.**, 6 suites – SB.

Holiday Inn Newcastle City, 1 New Bridge Street West, NE1 8BS, (0870) 400 9058, *Fax (0191) 261 8529,* – rm, rest, – 400. CY n
The Junction : **Meals** *(closed lunch Saturday and Sunday)* 15.00 and a la carte 23.00/28.50 **t.** 11.95 – 13.95 – **172 rm** 105.00 **st.** – SB.

Thistle Newcastle, Neville St, NE1 5DF, (0870) 3339142, *newcastle@thistle.co.uk, Fax (0870) 3339242* – rm, – 130. CZ a
Gengis : **Meals** 12.50/27.50 and a la carte 20.00/29.00 **st.** 12.00 – 13.50 – **115 rm** 122.00/157.00 **st.** – SB.

New Northumbria, 61-69 Osborne Rd, Jesmond, NE2 2AN, (0191) 281 4961, *reservations@newnorthumbriahotel.co.uk, Fax (0191) 281 8588,* – rm, – 120. BV a
Scalini's : **Meals** - Italian - a la carte 14.00/23.45 **t.** 9.75 – **50 rm** 75.00/115.00 **st.**

Novotel, Ponteland Rd, Kenton Bank, NE3 3HZ, at junction of A 1(M) with A 696 (0191) 214 0303, *h1118@accor-hotels.com, Fax (0191) 214 0633,* – rm, rest, – 220. AV a
Garden Brasserie : **Meals** 15.50 (dinner) and a la carte 17.00/26.00 **st.** 13.00 – 10.00 – **126 rm** 75.00 **st.** – SB.

Waterside, 48-52 Sandhill, Quayside, NE1 3JF, (0191) 230 0111, *enquiries@watersidehotel.com, Fax (0191) 230 1615* – rm, CZ r
Meals - Italian - *(closed Sunday)* a la carte 15.15/21.00 **st.** 6.95 – 9.95 – **36 rm** 65.00/88.00 **st.**

Premier Lodge, Exchange Buildings, The Quayside, NE1 3DW, (0870) 7001504, *Fax (0870) 7001505* – rm, – 35. CZ n
Meals (dinner only) a la carte approx. 12.45 **t.** 8.45 – **136 rm** 49.95 **t.** – SB.

Travel Inn Metro, City Rd, Quayside, NE2 2AQ, (0191) 232 6533, *Fax (0191) 232 6557* – rm, rest, BX a
Meals (grill rest.) (dinner only) – **81 rm** 49.95 **t.**

Travelodge without rest., Forster St, NE1 2NH, (0191) 261 5432, *Fax (0191) 261 7105* – – 25. CZ c
120 rm 59.95 **t.**

Fisherman's Lodge, Jesmond Dene, Jesmond, NE7 7BQ, (0191) 281 3281, *enquiries@fishermanslodge.co.uk, Fax (0191) 281 6410,* « Victorian country house in wooded valley » – BV e
closed 25-29 December, 1-7 January, Saturday lunch, Sunday and Bank Holidays – **Meals** 19.50 (lunch) and a la carte 29.50/57.30 **t.** 14.80.

Treacle Moon, 5-7 The Side, Quayside, NE1 3JE, (0191) 232 5537, *Fax (0191) 221 1745* – CZ x
closed 2 weeks August, Christmas, Saturday lunch, Sunday and Monday – **Meals** (booking essential) a la carte 28.05/34.85 **t.** 14.95.

Vujon, 29Queen St, Quayside, NE1 3UG, (0191) 221 0601, *mataj@vujon.demon.co.uk, Fax (0191) 221 0602* – CZ g
closed 25 December, 1 January and Sunday lunch – **Meals** - Indian - 20.00/22.00 and a la carte 20.40/31.60 **t.** 8.90.

Leela's, 20 Dean St, NE1 1PG, (0191) 230 1261 – CZ e
closed 2 weeks January, 25-26 December, Sunday and Bank Holidays – **Meals** - South Indian - 9.95 (lunch) and a la carte 14.20/21.80 **t.** 11.95.

ENGLAND

Valley Junction 397, The Old Station, Archbold Terr, NE2 1DB, (0191) 281 639 CY
Fax (0191) 281 6383 –
closed 25-26 December, Sunday lunch and Monday – **Meals** - Indian - a la carte appro 16.85.

Café 21, 19-21 Queen St, Princes Wharf, Quayside, NE1 3UG, (0191) 222 075 CZ
Fax (0191) 221 0761 – . VISA
closed Sunday and Bank Holidays – **Meals** (booking essential) 14.50 (lunch) and a la car 17.00/36.00 **t.** 10.50.

at Gosforth *North : 2½ m. by B 1318* – **AV** – *Newcastle upon Tyne.*

Newcastle Marriott H. Gosforth Park, High Gosforth Park, NE3 5HN, North : 2 on B 1318 at junction with A 1056 (0191) 236 4111, *Fax (0191) 236 8192*, , squash – , rm, rest, – 600. VISA
Chaps : **Meals** (bar lunch)/dinner a la carte 23.70/33.75 **st.** 13.75 – ***Park :*** **Meals** (dinn only) a la carte 23.70/33.75 **st.** – 13.50 – **173 rm** 110.00 **st.**, 5 suites – SB.

at Seaton Burn *North : 8 m. by B 1318* – **AV** – *Newcastle upon Tyne.*

Holiday Inn, Great North Rd, NE13 6BP, North : ¾ m. at junction with A (0191) 201 9988, *revnhi@queensmoat.co.uk, Fax (0191) 236 8091*, – r – 400. VISA JCB
Meals *(closed Saturday lunch)* 11.95/22.00 **t.** 11.95 – 11.50 – **150 rm** 115.00/135.00

Travelodge, Fisher Lane, NE13 6ED, North : ¾ m. at junction with A 1 (0191) 217 010
Fax (0191) 217 0107 – rm, rest, . VISA JCB.
Meals (grill rest.) – **40 rm** 49.95 **t.**

Horton Grange with rm, NE13 6BU, Northwest : 3 ½ m. by Blagdon rd on Ponteland (01661) 860686, *andrew@horton-grange.co.uk, Fax (01661) 860308*, – rest, VISA.
closed Christmas and New Year – **Meals** *(closed Sunday dinner to non-residents)* (booki essential) (dinner only) 27.00/37.00 **t.** 11.00 – **9 rm** 69.00/95.00 **t.** – SB.

at Holystone *Northeast : 6 m. by B 1318,* – **BV** – *A 189 on A 191* – *Newcastle upon Tyne.*

Travel Inn, Whitley Rd, NE27 0DA, at junction of A 19 and A 191 (0191) 270 270
Fax (0191) 259 9509 – , rest, . VISA JCB.
Meals (grill rest.) – **40 rm** 41.95 **t.**

at Annitsford *(Northd.) Northeast : 7 m. by B 1318 and A 189* – *Newcastle upon Tyne.*

Travel Inn, Moor Farm Industrial Estate, NE23 7RG, at junction of A 19 and A 1 (0191) 250 2770, *Fax (0191) 250 2216* – , rest, . VISA.
Meals (grill rest.) – **40 rm** 41.95 **t.**

at Newcastle Airport *Northwest : 6 ¾ m. by A 167 off A 696* – **AV** – *Newcastle upon Tyne.*

Travel Inn Metro, Ponteland Rd, Prestwick, NE20 9DB, (01661) 8250
Fax (01661) 824940, « Aeronautical themed restaurant » – , rest, – VISA.
Meals (grill rest.) – **86 rm** 49.95 **t.**

at Ponteland *Northwest : 8 ¼ m. by A 167 on A 696* – **AV** – *Newcastle upon Tyne.*

Café 21, 35 Broadway, Darras Hall Estate, NE20 9PW, Southwest : 1 ½ m. by B 6323 a Darras Hall Estate rd (01661) 820357, *Fax (01661) 820357* – VISA
closed Sunday and Bank Holidays – **Meals** - Bistro - (booking essential) (dinner only a Saturday lunch) a la carte 16.50/32.00 **t.** 10.50.

NEWENT *Glos.* 403 404 M 28 – *pop. 4 111.*

7 Church St (01531) 822468.

London 109 – *Gloucester 10* – *Hereford 22* – *Newport 44.*

at Clifford's Mesne *Southwest : 3 m. by B 4216* – *Newent.*

Yew Tree with rm, GL18 1JS, on Glasshouse rd (01531) 820719, – VISA
closed 2-8 January – **Meals** *(closed Monday)* 24.50 12.00 – **2 rm** 40.00/60.00 **st.** – SB

NEWHAVEN *E. Sussex* 404 U 31 – *pop. 11 208.*

to France (Dieppe) (Hoverspeed Ltd) 2-6 daily (2 h).

London 63 – *Brighton 9* – *Eastbourne 14* – *Lewes 7.*

Travel Inn, Avis Rd, BN9 0AG, East : ½ m. on A 259 (01273) 612356, *Fax (01273) 612*
– rm, . VISA
Meals (grill rest.) – **40 rm** 41.95 **t.**

EWICK *E. Sussex* 404 U 31 – *pop. 2 445.*

London 57 – Brighton 14 – Eastbourne 20 – Hastings 34 – Maidstone 30.

Newick Park ⛰, BN8 4SB, Southeast : 1 ½ m. following signs for Newick Park ☎ (01825) 723633, *bookings@newickpark.co.uk, Fax (01825) 723969,* ←, « Georgian house, extensive grounds », heated, ⛳, ☂, ☒, ✂ – ⇔ TV ♿ P. MC AE VISA
Meals (booking essential to non-residents) 19.50/27.50 and dinner a la carte 31.50/56.00 **t.** 9.75 – **15 rm** ☕ 95.00/235.00 **t.**, 1 suite – SB.

EWLYN *Cornwall* 403 D 33 – *see Penzance.*

EWMARKET *Suffolk* 404 V 27 – *pop. 16 498.*

18 Links, Cambridge Rd ☎ (01638) 663000.

Palace House, Palace St ☎ (01638) 667200.

London 64 – Cambridge 13 – Ipswich 40 – Norwich 48.

Bedford Lodge, Bury Rd, CB8 7BX, Northeast : ½ m. on A 1304 ☎ (01638) 663175, *info@bedfordlodgehotel.co.uk, Fax (01638) 667391,* ⚒, ≘s, ☒, ☂ – ⇕ ⇔ TV P – 200. MC AE VISA. ✗
Orangery : **Meals** *(closed Saturday lunch except during racing)* 12.00/23.50 and dinner a la carte 16.95/39.50 **st.** 16.00 – **50 rm** ☕ 105.00/140.00 **st.**, 6 suites – SB.

Rutland Arms, High St, CB8 8NB, ☎ (01638) 664251, *gapleisure@rutlandarmshotel.com, Fax (01638) 666298* – ⇔ rm, TV ☎ P – 80. MC AE ① VISA. ✗
Meals 12.50/17.50 and a la carte 21.45/30.65 **t.** 12.95 – ☕ 8.25 – **46 rm** 72.50/84.50 **t.** – SB.

Six Mile Bottom *(Cambs.) Southwest : 6 m. on A 1304 – ✉ Newmarket.*

Swynford Paddocks, CB8 0UE, ☎ (01638) 570234, *info@swynfordpaddocks.com, Fax (01638) 570283,* ←, ☂, ☒, ✂ – ⇔ rest, TV ☎ P – 25. MC AE ① VISA
Meals 31.50 and a la carte 20.00/31.50 **t.** 12.95 – **15 rm** ☕ 110.00/155.00 **t.** – SB.

*Keine Aufnahme in den **Michelin-Führer** durch*
– falsche Information oder
– Bezahlung!

EWMILLERDAM *W. Yorks. – see Wakefield.*

EW MILTON *Hants.* 403 404 P 31 – *pop. 24 324 (inc. Barton-on-Sea).*

18, 9 Barton-on-Sea, Milford Rd ☎ (01425) 615308.

London 106 – Bournemouth 12 – Southampton 21 – Winchester 34.

Chewton Glen ⛰, Christchurch Rd, BH25 6QS, West : 2 m. by A 337 and Ringwood Rd on Chewton Farm Rd ☎ (01425) 275341, *reservations@chewtonglen.com, Fax (01425) 272310,* ←, ☂, « Gardens », ⚒, ≘s, heated, ☒, 9, ☒, ✂ indoor/outdoor – ⇔ rest, ☰ rest, TV ☎ P – 120. MC AE ① VISA. ✗
Marryat Room and Conservatory : **Meals** 55.00 (dinner) and lunch a la carte 21.95/37.45 **st.** 18.50 – ☕ 20.00 – **43 rm** 250.00/380.00 **st.**, 19 suites 380.00/695.00 **st.**
Spec. Double baked Emmental soufflé. Braised pork cheeks and lobster with ginger and coriander. Chocolate fondant, pistachio ice cream.

EWPORT *Wrekin* 402 403 404 M 25 *Great Britain G.* – *pop. 10 964.*

Exc. : *Weston Park★★, SE : 6½ m. by A 41 and A 5.*

London 150 – Birmingham 33 – Shrewsbury 18 – Stoke-on-Trent 21.

Royal Victoria, St Mary's St, TF10 7AB, ☎ (01952) 820331, *info@royal-victoria.co.uk, Fax (01952) 820209* – TV P – 140. MC AE VISA
Meals *(closed Sunday dinner)* a la carte 11.75/15.00 **st.** – **24 rm** ☕ 44.00/59.00 **st.**

EWPORT PAGNELL *Milton Keynes* 404 R 27 – *pop. 12 285.*

London 57 – Bedford 13 – Luton 21 – Northampton 15.

Plan : see Milton Keynes

Swan Revived, High St, MK16 8AR, ☎ (01908) 610565, *swanrevived@btinternet.com, Fax (01908) 210995* – ⇕, ⇔ rest, ☰ rest, TV P – 70. MC AE ① VISA CU s
Meals *(closed Saturday lunch)* 15.00 (lunch) and a la carte 17.70/26.50 **t.** 9.95 – **40 rm** ☕ 78.00/95.00 **t.**, 2 suites – SB.

ENGLAND

The Limes, North Sq, MK16 8EP, ✆ (01908) 617041, *royandruth@8thelimes.freeserve.co.uk, Fax (01908) 217292,* « Georgian house », – TV P. MC AE VISA JCB CU
Meals (by arrangement) (communal dining) 19.50 **s.** – **4 rm** 45.00/65.00 – SB.

Robinsons, 18-20 St John St, MK16 8HJ, ✆ (01908) 611400, *info@robinsonsrestaurant.co.uk, Fax (01908) 216900* – MC AE VISA JCB CU
closed 1 week August, 26 December-2 January, Saturday lunch, Sunday and Bank Holiday Mondays – **Meals** 7.95/14.95 and a la carte 23.60/29.60 **t.** 12.75.

NEWQUAY *Cornwall* 403 E 32 *The West Country G. – pop. 17 390.*

Env. : *Penhale Point and Kelsey Head★ (≤★★), SW : by A 3075* **Y** *– Trerice★ AC, SE : 3 1/2 m. by A 392 –* **Y** *– and A 3058.*

Exc. : *St Agnes – St Agnes Beacon★★ (✳★★), SW : 12 1/2 m. by A 3075 –* **Y** *– and B 3285.*

Tower Rd ✆ (01637) 872091, **Z** *– Treloy ✆ (01637) 878554 – Merlin, Mawgan Porth ✆ (01841) 540222.*

Newquay Airport : ✆ (01637) 860834 **Y**.

Municipal Offices, Marcus Hill ✆ (01637) 854020.

London 291 – Exeter 83 – Penzance 34 – Plymouth 48 – Truro 14.

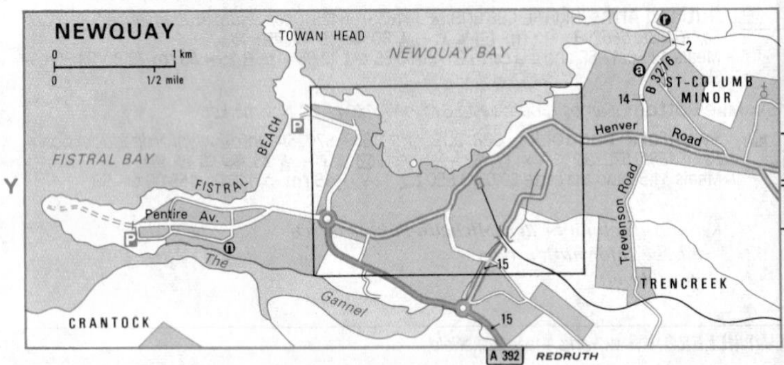

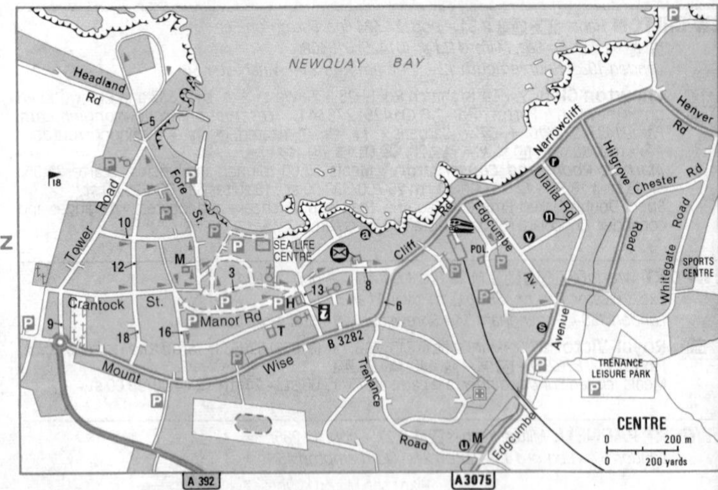

Alexandra Road . . . . **Y** 2
Bank Street . . . . **Z** 3
Beacon Road . . . . **Z** 5
Berry Road . . . . **Z** 6
East Street . . . . **Z** 8
Fore Street . . . . **Z**
Higher Tower Road . . . . **Z** 9
Hope Terrace . . . . **Z** 10
Jubilee Street . . . . **Z** 12
Marcus Hill . . . . **Z**
Porth Way . . . . **Y**
Trevemper Road . . . . **Y**
St. Georges Road . . . . **Z**
St. John's Road . . . . **Z**

ENGLAND

The Bristol, Narrowcliff, TR7 2PQ, (01637) 875181, *info@hotelbristol.co.uk, Fax (01637) 879347,* <, – – 200. MC AE VISA JCB Z r
Meals 12.50/16.00 and dinner a la carte 22.00/32.00 **st.** 9.50 – 9.50 – **73 rm** 54.00/98.00 **st.**, 1 suite – SB.

Trebarwith, Trebarwith Cres, TR7 1BZ, (01637) 872288, *enquiry@trebarwith-hotel.co.uk, Fax (01637) 875431,* < bay and coast, – rest, MC AE VISA. Z a
April-October – **Meals** (bar lunch)/dinner 14.00/28.00 **st.** 11.00 – **41 rm** (dinner included) 65.00/130.00 **t.** – SB.

Trenance Lodge, 83 Trenance Rd, TR7 2HW, (01637) 876702, *info@trenance-lodge.co.uk, Fax (01637) 878772,* heated, – MC VISA. Z u
Meals (lunch by arrangement)/dinner 17.50/21.50 and a la carte **t.** – **5 rm** 35.00/60.00 **s.** – SB.

Whipsiderry, Trevelgue Rd, Porth, TR7 3LY, Northeast : 2 m. by A 392 off B 3276 (01637) 874777, *whipsiderry@cornwall_net, Fax (01637) 874777,* <, heated, – MC AE VISA
April-December – **Meals** (bar lunch)/dinner 16.00 **t.** 9.95 – **20 rm** (dinner included) 50.00 **t.**

Windward, Alexandra Rd, Porth Bay, TR7 3NB, (01637) 873185, *caswind@aol.com, Fax (01637) 852436* – rest, MC AE VISA. Y r
closed 24-26 December – **Meals** (residents only) (dinner only) 10.00 **st.** 8.00 – **14 rm** 40.00/64.00 **st.**

Corisande Manor, Riverside Ave, Pentire, TR7 1PL, (01637) 872042, *relax@corisande.com, Fax (01637) 874557,* < Gannel Estuary, – rest, MC AE VISA. Y n
Meals (dinner only) 21.00 **st.** 10.00 – **9 rm** 75.00/130.00 **st.** – SB.

Porth Veor Manor, Porth Way, TR7 3LW, (01637) 873274, *info@porthveor.co.uk, Fax (01637) 851690,* – rest, MC AE VISA JCB Y a
Meals (lunch by arrangement)/dinner 14.25 and a la carte 15.85/22.20 **st.** 9.75 – **22 rm** 45.00/90.00 **t.** – SB.

Philadelphia without rest., 19 Eliot Gdns, TR7 2QF, (01637) 877747, *stay@thephiladelphia.co.uk, Fax (01637) 876860* – MC VISA. Z n
6 rm 30.00/56.00 **st.**

Wheal Treasure, 72 Edgcumbe Ave, TR7 2NN, (01637) 874136 – Z z
13 May-September – **Meals** (by arrangement) 9.50 **st.** 8.50 – **12 rm** 32.00/56.00 **st.** – SB.

Chynoweth Lodge without rest., 1 Eliot Gdns, TR7 2QE, (01637) 876684, *reg@chynowethlodge.co.uk, Fax (01637) 876684,* – Z v
closed November-December – **9 rm** 23.00/46.00 **st.**

at Crantock *Southwest : 4 m. by A 3075* – **Y** – *Newquay.*

Crantock Bay, West Pentire, TR8 5SE, West : ¾ m. (01637) 830229, *stay@crantockbayhotel.co.uk, Fax (01637) 831111,* < Crantock Bay, – rest, MC AE VISA JCB
closed December-January except New Year and restricted opening February-March – **Meals** (buffet lunch)/dinner 18.50 and a la carte approx. 26.95 **t.** 8.50 – **33 rm** (dinner included) 76.50/153.00 **t.** – SB.

NEW ROMNEY *Kent* 404 W 31.

London 71 – Brighton 60 – Folkestone 17 – Maidstone 36.

Romney Bay House, Coast Rd, Littlestone, TN28 8QY, East : 2 ¼ m. off B 2071 (01797) 364747, *Fax (01797) 367156,* <, « Beachside house designed by Sir Clough Williams-Ellis », – MC VISA.
closed 1 week Christmas – **Meals** (booking essential to non-residents) (dinner only) (set menu only) 29.50 **t.** 12.50 – **10 rm** 60.00/140.00 **t.** – SB.

NEWTON LONGVILLE *Bucks.* 404 R 28 – *see Milton Keynes.*

NEWTON ON THE MOOR *Northd.* 401 402 O 17 – *see Alnwick.*

NEWTON SOLNEY *Derbs.* 402 403 404 P 25 – *see Burton-upon-Trent (Staffs.).*

NITON *I.O.W.* 403 404 Q 32 – *see Wight (Isle of).*

NOMANSLAND *Wilts.* 403 404 P 31 – ✉ *Salisbury.*
London 96 – Bournemouth 26 – Salisbury 13 – Southampton 14 – Winchester 25.

XX **Les Mirabelles,** Forest Edge Rd, SP5 2BN, ☎ (01794) 390205, *Fax (01794) 390106,* ≤
MC AE VISA
closed first 2 weeks January, last week May, Monday and Sunday dinner – **Meals** - French
a la carte 16.00/35.00 **t.** 9.50.

NORMAN CROSS *Peterborough* 404 T 26 – *see Peterborough.*

NORTHALLERTON *N. Yorks.* 402 P 20 – *pop. 13 774.*
The Applegarth Car Park ☎ (01609) 776864.
London 238 – Leeds 48 – Middlesbrough 24 – York 33.

at Staddlebridge *Northeast : 7½ m. by A 684 on A 19 at junction with A 172* – ✉ *Northallerton*

The Tontine, DL6 3JB, on southbound carriageway (A 19) ☎ (01609) 882671, *enquiries mccoysatthetontine.co.uk, Fax (01609) 882660* – rm, TV P. MC AE VISA
closed 25-26 December and 1 January – **Meals** – (see ***McCoys Bistro*** below) – **6 r**
75.00/95.00 **t.**

X **McCoys Bistro** (at The Tontine H.), DL6 3JB, on southbound carriageway (A 1
☎ (01609) 882671, *Fax (01609) 882660* – P. MC AE VISA
closed 25-26 December and 1 January – **Meals** - Brasserie - (booking essential) 12.9
(lunch) and a la carte 25.50/30.70 **t.** 12.95.

at Newby Wiske *South : 2½ m. by A 167* – ✉ *Northallerton.*

Solberge Hall , DL7 9ER, Northwest : 1 ¼ m. on Warlaby rd ☎ (01609) 779191, *hote solberge.freeserve.co.uk, Fax (01609) 780472,* ≤, – rest, TV P – 100. MC
VISA
Meals 9.50/23.00 and dinner a la carte 21.70/26.80 **st.** 11.95 – **23 rm** 75.00/100.00 **s**
1 suite – SB.

Les prix — Pour toutes précisions sur les prix indiqués dans ce guide, reportez-vous aux pages de l'introduction.

NORTHAMPTON *Northants.* 404 R 27 *Great Britain G.* – *pop. 179 596.*
Exc. : *All Saints, Brixworth*★, *N : 7 m. on A 508 Y.*
18, 9 *Delapre, Eagle Drive, Nene Valley Way ☎ (01604) 764036* **Z** – 18 *Collingtree Pa Windingbrook Lane ☎ (01604) 700000.*
Mr Grant's House, St Giles Sq ☎ (01604) 622677.
London 69 – Cambridge 53 – Coventry 34 – Leicester 42 – Luton 35 – Oxford 41.

Plan opposite

Northampton Marriott, Eagle Drive, NN4 7HW, Southeast : 2 m. by A 428 off A
☎ (01604) 768700, *Fax (01604) 769011,* – rm, rest, TV P
220. MC AE VISA JCB. **Z**
La Fontana : **Meals** - Italian - 15.00/20.00 and dinner a la carte approx. 22.00 **st.** 15.0
13.00 – **118 rm** 105.00 **st.**, 2 suites – SB.

Hilton Northampton, 100 Watering Lane, Collingtree, NN4 0XW, South : 3 m. on A 5
☎ (01604) 700666, *Fax (01604) 702850,* – rm, rest, TV P
300. MC AE VISA JCB
Meals (carving lunch) (bar lunch Saturday) 14.25/19.95 and dinner a la carte 19.00/25.65
12.30 – 10.25 – **136 rm** 140.00/160.00, 3 suites – SB.

Northampton Moat House, Silver St, NN1 2TA, ☎ (01604) 739988, *ebnth@quee moat.co.uk, Fax (01604) 230614,* – rm, TV P – 600. MC AE V
JCB
Meals (buffet lunch)/dinner 16.50 and a la carte 19.60/27.80 **t.** 11.95 – 11.50 – **145 r**
108.00/120.00 **st.** – SB. **X**

Courtyard by Marriott, Bedford Rd, NN4 7YF, Southeast : 1 ½ m. on A 4
☎ (01604) 622777, *Fax (01604) 635454,* – TV P – 40. MC AE V
JCB. **Z**
Meals a la carte 14.00/24.00 11.75 – 10.50 – **104 rm** 90.00 **t.** – SB.

Travel Inn, Harpole Turn, Weedon Rd, NN7 4DD, West : 3 ¾ m. on A 45 ☎ (01604) 8323
Fax (01604) 831807 – , rest, TV P – 60. MC AE VISA.
Meals (grill rest.) – **51 rm** 41.95 **t.**

Travelodge, Upton Way (Ring Rd), NN5 6EG, Southwest : 1 ¾ m. by A
☎ (01604) 758395, *Fax (01604) 758395* – rm, TV P. MC AE VISA JCB. **Z**
Meals (grill rest.) – **62 rm** 49.95 **t.**

ɪORTHAMPTON

ɔington Square . . . . . . X 2
ɔington Street X
ɛwick Road . . . . Y 4
lling Road. . . . . X 5
ɪidge Street . . . . X 6
ampbell Street. . . . . . . X 7
astillian St. . . . . X 8
harnwood Avenue. . . . Y 10
ɪurch Lane. . . . . X 12
iftonville Rd . . . . Z 13
ollege Street . . . . X 14
erngate . . . . X 15
rapery . . . . X 18
old Street X
reyfriars . . . . X 23
rosvenor Centre X
uildhall Road . . . . X 24
azelwood Rd . . . . X 25
orse Shoe
Street. . . . . X 28
ettering Road. . . . . X 30
ngsthorpe Grove. . . . . Y 34
ower Mounts . . . . X 35
aklands Drive. . . . . Y 38
verstone Road. . . . . X 39
ark Avenue North . . . . Y 40
ark Avenue South . . . . Z 43
ushmere Road . . . . Z 44
. Andrew's Road . . . . Y 45
. Edmund's Road. . . . X 48
. Edmund's St. . . . . . . Z 49
. James's Road . . . . . Z 50
. John's Street . . . . . . X 51
. Leonard's Road . . . . Z 52
. Michael's Road . . . . X 53
St. Peters Way
Centre X
Sheep Street . . . . X 54
Silver Street . . . . X 55
Spencer Bridge
Road. . . . . X, Z 57
Towcester Road . . . . Z 58
Upper Mounts . . . . X 59
Waveney Way . . . . Y 60
West Bridge . . . . X 62
Weston Favell Centre . . . . Y
Windrush Way . . . . Y 63

A 5095 (A 508)
A 508
A 4500
A 5123
A 428 (A 45)
A 428
A 5123
A 508
Grafton St.
Robert St.
Earl St.
Andrew's St.
Broad St.
Lady's Lane
GROSVENOR CENTRE
Abington St.
Horse Market
York Rd
Mare Fair
Gold St.
St. Giles' St.
Cheyne Walk
ST-PETERS CENTRE
Peter's Way
Bedford Rd
Promenade
Victoria
POL.
X
0 200 m
0 200 yards

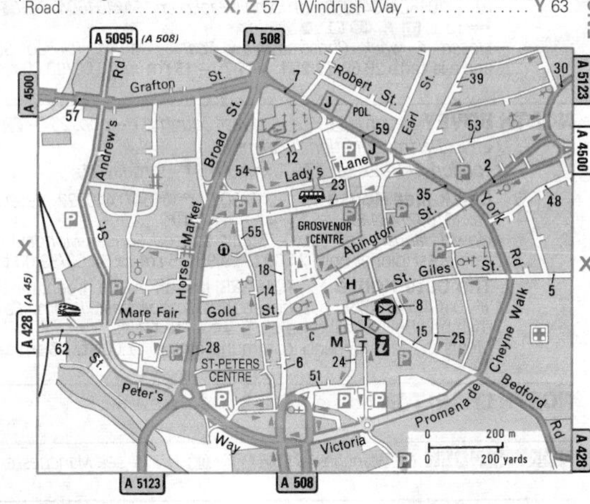

LEICESTER A 5199
A 508 MARKET HARBOROUGH
KETTERING A 43
(A 45)
WELLINGBOROUGH
A 4500
A 45 WELLINGBOROUGH
A 428 BEDFORD
A 43 OXFORD
A 508 (M 1),MILTON KEYNES
Welford Road
Harborough Rd
Holly Lodge Drive
Boughton Green Rd
Red House Road
MOULTON PARK
Talavera Way
KINGSTHORPE
Kettering Road
A 5123
Booth Lane
Lumbertubs Way
WESTON FAVELL CENTRE
WESTON FAVELL
Mill Lane
Kingsthorpe Rd
Balfour Rd
Kingsley Rd
A 508
Harlestone
DUSTON
DALLINGTON
ABINGTON PARK
A 428 Road
Wellingborough
A 4500 Billing Road
Billing Rd East
Valley Way
A 4500 Weedon Rd
Upton Way
A 45
Grand Union Canal
Bedford
A 428
Nene
Road
BRACKMILLS
Towcester Rd
London Rd
FAR COTTON
Danes Camp Way
Mere Way
Nene Valley Way
A 45
B 526
HARDINGSTONE
GREAT HOUGHTON
High St.
Y
Z
0 1 km
0 1 mile

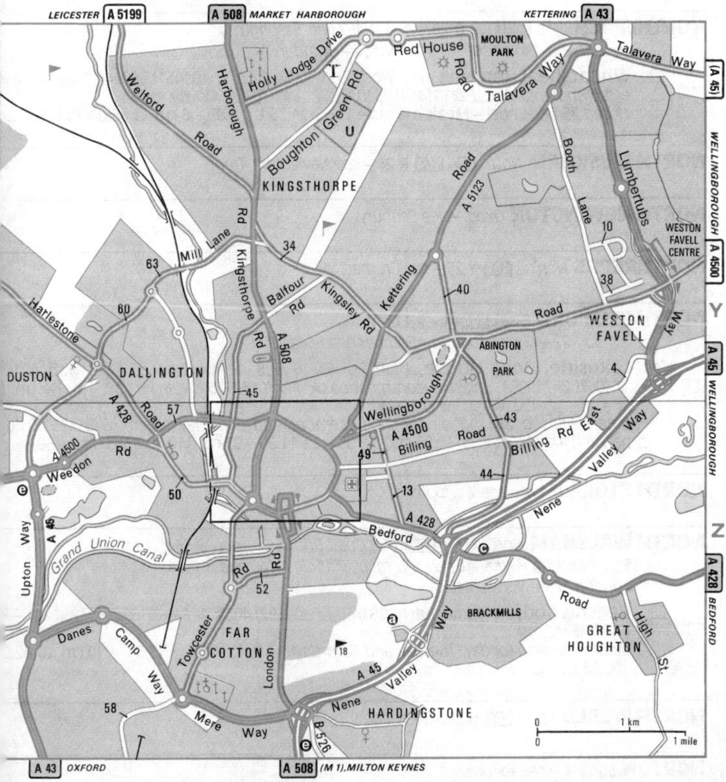

ENGLAND

at Spratton *North : 7 m. by A 508 off A 50 – Y – ✉ Northampton.*

Broomhill Country House, Holdenby Rd, NN6 8LD, Southwest : 1 m. on Holdenb rd ☎ (01604) 845959, *broomhill@aol.com, Fax (01604) 845834*, ≤, heated, –, rest, TV P. MC AE VISA.
closed 1 week Christmas-New Year – **Meals** *(closed Sunday dinner)* 14.50/23.9 and a la carte 28.60/32.25 **t.** 11.70 – **13 rm** 70.00/90.00 **t.**

NORTH BOVEY *Devon* 403 I 32 *The West Country G. – pop. 254 – ✉ Newton Abbot.*
Env. : *Dartmoor National Park★★.*
London 214 – Exeter 13 – Plymouth 34 – Torquay 21.

Blackaller House, TQ13 8QY, ☎ (01647) 440322, *peter@blackaller.fsbusiness.co.u Fax (01647) 441131*, ≤, –, TV P.
closed January-February – **Meals** *(closed Sunday-Monday)* (booking essential for nor residents) (dinner only) 24.00 **t.** 9.95 – **5 rm** 34.00/82.00 **t.** – SB.

The Gate House, TQ13 8RB, just off village green, past "Ring of Bells" public hous ☎ (01647) 440479, *gatehouseondartmoor@talk21.com, Fax (01647) 440479*, ≤, « 15 thatched Devon hallhouse », –, TV P.
Meals (by arrangement) (communal dining) 17.00 **st.** – **3 rm** 35.00/58.00 **st.**

NORTH CHARLTON *Northd.* 401 402 O 17 – *see Alnwick.*

NORTHENDEN *Gtr. Manchester* 402 403 404 N 23 – *see Manchester.*

NORTHFIELD *W. Mids.* 403 ㉒ 404 ⑳ – *see Birmingham.*

NORTHLEACH *Glos.* 403 404 O 28 – *pop. 1 462 (inc. Eastington).*
London 88 – Gloucester 18 – Oxford 30 – Swindon 24.

Wheatsheaf Inn with rm, West End, GL54 3EZ, ☎ (01451) 860244, *wheatsheaf establishment.ltd.uk, Fax (01451) 861037*, –, TV P. MC VISA
closed 25 December – **Meals** a la carte 15.35/21.35 **t.** 9.95 – **8 rm** 55.00/75.00 **t.**

NORTH MUSKHAM *Notts.* 402 404 R 24 – *see Newark-on-Trent.*

NORTH NEWINGTON *Oxon. – see Banbury.*

NORTHREPPS *Norfolk* 404 Y 25 – *see Cromer.*

NORTH STIFFORD *Essex* 404 ㊹ – ✉ *Grays.*
London 22 – Chelmsford 24 – Southend-on-Sea 20.

Lakeside Moat House, High Rd, RM16 5UE, at junction of A 13 with A 10 ☎ (01708) 719988, *cblak@queensmoat.co.uk, Fax (01375) 390426*, –, rm, P – 150. MC AE VISA JCB
Meals *(closed 25 and dinner 26 December and Saturday lunch)* 17.95/35.00 (di ner) and a la carte 24.95/30.95 **st.** 12.95 – 11.50 – **97 rm** 110.00/136.00 **st.** – SB.

NORTH STOKE *Oxon. – see Wallingford.*

NORTH WALSHAM *Norfolk* 403 404 Y 25 *Great Britain G. – pop. 9 534.*
Exc. : *Blicking Hall★★ AC, W : 8½ m. by B 1145, A 140 and B 1354.*
London 125 – Norwich 16.

Beechwood, 20 Cromer Rd, NR28 0HD, ☎ (01692) 403231, *Fax (01692) 407284*, – TV P. MC AE VISA
Meals *(closed Monday, Tuesday and Saturday)* 13.00/26.00 **t.** 13.50 – **10 rm** 62.0 100.00 **t.** – SB.

NORTH WEALD *Essex* 404 U 28 – *see Harlow.*

NORTON *Shrops. – see Telford.*

ORTON ST PHILIP *Somerset* 403 404 N 30 – *pop. 820* – ✉ *Bath.*
London 113 – Bristol 22 – Southampton 55 – Swindon 40.

George Inn, High St, BA3 6LH, ✆ (01373) 834224, *georgeinnsp@aol.com, Fax (01373) 834861,* « Historic 15C inn », – rest, TV P. MC AE VISA
accommodation closed 25 December – **Meals** 11.50 (dinner) and a la carte 16.85/24.85 **t.** 10.95 – **8 rm** 60.00/90.00 **t.**

Bath Lodge, BA2 7NH, East : 1 ¼ m. by A 366 on A 36 ✆ (01225) 723040, *walker@bath lodge.demon.co.uk, Fax (01225) 723737,* « Castellated former gatehouse », – TV P. MC AE VISA
Meals *(closed Sunday-Thursday)* (dinner only) 24.50 **st.** 10.25 – **6 rm** 50.00/130.00 **t.**

Monmouth Lodge without rest., BA2 7LH, on B 3110 ✆ (01373) 834367, – TV P. MC VISA.
closed 20 December-10 January – **3 rm** 55.00/70.00.

The Plaine without rest., BA2 7LT, ✆ (01373) 834723, *theplaine@easynet.co.uk, Fax (01373) 834101,* « 16C cottages » – TV P. MC VISA.
closed 25-26 December – **3 rm** 48.00/72.00 **st.**

ORWICH *Norfolk* 404 Y 26 *Great Britain G.* – *pop. 171 304.*

See : *City*** - *Cathedral*** Y – *Castle (Museum and Art Gallery* AC)* Z – *Market Place** Z.

Env. : *Sainsbury Centre for Visual Arts* AC, W : 3 m. by B 1108* X.

Exc. : *Blicking Hall** AC, N : 11 m. by A 140* – V – *and B 1354 – NE : The Broads*.*

Royal Norwich, Drayton High Rd, Hellesdon ✆ (01603) 425712, V – *Sprowston Park, Wroxham Rd ✆ (01603) 410657 – Costessy Park, Costessey ✆ (01603) 746333 – Bawburgh, Glen Lodge, Marlingford Rd ✆ (01603) 740404.*

Norwich Airport : ✆ (01603) 411923, N : 3½ m. by A 140 V.

The Guildhall, Gaol Hill ✆ (01603) 666071.

London 109 – Kingston-upon-Hull 148 – Leicester 117 – Nottingham 120.

Plans on following pages

Marriott Sprowston Manor H. & Country Club, Wroxham Rd, NR7 8RP, Northeast : 3 ¼ m. on A 1151 ✆ (01603) 410871, *Fax (01603) 423911,* – rest, TV P – 120. MC AE VISA.
Meals 11.95/37.50 **st.** 18.95 – 13.00
– **93 rm** 105.00 **st.**, 1 suite – SB.

Dunston Hall H. Golf & Country Club, Ipswich Rd, NR14 8PQ, South : 4 m. on A 140 ✆ (01508) 470444, *dhreception@devere-hotels.com, Fax (01508) 470689,* – rest, TV P – 300. MC AE VISA.
Meals (carvery) a la carte 22.20/28.55 – ***La Fontaine :*** **Meals** *(closed Sunday)* (dinner only) 28.50 and a la carte 29.70/41.40 **st.** 11.50
– **128 rm** 110.00/190.00 **st.**, 2 suites – SB.

Swallow Nelson, Prince of Wales Rd, NR1 1DX, ✆ (01603) 760260, *info@swallowhotels. com, Fax (01603) 620008,* – rm, rest, TV P – 90. MC AE VISA JCB. Z a
Trafalgar : **Meals** (dinner only and Sunday lunch)/dinner 16.95 and a la carte 17.90/ 25.50 **st.** 12.95 – ***Quarter-deck :*** **Meals** a la carte 10.45/19.50 **st.** 12.95 – 10.50 – **132 rm** 92.00/116.00 **st.** – SB.

Holiday Inn Norwich, Ipswich Rd, NR4 6EP, South : 2 ¼ m. on A 140 ✆ (0870) 400 9060, *gm1161@forte-hotels.com, Fax (01603) 506400,* – rm, TV P – 100. MC AE VISA JCB
Meals *(closed Saturday lunch)* 13.50/15.00 and dinner a la carte 15.00/26.00 **t.** 9.95 – 13.95 – **120 rm** 99.00 **st.** – SB.

Beeches, 2-6 Earlham Rd, NR2 3DB, ✆ (01603) 621167, *reception@beeches.co.uk, Fax (01603) 620151,* « Victorian gardens » – TV P. MC AE VISA JCB. VX e
closed 1 week Christmas – **Meals** (dinner only) 12.50/15.95 and a la carte 16.70/24.45 **st.** 10.50 – **36 rm** 64.00/82.00 **st.** – SB.

Annesley House, 6 Newmarket Rd, NR2 2LA, ✆ (01603) 624553, *annesleyhouse@best western.co.uk, Fax (01603) 621577,* – rest, TV P. MC AE VISA JCB. Z c
closed Christmas and New Year – **Meals** (dinner only) 22.50 **st.** 11.50 – **26 rm** 80.00/ 95.00 **st.** – SB.

Quality H. Norwich, 2 Barnard Rd, Bowthorpe, NR5 9JB, West : 3 ½ m. on A 1074 ✆ (01603) 741161, *admin@gb619.u-net.com, Fax (01603) 741500,* – rm, TV P – 200. MC AE VISA
Meals *(closed Saturday lunch)* (carvery) 12.50/15.50 **st.** 11.95 – 11.75 – **80 rm** 99.00 **t.** – SB.

Catton Old Hall, Lodge Lane, Old Catton, NR6 7HG, North : 3 ¼ m. by Catton Grove and St. Faiths Rd ℘ (01603) 419379, *enquiries@catton-hall.co.uk, Fax (01603) 4003* « 17C farmhouse », – TV P. MC AE VISA JCB. Meals *(closed Sunday)* (booking essential) (residents only) (dinner only) 21.00 6.95 – 7 60.00/85.00 **st.**

Travel Inn, Broadlands Business Park, Old Chapel Way, NR7 0WG, East : 3 m. by A 1242 A 1042 ℘ (01603) 307610, *Fax (01603) 307617* – rm, rest, TV P. – 30. MC VISA JCB. Meals (grill rest.) – **60 rm** 41.95 **t.**

Travel Inn, Longwater Interchange, New Costessey, NR5 0TL, Northwest : 5 ¼ m. A 1074 (junction with A 47) ℘ (01603) 749140, *Fax (01603) 749 1219* – rm, TV P. AE VISA – **Meals** (grill rest.) – **40 rm** 41.95 **t.**

The Gables without rest., 527 Earlham Rd, NR4 7HN, ℘ (01603) 4566 *Fax (01603) 250320*, – TV P. MC VISA JCB. X *closed 20 December-2 January* – **11 rm** 40.00/63.00 **st.**

Cumberland, 212-216 Thorpe Rd, NR1 1TJ, ℘ (01603) 434550, *cumberland@paston. uk, Fax (01603) 433355* – rest, TV P – 60. MC AE VISA. X **Meals** (booking essential) (dinner only and Sunday lunch) 15.95 and a la carte 15. 22.40 **st.** 9.95 – **25 rm** 49.95/69.95 **st.** – SB.

Arbor Linden Lodge without rest., 557 Earlham Rd, NR4 7HW, ℘ (01603) 4513 *Fax (01603) 250641*, – TV P. MC VISA. X **6 rm** 32.00/55.00.

Kingsley Lodge without rest., 3 Kingsley Rd, NR1 3RB, ℘ (01603) 615819, *kingsle paston.co.uk, Fax (01603) 615819* – TV. Z *closed Christmas-February* – **3 rm** 32.00/46.00.

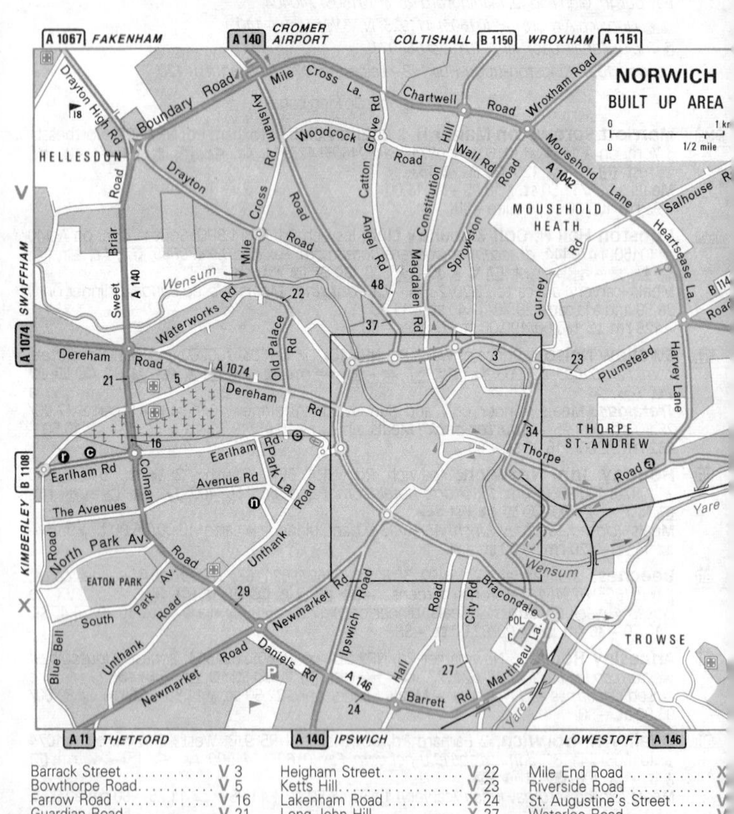

ENGLAND

XX **Adlard's,** 79 Upper St Giles St, NR2 1AB, ☎ (01603) 633522, *bookings@adlards.co.uk, Fax (01603) 617733* – ▤. MC AE ⓓ VISA JCB Z e
✿ *closed 1 week Christmas, Monday lunch, Sunday and Bank Holiday Mondays* – **Meals** 19.00 (lunch) and a la carte approx. 35.00 **t.** 🍷 14.50
Spec. Calf's sweetbread with onion purée and pommes Maxim. Roast turbot with pommes purée and roasted salsify. Compote of cherries, orange cake and ginger ice cream.

XX **By Appointment** with rm, 25-29 St Georges St, NR3 1AB, ☎ (01603) 630730, *Fax (01603) 630730* – ⇏ 📺. MC VISA. ✈ Y a
Meals *(closed Sunday)* (dinner only) a la carte 24.40/27.40 🍷 6.95 – **4 rm** ☕ 70.00/95.00 **t.**

XX **Marco's,** 17 Pottergate, NR2 1DS, ☎ (01603) 624044 – ⇏. MC AE VISA Y e
closed Sunday, Monday and Bank Holidays – **Meals** - Italian - 16.00 (lunch) and a la carte 23.90/28.90 **t.** 🍷 12.50.

NORWICH

nk Plain .... Y 2
thel Street .... Z 4
stle Mall
Shopping Centre .... Z
stle Meadow .... Z 6
ttle Market Street .... Z 7
apel Field North .... Z 9
Charing Cross .... Y 10
Coslany Street .... Y 14
Elm Hill .... Y
Exchange Street .... YZ 15
Gentleman's Walk .... Z 17
Grapes Hill .... Y 19
London Street .... YZ 26
Market Avenue .... Z 28
Rampant Horse Street .... Z 32
Red Lion Street .... Z 33
St. Andrew's Street .... Y 36
St. George Street .... Y 38
St. Stephen's Street .... Z
Thorn Lane .... Z 42
Timber Hill .... Z 43
Tombland .... Y 45
Upper King Street .... Y 46
Wensum Street .... Y 49
Westlegate .... Z 50
Whitefriars .... Y 51

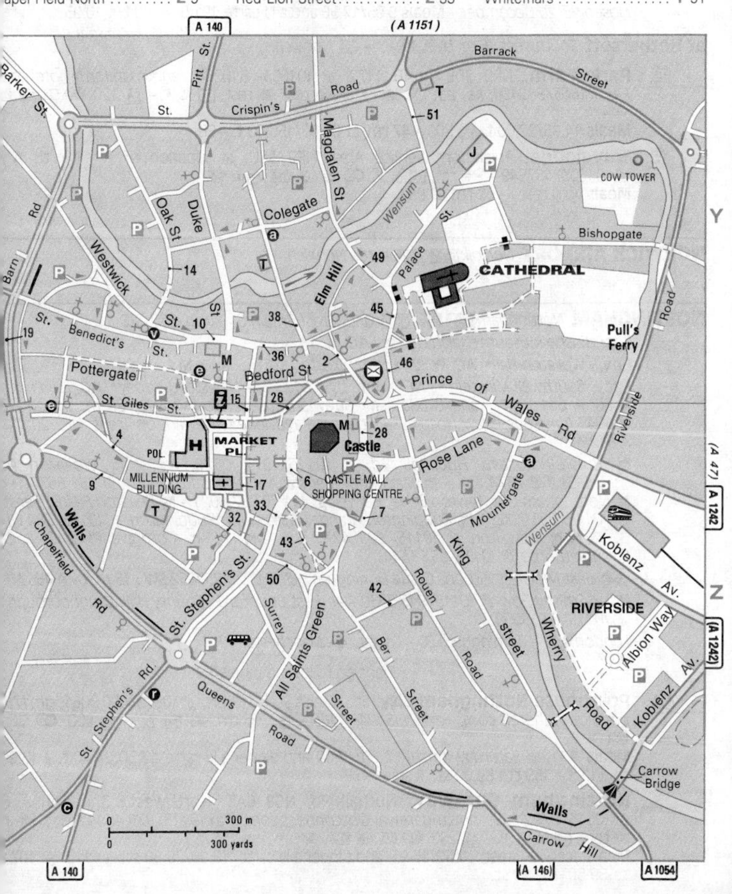

ENGLAND

St Benedicts, 9 St Benedicts St, NR2 4PE, ✆ (01603) 765377, *Fax (01603) 765377* – VISA Y
closed 25-31 December, Sunday and Monday – **Meals** a la carte 16.50/19.95 **t.** 8.50.

Mad Moose Arms, 2 Warwick St, NR2 3LB, off Dover St ✆ (01603) 627687, *mai animalinns.co.uk* – AE VISA X
closed 25 December – **Meals** a la carte 13.00/16.50 **t.** 9.50.

at Norwich Airport *North : 3½ m. by A 140* – **V** – ✉ *Norwich.*

Hilton Norwich, Cromer Rd, NR6 6JA, ✆ (01603) 410544, *reservations@norwich.stak co.uk, Fax (01603) 789935,* – rest, – 450. AE VIS
Meals (carvery) 9.95/19.00 and a la carte approx. 20.00 **st.** 12.30 – 14.25 – **121 r** 110.00/170.00 **st.** – SB.

at Caistor St Edmund *South : 4¼ m. by A 140* – **X** – ✉ *Norwich.*

Old Rectory , NR14 8QS, ✆ (01508) 492490, *pusey@paston.co.u Fax (01508) 495172,* « Georgian rectory », – . VISA
Meals (by arrangement) (communal dining) 18.00 **st.** – **3 rm** 30.00/60.00 **st.**

at Stoke Holy Cross *South : 5¾ m. by A 140* – **X** – ✉ *Norwich.*

Wildebeest Arms, 82-86 Norwich Rd, NR14 8QJ, ✆ (01508) 492497, *mail@animalinns. .uk, Fax (01508) 494353,* – . AE VISA
closed 25-26 December – **Meals** 9.95/17.50 and a la carte 19.00/25.00 **t.** 10.95.

at Hethersett *Southwest : 6 m. by A 11* – **X** – ✉ *Norwich.*

Park Farm, NR9 3DL, on B 1172 ✆ (01603) 810264, *enq@parkfarm-hotel.co.u Fax (01603) 812104,* – rest, rest, – 120. AE VIS
Meals 14.95/22.00 **t.** 11.00 – **47 rm** 80.00/150.00 **t.** – SB.

Travelodge, Thickthorn Service Area, NR9 3AU, at junction of A 11 with A ✆ (01603) 457549 – rm, . AE VISA JCB.
Meals (grill rest.) – **62 rm** 49.95 **t.**

NORWICH AIRPORT *Norfolk* 404 X 25 – *see Norwich.*

NOTTINGHAM *Nottingham* 402 403 404 Q 25 *Great Britain G. – pop. 270 222.*

See : *Castle Museum* (alabasters*) AC,* **CZ M.**

Env. : *Wollaton Hall* AC, W : 2½ m. by Ilkeston Rd, A 609* **AZ M.**

Exc. : *Southwell Minster**, NE : 14 m. by A 612* **BZ** – *Newstead Abbey* AC, N : 11 m. A 60, A 611 -* **AY** *- and B 683 – Mr Straw's House*, Worksop, N : 20 m. signed fro B 6045 (past Bassetlaw Hospital) – St Mary Magdalene*, Newark-on-Trent, NE : 20 m. A 612* **BZ**.

Bulwell Forest, Hucknall Rd ✆ (0115) 977 0576, **AY** – *Wollaton Pa ✆ (0115) 978 7574,* **AZ** – *Mapperley, Central Ave, Plains Rd ✆ (0115) 955 6672,* **BY** – *Nottingham City, Lawton Drive, Bulwell ✆ (0115) 927 8021* – *Beeston Fields, Beest ✆ (0115) 925 7062* – *Ruddington Grange, Wilford Rd, Ruddington ✆ (0115) 984 61* **BZ** – , *Edwalton ✆ (0115) 923 4775,* **BZ** – , , *Cotgrave Place G. & C. Stragglethorpe ✆ (0115) 933 3344.*

East Midlands Airport, Castle Donington : ✆ (01332) 852852 SW : 15 m. by A 453 **AZ**

1-4 Smithy Row ✆ (0115) 915 5330 – at West Bridgford : County Hall, Loughborough ✆ (0115) 977 3558.

London 135 – Birmingham 50 – Leeds 74 – Manchester 72.

Plans on following pages

Posthouse Nottingham City, St James's St, NG1 6BN, ✆ (0870) 400 9061, *gm176 posthouse_hotels.com, Fax (0115) 948 4366* – , rm, – 600. AE VISA CY
Meals *(closed Saturday lunch)* 12.00/17.00 and dinner a la carte 17.50/24.40 **t.** 12.95 11.95 – **159 rm** 89.00 **st.**, 1 suite – SB.

Nottingham Gateway, Nuthall Rd, NG8 6AZ, Northwest : 3 m. on A 6 ✆ (0115) 979 4949, *nottmgateway@btconnect.com, Fax (0115) 979 4744* – , r rest, – 250. AE VISA. AY
Meals (carving rest.) 9.50/15.95 and dinner a la carte 18.90/28.80 **st.** 11.45 – **107** 89.50/109.00 **st.**

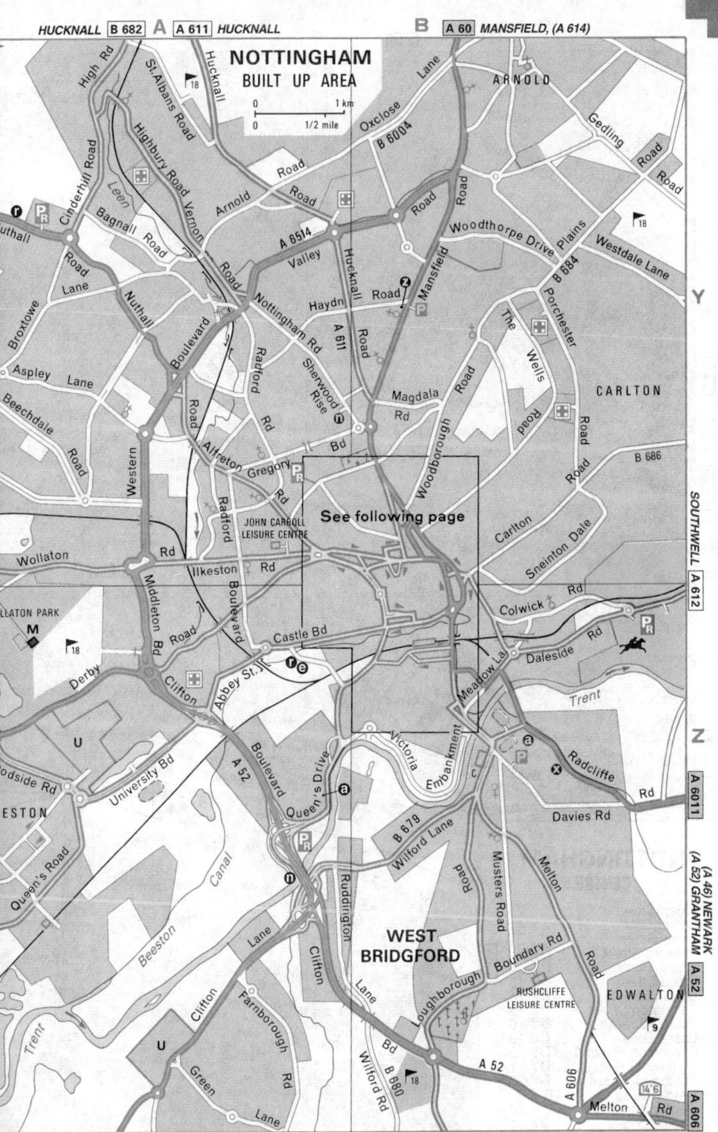

Hilton Nottingham, Milton St, NG1 3PZ, ✆ (0115) 934 9700, *rm_nottingham@hilton.com, Fax (0115) 934 9701,* ⅙, ☰, ☐ – ⊡, ▤ rest, TV ✆ ♿ P – 🏃 200. MC AE ⦾ VISA JCB. ✂ **DY e**

Bar Bacoa : Meals 8.75/19.50 and a la carte 25.45/42.00 **st.** ⌀ 16.45 – ☕ 14.50 – **177 rm** 125.00/160.00 **st.** – SB.

Rutland Square, St James's St, NG1 6FJ, ✆ (0115) 941 1114, *rutlandsquare@zoffanyhotels.co.uk, Fax (0115) 941 0014* – ⊡, ⊁ rm, ▤ rest, TV P – 🏃 200. MC AE ⦾ VISA ✂ **CZ c**

Woods : Meals (dinner only) 15.95 and a la carte 24.70/34.15 **st.** ⌀ 11.85 – **104 rm** ☕ 93.00/110.00 **st.**, 1 suite – SB.

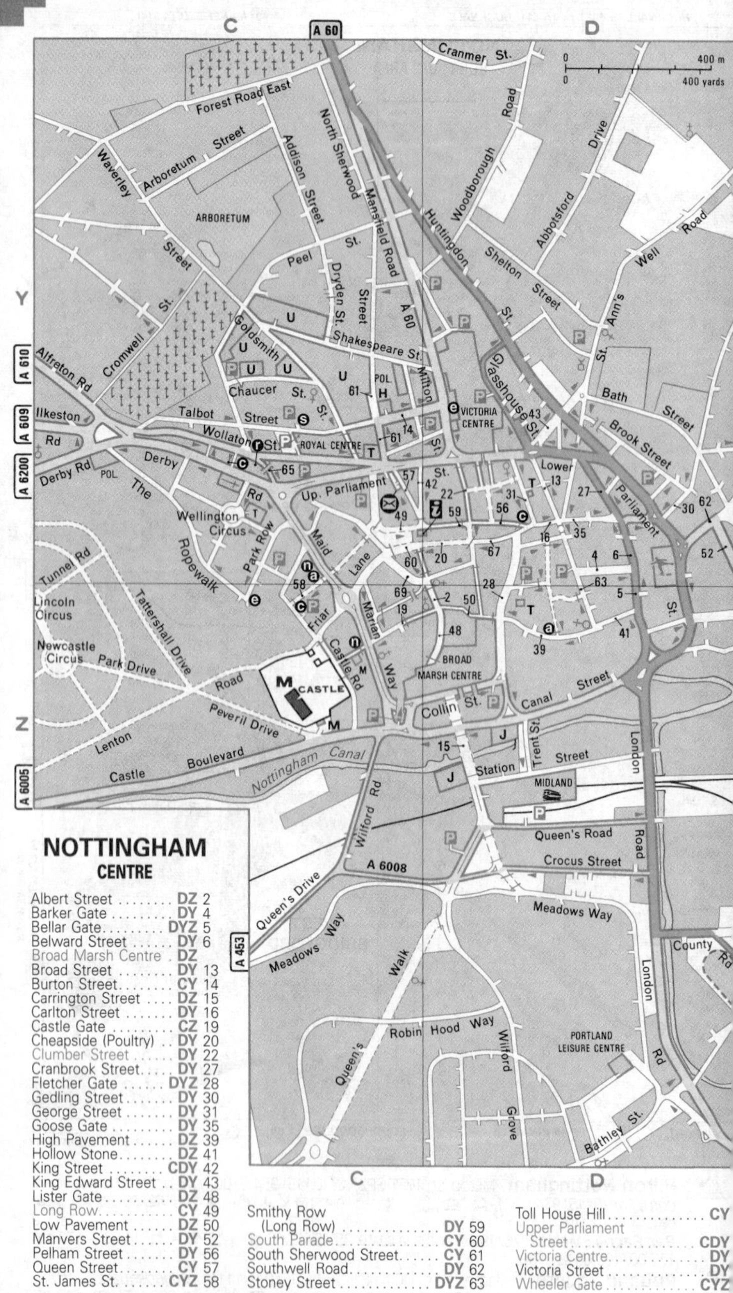

NOTTINGHAM
CENTRE

Albert Street . . . . **DZ** 2
Barker Gate . . . . **DY** 4
Bellar Gate. . . . . **DYZ** 5
Belward Street . . . . . . **DY** 6
Broad Marsh Centre . **DZ**
Broad Street . . . . **DY** 13
Burton Street. . . . . **CY** 14
Carrington Street . . . . **DZ** 15
Carlton Street . . . . **DY** 16
Castle Gate . . . . **CZ** 19
Cheapside (Poultry) . . **DY** 20
Clumber Street . . . . . . **DY** 22
Cranbrook Street. . . . . **DY** 27
Fletcher Gate . . . . . . **DYZ** 28
Gedling Street . . . . **DY** 30
George Street . . . . **DY** 31
Goose Gate . . . . **DY** 35
High Pavement . . . . . . **DZ** 39
Hollow Stone. . . . . **DZ** 41
King Street . . . . **CDY** 42
King Edward Street . . **DY** 43
Lister Gate . . . . **DZ** 48
Long Row. . . . . **CY** 49
Low Pavement . . . . . . **DZ** 50
Manvers Street . . . . . . **DY** 52
Pelham Street . . . . **DY** 56
Queen Street . . . . **CY** 57
St. James St. . . . . . . **CYZ** 58
Smithy Row (Long Row) . . . . **DY** 59
South Parade . . . . **CY** 60
South Sherwood Street. . . . . . **CY** 61
Southwell Road. . . . . **DY** 62
Stoney Street . . . . **DYZ** 63
Toll House Hill . . . . **CY**
Upper Parliament Street . . . . **CDY**
Victoria Centre. . . . . **DY**
Victoria Street . . . . **DY**
Wheeler Gate . . . . **CYZ**

If you find you cannot take up a hotel booking you have made, please let the hotel know immediately.

Welbeck, Talbot St, NG1 5GS, ☎ (0115) 841 1000, *info@welbeck-hotel.co.uk, Fax (0115) 841 1001* – |‡|, ⇎ rm, ▤ TV ☏ ♿ – 🏨 60. MC AE DC VISA. ✗ CY s
closed Christmas and New Year – **Meals** a la carte 15.60/21.60 **t.** – ☕ 8.50 – **96 rm** 92.00 **st.**

Lace Market, 29-31 High Pavement, The Lace Market, NG1 1HE, ☎ (0115) 852 3232, *Fax (0115) 852 3223*, « Contemporary interior » – |‡| TV ☏ – 🏨 35. MC AE VISA DZ a
Merchants : **Meals** *(closed Saturday lunch and Sunday dinner)* 9.50 and dinner a la carte 18.50/27.00 **t.** 🍷 9.50 – ☕ 10.95 – **29 rm** 89.00/169.00 **st.**

Strathdon, 44 Derby Rd, NG1 5FT, ☎ (0115) 941 8501, *info@strathdon-hotel-nottingham.com, Fax (0115) 948 3725* – |‡|, ⇎ rm, ▤ rest, TV ♿ P – 🏨 120. MC AE DC VISA JCB
Meals *(closed Saturday lunch)* 11.00/18.10 and a la carte 16.20/27.85 **st.** 🍷 10.50 – ☕ 9.50 – **68 rm** 95.00/125.00 **st.** – SB. CY c

Holiday Inn, Castle Marina Park, off Castle Boulevard, NG7 1GX, ☎ (0115) 993 5000, *holidayinn.nottingham@zoom.co.uk, Fax (0115) 993 4000*, Fø – |‡|, ⇎ rm, ▤ TV ♿ P – 🏨 45. MC AE DC VISA JCB AZ e
Meals *(closed lunch Saturday and Sunday)* (bar lunch Monday-Friday)/dinner a la carte approx. 18.00 🍷 9.95 – ☕ 10.50 – **130 rm** 93.00 **st.** – SB.

Novotel, Bostock Lane, Long Eaton, NG10 4EP, Southwest : 7 m. by A 52 following signs for M 1, taking Long Eaton rd off roundabout at junction 25 of M 1 ☎ (0115) 946 5111, *Fax (0115) 946 5900*, ⛱ heated, 🌳 – |‡|, ⇎ rm, TV ☏ ♿ P – 🏨 200. MC AE DC VISA
Meals 16.00 (dinner) and a la carte 12.95/24.25 **st.** 🍷 9.95 – ☕ 10.00 – **108 rm** 65.00 **st.**

Greenwood Lodge City without rest., Third Ave, Sherwood Rise, NG7 6JH, ☎ (0115) 962 1206, *coolspratt@aol.com, Fax (0115) 962 1206*, 🌳 – ⇎ TV P. MC VISA. ✗
6 rm ☕ 38.00/58.00. AY n

Citilodge, Wollaton St, NG1 5FW, ☎ (0115) 912 8000, *mail@citilodge.co.uk, Fax (0115) 912 8080* – |‡| ⇎ ▤ TV ☏ ♿ P – 🏨 100. MC AE VISA. ✗ CY r
closed 25-28 December – **Meals** 10.95 (lunch) and dinner a la carte 14.00/27.50 **t.** 🍷 10.00 – ☕ 5.00 – **90 rm** 55.00 **t.**

Travel Inn Metro, Castle Marina Park, off Castle Boulevard, NG7 1GX, ☎ (0115) 947 3419, *Fax (0115) 958 2362* – |‡| ⇎ TV ♿ P. MC AE DC VISA. ✗ AZ r
Meals (grill rest.) – **38 rm** 49.95 **t.**

Travelodge, Riverside Park, Queens Drive, NG2 1RT, ☎ (0115) 850934, *Fax (0115) 986 0467* – |‡|, ⇎ rm, TV ♿ P. MC AE DC VISA JCB. ✗ AZ a
Meals (grill rest.) – **61 rm** 52.95 **t.**

Travel Inn, Phoenix Centre, Millennium Way West, NG8 6AS, Northwest : 4 m. on A 610 ☎ (0115) 951 9971, *Fax (0115) 977 0113* – |‡|, ⇎ rm, ▤ rest, TV ♿ P. MC AE DC VISA. ✗
Meals (grill rest.) – **86 rm** 41.95 **t.**

Restaurant des Clos with rm, Old Lenton Lane, NG7 2SA, ☎ (0115) 986 6566, *enquiries@hoteldesclos, Fax (0115) 986 0343*, 🌳 – ⇎ TV P. MC AE DC VISA AZ n
closed 26-29 December – **Meals** *(closed Saturday lunch, Sunday and Bank Holidays)* 19.95/35.00 **t.** 🍷 13.50 – **6 rm** ☕ 89.50/99.50 **t.**, 2 suites – SB.

Hart's, Standard Court, Park Row, NG1 6GN, ☎ (0115) 911 0666, *enquiries@hartsnottingham.co.uk, Fax (0115) 911 0611*, 🏛 – MC AE VISA CZ e
closed 26 December, dinner 25 December and lunch 31 December – **Meals** 11.00/14.95 (lunch) and a la carte 20.25/34.00 **t.** 🍷 12.50.

World Service, Newdigate House, Castlegate, NG1 6AF, ☎ (0115) 847 5583, *Fax (0115) 847 5584*, « Part Georgian mansion house » – MC AE VISA CZ n
closed 2-9 January – **Meals** 9.50/13.00 (lunch) and a la carte 19.00/34.50 **t.** 🍷 14.00.

Sonny's, 3 Carlton St, NG1 1NL, ☎ (0115) 947 3041, *Fax (0115) 950 7776* – ▤. MC AE VISA JCB DY c
closed Bank Holidays – **Meals** a la carte 20.50/25.70 **t.** 🍷 10.45.

Mem-Saab, 12-14 Maid Marian Way, NG1 6HS, ☎ (0115) 957 0009, *Fax (0115) 941 2724* – MC AE VISA JCB CY n
closed 25-26 December, 1-2 January and Sunday – **Meals** - Indian - (dinner only) and a la carte 19.25/22.75 **t.** 🍷 9.50.

Saagar, 473 Mansfield Rd, Sherwood, NG5 2DR, ☎ (0115) 962 2014 – ▤. MC AE VISA
closed 25 December – **Meals** - Indian - a la carte 13.60/22.80 **t.** 🍷 11.75. BY z

West Bridgford *Southeast : 2 m. by A 52 on A 6011* – ✉ *Nottingham.*

Windsor Lodge, 116 Radcliffe Rd, NG2 5HG, ☎ (0115) 952 8528, *windsor@bt.internet.com, Fax (0115) 952 0020* – TV P – 🏨 40. MC AE DC VISA. ✗ BZ x
closed 25-26 December – **Meals** *(closed Sunday)* (residents only) (dinner only) 11.75 **st.** 🍷 5.00 – **46 rm** ☕ 52.00/59.00 **st.**

Swans, 84-90 Radcliffe Rd, NG2 5HH, ☎ (0115) 981 4042, *enquiries@swanshotel.co.uk, Fax (0115) 945 5745* – |‡| TV P – 🏨 50. MC AE DC VISA. ✗ BZ a
*closed 3 days Christmas*Meals *(in bar Sunday dinner)* 13.95 and a la carte 18.40/26.95 **t.** 🍷 9.95 – **29 rm** ☕ 55.00/65.00 **t.**, 1 suite.

ENGLAND

at Plumtree *Southeast : 5 ¾ m. by A 60 – BZ – off A 606 – ✉ Nottingham.*

Perkins, Old Railway Station, Station Rd, NG12 5NA, ✆ (0115) 937 3695, *perkinsrestaura@supanet.com, Fax (0115) 937 6405,* – P. MC AE VISA JCB
closed 1 week Christmas, Sunday dinner and Monday – **Meals** a la carte 19.50/23.95 7.50.

at Beeston *Southwest : 4 ¼ m. on A 6005 – AZ – ✉ Nottingham.*

Village H. & Leisure Club, Brailsford Way, Chilwell Meadows, NG9 6DL, Southwest : 2 ¾ by A 6005 ✆ (0115) 946 4422, *village.nottingham@village-hotels.com, Fax (0115) 946 442* squash – rest, – 400. MC AE VISA.
Meals (grill rest.) 10.00/14.95 and a la carte 11.15/22.00 **t.** 7.75 – **92 rm** 98.0 134.00 **t.**

La Toque, 61 Wollaton Rd, NG9 2NG, ✆ (0115) 922 2268, *Fax (0115) 922 2268* – . MC VISA JCB
closed Sunday – **Meals** - French - (lunch booking essential) 22.00 and a la carte appro 26.00 **st.** 12.00.

at Risley *(Derbs.) Southwest : 7 ½ m. by A 52 – AZ – on B 5010 – ✉ Derby.*

Risley Hall, Derby Rd, DE72 3SS, ✆ (0115) 939 9000, *Fax (0115) 939 7766,* « Victori manor house », – , rest, – 150. MC AE VISA.
Meals a la carte 26.50/41.95 12.95 – 10.95 – **16 rm** 85.00/125.00 **t.** – SB.

at Sandiacre *(Derbs.) Southwest : 7 ½ m. by A 52 – AZ – on B 5010 – ✉ Nottingham.*

Posthouse Nottingham/Derby, Bostocks Lane, NG10 5NJ, Southwest : ¾ m. junction 25 of M 1 ✆ (0870) 400 9062, *gm1163@forte-hotels.com, Fax (0115) 949 0469* rm, rest, – 50. MC AE VISA JCB
Meals a la carte 16.85/28.45 6.95 – 11.95 – **93 rm** 89.00/109.00 **st.** – SB.

NUNEATON *Warks.* 403 404 P 26 – *pop. 66 715.*

Purley Chase, Pipers Lane, Ridge Lane ✆ (024) 7639 3118.
Nuneaton Library, Church St ✆ (024) 7638 7006.
London 107 – Birmingham 25 – Coventry 10 – Leicester 18.

Travel Inn, Coventry Rd, CV10 7PJ, South : 2 ½ m. by A 444 on B 4113 ✆ (024) 7634 35 *Fax (024) 7632 7156,* – rm, rest, – 30. MC AE VISA.
Meals (grill rest.) – **48 rm** 41.95 **t.**

Travelodge without rest., CV10 7TF, South : 1 ½ m. on A 444 (southbound carriagew ✆ (024) 7638 2541, *Fax (024) 7638 2541* – . MC AE VISA JCB.
40 rm 42.95 **t.**

Travelodge, St Nicholas Park Drive, CV11 6EN, Northeast : 1 ½ m. by A 47 (Hinckley ✆ (024) 7635 3885, *Fax (024) 7635 3885* – rm, . MC AE VISA JCB.
Meals (grill rest.) – **28 rm** 42.95 **t.**

at Sibson *(Leics.) North : 7 m. on A 444 – ✉ Nuneaton.*

Millers', Twycross Rd, CV13 6LB, ✆ (01827) 880223, *Fax (01827) 880223* – – MC AE VISA
Meals *(closed Sunday dinner)* (bar lunch)/dinner 13.95/24.95 and a la carte 10.65/27.1 10.50 – **40 rm** 60.00/75.00 **t.** – SB.

NUNNINGTON *N. Yorks.* 402 Q 21 – *see Helmsley.*

OAKHAM *Rutland* 402 404 R 25 – *pop. 8 691.*

Flore's House, 34 High St ✆ (01572) 724329.
London 103 – Leicester 26 – Northampton 35 – Nottingham 28.

Barnsdale Lodge, The Avenue, Rutland Water, LE15 8AH, East : 2 ½ m. on A ✆ (01572) 724678, *barnsdale.lodge@btconnect.com, Fax (01572) 724961,* « Conver part 17C farmhouse », – – 300. MC AE VISA JCB
Meals a la carte approx. 19.85 **st.** 11.95 – **45 rm** 69.00/109.50 **st.** – SB.

Whipper-In, Market Pl, LE15 6DT, ✆ (01572) 756971, *whipper.in@lineone.r Fax (01572) 757759,* « Part 17C former coaching inn » – rest, – 60. MC AE
The George : **Meals** 12.95/18.95 and dinner a la carte 17.00/31.85 **t.** 10.50 – ***No*** *(✆ (01572) 740774) :* **Meals** a la carte 11.95/19.65 – **24 rm** 74.00/99.00 **t.** – SB.

Serpentine House without rest., Lodge Gdns, LE15 6EP, East : 3/4 m. by B 668, Vicarage Rd and St Albans Cl, bearing right into Lodge Gdns, entrance is on right hand bend ✆ (01572) 757878, *jenny.dryden@freeuk.com*, – rm, TV P.
3 rm 30.00/55.00 s.

Lord Nelson's House H. and Nicks Restaurant with rm, Market Pl, LE15 6DT, ✆ (01572) 723199, *nelsonshouse@compuserve.com, Fax (01572) 721694,* « 17C town house » – rm, TV. MC VISA.
closed 10 days Easter, 2 weeks late July and 24 December-9 January – **Meals** *(closed Sunday and Monday)* a la carte 22.40/29.40 7.50 – **4 rm** 65.00/90.00 **st.**

The Admiral Hornblower with rm, 64 High St, LE15 6AS, ✆ (01572) 723004, *david@hornblowerhotel.co.uk, Fax (01572) 722325,* – rm TV. MC VISA.
closed 25 December – **Meals** a la carte 13.85/28.65 **st.** 9.90 – **9 rm** 49.50/95.00 **st.**

Hambleton *East : 3 m. by A 606* – ✉ *Oakham.*

Hambleton Hall, LE15 8TH, ✆ (01572) 756991, *hotel@hambletonhall.com, Fax (01572) 724721,* « Victorian country house, ≤ Rutland Water », heated, – rest, TV P. MC AE VISA
Meals 21.50/35.00 and a la carte 40.50/69.00 **t.** 16.50 – 12.00 – **16 rm** 170.00/340.00 **t.**, 1 suite
Spec. Roast scallops with creamed endive. Assiette of rabbit. Assiette of citrus.

Finch's Arms with rm, Oakham Rd, LE15 8TL, ✆ (01572) 756575, *Fax (01572) 771142,* ≤, – TV P. MC VISA.
Meals a la carte 13.85/21.40 **t.** 10.95 – **6 rm** 55.00/65.00 **t.** – SB.

BORNE *Dorset* 403 404 M 31 – *see Sherborne.*

CKHAM *Surrey* 404 S 30 – *pop. 407* – ✉ *Ripley.*
London 27 – *Guildford 9.*

The Hautboy, Ockham Lane, GU23 6NP, ✆ (01483) 225355, *thehautboy@aol.com, Fax (01483) 211176,* – , rest, TV P. MC AE VISA
Oboe : **Meals** *(closed Sunday, Monday and Saturday lunch)* 12.50 (lunch) and a la carte 25.50/33.50 **t.** 15.50 – 7.00 – **5 rm** 100.00/125.00 **st.**

CKLEY *Surrey* 404 S 30.
Catton Manor Hotel G. & C.C., Standon Lane ✆ (01306) 627555.
London 31 – *Brighton 32* – *Guildford 23* – *Lewes 36* – *Worthing 29.*

Bryce's, The Old School House, RH5 5TH, ✆ (01306) 627430, *bryces.fish@virgin.net, Fax (01306) 628274* – P. MC VISA
closed 25-26 December, 1-2 January and Sunday dinner November-February – **Meals** - Seafood - 20.45/24.45 **st.** 10.95.

DINGLEY *Worcs.* 403 404 N 27 – *see Droitwich Spa.*

DIHAM *Hants.* 404 R 30 – *pop. 3 531* – ✉ *Hook.*
London 51 – *Reading 16* – *Winchester 25.*

George, 100 High St, RG29 1LP, ✆ (01256) 702081, *Fax (01256) 704213,* « 15C inn » – rm, TV P. MC AE VISA
Cromwell's : **Meals** *(closed Saturday lunch and Sunday dinner)* 16.95/19.95 (lunch) and a la carte 25.25/41.95 10.50 – ***Next door at the George :*** **Meals** a la carte 14.70/24.15 **t.** 10.50 – **28 rm** 80.00/120.00 **t.**

Grapevine, 121 High St, RG29 1LA, ✆ (01256) 701122, *Fax (01256) 704662* – . MC AE VISA
closed 1 week Christmas-New Year, Sunday, Saturday lunch and Bank Holidays – **Meals** 12.95 (lunch) and a la carte 17.75/25.80 **t.** 11.00.

KEHAMPTON *Devon* 403 H 31 *The West Country G.* – *pop. 4 841.*
Exc. : *S : Dartmoor National Park★★* – *Lydford★★, S : 8 m. by B 3260 and A 386.*
Okehampton ✆ (01837) 52113 – *Ashbury, Fowley Cross ✆ (01837) 55453.*
Museum Courtyard, 3 West St ✆ (01837) 53020.
London 226 – *Exeter 25* – *Plymouth 32.*

Travelodge, Sourton Cross, EX20 4LY, Southwest : 4 1/2 m. by B 3260 and A 30 on A 386 ✆ (01837) 52124, *Fax (01837) 52124* – rm, rest, TV P. MC AE VISA JCB.
Meals (grill rest.) – **42 rm** 49.95 **t.**

at Belstone *East : 2 ¾ m. by B 3260 – ✉ Okehampton.*

Tor Down House without rest., EX20 1QY, Northwest : ¾ m. turning right just pa telephone box ✆ (01837) 840731, *Fax (01837) 840731*, ≤, « 14C thatched longhouse », – ⇔ TV P. MC VISA. ✧
March-November – **3 rm** ☐ 45.00/70.00 **s.**

OLD BURGHCLERE *Hants.* 404 Q 29 – ✉ *Newbury.*
London 77 – Bristol 76 – Newbury 10 – Reading 27 – Southampton 28.

Dew Pond, RG20 9LH, ✆ (01635) 278408, *Fax (01635) 278580*, ≤ – ⇔ P. MC AE ⓓ JCB
closed 2 weeks August, Christmas-mid January, Sunday and Monday – **Meals** (dinner or 28.00/34.00 **t.** ♁ 11.95.

OLDBURY *W. Mids.* 402 403 404 N 26 – *see Birmingham.*

OLDHAM *Gtr. Manchester* 402 404 N 23 – *pop. 103 931.*
Crompton and Royton, High Barn, Royton ✆ (0161) 624 2154 – Werneth, Green La Garden Suburb ✆ (0161) 624 1190 – Lees New Rd ✆ (0161) 624 4986.
11 Albion St ✆ (0161) 627 1024.
London 212 – Leeds 36 – Manchester 7 – Sheffield 38.

Plan : see Manchester

Smokies Park, Ashton Rd, Bardsley, OL8 3HX, South : 2 ¾ m. on A 6 ✆ (0161) 785 5000, *sales@smokies.co.uk, Fax (0161) 785 5010*, ⇔ rm, ▤ re TV ♿ P – 110. MC AE ⓓ VISA. ✧
closed 1-2 January – **Meals** - Italian - *(closed Saturday lunch)* 6.95/17.50 and a la ca 17.60/33.00 **st.** ♁ 10.00 – **72 rm** ☐ 80.00/90.00 **t.**, 1 suite.

Avant, Windsor Rd, off Manchester St, OL8 4AS, ✆ (0161) 627 5500, *info@menzies-hot co.uk, Fax (0161) 627 5896*, – ⇔, ▤ rest, TV ♿ P – 250. MC AE ⓓ JCB
Meals 9.50/17.50 and a la carte 17.75/26.95 **st.** ♁ 13.25 – ☐ 12.95 – **101 rm** 85.(115.00 **st.**, 2 suites – SB.

Travel Inn, The Broadway, Chadderton, OL9 8DW, Southwest : 3 ½ m. by A 62 on A 610 junction with A 663 ✆ (0161) 681 1373, *Fax (0161) 682 7974* – ⇔ rm, ▤ rest, TV ♿ P. AE ⓓ VISA. ✧ BV
Meals (grill rest.) – **40 rm** 41.95 **t.**

White Hart Inn with rm, 51 Stockport Rd, Lydgate, OL4 4JJ, East : 3 m. by A 669 A 6050 ✆ (01457) 872566, *charles@thewhitehart.co.uk, Fax (01457) 875190* – ⇔, ▤ r TV P. MC AE VISA. ✧
Meals *(closed Sunday dinner and Monday)* (dinner only and Sunday lunch)/dinner a la ca 22.45/28.00 **t.** ♁ 13.25 – (see also ***Brasserie*** below) – **12 rm** ☐ 72.00/105.00.

Brasserie (at White Hart Inn), 51 Stockport Rd, Lydgate, OL4 4JJ, East : 3 m. by A 669 A 6050 ✆ (01457) 872566, *charles@thewhitehart.co.uk, Fax (01457) 875190* – P. MC AE
Meals (booking essential) 13.75 (lunch) and a la carte 21.20/25.90 **t.** ♁ 13.25.

OLD SODBURY *South Gloucestershire* 403 404 M 29 – ✉ *Bristol.*
Chipping Sodbury ✆ (01454) 312024.
London 110 – Bristol 14 – Gloucester 30 – Swindon 29.

Dornden, 15 Church Lane, BS37 6NB, ✆ (01454) 313325, *dorndenguesthouse@ world.co.uk, Fax (01454) 312263*, ≤, – ⇔ TV P. MC VISA. ✧
closed 3 weeks late September-October, Christmas and New Year – **Meals** (by arrangeme 12.00 **t.** – **9 rm** ☐ 29.00/64.00 **t.**

OLTON *W. Mids.* 402 ㉒ 403 ⑩ 404 ⑳ – *see Solihull.*

OMBERSLEY *Worcs.* 403 404 N 27 – *pop. 2 089.*
London 148 – Birmingham 42 – Leominster 33.

Greenlands without rest., Uphampton, WR9 0JP, Northwest : 1 ½ m. by A turning left at the Reindeer pub ✆ (01905) 620873, *xlandsgreenlands@onetel.net.uk,* « 16C cottage », – ⇔ TV P. ✧
3 rm ☐ 20.00/50.00 **st.**

ENGLAND

The Venture In, Main St, WR9 0EW, ✆ (01905) 620552, *Fax (01905) 620552,* « 15C » – 🚭 P. MC VISA
closed 2 weeks February, 2 weeks July, Sunday dinner and Monday – **Meals** 15.95/28.95 **t.** 11.00.

Kings Arms, Main Rd, WR9 0EW, ✆ (01905) 620142, « 15C inn » – P. MC AE VISA
– **Meals** a la carte 17.00/22.50 **t.** 9.50.

RFORD *Suffolk* 404 Y 27 – *pop. 1 153* – ✉ *Woodbridge.*
London 103 – Ipswich 22 – Norwich 52.

Crown and Castle, IP12 2LJ, ✆ (01394) 450205, *info@crownandcastle.co.uk, Fax (01394) 450176,* – TV P. MC VISA
closed 6-16 January – **Meals** – (see ***The Trinity*** below) – **18 rm** 65.00/120.00 **t.** – SB.

The Trinity (at Crown and Castle H.), IP12 2LJ, ✆ (01394) 450205, *info@crownandcastle.co.uk, Fax (01394) 450176,* – P. MC VISA
closed 6-16 January – **Meals** (booking essential) 13.95 (lunch) and a la carte 18.20/24.05 **t.** 6.80.

SMOTHERLEY *N. Yorks.* 402 Q 20 – *pop. 1 217* – ✉ *Northallerton.*
London 245 – Darlington 25 – Leeds 49 – Middlesbrough 20 – York 36.

The 3 Tuns with rm, 9 South End, DL6 3BN, ✆ (01609) 883301, *craig.robinson@steelriver.co.uk, Fax (01609) 883988,* – TV P. MC VISA.
Meals a la carte 20.20/25.00 **t.** 10.75 – **7 rm** 49.00/65.00 **t.**

Golden Lion, 6 West End, DL6 3AA, ✆ (01609) 883526, *Fax (01609) 884000* – MC VISA
closed dinner 25 December – **Meals** a la carte 12.50/24.65 **st.** 8.50.

Si vous cherchez un hôtel tranquille,
consultez d'abord les cartes de l'introduction
ou repérez dans le texte les établissements indiqués avec le signe ou .

SWESTRY *Shrops.* 402 403 K 25 – *pop. 15 612.*
Aston Park ✆ (01691) 610221 – Llanymynech, Pant ✆ (01691) 830542.
Mile End Services ✆ (01691) 662488 – The Heritage Centre, 2 Church Terr ✆ (01691) 657811.
London 182 – Chester 28 – Shrewsbury 18.

Wynnstay, Church St, SY11 2SZ, ✆ (01691) 655261, *info@wynnstayhotel.com, Fax (01691) 670606,* – 🚭 rm, rest, TV P – 250. MC AE VISA
The Wynnstay : **Meals** *(closed Sunday dinner)* 11.50/15.50 **st.** 9.25 – 9.45 – **28 rm** 75.00/95.00 **st.**, 1 suite – SB.

Travelodge, Mile End Service Area, SY11 4JA, Southeast : 1 ¼ m. at junction of A 5 with A 483 ✆ (01691) 658178 – 🚭 rm, TV P. MC AE VISA JCB.
Meals (grill rest.) – **40 rm** 39.95 **t.**

Sebastian's with rm, 45 Willow St, SY11 1AQ, ✆ (01691) 655444, *sebastians.rest@virgin.net, Fax (01691) 653452* – 🚭 TV. MC AE VISA.
closed 25 and 26 December – **Meals** - French - *(closed Sunday and Monday)* (dinner only) 27.00 **st.** 9.50 – 8.95 – **8 rm** 50.00/60.00 **st.**

Rhydycroesau *West : 3 ¼ m. on B 4580* – ✉ *Oswestry.*

Pen-Y-Dyffryn Country H., SY10 7JD, Southeast : ¼ m. by B 4580 ✆ (01691) 653700, *stay@peny.co.uk, Fax (01691) 650066,* – 🚭 rest, TV P. MC AE VISA JCB
– **Meals** (booking essential for non-residents) (dinner only) 23.00/27.00 **t.** 12.00 – **10 rm** 68.00/110.00 **t.** – SB.

TLEY *W. Yorks.* 402 O 22 – *pop. 13 596.*
West Busk Lane ✆ (01943) 465329.
8 Boroughgate ✆ (0113) 247 7707.
London 216 – Harrogate 14 – Leeds 12 – York 28.

Chevin Lodge, York Gate, LS21 3NU, South : 2 m. by B 6451 off East Chevin Rd ✆ (01943) 467818, *reception@chevinlodge.co.uk, Fax (01943) 850335,* « Pine lodge village in extensive woodland », – 🚭 rest, TV P – 120. MC AE VISA
Meals 13.50/21.00 and a la carte 25.40/29.40 **st.** 11.95 – **46 rm** 95.00/125.00 **st.**, 3 suites – SB.

OTTERBURN *Northd.* 401 402 N 18 – *pop. 497* – ✉ *Hexham.*
London 330 – Newcastle upon Tyne 32 – Carlisle 58.

Otterburn Tower, NE19 1NS, ☎ (01830) 520620, *reservations@otterburntower.co.* *Fax (01830) 521504,* « Part 14C and 17C fortified country house », – 70. VISA
Meals (dinner only) 20.00 and a la carte 14.95/26.50 **st.** 12.95 – **16 rm** 60.00/90.00
1 suite – SB.

OTTERY ST MARY *Devon* 403 K 31.
10b Broad St ☎ (01404) 813964.
London 171 – Exeter 15 – Southampton 87 – Taunton 13.

Normandy House, 5 Cornhill, EX11 1DW, ☎ (01404) 811088, *Fax (01404) 8110*
« Georgian town house », – . VISA JCB.
Meals a la carte 12.45/16.85 7.95 – **5 rm** 29.95/55.00 **t.**

OULTON BROAD *Suffolk* 404 Z 26 – *see Lowestoft.*

OUNDLE *Northants.* 404 S 26 – *pop. 3 996* – ✉ *Peterborough.*
18 *Benefield Rd ☎ (01832) 273267.*
14 West St ☎ (01832) 274333.
London 89 – Leicester 37 – Northampton 30.

Castle Farm without rest., Fotheringhay, PE8 5HZ, North : 3 ¾ m. by A 427 off A 6
☎ (01832) 226200, *Fax (01832) 226200,* « Riverside garden », – .
5 rm 35.00/58.00 **st.**

The Falcon Inn, Fotheringhay, PE8 5HZ, North : 3 ¾ m. by A 427 off A 6
☎ (01832) 226254, *Fax (01832) 226046,* , – . AE VISA
Meals a la carte 18.20/25.50 **st.** 11.50.

OUTLANE *W. Yorks.* – *see Huddersfield.*

OVERSTRAND *Norfolk* 404 Y 25 – *see Cromer.*

OXFORD *Oxon.* 403 404 Q 28 *Great Britain G.* – *pop. 118 795.*
See : *City*★★★ - *Christ Church*★★ *(Hall*★★ *AC, Tom Quad*★, *Tom Tower*★, *Cathedral*★ *A Choir Roof*★) **BZ** – *Merton College*★★ *AC* **BZ** - *Magdalen College*★★ **BZ** – *Ashmole Museum*★★ **BY M1** – *Bodleian Library*★★ *(Ceiling*★★, *Lierne Vaulting*★) *AC* **BZ A1** – *St Joh College*★ **BY** - *The Queen's College*★ **BZ** – *Lincoln College*★ **BZ** - *Trinity College (Chape* **BY** – *New College (Chapel*★) *AC*, **BZ** – *Radcliffe Camera*★ **BZ P1** – *Sheldonian Theatre*★ **BZ T** – *University Museum*★ **BY M4** – *Pitt Rivers Museum*★ **BY M3.**
Env. : *Iffley Church*★ **AZ A.**
Exc. : *Woodstock : Blenheim Palace*★★★ *(The Grounds*★★★) *AC, NW : 8 m. by A 4144 a A 34* **AY.**
Swinford Bridge (toll).
to Abingdon Bridge (Salter Bros. Ltd) (summer only).
The Old School, Gloucester Green ☎ (01865) 726871.
London 59 – Birmingham 63 – Brighton 105 – Bristol 73 – Cardiff 107 – Coventry 5 Southampton 64.

Plans on following pages

Randolph, Beaumont St, OX1 2LN, ☎ (0870) 4008200, *sales.randolph@heritage-hot com, Fax (01865) 791678* – – 250. AE VISA **BY**
***Oyster Bar* :** **Meals** 8.00/20.00 and a la carte 16.00/40.00 **t.** 13.95 – 13.95 – **114** 170.00/190.00 **st.**, 5 suites – SB.

Old Bank, 92-94 High St, OX1 4BN, ☎ (01865) 799599, *info@oldbank-hotel.co.* *Fax (01865) 799598,* , « Contemporary interior » – . AE VISA **BZ**
closed 25-26 December – ***Quod* :** **Meals** a la carte 19.55/24.25 **t.** 9.95 – 11.00 – **41** 135.00/225.00 **st.**, 1 suite.

Oxford Spires, Abingdon Rd, OX1 4PS, ☎ (01865) 324324, *spires@four-pillars.co.* *Fax (01865) 324325,* , – – 230. AE VISA JCB **AZ**
***Deacons* :** **Meals** 12.50/36.00 **st.** 6.95 – 12.95 – **103 rm** 139.00/169.00 **st.**, 12 suite SB.

Old Parsonage, 1 Banbury Rd, OX2 6NN, ✆ (01865) 310210, *oldparsonage@dial.pipex.com, Fax (01865) 311262,* « Part 17C house », – TV P. MC AE D VISA JCB.
closed 24-28 December – **Meals** (in bar) a la carte 19.00/25.00 t. 13.50 – **30 rm** 140.00/200.00 t. BY e

Cotswold Lodge, 66a Banbury Rd, OX2 6JP, ✆ (01865) 512121, *cotswoldlodge@netscapeonline.co.uk, Fax (01865) 512490* – TV P – 100. MC AE D VISA JCB.
Meals 12.95/22.85 and a la carte 22.85/31.85 t. 13.95 – **47 rm** 135.00/185.00 t., 1 suite. AY x

Eastgate, Merton St, OX1 4BE, ✆ (0870) 4008201, *heritagehotels-oxford.eastgate@forte-hotels.com, Fax (01865) 791681* – rm, TV P. MC AE D VISA BZ c
closed 25, 26 and 31 December – ***Cafe Boheme :*** **Meals** 14.50 and a la carte 18.50/29.50 t. 9.50 – 10.50 – **64 rm** 115.00/165.00 **st.**

Marlborough House without rest., 321 Woodstock Rd, OX2 7NY, ✆ (01865) 311321, *enquiries@marlbhouse.win-uk.net, Fax (01865) 515329* – TV. MC AE D VISA. AY v
16 rm 69.00/80.00 **s.**

Travelodge, Peartree Roundabout, Woodstock Rd, OX2 8JZ, ✆ (01865) 54301, *Fax (01865) 513474* – rm, rest, TV P – 80. MC AE D VISA JCB. AY n
Meals (grill rest.) – **120 rm** 59.95 t.

Burlington House without rest., 374 Banbury Rd, OX2 7PP, ✆ (01865) 513513, *stay@burlington-house.co.uk, Fax (01865) 311785,* « Contemporary interior » – TV P. MC AE VISA. – *closed 25-26 December* – **11 rm** 50.00/70.00 **st.** AY a

Cotswold House without rest., 363 Banbury Rd, OX2 7PL, ✆ (01865) 310558, *d.r.walker@talk21.com, Fax (01865) 310558* – TV P. MC VISA JCB. AY c
7 rm 48.00/76.00 **st.**

Chestnuts without rest., 45 Davenant Rd, OX2 8BU, ✆ (01865) 553375, *stay@chestnutsguesthouse.co.uk, Fax (01865) 553375* – TV P. MC AE VISA JCB. AY s
closed 22 December-7 January – **5 rm** 50.00/75.00 **st.**

Pine Castle, 290-292 Iffley Rd, OX4 4AE, ✆ (01865) 241497, *stay@pinecastle.co.uk, Fax (01865) 727230* – TV P. MC AE D VISA JCB. AZ r
Meals 22.00 **st.** – **8 rm** 57.00/71.00 **st.**

La Gousse D'Ail, 268 Woodstock Rd, OX2 7NW, ✆ (01865) 311936, *info@lagoussedail.co.uk, Fax (01865) 516613* – P. MC AE VISA AY u
closed first 2 weeks January, 2 weeks August, Sunday dinner and Monday – **Meals** a la carte 39.50/55.00 t. 17.00.

Gee's, 61Banbury Rd, OX2 6PE, ✆ (01865) 553540, *info@gees-restaurant.co.uk, Fax (01865) 310308,* « Conservatory » – . MC AE VISA AY r
closed 25 and 26 December – **Meals** (booking essential) a la carte 19.90/28.20 t. 11.85.

Le Petit Blanc, 71-72 Walton St, OX2 6AG, ✆ (01865) 510999, *oxford@lepetitblanc.co.uk, Fax (01865) 510700* – . MC AE D VISA AY z
closed 25 December – **Meals** - Brasserie - 15.00 (lunch) and a la carte 18.70/27.75 t. 11.00.

Branca, 111 Walton St, OX2 6AJ, ✆ (01865) 556111, *Fax (01865) 556501* – . MC AE VISA JCB BY a
closed 25-26 December – **Meals** - Italian influences - a la carte 16.00/23.00 t. 9.95.

Fishers, 36-37 St Clements, OX4 1AB, ✆ (01865) 243003, *Fax (01865) 243003* – . MC D VISA AZ a
closed Christmas and Monday lunch – **Meals** - Seafood - a la carte 17.25/25.95 t. 9.95.

Iffley *Southeast : 2 m. by A 4158* – ✉ *Oxford.*

Hawkwell House, Church Way, OX4 4DZ, ✆ (01865) 749988, *hawkwellhousehotel@corushotels.com, Fax (01865) 748525,* – , rest, TV P – 200. MC AE D VISA JCB. AZ c
Meals *(closed Saturday lunch)* 19.95 and a la carte 20.80/37.40 t. – 11.75 – **51 rm** 110.00/130.00 t. – SB.

Cowley *Southeast : 2½ m. by B 480* – ✉ *Oxford.*

Travel Inn, Garsington Rd, OX4 2JZ, ✆ (01865) 779230, *Fax (01865) 775887* – , rm, rest, TV P. MC AE D VISA. AZ s
Meals (grill rest.) – **121 rm** 41.95 t.

Sandford-on-Thames *Southeast : 5 m. by A 4158* – ✉ *Oxford.*

Oxford Thames Four Pillars, Henley Rd, OX4 4GX, ✆ (01865) 334444, *thames@four-pillars.co.uk, Fax (01865) 334400,* « Thames-side setting », , , , , , – , rest, TV P – 160. MC AE D VISA JCB AZ v
The River Room : **Meals** 12.50/36.00 6.95 – 12.95 – **60 rm** 139.00/169.00 **st.** – SB.

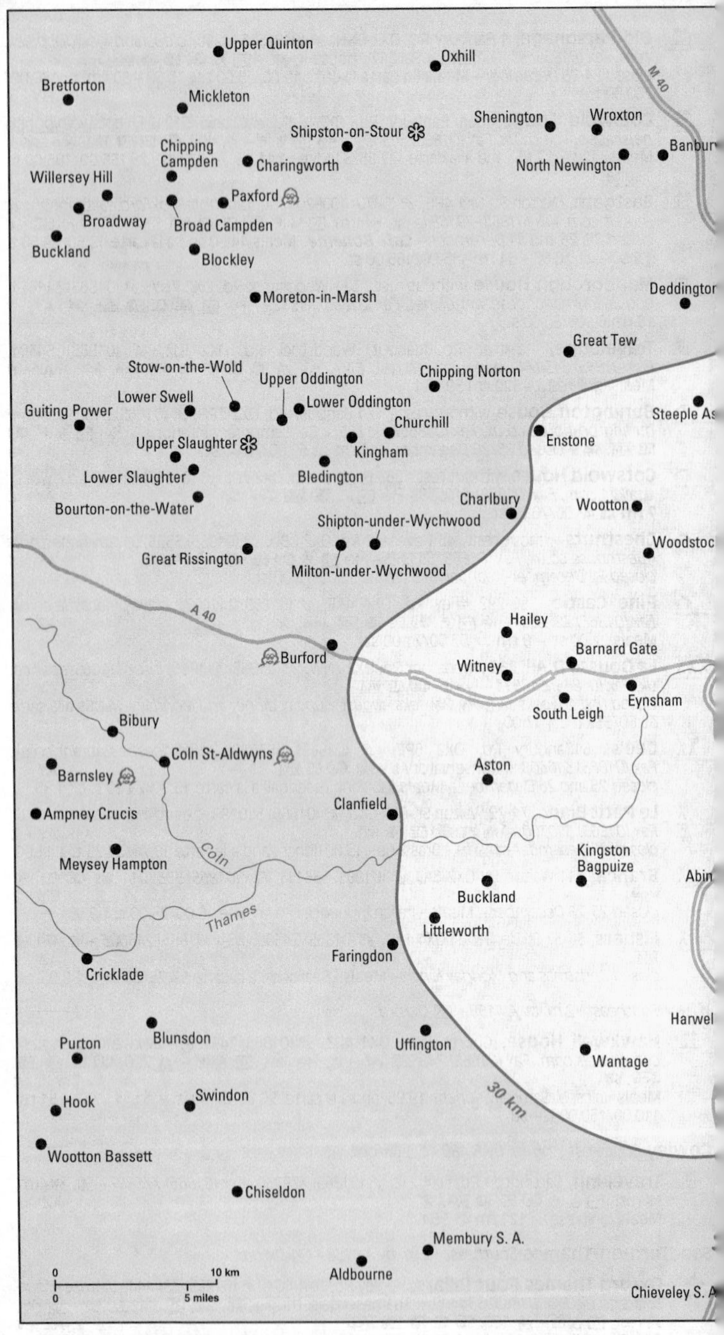

Upper Quinton
Oxhill
M 40
Bretforton
Mickleton
Shenington
Wroxton
Shipston-on-Stour
Banbur
Chipping Campden
Charingworth
North Newington
Willersey Hill
Paxford
Broadway
Broad Campden
Buckland
Blockley
Moreton-in-Marsh
Deddingtor
Great Tew
Stow-on-the-Wold
Upper Oddington
Chipping Norton
Lower Swell
Lower Oddington
Guiting Power
Churchill
Steeple As
Upper Slaughter
Kingham
Enstone
Lower Slaughter
Bledington
Bourton-on-the-Water
Charlbury
Wootton
Shipton-under-Wychwood
Woodstoc
Great Rissington
Milton-under-Wychwood
A 40
Hailey
Burford
Barnard Gate
Witney
Eynsham
South Leigh
Bibury
Coln St-Aldwyns
Aston
Barnsley
Ampney Crucis
Clanfield
Coln
Meysey Hampton
Kingston Bagpuize
Abin
Buckland
Thames
Littleworth
Faringdon
Cricklade
Harwel
Blunsdon
Purton
Uffington
Wantage
30 km
Hook
Swindon
Wootton Bassett
Chiseldon
Membury S. A.
0
10 km
0
5 miles
Aldbourne
Chieveley S. A

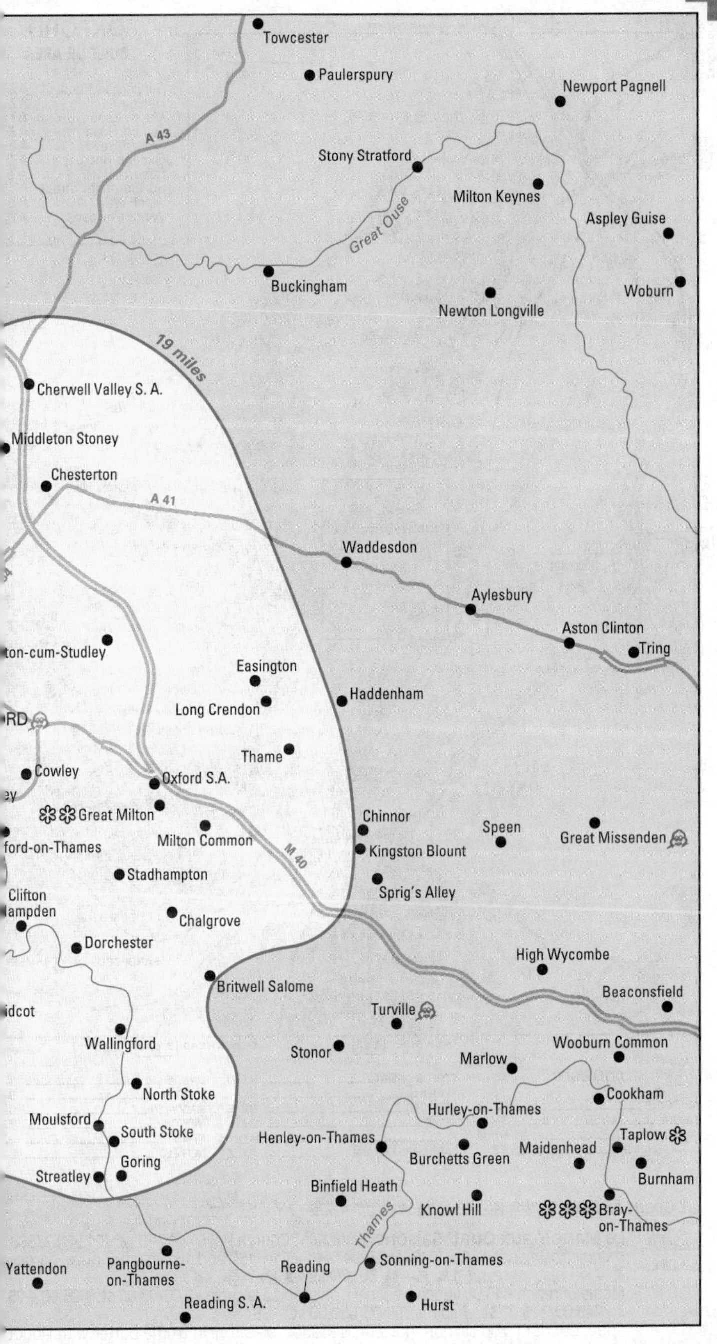
Towcester
Paulerspury
Newport Pagnell
A 43
Stony Stratford
Milton Keynes
Great Ouse
Aspley Guise
Buckingham
Woburn
Newton Longville
19 miles
Cherwell Valley S. A.
Middleton Stoney
Chesterton
A 41
Waddesdon
Aylesbury
Aston Clinton
Tring
ton-cum-Studley
Easington
Haddenham
Long Crendon
RD
Thame
Cowley
Oxford S.A.
Great Milton
Milton Common
Chinnor
Speen
Great Missenden
ford-on-Thames
M 40
Kingston Blount
Stadhampton
Sprig's Alley
Clifton
ampden
Chalgrove
Dorchester
High Wycombe
Britwell Salome
Beaconsfield
idcot
Turville
Wallingford
Stonor
Wooburn Common
Marlow
North Stoke
Cookham
Hurley-on-Thames
Moulsford
South Stoke
Henley-on-Thames
Taplow
Maidenhead
Burchetts Green
Goring
Streatley
Burnham
Binfield Heath
Knowl Hill
Bray-
on-Thames
Thames
Sonning-on-Thames
Yattendon
Pangbourne-
on-Thames
Reading
Reading S. A.
Hurst

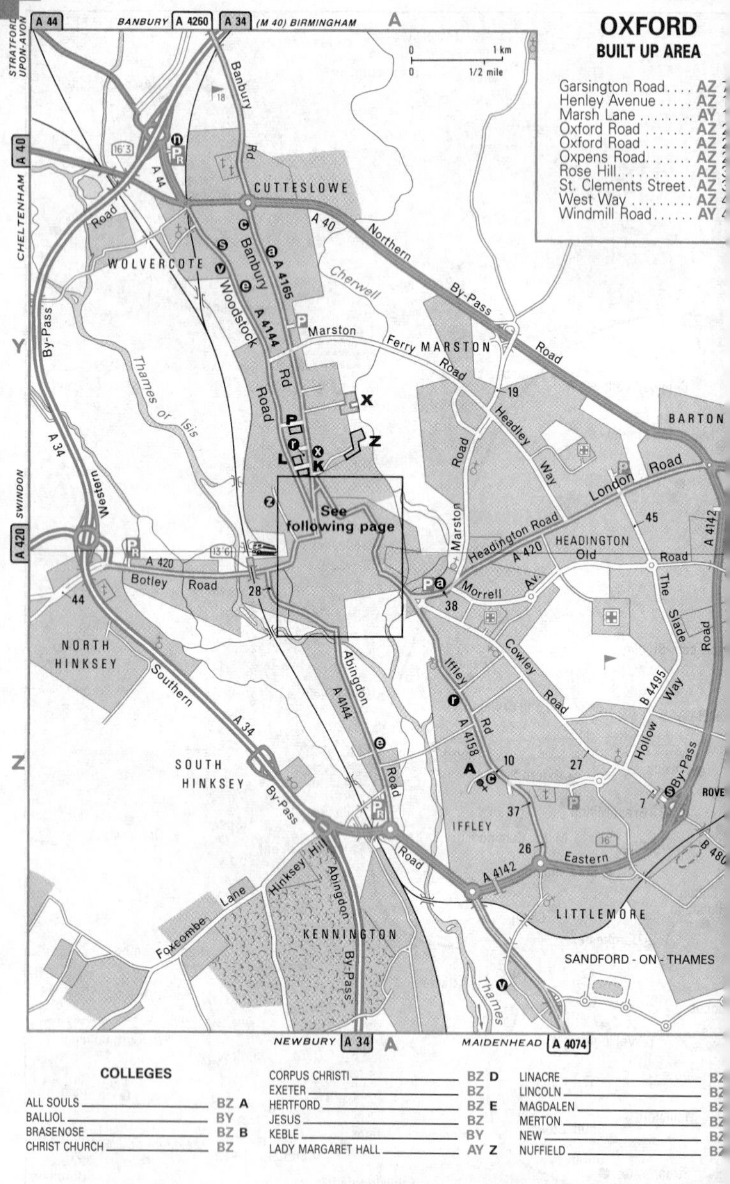

COLLEGES

ALL SOULS	BZ A	CORPUS CHRISTI	BZ D	LINACRE	BZ
BALLIOL	BY	EXETER	BZ	LINCOLN	BZ
BRASENOSE	BZ B	HERTFORD	BZ E	MAGDALEN	BZ
CHRIST CHURCH	BZ	JESUS	BZ	MERTON	BZ
		KEBLE	BY	NEW	BZ
		LADY MARGARET HALL	AY Z	NUFFIELD	BZ

at Great Milton *Southeast : 12 m. by A 40 off A 329 – AY – ✉ Oxford.*

Le Manoir aux Quat' Saisons (Blanc), Church Rd, OX44 7PD, ☎ (01844) 27888 *manoir@blanc.co.uk, Fax (01844) 278847,* ←, « Part 15C and 16C manor house, gardens – ✱ rest, ▤ rest, TV ☎ P – 🕴 50. MC AE ① VISA JCB. ✱

Meals - French - 45.00 (lunch weekdays only) and a la carte 70.00/77.00 **st.** 🍷 25.00 – 25 ☕ 245.00/375.00 **st.**, 7 suites 395.00/650.00 **st.** – SB

Spec. Confit of wild salmon, horseradish sauce. Macaroni in truffle butter with langou nes. Braised rabbit shoulder and roasted loin in tarragon mustard jus.

OXFORD

ue Boar Street . . . . BY 2
road Street . . . . BZ 3
astle Street . . . . BZ 5
arendon Shopping Centre BZ
ornmarket Street . . . . BZ 6
eorge Street . . . . BZ 9
gh Street . . . . BZ
Hythe Bridge Street . . . . . . BZ 12
Little Clarendon Street . . . . BY 13
Logic Lane . . . . BZ 14
Magdalen Street . . . . BYZ 16
Magpie Lane . . . . BZ 17
New Inn Hall Street . . . . . . BZ 20
Norfolk Street . . . . BZ 21
Old Greyfriars Street . . . . . BZ 23
Oriel Square . . . . BZ 24
Park End Street . . . . BZ 30
Pembroke Street . . . . BZ 31
Queen's Lane . . . . BZ 33
Queen Street . . . . BZ 34
Radcliffe Square . . . . BZ 35
St. Michael Street . . . . BZ 40
Turl Street . . . . BZ 41
Walton Crescent . . . . BY 42
Westgate Shopping Centre BZ
Worcester Street . . . . BZ 47

COLLEGES (CONTINUED)

EL	BZ F	ST CROSS	BY V	SOMERVILLE	BY Y
MBROKE	BZ Q	ST EDMUND HALL	BZ K	TRINITY	BY
EEN'S	BZ	ST HILDA'S	BZ W	UNIVERSITY	BZ L
ANNE'S	AY K	ST HUGH'S	AY P	WADHAM	BY Z
ANTHONY'S	AY L	ST JOHN'S	BY	WOLFSON	AY X
CATHERINE'S	BY R	ST PETER'S	BZ X	WORCESTER	BY

Kingston Bagpuize *Southwest : 10 m. by A 420 – AY – off A 415 – ✉ Oxford.*

Fallowfields Country House ⛍, Faringdon Rd, OX13 5BH, ✆ (01865) 820416, *stay@fallowfields.com, Fax (01865) 821275,* – **Meals** 13.95/33.50 and a la carte 25.50/29.50 t. 15.25 – **10 rm** 136.00/180.00 t. – SB.

OXFORD SERVICE AREA *Oxon. – ✉ Oxford.*

Days Inn without rest., Waterstock, OX33 1JN, at junction 8a of M
℘ (01865) 877000, Reservations (Freephone) 0800 0280400, *Fax (01865) 877016* –
P. VISA JCB
59 rm 60.00 t.

OXHILL *Warks.* 403 404 P 27 – *pop. 303* – ✉ *Stratford-upon-Avon.*

London 85 – Birmingham 32 – Oxford 25.

Nolands Farm without rest., CV35 0RJ, on A 422 ℘ (01926) 640309, *inthecour@nolandsfarm.co.uk, Fax (01926) 641662,* « Working farm », – P.
10 rm 35.00/102.00 st.

Don't confuse:

Comfort of hotels	:	... ,
Comfort of restaurants	:	XXXXX .... X,
Quality of the cuisine	:	✿✿✿, ✿✿, ✿, Meals

PADSTOW *Cornwall* 403 F 32 *The West Country G. – pop. 2 855.*

See : *Town★ – Prideaux Place★.*

Env. : *Trevone (Cornwall Coast Path★★) W : 3 m. by B 3276 – Trevose Head★ (≤★★) W : 6 by B 3276.*

Exc. : *Bedruthan Steps★, SW : 7 m. by B 3276 – Pencarrow★, SE : 11 m. by A 389.*

18, 9, 9 *Trevose, Constantine Bay ℘ (01841) 520208.*

Red Brick Building, North Quay ℘ (01841) 533449.

London 288 – Exeter 78 – Plymouth 45 – Truro 23.

The Metropole, Station Rd, PL28 8DB, ℘ (01841) 532486, *heritagehotels-padstowmetropole@forte-hotels.com, Fax (01841) 532867,* ≤ Camel Estuary, heated, – TV
VISA.
Meals (bar lunch Monday-Saturday)/dinner 23.00 t. 11.95 – 12.95 – **50 rm** 90.
120.00 t. – SB.

St Petroc's, 4 New St, PL28 8EA, ℘ (01841) 532700, *reservations@rickstein.co*
Fax (01841) 532942, – TV P. VISA
closed 1 week Christmas and 1 May – ***St. Petrocs Bistro*** **:** Meals *(closed Monc*
(booking essential) a la carte approx 27.00 t. 14.95 – **13 rm** 50.00/150.00 t
SB.

Old Custom House Inn, South Quay, PL28 8BL, ℘ (01841) 532359, *oldcustomho@westcountryhotelrooms.co.uk, Fax (01841) 533372,* ≤ Camel Estuary and harbour –
rest, TV. VISA
Meals – (see ***Pescadou*** below) – **24 rm** 86.00/175.00 st.

Cross House without rest., Church St, PL28 8BG, ℘ (01841) 532391, *info@crosshou*
co.uk, Fax (01841) 533633 – TV P. VISA JCB.
9 rm 60.00/120.00 t.

Dower House, Fentonluna Lane, PL28 8BA, ℘ (01841) 532317, *dower@btinternet.co*
Fax (01841) 532667 – TV P. VISA
closed December and January – **Meals** *(closed Tuesday and Thursday dinner)* a la ca
approx. 16.00 t. 10.00 – **6 rm** 52.00/90.00 t.

Rick Stein's Café, 10 Middle St, PL28 8AP, ℘ (01841) 532700, *reservations@rickst*
com, Fax (01841) 532942, – rm, TV. VISA
closed 1 May, 24-26 and 31 December – **Meals** *(closed Sunday)* (light lunch)/dinner 19.5
12.95 – **3 rm** 70.00/90.00 t. – SB.

Woodlands without rest., Treator, PL28 8RU, West : 1 ¼ m. by A 389 on B 32
℘ (01841) 532426, *Fax (01841) 532426,* ≤, – TV P
March-October – **9 rm** 28.00/60.00 s.

Treverbyn House without rest., Station Rd, PL28 8DA, ℘ (01841) 5328
Fax (01841) 532855, ≤, – rm, TV P.
closed Christmas and New Year – **5 rm** 80.00 st.

XX **The Seafood** with rm, Riverside, PL28 8BY, ✆ (01841) 532700, *reservations@rickstein.com, Fax (01841) 532942,* « Converted granary overlooking quayside and Camel Estuary » – ⇔ rest, ▤ rest, TV ✆ P. MC VISA
closed 1 week Christmas and 1 May – **Meals** - Seafood - (booking essential) a la carte 32.00/64.50 **t.** 16.00 – **19 rm** 95.00/170.00 **t.** – SB.

XX **Brocks,** The Strand, PL28 8AJ, ✆ (01841) 532565, *brockx@compuserve.com, Fax (01841) 533199* – ⇔. MC VISA
closed January, Sunday and Monday except Bank Holidays – **Meals** - Seafood - 21.50/24.50 (dinner) and a la carte 24.75/35.15 **t.** 13.50.

X **Pescadou** (at Old Custom House Inn), South Quay, PL28 8BL, ✆ (01841) 532359, *Fax (01841) 533372* – ▤. MC AE VISA
Meals - Seafood - (booking essential) a la carte 19.85/28.85 **t.** 10.00.

X **No 6** with rm, 6 Middle St, PL28 8AP, ✆ (01841) 532093, *karenscottnumber6inpadstow@amserve.net, Fax (01841) 532093,* – ⇔ TV. VISA
closed2 January-14 February – **Meals** - Seafood - *(closed Tuesday)* (booking essential) 15.00/24.50 **t.** 11.50 – **3 rm** 56.00/70.00 **t.**

X **Margot's,** 11 Duke St, PL28 8AB, ✆ (01841) 533441, *oliveradrian@hotmail.com* – ⇔. MC AE VISA JCB
closed January, Monday and Tuesday, Wednesday lunch and restricted opening November-December – **Meals** (dinner booking essential) (light lunch)/dinner a la carte 14.85/22.85 **t.** 9.95.

Little Petherick *South : 3 m. on A 389* – ✉ *Wadebridge.*

Molesworth Manor without rest., PL27 7QT, ✆ (01841) 540292, *molesworthmanor@aol.com,* ←, « Part 17C and 19C rectory », – P. ✗
closed November and December – **10 rm** 25.50/70.00 **t.**

Old Mill Country House without rest., PL27 7QT, ✆ (01841) 540388, *dwalker@oldmillbandb.demon.co.uk,* « Part 16C corn mill », – ⇔. MC VISA. ✗
April-October – **4 rm** 48.00/64.00 **st.**

St Issey *South : 3½ m. on A 389* – ✉ *Wadebridge.*

Olde Treodore House without rest., PL27 7QS, North : ¼ m. off A 389 ✆ (01841) 540291, ←, – ⇔ TV P. ✗
closed 21 December-2 January – **3 rm** 42.00/56.00 **t.**

Constantine Bay *Southwest : 4 m. by B 3276* – ✉ *Padstow.*

Treglos , PL28 8JH, ✆ (01841) 520727, *enquiries@treglos-hotel.co.uk, Fax (01841) 521163,* ←, , – , ⇔ rest, ▤ rest, TV P. MC VISA
mid March-October – **Meals** 11.00/25.00 and a la carte **st.** 10.00 – **41 rm** (dinner included) 80.00/160.00, 3 suites – SB.

Trevone Bay *West : 2¼ m. by B 3276* – ✉ *Padstow.*

The Old Cabbage Patch without rest., PL28 8QX, ✆ (01841) 520956, *info@theoldcabbagepatch.co.uk, Fax (01841) 520956,* – ⇔ TV P. MC AE VISA JCB
closed January – **3 rm** 61.75/65.00 **s.**

ADWORTH *Newbury* 403 404 Q 29 – *pop. 545* – ✉ *Reading.*
London 58 – Basingstoke 12 – Reading 10.

Courtyard by Marriott Reading, Bath Rd, RG7 5HT, on A 4 ✆ (0118) 9714411, *Fax (0118) 9714442,* , – ⇔ ▤ TV ✆ & P – 180. MC AE VISA JCB. ✗
Meals a la carte 17.50/24.70 **t.** 11.75 – 10.50 – **50 rm** 125.00/160.00 **st.**

IGNTON *Torbay* 403 J 32 *The West Country G.* – *pop. 42 989.*
See : *Torbay★ - Kirkham House★ AC* Y B.
Env. : *Paignton Zoo★★ AC, SW : ½ m. by A 3022* AY *(see Plan of Torbay)* – *Cockington★, N : 3 m. by A 3022 and minor roads.*
The Esplanade ✆ (01803) 558383.
London 226 – Exeter 26 – Plymouth 29.

Plan of Built up Area : see Torbay

Redcliffe, 4 Marine Drive, TQ3 2NL, ✆ (01803) 526397, *redclfe@aol.com, Fax (01803) 528030,* ← Torbay, , , heated, , – , ⇔ rest, TV P – 200. MC AE VISA. ✗ Y n
Meals (bar lunch Monday to Saturday)/dinner 16.75/17.75 and a la carte 19.00/23.50 **t.** 12.50 – **65 rm** 52.00/104.00 **t.**

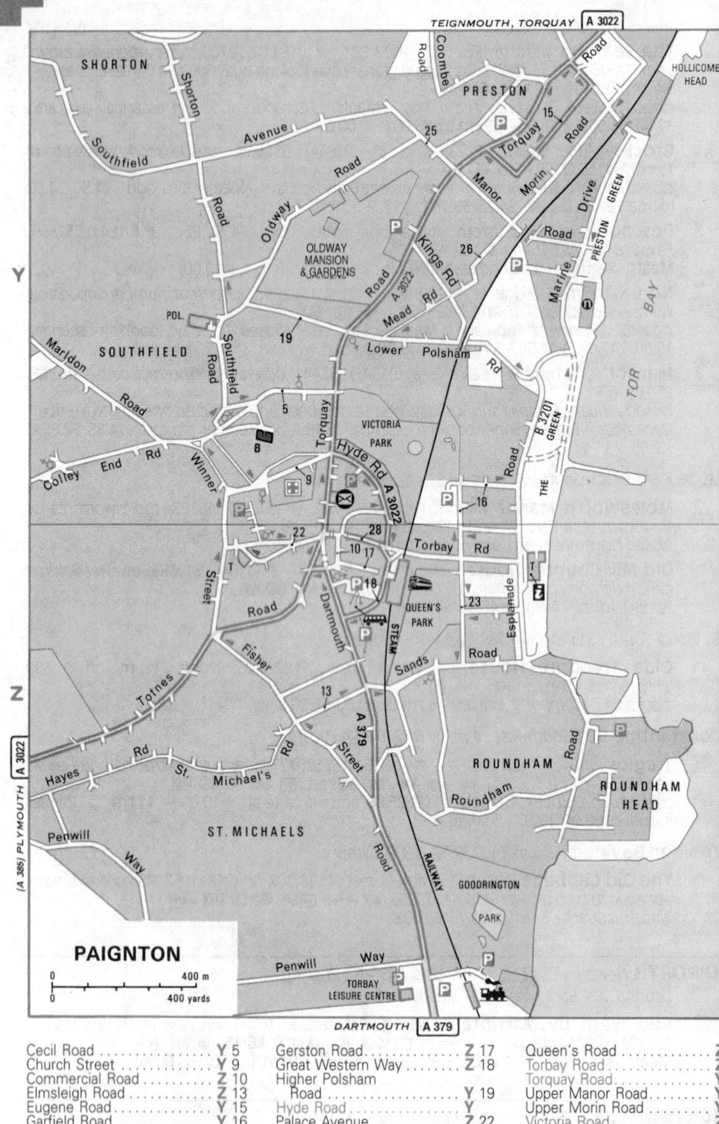

Cecil Road . . . . Y 5
Church Street . . . . Y 9
Commercial Road . . . . Z 10
Elmsleigh Road . . . . Z 13
Eugene Road . . . . Y 15
Garfield Road . . . . Y 16

Gerston Road . . . . Z 17
Great Western Way . . . . Z 18
Higher Polsham Road . . . . Y 19
Hyde Road . . . . Y
Palace Avenue . . . . Z 22

Queen's Road . . . . Z
Torbay Road . . . . Z
Torquay Road . . . . Y
Upper Manor Road . . . . Y
Upper Morin Road . . . . Y
Victoria Road . . . . Z

PAINSWICK *Glos.* **403** **404** N 28 *Great Britain G. – pop. 1 628.*

See : *Town*★.

London 107 – Bristol 35 – Cheltenham 10 – Gloucester 7.

Painswick ⛰, Kemps Lane, GL6 6YB, Southeast : ½ m. by Bisley St, St Marys St, Cross and Tibbiwell Lane ☎ (01452) 812160, *reservations@painswickhotel.c… Fax (01452) 814059,* ⌂, « Part 18C Palladian house », – ⚭ rest, TV P. MC AE VISA … **Meals** 16.00/27.50 and dinner a la carte 29.50/36.75 **st.** 🍷 13.75 – **19 rm** ☕ 75.… 180.00 **st.** – SB.

Cardynham House without rest., The Cross, GL6 6XX, by Bisley St and St Marys St ✆ (01452) 814006, *info@cardynham.co.uk, Fax (01452) 812321,* « Part 15C » – TV. MC VISA JCB. 🚭
9 rm ☕ 47.00/69.00 st.

ANGBOURNE-ON-THAMES *Newbury* 403 404 Q 29 – ✉ *Reading.*
London 53 – Basingstoke 18 – Newbury 16 – Oxford 22 – Reading 6.

Copper Inn, Church Rd, RG8 7AR, ✆ (01189) 842244, *reservations@copper-inn.co.uk, Fax (01189) 845542,* – TV ♿ – 🔊 60. MC AE ① VISA
Meals a la carte 23.95/31.85 **t.** 🍷 13.95 – ☕ 9.50 – **22 rm** 95.00/130.00 **t.** – SB.

ARKGATE *Mersey.* 402 403 K 24.
London 212 – Birkenhead 10 – Chester 16 – Liverpool 12.

Marsh Cat, 1 Mostyn Sq, CH64 6SL, ✆ (0151) 336 1963, *info@marshcat.com* – MC AE ① VISA
Meals a la carte 19.95/24.40 **st.** 🍷 8.95.

In this guide
a symbol or a character, printed in red or black, in **bold** or light type, does not have the same meaning.
Pay particular attention to the explanatory pages.

ARKHAM *Devon* 403 H 31 – ✉ *Bideford.*
London 229 – Barnstaple 14 – Exeter 87 – Plymouth 58.

Penhaven Country House 🐦, Rectory Lane, EX39 5PL, ✆ (01237) 451711, *restaurant @penhaven.co.uk, Fax (01237) 451878,* – 🚭 rest, TV P. MC AE ① VISA
Meals (dinner only and Sunday lunch)/dinner 17.00 and a la carte 24.95/31.95 **st.** 🍷 12.95 – **12 rm** ☕ (dinner included) 74.00/170.00 **st.** – SB.

ATCHWAY *South Gloucestershire* 403 404 M 29 – *see Bristol.*

ATELEY BRIDGE *N. Yorks.* 402 O 21 *Great Britain G.* – *pop. 2 504* – ✉ *Harrogate.*
Exc. : *Fountains Abbey★★★ AC - Studley Royal★★ AC (<★ from Anne Boleyn's Seat) - Fountains Hall (Façade★), NE : 8½ m. by B 6265.*
18 High St ✆ (01423) 711147.
London 225 – Leeds 28 – Middlesbrough 46 – York 32.

Grassfields Country House 🐦, Low Wath Rd, HG3 5HL, ✆ (01423) 711412, *Fax (01423) 712844,* « Part 18C », – 🚭 rest, TV P – 🔊 60. MC VISA
Meals *(closed Monday)* 9.25/19.95 **st.** 🍷 11.50 – **9 rm** ☕ 33.50/80.00 **st.** – SB.

Knottside Farm 🐦, The Knott, HG3 5DQ, Southeast : 1 m. by A 6165 ✆ (01423) 712927, *Fax (01423) 712927,* <, « 17C », – 🚭 TV P
Meals (by arrangement) 18.00 – **3 rm** ☕ 50.00/65.00.

Low Laithe *Southeast : 2 ¾ m. on B 6165* – ✉ *Harrogate.*

Dusty Miller, Main Rd, Summerbridge, HG3 4BU, ✆ (01423) 780837 – P. MC AE VISA *closed 1 week July, 25 December, 1 January, Sunday and Monday* – **Meals** (dinner only) 24.00 and a la carte 26.40/31.40 **t.** 🍷 12.90.

Summerbridge *Southeast : 3 ¾ m. on B 6165* – ✉ *Harrogate.*

North Pasture Farm 🐦 without rest., Brimham Rocks, HG3 4DW, Northeast : 2 ¾ m. by Hartwith Bank Rd ✆ (01423) 711470, *Fax (01423) 711470,* <, « Part 14C and 17C farmhouse, working farm », – 🚭 P. 🚭
March-early November – **3 rm** ☕ 30.00/45.00 **st.**

Wath-in-Nidderdale *Northwest : 2 ¼ m. by Low Wath Rd* – ✉ *Harrogate.*

Sportsman's Arms 🐦 with rm, HG3 5PP, ✆ (01423) 711306, *Fax (01423) 712524,* « Part 17C », – 🚭 TV P. MC VISA. 🚭
closed 25 December – **Meals** (booking essential to non-residents) a la carte 15.00/25.00 **t.** 🍷 7.00 – **13 rm** ☕ 50.00/90.00 **st.** – SB.

at Ramsgill-in-Nidderdale *Northwest : 5 m. by Low Wath Rd – ✉ Harrogate.*

Yorke Arms with rm, HG3 5RL, ✆ (01423) 755243, *enquiries@yorke-arms.co.u*
Fax (01423) 755330, « Part 17C former shooting lodge », – rest, P. VISA
closed 1 week February, 1 week July and 1 week November **Meals** *(closed Sunday dinne and Monday to non-residents)* a la carte 21.75/31.95 **t.** 12.50 – **14 rm** (dinner include 95.00/300.00 **t.** – SB.

PATRICK BROMPTON *N.Yorks.* 402 P 21 – ✉ *Bedale.*
London 242 – Newcastle upon Tyne 58 – York 43.

Elmfield House, Arrathorne, DL8 1NE, Northwest : 2 ¼ m. by A 684 on Richmond r
✆ (01677) 450558, *stay@elmfieldhouse.freeserve.co.uk, Fax (01677) 450557,*
rest, P. VISA.
Meals (residents only) (dinner only) 15.00 **st.** 9.00 – **9 rm** 35.00/60.00 **st.** – SB.

PAULERSPURY *Northants.* 403 404 R 27 – *see Towcester.*

PAXFORD *Glos.* 403 404 O 27 – *see Chipping Campden.*

PAYHEMBURY *Devon – see Honiton.*

PEASMARSH *E. Sussex* 404 W 31 – *see Rye.*

PELYNT *Cornwall* 403 G 32 – *see Looe.*

PEMBURY *Kent* 404 U 30 – *see Royal Tunbridge Wells.*

PENDLEBURY *Gtr. Manchester* 402 403 404 N 23 – *see Manchester.*

PENRITH *Cumbria* 401 402 L 19 – *pop. 12 049.*
Salkeld Rd ✆ (01768) 891919.
Robinsons School, Middlegate ✆ (01768) 867466 – Rheged, Redhills, Penrith ✆ (0176 860 034.
London 290 – Carlisle 24 – Kendal 31 – Lancaster 48.

North Lakes, Ullswater Rd, CA11 8QT, South : 1 m. by A 592 at junction 40 of M
✆ (01768) 868111, *nlakes@shireinns.co.uk, Fax (01768) 868291,* squash –
P – 200. VISA
Meals *(closed Saturday lunch)* a la carte 22.40/32.00 **st.** 13.45 – **84 rm** 102.0 122.00 **st.** – SB.

Travelodge, Redhills, CA11 0DT, Southwest : 1 ½ m. by A 592 on A 66 ✆ (01768) 86695
rm, P. VISA JCB.
Meals (grill rest.) – **40 rm** 49.95 **t.**

A Bit on the Side, Brunswick Sq, CA11 7LG, ✆ (01768) 892526 – . VISA
closed 25-26 December and 1 January – **Meals** (dinner only) a la carte 18.20/24.95 **t.** 9.9

at Temple Sowerby *East : 6 ¾ m. on A 66 – ✉ Penrith.*

Temple Sowerby House, CA10 1RZ, ✆ (01768) 361578, *stay@temple-sowerby.co*
Fax (01768) 361958, « Early 18C farmhouse with Georgian additions », – rest,
VISA
Meals (dinner only) a la carte 24.25/30.65 **st.** 14.75 – **13 rm** 68.00/98.00 **st.** – SB.

ENZANCE *Cornwall* **403** **D 33** *The West Country G. – pop. 20 284.*

See : *Town★ - Outlook★★★ – Western Promenade (<★★★)* **YZ** *– National Lighthouse Centre★* **AC Y** *– Chapel St.★* **Y** *– Maritime Museum★* **AC Y M1.**

Env. : *St Buryan★★ (church tower★★), SW : 5 m. by A 30 and B 3283 – Penwith★★ – Trengwainton Garden★★, NW : 2 m. – Sancreed - Church★★ (Celtic Crosses★★) - Carn Euny★, W : 3 ½ m. by A 30* **Z** *– St Michael's Mount★★ (<★★), E : 4 m. by B 3311 –* **Y** *– and A 30 – Gulval★ (Church★), NE : 1 m. – Ludgvan★ (Church★), NE : 3 ½ m. by A 30 – Chysauster Village★, N : 3 ½ m. by A 30, B 3311 and minor rd – Newlyn★ - Pilchard Works★, SW : 1 ½ m. by B 3315* **Z** *– Lanyon Quoit★, NW : 3 ½ m. by St Clare Street – Men-an-Tol★, NW : 5 m. by B 3312 – Madron Church★, NW : 1 ½ m. by St Clare Street* **Y**.

Exc. : *Morvah (<★★), NW : 6 ½ m. by St Clare Street* **Y** *– Zennor (Church★), NW : 6 m. by B 3311* **Y** *– Prussia Cove★, E : 8 m. by B 3311 –* **Y** *– and A 394 – Land's End★ (cliff scenery★★★), SW : 10 m. by A 30* **Z** *– Porthcurno★, SW : 8 ½ m. by A 30, B 3283 and minor rd.*

Access to the Isles of Scilly by helicopter, British International Heliport (01736) 363871, Fax (01736) 364293.

to the Isles of Scilly (Hugh Town) (Isles of Scilly Steamship Co. Ltd) (summer only) (approx. 2 h 40 mn).

Station Rd ℘ (01736) 362207.

London 319 – Exeter 113 – Plymouth 77 – Taunton 155.

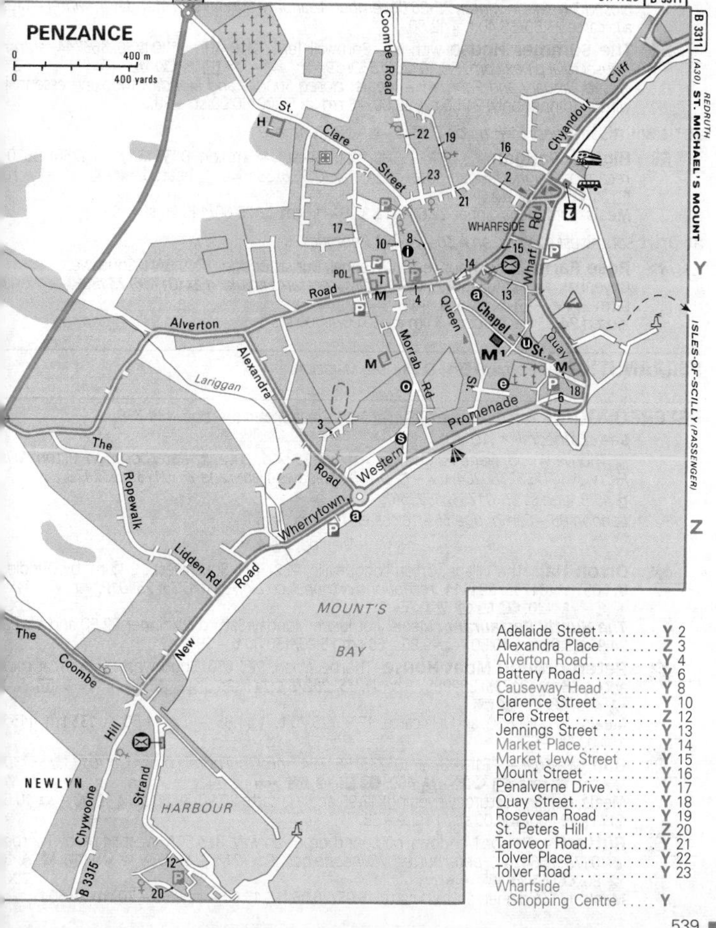

ENGLAND

Abbey, Abbey St, TR18 4AR, ℘ (01736) 366906, *glyn@abbeyhotel.fsnet.co* *Fax (01736) 351163*, « Attractively furnished 17C house », – rest, TV P. VISA Y
closed 1 week Christmas – **Meals** (booking essential) (dinner only) 24.50 **t.** 12.00 – 6
80.00/155.00 **t.**, 1 suite – SB.

Beachfield, The Promenade, TR18 4NW, ℘ (01736) 362067, *office@beachfield.co* *Fax (01736) 331100*, ← – TV. AE VISA JCB Z
closed 1 week Christmas-New Year – **Meals** (bar lunch)/dinner 15.95/17.95 and a la ca 12.00/26.00 **st.** 10.00 – **18 rm** 47.50/95.00 **st.**

Tarbert, 11 Clarence St, TR18 2NU, ℘ (01736) 363758, *reception@tarbert-hotel.co* *Fax (01736) 331336* – TV. AE VISA JCB. Y
closed December and January – **Meals** (dinner only) a la carte approx. 14.75 **t.** 7.9
12 rm 38.00/68.00 **t.** – SB.

Estoril without rest., 46 Morrab Rd, TR18 4EX, ℘ (01736) 362468, *estoril@aol.co* *Fax (01736) 367471* – TV. VISA. Y
closed Christmas and New Year – **9 rm** 30.00/60.00 **st.**

Chy-An-Mor without rest., 15 Regent Terr, TR18 4DW, ℘ (01736) 363441, *info@ch* *mor.co.uk, Fax (01736) 363441*, ←, – TV P. VISA. Y
closed December and January – **10 rm** 35.00/70.00 **st.**

Harris's, 46 New St, TR18 2LZ, ℘ (01736) 364408, *harriss.restaurant@lineone.* *Fax (01736) 333273* – . AE VISA Y
closed 3 weeks in winter, 25-26 December, 1 January, Sunday and Monday in winter – **Me** a la carte 23.50/38.40 **t.** 12.50.

The Summer House with rm, Cornwall Terr, TR18 4HL, ℘ (01736) 363744, *sum* *house@dial.pipex.com, Fax (01736) 360959*, , – TV P. VISA JCB Z
closed January and February – **Meals** *(closed Sunday and Monday)* (booking essentia winter) (dinner only) 21.50 **t.** 12.00 – **5 rm** 55.00/80.00 **st.** – SB.

at Newlyn *Southwest : 1½ m. on B 3315* – Z – ✉ *Penzance.*

Higher Faugan , TR18 5NS, Southwest : ¾ m. on B 3315 ℘ (01736) 362C *reception@higherfaugan-hotel.co.uk, Fax (01736) 351648*, heated, , , – r TV P. AE VISA
Meals (bar lunch)/dinner 22.50 **st.** 9.25 – **11 rm** 75.00/115.00 **st.** – SB.

at Drift *Southwest : 2½ m. on A 30* – Z – ✉ *Penzance.*

Rose Farm without rest., Chyenhal, Buryas Bridge, TR19 6AN, Southwest : ¾ m. Chyenhal rd ℘ (01736) 731808, *lally@rosefarm.co.uk*, *Fax (01736) 731808*, « Work farm », – TV P. VISA.
closed 24-25 December – **3 rm** 30.00/44.00 **st.**

PERRANUTHNOE *Cornwall* 403 D 33 – *see Marazion.*

PETERBOROUGH *Peterborough* 402 404 T 26 *Great Britain G.* – *pop. 134 788.*

See : *Cathedral*★★ *AC* Y.

Thorpe Wood, Nene Parkway ℘ *(01733) 267701*, BX – *Peterborough Milton, Mi Ferry* ℘ *(01733) 380204*, BX – *Orton Meadows, Ham Lane* ℘ *(01733) 237478*, BX.
45 Bridge St ℘ *(01733) 452336.*
London 85 – Cambridge 35 – Leicester 41 – Lincoln 51.

Plan opposite

Orton Hall, The Village, Orton Longueville, PE2 7DN, Southwest : 2 ½ m. by Oundle (A 605) ℘ (01733) 391111, *reception@ortonhall.co.uk, Fax (01733) 231912*, , –
P – 120. AE VISA JCB BX
The Huntly Restaurant : **Meals** (bar lunch Monday-Saturday)/dinner 22.50 and a la ca 24.95/33.95 **t.** 10.50 – 9.85 – **65 rm** 75.00/130.00 **t.** – SB.

Peterborough Moat House, Thorpe Wood, PE3 6SG, Southwest : 2 ¼ m. at rou about 33 ℘ (01733) 289988, *Fax (01733) 262737*, , , – , rest, TV
400. AE VISA BX
Meals 15.00/17.50 and a la carte 17.95/25.70 **t.** 11.85 – 11.50 – **133 rm** 113. 130.00 **st.** – SB.

Bull, Westgate, PE1 1RB, ℘ (01733) 561364, *info@bullhotel.co.uk, Fax (01733) 5573C* rm, rest, TV P – 400. AE VISA JCB Y
Meals (dancing Saturday evening) 17.95 and a la carte 20.90/38.50 **st.** 10.90 – 10.5
117 rm 94.00/104.00 **st.**, 1 suite – SB.

Butterfly, Thorpe Meadows, off Longthorpe Parkway, PE3 6GA, West : 1 m. by Thorpe ℘ (01733) 564240, *peterbutterfly@lineone.net, Fax (01733) 565538* – TV
80. AE VISA JCB BX
Meals 17.50 (dinner) and a la carte 15.95/26.95 **t.** 13.00 – 8.50 – **70 rm** 79.50 **t.**

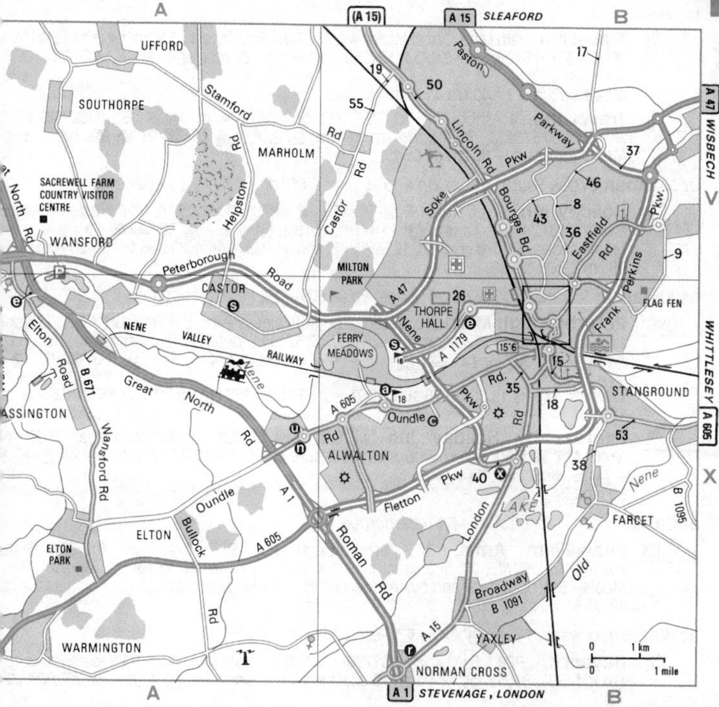

A B

(A 15) A 15 SLEAFORD

UFFORD
SOUTHORPE
Stamford Rd
MARHOLM
SACREWELL FARM COUNTRY VISITOR CENTRE
North Rd
WANSFORD
Helpston Rd
Castor Rd
Peterborough Road
CASTOR
MILTON PARK
NENE VALLEY RAILWAY
FERRY MEADOWS
Nene
Great North Rd
Elton Road
B 671
ASSINGTON
Wansford Rd
Oundle
ELTON
Bullock Rd
ELTON PARK
A 605
A 1
Roman Rd
WARMINGTON
ALWALTON
Oundle Rd
A 605
Fletton Pkw
London Rd
LAKE
Broadway B 1091
YAXLEY
A 15
NORMAN CROSS
Paston Parkway
Lincoln Rd
Pkw
Soke
Bourges Bd
Eastfield Rd
Frank Perkins Pkw.
A 47
Nene
THORPE HALL
A 1179
FLAG FEN
STANGROUND
Nene
Old
FARCET
B 1095
A 47 WISBECH
WHITTLESEY
A 605
19 50 55 17 37 46 8 43 36 9 26 15'6 15 35 18 53 38 40
0 1 km
0 1 mile
A 1 STEVENAGE, LONDON
V X

PETERBOROUGH

dge Street .... Z
ttle Market Road .... Y 2
urch Street .... YZ
y Road .... Y 3
wgate .... Y 5
ss Street.............. Z 6
gsthorpe Road .... BV 8
gerley Drain Road..... BV 9
bankment Road......... Z 12
change Street.......... Y 13
tton Avenue.......... BX 15
neva Street............ Y 16
ntons Road .... BV 17
h Street.............. BX 18
rn Road.............. BV 19
g Causeway .... Y 25
gthorpe
arkway................ BX 26
rket Way............... Y 28
dgate .... Y 29
w Road .... Y 34
w Road............... BX 35
k Road .... BV 36
ston Parkway......... BV 37
erborough Road...... BX 38
orpres Way .... BX 40
eensgate
hopping Centre......... Y
ergate .... Z 42
ergate
hopping Centre......... Z
Paul's Road .... BV 43
orpe Road .... Y 45
lland Road........... BV 46
entworth Street......... Z 48
rrington
arkway............... BV 50
eelyard .... Y 52
ittlesey Road .... BX 53
odcroft Road .... BV 55

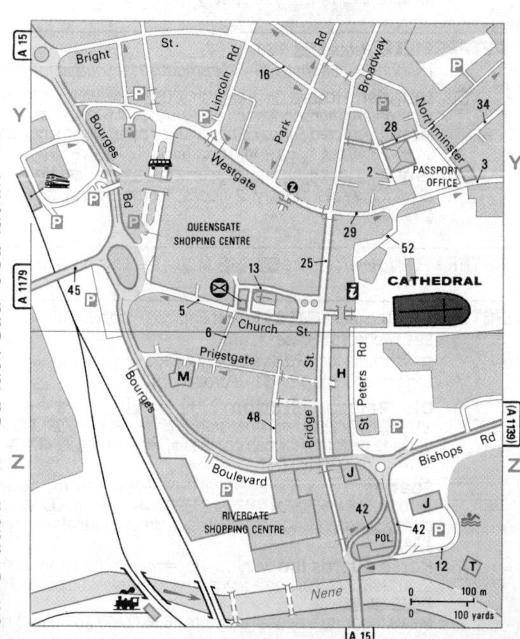

Travel Inn, Ham Lane, Orton Meadows, PE2 5UU, Southwest : 3 ½ m. by Oundle Rd (A 605) ☎ (01733) 235794, *Fax (01733) 391055* – rm, rest, TV & P. MC AE VISA BX
Meals (grill rest.) – **40 rm** 41.95 **t.**

Travel Inn, 4 Ashbourne Rd, PE7 8BT, South : 2 ¾ m. by A 15 ☎ (01733) 310772, *Fax (01733) 310923*, – |♦|, rm, rest, TV & P – 30. MC AE VISA. BX
Meals *(grill rest.)* – **80 rm** 41.95 **t.**

at Norman Cross *South : 5 ¾ m. on A 15 at junction 16 of A 1(M) – ✉ Peterborough.*

Holiday Inn, Great North Rd, PE7 3TB, ☎ (0870) 400 9063, *fc1428@forte-hotels.com*, *Fax (01733) 244455*, – rm, rest, TV & P – 50. MC AE VISA BX
Meals *(closed Saturday lunch)* 12.50/35.00 and a la carte 14.40/25.85 **t.** 11.25 – 10.95 – **96 rm** 89.00 **t.** – SB.

at Alwalton *Southwest : 5 ¾ m. on Oundle Rd (A 605) – ✉ Peterborough.*

Peterborough Marriott, Peterborough Business Park, Lynch Wood, PE2 6GB, (opposite East of England Showground) ☎ (01733) 371111, *peterborough@swallow_hotel.co.uk*, *Fax (01733) 236725*, – , rest, TV & P – 300. MC AE VISA JCB AX
Laurels : Meals 15.50/19.75 **st.** 12.75 – 13.00 – **155 rm** 89.00/115.00 **st.**, 2 suites – SB.

Express by Holiday Inn without rest., East of England Way, PE2 6H… ☎ (01733) 284450, *peterborough@oriel-leisure.co.uk, Fax (01733) 284451* – TV & … – 25. MC AE VISA JCB AX
80 rm 62.50 **st.**

at Castor *West : 5 m. off A 47 – ✉ Peterborough.*

Fitzwilliam Arms, 34 Peterborough Rd, PE5 7AX, ☎ (01733) 38025…, *Fax (01733) 380116*, « Characterful thatched inn » – P. MC AE VISA JCB. AX
Meals - Seafood, steak and oyster specialities - (bookings not accepted at dinner) a la carte 12.00/50.00 **st.** 10.50.

at Wansford *West : 8½ m. by A 47 – ✉ Peterborough.*

Haycock, PE8 6JA, ☎ (01780) 782223, *eventshaycock@arcadianhotels.co.uk*, *Fax (01780) 783031*, « Part 17C coaching inn », – TV & P – 200. MC AE VISA AX
Meals a la carte 18.00/26.00 **st.** 13.50 – 12.50 – **50 rm** 90.00/115.00 **st.** – SB.

PETERSFIELD *Hants.* 404 R 30.
London 60 – Brighton 45 – Portsmouth 21 – Southampton 34.

Langrish House , Langrish, GU32 1RN, West : 3 ½ m. by A 272 ☎ (01730) 26694…, *frontdesk@langrishhouse.co.uk, Fax (01730) 260543*, – TV P – 60. MC AE VISA
Meals *(restricted Sunday dinner)* (lunch by arrangement)/dinner 12.95/24.95 and a la carte 24.95/28.40 **t.** 10.50 – **14 rm** 63.00/120.00 **t.** – SB.

JSW, 1 Heath Rd, GU31 4JE, ☎ (01730) 262030 – MC VISA
closed 2 weeks January, 2 weeks August, Sunday and Monday – **Meals** 15.50/25.50 13.50.

PETERSTOW *Herefordshire* 403 404 M 28 – *see Ross-on-Wye.*

PETWORTH *W. Sussex* 404 S 31 *Great Britain G. – pop. 2 156.*
See : *Petworth House*★★ *AC.*
18 *Osiers, London Rd ☎ (01798) 344097.*
London 54 – Brighton 31 – Portsmouth 33.

Old Railway Station without rest., GU28 0JF, South : 1 ½ m. off A 2… ☎ (01798) 342346, *mlr@old-station.co.uk, Fax (01798) 342346*, « Converted late 19C station and restored Pullman coaches », – TV P. MC VISA JCB.
6 rm 65.00/116.00 **st.**

Soanes, Grove Lane, GU28 0HY, South : ½ m. by High St and Pulborough … ☎ (01798) 343659, *Fax (01798) 343659*, – P. MC VISA JCB
closed Sunday, Monday and 2 weeks January – **Meals** (dinner only) a la carte 30.40/42.45 14.00.

Horse Guards Inn with rm, Upperton Rd, Tillington, GU28 9AF, West : 1 ½ m. by A 2… ☎ (01798) 342332, *horseguardsinn@freeserve.co.uk, Fax (01798) 344351*, – rm, … MC AE VISA.
Meals (booking essential) a la carte 18.60/27.95 12.95 – **3 rm** 60.00/82.00 **t.**

Sutton *South : 5 m. by A 283 – ✉ Pulborough.*

White Horse Inn with rm, The Street, RH20 1PS, ✆ (01798) 869221, *Fax (01798) 869291,* – TV P. MO AE VISA JCB
Meals 12.25/16.75 and a la carte 18.45/25.75 **t.** 10.90 – **6 rm** 75.00 **t.**

Halfway Bridge *West : 3 m. on A 272 – ✉ Petworth.*

The Halfway Bridge Inn, GU28 9BP, ✆ (01798) 861281, *mail@thesussexpub.co.uk, Fax (01798) 861878,* « 17C coaching inn », – P. MO VISA
closed dinner 25-26 December – **Meals** a la carte 15.95/25.00 **t.**

Lickfold *Northwest : 6 m. by A 272 – ✉ Petworth.*

Lickfold Inn, GU28 9EY, ✆ (01798) 861285, *Fax (01798) 861342,* , « 15C inn », – P. MO AE VISA
Meals a la carte 23.70/27.25 **t.** 11.50.

PICKERING *N. Yorks.* 402 R 21 – *pop. 5 914.*
Eastgate Car Park ✆ (01751) 473791.
London 237 – Middlesbrough 43 – Scarborough 19 – York 25.

White Swan, Market Pl, YO18 7AA, ✆ (01751) 472288, *welcome@white-swan.co.uk, Fax (01751) 475554* – TV P. MO AE VISA JCB
Meals a la carte 15.85/27.90 **t.** 11.25 – **11 rm** 65.00/120.00 **t.**, 1 suite – SB.

Burgate House, 17 Burgate, YO18 7AU, ✆ (01751) 473463, *info@burgatehouse.co.uk, Fax (01751) 473463,* « Part 17C » – rest, TV P. MO AE VISA.
restricted opening in Winter – **Meals** (booking essential) 15.00 6.50 – **7 rm** 40.00/60.00 – SB.

Bramwood, 19 Hall Garth, YO18 7AW, ✆ (01751) 474066, – P. MO VISA.
Meals (by arrangement) 17.00 **s.** – **8 rm** 25.00/65.00 **s.**

Old Manse, Middleton Rd, YO18 8AL, ✆ (01751) 476484, *Fax (01751) 477124,* – TV P.
Meals 12.00 **st.** – **10 rm** 26.00/54.00 **st.**

Thornton-le-Dale *East : 2 m. by A 170 – ✉ Pickering.*

New Inn with rm, YO18 7LF, ✆ (01751) 474226, *newinntld@aol.com, Fax (01751) 477715,* « 18C » – TV P. MO VISA.
*closed 25 December***Meals** a la carte 12.70/23.15 **t.** 8.55 – **6 rm** 40.00/68.00 **t.** – SB.

Middleton *Northwest : 1½ m. on A 170 – ✉ Pickering.*

Cottage Leas , Nova Lane, YO18 8PN, North : 1 m. via Church Lane ✆ (01751) 472129, *cottageleas@aol.com, Fax (01751) 474930,* , – TV P. MO VISA
Meals (dinner only and Sunday lunch)/dinner 17.50 **t.** 9.95 – **12 rm** 49.50/154.00 **t.** – SB.

Sinnington *Northwest : 4 m. by A 170 – ✉ York.*

Fox and Hounds, Main St, YO62 6SQ, ✆ (01751) 431577, *foxhoundsinn@easynet.co.uk, Fax (01751) 432791,* – TV P. MO AE VISA
Meals a la carte 13.95/26.35 **t.** 11.50 – **10 rm** 44.00/70.00 **t.**

Cropton *Northwest : 4¾ m. by A 170 – ✉ Pickering.*

Burr Bank , YO18 8HL, North : ¼ m. ✆ (01751) 417777, *banb@burrbank.com., Fax (01751) 417789,* , – TV P.
Meals (by arrangement) 16.00 **st.** 6.00 – **3 rm** 27.00/54.00 **st.**

The New Inn with rm, YO18 8HH, ✆ (01751) 417330, *Fax (01751) 417310,* « Home of Cropton brewery » – TV P. MO VISA.
Meals a la carte 12.95/20.95 **st.** 8.95 – **9 rm** 37.00/62.00 – SB.

PICKHILL *N. Yorks.* 402 P 21 – *pop. 412 – ✉ Thirsk.*
London 229 – Leeds 41 – Middlesbrough 30 – York 34.

Nags Head Country Inn, YO7 4JG, ✆ (01845) 567391, *reservations@nagsheadpickhill.freeserve.co.uk, Fax (01845) 567212,* – TV P – 30. MO VISA JCB
Meals 15.00/20.00 and a la carte 14.40/20.95 **st.** 12.95 – **17 rm** 40.00/60.00 **st.** – SB.

Wenn Sie ein ruhiges Hotel suchen,
benutzen Sie zuerst die Karte in der Einleitung
oder wählen Sie im Text ein Hotel mit dem Zeichen oder .

ENGLAND

PILLING *Lancs.* 402 L 22 – *pop. 2 204* – ✉ *Preston.*
London 243 – Blackpool 11 – Burnley 43 – Manchester 49.

Springfield House ⛏, Wheel Lane, PR3 6HL, ✆ (01253) 790301, *recep@springf house.co.uk, Fax (01253) 790907*, ≤, « Victorian country house in Georgian style », ⛱ rest, TV P. MC AE VISA JCB
Meals *(closed Monday lunch)* 9.75/10.75 (lunch) and a la carte 12.45/16.75 **t.** 10.45 – 8
39.50/65.00 **t.** – SB.

PLUCKLEY *Kent* 404 W 30 – *pop. 883.*
London 53 – Folkestone 25 – Maidstone 18.

Elvey Farm Country H. without rest., TN27 0SU, West : 2 m. by Smarden rd Marley Farm rd, off Mundy Bois rd ✆ (01233) 840442, *Fax (01233) 840726*, ≤, « Conver oast house and barn », – TV P. MC VISA JCB
9 rm 55.50/65.50 **t.**

Dering Arms, Station Rd, TN27 0RR, South : 1 ½ m. on Bethersden rd ✆ (01233) 840 *info@deringarms.com, Fax (01233) 840498*, « Mid 19C former hunting lodge », – P. AE VISA
closed 26 to 29 December – **Meals** a la carte 20.85/25.15 **t.** 8.95.

PLUMTREE *Notts.* – *see Nottingham.*

The Guide is updated annually so renew your Guide every year.

PLUSH *Dorset.*
London 142 – Bournemouth 35 – Salisbury 44 – Taunton 52 – Weymouth 15 – Yeovil 23.

Brace of Pheasants, DT2 7RQ, ✆ (01300) 348357, *geoffreyknights@braceofpheasa freeserve.co.uk*, « 16C thatched inn », – rest, P. MC VISA JCB
restricted opening in winter and closed Monday except Bank Holidays – **Meals** a la c 14.55/22.85 **st.** 11.50.

PLYMOUTH *Plymouth* 403 H 32 *The West Country G.* – *pop. 245 295.*
See : *Town★ – Smeaton's Tower (≤★★) AC* **BZ A** – *Plymouth Dome★ AC* **BZ** – *Royal Cit (ramparts ≤★★) AC* **BZ** – *City Museum and Art Gallery★* **BZ M.**
Env. : *Saltram House★★ AC, E : 3 ½ m.* **BY A** – *Tamar River★★ – Anthony House★ W : 5 m. by A 374 – Mount Edgcumbe (≤★) AC, SW : 2 m. by passenger ferry f Stonehouse* **AZ.**
Exc. : *NE : Dartmoor National Park★★ – Buckland Abbey★★ AC, N : 7½ m. by A 386* **AB**
18 *Staddon Heights, Plymstock ✆ (01752) 402475 –* 9 *Elfordleigh Hotel G. & Colebrook, Plympton ✆ (01752) 336428.*
Tamar Bridge (toll) **AY.**
✈ *Plymouth City (Roborough) Airport : ✆ (01752) 204090, N : 3½ m. by A 386* **ABY.**
⛴ *to France (Roscoff) (Brittany Ferries) 1-3 daily (6 h) – to Spain (Santander) (Brit Ferries) 2 weekly (approx. 24 h) – to Spain (Bilbao) (P & O Portsmouth) 2 weekly (app 30 h) – to France (St Malo) (Brittany Ferries) (winter only) (8 h).*
ℹ *Island House, 9 The Barbican ✆ (01752) 264849 – Plymouth Discovery Centre, Crab ✆ (01752) 266030.*
London 242 – Bristol 124 – Southampton 161.

Plans on following pages

Plymouth Hoe Moat House, Armada Way, PL1 2HJ, ✆ (01752) 639988, *revp queensmoat.co.uk, Fax (01752) 673816*, ≤ city and Plymouth Sound, – rest, TV – 400. MC AE VISA. **BZ**
Elliotts : **Meals** (buffet lunch) 10.00/16.95 and dinner a la carte 19.05/33.00 11.9 11.50 – **210 rm** 125.00/150.00.

The Duke of Cornwall, Millbay Rd, PL1 3LG, ✆ (01752) 275850, *duke@bhere.cc Fax (01752) 275854* – TV P – 300. MC AE VISA. **AZ**
closed 24-30 December – **Meals** (bar lunch)/dinner 17.50/21.00 and a la carte 20 27.00 **t.** 12.95 – **69 rm** 89.50/99.50 **st.**, 3 suites – SB.

Copthorne Plymouth, Armada Centre, Armada Way, PL1 1AR, (via Western Appro southbound) ✆ (01752) 224161, *sales.plymouth@mill-cop.com, Fax (01752) 670688*, – rm, rest, TV P – 150. MC AE VISA JCB. **BZ**
Meals 18.50 (dinner) and a la carte 17.65/25.45 14.50 – ***Bentley's*** : **Meals** 18.50 ner) and a la carte 17.65/25.45 **st.** 14.50 – 13.95 – **135 rm** 123.00/173.00 **st.** – SB.

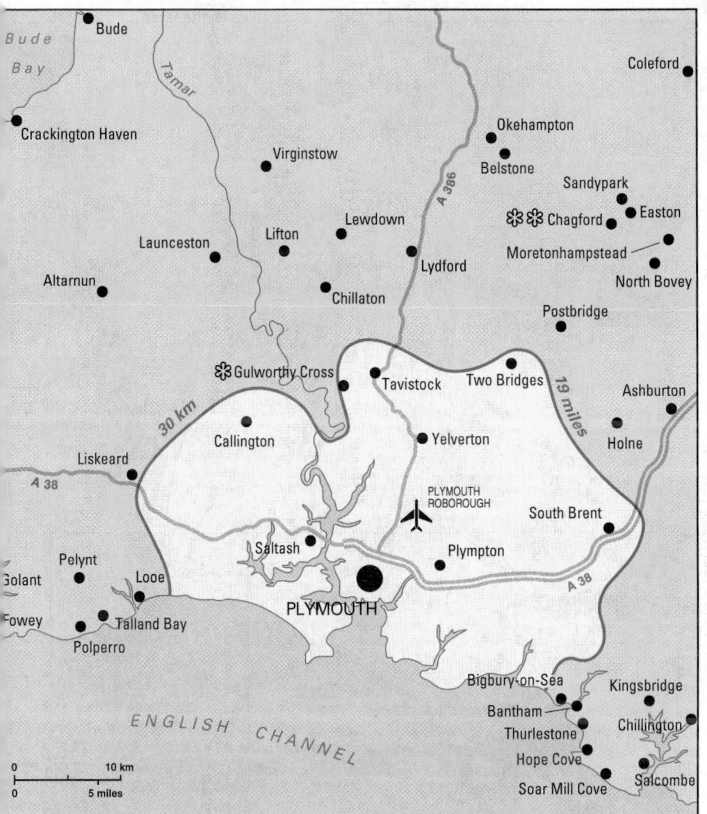

Grand, Elliot St, The Hoe, PL1 2PT, ✆ (01752) 661195, *info@plymouthgrand.com, Fax (01752) 600653*, < – |‡| ⇆ TV P – 70. MC AE VISA BZ a
Meals (dancing Saturday evening) a la carte 25.75/29.40 **st.** 10.50 – **77 rm** 90.00/150.00 **st.** – SB.

New Continental, Millbay Rd, PL1 3LD, ✆ (01752) 220782, *newconti@aol.com, Fax (01752) 227013*, ⅙, ≘s, ☒ – |‡|, ⇆ rm, ▤ rest, TV ✆ P – 400. MC AE VISA AZ s
closed 23 December-3 January – **Meals** *(closed dinner Friday and Sunday)* 11.25/28.00 and a la carte **t.** 9.95 – **99 rm** 93.00/170.00 **st.** – SB.

Travel Inn Metro, 1 Lockyers Quay, Coxside, PL4 0DX, ✆ (01752) 254180, *Fax (01752) 663872*, – ⇆ rm, ▤ rest, TV ♿ P – 20. MC AE ① VISA. ✂ BZ c
Meals (grill rest.) – **60 rm** 49.95 **t.**

Bowling Green without rest., 9-10 Osborne Pl, Lockyer St, The Hoe, PL1 2PU, ✆ (01752) 209090, *dave@bowlinggreenhotel.freeserve.co.uk, Fax (01752) 209092* – TV. MC AE ① VISA BZ r
closed 24 to 29 December – **12 rm** 40.00/54.00 **st.**

Berkeley's of St James without rest., 4 St James Place East, The Hoe, PL1 3AS, ✆ (01752) 221654, *Fax (01752) 221654* – ⇆ TV. MC VISA JCB. ✂ AZ n
closed 24 December-New Year – **5 rm** 28.00/50.00 **s.**

Athenaeum Lodge without rest., 4 Athenaeum St, The Hoe, PL1 2RQ, ✆ (01752) 665005, *Fax (01752) 665005* – ⇆ TV P. MC VISA JCB. ✂ BZ u
closed 24 December-2 January – **9 rm** 25.00/44.00 **st.**

Chez Nous, 13 Frankfort Gate, PL1 1QA, ✆ (01752) 266793, *Fax (01752) 266793* – MC AE ① VISA AZ e
closed 3 weeks February, 3 weeks September, Sunday, Monday and Saturday lunch – **Meals** - French - (lunch booking essential) 33.50 **t.** 12.50.

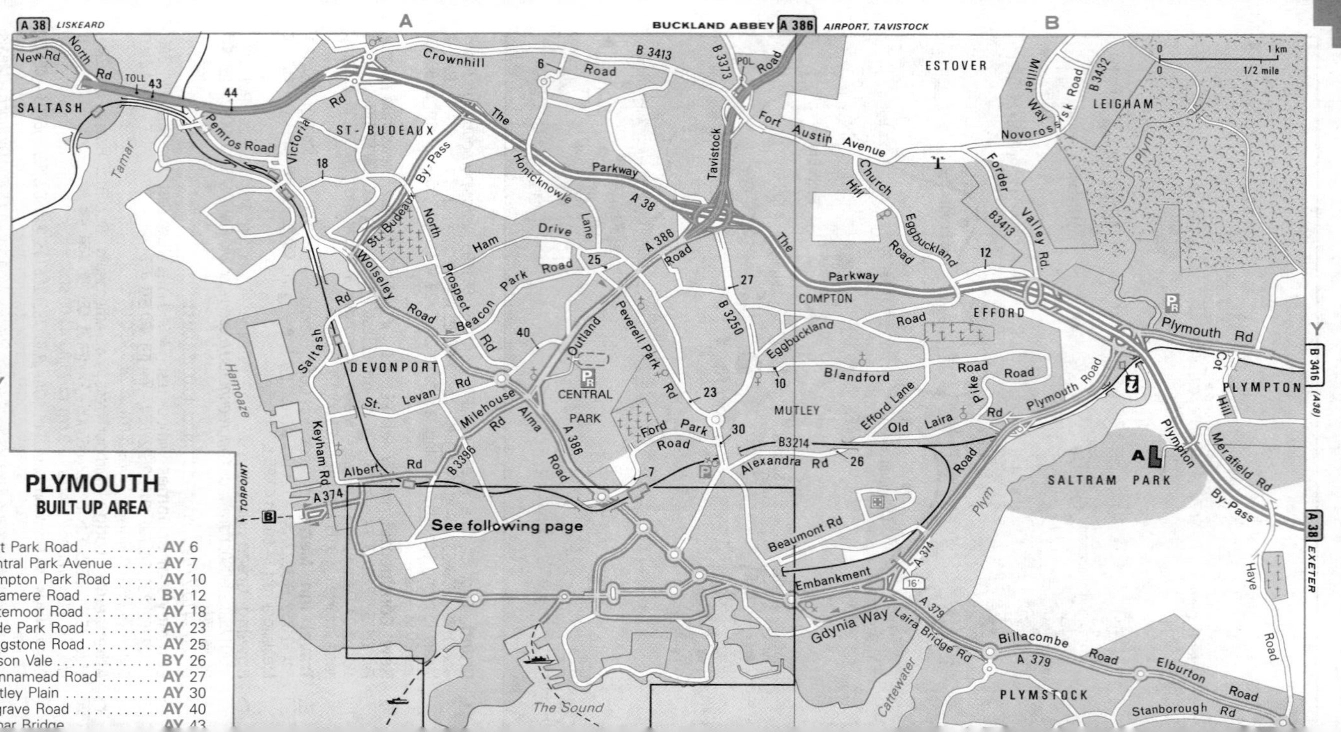

PLYMOUTH
BUILT UP AREA

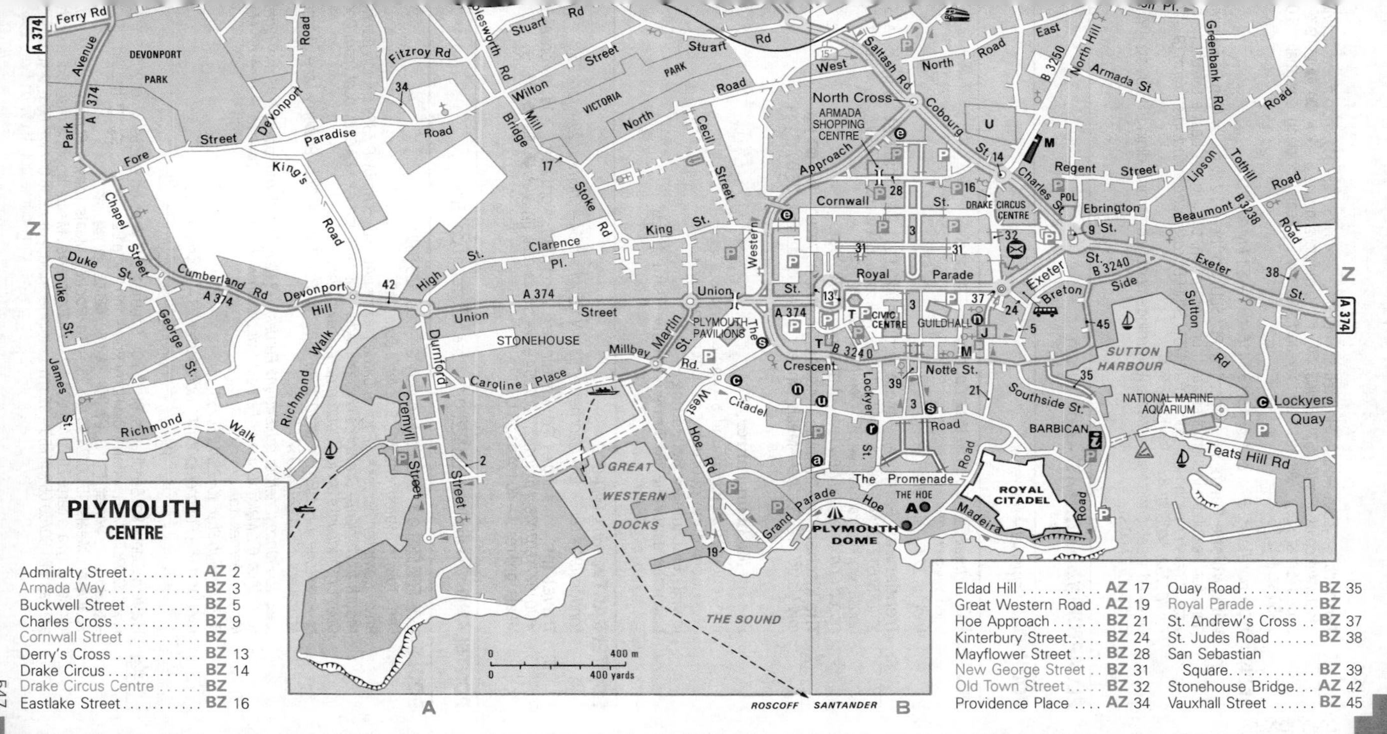

PLYMOUTH
CENTRE
Admiralty Street .... AZ 2
Armada Way .... BZ 3
Buckwell Street .... BZ 5
Charles Cross .... BZ 9
Cornwall Street .... BZ
Derry's Cross .... BZ 13
Drake Circus .... BZ 14
Drake Circus Centre .... BZ
Eastlake Street .... BZ 16
Eldad Hill .... AZ 17
Great Western Road . AZ 19
Hoe Approach .... BZ 21
Kinterbury Street .... BZ 24
Mayflower Street .... BZ 28
New George Street .. BZ 31
Old Town Street .... BZ 32
Providence Place .... AZ 34
Quay Road .... BZ 35
Royal Parade .... BZ
St. Andrew's Cross .. BZ 37
St. Judes Road .... BZ 38
San Sebastian Square .... BZ 39
Stonehouse Bridge ... AZ 42
Vauxhall Street .... BZ 45
DEVONPORT PARK
VICTORIA PARK
NORTH CROSS
ARMADA SHOPPING CENTRE
DRAKE CIRCUS CENTRE
STONEHOUSE
PLYMOUTH PAVILIONS
CIVIC CENTRE
GUILDHALL
SUTTON HARBOUR
NATIONAL MARINE AQUARIUM
BARBICAN
ROYAL CITADEL
THE HOE
PLYMOUTH DOME
GREAT WESTERN DOCKS
THE SOUND
ROSCOFF
SANTANDER
A 374
0 400 m
0 400 yards
A
B
Z

X **Tanners,** Prysten House, Finewell St, PL1 2AE, ☎ (01752) 252001, *goodfood@tann restaurant.co.uk, Fax (01752) 252105,* « 15C medieval house » – ✗. MC VISA BZ *closed Christmas, New Year, Sunday and Monday* – **Meals** (booking essential) 15.(27.50 **st.** 12.95.

at Plympton *Northeast : 5 m. by A 374 on B 3416* – BY – ✉ *Plymouth.*

Windwhistle Farm , Hemerdon, PL7 5BU, Northeast : 2 ½ m. by Glen Rd followi signs for Newnham industrial estate then Hemerdon, turning left beside telephone b after Miners Arms in Hemerdon ☎ (01752) 340600, *rosemarie@windwhistlefarm.f9.co. Fax (01752) 340600,* – ✗ TV P.
closed 1 week Christmas – **Meals** (by arrangement) (communal dining) 15.00 **st.** – **4** 30.00/52.00 **st.**

PLYMPTON *Plymouth* 403 H 32 – *see Plymouth.*

PODIMORE *Somerset* – *see Yeovil.*

POLPERRO *Cornwall* 403 G 33 *The West Country G.* – ✉ *Looe.*
See : *Village*★.
London 271 – *Plymouth 28.*

Trenderway Farm without rest., Pelynt, PL13 2LY, Northeast : 2 m. by A 3 ☎ (01503) 272214, *trenderwayfarm@hotmail.com, Fax (01503) 272991,* ≤, « 16C far house, working farm », – ✗ TV P. MC VISA.
closed Christmas and New Year – **4 rm** 45.00/70.00 **st.**

X **The Kitchen,** The Coombes, PL13 2RQ, ☎ (01503) 272780 – ✗. MC VISA
mid March-mid October – **Meals** (dinner only) a la carte 18.00/26.00 **t.** 11.00.

Die im **Michelin-Führer**
verwendeten Zeichen und Symbole haben
- **fett** oder dünn gedruckt, rot oder **schwarz** -
jeweils eine andere Bedeutung.
Lesen Sie daher die Erklärungen aufmerksam durch.

PONTEFRACT *N. Yorks.* 402 Q 22.
London 194 – *Leeds 16* – *Manchester 53* – *Nottingham 64* – *Sheffield 29* – *York 25.*

Travel Inn, Knottingley Rd, Knottingley, WF11 0BU, Northeast : 2 ½ m. on A 6 ☎ (01977) 607946, *Fax (01977) 607954* – ✗ rm, rest, TV & P. MC AE VISA
Meals (grill rest.) – **40 rm** 41.95 **t.**

PONTELAND *Tyne and Wear* 401 402 O 19 – *see Newcastle upon Tyne.*

POOLE *Poole* 403 404 O 31 *The West Country G.* – *pop. 133 050.*
See : *Town*★ *(Waterfront* **M1** *, Scaplen's Court* **M2** *).*
Env. : *Compton Acres*★★, *(English Garden* ≤★★★*)* **AC**, *SE : 3 m. by B 3369* BX *(on Bourn mouth town plan)* – *Brownsea Island*★ *(Baden-Powell Stone* ≤★★*)* **AC**, *by boat from Poo Quay or Sandbanks* BX *(on Bournemouth town plan).*
18 *Parkstone, Links Rd* ☎ *(01202) 707138* – 18 *The Bulbury Club, Bulberry Lane, Lytch Matravers* ☎ *(01929) 459574.*
to France (Cherbourg) (Brittany Ferries) 1-2 daily (4 h 15 mn) day (5 h 45 mn) nigh to France (St Malo) (Brittany Ferries) (winter only) 4 weekly (8 h) – *to France (St Ma (Condor Ferries Ltd).*
4 The High St ☎ *(01202) 253253.*
London 116 – *Bournemouth 4* – *Dorchester 23* – *Weymouth 28.*

Plan of Built up Area : see Bournemouth

Haven, Banks Rd, Sandbanks, BH13 7QL, Southeast : 4 ¼ m. on B 3369 ☎ (01202) 70733 *Fax (01202) 708796,* ≤ Ferry, Old Harry Rocks and Poole Bay, , , heated, , – , ✗ rest, rest, TV – 160. MC AE VISA.
Seaview **: Meals** 15.00/24.50 6.25 – ***La Roche*** **: Meals** *(closed Sunday and Mond* (dinner only) a la carte 26.00/43.00 12.00 – ***Brasserie*** **: Meals** (booking essential in winte a la carte 21.00/30.05 10.50 – **92 rm** (dinner included) 86.00/173.00 **t.**, 2 suites – on Bournemouth town plan BX

POOLE

urch Street ... 3
lphin Shopping Centre
ierson Road ... 4
Falkland Sq. ... 6
Fishermans Rd ... 7
Furnell Rd ... 8
High Street
Holes Bay Rd. ... 10
Labrador Drive ... 12
Longfleet Rd ... 13
Market St. ... 14
New Orchard ... 16
New Street ... 17
Serpentine Rd ... 18
Thames St. ... 19
Towngate Bridge ... 21
Westons Lane ... 22

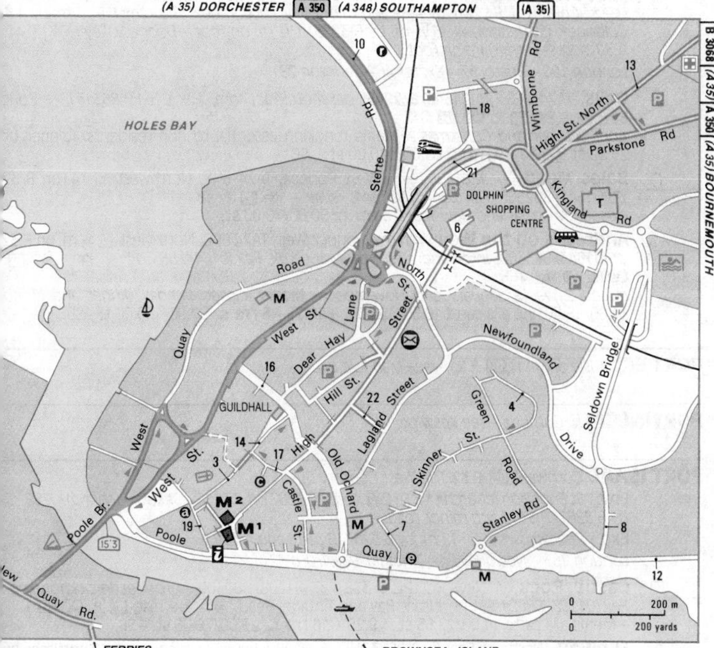

Salterns, 38 Salterns Way, Lilliput, BH14 8JR, (01202) 707321, *Fax (01202) 707488*, « Harbourside setting », – rm, rest, – 80. VISA. on Bournemouth town plan **BX** e

Waterside : **Meals** 25.00 and a la carte 26.00/33.50 **t.** 15.50 – 15.00 – **20 rm** 96.00/140.00 **t.** – SB.

Mansion House, 7-11 Thames St, BH15 1JN, off Poole Quay (01202) 685666, *enquiries@themansionhouse.co.uk, Fax (01202) 665709,* « 18C town house » – rest, – 40. VISA JCB. a

Benjamin's : **Meals** *(closed Sunday and Saturday lunch)* 15.95/27.00 and lunch a la carte approx. 22.00 **t.** 12.95 – ***JJ's Bistro :*** **Meals** *(closed Sunday lunch and Monday)* (residents only) 15.00 (dinner) and lunch a la carte approx. 12.45 **t.** 8.95 – **32 rm** 90.00/120.00 **st.** – SB.

Thistle Poole, The Quay, BH15 1HD, (0870) 333 9143, *poole@thistle.co.uk, Fax (0870) 333 9243,* – , rm, – 60. VISA JCB e

Meals *(closed lunch in July and August)* 19.95 **st.** 11.85 – 11.85 – **70 rm** 126.00/136.00 **st.** – SB.

Travel Inn, Holesbay Rd, BH15 2BD, (01202) 669944, *Fax (01202) 669954* – rm, VISA. r

Meals (grill rest.) – **40 rm** 41.95 **t.**

John B's, 20 High St, Old Town, BH15 1BP, (01202) 672440, *mark@markroberts.co.uk, Fax (01202) 672440* – VISA c

closed Sunday except dinner at Bank Holidays – **Meals** (dinner only) a la carte 24.15/29.20 **t.** 9.95.

Isabel's, 32 Station Rd, Lower Parkstone, BH14 8UD, (01202) 747885, *Fax (01202) 747885* – VISA JCB on Bournemouth town plan **BX** a

closed 26-27 December, 1-2 January, Sunday and Monday – **Meals** (dinner only) a la carte 21.90/28.30 **t.** 10.40.

POOLEY BRIDGE *Cumbria* 401 402 L 20 – *see Ullswater.*

PORLOCK *Somerset* 403 J 30 *The West Country G. – pop. 1 395 (inc. Oare) – ✉ Minehead.*

See : *Village★ – Porlock Hill (≤★★) – St. Dubricius Church★.*

Env. : *Dunkery Beacon★★★ (≤★★★), S : 5 ½ m. – Exmoor National Park★★ – Selworth (≤★★, Church★), E : 2 m. by A 39 and minor rd – Luccombe★ (Church★), E : 3 m. by A 3 Culbone★ (St Beuno), W : 3 ½ m. by B 3225, 1 ½ m. on foot – Doone Valley★, W : 6 m. A 39, access from Oare on foot.*

London 190 – Bristol 67 – Exeter 46 – Taunton 28.

Oaks, TA24 8ES, ☎ (01643) 862265, *oakshotel@aol.com, Fax (01643) 863131,* ≤ Porlc Bay, – TV P. MC VISA
April-October and Christmas – **Meals** (booking essential to non-residents) (dinner or 25.00 **st.** 9.00 – **9 rm** 65.00/110.00 **st.** – SB.

Bales Mead without rest., West Porlock, TA24 8NX, Northwest : 1 m. on B 32 ☎ (01643) 862565, *Fax (01643) 862544,* ≤, – TV P.
closed Christmas and New Year – **3 rm** 50.00/70.00 **st.**

Andrew's on the Weir with rm, Porlock Weir, TA24 8PB, Northwest : 1 ¾ m. on B 32 ☎ (01643) 863300, *info@andrewsontheweir.co.uk, Fax (01643) 863311,* ≤, – TV MC AE VISA JCB
closed 2 weeks January and November – **Meals** *(closed Sunday dinner and Mond* 14.00/18.50 and a la carte 18.50/32.50 **t.** 10.25 – **5 rm** 50.00/100.00 **t.** – SB.

PORT ERIN *Isle of Man* 402 F 21 – *see Man (Isle of).*

PORTINSCALE *Cumbria – see Keswick.*

PORT ISAAC *Cornwall* 403 F 32 *The West Country G.*

Env. : *St Endellion (church★★), S : 2½ m. by B 3267 on B 3314 – St Kew★ (church★), SE : 3 by B 3267, B 3314 and minor roads.*

Exc. : *Pencarrow★, SE : 12 m. by B 3267, B 3314 and A 389.*

London 266 – Newquay 24 – Tintagel 14 – Truro 32.

Castle Rock, 4 New Rd, PL29 3SB, ☎ (01208) 880300, *info@castlerockhotel.co. Fax (01208) 880219,* ≤ Port Isaac Bay and Tintagel Head, – rest, TV P. MC VISA
– **Meals** a la carte 14.00/22.65 **st.** 9.25 – **16 rm** 29.00/76.00 **st.** – SB.

Slipway, Harbour Front, PL29 3RH, ☎ (01208) 880264, *slipwayhotel@portisaac.co Fax (01208) 880408,* , « Part 16C inn » – MC AE VISA JCB
closed early January-mid February – **Meals** *(restricted opening in winter)* a la carte 17.0 36.00 **t.** 9.90.

PORTLOE *Cornwall* 403 F 33 – ✉ *Truro.*

London 296 – St. Austell 15 – Truro 15.

Lugger, TR2 5RD, ☎ (01872) 501322, *Fax (01872) 501691,* ≤, – rest, TV P. MC VISA.
March-November – **Meals** (bar lunch Monday to Saturday)/dinner 30.00 12.50 – **18 rm** (dinner included) 158.00/210.00 **t.** – SB.

PORTREATH *Cornwall* 403 E 33 – *pop. 1 251.*

London 309 – Falmouth 20 – Penzance 23 – Truro 14.

Tabb's, Tregea Terr, TR16 4LD, ☎ (01209) 842488, *Fax (01209) 842488* – MC VISA JCB
closed 2 weeks January, 2 weeks November and Tuesday – **Meals** (dinner only and Sunc lunch)/dinner 16.50 and a la carte 20.90/29.25 **t.** 9.95.

PORTSCATHO *Cornwall* 403 F 33 *The West Country G. – ✉ Truro.*

Env. : *St Just-in-Roseland Church★★, W : 4 m. by A 3078 – St Anthony-in-Roseland (≤★★) 3½ m.*

London 298 – Plymouth 55 – Truro 16.

Roseland House , Rosevine, TR2 5EW, North : 2 m. by A 3078 ☎ (01872) 5806 *anthony-hindley@btinternet.com, Fax (01872) 580801,* ≤ Gerrans Bay, – TV P. AE VISA.
February-October – **Meals** (booking essential) (bar lunch)/dinner 25.00 **t.** 12.00 – **10** (dinner included) 120.00/160.00 **t.** – SB.

Rosevine, Rosevine, TR2 5EW, North : 2 m. by A 3078 ℘ (01872) 580206, *info@rosevine.co.uk, Fax (01872) 580230,* ⛱, ⛐ – ⇝ rest, TV P. MC AE VISA JCB
closed January-8 February – **Meals** 25.00/47.00 and lunch a la carte 22.00/42.00 **t.** 17.00 – **17 rm** 116.00/200.00 **t.** – SB.

PORTSMOUTH and SOUTHSEA *Portsmouth* 403 404 Q 31 *Great Britain G. – pop. 174 690.*

See : *City★ – Naval Portsmouth* BY : *H.M.S. Victory★★★ AC, The Mary Rose★★, Royal Naval Museum★★ AC – Old Portsmouth★* BYZ : *The Point (≤★★) - St Thomas Cathedral★ – Southsea (Castle★ AC)* AZ *– Royal Marines Museum, Eastney★ AC,* AZ **M1.**

Env. : *Portchester Castle★ AC, NW : 5½ m. by A 3 and A 27* AY.

Great Salterns, Portsmouth Golf Centre, Burrfields Rd ℘ (023) 9266 4549 AY *– Crookhorn Lane, Widley, Waterlooville ℘ (023) 9237 2210 – Southwick Park, Pinsley Drive, Southwick ℘ (023) 9238 0131.*

to France (Cherbourg) (P & O Portsmouth) 3-4 daily (5 h) day, (7 h) night – to France (Le Havre) (P & O Portsmouth) 3 daily (5 h 30 mn/7 h 30 mn) – to France (St Malo) (Brittany Ferries) daily (8 h 45 mn) day (10 h 45 mn) night – to France (Caen) (Brittany Ferries) 2-3 daily (6 h) – to France (Cherbourg) (P & O Portsmouth) 2-3 daily (2 h 45 mn) – to Spain (Bilbao) (P & O European Ferries Ltd) 1-2 weekly (35 h) – to Spain (Santander) (Brittany Ferries) (winter only) (30 h) – to Guernsey (St Peter Port) and Jersey (St Helier) (Condor Ferries Ltd) daily except Sunday (10 h 30 mn) – to the Isle of Wight (Fishbourne) (Wightlink Ltd) frequent services daily (35 mn).

to the Isle of Wight (Ryde) (Wightlink Ltd) frequent services daily (15 mn) – from Southsea to the Isle of Wight (Ryde) (Hovertravel Ltd) frequent services daily (10 mn).

The Hard ℘ (023) 9282 6722 – Clarence Esplanade ℘ (023) 9283 2464 – 102 Commercial Rd ℘ (023) 9282 6722.

London 78 – Brighton 48 – Salisbury 44 – Southampton 21.

Plans on following pages

Hilton Portsmouth, Eastern Rd, Farlington, P06 1UN, Northeast : 5 m. on A 2030 ℘ (023) 9221 9111, *sales-portsmouth@hilton.com, Fax (023) 9221 0762,* ⛉, ⛆, ⛱, ⛳ – ⇝ rm, TV ☏ ♿ P – 230. MC AE ⓓ VISA. ⛔ AY c
Meals a la carte 14.70/24.65 **t.** 17.95 – 14.95 – **119 rm** 115.00/145.00 **st.** – SB.

Holiday Inn, Pembroke Rd, P01 2TA, ℘ (0870) 4009065, *gm1429@forte-hotels.com, Fax (023) 9275 6715,* ⛉, ⛆, ⛱ – |‡| ⇝ TV ☏ P – 250. MC AE ⓓ VISA JCB CZ o
Meals *(closed Saturday lunch and 24-27 December)* 15.00 (dinner) and a la carte 21.85/29.15 11.95 – 13.95 – **167 rm** 79.00/109.00 **st.** – SB.

Innlodge, Burrfields Rd, P03 5HH, ℘ (023) 9265 0510, *innlodge@bestwestern.co.uk, Fax (023) 9269 3458,* ⛐ – ⇝ rm, ▤ rest, TV ♿ P – 150. MC AE ⓓ VISA JCB. ⛔ AY u
Meals (grill rest.) a la carte 8.85/18.45 **st.** 8.95 – 6.95 – **74 rm** 59.95/69.95 **st.**

Beaufort, 71 Festing Rd, Southsea, PO4 0NQ, ℘ (023) 9282 3707, *enq@beauforthotel.co.uk, Fax (023) 9287 0270* – ⇝ TV P. MC AE ⓓ JCB. ⛔ AZ n
Meals (dinner only) 15.85/19.95 and a la carte 15.85/24.85 **st.** 8.95 – **20 rm** 50.00/78.00 **st.**

Seacrest, 11-12 South Par, Southsea, PO5 2JB, ℘ (023) 9273 3192, *seacrest@mcmail.com, Fax (023) 9283 2523,* ≤ – |‡| ⇝ TV P. MC AE VISA AZ e
closed Christmas and New Year – **Meals** (residents only) (dinner only) 14.95/16.95 **st.** 8.95 – **28 rm** 50.00/85.00 **st.** – SB.

Westfield Hall, 65 Festing Rd, Southsea, PO4 0NQ, ℘ (023) 9282 6971, *jdanie@westfield-hall-hotel.co.uk, Fax (023) 9287 0200* – ⇝ TV P. MC AE ⓓ VISA. ⛔ AZ a
closedChristmas and New Year – **Meals** (dinner only) 18.95/20.20 and a la carte 16.95/28.15 **t.** 9.95 – **20 rm** 54.00/90.00 **t.** – SB.

Upper Mount House, The Vale, Clarendon Rd, PO5 2EQ, ℘ (023) 9282 0456, *Fax (023) 9282 0456* – ⇝ TV P. MC VISA JCB. ⛔ CZ e
closed Christmas – **Meals** *(booking essential in summer)* (dinner only) 12.50 – **12 rm** 35.00/60.00 **t.**

Travel Inn, Long Curtain Rd, Southsea, PO4 3AA, ℘ (023) 9273 4622, *Fax (023) 9273 5048* – ⇝ rm, TV ♿ P. MC AE ⓓ VISA. ⛔ BZ r
Meals (grill rest.) – **40 rm** 41.95 **t.**

Fortitude Cottage without rest., 51 Broad St, Old Portsmouth, PO1 2JD, ℘ (023) 9282 3748, *fortcott@aol.com, Fax (023) 9282 3748* – ⇝ TV. MC VISA. ⛔ BY c
3 rm 30.00/50.00 **st.**

Glencoe without rest., 64 Whitwell Rd, Southsea, PO4 0QS, ℘ (023) 9273 7413, *Fax (023) 9273 7413* – ⇝ TV. MC VISA. ⛔ AZ u
7 rm 25.00/45.00 **st.**

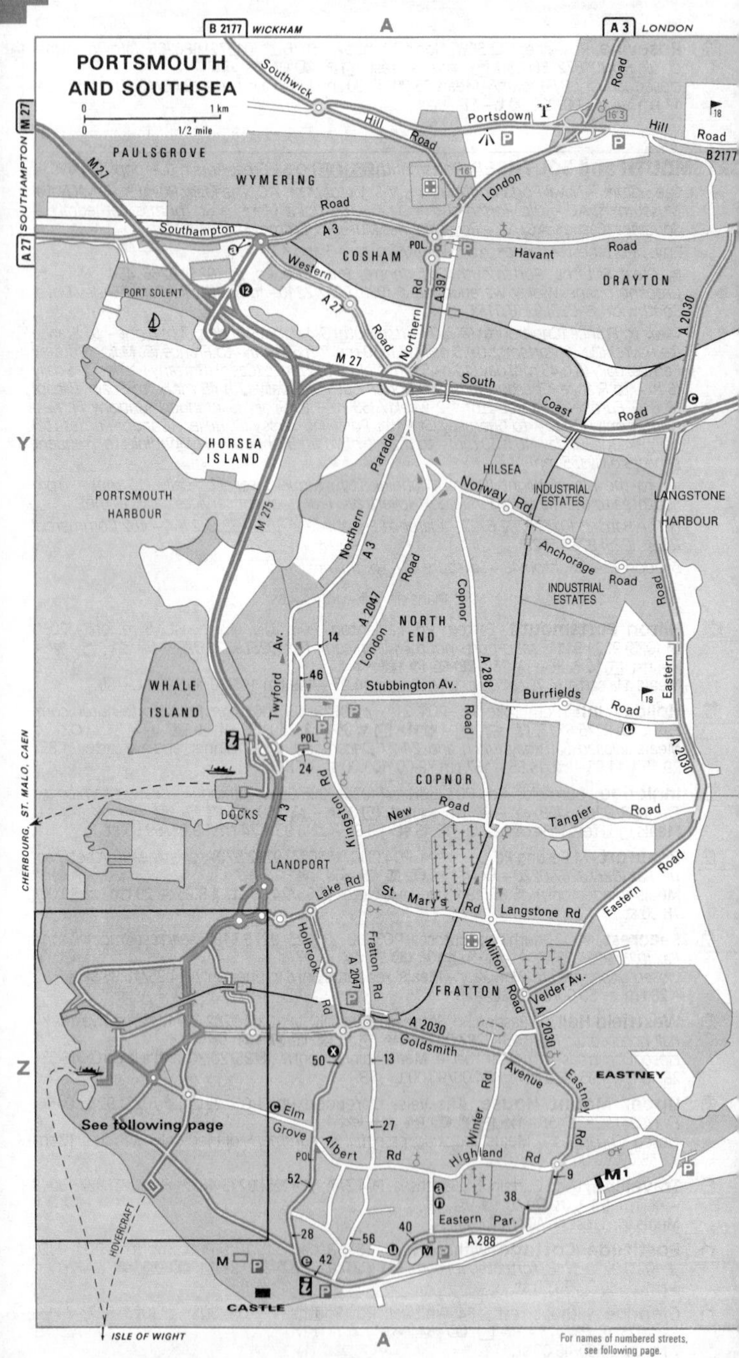
PORTSMOUTH AND SOUTHSEA
0 1 km
0 1/2 mile
B 2177 WICKHAM
A 3 LONDON
A 27 SOUTHAMPTON M 27
CHERBOURG, ST. MALO, CAEN
ISLE OF WIGHT
HOVERCRAFT
PAULSGROVE
WYMERING
COSHAM
DRAYTON
PORT SOLENT
HORSEA ISLAND
PORTSMOUTH HARBOUR
WHALE ISLAND
HILSEA
INDUSTRIAL ESTATES
LANGSTONE HARBOUR
NORTH END
COPNOR
DOCKS
LANDPORT
FRATTON
EASTNEY
CASTLE
See following page
Southwick Hill Road
Portsdown Hill Road
London Road
Southampton Road
Western Road
Northern Rd
Havant Road
South Coast Road
Northern Parade
Norway Rd.
Anchorage Road
Copnor Road
London Road
Twyford Av.
Stubbington Av.
Burrfields Road
Eastern Road
Kingston Rd
New Road
Tangier Road
Lake Rd
St. Mary's Rd
Langstone Rd
Holbrook Rd
Fratton Rd
Milton Road
Velder Av.
Goldsmith Avenue
Eastney Rd
Elm Grove
Albert Rd
Winter Rd
Highland Rd
Eastern Par.
For names of numbered streets, see following page.

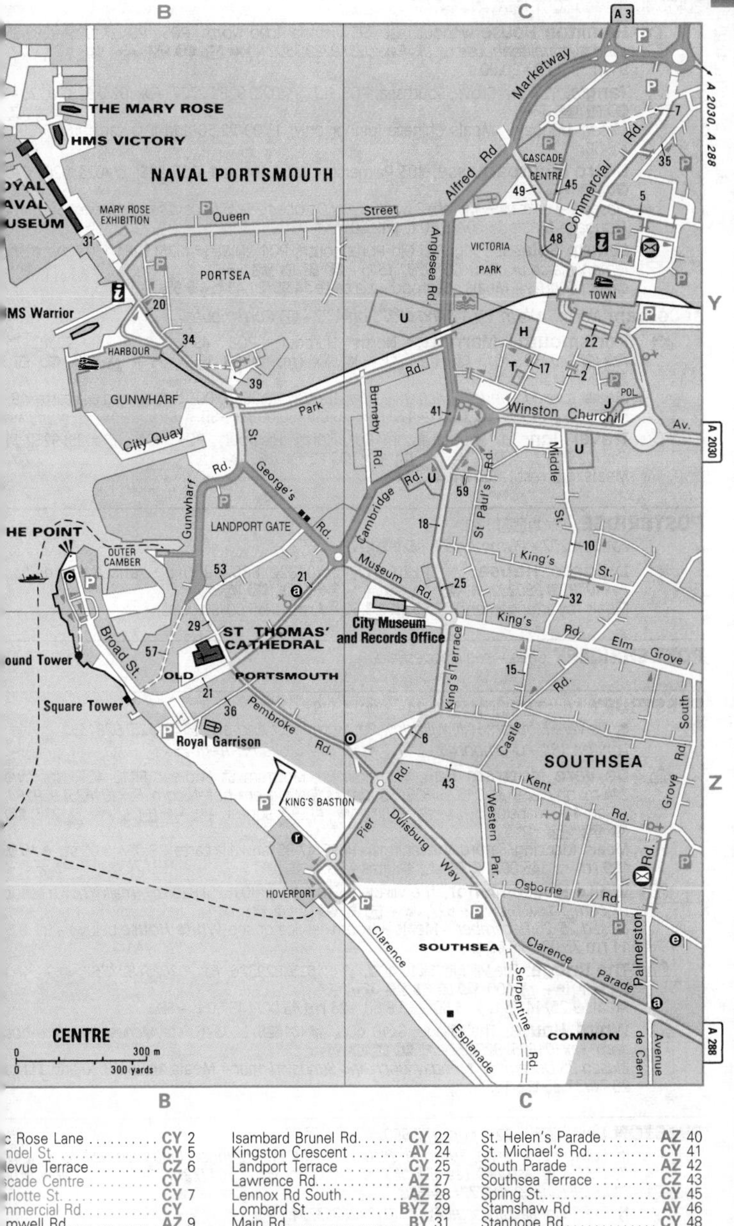

c Rose Lane .... CY 2
ndel St. .... CY 5
levue Terrace .... CZ 6
scade Centre .... CY
arlotte St. .... CY 7
mmercial Rd. .... CY
mwell Rd. .... AZ 9
on St. .... CY 10
ycett Rd .... AZ 13
dys Avenue .... AY 14
at Southsea St. .... CZ 15
dhall Walk .... CY 17
mpshire Terrace .... CY 18
d (The) .... BY 20
h St. .... BYZ 21

Isambard Brunel Rd. .... CY 22
Kingston Crescent .... AY 24
Landport Terrace .... CY 25
Lawrence Rd. .... AZ 27
Lennox Rd South .... AZ 28
Lombard St. .... BYZ 29
Main Rd. .... BY 31
Norfolk St. .... CYZ 32
Ordnance Row .... BY 34
Palmerston Rd .... CZ
Paradise St. .... CY 35
Penny St. .... BZ 36
St. George's Rd .... AZ 38
St. George's Square .... BY 39

St. Helen's Parade .... AZ 40
St. Michael's Rd. .... CY 41
South Parade .... AZ 42
Southsea Terrace .... CZ 43
Spring St. .... CY 45
Stamshaw Rd .... AY 46
Stanhope Rd. .... CY 48
Unicorn Rd .... CY 49
Victoria Rd North .... AZ 50
Victoria Rd South .... AZ 52
Warblington St. .... BY 53
Waverley Rd .... AZ 56
White Hart Rd .... BYZ 57
Wiltshire St. .... CY 59

ENGLAND

Hamilton House without rest., 95 Victoria Road North, PO5 1PS, ☎ (023) 9282 35 sandra@hamiltonhouse.co.uk, Fax (023) 9282 3502 – TV. MC VISA JCB. AZ
9 rm 40.00/50.00 s.

Tang's, 127 Elm Grove, Southsea, PO5 1LJ, ☎ (023) 9282 2722, Fax (023) 9283 8323 – MC AE VISA JCB AZ
closed Monday – **Meals** Chinese (dinner only) 15.00/22.50 and a la carte 16.50/38.0 8.50.

Bistro Montparnasse, 103 Palmerston Rd, Southsea, PO5 3PS, ☎ (023) 9281 675 MC VISA JCB CZ
closed 2 weeks early March, 2 weeks early October, 25-26 December, 1 January, Sunday Monday – **Meals** 15.00/23.50 **t.** 12.00.

Lemon Sole, 123 High St, Old Portsmouth, PO1 2HW, ☎ (023) 9281 1303, bestfish lemonsole.co.uk, Fax (023) 9281 1345 – MC AE VISA JCB BY
closed Sunday – **Meals** - Seafood - a la carte 14.95/21.45 **t.** 9.95.

at Cosham North : 4½ m. by A 3 and M 275 on A 27 – ✉ Portsmouth.

Portsmouth Marriott, North Harbour, PO6 4SH, ☎ (023) 9238 31 Fax (023) 9238 8701, TV – 300. MC AE VISA AY
Meals (closed Sunday lunch July and August) 20.95/30.00 (dinner) and a la carte 18. 37.25 **st.** 13.75 – 13.00 – **170 rm** 120.00/150.00 **st.** – SB.

Travel Inn, 1 Southampton Rd, North Harbour, PO6 4SA, ☎ (023) 9232 11 Fax (023) 9232 4895 – rm, TV P. MC AE VISA. AY
Meals (grill rest.) – **64 rm** 41.95 **t.**

POSTBRIDGE Devon 403 I 32.
London 207 – Plymouth 21 – Exeter 21.

Lydgate House, PL20 6TJ, ☎ (01822) 880209, lydgatehouse@email.cc Fax (01822) 880202, TV P. MC VISA
Meals (by arrangement) 17.50 **st.** 8.50 – **7 rm** 35.00/90.00 **st.**

POTT SHRIGLEY Ches. – see Macclesfield.

PRESTBURY Ches. 402 403 404 N 24 – pop. 3 346.
18 De Vere Mottram Hall, Wilmslow Rd, Mottram St Andrews ☎ (01625) 828135.
London 184 – Liverpool 43 – Manchester 17 – Stoke-on-Trent 25.

De Vere Mottram Hall, Wilmslow Rd, Mottram St Andrew, SK10 4QT, Northwe 2 ¼ m. on A 538 ☎ (01625) 828135, dmh.sales@devere-hotels.com, Fax (01625) 829284 « Part 18C mansion », 18, squash – TV P – 275. MC VISA JCB.
Meals (dancing Saturday evenings) 14.95/17.95 and a la carte 28.00/46.00 **st.** 16.0 **129 rm** 145.00/170.00 **st.**, 3 suites – SB.

White House Manor, The Village, SK10 4HP, ☎ (01625) 829376, mail@thewhiteho uk.com, Fax (01625) 828627, – TV P. MC AE VISA.
closed 25-26 December – **Meals** – (room service or see ***White House*** below) – 9.5 **11 rm** 75.00/125.00 **t.**

The Bridge, The Village, SK10 4DQ, ☎ (01625) 829326, Fax (01625) 827557, – TV P – 100. MC AE VISA JCB.
Meals 9.25/14.75 **t.** 13.50 – 8.50 – **23 rm** 45.00/145.00 **t.** – SB.

White House, The Village, SK10 4DG, ☎ (01625) 829376, stay@cheshire-white-hou com, Fax (01625) 828627 – P. MC AE VISA
closed 25 December, Monday lunch and Sunday dinner – **Meals** 14.25/18.50 and a la ca 25.70/37.35 **t.** 13.95.

PRESTON Lancs. 402 L 22 – pop. 177 660.
18 Fulwood Hall Lane, Fulwood ☎ (01772) 700011 – 18 Ingol, Tanterton Hall Rd ☎ (01 734556 – 18 Aston & Lea, Tudor Ave, Blackpool Rd ☎ (01772) 726480 – 18 Penworth Blundell Lane ☎ (01772) 744630.
The Guildhall, Lancaster Rd ☎ (01772) 253731.
London 226 – Blackpool 18 – Burnley 22 – Liverpool 30 – Manchester 34 – Stoke-Trent 65.

Posthouse Preston, The Ringway, PR1 3AU, ☎ (0870) 400 9066, gm1430@forte-ho .com, Fax (01772) 201923 – TV P – 120. MC AE VISA
Meals 15.00 (dinner) and a la carte 17.35/29.15 **t.** 11.45 – 11.95 – **129 rm** 69. 119.00 **st.** – SB.

Tulketh, 209 Tulketh Rd, PR2 1ES, Northwest : 2 ¼ m. by A 6 off A 5085 (01772) 726250, *Fax (01772) 723743* – TV P. VISA JCB.
closed Christmas and New Year – **Meals** *(closed Friday to Sunday)* (dinner only) a la carte 7.75/15.50 **st.** 8.50 – **13 rm** 37.50/60.00 **st.**

Claremont, 516 Blackpool Rd, Ashton, PR2 1HY, Northwest : 2 m. by A 6 on A 5085 (01772) 729738, *claremonthotel@btinternet.com, Fax (01772) 726274,* – rest, TV P. VISA
Meals (lunch by arrangement)/dinner 11.95 and a la carte 11.95/16.25 **st.** 7.50 – **15 rm** 38.50/55.00 **st.**

Travel Inn, Bluebell Way, Preston East Link Rd, PR2 5RU, Northeast : 3 ¼ by B 6243 (Longridge rd) off B 6242 (Preston East) (01772) 651580, *Fax (01772) 651619* – rest, TV P – 30. VISA.
Meals (grill rest.) – **65 rm** 41.95 **t.**

Simply Heathcotes, 23 Winckley Sq, PR1 3JJ, (01772) 252732, *preston@simplyheathcotes.co.uk, Fax (01772) 203433* – VISA JCB
closed 25-26 December, 1 January, Saturday lunch and Bank Holidays – **Meals** 13.50 (lunch) and a la carte 23.00/25.00 **t.** 11.50 – ***Downstairs on the Square :*** **Meals** *(closed Sunday and dinner Monday-Wednesday)* a la carte 11.00/14.00 **t.**.

Broughton *North : 3 m. on A 6 – Preston.*

Preston Marriott, 418 Garstang Rd, PR3 5JB, (01772) 864087, *Fax (01772) 861728,* – TV P – 200. VISA JCB.
Meals (dinner only) a la carte 18.25/32.65 **t.** 12.75 – 13.00 – **149 rm** 120.00 **st.**, 1 suite.

Ibis without rest., Garstang Rd, PR3 5JE, South : ¾ m. off A 6 (01772) 861800, *Fax (01772) 861900* – TV P – 40. VISA
82 rm 52.00 **st.**

Samlesbury *East : 2 ½ m. by A 59 – Preston.*

Swallow, Preston New Rd, PR5 0UL, East : 1 m. at junction of A 59 with A 677 (01772) 877351, *preston@swallowhotels.com, Fax (01772) 877424,* – rest, TV P – 250. VISA.
Meals (bar lunch Saturday) 12.95/19.50 and dinner a la carte 22.75/31.80 **st.** 12.75 – **78 rm** 85.00/110.00 **st.** – SB.

Bamber Bridge *South : 5 m. by A 6 on B 6258 – Preston.*

Novotel, Reedfield Pl, Walton Summit, PR5 8AA, Southeast : ¾ m. by A 6 at junction 29 of M 6 (01772) 313331, *h0838@accor-hotels.com, Fax (01772) 627868,* heated, – rm, rest, TV P – 180. VISA
Meals 13.50 and a la carte 14.65/23.40 **st.** 9.95 – 8.50 – **98 rm** 55.00 **st.** – SB.

Premier Lodge, Lobstock Lane, PR5 6BA, South : ½ m. on A 6 (0870) 7001512, *Fax (0870) 7001513* – rm, TV P. VISA.
Meals (grillrest.) a la carte approx. 12.50 **t.** 7.80 – **40 rm** 42.95 **t.**

Lea *West : 3 ½ m. on A 583 – Preston.*

Travel Inn, Blackpool Rd, PR4 0XL, on A 583 (01772) 720476, *Fax (01772) 729971* – rm, rest, TV P. VISA.
Meals (grill rest.) – **38 rm** 41.95 **t.**

RESTWICH *Gtr. Manchester* 402 403 404 N 23 – *pop. 31 801* – *Manchester.*
London 205 – Leeds 40 – Liverpool 30 – Manchester 5.

Plan : see Manchester

Village H & Leisure Club, George St, M25 9WS, South : 1 ¾ m. by A 56 (0161) 798 8905, *Fax (0161) 773 5562,* squash – rest, TV P – 150. VISA. AV c
Meals *(closed Saturday lunch)* 6.90/25.00 and a la carte 15.90/25.85 **st.** 9.45 – **39 rm** 74.00/84.00 **st.**, 2 suites.

Travel Inn, Bury New Rd, M25 3AJ, Northwest : ½ m. on A 56 (0161) 798 0827, *Fax (0161) 773 8099* – rm, rest, TV P. VISA.
Meals (grill rest.) – **60 rm** 41.95 **t.**

JCKRUP *Glos. – see Tewkesbury.*

JDDINGTON *Ches.* 402 403 K 24 – *see Chester.*

JDSEY *W. Yorks.* 402 P 22 – *see Leeds.*

PULBOROUGH *W. Sussex* 404 S 31 – *pop. 3 497.*
18, 9 West Chiltington, Broadford Bridge Rd (01798) 813574.
London 49 – Brighton 25 – Guildford 25 – Portsmouth 35.

Chequers, Old Rectory Lane, RH20 1AD, Northeast : ¼ m. on A 29 (01798) 8724
chequers@btinternet.com, Fax (01798) 872715, – TV P. MC AE VISA JCB
Meals (light lunch)/dinner 25.00 **t.** 11.50 – **11 rm** 49.50/95.00 **t.** – SB.

La PULENTE *Jersey (Channel Islands)* 403 P 33 and 230 ⑪ – *see Channel Islands.*

PULHAM MARKET *Norfolk* 404 X 26 – *pop. 919* – ✉ *Diss.*
London 106 – Cambridge 58 – Ipswich 29 – Norwich 16.

Old Bakery, Church Walk, IP21 4SL, (01379) 676492, *Fax (01379) 676492,* « Part 1 timbered house », – TV.
closed Christmas and New Year – **Meals** (by arrangement) 16.00 **st.** – **3 rm** 50. 54.00 **st.** – SB.

PURTON *Wilts.* 403 404 O 29 – *pop. 3 879* – ✉ *Swindon.*
London 94 – Bristol 41 – Gloucester 31 – Oxford 38 – Swindon 5.

Pear Tree at Purton, Church End, SN5 4ED, South : ½ m. by Church St. on Lydi Millicent rd (01793) 772100, *res@peartreepurton.co.uk, Fax (01793) 772369,* « Conservatory restaurant », – TV P – 60. MC AE VISA JCB
closed 26 to 30 December – **Meals** *(closed Saturday lunch)* 15.50/31.50 **st.** 11.50 – **16** 110.00/130.00 **st.**, 2 suites.

Le Grand Londres (GREATER LONDON) est composé de la City et de 32 arrondissements administratifs (Borough) eux-mêmes divisés en quartiers ou en villages ayant conservé leur caractère propre (Area).

QUORNDON *Leics.* 402 403 404 Q 25 – *see Loughborough.*

RAMSBOTTOM *Gtr. Manchester* 402 N 23 – *pop. 17 318.*
London 223 – Blackpool 39 – Burnley 12 – Leeds 46 – Manchester 13 – Liverpool 39.

Ramsons, 18 Market Pl, BL0 9HT, (01706) 825070, *rammy.vics@which.r Fax (01706) 822005* – . MC AE VISA JCB
closed dinner Sunday and Monday – **Meals** 12.95 (lunch) and a la carte 21.00/28.0 9.75.

RAMSEY *Isle of Man* 402 G 21 – *see Man (Isle of).*

RAMSGATE *Kent* 404 Y 30 – *pop. 37 895.*
19-21 Harbour St (01843) 583333.
London 77 – Dover 19 – Maidstone 45 – Margate 4.5.

Ramada Jarvis, Harbour Par, CT11 8LJ, (01843) 588276, *sales-ramsgate@ramadaja .co.uk, Fax (01843) 586866,* , , – rest, TV – 120. MC AE VISA.
Meals (bar lunch Monday to Saturday)/dinner 15.95 and a la carte 13.65/21.65 **t.** 11.7 10.95 – **58 rm** 90.00/100.00 **st.** – SB.

RAMSGILL-IN-NIDDERDALE *N.Yorks.* 402 O 21 – *see Pateley Bridge.*

RASKELF *N. Yorks.* 402 Q 21 – *see Easingwold.*

RAVENSTONEDALE *Cumbria* 402 M 20 – *pop. 886* – ✉ *Kirkby Stephen.*
London 280 – Carlisle 43 – Kendal 19 – Kirkby Stephen 5.

Black Swan, CA17 4NG, (015396) 23204, *reservations@blackswanhotel.co Fax (015396) 23604,* , – rest, TV P. MC AE VISA JCB
Meals 12.00/25.00 and a la carte 11.50/16.00 **t.** 6.00 – **16 rm** 50.00/80.00 **t.** – SB.

ADING *Reading* 403 404 Q 29 – *pop. 213 474.*

Calcot Park, Bath Rd, Calcot (0118) 942 7124.

Whitchurch Bridge (toll).

to Henley-on-Thames (Salter Bros. Ltd) (summer only).

Town Hall, Blagrave St (0118) 956 6226.

London 43 – Brighton 79 – Bristol 78 – Croydon 47 – Luton 62 – Oxford 28 – Portsmouth 67 – Southampton 46.

Plan on next page

Holiday Inn Reading, Caversham Bridge, Richfield Ave, RG1 8BD, (0118) 925 9988, *cbrhi@queensmoat.co.uk, Fax (0118) 939 1665,* « Thames-side setting », – rm, rest, – 200. VISA JCB. X e
Meals 18.25 and dinner a la carte 13.25 – 12.50 – **110 rm** 155.00 **st.**, 2 suites.

Renaissance Reading, Oxford Rd, RG1 7RH, (0118) 958 6222, *Fax (0118) 959 7842,* – rm, – 200. VISA JCB. Z i
Meals 14.50/22.50 and a la carte 19.20/25.15 **t.** 12.95 – 12.50 – **195 rm** 130.00 **t.**, 1 suite – SB.

Millennium Madejski, Madejski Stadium, RG2 0FL, South : 1 ½ m. by A 33 (0118) 925 3500, *sales.reading@mill-cop.com, Fax (0118) 925 3501,* « Adjacent to Madejski sports stadium », – rm, VISA JCB X v
Cilantro : **Meals** *(closed Sunday)* (dinner only) 35.00/40.00 **t.** 12.50 – ***Le Café :*** **Meals** *(closed Saturday lunch)* 18.95 (dinner) and a la carte 20.20/28.45 **t.** 8.75 – 13.95 – **132 rm** 205.00 **st.**, 8 suites – SB.

Holiday Inn, 500 Basingstoke Rd, RG2 0SL, South : 2 ½ m. by A 33 (0870) 4009067, *Fax (0118) 931 1958,* – rm, rest, – 110. VISA JCB. X a
Meals *(closed lunch Saturday and Bank Holidays)* a la carte approx. 35.00 15.95 – 15.95 – **204 rm** 160.00 **st.** – SB.

Rainbow Corner, 132-138 Caversham Rd, RG1 8AY, (0118) 958 8140, *info@rainbowhotel.co.uk, Fax (0118) 958 6500* – rest, rest, VISA JCB. X u
Meals *(closed Friday-Sunday)* (dinner only) a la carte 12.70/22.45 **t.** 7.50 – 6.50 – **24 rm** 80.00/100.00 **t.**

Travelodge, Oxthorn House, 60 Oxford Rd, RG1 7LT, (01189) 503179, *Fax (01189) 503257* – , rest, VISA JCB. Z v
Meals - Seafood - (grill rest.) – **80 rm** 69.95 **t.**

Old Siam, King's Walk, King St, RG1 2HG, (0118) 951 2600, *manager@oldsiam.co.uk, Fax (0118) 959 6300* – . VISA JCB Z a
closed 2 weeks Christmas, Sunday and Bank Holidays – **Meals** - Thai - 12.50/22.50 and a la carte 14.45/29.20 **st.** 10.50.

London Street Brasserie, 2-4 London St, RG1 4SE, (01189) 505036, *Fax (01189) 505031,* – VISA Z c
closed 25-26 December and 1 January – **Meals** (booking essential) 18.00 (lunch) and a la carte 21.70/33.40 **t.** 12.50.

Hurst *East : 5 m. by A 329 – X – on B 3030 – Reading.*

Castle, Church Hill, RG10 0SJ, (0118) 934 0034, *info@castlerestaurant.co.uk, Fax (0118) 934 0334,* « Part 16C », – – 30. VISA JCB
closed 26 December, Sunday dinner and Monday – **Meals** (booking essential) 25.95/37.50 **t.** 12.50.

Sindlesham *Southeast : 5 m. by A 329 on B 3030 – X – Wokingham.*

Reading Moat House, Mill Lane, RG41 5DF, Northwest : ½ m. by Mole Rd (0118) 949 9988, *cbrmt@queensmoat.co.uk, Fax (0118) 966 6530,* – – 80. VISA.
Meals (bar lunch Saturday) (carving lunch Sunday) a la carte 17.95/28.00 **st.** 11.95 – 11.50 – **100 rm** 156.00/171.00 **st.** – SB.

Shinfield *South : 4¼ m. on A 327 – X – Reading.*

L'Ortolan, Church Lane, RG2 9BY, (01189) 883783, *info@lortolan.com, Fax (01189) 889338,* « Former vicarage, contemporary interior », – . VISA
closed 23 December-9 January, Sunday and Monday – **Meals** 19.00/45.00 **t.** 28.00.

Grazeley Green *Southwest : 5½ m. by A 33 – X – Reading.*

Premier Lodge, Grazeley Rd, RG7 1LS, (0870) 7001500, *Fax (0870) 7001501,* – rm, VISA.
Meals (grill rest.) a la carte approx. 12.50 **t.** 7.80 – **32 rm** 49.95 **t.**

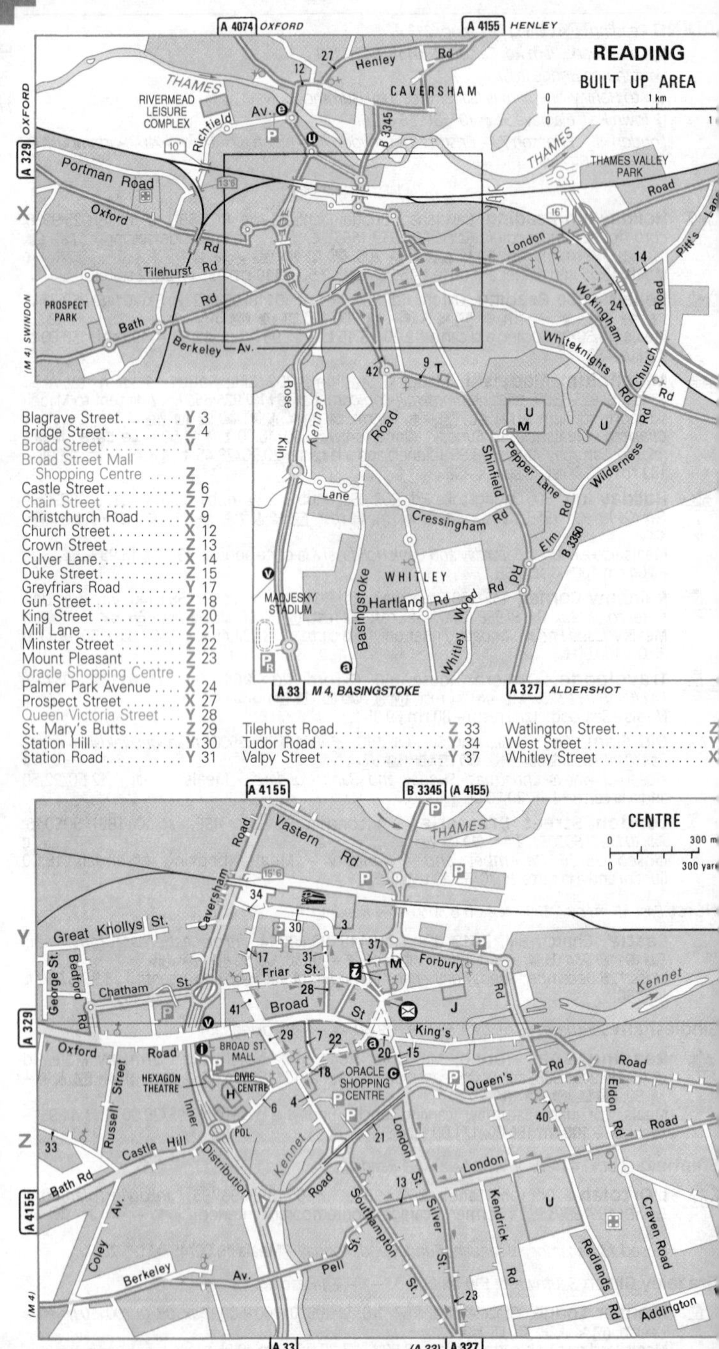

READING
BUILT UP AREA
0 1 km
A 4074 OXFORD
A 4155 HENLEY
A 329 OXFORD
(M 4) SWINDON
A 33 M 4, BASINGSTOKE
A 327 ALDERSHOT
THAMES
RIVERMEAD LEISURE COMPLEX
CAVERSHAM
Henley Rd
Richfield Av.
B 3345
THAMES VALLEY PARK
Portman Road
Oxford Rd
Tilehurst Rd
Bath Rd
Berkeley Av.
PROSPECT PARK
London Road
Wokingham Road
Pitt's Lane
Whiteknights Rd
Church Rd
Wilderness Rd
Pepper Lane
Shinfield Rd
Elm Rd
B 3350
Rose Kiln Lane
Kennet
Cressingham Rd
WHITLEY
Basingstoke Road
Hartland Rd
Whitley Wood Rd
MADJESKY STADIUM
Blagrave Street Y 3
Bridge Street Z 4
Broad Street Y
Broad Street Mall Shopping Centre Z
Castle Street Z 6
Chain Street Z 7
Christchurch Road X 9
Church Street X 12
Crown Street Z 13
Culver Lane X 14
Duke Street Z 15
Greyfriars Road Y 17
Gun Street Z 18
King Street Z 20
Mill Lane Z 21
Minster Street Z 22
Mount Pleasant Z 23
Oracle Shopping Centre Z
Palmer Park Avenue X 24
Prospect Street X 27
Queen Victoria Street Y 28
St. Mary's Butts Z 29
Station Hill Y 30
Station Road Y 31
Tilehurst Road Z 33
Tudor Road Y 34
Valpy Street Y 37
Watlington Street Z
West Street Y
Whitley Street X
CENTRE
0 300 m
0 300 yards
A 4155
B 3345 (A 4155)
A 329
A 4155
A 33
(A 33) A 327
(M 4)
Vastern Rd
Caversham Road
Great Knollys St.
George St.
Bedford Rd
Chatham St.
Friar St.
Broad St
Forbury Rd
King's Road
Queen's Rd
Eldon Rd
Oxford Road
BROAD ST. MALL
HEXAGON THEATRE
CIVIC CENTRE
ORACLE SHOPPING CENTRE
POL.
Russell Street
Inner Distribution Road
Castle Hill
Bath Rd
Coley Av.
Berkeley Av.
Pell St.
Southampton St.
London St.
Silver St.
London Road
Kendrick Rd
Redlands Rd
Craven Road
Addington

EADING SERVICE AREA *Newbury* 403 404 Q 29 – ✉ *Reading.*

Travelodge, RG30 3UQ, M 4 westbound between junctions 11 and 12 ✆ (01189) 566966, *Fax (01189) 582350* – ⇔ rm, TV & P. MC AE VISA JCB. ✗
Meals (grill rest.) – **102 rm** 69.95 **t.**

EDDITCH *Worcs.* 403 404 O 27 – *pop. 73 372.*

Abbey Park G. & C.C., Dagnell End Rd ✆ (01527) 63918 – Lower Grinsty, Green Lane, Callow Hill ✆ (01527) 543309 – Pitcheroak, Plymouth Rd ✆ (01527) 541054.
Civic Square, Alcester St ✆ (01527) 60806.
London 111 – Birmingham 15 – Cheltenham 33 – Stratford-upon-Avon 15.

Quality ⛰, Pool Bank, Southcrest, B97 4JS, ✆ (01527) 541511, *admin@gb646.u-net.com, Fax (01527) 402600,* – ⇔ rm, TV P – 100. MC AE VISA
Meals 9.95/16.50 **s.** 11.95 – 10.75 – **73 rm** 99.00 **t.** – SB.

Premier Lodge, Birchfield Rd, B97 6PX, West : 4 ¾ m. by A 441 and A 448 off Tardebigge rd ✆ (0870) 7001320, *Fax (0870) 7001321,* – ⇔ rm, TV & P – 150. MC AE VISA JCB. ✗
Meals (grill rest.) a la carte approx. 12.50 **t.** 7.80 – **33 rm** 46.95 **t.**

Old Rectory ⛰, Ipsley Lane, Ipsley, B98 0AP, ✆ (01527) 523000, *theoldrectory@aol.com, Fax (01527) 517003,* – ⇔ P. MC AE VISA JCB. ✗
Meals (booking essential to non-residents) (dinner only) 25.00 **t.** 9.95 – **10 rm** 80.00/ 120.00 **t.**

EDHILL *Surrey* 404 T 30 – *pop. 47 602 (inc. Reigate).*

Redhill & Reigate, Clarence Lodge, Pendleton Rd ✆ (01737) 244626 – Canada Ave ✆ (01737) 770204.
London 22 – Brighton 31 – Guildford 20 – Maidstone 34.

Nutfield Priory, Nutfield, RH1 4EN, East : 2 m. on A 25 ✆ (01737) 824400, *nutpriory@aol .com.uk, Fax (01737) 823321,* ≤, squash – ⇔ rest, TV P – 80. MC AE VISA JCB
Cloisters : Meals *(closed Saturday lunch)* 15.00/34.00 and a la carte 30.00/38.00 **st.** 16.00 – 12.50 – **59 rm** 130.00/160.00 **st.**, 1 suite – SB.

Salfords *South : 2½ m. on A 23 –* ✉ *Redhill.*

Travel Inn, Brighton Rd, RH1 5BT, ✆ (01737) 767277, *Fax (01737) 778099* – ⇔ rm, rest, TV & P. MC AE VISA. ✗
Meals (grill rest.) – **48 rm** 41.95 **t.**

EDMILE *Leics. – pop. 697.*

London 140 – Leicester 20 – Lincoln 37 – Nottingham 17 – Sheffield 52.

The Peacock Inn with rm, Church Corner, NG13 0GA, ✆ (01949) 842554, *peacock @redmile.fsbusiness.co.uk, Fax (01949) 843746,* « Part 17C » – ⇔ TV P. MC AE VISA JCB. ✗
Meals a la carte 19.15/30.20 **t.** 9.95 – **10 rm** 55.00/80.00 **t.**

EDWORTH *Durham – see Darlington.*

EEPHAM *Norfolk* 404 X 25 – *pop. 2 405 –* ✉ *Norwich.*

London 125 – Cromer 26 – King's Lynn 34 – Norwich 14.

Westwood Barn ⛰ without rest., Crabgate Lane South, Wood Dalling, NR11 6SW, North : 3 m. by Station Rd and Wood Dalling Rd ✆ (01263) 584108, ≤, « Converted barn », – ⇔ TV P. ✗
3 rm 35.00/52.00 **t.**

EETH *N. Yorks.* 402 O 20 – *pop. 939 –* ✉ *Richmond.*

The Literary Institute, The Green ✆ (01748) 884059.
London 253 – Leeds 53 – Middlesbrough 36.

Burgoyne, On The Green, DL11 6SN, ✆ (01748) 884292, *Fax (01748) 884292,* ≤, – ⇔ TV & P. MC VISA
closed 2 January-14 February – **Meals** (dinner only) 24.50 **t.** 12.50 – **8 rm** 80.00/ 150.00 **t.** – SB.

Arkleside, DL11 6SG, Northeast corner of the green ✆ (01748) 884200, *info@arkleside hotel.co.uk, Fax (01748) 884200,* ≤, – ⇔ TV P. MC VISA
– **Meals** (dinner only) 21.50 **t.** 11.00 – **10 rm** 47.50/75.00 **t.**, 1 suite.

REIGATE *Surrey* 404 T 30 – *pop. 47 602 (inc. Redhill).*
London 26 – Brighton 33 – Guildford 20 – Maidstone 38.

Bridge House, Reigate Hill, RH2 9RP, North : 1 ¼ m. on A 217 ☏ (01737) 24680[illegible] *Fax (01737) 223756,* ← – TV P – 🎤 100. MC AE ① VISA. ✗
Meals *(closed Saturday lunch and Bank Holidays)* (booking essential January and Decembe[illegible] (dancing Friday and Saturday evening) 24.50/31.50 **t.** 🍷 13.00 – ☕ 12.00 – **39 rm** 60.00[illegible] 135.00 **t.**

Cranleigh, 41 West St, RH2 9BL, ☏ (01737) 223417, *cranleighhotel@tinyworld.co.u[illegible]* *Fax (01737) 223734,* heated, ✗ – TV P. MC AE ① VISA JCB. ✗
closed 10 days Christmas – **Meals** *(closed Friday to Sunday)* (dinner only) a la carte 15.5[illegible] 27.50 **st.** 🍷 10.00 – **9 rm** ☕ 80.00/90.00 **st.**

The Dining Room, 59a High St, RH2 9AE, ☏ (01737) 226650 – ✗ ▤. MC AE ① VISA
closed Easter, 2 weeks August, 1 week Christmas, Saturday lunch, Sunday dinner and Ba[illegible] Holidays – **Meals** a la carte 22.90/29.95 **t.** 🍷 11.95.

La Barbe, 71 Bell St, RH2 7AN, ☏ (01737) 241966, *restaurant@labarbe.co.u[illegible]* *Fax (01737) 226387* – MC AE VISA JCB
closed 25 December, 1 January, Saturday lunch, Sunday and Bank Holidays – **Meals** - Frenc[illegible] - 19.95/27.95 **st.** 🍷 12.95.

RETFORD *Notts.* 402 403 404 R 24 – *pop. 20 679.*
40 Grove St (01777) 860780.
London 148 – Lincoln 23 – Nottingham 31 – Sheffield 27.

The Barns without rest., Morton Farm, Babworth, DN22 8HA, Southwest : 2 ¼ m. [illegible] A 6420 ☏ (01777) 706336, *harry@thebarns.co.uk, Fax (01777) 709773,* ✗ – ✗ TV P. [illegible] VISA. ✗
closed Christmas – **6 rm** ☕ 34.00/52.00 **st.**

Le Guide change, changez de ***guide Michelin*** *tous les ans.*

RHYDYCROESAU *Shrops.* 402 403 K 25 – *see Oswestry.*

RIBCHESTER *Lancs.* 402 M 22 – *pop. 1 654.*
London 234 – Blackburn 13 – Blackpool 26 – Burnley 19 – Lancaster 27.

Stonebridge Bistro, 19 Blackburn Rd, PR3 3ZP, ☏ (01254) 878664, *Fax (01254) 8781[illegible]* – P. MC AE VISA JCB
closed Saturday lunch and Monday – **Meals** 12.50/19.50 and a la carte 13.45/28.80 [illegible] 🍷 11.60.

RICHMOND *N. Yorks.* 402 O 20 *Great Britain G.* – *pop. 7 862.*
See : *Town★ – Castle★ AC – Georgian Theatre Royal and Museum★.*
Exc. : *Josephine and John Bowes Museum★, Barnard Castle, NW : 15 m. by B 6274, A and minor rd (right) – Raby Castle★, NE : 6 m. of Barnard Castle by A 688.*
Bend Hagg ☏ (01748) 825319 – Catterick, Leyburn Rd ☏ (01748) 833268.
Friary Gardens, Victoria Rd ☏ (01748) 850252.
London 243 – Leeds 53 – Middlesbrough 26 – Newcastle upon Tyne 44.

King's Head, Market Pl, DL10 4HS, ☏ (01748) 850220, *res@kingsheadrichmond.co.[illegible]* *Fax (01748) 850635* – ✗ TV P – 🎤 150. MC AE ① VISA JCB
Meals (bar lunch Monday to Saturday)/dinner 16.95 and a la carte 18.15/24.90 **t.** 🍷 10.5[illegible] **30 rm** ☕ 65.00/115.00 **t.** – SB.

West End without rest., 45 Reeth Rd, DL10 4EX, West : ½ m. on A 6108 ☏ (01748) 8247[illegible] *westend@richmond.org,* ✗ – ✗ TV P
closed 2 weeks Christmas and New Year – **5 rm** ☕ 23.50/47.00.

The Old Brewery without rest., 29 The Green, DL10 4RG, via Victoria Rd off Cravenga[illegible] ☏ (01748) 822460, *Fax (01748) 825561,* ✗ – ✗ TV. MC VISA. ✗
closed December and January – **4 rm** ☕ 30.00/47.00.

at Whashton *Northwest : 4½ m. by Ravensworth rd* – ✉ *Richmond.*

Whashton Springs Farm without rest., DL11 7JS, South : 1 ½ m. on Richmond ☏ (01748) 822884, *whashton@turnbullg-f.freeserve.co.uk, Fax (01748) 826285,* « Worki[illegible] farm », ✗, ✗ – ✗ TV P. ✗
closed mid December-1 february – **8 rm** ☕ 30.00/50.00 **s.**

The Hack and Spade, DL11 7JL, ☏ (01748) 823721 – ✗ P. MC VISA JCB
closed 25 December, 1 week January and Sunday dinner – **Meals** a la carte approx. 17.40

t Dalton *Northwest : 6 ¾ m. by Ravensworth rd and Gayles rd – ✉ Richmond.*

The Travellers Rest, DL11 7HU, ☎ (01833) 621225, *travs@fsmail.net* – P. MC VISA
closed 25-26 December, 1 January and Sunday – **Meals** (dinner only) a la carte 16.40/22.70 **t.** 9.90.

IDGEWAY *Derbs. – see Sheffield (S. Yorks.).*

INGWOOD *Hants.* 403 404 O 31 – *pop. 11 959.*

The Furlong ☎ (01425) 470896.

London 102 – Bournemouth 11 – Salisbury 17 – Southampton 20.

Moortown Lodge, 244 Christchurch Rd, BH24 3AS, South : 1 m. on B 3347 ☎ (01425) 471404, *hotel@moortownlodge.co.uk, Fax (01425) 476052* – TV P. MC AE VISA.
closed Christmas-mid January – **Meals** *(closed Sunday)* (dinner only) 19.95/22.95 **t.** 9.95 – **6 rm** 55.00/90.00 **t.** – SB.

IPLEY *N. Yorks.* 402 P 21 – *pop. 193* – ✉ *Harrogate.*

London 213 – Bradford 21 – Leeds 18 – Newcastle upon Tyne 79.

The Boar's Head, HG3 3AY, ☎ (01423) 771888, *reservations@boarsheadripley.co.uk, Fax (01423) 771509,* « 18C coaching inn within estate village of Ripley Castle », – rm, TV P. MC AE VISA JCB
The Restaurant : Meals 14.00/18.50 and a la carte 18.50/25.00 **st.** 12.25 – ***The Bistro :*** Meals 12.95 and a la carte 15.40/18.50 **st.** 9.95 – **25 rm** 99.00/140.00 **st.** – SB.

t Burnt Yates *West : 2 ¾ m. on B 6165* – ✉ *Harrogate.*

High Winsley Cottage, HG3 3EP, Northwest : 1 m. by Brimham Rocks rd ☎ (01423) 770662, ←, – P.
closed December and January – **Meals** (by arrangement) (communal dining) 14.00 6.90 – **4 rm** 38.00/56.00.

IPLEY *Surrey* 404 S 30 – *pop. 1 697.*

London 28 – Guildford 6.

Michels', 13 High St, GU23 6AQ, ☎ (01483) 224777, *Fax (01483) 222940,* – MC AE VISA
closed 2 weeks January, Sunday dinner and Monday – **Meals** (dinner only and Sunday lunch) 21.00 (lunch) and a la carte 34.00/43.00 **t.** 8.50.

IPON *N. Yorks.* 402 P 21 *Great Britain G.* – *pop. 13 806.*

See : *Town★ - Cathedral★ (Saxon Crypt★★) AC.*

Env. : *Fountains Abbey★★★ AC :- Studley Royal★★ AC (←★ from Anne Boleyn's Seat) - Fountains Hall (Façade★), SW : 2½ m. by B 6265 – Newby Hall (Tapestries★) AC, SE : 3½ m. by B 6265.*

Ripon City, Palace Rd ☎ (01765) 603640.

Minster Rd ☎ (01765) 604625.

London 222 – Leeds 26 – Middlesbrough 35 – York 23.

Ripon Spa, Park St, HG4 2BU, ☎ (01765) 602172, *spahotel@branco.co.uk, Fax (01765) 690770,* – rest, TV P – 150. MC AE VISA JCB
Meals 12.25/30.00 and a la carte 17.70/27.25 **t.** 14.00 – **40 rm** 80.00/105.00 **t.** – SB.

The Outside Inn, 2-4 Skellbank, HG4 2PT, ☎ (01765) 602600, *Fax (01765) 690736,* – MC AE VISA
closed 25 December – **Meals** a la carte 12.15/17.65 **t.** 8.95.

Aldfield *Southwest : 3 ¾ m. by B 6265* – ✉ *Ripon.*

Bay Tree Farm, HG4 3BE, ☎ (01765) 620394, *Fax (01765) 620394,* – TV P. VISA
Meals (by arrangement) (communal dining) 13.50 **st.** 7.00 – **6 rm** 40.00/55.00 **t.**

Wormald Green *South : 4¼ m. on A 61* – ✉ *Ripon.*

George with rm, HG3 3PR, ☎ (01765) 677214, *info@hotelgeorge.co.uk, Fax (01765) 676201* – TV P. MC VISA
Newboulds : Meals *(closed Sunday)* (booking essential) (dinner only) a la carte 29.50/45.50 **t.** 10.95 – **5 rm** 50.00/70.00 **t.**

Olives (at George H.), HG3 3PR, ☎ (01765) 677214, *info@hotelgeorge.co.uk, Fax (01765) 676201* – P. MC VISA
Meals 8.95/10.95 and a la carte 19.00/39.00 **t.** 10.95.

at Markington *Southwest : 5 m. by A 61 – ✉ Harrogate.*

Hob Green ⨂, HG3 3PJ, Southwest : ½ m. ✆ (01423) 770031, *info@hobgreen.com, Fax (01423) 771589,* ⩽, « Country house in extensive parkland », – TV P. MC AE Ⓓ VISA JCB
Meals 10.45/27.50 and a la carte 23.50/31.00 **st.** 10.95 – **11 rm** 85.00/140.00 **st.** 1 suite – SB.

RISLEY *Notts. – see Nottingham.*

ROADE *Northants.* 404 R 27 – *pop. 2 239.*
London 66 – Coventry 36 – Northampton 5.5.

Roade House with rm, 16 High St, NN7 2NW, ✆ (01604) 863372, *info@roadehousehotel.co.uk, Fax (01604) 862421* – ⇔, ▤ rest, TV P. MC AE VISA.
closed Bank Holidays – **Meals** *(closed lunch Saturday and Monday and Sunday dinner)* 16.5 (lunch) and dinner a la carte 23.50/29.75 **st.** 10.75 – **9 rm** 69.00/79.00 **st.**

ROCHDALE *Gtr. Manchester* 402 N 23 – *pop. 94 313.*
18 Edenfield Rd, Bagslate ✆ (01706) 646024 – 18 Marland, Springfield Park, Bolton R ✆ (01706) 649801 – 18, 9 Castle Hawk, Chadwick Lane, Castleton ✆ (01706) 640841.
The Clock Tower, Town Hall ✆ (01706) 356592.
London 224 – Blackpool 40 – Burnley 11 – Leeds 45 – Manchester 12 – Liverpool 40.

Royal Toby Lodge, Manchester Rd, Castleton, OL11 3HF, Southwest : 2 m. by A 58 on A 664 ✆ (01706) 861861, *Fax (01706) 868428,* – |‡|, ⇔ rm, ▤ rest, TV ♿ P – 120. MC AE Ⓓ VISA.
Meals 8.95/10.95 and a la carte 12.00/15.00 **t.** 11.00 – ***Fallen Angel :*** **Meals** - Italian (dinner only) a la carte 25.00/32.00 **t.** 15.00 – **44 rm** 77.50/100.00 **st.**

Nutters, Edenfield Rd, Norden, OL12 7TY, West : 5 m. on A 680 ✆ (01706) 650167, *Fax (01706) 650167,* ⩽ – ⇔ P. MC AE VISA
closed 2 weeks August and Tuesday – **Meals** 29.95 (dinner) and a la carte 23.85/28.85 10.95.

After Eight, 2 Edenfield Rd, OL11 5AA, West : 1 m. on A 680 ✆ (01706) 646432, *atayl@compuserve.com, Fax (01706) 646432,* – ⇔. MC AE Ⓓ VISA JCB
closed 25-26 December, Sunday and Monday – **Meals** (dinner only) a la carte 21.50/24.40 10.90.

at Milnrow *Southeast : 3 m. by A 640 – ✉ Rochdale.*

Travel Inn, Newhey Rd, OL16 4JF, ✆ (01706) 299999, *Fax (01706) 299074* – ⇔ rm, ▤ rest, TV ♿ P – 40. MC AE Ⓓ VISA.
Meals (grill rest.) – **40 rm** 41.95 **t.**

ROCHESTER *Medway* 404 V 29 *Great Britain G.* – *pop. 23 971* – ✉ *Chatham.*
See : *Castle★ AC – Cathedral★ AC.*
Env. : *The Historic Dockyard★, Chatham, NE : 2 m. of the Cathedral.*
Exc. : *Leeds Castle★, SE : 11 m. by A 229 and M 20.*
95 High St ✆ (01634) 843666.
London 30 – Dover 45 – Maidstone 8 – Margate 46.

Bridgewood Manor, Bridgewood Roundabout, ME5 9AX, Southeast : 3 m. by A 2 and A 229 on Walderslade rd ✆ (01634) 201333, *bridgewoodmanor@marstonhotels.com, Fax (01634) 201330,* ⅰ, ≘s, ⊠, ✂ – |‡| ⇔, ▤ rest, TV ♿ P – 200. MC AE Ⓓ VISA
Squires : **Meals** 19.50/27.00 and dinner a la carte approx. 35.00 **st.** 12.95 – **96 rm** 115.0 149.00 **st.**, 4 suites – SB.

Posthouse Rochester, Maidstone Rd, ME5 9SF, Southeast : 2 ½ m. by A 2 on A 2 ✆ (0870) 400 9069, *gm1431@forte-hotels.com, Fax (01634) 684512,* ⅰ, ≘s, ⊠, – |‡| ⇔ rm, TV ♿ P – 110. MC AE Ⓓ VISA
Meals *(closed Saturday lunch)* 10.00/15.00 and dinner a la carte 20.45/30.15 **t.** 11.95 – 11.95 – **145 rm** 105.00/125.00 **st.** – SB.

Bitte beachten Sie die Geschwindigkeitsbeschränkungen in Großbritannien
- 60 mph (= 96 km/h) außerhalb geschlossener Ortschaften
- 70 mph (= 112 km/h) auf Straßen mit getrennten Fahrbahnen und Autobahnen.

ROCHFORD *Essex* 404 W 29 – *pop. 15 081.*

Rochford Hundred, Rochford Hall, Hall Rd ☎ (01702) 544302.

London 46 – Chelmsford 19 – Colchester 39 – Southend-on-Sea 3.

Renouf, Bradley Way, SS4 1BU, ☎ (01702) 541334, *reception@hotelrenouf.fsnet.co.uk, Fax (01702) 549563,* – rest, rest, – 30. AE VISA
closed 26 to 30 December – **Meals** (residents only Sunday dinner and Bank Holidays) 15.50/30.00 **t.** 11.50 – 3.00 – **23 rm** 61.50/105.00 **t.**

ROCK *Cornwall* 403 F 32 *The West Country G.* – *pop. 4 593* – ✉ *Wadebridge.*

Exc. : *Pencarrow★, SE : 8½ m. by B 3314 and A 389.*

London 266 – Newquay 24 – Tintagel 14 – Truro 32.

St Enodoc, PL27 6LA, ☎ (01208) 863394, *enodoc@aol.com, Fax (01208) 863970,* ←, , , , heated, , squash – rm, . AE VISA.
closed 7 January-14 February and 6-27 December – ***Porthilly Grill :*** **Meals** (light lunch)/ dinner a la carte 18.00/27.00 **st.** 9.90 – 6.50 – **15 rm** 100.00/150.00 **st.**, 3 suites.

ROCQUE *Jersey (Channel Islands)* 230 ⑪ – *see Channel Islands.*

ROGATE *W. Sussex* 404 R 30 – *pop. 1 785* – ✉ *Petersfield (Hants.).*

London 63 – Brighton 42 – Guildford 29 – Portsmouth 23 – Southampton 36.

Mizzards Farm without rest., GU31 5HS, Southwest : 1 m. by Harting rd ☎ (01730) 821656, *julian.francis@hemscott.net, Fax (01730) 821655,* ←, « 17C farmhouse », heated, , – .
closed Christmas and New Year – **3 rm** 42.00/70.00 **st.**

ROMALDKIRK *Durham* 402 N 20 – *see Barnard Castle.*

ROMSEY *Hants.* 403 404 P 31 *Great Britain G.* – *pop. 17 032.*

See : *Abbey★ (interior★★).*

Env. : *Broadlands★ AC, S : 1 m.*

Dunwood Manor, Danes Rd, Awbridge ☎ (023) 8073 2218 – Nursling ☎ (023) 8073 2218 – , Wellow, Ryedown Lane, East Wellow ☎ (01794) 322872.

1 Latimer St ☎ (01794) 512987.

London 82 – Bournemouth 28 – Salisbury 16 – Southampton 8 – Winchester 10.

White Horse, Market Pl, SO51 8ZJ, ☎ (0870) 400 8123, *heritagehotels_romsey.white_horse@forte-hotels.com, Fax (01794) 517485* – rm, – 30. AE VISA JCB
Meals 10.95 (lunch) and a la carte 17.25/25.65 **t.** 9.95 – 11.85 – **33 rm** 80.00/100.00 **st.** – SB.

Ranvilles Farm House without rest., Ower, SO51 6AA, Southwest : 2 m. on A 3090 (southbound carriageway) ☎ (023) 8081 4481, *Fax (023) 8081 4481,* « Part 16C farmhouse », –
closed 25, 26 and 31 December and 1 January – **3 rm** 35.00/55.00 **st.**

Highfield House , Newtown Rd, Awbridge, SO51 0GG, Northwest : 3 ½ m. by A 3090 (old A 31) and A 27 ☎ (01794) 340727, *Fax (01794) 341450,* – .
Meals (by arrangement) (communal dining) 17.00 **s.** – **3 rm** 35.00/60.00 **s.**

Old Manor House, 21 Palmerston St, SO51 8GF, ☎ (01794) 517353, *Fax (01794) 513855,* « Timbered 16C house » – . AE VISA
closed 24-31 December, Sunday dinner and Monday – **Meals** - Italian - (booking essential) a la carte 25.00/31.50 **t.** 11.50.

East Tytherley *Northwest : 6 m. by A 3057 off B 3084* – ✉ *Romsey.*

Star Inn with rm, SO51 0LW, ☎ (01794) 340225, *info@starinn-uk.com,* , – .
VISA
closed 25-26 December – **Meals** a la carte 13.25/28.40 **t.** 12.00 – **3 rm** 45.00/60.00 **t.**

ROSEDALE ABBEY *N. Yorks.* 402 R 20 *Great Britain G.* – *pop. 332 (Rosedale)* – ✉ *Pickering.*

Env. : *←★ on road to Hutton-le-Hole.*

London 247 – Middlesbrough 27 – Scarborough 25 – York 36.

Milburn Arms, YO18 8RA, ☎ (01751) 417312, *info@milburnarms.com, Fax (01751) 417541,* – rest, . VISA
Priory : **Meals** *(closed Sunday dinner)* (bar lunch Monday-Saturday)/dinner a la carte 19.70/ 27.00 **st.** 9.95 – **11 rm** 41.50/68.00 **st.** – SB.

ROSS-ON-WYE *Herefordshire* 403 404 M 28 *Great Britain G. – pop. 9 606.*
See : *Market House★ – Yat Rock (<★).*
Env. : *SW : Wye Valley★ – Goodrich Castle★* AC, *SW : 3½ m. by A 40.*
Swan House, Edde Cross St (01989) 562768.
London 118 – Gloucester 15 – Hereford 15 – Newport 35.

The Chase, Gloucester Rd, HR9 5LH, (01989) 763161, *info@chasehotel.co*
Fax (01989) 768330, – TV P – 250. MC AE VISA JCB.
closed 24-29 December – **Meals** 14.95/22.50 **st.** 10.75 – **36 rm** 105.00/140.00 **st.**

Royal, Palace Pound, HR9 5HZ, (01989) 565105, *Fax (01989) 768058,* <, – TV
80. MC AE VISA
Meals (bar lunch Monday-Saturday)/dinner 16.95 and a la carte 13.95/26.65 **t.** 9.9
42 rm 65.00/95.00 **t.** – SB.

Travel Inn, Ledbury Rd, HR9 7QJ, Northeast : 1 ½ m. by A 40 at junction with A 449 a
M 50 (01989) 563861, *Fax (01989) 566124* – rm, TV P. MC AE VISA.
Meals (grill rest.) – **43 rm** 41.95 **t.**

China Boy Jo, 27 Gloucester Rd, HR9 5LE, (01989) 563533, *chinaboyjo@aol.cc*
Fax (01989) 563533 – MC VISA JCB
closed 25-26 December, Monday and Tuesday lunch except Bank Holidays – **Meals** - Chin
- 15.00/26.00 and a la carte 10.50/28.80 **t.**

The Pheasant, 52 Edde Cross St, HR9 7BZ, (01989) 565751, *Fax (01989) 763069* –
MC AE VISA
closed first week June, 23 December-2 January and Sunday-Wednesday – **Meals** (din
only) 25.00 **t.** 12.80.

The Lough Pool Inn, HR9 6LX, Northwest : 3 ¼ m. by B 4260 and A 49 on Hoarwithy
(01989) 730236, , « 16C inn », – P. MC VISA
closed 25 December and Sunday dinner November-March – **Meals** a la carte 19.00/23.9
10.50.

at Kerne Bridge *South : 3¾ m. on B 4234 – Ross-on-Wye.*

Lumleys without rest., HR9 5QT, (01600) 890040, *helen@lumleys.force9.co.uk,*
TV P
3 rm 25.00/55.00 **st.**

at Glewstone *Southwest : 3¼ m. by A 40 – Ross-on-Wye.*

Glewstone Court, HR9 6AW, (01989) 770367, *glewstone@aol.cc*
Fax (01989) 770282, <, « Part Georgian and Victorian country house », – TV P. MC
VISA JCB
closed 25-27 December – **Meals** (bar lunch Monday to Saturday)/dinner 26.00 **st.** 10.0
8 rm 45.00/105.00 **st.** – SB.

at Peterstow *West : 2½ m. on A 49 – Ross-on-Wye.*

Pengethley Manor, HR9 6LL, Northwest : 1 ½ m. on A 49 (01989) 7302
reservations@pengethleymanor.co.uk, Fax (01989) 730238, <, heated, , , –
P – 50. MC AE VISA
Meals a la carte 22.00/34.00 **t.** 13.90 – **22 rm** 75.00/120.00 **t.**, 3 suites – SB.

ROSTHWAITE *Cumbria* 402 K 20 – *see Keswick.*

ROTHBURY *Northd.* 401 402 O 18 *Great Britain G. – pop. 1 805 – Morpeth.*
See : *Cragside House★ (interior★) AC.*
National Park Centre, Church House, Church St (01669) 620887.
London 311 – Edinburgh 84 – Newcastle upon Tyne 29.

Lee Farm without rest., NE65 8JQ, South : 3 ¼ m. by B 6342 on The Lee
(01665) 570257, *enqs@leefarm.co.uk, Fax (01665) 570257,* <, « Working farm »,
P
closed Christmas-New Year – **3 rm** 30.00/46.00 **st.**

Orchard without rest., High St, NE65 7TL, (01669) 620684, *jpickard@orchardgu*
house.co.uk, – TV.
closed 2 weeks Christmas and New Year – **6 rm** 30.00/50.00 **s.**

ROTHERHAM *S. Yorks.* 402 403 404 P 23 – *pop. 121 380.*
Thrybergh Park (01709) 850466 – Grange Park, Upper Wortley Rd, Kimberwo
(01709) 558884 – Phoenix, Pavilion Lane, Brinsworth (01709) 363788.
Central Library, Walker Pl (01709) 835904.
London 166 – Kingston-upon-Hull 61 – Leeds 36 – Sheffield 6.

Courtyard by Marriott, West Bawtry Rd, S60 4NA, South : 2 ¼ m. on A 630 ✆ (01709) 830630, *Fax (01709) 830549*, rest, 300.
Meals (bar lunch Saturday) (carvery lunch) 9.95/20.50 **st.** 12.95 – 10.95 – **98 rm** 87.00 **st.**, 2 suites – SB.

Elton, Main St, Bramley, S66 2SF, East : 4 ¼ m. by A 6021, A 631 and Cross St. ✆ (01709) 545681, *bestwestern.eltonhotel@btinternet.com, Fax (01709) 549100* – rm, 50.
Meals 12.50/21.00 and a la carte 20.65/28.75 **st.** 10.95 – **29 rm** 60.00/98.00 **st.** – SB.

Ibis without rest., Moorhead Way, Bramley, S66 1YY, East : 4 ½ m. by A 6021 off A 631, at junction 1 of M 18 ✆ (01709) 730333, *Fax (01709) 730444* – 40.
86 rm 42.00 **st.**

Travel Inn, Bawtry Rd, S65 3JB, East : 2 m. by A 6021 on A 631 ✆ (01709) 543216, *Fax (01709) 531546* – rm, rest.
Meals (grill rest.) – **37 rm** 41.95 **t.**

OTHERWICK *Hants. – see Hook.*

OTHLEY *Leics.* 402 403 404 Q 25 – *see Leicester.*

OUGHAM GREEN *Suffolk – see Bury St. Edmunds.*

OWDE *Wilts.* 403 404 N 29 – *see Devizes*

OWNHAMS SERVICE AREA *Hants.* 403 404 P 31 – ✉ *Southampton.*
M 27 Services (westbound) ✆ (023) 8073 0345.

Travel Inn without rest., SO16 8AP, M 27 between junctions 3 and 4 (westbound carriage-way) ✆ (023) 8074 1144, *Fax (023) 8074 0204* –
closed Christmas and New Year – **40 rm** 41.95.

OWSLEY *Derbs.* 402 403 404 P 24 *Great Britain G. – pop. 451* – ✉ *Matlock.*
Env. : *Chatsworth★★★ (Park and Garden★★★) AC, N : by B 6012.*
London 157 – Derby 23 – Manchester 40 – Nottingham 30.

East Lodge, DE4 2EF, ✆ (01629) 734474, *info@eastlodge.com, Fax (01629) 733949*, – rest.
Meals 12.95/23.95 **st.** 11.50 – **15 rm** (dinner included) 160.00 **st.** – SB.

The Peacock, Bakewell Rd, DE4 2EB, ✆ (01629) 733518, *jpeacock.gm@jarvis.co.uk, Fax (01629) 732671*, « 17C stone house, antiques », – rest.
Meals 12.95/26.95 and a la carte 17.85/41.40 **t.** 12.95 – **16 rm** 95.00/165.00 **t.** – SB.

OWTON *Ches.* 402 403 L 24 – *see Chester.*

OYAL LEAMINGTON SPA *Warks.* 403 404 P 27 – *pop. 55 396.*
Leamington and County, Golf Lane, Whitnash ✆ (01926) 425961 (on plan of Warwick).
The Royal Pump Rooms, The Parade ✆ (01926) 742762.
London 99 – Birmingham 23 – Coventry 9 – Warwick 3.

Plan on next page

Mallory Court, Harbury Lane, Bishop's Tachbrook, CV33 9QB, South : 2 ¼ m. by B 4087 (Tachbrook Rd) ✆ (01926) 330214, *reception@mallory.co.uk, Fax (01926) 451714*, « Part Edwardian country house in Lutyens style, extensive landscaped gardens », – rest.
Meals (booking essential) 25.00/39.50 and a la carte 39.50/56.50 **st.** 20.00 – 10.00 – **18 rm** 185.00/340.00 **st.** – SB.

Courtyard by Marriott, Olympus Ave, Tachbrook Park, CV34 6RJ, Southwest : 1 ½ m. by A 452 ✆ (01926) 425522, *Fax (01926) 881322* – rm, rest, 70.
on Warwick town plan **Z v**
Meals a la carte 19.70/23.15 **st.** 11.75 – **91 rm** 92.00/117.00 **st.**

The Angel, 143 Regent St, CV32 4NZ, ✆ (01926) 881296, *angelhotel143@hotmail.com, Fax (01926) 881296* – 40. **U c**
Meals (bar lunch Monday-Saturday)/dinner 13.00/16.00 **t.** 8.95 – **46 rm** 65.00/75.00 **t.** – SB.

ROYAL LEAMINGTON SPA

Adelaïde Road V
Avenue Road . . . . V 2
Bath Street . . . . V 3
Beauchamp Avenue . . . . U
Beauchamp Hill . . . . U 4
Binswood Street . . . . U 6
Brandon Parade . . . . U 10
Church Hill . . . . UV 16
Clarendon Avenue . . . . U
Clarendon Place . . . . U 18
Dale Street . . . . UV
Hamilton Terrace . . . . V 21
High Street . . . . V 22
Holly Walk . . . . U
Kenilworth Road . . . . U
Leam Terrace V
Leicester Street . . . . U
Lillington Avenue . . . . U
Lillington Road . . . . U
Lower Avenue . . . . V 28
Newbold Terrace . . . . V 30
Northumberland Road . . . . U 33
Old Warwick Road V
Parade . . . . UV
Priory Terrace . . . . V 37
Radford Road V
Regent Grove . . . . UV 40
Regent Street . . . . UV
Royal Priors Shopping Centre . . . U
Rugby Road . . . . U
Russell Terrace V
Spencer Street . . . . V 44
Tachbrook Road . . . . V 47
Victoria Terrace . . . . V 49
Warwick Street . . . . U
Willes Road . . . . UV

Leamington H. & Bistro, 64 Upper Holly Walk, CV32 4JL, ✆ (01926) 8837... *Fax (01926) 330467,* – TV & P – 40. MC AE VISA. U
Meals a la carte 16.35/22.25 **t.** 9.95 – 6.95 – **30 rm** 70.00/90.00 **t.**

Lansdowne, 87 Clarendon St, CV32 4PF, ✆ (01926) 450505, *Fax (01926) 421313* rest, TV P. MC AE VISA. U
Meals (dinner only) 20.00 **st.** – **14 rm** 54.95/68.00 **t.** – SB.

Adams, 22 Avenue Rd, CV31 3PQ, ✆ (01926) 450742, *Fax (01926) 313110,* – TV P. AE VISA. V
Meals *(closed Saturday-Sunday)* (bar lunch)/dinner 18.00/25.00 and a la carte 21.5... 26.60 **t.** 12.50 – **15 rm** 69.00/75.00 **t.** – SB.

York House, 9 York Rd, CV31 3PR, ✆ (01926) 424671, *Fax (01926) 832272* – TV. MC VISA V
closed 23 December-1 January – **Meals** (by arrangement) 20.00 **st.** 6.50 – **8 rm** 28.5... 56.00 **t.** – SB.

The Emperors, Bath Pl, CV31 3BP, ✆ (01926) 313030, *Fax (01926) 435966* – . MC AE VISA. V
closed 14-31 August, 25-26 December, Sunday and Bank Holidays – **Meals** - Chine... (Canton and Peking) - a la carte 15.00/31.00 **st.** 10.00.

Solo, 23 Dormer Pl, CV32 5AA, ✆ (01926) 422422 – . MC VISA V
closed 1 week Christmas, Monday lunch and Sunday – **Meals** 18.00/25.00 **t.** 13.00.

ROYAL TUNBRIDGE WELLS *Kent* 404 U 30 *Great Britain G.* – *pop. 60 272.*
See : *The Pantiles*★ **B 26** – *Calverley Park*★ **B.**
Langton Rd ✆ *(01892) 523034* **A.**
The Old Fish Market, The Pantiles ✆ *(01892) 515675.*
London 36 – Brighton 33 – Folkestone 46 – Hastings 27 – Maidstone 18.

Plan opposite

Hotel du Vin, Crescent Rd, TN1 2LY, ✆ (01892) 526455, *reception@tunbridgewells.ho... duvin.co.uk, Fax (01892) 512044,* <, « Georgian house, contemporary wine them... interior », – TV P – 80. MC AE VISA. B
Meals – (see ***Bistro*** below) – 11.50 – **31 rm** 80.00/135.00 **t.**, 1 suite.

Spa, Mount Ephraim, TN4 8XJ, ✆ (01892) 520331, *info@spahotel.co... Fax (01892) 510575,* – TV & P – 350. MC AE VISA A
Meals *(closed Saturday lunch)* a la carte 27.25/39.50 **st.** 11.75 – 10.75 – **68 rm** 85... 105.00 **st.**, 3 suites – SB.

ROYAL TUNBRIDGE WELLS

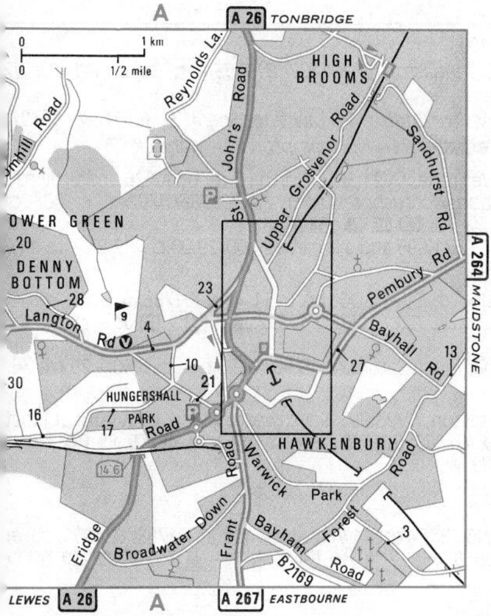

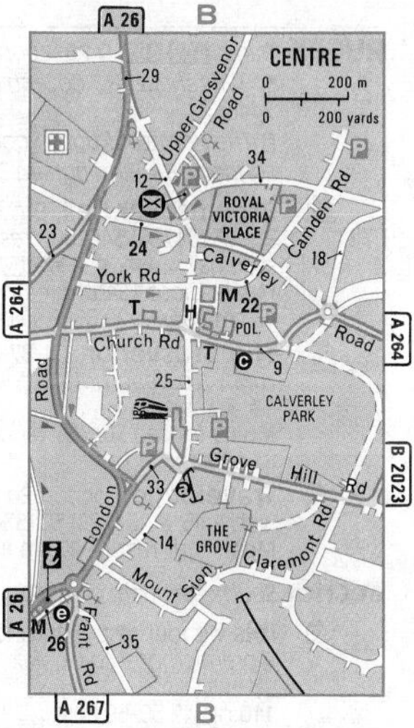

Danehurst without rest., 41 Lower Green Rd, Rusthall, TN4 8TW, West : 1 3/4 m. by A 264 (01892) 527739, *danehurst@zoom.co.uk, Fax (01892) 514804*, – TV P. MC AE VISA. — A e
closed last week August, Christmas and New Year – **4 rm** 60.00/79.00 **s.**

Signor Franco, 5a High St, TN1 1UL, (01892) 549199, *Fax (01892) 541378* – MC VISA JCB — B a
closed Sunday and Bank Holidays – **Meals** - Italian - a la carte 23.00/34.50 **t.** 12.50.

Bistro (at Hotel du Vin), TN1 2LY, (01892) 526455, *Fax (01892) 512044*, – P. MC AE VISA — B c
Meals (booking essential) a la carte approx. 24.00 **t.**

The Tagore, 4 Nevill St, TN2 5SA, (01892) 615100, *nurul-monie@aol.com, Fax (01892) 510139* – MC AE VISA JCB — B e
closed 25-26 December – **Meals** - Indian - (booking essential) 14.95 and a la carte 16.40/27.75 **t.** 10.95.

Pembury *Northeast : 4 m. by A 264 off B 2015 – A – Royal Tunbridge Wells.*

Jarvis International, 8 Tonbridge Rd, TN2 4QL, (01892) 823567, *jitunbridgewells.gm@jarvis.co.uk, Fax (01892) 823931*, – TV P – 180. MC AE VISA
Meals *(closed Saturday lunch)* 12.50/19.95 and dinner a la carte 22.50/26.75 **st.** 12.75 – 9.50 – **82 rm** 99.00/109.00 **st.**, 2 suites – SB.

Matfield *Northeast : 5 m. by A 264 – A – and A 21 on B 2160 – Royal Tunbridge Wells.*

Maynards, TN12 7DU, on B 2160 (01892) 723966, *mail@maynards-uk.com, Fax (01892) 723312*, «, « 13C timbered farmhouse, gardens », heated – TV P. MC VISA.
Meals (by arrangement) (communal dining) 28.00 **st.** – **3 rm** 60.00/130.00 **st.**

Frant *South : 2½ m. on A 267 – A – Royal Tunbridge Wells.*

Old Parsonage without rest., Church Lane, TN3 9DX, (01892) 750773, *oldparson@aol.com, Fax (01892) 750773*, «, « Georgian rectory », – TV P. MC VISA
4 rm 59.00/89.00.

Langton Green *West : 2 m. on A 264 – A – Royal Tunbridge Wells.*

The Hare, Langton Rd, TN3 0JA, (01892) 862419, *Fax (01892) 861275*, – P. MC AE VISA
Meals a la carte 15.65/26.85 **t.** 9.95.

ROZEL BAY *Jersey (Channel Islands)* 403 P 33 and 230 ⑪ – *see Channel Islands.*

RUAN-HIGH-LANES *Cornwall* 403 F 33 – *see Veryan.*

RUCKHALL *Herefordshire – see Hereford.*

RUGBY *Warks.* 403 404 Q 26 – *pop. 61 106.*

Whitefields H., Coventry Rd, Thurlaston ℘ (01788) 815555 – Clifton Rd ℘ (017 544637.

The Home of Rugby Football Visitor Centre, 4-5 Lawrence Sheriff St ℘ (01788) 534970

London 88 – Birmingham 33 – Leicester 21 – Northampton 20 – Warwick 17.

Brownsover Hall, Brownsover Lane, CV21 1HU, North : 2 m. by A 426 and Brownso Rd ℘ (01788) 546100, *reservations@corushotels.com, Fax (01788) 579241,* « 19C Got style hall », – rm, TV P – 70. MC AE VISA JCB
Meals *(closed Saturday lunch)* 12.95/17.95 and a la carte 24.00/29.00 **t.** 12.95 – 11.7
45 rm 99.00/129.00, 2 suites – SB.

The Grosvenor, 81-87 Clifton Rd, CV21 3QQ, on B 5414 ℘ (01788) 535686, *mail@ rugbygrosvenorhotel.freeserve.co.uk, Fax (01788) 541297,* – TV P – 35. MC VISA.
Meals *(closed Sunday dinner)* (bar lunch Saturday) 13.95/18.95 **t.** – 6.50 – **26 rm** 76. 87.50 **st.**

Travelodge, London Rd, Thurlaston, CV23 9LG, Southwest : 4 ¼ m. by A 4071 at junct with A 45 ℘ (01788) 521538, *Fax (01788) 521538* – rm, TV P. MC AE VISA JCB.
Meals (grill rest.) – **40 rm** 49.95 **t.**

at Crick *Southeast : 6 m. on A 428.*

Ibis without rest., Parklands, NN6 7EX, West : 1 ¼ m. on A 428 ℘ (01788) 824331, *daver @premierhotel.co.uk, Fax (01788) 824332* – TV P – 35. MC AE VISA
110 rm 49.50/69.00 **t.**

RUGELEY *Staffs.* 402 403 404 O 25 – *pop. 22 975.*

London 134 – Birmingham 31 – Derby 29 – Stoke-on-Trent 22.

Travelodge, Western Springs Rd, WS15 2AS, at junction of A 51 with A ℘ (01889) 570096, *Fax (01889) 570096* – rm, TV P. MC AE VISA JCB.
Meals (grill rest.) – **32 rm** 39.95 **t.**

RUMWELL *Somerset – see Taunton.*

RUNCORN *Ches.* 402 403 L 23 – *pop. 64 154.*

Clifton Rd ℘ (01928) 572093.

London 202 – Liverpool 17 – Manchester 29.

Holiday Inn Runcorn, Wood Lane, Beechwood, WA7 3HA, Southeast : 2 m. by A ℘ (0870) 4009070, *gm1432@forte-hotels.com, Fax (01928) 714611,* – rm, TV P – 500. MC AE VISA
Meals *(closed Saturday lunch)* 15.00 and a la carte 14.95/24.00 13.95 – 12.95 – **150** 95.00 **t.**

Travel Inn, Chester Rd, Preston Brook, WA7 3BB, Southeast : 6 m. by A 533 on A ℘ (01928) 716829, *Fax (01928) 719852* – rm, rest, TV P – 40. MC AE VISA.
Meals (grill rest.) – **40 rm** 41.95 **t.**

RUSHDEN *Northants.* 404 S 27 – *pop. 23 854.*

London 74 – Cambridge 42 – Northampton 14 – Peterborough 25.

Travelodge, NN10 9EP, on A 45 (eastbound carriageway) ℘ (01933) 357(*Fax (01933) 411325* – rm, TV P. MC AE VISA JCB.
Meals (grill rest.) – **40 rm** 39.95 **t.**

Se cercate un albergo tranquillo,
oltre a consultare le carte dell'introduzione,
rintracciate nell'elenco degli esercizi quelli con il simbolo o .

USHLAKE GREEN *E. Sussex* 404 U 31 – ✉ *Heathfield.*
London 54 – Brighton 26 – Eastbourne 13.

Stone House ⚘, TN21 9QJ, Northeast corner of the green ✆ (01435) 830553, *Fax (01435) 830726*, ≤, « Part 15C, part Georgian country house, antiques », ⚘, ⛱, ⚘ – TV P. MC VISA. ⚘
closed 23 December-1 January – **Meals** (residents only) (dinner only) 24.95 **st.** 9.95 – **6 rm** ☕ 90.00/225.00 **st.**, 1 suite.

YDE *I.O.W.* 403 404 Q 31 – *see Wight (Isle of).*

La guida cambia, cambiate la guida ogni anno.

YE *E. Sussex* 404 W 31 *Great Britain G. – pop. 3 708.*
See : *Old Town★★ : Mermaid Street★, St Mary's Church (≤★).*
The Heritage Centre, Strand Quay ✆ (01797) 226696.
London 61 – Brighton 49 – Folkestone 27 – Maidstone 33.

Mermaid Inn, Mermaid St, TN31 7EY, ✆ (01797) 223065, *mermaid@rye-tourism.co.uk, Fax (01797) 225069*, « Historic 15C inn » – ⚘ rest, TV P. MC AE ① VISA JCB. ⚘
Meals 17.50/35.00 and a la carte 32.00/56.00 **t.** 14.50 – **31 rm** ☕ 80.00/160.00 **st.** – SB.

Rye Lodge, Hilders Cliff, TN31 7LD, ✆ (01797) 223838, *info@ryelodge.co.uk, Fax (01797) 223585*, ⚘, ⚘ – ⚘ rest, TV P. MC AE ① VISA JCB
Meals (dinner only) 23.50 and a la carte 20.00/31.00 **t.** 12.00 – **18 rm** ☕ 59.50/150.00 **t.** – SB.

Jeake's House without rest., Mermaid St, TN31 7ET, ✆ (01797) 222828, *jeakeshouse @btinternet.com, Fax (01797) 222623*, « Part 17C » – TV P. MC VISA
12 rm ☕ 32.50/105.00 **st.**

King Charles II without rest., 4 High St, TN31 7JE, ✆ (01797) 224954, « Medieval house » – ⚘ TV. MC. ⚘
3 rm 55.00/95.00.

Old Vicarage without rest., 66 Church Sq, TN31 7HF, ✆ (01797) 222119, *oldvicaragerye @tesco.net, Fax (01797) 227466*, « Part 14C », ⛱ – ⚘ TV P. ⚘
closed 23-26 December – **4 rm** ☕ 60.00/80.00 **st.**

Little Orchard House without rest., West St, TN31 7ES, ✆ (01797) 223831, *Fax (01797) 223831*, ⛱ – ⚘ TV. MC VISA JCB. ⚘
3 rm ☕ 55.00/90.00 **st.**

Flushing Inn, 4 Market St, TN31 7LA, ✆ (01797) 223292, *j.e.flynn@talk21.com*, « 15C inn with 16C mural » – ⚘. MC AE ① VISA
closed first 2 weeks January and June, Monday dinner and Tuesday – **Meals** - Seafood - 17.00/35.00 and a la carte 17.00/22.50 **t.** 11.80.

Landgate Bistro, 5-6 Landgate, TN31 7LH, ✆ (01797) 222829 – MC AE ① VISA JCB
closed 2 weeks in summer, 2 weeks Christmas, Sunday and Monday – **Meals** (dinner only) a la carte 18.30/23.00 **st.** 8.90.

Peasmarsh *Northwest : 4 m. on A 268 – ✉ Rye.*

Flackley Ash, London Rd, TN31 6YH, on A 268 ✆ (01797) 230651, *flackleyash@marston hotels.co.uk, Fax (01797) 230510*, ⚘, ⚘, ⚘, ⛱ – ⚘ rest, TV ♿ P – ⚘ 100. MC AE ① VISA
Meals (bar lunch Monday-Saturday)/dinner 14.00/25.00 **st.** 10.95 – **43 rm** ☕ 79.00/119.00, 2 suites – SB.

YLSTONE *N. Yorks.* 402 N 21 – *see Skipton.*

YTON ON DUNSMORE *W. Mids.* 403 404 P 28 – *see Coventry.*

AFFRON WALDEN *Essex* 404 U 27 *Great Britain G. – pop. 13 201.*
See : *Audley End★★ AC.*
1 Market Pl, Market Sq ✆ (01799) 510444.
London 46 – Cambridge 15 – Chelmsford 25.

the restaurant, 2 Church St, CB10 1JW, ✆ (01799) 526444, *info@the-restaurantweb. com* – MC VISA
closed first week January, 25-26 December, Sunday and Monday – **Meals** (dinner only) a la carte 18.85/30.85 **t.** 12.95.

ST AGNES *Cornwall* 403 E 33 *The West Country G. – pop. 2 899.*

See : *St Agnes Beacon*★★ (☼★★).

Env. : *Portreath*★, *SW : 5½ m.*

Perranporth, Budnic Hill (01872) 572454.

London 302 – Newquay 12 – Penzance 26 – Truro 9.

Rose-in-Vale Country House, Mithian, TR5 0QD, East : 2 m. by B 32 (01872) 552202, *reception@rose-in-vale-hotel.co.uk, Fax (01872) 552700*, heat – rest, TV P. VISA
closed January-February – **Meals** (bar lunch Monday-Saturday)/dinner 25.95 and a la ca 21.90/27.90 **t.** – **18 rm** 57.50/119.00 **t.** – SB.

ST ALBANS *Herts.* 404 T 28 *Great Britain G. – pop. 80 376.*

See : *City*★ - *Cathedral*★ – *Verulamium*★ (*Museum*★ *AC*).

Env. : *Hatfield House*★★ *AC*, *E : 6 m. by A 1057.*

Batchwood Hall, Batchwood Drive (01727) 833349 – 18, 9 Redbourn, Kinsbou Green Lane (01582) 793493.

Town Hall, Market Pl (01727) 864511.

London 27 – Cambridge 41 – Luton 10.

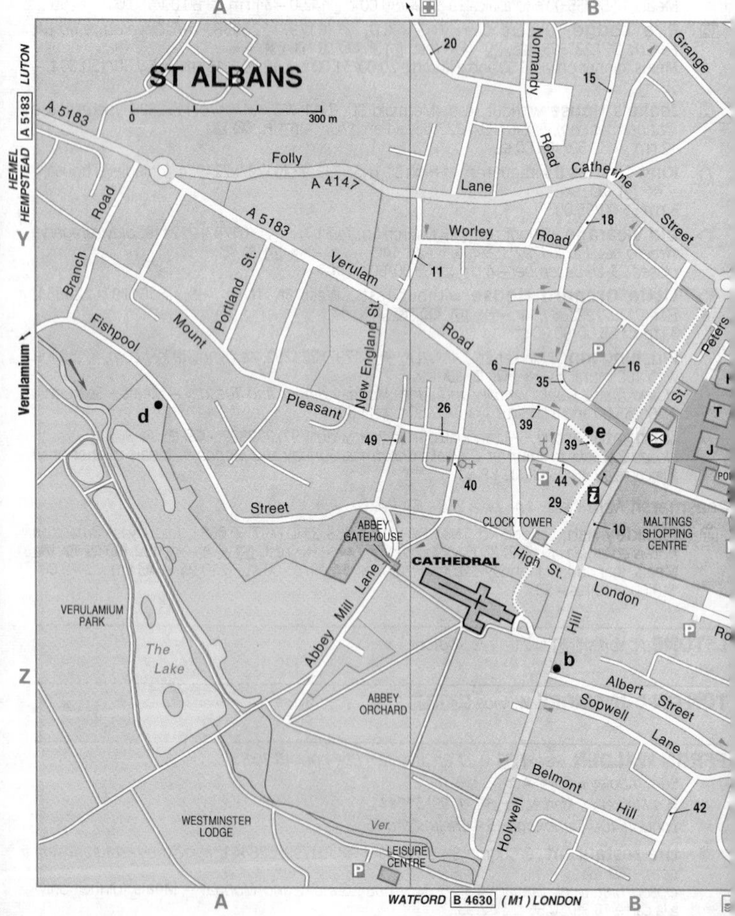

Sopwell House, Cottonmill Lane, AL1 2HQ, Southeast : 1 ½ m. by A 1081 and Mile House Lane ☎ (01727) 864477, *enquiries@sopwellhouse.co.uk, Fax (01727) 844741*, rm, – 450. VISA.
Magnolia : Meals *(closed Saturday lunch)* 15.95/19.95 **t.** 14.75 – ***Bejerano's Brasserie :*** Meals a la carte approx. 18.40 **t.** 13.25 – 12.50 – **126 rm** 130.00/170.00 **t.**, 2 suites – SB.

St Michael's Manor; 'St Michael's Village', Fishpool St, AL3 4RY, ☎ (01727) 864444, *smmanor@globalnet.co.uk, Fax (01727) 848909*, <, « Part 16C, part William and Mary manor house, lake and gardens » – VISA. AY **d**
Meals 21.00/35.00 **t.** 15.75 – **22 rm** 120.00/250.00 **t.**, 1 suite – SB.

Thistle St. Albans, Watford Rd, AL2 3DS, Southwest : 2 ½ m. at junction of A 405 with B 4630 ☎ (01727) 854252, *stalbans@thistle.co.uk, Fax (01727) 841906*, – rm, rest, – 50. VISA JCB.
Restaurant : Meals *(closed Saturday lunch)* 18.00/26.50 and a la carte 13.50 – ***Carvery :*** Meals *(closed Sunday dinner)* 18.00 **t.** 13.50 – 11.50 – **109 rm** 150.00/171.00 **st.**, 2 suites – SB.

Pré, Redbourn Rd, AL3 6JZ, Northwest : 1 ¼ m. on A 5183 ☎ (01727) 855259, *Fax (01727) 852239*, – rest, VISA.
closed 24-29 December – **Meals** (grill rest.) a la carte 12.00/19.00 **t.** 11.00 – **10 rm** 55.00/65.00 **t.**

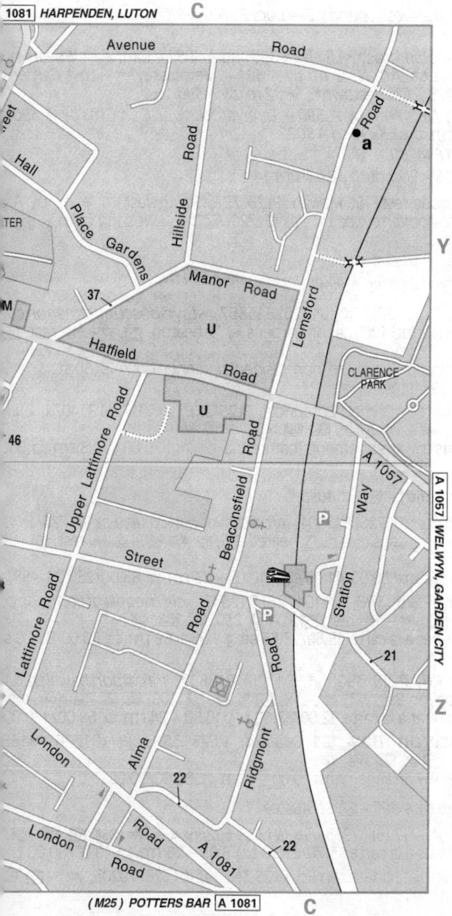

Abbey Mill Lane .... AZ
Albert Street .... BZ
Alma Road .... CZ
Avenue Road .... CY
Beaconsfield Road ... CYZ
Belmont Hill .... BZ
Branch Road .... AY
Bricket Road .... BCYZ 5
Britton Avenue .... BY 6
Carlisle Avenue ...... BCY 8
Catherine Street .... BY
Chequer Street .... BZ 10
Church Crescent ..... ABY 11
Cottonmill Lane ...... BCZ 13
Dalton Street .... BY 15
Drovers Way .... BY 16
Etna Road .... BY 18
Fishpool Street .... AYZ
Folly Avenue .... BY 20
Folly Lane .... ABY
Grange Street .... BY
Grimston Road .... CZ 21
Grosvenor Road .... CZ 22
Hall Place Gardens .... CY
Hatfield Road .... CY
High Street .... BZ
Hillside Road .... CY
Holywell Hill .... BZ
Lattimore Road .... CZ
Lemsford Road .... CY
London Road .... BCZ
Lower Dagnall Street .... BYZ 26
Maltings Shopping Centre .... BY
Manor Road .... CY
Marlborough Road ..... CZ 28
Market Place .... BZ 29
Mount Pleasant .... AY
New England Street .... AY
Normandy Road .... BY
Old London Road ...... CZ
Portland Street .... AY
Ridgemont Road .... CZ
Russell Avenue .... BY 35
Sopwell Lane .... BZ
St. Peter's Road .... CY 37
St. Peter's Street ..... BCY
Spencer Street .... BY 39
Spicer St. College .... BYZ 40
Station Way .... CZ
Thorpe Road .... BZ 42
Upper Dagnall Street .... BYZ 44
Upper Lattimore Road .... CYZ
Upper Marlborough Road .... CYZ 46
Verulam Road .... ABY
Victoria Street .... BCZ
Watson's Walk .... CZ 48
Welclose Street ..... AYZ 49
Worley Road .... BY

Comfort, Ryder House, Holywell Hill, AL1 1HG, (01727) 848849, *admin@gb055.u-n com, Fax (01727) 812210* – , rest, – 35. VISA. BZ
Meals *(closed Sunday lunch)* (light lunch)/dinner 12.95/20.50 **st.** 8.95 – 8.50 – **60 r** 67.50 **st.** – SB.

Ardmore House, 54 Lemsford Rd, AL1 3PR, (01727) 859313, *info@ardmorehou hotel.altodigital.co.uk, Fax (01727) 859313,* – rm, . VISA JCB. CY
Meals *(closed Saturday and Sunday lunch)* (dinner only) a la carte 13.50/23.50 **t.** 13.7
40 rm 55.00/95.00 **st.**

Sukiyaki, 6 Spencer St, AL3 5EG, (01727) 865009 – VISA JCB BY
closed 2 weeks in summer, 1 week Christmas, Sunday and Monday – **Meals** - Japanese 6.50/23.50 and a la carte 14.00/17.20 **st.** 10.50.

ST ANNE *Alderney (Channel Islands)* 403 Q 33 and 230 ⑨ – *see Channel Islands.*

ST ANNE'S *Lancs.* 402 K 22 – *see Lytham St Anne's.*

ST AUBIN *Jersey (Channel Islands)* 403 P 33 and 230 ⑪ – *see Channel Islands.*

ST AUSTELL *Cornwall* 403 F 32 *The West Country G.* – *pop. 21 622.*

See : *Holy Trinity Church★.*

Env. : *St Austell Bay★★ (Gribbin Head★★) E : by A 390 and A 3082 – Carthew : Wheal Mar China Clay Heritage Centre★★ AC, N : 2 m. by A 391 – Mevagissey★★ - Lost Gardens Heligan★, S : 5 m. by B 3273 – Charlestown★, SE : 2 m. by A 390.*

Exc. : *Trewithen★★★ AC, NE : 7 m. by A 390 – Lanhydrock★★, NE : 11 m. by A 390 a B 3269 – Polkerris★, E : 7 m. by A 390 and A 3082.*

18 *Carlyon Bay (01726) 814250.*

London 281 – Newquay 16 – Plymouth 38 – Truro 14.

Poltarrow Farm without rest., St Mewan, PL26 7DR, Southwest : 1 ¾ m. by A (01726) 67111, *enquire@poltarrow.co.uk, Fax (01726) 67111,* « Working farm », , – . VISA.
5 rm 30.00/50.00 **s.**

at Tregrehan *East : 2½ m. by A 390 –* ✉ *St. Austell.*

Boscundle Manor, PL25 3RL, (01726) 813557, *stay@boscundlemanor.co. Fax (01726) 814997,* « Converted 18C manor, gardens », heated, , – rest, VISA JCB
April-October – **Meals** *(closed Sunday to non-residents)* (dinner only) 22.50 **st.** 11.5
8 rm 80.00/140.00 **st.**, 2 suites.

Anchorage House, Nettles Corner, Boscundle, PL25 3RH, (01726) 814071, *enq @anchoragehouse.co.uk,* – . VISA JCB.
February-October – **Meals** (by arrangement) (communal dining) 25.00 **s.** – **3 rm** 55. 76.00 **st.**

at Carlyon Bay *East : 2½ m. by A 3601 –* ✉ *St. Austell.*

Carlyon Bay, PL25 3RD, (01726) 812304, *info@carlyonbay.co.uk, Fax (01726) 814* ≤ Carlyon Bay, « Extensive gardens », , heated, , 18, , – , rest, – 65. VISA.
Meals 12.50/24.00 and a la carte 30.00/41.00 **st.** 10.00 – **73 rm** 85.00/250.00 – SB.

Cliff Head, Sea Rd, PL25 3RB, (01726) 812345, *cliffhead@btconnect.co Fax (01726) 815511,* , , – rest, – 230. VISA.
Meals 7.25/12.95 and dinner a la carte 18.50/23.65 **st.** 8.95 – **59 rm** 50.00/82.00 **s** SB.

Porth Avallen, Sea Rd, PL25 3SG, (01726) 812802, *info@porthavallen.co Fax (01726) 817097,* ≤ Carlyon Bay, , – – 100. VISA JCB.
Meals 15.50/25.50 and dinner a la carte 22.00/37.00 **t.** 10.50 – **24 rm** 68.00/110.00

The Lodge at Carlyon Bay, 91 Sea Rd, PL25 3SH, (01726) 8155 *Fax (01726) 815543,* – . VISA.
closed Christmas – **Meals** (by arrangement) 20.00 – **6 rm** 50.00/90.00.

at Charlestown *Southeast : 2 m. by A 390 –* ✉ *St. Austell.*

Pier House, PL25 3NJ, (01726) 67955, *Fax (01726) 69246,* ≤ – rest, . VISA.
closed 25 December – **Meals** a la carte 15.70/27.90 **t.** 8.95 – **26 rm** 40.00/80.00 **t.**

T' Gallants without rest., 6 Charlestown Rd, PL25 3NJ, (01726) 70203, – . VISA.
8 rm 30.00/48.00 **s.**

T BLAZEY *Cornwall* 403 F 32 – *pop. 8 837 (inc. Par).*
London 276 – Newquay 21 – Plymouth 33 – Truro 19.

Nanscawen Manor House without rest., Prideaux Rd, PL24 2SR, West : 3/4 m. by Luxulyan rd (01726) 814488, *keith@nanscawen.com, Fax (01726) 814488,* ←, heated, – rm, TV P. MC VISA.
3 rm 68.00/84.00 **s.**

T BRELADE'S BAY *Jersey (Channel Islands)* 403 P 33 and 230 ⑪ – *see Channel Islands.*

T HELENS *Mersey.* 402 403 L 23 – *pop. 106 293.*
Sherdley Park Municipal, Sherdley Park (01744) 813149.
London 207 – Liverpool 16 – Manchester 27.

Hilton St. Helens, Linkway West, WA10 1NG, (01744) 453444, *reservations@sthelens.stakis.co.uk, Fax (01744) 454655,* – rm, TV P – 200. MC AE VISA JCB
Britisserie : **Meals** *(closed Saturday lunch)* 10.00/25.00 and a la carte 17.85/27.90 **t.** 11.95 – 13.50 – **81 rm** 125.00/145.00 **st.**, 3 suites – SB.

Travel Inn, Eurolink, Lea Green, WA9 4TT, South : 3 m. off A 570 (01744) 818971, *Fax (01744) 851427* – rm, rest, TV P. MC AE VISA JCB.
Meals (grill rest.) – **40 rm** 41.95 **t.**

T HELIER *Jersey (Channel Islands)* 403 P 33 and 230 ⑪ – *see Channel Islands.*

T. ISSEY *Cornwall* 403 F 32 – *see Padstow.*

T IVES *Cambs.* 404 T 27 – *pop. 15 312* – *Huntingdon.*
London 75 – Cambridge 14 – Huntingdon 6.

Oliver's Lodge, Needingworth Rd, PE27 5JP, (01480) 463252, *reception@oliverslodge.co.uk, Fax (01480) 461150,* – rest, TV P – 65. MC AE VISA JCB
Meals a la carte 19.25/23.00 **t.** 9.95 – **17 rm** 75.00/110.00 **t.** – SB.

Slepe Hall, Ramsey Rd, PE27 5RB, (01480) 463122, *mail@slepehall.co.uk, Fax (01480) 300706,* – rest, TV P – 200. MC AE VISA.
closed 4 days Christmas-New Year – **Meals** 15.50/17.50 **st.** 9.25 – **16 rm** 75.00/100.00 **st.**

Holywell *East : 3 m. by A 1123 – Huntingdon.*

Old Ferryboat Inn, PE27 4TG, (01480) 463227, *theoldferryboatinn@tinyworld.co.uk, Fax (01480) 463245,* – rm, TV P – 70. MC AE VISA JCB.
Meals a la carte 10.70/16.90 **t.** – **7 rm** 50.00/70.00 **t.**

T IVES *Cornwall* 403 D 33 *The West Country G.* – *pop. 10 092.*
See : *Town★★ - Barbara Hepworth Museum★★* AC Y M1 – *Tate St Ives★★ (←★★) - St Nicholas Chapel (←★★)* Y – *Parish Church★* Y A.
Env. : *S : Penwith★★* Y.
Exc. : *St Michael's Mount★★ (←★★) S : 10 m. by B 3306* – Y – *B 3311, B 3309 and A 30.*
Tregenna Castle H. (01736) 795254 ext: 121 Y – *West Cornwall, Lelant (01736) 753401.*
The Guildhall, Street-an-Pol (01736) 796297.
London 319 – Penzance 10 – Truro 25.

Plan on next page

Porthminster, The Terrace, TR26 2BN, (01736) 795221, *reception@porthminster-hotel.co.uk, Fax (01736) 797043,* ←, heated, – TV P. MC AE VISA — Y s
Meals (bar lunch Monday-Saturday)/dinner 15.00 and a la carte 15.80/24.70 **t.** 10.40 – **43 rm** (dinner included) 73.00/146.00 **st.** – SB.

Blue Hayes without rest., Trelyon Ave, TR26 2AD, (01736) 797129, ←, – TV P. MC AE VISA. — Y c
closed December-January – **7 rm** 39.00/120.00 **st.**

Old Vicarage without rest., Parc-an-Creet, TR26 2ES, (01736) 796124, *holidays@oldvicaragehotel.freeserve.co,.uk, Fax (01736) 796124,* – TV P. MC VISA JCB — Y i
Easter-October – **8 rm** 21.00/54.00 **t.**

Trewinnard without rest., 4 Parc Ave, TR26 2DN, (01736) 794168, *trewinnard@cwcom.net, Fax (01736) 798161,* ← – TV P. MC VISA JCB. — Y e
Easter-October – **7 rm** 30.00/60.00 **st.**

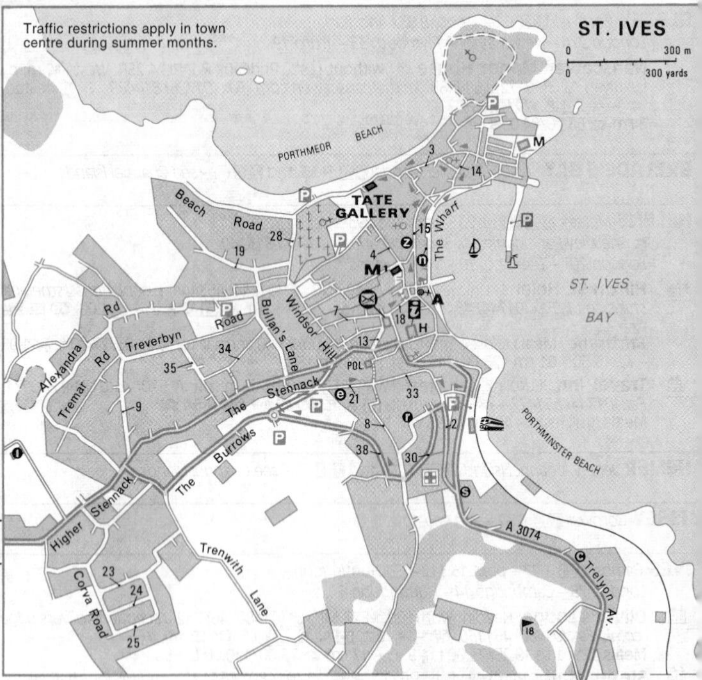

Traffic restrictions apply in town centre during summer months.

ST. IVES

0 300 m
0 300 yards

Albert Road . . . . . Y 2
Back Road West . . . . Y 3
Barnoon Hill . . . . . Y 4
Bedford Road . . . Y 7
Bishop's Road . . . Y 8
Carnellis Road . . . Y 9
Chapel Street . . . Y 13
Fish Street . . . . . . Y 14
Fore Street . . . . . Y 15
High Street . . . . . . Y 18
Orange Lane . . . . Y 19
Parc Owles . . . . . Z 20
Park Av. . . . . Y 21
Penwith Road . . . Y 23
Porthia Crescent . . . . . . Y 24
Porthia Road . . . . Y 25
Porthmeor Hill . . . Y 28
Porthrepta Road . . . . Z 29
Talland Road . . . . Y 30
Tregenna Terrace . . . . Y 33
Trelawney Road . Y 34
Trerice Road . . . . Y 35
Trewidden Road . Y 38
Wheal Whidden . Z 40

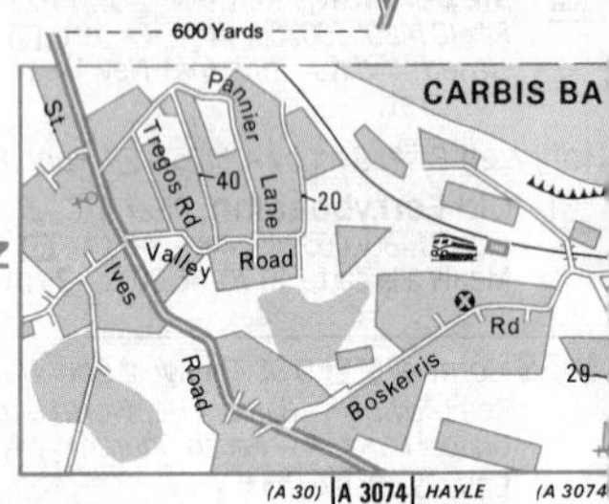

The Pondarosa, 10 Porthminster Terr, TR26 2DQ, ℘ (01736) 795875, *pondarosa-hot talk21.com, Fax (01736) 797811* – ⅔ TV P. MC AE VISA. ⅔ Y
Meals (by arrangement) 14.00 **st.** 9.00 – **10 rm** 21.00/48.00 **st.** – SB.

Russets, 18a Fore St, TR26 1AB, ℘ (01736) 794700, *russets@manutd.c Fax (01736) 794700* – ⅔. MC AE VISA Y
Meals (dinner only and lunch 25 December) a la carte 19.80/25.90 **t.** 8.90.

Alfresco, Wharf Rd, TR26 1LF, ℘ (01736) 793737, *alfresco@stivesharbour.c Fax (01736) 796831* – MC VISA Y
closed 25 December and 2-4 January – **Meals** a la carte 16.75/24.65 **t.** 9.50.

at Carbis Bay *South : 1¾ m. on A 3074* – ✉ *St. Ives.*

Boskerris, Boskerris Rd, TR26 2NQ, ℘ (01736) 795295, *boskerris.hotel@btinternet.c Fax (01736) 798632*, ≤, heated, – ⅔ rest, TV P. MC AE VISA Z
Easter-October – **Meals** (bar lunch)/dinner 16.50/25.00 **st.** 9.50 – **16 rm** 75. 110.00 **st.** – SB.

JUST *Cornwall* 403 C 33 *The West Country G. – pop. 2 092.*
See : *Church*★.
Env. : *Penwith*★★ – *Sancreed – Church*★★ *(Celtic Crosses*★★*), SE : 3 m. by A 3071 – St Buryan*★★ *(Church Tower*★★*), SE : 5 ½ m. by B 3306 and A 30 – Land's End*★ *(cliff scenery*★★★*), S : 5½ m. by B 3306 and A 30 – Cape Cornwall*★ *(≤*★★*), W : 1½ m. – Morvah (≤*★★*), NE : 4½ m. by B 3306 – Geevor Tin Mine*★ **AC**, *N : 3 m. by B 3306 – Carn Euny*★, *SE : 3 m. by A 3071 – Wayside Cross*★ *– Sennen Cove*★ *(≤*★*), S : 5½ m. by B 3306 and A 30.*
Exc. : *Porthcurno*★, *S : 9½ m. by B 3306, A 30 and B 3315.*
18 *Cape Cornwall G. & C.C.* ✆ *(01736) 788611.*
London 325 – Penzance 7.5 – Truro 35.

Boscean Country ⛟, TR19 7QP, Northwest : ½ m. by Boswedden Rd ✆ *(01736) 788748, boscean@aol.com, Fax (01736) 788748*, ≤, – P. VISA JCB.
Meals (dinner only) (residents only) 13.00 **t.** 9.95 – **12 rm** 31.00/46.00 **t.**

KEVERNE *Cornwall* 403 E 33 – *pop. 1 843.*
London 302 – Penzance 26 – Truro 28.

Valley View House, Porthallow Cove, TR12 6PN, Northeast : 2 ½ m. ✆ (01326) 280370, *hawthorne@valleyviewhouse.freeserve.co.uk, Fax (01326) 280370* – TV.
closed November-December – **Meals** (by arrangement) 12.95 **st.** – **3 rm** 19.00/44.00.

Pour visiter une ville ou une région : utilisez les ***Guides Verts Michelin.***

LAWRENCE *I.O.W.* 403 404 Q 32 – *see Wight (Isle of).*

LEONARDS *E. Sussex* 404 V 31 – *see Hastings and St Leonards.*

MARGARET'S AT CLIFFE *Kent* 404 Y 30 – *see Dover.*

MARTIN *Guernsey (Channel Islands)* 403 P 33 and 230 ⑩ – *see Channel Islands.*

MARTIN'S *Cornwall* 403 ㉚ – *see Scilly (Isles of).*

MARY'S *Cornwall* 403 ㉚ – *see Scilly (Isles of).*

MAWES *Cornwall* 403 E 33 *The West Country G.* – ✉ *Truro.*
See : *Town*★ - *Castle*★ **AC** *(≤*★*).*
Env. : *St Just-in-Roseland Church*★★, *N : 2½ m. by A 3078.*
London 299 – Plymouth 56 – Truro 18.

Tresanton ⛟, 27 Lower Castle Rd, TR2 5DR, ✆ (01326) 270055, *info@tresanton.com, Fax (01326) 270053*, ≤ St Mawes bay, St Anthony's head and lighthouse, – TV P – 50. AE VISA.
Meals (booking essential to non-residents) 33.00 **t.** 12.00 – **24 rm** 200.00/265.00 **st.**, 2 suites.

Idle Rocks, Harbourside, 1 Tredenham Rd, TR2 5AN, ✆ (01326) 270771, *reception@idlerocks.co.uk, Fax (01326) 270062*, ≤ harbour and estuary – rest, TV. AE VISA
Meals (light lunch)/dinner 28.95 **t.** 11.95 – **27 rm** (dinner included) 89.00/198.00 **t.**

Rising Sun, The Square, TR2 5DJ, ✆ (01326) 270233, *therisingsun@btclick.com, Fax (01326) 270198* – TV P. VISA
Meals (bar lunch Monday-Saturday)/dinner 27.00 **t.** 10.00 – **8 rm** 60.00/120.00 **t.**

The St Mawes, The Sea Front, TR2 5DW, ✆ (01326) 270266, *stmaweshotel@compuserve.com, Fax (01326) 270170*, ≤ – TV. VISA
Meals (light lunch)/dinner a la carte 14.45/23.90 **t.** 9.95 – **5 rm** 60.00/110.00 **t.** – SB.

MICHAELS-ON-WYRE *Lancs.* 402 L 22.
London 235 – Blackpool 24 – Burnley 35 – Manchester 43.

Compton House without rest., Garstang Rd, PR3 0TE, ✆ (01995) 679378, *dave@compton-hs.co.uk, Fax (01995) 679378*, – TV P. VISA JCB.
closed 20 December-5 January – **3 rm** 30.00/40.00.

ST NEOTS *Cambs.* 404 T 27 – *pop. 25 110.*
London 60 – Cambridge 19 – Northampton 33 – Peterborough 28.

Premier Lodge, 1 Great North Rd, Eaton Socon, PE19 8EN, Southwest : 2 m. by B at junction with A 421 ✆ (01480) 212232, *Fax (01480) 471077,* – |‡|, ⋟ rm, ▤ rest, ♿ P. MO AE ① VISA JCB
Meals (grill rest.) a la carte approx. 16.95 **t.** 8.75 – **63 rm** 42.95 **t.**

ST PETER *Jersey (Channel Islands)* 403 P 33 and 230 ⑪ – *see Channel Islands.*

ST. PETER IN THE WOOD *Guernsey (Channel Islands)* 403 P 33 and 230 ⑨ – *see Cha Islands.*

ST PETER PORT *Guernsey (Channel Islands)* 403 P 33 and 230 ⑩ – *see Channel Islands.*

ST SAVIOUR *Guernsey (Channel Islands)* 403 P 33 and 230 ⑨ – *see Channel Islands.*

ST SAVIOUR *Jersey (Channel Islands)* 403 P 33 and 230 ⑪ – *see Channel Islands.*

SALCOMBE *Devon* 403 I 33 *The West Country G. – pop. 2 189.*
Env. : *Sharpitor (Overbecks Museum and Garden★) (≤★★)* **AC**, *S : 2 m. by South Sands Z*
Exc. : *Prawle Point (≤★★★) E : 16 m. around coast by A 381 – Y – and A 379.*
Market St ✆ (01548) 843927.
London 243 – Exeter 43 – Plymouth 27 – Torquay 28.

SALCOMBE

Town plans
roads most used by traffic and those on which guide listed hotels and restaurants stand are fully drawn; the beginning only of lesser roads is indicated.

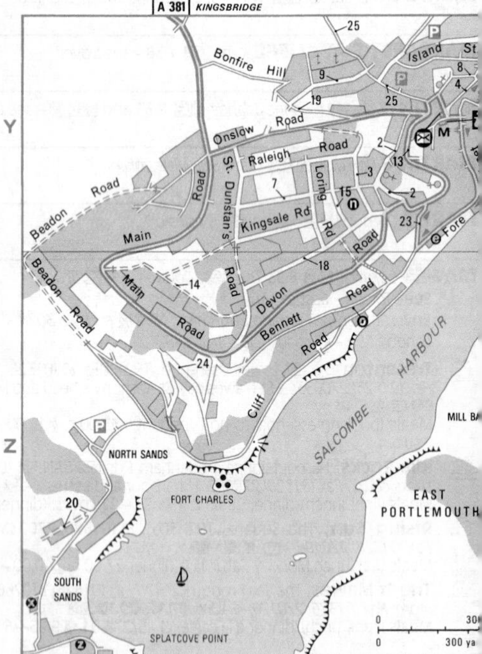

Tides Reach, South Sands, TQ8 8LJ, ✆ (01548) 843466, *enquire@tidesreach.c* *Fax (01548) 843954,* ≤ estuary, ⅃₆, ≘, ⊠, ⛟, squash – |‡| ⚓, ⋟ rest, TV P. MO AE ① JCB
closed December-January – **Meals** (bar lunch)/dinner 30.00 **st.** 13.75 – **35 rm** ⊒ (dir included) 115.00/260.00 **st.** – SB.

Marine, Cliff Rd, TQ8 8JH, ☎ (01548) 844444, *marine@menzies-hotels.co.uk, Fax (01548) 843109,* ≤ estuary, ... Y e
Meals 27.50 – **52 rm** (dinner included) 80.00/250.00 **st.**, 1 suite – SB.

Bolt Head, South Sands, TQ8 8LL, ☎ (01548) 843751, *info@boltheadhotel.com, Fax (01548) 843061,* ≤ estuary, heated – ... VISA Z z
11 March-October – **Meals** (dinner only) 25.00 **t.** 9.75 – 9.95 – **28 rm** 78.00/176.00 **st.** – SB.

Lyndhurst without rest., Bonaventure Rd, TQ8 8BG, ☎ (01548) 842481, *lyndhursthotel @salcombeonline.co.uk, Fax (01548) 842481,* ≤ – ... VISA JCB. Y n
March-October – **8 rm** 35.00/70.00 **s.**

Soar Mill Cove *Southwest : 4¼ m. by A 381 via Malborough village* – Y – ✉ *Salcombe.*

Soar Mill Cove , TQ7 3DS, ☎ (01548) 561566, *info@makepeacehotels.co.uk, Fax (01548) 561223,* ≤, heated, ... VISA JCB
closed 2 January-8 February – **Meals** (booking essential to non-residents) 25.00/40.00 **t.** 17.00 – **21 rm** 116.00/170.00 – SB.

Hope Cove *West : 4 m. by A 381 via Malborough village* – Y – ✉ *Kingsbridge.*

Lantern Lodge , TQ7 3HE, by Grand View Rd ☎ (01548) 561280, *Fax (01548) 561736,* ≤, ... rest, ... VISA JCB.
March-November – **Meals** (bar lunch)/dinner 18.00 **t.** – **14 rm** (dinner included) 84.00/140.00 **t.**

es prix Pour toutes précisions sur les prix indiqués dans ce guide, reportez-vous aux pages de l'introduction.

LE *Gtr. Manchester* 402 403 404 N 23 – *pop. 56 052* – ✉ *Manchester.*

Sale Lodge, Golf Rd ☎ (0161) 973 3404.

London 212 – Liverpool 36 – Manchester 6 – Sheffield 43.

Belmore, 143 Brooklands Rd, M33 3QN, ☎ (0161) 973 2538, *belmore-hotel@hotmail.com, Fax (0161) 973 2665,* ... – 80. ... VISA
***Classic* :** **Meals** *(closed Sunday dinner)* (booking essential to non-residents) 9.95/15.95 (lunch) and dinner a la carte approx. 35.00 **st.** 12.50 – ***Cada's* :** **Meals** 9.95/15.95 (lunch) and dinner a la carte approx. 21.00 **st.** 12.50 – **21 rm** 90.00/165.00 **st.**, 2 suites.

Amblehurst, 44 Washway Rd, M33 7QZ, on A 56 ☎ (0161) 973 8800, *amblehurst@aol.com, Fax (0161) 905 1697* – rm, rest, ... – 50. ... VISA
Meals *(closed Sunday dinner)* 9.95/13.95 and dinner a la carte **t.** – **64 rm** 75.00/95.00 **st.**

Travel Inn, Carrington Lane, Ashton-upon-Mersey, M33 5BL, Northwest : 1 ½ m. by B 5166 on A 6144 ☎ (0161) 962 8113, *Fax (0161) 905 1742* – rm, ... – 40. ... VISA.
Meals (grill rest.) – **40 rm** 41.95 **t.**

Cornerstones, 230 Washway Rd, M33 4RA, ☎ (0161) 283 6909, *info@cornerstoneshotel.com, Fax (0161) 283 6909,* ... VISA JCB.
closed Christmas-New Year – **Meals** (by arrangement) 15.00 **t.** 10.00 – 4.50 – **9 rm** 27.00/50.00.

LFORD QUAYS *Gtr. Manchester* – *see Manchester.*

LFORDS *Surrey* 404 T 30 – *see Redhill.*

LISBURY *Wilts.* 403 404 O 30 *The West Country G.* – *pop. 39 268.*

See : *City*★★ – *Cathedral*★★★ *AC* Z – *Salisbury and South Wiltshire Museum*★ *AC* Z **M2** – *Close*★ Z : *Mompesson House*★ *AC* Z **A** – *Sarum St Thomas Church*★ Y **B** – *Royal Gloucestershire, Berkshire and Wiltshire Regiment Museum*★.

Env. : *Wilton Village*★ *(Wilton House*★★ *AC, Wilton Carpet Factory*★ *AC), W : 3 m. by A 30* Y – *Old Sarum*★ *AC, N : 2 m. by A 345* Y – *Woodford (Heale House Garden*★*) AC, NW : 4½ m. by Stratford Rd* Y.

Exc. : *Stonehenge*★★★ *AC, NW : 10 m. by A 345* – Y – *and A 303* – *Wardour Castle*★ *AC, W : 15 m. by A 30* Y.

18, 9 *Salisbury & South Wilts., Netherhampton ☎ (01722) 742645* – 18 *High Post, Great Durnford ☎ (01722) 782356.*

Fish Row ☎ (01722) 334956.

London 91 – Bournemouth 28 – Bristol 53 – Southampton 23.

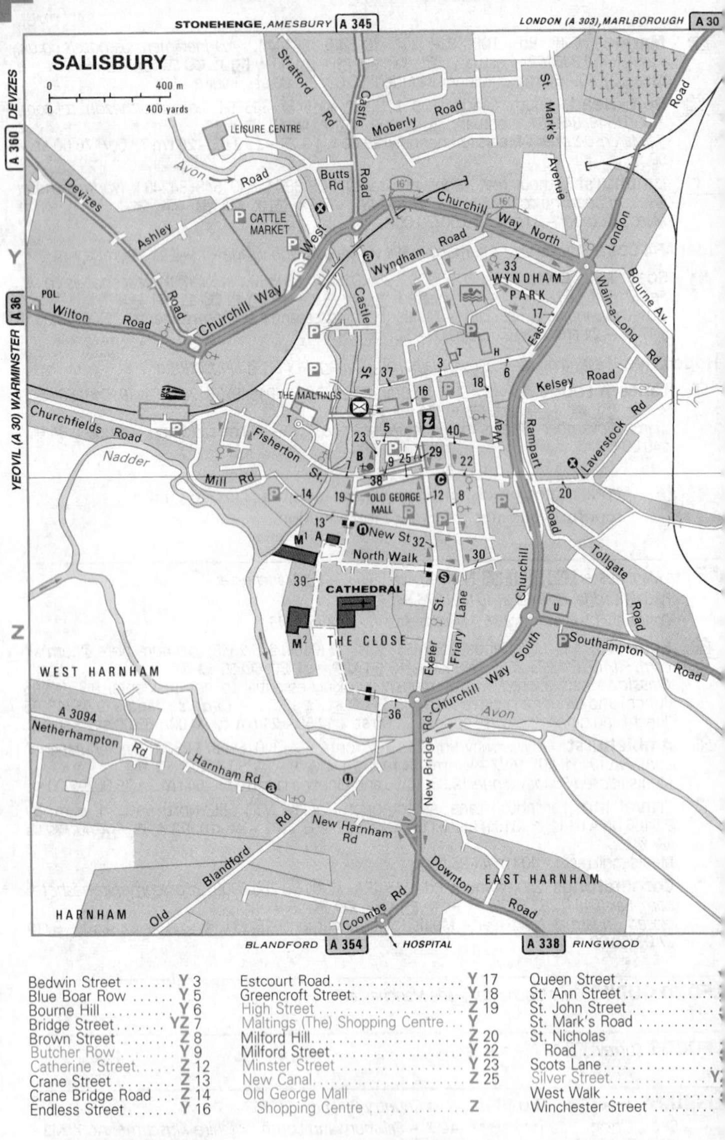

Bedwin Street . . . . Y 3	Estcourt Road . . . . Y 17	Queen Street . . . .
Blue Boar Row . . . . . . Y 5	Greencroft Street . . . . Y 18	St. Ann Street . . . .
Bourne Hill . . . . Y 6	High Street . . . . Z 19	St. John Street . . . .
Bridge Street . . . . YZ 7	Maltings (The) Shopping Centre . . . Y	St. Mark's Road . . . .
Brown Street . . . . Z 8	Milford Hill . . . . Z 20	St. Nicholas Road . . . .
Butcher Row . . . . Y 9	Milford Street . . . . Y 22	Scots Lane . . . .
Catherine Street . . . . . . Z 12	Minster Street . . . . Y 23	Silver Street . . . . Y
Crane Street . . . . Z 13	New Canal . . . . Z 25	West Walk . . . .
Crane Bridge Road . . . Z 14	Old George Mall Shopping Centre . . . . Z	Winchester Street . . . .
Endless Street . . . . Y 16		

White Hart, 1 St John's St, SP1 2SD, ☎ (0870) 400 8125, *Fax (01722) 412761* – – 80. MC AE VISA – **Meals** *(closed Saturday lunch)* a la carte 19.40/30.00 **t.** 12. – 11.95 – **68 rm** 95.00/140.00 **t.** – SB.

Red Lion, 4 Milford St, SP1 2AN, ☎ (01722) 323334, *reception@the-redlion.co* *Fax (01722) 325756* – – 100. MC AE VISA JCB. **Meals** a la carte 15.25/20.70 **t.** 12.95 – 9.50 – **51 rm** 84.00/122.00 **t.** – SB.

Milford Hall, 206 Castle St, SP1 3TE, ☎ (01722) 417411, *milfordhallhotel@cs.* *Fax (01722) 419444* – – 25. MC AE VISA *closed 24-27 December* – **Meals** a la carte 17.40/29.40 **st.** 10.00 – **35 rm** 100 115.00 **st.** – SB.

Cricket Field House, Wilton Rd, SP2 9NS, West : 1 ¼ m. on A 36 ☎ (01722) 322595, *cricketfieldcottage@btinternet.com, Fax (01722) 322595* – *Meals (closed Friday-Sunday)* (dinner only) 12.50/21.00 – **14 rm** 40.00/65.00 **st.** – SB.

Travel Inn, Pearce Way, Bishopdown, SP1 3YU, Northeast : 2 ½ m. on A 338 ☎ (01722) 339836, *Fax (01722) 337889* – rm. Meals (grill rest.) – **40 rm** 41.95 **t.**

Old House without rest., 161 Wilton Rd, SP2 7JQ, West : 1 m. on A 36 ☎ (01722) 333433, *Fax (01722) 335551*, – **6 rm** 30.00/50.00 **s.**, 1 suite.

Stratford Lodge, 4 Park Lane, SP1 3NP, off Castle Rd ☎ (01722) 325177, *enquiries@stratfordlodge.co.uk, Fax (01722) 325177*, – Meals (by arrangement) 19.95 **t.** 11.95 – **8 rm** 50.00/70.00 **t.** – SB.

Glen Lyn without rest., 6 Bellamy Lane, Milford Hill, SP1 2SP, ☎ (01722) 327880, *glen.lyn@btinternet.com, Fax (01722) 327880*, – YZ x
7 rm 34.00/62.50 **st.**

Malvern without rest., 31 Hulse Rd, SP1 3LU, ☎ (01722) 327995, *malvern_gh@madasafish.com, Fax (01722) 327995*, – Y x
3 rm 40.00/50.00.

LXIX, 69 New St, SP1 2PH, ☎ (01722) 340000, *lx1x69@aol.om, Fax (01722) 340000* – Z n
closed Christmas, New Year, Saturday lunch and Sunday – **Meals** 12.00/20.00 (lunch) and dinner a la carte 23.50/33.50 **t.** 10.50.

Middle Winterslow *Northeast : 6½ m. by A 30 – Y – ✉ Salisbury.*

Beadles, Middleton, SP5 1QS, ☎ (01980) 863565, *winterbead@aol.com, Fax (01980) 863565*, – Meals (by arrangement) (communal dining) 22.50 **st.** – **3 rm** 45.00/70.00 **st.** – SB.

Whiteparish *Southeast : 7½ m. by A 36 – Z – on A 27 – ✉ Salisbury.*

Brickworth Farmhouse without rest., Brickworth Lane, SP5 2QE, Northwest : 1 ½ m. off A 36 ☎ (01794) 884663, *Fax (01794) 884186*, « Georgian farmhouse », –
closed 20 December-3 January – **4 rm** 25.00/50.00.

Newton Farmhouse, Southampton Rd, SP5 2QL, Southwest : 1 ½ m. on A 36 ☎ (01794) 884416, *reservations@newtonfarmhouse.co.uk*, –
closed 2 weeks in spring – **Meals** (by arrangement) 20.00 **s.** – **8 rm** 25.00/60.00 **s.**

Woodfalls *South : 7 ¾ m. by A 338 – Z – on B 3080 – ✉ Salisbury.*

Woodfalls Inn, The Ridge, SP5 2LN, ☎ (01725) 513222, *woodfallsi@aol.com, Fax (01725) 513220* – 100.
Meals a la carte 11.40/22.40 **st.** 9.00 – **10 rm** 49.95/79.95 **st.** – SB.

Harnham *Southwest : 1½ m. by A 3094 – ✉ Salisbury.*

Rose & Crown, Harnham Rd, SP2 8JQ, ☎ (01722) 399955, *Fax (01722) 339816*, <, « Part 13C inn, riverside setting », – 80. Z u
Meals 12.95/19.50 and a la carte 20.95/25.40 **st.** 10.95 – 10.50 – **28 rm** 110.00/140.00 **st.** – SB.

Grasmere House, 70 Harnham Rd, SP2 8JN, ☎ (01722) 338388, *grasmerehotel@mistral.co.uk, Fax (01722) 333710*, <, – rm, 80. Z a
Meals 7.50/26.50 and a la carte 19.25/26.95 **st.** 10.50 – **20 rm** 72.50/145.00 **st.** – SB.

Teffont *West : 10¼ m. by A 36 – Y – and A 30 on B 3089 – ✉ Salisbury.*

Howard's House, Teffont Evias, SP3 5RJ, ☎ (01722) 716392, *enq@howardshousehotel.com, Fax (01722) 716820*, « Part 17C former dower house », – rest,
closed Christmas – **Meals** (booking essential to non-residents) (dinner only and Sunday lunch)/dinner 19.95 and a la carte 26.85/35.40 **t.** 9.95 – **9 rm** 85.00/155.00 **t.**

Stapleford *Northwest : 7 m. by A 36 – Y – on B 3083 – ✉ Salisbury.*

Elm Tree Cottage without rest., Chain Hill, SP3 4LH, ☎ (01722) 790507, *jaw.sykes@virgin.net*, –
restricted opening in winter – **3 rm** 35.00/52.00 **s.**

Little Langford *Northwest : 8 m. by A 36 – Y – and Great Wishford rd – ✉ Salisbury.*

Little Langford Farmhouse without rest., SP3 4NR, ☎ (01722) 790205, *bandb@littlelangford.co.uk, Fax (01722) 790086*, <, « Working farm », –
restricted opening in winter – **3 rm** 35.00/55.00 **st.**

SALTASH *Cornwall* 403 H 32 *The West Country G. – pop. 14 139.*
Env. : *Tamar River*★★.
Exc. : *St Germans Church*★*, SW : 7 m. by A 38 and B 3249.*
18, 18 *St Mellion G. & C.C. ℘ (01579) 351351 –* 18 *China Fleet C.C. ℘ (01752) 848668.*
London 246 – Exeter 38 – Plymouth 7 – Truro 49.

Travelodge, Callington Rd, Carkeel, PL12 6LF, Northwest : 1 ½ m. by A 388 on A 38 a Saltash Service Area ℘ (01752) 848414, *Fax (01752) 849028* – ⇔, ▤ rest, TV & P – 3
MC AE VISA JCB. ✈
Meals (grill rest.) – **31 rm** 52.95 **t.**

SALTFORD *Bath & North East Somerset* 403 404 M 29 – *see Bristol.*

SAMLESBURY *Lancs.* 402 M 22 – *see Preston.*

SAMPFORD PEVERELL *Devon* 403 J 31 *The West Country G. – pop. 1 091 – ✉ Tiverton.*
Env. : *Uffculme (Coldharbour Mill★★), SE : 3 m. by A 373, A 38 and minor roads.*
Exc. : *Knightshayes Court★, W : 7 m. by A 373 and minor roads.*
London 184 – Barnstaple 34 – Exeter 20 – Taunton 19.

Parkway House, EX16 7BJ, ℘ (01884) 820255, *Fax (01884) 820780,* – ⇔ rest, TV – 150. MC AE VISA. ✈
Meals a la carte 13.25/18.85 **t.** 8.95 – **10 rm** ☐ 37.50/55.00 **t.** – SB.

SAMPFORD PEVERELL SERVICE AREA *Devon* 403 J 31 – *✉ Tiverton.*
London 184 – Barnstaple 34 – Exeter 20 – Taunton 19.

Travelodge, EX16 7HD, M 5 junction 27 ℘ (01884) 821087, *Fax (01884) 821087* – ⇔ rm, ▤ rest, TV & P. MC AE VISA JCB. ✈
Meals (grill rest.) – **40 rm** 39.95 **t.**

SANDBACH *Ches.* 402 403 404 M 24 – *pop. 15 839.*
18 *Malkins Bank ℘ (01270) 765931.*
London 177 – Liverpool 44 – Manchester 28 – Stoke-on-Trent 16.

Chimney House, Congleton Rd, CW11 4ST, East : 1 ½ m. on A 534 ℘ (01270) 7641.. *chimneyhouse@corushotels.com, Fax (01270) 768916,* – ⇔ TV P – 100.
AE VISA
Meals *(closed Saturday lunch)* 14.00/18.00 and dinner a la carte 21.50/30.00 **st.** 14.00
☐ 10.25 – **48 rm** 85.00/95.00 **st.** – SB.

Curshaws, Town Mill, High St, CW11 1AH, ℘ (01270) 753009 – ⇔. MC AE VISA JCB
closed Sunday dinner – **Meals** a la carte 15.25/23.25 **t.** 9.50.

at Wheelock *South : 1½ m. by A 534 – ✉ Sandbach.*

Grove House with rm, Mill Lane, CW11 4RD, ℘ (01270) 762582, *grovehouseho... supanet.com, Fax (01270) 759465,* « Georgian manor house » – ⇔ rest, TV P. MC AE
JCB. ✈
closed Christmas and New Year – **Meals** *(closed Sunday dinner)* (dinner only and Sun... lunch)/dinner 14.50 and a la carte 14.50/25.00 **t.** 9.25 – **8 rm** ☐ 47.50/85.00 **t.**

SANDFORD-ON-THAMES *Oxon. – see Oxford.*

SANDGATE *Kent* 404 X 30 – *see Folkestone.*

SANDHOE *Northd. – see Corbridge.*

SANDIACRE *Derbs.* 402 403 404 Q 25 – *see Nottingham (Notts.).*

Remember the speed limits that apply in the United Kingdom, unless otherwise signposted.
- 60 mph on single carriageway roads
- 70 mph on dual carriageway roads and motorways

NDIWAY *Ches.* 402 403 404 M 24 – ✉ *Northwich.*
London 191 – Liverpool 34 – Manchester 22 – Stoke-on-Trent 26.

Nunsmere Hall ⛵, Tarporley Rd, CW8 2ES, Southwest : 1 ½ m. by A 556 on A 49 ✆ (01606) 889100, *reservations@nunsmere.co.uk, Fax (01606) 889055,* ←, 🏠, « Part Victorian house on wooded peninsula », 🌳, 🎾 – 🛗 ⚡ 📺 🅿 – 🏛 50. MC AE ⓓ VISA JCB. ✂
Crystal : **Meals** 25.00 (lunch) and dinner a la carte 31.20/48.50 **t.** 🍷 16.00 – ☕ 17.50 – **36 rm** 125.00/350.00 **t.**

Premier Lodge, 520 Chester Rd, CW8 2DN, on A 556 ✆ (01606) 883006, *Fax (01606) 889706* – ⚡ rm, ▤ rest, 📺 ♿ 🅿 – 🏛 60. MC AE ⓓ VISA. ✂
Meals (grill rest.) a la carte approx. 16.95 **t.** 🍷 8.75 – **54 rm** 46.95 **t.**

NDWICH *Kent* 404 Y 30 *Great Britain G. – pop. 4 164.*
See : *Town*★.
ℹ *Guildhall* ✆ *(01304) 613565.*
London 72 – Canterbury 13 – Dover 12 – Maidstone 41 – Margate 9.

Bell, The Quay, CT13 9EF, ✆ (01304) 613388, *hotel@princes-leisure.co.uk, Fax (01304) 615308* – ⚡ 📺 🅿 – 🏛 150. MC AE ⓓ VISA JCB. ✂
*closed 24-26 December***Meals** 11.95/17.50 and a la carte 🍷 5.70 – **33 rm** ☕ 75.00/150.00 **t.** – SB.

George & Dragon Inn, 24 Fisher St, CT13 9EJ, ✆ (01304) 613106, *Fax (01304) 621137,* 🏠 – MC AE VISA
closed 25 December – **Meals** a la carte 12.40/25.40 **t.** 🍷 8.95.

NDY *Beds.* 404 T 27 – *pop. 8 554.*
ℹ *Girtford Bridge, London Rd* ✆ *(01767) 682728.*
London 49 – Bedford 8 – Cambridge 24 – Peterborough 35.

Holiday Inn Garden Court, Girtford Bridge, London Rd, SG19 1DH, West : ¾ m. by B 1042 at junction of A 1 with A 603 ✆ (01767) 692220, *sandy@holidayinns.co.uk, Fax (01767) 680452* – ⚡ rm, 📺 📞 🅿 – 🏛 100. MC AE ⓓ VISA JCB. ✂
Meals (dinner only) 15.00/20.00 and a la carte 18.00/24.00 **st.** 🍷 10.00 – ☕ 7.50 – **57 rm** 69.00 **st.**

Highfield Farm without rest., Great North Rd, SG19 2AQ, North : 2 m. by B 1042 on A 1 (southbound carriageway) ✆ (01767) 682332, *margaret@highfield-farm.co.uk, Fax (01767) 692503,* « Working farm », 🌳, 🎾 – ⚡ 🅿. MC VISA. ✂
6 rm ☕ 35.00/60.00 **st.**

NDYPARK *Devon* 403 I 31 – *see Chagford.*

PPERTON *Glos.* 403 404 N 28 – *see Cirencester.*

RK 403 P 33 and 230 ⑩ – *see Channel Islands.*

UNTON *Devon* 403 H 30 – ✉ *Braunton.*
Env. : *Braunton*★ – *St Brannock's Church*★, *E : 2½ m. on B 3231* – *Braunton Burrows*★, *E : ½ m. on B 3231.*
⛳18, ⛳18 *Saunton, Braunton* ✆ *(01271) 812436.*
London 230 – Barnstaple 8 – Exeter 48.

Saunton Sands, EX33 1LQ, ✆ (01271) 890212, *info@sauntonsands.co.uk, Fax (01271) 890145,* ← Saunton Sands, 🏋, ≘s, 🏊 heated, 🏊, 🌳, 🎾, squash – 🛗, ⚡ rest, ▤ rest, 📺 ♿ 🧒 🅿 – 🏛 175. MC AE ⓓ VISA. ✂
Meals 13.50/25.00 **st.** 🍷 10.00 – **92 rm** ☕ 80.00/220.00 **st.** – SB.

Preston House, EX33 1LG, ✆ (01271) 890472, *prestonhouse-saunton@zoom.co.uk, Fax (01271) 890555,* ← Saunton Sands, ≘s, 🏊 heated, 🌳 – ⚡ 📺 🅿. MC VISA JCB. ✂
closed 21 December-14 February – **Meals** *(closed Sunday)* (dinner only) 24.00/28.00 **st.** 🍷 10.95 – **12 rm** ☕ 65.00/130.00 **st.** – SB.

WBRIDGEWORTH *Herts.* 404 U 28 – *pop. 9 432.*
London 26 – Cambridge 32 – Chelmsford 17.

Goose Fat & Garlic, 52 Bell St, CM21 9AN, ✆ (01279) 722554, *lwootton@goosefatandgarlic.co.uk, Fax (01279) 600766* – MC AE VISA
closed 2 weeks Christmas, Saturday lunch and Sunday dinner – **Meals** a la carte 23.20/30.00 **t.** 🍷 12.75.

SAWLEY *Lancs.* 402 M 22 – *pop. 237.*
London 242 – Blackpool 39 – Leeds 44 – Liverpool 54.

XX **Spread Eagle,** BB7 4NH, ℘ (01200) 441202, *Fax (01200) 441973* – ⅏ P. MC AE VISA
closed Sunday dinner and Monday – **Meals** a la carte 15.95/24.95 **t.**

SCALBY *N. Yorks.* 402 S 21 – *see Scarborough.*

SCARBOROUGH *N. Yorks.* 402 S 21 *Great Britain G.* – *pop. 38 809.*
Exc. : *Robin Hood's Bay*★, *N : 16 m. on A 171 and minor rd to the right (signposte[d]) Whitby Abbey*★, *N : 21 m. on A 171 – Sledmere House*★, *S : 21 m. on A 645, B 1249 B 1253 (right).*
Scarborough North Cliff, North Cliff Ave, Burniston Rd ℘ (01723) 360786, NW : 2 m A 165 Y – *Scarborough South Cliff, Deepdale Ave, off Filey Rd ℘ (01723) 360522, S : by A 165* Z.
Unit 3, Pavilion House, Valley Bridge Rd ℘ (01723) 373333.
London 253 – Kingston-upon-Hull 47 – Leeds 67 – Middlesbrough 52.

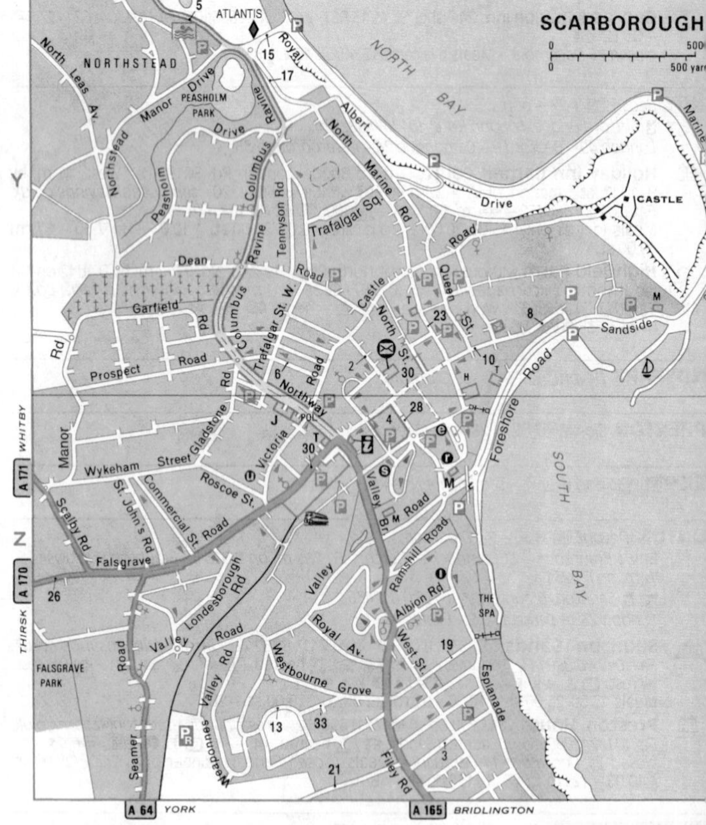

Beiderbecke's, 1-3 The Crescent, YO11 2PW, ✆ (01723) 365766, *info@beiderbeckes.com, Fax (01723) 367433* – rest, VISA. Z s
Meals – (see ***Marmalade's*** below) – **27 rm** 60.00/130.00 **t.** – SB.

The Crown, 7-11 Esplanade, YO11 2AG, ✆ (01723) 373491, *roomsales@scarboroughhotel.com, Fax (01723) 362271,* ← – – 160. AE VISA JCB Z i
Meals (bar lunch Monday to Saturday)/dinner 16.95 and a la carte 16.00/30.00 10.00 – **82 rm** 45.00/70.00 **st.**, 1 suite – SB.

Palm Court, St Nicholas Cliff, YO11 2ES, ✆ (01723) 368161, *Fax (01723) 371547,* – – 150. AE VISA. Z e
Meals (dancing Saturday evening) (bar lunch Monday to Saturday)/dinner 13.50/16.75 and a la carte 18.00/20.00 **st.** 9.50 – **45 rm** 41.00/86.00 **st.** – SB.

The Mount, Cliff Bridge Terr, YO11 2HA, ✆ (01723) 360961, *Fax (01723) 375850,* ← – . VISA Z r
Meals (dinner only and Sunday lunch)/dinner 16.50/22.50 12.50 – **50 rm** 45.00/86.00 **st.** – SB.

Ox Pasture Hall , Lady Edith's Drive, Raincliffe Woods, YO12 5TD, West : 3 ¼ m. by A 171 following signs for Raincliffe Woods ✆ (01723) 365295, *hawksmoor@oxpasture.freeserve.co.uk, Fax (01723) 355156,* ←, « Part 17C », , , – rest, . VISA
Meals (dinner only and Sunday lunch)/dinner 18.50 and a la carte 16.40/28.85 **t.** 9.95 – **23 rm** 45.50/90.00 **t.** – SB.

Old Mill, Mill St, YO11 1SZ, by Victoria Rd ✆ (01723) 372735, *info@windmill-hotel.co.uk, Fax (01723) 372735,* « Restored 18C windmill, toy museum » – rest, . VISA JCB. Z u
Meals (by arrangement) (residents only) (dinner only) 12.50 – **11 rm** 35.00/50.00 **st.**

Marmalade's (at Beiderbecke's H.), 1-3 The Crescent, YO11 2PN, ✆ (01723) 365766, *Fax (01723) 367433* – rest. VISA Z s
Meals (live jazz music Thursday-Saturday dinner and Sunday lunch) (dinner only) 15.95 and a la carte 13.50/25.00 **t.** 9.50.

Scalby *Northwest : 3 m. by A 171 – Z – ✉ Scarborough.*

Wrea Head Country House , Barmoor Lane, YO13 0PB, North : 1 m. by A 171 on Barmoor Lane ✆ (01723) 378211, *wreahead@englishrosehotels.co.uk, Fax (01723) 355936,* ←, « Victorian country house », , – rest, – 30. AE VISA JCB.
Meals 12.95/25.00 **t.** 14.95 – **19 rm** 75.00/190.00 **t.**, 1 suite – SB.

Hackness *Northwest : 7 m. by A 171 – Z – ✉ Scarborough.*

Hackness Grange , YO13 0JW, ✆ (01723) 882345, *hacknessgrange@englishrosehotels.co.uk, Fax (01723) 882391,* « 18C country house, gardens », , , – rest, . AE VISA.
Meals 12.95/25.00 **t.** 19.95 – **30 rm** 77.50/135.00 **t.**, 1 suite – SB.

AWTON *N. Yorks.* 402 Q 21 – *see Helmsley.*

ILLY (Isles of) *Cornwall* 403 ㉚ *The West Country G. – pop. 2 048.*

See : *Islands★ - The Archipelago (← ★★★).*

Env. : *St Agnes : Horsepoint★.*

Helicopter service from St Mary's and Tresco to Penzance : ✆ (01736) 363871.

St Mary's Airport : ✆ (01720) 422677, E : 1½ m. from Hugh Town.

from Hugh Town to Penzance (Isles of Scilly Steamship Co. Ltd) (summer only) (2 h 40 mn).

The Old Wesleyan Chapel, Well Lane, St Mary's ✆ (01720) (Scillonia) 422536.

yher *The West Country G. – pop. 78 – ✉ Scillonia.*

See : *Watch Hill (← ★) – Hell Bay★.*

Hell Bay , TR23 0PR, ✆ (01720) 422947, *hellbay@aol.com, Fax (01720) 423004,* – rest, . VISA JCB.
March-October – **Meals** (bar lunch)/dinner 28.00 **t.** 11.95 – **3 rm** (dinner included) 162.50/250.00, **14 suites** 160.00/250.00 **t** – SB.

Bank Cottage , TR23 0PR, ✆ (01720) 422612, *macmace@patrol.i-way.co.uk, Fax (01720) 422612,* ←, – .
April-October – **5 rm** (dinner included) 41.00/96.00 **st.**

ENGLAND

St Martin's *The West Country G. – pop. 113.*

See : *St Martin's Head (≤★★).*

St Martin's on the Isle ⛰, TR25 0QW, ✆ (01720) 422092, *stay@stmartinshotel.co.u* *Fax (01720) 422298,* ≤ Tean Sound and islands, « Idyllic island setting », ▣, ▣, ✂ ▣ rest, ▣ ▣. ▣ ▣ ▣ VISA
March-October – ***Tean :*** **Meals** (bar lunch)/dinner 35.00 **st.** 15.00 – **28 rm** ▣ (dinn included) 95.00/190.00 **st.**, 2 suites – SB.

St Mary's *The West Country G. – pop. 1 607.*

See : *Gig racing★★ – Garrison Walk★ (≤★★) – Peninnis Head★ – Hugh Town - Museum★.*
▣ ✆ *(01720) 422692.*

Star Castle ⛰, The Garrison, TR21 0JA, ✆ (01720) 422317, *reception@starcastlesci demon.co.uk, Fax (01720) 422343,* ≤, « Elizabethan fortress », ▣, ▣, ✂ – ▣ rest, ▣ ▣ VISA
mid March-mid October – **Meals** (bar lunch)/dinner 23.00/33.00 10.00 – **30 rm** ▣ (dinn included) 85.00/187.00 **t.**, 4 suites – SB.

Atlantic, Hugh St, Hugh Town, TR21 0PL, ✆ (01720) 422417, *atlantichotel@btintern com, Fax (01720) 423009,* ≤ St Mary's Harbour – ▣ ▣. ▣ VISA
March-October – **Meals** (dinner only) 16.00/25.00 **t.** 11.60 – **24 rm** ▣ (dinner include 90.00/190.00 **t.**

Carnwethers Country House ⛰, Pelistry Bay, TR21 0NX, ✆ (01720) 4224 *Fax (01720) 422415,* ▣, ▣ heated, ▣ – ▣ ▣
May-September – **Meals** (by arrangement) 6.00 – **9 rm** ▣ (dinner included) 67.0 124.00 **st.**

Crebinick House without rest., Church St, TR21 0JT, ✆ (01720) 422968, *enquirie crebinick.co.uk, Fax (01720) 422968* – ▣ ▣. ▣
April-October – **6 rm** ▣ 40.00/68.00.

Evergreen Cottage without rest., Parade, High Town, TR21 0LP, ✆ (01720) 42271 ▣
closed 24 December-3 January – **5 rm** ▣ 29.50/59.00 **st.**

Tresco *The West Country G. – pop. 167 – ✉ New Grimsby.*

See : *Island★ - Abbey Gardens★★ AC (Lighthouse Way ≤★★).*

The Island ⛰, Old Grimsby, TR24 0PW, ✆ (01720) 422883, *islandhotel@tresco.co. Fax (01720) 423008,* ≤ St Martin's and islands, « Idyllic island setting, sub-trop gardens », ▣ heated, ▣, ✂ – ▣ rest, ▣ ▣. ▣ ▣ VISA. ▣
March-October – **Meals** (bar lunch)/dinner 35.00/37.00 and a la carte **t.** 15.00 – **46 rm** (dinner included) 138.00/368.00 **t.**, 2 suites.

New Inn, TR24 0QQ, ✆ (01720) 422844, *newinn@tresco.co.uk, Fax (01720) 423200,* ▣ heated, ▣ – ▣ rest, ▣. ▣ VISA. ▣
Meals (booking essential to non-residents) (bar lunch)/dinner 26.50 **t.** 10.65 – **14 rm** (dinner included) 129.00/194.00 **t.** – SB.

SCOTCH CORNER *N. Yorks.* 402 P 20 – ✉ *Richmond.*

London 235 – Carlisle 70 – Middlesbrough 25 – Newcastle upon Tyne 43.

Quality H. Scotch Corner, DL10 6NR, ✆ (01748) 850900, *admin@gb609.u_net.co Fax (01748) 825417,* ▣, ▣, ▣ – ▣, ▣ rm, ▣ ▣ – ▣ 350. ▣ ▣ ▣ VISA
Meals *(closed Saturday lunch)* 17.95 (dinner) and a la carte approx. 23.15 **st.** 11.9 ▣ 10.75 – **90 rm** 85.00/95.00 **t.** – SB.

Travelodge, Middleton Tyas Lane, D10 6PQ, ✆ (01325) 377719, *Fax (01325) 37789* ▣ rm, ▣ rest, ▣ ▣ ▣. ▣ ▣ ▣ VISA JCB. ▣
Meals (grill rest.) – **50 rm** 49.95 **t.**

Travelodge, Skeeby, DL10 5EQ, South : 1 m. on A 1 (northbound carriagew ✆ (01748) 823768, *Fax (01748) 823768* – ▣ rm, ▣ rest, ▣ ▣ ▣. ▣ ▣ ▣ VISA JCB. ▣
Meals (grill rest.) – **40 rm** 49.95 **t.**

When travelling for business or pleasure in ***England, Wales, Scotland*** *and* ***Ireland:***

- use the series of five maps (nos 401, 402, 403, 404 and 923) at a scale of 1:400 000
- they are the perfect complement to this Guide

CUNTHORPE *North Lincolnshire* 402 S 23 – *pop. 75 982.*

Ashby Decoy, Burringham Rd (01724) 842913 – Kingsway (01724) 840945 – , Grange Park, Butterwick Rd, Messingham (01724) 762945.

Humberside Airport : (01652) 688456, E : 15 m. by A 18.

London 167 – Leeds 54 – Lincoln 30 – Sheffield 45.

Forest Pines, Ermine St, Broughton, DN20 0AQ, Southeast : 5 m. by A 1029 off A 18 (01652) 650770, *enquiries@forestpines.co.uk, Fax (01652) 650495,* – 250. VISA JCB.
Meals 17.25/29.95 (lunch) and a la carte 19.50/29.95 **st.** – **84 rm** 90.00/100.00 **st.**, 2 suites – SB.

Travel Inn, Lakeside Retail Park, Lakeside Parkway, DN16 3NA, Southeast : 2 ½ m. off A 1029 at junction with A 18 (01724) 870030, *Fax (01724) 851809* – rm, rest, VISA.
Meals (grill rest.) – **40 rm** 41.95 **t.**

EAHAM *Durham* 401 402 P/Q 19 – *pop. 4 137.*

London 284 – Newcastle upon Tyne 17 – Carlisle 77 – Leeds 84 – Middlesbrough 24.

Seaham Hall, Lord Byron's Walk, SR7 7AG, North : 1 ¼ m. by B 1287 (0191) 516 1400, *reservations@seaham-hall.com, Fax (0191) 516 1410,* « 17C and 19C hall, contemporary interior », – 140. VISA.
Meals (booking essential to non-residents) 25.00/34.00 and dinner a la carte 30.25/46.00 **t.** 13.95 – **16 rm** 185.00/325.00 **t.**, 3 suites – SB.

EAFORD *E. Sussex* 404 U 31 – *pop. 19 622.*

Seaford Head, Southdown Rd (01323) 890139 – East Blatchington (01323) 892442.

25 Clinton Pl (01323) 897426.

London 65 – Brighton 14 – Folkestone 64.

Westdean *East : 3 ¼ m by A 259.*

Old Parsonage without rest., BN25 4AL, (01323) 870432, *raymondj.woodhams@virgin.net, Fax (01323) 870432,* « 13C King John house », – .
closed Christmas and New Year – **3 rm** 70.00/85.00.

EAHOUSES *Northd.* 401 402 P 17 *Great Britain G.*

Env. : *Farne Islands★ (by boat from harbour).*

Beadnell Rd (01665) 720794.

Car Park, Seafield Rd (01665) 720884 (Easter-October).

London 328 – Edinburgh 80 – Newcastle upon Tyne 46.

Olde Ship, 9 Main St, NE68 7RD, (01665) 720200, *theoldeship@seahouses.co.uk, Fax (01665) 721383,* « Nautical memorabilia » – rest, VISA JCB.
Meals (bar lunch)/dinner 10.50/17.50 **st.** 8.00 – **18 rm** 40.00/80.00 **st.**, 4 suites – SB.

EATON BURN *Tyne and Wear* 402 P 18 – *see Newcastle upon Tyne.*

EATON CAREW *Hartlepool* 402 Q 20 – *see Hartlepool.*

EAVIEW *I.O.W.* 403 404 Q 31 – *see Wight (Isle of).*

EDGEFIELD *Durham* 401 402 P 20 – *pop. 90 530.*

London 270 – Carlisle 83 – Middlesbrough 15 – Newcastle upon Tyne 27 – Sunderland 23.

Travelodge, A 689 Roundabout, TS21 2JX, Southeast : ¾ m. on A 689 (01740) 623399, *Fax (01740) 623399* – rm, VISA JCB.
Meals (grill rest.) – **40 rm** 42.95 **t.**

Ministers, Lambton House, 8 Church View, TS21 2AY, (01740) 622201, *Fax (01740) 622201* – VISA JCB
closed first week January, 25-26 December, Monday, Saturday lunch and Sunday dinner – **Meals** 12.95/24.50 and a la carte 24.50/34.75 **t.** 9.75.

ENGLAND

SEDGEMOOR SERVICE AREA *Somerset* 403 L 30.
Somerset Visitor Centre, M 5 (southbound) (01934) 750833.

Days Inn without rest., BS21 0JL, M 5 (northbound carriageway) between junctions 2 and 21 (01934) 750831, Reservations (Freephone) 0800 0280400, *Fax (01934) 750808* VISA
7.45 **40 rm** 45.00/50.00 **t.**

SEDLESCOMBE *E. Sussex* 404 V 31 – *pop. 1 631 (inc. Whatlington)* – *Battle.*
London 56 – Hastings 7 – Lewes 26 – Maidstone 27.

Brickwall, The Green, TN33 0QA, (01424) 870253, *reception@brickwallhotel.totalserv co.uk, Fax (01424) 870785*, , heated, – VISA
Meals 17.50/23.50 and lunch a la carte 17.75/26.25 **t.** 12.50 – **26 rm** 55.00/98.00 **st.** SB.

SELSIDE *Cumbria – see Kendal.*

SEMINGTON *Wilts.* 403 404 N 29 – *see Trowbridge.*

SETTLE *N. Yorks.* 402 N 21 – *pop. 3 082.*
Giggleswick (01729) 825288.
Town Hall, Cheapside (01729) 825192.
London 238 – Bradford 34 – Kendal 30 – Leeds 41.

The Falcon Manor, Skipton Rd, BD24 9BD, (01729) 823814, *falconm@netcomu co.uk, Fax (01729) 822087*, – rest, – 50. VISA JCB
Meals (bar lunch Monday-Saturday)/dinner 21.75 10.50 – 9.75 – **19 rm** 75.0 110.00 **st.** – SB.

SEVENOAKS *Kent* 404 U 30 *Great Britain G.* – *pop. 24 489.*
Env. : *Knole★★ AC, SE : ½ m. – Ightham Mote★ AC, E : 5 m. by A 25.*
Woodlands Manor, Tinkerpot Lane (01959) 523805 – Darenth Valley, Station R Shoreham (01959) 522944.
Buckhurst Lane (01732) 450305.
London 26 – Guildford 40 – Maidstone 17.

Royal Oak, Upper High St, TN13 1HY, (01732) 451109, *roak@brook-hotels.co. Fax (01732) 740187* – rest, – 35. VISA
No 5 Restaurant : **Meals** a la carte 22.90/30.40 **st.** 11.95 – 11.95 – **36 rm** 90.0 110.00 **st.** – SB.

Sun Do, 61 High St, TN13 1JF, (01732) 453299, *Fax (01732) 461289* – . VI
closed 25-26 December – **Meals** - Chinese - 21.00 (dinner) and a la carte 12.95/43.9 9.75.

at Ivy Hatch *East : 4 ¾ m. by A 25 on Coach Rd* – *Sevenoaks.*

The Plough, High Cross Rd, TN15 0NL, (01732) 810268, *alisonhumbert@btconne com, Fax (01732) 810268*, , – VISA
closed Sunday dinner – **Meals** 15.95 and a la carte 14.20/26.40 **t.** 11.50.

SEVERN VIEW SERVICE AREA *South Gloucestershire* 403 404 M 29 – *Bristol.*
Severn Bridge (toll).

Travelodge without rest., BS12 3BH, M 48 junction 1 (01454) 6331 *Fax (01454) 632482* – VISA JCB.
51 rm 52.95 **t.**

SHAFTESBURY *Dorset* 403 404 N 30 *The West Country G.* – *pop. 6 203.*
See : *Gold Hill★ (≤★) – Local History Museum★ AC.*
Env. : *Wardour Castle★ AC, NE : 5 m.*
8 Bell St (01747) 853514.
London 115 – Bournemouth 31 – Bristol 47 – Dorchester 29 – Salisbury 20.

Royal Chase, Royal Chase Roundabout, SP7 8DB, Southeast : at junction of A 30 w A 350 (01747) 853355, *royalchasehotel@btinternet.com, Fax (01747) 851969*, ,
– 130. VISA
Meals 21.00/23.50 **st.** 12.50 – 8.50 – **33 rm** 84.50/115.00 – SB.

Paynes Place Barn without rest., New Rd, SP7 8QL, Northwest : ½ m. off B 3((01747) 855016, *xstal@globalnet.co.uk, Fax (01747) 855016*, ≤ Vale of Blackmore,

3 rm 48.00/58.00 **st.**

XX **La Fleur de Lys,** 25 Salisbury St, SP7 8EL, ✆ (01747) 853717, *info@lafleurdelys.co.uk, Fax (01747) 853717,* – MC AE VISA JCB
closed 2 weeks January, Sunday dinner, Monday lunch and Monday in winter – **Meals** 21.50/23.50 (dinner) and a la carte 23.00/32.00 **t.** 13.00.

XX **Wayfarers,** Sherborne Causeway, SP7 9PX, West : 2 ½ m. on A 30 ✆ (01747) 852821, *Fax (01747) 852821* – P. MC AE VISA
closed 26 December-14 January, 1 week June, Monday, Saturday lunch and Sunday dinner – **Meals** a la carte 16.50/29.75 **t.** 10.85.

t Compton Abbas *South : 4 m. on A 350 – ✉ Shaftesbury.*

Old Forge without rest., Chapel Hill, SP7 0NQ, ✆ (01747) 811881, *theoldforge@hotmail.com, Fax (01747) 811881,* « Thatched cottage and converted wheelwrights », – TV P.
3 rm 40.00/65.00 **s.**

t Motcombe *Northwest : 2½ m. by B 3081 – ✉ Shaftesbury.*

Coppleridge Inn, SP7 9HW, North : 1 m. on Mere rd ✆ (01747) 851980, *thecoppleridgeinn@btinternet.com, Fax (01747) 851858,* – TV P – 50. MC AE VISA
Meals 11.00 and a la carte 16.25/22.25 **t.** 9.50 – **10 rm** 42.50/75.00 **t.** – SB.

HALDON *Devon* 403 J 32 – *see Teignmouth.*

HANKLIN *I.O.W.* 403 404 Q 32 – *see Wight (Isle of).*

HEDFIELD *Hants.* 403 404 Q 31 – *pop. 3 558* – ✉ *Southampton.*

18, 9 *Marriott Meon Valley H. & C.C., Sandy Lane, off A 334 ✆ (01329) 833455.*

London 75 – Portsmouth 13 – Southampton 10.

Marriott Meon Valley H. & Country Club, Sandy Lane, SO32 2HQ, off A 334 ✆ (01329) 833455, *Fax (01329) 834411,* 18, – rm, rest, TV P – 80. MC AE VISA.
Treetops : **Meals** (dinner only and Sunday lunch)/dinner 27.00 **st.** 12.75 – ***The Long Weekend :*** **Meals** a la carte 9.50/23.15 **st.** – **112 rm** 129.00/168.00 **st.** – SB.

HEFFIELD *S. Yorks.* 402 403 404 P 23 *Great Britain G. – pop. 431 607.*

See : *Cutlers' Hall★* **CZ A** – *Cathedral Church of SS. Peter and Paul* **CZ B** : *Shrewsbury Chapel (Tomb★).*

18 *Tinsley Park, High Hazel Park, Darnall ✆ (0114) 203 7435* **BY** – 18 *Beauchief Municipal, Abbey Lane ✆ (0114) 236 7274* **AZ** – 18 *Birley Wood, Birley Lane ✆ (0114) 264 7262* **BZ** – 18 *Concord Park, Shiregreen Lane ✆ (0114) 257 7378* **BY** – 18 *Hillsborough, Worrall Rd ✆ (0114) 234 3608* **AY** – 18 *Abbeydale, Twentywell Lane, Dore ✆ (0114) 236 0763* **AZ** – 18 *Lees Hall, Hemsworth Rd, Norton ✆ (0114) 255 4402* **AZ**.

1 Tudor Sq ✆ (0114) 273 4671.

London 174 – Leeds 36 – Liverpool 80 – Manchester 41 – Nottingham 44.

Plans on following pages

Hilton Sheffield, Victoria Quays, Furnival Rd, S4 7YA, ✆ (0114) 252 5500, *Fax (0114) 252 5511,* « Canalside setting », – rm, rest, TV P – 260. MC AE VISA JCB. **DY e**
Meals 7.95 (lunch) and a la carte 17.45/25.00 **t.** 12.30 – 14.00 – **128 rm** 120.00/140.00 **st.**

Sheffield Marriott, Kenwood Rd, S7 1NQ, ✆ (0114) 258 3811, *info@swallowhotels.com, Fax (0114) 250 0138,* – TV P – 200. MC AE VISA **AZ r**
Meals 16.00/30.00 and dinner a la carte 23.00/34.00 **st.** 12.95 – 11.00 – **116 rm** 95.00/130.00 **st.** – SB.

Holiday Inn Royal Victoria Sheffield, Victoria Station Rd, S4 7YE, ✆ (0114) 276 8822, *Fax (0114) 272 4519,* – rm, TV P – 400. MC AE VISA JCB. **DY a**
Meals (carvery lunch)/dinner 19.95 and a la carte 28.00/37.00 **st.** 10.95 – 10.50 – **99 rm** 115.00 **st.**, 1 suite – SB.

Beauchief, 161 Abbeydale Road South, S7 2QW, Southwest : 3 ½ m. on A 621 ✆ (0114) 262 0500, *Fax (0114) 235 0197* – TV P – 100. MC AE VISA
Meals 11.95/20.95 and a la carte 21.00/33.00 **st.** 11.95 – 10.95 – **50 rm** 95.00/125.00 **st.** – SB.

SHEFFIELD
BUILT UP AREA

Barrow Road .... BY 4
Bawtry Road .... BY 5
Bradfield Road .... AY 7
Brocco Bank.............. AZ 8
Broughton Lane .... BY 10
Burngreave Road .... AY 12
Handsworth Road .... BZ 24
Holywell Road .... BY 29
Main Road................ BZ 32
Meadow Hall Road .... BY 33
Meadowhall Shopping Centre .... BY
Middlewood Road .... AY 3
Newhall Road............. BY 3
Westbourne Road.......... AZ 4
Western Bank .... AZ 4
Whitham Road .... AZ 4
Woodbourn Road .... BYZ 5
Woodhouse Road .... BZ 5

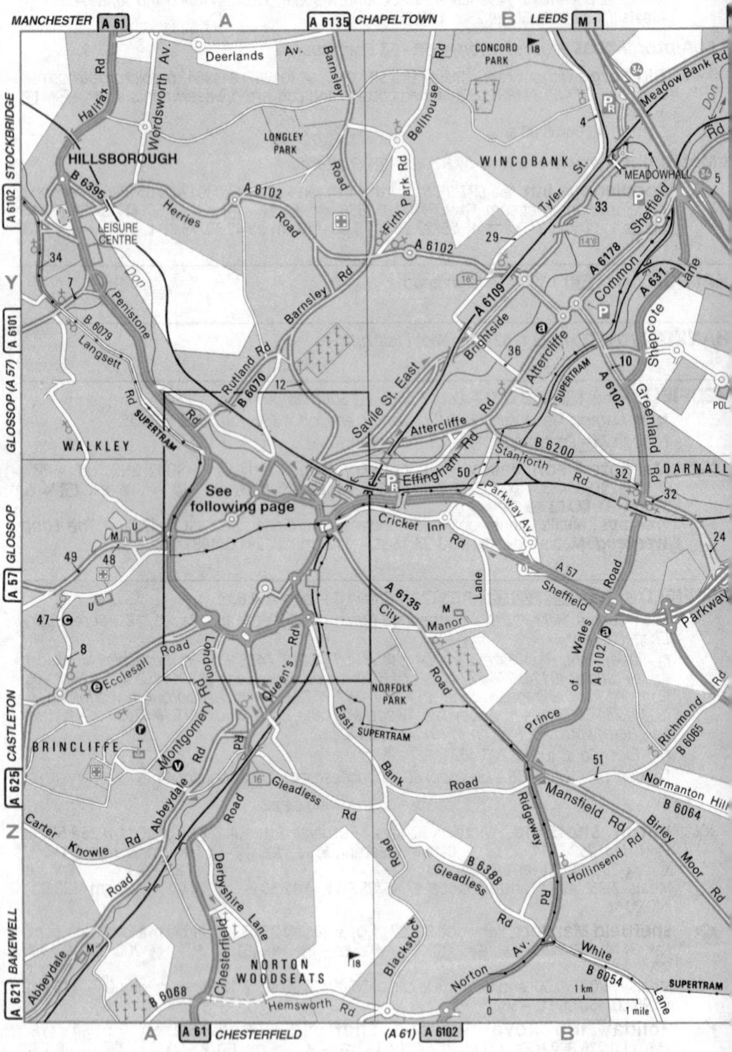

Ne confondez pas :

Confort des hôtels : 🏨🏨🏨🏨🏨 ... 🏨, ⌂
Confort des restaurants : ✕✕✕✕✕ ..... ✕, 🍺
Qualité de la table : ✿✿✿, ✿✿, ✿, Meals ☺

SHEFFIELD
CENTRE

gel Street	DY	3
nk Street	DY	6
tle Gate	DY	13
rter Row	CZ	14
urch Street	CZ	15
Commercial Street	DZ	16
Cumberland Street	CZ	17
Fargate	CZ	
Fitzwilliam Gate	CZ	19
Flat Street	DZ	20
Furnival Gate	CZ	21
Furnival Street	CZ	22
Haymarket	DY	25
High Street	DZ	
Leopold Street	CZ	31
Moorfields	CY	35
Pinstone Street	CZ	37
Queen Street	CY	38
St. Mary's Gate	CZ	40
Shalesmoor	CY	41
Snig Hill	DY	42
Waingate	DY	44
West Bar Green	CY	45
West Street	CZ	

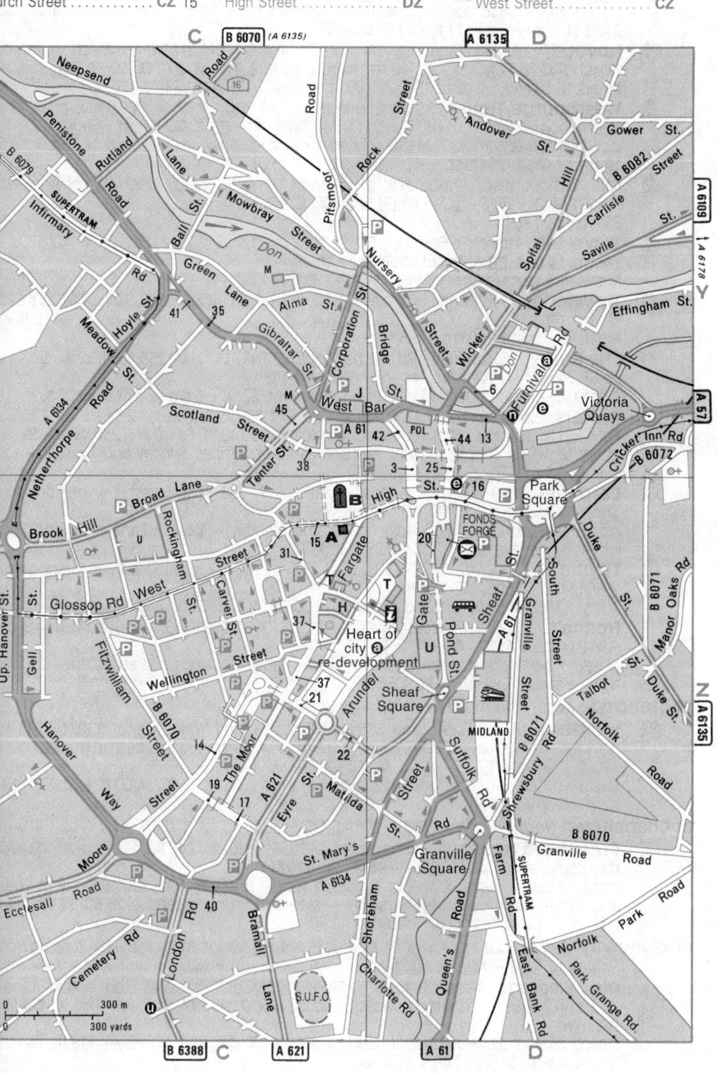

confondete :

Confort degli alberghi : ... ,
Confort dei ristoranti : ..... ,
Qualità della tavola : , , , Meals

ENGLAND

Charnwood, 10 Sharrow Lane, S11 8AA, ☎ (0114) 258 9411, *Fax (0114) 255 510*
rm, – 100. VISA. CZ
closed 24-31 December – **Meals** *(closed Sunday and Bank Holiday Mondays)* (lunch book essential) 15.95 and a la carte approx. 25.00 **st.** 10.25 – **22 rm** 83.00/98.00 **t.** – SB.

Bristol, Blonk St, S1 2AU, ☎ (0114) 220 4000, *sheffield@bhg.co.uk, Fax (0114) 220 390*
– , rm, rest, – 40. VISA. DY
closed 24-27 December – **Meals** (bar lunch)/dinner 14.00/25.00 and a la carte 15. 21.95 **st.** – 8.50 – **111 rm** 69.50 **st.** – SB.

Novotel, Arundel Gate, S1 2PR, ☎ (0114) 278 1781, *h1348-gm@accor-hotels.c* *Fax (0114) 278 7744,* – , rm, rest, – 200. VISA DZ
Meals 16.50 and a la carte 15.95/20.90 **st.** – 9.75 – **144 rm** 79.00/120.00 **st.**

Westbourne House, 25 Westbourne Rd, S10 2QQ, ☎ (0114) 266 0109, *guests@w bournehouse.demon.co.uk, Fax (0114) 266 7778,* – . VISA JCB. AZ
closed 24-26 December – **Meals** *(closed Friday to Sunday)* (dinner only) 14.50 **t.** 10.5
10 rm 45.00/75.00 **st.**

Ibis without rest., Shude Hill, S1 2AR, ☎ (0114) 241 9600, *h2891@accor-hotels.c* *Fax (0114) 241 9610* – . VISA JCB DZ
95 rm 42.00 **st.**

Travel Inn, Attercliffe Common Rd, S9 2LU, ☎ (0114) 242 2802, *Fax (0114) 242 3703* –
rm, rest, . VISA. BY
Meals (grill rest.) (dinner only) – **61 rm** 41.95 **t.**

Travelodge, 340 Prince of Wales Rd, S2 1FF, ☎ (0114) 253 0935, *Fax (0114) 253 093*
rm, – 80. VISA JCB. BZ
Meals (grill rest.) – **60 rm** 52.95 **t.**

The Briary, 12 Moncrieffe Rd, Nether Edge, S7 1HR, ☎ (0144) 255 1951, *briary@briary co.uk, Fax (0114) 249 4746,* – . VISA AZ
closed 22-29 December – **Meals** (by arrangement) 22.00 – **6 rm** 37.00/60.00 **s.**

Rafters, 220 Oakbrook Rd, Nether Green, S11 7ED, Southwest : 2 ½ m. by A 625
Fulwood rd, turning left at roundabout ☎ (0114) 230 4819, *Fax (0114) 230 4819* –
closed 2 weeks August, 1 week January, 25-26 December, Sunday and Tuesday – **Me**
(dinner only) 24.95/27.45 **t.** 9.50.

Carriages, 289 Abbeydale Road South, S17 3LB, Southwest : 4 m. on A
☎ (0114) 235 0101 – . VISA
closed 2 weeks January, Sunday dinner and Monday – **Meals** (dinner only and Sun lunch)/dinner a la carte 22.50/28.95 **t.** 11.00.

Thyme, 34 Sandygate Rd, S10 5RY, West : 2 ¼ m. by A 57, turning left at Crosspool Tav
☎ (0114) 266 6096 – VISA
Meals 12.00/17.50 (lunch) and a la carte 22.50/28.00 **t.** 10.00.

Nonna's, 537-541 Ecclesall Rd, S11 8PR, ☎ (0114) 268 6166, *enquiries@nonnas.co* *Fax (0114) 266 6122* – VISA AZ
closed 1 week Christmas – **Meals** - Italian - (lunch bookings not accepted) 16.00/18 and a la carte 17.90/26.40 **st.** 5.50.

at Grenoside *North : 4½ m. on A 61* – **AY** – ✉ *Sheffield.*

Whitley Hall , Elliott Lane, S35 8NR, East : 1 m. off Whitley Lane ☎ (0114) 245 44 *reservations@whitleyhall.com, Fax (0114) 245 5414,* « Part 16C Elizabethan manor hous
, – rest, – 70. VISA.
Meals *(closed Saturday lunch)* 12.50/23.50 and a la carte 22.00/34.00 **t.** 13.00 – **19**
78.00/110.00 **t.**

at Chapeltown *North : 6 m. on A 6135* – **AY** – ✉ *Sheffield.*

Greenhead House, 84 Burncross Rd, S35 1SF, ☎ (0114) 246 9004, *allengreenhead@ mail.com, Fax (0114) 246 9004* – . VISA
closed 2 weeks Easter, 2 weeks August, 1 week Christmas-New Year, Sunday to Tues and lunch Wednesday and Saturday – **Meals** (booking essential) 28.50/34.00 (din and lunch a la carte approx. 16.00 **t.** 12.90.

at Ridgeway *(Derbs.) Southeast : 6 ¾ m. by A 6135 (signed Manor Park) on B 6054 turning righ Ridgeway Arms* – **BZ** – ✉ *Sheffield.*

Old Vicarage (Tessa Bramley), Ridgeway Moor, S12 3XW, on Marsh Lane
☎ (0114) 247 5814, *eat@theoldvicarage.co.uk, Fax (0114) 247 7079,* – .
VISA JCB
closed 26 and 31 December, 1 January, Sunday dinner and Monday – **Meals** (lunch arrangement) 33.00/43.00 **t.** 16.50
Spec. Pan-fried calves liver, grain mustard mash, Madeira sauce. Roast squab, minted p foie gras and apple. Chocolate brownie, pistachio ice cream.

at Meadow Head *South : 5¼ m. on A 61* – **AZ** – ✉ *Sheffield.*

Sheffield Moat House, Chesterfield Rd South, S8 8BW, ☎ (0114) 282 9988, *gms queensmoat.co.uk, Fax (0114) 237 8140,* , , , – , rest, ,
500. VISA
Meals a la carte 23.35/30.40 **st.** 11.95 – 10.50 – **93 rm** 108.00/135.00 **st.**, 2 suites –

EFFORD *Beds.* 404 S 27 – *pop. 3 319.*
London 48 – Bedford 10 – Luton 16 – Northampton 37.

The Black Horse with rm, Ireland, SG17 5QL, Northwest : 1 ¾ m. by Northbridge St. and B 658 on Ireland rd ✆ (01462) 811398, *Fax (01462) 817238*, , « Part 18C » – ⇔ TV P. MC AE VISA
closed 25 December – **Meals** *(closed Sunday dinner)* a la carte 20.15/26.85 **t.** 9.90 – **2 rm** 49.95.

ELLEY *W. Yorks.* 402 404 O 23 – *see Huddersfield.*

ENINGTON *Oxon.* – *see Banbury.*

EPTON MALLET *Somerset* 403 404 M 30 *The West Country G.* – *pop. 7 581.*
See : *Town★ - SS. Peter and Paul's Church★.*
Env. : *Downside Abbey★ (Abbey Church★) N : 5½ m. by A 37 and A 367.*
Exc. : *Longleat House★★★ AC, E : 15 m. by A 361 and B 3092 – Wells★★ - Cathedral★★★, Vicars' Close★, Bishop's Palace★ AC (≤★★) W : 6 m. by A 371 – Wookey Hole★ (Caves★ AC, Papermill★) W : 6 ½ m. by B 371 – Glastonbury★★ - Abbey★★ (Abbot's Kitchen★) AC, St John the Baptist★★, Somerset Rural Life Museum★ AC – Glastonbury Tor★ (≤★★★) SW : 9 m. by B 3136 and A 361 - Nunney★, E : 8½ m. by A 361.*
18 *The Mendip, Gurney Slade ✆ (01749) 840570.*
London 127 – Bristol 20 – Southampton 63 – Taunton 31.

Charlton House, BA4 4PR, East : 1 m. on A 361 (Frome rd) ✆ (01749) 342008, *enquiries @charltonhouse.com, Fax (01749) 346362*, , « Part Georgian country house », , , , – ⇔ rest, TV P. MC AE VISA JCB.
Mulberry : **Meals** 18.50/38.50 **t.** 14.50 – **16 rm** 112.50/315.00 **t.** – SB
Spec. Layers of red pepper and feta cheese with Greek salad. Pan-fried scallops with baby artichokes, parma ham and sage. Layers of raspberries and brandy snap biscuits, raspberry sorbet.

The Shrubbery, 17 Commercial Rd, BA4 5BU, ✆ (01749) 346671, *Fax (01749) 346581*, – ⇔ rest, TV P. MC AE VISA
Meals *(closed Sunday dinner)* 17.70/26.40 and a la carte **t.** 11.95 – **11 rm** 52.50/75.00 **t.**

Bowlish House, Wells Rd, BA4 5JD, West : ½ m. on A 371 ✆ (01749) 342022, *Fax (01749) 342022*, – ⇔ TV P. MC VISA JCB
closed 2 weeks in winter – **Meals** *(closed Sunday and Monday)* (booking essential) (dinner only) 25.95 **t.** 10.95 – 5.00 – **3 rm** 55.00/65.00.

Pennard Hill Farm , Stickleball Hill, East Pennard, BA4 6UG, Southwest : 6 ¼ m. by A 37 off A 361 turning left 300 metres after Stonecross Farm (Stickleball Lane) ✆ (01749) 890221, *phebejudah@aol.com, Fax (01749) 890665*, ≤, « Working sheep farm », , , – TV P.
Meals (by arrangement) 17.50/30.00 **st.** 8.00 – **5 rm** 70.00/120.00 **s.** – SB.

ERBORNE *Dorset* 403 404 M 31 *The West Country G.* – *pop. 7 606.*
See : *Town★ - Abbey★★ – Castle★ AC.*
Env. : *Sandford Orcas Manor House★ AC, NW : 4 m. by B 3148 – Purse Caundle Manor★ AC, NE : 5 m. by A 30.*
Exc. : *Cadbury Castle (≤★★) N : 8 m. by A 30 – Parish Church★, Crewkerne, W : 14 m. on A 30.*
18 *Higher Clatcombe ✆ (01935) 812475.*
3 Tilton Court, Digby Rd ✆ (01935) 815341.
London 128 – Bournemouth 39 – Dorchester 19 – Salisbury 36 – Taunton 31.

Eastbury, Long St, DT9 3BY, ✆ (01935) 813131, *eastbury.sherbourne@village.net, Fax (01935) 817296*, , « Walled garden », – ⇔ TV P – 60. MC AE VISA JCB.
closed 1-7 January – **Meals** (bar lunch Monday and Tuesday) 13.50/19.95 **t.** 9.95 – **14 rm** 55.50/91.00 **t.** – SB.

Pheasants with rm, 24 Greenhill, DT9 4EW, ✆ (01935) 815252, *andrew@pheasants.co.uk, Fax (01935) 815252* – TV P. MC VISA.
closed 2 weeks January – **Meals** *(closed lunch Tuesday to Friday, Sunday dinner and Monday)* 17.50/27.00 **t.** 10.20 – **6 rm** 45.00/70.00 **t.** – SB.

Oborne Northeast : 2 m. by A 30 – ✉ Sherborne.

The Grange , DT9 4LA, ✆ (01935) 813463, *karen@thegrangehotel-dorset.co.uk, Fax (01935) 817464*, – ⇔ TV P. MC AE VISA.
closed 26 December-10 January – **Meals** *(closed Sunday dinner)* (dinner only and Sunday lunch)/dinner 19.50/24.50 12.50 – **10 rm** 65.00/105.00 **t.** – SB.

ENGLAND

at Milborne Port *Northeast : 3 m. on A 30 – ✉ Sherborne.*

Old Vicarage, Sherborne Rd, DT9 5AT, ☎ (01963) 251117, *Fax (01963) 251515,* ←, ✻ – TV P. MC AE VISA. ✻
closed January – **Meals** *(closed Sunday to Thursday)* (dinner only) 21.90 ₰ 11.90 – **7**
☕ 32.50/96.00 **t.**

at Hermitage *South : 7½ m. by A 352 – ✉ Sherborne.*

Almshouse Farm ⚘ without rest., DT9 6HA, ☎ (01963) 210296, *Fax (01963) 210296,* « Former monastery, working farm », ✻ – TV P. ✻
closed December and January – **3 rm** ☕ 30.00/55.00.

at Yetminster *Southwest : 5½ m. by A 352 and Yetminster rd – ✉ Sherborne.*

Manor Farmhouse, DT9 6LF, ☎ (01935) 872247, *Fax (01935) 872247,* « 17C », ✻ – TV P. MC VISA. ✻
closed 1 week Christmas – **Meals** (by arrangement) 20.00 – **3 rm** ☕ 35.00/70.00.

at Leigh *Southwest : 6¼ m. by A 352 – ✉ Sherborne.*

Huntsbridge Farm ⚘ without rest., DT9 6JA, Southeast : ¼ m. on Batcombe ☎ (01935) 872150, *huntsbridge@lineone.net, Fax (01935) 872150,* ←, « Working farm ✻ – ✻ TV P. MC AE VISA. ✻
closed mid December-February – **3 rm** ☕ 56.00 **s.**

SHERBOURNE *Warks. – see Warwick.*

SHERE *Surrey* **404** S 30 – *see Guildford.*

SHIFNAL *Shrops.* **402** **403** **404** M 25 – *pop. 5 893 – ✉ Telford.*
London 150 – Birmingham 28 – Shrewsbury 16.

Park House, Park St, TF11 9BA, ☎ (01952) 460128, *parkhouse@macdonald-hotels.co. Fax (01952) 461658,* ≘, ◻, ✻ – |‡| ✻ TV ♿ P – 🏛 180. MC AE ① VISA. ✻
Meals *(closed Saturday lunch)* 14.50/21.50 and a la carte 18.00/30.00 **t.** ₰ 14.50 – ☕ 10.5
52 rm 120.00 **t.**, 2 suites – SB.

SHIMPLING *Suffolk – see Long Melford.*

SHINCLIFFE *Durham – see Durham.*

SHINFIELD *Reading* **404** R 29 – *see Reading.*

SHIPHAM *Somerset* **403** L 30 *The West Country G. – pop. 1 094 – ✉ Winscombe.*
Env. : *Cheddar Gorge★★ (Gorge★★, Caves★, Jacobs's Ladder ✻★) – Axbridge★★ – K John's Hunting Lodge★ – St John the Baptist★, SW : 5 m. on A 38 – St Andrew's Churc S : 2½ m.*
⛳18, ⛳9 *Mendip Spring, Honeyhall Lane, Congresbury, Avon ☎ (01934) 853337.*
London 135 – Bristol 14 – Taunton 20.

Daneswood House, Cuck Hill, BS25 1RD, ☎ (01934) 843145, *info@daneswoodhotel uk, Fax (01934) 843824,* ←, ✻ – ✻ TV P – 🏛 40. MC AE ① VISA. ✻
closed 25 December-3 January – **Meals** 19.95/29.95 **st.** ₰ 11.95 – **14 rm** ☕ 89. 105.00 **st.**, 3 suites – SB.

SHIPLEY *W. Yorks.* **402** O 22 – *pop. 28 165.*
⛳18 *Northcliffe, High Bank Lane ☎ (01274) 584085 –* ⛳18 *Beckfoot Lane, Cottingley Bric Bingley ☎ (01274) 563212.*
London 216 – Bradford 4 – Leeds 12.

Marriott Hollins Hall H. and Country Club ⚘, Hollins Hill, Baildon, BD17 7(Northeast : 2½ m. on A 6038 ☎ (01274) 530053, *Fax (01274) 530187,* ←, ✻, ≘, ◻, ⛳18, ✻ – |‡|, ✻ rm, TV ✆ ♿ P – 🏛 200. MC AE ① VISA JCB. ✻
Meals a la carte approx. 25.00 **st.** ₰ 12.75 – ☕ 13.00 – **121 rm** 109.00/149.00 **st.**, 1 suite

Ibis without rest., Salts Mill Rd, BD18 3ST, ☎ (01274) 589333, Reservations (F phone) 0800 897121, *Fax (01274) 589444* – |‡| ✻ TV ✆ ♿ P – 🏛 30. MC AE ① VISA JCB
78 rm 45.00 **st.**

XX **Aagrah,** 27 Westgate, BD18 3HN, ☎ (01274) 530880, *Fax (01274) 669803* – ▤. MC AE VISA JCB
closed 25 December – **Meals** - Indian (Kashmiri) - (booking essential) (dinner only) a la carte 13.30/17.25 **t.** 🍷 9.95.

IPSTON-ON-STOUR *Warks.* 403 404 P 27 – *pop. 3 882.*
London 89 – Oxford 32 – Birmingham 33 – Coventry 29 – Stratford-upon-Avon 11.

XXX ✿ **Chavignol at the Old Mill** with rm, Mill St, CV36 4AW, ☎ (01608) 663888, *chavignol@virginbiz.com, Fax (01608) 663188,* – ⇔ rest, TV P. MC AE VISA
Meals 25.00/40.00 **t.** 🍷 13.00 – **5 rm** ☕ (dinner included) 125.00/340.00 **t.**
Spec. Duo of scallops with haricot vert and blinis. Squab pigeon on carrot and swede purée, fondant potato. Chocolate marquise.

IPTON GORGE *Dorset – see Bridport.*

IPTON-UNDER-WYCHWOOD *Oxon.* 403 404 P 28 – *pop. 1 154.*
London 81 – Birmingham 50 – Gloucester 37 – Oxford 25.

⌂ **Shipton Grange House** without rest., OX7 6DG, ☎ (01993) 831298, *Fax (01993) 832082,* « Georgian former coach house and stables, walled garden » – ⇔ TV P. ✈
closed 24-26 December – **3 rm** ☕ 68.00.

IRLEY *W. Mids.* 403 404 O 26 – *see Solihull.*

OBDON *Herefordshire* 403 L 27 – *pop. 741* – ✉ *Leominster.*
London 158 – Birmingham 55 – Hereford 18 – Shrewsbury 37 – Worcester 33.

⌂ **The Paddock,** HR6 9NQ, West : ¼ m. on B 4362 ☎ (01568) 708176, *thepaddock@talk21.com, Fax (01568) 708829* – ⇔ TV P. ✈
Meals (by arrangement) 15.00 **st.** – **5 rm** ☕ 34.00/48.00 **st.**

OTTISHAM *Suffolk* 404 X 27 – *see Woodbridge.*

OTTLE *Derbs. – see Belper.*

IREWSBURY *Shrops.* 402 403 L 25 *Great Britain G.* – *pop. 64 219.*
See : *Abbey*★ D.
Exc. : *Ironbridge Gorge Museum*★★ *AC (The Iron Bridge*★★ *- Coalport China Museum*★★ *- Blists Hill Open Air Museum*★★ *– Museum of the River and Visitor Centre*★*) SE : 12 m. by A 5 and B 4380.*
18 *Condover ☎ (01743) 872976* – 9 *Meole Brace ☎ (01743) 364050.*
ℹ *The Music Hall, The Square ☎ (01743) 350761.*
London 164 – Birmingham 48 – Chester 43 – Derby 67 – Gloucester 93 – Manchester 68 – Stoke-on-Trent 39 – Swansea 124.

Plan on next page

Prince Rupert, Butcher Row, SY1 1UQ, ☎ (01743) 499955, *post@prince-rupert-hotel.co.uk, Fax (01743) 357306,* Fø, ≘s – |‡|, ▤ rest, TV P – 🏟 100. MC AE ① VISA JCB. ✈ n
Meals 10.50/27.00 (lunch) and a la carte 16.95/30.95 **st.** 🍷 12.50 – ☕ 10.50 – **67 rm** 75.00/95.00 **st.**, 2 suites – SB.

Lord Hill, Abbey Foregate, SY2 6AX, East : 1 m. ☎ (01743) 232601, *reservations@lordhill.u-net.com, Fax (01743) 369734* – ⇔ rest, ▤ rest, TV P – 🏟 180. MC AE ① VISA JCB
Meals 18.50 and a la carte 18.15/27.95 **st.** 🍷 11.95 – **35 rm** ☕ 63.50/82.00 **st.**, 1 suite – SB.

Travelodge, Bayston Hill Service Area, SY3 0DA, South : 2 ¾ m. by Belle Vue Rd (A 5191) and A 5112 at junction with A 5 ☎ (01743) 874256 – ⇔ rm, TV ♿ P. MC AE ① VISA JCB. ✈
Meals (grill rest.) – **40 rm** 49.95 **t.**

The Bellstone, Bellstone, SY1 1HU, ☎ (01743) 242100, *admin@bellstone-hotel.co.uk, Fax (01743) 242103* – ⇔ rm, TV. MC AE VISA JCB. ✈ c
closed 25 Decemeber – ***Brasserie :*** **Meals** a la carte 15.80/17.20 **t.** 🍷 9.00 – ☕ 5.95 – **23 rm** 39.50 **t.**

⌂ **Pinewood House** without rest., Shelton Park, The Mount, SY3 8BL, Northwest : 1 ½ m. on A 458 ☎ (01743) 364200, « Victorian coach house », – TV P
closed 2 weeks spring and 1 week Christmas – **3 rm** ☕ 40.00/60.00 **s.**

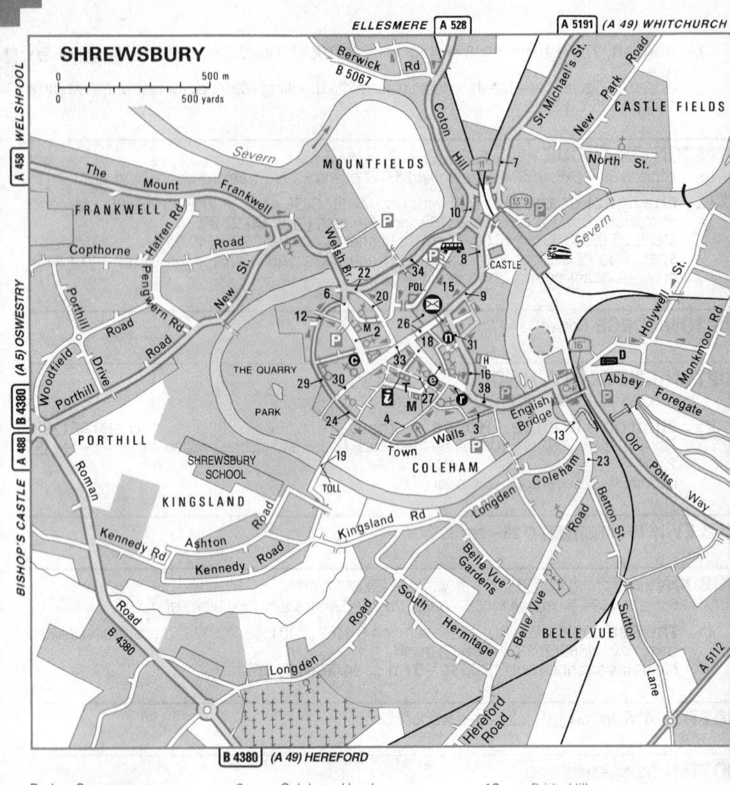

Tudor House without rest., 2 Fish St, SY1 1UR, (01743) 351735, « 15C » –
closed 25 and 26 December – **3 rm** 30.00/54.00 **st.**

Fieldside without rest., 38 London Rd, SY2 6NX, East : 1 ¼ m. by Abbey Foregate A 5064 (via Shirehall) (01743) 353143, *Fax (01743) 354687*, –
5 rm 22.00/55.00 **s.**

Sol (Williams), 82 Wyle Cop, SY1 1UT, (01743) 340560, *Fax (01743) 340552* – VISA
closed Sunday and Monday – **Meals** 15.00/35.00 and lunch a la carte 21.50/32.50 **t.** 9.9
Spec. Seared salmon with smoked salmon brandade. Rump of lamb, lentils and Ca potatoes. Banana bavarois with caramelised figs.

at Albrighton *North : 3 m. on A 528* – *Shrewsbury.*

Albrighton Hall, Ellesmere Rd, SY4 3AG, (01939) 291000, *info@albrighton.macdor hotels.uk, Fax (01939) 291123*, , squash – , rm, – 400. AE VISA
Meals *(closed Saturday lunch)* 16.50/30.00 a la carte **st.** 14.95 – 12.95 – **71 rm** 95. 125.00 **st.** – SB.

Albright Hussey , Ellesmere Rd, SY4 3AF, (01939) 290571, *abhhotel@aol.co Fax (01939) 291143*, , « 16C moated manor house », – – 200. VISA JCB
Meals 12.50/16.00 and a la carte 22.40/25.00 **t.** 11.95 – **13 rm** 79.00/148.50 **t.**, 1 su – SB.

Cross Houses *Southeast : 5 m. on A 458 – ✉ Shrewsbury.*

Upper Brompton Farm ⑤, SY5 6LE, East : ½ m. by Lower Cross ☎ (01743) 761629, *upper.bromtonfarm@dial.pipex.com, Fax (01743) 761679,* « Working farm », – TV P. MC AE VISA JCB.
Meals (by arrangement) 25.00 **s.** 9.95 – **5 rm** 49.50/100.00 **s.** – SB.

Dorrington *South : 7 m. on A 49 – ✉ Shrewsbury.*

Country Friends, SY5 7JD, ☎ (01743) 718707, *countryfriends@ukonline.co.uk, Fax (01743) 718707,* – P. MC VISA JCB
closed 2 weeks mid July and Sunday-Tuesday – **Meals** 27.50/29.90 and lunch a la carte 15.70/21.65 **t.** 12.75.

Hanwood *Southwest : 4 m. on A 488 – ✉ Shrewsbury.*

White House, SY5 8LP, ☎ (01743) 860414, *mgm@whitehousehanwood.freeserve.co.uk, Fax (01743) 860414,* « 16C farmhouse », – P.
Meals (by arrangement) 20.00 **s.** 9.00 – **6 rm** 30.00/65.00 **s.** – SB.

URDINGTON *Glos.* 403 404 N 28 – *see Cheltenham.*

BSON *Leics. – see Nuneaton (Warks.).*

DFORD *Devon* 403 K 31 – *see Sidmouth.*

DMOUTH *Devon* 403 K 31 *The West Country G. – pop. 12 982.*

Env. : *Bicton★ (Gardens★) AC, SW : 5 m.*

Cotmaton Rd ☎ (01395) 513023.

Ham Lane ☎ (01395) 516441.

London 176 – Exeter 14 – Taunton 27 – Weymouth 45.

Victoria, The Esplanade, EX10 8RY, ☎ (01395) 512651, *info@victoriahotel.co.uk, Fax (01395) 579154,* ≤, heated, – |‡|, rest, rest, TV P. MC AE VISA.
Meals (dancing Saturday evening) 16.00/27.50 **st.** 9.75 – **58 rm** 105.00/240.00, 3 suites – SB.

Riviera, The Esplanade, EX10 8AY, ☎ (01395) 515201, *enquiries@hotelriviera.co.uk, Fax (01395) 577775,* ≤, – |‡|, rest, rest, TV – 85. MC AE VISA
Meals 18.00/28.00 and a la carte 29.50/34.90 **t.** 12.75 – **27 rm** (dinner included) 100.00/216.00 **t.** – SB.

Belmont, The Esplanade, EX10 8RX, ☎ (01395) 512555, *info@belmont_hotel.co.uk, Fax (01395) 579101,* ≤, – |‡|, rest, rest, TV P. MC AE VISA.
Meals (dancing Saturday evening) 15.00/25.00 **st.** 9.00 – **50 rm** 90.00/230.00 **st.** – SB.

Salcombe Hill House ⑤, Beatlands Rd, EX10 8JQ, ☎ (01395) 514697, *salcombehill househotel@eclipse.co.uk, Fax (01395) 578310,* heated, – |‡|, rest, TV P. MC VISA JCB
March-9 November – **Meals** (bar lunch Monday to Saturday)/dinner 15.50 and a la carte 19.85/25.85 **t.** 8.25 – **28 rm** (dinner included) 64.50/129.00 **t.** – SB.

Hunters Moon, Sid Rd, EX10 9AA, ☎ (01395) 513380, *huntersmoon.hotel@virgin.net, Fax (01395) 514270,* – TV P. MC VISA JCB
closed January-February – **Meals** (booking essential to non-residents) (dinner only) 17.95 **st.** 8.95 – **21 rm** (dinner included) 56.00/112.00 **st.**

Mount Pleasant, Salcombe Rd, EX10 8JA, ☎ (01395) 514694, – TV P.
March-October – **Meals** (residents only) (dinner only) 12.95/14.95 5.50 – **16 rm** (dinner included) 47.00/94.00 **st.** – SB.

Woodlands, Station Rd, Cotmaton Cross, EX10 8HG, ☎ (01395) 513120, *info@woodlands -hotel.com, Fax (01395) 513348,* – TV P. MC VISA JCB
Meals (dinner only) 14.95 and a la carte 14.95/25.00 **t.** 8.25 – **19 rm** 39.00/99.00 **t.** – SB.

Sidford *North : 2 m. – ✉ Sidmouth.*

Salty Monk, Church St, EX10 9QP, on A 3052 ☎ (01395) 513174, *andy@saltymonkhotel sidmouth.co.uk, Fax (01395) 514722,* « Part 16C », – TV P. MC VISA JCB
closed 2 weeks January and November – **Meals** (booking essential) (lunch by arrangement) 9.00/22.00 and a la carte 17.00/27.50 **st.** 10.50 – **5 rm** 45.00/88.00 **st.** – SB.

SILCHESTER *Hants.* 403 404 Q 29 – *pop. 1 428* – ✉ *Reading (Berks.).*
London 62 – Basingstoke 8 – Reading 14 – Winchester 26.

Romans, Little London Rd, RG7 2PN, ☎ (01189) 700421, *romanhotel@hotmail.cc* *Fax (01189) 700691,* heated, – rest, – 80. VISA JCB
Meals 18.50 and a la carte 22.65/28.20 **t.** 13.00 – **25 rm** 95.00/105.00 **t.** – SB.

SIMONSBATH *Somerset* 403 I 30 *The West Country G.* – ✉ *Minehead.*
Env. : *Exmoor National Park★★ – Exford (Church★) E : 5½ m. by B 3223 and B 3224.*
London 200 – Exeter 40 – Minehead 19 – Taunton 38.

Simonsbath House, TA24 7SH, ☎ (01643) 831259, *simonsbath@talk21.cc* *Fax (01643) 831557,* ≤, « 17C country house », – rest, . VISA
Meals (dinner only) 22.50 **st.** 8.50 – **7 rm** 40.00/80.00 **st.**

SINDLESHAM *Wokingham – see Reading.*

SINGLETON *Lancs.* 402 L 22 – *see Blackpool.*

SINNINGTON *N. Yorks.* 402 R 21 – *see Pickering.*

SISSINGHURST *Kent* 404 V 30 – *see Cranbrook.*

SITTINGBOURNE *Kent* 404 W 29.
London 44 – Canterbury 18 – Maidstone 15 – Sheerness 9.

Hempstead House, London Rd, Bapchild, ME9 9PP, East : 2 m. on A ☎ (01795) 428020, *info@hempsteadhouse.co.uk, Fax (01795) 436362,* « Part Victor country house », heated, – . VISA JCB
Meals *(closed Sunday)* a la carte 20.00/28.50 **t.** 10.95 – **14 rm** 70.00/80.00 **t.** – SB.

Travel Inn, Bobbing Corner, Sheppey Way, Bobbing, ME9 8PD, Northwest : 2 ¼ m. by on Sheerness rd ☎ (01795) 431890, *Fax (01795) 436748* – rm, rest, . VISA.
Meals (grill rest.) – **40 rm** 41.95 **t.**

Beaumont without rest., 74 London Rd, ME10 1NS, West : ½ m. on A ☎ (01795) 472536, *beaumont74@aol.com, Fax (01795) 425921* – . VISA
closed Christmas and New Year – **9 rm** 35.00/65.00 **t.**

SIX MILE BOTTOM *Cambs. – see Newmarket (Suffolk).*

SKELTON *N. Yorks.* 402 Q 22 – *see York.*

SKELWITH BRIDGE *Cumbria* 402 K 20 – *see Ambleside.*

SKIPTON *N. Yorks.* 402 N 22 *Great Britain G.* – *pop. 13 583.*
See : *Castle★ AC.*
18 *off NW Bypass* ☎ *(01756) 793922.*
Craven Court Shopping Centre ☎ *(01756) 792809.*
London 217 – Kendal 45 – Leeds 26 – Preston 36 – York 43.

Hanover International, Keighley Rd, BD23 2TA, South : 1 ¼ m. on A 6 ☎ (01756) 700100, *hihskipton@totalise.co.uk, Fax (01756) 700107,* ≤, , squas – 400. VISA.
closed 24-27 December – **Meals** (bar lunch)/dinner 15.20/20.20 and a la carte **st.** 11.C 9.50 – **75 rm** 88.00/100.00 **st.** – SB.

Travelodge, Gargrave Rd, BD23 1UD, Northwest : 1 ¼ m. by Water St. at A 65/A roundabout ☎ (01756) 798091, *Fax (01756) 798091* – rm, . VISA
Meals (grill rest.) – **32 rm** 49.95 **t.**

Aagrah, Unit 4, Unicorn House, Devonshire Pl, Keighley Rd, BD23 2LP, ☎ (01756) 7908C . VISA JCB
closed 25 December – **Meals** - Indian (Kashmiri) - (booking essential) (dinner only) a la ca 13.30/17.25 **t.** 9.95.

at Rylstone *North : 5 m. on B 6265 – ✉ Skipton.*

The Manor House without rest., BD23 6LH, ✆ (01756) 730226, ≤, « Working farm », 🌳, 🐎 – TV P. ✗
3 rm ☕ 45.00/70.00 **t.**

at Hetton *North : 5¾ m. by B 6265 – ✉ Skipton.*

Angel Inn, BD23 6LT, ✆ (01756) 730263, *info@angelhetton.co.uk, Fax (01756) 730363,* « Characterful 18C inn » – ⚞ ▤ P. MC AE VISA
closed 25 December and Sunday dinner – ***The Restaurant :*** Meals (dinner only and Sunday lunch)/dinner a la carte 19.95/29.50 **t.** 🍷 11.90 – (see also below).

Angel Inn, BD23 6LT, ✆ (01756) 730263, *info@angelhetton.co.uk, Fax (01756) 730363,* 🍽, « Characterful 18C inn » – ⚞ P. MC AE VISA
Bar/Brasserie : Meals (bookings not accepted) 7.50 (lunch) and a la carte 14.30/23.75 **t.** 🍷 11.90.

at Elslack *West : 5¼ m. by A 59 off A 56 – ✉ Skipton.*

The Tempest Arms, BD23 3AY, ✆ (01282) 842450, *Fax (01282) 843331* – TV P – 🏫 50. MC AE VISA. ✗
Meals a la carte 12.15/22.95 **t.** – **10 rm** ☕ 52.50/65.00 **t.**

at Coniston Cold *Northwest : 6½ m. on A 65 – ✉ Skipton.*

Coniston Hall Lodge, BD23 4EB, on A 65 ✆ (01756) 748080, *conistonhall@clara.net, Fax (01756) 749487,* ≤, 🎣, 🌳, 🐎 – ⚞ TV ♿ P – 🏫 40. MC AE ⊙ VISA
Meals 18.50 (dinner) and a la carte 17.40/31.95 **st.** 🍷 9.95 – ***Winston's Bistro :*** Meals (dinner only) 18.50/19.95 and a la carte **st.** 🍷 9.95 – ☕ 11.50 – **40 rm** 65.00 **st.** – SB.

SLALEY *Northd.* 401 402 N 19 – *see Hexham.*

SLEAFORD *Lincs.* 402 404 S 25 – *pop. 10 388.*

Willoughby Rd, South Rauceby ✆ (01529) 488273.
Money's Yard, Carre St ✆ (01529) 414294.
London 119 – Leicester 45 – Lincoln 17 – Nottingham 39.

Lincolnshire Oak, East Rd, NG34 7EH, Northeast : ¾ m. on B 1517 ✆ (01529) 413807, *reception@lincolnshire-oak.co.uk, Fax (01529) 413710,* 🌳 – ⚞ TV P – 🏫 140. MC AE ⊙ VISA. ✗
Meals (booking essential) a la carte 16.20/21.70 **t.** 🍷 10.95 – **17 rm** ☕ 55.00/84.00 **t.** – SB.

Travelodge, NG34 8NP, Northwest : 1 m. on A 15 at junction with A 17 ✆ (01529) 414752, *Fax (01529) 414752* – ⚞ rm, TV ♿ P. MC AE ⊙ VISA JCB. ✗
Meals (grill rest.) – **40 rm** 39.95 **t.**

Tally Ho Inn with rm, Aswarby, NG34 8SA, South : 4½ m. on A 15 ✆ (01529) 455205, *Fax (01529) 455205,* ≤, 🌳 – TV P. MC VISA
closed 26 December – **Meals** a la carte 14.20/22.85 **t.** 🍷 9.75 – **6 rm** ☕ 35.00/50.00 **t.**

SLEIGHTS *N. Yorks. – see Whitby.*

SLINFOLD *W. Sussex – see Horsham.*

SLOUGH *Slough* 404 S 29 – *pop. 110 708.*

London 29 – Oxford 39 – Reading 19.

Slough/Windsor Marriott, Ditton Rd, Langley, SL3 8PT, Southeast : 2½ m. on A 4 ✆ (01753) 544244, *Fax (01753) 540272,* 🏋, ♨, 🏊, 🎾 – 🛗, ⚞ rm, ▤ TV 📞 ♿ P – 🏫 400. MC AE ⊙ VISA. ✗
Meals *(closed lunch Saturday, Sunday and Bank Holidays)* 16.00/19.95 and dinner a la carte 21.00/28.50 **st.** 🍷 13.95 – ☕ 13.00 – **381 rm** 135.00 **st.**, 1 suite – SB.

Copthorne, Cippenham Lane, SL1 2YE, Southwest : 1¼ m. by A 4 on A 355 off M 4 junction 6 ✆ (01753) 516222, *copthorne@mill.cop.com, Fax (01753) 516237,* 🏋, ♨, 🏊 – 🛗, ⚞ rm, ▤ TV 📞 ♿ P – 🏫 250. MC AE ⊙ VISA. ✗
Veranda : Meals (bar lunch Saturday and Sunday) 16.00 (dinner) and a la carte 17.00/35.00 **st.** 🍷 14.75 – ☕ 13.50 – **217 rm** 175.00/195.00 **st.**, 2 suites – SB.

Courtyard by Marriott Slough/Windsor, Church St, Chalvey, SL1 2NH, Southwest : 1¼ m. by A 4 on A 355 off M 4 junction 6 ✆ (01753) 551551, *Fax (01753) 553333,* 🏋 – 🛗, ⚞ rm, ▤ TV 📞 ♿ P – 🏫 40. MC AE ⊙ VISA. ✗
Meals (bar lunch)/dinner a la carte 19.50/24.50 **st.** 🍷 12.00 – **150 rm** ☕ 135.00/149.00 **st.** – SB.

SMITE *Worcs. – see Droitwich Spa.*

SNAPE *Suffolk* 404 Y 27 – *pop. 1 509.*
London 113 – Ipswich 19 – Norwich 50.

Crown Inn with rm, Bridge Rd, IP17 1SL, ☎ (01728) 688324, « 15C inn », – rm, P
closed 25-26 December – **Meals** a la carte 17.65/24.65 **t.** 10.50 – **3 rm** 45.00/65.00 **t.**

SNETTISHAM *Norfolk* 402 404 V 25 – *pop. 2 294.*
London 115 – Cambridge 58 – Norwich 45 – Peterborough 49.

Rose and Crown with rm, Old Church Rd, PE31 7LX, ☎ (01485) 541382, *roseandcrown@btclick.com, Fax (01485) 543172,* , « Part 14C inn », – P. VISA
Meals a la carte 16.75/23.25 **t.** 10.25 – **11 rm** 60.00/90.00 **t.** – SB.

SOAR MILL COVE *Devon – see Salcombe.*

SOLIHULL *W. Mids.* 403 404 O 26 – *pop. 199 859.*
Central Library, Homer Rd ☎ (0121) 704 6130.
London 109 – Birmingham 7 – Coventry 13 – Warwick 13.

Solihull Moat House, Homer Rd, B91 3QD, ☎ (0121) 623 9988, *revsol@queensmoat.co.uk, Fax (0121) 711 2696,* – rm, rest, P – 200. AE VISA JCB
Meals *(closed Saturday lunch)* 17.50 and a la carte 17.10/29.25 **st.** 12.95 – 13.50 – **113 rm** 165.00/185.00 **st.**, 2 suites – SB.

Renaissance Solihull, 651 Warwick Rd, B91 1AT, ☎ (0121) 711 3000, *reservations.solihull@whitbread.com, Fax (0121) 711 3963,* – rm, rest, – 700. AE VISA
651 **:** **Meals** a la carte 22.50/26.50 **st.** 13.50 – 11.75 – **177 rm** 125.00 **st.**, 1 suite – SB.

Ramada Jarvis, The Square, B91 3RF, ☎ (0121) 711 2121, *sales.solihull@ramadajarvis.co.uk, Fax (0121) 711 3374* – rm, P – 200. AE VISA
Meals a la carte 13.45/23.15 **st.** 12.15 – 10.95 – **135 rm** 160.00/170.00 **st.**, 10 suites – SB.

at Shirley *West : 2½ m. by B 4102 on A 34 –* ✉ *Solihull.*

Regency, Stratford Rd, B90 4EB, Southeast : 1 m. on A 34 ☎ (0121) 745 6119, *regency.hotel.regalhotels@pop3.hiway.com, Fax (0121) 733 3801,* – rm, P – 150. AE VISA JCB
– **Meals** (bar lunch Saturday and Sunday) 20.00 (dinner) and a la carte 20.00/35.00 **st.** – **110 rm** 145.00/155.00 **st.**, 2 suites – SB.

Travel Inn, Stratford Rd, B90 4EP, Southeast : 1 ½ m. on A 34 ☎ (0121) 744 294..., *Fax (0121) 733 7075* – rm, P. AE VISA.
Meals (grill rest.) – **51 rm** 41.95 **t.**

Chez Julien, 1036 Stratford Rd, Monkspath, B90 4EE, Southeast : 1 ½ m. on A 3... ☎ (0121) 744 7232, *chezjulien@yahoo.com, Fax (0121) 745 4775,* – P. AE VISA JCB
closed Saturday lunch, Sunday and Bank Holidays – **Meals** - French - 10.9... (lunch) and a la carte 24.40/30.50 **st.** 11.90.

at Olton *Northwest : 2½ m. on A 41 –* ✉ *Solihull.*

Rajnagar, 256 Lyndon Rd, B92 7QW, ☎ (0121) 742 8140, *info@rajnagar.co..., Fax (0121) 743 3147* – . AE VISA JCB
Meals - Indian - (dinner only) 12.95/17.95 and a la carte 9.00/11.95 **t.** 9.95.

SOMERTON *Somerset* 403 L 30 *The West Country G. – pop. 4 489.*
See : *Town★ - Market Place★ (cross★) – St Michael's Church★.*
Env. : *Long Sutton★ (Church★★) SW : 2½ m. by B 3165 – Huish Episcopi (St Mary's Church Tower★★) SW : 4½ m. by B 3153 – Lytes Cary★, SE : 3½ m. by B 3151 – Street - The Sh... Museum★, N : 5 m. by B 3151.*
Exc. : *Muchelney★★ (Parish Church★★) SW : 6½ m. by B 3153 and A 372 – High Ham (≤★... St Andrew's Church★), NW : 9 m. by B 3153, A 372 and minor rd – Midelney Manor★ A... SW : 9 m. by B 3153 and A 378.*
London 138 – Bristol 32 – Taunton 17.

Lynch Country House without rest., 4 Behind Berry, TA11 7PD, ☎ (01458) 272316, *the_lynch@talk21.com, Fax (01458) 272590*, <, « Regency house », ... – ... TV P. MC AE O VISA. ✻
5 rm ☕ 50.00/85.00 t.

...NNING-ON-THAMES *Wokingham 404 R 29 – pop. 1 354.*

London 48 – Reading 4.

French Horn with rm, RG4 6TN, ☎ (01189) 692204, *thefrenchhorn@compuserve.com, Fax (01189) 442210*, < River Thames and gardens – ... TV ... P. MC AE O VISA. ✻
closed 25-30 December – **Meals** (booking essential) 25.00/39.00 and a la carte 46.00/61.00 **st.** 25.00 – **16 rm** ☕ 120.00/150.00 **st.**, 4 suites.

...UTHAMPTON *Southampton 403 404* **P 31** *Great Britain G. – pop. 210 138.*

See : *Old Southampton* AZ : *Bargate*★ **B** - *Tudor House Museum*★ **M1.**

18, 9 Southampton Municipal, Golf Course Rd, Bassett ☎ (023) 8076 8407, AY – *18 Stoneham, Monks Wood Close, Bassett ☎ (023) 8076 8151,* AY – *18 Chilworth Golf Centre, Main Rd, Chilworth ☎ (023) 8074 0544,* AY – *Itchen Bridge (toll)* AZ.

Southampton/Eastleigh Airport : ☎ (023) 8062 0021, N : 4 m. BY.

to France (Cherbourg) (Stena Line) 1-2 daily (5 h) – to the Isle of Wight (East Cowes) (Red Funnel Ferries) frequent services daily (1 h).

to Hythe (White Horse Ferries Ltd) frequent services daily (12 mn) – to the Isle of Wight (Cowes) (Red Funnel Ferries) frequent services daily (approx. 22 mn).

9 Civic Centre Rd ☎ (023) 8022 1106.

London 87 – Bristol 79 – Plymouth 161.

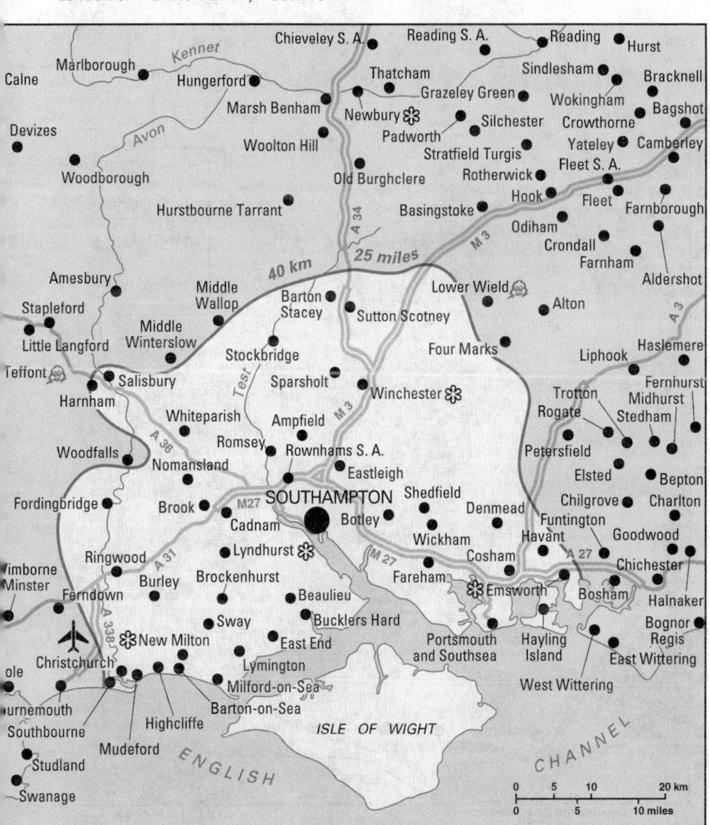

SOUTHAMPTON

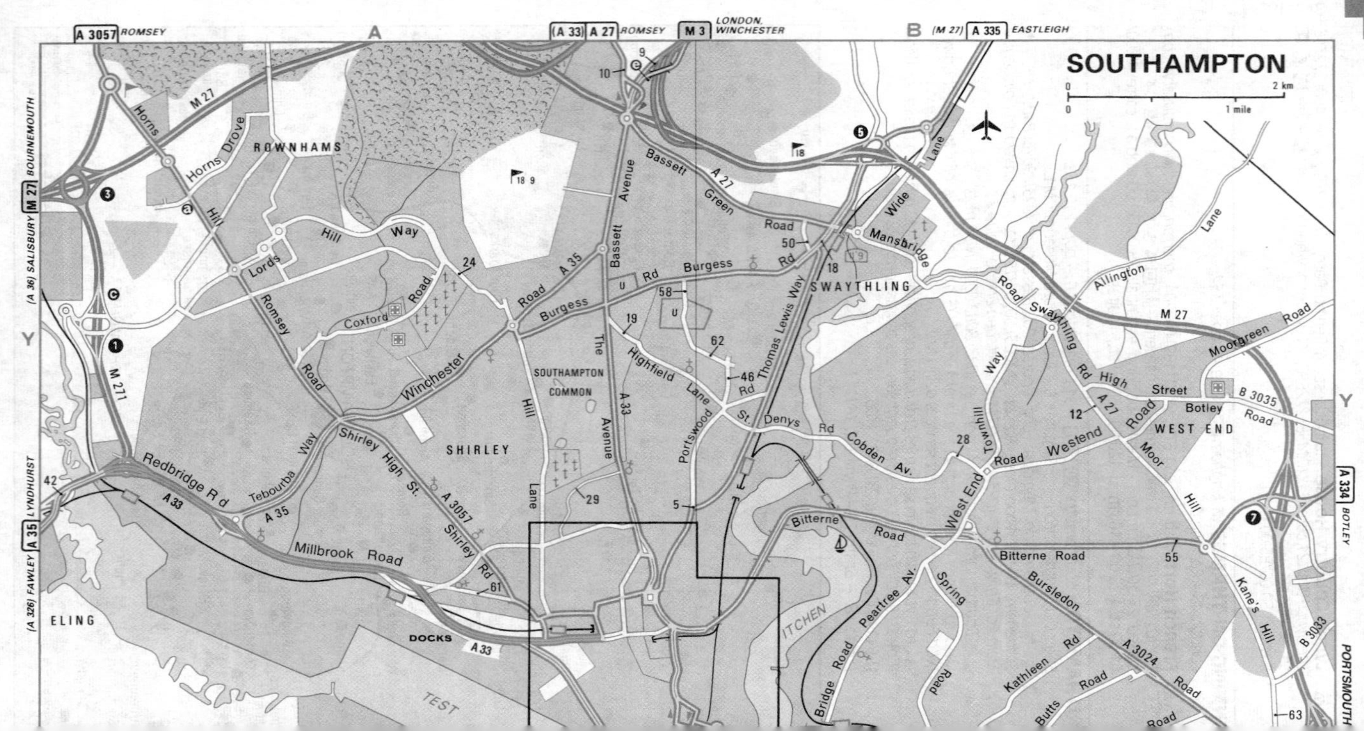

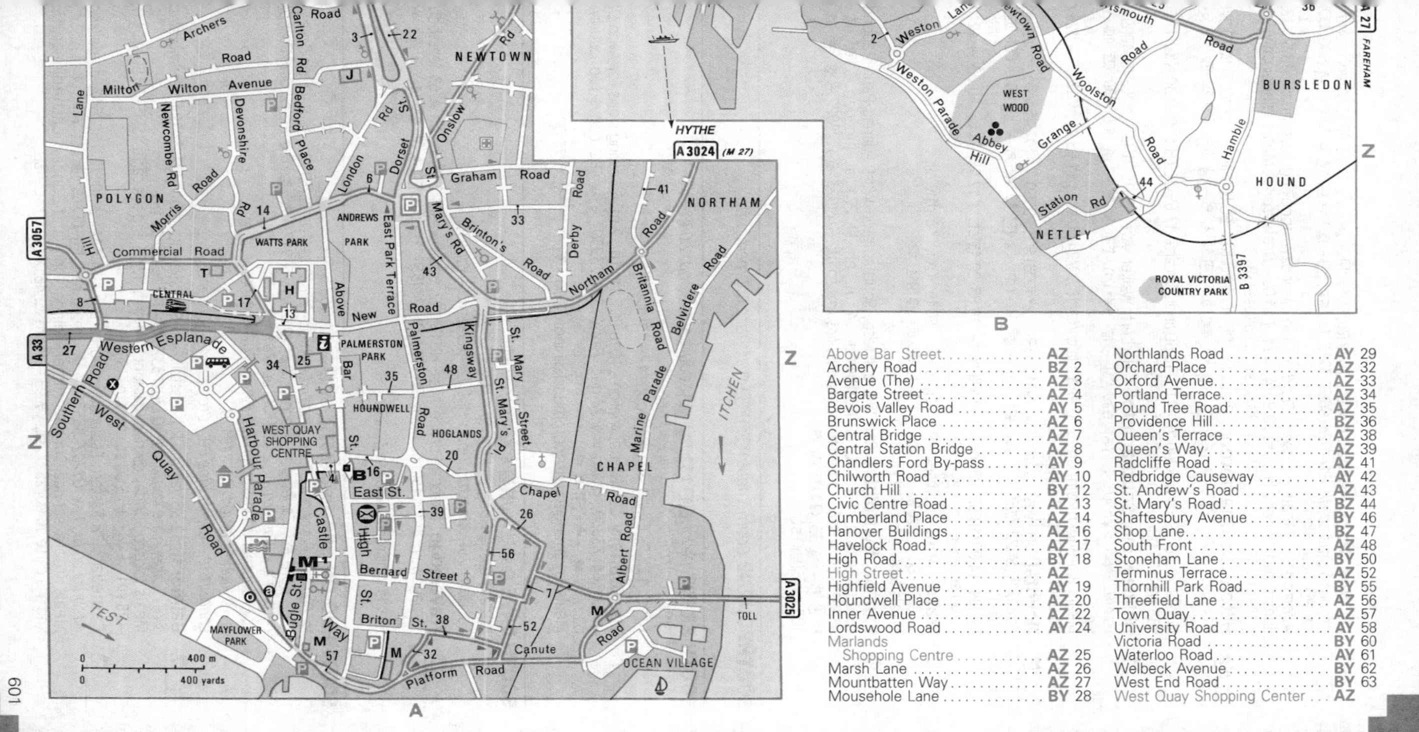

Street		No.	Street		No.
Above Bar Street	AZ		Northlands Road	AY	29
Archery Road	BZ	2	Orchard Place	AZ	32
Avenue (The)	AZ	3	Oxford Avenue	AZ	33
Bargate Street	AZ	4	Portland Terrace	AZ	34
Bevois Valley Road	AY	5	Pound Tree Road	AZ	35
Brunswick Place	AZ	6	Providence Hill	BZ	36
Central Bridge	AZ	7	Queen's Terrace	AZ	38
Central Station Bridge	AZ	8	Queen's Way	AZ	39
Chandlers Ford By-pass	AY	9	Radcliffe Road	AZ	41
Chilworth Road	AY	10	Redbridge Causeway	AY	42
Church Hill	BY	12	St. Andrew's Road	AZ	43
Civic Centre Road	AZ	13	St. Mary's Road	BZ	44
Cumberland Place	AZ	14	Shaftesbury Avenue	BY	46
Hanover Buildings	AZ	16	Shop Lane	BZ	47
Havelock Road	AZ	17	South Front	AZ	48
High Road	BY	18	Stoneham Lane	BY	50
High Street	AZ		Terminus Terrace	AZ	52
Highfield Avenue	AY	19	Thornhill Park Road	BY	55
Houndwell Place	AZ	20	Threefield Lane	AZ	56
Inner Avenue	AZ	22	Town Quay	AZ	57
Lordswood Road	AY	24	University Road	AY	58
Marlands Shopping Centre	AZ	25	Victoria Road	BY	60
Marsh Lane	AZ	26	Waterloo Road	AY	61
Mountbatten Way	AZ	27	Welbeck Avenue	BY	62
Mousehole Lane	BY	28	West End Road	BY	63
			West Quay Shopping Center	AZ	

De Vere Grand Harbour, West Quay Rd, SO15 1AG, ☏ (023) 8063 3033, *grand.southampton@airtime.co.uk, Fax (023) 8063 3066,* ⛶, ⛶, ⛶ – ⛶ ⛶ ⛶ ⛶ ⛶ ⛶ ⛶ – ⛶ 500. ⛶ ⛶ ⛶ VISA JCB. ⛶ AZ
Allerton's : **Meals** *(closed Sunday and Monday)* (booking essential) 15.50/17.5 (lunch) and dinner a la carte 30.90/45.45 **t.** 14.00 – ***Brewster's :*** **Meals** (dinner only) 26.0 19.00 – **169 rm** 160.00/180.00 **st.**, 3 suites – SB.

Hilton Southampton, Bracken Pl, Chilworth, SO16 3RB, ☏ (023) 8070 2700, *Fax (023) 8076 7233,* ⛶, ⛶, ⛶ – ⛶ ⛶, ⛶ rest, ⛶ ⛶ ⛶ ⛶ – ⛶ 200. ⛶ AE ⛶ VISA JCB ⛶ AY
Meals *(closed Saturday lunch)* 14.00/18.50 and a la carte 17.65/30.65 **t.** 12.30 – 11.50 **133 rm** 135.00/180.00 **t.**, 2 suites – SB.

Holiday Inn Southampton, Herbert Walker Ave, SO15 1HJ, ☏ (0870) 4009073, *Fax (023) 8033 2510,* ⛶, ⛶, ⛶, ⛶ – ⛶, ⛶ rm, ⛶ ⛶ ⛶ – ⛶ 200. ⛶ AE ⛶ VISA ⛶ AZ
Meals (bar lunch)/dinner 15.00 and a la carte 18.00/24.00 **st.** 11.95 – 13.95 – **126 rm** 99.00/110.00 **st.**, 2 suites – SB.

Novotel, 1 West Quay Rd, SO15 1RA, ☏ (023) 8033 0550, *h1073@accor-hotel.com, Fax (023) 8022 2158,* ⛶, ⛶, ⛶, ⛶ – ⛶, ⛶ rm, ⛶ ⛶ ⛶ ⛶ ⛶ – ⛶ 450. ⛶ AE ⛶ VISA AZ
Meals 14.00/18.00 (dinner) and a la carte 16.85/20.15 **st.** 12.95 – 10.00 – **121 rm** 82.00 **st.** – SB.

Travel Inn, Romsey Rd, Nursling, SO16 0XJ, Northwest : 4 m. on A 305 ☏ (023) 8073 2262 – ⛶ rm, ⛶ ⛶ ⛶. ⛶ AE ⛶ VISA. ⛶ AY
Meals (grill rest.) – **32 rm** 41.95 **t.**

Express by Holiday Inn without rest., Southampton West Adanac Park, Redbridge Lane, Nursling, SO16 0YP, Northwest : 4 m. on M 271 at junction 3 of M 2 ☏ (023) 8074 3100, *southampton@ariel-liesurre.co.uk, Fax (023) 8073 1827* – ⛶ ⛶ ⛶ ⛶ ⛶ ⛶ ⛶ – ⛶ 35. ⛶ AE ⛶ VISA AY
105 rm 69.50 **st.**

SOUTHBOURNE *Bournemouth* 403 404 O 31 – *see Bournemouth.*

SOUTH BRENT *Devon* 403 I 32 *The West Country G.* – *pop. 2 087.*

Env. : *Dartmoor National Park★★.*

London 227 – Exeter 29 – Plymouth 17 – Torquay 16.

The Granary ⛶, Harbourneford, TQ10 9DT, North : 2 m. following signs for Avon Da ☏ (01364) 73930, *granary@ic24.net, Fax (01364) 73930,* ⛶, « 18C converted courtyard barn », ⛶ – ⛶ ⛶ ⛶. ⛶
Meals (by arrangement) (communal dining) 22.00 – **3 rm** 35.00/70.00.

SOUTH CAVE *East Riding* 402 S 22 – *pop. 2 669.*

⛳18 *Cave Castle Hotel* ☏ *(01430) 421286.*

London 176 – Kingston-upon-Hull 12 – Leeds 40 – York 30.

Travelodge, Beacon Service Area, HU15 1RZ, Southwest : 2 ½ m. on A 63 (eastbound carriageway) ☏ (01430) 424455, *Fax (01430) 424455* – ⛶ rm, ⛶ ⛶ ⛶. ⛶ AE ⛶ VISA JCB ⛶
Meals (grill rest.) – **40 rm** 39.95 **t.**

SOUTHEND-ON-SEA *Southend* 404 W 29 – *pop. 158 517.*

⛳18 *Belfairs, Eastwood Road North, Leigh-on-Sea* ☏ *(01702) 525345* – ⛳18 *Ballards Gore G.C.C., Gore Rd, Canewdon, Rochford* ☏ *(01702) 258917* – ⛳18, ⛳9 *The Essex Golf Complex Garon Park, Eastern Av.* ☏ *(01702) 601701.*

✈ *Southend-on-Sea Airport :* ☏ *(01702) 608100, N : 2 m.*

ℹ *19 High St* ☏ *(01702) 215120.*

London 39 – Cambridge 69 – Croydon 46 – Dover 85.

Balmoral, 32-36 Valkyrie Rd, Westcliff-on-Sea, SS0 8BU, ☏ (01702) 342947, *balmoralho@netscapeonline.co.uk, Fax (01702) 337828* – ⛶ ⛶. ⛶ AE VISA
Meals *(closed Sunday dinner)* (bar lunch)/dinner 12.95 and a la carte 13.15/22.50 **st.** 8. – **28 rm** 44.00/75.00 **st.**, 1 suite – SB.

Camelia, 178 Eastern Esplanade, Thorpe Bay, SS1 3AA, ☏ (01702) 587917, *cameliaho@fsbdial.co.uk, Fax (01702) 585704* – ⛶ rm, ⛶ rest, ⛶. ⛶ AE ⛶ VISA JCB. ⛶
Meals (room service Sunday dinner) (dinner only and Sunday lunch)/dinner 13. and a la carte 10.00/25.00 **st.** 7.95 – **21 rm** 46.00/60.00 **st.** – SB.

Travel Inn, Thanet Grange, SS2 6GB, Northwest : 2 ½ m. by A 127 off B 1013 ✆ (01702) 338787, *Fax (01702) 430838* – |‡|, ⇔ rm, TV ♿ P. MC AE ⓓ VISA. ✻
Meals (grill rest.) – **60 rm** 41.95 **t.**

Beaches without rest., 192 Eastern Esplanade, Thorpe Bay, SS1 3AA, ✆ (01702) 586124, *beaches@quista.net, Fax (01702) 588377*, ← – TV. MC AE VISA JCB. ✻
8 rm 25.00/60.00 **s.**

Pebbles without rest., 190 Eastern Esplanade, Thorpe Bay, SS1 3AA, ✆ (01702) 582329, *pebbles.guesthouse@virgin.net, Fax (01702) 582329*, ← – ⇔ TV. MC VISA. ✻
5 rm ☕ 35.00/65.00 **st.**

The Bay without rest., 187 Eastern Esplanade, Thorpe Bay, SS1 3AA, ✆ (01702) 588415, *thebayguesthouse@hotmail.com* – ⇔ TV. MC AE VISA JCB. ✻
4 rm ☕ 35.00/50.00 **s.**

Moorings without rest., 172 Eastern Esplanade, Thorpe Bay, SS1 3AA, ✆ (01702) 587575, *Fax (01702) 586791* – TV. ✻
3 rm ☕ 35.00/47.50 **s.**

Paris, 719 London Rd, Westcliff-on-Sea, SS0 9ST, ✆ (01702) 344077, *Fax (01702) 344077* – MC AE VISA
closed Saturday lunch, Sunday dinner and Monday – **Meals** 15.95/25.95 **st.** 🍷 10.50.

Fleur de Provence, 52 Alexandra St, SS1 1BJ, ✆ (01702) 352987, *Fax (01702) 431123*. MC AE ⓓ VISA
closed first week January, Saturday lunch and Sunday – **Meals** 25.00 **st.** 🍷 12.00.

)UTH LEIGH *Oxon.* 403 404 P 28 – *see Witney.*

)UTH MIMMS SERVICE AREA *Herts.* 404 T 28 – ✉ *Potters Bar.*

London 21 – Luton 17.

Holiday Inn South Mimms, Bignells Corner, EN6 3NH, M 25 junction 23 at junction with A 1 (M) ✆ (0870) 400 9072, *Fax (01707) 646728*, Fá, ≘s, ▣ – ⇔ rm, TV ♿ P – 🏛 100. MC AE ⓓ VISA JCB
Meals *(closed Saturday lunch)* 10.00/11.95 (lunch) and dinner a la carte 17.35/29.15 **st.** 🍷 11.95 – ☕ 13.95 – **144 rm** 121.00 **t.** – SB.

Days Inn, Bignells Corner, EN6 3QQ, M 25 junction 23 at junction with A 1(M) ✆ (01707) 665440, Reservations (Freephone) 0800 0280400, *south.mimms.hotel@welcomebreak.co.uk, Fax (01707) 660189* – ⇔ rm, TV ♿ P. MC AE ⓓ VISA JCB
Meals (grill rest.) a la carte approx. 11.00 **t.** – **74 rm** 69.00/74.00 **t.**

)UTH NORMANTON *Derbs.* 402 403 404 Q 24 – *pop. 13 044 (inc. Pinxton).*

London 130 – Derby 17 – Nottingham 15 – Sheffield 31.

Renaissance Derby/Nottingham, Carter Lane East, DE55 2EH, on A 38 ✆ (01773) 812000, *info@swallowhotels.com, Fax (01773) 580032*, Fá, ≘s, ▣ – ⇔ ▤ TV ✆ ♿ P – 🏛 220. MC AE ⓓ VISA
Meals 16.95/21.00 **st.** 🍷 12.95 – **157 rm** 89.00/108.00.

Travel Inn, Carter Lane East, DE55 2EH, on A 38 ✆ (01773) 862899, *Fax (01773) 861155* – ⇔ rm, ▤ rest, TV ♿ P. MC AE ⓓ VISA. ✻
Meals (grill rest.) – **82 rm** 41.95 **t.**

)UTHPORT *Mersey.* 402 K 23 – *pop. 90 959.*

18 Southport Municipal, Park Road West ✆ (01704) 535286.
112 Lord St ✆ (01704) 533333.
London 221 – Liverpool 25 – Manchester 38 – Preston 19.

Scarisbrick, 239 Lord St, PR8 1NZ, ✆ (01704) 543000, *scarisbrickhotel@talk21.com, Fax (01704) 533335*, Fá, ≘s, ▣ – |‡|, ⇔ rest, TV P – 🏛 180. MC AE ⓓ VISA
Meals (dancing Saturday evening) (carving lunch Sunday) (dinner only and Sunday lunch)/dinner 12.00/16.00 and a la carte **st.** 🍷 10.25 – ***Cloisters*** *(✆ (01704) 535153)* : **Meals** a la carte 8.95/19.65 **st.** 🍷 10.00 – **89 rm** ☕ 77.00/105.00 **st.**, 1 suite – SB.

Prince of Wales, Lord St, PR8 1JS, ✆ (01704) 536688, *res.719@britanniahotels.com, Fax (01704) 543932* – |‡| ⇔ TV ♿ P – 🏛 450. MC AE ⓓ VISA JCB. ✻
Meals 10.95/17.00 🍷 12.95 – **100 rm** ☕ 99.00/115.00 **t.**, 3 suites – SB.

Cambridge House, 4 Cambridge Rd, PR9 9NG, Northeast : 1 ½ m. on A 565 ✆ (01704) 538372, *info@cambridgehousehotel.co.uk, Fax (01704) 547183*, 🌳 – ⇔ TV P. MC VISA. ✻
Meals (dinner only and Sunday lunch)/dinner 15.95 and a la carte approx. 21.00 **t.** 🍷 10.75 – **16 rm** ☕ 55.00/140.00 **t.**

Stutelea, Alexandra Rd, PR9 0NB, ✆ (01704) 544220, *info@stutelea.co.u*
Fax (01704) 500232, ... rest, ...
closed 24-26 December and 1 January – **Meals** (bar lunch)/dinner a la carte 15.20/23.60
8.95 – **20 rm** 65.00/120.00 **st.** – SB.

Bay Trees without rest., 4 Queens Rd, PR9 9HN, ✆ (01704) 536513, *Fax (01704) 53651*
...
12 rm 24.00/48.00.

Ambassador, 13 Bath St, PR9 0DP, ✆ (01704) 543998, *ambassador.walton@virgin.ne*
Fax (01704) 536269 – ...
closed Christmas and New Year – **Meals** (by arrangement) 10.00 **st.** – **8 rm** 36.0
50.00 **s.**

Warehouse Brasserie, 30 West St, PR8 1QN, ✆ (01704) 544662, *info@warehou*
brasserie.co.uk, Fax (01704) 500074 – ...
closed 25-26 December, 1 January and Sunday – **Meals** (light lunch)/dinner a la car
20.40/26.40 **t.** 9.95.

New Ho Lee Chow, Rotton Row, Victoria Park, PR8 2BZ, ✆ (01704) 55116
Fax (01704) 551166 – ...
closed 25 December – **Meals** - Chinese - (dinner only and Sunday lunch)/dinner 12.00/33.
and a la carte 9.95/23.00 **t.** 9.95.

SOUTHSEA *Portsmouth* 403 404 Q 31 – *see Portsmouth and Southsea.*

When looking for a quiet hotel
use the maps found in the introduction
or look for establishments with the sign ... *or* ....

SOUTH STOKE *Oxon.* 403 404 Q 29 – *see Goring.*

SOUTHWAITE SERVICE AREA *Cumbria* 401 402 L 19 – ✉ *Carlisle.*
M 6 Service Area ✆ (016974) 73445.
London 300 – Carlisle 14 – Lancaster 58 – Workington 48.

Travelodge, CA4 0NT, M 6 between junctions 41 and 42 ✆ (016974) 7331
Fax (016974) 73669 – ... rm, ...
Meals (grill rest.) – **39 rm** 49.95 **t.**

SOUTHWATER *W. Sussex* 404 T 30 – *see Horsham.*

SOUTHWELL *Notts.* 402 404 R 24 *Great Britain G.* – *pop. 6 498.*
See : *Minster★★ AC.*
London 135 – Lincoln 24 – Nottingham 14 – Sheffield 34.

Old Forge without rest., 2 Burgage Lane, NG25 0ER, ✆ (01636) 8128
Fax (01636) 816302, ...
5 rm 35.00/68.00.

SOUTHWOLD *Suffolk* 404 Z 27 – *pop. 3 905.*
The Common ✆ (01502) 723234.
Town Hall, Market Pl ✆ (01502) 724729.
London 108 – Great Yarmouth 24 – Ipswich 35 – Norwich 34.

Swan, Market Pl, IP18 6EG, ✆ (01502) 722186, *swan.hotel@adnams.co.*
Fax (01502) 724800, ... rest, ... 40. ...
closed 3 weeks January – **Meals** *(closed lunch October-Easter)* 18.00/27.50 and d
ner a la carte 24.25/37.75 **t.** 9.50 – **41 rm** 70.00/150.00 **t.**, 2 suites – SB.

Crown, 90 High St, IP18 6DP, ✆ (01502) 722275, *crownhotelreception/adnams@adnar*
co.uk, Fax (01502) 727263, « Part 18C inn » – ... 40. ...
Meals 16.50/27.00 and a la carte 18.00/22.95 **st.** 12.00 – **14 rm** 57.00/82.00.

at Uggeshall *Northwest : 4 m. by A 1095 and B 1126 over A 12 at Wangford* – ✉ *Southwold.*

Uggeshall Manor Farm ... without rest., NR34 8BD, ✆ (01502) 5785
Fax (01502) 578663, ..., « Working farm », ...
3 rm 50.00/70.00 **st.**

OWERBY BRIDGE *W. Yorks.* 402 O 22 – *pop. 9 901* – ✉ *Halifax.*
London 211 – Bradford 10 – Burnley 35 – Manchester 32 – Sheffield 40.

The Millbank, Mill Bank, HX6 3DY, Southwest : 2 ¼ m. by A 58 ✆ (01422) 825588, *millbankph@ukonline.co.uk, Fax (01422) 822080,* – . MO VISA
closed 2 weeks October, 1 week March, Monday, Sunday dinner and Tuesday lunch – **Meals** (booking essential) a la carte 19.45/24.15 **t.** 9.10.

PALDING *Lincs.* 402 404 T 25 – *pop. 18 731.*
Ayscoughfee Hall Museum, Churchgate ✆ (01775) 725468.
London 111 – Lincoln 40 – Leicester 56 – Norwich 65.

Bedford Court without rest., 10 London Rd, PE11 2TA, ✆ (01775) 722377, *Fax (01775) 722377,* – TV P.
4 rm 30.00/45.00.

PARSHOLT *Hants.* 403 404 P 30 – *see Winchester.*

PEEN *Bucks.* 404 R 28 – ✉ *Princes Risborough.*
London 41 – Aylesbury 15 – Oxford 33 – Reading 25.

Old Plow (Restaurant), Flowers Bottom, HP27 0PZ, West : ½ m. by Chapel Hill and Highwood Bottom ✆ (01494) 488300, *Fax (01494) 488702,* – P. MO AE VISA
closed August, Monday, Saturday lunch, Sunday dinner and Bank Holidays – **Meals** 25.95/ 29.95 **t.** 13.95 – (see also ***Bistro*** below).

Bistro (at Old Plow), Flowers Bottom, HP27 0PZ, West : ½ m. by Chapel Hill and Highwood Bottom ✆ (01494) 488300, *Fax (01494) 488702,* , – P. MO AE VISA
closed August, Monday, Saturday lunch, Sunday dinner and Bank Holidays – **Meals** (booking essential) a la carte 27.85/39.85 **t.** 13.95.

PEKE *Mersey.* 402 403 L 23 – *see Liverpool.*

PENNYMOOR *Durham* 401 402 P 19 – *pop. 6 462* – ✉ *Darlington.*
London 275 – Newcastle upon Tyne 24 – Durham 6 – Leeds 75.

Whitworth Hall Country Park H. , DL16 7QX, Northwest : 1 ½ m. by Middlestone Moor rd on Brancepeth rd ✆ (01388) 811772, *reception@whitworthhall.co.uk, Fax (01388) 818669,* <, « 19C country house in Deer park », , – TV P – 150. MO AE VISA.
Four Seasons : **Meals** (dinner only and Sunday lunch) 22.95 **t.** 11.25 – ***Silver Buckles Brasserie :*** **Meals** *(closed Sunday dinner)* 9.95/22.95 11.25 – **29 rm** 99.00/135.00 **t.** – SB.

Idsley House without rest., 4 Green Lane, Mount Pleasant, DL16 6HD, Northeast : 1 ¼ m. by A 688 off the B 6288 turning right at lights ✆ (01388) 814237 – TV P. MO VISA JCB
closed Christmas-New Year – **5 rm** 32.00/48.00 **s.**

PRATTON *Northants.* 404 R 27 – *see Northampton.*

PRIG'S ALLEY *Oxon.* – *see Chinnor.*

TADDLEBRIDGE *N. Yorks.* – *see Northallerton.*

TADHAMPTON *Oxon.* 403 404 Q 28 – *pop. 718.*
London 53 – Aylesbury 18 – Oxford 10.

Crazy Bear with rm, Bear Lane, OX44 7UR, off Wallingford rd ✆ (01865) 890714, *hunt crazybear@cs.co.uk, Fax (01865) 400481,* , – TV P. MO AE VISA.
closed 24 December-2 January – **Meals** *(closed Sunday dinner and Monday)* 10.00/15.00 (lunch) and a la carte 27.50/37.50 **t.** 12.50 – ***Thai Thai :*** **Meals** *(closed Sunday lunch)* (booking essential) 19.00/24.00 and a la carte 20.00/26.00 **t.** 12.50 – 10.00 – **11 rm** 60.00/120.00 **t.**, 1 suite – SB.

***Le Grand Londres** (GREATER LONDON) est composé de la City et de 32 arrondissements administratifs (Borough) eux-mêmes divisés en quartiers ou en villages ayant conservé leur caractère propre (Area).*

STAFFORD *Staffs.* 402 403 404 N 25 – *pop. 61 885.*

Stafford Castle, Newport Rd (01785) 223821.

The Ancient High House, Greengate St (01785) 619136.

London 142 – Birmingham 26 – Derby 32 – Shrewsbury 31 – Stoke-on-Trent 17.

Garth, Wolverhampton Rd, ST17 9JR, South : 2 m. on A 449 (01785) 256124, *thegarth corushotels.com, Fax (01785) 255152,* – rm, rest, – 175.
Meals *(closed Saturday lunch)* 15.50 (dinner) and a la carte 16.15/23.75 **t.** 11.75 – 10.
– **60 rm** 82.00/92.00 **st.** – SB.

Express by Holiday Inn without rest., Acton Court, Acton Gate, ST18 9AR, South : 3 m. on A 449 (01785) 212244, *express.stafford@ingramhotels.co.uk, Fax (01785) 212377* – – 40. VISA JCB
closed 24-26 December – **103 rm** 58.00 **st.**

STAFFORD SERVICE AREA *Staffs.* 403 404 N 25 – *Stafford.*

Travelodge, Stone, ST15 0EU, M 6 between junctions 14 and 15 (northbound carriageway) (01785) 811188, *Fax (01785) 810500* – VISA JCB.
Meals (grill rest.) – **49 rm** 52.95 **t.**

Travel inn without rest., Stone, ST15 0EU, M 6 between junctions 15 and 14 (southbound carriageway) (01785) 826300, *Fax (01785) 826303* – – 50. VISA
42 rm 41.95 **t.**

STAINES *Middx.* 404 S 29 – *pop. 51 167.*

London 26 – Reading 25.

Thames Lodge, Thames St, TW18 4SF, (0870) 4008121, *heritagehotels-staines thames-lodge@forte-hotels.com, Fax (01784) 466772,* <, « Riverside setting » – rest, – 50. VISA
Meals (dinner only) a la carte 18.20/25.45 **t.** 13.50 – **78 rm** 176.00 **st.** – SB.

STAITHES *Redcar & Cleveland* 402 R 20 – *Saltburn (Cleveland).*

London 269 – Middlesbrough 22 – Scarborough 31.

Endeavour, 1 High St, TS13 5BH, (01947) 840825 –
closed mid January-mid March, November, Sunday and Monday – **Meals** - Seafood - (lunch booking essential) a la carte 21.35/24.65 **t.** 9.25.

STAMFORD *Lincs.* 402 404 S 26 *Great Britain G.* – *pop. 17 492.*

See : *Town★★ - St Martin's Church★ – Lord Burghley's Hospital★ – Browne's Hospital★ A*

Env. : *Burghley House★★ AC, SE : 1½ m. by B 1443.*

The Arts Centre, 27 St Mary's St (01780) 755611.

London 92 – Leicester 31 – Lincoln 50 – Nottingham 45.

The George of Stamford, 71 St Martin's, PE9 2LB, (01780) 750750, *reservations @georgehotelofstamford.com, Fax (01780) 750701,* , « Part 16C coaching inn with walled monastic garden » – – 50. VISA JCB
Dining Room : **Meals** a la carte 30.25/45.75 **st.** 11.00 – ***Garden Lounge :*** **Meals** a la carte 19.25/36.40 **st.** 11.00 – **46 rm** 78.00/175.00 **st.**, 1 suite – SB.

Garden House, 42 High St, St Martin's, PE9 2LP, (01780) 763359, *gardenhousehotel stamford60.freeserve.co.uk, Fax (01780) 763339,* , – rest, VISA JCB
Meals 17.00 and dinner a la carte 16.25/20.50 **st.** 8.75 – **20 rm** 62.00/88.00 **st.** – SB.

at Stretton *(Rutland) Northwest : 8 m. by B 1081 off A 1* – *Stamford.*

Ram Jam Inn, Great North Rd, LE15 7QX, on A 1 (northbound carriageway) (01780) 410776, *rji@rutnet.co.uk, Fax (01780) 410361,* – – 30. VISA
closed 25 December and 1 January – **Meals** a la carte 15.15/22.85 **t.** 11.95 – 5.75
7 rm 47.00/57.00 **t.**

at Clipsham *(Rutland) Northwest : 9½ m. by B 1081 off A 1* – *Stamford.*

The Olive Branch (Hope), Main St, LE15 7SH, (01780) 410355, *Fax (01780) 410000,* – VISA
closed Sunday dinner – **Meals** (booking essential) 11.50 (lunch) and a la carte 17.25/22.95 10.00
Spec. Mushroom risotto, truffle oil and parmesan. Pan-fried plaice with Welsh rarebit and sauté potatoes. Chocolate brownie with pistachio ice cream.

STANBRIDGE *Beds.* 404 S 28 – *pop. 1 496.*

London 42 – Milton Keynes 14 – Luton 10.

The Five Bells, Station Rd, LU7 9JF, ☎ (01525) 210224, *Fax (01525) 211164*, « Characterful inn », – rest, P. **Meals** (booking essential) a la carte 17.40/22.50 **t.** 9.95.

STANDISH *Gtr. Manchester* 402 404 M 23 – *pop. 12 196* – ✉ *Wigan.*

London 210 – Liverpool 25 – Manchester 21 – Preston 15.

Wigan/Standish Moat House, Almond Brook Rd, WN6 0SR, West : 1 m. on A 5209 ☎ (01257) 499988, *revwig@queensmoat.co.uk, Fax (01257) 426632*, – rest, – 55. **Meals** *(closed Saturday lunch)* 11.00 (dinner) and a la carte 11.95/20.00 **st.** 11.95 – 10.50 – **124 rm** 89.00/120.00 **st.** – SB.

Ashfield House, Ashfield Park Drive, WN6 0EQ, Southeast : ¾ m. by A 49 ☎ (01257) 473500, *arb355@compuserve.com, Fax (01257) 400311*, – – 50.

Barkers : **Meals** *(closed lunch Monday and Saturday and Sunday dinner)* 7.95/15.95 and a la carte 21.85/27.15 **t.** 10.95 – **15 rm** 65.00/85.00 **t.** – SB.

Premier Lodge, Almond Brook Rd, WN6 0SS, West : 1 m. on A 5209 ☎ (0870) 7001574, *Fax (0800) 7001575* – rm, rest, – 30. **Meals** (grill rest.) a la carte approx. 12.50 **t.** 7.80 – **36 rm** 42.95 **t.**

Wrightington Bar *Northwest : 3½ m. by A 5209 on B 5250* – ✉ *Wigan.*

The Mulberry Tree, WN6 9SE, ☎ (01257) 451400, *Fax (01257) 451400* – P. *closed 1-14 January, 27 May-3 June, 28 October-3 November, dinner 25-26 December and Monday* – **Meals** a la carte 19.70/25.40 **t.** 9.50.

STANLEY *Durham* 401 402 O 19 – *pop. 1 733.*

London 284 – Newcastle upon Tyne 11 – Carlisle 68 – Darlington 31 – Middlesbrough 39.

Beamish Park, Beamish Burn Rd, Marley Hill, NE16 5EG, North : 2 ½ m. by A 6076 ☎ (01207) 230666, *reception@beamish-park-hotel.co.uk, Fax (01207) 281260*, – rm, – 40.

The Bistro : **Meals** a la carte 14.70/25.70 **st.** 10.95 – 8.95 – **47 rm** 44.50/69.00 **st.** – SB.

STANNERSBURN *Northd.* 401 402 M 18 – ✉ *Hexham.*

London 363 – Carlisle 56 – Newcastle upon Tyne 46.

Pheasant Inn with rm, Falstone, NE48 1DD, ☎ (01434) 240382, *thepheasantinn @kielderwater.demon.co.uk, Fax (01434) 240382* – P. *closed 25 December and 1 January* – **Meals** a la carte 12.70/17.00 **t.** 9.75 – **8 rm** 30.00/65.00 **t.** – SB.

STANSTEAD ABBOTTS *Herts.* 404 U 28 – *pop. 1 909* – ✉ *Ware.*

Briggens House Hotel, Briggens Park, Stanstead Rd ☎ (01279) 793742.

London 22 – Cambridge 37 – Luton 32 – Ipswich 66.

Briggens House, Stanstead Rd, SG12 8LD, East : 2 m. by A 414 ☎ (01279) 829955, *Fax (01279) 793685*, ≤, heated, – – rest, – 100. **Meals** *(closed Saturday lunch)* 12.95/30.00 **t.** 13.50 – 12.00 – **53 rm** 110.00/125.00 **st.**, 1 suite – SB.

STANSTED AIRPORT *Essex* 404 U 28 – ✉ *Stansted Mountfitchet.*

London 37 – Cambridge 29 – Chelmsford 18 – Colchester 29.

Hilton London Stansted Airport, Round Coppice Rd, CM24 8SE, ☎ (01279) 680800, *Fax (01279) 680890*, – rm, rest, – 300. **Meals** *(closed Saturday lunch)* 14.95/20.95 and dinner a la carte 26.50/32.50 **t.** 12.50 – 14.00 – **236 rm** 150.00/170.00 **st.**, 3 suites.

Broxted *Northeast : 3 ¾ m. by Broxted rd* – ✉ *Great Dunmow.*

Whitehall, Church End, CM6 2BZ, on B 1051 ☎ (01279) 850603, *sales@whitehallhotel.co.uk, Fax (01279) 850385*, ≤, « Part 12C and 15C manor house », – – 100. *accommodation closed 25-31 December* – **Meals** *(closed Saturday lunch, Sunday dinner residents only)* 23.50 and dinner a la carte 27.00/35.00 **t.** 14.75 – 11.00 – **26 rm** 98.00/220.00 **t.** – SB.

STANTON *Suffolk* 404 W 27 – *pop. 2 490.*
London 88 – Cambridge 38 – Ipswich 40 – King's Lynn 38 – Norwich 39.

Leaping Hare, Wyken Vineyards, IP31 2DW, South : 1 ¼ m. by Wyken ... (01359) 250287, *Fax (01359) 252372*, « 17C converted barn, vineyard, working fa... and gardens » – P. VISA
closed 25 December-9 January – **Meals** (booking essential) (lunch only and dinner Frid... and Saturday) a la carte 18.25/26.75 **t.** 11.00.

STANTON SAINT QUINTIN *Wilts.* 403 404 N 29 – *see Chippenham.*

STANTON WICK *Bath & North East Somerset* 403 404 M 29 – *see Bristol.*

STAPLEFORD *Wilts.* 403 404 O 30 – *see Salisbury.*

STAVERTON *Devon* 403 I 32 – *pop. 682* – ✉ *Totnes.*
London 220 – Exeter 20 – Torquay 33.

Kingston House, TQ9 6AR, Northwest : 1 m. on Kingston rd (01803) 762235, *in... @kingston-estate.com, Fax (01803) 762444*, ≤, « Georgian mansion, antiques and m... quetry staircase », – P. AE VISA JCB.
closed Christmas and New Year – **Meals** (set menu only) (residents only) (dinner on... 32.50/34.50 **st.** 9.95 – **3 rm** 85.00/150.00 **st.** – SB.

Sea Trout Inn with rm, TQ9 6PA, (01803) 762274, *Fax (01803) 762506*, – re... TV P. AE VISA
closed 25 December – **Meals** 19.75 (dinner) and lunch a la carte approx. 14.00 **t.** 9.75... **10 rm** 45.00/75.00 **t.** – SB.

When looking for a quiet hotel
use the maps found in the introduction
or look for establishments with the sign or .

STAVERTON *Northants.* 404 Q 27 – *see Daventry.*

STEDHAM *W. Sussex* 404 R 31 – *see Midhurst.*

STEEPLE ASTON *Oxon.* 403 404 Q 28 – *pop. 874* – ✉ *Bicester.*
London 69 – Coventry 38 – Oxford 10.

The Holt, OX25 5QQ, Southwest : 1 ¼ m. at junction of A 4260 with B 40... (01869) 340259, *info@holthotel-oxford.co.uk, Fax (01869) 340865*, – TV P... 120. AE VISA JCB
Meals *(closed Sunday dinner)* (carvery lunch Monday-Friday)/dinner 14.95/24... and a la carte 24.65/34.40 **t.** 10.95 – **86 rm** 99.90/128.00 **t.**

STEVENAGE *Herts.* 404 T 28 *Great Britain G.* – *pop. 76 064.*
Env. : *Knebworth House★ AC, S : 2½ m.*
18, 9 *Aston Lane (01438) 880424* – 18, 9 *Chesfield Downs, Jack's Hill, Graveley (014... 482929.*
London 36 – Bedford 25 – Cambridge 27.

Cromwell, High St, Old Town, SG1 3AZ, (01438) 779954, *cromwell@corushotels.co... Fax (01438) 742169*, – , rest, TV P – 200. AE VISA.
Meals *(closed Sunday dinner)* a la carte 18.50/31.00 **st.** 11.50 – 11.50 – **76 rm** 104.0... 120.00 **st.** – SB.

Novotel Stevenage, Knebworth Park, SG1 2AX, Southwest : 1 ½ m. by A 602 at juncti... 7 of A 1(M) (01438) 346100, *h0992@accor-hotels.com, Fax (01438) 723872*, heated... rm, rest, TV P – 120. AE VISA
Meals 12.50/16.75 and a la carte 13.00/26.85 **st.** 11.25 – 10.50 – **100 rm** 99.0... 109.00 **st.**

Travel Inn, Corey's Mill Lane, SG1 4AA, Northwest : 2 m. on A 602 (01438) 3513... *Fax (01438) 721609* – rm, rest, TV P. AE VISA.
Meals (grill rest.) – **40 rm** 41.95 **t.**

ENGLAND

TEYNING *W. Sussex* 404 T 31 – *pop. 8 692 (inc. Upper Beeding).*
London 52 – Brighton 12 – Worthing 10.

The Old Tollgate, The Street, Bramber, BN44 3WE, Southwest : 1 m. (01903) 879494, *otr@fastnet.co.uk, Fax (01903) 813399,* – VISA JCB.
Meals (carving rest.) 14.65/21.95 **t.** 11.25 – 7.65 – **31 rm** 75.00 **t.** – SB.

Springwells without rest., 9 High St, BN44 3GG, (01903) 812446, *contact@springwells.co.uk, Fax (01903) 879823,* heated, – VISA
closed 2 weeks Christmas-New Year – **10 rm** 45.00/75.00 **t.**

TILTON *Cambs.* 404 T 26 – *pop. 2 219* – *Peterborough.*
London 76 – Cambridge 30 – Northampton 43 – Peterborough 6.

Bell Inn, Great North Rd, PE7 3RA, (01733) 241066, *reception@thebellstilton.co.uk, Fax (01733) 245173,* « Part 16C », – rm, – 100. VISA JCB.
closed 25 December – **Meals** *(closed Saturday lunch)* 22.95 **t.** 10.95 – (see also ***Village Bar*** below) – **19 rm** 69.50/109.50 **st.**

Village Bar (at Bell Inn), Great North Rd, PE7 3RA, (01733) 241066, « Part 16C » – VISA
closed 25 December – **Meals** a la carte 15.25/21.20 **t.** 10.95.

TOCKBRIDGE *Hants.* 403 404 P 30 – *pop. 570.*
London 75 – Salisbury 14 – Winchester 9.

Carbery, Salisbury Hill, SO20 6EZ, on A 30 (01264) 810771, *Fax (01264) 811022,* heated, – rest, VISA.
closed 2 weeks Christmas – **Meals** (by arrangement) 14.50 **st.** – **11 rm** 29.00/55.00 **t.**

Peat Spade Inn with rm, Longstock, SO20 6DR, North : 1 ½ m. on A 3057 (01264) 810612, *peat.spade@virgin.net, Fax (01264) 810612,* « 18C inn », –
closed 1 January and 25 December – **Meals** *(closed Sunday dinner and Monday)* a la carte 15.45/23.50 **t.** 9.50 – **2 rm** 60.00/65.00 **st.**

There is no paid advertising in this Guide.

TOCKPORT *Gtr. Manchester* 402 403 404 N 23 – *pop. 132 813.*
18 Heaton Moor, Mauldeth Rd (0161) 432 2134 – 18 Romiley, Goosehouse Green (0161) 430 2392 – 18 Ladythorn Rd, Bramhall (0161) 439 4057 – 18 Hazel Grove (0161) 483 3217.
Graylaw House, Chestergate (0161) 474 4444.
London 201 – Liverpool 42 – Manchester 6 – Sheffield 37 – Stoke-on-Trent 34.

Alma Lodge, 149 Buxton Rd, SK2 6EL, South : 1 ¼ m. on A 6 (0161) 483 4431, *Fax (0161) 483 1983* – rm, rest, – 200. VISA.
closed 26 December **Meals** - Italian - *(closed Saturday lunch)* 9.00 (lunch) a la carte 20.25/35.00 **t.** 11.00 – 8.00 – **52 rm** 65.00/75.00 **t.** – SB.

Wycliffe, 74 Edgeley Rd, Edgeley, SK3 9NQ, West : 1 m. on B 5465 (0161) 477 5395, *wycliffe-hotel@yahoo.co.uk, Fax (0161) 476 3219* – rm, – 30. VISA.
Meals - Italian - *(closed Saturday lunch and Bank Holidays)* 10.00/18.00 and a la carte 18.50/34.00 **st.** 11.00 – **20 rm** 50.00/65.00 **st.**

Premier Lodge, Churchgate, SK1 1YG, East : ¼ m. by Wellington St (0870) 7001484, *Fax (0870) 7001485* – rm, rest, – 30. VISA.
Meals (grill rest.) a la carte approx. 13.00 **t.** 8.95 – **46 rm** 46.95 **t.**

Travel Inn, Buxton Rd, SK2 6NB, South : 1 m. on A 6 (0161) 480 2968, *Fax (0161) 477 8320* – rm, rest, VISA.
Meals (grill rest.) – **40 rm** 41.95 **t.**

TOCKTON-ON-TEES *Stockton-on-Tees* 402 P 20 – *pop. 83 576.*
18 Eaglescliffe, Yarm Rd (01642) 780098 – 18 Knotty Hill Golf Centre, Sedgefield (01740) 620320 – 18 Norton, Junction Rd (01642) 676385.
Teesside Airport : (01325) 332811, SW : 6 m. by A 1027, A 135 and A 67.
Theatre Yard, off High St (01642) 393936.
London 251 – Leeds 61 – Middlesbrough 4.

Travel Inn, Yarm Rd, TS18 3RT, Southwest : 1 ¾ m. on A 135 at junction with A 66 (01642) 633354, *Fax (01642) 633339* – rm, rest, VISA.
Meals (grill rest.) – **40 rm** 41.95 **t.**

at Eaglescliffe *South : 3½ m. on A 135 – ✉ Stockton-on-Tees.*

Parkmore, 636 Yarm Rd, TS16 0DH, ☎ (01642) 786815, *enquiries@parkmorehotel.co.* *Fax (01642) 790485,* – 120. *VISA*
Reeds at Six Three Six : **Meals** a la carte 15.50/23.75 **st.** 8.95 – **54 rm** 59.00/80.00 s 1 suite – SB.

STOKE BRUERNE *Northants.* 404 R 27 – *pop. 347 – ✉ Towcester.*
London 69 – Coventry 33 – Northampton 9 – Oxford 33.

Bruerne's Lock, 5 The Canalside, NN12 7SB, ☎ (01604) 863654, *bruerneslock@ma com, Fax (01604) 863330,* « Canalside setting » – . *VISA*.
closed 26 December to 8 January, 1 week March, 1 week October, Monday, Sunday dinr and Saturday lunch – **Meals** 17.00 (lunch) and dinner a la carte 25.15/32.40 **t.** 14.95.

STOKE BY NAYLAND *Suffolk* 404 W 28.
London 70 – Bury St. Edmunds 24 – Cambridge 54 – Colchester 11 – Ipswich 14.

The Stoke by Nayland Club, Keepers Lane, Leavenheath, CO6 4PZ, Northwest : 1½ on B 1068 ☎ (01206) 262836, *info@golf-club.co.uk, Fax (01206) 263356,* – rm, – 600. *VISA*
Meals (bar lunch Monday to Saturday) (carvery lunch Sunday)/dinner 13.00/17. and a la carte 15.50/28.00 **t.** 9.95 – **30 rm** 79.00/130.00 **st.** – SB.

Ryegate House without rest., CO6 4RA, ☎ (01206) 263679, *ryegate@lineone.net,* –
closed 1 week in spring, 1 week in autumn and 5 days at Christmas – **3 rm** 36.7 52.50 **st.**

Angel Inn with rm, Polstead St, CO6 4SA, ☎ (01206) 263245, *Fax (01206) 263373,* « P timbered 17C inn » – rm, . *VISA*.
closed 25-26 December and 1 January – **Meals** a la carte 15.15/26.00 **t.** 8.90 – **6 r** 52.50/67.50 **t.**

Se cercate un albergo tranquillo,
oltre a consultare le carte dell'introduzione,
rintracciate nell'elenco degli esercizi quelli con il simbolo o .

STOKE CANON *Devon* 403 J 31 – *see Exeter.*

STOKE D'ABERNON *Surrey* 404 ㊷ – *see Cobham.*

STOKE FLEMING *Devon* 403 J 33 – *see Dartmouth.*

STOKE HOLY CROSS *Norfolk* 404 X 26 – *see Norwich.*

STOKE-ON-TRENT *Stoke-on-Trent* 402 403 404 N 24 *Great Britain G.* – *pop. 266 543.*
See : *The Potteries Museum and Art Gallery*★ Y **M** – *Gladstone Pottery Museum*★ *AC* V.
Env. : *Wedgwood Visitor Centre*★ *AC, S : 7 m. on A 500, A 34 and minor rd* V.
Exc. : *Little Moreton Hall*★★ *AC, N : 10 m. by A 500 on A 34* U.
Greenway Hall, Stockton Brook ☎ (01782) 503158, U – *Parkhall, Hulme Rd, West Coyney ☎ (01782) 599584,* V.
Quadrant Rd, Hanley ☎ (01782) 236000.
London 162 – Birmingham 46 – Leicester 59 – Liverpool 58 – Manchester 41 – Sheffield 5

Plans on following pages

Stoke-on-Trent Moat House, Etruria Hall, Festival Park, Etruria, ST1 5E ☎ (01782) 609988, *Fax (01782) 284500,* – – 600. U
Meals *(closed Saturday lunch)* a la carte approx. 16.50 **st.** 11.95 – 10.50 – **147 r** 132.00/156.00 **st.** – SB.

Express by Holiday Inn without rest., Stanley Matthews Way, Trentham Lakes, ST4 4E ☎ (01782) 377000, *stoke@expressholidayinn.co.uk, Fax (01782) 377037* – – 30. *VISA* JCB V
123 rm 56.00 **t.**

STOKE-ON-TRENT
NEWCASTLE-UNDER-LYME
BUILT UP AREA

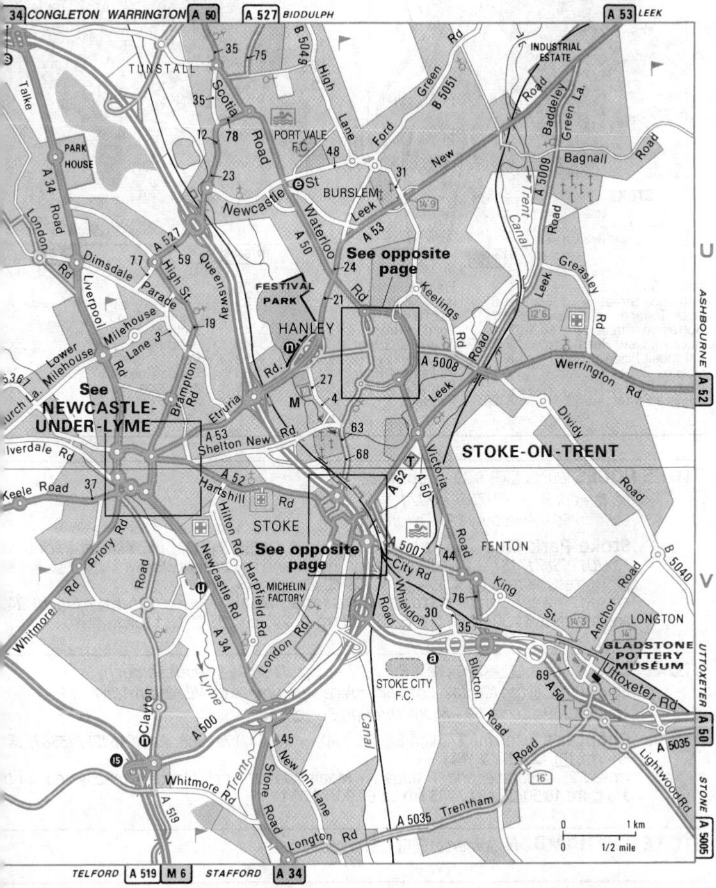

Burslem *North : 3½ m. by A 500 and A 53 on A 50 – ✉ Stoke-on-Trent.*

The George, Swan Sq, ST6 2AE, ✆ (01782) 577544, *georgestoke@btinternet.com, Fax (01782) 837496* – 🛗 TV P – 🏛 200. MC AE Ⓓ VISA JCB. ✂ U e
closed 24-26 December – **Meals** 16.95/25.85 and dinner a la carte **t.** 🍷 9.95 – **39 rm** 65.00/85.00 **t.** – SB.

Talke *Northwest : 4 m. by A 500 on A 34 – ✉ Stoke-on-Trent.*

Travelodge, Newcastle Rd, ST7 1UP, at junction of A 500 and A 34 ✆ (01782) 777000, *Fax (01782) 777000* – ⇔ rm, TV ♿ P. MC AE Ⓓ VISA JCB. ✂ U s
Meals (grill rest.) – **62 rm** 49.95 **t.**

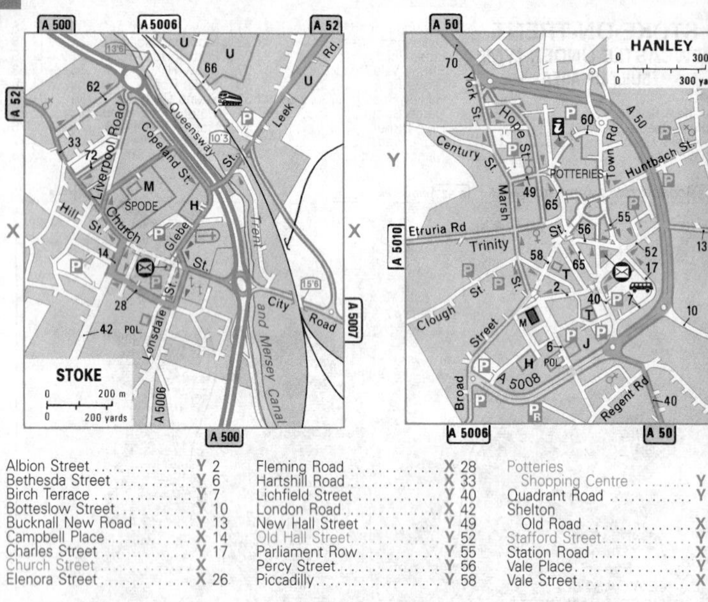

Albion Street .... Y 2
Bethesda Street .... Y 6
Birch Terrace .... Y 7
Botteslow Street.......... Y 10
Bucknall New Road .... Y 13
Campbell Place............ X 14
Charles Street .... Y 17
Church Street X
Elenora Street .... X 26
Fleming Road .... X 28
Hartshill Road .... X 33
Lichfield Street .... Y 40
London Road............... X 42
New Hall Street .... Y 49
Old Hall Street............ Y 52
Parliament Row............ Y 55
Percy Street............... Y 56
Piccadilly.................. Y 58
Potteries Shopping Centre......... Y
Quadrant Road .... Y
Shelton Old Road X
Stafford Street............. Y
Station Road X
Vale Place................. Y
Vale Street................. X

STOKE POGES *Bucks.* 404 S 29 – *pop. 4 508.*

⛳18, ⛳9 *Park Rd ☎ (01753) 717171.*

London 30 – Aylesbury 28 – Oxford 44.

Stoke Park Club ⛰, Park Rd, SL2 4PG, ☎ (01753) 717171, *info@stokeparkclub.co* *Fax (01753) 717181*, « Palladian mansion in parkland by Capability Brown », ⛳18, ⛰, ⛱, ⚔, 🛗, ⊗ rest, ▤ rest, TV ☎ P – 🏛 80. MC AE ⓓ VISA JCB. ✗
closed 1 week January ***Stoke's Brasserie*** **:** **Meals** *(closed Saturday lunch)* 24. and a la carte 34.50/46.50 **t.** 🍷 15.50 – **19 rm** ☕ 245.00/285.00 **t.**, 1 suite.

STOKESLEY *N. Yorks.* 402 Q 20 *Great Britain G. – pop. 4 008 –* ✉ *Middlesbrough.*

Env. : *Great Ayton (Captain Cook Birthplace Museum★ AC), NE : 2½ m. on A 173.*

London 239 – Leeds 59 – Middlesbrough 8 – York 52.

Chapter's with rm, 27 High St, TS9 5AD, ☎ (01642) 711888, *Fax (01642) 713387*, ⛱ ⊗ rm, TV. MC AE ⓓ VISA
closed 25 December and 1 January – **Meals** *(closed lunch Monday-Tuesday and Sund* a la carte 16.50/28.45 **t.** – **13 rm** ☕ 60.00/73.00 **t.**

STOKE SUB HAMDON *Somerset* 403 L 31 – *see Yeovil.*

STONE *Staffs.* 402 403 404 N 25 – *pop. 12 305.*

⛳18 *Barlaston, Meaford Rd ☎ (01782) 372867.*

London 150 – Birmingham 36 – Stoke-on-Trent 9.

Stone House, ST15 0BQ, South : 1 ¼ m. by A 520 on A 34 ☎ (01785) 81555 *Fax (01785) 814764*, 🏋, ♨, 🏊, ⛱, ⚔ – ⊗ TV ☎ ♿ P – 🏛 180. MC AE ⓓ VISA JCB
Meals (bar lunch Saturday) 8.95/19.95 **st.** – ☕ 10.50 – **50 rm** 89.00/109.00 **st.** – SB.

STON EASTON *Somerset* 403 404 M 30 – *pop. 579 –* ✉ *Bath (Bath & North East Somerset).*

London 131 – Bath 12 – Bristol 11 – Wells 7.

Ston Easton Park ⛰, BA3 4DF, ☎ (01761) 241631, *stoneastonpark@stoneaston.co.* *Fax (01761) 241377*, ←, « Palladian mansion in classical parkland designed by Humph Repton », ⛱, ⚔ – ⊗ TV P. MC AE ⓓ VISA
The Parlour **:** **Meals** (booking essential to non-residents) 16.50/39.50 and dinner a la ca 37.50/50.00 **t.** 🍷 19.00 – ☕ 12.50 – **21 rm** 130.00/225.00 **t.**, 2 suites.

ENGLAND

ONOR *Oxon.* 404 R 29 – *see Henley-on-Thames.*

ONY STRATFORD *Milton Keynes* 404 R 27 – *pop. 55 733 (inc. Wolverton).*
London 58 – Birmingham 68 – Northampton 14 – Oxford 32.
Plans : see Milton Keynes

Peking, 117 High St, MK11 1AT, (01908) 563120, *Fax (01908) 560084* – . VISA JCB AV p
Meals - Chinese (Peking, Szechuan) - 15.00 and a la carte.

ORRINGTON *W. Sussex* 404 S 31 – *pop. 7 429.*
London 54 – Brighton 20 – Portsmouth 36.

No. 1 Lime Chase without rest., RH20 4LX, by B 2139 (Thakeham Rd) off Fryern Rd (01903) 740437, *fionawarton@limechase.co.uk, Fax (01903) 740437,* – P.
3 rm 45.00/70.00.

Fleur de Sel (Perraud), Manleys Hill, RH20 4BT, East : ¼ m. on A 283 (01903) 742331, *Fax (01903) 740649* – P. VISA
closed first 2 weeks January and September, Saturday lunch, Sunday dinner and Monday – **Meals** - French - 33.00 **t.** 12.50
Spec. Cornish crab cake with prawns, herb butter sauce. Fillet of salmon with scallops, tomato, orange and basil sauce. Crispy Gressingham duck, honey and ginger sauce.

Old Forge, 6 Church St, RH20 4LA, (01903) 743402, *enquiry@oldforge.co.uk, Fax (01903) 742540* – VISA
closed 2 weeks in spring and autumn, Christmas, New Year, Saturday lunch, Sunday dinner, Monday and Wednesday – **Meals** 14.50/25.00 **t.** 12.00.

OURBRIDGE *W. Mids.* 403 404 N26 – *pop. 55 624.*
London 147 – Birmingham 14 – Wolverhampton 10 – Worcester 21.
Plan : see Birmingham p. 4

Travel Inn, Birmingham Rd, Hagley, DY9 9JS, Southeast : 3 ½ m. by A 491 on A 456 (eastbound carriageway) (01562) 883120, *Fax (01562) 884416* – rm, P. VISA. AU r
Meals (grill rest.) – **40 rm** 41.95 **t.**

OURPORT-ON-SEVERN *Worcs.* 403 404 N 26 – *pop. 18 283.*
London 137 – Birmingham 21 – Worcester 12.

Stourport Manor, Hartlebury Rd, DY13 9LT, East : 1 ¼ m. on B 4193 (01299) 289955, *stourport@menzies-hotels.co.uk, Fax (01299) 878520,* heated, squash – P – 350. VISA JCB
Meals 11.95/15.95 and a la carte 15.85/29.40 **st.** 12.95 – 12.95 – **66 rm** 95.00 **st.**, 2 suites – SB.

OWMARKET *Suffolk* 404 W/X 27 – *pop. 13 229.*
Wilkes Way (01449) 676800.
London 81 – Cambridge 42 – Ipswich 12 – Norwich 38.

Travelodge, IP14 3PY, Northwest : 2 m. by A 1038 on A 14 (westbound) (01449) 615347, *Fax (01449) 615347* – rm, P. VISA JCB.
Meals (grill rest.) – **40 rm** 42.95 **t.**

Gipping Heights, Creeting Rd, IP14 5BT, East : 1 m. by Station Rd East (01449) 675264, *gipping.heights@virgin.net* – P. VISA.
Meals 13.50 **s.** 8.95 – **3 rm** 38.00/50.00 **s.**

Mendlesham Green *Northeast : 6 ¼ m. by B 1115, A 1120 and Mendlesham rd – Stowmarket.*

Cherry Tree Farm, Mendlesham Green, IP14 5RQ, (01449) 766376, « Part Elizabethan house », – P.
closed Christmas and New Year – **Meals** (by arrangement) (communal dining) 17.50 **st.** 8.50 – **3 rm** 37.00/55.00 **st.**

***Le Grand Londres** (GREATER LONDON) est composé de la City et de 32 arrondissements administratifs (Borough) eux-mêmes divisés en quartiers ou en villages ayant conservé leur caractère propre (Area).*

ENGLAND

STOW-ON-THE-WOLD *Glos.* 403 404 O 28 *Great Britain G. – pop. 1 999.*

Exc. : *Chastleton House*★★, *NE : 6½ m. by A 436 and A 44.*

Hollis House, The Square ✆ *(01451) 831082.*

London 86 – Birmingham 44 – Gloucester 27 – Oxford 30.

Wyck Hill House, GL54 1HY, South : 2 ¼ m. by A 429 on A 424 ✆ (01451) 8319 *wyckhill@wrensgroup.com, Fax (01451) 832243*, ≤, « Part 18C country mansion », , rest, rest, – 50. VISA JCB
Meals 10.95/36.50 and dinner a la carte 14.95/36.50 **t.** 14.95 – **31 rm** 110.00/236.0 1 suite – SB.

Unicorn, Sheep St, GL54 1HQ, ✆ (01451) 830257, *bookings@cotswold-inns-hotels.co Fax (01451) 831090* – – 40. VISA JCB.
Meals (bar lunch Monday to Saturday)/dinner 22.95 **st.** 10.95 – **20 rm** 50.00/115.00 – SB.

The Royalist, Digbeth St, GL54 1BN, ✆ (01451) 830670, *info@theroyalisthotel.co Fax (01451) 870048*, « Part 10C inn » – . VISA.
947 AD : **Meals** *(closed Sunday dinner and Monday)* 12.50 (lunch) and a la carte 20 34.50 **t.** 12.25 – (see also ***Eagle & Child*** below) – 7.50 – **8 rm** 60.00/130.00 **t.**

Grapevine, Sheep St, GL54 1AU, ✆ (01451) 830344, *enquiries@vines.co Fax (01451) 832278*, « Mature grapevine in restaurant » – – 25. JCB.
Meals 26.00/36.00 (dinner) a la carte 18.20/34.00 **st.** 12.50 – **22 rm** 85.00/180.00 s SB.

Fosse Manor, Fosse Way, GL54 1JX, South : 1 ¼ m. on A 429 ✆ (01451) 830354, *enqu @fossemanor.co.uk, Fax (01451) 832486*, – rest, – 40. JCB
closed 21-29 December – **Meals** 12.50 (lunch) and dinner a la carte approx. 30.00 **t.** 1 – **21 rm** 59.00/120.00 **t.**

Stow Lodge, The Square, GL54 1AB, ✆ (01451) 830485, *enquiries@stowlodge.c Fax (01451) 831671*, – . VISA JCB.
closed Christmas and 31 December – **Meals** (bar lunch)/dinner 19.00 and a la carte 24 33.50 **t.** 15.00 – **21 rm** 65.00/120.00 **t.** – SB.

Number Nine without rest., 9 Park St, GL54 1AQ, ✆ (01451) 870333, *numbernine@ta .com, Fax (01451) 870445* – . VISA.
3 rm 40.00/54.00 **s.**

Wyck Hill Lodge without rest., Wyck Hill, GL54 1HT, South : 2 m. by A 429 on A ✆ (01451) 830141, *gkhwyck@compuserve.com*, ≤, – .
March-November – **3 rm** 50.00.

Hamiltons, Park St, GL54 1AQ, ✆ (01451) 831700, *goodfood@hamiltons.br.c Fax (01451) 831388* – . VISA JCB
closed Sunday dinner and 25 December – **Meals** (booking essential) a la carte 20.25/24.7 11.00.

Eagle & Child (at The Royalist H.), Digbeth St, GL54 1BN, ✆ (01451) 8306 *Fax (01451) 870048*, – VISA
Meals (bookings not accepted) 10.00 (lunch) and a la carte 12.00/23.95 **t.** 11.95.

at Upper Oddington *East : 2 m. by A 436 – ✉ Stow-on-the-Wold.*

Horse and Groom with rm, GL56 0XH, ✆ (01451) 830584, « Part 16C former coach inn », – rm, . VISA.
closed 25 December – **Meals** and a la carte approx. 16.40 **t.** – **7 rm** 45.00/60.00 **t.**

at Lower Oddington *East : 3 m. by A 436 – ✉ Stow-on-the-Wold.*

Fox Inn with rm, GL56 0UR, ✆ (01451) 870555, *info@foxinn.net, Fax (01451) 870669*, rm, . VISA JCB
closed 25, 26 and 31 December and 1 January – **Meals** (bookings not accepted) a la c 14.00/19.75 **t.** 9.75 – **3 rm** 58.00/85.00 **t.**

at Bledington *Southeast : 4 m. by A 436 on B 4450 – ✉ Kingham.*

Kings Head Inn, OX7 6XQ, ✆ (01608) 658365, *kingshead@orr-ewing.c Fax (01608) 658902*, « Part 15C inn » – rm, . VISA.
closed 25 and 26 December – **Meals** a la carte 13.40/24.50 **t.** 10.00 – **12 rm** 45 75.00 **st.**

at Lower Swell *West : 1¼ m. on B 4068 – ✉ Stow-on-the-Wold.*

Rectory Farmhouse without rest., GL54 1LH, by Rectory Barns ✆ (01451) 832351, *rectory.farmhouse@cw-warwick.co.uk*, ≤, –
closed Christmas and New Year – **2 rm** 40.00/80.00 **st.**, 1 suite.

TRATFIELD TURGIS *Hants.* 403 404 Q 29 – *pop. 94* – ✉ *Basingstoke.*
London 46 – Basingstoke 8 – Reading 11.

Wellington Arms, RG27 0AS, on A 33 ✆ (01256) 882214, *wellington.arms@virgin.net, Fax (01256) 882934,* – rm, TV P – 200. MC AE VISA.
Meals *(closed Saturday lunch and Sunday dinner)* a la carte 20.15/31.95 **t.** 9.95 – **28 rm** 105.00/140.00 **st.**, 2 suites.

TRATFORD-UPON-AVON *Warks.* 403 404 P 27 *Great Britain G.* – *pop. 22 231.*
See : *Town★ - Shakespeare's Birthplace★ AC, AB.*
Env. : *Mary Arden's House★ AC, NW : 4 m. by A 3400 A.*
Exc. : *Ragley Hall★ AC, W : 9 m. by A 422 A.*
Tiddington Rd ✆ (01789) 297296, B – Welcombe Hotel, Warwick Rd ✆ (01789) 299012, B – Stratford Oaks, Bearley Rd, Snitterfield ✆ (01789) 731982, B.
Bridgefoot ✆ (01789) 293127.
London 96 – Birmingham 23 – Coventry 18 – Oxford 40.

STRATFORD-UPON-AVON

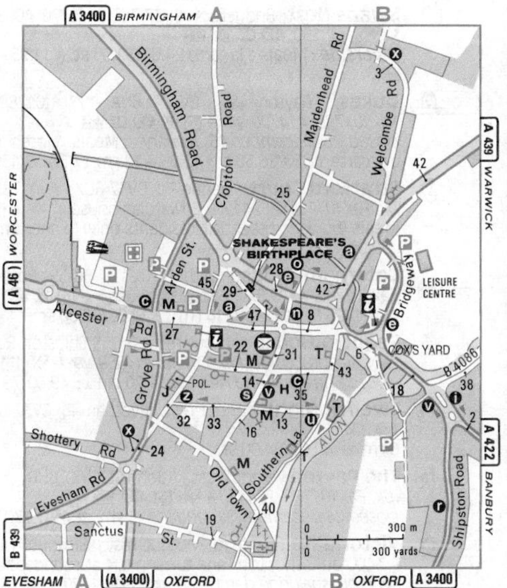

r maximum information
om town plans:
nsult the
nventional signs key.

Welcombe H. & Golf Course, Warwick Rd, CV37 0NR, Northeast : 1 ½ m. on A 439 ✆ (01789) 295252, *sales@welcombe.co.uk, Fax (01789) 414666,* ≤, « 19C Jacobean style mansion, formal garden », – rest, TV P – 100. MC AE VISA JCB.
Trevelyan : **Meals** 17.00/35.00 and a la carte 31.95/39.40 **st.** 16.00 – **59 rm** 135.00/295.00 **st.**, 5 suites – SB.

Alveston Manor, Clopton Bridge, CV37 7HP, ✆ (0870) 4008181, *Fax (01789) 414095,* « Part Elizabethan house », – TV P – 120. MC AE VISA JCB. B i
Manor : **Meals** a la carte 25.40/33.70 **st.** – 13.95 – **109 rm** 115.00/150.00, 4 suites – SB.

Stratford Moat House, Bridgefoot, CV37 6YR, ✆ (01789) 279988, *revsfd@queens moat.co.uk, Fax (01789) 298589,* – rm, TV P – 600. MC AE VISA B e
The Terrace : **Meals** (dinner only) 17.00 and a la carte approx. 22.00 6.80 – ***The Riverside :*** **Meals** (carving rest.) 11.95/17.00 6.00 – 11.50 – **249 rm** 135.00/155.00 **st.**, 2 suites – SB.

Stratford Victoria, Arden St, CV37 6QQ, ✆ (01789) 271000, *stratfordvictoria@marston hotels.com, Fax (01789) 271001,* – rm, rest, TV P – 140. MC AE VISA A c
Meals (carvery lunch Sunday) 19.50/22.00 and a la carte approx. 25.00 **st.** 12.95 – **101 rm** 100.00/135.00 **st.**, 1 suite – SB.

The Shakespeare, Chapel St, CV37 6ER, ☎ (0870) 4008182, *Fax (01789) 415411,* « timbered inn » – 100. A
David Garrick : **Meals** 13.95 (lunch) and dinner a la carte 24.00/66.90 **st.** – 13.95
73 rm 125.00/165.00 **st.**, 1 suite – SB.

Thistle Stratford-Upon-Avon, Waterside, CV37 6BA, ☎ (01789) 294949, *reservations stratforduponavon@thistle.co.uk, Fax (01789) 415874,* – 60. B
Bards : **Meals** 14.95/24.95 (dinner) and a la carte 23.85/33.85 **st.** 11.95 – 10.50
62 rm 126.00/176.00 **st.** – SB.

Stratford Manor, Warwick Rd, CV37 0PY, Northeast : 3 m. on A 439 ☎ (01789) 7311 *stratfordmanor@marstonhotels.com, Fax (01789) 731131,* rest, – 350.
Meals *(closed Saturday lunch)* 19.50/27.00 and dinner a la carte approx. 35.00 **st.** 12.9
104 rm 115.00/149.00 **st.** – SB.

Grosvenor, 12-14 Warwick Rd, CV37 6YT, ☎ (01789) 269213, *info@groshotelstratford. uk, Fax (01789) 266087,* – rm, – 100. B
Meals 11.50/16.50 and a la carte 18.90/25.30 **st.** 8.00 – 8.95 – **67 rm** 85.00/99.00 **st** SB.

Swans Nest, Bridgefoot, CV37 7LT, ☎ (0870) 4008183, *Fax (01789) 414547,* – – 150. B
Riverside : **Meals** a la carte 24.00/32.00 **st.** 11.95 – 13.95 – **67 rm** 115.00/125.00 **st** SB.

Dukes, Payton St, CV37 6UA, ☎ (01789) 269300, *info@dukes-hotel.co. Fax (01789) 414700,* – . AB
closed 15 December-15 January – **Meals** *(closed Sunday)* (residents only) (dinner on a la carte 19.50/25.50 **t.** 12.95 – **22 rm** 58.50/130.00 **t.** – SB.

Stratford Court, Avenue Rd, CV37 6UX, ☎ (01789) 297799, *stratfordcourt@easynet. uk, Fax (01789) 262449,* « Edwardian house », – . B
Meals (booking essential) (residents only) (dinner only) 17.50 **st.** 11.50 – **13 rm** 65.0 150.00.

Caterham House without rest., 58-59 Rother St, CV37 6LT, ☎ (01789) 2673 *Fax (01789) 414836,* « Georgian house » – . A
closed 25 December – **14 rm** 74.00/90.00 **st.**

Sequoia House without rest., 51-53 Shipston Rd, CV37 7LN, ☎ (01789) 268852, *inf sequoiahotel.co.uk, Fax (01789) 414559,* – – 40. . B
closed Christmas and New Year – **20 rm** 49.00/79.00.

Twelfth Night without rest., Evesham Pl, CV37 6HT, ☎ (01789) 414595 – . A
6 rm 40.00/64.00 **st.**

The Payton without rest., 6 John St, CV37 6UB, ☎ (01789) 266442, *payton@waverider .uk, Fax (01789) 294410* – . A
closed 24 December-31 January – **5 rm** 45.00/70.00 **t.**

Victoria Spa Lodge without rest., Bishopton Lane, CV37 9QY, Northwest : 2 m. A 3400 on Bishopton Lane turning left at roundabout with A 46 ☎ (01789) 267985, *pto @victoriaspalodge.demon.co.uk, Fax (01789) 204728,* – . .
7 rm 65.00 **t.**

Virginia Lodge without rest., 12 Evesham Pl, CV37 6HT, ☎ (01789) 2921 *Fax (01789) 292157,* – . A
closed 24-26 December – **6 rm** 25.00/52.00 **s.**

Desport's, 13-14 Meer St, CV37 6QB, ☎ (01789) 269304, *bookings@desports.co. Fax (01789) 269304* – A
closed, Sunday and Monday – **Meals** 7.50 (lunch) and a la carte 23.95/33.85 **t.** 10.50.

Restaurant Margaux, 6 Union St, CV37 6QT, ☎ (01789) 269106, *Fax (01789) 26910* A
closed 25-26 December, 1 January, Sunday and Monday – **Meals** a la carte 19.40/29.4 11.75.

Lambs, 12 Sheep St, CV37 6EF, ☎ (01789) 292554, *lambs@ukgateway.net,* « 16C » – B
closed 25-26 December – **Meals** 14.50 (lunch) and a la carte 18.50/27.40 **t.** 9.75.

at Charlecote *East : 4 ¾ m. by B 4086* – **B** – ✉ *Stratford-upon-Avon.*

The Charlecote Pheasant, CV35 9EW, ☎ (01789) 279954, *Fax (01789) 4702* heated, – – 160.
Meals (carvery rest.) 11.50/18.50 and dinner a la carte 19.95/25.00 **st.** 11.50 – 9.9
70 rm 105.00/120.00 – SB.

Loxley *Southeast : 3 m. by B 4086 – B – and Loxley Rd – ✉ Stratford-upon-Avon.*

Glebe Farm House, Stratford Rd, CV35 9JW, ☎ (01789) 842501, *scorpiolimited@msn.com, Fax (01789) 841194,* ←, « Rare breed farm animals » – ⇐ TV 🚗 P. MC VISA JCB
Meals - Organic - 22.50 **st.** 🍷 12.00 – **4 rm** ☕ 69.50/120.00 **st.** – SB.

Binton *Southwest : 4½ m. by B 439 – A – ✉ Stratford-upon-Avon.*

Gravelside Barn 🔇 without rest., CV37 9TU, Northwest : ¾ m. by Binton Hill ☎ (01789) 750502, *denise@gravelside.fsnet.co.uk, Fax (01789) 750502,* ←, « Converted barn », 🌳, 🎾 – ⇐ TV P. MC VISA. ✗
3 rm ☕ 40.00/70.00 **s.**

Billesley *West : 4½ m. by A 422 – A – off A 46 – ✉ Stratford-upon-Avon.*

Billesley Manor 🔇, B49 6NF, ☎ (01789) 279955, *Fax (01789) 764145,* ←, « Part Elizabethan manor, topiary garden », 🏊, 🌳, 🎾 – ⇐ TV P – 🎤 120. MC AE ◐ VISA
Meals (bar lunch Monday-Friday) 24.95 and a la carte approx. 35.95 **t.** 🍷 14.50 – **59 rm** ☕ 105.00/160.00 **t.**, 2 suites – SB.

Wilmcote *Northwest : 3½ m. by A 3400 – A – ✉ Stratford-upon-Avon.*

Pear Tree Cottage 🔇 without rest., 7 Church Rd, CV37 9UX, ☎ (01789) 205889, *mander@peartreecot.co.uk, Fax (01789) 262862,* « Part Elizabethan », 🌳 – ⇐ TV P. ✗
closed 25 December-1 January – **5 rm** ☕ 40.00/56.00 **st.**

STREATLEY *Newbury* 403 404 Q 29 *Great Britain G. – pop. 4 193 (inc. Goring) – ✉ Goring.*

Env. : *Basildon Park★ AC, SE : 2½ m. by A 329 – Mapledurham★ AC, E : 6 m. by A 329, B 471 and B 4526.*

Exc. : *Ridgeway Path★★.*

🏌18 *Goring & Streatley, Rectory Rd ☎ (01491) 873229.*

London 56 – Oxford 16 – Reading 11.

Swan Diplomat, High St, RG8 9HR, ☎ (01491) 878800, *sales@swan-diplomat.co.uk, Fax (01491) 872554,* 🏨, « ← Thames-side setting », 🏋, ≘s, 🏊, 🌳 – ⚓, ⇐ rest, TV 📞 ♿ P – 🎤 80. MC AE ◐ VISA
The Racing Swan : **Meals** a la carte 24.00/34.00 **st.** 🍷 12.00 – ☕ 9.50 – **45 rm** 108.00/155.00 **st.**, 1 suite – SB.

STRENSHAM SERVICE AREA *Worcs.* 403 N 27.

London 114 – Birmingham 37 – Gloucester 17.

Travel Inn without rest., WR8 0BZ, M 5 between junctions 7 and 8 (northbound carriageway) ☎ (01684) 293004, *Fax (01684) 273606* – ⇐ TV ♿ P. MC AE ◐ VISA. ✗
closed Christmas-New Year – **40 rm** 41.95, 1 suite.

STRETTON *Ches.* 402 403 404 M 23 – *see Warrington.*

STRETTON *Rutland – see Stamford.*

STRETTON *Staffs.* 402 403 404 P 25 – *see Burton-upon-Trent.*

STROUD *Glos.* 403 404 N 28 – *pop. 38 835.*

🏌18, 🏌18, 🏌18 *Minchinhampton ☎ (01453) 832642 (old course) (01453) 833840 (new course) – 🏌18 Painswick ☎ (01452) 812180.*

ℹ *Subscription Rooms, George St. ☎ (01453) 765768.*

London 113 – Bristol 30 – Gloucester 9.

Travelodge, Easington, Stonehouse, GL10 3SQ, West : 5 ¼ m. off A 419 ☎ (01453) 828590 – ⇐ rm, TV ♿ P. MC AE ◐ VISA JCB. ✗
Meals (grill rest.) – **40 rm** 49.95 **t.**

Brimscombe *Southeast : 2¼ m. on A 419 – ✉ Stroud.*

Burleigh Court 🔇, Burleigh Lane, GL5 2PF, South : ½ m. by Burleigh rd via The Roundabouts ☎ (01453) 883804, *info@burleighcourthotel.co.uk, Fax (01453) 886870,* ←, 🏊 heated, 🌳 – ⇐ rest, TV P. MC ◐ VISA JCB
Meals 17.95/31.95 **t.** 🍷 12.50 – **18 rm** ☕ 80.00/170.00 **t.** – SB.

STUDLAND *Dorset* 403 404 O 32 – *pop. 471.*
London 135 – Bournemouth 25 – Southampton 53 – Weymouth 29.

Shell Bay, Ferry Rd, BH19 3BA, North : 3 m. or via car ferry from Sandbar *(01929) 450363, Fax (01929) 450570,* ≤ Poole Harbour and Brownsea Island, – *April-September and restricted opening in winter* – **Meals** - Seafood - a la carte 19.95/32 10.50.

STUDLEY *Warks.* 403 404 O 27 – *pop. 5 883* – *Redditch.*
London 109 – Birmingham 15 – Coventry 33 – Gloucester 39.

Peppers, 45 High St, B80 7HN, (01527) 853183 – . VISA
closed 25 December – **Meals** - Indian - (dinner only) a la carte 11.65/22.60 7.90.

STURMINSTER NEWTON *Dorset* 403 404 N 31 *The West Country G.* – *pop. 2 155.*
See : *Mill★ AC.*
London 123 – Bournemouth 30 – Bristol 49 – Salisbury 28 – Taunton 41.

Stourcastle Lodge, Gough's Close, DT10 1BU, (off the Market Pla *(01258) 472320, enquiries@stourcastle-lodge.co.uk, Fax (01258) 473381,* – VISA.
Meals 19.00 **st.** – **5 rm** (dinner included) 41.00/78.00 **st.**

Plumber Manor with rm, DT10 2AF, Southwest : 1 ¾ m. by A 357 on Hazelbury Bry rd (01258) 472507, *enquiries@plumbermanor.com, Fax (01258) 473370,* ≤, « 18C mar house », , , – – 25. VISA
closed February – **Meals** (dinner only and Sunday lunch)/dinner 21.50/30.00 11.50
16 rm 85.00/155.00 – SB.

The Guide is updated annually so renew your Guide every year.

SUDBURY *Suffolk* 404 W 27 *Great Britain G.* – *pop. 19 512.*
See : *Gainsborough's House★ AC.*
Town Hall, Market Hill (01787) 881320.
London 59 – Cambridge 37 – Colchester 15 – Ipswich 21.

Mill, Walnut Tree Lane, CO10 1BD, (01787) 375544, *Fax (01787) 373027,* ≤, « Convert 19C mill » – rest, – 70. VISA JCB
Meals *(closed dinner 25 December-lunch 27 December)* 15.95/28.00 (lunch) and a la ca 25.00/31.00 10.40 – 11.50 – **56 rm** 59.00/119.00 **t.** – SB.

SUMMERBRIDGE *N. Yorks.* 402 O 21 – *see Pateley Bridge.*

SUNDERLAND *Tyne and Wear* 401 402 P 19 – *pop. 183 310.*
See : *National Glass Centre★.*
18 Whitburn, Lizard Lane, South Shields (0191) 529 2144.
50 Fawcett St (0191) 553 2000.
London 272 – Leeds 92 – Middlesbrough 29 – Newcastle upon Tyne 12.

Plan on next page

Sunderland Marriott, Queens Par, Seaburn, SR6 8DB, (0191) 529 2041, *sunderla marriott@whitbread.com, Fax (0191) 529 4227,* ≤, , , – , rest, 300. VISA JCB A
The Promenade : **Meals** 11.95/21.95 a la carte 15.00/25.00 **st.** 12.75 – 13.00 – **82** 99.00/155.00 **st.** – SB.

Premier Lodge, Timber Beach Rd, off Wessington Way, SR5 3XG, West : 2 ½ m. by A 12 (0870) 7001550, *Fax (0870) 7001551* – rm, . VISA JCB.
Meals (grill rest.) a la carte approx. 17.00 **t.** 9.85 – **63 rm** 46.95 **t.**

Travel Inn, Wessington Way, SR5 3HR, West : 3 ¾ m. by A 1231 (0191) 548 93 *Fax (0191) 548 4148* – rm, rest, – 25. VISA.
Meals (grill rest.) – **41 rm** 41.95 **t.**

at Boldon *Northwest : 3 ¾ m. by A 1018 on A 184* – **A** – *Newcastle upon Tyne.*

Forsters, 2 St Bedes, Station Rd, East Boldon, NE36 OLE, (0191) 519 0929, *inf forsters-restaurant.co.uk* – . VISA
closed 2 weeks in summer, 1 week in winter, 25 December and Monday – **Meals** (dinn only) a la carte 18.50/30.50 **t.** 10.00.

Albion Place	B 2
Barnes Park Road	A 3
Bedford Street	B 4
Borough Road	B 5
Bridge Street	B 6
Charlton Road	A 8
Chester Road	B 10
Crowtree Road	B 11
Dame Dorothy Street	A 12
Derwent Street	B 13
Fawcett Street	B
Harbour View	A 14
High Street West	B 15
Holmeside	B
John Street	B 16
Kayll Road	A 17
Livingstone Road	B 18
New Durham Road	B 19
Ormonde Street	A 21
Pallion Road	A 22
Park Lane	B 23
Queens Road	A 24
Roker Terrace	A 25
St. Luke's Terrace	A 26
St. Mary's Way	B 27
Shields Road	A 29
Southwick Road	B 30
Station Road	A 32
The Bridges	B
Trimdon Street	A 35
Vine Place	B 36
Wessington Way	A 38

***Town plans:** the names of main shopping streets are indicated in red at the beginning of the list of streets.*

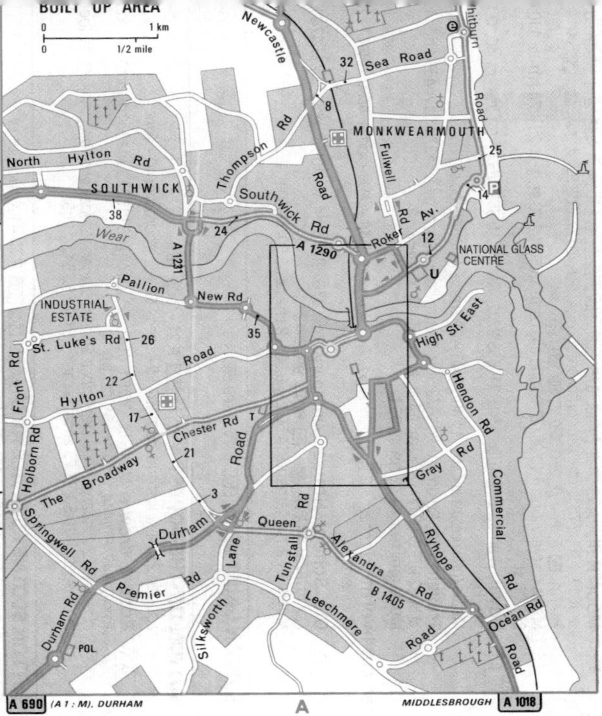

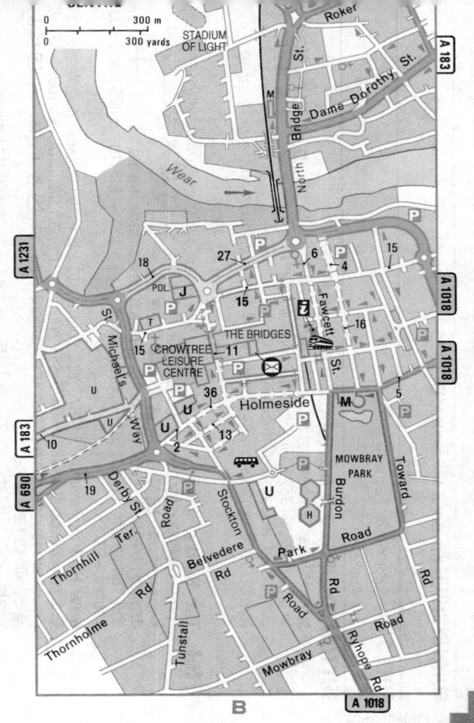

SUNNINGHILL *Windsor & Maidenhead* 404 S 29 – *see Ascot.*

SUTTON *W. Sussex – see Petworth.*

SUTTON COLDFIELD *W. Mids.* 403 404 O 26 – *pop. 106 001.*

Pype Hayes, Eachelhurst Rd, Walmley (0121) 351 1014, DT – Boldmere, Monmo… Dr. (0121) 354 3379, DT – 110 Thornhill Rd (0121) 353 2014, DT – The Bel… Lichfield Rd, Wishaw (01675) 470301 DT.

London 124 – Birmingham 8 – Coventry 29 – Nottingham 47 – Stoke-on-Trent 40.

Plan : see Birmingham pp. 4 and 5

The Belfry, Wishaw, B76 9PR, East : 6 ½ m. by A 453 on A 446 (01675) 4703… *enquiries@thebelfry.com, Fax (01675) 470178,* ≤, squash – rm, rest, 450. VISA.
Atrium : **Meals** 14.95/24.95 16.10 – ***French Restaurant :*** **Meals** *(closed Saturday lu… and Sunday dinner)* a la carte approx. 29.95 **st.** 16.10 – **315 rm** 175.00/200.00 … 9 suites – SB.

New Hall, Walmley Rd, B76 1QX, Southeast : 1 ½ m. by Coleshill St, Coleshill Rd … Reddicap Hill on B 4148 (0870) 333 9147, *new.hall@thistle.co.uk, Fax (0870) 333 92…* « Part 13C moated manor house, gardens », – 50. VISA. DT
Meals 29.50/39.50 **st.** 17.50 – 15.75 – **55 rm** 165.00/201.00 **st.**, 5 suites.

Moor Hall, Moor Hall Drive, B75 6LN, Northeast : 2 m. by A 453 and Weeford (0121) 308 3751, *mail@moorhallhotel.co.uk, Fax (0121) 308 8974,* – rm, – 250. VISA JCB. DT
Meals (carvery lunch) 10.95/22.00 and a la carte 13.50/22.00 **st.** 11.25 – **74 rm** 110.… 205.00 **st.** – SB.

Royal, High St, B72 1UD, (0121) 355 8222, *Fax (0121) 355 1837* – – 40. VISA. DT
Meals (grill rest.) a la carte 11.40/20.40 – **22 rm** 45.00/75.00 **st.**

Travelodge, Boldmere Rd, B72 5UP, Southwest : 1 ¼ m. by A 5127 and A 453 on B 41… (0121) 355 0017 – rm, VISA JCB. DT
Meals (grill rest.) – **32 rm** 49.95 **t.**

at Curdworth *Southeast : 6 ½ m. by A 5127, A 452 and A 38 – DT – on A 4097 – Sutt… Coldfield.*

Old School House, Kingsbury Rd, B76 9DR, on A 4097 (01675) 4701… *Fax (01675) 470884,* – VISA.
Meals (by arrangement) 14.50 **t.** 8.50 – **8 rm** 39.50/48.00 **t.**

SUTTON GAULT *Cambs.* 404 U 26 – *see Ely.*

SUTTON-ON-THE-FOREST *N. Yorks.* 402 P 21 – *pop. 281.*

London 230 – Kingston-upon-Hull 50 – Leeds 52 – Scarborough 40 – York 12.

Rose & Crown, Main St, YO61 1DP, (01347) 811333, *mail@rosecrown.co.… Fax (01347) 811444,* – VISA
closed 2-22 January, 25-26 December, Sunday dinner, Monday and Tuesday – **Meals** (boo… ing essential) 16.50/23.75 and a la carte 25.00/35.75 **t.** 11.95.

SUTTON SCOTNEY SERVICE AREA *Hants.* 403 404 P 30 – *Winchester.*

London 66 – Reading 32 – Salisbury 21 – Southampton 19.

Travelodge, SO21 3JY, on A 34 (01962) 761016 (northside), 7607779 (southside… rm, VISA JCB.
Meals (grill rest.) – **71 rm** 52.95 **t.**

SWAFFHAM *Norfolk* 404 W 26 *Great Britain G.* – *pop. 5 332.*

Exc. : *Oxburgh Hall★★ AC, SW : 7½ m.*

London 97 – Cambridge 46 – King's Lynn 16 – Norwich 27.

Strattons, 4 Ash Close, PE37 7NH, off Market Sq. (01760) 723845, *strattonshote… btinternet.com, Fax (01760) 720458,* « Queen Anne house with Victorian additions », VISA JCB.
closed 1 week Christmas – **Meals** (booking essential to non-residents) (dinner o… 34.50 **st.** 13.00 – **6 rm** 80.00/180.00 **st.**

ANAGE *Dorset* 403 404 O 32 *The West Country G. – pop. 9 037.*

See : *Town*★.

Env. : *St. Aldhelm's Head*★★ *(≤★★★), SW : 4 m. by B 3069 – Durlston Country Park (≤★★), S : 1 m. – Studland (Old Harry Rocks*★★*, Studland Beach (≤*★*), St. Nicholas Church*★*), N : 3 m. – Worth Matravers (Anvil Point Lighthouse ≤*★★*), S : 2 m. – Great Globe*★*, S : 1¼m.*

Exc. : *Corfe Castle*★ *(≤★★)* AC*, NW : 6 m. by A 351 – Blue Pool*★*, NW : 9 m. by A 351 and minor roads – Lulworth Cove*★*, W : 18 m. by A 351 and B 3070.*

18, 9 *Isle of Purbeck, Studland ☎ (01929) 450361.*

The White House, Shore Rd ☎ (01929) 422885.

London 130 – Bournemouth 22 – Dorchester 26 – Southampton 52.

Cauldron Bistro, 5 High St, BH19 2LN, ☎ (01929) 422671 – MC AE VISA
closed 2 weeks November-December, 2 weeks January, Monday, Tuesday lunch, Wednesday lunch in summer and Tuesday dinner in winter – **Meals** a la carte 22.95/28.95 **t.** 13.50.

The Galley, 9 High St, BH19 2LN, ☎ (01929) 427299, *thegalleyswanage@aol.com, Fax (01929) 427364* – MC AE VISA
closed January-February and restricted opening November-May – **Meals** (dinner only) 15.50/22.50 **t.** 9.75.

ARLAND *Northd.* 401 402 O 18 – *see Alnwick.*

AY *Hants.* 403 404 P 31 – *see Brockenhurst.*

The Guide is updated annually so renew your Guide every year.

INDON *Swindon* 403 404 O 29 *The West Country G. – pop. 145 236.*

See : *Great Western Railway Museum*★ AC *– Railway Village Museum*★ AC Y **M.**

Env. : *Lydiard Park (St. Mary's*★*) W : 4 m.* U.

Exc. : *Ridgeway Path*★★*, S : 8½ m. by A 4361 – Whitehorse (≤*★*)E : 7½ m. by A 4312, A 420 and B 400 off B 4057.*

18, 9 *Broome Manor, Pipers Way ☎ (01793) 532403 –* 18 *Shrivenham Park, Penny Hooks, Shrivenham ☎ (01793) 783853 –* 18 *The Wiltshire, Vastern, Wootton Bassett ☎ (01793) 849999 –* 18 *Wrag Barn G & C.C., Shrivenham Rd, Highworth ☎ (01793) 861327.*

37 Regent St. ☎ (01793) 530328.

London 83 – Bournemouth 69 – Bristol 40 – Coventry 66 – Oxford 29 – Reading 40 – Southampton 65.

Plans on following pages

De Vere, Shaw Ridge Leisure Park, Whitehill Way, SN5 7DW, West : 2 ¾ m. by A 3102 off B 4553 ☎ (01793) 878785, *devere.swindon@airtime.co.uk, Fax (01793) 877822,* – rest, – 400. MC AE VISA U e
Meals *(closed Saturday lunch)* 14.50/25.00 and a la carte 21.70/34.40 **t.** 12.95 – 12.95 – **154 rm** 125.00/145.00 **t.**, 4 suites – SB.

Swindon Marriott, Pipers Way, SN3 1SH, South : 1 ½ m. by Marlborough Road off B 4006 ☎ (01793) 512121, *Fax (01793) 513114,* – , rm, – 280. MC AE VISA V s
Meals *(closed Saturday lunch)* a la carte 19.40/28.65 **st.** 12.95 – 13.00 – **153 rm** 120.00/163.00 **st.** – SB.

Hilton Swindon, Lydiard Fields, Great Western Way, SN5 8UZ, West : 3 ½ m. by A 3102 at junction 16 of M 4 ☎ (01793) 881777, *Fax (01793) 881881,* – , rm, – 350. MC AE VISA V a
Meals *(closed lunch Saturday and Bank Holiday Monday)* 18.00 and a la carte 18.25/28.00 **st.** 12.50 – 12.95 – **171 rm** 135.00/180.00 **st.** – SB.

Holiday Inn Swindon, Marlborough Rd, SN3 6AQ, Southeast : 2 ½ m. on A 4259 ☎ (0870) 400 9079, *reservations.swindon@posthouse-hotels.com, Fax (01793) 512887,* – rm, – 70. MC AE VISA V b
Meals a la carte 17.85/24.45 **t.** 9.95 – 11.95 – **100 rm** 121.00 **st.** – SB.

Thistle Swindon, Fleming Way, SN1 1TN, ☎ (0870) 333 9148, *swindon@thistle.co.uk, Fax (01793) 541283* – – 150. MC AE VISA JCB. Y c
Meals *(closed lunch Saturday and Bank Holidays)* 18.50 and a la carte 16.95/27.50 **t.** 11.50 – **94 rm** 123.00/180.00.

Goddard Arms, High St, Old Town, SN1 3EG, ☎ (01793) 692313, *customercare@zoffany hotels.co.uk, Fax (01793) 512984,* – – 200. MC AE VISA. Z a
Meals (bar lunch Monday to Saturday)/dinner a la carte 15.00/22.50 12.50 – **65 rm** 90.00/95.00 **st.**

SWINDON

Beechcroft Road . . . . U 4
Bridge End Road . . . . U 6
Cheney Manor Road . . . . . . U 10
Cirencester Way . . . . U 12
Devises Road . . . . V 18
Gipsy Lane . . . . U 25
Great Western Retail Outlet U 26
Hobley Drive . . . . U 28
Kingsdown Road . . . . U 30
Newport Street . . . . V 36
Oxford Road . . . . U 42
Park Lane . . . . U 43
Rodbourne Road . . . . U
Slade Drive . . . . U
Swindon Road . . . . U
Vicarage Road . . . . U
Westcott Place . . . . U
Whitworth Road . . . . U
Wootton Basset Road . . . . . . U

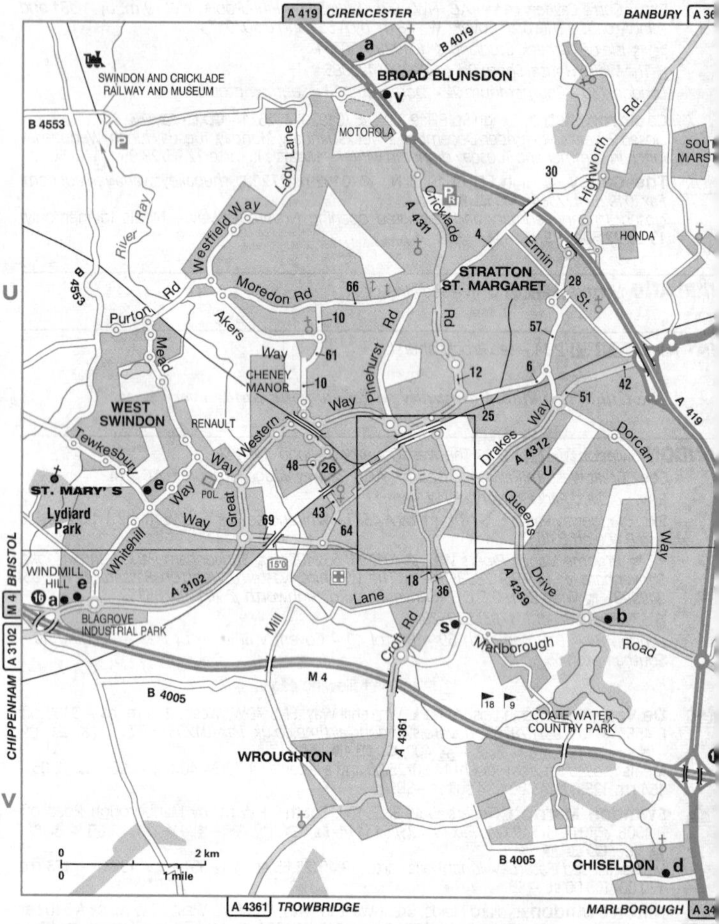

Travel Inn, Lydiard Fields, Great Western Way, SN5 8UY, West : 3 ½ m. by A 3102 junction 16 of M 4 ✆ (01793) 881490, *Fax (01793) 886890* – ⇔ rm, TV ♿ P. MO AE VISA
Meals (grill rest.) – **63 rm** 41.95 **t.**

at Blunsdon *North : 4½ m. by A 4311 on A 419 – ✉ Swindon.*

Blunsdon House, SN26 4AD, ✆ (01793) 721701, *info@blunsdonhouse.co*
Fax (01793) 721056, ⚒, ≘s, ⛆, ⛳9, ⛳, ⛳, ✂, squash – |‡| ⇔ TV ✆ ♿ P – 🏔 300. MO ⓓ VISA. ✂
The Ridge : Meals (dinner only and Sunday lunch)/dinner a la carte 19.50/32.50 🍷 12.5
Christophers : Meals (carvery rest.) 15.00/20.00 a la carte 15.00/23.50 **t.** 🍷 11.00 – **116**
⊏ 115.00/145.00 **t.**, 4 suites – SB.

Premier Lodge, Ermine St, SN2 4DJ, on A 419 ✆ (0870) 7001554, *Fax (0870) 700155*
⇔ rm, TV ♿ P. MO AE ⓓ VISA. ✂
Meals (grill rest.) 11.75 and a la carte approx. 11.95 **t.** 🍷 8.95 – **40 rm** 46.95 **t.**

SWINDON

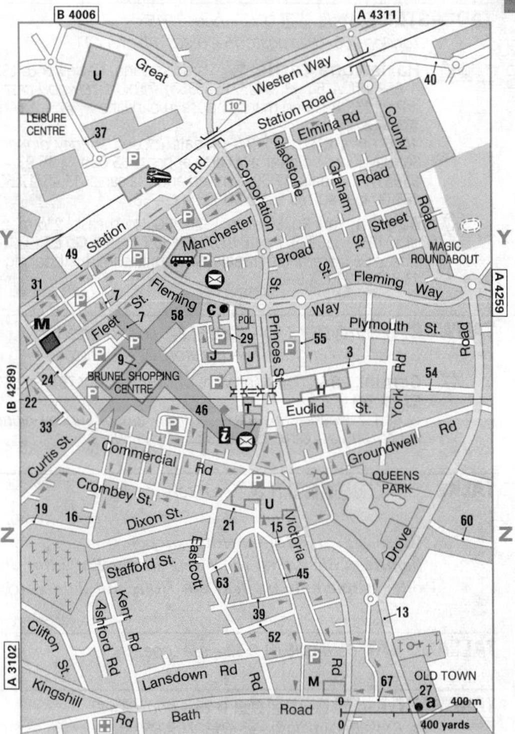

Chiseldon *South : 6¼ m. by A 4259, A 419 and A 346 on B 4005 – ✉ Swindon.*

Chiseldon House, New Rd, SN4 0NE, ☎ (01793) 741010, *chiseldonhousehotel@ukonline.co.uk, Fax (01793) 741059,* heated, – TV P – 50. MO AE VISA JCB V d
Orangery : **Meals** 14.95 (lunch) and a la carte 24.15/31.15 **st.** 12.50 – **21 rm** 80.00/120.00 **st.** – SB.

Wootton Bassett *West : 6¼ m. on A 3102 – V – ✉ Swindon.*

Marsh Farm, SN4 8ER, North : 1 m. by A 3102 on Purton rd ☎ (01793) 848044, *marshfarmhotel@btconnect.com, Fax (01793) 851528,* – rest, TV P – 120. MO AE VISA.
closed 24-30 December – **Meals** *(closed lunch Saturday)* 14.50/22.50 and a la carte 20.75/32.50 **st.** 12.50 – **38 rm** 100.00/140.00 **st.** – SB.

Hook *West : 6¼ m. by A 3102 – V – , B 4534 and Hook rd – ✉ Swindon.*

The School House, Hook St, SN4 8EF, ☎ (01793) 851198, *schoolhotel@email.msn.com, Fax (01793) 851025,* – rest, TV P. MO AE VISA.
Meals a la carte 18.00/27.50 **t.** 7.50 – **11 rm** 99.00 **t.**

VINTON *Gtr.Manchester* 402 403 404 N 23 – *see Manchester.*

MONDS YAT WEST *Herefordshire* 403 404 M 28 *Great Britain G.* – ✉ *Ross-on-Wye.*

See : *Town* ★ – *Yat Rock* (≤★) – **Env.** : *S : Wye Valley* ★.
London 126 – Gloucester 23 – Hereford 17 – Newport 31.

Norton House, Whitchurch, HR9 6DJ, ☎ (01600) 890046, *norton@osconwhi.source.co.uk, Fax (01600) 890045,* « 18C farmhouse of 15C origins », – TV P
closed 25 December – **Meals** (by arrangement) (communal dining) 16.95 – **3 rm** 30.00/46.00 **s.**

TADCASTER *N. Yorks.* 402 Q 22 – *pop. 6 915.*

London 206 – Harrogate 16 – Leeds 14 – York 11.

Hazlewood Castle ♘, Paradise Lane, Hazlewood, LS24 9NJ, Southwest : 2 ¾ m A 659 off A 64 ✆ (01937) 535353, *info@hazlewood-castle.co.uk, Fax (01937) 530630* « Part 13C fortified manor house in parkland », – ⇔ rest, TV ✆ P – 120. MC AE VISA JCB.
1086 *(✆ (01937) 535354)* **: Meals** *(closed Sunday dinner and Monday)* (dinner only Sunday lunch)/dinner a la carte approx. 35.00 **t.** 15.95 – ***Prickly Pear Café*** *(✆ (01 535317)* **: Meals** 17.50 (dinner) and a la carte 13.45/17.50 **t.** 9.95 – **12 rm** 105 165.00 **t.**, **9 suites** 195.00/300.00 **t.** – SB.

Aagrah, York Rd, Steeton, LS24 8EG, Northeast : 2 ½ m. on A 64 (westbound carriage ✆ (01937) 530888, *Fax (01937) 531535* – P. MC AE VISA JCB
closed 25 December – **Meals** - Indian (Kashmiri) - (booking essential) (dinner only) a la c 13.30/17.25 **t.** 9.95.

TADWORTH *Surrey* 404 T 30 – *pop. 37 245 (inc. Banstead).*

London 23 – Brighton 36 – Guildford 22 – Maidstone 41.

Gemini, 28 Station Approach, KT20 5AH, ✆ (01737) 812179, *Fax (01737) 812179* – ⇔ AE VISA
closed 2 weeks Christmas, Saturday lunch, Sunday dinner and Monday – **Meals** 1 (lunch) and a la carte 23.80/29.35 **t.** 11.50.

TALKE *Staffs.* 402 403 404 N 24 – *see Stoke-on-Trent.*

Wenn Sie ein ruhiges Hotel suchen,
benutzen Sie zuerst die Karte in der Einleitung
oder wählen Sie im Text ein Hotel mit dem Zeichen ♘ oder ♘.

TALLAND BAY *Cornwall* 403 G 32 – *see Looe.*

TAMWORTH *Staffs.* 402 403 404 O 26 – *pop. 68 440.*

Eagle Dr., Amington ✆ (01827) 53850.

29 Market St ✆ (01827) 709581.

London 128 – Birmingham 12 – Coventry 29 – Leicester 31 – Stoke-on-Trent 37.

Travel Inn, Bitterscote, Bonehill Rd, B78 3HQ, on A 51 ✆ (01827) 544 *Fax (01827) 310420* – ⇔, rest, TV P – 60. MC AE VISA.
Meals (grill rest.) – **40 rm** 41.95 **t.**

at Bodymoor Heath *South : 6 ¾ m. by A 4091 – ✉ Sutton Coldfield.*

Marston Farm, B76 9JD, ✆ (01827) 872133, *marston.farm@lineone.* *Fax (01827) 875043*, , – ⇔ TV P – 50. MC AE VISA JCB
Meals 21.95 and a la carte **t.** 11.75 – 10.75 – **37 rm** 105.00/130.00 **st.** – SB.

at Hopwas *Northwest : 2 m. on A 51 – ✉ Tamworth.*

Oak Tree Farm without rest., Hints Rd, B78 3AA, ✆ (01827) 56807, *Fax (01827) 56* , – ⇔ rm, TV P. MC AE VISA
7 rm 57.00/100.00 **st.**

TAMWORTH SERVICE AREA *Staffs.* 402 403 404 P 26 – *✉ Tamworth.*

Travelodge, Green Lane, B77 5PS, at junction 10 of M 42 ✆ (01827) 260 *Fax (01827) 260145* – ⇔ TV ✆ P – 25. MC AE VISA JCB.
Meals (grill rest.) – **62 rm** 49.95 **t.**

TAPLOW *Windsor & Maidenhead* 404 R 29.

London 33 – Maidenhead 2 – Reading 12.

Cliveden ♘, SL6 0JF, North : 2 m. by Berry Hill ✆ (01628) 668561, *reservations@clive house.co.uk, Fax (01628) 661837*, « Mid-Victorian stately home ≤ National Trust Garde parterre and River Thames », , heated, , , indoor/outdoor, squash ⇔ TV ✆ P – 40. MC AE VISA JCB
Terrace **: Meals** 26.00 (lunch) and a la carte 57.50/70.50 **t.** 10.00 – (see also ***Wald*** below) – **33 rm** 365.00/515.00 **st.**, 6 suites 550.00/955.00 **st.** – SB.

Taplow House, Berry Hill, SL6 0DA, ☎ (01628) 670056, *taplow@wrensgroup.com, Fax (01628) 773625,* « Part 16C mansion », – 100. **Meals** 23.00/27.50 and a la carte 29.70/39.45 **t.** 16.00 – **31 rm** 160.00/265.00 **st.**, 1 suite – SB.

Waldo's (at Cliveden H.), SL6 0JF, North : 2 m. by Berry Hill ☎ (01628) 668561, *Fax (01628) 661837* –
April-December – **Meals** *(closed Sunday and Monday)* (booking essential) (dinner only) 58.00/84.00 **t.** 19.00
Spec. Vanilla-roasted monkfish with lobster risotto. Best end of lamb, tian of vegetables, red pepper jus. Caramelised banana soufflé, rum and coconut ice cream.

ARPORLEY *Ches.* 402 403 404 L/M 24 – *pop. 2 308.*

Portal G & C.C., Cobblers Cross Lane ☎ (01829) 733933 – Portal Premier, Forest Rd ☎ (01829) 733884.

London 186 – Chester 11 – Liverpool 27 – Shrewsbury 36.

Wild Boar, Whitchurch Rd, Beeston, CW6 9NW, South : 2 ¼ m. on A 49 ☎ (01829) 260309, *wildboarpop@hotmail.com, Fax (01829) 261081,* « Part 17C timbered house » – , rest, – 100.
Meals 14.95/21.95 and a la carte 12.95/33.95 **st.** 11.95 – **37 rm** 75.00/90.00 **st.** – SB.

Cotebrook *Northeast : 2½ m. on A 49 – ✉ Tarporley.*

Fox and Barrel, CW6 9DZ, ☎ (01829) 760529, *martin@thefoxandbarrel.co.uk, Fax (01829) 760529,*
closed 25 December – **Meals** (live jazz Monday evening) a la carte 16.75/23.00 **t.** 9.50.

Bunbury *South : 3 ¼ m. by A 49 – ✉ Tarporley.*

Dysart Arms, Bowes Gate Rd, CW6 9PH, by Bunbury Mill rd ☎ (01829) 260183, *dysart.arms@brunningandprice.co.uk, Fax (01829) 261286,*
closed 25 December – **Meals** a la carte 12.75/21.50 **t.** 10.25.

Willington *Northwest : 3 ¼ m. by Utkinton Rd – ✉ Tarporley.*

Roughlow Farm without rest., CW6 0PG, Northeast : ½ m. on Chapel Lane ☎ (01829) 751199, *Fax (01829) 751199,*
2 rm 40.00/70.00 **s.**, 1 suite.

ATTENHALL *Ches.* 402 403 404 L 24 – *pop. 1 854.*

London 200 – Birmingham 71 – Chester 10 – Liverpool 29 – Manchester 38 – Stoke-on-Trent 30.

Higher Huxley Hall, CH3 9BZ, North : 2 ¼ m. on Huxley rd ☎ (01829) 781484, *info@huxleyhall.co.uk, Fax (01829) 781142,*
booking essential – **Meals** (by arrangement) (communal dining) 22.50 **s.** 8.00 – **4 rm** 45.00/80.00 **s.** – SB.

Newton Hall without rest., CH3 9NE, North : 1 m. by Huxley rd on Gatesheath rd ☎ (01829) 770153, *newton.hall@farming.co.uk, Fax (01829) 770655,* « Working farm »,
3 rm 25.00/55.00 **s.**

AUNTON *Somerset* 403 K 30 *The West Country G. – pop. 55 855.*

See : *Town★ – St. Mary Magdalene★* **V** *– Somerset County Museum★* **AC U** *– St. James'★* **U** *– Hammett St.★* **V 25** *– The Crescent★* **V** *– Bath Place★* **V 3**.

Env. : *Trull (Church★), S : 2½ m. by A 38.*

Exc. : *Bishops Lydeard★ (Church★), NW : 6 m. – Wellington : Church★, Wellington Monument (≤★★), SW : 7½ m. by A 38 – Combe Florey★, NW : 8 m. – Gaulden Manor★* **AC**, *NW : 10 m. by A 358 and B 3227.*

Taunton Vale, Creech Heathfield ☎ (01823) 412220 – Vivary, Vivary Park ☎ (01823) 289274 – Taunton and Pickeridge, Corfe ☎ (01823) 421240.

Paul St. ☎ (01823) 336344.

London 168 – Bournemouth 69 – Bristol 50 – Exeter 37 – Plymouth 78 – Southampton 93 – Weymouth 50.

Plan on next page

The Castle, Castle Green, TA1 1NF, ☎ (01823) 272671, *reception@the-castle-hotel.com, Fax (01823) 336066,* « Part 12C castle with Norman garden » – , rest, – 100. V a
Meals *(closed Sunday dinner)* 16.95/37.00 **t.** 12.00 – **44 rm** 110.00/240.00 **t.**
Spec. Home cured beef with a radish and gherkin salad. Steamed mutton and caper pudding, buttered cabbage and fennel. Rhubarb and custard.

TAUNTON

Street	Grid	No.
Bath Place	V	3
Billet Street	V	4
Billetfield	V	6
Birch Grove	U	7
Bishop's Hull Road	AZ	9
Bridge (The)	U	10
Bridge Street	U	12
Burton Place	V	13
Cann Street	V	15
Cleveland Street	U	16
Comeytrowe Lane	AZ	18
Corporation Street	V	19
County Walk Shopping Centre	V	
Duke Street	V	21
East Street	V	
Fore Street	V	22
Hamilton Road	BZ	24
Hammet Street	V	25
High Street	V	
Hurdle Way	V	27
Ilminster Road	BZ	28
Magdalene Street	V	30
Middleway	AZ	31
North Street	V	33
Obridge Viaduct	BY	34
Old Market Shopping Centre	V	
Portland Street	U	36
Priory Avenue	U	37
Shoreditch Road	BZ	39
Shuttern	V	40
Silver Street South	VZ	42
Upper High Street	V	43
Upper Wood Street	U	44
Victoria Parkway	BYZ	45
Wellington New Road	AZ	46
Wilton Street	V	48
Winchester Street	U	49
Wood Street	U	51

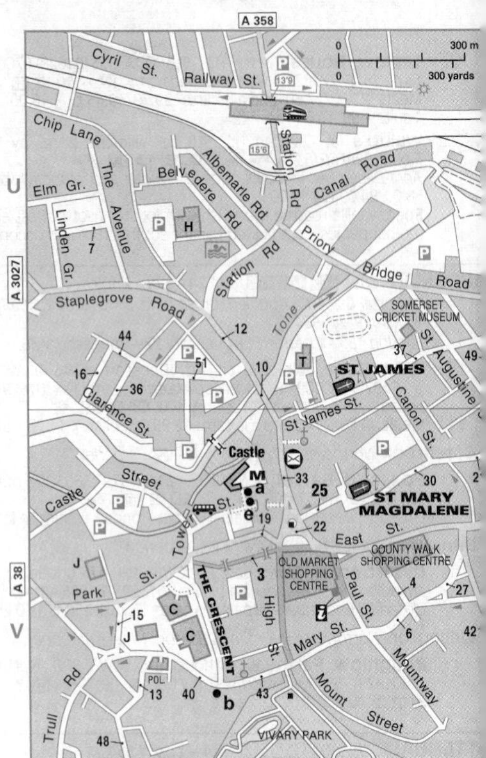

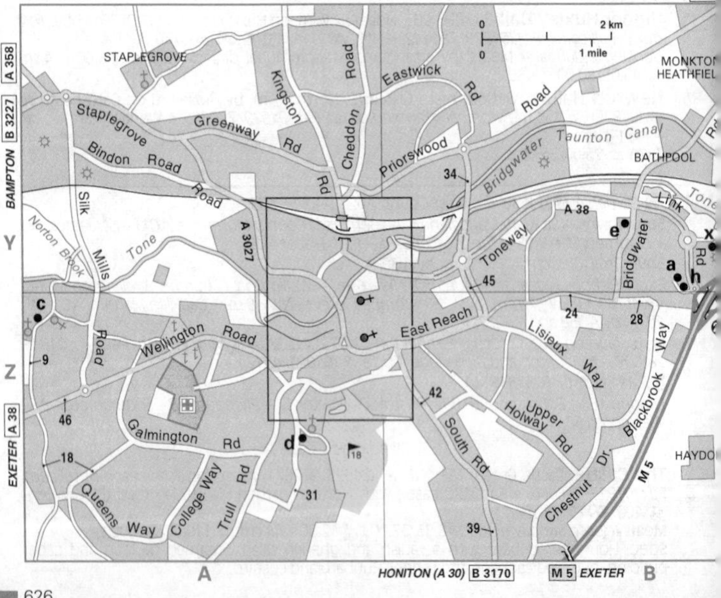

Holiday Inn, Deane Gate Ave, TA1 2UA, East : 2 ½ m. by A 358 at junction with M 5 (0870) 400 9080, *Fax (01823) 332266*, – rm, rest, – 300. VISA JCB BY h
Meals (bar lunch Saturday) 10.00/15.00 and a la carte 18.85/29.80 **st.** 11.95 – 13.95 – **99 rm** 99.00/164.00 **st.**

Express by Holiday Inn without rest., Blackbrook Business Park, TA1 2RW, (01823) 624000, *taunton@expresshidayinn.co.uk, Fax (01823) 624024*, – – 30. VISA JCB. BY a
92 rm 53.00 **t.**

Travel Inn, 81 Bridgwater Rd, TA1 2DU, East : 1 ¾ m. by A 358 (01823) 321112, *Fax (01823) 322054* – rm, VISA. BY e
Meals (grill rest.) – **40 rm** 41.95 **t.**

Travelodge without rest., Riverside Retail Park, Hankridge Farm, TA1 2LR, East : 2 m. by A 358 (01823) 444702, *Fax (01823) 444702* – rm, VISA JCB. BY x
48 rm 49.95 **t.**

Orchard House without rest., Fons George, Middleway, TA1 3JS, off Wilton St (01823) 351783, *orch-hse@dircon.co.uk, Fax (01823) 351785*, « Georgian house », – VISA. AZ d
6 rm 35.00/55.00.

Forde House without rest., 9 Upper High St, TA1 3PX, (01823) 279042, *Fax (01823) 279042*, – VISA. V b
closed Christmas and New Year – **5 rm** 32.00/52.00 **s.**

Gatchells, Angersleigh, TA3 7SY, South : 3 ½ m. by Trull rd turning right on Dipford Rd (01823) 421580, *gatchells@somerweb.co.uk*, «, « 16C thatched cottage », – VISA
Meals (by arrangement) 13.00 **s.** – **3 rm** 30.00/54.00.

Brazz, Castle Bow, TA1 1NF, (01823) 252000, *enquiries@brazz.co.uk, Fax (01823) 336066* – VISA V e
Meals a la carte 15.85/27.40 **t.** 10.50.

West Monkton *Northeast : 3½ m. by A 361* – **AZ** – *off A 38* – *Taunton.*

Springfield House without rest., Walford Cross, TA2 8QW, on A 38 (01823) 412116, *tina@ridout13.freeserve.co.uk, Fax (01823) 412844*, – .
closed 24, 25 and 31 December – **5 rm** 30.00/50.00 **st.**

Henlade *East : 3½ m. on A 358* – **BZ** – *Taunton.*

Mount Somerset, Lower Henlade, TA3 5NB, South : ½ m. by Stoke Rd and Ash Cross rd (01823) 442500, *info@mountsomersethotel.co.uk, Fax (01823) 442900*, «, « Regency country house », – , rest, – 60. VISA JCB.
Meals 19.95/25.95 and dinner a la carte 30.00/35.00 **t.** 15.00 – **11 rm** 95.00/195.00 **t.** – SB.

Hatch Beauchamp *Southeast : 6 m. by A358* – **BZ** – *Taunton.*

Farthings, TA3 6SG, (01823) 480664, *farthings1@aol.com, Fax (01823) 481118*, « Georgian country house », – VISA.
Meals (dinner only and Sunday lunch)/dinner 23.50 **t.** 11.00 – **10 rm** 64.00/120.00 **t.** – SB.

Frog Street Farm, Beercrocombe, TA3 6AF, Southeast : 1 ¼ m. by Beercrocombe Rd (01823) 480430, *Fax (01823) 480430*, « 15C farmhouse, working farm », – .
Meals (by arrangement) 16.00 – **3 rm** 30.00/60.00 **st.** – SB.

Rumwell *Southwest : 2½ m. on A 38* – **AZ** – *Taunton.*

Rumwell Manor, TA4 1EL, (01823) 461902, *reception@rumwellmanor.co.uk, Fax (01823) 254861*, – rest, – 40. VISA JCB.
closed 27 December-2 January – **Meals** (bar lunch)/dinner 18.50 and a la carte 16.00/26.25 **st.** 9.50 – 8.00 – **20 rm** 61.00/100.00 **st.** – SB.

Bishop's Hull *West : 1 ¾ m. by A 38* – *Taunton.*

Meryan House, Bishop's Hull Rd, TA1 5EG, (01823) 337445, *anglo@dircon.co.uk, Fax (01823) 322355*, – VISA JCB AZ c
Meals *(closed Sunday)* (dinner only) 16.00/20.00 **st.** 10.50 – **12 rm** 49.00/80.00 **st.** – SB.

at West Bagborough *Northwest : 10½ m. by A 358 – AY – ✉ Taunton.*

Bashfords Farmhouse ⑤, TA4 3EF, ☎ (01823) 432015, *charlieritchie@netscapeonli .co.uk, Fax (0870) 1671587, « 18C »*, – TV P.
Meals (by arrangement) (communal dining) 20.00 **st.** – **3 rm** 30.00/50.00 **s.**

Tilbury Farm ⑤ without rest., Cothelstone, TA4 3DY, East : ¾ m. ☎ (01823) 43239 ← Vale of Taunton, « 18C », – TV P.
3 rm 30.00/50.00.

TAUNTON DEANE SERVICE AREA *Somerset* 403 K 31 – ✉ *Taunton.*

Travel Inn without rest., TA3 7PF, M 5 between junctions 25 and 26 (southbou carriageway) ☎ (01823) 332228, *Fax (01823) 338131* – TV P. VISA.
closed Christmas and New Year – **40 rm** 41.95 **t.**

TAVISTOCK *Devon* 403 H 32 *The West Country G. – pop. 10 222.*

Env. : *Morwellham** **AC**, *SW : 4½ m.*
Exc. : *E : Dartmoor National Park** – Buckland Abbey*** **AC**, *S : 7 m. by A 386 – Lydford* N : 8½ m. by A 386.*
Down Rd ☎ (01822) 612344 – Hurdwick, Tavistock Hamlets ☎ (01822) 612746.
Town Hall, Bedford Sq ☎ (01822) 612938.
London 239 – Exeter 38 – Plymouth 16.

Browns, 80 West St, PL19 8AQ, ☎ (01822) 618686, *enquiries@brownsdevon.co. Fax (01822) 618646,* – TV P. VISA
Brasserie : Meals (light lunch Monday-Saturday)/dinner 17.50 and a la carte **st.** 6.00
20 rm 55.00/110.00 **st.** – SB.

Bedford, 1 Plymouth Rd, PL19 8BB, ☎ (01822) 613221, *enquiries@bedford-hotel.co. Fax (01822) 618034* – TV P – 60. VISA
Meals a la carte 14.50/23.45 **st.** 10.95 – **29 rm** 42.50/85.00 **st.** – SB.

Quither Mill ⑤, PL19 0PZ, Northwest : 5 ¾ m. by Chillaton rd on Quither ☎ (01822) 860160, *quither.mill@virgin.net, Fax (01822) 860160,* ←, « 18C converted wa mill », – TV P. VISA.
closed Christmas and New Year – **Meals** (communal dining) 19.00 9.95 – **2 rm** 40.0 70.00, 1 suite.

April Cottage without rest., Mount Tavy Rd, PL19 9JB, ☎ (01822) 613280 – TV P
3 rm 30.00/45.00 **s.**

Colcharton Farm ⑤, Gulworthy, PL19 8HU, West : 2 ½ m. by A 390 on Colcharton ☎ (01822) 616435, *Fax (01822) 616435,* « Working farm », – P.
Meals (by arrangement) (communal dining) 10.00 **st.** – **3 rm** 25.00/45.00 **st.**

at Gulworthy Cross *West : 3 m. on A 390 – ✉ Tavistock.*

XXX ✿ **Horn of Plenty** ⑤ with rm, PL19 8JD, Northwest : 1 m. by Chipshop ☎ (01822) 832528, *enquiries@hornofplenty.co.uk, Fax (01822) 832528,* ← Tamar Valley a Bodmin Moor, – TV P. VISA.
closed 25-26 December – **Meals** *(closed Monday lunch)* 18.50/37.00 **t.** 17.00 – **10** 95.00/200.00 **t.** – SB
Spec. Roast squab pigeon salad, quails eggs and red wine dressing. Pan-fried sea ba artichoke purée, sauce vierge. Chocolate and cognac cake with cherries.

at Chillaton *Northwest : 6¼ m. by Chillaton rd – ✉ Tavistock.*

Tor Cottage ⑤ without rest., PL16 0JE, Southwest : ¼ m. by Tavistock rd, turning rig at bridle path sign, down unmarked track for ½ m. ☎ (01822) 860248, *info@torcottage. uk, Fax (01822) 860126,* ←, heated, – TV P. VISA JCB.
closed 2 weeks Christmas-New Year – **4 rm** 89.30/115.00 **t.**, 1 suite.

TEFFONT *Wilts.* – *see Salisbury.*

TEIGNMOUTH *Devon* 403 J 32 – *pop. 13 403.*

The Den, Sea Front ☎ (01626) 779769.
London 216 – Exeter 16 – Torquay 8.

Thomas Luny House without rest., Teign St, TQ14 8EG, follow signs for the Quays, the A 381 ☎ (01626) 772976, *alisonandjohn@thomas-luny-house.co.uk,* « Georgian hou built by Thomas Luny », – TV P. VISA.
4 rm 40.00/75.00 **s.**

Shaldon *South : 1 m. on B 3199 – Teignmouth.*

Ness House, Marine Drive, TQ14 0HP, (01626) 873480, *nesshouse@talk21.com, Fax (01626) 873486,* – rest, .
closed 24-25 December – **Meals** (carving lunch Sunday) 19.50 (dinner) and a la carte 17.40/24.50 **t.** 9.25 – **12 rm** 45.00/125.00 **t.** – SB.

LFORD *Wrekin* 402 403 404 M 25 *Great Britain G. – pop. 119 340.*

Env. : *Ironbridge Gorge Museum★★ AC (The Iron Bridge★★, Coalport China Museum★★, Blists Hill Open Air Museum★★, Museum of the River and Visitor Centre★) S : 5 m. by B 4373.*

Exc. : *Weston Park★★ AC, E : 7 m. by A 5.*

Telford, Great Hay, Sutton Heights (01952) 429977 – Wrekin, Wellington (01952) 244032 – The Shropshire, Muxton Grange, Muxton (01952) 677866.

Wyre Hall, The Telford Centre (01952) 238008.

London 152 – Birmingham 33 – Shrewsbury 12 – Stoke-on-Trent 29.

Clarion H. Madeley Court, Castlefields Way, Madeley, TF7 5DW, South : 4 ½ m. by A 442 and A 4169 on B 4373 (01952) 680068, *admin@gb068u-net.com, Fax (01952) 684275,* « Part 16C manor house », – rest, – 200.
Priory : **Meals** (dinner only and Sunday lunch)/dinner 23.00 **st.** 12.75 – ***Cellar Vaults :*** **Meals** *(closed Saturday lunch)* 23.00 **st.** 12.75 – 11.75 – **47 rm** 110.00/125.00 **t.** – SB.

Telford Moat House, Forgegate, Telford Centre, TF3 4NA, (01952) 429988, *revtel@queensmoat.co.uk, Fax (01952) 292012,* – , rest, – 400.
Casa Med : **Meals** (bar lunch Monday-Saturday)/dinner 15.95 and a la carte 16.50/24.00 **st.** 12.95 – 10.95 – **151 rm** 107.00/127.00 **st.** – SB.

Travel Inn, Euston Way, TF3 4LY, North : ½ m. by Cannock rd at jucntion with A 442 (01952) 201075, *Fax (01952) 290742* – , rm, rest, – 30.
Meals (grill rest.) – **60 rm** 41.95 **t.**

Travelodge, Shawbirch Crossroads, Shawbirch, TF1 3QA, Northwest : 5 ½ m. by A 442 at junction with B 5063 (01952) 251244, *Fax (01952) 246534* – rm, .
Meals (grill rest.) – **40 rm** 49.95 **t.**

White House, Wellington Rd, Muxton, TF2 8NG, North : 4 ½ m. by A 442 off A 518 (01952) 604276, *reception@whhotel.co.uk, Fax (01952) 670336,* – .
Meals *(closed Bank Holiday lunch)* 10.50/13.50 and a la carte 17.70/25.75 **st.** 8.95 – **32 rm** 62.50/82.50 **st.** – SB.

Norton *South : 7 m. on A 442 – Shifnal.*

Hundred House with rm, Bridgnorth Rd, TF11 9EE, (01952) 730353, *hphundredhouse@messages.co.uk, Fax (01952) 730355,* « Characterful inn, gardens » – .
Meals a la carte 17.75/27.50 **t.** 12.50 – **10 rm** 69.00/120.00 **t.** – SB.

MPLE SOWERBY *Cumbria* 402 M 20 – *see Penrith.*

NBURY WELLS *Worcs.* 403 404 M 27 – *pop. 2 219.*

London 144 – Birmingham 36 – Hereford 20 – Shrewsbury 37 – Worcester 28.

Cadmore Lodge, St Michaels, WR15 8TQ, Southwest : 2 ¾ m. by A 4112 (01584) 810044, *info@cadmorelodge.demon.co.uk, Fax (01584) 810044,* – – 100.
Meals 11.25/18.50 and a la carte 14.00/21.50 **st.** 7.80 – **14 rm** 47.50/115.00 **st.** – SB.

NTERDEN *Kent* 404 W 30 – *pop. 6 803.*

Town Hall, High St. (01580) 763572 (summer only).

London 57 – Folkestone 26 – Hastings 21 – Maidstone 19.

White Lion, High St, TN30 6BD, (01580) 765077, *whitelion@lionheartinns.co.uk, Fax (01580) 764157* – – 40.
Meals a la carte 12.75/20.85 **st.** 8.95 – **15 rm** 59.00/74.00 **t.** – SB.

Little Silver Country H., Ashford Rd, St Michaels, TN30 6SP, North : 2 m. on A 28 (01233) 850321, *enquiries@little-silver.co.uk, Fax (01233) 850647,* – rest, – 120.
Meals (booking essential) a la carte 21.20/26.70 **t.** 10.95 – **10 rm** 60.00/110.00 **t.** – SB.

ENGLAND

Collina House, 5 East Hill, TN30 6RL, ✆ (01580) 764852, *collina.house@dial.pipex.co* *Fax (01580) 762224* – ⇔ TV P. MC AE VISA. ✻
closed 10 days Christmas – **Meals** (lunch by arrangement)/dinner a la carte 20.50/26.50 🍷 8.50 – **14 rm** ☐ 45.00/75.00 **st.** – SB.

TETBURY *Glos.* 403 404 N 29 *Great Britain G.* – *pop. 4 618.*
Env. : *Westonbirt Arboretum★ AC, SW : 2½ m. by A 433.*
Westonbirt ✆ (01666) 880242.
33 Church St. ✆ (01666) 503552.
London 113 – *Bristol 27* – *Gloucester 19* – *Swindon 24.*

The Close, 8 Long St, GL8 8AQ, ✆ (01666) 502272, *reception@theclosehotel.co* *Fax (01666) 504401,* « 16C town house with walled garden » – ⇔ rest, TV P – 🎪 70. AE VISA
Meals 16.50/32.50 **t.** 🍷 14.50 – **15 rm** ☐ 75.00/120.00 **t.** – SB.

Snooty Fox, Market Pl, GL8 8DD, ✆ (01666) 502436, *res@snooty-fox.co* *Fax (01666) 503479* – ⇔ rest, TV. MC AE ① VISA JCB. ✻
Meals (bar lunch)/dinner a la carte 18.95/23.95 **t.** 🍷 11.95 – **12 rm** ☐ 69.50/130.00 **st.** –

The Trouble House, GL8 8SG, Northeast : 2 m. on A 433 ✆ (01666) 5022 *Fax (01666) 504508,* 🏠 – P. MC AE ① VISA JCB
closed 25 December and Mondays except Bank Holidays – **Meals** a la carte 22.50/29.0 🍷 10.00.

at Willesley *Southwest : 4 m. on A 433* – ✉ *Tetbury.*

Tavern House without rest., GL8 8QU, ✆ (01666) 880444, *Fax (01666) 880254,* « Part former inn and staging post », 🌳 – ⇔ TV P. ✻
4 rm ☐ 65.00/85.00 **st.**

at Calcot *West : 3½ m. on A 4135* – ✉ *Tetbury.*

Calcot Manor ⛰, GL8 8YJ, ✆ (01666) 890391, *reception@calcotmanor.co* *Fax (01666) 890394,* 🏠, « Converted Cotswold farm buildings », ⛱ heated, 🌳, ⇔ rest, TV ✆ 🏃 P – 🎪 65. MC AE ① VISA. ✻
Conservatory **: Meals** (booking essential) a la carte 23.25/36.00 **t.** 🍷 12.75 – (see also ***Gumstool Inn*** below) – **24 rm** ☐ 120.00/175.00 **t.**, 4 suites – SB.

The Gumstool Inn (at Calcot Manor H.), GL8 8YJ, ✆ (01666) 890391, *reception@ca manor.com, Fax (01666) 890394,* 🏠, 🌳 – P. MC AE ① VISA
Meals (booking essential) a la carte 14.75/21.75 **t.** 🍷 9.50.

TEWKESBURY *Glos.* 403 404 N 28 *Great Britain G.* – *pop. 9 488.*
See : *Town★* – *Abbey★★ (Nave★★, vault★).*
Env. : *St. Mary's, Deerhurst★, SW : 4 m. by A 38 and B 4213.*
Tewkesbury Park Hotel, Lincoln Green Lane ✆ (01684) 295405.
64 Barton St. ✆ (01684) 295027.
London 108 – *Birmingham 39* – *Gloucester 11.*

Jessop House, 65 Church St, GL20 5RZ, ✆ (01684) 292017, *lestms@aol.co* *Fax (01684) 273076* – ⇔ rest, TV P. MC VISA JCB. ✻
closed 24 December-2 January – **Meals** (booking essential) (dinner only) 20.00/25.00 – 8 ☐ 58.00/78.00 **st.**

Evington Hill Farm, Tewkesbury Rd, The Leigh, GL19 4AQ, South : 5 m. on A ✆ (01242) 680255, 🌳 – ⇔ TV P. ✻
Meals (by arrangement) (communal dining) 15.00 **st.** 🍷 10.00 – **6 rm** ☐ 48.00/80.00 **st.**

at Puckrup *North : 2½ m. by A 38* – ✉ *Tewkesbury.*

Hilton Puckrup Hall, GL20 6EL, ✆ (01684) 296200, *Fax (01684) 850788,* 🏋, ≘s, ⛱, 🌳, 🏌 – 🛗 ⇔, ▤ rest, TV ✆ ♿ P – 🎪 200. MC AE ① VISA
Meals *(closed Saturday lunch)* 19.95 (dinner) and a la carte 23.85/34.40 **st.** 🍷 13.75 – **110** ☐ 170.00/300.00 **st.**, 2 suites – SB.

at Corse Lawn *Southwest : 6 m. by A 38 and A 438 on B 4211* – ✉ *Gloucester.*

Corse Lawn House ⛰, GL19 4LZ, ✆ (01452) 780771, *hotel@corselawnhouse.u-com, Fax (01452) 780840,* « Part Queen Anne house », ⛱, 🌳, 🎾 – ⇔ rm, TV P – 🎪 MC AE ① VISA
closed 24-26 December – ***Bistro*** **: Meals** a la carte 16.40/32.40 **t.** 🍷 10.50 – (see ***The Restaurant*** below) – **17 rm** ☐ 80.00/125.00 **t.**, 2 suites – SB.

XXX **The Restaurant** (at Corse Lawn House H.), GL19 4LZ, ✆ (01452) 780771, *hotel@co lawnhouse.u_net.com, Fax (01452) 780840,* 🌳 – ⇔ P. MC AE ① VISA
closed 24-26 December – **Meals** 18.50/27.50 and a la carte 24.40/37.35 **t.** 🍷 10.50.

ENGLAND

[T]HAME *Oxon.* 404 R 28 *The West Country G. – pop. 10 806.*
Exc. : *Ridgeway Path*★★.
Market House, North St. ✆ *(01844) 212834.*
London 48 – Aylesbury 9 – Oxford 13.

Spread Eagle, 16 Cornmarket, OX9 2BW, ✆ (01844) 213661, *enquiries@spreadeagle thame.co.uk, Fax (01844) 261380* – TV P – 250. MC AE VISA.
closed 28-30 December – **Meals** *(closed Sunday dinner)* a la carte 20.50/31.40 **st.** 10.95 – 9.95 – **31 rm** 96.55/132.25 **st.**, 2 suites – SB.

Travelodge, OX9 3XA, Northwest : 1 m. by B 4445 on B 4011 at junction with A 418 ✆ (01844) 218740, *Fax (01844) 218740* – rm, rest, TV P. MC AE VISA JCB.
Meals (grill rest.) – **31 rm** 59.95 **t.**

The Dairy without rest., Moreton, OX9 2HX, Southwest : 2 m. by A 329 ✆ (01844) 214075, *Fax (01844) 214075*, « Former milking parlour », – TV P
closed Christmas – **3 rm** 62.00/86.00 **s.**

The Old Trout with rm, 29-30 Lower High St, OX9 2AA, ✆ (01844) 212146, *mj4trout@aol. com, Fax (01844) 212614*, « 15C thatched inn » – TV P. MC VISA.
closed 2 weeks from 24 December – **Meals** *(closed Sunday)* 12.00 (lunch) and a la carte 19.50/27.00 **st.** 14.00 – **7 rm** 60.00/85.00 **st.**

Milton Common *Southwest : 4 m. by A 329 on A 40 – ✉ Thame.*

Lower Chilworth Farm without rest., OX9 2JS, Northwest : ¾ m. on A 40 ✆ (01844) 279593, « Part 15C and 18C house, working farm », – TV P.
closed 25 and 31 December – **3 rm** 35.00/70.00 **st.**

***Groß-London** (GREATER LONDON) besteht aus der City und 32 Verwaltungsbezirken (Borough). Diese sind wiederum in kleinere Bezirke (Area) unterteilt, deren Mittelpunkt ehemalige Dörfer oder Stadtviertel sind, die oft ihren eigenen Charakter bewahrt haben.*

[TH]ANET WAY SERVICE AREA *Kent* 404 W 30 – *see Whitstable.*

[TH]ATCHAM *Newbury* 403 404 Q 29 – *pop. 20 726 – ✉ Newbury.*
London 69 – Bristol 68 – Oxford 30 – Reading 15 – Southampton 40.

Premier Lodge, Bath Rd, Midgham, RG7 5UX, East : 2 m. on A 4 ✆ (0870) 7001498, *Fax (0870) 7001499* – rm, TV P. MC AE VISA.
Meals (grill rest.) a la carte approx. 12.50 **t.** 7.80 – **29 rm** 49.95 **t.**

[TH]AXTED *Essex* 404 V 28 – *pop. 1 899.*
London 44 – Cambridge 24 – Colchester 31 – Chelmsford 20.

Crossways without rest., 32 Town St, CM6 2LA, ✆ (01371) 830348, – TV.
restricted opening in winter – **3 rm** 38.00/58.00.

[TH]IRSK *N. Yorks.* 402 P 21 – *pop. 6 860.*
Thornton-Le-Street ✆ *(01845) 522170.*
The World of James Herriot, 23 Kirkgate ✆ *(01845) 522755.*
London 227 – Leeds 37 – Middlesbrough 24 – York 24.

Golden Fleece, 42 Market Pl, YO7 1LL, ✆ (01845) 523108, *goldenfleece@bestwestern.co .uk, Fax (01845) 523996* – rest, TV P – 80. MC AE VISA
Meals (bar lunch)/dinner 17.50 and a la carte 14.35/22.35 **t.** 12.50 – **18 rm** 65.00/ 105.00 **t.** – SB.

Sheppard's, Front St, Sowerby, YO7 1JF, South : ½ m. ✆ (01845) 523655, *sheppards @thirskny.freeserve.co.uk, Fax (01845) 524720* – rm, TV P. MC VISA.
closed first week January – ***Bistro :*** **Meals** *(closed Monday lunch and Sunday)* a la carte 17.50/29.15 **st.** 11.95 – **8 rm** 62.00/88.00 **st.**

Spital Hill, York Rd, YO7 3AE, Southeast : 1 ¾ m. on A 19, entrance between 2 white posts ✆ (01845) 522273, *Fax (01845) 524970*, – P. MC AE VISA.
Meals (by arrangement) (communal dining) 28.00 **st.** 7.50 – **3 rm** 51.00/90.00 **st.** – SB.

Topcliffe *Southwest : 4½ m. by A 168 – ✉ Thirsk.*

Angel Inn, Long St, YO7 3RW, ✆ (01845) 577237, *Fax (01845) 578000*, – TV P – 150. MC VISA.
Meals a la carte 12.40/17.50 **t.** 8.95 – **15 rm** 44.50/60.00 **t.** – SB.

at Asenby *Southwest : 5 1/4 m. by A 168 – ✉ Thirsk.*

Crab Manor, Dishforth Rd, YO7 3QL, ☎ (01845) 577286, *info@crabandlobster.co.*
Fax (01845) 577109, « Part Georgian manor, memorabilia », – P. MC AE VISA
Meals – (see ***Crab and Lobster*** below) – **12 rm** 90.00/150.00 **t.**

Crab and Lobster, Dishforth Rd, YO7 3QL, ☎ (01845) 577286, *Fax (01845) 577109,*
« Thatched inn, memorabilia », – P. MC AE VISA
The Restaurant : **Meals** - Seafood - (booking essential) 13.50 (lunch) and a la carte 20.4
25.00 **t.** 12.50 – ***The Brasserie :*** **Meals** - Seafood - (bookings not accepted) 13.
(lunch) and a la carte 20.45/25.00 **t.** 12.50.

THORNABY-ON-TEES *Stockton-on-Tees* 402 Q 20 – *pop. 12 108* – ✉ *Middlesbrough.*
London 250 – Leeds 62 – Middlesbrough 3 – York 49.

Travel Inn, Whitewater Way, TS17 6QB, Northeast : 1 1/2 m. by A 66 following signs
Teeside Park then Teesdale ☎ (01642) 671573, *Fax (01642) 671464* – rm, rest, TV
P. MC AE VISA.
Meals (grill rest.) – **62 rm** 41.95 **t.**

THORNBURY *South Gloucestershire* 403 404 M 29 – *pop. 12 108* – ✉ *Bristol.*
London 128 – Bristol 12 – Gloucester 23 – Swindon 43.

Thornbury Castle, Castle St, BS35 1HH, ☎ (01454) 281182, *thornburycastl*
compuserve.com, Fax (01454) 416188, « 16C castle, antiques, gardens and vineyard »,
rest, TV P. MC AE VISA.
closed 4 days January – **Meals** 22.50/42.50 **t.** 12.00 – 8.95 – **23 rm** 105.00/175.00
2 suites.

THORNHAM MAGNA *Suffolk* – ✉ *Eye.*
London 96 – Cambridge 47 – Ipswich 20 – Norwich 30.

Thornham Hall, IP23 8HA, ☎ (01379) 783314, *lhenniker@aol.co*
Fax (01379) 788347, ←, « Within grounds of Thornham estate », – P. MC
VISA JCB
Meals (by arrangement) (communal dining) 20.00 – **3 rm** 45.00/70.00.

THORNTHWAITE *Cumbria* 402 K 20 – *see Keswick.*

THORNTON CLEVELEYS *Lancs.* 402 K/L 22.
London 447 – Blackpool 4 – Carlisle 94 – Liverpool 59 – Manchester 54.

Twelve, Marsh Mill Village, Marsh Mill in Wyre, FY5 4JZ, ☎ (01253) 821212, *info@twe*
restaurant.co.uk, Fax (01253) 821212 – MC AE VISA JCB
closed first 2 weeks January, Monday and lunch Saturday and Sunday – **Meals** 11
(lunch) and dinner a la carte 19.70/29.15 **t.** 9.95.

THORNTON HOUGH *Mersey.* 402 403 K 24 – ✉ *Wirral.*
London 215 – Birkenhead 12 – Chester 17 – Liverpool 12.

Thornton Hall, CH63 1JF, on B 5136 ☎ (0151) 336 3938, *thorntonhallhotel@btinter*
com, Fax (0151) 336 7864, – TV P – 250. MC AE VISA
closed 1 January – ***The Italian Room :*** **Meals** (bar lunch Saturday) 11.00/25.00 and c
ner a la carte 26.85/31.85 **t.** 11.95 – **62 rm** 95.00/105.00 **t.**, 1 suite – SB.

THORNTON-LE-DALE *N. Yorks.* 402 R 21 – *see Pickering.*

Besonders angenehme Hotels oder Restaurants
sind im Führer rot gekennzeichnet.
Sie können uns helfen, wenn Sie uns die Häuser angeben,
in denen Sie sich besonders wohl gefühlt haben.
Jährlich erscheint eine komplett überarbeitete Ausgabe
aller Roten **Michelin-Führer**.

HORPE *Derbs.* 402 403 404 O 24 *Great Britain G. – pop. 201 – ✉ Ashbourne.*
See : *Dovedale★★ (Ilam Rock★).*
London 151 – Derby 16 – Sheffield 33 – Stoke-on-Trent 26.

Peveril of the Peak ⛰, DE6 2AW, ☎ (0870) 4008109, *Fax (01335) 350507*, ≤, 🌳, 🎾 – ⇔ TV P – 🏛 50. MC AE ⊙ VISA JCB. ✈
Meals 12.95/21.95 **t.** 🍷 14.95 – ☕ 10.95 – **46 rm** 90.00/115.00 **st.** – SB.

HORPE MARKET *Norfolk* 404 X 25 – *pop. 303* – ✉ *North Walsham.*
London 130 – Norwich 21.

Elderton Lodge ⛰, Gunton Park, NR11 8TZ, South : 1 m. on A 149 ☎ (01263) 833547, *enquiries@eldertonlodge.co.uk, Fax (01263) 834673*, ≤, 🌳 – TV P. MC AE VISA
Meals 9.75/27.50 and a la carte 12.85/28.85 **t.** 🍷 13.95 – **11 rm** ☕ 60.00/115.00 **t.** – SB.

HRAPSTON SERVICE AREA *Northants.* 404 S 26 – ✉ *Kettering.*

Travelodge, NN14 4UR, at junction of A 14 with A 605 and A 45 ☎ (01832) 735199, *Fax (01832) 735199* – ⇔ rm, TV ♿ P. MC AE ⊙ VISA JCB. ✈
Meals (grill rest.) – **40 rm** 39.95 **t.**

HREE BRIDGES *W. Sussex – see Crawley.*

HRELKELD *Cumbria* 402 K 20 – *see Keswick.*

HRUSSINGTON *Leics.* 402 403 404 Q 25 – *pop. 512* – ✉ *Leicester.*
London 101 – Leicester 10 – Nottingham 22 – Lincoln 50.

Travelodge, Green Acres Filling Station, LE7 8TF, on A 46 (southbound carriageway) ☎ (01664) 424525, *Fax (01664) 424525* – ⇔ rm, ▤ rest, TV ♿ P. MC AE ⊙ VISA JCB. ✈
Meals (grill rest.) – **32 rm** 39.95 **t.**

HURLESTONE *Devon* 403 I 33 – *see Kingsbridge.*

HURROCK *Essex* 404 U 29 – *pop. 127 819.*
London 21 – Cambridge 60 – Dover 69 – Southend-on-Sea 20.

Travel Inn, Fleming Rd, Unicorn Estate, Chafford Hundred, Grays, RM16 6YJ, ☎ (01375) 481908, *Fax (01375) 481876* – ⇔ rm, ▤ rest, TV ♿ P. MC AE ⊙ VISA JCB. ✈
Meals (grill rest.) – **62 rm** 41.95 **t.**

HURROCK SERVICE AREA *Thurrock* 404 V 29 – ✉ *West Thurrock.*
⛳18 *Belhus Park, South Ockendon ☎ (01708) 854260.*
ℹ *Granada Motorway Service Area (M 25), Thurrock, Grays ☎ (01708) 863733.*

Travelodge, RM16 3BG, ☎ (01708) 865487, *Fax (01708) 860971* – |‡|, ⇔ rm, TV ♿ P. MC AE ⊙ VISA JCB. ✈
Meals (grill rest.) – **48 rm** 59.95 **t.**

BSHELF SERVICE AREA *Derbs.* – ✉ *Derby.*

Travel Inn without rest., DE55 5TZ, M 1 between junctions 28 and 29 (northbound carriageway) ☎ (01773) 876607, *Fax (01773) 876609* – ⇔ TV ♿ P – 🏛 30. MC AE ⊙ VISA. ✈
40 rm 41.95 **t.**

When travelling for business or pleasure
in **England, Wales, Scotland** *and* **Ireland***:*
- use the series of five maps
(nos 401, 402, 403, 404 and 923) at a scale of 1:400 000
- they are the perfect complement to this Guide

TICEHURST *E. Sussex* 404 V 30 – *pop. 3 118* – ✉ *Wadhurst.*
Dale Hill (01580) 200112.
London 49 – Brighton 44 – Folkestone 38 – Hastings 15 – Maidstone 24.

Dale Hill, TN5 7DQ, Northeast : ½ m. on B 2087 (01580) 200112, *info@dalehill.co.*
Fax (01580) 201249, – 30. VISA JCB
Meals (restricted lunch)/dinner 18.00 and a la carte 19.85/32.85 **t.** 11.25 – **31 r**
70.00/80.00 **t.**, 1 suite.

King John's Lodge, Sheepstreet Lane, Etchingham, TN19 7AZ, South : 2 m.
Church St (01580) 819232, *Fax (01580) 819562*, « Part Tudor hunting lodge w
Jacobean additions, gardens », heated, – rm,
closed Christmas and New Year – **Meals** (by arrangement) (communal dining) 25.00 **st**
4 rm 55.00/80.00 **st.**

TINTAGEL *Cornwall* 403 F 32 *The West Country G.* – *pop. 1 721.*
See : *Arthur's Castle (site★★★) AC – Church★ – Old Post Office★ AC.*
Env. : *Boscastle★, E : off B 3263 – W : Hell's Mouth★.*
Exc. : *Camelford★, SE : 6½ m. by B 3263 and B 3266.*
London 264 – Exeter 63 – Plymouth 49 – Truro 41.

Trebrea Lodge, Trenale, PL34 0HR, Southeast : 1 ¼ m. by Boscastle Rd (B 3263) a
Trenale Lane on Trewarmett rd (01840) 770410, *Fax (01840) 770092*, « Part 18C mar
house, 14C origins », – VISA
closed January – **Meals** (booking essential to non-residents) (dinner only) (set menu or
24.50 **t.** 9.75 – **7 rm** 63.50/98.00 **t.** – SB.

Polkerr without rest., Molesworth St, PL34 0BY, (01840) 770382, –
7 rm 25.00/50.00 **s.**

Old Borough House, Bossiney, PL34 0AY, Northeast : ½ m. on B 32
(01840) 770475, *oldboroughhouse@hotmail.com, Fax (01840) 779000* –
VISA.
Meals (by arrangement) 22.00 **st.** 10.00 – **4 rm** 35.00/80.00 **st.**

TITLEY *Herefordshire* 403 L 27 – *see Kington.*

TIVERTON *Devon* 403 J 31 – *pop. 17 213.*
London 191 – Bristol 64 – Exeter 15 – Plymouth 63.

Hornhill Farmhouse, Exeter Hill, EX16 4PL, East : ½ m. by A 361 and Butterleigh
(01884) 253352, *hornhill@tinyworld.co.uk, Fax (01884) 253352*, « Part 17C »,
VISA
Meals (by arrangement) (communal dining) 15.00 – **3 rm** 25.00/46.00 **s.**

TODDINGTON SERVICE AREA *Beds.* 404 S 28 – *pop. 4 500* – ✉ *Luton.*
Chalgrave Manor, Dunstable Rd, Toddington (01525) 876556.

Travelodge, LU5 6HR, M 1 (southbound carriageway) (01525) 8784
Fax (01525) 878452 – rm, VISA JCB.
Meals (grill rest.) – **66 rm** 59.95 **t.**

TODMORDEN *W. Yorks.* 402 N 22.
London 217 – Burnley 10 – Leeds 35 – Manchester 22.

Scaitcliffe Hall, Burnley Rd, OL14 7DQ, Northwest : 1 m. on A 646 (01706) 8188
enquiries@scaitcliffehall.com, Fax (01706) 818825, – – 30. VISA.
Meals (bar lunch)/dinner a la carte 20.00/25.75 **st.** 8.50 – **28 rm** 45.00/84.00 **t.**

TOPCLIFFE *N. Yorks.* 402 P 21 – *see Thirsk.*

TOPSHAM *Devon* 403 J 31 – *pop. 4 155.*
London 182 – Bristol 75 – Exeter 5 – Plymouth 47.

No 5 The Garden Café and Gallery, 6-7 Fore St, EX3 0HF, (01392) 8778
Fax (01392) 879048, – VISA
closed Sunday dinner and Monday – **Meals** 11.95/19.95 and a la carte 18.85/30.15
10.50.

ORQUAY *Torbay* 403 J 32 *The West Country G. – pop. 59 587.*

See : *Torbay*★ – *Kent's Cavern*★ *AC* **CX A.**

Env. : *Paignton Zoo*★★ *AC, SE : 3 m. by A 3022 – Cockington*★, *W : 1 m.* **AX.**

18 *Petitor Rd, St. Marychurch* ☎ *(01803) 327471,* **B.**

Vaughan Par. ☎ *(01803) 297428.*

London 223 – Exeter 23 – Plymouth 32.

Plans on following pages

Imperial, Parkhill Rd, TQ1 2DG, ☎ (01803) 294301, *imperialtorquay@paramount-hotels.co.uk, Fax (01803) 298293,* ≤ Torbay, squash – rest, – 350. VISA. — **CZ a**
Regatta : **Meals** (dinner only) 25.00 and a la carte approx. 40.00 **st.** 12.95 – ***TQ1 :*** **Meals** a la carte 19.00/36.00 **st.** 12.95 – 9.50 – **136 rm** 140.00/250.00 **t.**, 17 suites – SB.

Palace, Babbacombe Rd, TQ1 3TG, ☎ (01803) 200200, *info@palacetorquay.co.uk, Fax (01803) 299899,* ≤, « Extensive gardens », heated, 9, indoor/outdoor, squash – rest, – 350. VISA. — **CX u**
Meals 25.00 (dinner) and a la carte 26.50/37.00 **st.** 12.50 – **135 rm** 71.00/196.00 **st.**, 6 suites – SB.

Grand, Sea Front, TQ2 6NT, ☎ (01803) 296677, *grandhotel@netsite.co.uk, Fax (01803) 213462,* ≤, heated, – rest, – 300. VISA JCB — **BZ z**
Meals (bar lunch Monday to Saturday)/dinner and a la carte approx. 25.00 **t.** 12.50 – **99 rm** 65.00/190.00 **t.**, 11 suites – SB.

Osborne, Hesketh Cres, Meadfoot, TQ1 2LL, ☎ (01803) 213311, *enq@osborne-torquay.co.uk, Fax (01803) 296788,* ≤, « Regency town houses », heated, – rest, – 80. VISA. — **CX n**
Langtry's : **Meals** (dinner only) 22.00 and a la carte 24.00/31.00 **st.** 11.95 – ***The Brasserie :*** **Meals** a la carte 12.30/18.80 **st.** 11.95 – **29 rm** 70.00/210.00 **st.** – SB.

Livermead Cliff, Seafront, TQ2 6RQ, ☎ (01803) 299666, *enquiries@livermeadcliff.co.uk, Fax (01803) 294496,* ≤, heated, – rest, – 70. VISA. — **BX r**
Meals 9.95/17.95 and a la carte 16.95/24.85 **st.** 9.75 – **64 rm** 59.00/129.00 **st.** – SB.

Albaston House, 27 St Marychurch Rd, TQ1 3JF, ☎ (01803) 296758, *Fax (01803) 211509* – VISA JCB — **CY a**
closed 1 week Christmas – **Meals** (dinner only) 12.00/15.00 **st.** 7.00 – **13 rm** 34.00/70.00 – SB.

Fairmount House, Herbert Rd, Chelston, TQ2 6RW, ☎ (01803) 605446, *Fax (01803) 605446,* – rest, VISA JCB — **AX a**
Meals (residents only) (bar lunch)/dinner 10.00 5.50 – **8 rm** 33.00/66.00 **st.**

Cranborne, 58 Belgrave Rd, TQ2 5HY, ☎ (01803) 298046, *Fax (01803) 215477* – rest, VISA. — **BY i**
closed October and November **Meals** (by arrangement) 12.50 **st.** 7.00 – **11 rm** 40.00/60.00.

Belmont without rest., 66 Belgrave Rd, TQ2 5HY, ☎ (01803) 295028, *belmont@fsbdial.co.uk, Fax (01803) 211668* – rest, VISA JCB — **BY i**
13 rm 16.00/50.00.

Glenorleigh, 26 Cleveland Rd, TQ2 5BE, ☎ (01803) 292135, *glenorleighhotel@btinternet.com, Fax (01803) 213717,* heated, – VISA. — **BY n**
Meals 12.00 – **16 rm** 34.00/68.00 **st.** – SB.

Cedar Court, 3 St Matthews Rd, Chelston, TQ2 6JA, ☎ (01803) 607851 – — **BY a**
closed 20 January-8 February **Meals** (by arrangement) 11.00 – **8 rm** 28.00/56.00 **s.** – SB.

Remy's, 3 Croft Rd, TQ2 5UF, ☎ (01803) 292359, *gonescah@madasafish.com* – . VISA — **CY x**
closed 25-26 December, Sunday and Monday – **Meals** - French - (booking essential) (lunch by arrangement)/dinner 18.75/27.75 **t.** 9.00.

Mulberry House with rm, 1 Scarborough Rd, TQ2 5UJ, ☎ (01803) 213639 – . — **CY x**
Meals *(closed lunch Monday-Thursday)* (booking essential) (residents by arrangement Sunday-Tuesday dinner) a la carte 15.50/22.50 **st.** 10.00 – **3 rm** 35.00/55.00 **st.**

Maidencombe *North : 3½ m. by B 3199* – **BX** – ✉ *Torquay.*

Orestone Manor, Rockhouse Lane, TQ1 4SX, ☎ (01803) 328098, *enquiries@orestone.co.uk, Fax (01803) 328336,* ≤, heated, – rest, VISA
Meals 30.00 (dinner) and lunch a la carte 16.50/26.95 **st.** 11.50 – **12 rm** 50.00/160.00 **st.** – SB.

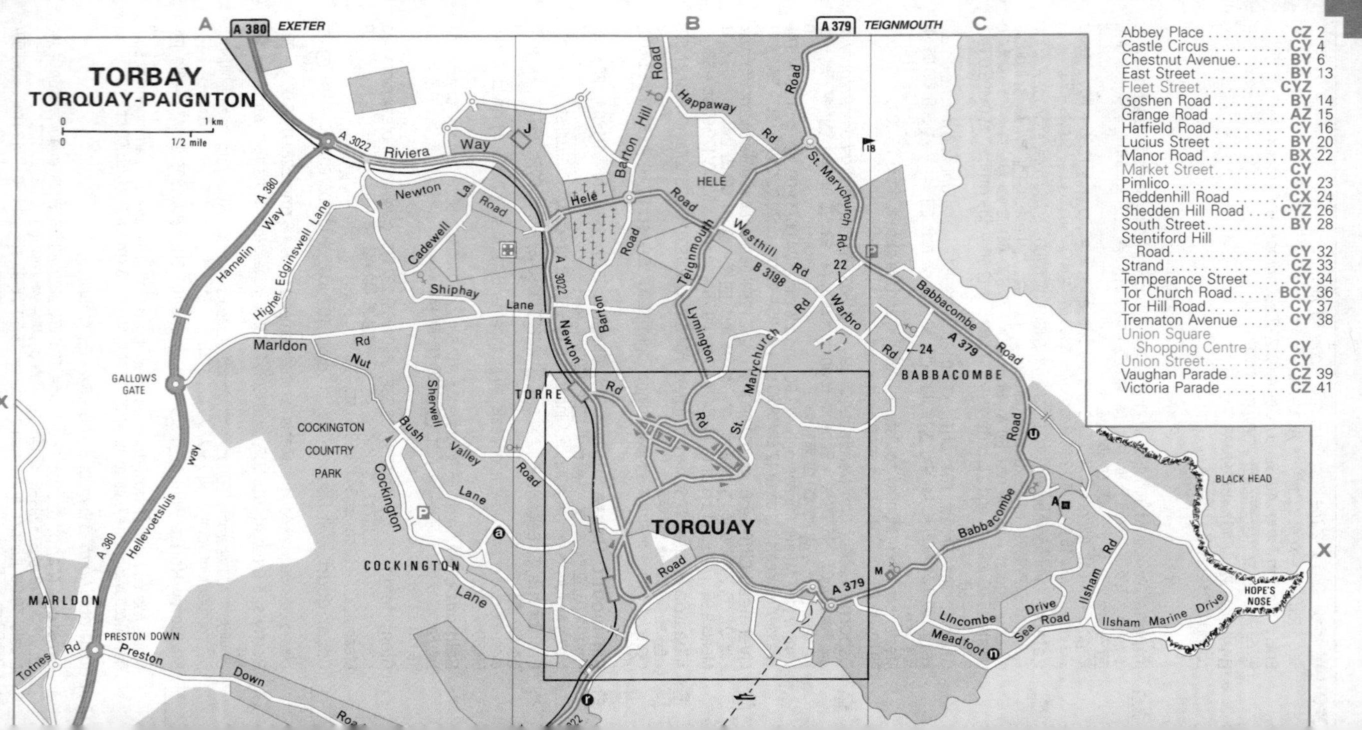
TORBAY
TORQUAY-PAIGNTON
0 1 km
0 1/2 mile
A
B
C
X
X
A 380 EXETER
A 379 TEIGNMOUTH
Abbey Place . . . . CZ 2
Castle Circus . . . . CY 4
Chestnut Avenue . . . . BY 6
East Street . . . . BY 13
Fleet Street . . . . CYZ
Goshen Road . . . . BY 14
Grange Road . . . . AZ 15
Hatfield Road . . . . CY 16
Lucius Street . . . . BY 20
Manor Road . . . . BX 22
Market Street . . . . CY
Pimlico . . . . CY 23
Reddenhill Road . . . . CX 24
Shedden Hill Road . . . . CYZ 26
South Street . . . . BY 28
Stentiford Hill Road . . . . CY 32
Strand . . . . CZ 33
Temperance Street . . . . . CY 34
Tor Church Road . . . . . BCY 36
Tor Hill Road . . . . CY 37
Trematon Avenue . . . . . . CY 38
Union Square Shopping Centre . . . . . CY
Union Street . . . . CY
Vaughan Parade . . . . CZ 39
Victoria Parade . . . . CZ 41
A 3022
Riviera Way
A 380
Hamelin Way
Higher Edginswell Lane
Newton La
Road
Cadewell
Shiphay
Lane
Hele
Barton Hill Road
Happaway Rd
HELE
Road
Westhill Rd
B 3198
Teignmouth
St. Marychurch Rd.
22
Warbro Rd
24
Babbacombe Road
A 379
BABBACOMBE
Lymington
Barton Road
Newton Rd
St. Marychurch Rd
Marldon Rd
Nut
GALLOWS GATE
TORRE
COCKINGTON COUNTRY PARK
Bush
Sherwell Valley Road
Lane
Cockington
COCKINGTON
Lane
TORQUAY
Road
A 379
M
Babbacombe
Road
A
BLACK HEAD
HOPE'S NOSE
Ilsham Rd
Ilsham Marine Drive
Lincombe Drive
Sea Road
Meadfoot
Hellevoetsluis Way
A 380
MARLDON
PRESTON DOWN
Preston Down Road
Totnes Rd

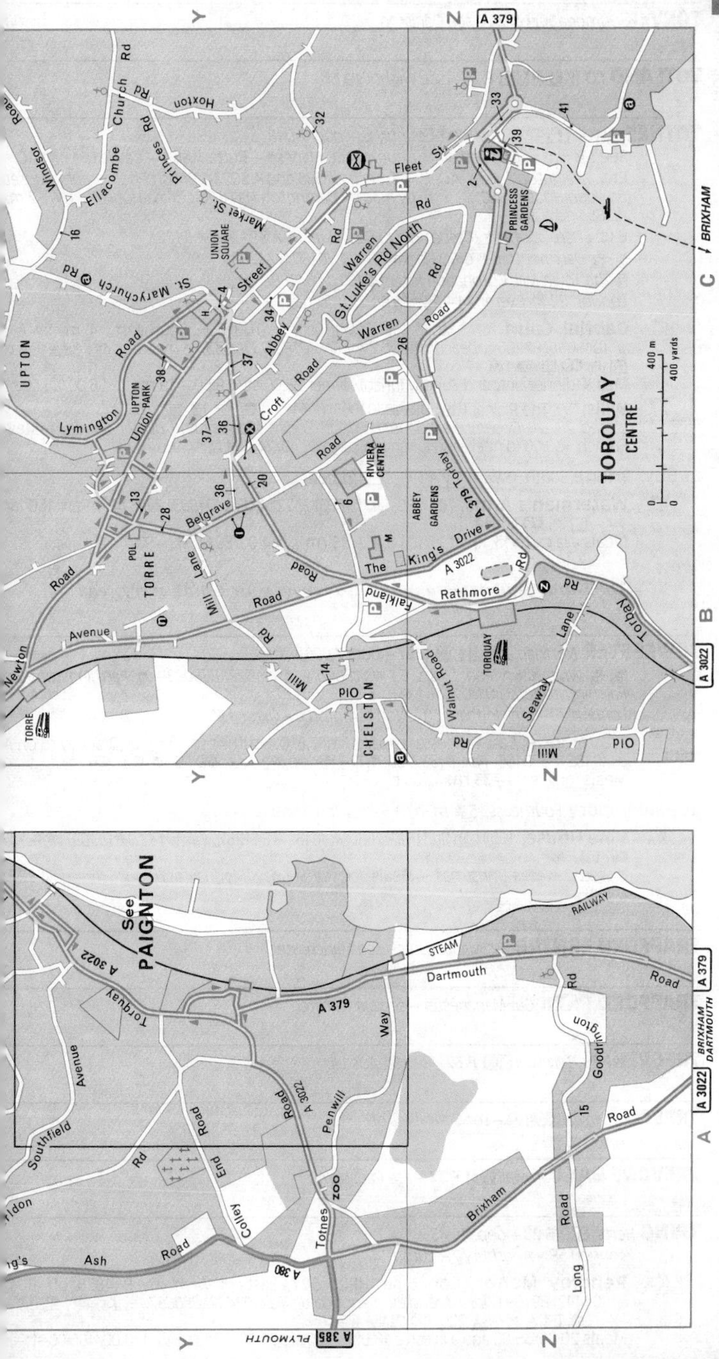

TORQUAY
CENTRE

0 400 m
0 400 yards

UPTON
TORRE
CHELSTON
UPTON PARK
UNION SQUARE
RIVIERA CENTRE
ABBEY GARDENS
PRINCESS GARDENS
POL

Windsor Road
Ellacombe Church Rd
Princes Rd
Hoxton
St. Marychurch Rd
Market St.
Union Street
Lymington Road
Fleet St
Warren Rd
St.Luke's Rd North
Abbey Road
Croft Road
Belgrave Road
Newton Road
Avenue Road
Mill Lane
Falkland Road
The King's Drive
A 379 Torbay Road
A 3022 Rathmore Rd
Torbay Rd
Lane
Walnut Road
Seaway
Old Mill Rd
Old Mill Rd

A 379
A 3022
BRIXHAM
TORQUAY
TORRE

See
PAIGNTON

Southfield Avenue
A 3022 Torquay
A 379
STEAM RAILWAY
Dartmouth Road
Goodrington Rd
Way
Penwill
A 3022 Road
Colley End Road
Rd
ZOO
Totnes
Brixham Road
Long Road
A 380
Ash Road
A 385 PLYMOUTH
A 3022
BRIXHAM DARTMOUTH
A 379

Y Z A B C

TORVER *Cumbria* 402 K 20 – *see Coniston.*

TOTLAND *I.O.W.* 403 404 P 31 – *see Wight (Isle of).*

TOTNES *Devon* 403 I 32 *The West Country G. – pop. 7 018.*

See : *Town★ – Elizabethan Museum★ – St. Mary's★ – Butterwalk★ – Castle (≤★★★) AC.*
Env. : *Paignton Zoo★★ AC, E : 4½ m. by A 385 and A 3022 – British Photographic Museu Bowden House★ AC, S : 1 m. by A 381 – Dartington Hall (High Cross House★), NW : 2 m. A 385 and A 384.*
Exc. : *Dartmouth★★ (Castle ≤★★★) SE : 12 m. by A 381 and A 3122.*
18, 9 *Dartmouth G & C.C., Blackawton ℘ (01803) 712686.*
The Town Mill, Coronation Rd ℘ (01803) 863168.
London 224 – Exeter 24 – Plymouth 23 – Torquay 9.

Gabriel Court ⛰, Stoke Hill, Stoke Gabriel, TQ9 6SF, Southeast : 4 m. by A 3 ℘ (01803) 782206, *obeacom@aol.com, Fax (01803) 782333,* heated, – re TV P. MC AE ① VISA
Meals (dinner only and Sunday lunch)/dinner 28.00 **st.** 9.50 – **19 rm** 56.00/86.00 **st.**

Wills, 2/3 The Plains, TQ9 5DR, ℘ (01803) 865192 – MC AE ① VISA JCB
closed 25, 26 December, 1 January, good Friday, Monday and dinner Sunday – **Meal** French - 30.00 (dinner) and lunch a la carte 15.40/24.40 **t.** 14.00.

at Bow Bridge *South : 3½ m. by A 381 – ✉ Totnes.*

Waterman's Arms, TQ9 7EG, ℘ (01803) 732214, *Fax (01803) 732314,* « Part 15C inn – TV P. MC AE VISA
Meals a la carte 13.15/21.25 **t.** 8.95 – **15 rm** 64.00/89.00 **st.** – SB.

The Guide is updated annually so renew your Guide every year.

TOWCESTER *Northants.* 403 404 R 27 – *pop. 7 006.*

18, 18 *Whittelbury Park G. & C.C., Whittlebury ℘ (01327) 858092 – 18 Farthingstone Ho Farthingstone ℘ (01327) 361291.*
London 70 – Birmingham 50 – Northampton 9 – Oxford 36.

Travelodge, East Towcester bypass, NN12 6TQ, Southwest : ½ m. by Brackley rd on A ℘ (01327) 359105, *Fax (01327) 359105* – rm, TV ♿ P. MC AE ① VISA JCB.
Meals (grill rest.) – **33 rm** 42.95 **t.**

at Paulerspury *Southeast : 3¼ m. by A 5 – ✉ Towcester.*

Vine House, 100 High St, NN12 7NA, ℘ (01327) 811267, *Fax (01327) 811309,* – MC VISA.
closed 2 weeks Christmas – **Meals** *(closed Sunday, Monday and lunch Tuesday)* 28.5 11.95.

TRAFFORD CENTRE *Gtr. Manchester – see Manchester.*

TRAFFORD PARK *Gtr. Manchester – see Manchester.*

TREGREHAN *Cornwall* 403 F 32 – *see St. Austell.*

TRESCO *Cornwall* 403 ㉚ – *see Scilly (Isles of).*

TREVONE BAY *Cornwall* 403 F 32 – *see Padstow.*

TRING *Herts.* 404 S 28 – *pop. 11 455.*

London 38 – Aylesbury 7 – Luton 14.

Pendley Manor, Cow Lane, HP23 5QY, East : 1 ½ m. by B 4635 off B 4 ℘ (01442) 891891, *info@pendley-manor.co.uk, Fax (01442) 890687,* ≤, – rest, TV ♿ P – 220. MC AE ① VISA JCB
Meals 20.00/35.00 and a la carte 18.00/35.00 **st.** 7.00 – **74 rm** 110.00/160.00 **st.** –

Rose and Crown, High St, HP23 5AH, ☎ (01442) 824071, *Fax (01442) 890735* – ⇔ rest, TV P – 60. MC AE D VISA
Meals (dinner only and Sunday lunch)/dinner 19.95 **t.** 11.50 – **27 rm** 95.00/105.00 **t.** – SB.

Travel Inn, Tring Hill, HP23 4LD, West : 1 ½ m. on A 41 ☎ (01442) 824819, *Fax (01442) 890787* – ⇔ rm, ≡ rest, TV & P. MC AE D VISA. ※
Meals (grill rest.) – **30 rm** 41.95 **t.**

TRINITY *Jersey (Channel Islands)* 403 P 33 and 230 ⑪ – *see Channel Islands.*

TROTTON *W. Sussex – see Midhurst.*

TROUTBECK *Cumbria* 402 L 20 – *see Windermere.*

TROWBRIDGE *Wilts.* 403 404 N 30 *The West Country G. – pop. 25 279.*

Env. : *Westwood Manor★, NW : 3 m. by A 363 – Farleigh Hungerford★ (St. Leonard's Chapel★) AC, W : 4 m.*

Exc. : *Longleat House★★★ AC, SW : 12 m. by A 363, A 350 and A 362 - Bratton Castle (≤★★) SE : 7½ m. by A 363 and B 3098 – Steeple Ashton★ (The Green★) E : 6 m. – Edington (St. Mary, St. Katherine and All Saints★) SE : 7½ m.*

St. Stephen's Pl. ☎ (01225) 777054.

London 115 – Bristol 27 – Southampton 55 – Swindon 32.

Old Manor, Trowle, BA14 9BL, Northwest : 1 m. on A 363 ☎ (01225) 777393, *olderbeams @oldmanorhotel.com, Fax (01225) 765443,* « Queen Anne house of 15C origins », – ⇔ TV & P. MC AE D VISA JCB. ※
closed 4 days Christmas – **Meals** *(closed Sunday and Bank Holiday Mondays)* (residents only) (dinner only) 17.00 and a la carte 10.70/17.70 **st.** 6.95 – **18 rm** 49.50/125.00 **t.**

Welam House without rest., Bratton Rd, West Ashton, BA14 6AZ, Southeast : 2 m. by A 361 on West Ashton Rd ☎ (01225) 755908, – ⇔ P. ※
April-October – **3 rm** 36.00.

Holt *North : 3¼ m. by B 3106 off B 3105 – ✉ Trowbridge.*

Tollgate Inn, Ham Green, BA14 6PX, ☎ (01225) 782326, *Fax (01225) 782805* – ⇔ P. MC VISA
Meals (booking essential) 11.50 (lunch) and a la carte 17.50/26.85 10.50.

Semington *Northeast : 2½ m. by A 361 – ✉ Trowbridge.*

Lamb on the Strand, 99 The Strand, BA14 6LL, East : 1 ½ m. on A 361 ☎ (01380) 870263, *Fax (01380) 871203,* – P. MC AE VISA
closed 25 December, 1 January and Sunday dinner – **Meals** a la carte 15.75/19.00 **st.** 10.75.

TROWELL SERVICE AREA *Notts.* 404 Q 25 – ✉ *Ilkeston.*

Travelodge, NG9 3PL, at junction 25/6 on M 1 (northbound carriageway) ☎ (0115) 932 0291, *Fax (0115) 930 7261* – ⇔ TV & P. MC AE D VISA JCB. ※
Meals (grill rest.) – **35 rm** 49.95 **t.**

TRURO *Cornwall* 403 E 33 *The West Country G. – pop. 16 522.*

See : *Royal Cornwall Museum★★ AC.*

Env. : *Trelissick Garden★★ (≤★★) AC, S : 4 m. by A 39 – Feock (Church★) S : 5 m. by A 39 and B 3289.*

Exc. : *Trewithen★★★, NE : 7½ m. by A 39 and A 390 – Probus★ (tower★ - garden★) NE : 9 m. by A 39 and A 390.*

18 Treliske ☎ (01872) 272640 – 18 Killiow Park, Killiow, Kea ☎ (01872) 270246.

Municipal Buildings, Boscawen St. ☎ (01872) 274555.

London 295 – Exeter 87 – Penzance 26 – Plymouth 52.

Alverton Manor, Tregolls Rd, TR1 1ZQ, ☎ (01872) 276633, *reception@alvertonmanor.demon.co.uk, Fax (01872) 222989,* « Mid 19C manor house, former Bishop's residence and convent », – |‡|, ⇔ rest, TV P – 200. MC VISA JCB
Meals 20.00/23.50 and dinner a la carte **t.** 12.50 – **30 rm** 72.00/165.00 **t.**, 4 suites – SB.

Royal, Lemon St, TR1 2QB, ☎ (01872) 270345, *reception@royalhotelcornwall.co.uk, Fax (01872) 242453* – ⇔ rm, TV P. MC AE D VISA JCB. ※
closed 25 and 26 December – **Meals** *(closed Sunday lunch)* (grill rest.) a la carte 19.00/32.00 **t.** 10.50 – 5.50 – **35 rm** 59.00/85.00 **t.**

at Carnon Downs *Southwest : 3¼ m. by A 39 – ✉ Truro.*

Travel Inn, Old Carnon Hill, TR3 6JT, ☎ (01872) 863370, *Fax (01872) 865620,* – rest, .
Meals (grill rest.) – **40 rm** 41.95 **t.**

at Blackwater *West : 7 m. by A 390 – ✉ Truro.*

Rock Cottage without rest., TR4 8EU, ☎ (01872) 560252, *rockcottage@yahoo.co* *Fax (01872) 560252* – .
closed Christmas and New Year – **3 rm** 26.00/44.00 **s.**

TUNBRIDGE WELLS *Kent* 404 U 30 – *see Royal Tunbridge Wells.*

TURNERS HILL *W. Sussex* 404 T 30 – *pop. 1 534.*
London 33 – Brighton 24 – Crawley 7.

Alexander House, East St, RH10 4QD, East : 1 m. on B 2110 ☎ (01342) 714914, *i @alexanderhouse.co.uk, Fax (01342) 717328,* ≤, « Part 17C country house in extens parkland », – rest, – 60. .
Meals *(closed Saturday lunch)* 21.50/34.00 and a la carte 34.00/48.00 **t.** 16.80 – 9 135.00/165.00 **t.**, 6 suites – SB.

Si vous cherchez un hôtel tranquille,
consultez d'abord les cartes de l'introduction
ou repérez dans le texte les établissements indiqués avec le signe ou

---

TURVILLE *Bucks. – ✉ Henley-on-Thames.*
London 45 – Oxford 22 – Reading 17.

Bull & Butcher, RG9 6QU, ☎ (01491) 638283, *nick@bullandbutcher.com,* –
Meals a la carte 19.85/28.85 **t.** 13.95.

TUTBURY *Staffs.* 402 403 404 O 25 *Great Britain G. – pop. 5 646 (inc. Hatton) – ✉ Burton-up Trent.*
Env. : *Sudbury Hall★★ AC, NW : 5½ m. by A 50.*
London 132 – Birmingham 33 – Derby 11 – Stoke-on-Trent 27.

Ye Olde Dog and Partridge, High St, DE13 9LS, ☎ (01283) 813030, *info@dogandpa dge.net, Fax (01283) 813178,* « Part 15C timbered inn », – rm, rest,
Meals (carvery rest.) 13.50/15.00 **st.** 9.95 – (see also ***Brasserie at The Dog*** below **20 rm** 55.00/99.00 **st.** – SB.

Brasserie at The Dog (at Ye Olde Dog and Partridge H.), High St, DE13 9 ☎ (01283) 813030, *Fax (01283) 813178* –
closed Sunday dinner and Monday – **Meals** a la carte 18.50/27.15 **st.** 13.50.

TWO BRIDGES *Devon* 403 I 32 *The West Country G. – ✉ Yelverton.*
Env. : *Dartmoor National Park★★.*
London 226 – Exeter 25 – Plymouth 17.

Prince Hall, PL20 6SA, East : 1 m. on B 3357 ☎ (01822) 890403, *bookings@princel co.uk, Fax (01822) 890676,* ≤, – rest,
closed mid December-12 February – **Meals** (booking essential to non-residents) (din only) 29.00 **st.** 10.80 – **8 rm** (dinner included) 90.00/170.00 **st.** – SB.

TYNEMOUTH *Tyne and Wear* 401 402 P 18 – *pop. 17 422.*
London 290 – Newcastle upon Tyne 8 – Sunderland 7.

Grand, Grand Par, NE30 4ER, ☎ (0191) 293 6666, *info@grand-hotel.demon.co Fax (0191) 293 6665,* ≤, « Victorian mansion » – – 130. .
Meals 12.75/16.75 and a la carte approx. 21.25 **t.** – **45 rm** 75.00/150.00 **t.**

Sidney's, 3-5 Percy Park Rd, NE30 4LZ, ☎ (0191) 257 8500, *bookings@sidneys.co Fax (0191) 257 9800* –
closed dinner Sunday and Bank Holidays except Good Friday – **Meals** (booking essen 10.95 (lunch) and a la carte 15.70/22.85 **t.** 9.95.

ENGLAND

CKFIELD *E. Sussex* 404 U 31 – *pop. 13 531.*
London 45 – Brighton 17 – Eastbourne 20 – Maidstone 34.

Horsted Place, Little Horsted, TN22 5TS, South : 2 ½ m. by B 2102 and A 22 on A 26 (01825) 750581, *hotel@horstedplace.co.uk, Fax (01825) 750459*, « Victorian Gothic country house and gardens », – rest, – 80. VISA.
Meals 14.95/32.00 and a la carte 31.00/45.00 **st.** 16.50 – **15 rm** 110.00/245.00 **st.**, 5 suites – SB.

Hooke Hall without rest., 250 High St, TN22 1EN, (01825) 761578, *Fax (01825) 768025*, « Queen Anne town house », – VISA
closed 24 December-2 January – 7.50 – **10 rm** 50.00/120.00 **st.**

FFINGTON *Oxon.* 403 404 P 29.
London 75 – Oxford 29 – Reading 32 – Swindon 17.

Craven, Fernham Rd, SN7 7RD, (01367) 820449, « 17C thatched house », – VISA.
Meals (by arrangement) (communal dining) 18.00 7.50 – **6 rm** 25.00/80.00 – SB.

GGESHALL *Suffolk – see Southwold.*

LLINGSWICK *Herefordshire* 403 404 M 27 – *pop. 237* – Hereford.
London 134 – Hereford 12 – Shrewsbury 52 – Worcester 19.

Steppes Country House, HR1 3JG, (01432) 820424, *bookings@steppeshotel.fsbusiness.co.uk, Fax (01432) 820042*, « Converted farmhouse of 14C origins », – VISA JCB
closed December and January – **Meals** (dinner only) (residents only) 27.00 **st.** 8.50 – **6 rm** 45.00/90.00 **st.** – SB.

LLSWATER *Cumbria* 402 L 20 – *pop. 1 199* – Penrith.
Main Car Park, Glenridding, Penrith (017684) 82414.
London 296 – Carlisle 25 – Kendal 31 – Penrith 6.

Pooley Bridge *on B 5320* – *Penrith.*

Sharrow Bay Country House, CA10 2LZ, South : 2 m. on Howtown rd (017684) 86301, *enquiries@sharrow-bay.com, Fax (017684) 86349*, Ullswater and fells, « Victorian country house on the shores of Lake Ullswater, gardens », –, rest, VISA JCB.
March-early December – **Meals** (booking essential) 30.00/47.25 **st.** 29.00 – **21 rm** (dinner included) 140.00/210.00 **st.**, 5 suites
Spec. Foie gras with apples and grapes, peach chutney. Noisette of local venison, rosemary and juniper sauce. Aniseed parfait with blackberry compote.

Watermillock *on A 592* – *Penrith.*

Leeming House, CA11 0JJ, on A 592 (017684) 86622, *Fax (017684) 86443*, « Lakeside country house and gardens », – – 35. VISA JCB.
Regency : **Meals** 13.95/29.50 and dinner a la carte 13.70/24.85 **t.** 14.50 – 14.00 – **40 rm** 90.00/160.00 **t.** – SB.

Rampsbeck Country House, CA11 0LP, (017684) 86442, *enquiries@rampsbeck.fsnet.co.uk, Fax (017684) 86688*, Ullswater and fells, « Lakeside setting », – VISA JCB
closed early January-mid February – **Meals** – (see ***The Restaurant*** below) – **19 rm** 60.00/150.00 **t.**, 1 suite – SB.

Old Church, CA11 0JN, (017684) 86204, *info@oldchurch.co.uk, Fax (017684) 86368*, Ullswater and fells, « Georgian country house on the shores of Lake Ullswater », –, rest, VISA.
March-November – **Meals** *(closed Sunday)* (booking essential) (dinner only) 25.00 and a la carte 23.00/27.00 **st.** 12.50 – **10 rm** 65.00/155.00 **st.** – SB.

The Restaurant (at Rampsbeck Country House H.), CA11 0LP, (017684) 86442, *Fax (017684) 86688*, Ullswater and fells, « Lakeside setting », – VISA JCB
closed early January-mid February – **Meals** (booking essential) (lunch by arrangement Monday to Saturday)/dinner 30.00/41.00 **t.** 11.95.

Brackenrigg Inn with rm, CA11 0LP, (017684) 86206, *enquiries@brackenrigginn.co.uk, Fax (017684) 86945*, – rest, VISA JCB.
Meals 10.00/19.00 and a la carte 15.50/24.20 **st.** 8.50 – **11 rm** 37.00/64.00 **st.**

at Glenridding *on A 592 – ✉ Penrith.*

The Inn on the Lake, CA11 0PE, ✆ (017684) 82444, *info@innonthelakeullswater.co. Fax (017684) 82303,* ≤ Ullswater and fells, « Lakeside setting », – rest, 50. MC AE VISA
Meals (dinner only and Sunday lunch) 12.95/24.95 **t.** 9.50 – **46 rm** 55.00/130.00 t
SB.

ULVERSTON *Cumbria* 402 K 21 – *pop. 11 866.*
Coronation Hall, County Sq. ✆ (01229) 587120.
London 278 – Kendal 25 – Lancaster 36.

Trinity House without rest., 1 Princes St, LA12 7NB, off A 590 ✆ (01229) 588889, *trir househotel@fitness.co.uk, Fax (01229) 588552* – TV P. MC AE VISA
6 rm 49.00/69.00 **st.**

Church Walk House without rest., Church Walk, LA12 7EW, ✆ (01229) 582211, *chu walk@m.chadderton.freeserve.co.uk* –
closed Christmas-New Year – **3 rm** 25.00/50.00 **st.**

Bay Horse with rm, Canal Foot, LA12 9EL, East : 2 ¼ m. by A 5087, turning left Morecambe Tavern B&B and beyond Industrial area, on the coast ✆ (01229) 5839 *reservations@bayhorsehotel.co.uk, Fax (01229) 580502,* ≤ Morecambe bay – rest, P. MC VISA
Meals (booking essential) (bar lunch Sunday and Monday) 17.75 (lunch) and a la carte 26.7 32.65 **t.** 15.00 – **9 rm** (dinner included) 90.00/170.00 **t.** – SB.

UMBERLEIGH *Devon* 403 I 31.
London 218 – Barnstaple 7 – Exeter 31 – Taunton 49.

Rising Sun Inn, EX37 9DU, on A 377 ✆ (01769) 560447, *risingsuninn@btinternet.cc Fax (01769) 560764* – TV P – 50. MC VISA.
closed 25 December – **Meals** a la carte 14.40/24.40 **t.** 8.95 – **9 rm** 40.00/77.00 **st.** –

UP HOLLAND *Lancs.* 402 M 23 – *see Wigan.*

UPPER HARBLEDOWN SERVICE AREA *Kent – see Canterbury.*

UPPER ODDINGTON *Glos. – see Stow-on-the-Wold.*

UPPER QUINTON *Warks. – ✉ Stratford-upon-Avon.*
London 95 – Cheltenham 24 – Oxford 43 – Stratford-upon-Avon 6.

Winton House without rest., The Green, CV37 8SX, ✆ (01789) 720500, *gail@wint house.com,* « Victorian farmhouse », – P.
3 rm 60.00 **st.**

UPPER SLAUGHTER *Glos.* 403 404 O 28 – *see Bourton-on-the-Water.*

UPPINGHAM *Rutland* 404 R 26 – *pop. 3 140.*
London 101 – Leicester 19 – Northampton 28 – Nottingham 35.

Rutland House without rest., 61 High St East, LE15 9PY, ✆ (01572) 822497, *rutla house@virgin.net, Fax (01572) 820065* – TV P. MC VISA
5 rm 35.00/45.00 **st.**

Lake Isle with rm, 16 High St East, LE15 9PZ, ✆ (01572) 822951, *info@lakeisle.cc Fax (01572) 822951* – rest, TV P. MC AE VISA
Meals *(closed Monday lunch)* 23.50 (dinner) and lunch a la carte 12.25/19.50 **st.** 11.5
10 rm 53.00/74.00 **st.**, 2 suites – SB.

at Morcott Service Area *East : 4 ¼ m. by A 6003 on A 47 – ✉ Uppingham.*

Travelodge, Glaston Rd, LE15 8SA, ✆ (01572) 747719, *Fax (01572) 747719* – rm, TV P. MC AE VISA JCB.
Meals (grill rest.) – **40 rm** 39.95 **t.**

UPTON ST. LEONARDS *Glos. – see Gloucester.*

ENGLAND

PTON-UPON-SEVERN *Worcs.* 403 404 N 27 – *pop. 1 756.*
4 High St. ℘ (01684) 594200.
London 116 – Hereford 25 – Stratford-upon-Avon 29 – Worcester 11.

Welland Court without rest., WR8 0ST, West : 3 ¾ m. by A 4104 ℘ (01684) 594426, *arher@wellandcourt.co.uk, Fax (01684) 594426,* ≤ The Malvern Hills, « Georgian manor house of 13C origins », –
closed 25 December – **3 rm** 45.00/70.00.

Tiltridge Farm without rest., Upper Hook Rd, WR8 0SA, West : 1 ½ m. by A 4104 and Greenfields Rd off Hyde Lane ℘ (01684) 592906, *elgarwine@aol.com, Fax (01684) 594142,* « Part 17C farmhouse, working vineyard », –
closed Christmas-New Year – **3 rm** 30.00/48.00.

Welland Stone *Southwest : 3 ¼ m. by A 4104 – Upton-upon-Severn.*

Bridge House without rest., WR8 0RW, ℘ (01684) 593046, *merrymichael@data.net, Fax (01684) 593046,* ≤, –
closed 25 December and 1 January – **3 rm** 30.00/90.00.

TTOXETER *Staffs.* 402 403 404 O 25 *Great Britain G. – pop. 10 329.*
Env. : *Sudbury Hall★★ AC, E : 5 m. by A 518 and A 50.*
Wood Lane ℘ (01889) 566552 – Manor (Kingstone), Leese Hill ℘ (01889) 563234.
London 145 – Birmingham 33 – Derby 19 – Stafford 13 – Stoke-on-Trent 16.

Travelodge, Ashbourne Rd, ST14 5AA, at junction of A 50 with B 5030 ℘ (01889) 562043, *Fax (01889) 562043* – rm, rest,
Meals (grill rest.) – **32 rm** 52.95 **t.**

Le Grand Londres (GREATER LONDON) est composé de la City et de 32 arrondissements administratifs (Borough) eux-mêmes divisés en quartiers ou en villages ayant conservé leur caractère propre (Area).

LE *Guernsey (Channel Islands)* 403 O/P 33 – *see Channel Islands.*

ZON BAY *Guernsey (Channel Islands)* 403 P 33 and 230 ⑨ – *see Channel Islands.*

NTNOR *I.O.W.* 403 404 Q 32 – *see Wight (Isle of).*

RYAN *Cornwall* 403 F 33 *The West Country G. – pop. 877 – Truro.*
See : *Village★.*
London 291 – St. Austell 13 – Truro 13.

Nare , Carne Beach, TR2 5PF, Southwest : 1 ¼ m. ℘ (01872) 501111, *office@narehotel.co.uk, Fax (01872) 501856,* ≤ Carne Bay, heated,
Meals 13.50/34.00 and a la carte 35.00/50.00 **t.** 13.00 – **34 rm** (dinner included) 158.00/286.00 **t.**, 2 suites.

Crugsillick Manor , TR2 5LJ, West : 1 m. on St. Mawes rd ℘ (01872) 501214, *barstow@adtel.co.uk, Fax (01872) 501228,* « Queen Anne manor house of Elizabethan origins », – rm,
Meals (by arrangement) (communal dining) 25.00/35.00 8.50 – **3 rm** 45.00/98.00 **st.**

Ruan High Lanes *West : 1 ¼ m. on A 3078 – Truro.*

The Hundred House, TR2 5JR, ℘ (01872) 501336, *eccles@hundredhousehotel.co.uk, Fax (01872) 501151,* –
March-October – **Meals** (dinner only) 25.00 **t.** 11.00 – **10 rm** 47.00/94.00 **t.** – SB.

RGINSTOW *Devon* 403 H 31.
London 227 – Bideford 25 – Exeter 41 – Launceston 11 – Plymouth 33.

Percy's with rm, Coombeshead Estate, EX21 5EA, Southwest : 1 ¼ m. on Tower Hill rd ℘ (01409) 211236, *info@percys.co.uk, Fax (01409) 211275,* ≤, –
Meals 32.50 12.00 – **8 rm** 79.50/165.00 **t.** – SB.

WADDESDON *Bucks.* 404 R 28 *Great Britain G. – pop. 1 864 –* ✉ *Aylesbury.*

See : *Chiltern Hills*★.

Env. : *Waddesdon Manor*★★, *S : ½ m. by a 41 and minor rd – Claydon House*★, *N : by min rd.*

London 51 – Aylesbury 5 – Northampton 32 – Oxford 31.

Five Arrows with rm, High St, HP18 0JE, ☎ (01296) 651727, *thefivearrows@netscaj online.co.uk, Fax (01296) 658596,* , « Characterful Waddesdon Estate inn », – [P. VISA.

Meals a la carte 19.60/24.85 **t.** 10.75 – **10 rm** 65.00/95.00 **t.**, 1 suite.

WADDINGTON *Lancs.* 402 M 22 – *see Clitheroe.*

WAKEFIELD *W. Yorks.* 402 P 22 *Great Britain G. – pop. 73 955.*

Env. : *Nostell Priory*★ *AC, SE : 4½ m. by A 638.*

City of Wakefield, Lupset Park, Horbury Rd ☎ (01924) 367442 – 28 Woodthorpe Lar Sandal ☎ (01924) 255104 – Painthorpe House, Painthorpe Lane, Crigglestone ☎ (0192 255083.

Town Hall, Wood St. ☎ (01924) 305000.

London 188 – Leeds 9 – Manchester 38 – Sheffield 23.

Cedar Court, Denby Dale Rd, Calder Grove, WF4 3QZ, Southwest : 3 m. on A 636 junction 39 of M 1 ☎ (01924) 276310, *sales@cedarcourthotels.co.uk, Fax (01924) 28022* – , rm, rest, P – 400. AE VISA

Meals 12.00/18.50 **t.** 10.95 – 10.95 – **146 rm** 99.00 **t.**, 5 suites – SB.

Holiday Inn, Queen's Drive, Ossett, WF5 9BE, West : 2 ½ m. on A 638 ☎ (0870) 400 908 *Fax (01924) 276437,* – , rm, rest, P – 160. AE VISA.

Meals a la carte 14.00/26.00 **st.** 11.25 – 12.95 – **105 rm** 89.00 **st.** – SB.

Travel Inn, Denby Dale Rd, Thornes Park, WF2 8DY, West : ½ m. on A 6 ☎ (01924) 367901, *Fax (01924) 373620,* – rm, rest, P – 60. AE VISA.

Meals (grill rest.) – **42 rm** 41.95 **t.**

Aagrah, 108 Barnsley Rd, Sandal, WF1 5NX, South : 1 ¼ m. on A 61 ☎ (01924) 24222 *Fax (01924) 240562* – P. AE VISA JCB

closed 25 December – **Meals** - Indian (Kashmiri) - (booking essential) (dinner only) a la ca 13.30/17.25 **t.** 9.95.

at Newmillerdam *South : 3½ m. on A 61 –* ✉ *Wakefield.*

St Pierre, Barnsley Rd, WF2 6QG, ☎ (01924) 255596, *enq@hotelstpierre.co. Fax (01924) 252746,* – , , rest, P – 120. AE VISA.

Meals (bar lunch Saturday) 9.95/15.95 and a la carte 19.65/23.65 **st.** 9.95 – 8.50 **52 rm** 73.00/83.00 **st.**, 2 suites – SB.

at Midgley *Southwest : 6¼ m. by A 636 on A 637 –* ✉ *Wakefield.*

Midgley Lodge Motel without rest., Barr Lane, WF4 4JJ, ☎ (01924) 8300 *Fax (01924) 830087,* – P. AE VISA JCB.

closed 24 December-2 January – 5.50 – **25 rm** 38.00/45.00 **t.**

WALBERTON *W. Sussex – see Arundel.*

WALKINGTON *East Riding* 402 S 22 – *see Beverley.*

WALLASEY *Mersey.* 402 403 K 23 – *pop. 15 642 –* ✉ *Wirral.*

Wallasey, Bayswater Rd ☎ (0151) 639 3630.

London 222 – Birkenhead 3 – Liverpool 4.

Grove House, Grove Rd, CH45 3HF, ☎ (0151) 639 3947, *Fax (0151) 639 0028,* rest, P – 100. AE VISA.

Meals *(closed Bank Holidays)* (dinner only) 15.95/16.95 and a la carte 12.65/33.10 **t.** 9.9 5.95 – **14 rm** 54.50 **t.** – SB.

Bitte beachten Sie die Geschwindigkeitsbeschränkungen in Großbritannien
- 60 mph (= 96 km/h) außerhalb geschlossener Ortschaften
- 70 mph (= 112 km/h) auf Straßen mit getrennten Fahrbahnen und Autobahnen.

WALLINGFORD *Oxon.* 403 404 Q 29 *The West Country G. – pop. 9 315.*

Exc. : *Ridgeway Path*★★.

Town Hall, Market Pl. (01491) 826972.

London 54 – Oxford 12 – Reading 16.

George, High St, OX10 0BS, (01491) 836665, *info@george-hotel-wallingford.com, Fax (01491) 825359* – rest, TV P – 140. MC AE VISA

Meals (bar lunch Monday-Saturday)/dinner a la carte 19.45/25.70 **t.** 10.95 – 10.75 – **39 rm** 95.00/125.00.

at North Stoke *South : 2 ¾ m. by A 4130 and A 4074 on B 4009 – Wallingford.*

The Springs, Wallingford Rd, OX10 6BE, (01491) 836687, *info@thespringshotel.co.uk, Fax (01491) 836877*, ≤, « Lakeside setting », , heated, 18, , , – rest, TV P – 70. MC AE VISA.

Meals (carving lunch Sunday) 15.00 (dinner) and a la carte 20.00/34.20 **t.** 14.00 – **29 rm** 90.00/100.00 **t.**, 2 suites – SB.

WALMERSLEY *Gtr. Manchester* 402 ㉒ 403 ③ 404 ⑨ – *see Bury.*

WALSALL *W. Mids.* 403 404 O 26 – *pop. 174 739.*

18 *Calderfields, Aldridge Rd (01922) 632243* **CT** – 18 *Broadway (01922) 613512.*

London 126 – Birmingham 9 – Coventry 29 – Shrewsbury 36.

Plan of enlarged area : see Birmingham pp. 4 and 5

Travel Inn, Bentley Green, Bentley Road North, WS2 0WB, West : 2 ¾ m. by A 454 and Bentley South rd (01922) 724485, *Fax (01922) 724098* – rm, rest, TV & P. MC AE VISA **BT e**

Meals (grill rest.) – **40 rm** 41.95 **t.**

WALTHAM *Kent* 404 X 30 – *pop. 397 – Canterbury.*

London 59 – Canterbury 12 – Folkestone 14 – Maidstone 24.

Beech Bank without rest., Duckpit Lane, CT4 5QA, East : 1 ¾ m. by Church Lane (01227) 700302, *Fax (01227) 700302*, « Converted 15C coach house », – TV P.

closed 1 week Christmas – **3 rm** 35.00/47.00 **st.**

WALTHAM ABBEY *Essex* 404 U 28 – *pop. 15 629.*

4 Highbridge St. (01992) 652295.

London 15 – Cambridge 44 – Ipswich 66 – Luton 30 – Southend-on-Sea 35.

Marriott Waltham Abbey, Old Shire Lane, EN9 3LX, Southeast : 1 ½ m. on A 121 (01992) 717170, *Fax (01992) 711841*, , , – TV & P – 220. MC AE VISA

Meals a la carte 16.00/33.00 **st.** – 12.50 – **162 rm** 119.00 **st.**

WANSFORD *Peterborough* 404 S 26 – *see Peterborough.*

WANTAGE *Oxon.* 403 404 P 29 – *pop. 9 452.*

Vale and Downland Museum, 19 Church St. (01235) 760176.

London 71 – Oxford 16 – Reading 24 – Swindon 21.

Boar's Head, Church St, Ardington, OX12 8QA, East : 2 ½ m. by A 417 (01235) 833254, *Fax (01235) 833254*, – P. MC AE VISA

closed between Christmas and New Year – **Meals** 12.00/32.50 and a la carte 17.00/22.50 **t.**

WARE *Herts.* 404 T 28 – *pop. 17 000.*

18 *Whitehill, Dane End (01920) 438495.*

London 24 – Cambridge 30 – Luton 22.

Marriott Hanbury Manor H. & Country Club, Thundridge, SG12 0SD, North : 1 ¾ m. by A 1170 on A 10 (01920) 487722, *Fax (01920) 487692*, ≤, , « Jacobean style mansion in extensive grounds, walled garden », , , , 18, , – , rest, TV & P – 120. MC AE VISA JCB.

Oakes* : Meals** 23.50 and a la carte **t.** 19.50 – (see also ***Zodiac below) – 15.75 – **152 rm** 154.00/254.00 **st.**, 9 suites – SB.

Zodiac (at Marriott Hanbury Manor H. & Country Club), Thundridge, SG12 0SD, North : 1 ¾ m. by A 1170 on A 10 (01920) 487722, *Fax (01920) 487692* – P. MC AE VISA JCB

Meals 23.50/35.00 and a la carte **st.** 19.50.

WAREHAM *Dorset* 403 404 N 31 *The West Country G. – pop. 5 644.*

See : *Town★ – St. Martin's★★.*

Env. : *Blue Pool★ AC, S : 3 ½ m. by A 351 – Bovington Tank Museum★ AC, Woolbridg Manor★, W : 5 m. by A 352.*

Exc. : *Moreton Church★★, W : 9½ m. by A 352 – Corfe Castle★ (≤★★) AC, SE : 6 m. by A 35 – Lulworth Cove★, SW : 10 m. by A 352 and B 3070 – Bere Regis★ (St. John the Bapti Church★), NW : 6½ m. by minor rd.*

Holy Trinity Church, South St (01929) 552740.

London 123 – Bournemouth 13 – Weymouth 19.

Springfield Country H., Grange Rd, BH20 5AL, South : 1 ¼ m. by South St and Wes Lane (01929) 552177, *enquiries@springfield-country-hotel.co.uk, Fax (01929) 55186*, heated, squash – rest, – 200. JCB

Millview : **Meals** (bar lunch)/dinner 20.00/25.00 **t.** 12.95 – ***Springers :*** **Meals** *(close Sunday)* (dinner only) a la carte 15.40/25.40 **t.** 12.95 – **48 rm** 70.00/140.00 **t.** SB.

Priory, Church Green, BH20 4ND, (01929) 551666, *reception@theprioryhotel.co.u Fax (01929) 554519*, «, « Part 16C priory, riverside gardens », – rest, VISA.

Meals 31.50 (dinner) and a la carte 18.20/46.25 **t.** 14.95 – **17 rm** 85.00/185.00 t 2 suites – SB.

Gold Court House, St John's Hill, BH20 4LZ, (01929) 553320, *Fax (01929) 55332* « Georgian house », –

closed Christmas and New Year – **Meals** *(winter only)* (by arrangement) (communal dinin 12.00 – **3 rm** 35.00/50.00.

WAREN MILL *Northd.* 401 402 O 17 – *see Bamburgh.*

WARMINSTER *Wilts.* 403 404 N 30 *The West Country G. – pop. 16 379.*

Env. : *Longleat House★★★ AC, SW : 3 m.*

Exc. : *Stonehenge★★★ AC, E : 18 m. by A 36 and A 303 – Bratton Castle (≤★★) NE : 6 m. A 350 and B 3098.*

Central Car Park (01985) 218548.

London 111 – Bristol 29 – Exeter 74 – Southampton 47.

Bishopstrow House, BA12 9HH, Southeast : 1 ½ m. on B 3414 (01985) 212312, *enq ries@bishopstrow.co.uk, Fax (01985) 216769*, «, « Georgian country house », heated, indoor/outdoor – rest, – 60. JCB

Meals 38.00 (dinner) and a la carte 18.00/25.50 **t.** 14.00 – 7.00 – **29 rm** 99.00/330.00 3 suites – SB.

Travelodge, BA12 7RU, Northwest : 1 ¼ m. by B 3414 at junction of A 36 ar A 350 (01985) 21953, *Fax (01985) 214380* – rm, VISA JC

Meals (grill rest.) – **30 rm** 49.95 **t.**

at Heytesbury *Southeast : 3 ¾ m. by B 3414 – ✉ Warminster.*

Angel Inn with rm, High St, BA12 0ED, (01985) 840330, *angelheytesbury@aol.co Fax (01985) 840931*, « 17C » – VISA

Meals a la carte 14.20/25.25 **st.** 13.95 – **9 rm** 45.00/90.00 **st.**

at Crockerton *South : 1 ¾ m. by A 350 – ✉ Warminster.*

Springfield House without rest., BA12 8AU, on Potters Hill rd (01985) 21369 *Fax (01985) 213696*, « Part 16C cottage », –

closed January-February – **3 rm** 50.00/65.00.

ENGLAND

ARRINGTON *Warrington 402 403 404 M 23 – pop. 82 812.*

Hill Warren, Appleton ℘ (01925) 261620 – Walton Hall, Warrington Rd, Higher Walton ℘ (01925) 266775 – Birchwood, Kelvin Close ℘ (01925) 818819 – Leigh, Kenyon Hall, Culcheth ℘ (01925) 763130 – Alder Root, Alder Root Lane, Winwick ℘ (01925) 291919.

21 Rylands St. ℘ (01925) 442180.

London 195 – Chester 20 – Liverpool 18 – Manchester 21 – Preston 28.

Village H. and Leisure Club, Centre Park, WA1 1QA, South : ¾ m. by A 49 ℘ (01925) 240000, *Fax (01925) 445240*, squash – rest, – 250. MC AE VISA.
Meals 14.95 (lunch) and a la carte 11.35/25.15 **st.** 9.65 **89 rm** 99.00/111.00 **t.** – SB.

Holiday Inn, Woolston Grange Ave, Woolston, WA1 4PX, East : 3 ¼ m. by A 57 on B 5210 at junction 21 of M 6 ℘ (01925) 838779, *Fax (01925) 838859*, – rm, rest, – 25. MC AE VISA JCB
Meals a la carte approx. 17.00 11.95 – 13.95 – **97 rm** 92.00 **st.** – SB.

Travel Inn, 1430 Centre Park, Park Boulevard, WA1 1QA, South : ¾ m. by A 49 ℘ (01925) 242692, *Fax (01925) 244259* – rm, rest, MC AE VISA.
Meals (grill rest.) – **42 rm** 41.95 **t.**

Travelodge without rest., Kendrick St, WA1 1UZ, off A 57 (Liverpool rd) ℘ (01925) 636979, *Fax (01925) 639432* – MC AE VISA JCB.
63 rm 42.95 **t.**

Stretton *South : 3½ m. by A 49 on B 5356 – ✉ Warrington.*

Hanover International, Stretton Rd, WA4 4NS, ℘ (01925) 730706, *Fax (01925) 730740*, – rm, rest, – 400. MC AE VISA JCB.
The Harlequin : **Meals** 13.95/20.15 and a la carte 22.45/41.85 **t.** 10.00 – 10.25 – **139 rm** 101.50/111.50 **t.**, 3 suites – SB.

Premier Lodge, Tarporley Rd, WA4 4NB, ℘ (01925) 730451, *Fax (01925) 730709* – rm, MC AE VISA.
Meals (grill rest.) a la carte approx. 12.50 **t.** 7.80 – **29 rm** 46.95 **t.**

ARTLING *E. Sussex 404 V 31 – see Herstmonceux.*

ARWICK *Warks. 403 404 P 27 Great Britain G. – pop. 22 476.*

See : *Town★ – Castle★★ AC* Y – *Leycester Hospital★ AC* Y B – *Collegiate Church of St. Mary★ (Tomb★)* Y A.

Warwick Racecourse ℘ (01926) 494316 Y.

The Court House, Jury St. ℘ (01926) 492212.

London 96 – Birmingham 20 – Coventry 11 – Oxford 43.

Plan on next page

Old Fourpenny Shop, 27-29 Crompton St, CV34 6HJ, ℘ (01926) 491360, *Fax (01926) 411892* – MC AE VISA JCB Y a
Meals a la carte 18.95/29.45 **t.** 9.50 – **11 rm** 43.50/75.00 **t.** – SB.

Charter House without rest., 87 West St, CV34 6AH, ℘ (01926) 496965, *penon@charterhouse8.freeserve.co.uk*, *Fax (01926) 411910*, « Part 15C », – MC VISA JCB. Y c
3 rm 56.00/80.00.

Park Cottage without rest., 113 West St, CV34 6AH, ℘ (01926) 410319, *parkcott@aol.com*, *Fax (01926) 410319*, « Part 16C » – MC VISA. Y e
closed Christmas – **4 rm** 45.00/65.00.

Saffron, Unit 1, Westgate House, Market St, CV34 4DE, ℘ (01926) 402061 – MC AE VISA JCB Y n
closed 25 December – **Meals** - Indian - (dinner only) a la carte 8.35/13.00 **t.** 7.50.

Prym's, 48 Brook St, CV34 4BL, ℘ (01926) 493504 – MC VISA JCB Y z
closed Sunday dinner – **Meals** (light lunch) a la carte 18.95/27.50 **t.** 10.50.

The Cellar, 5-6 The Knibbs, Smith St, CV34 4UW, ℘ (01926) 400809, *Fax (01926) 400809*, – MC VISA Y x
closed 24 December-4 January, Sunday and Monday – **Meals** 15.00 and a la carte 19.00/26.50 **t.** 9.95.

Barford *South : 3½ m. on A 429 – Z – ✉ Warwick.*

Glebe, Church St, CV35 8BS, on B 4462 ℘ (01926) 624218, *sales@glebehotel.co.uk*, *Fax (01926) 624625*, – rest, – 120. MC AE VISA JCB
Meals 19.95 (dinner) and a la carte 17.85/26.85 **t.** 10.25 – **38 rm** 98.00/118.00 **st.**, 1 suite – SB.

WARWICK
ROYAL LEAMINGTON SPA

Birmingham Road . . . . Z 7
Bowling Green Street. . . . . Y 9
Brook Street . . . . Y 12
Butts (The) . . . . Y 13
Castle Hill . . . . Y 15
Church Street. . . . . Y 17
High Street . . . . Y 23
Jury Street . . . . Y
Lakin Road . . . . Y 25
Linen Street . . . . Y 26
Market Place . . . . Y 29
North Rock . . . . Y 32
Old Square . . . . Y 35
Old Warwick Road . . . . Z 36
Radford Road . . . . Z 39
St. John's Road . . . . Y 42
St. Nicholas Church Street . . . . Y 43
Shires Retail Park . . . . Z
Smith Street . . . . Y
Swan Street . . . . Y 46
Theatre Street . . . . Y 48
West Street . . . . Y 50

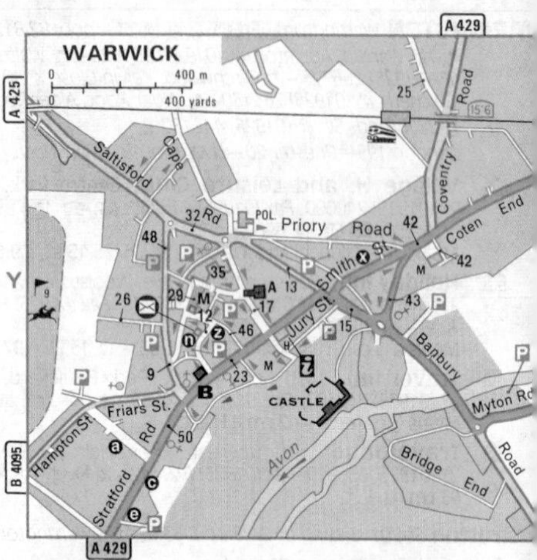

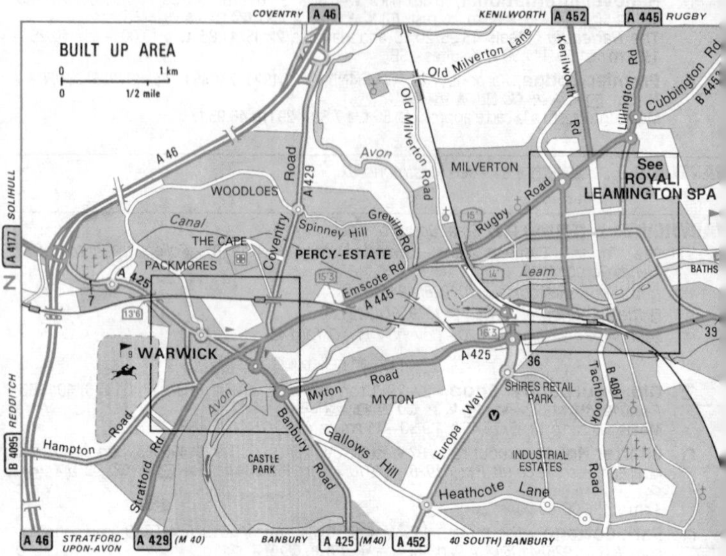

at Longbridge *Southwest : 2 m. on A 429 – Z – ✉ Warwick.*

Hilton Warwick, Stratford Rd, CV34 6RE, on A 429 at junction 15 of M 40 ✆ (01926) 499555, *Fax (01926) 410020*, rest, – 250. AE VISA JCB.
Meals *(closed Saturday lunch)* a la carte 24.00/30.00 **st.** 13.50 – 11.50 – **181 rm** 140.00/160.00 **st.** – SB.

Express by Holiday Inn without rest., Stratford Rd, CV34 6TW, on A 429 at junction of M 40 ✆ (01926) 483000, *Fax (01926) 483033* – – 25. AE JCB
117 rm 65.00 **st.**

at Sherbourne *Southwest : 2¾ m. by A 429 – Z – ✉ Warwick.*

Old Rectory, Vicarage Lane, CV35 8AB, at junction with A 46 ✆ (01926) 62456 *Fax (01926) 624995*, – rest, VISA
Meals (dinner only) a la carte approx. 16.95 **st.** 10.00 – **7 rm** 50.00/88.00 **st.** – SB.

t Hatton *Northwest : 3½ m. by A 425 on A 4177 – Z – ✉ Warwick.*

Northleigh House without rest., Five Ways Rd, CV35 7HZ, Northwest : 2½ m. by A 4177, turning left at roundabout with A 4141 ☎ (01926) 484203, *Fax (01926) 484006*, – P. VISA.
closed December and January – **7 rm** 36.00/62.00 **st.**

t Honiley *Northwest : 6¾ by A 425 on A 4177 – Z – ✉ Warwick.*

Honiley Court, CV8 1NP, on A 4177 ☎ (01926) 484234, *honileycourt@corushotels.co.uk, Fax (01926) 484474* – P – 200. VISA
Meals 12.00/25.00 and a la carte 15.00/26.45 **st.** 9.95 – 10.50 – **62 rm** 100.00/120.00 **st.** – SB.

VARWICK SERVICE AREA *Warks.* 404 P 27.
The Court House, Jury St. ☎ *(01926) 492212.*

Days Inn, Banbury Rd, Ashorn, CV35 0AA, M 40 (northbound) between junctions 12 and 13 ☎ (01926) 651681, Reservations (Freephone) 0800 0280400, *warwickhotelnorth@welcomebreak.co.uk, Fax (01926) 651634* – rm, P. VISA JCB
Meals (grill rest.) a la carte approx. 11.00 **st.** – 7.45 – **54 rm** 49.00 **t.**

Days Inn, Banbury Rd, Ashorn, CV35 0AA, M 40 (southbound) between junctions 12 and 13 ☎ (01926) 651699, Reservations (Freephone) 0800 0280400, *Fax (01926) 651601* – rm, P. VISA JCB
Meals (grill rest.) a la carte approx. 11.00 **st.** – 7.45 – **40 rm** 49.00 **t.**

VASDALE HEAD *Cumbria* 402 K 20 – ✉ *Gosforth.*
London 324 – Kendal 72 – Workington 30.

Wasdale Head Inn, CA20 1EX, ☎ (019467) 26229, *wasdaleheadinn@msn.com, Fax (019467) 26334*, ← Wasdale Head, – rest, P. VISA JCB
Meals (bar lunch)/dinner 22.00 **st.** 11.00 – **14 rm** 45.00/110.00 **st.**

VASHINGBOROUGH *Lincs.* 402 404 S 24 – *see Lincoln.*

VASHINGTON *Tyne and Wear* 401 402 P 19 – *pop. 56 848.*
Washington Moat House, Stone Cellar Rd, Usworth ☎ *(0191) 402 9988.*
London 278 – Durham 13 – Middlesbrough 32 – Newcastle upon Tyne 7.

George Washington, Stone Cellar Rd, District 12, NE37 1PH, ☎ (0191) 402 9988, *georgewashington@corushotels.com, Fax (0191) 415 1166*, , squash – P – 200. VISA.
Lincolns : **Meals** 10.00/30.00 **st.** 12.00 – 10.95 – **102 rm** 79.00/89.00 **st.**, 1 suite – SB.

Holiday Inn, Emerson, District 5, NE37 1LB, at junction of A 1(M) with A 195 ☎ (0870) 400 9084, *Fax (0191) 415 3371* – rm, P – 100. VISA JCB
Meals 15.00/30.00 (dinner) and a la carte 17.35/29.15 **t.** 11.45 – 12.95 – **138 rm** 85.00 **st.** – SB.

VASS *N. Yorks. – see Helmsley.*

VATERHEAD *Cumbria* 402 L 20 – *see Ambleside.*

VATERINGBURY *Kent* 404 V 30 – *see Maidstone.*

VATERMILLOCK *Cumbria* 402 L 20 – *see Ullswater.*

VATER YEAT *Cumbria – see Coniston.*

Die im **Michelin-Führer**
verwendeten Zeichen und Symbole haben
- **fett** oder dünn gedruckt, rot oder **schwarz** -
jeweils eine andere Bedeutung.
Lesen Sie daher die Erklärungen aufmerksam durch.

WATFORD *Herts.* 404 S 29 – *pop. 113 080.*

West Herts., Cassiobury Park ℘ (01923) 224264 – Oxhey Park, Prestwick Rd, Sout Oxhey ℘ (01923) 248312, AT.

London 21 – Aylesbury 23.

Plan : see Greater London (North-West) p. 8

Hilton Watford, Elton Way, WD2 8HA, Watford Bypass, East : 3 ½ m. on A 41 at junctic with B 462 ℘ (01923) 235881, *rm_watford@hilton.com, Fax (01923) 220836,* rm, rest, – 375. VISA JCB BT
Patio rest. : **Meals** *(closed lunch Saturday)* (carving rest.) (live music and dancing Saturda a la carte 24.80/30.80 **t.** 12.30 – ***Patio Brasserie :*** **Meals** *(closed dinner 25 Decembe lunch Saturday and Bank Holidays)* 15.95/24.50 12.30 – 10.85 – **199 rm** 150.0 170.00 **t.**, 2 suites – SB.

Premier Lodge, Water Lane, WD17 2NJ, ℘ (0870) 7001570, *Fax (0870) 7001571* – rm, rest, VISA AT
Meals (grill rest.) (dinner only) a la carte approx. 12.45 **t.** 8.45 – **105 rm** 54.95 **t.**

WATFORD GAP SERVICE AREA *Northants.* 403 404 Q 27 – ✉ *Northampton.*

Travel Inn without rest., NN6 7UZ, M 1 between junctions 16 and 17 ℘ (01327) 87900 *Fax (01327) 871333* – VISA
closed Christmas and New Year – **36 rm** 41.95.

WATH-IN-NIDDERDALE *N. Yorks. – see Pateley Bridge.*

WEAVERHAM *Ches.* 402 403 404 M 24 – *pop. 6 604.*

London 191 – Chester 15 – Liverpool 28 – Manchester 28.

Oaklands, Millington Lane, Gorstage, CW8 2SU, Southwest : 2 m. by A ℘ (01606) 853249, *Fax (01606) 852419,* – – 150. VISA.
Meals a la carte 19.00/22.00 **t.** 9.95 – **11 rm** 49.00/65.00 **t.**

Tall Trees Lodge without rest., Tarporley Rd, Lower Whitley, WA4 4EZ, North : 2 ¾ m. A 49 at junction with A 533 ℘ (01928) 790824, *bookings@talltreeslodge.co.u Fax (01928) 791330* – VISA
20 rm 39.95 **st.**

WELLAND *Worcs.* 403 404 N 27 – *see Great Malvern.*

WELLAND STONE *Worcs.* 403 404 N 27 – *see Upton-upon-Severn.*

WELLINGBOROUGH *Northants.* 404 R 27 – *pop. 41 602.*

Library, Pebble Lane ℘ (01933) 276412.

London 73 – Cambridge 43 – Leicester 34 – Northampton 10.

Ibis without rest., Enstone Court, NN9 2DR, Southwest : 2 ½ m. by A 5128 (Northampt rd) on A 509 at junction with A 45 ℘ (01933) 228333, *Fax (01933) 228444* – – 25. VISA
78 rm 49.50 **st.**

Travel Inn, London Rd, NN8 2DP, Southeast : ¾ m. on A 5193 ℘ (01933) 2786 *Fax (01933) 275947* – rm, rest, VISA
Meals (grill rest.) – **40 rm** 41.95 **t.**

at Finedon *Northeast : 3½ m. by A 510 – ✉ Wellingborough.*

Tudor Gate, High St, NN9 5JN, ℘ (01933) 680408, *info@tudorgate-hotel.co. Fax (01933) 680745* – rest, – 45. VISA JCB
Meals 18.95 and a la carte 19.95/39.45 **t.** 10.95 – **27 rm** 49.00/110.00 **t.** – SB.

WELLINGTON *Somerset* 403 K 31 – *pop. 11 302.*

London 176 – Barnstaple 42 – Exeter 32 – Taunton 10.

Bindon Country House , Langford Budville, TA21 0RU, Northwest : 4 ½ m. B 3187 via Langford Budville village following signs for Wiveliscombe ℘ (01823) 4000 *stay@bindon.com, Fax (01823) 400071,* , , « Part 17C country house with distinct Flemish gables », heated, , – – 45. VISA.
The Wellesley : **Meals** 16.95/29.95 **t.** 15.00 – **12 rm** 85.00/195.00 **t.** – SB.

ELLS *Somerset* 403 404 M 30 *The West Country G. – pop. 9 763.*

See : *City*★★ – *Cathedral*★★★ – *Vicars' Close*★ – *Bishop's Palace*★ (≤★★) **AC** – *St. Cuthbert*★.

Env. : *Glastonbury*★★ – *Abbey*★★ *(Abbot's Kitchen*★*)* **AC**, *St. John the Baptist*★★, *Somerset Rural Life Museum*★ **AC**, *Glastonbury Tor*★ (≤★★★), *SW : 5½ m. by A 39 – Wookey Hole*★ *(Caves*★ **AC**, *Papermill*★*), NW : 2 m.*

Exc. : *Cheddar Gorge*★★ *(Gorge*★★, *Caves*★, *Jacob's Ladder* ✳★*) – St. Andrew's Church*★, *NW : 7 m. by A 371 – Axbridge*★★ *(King John's Hunting Lodge*★, *St. John the Baptist Church*★*), NW : 8½ m. by A 371.*

East Horrington Rd ☏ *(01749) 675005.*

Town Hall, Market Pl. ☏ *(01749) 672552.*

London 132 – Bristol 20 – Southampton 68 – Taunton 28.

Swan, 11 Sadler St, BA5 2RX, ☏ (01749) 836300, *swan@bhere.co.uk, Fax (01749) 836301* – rest, TV P – 150. MC AE VISA
Meals 19.95/25.00 **t.** 11.00 – 9.50 – **35 rm** 75.00/109.00 **t.** – SB.

Beryl, BA5 3JP, East : 1 ¼ m. by B 3139 off Hawkers Lane ☏ (01749) 678738, *stay@beryl-wells.co.uk, Fax (01749) 670508*, ≤, « Victorian Gothic country house, antique furnishings », heated, – TV P. MC VISA
closed 25-26 December – **Meals** *(closed Sunday)* (booking essential) (residents only) (communal dining) (dinner only) 22.50 **st.** 10.00 – **8 rm** 50.00/95.00 **st.**

White Hart, Sadler St, BA5 2RR, ☏ (01749) 672056, *info@whitehart-wells.co.uk, Fax (01749) 671074* – TV P – 60. MC AE VISA
Meals (bar lunch Monday-Saturday)/dinner 15.00 and a la carte 14.35/19.00 **t.** 9.50 – **15 rm** 63.00/80.00 **t.** – SB.

Infield House, 36 Portway, BA5 2BN, ☏ (01749) 670989, *infield@talk21.com, Fax (01749) 679093*, – TV P. MC AE VISA JCB
Meals (by arrangement) 12.45 **s.** – **3 rm** 34.50/49.00 **s.**

Littlewell Farm, Coxley, BA5 1QP, Southwest : 1 ½ m. on A 39 ☏ (01749) 677914, – TV P.
Meals (by arrangement) (communal dining) 21.00 **st.** – **5 rm** 28.00/50.00 **st.**

Ritchers, 5A Sadler St, BA5 2RR, ☏ (01749) 679085, *ritcher@btinternet.co.uk, Fax (01749) 673866*, – MC VISA
closed 26 December and 1 January – **Meals** (booking essential) 10.95/21.50 **t.** 9.95.

Wookey Hole *Northwest : 1 ¾ m. by A 371 – ✉ Wells.*

Glencot House, Glencot Lane, BA5 1BH, ☏ (01749) 677160, *glencot@ukonline.co.uk, Fax (01749) 670210*, « Victorian mansion built in Jacobean style », – TV P – 40. MC AE VISA JCB.
Meals (dinner only) 25.50 **t.** 9.95 – **13 rm** 67.00/110.00 **t.** – SB.

Easton *Northwest : 3 m. on A 371 – ✉ Wells.*

Beaconsfield Farm without rest., BA5 1DU, on A 371 ☏ (01749) 870308, *carol@beaconsfieldfarm.co.uk, Fax (01749) 870166*, – TV P.
Easter-mid November – **3 rm** 40.00/48.00 **st.**

ELLS-NEXT-THE-SEA *Norfolk* 404 W 25 – *pop. 2 400.*

The Crown, The Buttlands, NR23 1EX, ☏ (01328) 710209, *Fax (01328) 711432*, – rm, TV. MC AE VISA JCB
Jewel : **Meals** a la carte 14.90/22.00 **t.** 10.95 – (see also ***Rococo*** below) – **11 rm** 85.00/120.00 **t.**

Rococo (Anderson) (at The Crown H.), The Buttlands, NR23 1EX, ☏ (01328) 710209, *rococorest@aol.com, Fax (01328) 711432* – . MC AE VISA JCB
Meals (dinner only) 25.50/35.50 **t.** 12.75
Spec. Open ravioli of smoked salmon and shrimps. Roast squab with dauphinoise potatoes and a thyme jus. Iced liquorice parfait with caramelised almonds.

ELWYN *Herts.* 404 T 28 – *pop. 10 512 (inc. Codicote).*

London 31 – Bedford 31 – Cambridge 31.

Tewin Bury Farm, AL6 0JB, Southeast : 3 ½ m. by A 1000 on B 1000 ☏ (01438) 717793, *hotel@tewinbury.co.uk, Fax (01438) 840440*, « Converted farm buildings », – rest, TV P – 70. MC AE VISA.
closed 24 December-1 January – **Meals** 10.60/22.00 and a la carte 12.95/27.55 **t.** 10.50 – **29 rm** 95.00/135.00 **t.**

Le Guide change, changez de **guide Michelin** *tous les ans.*

WELWYN GARDEN CITY *Herts.* 404 T 28.

18, 9 *Panshanger Golf Complex, Old Herns Lane ℘ (01707) 333312.*
London 22 – Luton 21.

Travel Inn, Stanborough Rd, AL8 6DQ, South : ¾ m. on A 6129 ℘ (01707) 39134 *Fax (01707) 393789* – rm, rest, TV P. VISA JCB.
Meals (grill rest.) – **60 rm** 41.95 **t.**

XXX **Auberge du Lac** with rm, Brocket Hall, AL8 7XG, West : 3 m. by A 6129 on B 65 ℘ (01707) 368888, *aubergedulac@brocket-hall.co.uk, Fax (01707) 368898,* ≤, « Pa 18C former hunting lodge in the grounds of Brocket Hall estate, lakeside setting », rest, TV P. AE VISA
closed 27-30 December, Monday and dinner Sunday – **Meals** 25.00/38.00 **t.** 20.00 – **16 r** 150.00/170.00 **t.**

WEM *Shrops.* 402 403 L 25 – *pop. 4 882* – ✉ *Shrewsbury.*
London 167 – Birmingham 50 – Chester 32 – Stoke-on-Trent 36 – Shrewsbury 8.

Soulton Hall, SY4 5RS, East : 2 m. on B 5065 ℘ (01939) 232786, *j.ashton@soultonha fsbusiness.co.uk, Fax (01939) 234097,* « Part 15C manor house », – TV P. AE VISA JCB.
Meals (booking essential) (dinner only) a la carte 16.50/22.00 **t.** 9.50 – **7 rm** 47.0 77.00 **t.**, 1 suite – SB.

WENDLING *Norfolk* 404 W 25 – *see East Dereham.*

WENTBRIDGE *W. Yorks.* 402 404 Q 23 – ✉ *Pontefract.*
London 183 – Leeds 19 – Nottingham 55 – Sheffield 28.

Wentbridge House, Old Great North Rd, WF8 3JJ, ℘ (01977) 620444, *info@wentbrid house.co.uk, Fax (01977) 620148,* – TV P – 120. AE VISA JCB.
closed 25 December – **Meals** 12.50/23.00 and a la carte 28.85/42.25 **t.** 10.95 – **18 r** 75.00/110.00 **t.** – SB.

WEOBLEY *Herefordshire* 403 L 27 – *pop. 1 076* – ✉ *Hereford.*
London 145 – Brecon 30 – Hereford 12 – Leominster 9.

Red Lion, HR4 8SE, ℘ (01544) 318220, *Fax (01544) 319075,* « 14C former inn » – TV P. VISA.
March-Christmas – **Meals** (residents only) (dinner only) 19.50/25.00 9.95 – **5 rm** 42.5 62.50 **t.**

XX **The Salutation Inn** with rm, Market Pitch, HR4 8SJ, ℘ (01544) 318443, *info@salutati inn.com, Fax (01544) 318216,* « Part 13C former cider house » – TV P. AE VISA.
Meals 25.00 and a la carte 15.90/31.45 **t.** 9.50 – **4 rm** 45.00/95.00 **st.**

WEST BAGBOROUGH *Somerset* 403 K 30 – *see Taunton.*

WEST BEXINGTON *Dorset* 403 404 M 31 – ✉ *Dorchester.*
London 150 – Bournemouth 43 – Bridport 6 – Weymouth 13.

Manor, Beach Rd, DT2 9DF, ℘ (01308) 897616, *themanorhotel@btconnect.cc Fax (01308) 897035,* ≤, – TV P. AE VISA.
Meals 20.95/23.95 **t.** – **13 rm** 60.00/100.00 **t.** – SB.

WEST BRIDGFORD *Nottingham* 403 404 Q 25 – *see Nottingham.*

WEST BROMWICH *W. Mids.* 403 404 O 26 – *see Birmingham.*

WEST BURTON *N. Yorks.* 402 O 21 – ✉ *Leyburn.*
London 260 – Carlisle 81 – Darlington 34 – Kendal 40 – Leeds 62 – York 58.

The Grange, DL8 4JR, ℘ (01969) 663348, – rm, TV P
Meals (by arrangement) (communal dining) 16.50 **st.** 10.00 – **3 rm** 35.00/60.00 **st** SB.

WESTDEAN *E. Sussex* – *see Seaford.*

WEST DOWN *Devon* 403 H 30.

Env. : *Exmoor National Park*★★ – *Ilfracombe : Hillsborough* (≤★★) *AC, Capstone Hill*★ (≤★), *St. Nicholas' Chapel* (≤★) *AC, N : 3 m. by A 361 and minor rd.*

London 221 – Exeter 52 – Taunton 59.

Long House, The Square, EX34 8NF, ✆ (01271) 863242, – .
March-October – **Meals** (by arrangement) 14.00 **st.** 7.50 – **3 rm** 30.00/52.00 **st.** – SB.

WESTFIELD *E. Sussex* 404 V 31 – *pop. 2 461.*

London 66 – Brighton 38 – Folkestone 45 – Maidstone 30.

The Wild Mushroom, Woodgate House, Westfield Lane, TN35 4SB, Southwest : ½ m. on A 28 ✆ (01424) 751137, *info@wildmushroom.co.uk, Fax (01424) 753405,* – P. AE VISA
closed 24 December-23 January, Monday, Saturday lunch and Sunday dinner – **Meals** (booking essential) 15.95 (lunch) and dinner a la carte 18.70/29.40 **st.** 10.50.

WESTLETON *Suffolk* 404 Y 27 – *pop. 1 317* – ✉ *Saxmundham.*

London 97 – Cambridge 72 – Ipswich 28 – Norwich 31.

Pond House without rest., The Hill, IP17 3AN, ✆ (01728) 648773, *john.wade3@btinternet.com,* – P.
3 rm 40.00/46.00.

When looking for a quiet hotel
use the maps found in the introduction
or look for establishments with the sign or .

WEST LULWORTH *Dorset* 403 404 N 32 *The West Country G.* – *pop. 838* – ✉ *Wareham.*

See : *Lulworth Cove*★.

London 129 – Bournemouth 21 – Dorchester 17 – Weymouth 19.

Cromwell House, Main Rd, BH20 5RJ, ✆ (01929) 400253, *catriona@lulworthcove.co.uk, Fax (01929) 400566,* ≤, heated, – rest, TV P. AE VISA JCB
closed 21 December-3 January – **Meals** (dinner only) 15.00 and a la carte 19.00/31.00 **t.** 7.75 – **17 rm** 38.50/67.00 **t.** – SB.

Gatton House without rest., Main Rd, BH20 5RU, ✆ (01929) 400252, *avril.mike@gattonhouse.co.uk, Fax (01929) 400252,* – TV P. VISA JCB
March-October – **8 rm** 43.00/66.00 **st.**

WEST MALLING *Kent* 404 V 30 – *pop. 2 479.*

18, 18 *Addington, Maidstone ✆ (01732) 844785.*

London 35 – Maidstone 7 – Royal Tunbridge Wells 14.

Travel Inn, Leybourne, ME19 5TR, Northeast : 1 m. on A 228 ✆ (01732) 521630, *Fax (01732) 521609* – rm, rest, TV P. AE VISA.
Meals (grill rest.) – **40 rm** 41.95 **t.**

Scott House without rest., 37 High St, ME19 6QH, ✆ (01732) 841380, *mail@scott-house.co.uk, Fax (01732) 522367,* « Part Georgian town house » – TV. AE VISA JCB.
closed Christmas-New Year – **3 rm** 55.00/75.00.

The Swan, 35 Swan St, ME19 6JU, ✆ (01732) 521910, *Fax (01732) 522898,* , – . AE VISA
closed 26 December and 1 January – **Meals** a la carte 19.75/27.00 **t.** 11.95.

WEST MONKTON *Somerset* 403 K 30 – *see Taunton.*

WESTON-SUPER-MARE *North Somerset* 403 K 29 *The West Country G.* – *pop. 69 372.*

See : *Seafront* (≤★★) BZ.

Exc. : *Axbridge*★★ *(King John's Hunting Lodge*★*, St. John the Baptist Church*★*) SE : 9 m. by A 371* – BY – *and A 38 – Cheddar Gorge*★★ *(Gorge*★★*, Caves*★*, Jacob's Ladder* ★*) – Clevedon*★ *(≤★★, Clevedon Court*★*), NE : 10 m. by A 370 and M 5 – St. Andrew's Church*★*, SE : 10½ m. by A 371.*

18 *Worlebury, Monks Hill ✆ (01934) 623214* BY.

Beach Lawns ✆ (01934) 888800.

London 147 – Bristol 24 – Taunton 32.

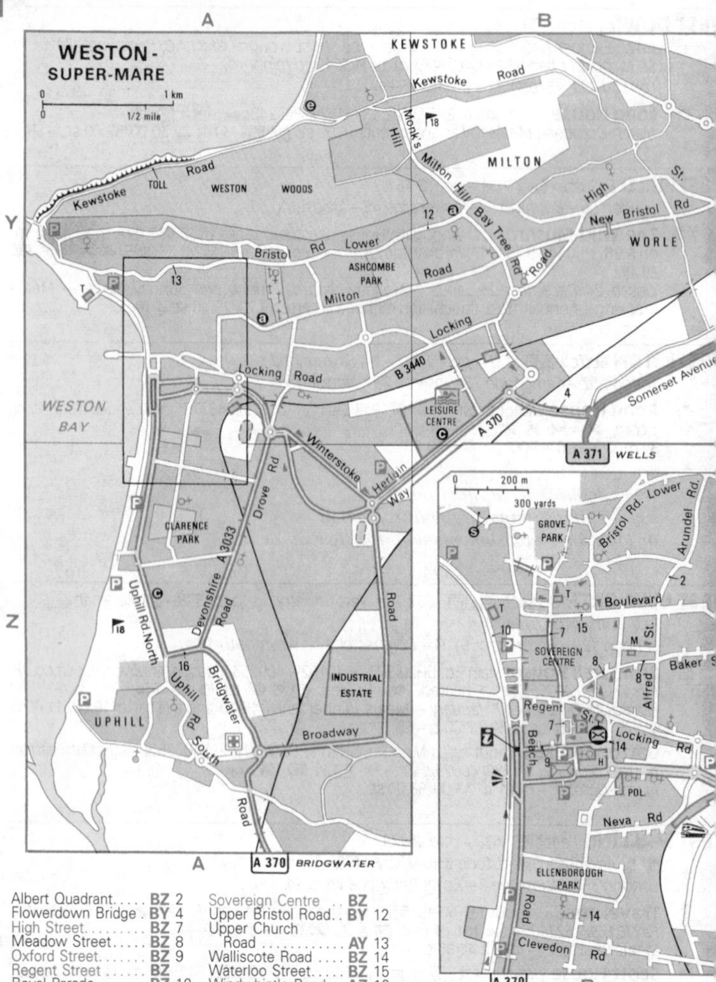

Albert Quadrant	BZ	2
Flowerdown Bridge	BY	4
High Street	BZ	7
Meadow Street	BZ	8
Oxford Street	BZ	9
Regent Street	BZ	
Royal Parade	BZ	10
Sovereign Centre	BZ	
Upper Bristol Road	BY	12
Upper Church Road	AY	13
Walliscote Road	BZ	14
Waterloo Street	BZ	15
Windwhistle Road	AZ	16

Beachlands, 17 Uphill Road North, BS23 4NG, ☎ (01934) 621401, *info@beachlandsho com, Fax (01934) 621966*, – rest, – 60. VISA AZ

closed 23 December-3 January – **Meals** (bar lunch Monday to Saturday)/dinner 12.0 18.00 **t.** 12.50 – **24 rm** 49.50/89.50 **t.** – SB.

Commodore, Beach Rd, Sand Bay, Kewstoke, BS22 9UZ, by Kewstoke rd (t ☎ (01934) 415778, *comm@latonahotels.co.uk, Fax (01934) 636483* – – 120. VISA. AY

Meals (bar lunch Monday-Saturday)/dinner a la carte 15.00/22.00 **t.** 7.95 – **19** 60.00/89.00 **t.** – SB.

Queenswood, Victoria Park, BS23 2HZ, off Upper Church Rd ☎ (01934) 416141, *sta queenswoodhotel.com, Fax (01934) 621759* – rest, . VISA JCB BZ

closed Christmas and New Year – **Meals** (bar lunch)/dinner 17.50 8.50 – **18 rm** 50.0 80.00 **st.**

Travel Inn, Hutton Moor Rd, BS22 8LY, East : 1 ½ m. by A 370 ☎ (01934) 6226 *Fax (01934) 627401*, – rm, VISA. BY

Meals (grill rest.) – **60 rm** 41.95 **t.**

Ashcombe Court, 17 Milton Rd, BS23 2SH, ☎ (01934) 625104, *Fax (01934) 625104* – ⅍ TV P. ✻ AY a
February-October – **Meals** (by arrangement) 10.00 – **6 rm** ⊡ 33.00/46.00.

Braeside without rest., 2 Victoria Park, BS23 2HZ, off Upper Church Rd ☎ (01934) 626642, *braeside@tesco.net, Fax (01934) 626642* – TV BZ s
closed Christmas and New Year – **9 rm** ⊡ 25.00/50.00 **s.**

Duets, 103 Upper Bristol Rd, BS22 8ND, ☎ (01934) 413428 – MC VISA BY a
closed 2 weeks May, 1 week October, Sunday dinner and Monday – **Meals** (dinner only) 17.95/19.95 and a la carte 23.95/26.40 **t.** 9.95.

'ESTON-UNDER-REDCASTLE *Shrops.* 402 M 25 – ✉ *Shrewsbury.*

18, 18 *Hawkstone Park ☎ (01939) 200611.*
London 178 – Birmingham 58 – Chester 30 – Stoke-on-Trent 30 – Shrewsbury 13.

The Citadel ⛹, SY4 5JY, East : ½ m. on Hodnet rd ☎ (01630) 685204, *griffiths@citadel2000.freeserve.co.uk, Fax (01630) 685204*, ←, « Castellated Georgian house », ⛬ – ⅍ TV P. MC VISA. ✻
April-October – **Meals** (by arrangement) (communal dining) 16.00/25.00 – **3 rm** ⊡ 60.00/90.00 **s.**

'ESTON UNDERWOOD *Derbs. – see Derby.*

'EST RUNTON *Norfolk* 404 X 25 – ✉ *Cromer.*

9 *Links Country Park Hotel ☎ (01263) 838383.*
London 135 – King's Lynn 42 – Norwich 24.

Links Country Park H., Sandy Lane, NR27 9QH, ☎ (01263) 838383, *sales@links_hotel.co.uk, Fax (01263) 838264*, ≘s, ⊡, 9, ⛬, ✂ – ⧈, ⅍ rest, ▤ rest, TV P – ⛺ 200. MC VISA
Meals (bar lunch Monday to Saturday)/dinner 21.75 and a la carte 12.65/25.50 **st.** 12.95 – **43 rm** ⊡ 67.50/147.50 **st.** – SB.

Dormy House, Cromer Rd, NR27 9QA, on A 149 ☎ (01263) 837537, *jjjarvis@freenetname.co.uk, Fax (01263) 837537*, ⛬ – ⧈ TV P. MC AE VISA. ✻
Meals (carving rest.) 12.40/14.20 7.50 – **14 rm** ⊡ 48.00/76.00 **t.** – SB.

'EST TANFIELD *N. Yorks.* 402 P 21 – *pop. 551* – ✉ *Ripon.*

London 237 – Darlington 29 – Leeds 32 – Middlesbrough 39 – York 36.

The Bruce Arms with rm, Main St, HG4 5JJ, ☎ (01677) 470325, *iwanttostay@brucearms.com, Fax (01677) 470796* – TV P. MC VISA. ✻
closed 2 weeks February, Monday, Tuesday lunch and Sunday dinner. – **Meals** a la carte 15.50/22.50 **t.** 9.95 – **3 rm** ⊡ 35.00/50.00 **t.** – SB.

'EST WITTERING *W. Sussex* 404 R 31 – *pop. 2 750.*

London 76 – Brighton 37 – Portsmouth 24 – Southampton 37.

Home Farm House ⛹ without rest., Elms Lane, PO20 8LW, ☎ (01243) 514252, *Fax (01243) 512804*, ⛬ – ⅍ TV P. ✻
closed Christmas and New Year – **3 rm** ⊡ 30.00/60.00 **s.**

'EST WITTON *N. Yorks.* 402 O 21 – *pop. 325* – ✉ *Leyburn.*

London 241 – Kendal 39 – Leeds 60 – York 53.

Wensleydale Heifer Inn, Main St, DL8 4LS, ☎ (01969) 622322, *heifer@daelnet.co.uk, Fax (01969) 624183*, « Part 17C », ⛬ – TV P. MC AE ① VISA
Meals a la carte 15.00/17.95 **t.** 9.25 – **9 rm** ⊡ 60.00/98.00 **st.** – SB.

Ivy Dene, DL8 4LP, ☎ (01969) 622785, *Fax (01969) 622785* – ⅍ TV P. ✻
closed 24-26 December – **Meals** (by arrangement) 14.50 7.50 – **5 rm** ⊡ 33.00/48.00 – SB.

ETHERAL *Cumbria* 401 402 L 19 – *see Carlisle.*

ETHERBY *W. Yorks.* 402 P 22 *Great Britain G.* – *pop. 8 154.*

Env. : *Harewood House★★ (The Gallery★) AC, SW : 5½ m. by A 58 and A 659.*
18 *Linton Lane, Linton ☎ (01937) 580089.*
Council Offices, 24 Westgate ☎ (0113) 247 7251.
London 208 – Harrogate 8 – Leeds 13 – York 14.

ENGLAND

Wood Hall ⛰, Trip Lane, Linton, LS22 4JA, Southwest : 3 m. by A 661 and Linton R
(01937) 587271, *woodhall@arcadianhotels.co.uk, Fax (01937) 584353,* ≤, « Part Jacc
bean and Georgian country house in park », Fб, ⊠, ⊗, ⊕ – |‡|, ✻ rest, TV ✆ P – 🚶 14
MC AE ⓓ VISA JCB
Meals *(closed Saturday lunch)* 15.95/24.95 **t.** – ☐ 12.00 – **42 rm** 90.00/125.00 **st.** – SB.

Linton Springs ⛰, Sicklinghall Rd, LS22 4AF, West : 1 ¾ m. by A 661 (01937) 58535
info@lintonsprings.co.uk, Fax (01937) 587579, ⊕, ⊕, ✕ – TV P – 🚶 70. MC AE ⓓ VISA.
closed 1 to 3 January ***The Gun Room :*** **Meals** *(closed Sunday dinner)* (dinner only ar
Sunday lunch)/dinner 11.00/14.75 and a la carte 18.10/23.10 **t.** 🍷 11.75 – **11 rm** ☐ 75.0
95.00 **st.**, 1 suite.

WETHERSFIELD *Essex* 404 V 28 – *pop. 1 204* – ✉ *Braintree.*

London 52 – Cambridge 31 – Chelmsford 19 – Colchester 22.

Dicken's Brasserie, The Green, CM7 4BS, (01371) 850723, *dickensbrasserie@hotma
com, Fax (01371) 850727,* « Part 17C house » – ✻ P. MC VISA
Meals a la carte 18.00/23.50 **st.** 🍷 10.00.

WEYBRIDGE *Surrey* 404 S 29 – *pop. 52 802 (inc. Walton).*

London 23 – Crawley 27 – Guildford 17 – Reading 33.

Oatlands Park, Oatlands Drive, KT13 9HB, Northeast : ¾ m. by A 317 on A 305
(01932) 847242, *info@oaklandsparkhouse.com, Fax (01932) 842252,* Fб, ⛳9, ⊕, ⊕, ✕
|‡|, ✻ rm, TV ✆ P – 🚶 300. MC AE ⓓ VISA
Meals 23.00/28.00 and dinner a la carte 26.50/32.50 **st.** 🍷 16.00 – ☐ 13.50 – **141 r**
120.00/185.00 **st.**, 3 suites.

The Ship, Monument Green, High St, KT13 8BQ, off A 317 (01932) 848364, *info@shi
hotel.weybridge.com, Fax (01932) 857153* – ✻ rest, ▤ rest, TV P – 🚶 150. MC AE ⓓ V
JCB. ✻
Meals 14.50/22.50 and a la carte 23.65/33.60 **st.** 🍷 11.95 – ☐ 11.50 – **39 rm** 128.0
160.00 **st.** – SB.

Casa Romana, 2 Temple Hall, Monument Hill, KT13 8RH, on A 317 (01932) 84347
Fax (01932) 854221 – ▤ P. MC AE ⓓ VISA JCB
closed 25-26 December, Saturday lunch and Bank Holidays – **Meals** - Italian - 14.95/18.
and a la carte 14.95/32.85 **t.** 🍷 10.95.

WEYMOUTH *Dorset* 403 404 M 32 *The West Country G.* – *pop. 46 065.*

See : *Town★ – Timewalk★ AC – Nothe Fort (≤★) AC – Boat Trip★ (Weymouth Bay a
Portland Harbour) AC.*
Env. : *Chesil Beach★★ – Portland★ - Portland Bill (✱★★) S : 2½ m. by A 354.*
Exc. : *Maiden Castle★★ (≤★) N : 6 ½ m. by A 354 – Abbotsbury★★ (Swannery★ A
Sub-Tropical Gardens★ AC, St. Catherine's Chapel★) NW : 9 m. by B 3157.*
⛳18 *Links Rd (01305) 773981.*
to Guernsey (St. Peter Port) and Jersey (St. Helier) (Condor Ferries Ltd).
The King's Statue, The Esplanade (01305) 785747.
London 142 – Bournemouth 35 – Bristol 68 – Exeter 59 – Swindon 94.

Moonfleet Manor ⛰, DT3 4ED, Northwest : 4 ½ m. by B 3157 (01305) 786948, *info
moonfleetmanor.com, Fax (01305) 774395,* ≤, ≘s, ⊠, ⊕, ✕, squash – ✻ rest, TV
P – 🚶 60. MC AE ⓓ VISA
Meals (bar lunch Monday-Saturday)/dinner 22.50/26.50 and a la carte 22.50/26.50
🍷 12.50 – **37 rm** ☐ 75.00/200.00 **st.**, 2 suites – SB.

Rex, 29 The Esplanade, DT4 8DN, (01305) 760400, *rex@kingshotel.co.u
Fax (01305) 760500,* ≤ – |‡| TV ⊖. MC AE ⓓ VISA
closed Christmas – **Meals** (bar lunch)/dinner 13.75 and a la carte 18.00/23.25 **t.** 🍷 8.50
31 rm ☐ 59.00/105.00 **t.** – SB.

Bay Lodge without rest., 27 Greenhill, DT4 7SW, (01305) 782419, *barbara@baylod
co.uk, Fax (01305) 782828* – TV P. MC AE ⓓ VISA
12 rm ☐ 55.50/78.00 **st.**

Travel Inn, Greenhill, DT4 7SX, East : ½ m. on A 353 (01303) 76796
Fax (01303) 768113 – ✻ rm, TV ♿ P. MC AE ⓓ VISA. ✻
Meals (grill rest.) – **40 rm** 41.95 **t.**

Chatsworth, 14 The Esplanade, DT4 8EB, (01305) 785012, *david@thechatsworth.co
, Fax (01305) 766342,* ≤, ⊕ – TV. MC VISA. ✻
Meals (by arrangement) 15.00 **st.** 🍷 7.95 – **8 rm** ☐ 35.00/75.00 **t.**

Bay View without rest., 35 The Esplanade, DT4 8DH, (01305) 78208
Fax (01305) 782083, ≤ – TV P. MC ⓓ VISA JCB. ✻
15 February-14 November – **8 rm** ☐ 40.00/60.00.

Perry's, The Old Harbour, 4 Trinity Rd, DT4 8TJ, (01305) 785799, *enquiries@perry restaurant.co.uk, Fax (01305) 787002* – MC AE VISA
closed 25-26 December, 1 January, lunch Monday and Saturday and Sunday dinner in winter – **Meals** a la carte 18.00/26.00 **t.** 9.95.

WHALLEY *Lancs.* 402 M 22 – *pop. 5 364* – *Blackburn.*
Long Leese Barn, Clerkhill (01254) 822236.
London 233 – Blackpool 32 – Burnley 12 – Manchester 28 – Preston 15.

Clarion H. Foxfields, Whalley Rd, Billington, BB7 9HY, Southwest : 1 ¼ m. (01254) 822556, *admin@gb065.u-net.com, Fax (01254) 824613,* – rest, P – 180. MC AE VISA
Expressions : **Meals** (bar lunch Saturday) (dancing Saturday evening) 7.50/19.50 **st.** 11.95 – 11.75 – **18 rm** 110.00 **t., 26 suites** 125.00 **t.** – SB.

WHASHTON *N. Yorks.* – *see Richmond.*

WHEELOCK *Ches.* – *see Sandbach.*

WHICKHAM *Tyne and Wear* 401 402 O/P 19 – *see Gateshead.*

WHIMPLE *Devon* 403 J 31 – *see Exeter.*

WHITBY *N. Yorks.* 402 S 20 *Great Britain G.* – *pop. 13 640.*
See : Abbey★.
Sandsend Rd, Low Straggleton (01947) 602768.
Langborne Rd (01947) 602674.
London 257 – Middlesbrough 31 – Scarborough 21 – York 45.

Bagdale Hall, 1 Bagdale, YO21 1QL, (01947) 602958, *Fax (01947) 820714,* « Part 16C » – rest, P. MC AE VISA.
Meals (dinner only and Sunday lunch)/dinner a la carte 21.30/26.20 **t.** 6.50 – **19 rm** 49.00/118.00 **st.**

Crescent House, 6 East Cres, YO21 3HD, (01947) 600091, *Fax (01947) 600091,* –
mid March-mid November – **Meals** (by arrangement) 9.50 **s.** 7.00 – **6 rm** 40.00/44.00 **s.**

at **Sleights** *Southwest : 3 m. by A 171 and A 169* – *Whitby.*

The Lawns, 73 Carr Hill Lane, Briggswath, YO21 1RS, North : ½ m. by B 1410 (01947) 810310, *thelortons@tesco.net, Fax (01947) 810310,* – P.
Meals (by arrangement) 16.00 **st.** – **3 rm** 26.00/52.00 **st.**

at **Dunsley** *West : 3 ¼ m. by A 171* – *Whitby.*

Dunsley Hall Country House, YO22 5PW, (01947) 893437, *reception@dunsley hall.com, Fax (01947) 893505,* – P. MC AE VISA.
Meals 24.95 (dinner) and a la carte 18.95/28.90 **st.** – **18 rm** 69.85/151.70 **st.** – SB.

WHITEHAVEN *Cumbria* 402 J 20.
London 332 – Carlisle 39 – Keswick 28 – Penrith 47.

Travel Inn, Howgate, CA28 6PL, Northeast : 3 m. by A 5094 on A 595 (01946) 66286, *Fax (01946) 63407* – rm, rest, P. MC AE VISA JCB.
Meals (grill rest.) – **38 rm** 41.95 **t.**

WHITEPARISH *Wilts.* 403 404 P 30 – *see Salisbury.*

WHITEWELL *Lancs.* 402 M 22 – *pop. 5 617* – *Clitheroe.*
London 281 – Lancaster 31 – Leeds 55 – Manchester 41 – Preston 13.

Inn at Whitewell, Forest of Bowland, BB7 3AT, (01200) 448222, *Fax (01200) 448298,* « Memorabilia », – P. MC AE VISA.
Meals (bar lunch)/dinner a la carte 20.40/33.00 **t.** 9.80 – **16 rm** 62.00/99.00 **st.**, 1 suite.

WHITLEY *W. Yorks.* 402 P 23 – *see Dewsbury.*

WHITLEY *Wilts. – see Melksham.*

WHITLEY BAY *Tyne and Wear* 401 402 P 18 – *pop. 33 335.*
Park Rd ☏ *(0191) 200 8535.*
London 295 – Newcastle upon Tyne 10 – Sunderland 10.

Windsor, South Parade, NE26 2RF, ☏ (0191) 251 8888, *info@windsor-hotel.demo.co.uk, Fax (0191) 297 0272* – |$|, ▤ rest, TV P – 80. MC AE VISA.
Meals (bar lunch)/dinner and a la carte approx. 20.00 **t.** – **69 rm** 65.00/75.00 **t.**

Bay's Bistro, 183 Park View, NE26 3RE, ☏ (0191) 251 3567, *Fax (0191) 251 8688* – ▤. VISA
closed 25-26 December, 1 January, Monday, Sunday dinner and Bank Holidays – **Me**... (dinner only and Sunday lunch) 15.95 (dinner) and a la carte 14.40/25.40 **t.** 11.20.

WHITNEY-ON-WYE *Herefordshire* 403 K 27 – *pop. 133* – ✉ *Hereford.*
London 150 – Birmingham 56 – Cardiff 73 – Hereford 17.

Rhydspence Inn, HR3 6EU, West : 1 ½ m. on A 438 ☏ (01497) 8312... *Fax (01497) 831751,* « Part 14C », – TV P. MC AE VISA.
closed 25 December – **Meals** (bar lunch) a la carte 21.00/36.20 **t.** 9.75 – **7 rm** 37.5... 75.00 **t.** – SB.

WHITSTABLE *Kent* 404 X 29 – *pop. 28 907* – ✉ *Whitstable.*
7 Oxford St. ☏ *(01227) 275482.*
London 68 – Dover 24 – Maidstone 37 – Margate 12.

Continental, 29 Beach Walk, CT5 2BP, East : ½ m. by Sea St. and Harbour ... ☏ (01227) 280280, *Fax (01227) 280257*, ←, – rm, TV P. MC AE VISA.
Meals a la carte 12.85/28.00 **t.** 11.50 – **23 rm** 55.00/125.00 **st.** – SB.

Travel Inn, Thanet Way, CT5 3BD, Southwest : 2 m. by A 290 ☏ (01227) 2724... *Fax (01227) 263151* – rm, TV P. MC AE VISA.
Meals (grill rest.) – **40 rm** 41.95 **t.**

Windyridge , Wraik Hill, CT5 3BY, Southwest : 2 m. off A 290 ☏ (01227) 2635... *Fax (01227) 771191,* ←, – rest, TV P. MC VISA
Meals (by arrangement) 17.50 **st.** 8.00 – **10 rm** 30.00/60.00 **st.**

Whitstable Oyster Fishery Co., Royal Native Oyster Stores, The Horsebridge, C... 1BU, ☏ (01227) 276856, *Fax (01227) 770666,* ←, « Converted warehouse on beach » – AE VISA JCB
closed 25-26 December and Monday except Bank Holidays – **Meals** - Seafood - a la ca... 24.50/31.30 **t.**

at Thanet Way Service Area *Southwest : 3 ¼ m. by A 290 on A 299* – ✉ *Faversham.*

Travelodge, ME13 9EL, (eastbound carriageway) ☏ (01227) 770980, *Fax (01227) 28113...* rm, TV P. MC AE VISA JCB.
Meals (grill rest.) – **40 rm** 59.95 **t.**

WHITTLE-LE-WOODS *Lancs.* 402 M 23 – *see Chorley.*

WHITWELL-ON-THE-HILL *N. Yorks.* 402 R 21 – *pop. 136* – ✉ *York.*
London 240 – Kingston-upon-Hull 47 – Scarborough 29 – York 13.

The Stone Trough Inn, Kirkham Abbey, YO60 7JS, East : 1 m. ☏ (01653) 618713, *inf... stonetroughinn.co.uk, Fax (01653) 618819,* – P. MC VISA
closed 25 December and Monday except Bank Holidays – **Meals** a la carte 18.65/24.95 9.75.

WICK *South Gloucestershire* 403 404 M 29 – *see Bristol.*

WICKFORD *Essex* 404 V 29 – *see Basildon.*

WICKHAM *Hants.* 403 404 Q 31 – *pop. 2 941.*
London 74 – Portsmouth 12 – Southampton 11 – Winchester 16.

The Old House, The Square, PO17 5JG, ☏ (01329) 833049, *enq@theoldhotel.co... Fax (01329) 833672,* « Queen Anne house », – rest, TV P. MC AE VISA.
closed 27 December-9 January – **Meals** *(closed Monday lunch and Sunday dinner)* 15.0... 21.50 and a la carte 32.45/36.30 **t.** 14.95 – 5.00 – **9 rm** 65.00/75.00 **t.** – SB.

IDNES *Halton* 402 403 404 L 23 – *pop. 57 162.*

Highfield Rd ☏ *(0151) 424 2440.*

London 205 – Liverpool 15 – Manchester 27 – Stoke-on-Trent 42.

Hillcrest, Cronton Lane, Cronton, WA8 9AR, Northwest : 2 m. by A 568 on A 5080 ☏ (0151) 424 1616, *Fax (0151) 495 1348* – rm, TV P – 120. MC AE VISA
Meals (bar lunch)/dinner 14.95 and a la carte 11.85/27.20 **t.** 8.25 – **50 rm** 69.00/125.00 **st.** – SB.

Travelodge, Fiddlers Ferry Rd, WA8 2NR, East : 1 m. on A 562 ☏ (0151) 424 8930, *Fax (0151) 424 8930* – rm, rest, TV P. MC AE VISA JCB.
Meals (grill rest.) – **32 rm** 42.95 **t.**

IGAN *Gtr. Manchester* 402 M 23 – *pop. 85 819.*

Trencherfield Mill, Wallgate ☏ *(01942) 825677.*

London 203 – Liverpool 22 – Manchester 24 – Preston 18.

Quality H. Wigan, Riverway, WN1 3SS, access by Orchard St ☏ (01942) 826888, *admin@gb058.u-net.com, Fax (01942) 825800* – TV P – 200. MC AE VISA
Meals 15.95 and a la carte approx. 25.00 **st.** 11.95 – 10.95 – **88 rm** 95.00 **t.**

Travel Inn, Warrington Rd, Marus Bridge, WN3 6XB, South : 2 ¾ m. on A 49 ☏ (01942) 493469, *Fax (01942) 498679* – rm, rest, TV P. MC AE VISA
Meals (grill rest.) – **41 rm** 41.95 **t.**

Travel Inn, Orrell Rd, Orrell, WN5 8HQ, West : 3 ½ m. on A 577 ☏ (01942) 211516, *Fax (01942) 215002* – TV P – 80. MC AE VISA.
Meals (grill rest.) – **40 rm** 41.95 **t.**

Up Holland *West : 4 ¾ m. on A 577* – ✉ *Wigan.*

Quality H. Skelmersdale, Prescott Rd, WN8 9PU, Southwest : 2 ¾ m. by A 577 and Stannanought Rd ☏ (01695) 720401, *admin@gb656.u-net.com, Fax (01695) 50953,* – , rest, TV P – 200. MC AE VISA
Meals (bar lunch Monday-Saturday)/dinner 17.75 **st.** 9.95 – 10.95 – **55 rm** 79.00/89.00 **st.** – SB.

IGHT (Isle of) 403 404 PQ 31 32 *Great Britain G.* – *pop. 124 577.*

See : Island★★.

Env. : *Osborne House, East Cowes★★ AC – Carisbrooke Castle, Newport★★ AC (Keep ≤★) – Brading★ (Roman Villa★ AC, St. Mary's Church★, Nunwell House★ AC) – Shorwell : St. Peter's Church★ (wall paintings★).*

from East Cowes to Southampton (Red Funnel Ferries) frequent services daily (1 h) – from Yarmouth to Lymington (Wightlink Ltd) frequent services daily (30 mn) – from Fishbourne to Portsmouth (Wightlink Ltd) frequent services daily (35 mn).

from Ryde to Portsmouth (Hovertravel Ltd) frequent services daily (10 mn) – from Ryde to Portsmouth (Wightlink Ltd) frequent services daily (15 mn) – from West Cowes to Southampton (Red Funnel Ferries) frequent services daily (22 mn).

reshwater – *pop. 7 317 (inc. Totland)* – ✉ *Isle of Wight.*

Newport 13.

Sandpipers, Coastguard Lane, Freshwater Bay, PO40 9QX, South : 1 ½ m. by A 3055 ☏ (01983) 758500, *sandpipers@fatcattrading.demon.co.uk, Fax (01983) 754364,* – TV P. MC VISA
Meals (bar lunch Monday-Saturday)/dinner 19.95 **t.** 7.75 – **15 rm** 35.00/80.00 **t.** – SB.

Rockstone Cottage without rest., Colwell Chine Rd, PO40 9NR, Northwest : ¾ m. by A 3055 off A 3054 ☏ (01983) 753723, *enquiries@rockstonecottage.co.uk, Fax (01983) 753721,* – TV P.
5 rm 32.00/56.00 **st.**

Red Lion, Church Pl, PO40 9BP, via Hooke Hill ☏ (01983) 754925, *info@redlion-wright.co.uk, Fax (01983) 754925,* , « Part 14C » – P. MC VISA JCB
closed 25 December – **Meals** a la carte 15.75/22.00 **t.** 10.75.

iton – ✉ *Isle of Wight.*

Windcliffe Manor , Sandrock Rd, Undercliffe, PO38 2NG, ☏ (01983) 730215, *enquiries@windcliffe.co.uk, Fax (01983) 730215,* heated, – rest, TV P. MC AE VISA JCB
Meals (light lunch Monday-Saturday)/dinner a la carte approx. 25.00 **t.** 9.95 – **14 rm** (dinner included) 70.50/140.00 **t.** – SB.

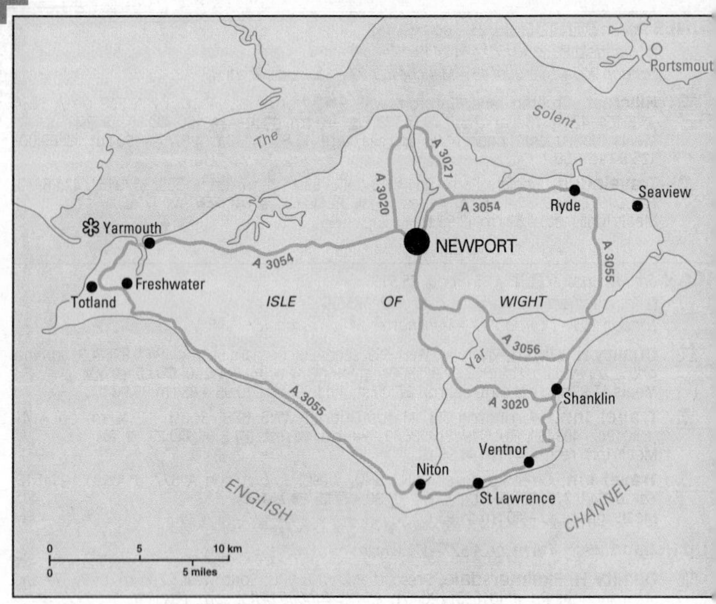

Ryde – ✉ *Isle of Wight.*

Binstead Rd ✆ (01983) 614809.

81-83 Union St. ✆ (01983) 562905.

Newport 7.

Biskra Beach, 17 St Thomas's St, PO33 2DL, ✆ (01983) 567913, *info@biskrahotel.co Fax (01983) 616976,* ≤, – TV P. MC AE VISA
closed 25-26 December – **Meals** 15.95 (dinner) and a la carte 12.45/29.90 **t.** 8.75 – **14** 60.00/140.00 **t.** – SB.

Little Upton Farm without rest., Gatehouse Rd, Ashey, PO33 4BS, Southwest : 2 by West St. ✆ (01983) 563236, *Fax (01983) 563236,* ≤, « 17C farmhouse, working farm , – TV P.
closed Christmas-New Year – **3 rm** 35.00/60.00.

St Lawrence – ✉ *Isle of Wight.*

Newport 16.

Little Orchard without rest., Undercliffe Drive, PO38 1YA, West : 1 m. on A 30 ✆ (01983) 731106, – TV P.
3 rm 27.00/40.00.

Seaview – *pop. 2 181* – ✉ *Isle of Wight.*

Priory Bay , Priory Drive, PO34 5BU, Southeast : 1 ½ m. by B 3330 ✆ (01983) 6131 *reception@priorybay.co.uk, Fax (01983) 616539,* , « Medieval priory with Georg extensions, extensive woodland », , , , , – TV P. MC AE VISA.
The Restaurant : **Meals** 25.00 and dinner a la carte 25.00/31.00 **t.** 14.00 – ***The Pric Oyster :*** **Meals** *(summer only)* a la carte 16.40/39.45 **t.** 14.00 – **17 rm** 140.00/200.00 2 suites.

Seaview, High St, PO34 5EX, ✆ (01983) 612711, *Fax (01983) 613729,* – , rest, P. MC AE VISA
closed 3 days Christmas – ***The Restaurant and Sunshine Room :*** **Meals** (booking esse tial) (in bar Sunday dinner except Bank Holidays) a la carte 18.70/26.95 **t.** 9.95 – **14** 55.00/130.00 **t.**, 2 suites – SB.

anklin – *pop. 17 305 (inc. Sandown)* – ✉ *Isle of Wight.*
The Fairway, Lake Sandown ✆ (01983) 403217.
67 High St ✆ (01983) 862942.
Newport 9.

Brunswick, Queens Rd, PO37 6AN, ✆ (01983) 863245, *enquiries@brunswick-hotel.co.uk, Fax (01983) 868398,* heated, – rest, VISA
mid March-mid November – **Meals** (residents only) (dinner only) 15.00 **t.** 8.95 – **35 rm** (dinner included) 66.00/117.00 **t.**

Bourne Hall, Luccombe Rd, PO37 6RR, ✆ (01983) 862820, *bhch@dialstart.net, Fax (01983) 865138,* heated, – rest, VISA.
Meals (bar lunch)/dinner 15.50 **st.** 8.95 – **30 rm** (dinner included) 53.50/134.00 **st.** – SB.

Foxhills, 30 Victoria Ave, PO37 6LS, ✆ (01983) 862329, *info@foxhillshotel.co.uk, Fax (01983) 866666,* – VISA.
Meals *(closed Monday)* (dinner only and Sunday lunch)/dinner 13.50/21.00 **t.** 8.50 – **9 rm** 38.00/76.00 **t.**

Rylstone Manor, Rylstone Gdns, PO37 6RG, ✆ (01983) 862806, *rylstone@dialstart.net,* « Part Victorian », – VISA JCB.
closed November and January – **Meals** (dinner only) 14.00/20.00 **t.** 8.95 – **8 rm** 41.00/82.00 **t.**

Grange Bank, Grange Rd, PO37 6NN, ✆ (01983) 862337, *grangebank@aol.com, Fax (01983) 862737* –
Easter-October – **Meals** (booking essential) (residents only) (dinner only) (unlicensed) 7.50 **s.** – **9 rm** 25.50/51.00 – SB.

tland – *pop. 7 317 (inc. Freshwater)* – ✉ *Isle of Wight.*
Newport 13.

Sentry Mead, Madeira Rd, PO39 0BJ, ✆ (01983) 753212, *enquiry@sentry-mead.co.uk, Fax (01983) 753212,* – VISA JCB
closed 20 December-2 January – **Meals** (bar lunch)/dinner 15.50 **t.** – **14 rm** 45.00/90.00 **t.**

ntnor – *pop. 5 978* – ✉ *Isle of Wight.*
Steephill Down Rd ✆ (01983) 853326.
34 High St. ✆ (01983) 853625 (summer only).
Newport 10.

Royal, Belgrave Rd, PO38 1JJ, ✆ (01983) 852186, *royalhotel@zetnet.co.uk, Fax (01983) 855395,* – – 40. VISA
Meals (bar lunch Monday-Saturday)/dinner 27.50/37.50 **t.** 11.50 – **54 rm** 70.00/120.00 **t.**, 1 suite – SB.

Lake, Shore Rd, Bonchurch, PO38 1RF, ✆ (01983) 852613, *mich@lakehotel.co.uk,* –
March-October – **Meals** (dinner only) 10.00 8.50 – **20 rm** 30.00/60.00 **st.**

rmouth – ✉ *Isle of Wight.*
Newport 10.

The George, Quay St, PO41 0PE, ✆ (01983) 760331, *res@thegeorge.co.uk, Fax (01983) 760425,* <, « 17C former governor's residence », – rm, rest, . VISA JCB
The Restaurant : **Meals** *(closed Sunday-Monday)* (booking essential) (dinner only) 50.00 **t.** 15.00 – (see also ***The Brasserie*** below) – **16 rm** 120.00/165.00 **t.**, 1 suite – SB
Spec. Trio of duck tastings. Halibut and langoustine, samphire and courgette flower. Trio of chocolate desserts on a raspberry sauce.

The Brasserie (at The George H.), Quay St, PO41 0PE, ✆ (01983) 760331, *Fax (01983) 760425,* – VISA JCB
Meals 17.95 (lunch) and a la carte 28.15/33.40 **t.** 15.00.

GSTON *Leics.* 402 403 404 Q 26 – *see Leicester.*

LLERBY *East Riding* 402 S 22 – *see Kingston-upon-Hull.*

LLERSEY HILL *Glos.* 403 404 O 27 – *see Broadway (Worcs.).*

WILLESLEY *Glos.* 403 404 N 29 – *see Tetbury.*

WILLINGTON *Ches. – see Tarporley.*

WILLITON *Somerset* 403 K 30 *The West Country G. – pop. 2 025 –* ✉ *Taunton.*
Env. : *Exmoor National Park★★ – Cleeve Abbey★★ AC, W : 2 m. by A 39.*
London 177 – Minehead 8 – Taunton 16.

White House, 11 Long St, TA4 4QW, ✆ (01984) 632306 – ⅍ rest, TV P. ✻
May-November – **Meals** (dinner only) 34.00 **t.** ₫ 12.00 – **10 rm** ☐ 49.00/108.00 **t.** – SB.

WILMCOTE *Warks.* 403 404 O 27 – *see Stratford-upon-Avon.*

WILMINGTON *Devon* 403 K 31 – *see Honiton.*

WILMINGTON *East Sussex* 404 U 31 – *see Eastbourne.*

WILMSLOW *Ches.* 402 403 404 N 24 – *pop. 28 604.*
18 *Great Warford, Mobberley ✆ (01565) 872148.*
London 189 – Liverpool 38 – Manchester 12 – Stoke-on-Trent 27.

Stanneylands, Stanneylands Rd, SK9 4EY, North : 1 m. by A 34 ✆ (01625) 5252
enquiries@stanneylandshotel.co.uk, Fax (01625) 537282, « Gardens » – ⅍ rm, ▤ rest,
P – 🏛 100. MC AE ⓓ VISA. ✻
The Restaurant : **Meals** (residents only dinner Sunday) 13.00/23.00 and a la carte 30.
42.50 **t.** ₫ 13.50 – ☐ 10.50 – **31 rm** 89.00/108.00 **t.**, 1 suite – SB.

Manchester Airport Moat House, Oversley Ford, Altrincham Rd, SK9 4LR, Nor
west : 2 ¾ m. on A 538 ✆ (01625) 889988, *Fax (01625) 531876,* 🏋, ≘s, ☐, squash – |‡|
TV ♿ P – 🏛 300. MC AE ⓓ VISA. ✻
Meals *(closed Saturday lunch)* 14.95 (dinner) and a la carte 16.40/26.95 **t.** ₫ 11.95 – ☐ 1
– **126 rm** 99.00/140.00 **st.** – SB.

Premier Lodge, Racecourse Rd, SK9 5LR, West : 1 m. by A 538 ✆ (01625) 5258
Fax (01625) 548382 – |‡| ⅍, ▤ rest, TV ✆ ♿ P. MC AE ⓓ VISA. ✻
Meals (grill rest.) a la carte approx. 13.00 **t.** ₫ 8.95 – **37 rm** 46.95 **t.**

Bank Square, 4-6 Bank Sq, SK9 1AN, ✆ (01625) 539754 – ▤. MC AE VISA
closed Sunday – **Meals** (booking essential) (dinner only) 10.00/11.95 and a la carte 14.
23.00 ₫ 12.50.

at Handforth *North : 3 m. on A 34 –* ✉ *Wilmslow.*

Belfry House, Stanley Rd, SK9 3LD, ✆ (0161) 437 0511, *office@belfryhouseho*
Fax (0161) 499 0597, 🏋, ≘s, ☐ – |‡|, ⅍ rm, TV ✆ P – 🏛 180. MC AE ⓓ VISA. ✻
Meals (dancing Friday and Saturday evening) 17.50/19.95 and a la carte 33.75/43.7
₫ 14.50 – **79 rm** ☐ 96.00/112.00 **st.**, 2 suites – SB.

WIMBORNE MINSTER *Dorset* 403 404 O 31 *The West Country G. – pop. 15 274.*
See : *Town★ – Minster★ – Priest's House Museum★ AC.*
Env. : *Kingston Lacy★★ AC, NW : 3 m. by B 3082.*
ℹ *29 High St. ✆ (01202) 886116.*
London 112 – Bournemouth 10 – Dorchester 23 – Salisbury 27 – Southampton 30.

Beechleas, 17 Poole Rd, BH21 1QA, ✆ (01202) 841684, *beechleas@hotmail.c*
Fax (01202) 849344, « Georgian town house » – ⅍ rest, TV P. MC AE ⓓ VISA JCB
closed 24 December-mid January – **Meals** (lunch by arrangement)/dinner 19.95/24.7
₫ 12.75 – **9 rm** ☐ 69.00/79.00 **t.** – SB.

Les Bouviers, Oakley Hill, Merley, BH21 1RJ, South : 1 ¼ m. on A 349 ✆ (01202) 8895
nfo@lesbouviers.co.uk, Fax (01202) 889555 – P. MC AE ⓓ VISA
closed first week January, Saturday lunch, Sunday dinner and Monday except Decemb
Meals 13.95/24.95 and a la carte 26.95/34.75 **t.** ₫ 15.00.

***Le Grand Londres** (GREATER LONDON) est composé de la City*
et de 32 arrondissements administratifs (Borough)
eux-mêmes divisés en quartiers ou en villages
ayant conservé leur caractère propre (Area).

INCHCOMBE *Glos.* 403 404 O 28 – *pop. 4 243.*

Town Hall, High St. (01242) 602925.

London 100 – Birmingham 43 – Gloucester 26 – Oxford 43.

Westward, Sudeley Lodge, GL54 5JB, East : 1 ½ m. by Castle St. on Sudeley Lodge/ Parks/Farm rd (01242) 604372, *jimw@haldon.co.uk, Fax (01242) 602206,* – rm, TV P. MC VISA
closed December-early January – **Meals** (by arrangement) (communal dining) 22.50 8.00 – **3 rm** 45.00/85.00 **s.**

Isbourne Manor House without rest., Castle St, GL54 5JA, (01242) 602281, *Fax (01242) 602281,* « Part Georgian and Elizabethan manor house », – TV P.
closed Christmas – **3 rm** 45.00/80.00.

Sudeley Hill Farm without rest., GL54 5JB, East : 1 m. by Castle St (01242) 602344, *scudamore4@aol.com, Fax (01242) 602344,* « Part 15C house, working farm », – TV P.
closed Christmas – **3 rm** 30.00/50.00.

Wesley House with rm, High St, GL54 5LJ, (01242) 602366, *enquiries@wesleyhouse.co.uk, Fax (01242) 609046,* « Part 15C » – TV. MC AE VISA.
closed Sunday dinner – **Meals** 14.00/21.50 **st.** 12.50 – **6 rm** 40.00/75.00 **st.** – SB.

Poachers, 5 North St, GL54 5LH, (01242) 604566 – . MC VISA
closed 5-13 November, 14-31 January, Sunday dinner and Monday – **Meals** (booking essential) (dinner only and Sunday lunch) 20.00/26.00 **st.** 10.00.

INCHELSEA *E. Sussex* 404 W 31 *Great Britain G.*

See : *Town★ – St. Thomas Church (effigies★).*

London 64 – Brighton 46 – Folkestone 30.

The Strand House without rest., Tanyard's Lane, TN36 4JT, East : ¼ m. on A 259 (01797) 226276, *strandhouse@winchelsea.freeserve.co.uk, Fax (01797) 224806,* « Part 14C and 15C », – TV P. MC VISA JCB.
closed Christmas and New Year – **10 rm** 38.00/72.00 **st.**

INCHESTER *Hants.* 403 404 P 30 *Great Britain G.* – *pop. 36 121.*

See : *City★★ - Cathedral★★★ AC* B – *Winchester College★ AC* B B – *Castle Great Hall★* B D – *God Begot House★* B A.

Env. : *St. Cross Hospital★★ AC* A.

Guildhall, The Broadway (01962) 840500.

London 72 – Bristol 76 – Oxford 52 – Southampton 12.

Plan on next page

Wessex, Paternoster Row, SO23 9LQ, (0870) 400 8126, *wessex@wessexhotel.co.uk, Fax (01962) 841503,* – , rest, TV P – 100. MC AE VISA JCB — B c
William Walker : **Meals** 17.00/23.00 **t.** 13.95 – 13.95 – **93 rm** 138.00/150.00 **st.**, 1 suite – SB.

Hotel du Vin, 14 Southgate St, SO23 9EF, (01962) 841414, *info@winchester.hotelduvin.com, Fax (01962) 842458,* « Georgian town house, wine themed interior », – TV P – 30. MC AE VISA. — B i
Meals – (see ***Bistro*** below) – 11.50 – **22 rm** 99.00/135.00 **t.**, 1 suite.

Winchester Royal, St Peter St, SO23 8BS, (01962) 840840, *royal@marstonhotels.com, Fax (01962) 841582,* – , rest, TV P – 100. MC AE VISA — B n
Meals 7.50/24.00 and dinner a la carte 24.00/28.40 **t.** 12.95 – **75 rm** 109.00/169.00 **st.** – SB.

Winchester Moat House, Worthy Lane, SO23 7AB, (01962) 709988, *Fax (01962) 840862,* , , – , rest, TV P – 200. MC AE VISA. — B e
Meals a la carte 17.00/30.00 **st.** 12.50 – 10.50 – **71 rm** 111.00 **st.** – SB.

Dawn Cottage without rest., Romsey Rd, SO22 5PQ, (01962) 869956, *Fax (01962) 869956,* – TV P. MC VISA JCB. — A c
3 rm 48.00/62.00 **st.**

East View without rest., 16 Clifton Hill, SO22 5BL, (01962) 862986, – TV P. MC VISA. — B v
closed Easter, Christmas and New Year – **3 rm** 50.00/55.00 **t.**

Portland House without rest., 63 Tower St, SO23 8TA, (01962) 865195, *tony@knightworld.com, Fax (01962) 865195* – TV. — B a
4 rm 50.00/60.00 **s.**

Florum House, 47 St Cross Rd, SO23 9PS, (01962) 840427, *florum.house@barclays.net, Fax (01962) 862287,* – TV P. MC VISA — A a
closed 1 week Christmas – **Meals** (by arrangement) 16.00 – **9 rm** 48.00/67.00 **st.** – SB.

WINCHESTER

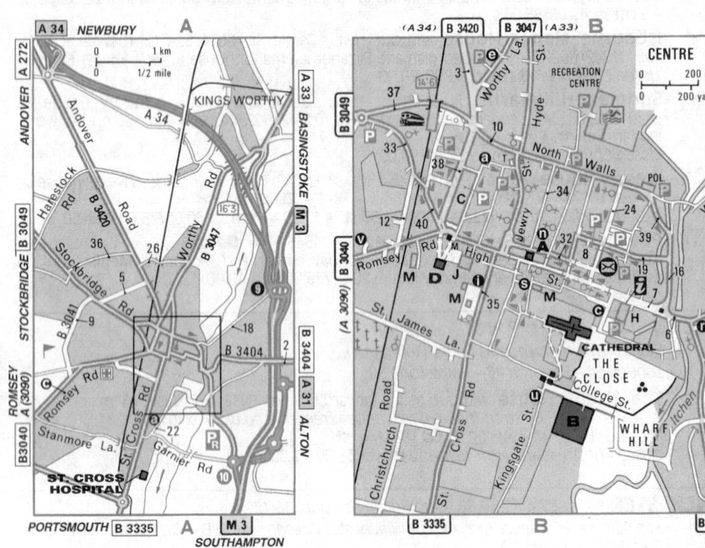

Chesil Rectory (Storey), Chesil St, SO23 8HU, ☎ (01962) 851555, *Fax (01962) 8697* B
« 15C » – MC AE ⓓ VISA JCB
closed 1 week Christmas, Sunday and Monday – **Meals** 25.00/40.00 **t.** 16.00
Spec. Twice baked cheddar soufflé. Pork and black pudding, spinach and mustard ma apple butter sauce. Passion fruit soufflé, mango sorbet.

Nine The Square, 9 Great Minster St, The Square, SO23 9HA, ☎ (01962) 8640 B
Fax (01962) 879586 – MC AE ⓓ VISA
closed 25-26 December, 1 January and Sunday – **Meals** a la carte 14.70/25.40 **t.** 12.95.

Bistro (at Hotel du Vin), 14 Southgate St, SO23 9EF, ☎ (01962) 8414 B
Fax (01962) 842458, – P. MC AE ⓓ VISA
Meals (booking essential) a la carte 26.40/32.40 **t.** 12.95.

Wykeham Arms with rm, 75 Kingsgate St, SO23 9PE, ☎ (01962) 853834, *doree wykehamarms.fsnet.com, Fax (01962) 854411*, « Characterful 18C inn, memorabilia B
– rm, TV P. MC AE ⓓ VISA JCB.
closed 25 December – **Meals** *(closed Sunday)* (booking essential) a la carte 18.45/23.0 12.95 – **13 rm** 45.00/97.50 **t.**, 1 suite.

at Sparsholt *Northwest : 3½ m. by B 3049 – A – ✉ Winchester.*

Lainston House , SO21 2LT, ☎ (01962) 863588, *enquiries@lainstonhouse.co Fax (01962) 776672*, , « 17C manor house, gardens and parkland », – r
TV P – 80. MC AE ⓓ VISA
Meals 17.00/37.00 and a la carte 49.40/57.90 **st.** 21.00 – 13.00 – **48 rm** 100. 275.00 **st.**, 2 suites – SB.

Plough Inn, SO21 2NW, ☎ (01962) 776353, *Fax (01962) 776400*, – P. MC VISA
closed 25 December – **Meals** (booking essential) a la carte 18.40/25.85 **st.** 10.95.

WINDERMERE *Cumbria* 402 L 20 *Great Britain G. – pop. 6 847.*

Env. : *Lake Windermere*★★ – *Brockhole National Park Centre*★ *AC, NW : 2 m. by A 591.*

Victoria St. ☎ *(015394) 46499.*

London 274 – Blackpool 55 – Carlisle 46 – Kendal 10.

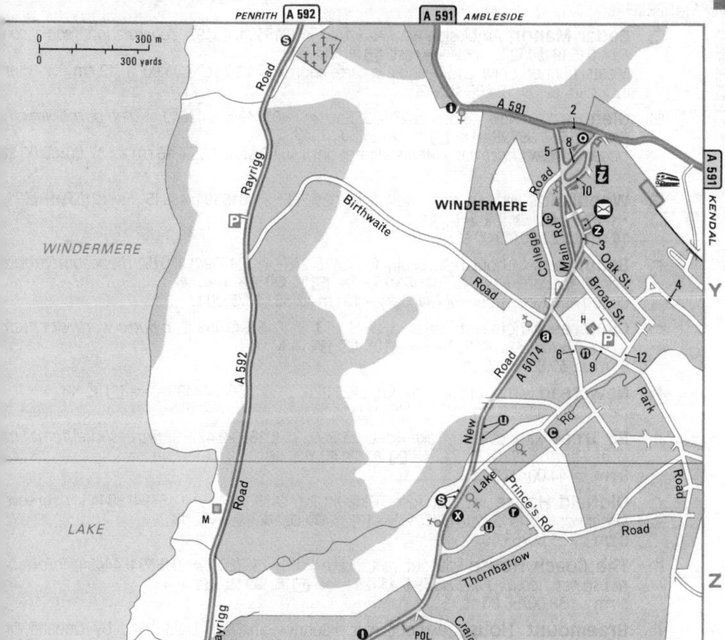

WINDERMERE

Church Street . . . . Y 2
Crescent Road . . . . Y 3
Droomer Drive . . . . Y 4
Elleray Road. . . . . Y 5
Ellerthwaite Road . . . . Y 6
Glebe Road . . . . Z 7
High Street . . . . Y 8
Holly Road . . . . Y 9
Victoria Street . . . . Y 10
Woodland Road . . . . Y 12

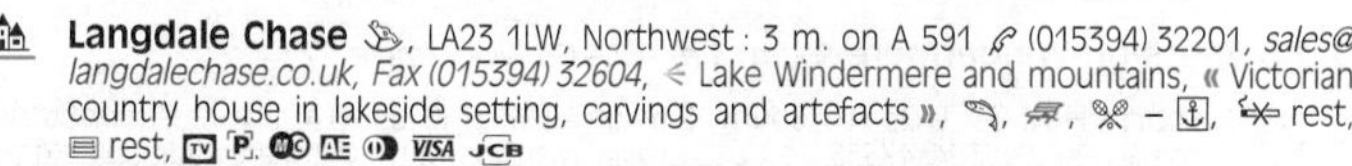

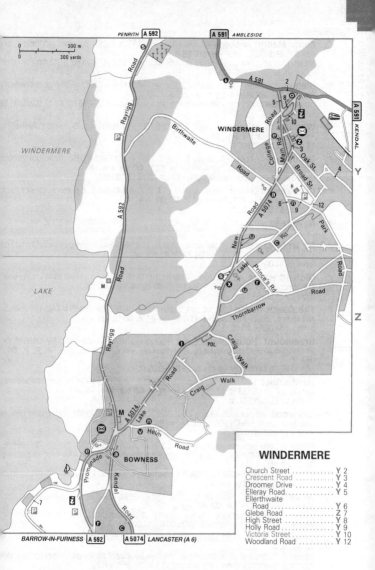

Langdale Chase, LA23 1LW, Northwest : 3 m. on A 591 (015394) 32201, *sales@langdalechase.co.uk, Fax (015394) 32604*, Lake Windermere and mountains, « Victorian country house in lakeside setting, carvings and artefacts », – rest, rest,
Meals 14.95/30.00 and a la carte 22.00/30.00 **st.** 16.00 – **27 rm** (dinner included) 70.00/180.00 **t.**, 1 suite – SB.

Holbeck Ghyll, Holbeck Lane, LA23 1LU, Northwest: 3 ¼ m. by A 591 (015394) 32375, *stay@holbeckghyll.com, Fax (015394) 34743*, Lake Windermere and mountains, « Victorian former hunting lodge, gardens », –
Meals 27.50/47.50 **t.** 17.95 – **19 rm** (dinner included) 145.00/280.00 **t.**, 1 suite – SB
Spec. Roast quail with onion compote and boudin blanc. Turbot with ragoût of girolles, bacon and celery. Assiette of apple.

ENGLAND

Cedar Manor, Ambleside Rd, LA23 1AX, ✆ (015394) 43192, *cedarmanor@fsbdial.co.u Fax (015394) 45970,* – rest, . Y
Meals (dinner only) 21.50 and a la carte approx. 24.50 **st.** 11.00 – **12 rm** (dinn included) 62.00/124.00 **st.** – SB.

Glenburn, New Rd, LA23 2EE, ✆ (015394) 42649, *glen.burn@virgin.ne Fax (015394) 88998* – . Y
closed 1 week Christmas – **Meals** (dinner only) 16.50 **st.** 9.95 – **16 rm** 37.00/85.00 **st.** SB.

Woodlands without rest., New Rd, LA23 2EE, ✆ (015394) 43915, *Fax (015394) 43915* . Y
14 rm 27.00/40.00 **st.**

Beaumont without rest., Holly Rd, LA23 2AF, ✆ (015394) 47075, *thebeaumonthote btinternet.com, Fax (015394) 47075* – . Y
closed mid November-mid January – **10 rm** 36.00/75.00 **t.**

Glencree without rest., Lake Rd, LA23 2EQ, ✆ (015394) 45822, *h.butterworth@btintern .com, Fax (015394) 45822* – . Z
6 rm 30.00/50.00 **st.**

Newstead without rest., New Rd, LA23 2EE, ✆ (015394) 44485 – . Y
closed January – **8 rm** 32.50/55.00 **st.**

Fir Trees without rest., Lake Rd, LA23 2EQ, ✆ (015394) 42272, *firtreeshotel@email.ms com, Fax (015394) 42512* – . Z
8 rm 44.00/64.00 **t.**

Oldfield House without rest., Oldfield Rd, LA23 2BY, ✆ (015394) 88445, *pat.reeve virgin.net, Fax (015394) 43250* – . Y
8 rm 25.00/65.00.

The Coach House without rest., Lake Rd, LA23 2EQ, ✆ (015394) 44494, *info@coa house.net.1.co.uk, Fax (015394) 43476* – Z
5 rm 38.00/56.00 **st.**

Braemount House without rest., Sunny Bank Rd, LA23 2EN, by Queens Dri ✆ (015394) 45967, *braemount.house@virgin.net, Fax (015394) 45967* – Z
closed 25-26 December – **9 rm** 35.00/60.00 **st.**

Hawksmoor without rest., Lake Rd, LA23 2EQ, ✆ (015394) 42110, *tyson@hawksmo net1.co.uk, Fax (015394) 42110,* – . Z
10 rm 56.00/65.00 **st.**

Kirkwood without rest., Prince's Rd, LA23 2DD, ✆ (015394) 43907, *neil.cox@kirkwood freeserve.co.uk, Fax (015394) 43907* – . Z
7 rm 30.00/60.00 **st.**

Miller Howe with rm, Rayrigg Rd, LA23 1EY, ✆ (015394) 42536, *lakeview@millerhou com, Fax (015394) 45664,* ≤ Lake Windermere and mountains, – rest, rest, Y
closed 8-16 January – **Meals** (booking essential) 17.50/39.50 **t.** 17.50 – **15 rm** (dinr included) 95.00/270.00 **t.** – SB.

Jerichos, Birch St, LA23 1EG, ✆ (015394) 42522, *enquiries@jerichos.co. Fax (015394) 42522* – . Y
closed 3 weeks November, 1 week January, 25-26 December, 1 January and Monda **Meals** (dinner only) a la carte 23.00/26.50 **t.** 12.00.

Oregano, High St, LA23 1AF, ✆ (015394) 44954, *alison@oregano-restaurant.co.uk* – Y
closed 2-16 January, 25-26 December and Sunday except Bank Holiday weekends – **Me** (booking essential) (dinner only) a la carte 20.00/28.65 **t.** 8.75.

at Bowness-on-Windermere *South : 1 m.* – **Z** – ✉ *Windermere.*

Storrs Hall , LA23 3LG, South : 2 m. on A 592 ✆ (015394) 47111, *reception@storrsh co.uk, Fax (015394) 47555,* ≤, « Georgian mansion with Victorian additions extensiv furnished with antiques, on the shores of Lake Windermere », , , – , rest, .
closed January – **Meals** 18.50/35.00 **st.** 14.50 – **25 rm** (dinner included) 130.0 305.00 **st.** – SB.

Old England, Church St, LA23 3DF, ✆ (015394) 42444, *heritagehotels-windermere.c england@forte-hotels.com, Fax (015394) 43432,* ≤ Lake Windermere, heated, – – 120. . Z
Vinland : **Meals** *(closed Saturday lunch)* 11.95/30.00 **t.** 11.45 – **76 rm** 85.00/240.00 – SB.

Linthwaite House ⛶, Crook Rd, LA23 3JA, South : ¾ m. by A 5074 on B 5284 ☎ (015394) 88600, *admin@linthwaite.com, Fax (015394) 88601,* ≤ Lake Windermere and fells, « Extensive grounds and private lake », – ⅍ TV & P. MC AE VISA JCB. ⅍
Meals (light lunch Monday-Saturday)/dinner 39.00 **st.** 20.50 – **26 rm** 115.00/260.00 **st.** – SB.

Lindeth Howe ⛶, Storrs Park, LA23 3JF, South : 1 ¼ m. by A 592 off B 5284 ☎ (015394) 45759, *hotel@lindeth-howe.co.uk, Fax (015394) 46368,* ≤, ≘s, ⛶, – ⅍ TV & P. MC VISA JCB. ⅍
Meals (light lunch Monday-Saturday)/dinner 14.95/28.50 **st.** 10.95 – **36 rm** 48.00/174.00 **st.** – SB.

Gilpin Lodge ⛶, Crook Rd, LA23 3NE, Southeast : 2 ½ m. by A 5074 on B 5284 ☎ (015394) 88818, *hotel@gilpin-lodge.co.uk, Fax (015394) 88058,* ≤, , – ⅍ rest, TV P. MC AE VISA JCB. ⅍
Meals (booking essential to non-residents) 35.00 (dinner) and lunch a la carte 16.50/24.00 **st.** 12.50 – **14 rm** 105.00/210.00 **st.** – SB.

Fayrer Garden House ⛶, Lyth Valley Rd, LA23 3JP, South : 1 m. on A 5074 ☎ (015394) 88195, *lakescene@fayrergarden.com, Fax (015394) 45986,* ≤, – ⅍, rest, TV P. MC AE VISA
closed 6-19 January – **Meals** (bar lunch)/dinner 25.00/29.50 **t.** 12.50 – **18 rm** (dinner included) 70.00/195.00 **t.** – SB.

Lindeth Fell ⛶, Lyth Valley Rd, LA23 3JP, South : 1 m. on A 5074 ☎ (015394) 43286, *kennedy@lindethfell.co.uk, Fax (015394) 47455,* ≤ Lake Windermere and mountains, « Country house atmosphere, gardens », – ⅍ TV P. MC VISA. ⅍
closed 2-23 January – **Meals** 12.00/23.00 **t.** 10.50 – **14 rm** 52.00/138.00 **st.** – SB.

Burn How Garden House, Back Belsfield Rd, LA23 3HH, ☎ (015394) 46226, *info@burnhow.co.uk, Fax (015394) 47000,* – ⅍ rest, TV P. MC AE VISA JCB. ⅍ Z r
closed first 2 weeks January – **Meals** (light lunch)/dinner 18.50 8.50 – **28 rm** 75.00/94.00 **st.** – SB.

Burnside, Kendal Rd, LA23 3EP, ☎ (015394) 42211, *stay@burnsidehotel.com, Fax (015394) 43824,* ⅍, ≘s, ⛶, , squash – ⅍ TV & P – 100. MC AE VISA JCB Z c
Meals (bar lunch Monday-Saturday)/dinner 16.00/23.00 and a la carte 20.85/30.85 **t.** 10.95 – **57 rm** 80.00/140.00 **t.** – SB.

Craig Manor, Lake Rd, LA23 2JF, ☎ (015394) 88877, *craig.manor@btinternet.com, Fax (015394) 88878,* ≤ – ⅍ rest, TV P. MC AE VISA Z i
Paisley's : **Meals** (dinner only and Sunday lunch)/dinner 22.50 and a la carte 20.20/26.70 **t.** 12.00 – **16 rm** 60.00/114.00 – SB.

Wild Boar, Crook Rd, LA23 3NF, Southeast : 4 m. by A 5074 on B 5284 ☎ (015394) 45225, *wildboar@elh.co.uk, Fax (015394) 42498,* – ⅍ TV P – 40. MC AE VISA JCB. ⅍
Meals 23.95 and a la carte 16.50/37.65 **st.** 10.95 – **36 rm** 59.00/138.00 **st.** – SB.

Crag Brow Cottage, Helm Rd, LA23 3BU, ☎ (015394) 44080, *cragbrow@aol.com, Fax (015394) 46003,* – ⅍ TV P. MC VISA JCB. ⅍ Z v
Meals (dinner only and Sunday lunch)/dinner 22.50 **st.** – **11 rm** 45.00/100.00 – SB.

Oakbank House without rest., Helm Rd, LA23 3BU, ☎ (015394) 43386, *enquiries@oakbankhousehotel.co.uk, Fax (015394) 47965,* ≤ – ⅍ TV P. MC VISA JCB Z n
12 rm 45.00/80.00 **st.**

Laurel Cottage without rest., St Martins Sq, Kendal Rd, LA23 3EF, ☎ (015394) 45594, *enquiries@laurelcottage-bnb.co.uk, Fax (015394) 45594* – ⅍ TV P. MC VISA JCB. ⅍ Z a
13 rm 25.00/68.00 **t.**

Troutbeck *North : 4 m. by A 592 – Y – ✉ Windermere.*

Broadoaks ⛶, Bridge Lane, LA23 1LA, South : 1 m. ☎ (015394) 45566, *trev@broadoaksf9.co.uk, Fax (015394) 88766,* ≤, , – ⅍ TV P. MC VISA. ⅍
Meals 13.95/35.00 and a la carte 17.70/51.00 **st.** 12.50 – **13 rm** 69.50/190.00 **st.** – SB.

Queens Head with rm, LA23 1PW, East : ¼ m. on A 592 ☎ (015394) 32174, *enquiries@queensheadhotel.com, Fax (015394) 31938,* ≤, « 17C inn » – ⅍ rm, TV P. MC VISA
closed 25 December – **Meals** 15.50 and a la carte 11.50/24.20 **t.** 9.95 – **15 rm** 56.50/75.00 **t.** – SB.

INDLESHAM *Surrey* 404 S 29 – *pop. 4 525.*
London 40 – *Reading 18 – Southampton 53.*

The Brickmakers, Chertsey Rd, GU20 6HT, East : 1 m. on B 386 ☎ (01276) 472267, *brickmakers@theoldmonk.co.uk, Fax (01276) 451014,* – P. MC AE VISA JCB
Meals a la carte 23.00/28.00 **t.** 9.95.

La guida cambia, cambiate la guida ogni anno.

WINDSOR

Bexley Street . . . . Z 2
Bolton Road . . . . Y 3
Castle Hill . . . . Z 4
Charles Street . . . . Z 5
Claremont Road . . . . Z 6
Clarence Crescent . . . . Z 7
Clewer Crescent Road . . . Z 8
Datchet Rd . . . . Z 9
Goswell Road . . . . Z 10
Grove Road . . . . Z 12
High Street . . . . Z 13
High Street (DATCHET) . . . . Y 14
Horton Road . . . . Y 16
Keats Lane . . . . Z 17
King Edward Court Centre . . . . Z
Peascod Street . . . . Z 19
Ragstone Road . . . . Y 20
River Street . . . . Z 21
Sheet Street Road . . . . Y 22
Stovell Road . . . . Z 23
Thames Avenue . . . . Z 24
Thames Street . . . . Z 25
Trinity Place . . . . Z 27
Windsor Bridge . . . . Z 28
Windsor Road . . . . Y 29

North is at the top on all town plans.

M 4 READING
A 355 SLOUGH WEST
A 332 SLOUGH
UPTON
UPTON PARK
Upton Court Rd
ETON WICK
MYRKE
B 3022
Pococks Lane
B 3026
Eton Wick
Slough Rd
Slough By-Pass
Eton Road
ETON
Southlea Rd
WINDSOR
DATCHET
B 3024
Hatch Lane
B 3173
St. Leonards Road
SPITAL
THE HOME PARK
Southlea Road
B 3021
Thames
Albert Road
MAIDENHEAD A 308
Y
2 km
1 mile
A 332 ASCOT
A 308 STAINES

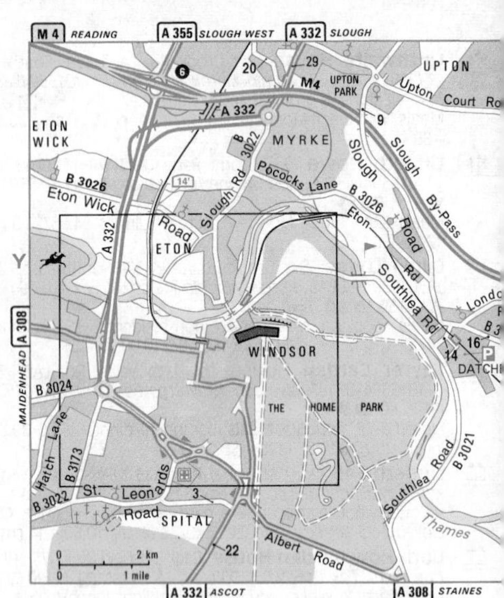

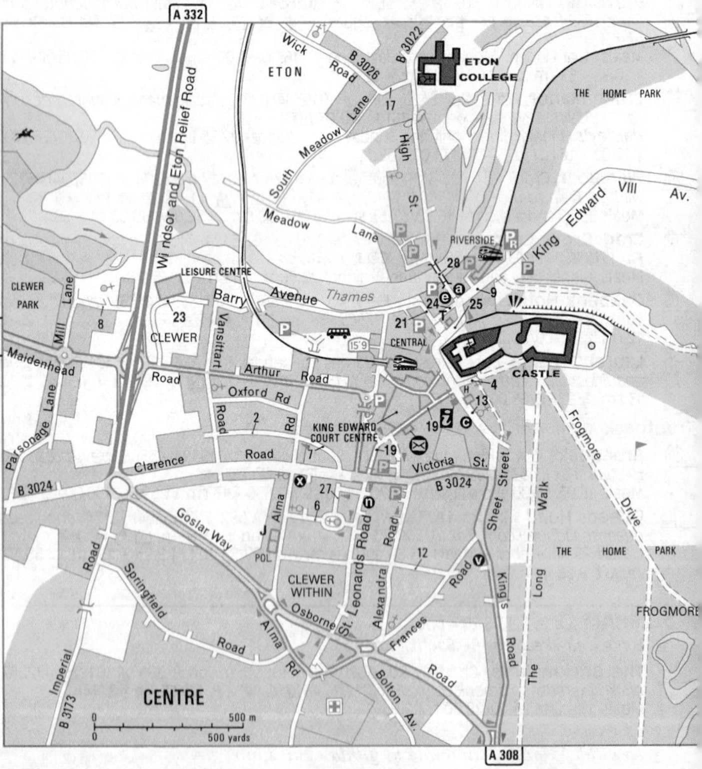

A 332
Wick Road
B 3026
B 3022
ETON
ETON COLLEGE
THE HOME PARK
Keats Lane
High St.
South Meadow Lane
Meadow Lane
Windsor and Eton Relief Road
RIVERSIDE
King Edward VIII Av.
LEISURE CENTRE
Barry Avenue
Thames
CLEWER PARK
Mill Lane
CLEWER
Vansittart Road
CENTRAL
CASTLE
A 308
Maidenhead Road
Arthur Road
Oxford Rd
KING EDWARD COURT CENTRE
Victoria St.
Parsonage Lane
Clarence Road
B 3024
Goslar Way
Alma Road
POL
CLEWER WITHIN
St. Leonards Road
Alexandra Road
Sheet Street
Long Walk
Frogmore Drive
THE HOME PARK
FROGMORE
Springfield Road
Osborne Road
Frances Road
King's Road
The Long Walk
Imperial Road
B 3173
Alma Rd
Bolton Av.
CENTRE
Z
500 m
500 yards
A 308

NDSOR *Windsor & Maidenhead* 404 S 29 *Great Britain G. – pop. 30 136 (inc. Eton).*

See : *Town★ – Castle★★★ : St. George's Chapel★★★ AC (stalls★★★), State Apartments★★ AC, North Terrace (≤★★) Z – Eton College★★ AC (College Chapel★★, Wall paintings★) Z.*

Env. : *Windsor Park★ AC Y.*

to Marlow, Maidenhead and Cookham (Salter Bros. Ltd) (summer only).

24 High St. (01753) 743900.

London 28 – Reading 19 – Southampton 59.

Plan opposite

Oakley Court, Windsor Rd, Water Oakley, SL4 5UR, West : 3 m. on A 308 (01753) 609988, *Fax (01628) 637011,* ≤, « Part Gothic mansion on banks of River Thames », rm, – 160. AE VISA.

The Oakleaf : Meals *(closed Saturday lunch)* 29.50/35.00 and a la carte **st.** 15.90 – 11.50 – **118 rm** 192.00/300.00 **st.**

Castle, High St, SL4 1LJ, (01753) 851011, *candb.castle@heritage-hotels.com, Fax (01753) 830244,* « Former inn built by monks » – – 400. AE VISA — Z c

Castle restaurant : Meals 22.50/24.95 **t.** 14.95 – ***Freshfields :*** Meals 15.95 and a la carte 15.85/25.80 **t.** 14.95 – **111 rm** 176.00/253.00 **st.**, 3 suites – SB.

Sir Christopher Wren's House, Thames St, SL4 1PX, (01753) 861354, *reservations@wrensgroup.com, Fax (01753) 860172,* – – 90. AE VISA JCB. — Z e

Meals 27.75 and a la carte 31.10/43.70 **st.** 16.00 – **81 rm** 170.00/225.00 **st.**, 5 suites – SB.

Royal Adelaide, 46 Kings Rd, SL4 2AG, (01753) 863916, *royaladelaide@meridianleisure.com, Fax (01753) 830682* – rest, – 75. AE VISA. — Z v

Meals (dinner only) 18.95 **st.** 9.95 – **42 rm** 99.00/129.00 **st.** – SB.

The Dorset without rest., 4 Dorset Rd, SL4 3BA, (01753) 852669, *Fax (01753) 852669* – AE VISA JCB. — Z x

closed 21 December-2 January – **4 rm** 64.00/80.00 **st.**

Al Fassia, 27 St Leonards Rd, SL4 3BP, (01753) 855370, *Fax (01753) 855370* – AE VISA — Z n

closed 25-26 December, Sunday and Bank Holidays – **Meals** - Moroccan - (booking essential) 13.50/19.95 and a la carte 16.95/23.40 **t.** 10.50.

Bel and the Dragon, Thames St, SL4 1PQ, (01753) 866056, *windsor@belandthedragon.co.uk, Fax (01753) 865707,* – AE VISA JCB — Z a

Meals 12.95/30.00 a la carte 26.45/36.35 **t.** 11.95.

NEHAM *W. Sussex* 404 T 31 – *see Henfield.*

NFORTON *Herefordshire* 403 K 27 – ✉ *Hereford.*

London 155 – Birmingham 71 – Cardiff 66 – Hereford 15.

Winforton Court without rest., HR3 6EA, (01544) 328498, *winfortoncourt@talk21.com, Fax (01544) 328498,* « 16C », –

closed 23-28 December – **3 rm** 40.00/72.00 **st.**

Sun Inn with rm, HR3 6EA, (01544) 327677, *Fax (01544) 327677,* « Part 17C », – rm,

closed 1 week spring, 1 week autumn, 25 December and Tuesday – **Meals** a la carte 14.50/23.50 **t.** – **3 rm** 35.00/65.00 **t.**

NGFIELD *Suffolk – see Diss.*

NKLEIGH *Devon* 403 I 31 – *pop. 1 063.*

London 218 – Barnstaple 25 – Exeter 23 – Plymouth 43 – Truro 76.

Pophams, Castle St, EX19 8HU, (01837) 83767 – . VISA

closed February and Saturday-Tuesday – **Meals** (booking essential) (lunch only) (unlicensed) a la carte 25.15/30.85.

Dieser Führer ist kein vollständiges Hotel- und Restaurantverzeichnis.
Um den Ansprüchen aller Touristen gerecht zu werden,
haben wir uns auf eine Auswahl in jeder Kategorie beschränkt.

ENGLAND

WINSCOMBE *Somerset* 403 L 30 *The West Country G. – pop. 4 192.*

Env. : *Axbridge★★ (King John's Hunting Lodge★, St. John the Baptist Church★), S : 1¾ m. A 38 and A 371.*

London 137 – Bristol 16 – Taunton 22.

Premier Lodge, Bridgwater Rd, BS25 1NN, on A 38 ☎ (0870) 70013 *Fax (0870) 7001341,* – rm, TV & P. MC AE VISA.

Meals (grill rest.) a la carte approx. 13.00 **t.** 8.95 – **31 rm** 46.95 **t.**

WINSFORD *Somerset* 403 J 30 *The West Country G. – pop. 270 – ✉ Minehead.*

See : *Village★.*

Env. : *Exmoor National Park★★.*

London 194 – Exeter 31 – Minehead 10 – Taunton 32.

Royal Oak Inn, Exmoor National Park, TA24 7JE, ☎ (01643) 851455, *enquiries@royalo somerset, Fax (01643) 851009,* « Attractive part 12C thatched inn », – TV P. MC AE VISA

Meals (bar lunch Monday-Saturday)/dinner a la carte 22.60/27.85 **t.** – **14 rm** 86 150.00 **t.** – SB.

Karslake House with rm, Halse Lane, Exmoor National Park, TA24 ☎ (01643) 851242, *karslakehouse@aol.com, Fax (01643) 851242,* – TV P. MC VISA *closed Christmas, February and March* – **Meals** (dinner only) (residents only Sunday-M day) 27.50 **t.** 15.00 – **6 rm** (dinner included) 95.00/150.00 **t.** – SB.

Pour les grands voyages d'affaires ou de tourisme, Guide Rouge ***MICHELIN : Main Cities EUROPE.***

WINSLEY *Wilts.* 403 404 N 29 – *see Bradford-on-Avon.*

WINTERBOURNE *South Gloucestershire* 403 404 M 29 – *see Bristol.*

WINTERBOURNE STEEPLETON *Dorset* 403 404 M 31 – *see Dorchester.*

WINTERINGHAM *North Lincolnshire* 402 S 22 – *pop. 4 714 – ✉ Scunthorpe.*

London 176 – Kingston-upon-Hull 16 – Sheffield 67.

Winteringham Fields (Schwab) with rm, Silver St, DN15 9PF, ☎ (01724) 733 *wintfields@aol.com, Fax (01724) 733898,* « Part 16C manor house » – TV P. MC VISA

✿✿ *closed last week March, first week August, last week October and 2 weeks Christm* **Meals** *(closed Sunday-Monday)* (booking essential to non-residents) 26.00/35 and a la carte 56.00/67.00 **st.** 17.50 – 10.00 – **8 rm** 75.00/165.00 **st.**, 2 suites

Spec. Pan-fried langoustine, tuile of aubergine marmalade. Duo of squab with b pudding and truffle potato purée. Rhubarb poached in rapsberry syrup with puff pastr

WITCHFORD *Cambs.* 404 U 26 – *see Ely.*

WITCOMBE *Glos. – see Gloucester.*

WITHERSLACK *Cumbria* 402 L 21 – *see Grange-over-Sands.*

WITNEY *Oxon.* 403 404 P 28 – *pop. 20 377.*

51A Market Sq. ☎ (01993) 775802.

London 69 – Gloucester 39 – Oxford 13.

Witney Four Pillars, Ducklington Lane, OX8 7TJ, South : 1 ½ m. on A ☎ (01993) 779777, *witney@fourpillars.co.uk, Fax (01993) 703467,* – rest, TV & P – 160. MC AE VISA JCB

Meals 7.95/18.95 and a la carte approx. 28.00 **st.** 5.25 – 8.75 – **83 rm** 89.00/99.00 s SB.

at Hailey *North : 1¼ m. on B 4022 – ✉ Witney.*

Bird in Hand, White Oak Green, OX29 9XP, North : 1 m. on B 4022 ☎ (01993) 8683 *birdinhand@heavitreeinns.co.uk, Fax (01993) 868702,* – TV & P. MC VISA JCB.

Meals a la carte 13.15/25.40 **t.** 9.20 – **16 rm** 49.50/58.00 **t.** – SB.

ENGLAND

Barnard Gate *East : 3 1/4 m. by B 4022 off A 40 – ✉ Eynsham.*

The Boot Inn, OX8 6XE, ✆ (01865) 881231, *bootinn@barnardgate.fsnet.co.uk, Fax (01865) 882119,* , « Collection of celebrities boots » – P. MC AE VISA
Meals (booking essential) a la carte 19.95/25.00 ₰ 9.75.

South Leigh *Southeast : 3 m. by B 4022 – ✉ Witney.*

Mason Arms with rm, OX8 6XN, ✆ (01993) 702485, « 15C thatched inn », – TV P. AE.
closed 1 week Christmas and 2 weeks August – **Meals** a la carte 23.95/36.90 **t.** ₰ 14.00 – **2 rm** 35.00/60.00 **t.**

WITTERSHAM *Kent* 404 W 30 – *pop. 1 431* – ✉ *Tenterden.*
London 59 – Brighton 54 – Folkestone 22 – Maidstone 28.

Wittersham Court , The Street, TN30 7EA, ✆ (01797) 270425, *watsoni5@aol.com, Fax (01797) 270425,* « Part 17C », , – P. MC VISA.
closed Christmas and New Year – **Meals** (by arrangement) (communal dining) 25.00 **st.** – **3 rm** 55.00/80.00.

WIVELISCOMBE *Somerset* 403 K 30 *The West Country G.* – *pop. 1 753* – ✉ *Taunton.*
Env. : *Gaulden Manor★ AC, NE : 3 m. by B 3188.*
London 185 – Barnstaple 38 – Exeter 37 – Taunton 14.

Langley House, Langley Marsh, TA4 2UF, North : 3/4 m. ✆ (01984) 623318, *user@langley.in2home.co.uk, Fax (01984) 624573,* – rest, TV P. MC AE VISA
Meals (booking essential to non-residents) (dinner only) (set menu only) 27.50 **st.** ₰ 12.50 – **8 rm** 82.50/127.50 **st.** – SB.

WIX *Essex* 404 X 28 – ✉ *Manningtree.*
London 70 – Colchester 10 – Harwich 7 – Ipswich 16.

Dairy House Farm without rest., Bradfield Rd, CO11 2SR, Northwest : 1 m. ✆ (01255) 870322, *bridgetwhitworth@hotmail.com, Fax (01255) 870186,* ←, « Working farm », , – TV P.
3 rm 28.00/44.00.

WOBURN *Beds.* 404 S 28 *Great Britain G.* – *pop. 1 534* – ✉ *Milton Keynes.*
See : *Woburn Abbey★★.*
London 49 – Bedford 13 – Luton 13 – Northampton 24.

Bedford Arms, George St, MK17 9PX, ✆ (01525) 290441, *hotel@woburn_fsbusiness.co.uk, Fax (01525) 290432* – rm, rest, TV P – 60. MC AE VISA JCB.
closed January-April – **Meals** a la carte 15.95/22.50 **t.** ₰ 10.50 – 11.00 – **51 rm** 105.00/148.00, 2 suites – SB.

Paris House, Woburn Park, MK17 9QP, Southeast : 2 1/4 m. on A 4012 ✆ (01525) 290692, *gailbaker@parishouse.co.uk, Fax (01525) 290471,* « Reconstructed timbered house in park », – P. MC AE VISA
closed February, 26 December, 1 January, Sunday dinner and Monday – **Meals** 25.00/50.00 **t.** ₰ 15.00.

The Birch, 20 Newport Rd, MK17 9HX, North : 1/2 m. on A 5130 ✆ (01525) 290295, *Fax (01525) 290899,* – rest, P. MC AE VISA
closed 25 December, 1 January and Sunday dinner – **Meals** (booking essential) a la carte 20.40/25.40 **t.** ₰ 14.95.

WOKING *Surrey* 404 S 30.

Holiday Inn, Victoria Way (A 320), GU21 1EW, ✆ (01483) 221000, *Fax (01483) 221021,* , – , rm, TV P – 90. MC AE VISA
Meals a la carte 22.50/27.00 **t.** ₰ 13.00 – 13.00 – **161 rm** 157.00.

WOKINGHAM *Wokingham* **404** R 29 – *pop. 38 063.*

Sand Martins, Finchampstead Rd ☏ (0118) 979 2711 – *Hurst, Sandford Lane ☏ (01 344355.*

London 43 – Reading 7 – Southampton 52.

Hilton St Anne's Manor, London Rd, RG40 1ST, East : 1 ½ m. on A ☏ (0118) 9772550, *reservations@stannes.stakis.co.uk, Fax (0118) 9772526*, rm, TV 250. AE VISA.
closed 27-29 December – **Meals** *(closed Saturday lunch)* (carving lunch)/dinner 2 and a la carte 25.00/44.85 **t.** 15.10 – 13.45 – **170 rm** 220.00/240.00 **st.**

Rose Street, 6 Rose St, RG40 1XU, ☏ (0118) 9788025, *Fax (0118) 9891314* – VISA
closed Sunday and Bank Holidays – **Meals** 14.95/18.95 (lunch) and a la carte 24.95/36.7 13.75.

WOLVERHAMPTON *W. Mids.* **402 403 404** N 26 – *pop. 257 943.*

18 Queen Sq. ☏ (01902) 556110.

London 132 – Birmingham 15 – Liverpool 89 – Shrewsbury 30.

Plan of Enlarged Area : see Birmingham pp. 4 and 5

WOLVERHAMPTON

Quality, 126 Penn Rd, WV3 0ER, (01902) 429216, *Fax (01902) 710419*, – 120. . B c
Meals (bar lunch Saturday) 10.50/16.95 **st.** 11.95 – 10.75 – **92 rm** 89.00/99.00 **t.** – SB.

Novotel, Union St, WV1 3JN, (01902) 871100, *Fax (01902) 870054*, heated – , rm, rest, – 200. . B a
Meals 10.00/17.00 and a la carte 13.45/23.45 **st.** 11.70 – 10.00 – **132 rm** 72.00 **st.**

Holiday Inn Garden Court, Dunstall Park, WV6 0PE, North : 1 ¾ m. by A 449 (01902) 713313, *enquiries@dunstallpark.com*, *Fax (01902) 714364*, – , rm, . A c
closed 25 December, 1 January **Meals** (bar lunch Sunday) 14.00 (dinner) and a la carte 12.00/24.00 **st.** 12.50 – 9.50 – **54 rm** 70.00 **st.** – SB.

Ely House, 53 Tettenhall Rd, WV3 9NB, (01902) 311311, *mail@elyhousehotel.co.uk*, *Fax (01902) 421098* – . B u
closed 25-30 December
Meals *(closed Sunday dinner)* 12.95/21.00 **st.** 9.50 – **19 rm** 69.00/99.00 **st.**

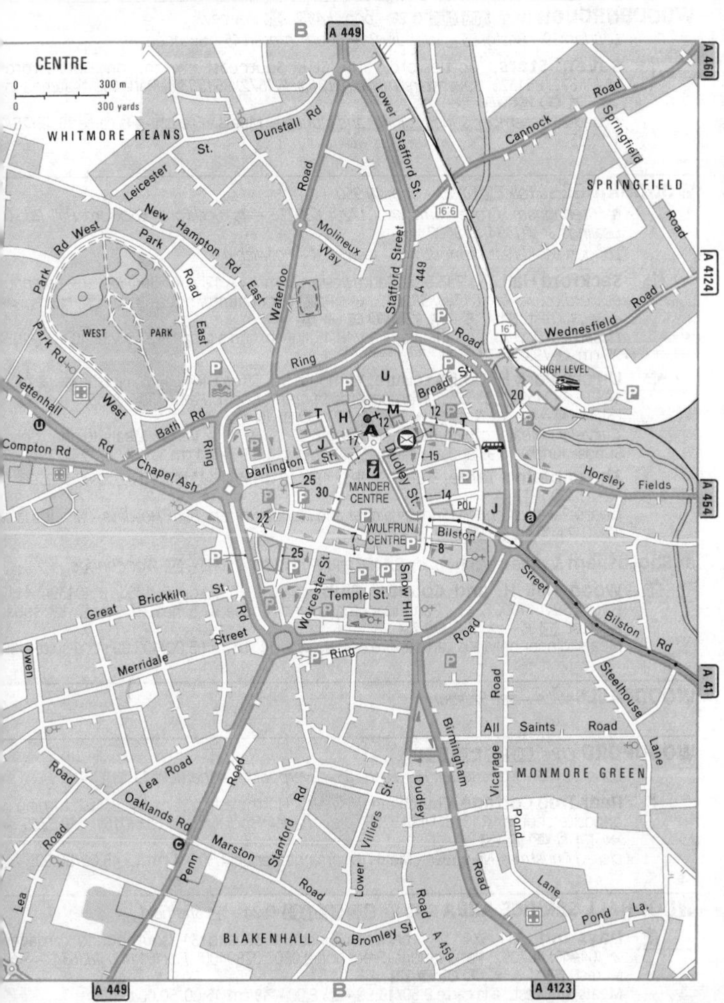

ENGLAND

Travel Inn, Wolverhampton Business Park, Greedfield Lane, Stafford Rd, WV10
North : 3 ½ m. by A 449 at junction with M 54 (01902) 397755, *Fax (01902) 785260*
, rest, – 50. .
Meals (grill rest.) – **54 rm** 41.95 **t.**

WOLVISTON *Cleveland 402 Q 20 – pop. 2 482 – Stockton-on-Tees.*
London 280 – Carlisle 93 – Middlesbrough 8 – Newcastle upon Tyne 37 – Sunderland 23

Express by Holiday Inn without rest., Wynyard Park Services, Coal Lane, TS22 5PZ
A 689 at junction with A 19 (01740) 644000, *Fax (01740) 644111* – –
.
49 rm 52.50 **st.**

WOOBURN COMMON *Bucks. – see Beaconsfield.*

WOODBOROUGH *Wilts. 403 404 O 29 – pop. 1 495 – Pewsey.*
London 89 – Bristol 53 – Salisbury 21 – Southampton 45 – Swindon 19.

Seven Stars, Bottlesford, SN9 6LU, Southeast : ¾ m. on Bottlesford
(01672) 851325, *sevenstars@dialin.net, Fax (01672) 851583,* « Part 16C thatched in
– . .
closed 25 December, Sunday dinner and Monday – **Meals** - French - a la carte 16.45/25.4
10.25.

WOODBRIDGE *Suffolk 404 X 27 – pop. 10 950.*
*Cretingham, Grove Farm (01728) 685275 – Seckford, Seckford Hall Rd, G
Bealings (01394) 388000.*
London 81 – Great Yarmouth 45 – Ipswich 8 – Norwich 47.

Seckford Hall , IP13 6NU, Southwest : 1 ¼ m. by A 12 (01394) 385678, *receptio
eckford.co.uk, Fax (01394) 380610,* <, « Part Tudor country house », , , , ,
– , rest, – 120.
closed 25 December – **Meals** 14.90/18.45 (lunch) and a la carte 22.90/36.40 **st.** 10.9
25 rm 79.00/170.00 **st.**, 7 suites – SB.

Ufford Park H. Golf & Leisure, Yarmouth Rd, Ufford, IP12 1QW, Northeast : 2 m.
1438 (01394) 383555, *uffordparkltd@btinternet.com, Fax (01394) 383582,* <, ,
, , – , rest, – 200. .
Carvery : **Meals** (carvery) (dinner only) 16.95 **t.** 9.95 – ***Vista :*** **Meals** (dinner only
Sunday lunch) 16.95 and a la carte 16.55/22.85 **t.** 9.95 – **44 rm** 77.00/125.00 **st.** – S

The Captain's Table, 3 Quay St, IP12 1BX, (01394) 383145, *Fax (01394) 388508,*
.
closed 2 weeks January, Sunday dinner and Monday except Bank Holidays – **Meals** a la c
12.70/21.00 **st.** 8.95.

at Shottisham *Southeast : 5 ¾ m. by B 1438 and A 1152 on B 1083 – Woodbridge.*

Wood Hall H. and Country Club , IP12 3EG, on B 1083 (01394) 4111
Fax (01394) 410007, <, « Part Elizabethan manor house », heated, , , , squa
rest, – 150.
Meals (dinner only) a la carte approx. 20.00 **st.** – **14 rm** 65.00/105.00 **st.**, 1 suite – SB

WOODFALLS *Wilts. – see Salisbury.*

WOODFORD *Ches. 402 ㉝ 403 404 ⑩.*
London 193 – Manchester 13 – Leeds 55 – Liverpool 45 – Sheffield 49.

Pear Tree Cottage, Church Lane, SK7 1PQ, Northwest : 1 ½ m. by A 5102, turning r
opposite church (0161) 439 5755, *p.t.cottage@fsbdial.co.uk, Fax (0161) 439 5755,*
.
closed Christmas-New Year – **Meals** (by arrangement) 14.50 – **4 rm** 45.00/80.00.

WOODHALL SERVICE AREA *S. Yorks. 402 403 404 Q 24 – Sheffield.*

Days Inn, S31 8XR, M 1 between junctions 30 and 31 (southbound carriagew
(01142) 487992, Reservations (Freephone) 0800 0280400, *Fax (01142) 485634* –
rest, .
Meals (grill rest.) a la carte 8.60/13.90 – 8.00 – **38 rm** 45.00/50.00 **t.**

OODHALL SPA *Lincs.* 402 404 T 24 *Great Britain G. – pop. 3 337.*

Env. : *Tattershall Castle★ AC, SE : 4 m. by B 1192 and A 153.*

Woodhall Spa ✆ (01526) 351835.

The Cottage Museum, Iddesleigh Rd ✆ (01526) 353775 (summer only).

London 138 – Lincoln 18.

The Petwood, Stixwould Rd, LN10 6QF, ✆ (01526) 352411, *reception@petwood.co.uk, Fax (01526) 353473,* ≤, « Gardens », 18, – – 150. MO AE VISA
Meals (bar lunch Monday-Saturday)/dinner 20.50/36.00 **t.** 11.75 – **49 rm** 60.00/120.00 **t.**, 1 suite – SB.

OODSTOCK *Oxon.* 403 404 P 28 *Great Britain G. – pop. 2 898.*

See : *Blenheim Palace★★★ (The Grounds★★★) AC.*

Oxfordshire Museum, Park St. ✆ (01993) 813276.

London 65 – Gloucester 47 – Oxford 8.

Bear, Park St, OX20 1SZ, ✆ (0870) 4008202, *heritagehotels-woodstock.bear@forte-hotels.com, Fax (01993) 813380,* « Part 16C inn » – TV – 30. MO AE VISA
Meals 14.50/23.00 and a la carte 19.00/36.00 **t.** 14.50 – 14.50 – **51 rm** 135.00/155.00 **t.**, 3 suites – SB.

Feathers, Market St, OX20 1SX, ✆ (01993) 812291, *enquiries@feathers.co.uk, Fax (01993) 813158,* « Restored 17C houses » – rest, rest, TV. MO AE VISA JCB
Meals (booking essential) 19.50 (lunch) and dinner a la carte 34.50/47.50 **t.** 12.50 – **16 rm** 115.00/185.00 **t.**, 4 suites – SB.

Shipton Glebe, OX20 1QQ, East : 2 ½ m. by A 44 and A 4095 turning left onto unmarked rd after Shipton Rd ✆ (01993) 812688, *stay@shipton-glebe.com, Fax (01993) 813142,* – TV . MO VISA
Meals (by arrangement) 25.00 **st.** – **3 rm** 60.00/85.00 **st.** – SB.

The Townhouse without rest., 15 High St, OX20 1TE, ✆ (01993) 810843, *info@woodstock-townhouse.com, Fax (01993) 810843* – TV. MO AE VISA
5 rm 45.00/75.00.

Plane Tree House without rest., 48 Oxford St, OX20 1TT, ✆ (01993) 813075 – TV
3 rm 50.00/80.00 **t.**

The Laurels without rest., Hensington Rd, OX20 1JL, ✆ (01993) 812583, *malnikk@aol.com, Fax (01993) 812583* – TV. MO VISA JCB.
closed 14 December-3 January – **3 rm** 45.00/60.00.

Wootton *North : 2½ m. by A 44 – ✉ Woodstock.*

Kings Head with rm, Chapel Hill, OX20 1DX, ✆ (01993) 811340, *t.fay@kings-head.co.uk, Fax (01993) 813131* – TV . MO VISA.
closed 25 December, Sunday dinner and Monday lunch – **Meals** a la carte 17.80/27.40 **t.** 10.95 – **3 rm** 70.00/105.00 **t.** – SB.

OOFFERTON *Shrops. – see Ludlow.*

OOKEY HOLE *Somerset* 403 L 30 – *see Wells.*

OOLACOMBE *Devon* 403 H 30 *The West Country G.*

Env. : *Exmoor National Park★★ – Mortehoe★★ (St. Mary's Church★, Morte Point – vantage point★) N : ½ m. – Ilfracombe : Hillsborough (≤★★) AC, Capstone Hill★ (≤★), St. Nicholas' Chapel (≤★) AC, NE : 5½ m. by B 3343 and A 361.*

Exc. : *Braunton★ (St. Braunton's Church★, Braunton Burrows★), S : 8 m. by B 3343 and A 361.*

The Esplanade ✆ (01271) 870553.

London 237 – Barnstaple 15 – Exeter 55.

Woolacombe Bay, South St, EX34 7BN, ✆ (01271) 870388, *woolacombebayhotel@btinternet.com, Fax (01271) 870613,* ≤, , , heated, , , , squash – , rest, rest, TV – 200. MO AE VISA JCB.
closed January-mid February – **Meals** (dancing Thursday and Saturday evening) (dinner only and Sunday lunch)/dinner 30.00 **st.** 9.95 – **64 rm** 115.00/230.00 **st.** – SB.

Little Beach without rest., The Esplanade, EX34 7DJ, ✆ (01271) 870398, ≤ – TV . MO VISA
March-October – **8 rm** 34.00/64.00 **s.**

ENGLAND

at Mortehoe *North : ½ m. – ✉ Woolacombe.*

Watersmeet, The Esplanade, EX34 7EB, ☎ (01271) 870333, *info@watersmeeth co.uk, Fax (01271) 870890,* ≤ Morte Bay, heated, , , – rest, P.
closed January – **Meals** (bar lunch Monday-Saturday)/dinner 20.00/28.00 **t.** 11.95 – 22 (dinner included) 102.00/240.00 **t.**

Cleeve House, EX34 7ED, ☎ (01271) 870719, *cleevehouse@mcmail.c Fax (01271) 870719,* – P. VISA.
April-October – **Meals** (by arrangement) (dinner only) 14.00/17.00 **t.** 8.00 – 7 43.00/64.00 **s.** – SB.

WOOLAVINGTON *Somerset* 403 L 30 – *see Bridgwater.*

WOOLLEY EDGE SERVICE AREA *W. Yorks.* 402 404 P 23 – ✉ *Wakefield.*

Travelodge without rest., WF4 4LQ, M 1 between junctions 38 and 39 (northbo carriageway) ☎ (01924) 830371, *Fax (01924) 830609* – P. VISA JCB.
32 rm 49.95 **t.**

WOOLSTHORPE-BY-BELVOIR *Lincs.* 402 404 R 25 – *see Grantham.*

In alta stagione, *e soprattutto nelle stazioni turistiche, è prudente prenotare con un certo anticipo. Avvertite immediatamente l'albergatore se non potete più occupare la camera prenotata.*

Se scrivete ad un albergo all'estero, allegate alla vostra lettera un tagliando-risposta internazionale (disponibile presso gli uffici postali).

WOOLTON *Mersey.* 402 403 L 23 – *see Liverpool.*

WOOLVERSTONE *Suffolk* 404 X 27 – *see Ipswich.*

WOOTTON *Oxon.* 403 404 P 28 – *see Woodstock.*

WOOTTON BASSETT *Wilts.* 403 404 O 29 – *see Swindon.*

WORCESTER *Worcs.* 403 404 N 27 *Great Britain G. – pop. 82 661.*
See : *City*★ – *Cathedral*★★ – *Royal Worcester Porcelain Works*★ *(Dyson Per Museum*★*)* **M.**
Exc. : *The Elgar Trail*★.
Perdiswell Park, Bilford Rd ☎ (01905) 754668.
The Guildhall, High St. ☎ (01905) 726311.
London 124 – Birmingham 26 – Bristol 61 – Cardiff 74.

Plan opposite

Diglis House, Severn St, WR1 2NF, ☎ (01905) 353518, *diglishouse@yahoo.c Fax (01905) 767772,* ≤, , « Georgian house on banks of River Severn », – rest P. VISA.
Meals (bar lunch)/dinner 19.50 **st.** 13.00 – **25 rm** 80.00/125.00 **st.**, 1 suite – SB.

Travel Inn, Wainwright Way, Warndon, WR4 9FA, Northeast : 5 ½ m. by A 449 (at junc 6 of M 5) ☎ (01905) 451240, *Fax (01905) 756601* – rm, . VISA.
Meals (grill rest.) – **60 rm** 41.95 **t.**

Glass House, Church St, WR1 2RH, ☎ (01905) 611120, « Part 16C » – . VISA
closed first 2 weeks January, Sunday and Monday – **Meals** 13.95 (lunch) and a la c 21.95/31.85 **t.** 11.50.

Brown's, 24 Quay St, WR1 2JJ, ☎ (01905) 26263, *Fax (01905) 25768,* « Converted ri side corn mill » – VISA JCB
closed 1 week Christmas, Monday, Sunday dinner and Saturday lunch – **Meals** 19 36.50 **st.** 11.95.

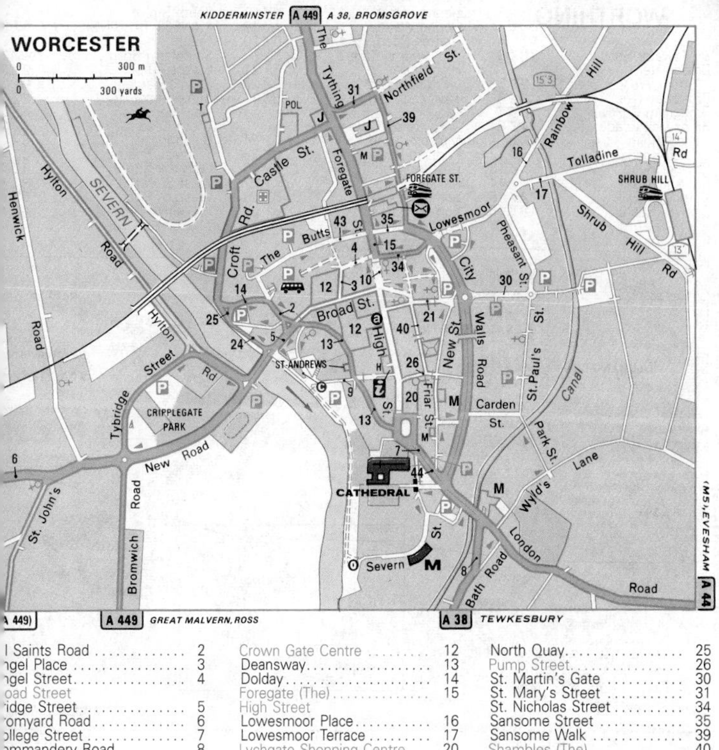

l Saints Road	2	Crown Gate Centre	12	North Quay	25
ngel Place	3	Deansway	13	Pump Street	26
ngel Street	4	Dolday	14	St. Martin's Gate	30
oad Street		Foregate (The)	15	St. Mary's Street	31
idge Street	5	High Street		St. Nicholas Street	34
omyard Road	6	Lowesmoor Place	16	Sansome Street	35
ollege Street	7	Lowesmoor Terrace	17	Sansome Walk	39
ommandery Road	8	Lychgate Shopping Centre	20	Shambles (The)	40
openhagen Street	9	Mealcheapen Street	21	Shaw Street	43
oss (The)	10	North Parade	24	Sidbury	44

Bitte beachten Sie die Geschwindigkeitsbeschränkungen in Großbritannien
- 60 mph (= 96 km/h) außerhalb geschlossener Ortschaften
- 70 mph (= 112 km/h) auf Straßen mit getrennten Fahrbahnen und Autobahnen.

ORFIELD *Shrops. – see Bridgnorth.*

ORKSOP *Notts.* 402 403 404 Q 24 *Great Britain G. – pop. 37 247.*

See : *Mr. Straw's House*★.

18 *Kilton Forest, Blyth Rd ☎ (01909) 472488.*

Worksop Library, Memorial Av. ☎ (01909) 501148.

London 163 – Derby 47 – Lincoln 28 – Nottingham 30 – Sheffield 19.

Clumber Park, Clumber Park, S80 3PA, Southeast : 6 ½ m. by B 6040 and A 57 on A 614 ☎ (01623) 835333, *Fax (01623) 835525*, – rm, – 180. AE VISA.
Limetree : Meals 11.50/21.50 and a la carte 20.25/32.75 **st.** 11.95 – 10.95 – **48 rm** 65.00/110.00 **st.** – SB.

Travelodge, Dukeries Mill, St Anne's Drive, S80 3QD, West : ½ m. off A 57 ☎ (01909) 501528, *Fax (01909) 501528* – rm, AE VISA JCB.
Meals (grill rest.) – **40 rm** 39.95 **t.**

ORMALD GREEN *N. Yorks.* 402 P 21 – *see Ripon.*

ORSLEY *Gtr. Manchester* 402 403 404 MN 23 – *see Manchester.*

WORTHING

Broadwater Road .... BZ 3
Broadwater Street West .... BY 5
Broadway (The) .... BZ 6
Brougham Road .... BY 7
Brunswick Road .... AZ 8
Chapel Road .... BZ
Church Road .... AY 12
Cowper Road .... AZ 13
Crockhurst Hill .... AY 14
Durrington Hill .... AY 15
Eriswell Road .... ABZ 16
Goring Street .... AY 17
Goring Way .... AY 18
Grafton Road .... BZ 20
Guildbourne Centre .... BZ
High Street .... BZ 21
Liverpool Road .... BZ 22
Montague Street .... BZ
Montague Centre Shopping Centre .... BZ
Mulberry Lane .... AY 24
Portland Road .... BZ 25
Rectory Road .... AY 26
Reigate Road .... AY 27
Sompting Avenue .... BY 28
Sompting Road .... BY 29
South Street (WEST TARRING) .... AY, AZ
South Street (WORTHING) .... BZ
Southfarm Road .... ABZ
Steyne (The) .... BZ
Steyne Garden .... BZ
Stoke Abbot Road .... BZ
Tennyson Road .... AZ
Thorn Road .... AZ
Union Place .... BZ
Warwick Road .... BZ
Warwick Street .... BZ
West Street .... BZ
Western Place .... BZ
Wykeham Road .... AZ

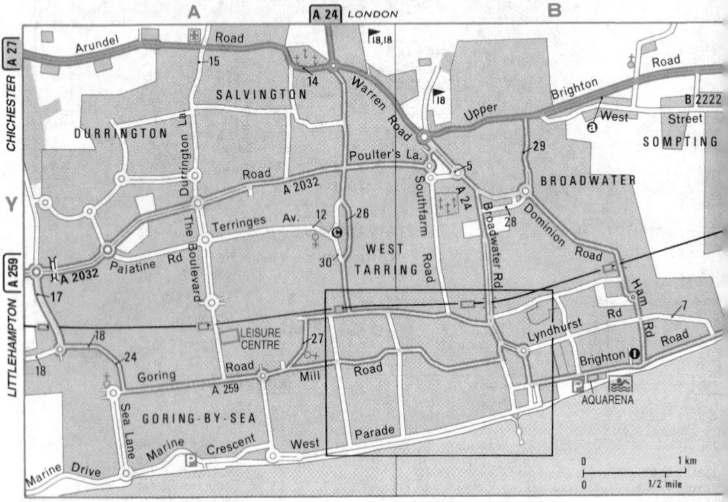

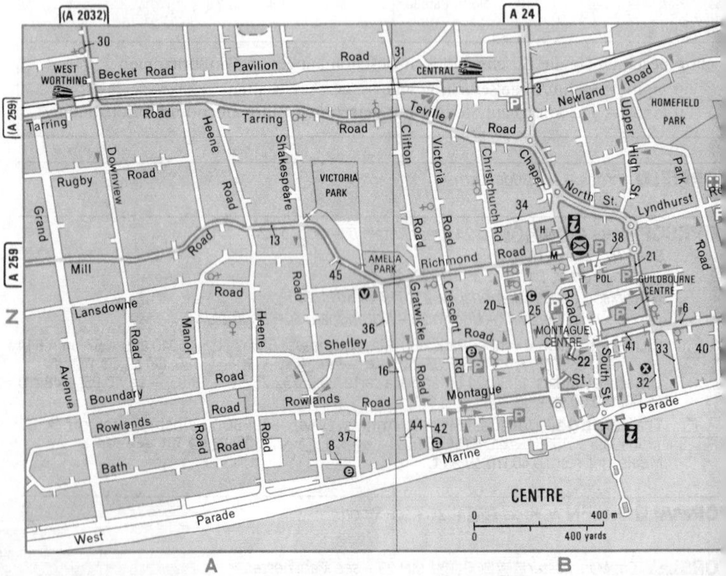

WORTHING *W. Sussex* 404 S 31 – *pop. 95 732.*

Hill Barn, Hill Barn Lane ☎ (01903) 237301 BY – *Links Rd ☎ (01903) 260801* AY.
Shoreham Airport : ☎ (01273) 296900, E : 4 m. by A 27 BY.
Chapel Rd ☎ (01903) 210022 – Marine Par. ☎ (01903) 210022.
London 59 – Brighton 11 – Southampton 50.

Plan opposite

Beach, Marine Par, BN11 3QJ, ☎ (01903) 234001, *thebeachhotel@btinternet.com, Fax (01903) 234567,* ← – |‡| TV ♿ P – 🎓 250. MC AE ① VISA. ✗ AZ e
Meals (bar lunch Monday-Saturday)/dinner 19.50/25.00 **st.** 10.50 – **79 rm** 59.75/100.00 **st.**, 4 suites – SB.

Chatsworth, Steyne, BN11 3DU, ☎ (01903) 236103, *chatsworth@wakefordhotels.co.uk, Fax (01903) 823726* – |‡|, ⇔ rest, TV – 🎓 150. MC AE ① VISA BZ x
Meals (dinner only) 15.95 **t.** 9.95 – **107 rm** 59.00/92.00 **t.** – SB.

Berkeley, 86-95 Marine Par, BN11 3QD, ☎ (01903) 820000, *berkeley@wakefordhotels.co.uk, Fax (01903) 821333,* ← – |‡| TV ♿ P – 🎓 150. MC AE ① VISA. ✗ BZ a
Meals (bar lunch Monday-Saturday)/dinner 15.00 10.00 – **80 rm** 79.00/102.00 **t.** – SB.

The Windsor, 14-20 Windsor Rd, BN11 2LX, ☎ (01903) 239655, Reservations (Freephone) 0800 9804242, *enquiries@thewindsor.co.uk, Fax (01903) 210763,* ⇔ – ⇔ rest, ▤ rest, TV P – 🎓 120. MC AE ① VISA JCB. ✗ BY i
closed 24-31 December – **Meals** (buffet lunch)/dinner 16.95 and a la carte 17.70/26.95 **t.** 10.95 – **30 rm** 70.00/115.00 **t.** – SB.

Beacons without rest., 18 Shelley Rd, BN11 1TU, ☎ (01903) 230948, *Fax (01903) 230948* – ⇔ TV P. MC VISA BZ e
8 rm 32.00/60.00 **st.**

Bonchurch House without rest., 1 Winchester Rd, BN11 4DJ, ☎ (01903) 202492, *bonchurch@enta.net, Fax (01903) 202492* – TV P. MC VISA JCB. ✗ AZ v
7 rm 25.00/52.00 **t.**

Upton Farm House without rest., Upper Brighton Rd, Sompting Village, BN14 9JU, ☎ (01903) 233706, ⇔ – ⇔ TV P BY a
3 rm 25.00/50.00 **st.**

Trenchers, 118-120 Portland Rd, BN11 1QA, ☎ (01903) 820287, *Fax (01903) 820305* – MC ① VISA BZ c
closed Sunday dinner and Monday – **Meals** 25.00/30.00 and a la carte 39.00/52.00 7.00.

Parsonage, 6-10 High St, Tarring, BN14 7NN, ☎ (01903) 820140, *Fax (01903) 523233,* 🏠, « 15C cottages » – MC AE VISA. ✗ AY c
closed 25-26 December, 1 January, Sunday and Bank Holidays – **Meals** 22.50 and a la carte 24.85/34.00 **t.**

The Brasserie (at Trenchers), 118-120 Portland Rd, BN11 1QA, ☎ (01903) 820287, *Fax (01903) 820305* – ⇔ BZ c
closed Sunday dinner and Monday – **Meals** a la carte 16.40/25.95.

WREA GREEN *Lancs.* 402 L 22 – *see Kirkham.*

WRESSLE *East Riding* 402 R 22 *Great Britain G.* – ✉ *Selby (N. Yorks.).*
Env. : *Selby (Abbey Church★), W : 5 m. by minor road and A 63.*
London 208 – Kingston-upon-Hull 31 – Leeds 31 – York 19.

Loftsome Bridge Coaching House, YO8 6EN, South : ½ m. ☎ (01757) 630070, *reception@loftsomebridge-hotel.co.uk, Fax (01757) 633900,* ⇔ – ⇔, ▤ rest, TV P. MC AE VISA. ✗
Meals (dinner only and Sunday lunch)/dinner 18.95/19.95 **st.** 8.90 – **16 rm** 44.50/57.00 **st.**, 1 suite.

WRIGHTINGTON BAR *Gtr. Manchester* 402 404 L 23 – *see Standish.*

WROTHAM HEATH *Kent* 404 U 30 – *pop. 1 767* – ✉ *Sevenoaks.*
London 35 – Maidstone 10.

Holiday Inn, London Rd, TN15 7RS, on A 20 ☎ (0870) 400 9054, *Fax (01732) 885850,* 🏋, ≘s, 🏊, ⇔ – ⇔ rm, TV ♿ P – 🎓 60. MC AE ① VISA
Meals 15.00 and a la carte 20.85/29.15 **t.** 11.95 – 13.95 – **106 rm** 104.00/124.00 **st.** – SB.

Travel Inn, London Rd, TN15 7RX, on A 20 ☎ (01732) 884214, *Fax (01732) 780368* – ⇔ rm, TV ♿ P. MC AE ① VISA. ✗
Meals (grill rest.) – **40 rm** 41.95 **t.**

WROXHAM *Norfolk* 404 Y 25 *Great Britain G. – pop. 3 247 (inc. Hoveton).*
Env. : *The Broads*★.
London 118 – Great Yarmouth 21 – Norwich 7.

Garden Cottage, 96 Norwich Rd, NR12 8RY, ☎ (01603) 784376, *Fax (01603) 78373*
Meals (by arrangement) 15.00 **st.** 8.00 – **3 rm** 35.00/55.00 **st.** – SB.

WROXTON *Oxon.* 403 404 P 27 – *see Banbury.*

WYCH CROSS *E. Sussex* 404 U 30 – *see Forest Row.*

WYE *Kent* 404 W 30 – *pop. 1 608* – ✉ *Ashford.*
London 60 – Canterbury 10 – Dover 28 – Hastings 34.

Wife of Bath with rm, 4 Upper Bridge St, TN25 5AF, ☎ (01233) 812540, *reservation wifeofbath.com, Fax (01233) 813630,* – rm, VISA
closed 1 week after Christmas – **Meals** *(closed Sunday-Monday)* 15.75/25. and lunch a la carte 20.95/27.50 **t.** 13.75 – 5.00 – **5 rm** 45.00/95.00 **t.**

WYMONDHAM *Norfolk* 404 X 26 – *pop. 10 869.*
London 102 – Cambridge 55 – King's Lynn 49 – Norwich 12.

Wymondham Consort, 28 Market St, NR18 0BB, ☎ (01953) 606721, *wymondh @bestwestern.co.uk, Fax (01953) 601361,* – VISA
Meals 10.95/17.00 and dinner a la carte 18.45/23.50 **t.** 8.00 – **20 rm** 55.00/75.00 **t** SB.

In alta stagione, e soprattutto nelle stazioni turistiche, è prudente prenotare con un certo anticipo.
Avvertite immediatamente l'albergatore se non potete più occupare la camera prenotata.

Se scrivete ad un albergo all'estero, allegate alla vostra lettera un tagliando-risposta internazionale (disponibile presso gli uffici postali).

YARCOMBE *Devon* 403 K 31 – *see Honiton.*

YARM *Stockton-on-Tees* 402 P 20 – *pop. 8 929.*
London 242 – Middlesbrough 8.

Crathorne Hall, Crathorne, TS15 0AR, South : 3 ½ m. by A 67 ☎ (01642) 7003 *enquiries@crathornehall.com, Fax (01642) 700814,* ←, « Converted Edwardian mansion – 140. VISA JCB
Leven : Meals 14.95/27.50 and dinner a la carte 19.00/31.00 **t.** 14.50 – 12.50 – **36** 105.00/115.00 **t.**, 1 suite – SB.

Judges at Kirklevington Hall, Kirklevington, TS15 9LW, South : 1 ½ m. on A ☎ (01642) 789000, *enquiries@judgeshotel.co.uk, Fax (01642) 782878,* ←, « Former Vict ian judges residence », – rest, – 200. VISA JCB.
Meals *(closed Saturday lunch)* 14.95/29.95 and a la carte 31.00/45.00 **st.** 21.00 – **21** 135.00/150.00 **st.** – SB.

Chadwick's, 104b High St, TI5 9AU, ☎ (01642) 788558, *Fax (01642) 788558* – VISA
closed 25 December, 1 week October, Sunday, Monday and Bank Holidays – **Meals** a la ca 16.95/29.85 **t.** 10.95.

YARMOUTH *I.O.W.* 403 404 P 31 – *see Wight (Isle of).*

YATELEY *Hants.* 404 R 29 – *pop. 15 663* – ✉ *Camberley.*
London 37 – Reading 12 – Southampton 58.

Casa Dei Cesari, Handford Lane, Cricket Hill, GU46 6BT, ☎ (01252) 8732 *Fax (01252) 870614,* – VISA.
closed 26 December and 1 January – **Meals** - Italian - 17.95 and a la carte 20.00/32.95 **t** **42 rm** 87.50/102.50, 2 suites.

TTENDON *Newbury* 403 404 Q 29 – *pop. 288* – ✉ *Newbury.*
London 61 – Oxford 23 – Reading 12.

XX **Royal Oak** with rm, The Square, RG18 0UG, ✆ (01635) 201325, *theroyaloakhotel@hotmail.com, Fax (01635) 201926,* « Part 17C coaching inn », – rest, TV P. MO AE VISA JCB
Meals *(closed Sunday)* (booking essential) (dinner only) 35.00 **st.** 11.00 – (see also below) – ☕ 11.00 – **5 rm** 115.00 **st.** – SB.

Royal Oak, The Square, RG18 0UG, ✆ (01635) 201325, *Fax (01635) 201926,* , – P. MO AE VISA JCB
Meals (booking essential) a la carte 19.20/38.00 **t.** 11.50.

EADON *W. Yorks.* 402 O 22 – *see Leeds.*

ELVERTON *Devon* 403 H 32 *The West Country G. – pop. 3 609 (inc. Horrabridge).*
See : *Yelverton Paperweight Centre★.*
Env. : *Buckland Abbey★★ AC, SW : 2 m.*
Exc. : *E : Dartmoor National Park★★.*
18 *Golf Links Rd* ✆ *(01822) 852824.*
London 234 – Exeter 33 – Plymouth 10.

Moorland Links , PL20 6DA, South : 2 m. on A 386 ✆ (01822) 852245, *moorland.links@forestdale.com, Fax (01822) 855004,* ≤, , – TV P – 200. MO AE VISA
Meals (bar lunch Saturday) 21.00/25.00 **t.** 9.95 – **44 rm** ☕ 85.00/127.00 **t.**, 1 suite – SB.

In this guide
a symbol or a character, printed in red or black, in **bold** or light type, does not have the same meaning.
Pay particular attention to the explanatory pages.

OVIL *Somerset* 403 404 M 31 *The West Country G. – pop. 28 317.*
See : *St John the Baptist★.*
Env. : *Monacute House★★ AC, W : 4 m. on A 3088 – Fleet Air Arm Museum, Yeovilton★★ AC, NW : 5 m. by A 37 – Tintinhull House Garden★ AC, NW: 5½ m. – Ham Hill (≤★★) W : 5½ m. by A 3088 – Stoke sub-Hamdon (parish church★) W : 5¼m. by A 3088.*
Exc. : *Muchelney★★ (Parish Church★★) NW : 14 m. by A 3088, A 303 and B 3165 – Lytes Cary★, N : 7½ m. by A 37, B 3151 and A 372 – Sandford Orcas Manor House★, NW : 8 m. by A 359 – Cadbury Castle (≤★★) NE : 10½ m. by A 359 – East Lambrook Manor★ AC, W : 12 m. by A 3088 and A 303.*
18, 9 *Sherborne Rd* ✆ *(01935) 475949.*
Petter's House, Petter's Way ✆ *(01935) 471279 – at Podimore : South Somerset Visitor Centre, Service Area (A 303)* ✆ *(01935) 841302.*
London 136 – Exeter 48 – Southampton 72 – Taunton 26.

Yeovil Court, West Coker Rd, BA20 2HE, Southwest : 2 m. on A 30 ✆ (01935) 863746, *verne@yeovilcourt.freeserve.co.uk, Fax (01935) 863990* – TV P – 60. MO AE VISA JCB.
closed 26 December-2 January – **Meals** *(closed Saturday lunch and Sunday dinner)* 12.50/22.95 and a la carte 13.10/21.85 **t.** 9.00 – **29 rm** ☕ 69.00/85.00 **t.**, 1 suite – SB.

Holywell House without rest., Holywell, East Coker, BA22 9NQ, Southwest : 2 ¾ m. by A 30 on Hardington rd ✆ (01935) 862612, *b&b@holywellhouse.freeserve.co.uk, Fax (01935) 863035,* « Georgian manor house », , – TV P.
closed 18 December-7 January – **2 rm** ☕ 45.00/65.00, 1 suite.

Podimore *North : 9½ m. by A 37 off A 303* – ✉ *Yeovil.*

Travelodge, BA22 8JG, West : ½ m. ✆ (01935) 840074 – rm, TV P. MO AE VISA JCB.
Meals (grill rest.) – **31 rm** 52.95 **t.**

Barwick *South : 2 m. by A 30 off A 37* – ✉ *Yeovil.*

XX **Little Barwick House** with rm, BA22 9TD, ✆ (01935) 423902, *reservations@barwick7.fsnet.co.uk, Fax (01935) 420908,* « Georgian dower house », – TV P. MO AE VISA
closed 2 weeks January – **Meals** *(closed Monday and Sunday dinner)* 12.50/27.95 **t.** 12.50 – **6 rm** ☕ (dinner included) 60.00/147.00 **st.** – SB.

at Stoke sub Hamdon *West : 6 m. by A 3088 – ✉ Yeovil.*

Priory House (Hadden), 1 High St, TA14 6PP, ☎ (01935) 822826, *martinhadden@hotm com, Fax (01935) 822826* – . VISA JCB
closed 2 weeks Christmas, 2 weeks August, Sunday and Monday – **Meals** 14.00/28.0(13.00
Spec. Seared scallops with spring onion and ginger butter. Grilled red mullet, red pepp sauce and tapenade. Chocolate tart with almond cream.

YETMINSTER *Dorset* 403 404 M 31 – *see Sherborne.*

YORK *N. Yorks.* 402 Q 22 *Great Britain G. – pop. 124 609.*

See : *City*★★★ – *Minster*★★★ *(Stained Glass*★★★, *Chapter House*★★, *Choir Screen*★★*)* **CD** *National Railway Museum*★★★ **CY** – *The Walls*★★ **CDXYZ** – *Castle Museum*★ *AC* **DZ M** *Jorvik Viking Centre*★ *AC* **DY M1** – *Fairfax House*★ *AC* **DY A** – *The Shambles*★ **DY 54**.

18 *Lords Moor Lane, Strensall* ☎ *(01904) 491840* **BY** – 9 *Heworth, Muncaster Hou Muncastergate* ☎ *(01904) 424618* **BY**.

The De Grey Rooms, Exhibition Sq ☎ *(01904) 621756 – York Railway Station, Ou Concourse* ☎ *(01904) 621756 – 20 George Hudson St* ☎ *(01904) 554488.*

London 203 – Kingston-upon-Hull 38 – Leeds 26 – Middlesbrough 51 – Nottingham 8 Sheffield 62.

Plan opposite

Middlethorpe Hall, Bishopthorpe Rd, YO23 2GB, South : 1 ¾ m. ☎ (01904) 641241, *i @middlethorpe.com, Fax (01904) 620176*, ≤, « William and Mary house, gardens », , – , rest, ☎ – 50. VISA.
Meals (booking essential to non-residents) 16.00/45.00 **st.** – 14.50 – **23 rm** 109. 200.00 **st.**, 7 suites – SB.

The Grange, Clifton, YO30 6AA, ☎ (01904) 644744, *info@grangehotel.co. Fax (01904) 612453*, « Regency town house » – ☎ – 45. AE JCB **CX**
The Ivy : **Meals** *(closed Sunday)* (dinner only) 26.00 and a la carte 27.70/34.20 **t.** 10.0
The Brasserie : **Meals** *(closed Sunday lunch)* a la carte 21.00/26.45 **t.** 10.00 – **29** 100.00/190.00 **st.**, 1 suite – SB.

Marriott, Tadcaster Rd, YO24 1QQ, ☎ (01904) 701000, *york@swallow.hotels.co Fax (01904) 702308*, , , , , – , rest, ☎ – 170. AE **AZ**
Ridings : **Meals** 14.50/21.50 and a la carte **st.** 12.95 – 12.50 – **107 rm** 104.00 1 suite – SB.

York Moat House, North St, YO1 6JF, ☎ (01904) 459988, *cbyrk@queensmoat.co Fax (01904) 641793*, ≤, , – ☎ – 390. AE VISA JCB **CY**
Meals *(closed Sunday lunch)* 13.50/18.95 and a la carte 18.00/32.00 **t.** 11.95 – 11.9 **199 rm** 123.00/146.00 **st.**, 1 suite – SB.

Dean Court, Duncombe Pl, YO1 7EF, ☎ (01904) 625082, *info@deancourt-york.co Fax (01904) 620305* – – 50. AE VISA JCB. **CY**
Meals 9.75/25.00 and dinner a la carte 26.00/31.75 **t.** 11.95 – **38 rm** 85.00/170.0(1 suite – SB.

Monkbar, St Maurice's Rd, YO31 7JA, ☎ (01904) 638086, *sales@monkbar-hotel.co Fax (01904) 629195* – – 200. AE VISA **DX**
Meals 12.50/18.00 and dinner a la carte 19.50/25.50 **t.** – **99 rm** 90.00/175.00 **st.**

Ambassador, 123-125 The Mount, YO24 1DU, ☎ (01904) 641316, *stay@ambassadorh .co.uk, Fax (01904) 640259*, – , rest, ☎ – 50. AE VISA. **AZ**
closed 25-28 December – ***Gray's :*** **Meals** (dinner only) 19.50 and a la carte 19.50/26.5 10.50 – **25 rm** 98.00/128.00 **t.** – SB.

York Pavilion, 45 Main St, Fulford, YO10 4PJ, South : 1 m. on A 19 ☎ (01904) 622(*reservations@yorkpavilionhotel.com, Fax (01904) 626939* – – 200. AE VISA.
Langtons Brasserie : **Meals** 14.95 (lunch) and dinner a la carte 22.95/29.45 **t.** 12.5 **57 rm** 75.00/150.00 **t.** – SB.

Judges' Lodging, 9 Lendal, YO1 2AQ, ☎ (01904) 638733, *judgeshotel@aol.c Fax (01904) 679947*, « 18C former judges' residence » – . AE VISA. **CY**
closed 25 December – **Meals** (dinner only) a la carte 11.75/17.20 **t.** 9.95 – **12 rm** 75 130.00 **t.**, 2 suites.

Novotel, Fishergate, YO10 4FB, ☎ (01904) 611660, *h0949@accor-hotels.c Fax (01904) 610925*, – , rest, ☎ – 210. AE VISA JCB **DZ**
Meals 16.00 and a la carte **st.** 12.00 – 11.00 – **124 rm** 80.00/85.00 **st.** – SB.

Bishopgate Street	CZ 3	Fetter Lane	CY 22	Penley's Grove Street	DX 46
Bishophill Senior	CZ 4	Goodramgate	DY 25	Queen Street	CZ 49
Blake Street	CY 5	High Ousegate	DY 26	St. Helen's Road	AZ 50
Campleshon Road	AZ 7	High Petergate	CY 28	St. Leonard's Place	CY 52
Church Street	DY 8	Knavesmire Road	AZ 29	St. Maurice's Road	DXY 53
Clifford Street	DY 10	Leeman Road	AY, CY 30	Shambles (The)	DY 54
Colliergate	DY 12	Lendal	CY 32	Station Road	CY 55
Coney Street	CY 13	Lord Mayor's Walk	DX 33	Stonebow (The)	DY 56
Cromwell Road	CZ 15	Low Petergate	DY 35	Stonegate	CY 58
Davygate	CY 16	Melrosegate	BY 36	Tower Street	DZ 59
Deangate	DY 18	Museum Street	CY 39	University Road	BZ 60
		Parliament Street	DY 42		

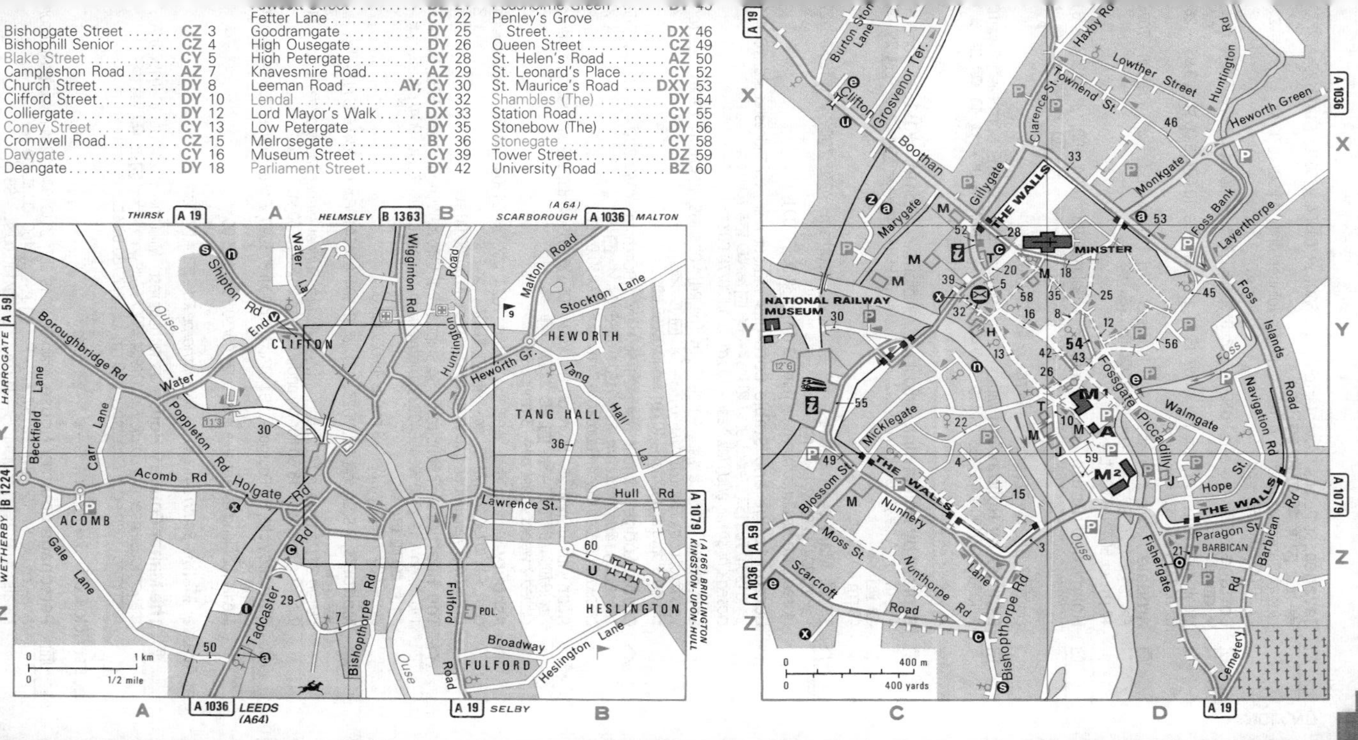

ENGLAND

Savages, St Peter's Grove, Clifton, YO30 6AQ, (01904) 610818, *Fax (01904) 62772* rest, TV P. MC AE VISA. CX
closed Christmas and New Year – **Meals** (dinner only) 11.50/16.00 **st.** 9.95 – **21**
30.00/60.00 **st.** – SB.

Cottage, 3 Clifton Green, YO30 6LH, (01904) 643711, *Fax (01904) 611230* – rest, P. MC VISA. AY
Meals (residents only) (dinner only) 15.00 and a la carte 10.00/16.00 **st.** 9.95 – **26**
35.00/70.00 **st.** – SB.

Arndale without rest., 290 Tadcaster Rd, YO24 1ET, (01904) 702 *Fax (01904) 709800*, – TV P. MC VISA JCB. AZ
12 rm 50.00/80.00 **t.**

Holmwood House without rest., 114 Holgate Rd, YO24 4BB, (01904) 626 *holmwood.house@dial.pipex.com, Fax (01904) 670899*, – TV P. MC AE VISA AZ
closed 7 January-7 February – **14 rm** 45.00/85.00 **st.**

Express by Holiday Inn without rest., Malton Rd, YO32 9TE, Northeast : 2 ¾ m. A 1036 (01904) 438660, *Fax (01904) 438560* – TV P – 30. MC AE
49 rm 55.00 **t.**

Express by Holiday Inn without rest., Shipton Rd, Clifton Park, YO30 5PA, Northw 1 ½ m. on A 19 (01904) 659992, *Fax (01904) 659994*, – TV P – 25. VISA. AY
49 rm 60.00 **st.**

23 St Mary's without rest., 23 St Mary's, Bootham, YO30 7DD, (01904) 622 *Fax (01904) 628802* – TV. CX
closed 2 weeks Christmas-New Year – **9 rm** 38.00/80.00 **t.**

Curzon Lodge and Stable Cottages without rest., 23 Tadcaster Rd, YO24 (01904) 703157, *Fax (01904) 703157* – TV P. MC VISA JCB. AZ
closed Christmas and New Year – **10 rm** 48.00/70.00 **st.**

Eastons's without rest., 90 Bishopthorpe Rd, YO23 1JS, (01904) 626646, *easton york@aol.com, Fax (01904) 626165* – TV P. CZ
closed 3 days Christmas – **10 rm** 40.00/69.00.

Crook Lodge without rest., 26 St Mary's, Bootham, YO30 7DD, (01904) 655 *crooklodge@hotmail.com, Fax (01904) 655614* – TV P. CX
closed 24 December-1 February – **7 rm** 35.00/60.00 **st.**

Acer without rest., 52 Scarcroft Hill, YO24 1DE, (01904) 653839, *info@acerhotel.co Fax (01904) 677017* – TV. MC AE VISA JCB. CZ
closed 2 weeks Christmas – **3 rm** 35.00/78.00 **s.**

Ashbury without rest., 103 The Mount, YO24 1AX, (01904) 647339, *ashbury@tal com, Fax (01904) 647339*, – TV. MC VISA. CZ
closed mid December-mid January – **5 rm** 40.00/60.00 **st.**

The Heathers without rest., 54 Shipton Rd, Clifton-Without, YO30 5RQ, Northw 1 ½ m. on A 19 (01904) 640989, *thghyork@globalnet.co.uk, Fax (01904) 640989*, – TV P. MC AE VISA. AY
closed 24-26 December – **8 rm** 46.00/108.00.

Melton's, 7 Scarcroft Rd, YO23 1ND, (01904) 634341, *Fax (01904) 635115* – VISA JCB CZ
closed 24 December-14 January, 1 week August, Sunday dinner and Monday lunch – **M** (booking essential) 16.50 (lunch) and a la carte 20.80/29.60 **st.** 14.00.

Blue Bicycle, 34 Fossgate, YO1 9TA, (01904) 673990, *Fax (01904) 677688* – VISA DY
Meals (booking essential) a la carte 21.00/30.50 **t.** 13.00.

at Acaster Malbis *South : 4 ¾ m. by Bishopthorpe Rd* – **BZ** – *York.*

The Manor Country House without rest., Mill Lane, YO23 2UL, (01904) 706 *manorhouse@selcom.co.uk, Fax (01904) 700737*, – TV P. MC VISA.
restricted opening in December – **10 rm** 42.00/80.00 **st.**

at Escrick *South : 5 ¾ m. on A 19* – **BZ** – *York.*

Parsonage Country House, Main St, YO19 6LF, (01904) 728111, *sales@parsor hotel.co.uk, Fax (01904) 728151*, – TV P – 160. MC AE VISA.
Meals 14.00/24.50 **st.** 11.25 – **21 rm** 95.00/140.00 **st.** – SB.

at Bilbrough *Southwest : 5½ m. by A 1036 – AZ – off A 64 – ✉ York.*

Travel Inn, Bilbrough Top, Colton, YO23 3PP, South : ½ m. on A 64 (westbound carriageway) ✆ (01937) 835067, *Fax (01937) 835934* – |♦|, ⇔ rm, ≡ rest, TV & P – 30. MC AE O VISA.
Meals (grill rest.) (dinner only) – **60 rm** 41.95 **t.**

Travelodge, Steeton, LS24 8EG, Southwest : ¾ m. on A 64 (eastbound carriageway) ✆ (01937) 531823, *Fax (01937) 531823* – ⇔ rm, TV & P. MC AE O VISA JCB.
Meals (grill rest.) – **62 rm** 59.95 **t.**

at Skelton *Northwest : 3 m. on A 19 – AY – ✉ York.*

Jarvis International, Shipton Rd, YO30 1XW, ✆ (01904) 670222, *j1york.rs@jarvis.co.uk, Fax (01904) 670311,* – |♦| ⇔, ≡ rest, TV & P – 200. MC AE O VISA
Meals *(closed Saturday lunch)* a la carte 21.00/26.95 **st.** 12.25 – ☕ 10.95 – **83 rm** 110.00/130.00 **st.**, 6 suites – SB.

at York Business Park *Northwest : 3¾ m. by A 59 – AY – on A 1237 – ✉ York.*

Travel Inn, White Rose Close, YO26 6RL, ✆ (01904) 787630, *Fax (01904) 787663* – |♦|, ⇔ rm, ≡ rest, TV & P. MC AE O VISA.
Meals (grill rest.) – **44 rm** 41.95 **t.**

XX **Maxi's,** Ings Lane, Nether Poppleton, YO26 6RA, ✆ (01904) 783898, *info@maxi_s.co.uk, Fax (01904) 783818,* « Pagoda, ornate decor » – ≡ P. MC AE O VISA
closed 25-26 December – **Meals** - Chinese (Canton, Peking) - 5.90/24.00 and a la carte 12.60/35.60 **t.** 9.90.

YOXFORD *Suffolk* 404 Y 27 – *pop. 1 512.*

London 99 – Ipswich 24 – Norwich 34.

Church Farm without rest., Yoxford Rd, Sibton, Saxmundham, IP17 2LX, Northwest : 1 ½ m. on A 1120 ✆ (01728) 660101, *dixons@church-farmhouse.demon.co.uk, Fax (01728) 660102,* « 17C house with Victorian additions », – ⇔ TV P
closed 25-26 December – **3 rm** ☕ 25.00/58.00 **s.**

Scotland

Place with at least

a hotel or restaurant ● Tongue
a pleasant hotel or restaurant 🏨, 🏠, ✕
a quiet, secluded hotel 🐎
a restaurant with ✿, ✿✿, ✿✿✿, 🙂 Meals

La località possiede come minim

una risorsa alberghiera ● Tong
Albergo o ristorante ameno 🏨, 🏠,
un albergo molto tranquillo, isolato
un'ottima tavola con ✿, ✿✿, ✿✿✿, 🙂 Mea

Localité offrant au moins

une ressource hôtelière ● Tongue
un hôtel ou restaurant agréable 🏨, 🏠, ✕
un hôtel très tranquille, isolé 🐎
une bonne table à ✿, ✿✿, ✿✿✿, 🙂 Meals

Ort mit mindestens

einem Hotel oder Restaurant ● Tong
ein angenehmes Hotel oder Restaurant 🏨, 🏠,
einem sehr ruhigen und abgelegenen Hotel
einem Restaurant mit ✿, ✿✿, ✿✿✿, 🙂 Mea

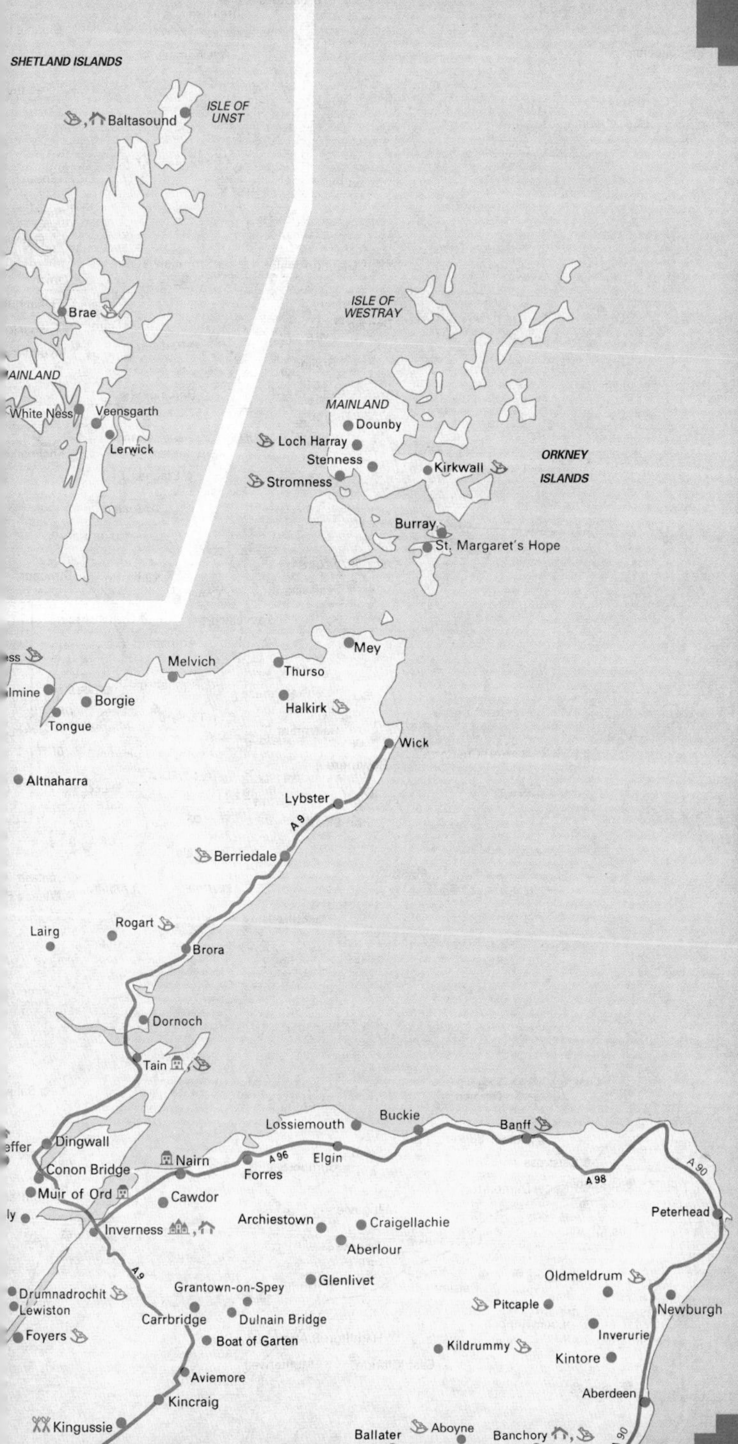
SHETLAND ISLANDS
Baltasound
ISLE OF UNST
Brae
MAINLAND
White Ness
Veensgarth
Lerwick
ISLE OF WESTRAY
MAINLAND
Dounby
Loch Harray
Stenness
Stromness
Kirkwall
ORKNEY ISLANDS
Burray
St. Margaret's Hope
Mey
Melvich
Thurso
Borgie
Halkirk
Tongue
Wick
Altnaharra
Lybster
A 9
Berriedale
Rogart
Lairg
Brora
Dornoch
Tain
Lossiemouth
Buckie
Banff
Dingwall
Nairn
A 96
Elgin
Conon Bridge
Forres
A 98
A 90
Muir of Ord
Cawdor
Peterhead
Archiestown
Craigellachie
Inverness
Aberlour
A 9
Oldmeldrum
Glenlivet
Drumnadrochit
Grantown-on-Spey
Pitcaple
Newburgh
Lewiston
Carrbridge
Dulnain Bridge
Inverurie
Foyers
Boat of Garten
Kildrummy
Kintore
Aviemore
Aberdeen
Kincraig
Kingussie
Ballater
Aboyne
Banchory
A 90

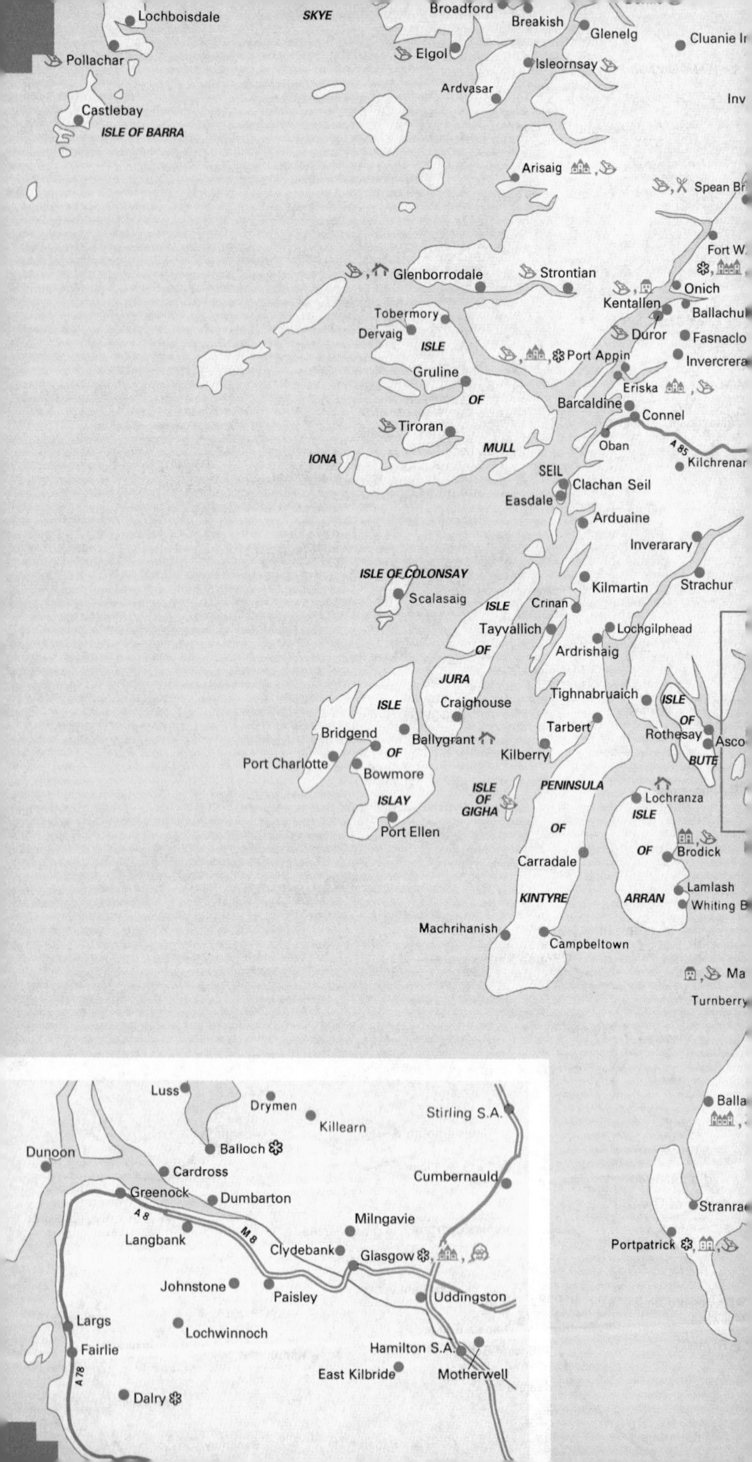
Lochboisdale
SKYE
Broadford
Breakish
Glenelg
Cluanie In
Pollachar
Elgol
Isleornsay
Castlebay
ISLE OF BARRA
Ardvasar
Inv
Arisaig
Spean Br
Fort W.
Glenborrodale
Strontian
Onich
Kentallen
Ballachu
Tobermory
Dervaig
ISLE
Duror
Fasnaclo
Port Appin
Invercrera
Gruline
OF
Eriska
Barcaldine
Connel
Tiroran
Oban
A 85
IONA
MULL
SEIL
Kilchrenar
Clachan Seil
Easdale
Arduaine
Inverarary
ISLE OF COLONSAY
Scalasaig
Kilmartin
Strachur
ISLE
Crinan
Tayvallich
Lochgilphead
OF
Ardrishaig
JURA
Tighnabruaich
ISLE
Craighouse
ISLE
OF
Bridgend
Tarbert
Rothesay
Ballygrant
Asco
Port Charlotte
OF
Kilberry
BUTE
Bowmore
ISLE OF GIGHA
PENINSULA
Lochranza
ISLAY
ISLE
Port Ellen
OF
OF
Brodick
Carradale
Lamlash
KINTYRE
ARRAN
Whiting B
Machrihanish
Campbeltown
Ma
Turnberry
Luss
Drymen
Stirling S.A.
Killearn
Balla
Dunoon
Balloch
Cardross
Cumbernauld
Greenock
Dumbarton
A 8
Stranra
M 8
Milngavie
Langbank
Portpatrick
Clydebank
Glasgow
Johnstone
Paisley
Uddingston
Largs
Lochwinnoch
Fairlie
Hamilton S.A.
A 78
East Kilbride
Motherwell
Dalry

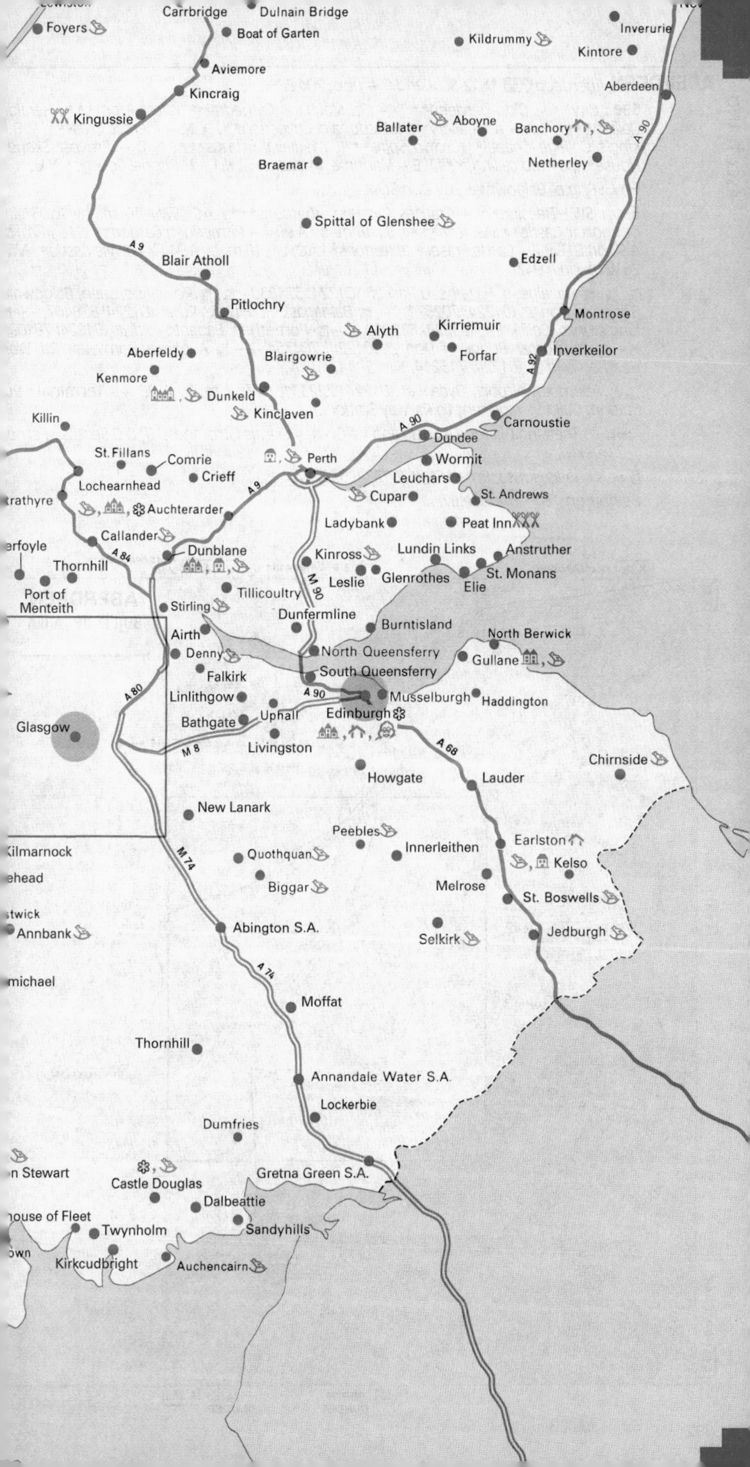
Carrbridge
Dulnain Bridge
Foyers
Boat of Garten
Kildrummy
Inverurie
Kintore
Aviemore
Kincraig
Aberdeen
Kingussie
Ballater
Aboyne
Banchory
A 90
Braemar
Netherley
Spittal of Glenshee
A 9
Blair Atholl
Edzell
Pitlochry
Montrose
Alyth
Kirriemuir
Aberfeldy
Forfar
Inverkeilor
Blairgowrie
A 92
Kenmore
Dunkeld
Kinclaven
Killin
A 90
Carnoustie
Dundee
St. Fillans
Comrie
Perth
Wormit
Crieff
Leuchars
Lochearnhead
A 9
Cupar
St. Andrews
trathyre
Auchterarder
Ladybank
Peat Inn
Callander
erfoyle
A 84
Dunblane
Kinross
Lundin Links
Anstruther
Thornhill
Leslie
Glenrothes
St. Monans
Elie
Port of Menteith
Tillicoultry
M 90
Stirling
Dunfermline
Burntisland
Airth
North Queensferry
North Berwick
Denny
Gullane
Falkirk
South Queensferry
A 80
Linlithgow
A 90
Musselburgh
Haddington
Uphall
Edinburgh
Glasgow
Bathgate
A 68
Livingston
M 8
Chirnside
Howgate
Lauder
New Lanark
Peebles
Earlston
Kilmarnock
Quothquan
Innerleithen
Kelso
ehead
M 74
Biggar
Melrose
St. Boswells
stwick
Annbank
Abington S.A.
Selkirk
Jedburgh
A 74
michael
Moffat
Thornhill
Annandale Water S.A.
Lockerbie
Dumfries
n Stewart
Gretna Green S.A.
Castle Douglas
Dalbeattie
ouse of Fleet
Twynholm
Sandyhills
own
Kirkcudbright
Auchencairn

ABERDEEN *Aberdeen* **401** N 12 *Scotland G.* – *pop. 204 885.*

See : *City★★ – Old Aberdeen★★* X – *St. Machar's Cathedral★★ (West Front★★★, Heraldi Ceiling★★★)* X **A** – *Art Gallery★★ (Macdonald Collection★★)* Y **M** – *Mercat Cross★★* Y **B** – *King's College Chapel★ (Crown Spire★★★, medieval fittings★★★)* X **D** – *Provost Skene House★ (painted ceilings★★)* Y **E** – *Maritime Museum★* Z **M1** – *Marischal College★* Y **U**.

Env. : *Brig o' Balgownie★, by Don St.* X.

Exc. : *SW : Deeside★★ – Crathes Castle★★ (Gardens★★★)* **AC**, *SW : 16 m. by A 93* X – *Dunnottar Castle★★* **AC** *(site★★★), S : 18 m. by A 90* X – *Pitmedden Garden★★, N : 14 m. b A 90 on B 999* X – *Castle Fraser★ (exterior★★)* **AC**, *W : 16 m. by A 944* X – *Fyvie Castle★, NW 26½ m. on A 947.*

18, 18, 9 Hazelhead, Hazelhead Park ☎ (01224) 321830 – 18, 18 Royal Aberdeen, Balgownie Bridge of Don ☎ (01224) 702571, X – *18 Balnagask, St. Fitticks Rd ☎ (01224) 876407,* X – *King's Links, Golf Rd ☎ (01224) 632269,* X – *18 Portlethen, Badentoy Rd ☎ (01224) 78109* X – *18, 9 Murcar, Bridge of Don ☎ (01224) 704354,* X – *18 Auchmill, Bomyview Rd, We Heatheryfold ☎ (01224) 715214,* X.

✈ *Aberdeen Airport, Dyce : ☎ (01224) 722331, NW : 7 m. by A 96* X – **Terminal :** *Bu Station, Guild St. (adjacent to Railway Station).*

⛴ *to Shetland Islands (Lerwick) and via Orkney Islands (Stromness) (P & O Scottish Ferrie 1-2 weekly.*

ℹ *St Nicholas House, Broad St ☎ (01224) 632727.*

Edinburgh 130 – Dundee 67.

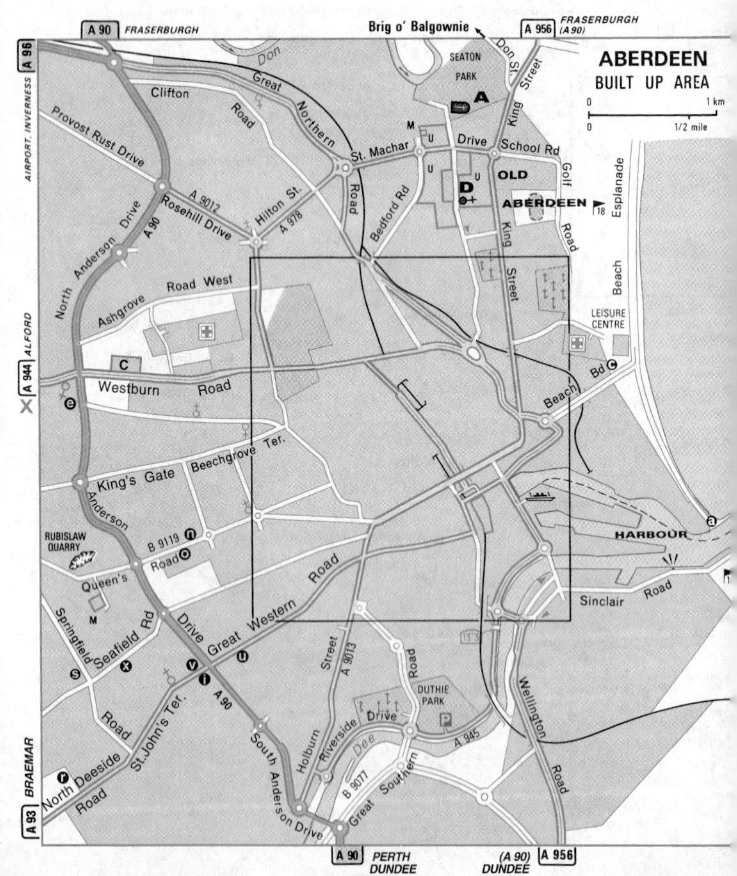

ABERDEEN

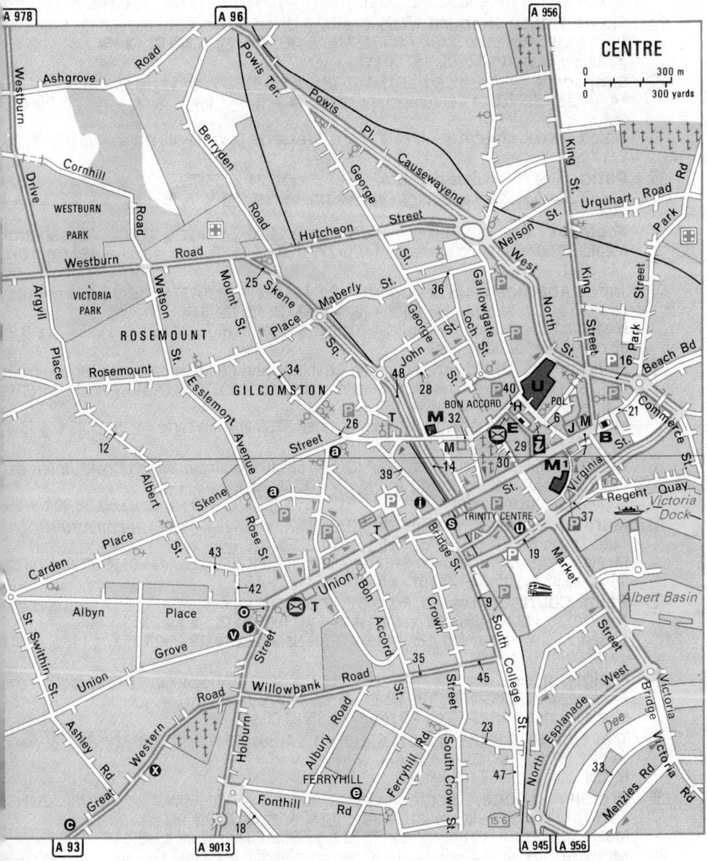

The Marcliffe at Pitfodels, North Deeside Rd, AB15 9YA, ✆ (01224) 861000, *enquiries@marcliffe.com, Fax (01224) 868860,* – |‡| ⅔, ▤ rest, TV ✆ ♿ P – 🏛 400. MC AE ⓓ VISA JCB X r
Conservatory : **Meals** a la carte 27.00/38.00 **st.** 14.50 – **42 rm** 145.00/275.00 **st.** – SB.

Ardoe House ⛰, South Deeside Rd, Blairs, AB12 5YP, Southwest : 5 m. on B 9077 ✆ (01224) 860600, *info.ardoe@macdonald-hotels.co.uk, Fax (01224) 861283*, ≤, « Part 19C baronial mansion », TV ✆ ♿ P – 🏛 500. MC AE ⓓ VISA
Meals *(closed Saturday lunch)* a la carte approx. 30.00 **t.** 14.50 – 10.95 – **110 rm** 120.00/135.00 **t.**, 2 suites – SB.

Thistle Aberdeen Caledonian, 10-14 Union Terr, AB10 1WE, ✆ (01224) 640233, *aberdeen.caledonian@thistle.co.uk, Fax (01224) 641627* – |‡| TV ✆ P – 🏛 45. MC AE ⓓ VISA JCB Z i
Meals (bar lunch)/dinner 19.95 and a la carte 19.95/31.85 **st.** 12.05 – 12.50 – **75 rm** 145.00/168.00 **st.**, 2 suites – SB.

SCOTLAND

Hilton Aberdeen Tree Tops, 161 Springfield Rd, AB15 7AQ, (01224) 313377, *sal aberdeen@hilton.com, Fax (01224) 312028,* – rm, – 900. VISA X
Bar Bacoa : **Meals** a la carte 16.20/28.50 **st.** 12.30 – 10.95 – **111 rm** 116.00/126.00 s 1 suite – SB.

Copthorne, 122 Huntly St, AB10 1SU, (01224) 630404, *reservations.aberdeen@m cop.com, Fax (01224) 640573* – rm, rest, – 220. VISA Z
closed 24-26 December – **Meals** (bar lunch Saturday and Sunday) 12. (lunch) and a la carte approx. 25.00 **st.** 14.25 – 13.50 – **89 rm** 160.00 **st.**

Skene House Holburn without rest., 6 Union Grove, AB10 6SY, (01224) 5800 *holburn@skene-house.co.uk, Fax (01224) 585193* – VISA. Z
12.95, **39 suites** 125.00/137.00 **st.**

Simpson's, 59 Queen's Rd, AB15 4YP, (01224) 327777, *address@simpsonshotel.co. Fax (01224) 327700,* « Contemporary interior » – – 25. VISA X
closed 1 week Christmas – **Meals** – (see ***Brasserie*** below) – **48 rm** 125.00/145.00 2 suites.

Patio, Beach Boulevard, AB24 5EF, (01224) 633339, *patioab@globalnet.co. Fax (01224) 638833,* – rm, rest, – 150. JCB X
Footdee's : **Meals** 10.50 (lunch) and a la carte 14.20/27.70 **st.** 11.50 – ***Conservator*** **Meals** 10.50/11.50 and a la carte 14.20/27.70 **st.** 11.50 – 13.25 – **124 rm** 125.C 145.00 **st.** – SB.

Jarvis Aberdeen, 448 Great Western Rd, AB10 6NP, (01224) 318724, *003rs@jarvis. uk, Fax (01224) 312716* – – 400. VISA JCB X
Meals (bar lunch Monday-Saturday)/dinner a la carte 16.75/24.65 **t.** 11.45 – 8.95 **53 rm** 92.00/102.00 **st.** – SB.

Holiday Inn Aberdeen, Aberdeen Exhibition and Conference Centre, Bridge of Dc AB23 8BL, North : 3 m. by A 956 at junction with A 90 (0870) 4009046, *Fax (01224) 8239* – rm, VISA JCB.
Meals (bar lunch Monday to Saturday)/dinner 10.00 and a la carte 14.15/23.45 **t.** 13.95 11.95 – **123 rm** 69.00/89.00 – SB.

Grampian, Stirling St, AB11 6JU, (01224) 589101, *grampion@macdonald_hotels.co. Fax (01224) 574288* – – 150. VISA. Z
Meals (bar lunch)/dinner a la carte 11.70/23.85 **t.** 11.95 – **49 rm** 82.50/98.00 **t.** – SB.

Mariner, 349 Great Western Rd, AB10 6NW, (01224) 588901, *enquires@vagabor hotels.com, Fax (01224) 571621* – VISA JCB. X
Meals - Seafood - (bar lunch Saturday) (carvery lunch Sunday) 12.00/14.00 and a la ca 14.50/23.75 **t.** 15.00 – **23 rm** 65.00/105.00 **t.** – SB.

Palm Court, 81 Seafield Rd, AB15 7YX, (01224) 310351, *info@palmcourt.co. Fax (01224) 312707* – , rest, – 100. VISA. X
closed 25 December and 1-3 January – **Meals** a la carte 12.45/23.75 **t.** 11.95 – **24 r** 79.00/99.00 **t.** – SB.

Craiglynn, 36 Fonthill Rd, AB11 6UJ, (01224) 584050, *info@craiglynn.co. Fax (01224) 212225* – VISA JCB. Z
Meals (dinner only) 17.50 **st.** – **9 rm** 49.95/80.00 **st.** – SB.

Travelodge, 9 Bridge St, AB11 6JL, (01224) 584555, *Fax (01224) 584587* – , r rest, VISA JCB. Z
Meals (cafe bar) – **97 rm** 49.95 **t.**

Premier Lodge, North Anderson Drive, AB15 6DW, (0870) 700130 *Fax (0870) 7001301* – rm, rest, VISA. X
Meals (grill rest.) a la carte approx. 12.50 **t.** 7.80 – **60 rm** 42.95 **t.** – SB.

Mannofield, 447 Great Western Rd, AB10 6NL, (01224) 315888, *mannofieldhc @btconnect.com, Fax (01224) 208971* – rest, VISA JCB X
Meals (by arrangement) 20.00 **st.** 9.95 – **9 rm** 50.00/74.00 **st.** – SB.

Penny Meadow without rest., 189 Great Western Rd, AB10 6PS, (01224) 5880 *Fax (01224) 573639,* – VISA JCB. Z
3 rm 40.00/55.00 **st.**

Manorville without rest., 252 Great Western Rd, AB10 6PJ, (01224) 594190, *manorv abz@aol.com, Fax (01224) 594190,* – VISA. Z
3 rm 25.00/42.00.

Silver Darling, Pocra Quay, North Pier, AB11 5DQ, (01224) 5762 *Fax (01224) 588119,* , « Quayside setting » – VISA X
closed 2 weeks Christmas-New Year, Saturday lunch and Sunday – **Meals** - Seafood - 24 (lunch) and dinner a la carte 31.50/36.50 **t.** 11.50.

Brasserie (at Simpson's H.), 59 Queens Rd, AB15 4YP, (01224) 327799, – VISA JCB X
Meals a la carte 13.95/21.50 **t.** 13.50.

XX **Olive Tree,** 32 Queens Rd, AB15 4YF, (01224) 208877, *info@olive-tree.co.uk, Fax (01224) 314255* – P. VISA X n
closed 25-26 December, 1-3 January, Saturday lunch and Sunday – **Meals** 14.80 (lunch) and a la carte 14.80/28.00 **st.** 14.50.

XX **Babylon,** 9 Alford Pl, AB10 1YD, (01224) 595001, *Fax (01224) 582245* – . VISA Z o
closed 25 December-4 January, Sunday and Monday – **Meals** (dinner only and Friday lunch)/dinner a la carte 19.00/23.00 **t.** 10.95.

XX **Nargile,** 77-79 Skene St, AB10 1QD, (01224) 636093, *nargile@freeserve.co.uk, Fax (01224) 636202* – . VISA Y a
closed 25-26 December and 1 January – **Meals** - Turkish - (dinner only) 16.95/20.75 and a la carte 16.85/21.70 **st.** 9.95.

X **Courtyard,** 1 Alford Lane, AB1 1YD, (01224) 213795, *courtyardcitycafe@hotmail.com, Fax (01224) 212961* – VISA Z r
closed 25 December and Sunday – **Meals** (light lunch)/dinner a la carte approx. 19.45 11.25.

Murcar *North : 4½ m. by A 90* – X – *Aberdeen.*

Travel Inn, AB23 8BP, on B 999 (01224) 821217, *Fax (01224) 706869* – P. VISA.
Meals (grill rest.) – **40 rm** 41.95 **t.**

Altens *(Aberdeenshire) South : 3 m. on A 956* – X – *Aberdeen.*

Thistle Aberdeen Alterns, Souter Head Rd, AB12 3LF, (0870) 3339150, *reservations.aberdeen@thistle.co.uk, Fax (0870) 3339250,* , rest, P – 400. VISA JCB
Cairngorm : **Meals** a la carte 9.50/24.00 **st.** 11.95 – ***Brasserie :*** **Meals** (lunch only) a la carte 9.10/24.00 **st.** 11.95 – 10.95 – **215 rm** 70.00/90.00 **st.**, 1 suite – SB.

Portlethen *(Aberdeenshire) South : 6 m. on A 90* – X – *Aberdeen.*

Travel Inn, Mains of Balquuarn, AB12 4QS, (01224) 783856, *Fax (01224) 783836* – rm, P. VISA
Meals (grill rest.) – **40 rm** 41.95 **t.**

Kirkton of Maryculter *(Aberdeenshire) Southwest : 8 m. by B 9077* – X – *Aberdeen.*

Maryculter House , South Deeside Rd, AB12 5GB, Southwest : 1 ½ m. on B 9077 (01224) 732124, *info@maryculterhousehotel.co.uk, Fax (01224) 733510,* , « Part 13C house on River Dee », – P – 200. VISA
Priory : **Meals** *(closed Sunday)* (dinner only) a la carte 21.70/32.45 **t.** 14.95 – ***Poachers Pocket :*** **Meals** 7.95 (lunch) and a la carte 13.00/24.00 **t.** 14.95 – **23 rm** 75.00/90.00 **t.** – SB.

Bankhead *(Aberdeenshire) Northwest : 4½ m. by A 96* – X – *Aberdeen.*

Craighaar, Waterton Rd, AB21 9HS, (01224) 712275, *info@craighaar.co.uk, Fax (01224) 716362* – P – 90. VISA.
closed 26 December and 1-2 January – **Meals** a la carte 13.15/30.90 **st.** 10.95 – **49 rm** 79.00/89.00 **st.**, 6 suites – SB.

Dyce *(Aberdeenshire) Northwest : 5½ m. by A 96* – X – *on A 947* – *Aberdeen.*

Aberdeen Marriott, Overton Circle, AB21 7AZ, (01224) 770011, *Fax (01224) 722347,* , – rm, P – 400. VISA.
Meals (bar lunch Saturday) a la carte 18.00/38.00 **st.** 12.75 – 12.50 – **154 rm** 120.00 **st.**, 1 suite – SB.

Travel Inn, Burnside Drive, AB21 7HW, off Wellheads Rd (01224) 772787, *Fax (01224) 772968,* – rm, rest, P. VISA.
Meals (grill rest.) – **40 rm** 41.95 **t.**

Aberdeen Airport *(Aberdeenshire) Northwest : 6 m. by A 96* – X – *Aberdeen.*

Thistle Aberdeen Airport, Argyll Rd, AB21 7DU, (0870) 3339149, *Fax (0870) 3339249,* , – rm, P – 600. VISA
Meals (bar lunch Saturday and Sunday) 13.95/21.00 and dinner a la carte 20.50/29.75 6.90 – 11.75 – **146 rm** 147.00/168.00 **st.**, 1 suite – SB.

Speedbird Inn, Argyll Rd, AB21 0AF, (01224) 772884, *reception@speedbirdinns.co.uk, Fax (01224) 772560* – , rest, P – 35. VISA JCB
Meals *(closed lunch Saturday and Sunday)* (bar lunch)/dinner a la carte 13.75/23.90 **st.** 8.95 – 4.95 – **99 rm** 45.50 **st.**

BERDEEN AIRPORT *Aberdeenshire* 401 N 12 – *see Aberdeen.*

SCOTLAND

ABERFELDY *Perth and Kinross* 401 I 14 *Scotland G. – pop. 4 083.*

See : *Town★.*
Env. : *St. Mary's Church (painted ceiling★) NE : 2 m. by A 827.*
Exc. : *Loch Tay★★, SW : 6 m. by A 827 – Ben Lawers★★, SW : 16 m. by A 827 – Blair Castle★ AC, N : 20½ m. by A 827 and A 9.*
18 Taybridge Rd (01887) 820535.
The Square (01887) 820276.
Edinburgh 76 – Glasgow 73 – Oban 77 – Perth 32.

Guinach House, Urlar Rd, PH15 2ET, off Crieff Rd (01887) 82025 *Fax (01887) 829607*, – – *closed 4 days Christmas* – **Meals** (dinner only) 25.00 **st.** 11.95 – **6 rm** 45.50/91.00 **st.**

Fernbank House without rest., Kenmore St, PH15 2BL, on A 827 (Killin r (01887) 820345, – *April-October* – **7 rm** 30.00/64.00 **st.**

ABERFOYLE *Stirling* 401 G 15.

Trossachs Discovery Centre, Main St. (01877) 382352.
Edinburgh 57 – Glasgow 30 – Perth 49.

Forest Hills, Kinlochard, FK8 3TL, West : 4 ¼ m. on B 829 (01877) 387277, *fores hills@macdonald-hotels.co.uk, Fax (01877) 387307,* Loch Ard, – – 120. ***Garden :*** **Meals** (dinner only) 27.95 and a la carte 15.00/27.95 **t.** 14.50 – ***Rafters :*** **Mea** a la carte approx. 15.00 14.50 – **53 rm** (dinner included) 100.00/160.00 **t.**, 2 suites.

Les prix — Pour toutes précisions sur les prix indiqués dans ce guide, reportez-vous aux pages de l'introduction.

ABERLOUR *Aberdeenshire* 401 K 11 *Scotland G. – pop. 1 780.*

Env. : *Dufftown (Glenfiddich Distillery★), SE : 6 m. by A 95 and A 941.*
9 Rothes, Blackhall (01340) 831443.
Edinburgh 192 – Aberdeen 60 – Elgin 15 – Inverness 55.

Dowans, AB38 9LS, Southwest : ¾ m. by A 95 (01340) 871488, *penny@thedowans.fr serve.co.uk, Fax (01340) 871038,* – rest, *closed 23 December-10 March* – **Meals** 24.50 **t.** 9.90 – **19 rm** 49.00/98.00 **t.**

ABINGTON SERVICE AREA *South Lanarkshire* 401 I 17 – *Biggar.*

Welcome Break Service Area, junction 13, M 74 (01864) 502436.
Edinburgh 43 – Dumfries 37 – Glasgow 38.

Days Inn, ML12 6RG, at junction 13 of M 74 (01864) 502782, Reservations (Fre phone) 0800 0280400, *Fax (01864) 502759* – rm, **Meals** (grill rest.) a la carte 8.70/13.90 – 8.00 – **54 rm** 45.00/50.00 **t.**

ABOYNE *Aberdeenshire* 401 L 12 *Scotland G. – pop. 3 793 (inc. Cromar).*

Exc. : *Craigievar Castle★ AC, NE : 12 m. by B 9094, B 9119 and A 980.*
18 Formanston Park (013398) 86328.
Edinburgh 131 – Aberdeen 30 – Dundee 68.

Struan Hall without rest., Ballater Rd, AB34 5HY, (013398) 87241, *struanhall@zetn co.uk, Fax (013398) 87241,* – *March-October* – **4 rm** 28.50/57.00 **st.**

Arbor Lodge without rest., Ballater Rd, AB34 5HY, (013398) 86951, *arborlodge@a com, Fax (013398) 86951,* – *March-November* – **3 rm** 30.00/52.00 **st.**

Birse Lodge without rest., Charleston Rd, AB34 5EL, on B 968 (013398) 86253, *bi lodgehouse@btinternet.com, Fax (013398) 87796,* – *closed Christmas and New Year* – **3 rm** 32.00/54.00 **st.**

at Migvie *Northwest : 10 m. by A 93 off A 97 – Aboyne.*

Migvie House, by Logie Coldstone, AB34 4XL, (013398) 81313, *migviehous yahoo.co.uk, Fax (013398) 81635,* – *March-October* – **Meals** (by arrangement) (communal dining) 18.00 – **3 rm** 35.C 50.00 **s.**

CHILTIBUIE *Highland* 401 D 9.
Edinburgh 243 – Inverness 84 – Ullapool 25.

Summer Isles ⑤, IV26 2YG, ☎ (01854) 622282, *summerisleshotel@aol.com, Fax (01854) 622251,* « Picturesque setting ≤ Summer Isles », – ⊁ P. MC VISA
27 March-12 October – **Meals** (booking essential) (set menu at dinner) (light seafood lunch)/dinner 40.00 **st.** 12.50 – (see also ***Summer Isles Bar*** below) – **10 rm** 69.00/130.00 **st.**, 3 suites
Spec. Goujons of monkfish and langoustine tails with ginger and lime. Carpaccio of Aberdeen Angus. Local scallops with champ, leeks and basil.

Summer Isles Bar (at Summer Isles H.), IV26 2YG, ☎ (01854) 622282, *Fax (01854) 622251,* – P. MC VISA
27 March-12 October – **Meals** - Seafood - (bookings not accepted) a la carte 12.10/18.05 **st.** 8.50.

IRTH *Falkirk* 401 I 15 – *pop. 1 519* – ✉ *Falkirk.*
Edinburgh 30 – Dunfermline 14 – Falkirk 7 – Stirling 8.

Radisson SAS Airth Castle, FK2 8JF, South : ¼ m. on A 905 ☎ (01324) 831411, *Fax (01324) 831419,* – ⊁ TV P – 380. MC AE VISA JCB
The Castle : **Meals** *(closed Sunday)* (dinner only) 32.50 and a la carte 24.45/34.20 **st.** 14.25 – ***The Conservatory :*** **Meals** 18.00 (dinner) and a la carte 16.25/26.00 **st.** 13.95 – 11.95 – **122 rm** 110.00/170.00 **st.** – SB.

Travel Inn, Bowtrees Roundabout, FK2 8PJ, South : 1 m. by A 905 at junction with M 876/A 876 ☎ (01324) 831125, *Fax (01324) 831934* – ⊁ rm, TV P. MC AE VISA.
Meals (grill rest.) – **40 rm** 41.95 **t.**

LLOWAY *South Ayrshire* 401 402 G 17 – *see Ayr.*

LTENS *Aberdeenshire – see Aberdeen.*

LTNAHARRA *Highland* 401 G 9 *Scotland G.* – ✉ *Lairg.*
Exc. : *Ben Loyal★★, N : 10 m. by A 836 – Ben Hope★ (≤★★★) NW : 14 m.*
Edinburgh 239 – Inverness 83 – Thurso 61.

Altnaharra ⑤, IV27 4UE, ☎ (01549) 411222, *altnaharra@btinternet.com, Fax (01549) 411222,* ≤, – ⊁ rest, P. MC VISA
March-October – **Meals** (bar lunch)/dinner 30.00 **t.** 10.00 – **16 rm** (dinner included) 85.00/170.00 **t.** – SB.

LYTH *Perthshire and Kinross* 401 J 14 – *pop. 4 650.*
Pitcrocknie ☎ (01828) 632268.
Edinburgh 63 – Aberdeen 69 – Dundee 16 – Perth 21.

Lands of Loyal ⑤, Loyal Rd, PH11 8JQ, North : ½ m. by B 952 ☎ (01828) 633151, *enq@landsofloyal.co.uk, Fax (01828) 633313,* ≤, – TV P. MC AE VISA
Meals a la carte 19.90/30.35 **t.** 11.90 – **14 rm** 59.00/89.00 **t.**

Drumnacree House ⑤, St Ninians Rd, PH11 8AP, ☎ (01828) 632194, *derek@drumnacreehouse.co.uk, Fax (01828) 632194,* – ⊁ TV P. MC VISA
Meals *(closed Monday)* (booking essential) (residents only) a la carte 12.00/17.50 **t.** 9.00 – ***The Oven Bistro*** *(☎ (01828) 633355)* **: Meals** *(closed Monday)* a la carte 12.00/17.50 **t.** 9.00 – **6 rm** 45.00/80.00 **st.** – SB.

NNANDALE WATER SERVICE AREA *Dumfries and Galloway* 401 J 18 – ✉ *Lockerbie.*

Travel Inn without rest., Johnstonebridge, DG11 1HD, junction 16 A 74 (M) ☎ (01576) 470870, *Fax (01576) 470644,* ≤, – ⊁ TV P. MC AE VISA.
closed Christmas and New Year – **42 rm** 41.95 **t.**

NNBANK *South Ayrshire* 401 G 17.
Edinburgh 84 – Glasgow 38 – Ayr 6 – Dumfries 54.

Enterkine ⑤, KA6 5AL, Southeast : ½ m. on B 742 (Coylton rd) ☎ (01292) 521608, *mail@enterkine.com, Fax (01292) 520580,* ≤, « 1930's country house, extensive gardens, woodlands », – ⊁ rest, TV P. MC AE VISA
closed January – **Meals** *(closed Sunday-Monday to non-residents)* (booking essential) 15.50/32.50 **t.** 13.95 – **5 rm** (dinner included) 180.00/300.00 **t.**, 1 suite – SB.

ANSTRUTHER *Fife* 401 L 15 *Scotland G.* – *pop. 1 307.*
See : *Scottish Fisheries Museum★★ AC.*
Env. : *The East Neuk★★ – Crail★★ (Old Centre★★, Upper Crail★) NE : 4 m. by A 917.*
Exc. : *Kellie Castle★ AC, NW : 7 m. by B 9171, B 942 and A 917.*
Marsfield Shore Rd ☎ (01333) 310956.
Scottish Fisheries Museum,Harbourhead ☎ (01333) 311073 (April-October).
Edinburgh 46 – Dundee 23 – Dunfermline 34.

The Spindrift, Pittenweem Rd, KY10 3DT, ☎ (01333) 310573, *info@thespindrift.co.u* *Fax (01333) 310573* – ⇔ TV P. MC VISA JCB
closed 2 weeks January and Christmas – **Meals** (by arrangement) 15.00 **st.** 7.50 – **8 r** 43.00/62.00 **st.** – SB.

The Grange without rest., 45 Pittenweem Rd, KY10 3DT, ☎ (01333) 310842, *pamela@t grangeanstruther.fsnet.co.uk, Fax (01333) 310842,* – ⇔ P.
April-October – **4 rm** 30.00/60.00.

Cellar, 24 East Green, KY10 3AA, ☎ (01333) 310378, *Fax (01333) 312544* – ⇔. MC AE VISA
closed 24-26 December, Monday and Tuesday lunch and Sunday November-April – **Meal** Seafood - (booking essential) 16.50/28.50 15.00.

ARCHIESTOWN *Moray* 401 K 11 – ✉ *Aberlour (Aberdeenshire).*
Edinburgh 194 – Aberdeen 62 – Inverness 49.

Archiestown, AB38 7QL, ☎ (01340) 810218, *Fax (01340) 810239,* – P. MC VISA
February-mid December – ***Bistro :*** **Meals** a la carte 16.50/26.50 **t.** 12.50 – **9 rm** 45.0 90.00 **t.** – SB.

ARDEONAIG *Perth and Kinross* 401 H 14 – *see Killin (Stirling).*

ARDRISHAIG *Argyll and Bute* 401 D 15 – *pop. 1 315* – ✉ *Lochgilphead.*
Edinburgh 132 – Glasgow 86 – Oban 40.

Fascadale House, Tarbert Rd, PA30 8EP, on A 83 ☎ (01546) 603845, *info@fascada com, Fax (01546) 602152,* ≤, – ⇔ TV P. MC VISA JCB.
Meals 24.95 **st.** – **3 rm** 50.00/70.00 **st.** – SB.

Allt-na-Craig, Tarbert Rd, PA30 8EP, on A 83 ☎ (01546) 603245, ≤, – ⇔ rest, P
closed Christmas and New Year – **Meals** (by arrangement) 17.50 **s.** 9.50 – **6 rm** 32.0 64.00 – SB.

ARDUAINE *Argyll and Bute* 401 D 15 *Scotland G.* – ✉ *Oban.*
Exc. : *Loch Awe★★, E : 12 m. by A 816 and B 840.*
Edinburgh 142 – Oban 20.

Loch Melfort , PA34 4XG, ☎ (01852) 200233, *lmhotel@aol.com, Fax (01852) 2002* ≤ Asknish bay and Islands of Jura, Shuna and Scarba, , , – ⇔ rest, TV P – 4
MC AE VISA
Meals - Seafood specialities - (bar lunch)/dinner 25.00/30.00 **t.** 12.95 – **26 rm** 79.0 118.00 **t.**

ARDVASAR *Highland* 401 C 12 – *see Skye (Isle of).*

ARDVOURLIE *Western Isles (Outer Hebrides)* 401 Z 10 – *see Lewis and Harris (Isle of).*

ARISAIG *Highland* 401 C 13 *Scotland G.*
See : *Village★.*
Env. : *Silver Sands of Morar★, N : 5½ m. by A 830.*
Traigh ☎ (01687) 450337.
Edinburgh 172 – Inverness 102 – Oban 88.

Arisaig House , Beasdale, PH39 4NR, Southeast : 3 ¼ m. on A 830 ☎ (01687) 4506 *arisaighse@aol.com, Fax (01687) 450626,* ≤ Loch nan Uamh and Roshven, « Gardens », ⇔ TV P. MC VISA.
March-November – **Meals** (restricted lunch) (dinner booking essential to non-reside 25.00/34.50 **t.** 14.50 – **12 rm** 130.00/295.00 **t.**

Arisaig, PH39 4NH, ✆ (01687) 450210, *arisaighotel@dial.pipex.com, Fax (01687) 450310,* ≤ Loch nan Ceall and Inner Hebridean Isles – ⇔ TV P. MC VISA
closed 24-27 December – **Meals** (bar lunch)/dinner a la carte 12.00/23.00 **t.** 8.50 – **13 rm** 38.00/76.00 **t.**

Old Library Lodge with rm, High St, PH39 4NH, ✆ (01687) 450651, *reception@oldlibrary.co.uk, Fax (01687) 450219,* ≤ Loch nan Ceall and Inner Hebridean Isles, – ⇔ TV. MC AE VISA JCB.
March-October – **Meals** *(closed Tuesday lunch)* a la carte 13.55/24.50 **st.** 12.50 – **6 rm** 45.00/80.00 **st.**

RRAN (Isle of) *North Ayrshire* 401 402 DE 16 17 *Scotland G. – pop. 4 474.*
See : *Island★★ - Brodick Castle★★ AC.*
from Brodick to Ardrossan (Caledonian MacBrayne Ltd) 4-6 daily (55 mn) – from Lochranza to Kintyre Peninsula (Claonaig) (Caledonian MacBrayne Ltd) frequent services daily (30 mn) – from Brodick to Isle of Bute (Rothesay) (Caledonian MacBrayne Ltd) 3 weekly (2 h 5 mn).

rodick – *pop. 822.*
18 Brodick ✆ (01770) 302349 – 9 Machrie Bay ✆ (01770) 850232.
The Pier ✆ (01770) 302140.

Auchrannie Country House, KA27 8BZ, ✆ (01770) 302234, *hotel@auchrannie.co.uk, Fax (01770) 302812,* , – ⇔ rest, TV & P. MC AE VISA.
Meals a la carte approx. 9.85 **t.** 11.95 – ***The Garden :*** **Meals** (dinner only) 22.50 **t.** 11.95 – **26 rm** 63.50/121.50 **t.**, 2 suites – SB.

Kilmichael Country House , Glen Cloy, KA27 8BY, West : 1 m. by Shore Rd, taking left turn opposite Golf Club ✆ (01770) 302219, *enquiries@kilmichael.com, Fax (01770) 302068,* – ⇔ TV P. MC VISA JCB
March-October – **Meals** (booking essential) (dinner only) 29.50 **t.** 11.95 – **4 rm** 85.00/130.00 **t.**, 3 suites.

Dunvegan House, Shore Rd, KA27 8AJ, ✆ (01770) 302811, *Fax (01770) 302811,* ≤, – ⇔ TV P.
closed Christmas and New Year – **Meals** (residents only) 18.00 **st.** 10.90 – **9 rm** 35.00/60.00 **st.**

amlash – *pop. 900 – ✉ Brodick.*
18 Lamlash ✆ (01770) 600296.

Lilybank without rest., Shore Rd, KA27 8LS, ✆ (01770) 600230, *colin369.richardson@virgin.net, Fax (01770) 600230,* ≤, – ⇔ TV P
March-November – **7 rm** 55.00.

ochranza.
9 Lochranza ✆ (0177083) 0273.

Apple Lodge, KA27 8HJ, South : ½ m. on Brodick rd ✆ (01770) 830229, *applelodge@easicom.com, Fax (01770) 830229,* ≤, – ⇔ TV P.
closed Christmas and New Year, minimum stay 2 nights – **Meals** (by arrangement) 19.00 **st.** – **3 rm** 50.00/64.00 **st.**, 1 suite.

hiting Bay – ✉.
18 Whiting Bay, Golf Course Rd ✆ (01770) 700775.

Argentine House, Shore Rd, KA27 8PZ, ✆ (01770) 700662, *info@argentinearran.co.uk, Fax (01770) 700693,* ≤, – ⇔ rest, TV P. MC VISA JCB
closed 1 week Easter and 1 week November – **Meals** (by arrangement) 20.00 **st.** 12.00 – **5 rm** 49.00/84.00 **st.** – SB.

Royal, Shore Rd, KA27 8PZ, ✆ (01770) 700286, *royalarran@aol.com, Fax (01770) 700286,* ≤, – ⇔ rest, TV P
mid March-October – **Meals** (by arrangement) 16.00 **st.** – **5 rm** 26.00/52.00.

SCOG *Argyll and Bute* 401 E 16 – *see Bute (Isle of).*

Bitte beachten Sie die Geschwindigkeitsbeschränkungen in Großbritannien
- 60 mph (= 96 km/h) außerhalb geschlossener Ortschaften
- 70 mph (= 112 km/h) auf Straßen mit getrennten Fahrbahnen und Autobahnen.

AUCHENCAIRN *Dumfries and Galloway* 401 402 I 19 – ✉ *Castle Douglas.*
Edinburgh 94 – Dumfries 21 – Stranraer 60.

Balcary Bay, DG7 1QZ, Southeast : 2 m. on Balcary rd (01556) 640217, *reservatior@balcary-bay-hotel.co.uk, Fax (01556) 640272,* Auchencairn Bay and Solway Firth, AE VISA JCB
March-November – **Meals** (bar lunch Monday-Saturday)/dinner 26.50 and a la carte 12.2 29.25 **st.** 11.50 – **20 rm** 61.00/122.00 **st.** – SB.

AUCHTERARDER *Perth and Kinross* 401 I 15 *Scotland G. – pop. 3 910.*
Env. : *Tullibardine Chapel*★, *NW : 2 m.*
Ochil Rd (01764) 662804 – Dunning, Rollo Park (01764) 684747.
90 High St (01764) 663450 (April-October).
Edinburgh 55 – Glasgow 45 – Perth 14.

Gleneagles, PH3 1NF, Southwest : 2 m. by A 824 on A 823 (01764) 662231, *resort.sal@gleneagles.com, Fax (01764) 662134,* « Championship golf courses and extensiv leisure facilities », squash – rm, rest, – 360. AE VISA JCB
Strathearn : **Meals** (dinner only and Sunday lunch)/dinner 43.50 and a la carte 43.5 70.00 **t.** 18.50 – ***The Club :*** **Meals** a la carte 15.50/34.50 **t.** – (see also ***Andrew Fairlie Gleneagles*** below) – **206 rm** 180.00/410.00 **t.**, 14 suites – SB.

Auchterarder House, PH3 1DZ, North : 1 ½ m. on B 8062 (01764) 66364 *auchterarder@wrensgroup.com, Fax (01764) 662939,* « Victorian mansion in Jacobea style », – rest, – 65. AE VISA
Meals *(closed Saturday lunch)* (dinner booking essential to non-residents) 39.50 (di ner) and lunch a la carte 16.70/18.90 **t.** 22.00 – **14 rm** 135.00/170.00 **t.**, 1 suite – SB.

Cairn Lodge, Orchil Rd, PH3 1LX, (01764) 662634, *email@cairnlodge.co.u Fax (01764) 664866,* – AE VISA JCB.
Meals (bar lunch)/dinner 16.00/29.50 **t.** 13.50 – **11 rm** 60.00/180.00 **t.** – SB.

Coll Earn House, PH3 1DF, (01764) 663553, *reservations@collearnhousehotel.co.u Fax (01764) 662376,* – rm, – 60. AE VISA.
Meals a la carte 15.00/22.00 **t.** 10.50 – **8 rm** 55.00/110.00 **t.**

Andrew Fairlie at Gleneagles, PH3 1NF, Southwest : 2 m. by A 824 on A 8 (01764) 694267, *andrew.fairlie@gleneagles.com, Fax (01764) 694163* – . AE V JCB
closed 25 December, 1 January and Sunday – **Meals** (dinner only) 55.00/75.00 **t.** 24.00
Spec. Home smoked lobster, herb and lime butter sauce. Assiette of pork. Passion fru tart, coconut sorbet.

AVIEMORE *Highland* 401 I 12 *Scotland G. – pop. 2 214 – Winter sports.*
See : *Town*★.
Exc. : *The Cairngorms*★★ (★★★) – ★★★ *from Cairn Gorm, SE : 11 m. by B 970 – Landma Visitor Centre (The Highlander*★*)* **AC**, *N : 7 m. by A 9 – Highland Wildlife Park*★ **AC**, *SW : 7 by A 9.*
Grampian Rd (01479) 810363.
Edinburgh 129 – Inverness 29 – Perth 85.

Hilton Aviemore, PH22 1PF, (01479) 810681, *Fax (01479) 810534,* Cairngorms, – rest, – 110. AE VISA JCB
Meals (dancing Saturday evening) (bar lunch)/dinner 20.50 and a la carte 27.00/33.00 12.80 – 9.50 – **88 rm** 80.00/180.00 **st.** – SB.

Corrour House, Inverdruie, PH22 1QH, Southeast : 1 m. on B 970 (01479) 81022 *Fax (01479) 811500,* – rest, AE VISA
February-October – **Meals** (dinner only) 20.00/30.00 **t.** 12.00 – **8 rm** 45.00/90.00 **t.** SB.

Lynwilg House, Lynwilg, PH22 1PZ, South : 2 m. by B 9152 on A 9 (01479) 8116 *marge@lynwilg.co.uk, Fax (01479) 811685,* – VISA
closed November-December – **Meals** (by arrangement) 25.00 **s.** – **3 rm** 35.00/80.00 – SB.

Remember the speed limits that apply in the United Kingdom, unless otherwise signposted.

- 60 mph on single carriageway roads
- 70 mph on dual carriageway roads and motorways

R *South Ayrshire* **401** **402** G 17 *Scotland G. – pop. 47 872.*

Env. : *Alloway★ (Burns Cottage and Museum★ **AC**) S : 3 m. by B 7024* **BZ**.

Exc. : *Culzean Castle★ **AC** (setting★★★, Oval Staircase★★) SW : 13 m. by A 719* **BZ**.

18 Belleisle, Bellisle Park, Doonfoot Rd ☎ (01292) 441258, **BZ** *– 18 Dalmilling, Westwood Av. ☎ (01292) 263893,* **BZ** *– 9 Doon Valley, Hillside, Patna ☎ (01292) 531607,* **BZ**.

22 Sandgate ☎ (01292) 290300.

Edinburgh 81 – Glasgow 35.

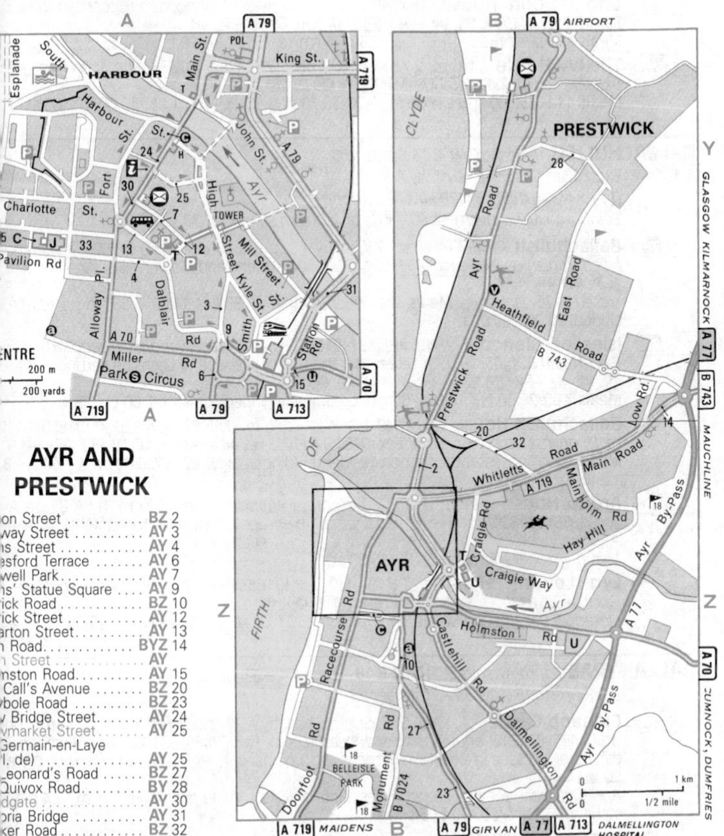

Fairfield House, 12 Fairfield Rd, KA7 2AR, ☎ (01292) 267461, *reservations@fairfieldhotel.co.uk, Fax (01292) 261456,* – 120. **AY a**
Meals a la carte 14.00/30.15 t. 11.95 – 5.00 – **44 rm** 100.00/180.00 t. – SB.

No 26 The Crescent without rest., 26 Bellevue Cres, KA7 2DR, ☎ (01292) 287329, *carrie@26crescent.freeserve.co.uk, Fax (01292) 286779* – **BZ c**
6 rm 32.00/54.00 st.

Coila without rest., 10 Holmston Rd, KA7 3BB, ☎ (01292) 262642, *hazel@coila.co.uk, Fax (01292) 285439* – **AY u**
5 rm 30.00/44.00 st.

Langley Bank without rest., 39 Carrick Rd, KA7 2RD, ☎ (01292) 264246, *Fax (01292) 282628,* – **BZ a**
4 rm 45.00/50.00 s.

Chaz-Ann without rest., 17 Park Circus, KA7 2DJ, ✆ (01292) 611215, *chazannayr@a com, Fax (01292) 611215* – ⇔ TV. ✻ AY
closed 25 December-7 January – **3 rm** ☐ 30.00/44.00 **st.**

Fouters Bistro, 2a Academy St, KA7 1HS, ✆ (01292) 261391, *laurie-fran@fouters.dem .co.uk, Fax (01292) 619323* – MC AE ① VISA AY
closed 1-3 January, 25-27 December and Sunday – **Meals** a la carte 16.75/23.25 **t.** 11.9

at Alloway *South : 3 m. on B 7024* – **BZ** – ✉ *Ayr.*

Brig O'Doon House, KA7 4PQ, ✆ (01292) 442466, *brigodoon@costleyhotels.co. Fax (01292) 441999,* – ⇔ TV – 220. MC AE VISA. ✻
Meals a la carte 16.25/18.75 **t.** 12.50 – **5 rm** ☐ 75.00/100.00 **t.**

The Ivy House with rm, 2 Alloway, KA7 4NL, ✆ (01292) 442336, *enquiries@theivyho uk.com, Fax (01292) 445572* – ⇔ TV P. MC AE VISA. ✻
Meals 11.50/32.00 and a la carte 18.00/30.70 **st.** 15.95 – **5 rm** ☐ 110.00/220.00 **st.** – S

BALLACHULISH *Highland* 401 E 13 *Scotland G.*

Exc. : *Glen Coe★★, E : 6 m. by A 82.*
Argyll ✆ (01855) 811296 (April-October).
Edinburgh 117 – Inverness 80 – Kyle of Lochalsh 90 – Oban 38.

Ballachulish, PH49 4JY, West : 2 ¼ m. by A 82 on A 828 ✆ (01855) 811606, *reservatior freedomglen.co.uk, Fax (01855) 821463,* ≤ Loch Linnhe and Morven Hills, – ⇔ rest, P. MC VISA
closed 6-26 January – **Meals** (bar lunch)/dinner 25.50 **t.** 14.00 – **56 rm** ☐ (dinner cluded) 90.00/200.00 **t.** – SB.

Isles of Glencoe, PH49 4HL, ✆ (01855) 811602, *reservations@freedomglen.co. Fax (01855) 821463,* ≤ Loch Leven and the Pap of Glencoe, « Lochside setting », , – ⇔ TV P – 40. MC VISA
Meals 7.00/25.50 **t.** 14.00 – **59 rm** ☐ (dinner included) 75.50/190.00 **t.** – SB.

Ballachulish House , PH49 4JX, West : 2 ½ m. by A 82 on A 828 ✆ (01855) 8112 *mclaughlins@btconnect.com, Fax (01855) 811498,* ≤, – ⇔ P. MC AE VISA JCB. ✻
Meals (booking essential to non-residents) (dinner only) 22.00/30.00 **st.** 12.00 – 8 ☐ 40.00/140.00 **st.** – SB.

Ardno House without rest., Lettermore, PH49 4JD, West : 3 ½ m. by A 82 on A ✆ (01855) 811830, *pamweir@globalnet.co.uk,* ≤ Loch Linnhe and Morven Hills, – ⇔ P. ✻
March-October – **3 rm** ☐ 50.00/55.00 **st.**

Lyn Leven, White St, PH49 4JP, ✆ (01855) 811392, *lynleven@amserve.r Fax (01855) 811600,* ≤, – ⇔ rest, TV P. MC VISA
closed 25 December – **Meals** (by arrangement) 9.00 **st.** 7.20 – **8 rm** ☐ 25.00/40.00 – S

BALLANTRAE *South Ayrshire* 401 402 E 18 – *pop. 672* – ✉ *Girvan.*

Edinburgh 115 – Ayr 33 – Stranraer 18.

Glenapp Castle , KA26 0NZ, South : 1 m. by A 77 taking first right turn after bric ✆ (01465) 831212, *enquiries@glenappcastle.com, Fax (01465) 831000,* ≤, « Victorian Sc tish Baronial castle in extensive gardens and woodland », , , – , ⇔ rest, TV P. AE VISA JCB
April-October – **Meals** - French - (residents only) (set menu only) (light lunch) – **14 rm** (f inclusive) 300.00/500.00 **t.**, 3 suites.

Cosses Country House , KA26 0LR, East : 2 ¼ m. by A 77 (south) taking first turn after bridge ✆ (01465) 831363, *cosses@compuserve.com, Fax (01465) 831598,* « Part former shooting lodge », , – ⇔ TV P. MC VISA
closed Christmas and New Year, restricted opening in winter – **Meals** (by arrangeme (communal dining) 25.00 **st.** 8.20 – **1 rm** ☐ 42.00/76.00 **st.**, **2 suites** 76.00 **st.** – SB.

BALLATER *Aberdeenshire* 401 K 12 – *pop. 1 362.*

18 *Victoria Rd ✆ (013397) 55567.*
Albert Hall, Station Sq ✆ (013397) 55306 (Easter-November).
Edinburgh 111 – Aberdeen 41 – Inverness 70 – Perth 67.

Hilton Craigendarroch, Braemar Rd, AB35 5XA, on A 93 ✆ (013397) 558 *Fax (013397) 55447,* ≤ Dee Valley and Grampians, , , , , , , squash – ⇔ rest, TV P – 110. MC AE ① VISA. ✻
Meals (bar lunch Monday-Saturday)/dinner 31.00 and a la carte 10.30/26.05 **st.** 11.8
Oaks : **Meals** (dinner only) 31.00 and a la carte 32.25/41.50 **st.** 11.80 – ☐ 10.95 – 40 140.00/160.00 **st.**, 5 suites – SB.

Darroch Learg, Braemar Rd, AB35 5UX, ☎ (013397) 55443, *nigel@darrochlearg.co.uk, Fax (013397) 55252,* ≤ Dee Valley and Grampians, – rest, TV P. MC AE VISA JCB
closed 3 weeks January and Christmas – **Meals** – (see ***Conservatory*** below) – **18 rm** 62.50/155.00 **st.** – SB.

Glen Lui, Invercauld Rd, AB35 5RP, ☎ (013397) 55402, *infos@glen-lui-hotel.co.uk, Fax (013397) 55545,* ≤, – TV P. MC AE VISA
Meals a la carte 12.50/21.00 **st.** 9.50 – **17 rm** 40.00/100.00 **t.**, 2 suites – SB.

Balgonie Country House, Braemar Pl, AB35 5NQ, ☎ (013397) 55482, *balgoniech@aol.com, Fax (013397) 55482,* ≤, – rest, TV P. MC AE VISA JCB.
closed 5 January-10 February – **Meals** (booking essential) (lunch by arrangement)/dinner 30.00 **t.** 17.50 – **9 rm** 72.50/125.00 **t.** – SB.

Auld Kirk, Braemar Rd, AB35 5RQ, ☎ (013397) 55762, *auldkirkhotel@aol.com, Fax (013397) 55707,* « Former 19C church » – rest, TV P. MC VISA
closed 25-27 December – **Meals** a la carte 17.20/22.10 **t.** 9.80 – **7 rm** 39.50/56.00 **t.** – SB.

Moorside House without rest., 26 Braemar Rd, AB35 5RL, ☎ (013397) 55492, *moorside house@virgin.net, Fax (013397) 55492,* – TV P. MC VISA.
April-October – **9 rm** 44.00 **st.**

Conservatory (at Darroch Learg H.), Braemar Rd, AB35 5UX, ☎ (013397) 55443, *Fax (013397) 55252,* ≤, – P. MC AE VISA
closed 3 weeks January and Christmas – **Meals** 19.50/39.00 and lunch a la carte 16.00/27.50 **st.**

Green Inn with rm, 9 Victoria Rd, AB35 5QQ, ☎ (013397) 55701, *info@green-inn.com, Fax (013397) 55701,* – TV. MC AE VISA JCB
closed 2 weeks November, Christmas and Sunday and Monday November-March – **Meals** (dinner only) 31.50 **t.** 11.25 – **3 rm** (dinner included) 75.00/119.00 **t.** – SB.

BALLOCH *West Dunbartonshire* 401 G 15 *Scotland G.* – ✉ *Alexandria.*

Env. : *N : Loch Lomond★★.*

The Old Station Building, Balloch Rd ☎ (01389) 753533 (April-October).

Edinburgh 72 – Glasgow 20 – Stirling 30.

Cameron House, Loch Lomond, G83 8QZ, Northwest : 1 ½ m. by A 811 on A 82 ☎ (01389) 755565, *devere.cameron@airtime.co.uk, Fax (01389) 759522,* ≤ Loch Lomond, « Lochside setting », , , , 9, , , , , squash – rest, TV P – 300. MC AE VISA.
Smolletts : **Meals** *(closed lunch Saturday, Sunday and Bank Holiday Mondays)* 18.50/25.00 and dinner a la carte approx. 28.00 **t.** 16.00 – ***Breakers :*** **Meals** a la carte 18.30/23.80 **t.** 16.00 – (see also ***Georgian Room*** below) – **89 rm** 170.00/235.00 **t.**, 7 suites – SB.

Georgian Room (at Cameron House H.), Loch Lomond, G83 8QZ, Northwest : 1 ½ m. by A 811 on A 82 ☎ (01389) 755565, *Fax (01389) 759522,* ≤ Loch Lomond, « Lochside setting », – P. MC AE VISA
closed Monday – **Meals** (booking essential) (dinner only) 47.50 **t.** 25.00
Spec. Foie gras with apple purée and clove jus. Roast squab pigeon with shallot tart, raspberry vinegar sauce. Honey crème brûlée, raspberry sorbet.

BALLYGRANT *Argyll and Bute* 401 B 16 – *see Islay (Isle of).*

BALTASOUND *Shetland Islands* 401 R 1 – *see Shetland Islands (Island of Unst).*

BANAVIE *Highland* 401 E 13 – *see Fort William.*

BANCHORY *Aberdeenshire* 401 M 12 *Scotland G.* – *pop. 6 230.*

Env. : *Crathes Castle★★ (Gardens★★★) AC, E : 3 m. by A 93 – Cairn o'Mount Road★ (≤★★), S : by B 974.*

Exc. : *Dunnottar Castle★★ (site★★★) AC, SW : 15 ½ m. by A 93 and A 957 – Aberdeen★★, NE : 17 m. by A 93.*

18 *Kinneskie ☎ (01330) 822365* – 9 *Torphins ☎ (013398) 82115.*

Bridge St ☎ (01330) 822000 (Easter-October).

Edinburgh 118 – Aberdeen 17 – Dundee 55 – Inverness 94.

Raemoir House, AB31 4ED, North : 2 ½ m. on A 980 ☎ (01330) 824884, *enquiries@raemoir.com, Fax (01330) 822171,* ≤, « 18C mansion with 16C Ha-Hoose », , , – rest, TV P – 50. MC AE VISA
Meals 17.50/29.50 **t.** 14.00 – **21 rm** 65.00/120.00 **t.** – SB.

Banchory Lodge ⛱, Dee St, AB31 5HS, ☎ (01330) 822625, *banchorylodgeht@connect.com, Fax (01330) 825019*, ≤, « Part 16C former coaching inn on River Dee », – ⇔ rm, TV P – 🏛 30. MC AE ① VISA
Meals a la carte 13.50/24.50 **st.** 🍷 10.50 – **22 rm** ☕ 55.00/150.00 **st.** – SB.

Tor-na-Coille, Inchmarlo Rd, AB31 4AB, ☎ (01330) 822242, *tornacoille@btinternet.cc Fax (01330) 824012*, – |≡| ⇔ TV ♿ P – 🏛 90. MC AE VISA JCB
closed 25-28 December – **Meals** (bar lunch Monday-Saturday)/dinner 26.50 **t.** 🍷 12.50 – **24 rm** ☕ 69.00/120.00 **st.** – SB.

Old West Manse, 71 Station Rd, AB31 5UD, ☎ (01330) 822202, *Fax (01330) 822202*, ⇔ TV P. MC VISA JCB
Meals (by arrangement) 18.50 **s.** 🍷 10.00 – **3 rm** ☕ 35.00/55.00 **s.**

Milton, Milton of Crathes, North Deeside Rd, Crathes, AB31 5QH, East : 3 m. on A ☎ (01330) 844566, *reservations@themilton.co.uk, Fax (01330) 844666* – ⇔ P. MC AE VIS
closed 24-25 December, 1 January and Sunday dinner – **Meals** a la carte 15.60/32.60 **t.**

BANFF *Aberdeenshire* 401 M 10 *Scotland G. – pop. 4 402.*

See : *Town★ – Duff House★★ (baroque exterior★) AC – Mercat Cross★.*
Royal Tarlair, Buchan St., Macduff ☎ (01261) 832897 – Duff House Royal, The Barnya ☎ (01261) 812062.
Collie Lodge ☎ (01261) 812419 (Easter-October).
Edinburgh 177 – Aberdeen 47 – Fraserburgh 26 – Inverness 74.

The Orchard ⛱ without rest., Duff House, AB45 3TA, by Duff House rd and Wrack Wc rd ☎ (01261) 812146, *jma6914291@aol.com, Fax (01261) 812146*, – ⇔ TV P. ✂
February-November – **5 rm** ☕ 25.00/50.00.

Milo's, 2 Crook 'o' Ness St, Macduff, AB44 1TR, East : 1 ½ m. on A 98 ☎ (01261) 83122 ⇔. MC VISA
closed Monday, 25-26 December and 1-2 January – **Meals** (dinner booking essent a la carte 12.10/21.75 **st.** 🍷 8.95.

Les prix — Pour toutes précisions sur les prix indiqués dans ce guide, reportez-vous aux pages de l'introduction.

BANKHEAD *Aberdeenshire* 401 N 12 – *see Aberdeen.*

BARCALDINE *Argyll and Bute* 401 E 14 – ✉ *Oban.*

Edinburgh 128 – Dundee 122 – Glasgow 105 – Inverness 103 – Oban 13.

Barcaldine House ⛱, PA37 1SG, ☎ (01631) 720219, *barcaldine@breathe.co. Fax (01631) 720219*, « 18C country house », – ⇔ TV P. MC ① VISA
Meals *(closed Monday dinner to non-residents)* (booking essential to non-residents) (d ner only) a la carte 22.25/29.25 **st.** 🍷 10.50 – **7 rm** ☕ 60.00/90.00 **st.**

BARRA (Isle of) *Western Isles* 401 X 12/13 – *pop. 1 316* – ✉ *Castlebay.*

from Castlebay to Oban, South Uist (Lochboisdale) and Mallaig (Caledonian MacBra Ltd) (summer only).

Castlebay.

Castlebay, HS9 5XD, ☎ (01871) 810223, *castlebayhotel@aol.com, Fax (01871) 8104* ≤ Kisimul Castle and Island of Vatersay – ⇔ rest, TV P. MC VISA
Meals a la carte 13.15/25.50 **st.** 🍷 7.95 – **12 rm** ☕ 40.00/70.00 **st.** – SB.

Grianamul without rest., HS9 5XD, ☎ (01871) 810416, *ronnie.macneil@virgin.n Fax (01871) 810319*, – ⇔ TV P. MC VISA. ✂
April-October – **3 rm** ☕ 25.00/50.00 **t.**

Tigh na Mara without rest., HS9 5XD, ☎ (01871) 810304, *tighnamara@aol.cc Fax (01871) 810858*, ≤ – ⇔ TV P. ✂
5 rm ☕ 22.00/44.00.

BATHGATE *West Lothian* 401 J 16 – *pop. 23 368.*

Edinburgh 24 – Dundee 62 – Glasgow 29 – Perth 50.

Express by Holiday Inn without rest., Starlaw Rd, EH48 1LQ, ☎ (01506) 6506 *Fax (01506) 650651* – |≡| ⇔ TV ☎ ♿ P – 🏛 30. MC AE ① VISA JCB. ✂
74 rm 52.50 **st.**

:AULY *Highland* 401 G 11 – *pop. 1 154.*
Edinburgh 169 – Inverness 13 – Wick 125.

Lovat Arms, High St, IV4 7BS, ☎ (01463) 782313, *lovatarms@cali.co.uk, Fax (01463) 782862* – ⇔ rest, TV P – 60. MC VISA JCB
Meals 20.00/25.00 (dinner) and a la carte 9.80/26.25 **t.** 9.50 – **22 rm** 32.00/90.00 – SB.

Priory, The Square, IV4 7BX, ☎ (01463) 782309, *reservations@priory-hotel.com, Fax (01463) 782531* – TV. MC AE VISA JCB
Meals 19.95 (dinner) and a la carte 8.50/29.50 **t.** 8.50 – **36 rm** 47.50/104.00 **t.** – SB.

:NBECULA *Western Isles* 401 X/Y 11 – *see Uist (Isles of).*

:RRIEDALE *Highland* 401 J 9.
Edinburgh 251 – Inverness 94 – Thurso 28 – Wick 14.

The Factor's House, Langwell, KW7 6HD, take private road to Langwell House - 2.9 m. ☎ (01593) 751280, *robert@welbeck2.freeserve.co.uk, Fax (01593) 751251,* ←, – ⇔ rm, P
closed Christmas and New Year – **Meals** (communal dining) 20.00 **t.** 5.00 – **3 rm** 35.00/70.00 **t.**

GGAR *South Lanarkshire* 401 J 17 – *pop. 2 238.*
The Park, Broughton Rd ☎ (01899) 220319.
155 High St ☎ (01899) 221066 (Easter-September).
Edinburgh 31 – Dumfries 49 – Glasgow 40.

Lindsaylands, Lindsaylands Rd, ML12 6NR, Southwest : ¾ m. via Park Place and The Wynd ☎ (01899) 220033, *elspeth@lindsaylands.co.uk, Fax (01899) 221009,* ←, – ⇔ P.
March-November – **Meals** (by arrangement) 15.00 **st.** – **3 rm** 30.00/52.00 **st.**

Le Grand Londres (GREATER LONDON) est composé de la City et de 32 arrondissements administratifs (Borough) eux-mêmes divisés en quartiers ou en villages ayant conservé leur caractère propre (Area).

.AIR ATHOLL *Perth and Kinross* 401 I 13 – *pop. 906.*
Blair Atholl, Invertilt Rd ☎ (01796) 481407.
Edinburgh 79 – Inverness 83 – Perth 35.

The Loft, Golf Course Rd, PH18 5TE, ☎ (01796) 481377, *Fax (01796) 481511,* « Converted hayloft » – ⇔ P. MC AE VISA JCB
closed Sunday and Monday – **Meals** (lunch booking essential) 27.50/32.50 and a la carte 16.80/32.50 **t.** 9.50.

.AIRGOWRIE *Perth and Kinross* 401 J 14 *Scotland G.* – *pop. 5 208.*
Exc. : *Scone Palace★★ AC, S : 12 m. by A 93.*
26 Wellmeadow ☎ (01250) 872960.
Edinburgh 60 – Dundee 19 – Perth 16.

Kinloch House, PH10 6SG, West : 3 m. on A 923 ☎ (01250) 884237, *info@kinlochhouse.com, Fax (01250) 884333,* ←, « Victorian country house », – ⇔ rest, TV P. MC AE VISA JCB
closed 18-30 December – **Meals** (bar lunch Monday-Saturday)/dinner 35.00 18.95 – **20 rm** (dinner included) 105.00/260.00 **st.** – SB.

Laurels, PH10 6LH, Southwest : 1 ¼ m. on A 93 ☎ (01250) 874920, *Fax (01250) 874920,* – ⇔ TV P. MC AE VISA.
closed mid November-mid January – **Meals** 11.00 **s.** 7.50 – **6 rm** 20.00/40.00 **s.**

Altamount House with rm, Coupar Angus Rd, PH10 6JN, on A 923 ☎ (01250) 873512, *althotel@netcomuk.co.uk, Fax (01250) 876200,* – ⇔ rest, TV P – 150. MC AE VISA.
closed first 2 weeks January and 25 December – **Meals** (booking essential to non-residents) (light lunch)/dinner 24.50 13.25 – **7 rm** 50.00/100.00 **st.** – SB.

Cargills, Lower Mill St, PH10 6AQ, ☎ (01250) 876735, *exceed@btconnect.com, Fax (01250) 876735,* « Former grain store » – P. MC VISA
closed 1-2 January and Monday-Tuesday in winter – **Meals** a la carte 13.15/22.75 **t.** 11.00.

BOAT OF GARTEN *Highland* 401 I 12.

Boat of Garten (01479) 831282.
Edinburgh 133 – Inverness 28 – Perth 89.

The Boat, PH24 3BH, (01479) 831258, *holidays@boathotel.co.uk, Fax (01479) 831*
– P – 60. VISA
closed 2 weeks January – **Meals** (bar lunch)/dinner 29.50 **st.** 11.95 – **32 rm** (din
included) 45.00/90.00 **st.** – SB.

BONNYRIGG *Midlothian* 401 K 16 – *see Edinburgh.*

BORGIE *Highland* 401 H 8.

Edinburgh 262 – Inverness 93 – Thurso 31.

Borgie Lodge, KW14 7TH, (01641) 521332, *info@borgielodgehotel.co.*
Fax (01641) 521332, , – rest, P. VISA JCB
booking essential November-February – **Meals** (bar lunch)/dinner 25.00 **t.** 11.30 – **7**
60.00/85.00 **st.** – SB.

BOWMORE *Argyll and Bute* 401 B 16 – *see Islay (Isle of).*

BRAE *Shetland Islands* 401 P 2 – *see Shetland Islands (Mainland).*

BRAEMAR *Aberdeenshire* 401 J 12 *Scotland G.*

Env. : *Lin O'Dee*★, *W : 5 m.*
Cluniebank Rd (013397) 41618.
The Mews, Mar Rd (013397) 41600.
Edinburgh 85 – Aberdeen 58 – Dundee 51 – Perth 51.

Braemar Lodge, Glenshee Rd, AB35 5YQ, (013397) 41627, *Fax (013397) 41627,*
P. VISA JCB
Meals (dinner only) a la carte 14.40/26.85 **t.** 11.95 – **7 rm** 35.00/70.00.

BREAKISH *Highland* 401 C 12 – *see Skye (Isle of).*

BREASCLETE *Western Isles (Outer Hebrides)* 401 Z 9 – *see Lewis and Harris (Isle of).*

BRIDGEND *Argyll and Bute* 401 B 16 – *see Islay (Isle of).*

BROADFORD *Highland* 401 C 12 – *see Skye (Isle of).*

BRODICK *North Ayrshire* 401 402 E 17 – *see Arran (Isle of).*

BRORA *Highland* 401 I 9 – *pop. 1 687.*

Golf Rd (01408) 621417.
Edinburgh 234 – Inverness 78 – Wick 49.

Royal Marine, Golf Rd, KW9 6QS, (01408) 621252, *info@highlandescape.co*
Fax (01408) 621181, , , , , – rest, P – 90. AE VISA
Meals a la carte 14.00/26.00 **t.** 11.00 – **22 rm** 68.00/110.00 **t.** – SB.

Links, Golf Rd, KW9 6QS, (01408) 621225, *info@highlandescape.co*
Fax (01408) 621181, , , – rest, P. AE VISA
April-mid October – **Meals** (bar lunch)/dinner 25.00 **t.** 11.00 – **20 rm** 68.00/110.00
2 suites – SB.

Glenaveron without rest., Golf Rd, KW9 6QS, (01408) 621601, *glenaveron@hotm*
com, Fax (01408) 621601, – P. VISA.
closed 2 weeks October and Christmas – **3 rm** 35.00/56.00 **st.**

Tigh Fada without rest., 18 Golf Rd, KW9 6QS, (01408) 621332, *clarkson@tighfa*
fsnet.co.uk, Fax (01408) 621332, , – P.
closed Christmas and New Year – **3 rm** 25.00/50.00 **s.**

BROUGHTY FERRY *Dundee City* 401 L 14 – *see Dundee.*

CKIE *Moray* 401 L 10 – *pop. 8 324.*

Buckpool, Barhill Rd ✆ (01542) 832236 – Strathlene, Portessie ✆ (01542) 831798 – Cullen, The Links ✆ (01542) 840685.

Edinburgh 195 – Aberdeen 66 – Inverness 56.

Rosemount without rest., 62 East Church St, AB56 1ER, ✆ (01542) 833434, *rosemount_bck@btinternet.com, Fax (01542) 833434,* – P.
closed 23 December-5 January – **3 rm** 27.50/45.00.

Old Monastery, Drybridge, AB56 5JB, Southeast : 3 ½ m. by A 942 on Deskford rd ✆ (01542) 832660, *calumorvale@oldmonastery.com, Fax (01542) 839437,* « Former chapel overlooking Spey Bay » – P. MO AE VISA
closed 3 weeks January, Sunday and Monday – **Meals** a la carte 24.60/31.15 **t.** 11.50.

INCHREW *Highland* – *see Inverness.*

RNTISLAND *Fife* 401 K 15 *Scotland G.* – *pop. 5 951.*

Env. : *Aberdour★ – Aberdour Castle★ AC, W : 3 m. by A 921.*

Burntisland Golf House Club, Dodhead ✆ (01592) 874093 – Kinghorn Municipal, McDuff Cres., Kingham ✆ (01592) 890345.

Edinburgh 20 – Dunfermline 10 – Kirkcaldy 6.

The Kingswood, Kinghorn Rd, KY3 9LL, East : 1 m. on A 921 ✆ (01592) 872329, *rankin@kingswoodhotel.co.uk, Fax (01592) 873123,* – TV P. – 100. MO AE VISA
closed 26 December – **Meals** (bar lunch)/dinner a la carte 11.15/21.20 **st.** 8.50 – **10 rm** 52.00/85.00 **st.** – SB.

RRAY *Orkney Islands* 401 L 7 – *see Orkney Islands.*

TE (Isle of) *Argyll and Bute* 401 402 E 16 – *pop. 7 354.*

from Rothesay to Wemyss Bay (Mainland) (Caledonian MacBrayne Ltd) frequent services daily (35 mn) – from Rhubodach to Colintraive (Mainland) (Caledonian MacBrayne Ltd) frequent services daily (5 mn).

cog.

Balmory Hall without rest., Balmory Rd, PA20 9LL, ✆ (01700) 500669, *enquiries@balmoryhall.com, Fax (01700) 500669,* ←, « Mid 19C Italianate mansion », – TV P. MO VISA JCB.
closed 23-28 December – **3 rm** 75.00/110.00 **t.**

thesay.

Canada Hill ✆ (01700) 502244 – Sithean, Academy Rd ✆ (01700) 504369 – Port Bannatyne, Bannatyne Mains Rd ✆ (01700) 504544.

Isle of Bute Discovery Centre, The Winter Garden, Victoria St. ✆ (01700) 502151.

Cannon House, 5 Battery Pl, PA20 9DP, ✆ (01700) 502819, *Fax (01700) 505725,* ←, « Georgian town house » – rest, TV. MO VISA.
Meals (booking essential to non-residents) (dinner only) 15.00 **st.** 7.50 – **8 rm** 40.00/80.00 **st.** – SB.

DBOLL *Highland* – *see Tain.*

IRNBAAN *Argyll and Bute* 401 D 15 – *see Lochgilphead.*

LLANDER *Stirling* 401 H 15 *Scotland G.* – *pop. 3 268.*

See : *Town★.*

Exc. : *The Trossachs★★★ (Loch Katrine★★) – Hilltop Viewpoint★★★ (★★★) W : 10 m. by A 821.*

Aveland Rd ✆ (01877) 330090.

Rob Roy & Trossachs Visitor Centre, Ancaster Sq ✆ (01877) 330342.

Edinburgh 52 – Glasgow 43 – Oban 71 – Perth 41.

Roman Camp, Main St, FK17 8BG, ✆ (01877) 330003, *mail@roman-camp-hotel.co.uk, Fax (01877) 331533,* ←, « Part 17C hunting lodge in extensive gardens », – TV P. MO AE VISA JCB
Meals – (see ***The Restaurant*** below) – **10 rm** 90.00/180.00 **t.**, 4 suites – SB.

SCOTLAND

Invertrossachs Country House ⛰, Invertrossachs Rd, FK17 8HG, Southwe 5 ½ m. by A 81 and Invertrossachs rd taking no through road after 1 ¾ ☎ (01877) 331126, *reservations@invertrossachs.freeserve.co.uk, Fax (01877) 331229,* « Edwardian hunting lodge in extensive grounds », – rest, TV P. MO AE ⓓ JCB
Meals (by arrangement) (dinner only) (unlicensed) 22.50 **st.** – **3 rm** 60.00/120.00 **st.**

Lubnaig without rest., Leny Feus, FK17 8AS, ☎ (01877) 330376, *reception@lubnaighc co.uk, Fax (01877) 330376,* – TV P. MO VISA JCB.
April-October – **10 rm** 34.00/68.00 **t.**

Priory ⛰ without rest., Bracklinn Rd, FK17 8EH, ☎ (01877) 330001, *judith@bracklinnr .fsnet.co.uk, Fax (01877) 339200,* – TV P. MO VISA JCB.
April-October – **7 rm** 40.00/80.00 **t.**

Brook Linn ⛰ without rest., Leny Feus, FK17 8AU, ☎ (01877) 330103, *derek@blinn.f serve.co.uk, Fax (01877) 330103,* ≤, – TV P. MO VISA.
mid March-October – **6 rm** 27.00/60.00 **st.**

East Mains House without rest., Bridgend, FK17 8AG, ☎ (01877) 330535, *east.ma @tesco.net, Fax (01877) 330535,* – TV P. MO VISA
6 rm 29.00/48.00 **t.**

Dunmor without rest., Leny Rd, FK17 8AL, ☎ (01877) 330756 – TV P. MO VISA
closed mid November-mid January – **4 rm** 35.00/60.00 **s.**

XXX **The Restaurant** (at Roman Camp H.), Main St, FK19 8BG, ☎ (01877) 330003, *ma roman-camp-hotel-co.uk, Fax (01877) 331533* – P. MO AE ⓓ VISA JCB
Meals 18.00/36.50 and a la carte 38.45/55.15 **t.** 17.50.

CAMPBELTOWN *Argyll and Bute* 401 D 17 – *see Kintyre (Peninsula).*

CANNICH *Highland* 401 F 11 – ✉ *Beauly.*
Edinburgh 184 – Inverness 28 – Kyle of Lochalsh 54.

Mullardoch House ⛰, IV4 7LX, West : 8 ½ m. ☎ (01456) 415460, *andy@mullhous demon.co.uk, Fax (01456) 415460,* ≤ Loch Sealbanach and Affric Hills, « Former hunt lodge », – TV P. MO AE VISA
Meals (booking essential to non-residents) (set menu only) (bar lunch)/dinner 24.0 8.95 – **7 rm** 62.00/108.00 **t.**

CARBOST *Highland* 401 A 12 – *see Skye (Isle of).*

CARDROSS *Argyll and Bute* 401 G 16 *Scotland G.*
Env. : *The Clyde Estuary*★.
Edinburgh 63 – Glasgow 17 – Helensburgh 5.

Kirkton House ⛰, Darleith Rd, G82 5EZ, ☎ (01389) 841951, *mich@kirktonhouse.co Fax (01389) 841868,* ≤, – TV P. MO AE ⓓ VISA JCB
closed December and January – **Meals** (by arrangement) 22.75 **st.** 8.50 – **6 rm** 45. 70.00 **st.** – SB.

CARNOUSTIE *Angus* 401 L 14 – *pop. 12 337.*
18, 18 *Monifieth Golf Links, Medal Starter's Box, Princes St., Monifieth ☎ (01382) 532767 - Burnside, Links Par. ☎ (01241) 853789 – 18 Panmure, Barry ☎ (01241) 853120 – 18 Budd Links, Links Par. ☎ (01241) 853789.*
1B High St ☎ (01241) 852258 (Easter-September).
Edinburgh 68 – Aberdeen 59 – Dundee 12.

The Carnoustie Golf Course H., The Links, DD7 7JE, ☎ (01241) 411999, *enqui @carnoustie-hotel.com, Fax (01241) 411998,* ≤, 18, – rest, TV P. – 280. MO AE ⓓ VISA
Dalhousie : **Meals** (light lunch)/dinner 31.50/37.50 and a la carte 32.50/37.50 **t.** 19.0 **81 rm** 165.00/230.00 **t.**, 4 suites – SB.

XX **11 Park Avenue,** 11 Park Ave, DD7 7JA, ☎ (01241) 853336, *parkavenue@genie.co. Fax (01241) 859333* – MO AE ⓓ VISA JCB
closed first week January, Sunday, Monday and Friday dinner – **Meals** (dinner only a lunch by arrangement April-September) a la carte 19.70/29.65 **t.** 11.50.

CARRADALE *Argyll and Bute* 401 D 17 – *see Kintyre Peninsula.*

ARRBRIDGE *Highland* 401 I 12.

Carrbridge (01479) 841623.

Edinburgh 135 – Aberdeen 92 – Inverness 23.

Fairwinds, PH23 3AA, (01479) 841240, *enquiries@fairwindshotel.com, Fax (01479) 841240,* – *closed mid-late November and 25-26 December –* **Meals** *(closed Monday to non-residents)* (booking essential) (dinner only) a la carte 15.75/25.40 **t.** 8.50 – **5 rm** 35.00/70.00 **t.** – SB.

Feith Mho'r Lodge without rest., Station Rd, PH23 3AP, West : 1 ¼ m. (01479) 841621, *feith.mhor@btinternet.com,* – *closed 25 December –* **6 rm** 28.00/56.00 **st.**

ASTLEBAY *Western Isles* 401 X 12/13 – *see Barra (Isle of).*

ASTLE DOUGLAS *Dumfries and Galloway* 401 402 I 19 *Scotland G. – pop. 4 187.*

Env. : *Threave Garden★★ AC, SW : 2½ m. by A 75 – Threave Castle★ AC, W : 1 m.*

Abercromby Rd (01556) 502801.

Markethill Car Park (01556) 502611 (Easter-October).

Edinburgh 98 – Ayr 49 – Dumfries 18 – Stranraer 57.

Longacre Manor, Ernespie Rd, DG7 1LE, Northeast : ¾ m. on Dumfries rd (A 75) (01556) 503576, *ball.longacre@btinternet.com, Fax (01556) 503886,* – rest,

Meals (by arrangement) (communal dining) 17.50 **s.** 7.75 – **4 rm** 45.00/90.00 **s.** – SB.

t Kirkpatrick Durham *North : 5½ m. by A 75 and B 794 – Castle Douglas.*

Chipperkyle without rest., DG7 3EY, (01556) 650223, *dickson@chipperkyle.freeserve.co.uk, « Georgian manor house »,* – *closed 15-28 December –* **3 rm** 36.00/72.00 **st.**

t Crossmichael *Northwest : 3 ¾ m. on A 713 – Castle Douglas.*

Plumed Horse (Borthwick), Main St, DG7 3AU, (01556) 670333, *plumed.horse@virgin.net, Fax (01556) 670333* – *closed first 2 weeks September, 2 weeks January, Christmas, Monday, Saturday lunch and Sunday dinner –* **Meals** (booking essential) 14.95/16.95 (lunch) and a la carte 25.70/36.95 **st.** 12.60

Spec. Assiette of foie gras. Salmon with langoustine tortellini, Nantua sauce. Peach and Champagne soup, rose sorbet.

AWDOR *Highland* 401 I 11 – *pop. 812 – Inverness.*

Edinburgh 170 – Aberdeen 100 – Inverness 14.

Cawdor Tavern, The Lane, IV12 5XP, (01667) 404777, *Fax (01667) 404777,* – *closed 1 week January and 25 December –* **Meals** (booking essential Saturday and Sunday) a la carte 14.40/24.75 **t.** 12.95.

HIRNSIDE *Borders* 401 N 16 – *pop. 1 680 – Duns.*

Edinburgh 52 – Berwick-upon-Tweed 8 – Glasgow 95 – Newcastle upon Tyne 70.

Chirnside Hall, TD11 3LD, East : 1 ¼ m. on A 6105 (01890) 818219, *chirnsidehall@globalnet.co.uk, Fax (01890) 818231,* – rest,

Meals (booking essential to non-residents) (dinner only) 23.50 12.50 – **10 rm** 75.00/130.00 **t.** – SB.

LACHAN SEIL *Argyll and Bute* 401 D 15 – *see Seil (Isle of).*

LEISH *Perth and Kinross* 401 J 15 – *see Kinross.*

LUANIE INN *Highland – Glenmoriston.*

Edinburgh 176 – Inverness 39 – Kyle of Lochalsh 32 – Oban 135.

Cluanie Inn, IV3 6YW, (01320) 340238, *cluanie@ecosse.net, Fax (01320) 340293,* –

Meals (bar lunch)/dinner 14.50/18.50 – **14 rm** 39.50/87.00 **st.**

SCOTLAND

CLYDEBANK *West Dunbartonshire* 401 G 16 – *pop. 45 717.*

Clydebank Municipal, Overtoun Rd, Dalmuir ☎ (0141) 952 8698.

Edinburgh 52 – Glasgow 6.

The Beardmore, Beardmore St, G81 4SA, off A 814 ☎ (0141) 951 6000, *beardmore.hc@hei.co.uk, Fax (0141) 951 6018,* – 170.

Citrus : **Meals** *(closed Sunday)* (dinner only) 21.00 and a la carte **st.** – ***B bar cafe :*** **Me** a la carte 18.00/31.00 **st.** 13.00 – 13.95 – **162 rm** 94.00 **st.**, 6 suites – SB.

COLONSAY (Isle of) *Argyll and Bute* 401 B 15 – *pop. 106 (inc. Oronsay).*

Isle of Colonsay ☎ (019512) 316.

– from Scalasaig to Oban (Caledonian MacBrayne Ltd) 3 weekly (2 h) – from Scalas to Kintyre Peninsula (Kennacraig) via Isle of Islay (Port Askaig) (Caledonian MacBrayne L weekly.

Scalasaig – *Colonsay.*

Isle of Colonsay, PA61 7YP, ☎ (01951) 200316, *colonsay.hotel@pipemedia.co. Fax (01951) 200353,* –

Meals (booking essential) (bar lunch)/dinner a la carte 12.20/18.15 **t.** 8.00 – **8 rm** (dinner included) 65.00/130.00 **t.**

COMRIE *Perthshire* 401 I 14 – *pop. 1 926.*

Comrie, Laggan Braes ☎ (01764) 70055.

Edinburgh 66 – Glasgow 56 – Oban 70 – Perth 24.

The Royal, Melville Sq, PH6 2DN, ☎ (01764) 679200, *reception@royalhotel.co. Fax (01764) 679219,* « Attractively furnished », –

Meals 26.50 (dinner) and a la carte 18.70/26.50 **t.** 9.50 – **11 rm** 70.00/150.00 **t.** – SB.

CONNEL *Argyll and Bute* 401 D 14 – *Oban.*

Edinburgh 118 – Glasgow 88 – Inverness 113 – Oban 5.

Ards House, PA37 1PT, on A 85 ☎ (01631) 710255, *jb@ardshouse.com,* –

closed mid November-mid February – **Meals** 30.00 **t.** 12.15 – **7 rm** (dinner include 64.00/128.00 **t.** – SB.

Ronebhal without rest., PA37 1PJ, on A 85 ☎ (01631) 710310, *ronebhal@btintern co.uk, Fax (01631) 710310,* –

closed January and December – **6 rm** 25.00/60.00.

CONON BRIDGE *Highland* 401 G 11.

Edinburgh 168 – Inverness 12.

Kinkell House, Easter Kinkell, IV7 8HY, Southeast : 3 m. by B 9163 and A 835 B 9169 ☎ (01349) 861270, *kinkell@aol.com, Fax (01349) 865902,* –

Meals (booking essential) (dinner only and Sunday lunch) a la carte approx. 25.00 **st.** 11. – **7 rm** 55.00/90.00 **st.**

CONTIN *Highland* 401 G 11 – *pop. 1 194 – Strathpeffer.*

Edinburgh 175 – Inverness 19.

Coul House, IV14 9EY, ☎ (01997) 421487, *coulhouse@bestwestern.co. Fax (01997) 421945,* – rest,

Mackenzie's : **Meals** 24.95 (dinner) and a la carte 21.50/31.00 **t.** 14.00 – ***Tartan Bistr*** **Meals** (dinner only) a la carte 12.00/21.50 **t.** 12.00 – **19 rm** 70.00/124.00 **t.**, 1 suite SB.

Achilty, IV14 9EG, Northwest : ¾ m. on A 835 ☎ (01997) 421355, *Fax (01997) 421923* –

Meals a la carte 13.45/27.95 **t.** 9.95 – **12 rm** 53.00/76.00 **t.** – SB.

CRAIGELLACHIE *Moray* 401 K 11 *Scotland G.*

Env. : *Dufftown (Glenfiddich Distillery★), SE : 5 m. by A 941.*

Edinburgh 190 – Aberdeen 58 – Inverness 53.

Craigellachie, Victoria St, AB38 9SR, ☎ (01340) 881204, *info@craigellachie.co Fax (01340) 881253,* – rest, – 60.

Meals 28.00/35.00 and lunch a la carte 15.85/25.00 **st.** 15.00 – **25 rm** 95.00/190.00 – SB.

RAIGHOUSE *Argyll and Bute* 401 C 16 – *see Jura (Isle of).*

RIEFF *Perth and Kinross* 401 I 14 *Scotland G.* – *pop. 6 096.*

See : *Town*★.

Env. : *Drummond Castle Gardens*★ *AC, S : 2 m. by A 822 – Comrie (Scottish Tartans Museum*★*) W : 6 m. by A 85.*

Exc. : *Scone Palace*★★ *AC, E : 16 m. by A 85 and A 93.*

18, 9 *Perth Rd* ☎ *(01764) 652909* – 9 *Muthill, Peat Rd* ☎ *(01764) 681523.*

ℹ *High St* ☎ *(01764) 652578.*

Edinburgh 60 – Glasgow 50 – Oban 76 – Perth 18.

Murraypark, Connaught Terr, PH7 3DJ, ☎ (01764) 658000, *Fax (01764) 655311,* – rest, TV & P – 25. MC AE VISA
Meals (bar lunch)/dinner a la carte 10.40/25.45 **t.** 9.95 – **19 rm** 37.50/110.00 **t.**, 1 suite.

Gwydyr House, Comrie Rd, PH7 4BP, West : ½ m. on A 85 ☎ (01764) 653277, *enquiries@gwdyrhouse.co.uk, Fax (01764) 653277,* ≤, – rest, TV P. MC VISA
closed 1 week spring, 2 weeks October, Christmas and New Year – **Meals** (by arrangement) 17.95 **st.** 10.50 – **8 rm** 40.00/70.00 **st.** – SB.

RINAN *Argyll and Bute* 401 D 15 *Scotland G.* – ✉ *Lochgilphead.*

See : *Hamlet*★.

Exc. : *Kilmory Knap (Macmillan's Cross*★*) SW : 14 m.*

Edinburgh 137 – Glasgow 91 – Oban 36.

Crinan, PA31 8SR, ☎ (01546) 830261, *nryan@crinanhotel.com, Fax (01546) 830292,* « Commanding setting, ≤ Loch Crinan and Sound of Jura », – |‡|, rest, TV P. MC AE VISA
closed 25 December – **Meals** (bar lunch)/dinner 42.50 **t.** 15.50 – (see also ***Lock 16*** below) – **20 rm** (dinner included) 95.00/260.00 **t.** – SB.

Lock 16 (at Crinan H.), PA31 8SR, ☎ (01546) 830261, *nryan@crinanhotel.com, Fax (01546) 830292,* « Commanding setting, ≤ Loch Crinan and Sound of Jura » – P. MC AE VISA
May-September – **Meals** - Seafood - *(closed 25 December, Sunday and Monday)* (booking essential) (dinner only) 42.50 **t.** 15.50.

ROSSFORD *Fife* 401 J 15 – *see Dunfermline.*

ROSSMICHAEL *Dumfries and Galloway* 401 402 I 19 – *see Castle Douglas.*

ULLODEN *Highland* 401 H 11 – *see Inverness.*

ULNAKNOCK *Highland* 401 B 11 – *see Skye (Isle of).*

UMBERNAULD *North Lanarkshire* 401 I 16 – *pop. 62 412.*

Edinburgh 40 – Glasgow 11 – Stirling 13.

Travel Inn, 4 South Muirhead Rd, G67 1AX, off A 8011 ☎ (01236) 725339, *Fax (01236) 736380* – rm, rest, TV & P. MC AE VISA.
Meals (grill rest.) – **37 rm** 41.95 **t.**

UPAR *Fife* 401 K 15 – *pop. 8 174.*

Edinburgh 45 – Dundee 15 – Perth 23.

Westfield House without rest., Westfield Rd, KY15 5AR, West : ½ m. by A 91 off Westfield Ave ☎ (1334) 655699, *westfieldhouse@standrews4.freeserve.co.uk, Fax (01334) 650075,* « Georgian house », – TV P.
3 rm 35.00/70.00 **st.**

Todhall House, Dairsie, KY15 4RQ, East : 2 m. by A 91 ☎ (01334) 656344, *todhallhouse@ukgateway.net, Fax (01334) 650791,* ≤, « Part Georgian, part Victorian country house », – TV P. MC VISA.
March-mid November – **Meals** (by arrangement) (communal dining) 20.00 – **3 rm** 34.00/68.00.

Ostler's Close, 25 Bonnygate, KY15 4BU, ☎ (01334) 655574, *Fax (01334) 654036* – MC AE VISA JCB
closed Sunday, Monday and lunch Tuesday-Thursday – **Meals** a la carte 17.45/33.00 **t.** 13.00.

DALBEATTIE *Dumfries and Galloway* 401 402 I 19 *Scotland G. – pop. 4 421.*
Env. : *Kippford*★, *S : 5 m. by A 710.*
Dalbeattie ☎ (01556) 611421.
Edinburgh 94 – Ayr 56 – Dumfries 14 – Stranraer 62.

Auchenskeoch Lodge, DG5 4PG, Southeast : 6 ¼ m. by A 711 on B 7
☎ (01387) 780277, *brmsmth@aol.com, Fax (01387) 780277,* – rest, TV
VISA
Easter-October – **Meals** (by arrangement) (communal dining) 17.50 **st.** 7.00 – 2
39.00/62.00 **st.**, 1 suite – SB.

DALRY *North Ayrshire* 401 402 F 16.
Edinburgh 70 – Ayr 21 – Glasgow 25.

Braidwoods, Drumastle Mill Cottage, KA24 4LN, Southwest : 1 ½ m. by A 737
Saltcoats rd ☎ (01294) 833544, *keithbraidwood@btconnect.com, Fax (01294) 833553* –
P. AE VISA
closed first 3 weeks January, 2 weeks September, 25 December, Monday, Sunday dinner a Tuesday lunch – **Meals** (booking essential) 18.00/30.00 **t.** 13.95
Spec. Roast quail with black pudding, braised Puy lentils. Baked medley of seafood. Var panna cotta with passion fruit and mango soup.

DENNY *Falkirk* 401 I 15 *Scotland G. – pop. 11 061.*
Exc. : *Stirling*★★, *N : 8 m. by A 872.*
Edinburgh 34 – Glasgow 25 – Stirling 7.

Topps Farm, Fintry Rd, FK6 5JF, West : 4 m. on B 818 ☎ (01324) 822471, *2lan @onetel.net, Fax (01324) 823099,* ← – TV P. VISA
Meals 15.50 **st.** 8.50 – **8 rm** 34.00/46.00 **st.** – SB.

DERVAIG *Argyll and Bute* 401 B 14 – *see Mull (Isle of).*

DINGWALL *Highland* 401 G 11 – *pop. 5 572.*
Edinburgh 172 – Inverness 14.

Cafe India Brasserie, Lockhart House, Tulloch St, IV15 9JZ, ☎ (01349) 862552 –
VISA
Meals - Indian - 6.95 (lunch) and a la carte 14.20/23.95 **t.** 9.50.

DORNIE *Highland* 401 D 12 *Scotland G.* – ✉ *Kyle of Lochalsh.*
See : *Eilean Donan Castle*★ *AC (site*★★*).*
Env. : *Glen Shiel*★, *SE : 4 m. on A 87.*
Edinburgh 212 – Inverness 74 – Kyle of Lochalsh 8.

Conchra House, Ardelve, IV40 8DZ, North : 1 ¾ m. by A 87 on Conchra
☎ (01599) 555233, *email@conchra.co.uk, Fax (01599) 555433,* ← Loch Long, « Part Georgian country house », – P – 40. AE VISA.
closed Christmas and New Year, booking essential in winter – **Meals** (booking essential non-residents) (dinner only) 15.50/19.50 **s.** 8.50 – **6 rm** 39.00/72.00 **s.** – SB.

DORNOCH *Highland* 401 H 10 *Scotland G. – pop. 2 042.*
See : *Town*★.
Royal Dornoch, Golf Rd ☎ (01862) 810219.
The Square ☎ (01862) 810400.
Edinburgh 219 – Inverness 63 – Wick 65.

Highfield House without rest., Evelix Rd, IV25 3HR, ☎ (01862) 810909, *enquiries@hi fieldhouse.co.uk, Fax (01862) 811605,* ←, – TV P
3 rm 40.00/58.00 **s.**

2 Quail with rm, Castle St, IV25 3SN, ☎ (01862) 811811, *bookings@2quail.com* – r
TV. AE VISA.
closed two weeks spring, Christmas and New Year – **Meals** *(closed Sunday and Mond*
(dinner only) 30.00/35.00 **t.** 13.00 – **2 rm** 70.00/80.00 **t.**

DOUNBY *Orkney Islands* 401 K 6 – *see Orkney Islands (Mainland).*

UMBEG *Highland* 401 E 9 – ✉ *Lairg.*
Edinburgh 262 – Inverness 105 – Ullapool 48.

Drumbeg, Assynt, IV27 4NW, ✆ (01571) 833236, *Fax (01571) 833333,* ≤ – ⇔ rest, TV P. MC VISA. ✻
April-October – **Meals** (booking essential to non-residents) (bar lunch) a la carte 11.00/19.00 **st.** 8.00 – **6 rm** 30.00/50.00 **st.**

UMNADROCHIT *Highland* 401 G 11 *Scotland G. – pop. 852 –* ✉ *Milton.*
Env. : *Loch Ness★★ – Loch Ness Monster Exhibition★ AC – The Great Glen★.*
Edinburgh 172 – Inverness 16 – Kyle of Lochalsh 66.

Polmaily House , IV63 6XT, West : 2 m. on A 831 ✆ (01456) 450343, *polmaily@btinternet.com, Fax (01456) 450813,* , , , – ⇔ TV P. MC VISA
Meals (bar lunch)/dinner 22.00/27.00 and a la carte 15.00/26.95 **t.** 14.00 – **12 rm** 72.00/144.00 **st.** – SB.

Drumbuie Farm without rest., Drumbuie, IV3 6XP, East : 3/4 m. by A 82 ✆ (01456) 450634, *drumbuie@amserve.net, Fax (01456) 450595,* ≤, « Working farm », – ⇔ TV P. MC VISA. ✻
3 rm 50.00.

YMEN *Stirling* 401 G 15 *Scotland G. – pop. 1 565.*
Env. : *Loch Lomond★★, W : 3 m.*
Drymen Library, The Square ✆ (01360) 660068 (May-September).
Edinburgh 64 – Glasgow 18 – Stirling 22.

Buchanan Arms, Main St, G63 0BQ, ✆ (01360) 660588, *enquiries@buchananarms.co.uk, Fax (01360) 660943,* , , , – ⇔ TV P – 150. MC AE VISA JCB
Meals 12.50/24.50 **st.** 11.75 – **52 rm** (dinner included) 70.00/160.00 **st.** – SB.

LNAIN BRIDGE *Highland* 401 J 12 – *see Grantown-on-Spey.*

MBARTON *West Dunbartonshire* 401 G 16 *Scotland G. – pop. 77 173.*
See : *Dumbarton Castle (site★) AC.*
Env. : *Loch Lomond★★, N : 5½ m. by A 82.*
18 Vale of Leven, Northfield Rd, Bonhill, Alexandria ✆ (01389) 752351 – 18 Broadmeadow ✆ (01389) 732830.
Milton, by Dumbarton A 82 (northbound) ✆ (01389) 742306.
Edinburgh 64 – Glasgow 12 – Greenock 17.

Travelodge, Milton, G82 2TY, East : 3 m. by A 814 on A 82 ✆ (01389) 65202, *Fax (01389) 65202* – ⇔ rm, TV P. MC AE VISA JCB. ✻
Meals (grill rest.) – **32 rm** 42.95 **t.**

MFRIES *Dumfries and Galloway* 401 402 J 18 *Scotland G. – pop. 21 164.*
See : *Town★ – Midsteeple★* A *A.*
Env. : *Lincluden College (Tomb★) AC, N : 1½ m. by College St.* A.
Exc. : *Drumlanrig Castle★★ (cabinets★) AC, NW : 16 ½ m. by A 76* A *– Shambellie House Museum of Costume (Costume Collection★) S : 7¼m. by A 710* A *– Sweetheart Abbey★ AC, S : 8 m. by A 710* A *– Caerlaverock Castle★ (Renaissance façade★★) AC, SE : 9 m. by B 725* B *– Glenkiln (Sculptures★) W : 9 m. by A 780 –* A *– and A 75 – Ruthwell Cross★, SE : 12 m. by A 780 –* B *– A 75 and B 724.*
18 Dumfries & Galloway, 2 Laurieston Av., Maxwelltown ✆ (01387) 253582 A *– 18 Dumfries & County, Nuffield, Edinburgh Rd ✆ (01387) 253585 – 9 Crichton, Bankend Rd ✆ (01387) 247894,* B.
Whitesands ✆ (01387) 253862, A.
Edinburgh 80 – Ayr 59 – Carlisle 34 – Glasgow 79 – Manchester 155 – Newcastle upon Tyne 91.

Plan on next page

Cairndale, English St, DG1 2DF, ✆ (01387) 254111, *sales@cairndale.fsnet.co.uk, Fax (01387) 250555,* , , – , ⇔ rm, TV P – 300. MC AE VISA B a
Meals 20.00/25.00 12.75 – **89 rm** 85.00/145.00 **st.**, 2 suites – SB.

Station, 49 Lovers Walk, DG1 1LT, ✆ (01387) 254316, *info@stationhotel.co.uk, Fax (01387) 250388* – , ⇔ rm, TV P – 70. MC AE VISA. ✻ B e
Meals (bar lunch Monday-Saturday) 6.95/11.95 and dinner a la carte 15.00/24.00 **st.** 10.00 – **32 rm** 75.00/110.00 **st.** – SB.

DUMFRIES

Aldermanhill Road	B 2	Friars Vennel	A 13	St. Michael's Bridge Road	A
Bank Street	A 3	Galloway Street	A 14	Shakespeare Street	B
Buccleuch Street	A 4	Glebe Street	B 15	Union Street	A
Cardoness Street	B 5	Great King Street	A 16	Whitesands	A
Cassalands	A 6	Hermitage Drive	A 17		
Castle Street	A 7	High Street	A 18		
Castle Douglas Road	A 8	Loreburn Centre	A 20		
Catherine Street	B 9	Loreburn Street	A 21		
Corberry Avenue	A 10	Nith Street	AB 22		
Cornwall Mount Rd	B 12	Queen Street	B 23		
		Queensberry Street	A 24		
		Rae Street	B 26		
		St. Mary's Street	B 27		
		St. Michael Street	B 28		

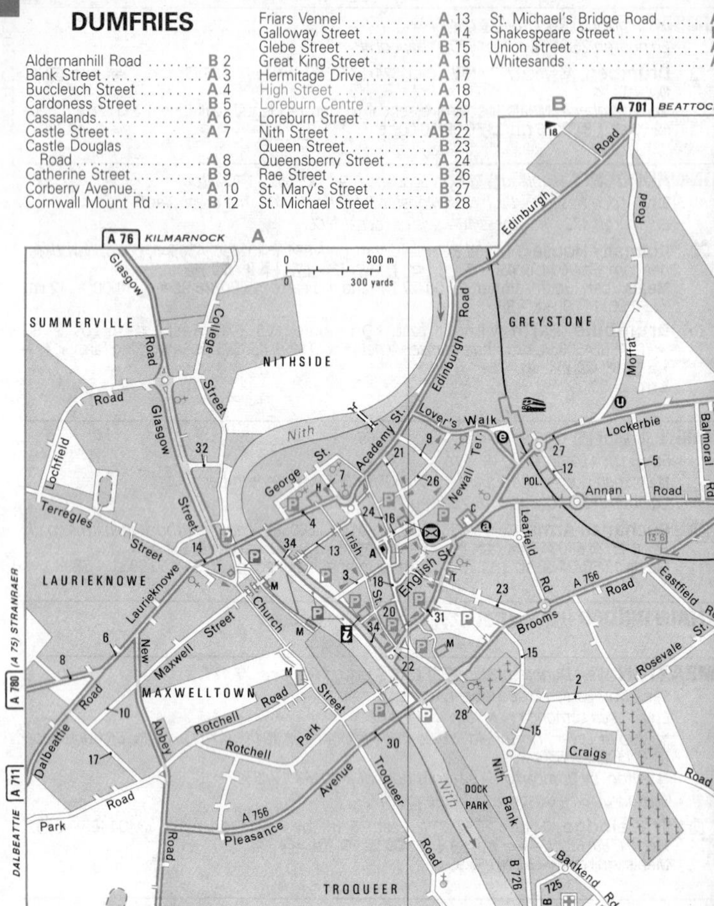

Travel Inn, Annan Rd, Collin, DG1 3JX, East : 2 m. on A 780 (Carlisle rd) at junction with A 75 ✆ (01387) 249785, *Fax (01387) 249287* – ⇔ rm, ▤ rest, TV & P. MC AE ⓓ VISA. ✂
Meals (grill rest.) – **40 rm** 41.95 t.

Travelodge, Annan Rd, Collin, DG1 3SE, East : 2 ¼ m. by A 780 (Carlisle rd) on A
✆ (01387) 750658, *Fax (01387) 750658* – ⇔ rm, TV & P. MC AE ⓓ VISA JCB. ✂
Meals (grill rest.) – **40 rm** 39.95 t.

Redbank House without rest., New Abbey Rd, DG2 8EW, South : 1 ½ m. by A (Stranraer rd) on A 710 ✆ (01387) 247034, *Fax (01387) 266220*, ≘s, 🌳 – ⇔ TV P. MC VISA JCB. ✂
5 rm ☐ 35.00/50.00 s.

Hazeldean without rest., 4 Moffat Rd, DG1 1NJ, ✆ (01387) 266178, *info@hazeld house.com, Fax (01387) 266178*, 🌳 – ⇔ TV P. MC VISA. ✂ B
7 rm ☐ 30.00/44.00 s.

DUNAIN PARK *Highland – see Inverness.*

Jährlich eine neue Ausgabe
Aktuellste Informationen, jährlich für Sie!

NBLANE *Stirling* 401 I 15 *Scotland G. – pop. 8 007 (inc. Lecropt).*

See : *Town★ – Cathedral★ (west front★★).*

Env. : *Doune★ (castle★ AC) W : 4½ m. by A 820 – Doune Motor Museum★ AC, W : 5½ m. by A 820 and A 84.*

Stirling Rd (01786) 824428 (May-September).

Edinburgh 42 – Glasgow 33 – Perth 29.

Cromlix House, Kinbuck, FK15 9JT, North : 3 ½ m. on B 8033 (01786) 822125, *reservations@cromlixhouse.com, Fax (01786) 825450,* « Antique furnishings, 19C chapel », – rest, P. VISA
closed 2-25 January – **Meals** (booking essential) (lunch by arrangement)/dinner 40.00 **st.** 17.00 – **6 rm** 160.00/245.00 **st.**, **8 suites** 260.00/325.00 **st.** – SB.

Rokeby House, Doune Rd, FK15 9AT, (01786) 824447, *rokeby.house@btconnect.com, Fax (01786) 821399,* « Edwardian house », – P. VISA JCB.
Meals (booking essential) (set menu only Monday-Friday) (dinner only) 15.00/28.00 **st.** 14.50 – **4 rm** 65.00/90.00 **st.**

NDEE *Dundee* 401 L 14 *Scotland G. – pop. 165 873.*

See : *Town★ – The Frigate Unicorn★ AC* Y A *– Discovery Point★ AC* Y B *– Verdant Works★ – McManus Galleries★.*

18, 9, 9 Caird Park, Mains Loan (01382) 453606 – 18 Camperdown, Camperdown Park (01382) 623398 – 18 Downfield, Turnberry Av. (01382) 825595.

Tay Road Bridge (toll) Y.

Dundee Airport : (01382) 643242, SW : 1½ m. Z.

21 Castle St (01382) 527527.

Edinburgh 63 – Aberdeen 67 – Glasgow 83.

Plan on next page

Hilton Dundee, Earl Grey Pl, DD1 4DE, (01382) 229271, *reservations@dundee-stakis.co.uk, Fax (01382) 200072,* – rest, P – 400. VISA JCB Y a
Meals (bar lunch Saturday) 12.95/21.00 and dinner a la carte 14.75/24.00 **t.** 12.30 – 11.50 – **128 rm** 120.00/140.00 **st.**, 1 suite – SB.

Swallow, Kingsway West (Dundee Ring Rd), DD2 5JT, West : 4 ¾ m. at junction of A 85 with A 90 (01382) 631200, *swallowsales@ukonline.co.uk, Fax (01382) 631201,* – rest, P – 100. VISA
Meals a la carte 19.95/29.00 **st.** 12.00 – **105 rm** 98.00/118.00 **st.**, 1 suite.

Premier Lodge, Dayton Drive, Camperdown Retail Park, Kingsway, DD2 3SQ, Northwest : 3 ¼ m. by A 923 at junction with A 90 (01382) 880170, *Fax (01382) 880172* – rm, rest, P. VISA. Z e
Meals (grill rest.) a la carte approx. 14.20 **t.** 8.75 – **78 rm** 42.95 **t.**

Premier Lodge, Panmurefield, DD5 3TS, East : 4 ¾ m. on A 92 (01382) 738112, *Fax (01382) 736042* – rm, rest, P. VISA.
Meals (grill rest.) a la carte approx. 16.95 **t.** 8.75 – **60 rm** 42.95 **t.**

Travel Inn, Discovery Quay, Riverside Drive, DD1 4XA, (01382) 203240, *Fax (01382) 203237,* – rm, rest, P. VISA. Z a
Meals (grill rest.) – **40 rm** 41.95 **t.**

Travel Inn, Ethiebeaton Park, Monifieth, DD5 4HB, East : 5 ¾ m. on A 92 (01382) 530565, *Fax (01382) 530468* – rm, rest, P. VISA.
Meals (grill rest.) – **40 rm** 41.95 **t.**

Travel Inn, Kingsway West, Invergowrie, DD2 5JU, West : 5 m. by A 85 on A 90 (01382) 561115, *Fax (01382) 568431* – rm, rest, P. VISA.
Meals (grill rest.) – **64 rm** 41.95 **t.**

Travelodge, Kingsway West, Invergowrie, DD2 4TD, Northwest : 3 ¾ m. by A 923 on A 90 (01382) 610488, *Fax (01382) 610488* – rm, P. VISA.
Meals (grill rest.) – **32 rm** 39.95 **t.**

Hillside without rest., 43 Constitution St, DD3 6JH, (01382) 223443, *info@tildab.co.uk, Fax (01382) 800222,* – P. VISA. Y e
3 rm 30.00/48.00.

Broughty Ferry *East : 4½ m. by A 930 –* Z *– (Dundee Rd) – Dundee.*

Broughty Ferry, 16 West Queen St, DD5 1AR, (01382) 480027, *jghm@hotelbroughtyferry.co.uk, Fax (01382) 477660,* – P. VISA.
Meals – (see ***Bombay Brasserie*** below) – **15 rm** 59.00/74.00 **t.** – SB.

Beach House, 22 Esplanade, DD5 2EN, (01382) 776614, *Fax (01382) 480241* – rest, VISA JCB.
Meals 12.50 8.50 – **5 rm** 38.00/48.00 **s.** – SB.

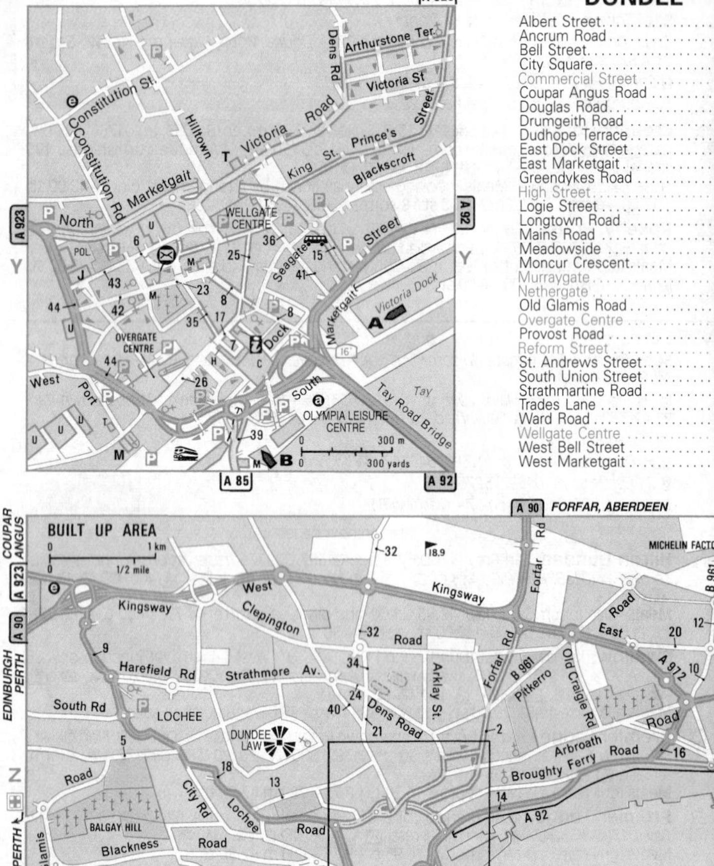

🏠 **Invermark House** without rest., 23 Monifieth Rd, DD5 2RN, ✆ (01382) 739 *invermarkhouse@onetel.net.uk, Fax (01382) 739430,* – TV P. MC VISA. *closed Christmas and New Year* – **5 rm** 30.00/45.00 **s.**

XX **Bombay Brasserie** (at Broughty Ferry H.), 16 West Queen St, DD5 ✆ (01382) 480490, *Fax (01382) 477660* – P. MC AE VISA *closed lunch Sunday and Monday* – **Meals** - Indian - (lunch by arrangement) a la c 15.00/23.90 9.75.

X **Cafe Montmartre,** 289 Brook St, DD5 2DS, ✆ (01382) 739313, *thierryhaddanou@ mail.com, Fax (01382) 739636* – MC AE VISA JCB *closed 2 weeks July, 25 December, 1 January and Sunday* – **Meals** - French - a la c 9.85/25.05 **t.** 10.90.

Les prix — Pour toutes précisions sur les prix indiqués dans ce guide, reportez-vous aux pages de l'introduction.

DUNDONNELL *Highland* 401 E 10 *Scotland G.* – ✉ *Garve.*

Env. : *Wester Ross★★★ – Loch Broom★★, N : 4½ m. via Allt na h–Airbhe.*

Exc. : *Falls of Measach★★, SE : 10 m. by A 832 – Corrieshalloch Gorge★, SE : 11 ½ m. by A 832 and A 835.*

Edinburgh 215 – Inverness 59.

Dundonnell, Little Loch Broom, IV23 2QR, ℘ (01854) 633204, *selbie@dundonnellhotel.co.uk, Fax (01854) 633366,* ≤ Dundonnell Valley – ⇔ TV P – 60. MO AE VISA
closed January-February – **Meals** (booking essential in winter) (bar lunch)/dinner a la carte 21.45/25.75 **t.** – **28 rm** 60.00/120.00 **t.** – SB.

DUNFERMLINE *Fife* 401 J 15 *Scotland G. – pop. 29 436.*

See : *Town★ – Abbey★ (Abbey Church★★) AC.*

Env. : *Forth Bridges★★, S : 5 m. by A 823 and B 980.*

Exc. : *Culross★★ (Village★★★, Palace★★ AC, Study★ AC), W : 7 m. by A 994 and B 9037.*

18 *Canmore, Venturefair Av.* ℘ *(01383) 724969* – 18 *Pitreavie, Queensferry Rd* ℘ *(01383) 722591* – 18 *Pitfirrane, Crossford* ℘ *(01383) 723534* – 9 *Saline, Kinneddar Hill* ℘ *(01383) 852591.*

13-15 Maygate ℘ *(01383) 720999 (April-October).*

Edinburgh 16 – Dundee 48 – Motherwell 39.

Garvock House, St John's Drive, Transy, KY12 7TU, East : ¾ m. by A 907 off Garvock hill ℘ (01383) 621067, *sales@garvock.co.uk, Fax (01383) 621168,* – ⇔ TV P – 40. MO AE VISA
Meals (light dinner Sunday) 8.25/16.25 (lunch) and dinner a la carte 16.75/27.95 **t.** 12.75 – **12 rm** 70.00/110.00 **t.** – SB.

King Malcolm, Queensferry Rd, KY11 8DS, South : 1 m. on A 823 ℘ (01383) 722611, *info@kingmalcolm-hotel.dunfermline.com, Fax (01383) 730865* – ⇔ rm, ▤ rest, TV P – 150. MO AE ⓓ VISA JCB
Meals (bar lunch Saturday and Sunday)/dinner a la carte 12.50/18.50 **st.** 8.90 – 10.25 – **48 rm** 80.00/120.00 **st.** – SB.

Crossford *Southwest : 1 ¾ m. on A 994* – ✉ *Dunfermline.*

Keavil House, Main St, KY12 8QW, ℘ (01383) 736258, *keavil@queensferry-hotels.co.uk, Fax (01383) 621600,* – ⇔ TV ♿ P – 350. MO AE ⓓ VISA.
Meals (buffet lunch)/dinner a la carte 13.00/25.00 13.50 – **47 rm** 70.00/105.00 **st.** – SB.

DUNKELD *Perth and Kinross* 401 J 14 *Scotland G. – pop. 4 069.*

See : *Village★ – Cathedral Street★.*

9 *Dunkeld & Birnam, Fungarth* ℘ *(01350) 727524.*

The Cross ℘ *(01350) 727688 (April-October).*

Edinburgh 58 – Aberdeen 88 – Inverness 98 – Perth 14.

Kinnaird , PH8 0LB, Northwest : 6 ¾ m. by A 9 on B 898 ℘ (01796) 482440, *enquiry@kinnairdestate.com, Fax (01796) 482289,* ≤ Tay valley and hills, « Sporting estate, antique furnishings », – , ⇔ rest, TV P. MO AE VISA.
closed Monday to Wednesday January-February – **Meals** 30.00/45.00 **t.** 17.00 – **8 rm** (dinner included) 320.00/475.00 **st.**, 1 suite.

Hilton Dunkeld House , PH8 0HX, ℘ (01350) 727771, *gm_dunkeld@hilton.com, Fax (01350) 728924,* ≤, « Tayside setting », – ⇔ TV ♿ P – 80. MO AE ⓓ VISA JCB.
Meals (bar lunch)/dinner 27.00/35.00 and a la carte 16.00/26.50 **t.** 15.00 – 10.75 – **89 rm** 110.00/150.00 **t.**, 7 suites – SB.

Letter Farm without rest., Loch of the Lowes, PH8 0HH, Northeast : 3 m. by A 923 on Loch of Lowes rd ℘ (01350) 724254, *Fax (01350) 724341,* « Working farm », – ⇔ P. MO VISA.
closed Christmas, New Year and April – – **3 rm** 27.00/44.00 **t.**

DUNOON *Argyll and Bute* 401 F 16 *Scotland G. – pop. 13 781 (inc. Kilmun).*

Env. : *The Clyde Estuary★.*

18 *Cowal, Ardenslate Rd* ℘ *(01369) 702216* – 9 *Innellan, Knockamillie Rd* ℘ *(01369) 830242.*

from Dunoon Pier to Gourock Railway Pier (Caledonian MacBrayne Ltd) frequent services daily (20 mn) – from Hunters Quay to McInroy's Point, Gourock (Western Ferries (Clyde) Ltd) frequent services daily (20 mn).

7 Alexandra Par ℘ *(01369) 703785.*

Edinburgh 73 – Glasgow 27 – Oban 77.

SCOTLAND

Enmore, Marine Par, Kirn, PA23 8HH, North : 1 ¼ m. on A 815 ☎ (01369) 702230, *enm hotel@btinternet.com, Fax (01369) 702148,* ≤ Firth of Clyde, ⛱, squash – ⊭ rest, TV MO AE VISA
closed December-January – **Meals** (lunch booking essential) 15.00/27.00 and a la ca 18.00/26.00 **st.** 🌢 13.95 – **8 rm** ☕ 49.00/160.00 **st.**, 1 suite – SB.

Anchorage, Shore Rd, Ardanadam, PA23 8QG, North : 3 m. on A 815 ☎ (01369) 7051 *info@anchorage.co.uk, Fax (0870) 7061099,* ≤, ⛱ – ⊭ TV P. MO VISA. ✗
closed November restricted opening in winter – **Meals** *(closed Sunday-Tuesday)* (book essential to non-residents) (dinner only) 20.00 **t.** 🌢 12.50 – **5 rm** ☕ 45.00/80.00 **t.** – SB.

DUNVEGAN *Highland* 401 A 11 – *see Skye (Isle of).*

DURNESS *Highland* 401 F 8 – ✉ *Lairg.*
Durness, Balnakeil ☎ (01971) 511364.
Durine ☎ (01971) 511259 (April-October).
Edinburgh 266 – Thurso 78 – Ullapool 71.

Port-na-Con House ⛵, Loch Eribol, IV27 4UN, Southeast : 6 m. on A 8 ☎ (01971) 511367, *portnacon70@hotmail.com, Fax (01971) 511367,* ≤ Loch Eribol, « Lo side setting » – ⊭ P. MO VISA JCB
restricted opening in winter – **Meals** (by arrangement) 13.00 **s.** 🌢 7.50 – **3 rm** ☕ 27.(41.00 **s.** – SB.

DUROR *Argyll and Bute* 401 E 14.
Edinburgh 126 – Dundee 120 – Glasgow 103 – Inverness 88 – Oban 28.

Druimgrianach ⛵ without rest., Cuil Bay, PA38 4DA, Southwest : ¾ m. by A 828 on (rd ☎ (01631) 740286, ≤ Loch Linnhe and Morven Hills, ⛱ – ⊭ P. ✗
closed Christmas and New Year – **3 rm** ☕ 20.00/50.00.

DYCE *Aberdeenshire* 401 N 12 – *see Aberdeen.*

EARLSTON *Borders* 401 402 L 17 – *pop. 1 968.*
Edinburgh 34 – Hawick 22 – Newcastle upon Tyne 71.

Birkhill ⛵, TD4 6AR, North : 3 ¼ m. by A 68 and Birkenside rd on Lauder ☎ (01896) 849307, *birkhill@btinternet.com, Fax (01896) 848206,* ≤, « Georgian cour house », ⛱, 🌳 – ⊭ P. MO VISA. ✗
closed Christmas and New Year – **Meals** (by arrangement) (communal dining) 25.00 **st** **3 rm** ☕ 45.00/90.00 **st.**

EASDALE *Argyll and Bute* 401 D 15 – *see Seil (Isle of).*

EAST KILBRIDE *South Lanarkshire* 401 402 H 16 – *pop. 73 378.*
Torrance House, Strathaven Rd ☎ (01355) 248638.
Edinburgh 46 – Ayr 35 – Glasgow 10.

Crutherland House, Strathaven Rd, G75 0QZ, Southeast : 2 m. on A 7 ☎ (01355) 577000, *crutherland@macdonald-hotels.co.uk, Fax (01355) 220855,* Fø, ≘s, ⛱, 🌳 – |♦| ⊭ TV ☎ ♿ P – 🔺 500. MO AE ⓓ VISA JCB. ✗
Meals (bar lunch Saturday) 26.50 (dinner) and a la carte 15.00/31.00 **st.** 🌢 14.50 – **75** ☕ 79.00/109.00 **st.** – SB.

Hilton East Kilbride, Stewartfield Way, G74 5LA, Northwest : 2 ¼ m. on A 7 ☎ (01355) 236300, *reservations@stakis.co.uk, Fax (01355) 233552,* Fø, ≘s, 🏊 – |♦| ⊭ ▤ rest, TV ☎ ♿ P – 🔺 400. MO AE ⓓ VISA JCB. ✗
Meals 9.95/17.50 and a la carte 23.00 **st.** 🌢 13.50 – ☕ 11.50 – **99 rm** 105.00 **st.**, 2 suite SB.

Premier Lodge, Eaglesham Rd, G75 8LW, Northwest : 1 ½ m. off A 7 ☎ (0870) 7001398, *Fax (0870) 7001399* – ⊭ rm, TV ♿ P. MO AE ⓓ VISA. ✗
Meals (grill rest.) a la carte approx. 12.50 **t.** 🌢 7.80 – **40 rm** 42.95 **t.**

Travel Inn, Brunel Way, The Murray, G75 0JY, ☎ (01355) 222809, *Fax (01355) 23051* ⊭ rm, ▤ rest, TV ♿ P. MO AE ⓓ VISA. ✗
Meals (grill rest.) – **40 rm** 41.95 **t.**

EDINBURGH

401 K 16 *Scotland G. – pop. 418 914.*

Glasgow 46 – Newcastle upon Tyne 105.

TOURIST INFORMATION

Edinburgh & Scotland Information Centre, 3 Princes St. ℘ (0131) 473 3800.
Edinburgh Airport, Tourist Information Desk ℘ (0131) 473 3800.

PRACTICAL INFORMATION

18, 18 *Braid Hills, Braid Hills Rd ℘ (0131) 447 6666,* **BX**.
18 *Carrick Knowe, Glendevon Park ℘ (0131) 337 1096,* **AX**.
18 *Duddingston, Duddingston Road West ℘ (0131) 661 1005,* **BV**.
18 *Silverknowes, Parkway ℘ (0131) 336 3843,* **AV**.
18 *Liberton, 297 Gilmerton Rd ℘ (0131) 664 3009,* **BX**.
18, 18 *Marriott Dalmahoy Hotel C.C., Kirknewton ℘ (0131) 333 4105,* **AX**.
9 *Portobello, Stanley St. ℘ (0131) 669 4361,* **BV**.
Edinburgh Airport : ℘ (0131) 333 1000, W : 6 m. by A 8 **AV** – **Terminal :** *Waverley Bridge.*

SIGHTS

See : *City★★★ – Edinburgh International Festival★★★ (August) – Royal Museum of Scotland* **EZ M2** – *National Gallery of Scotland★★* **DY M4** – *Royal Botanic Garden★★★* **AV** – *The Castle★★ AC* **DYZ** : *Site★★★ – Palace Block (Honours of Scotland★★★) – St. Margaret's Chapel (※★★★) – Great Hall (Hammerbeam Roof★★) – ≤★★ from Argyle and Mill's Mount* **DZ** – *Abbey and Palace of Holyroodhouse★★ AC (Plasterwork Ceilings★★★, ※★★ from Arthur's Seat)* **BV** – *Royal Mile★★ : St. Giles' Cathedral★★ (Crown Spire★★★)* **EYZ** – *Gladstone's Land★ AC* **EYZ A** – *Canongate Talbooth★* **EY B** – *New Town★★ (Charlotte Square★★★* **CY 14** – *The Georgian House★ AC* **CY D** – *Scottish National Portrait Gallery★* **EY M3** – *Dundas House★* **EY E** *) – Scottish National Gallery of Modern Art★* **AV M1** – *Victoria Street★* **EZ 84** – *Scott Monument★ (≤★) AC* **EY F** – *Craigmillar Castle★ AC* **BX** – *Calton Hill (※★★★ AC from Nelson's Monument)* **EY**.

Env. : *Edinburgh Zoo★★ AC* **AV** – *Hill End Ski Centre (※★★) AC, S : 5½ m. by A 702* **BX** – *The Royal Observatory (West Tower ≤★) AC* **BX** – *Ingleston, Scottish Agricultural Museum★, W : 6½ m. by A 8* **AV**.

Exc. : *Rosslyn Chapel★★ AC (Apprentice Pillar★★★) S : 7½ m. by A 701 –* **BX** *– and B 7006 – Forth Bridges★★, NW : 9½ m. by A 90* **AV** – *Hopetoun House★★ AC, NW : 11½ m. by A 90 –* **AV** *– and A 904 – Dalmeny★ – Dalmeny House★ AC, St. Cuthbert's Church★ (Norman South Doorway★★) NW : 7 m. by A 90* **AV** – *Crichton Castle (Italianate courtyard range★) AC, SE : 10 m. by A 7 –* **X** *– and B 6372.*

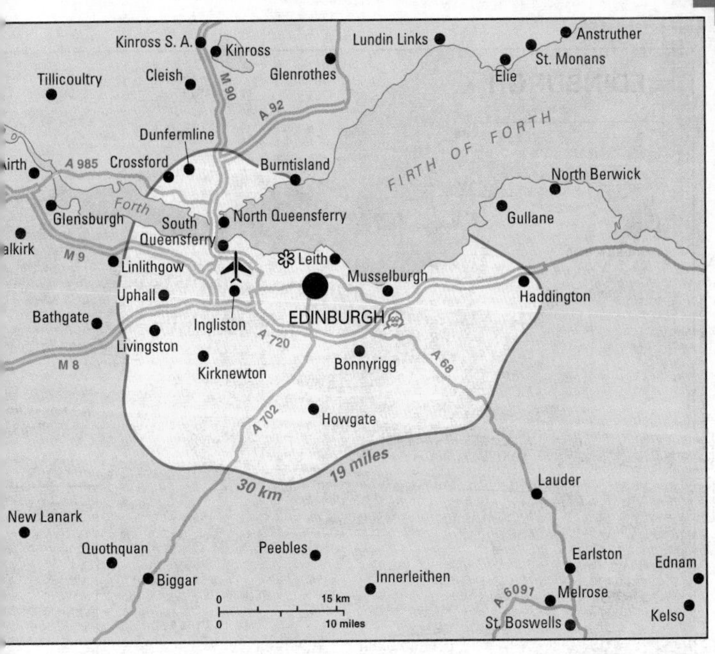

Balmoral, 1 Princes St, EH2 2EQ, ✆ (0131) 556 2414, *reservations@thebalmoralhotel.com, Fax (0131) 557 3747,* – 400. VISA JCB
EY n
Meals – (see ***Number One*** and ***Hadrian's*** below) – 16.75 – **167 rm** 184.00/268.00 **st.**, 21 suites.

Caledonian Hilton, Princes St, EH1 2AB, ✆ (0131) 222 8888, *ednchhirm@hilton.com.net, Fax (0131) 222 8889,* rm, rest, – 250. VISA.
CY n
La Pompadour : **Meals** 15.50/18.50 (lunch) and a la carte 13.25/31.95 **st.** 18.50 – ***Chisholms :*** **Meals** a la carte 16.50/30.50 **st.** 15.50 – 14.95 – **236 rm** 190.00/380.00 **st.**, 13 suites – SB.

Sheraton Grand, 1 Festival Sq, EH3 9SR, ✆ (0131) 229 9131, *grandedinburgh.sheraton@sheraton.com, Fax (0131) 229 6254,* rm, – 500. VISA JCB.
CDZ v
Terrace : **Meals** (buffet only) 19.95 and a la carte 15.75/23.00 **t.** 19.00 – (see also ***Grill Room*** below) – 15.95 – **243 rm** 192.00/272.00 **t.**, 17 suites – SB.

George Inter-Continental, 19-21 George St, EH2 2PB, ✆ (0131) 225 1251, *edinburgh@interconti.com, Fax (0131) 226 5644* – rm, – 200. VISA JCB.
DY z
Le Chambertin *(✆ (0131) 240 7178)* **: Meals** *(closed Saturday lunch, Sunday)* 15.50 and a la carte 31.00/39.00 **st.** 13.50 – ***Carvers*** *(✆ (0131) 459 2305)* **: Meals** 19.00 and a la carte 26.50/32.00 **st.** 13.50 – 16.50 – **192 rm** 180.00/230.00 **st.**, 3 suites.

The Howard, 34 Great King St, EH3 6QH, ✆ (0131) 557 3500, *reserve@thehoward.com, Fax (0131) 557 6515,* « Georgian town houses » – – 30. VISA.
DY s
closed 23-27 December – **Meals** (room service only) – **13 rm** 175.00/295.00, 5 suites – SB.

The Scotsman, 20 North Bridge, EH1 1YT, ✆ (0131) 556 5565, *reservations@thescotsmanhotel.co.uk, Fax (0131) 652 3652,* rm, rest, – 80. VISA JCB
EY x
North Bridge Brasserie : **Meals** a la carte 18.25/27.00 **st.** 14.00 – 15.50 – **56 rm** 175.00/350.00 **st.**, 12 suites.

The Edinburgh Residence, 7 Rothesay Terr, EH3 7RY, ✆ (0131) 226 3380, *Fax (0131) 226 3381,* « Georgian town houses » – VISA JCB.
closed one week January **Meals** (room service only) – 9.65 – **21 rm** 175.00/525.00 **t.**, 8 suites.
CY x

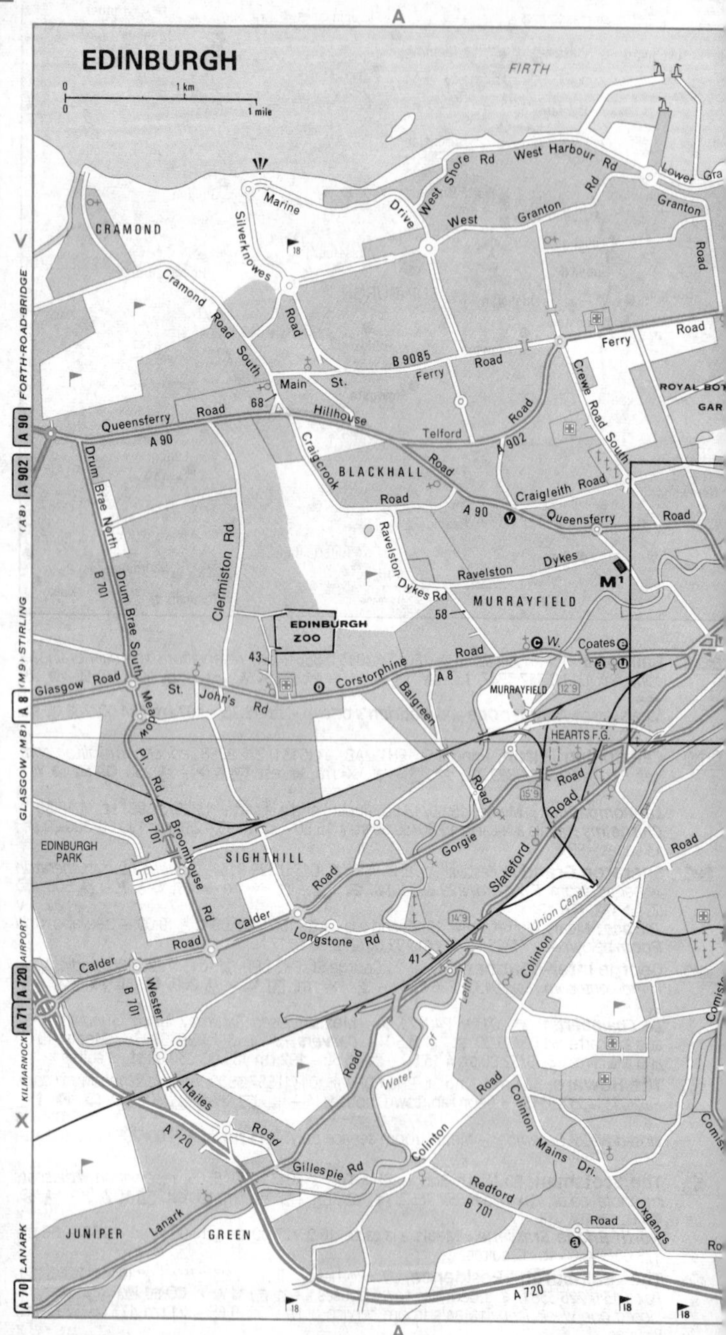

EDINBURGH
FIRTH
West Harbour Rd
West Shore Rd
Marine Drive
West Granton Rd
Granton Road
CRAMOND
Silverknowes Road
Cramond Road South
Main St.
B 9085
Ferry Road
Crewe Road South
ROYAL BOT GAR
Queensferry Road
A 90
Hillhouse Road
Telford Road
A 902
Craigcrook Road
BLACKHALL
Craigleith Road
Drum Brae North
B 701
Clermiston Rd
Ravelston Dykes Rd
Ravelston Dykes
MURRAYFIELD
EDINBURGH ZOO
Corstorphine Road
A 8
W. Coates
MURRAYFIELD
Glasgow Road
St. John's Rd
Drum Brae South
Meadow Pl. Rd
Balgreen Road
HEARTS F.C.
Broomhouse Rd
SIGHTHILL
EDINBURGH PARK
Gorgie Road
Slateford Road
Union Canal
Calder Road
Longstone Rd
Calder Road
Wester Hailes Road
Water of Leith
Colinton Road
Colinton Mains Dri.
Redford Road
Oxgangs Road
Gillespie Rd
A 720
Lanark
JUNIPER GREEN
FORTH-ROAD-BRIDGE
A 90
A 902
(A 8)
(M 9) STIRLING
A 8
GLASGOW (M 8)
AIRPORT
A 720
A 71
KILMARNOCK
LANARK
A 70

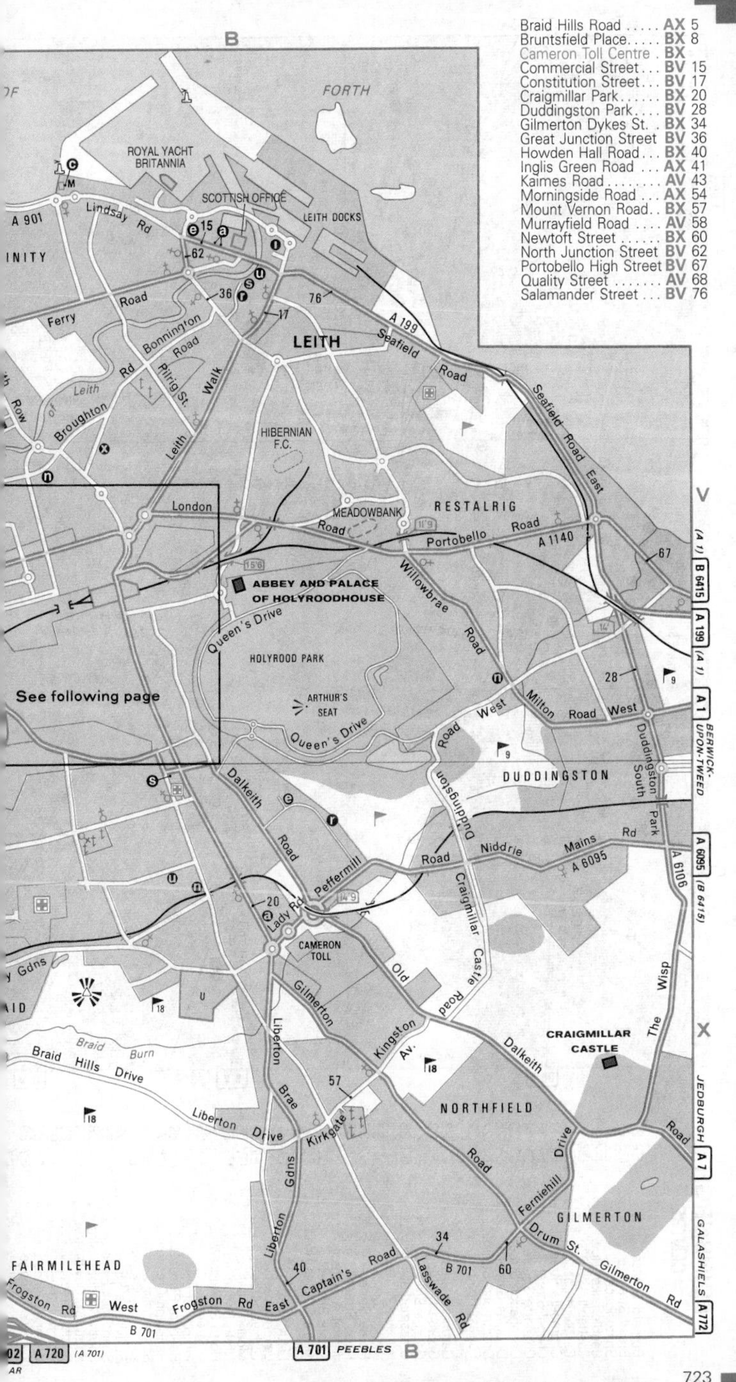
B
FORTH
ROYAL YACHT
BRITANNIA
SCOTTISH OFFICE
LEITH DOCKS
A 901
Lindsay Rd
INITY
Ferry
Road
Bonnington
Road
Pilrig St.
Rd
Leith
Walk
Broughton
Row
LEITH
A 199
Seafield
Road
Seafield
Road
East
HIBERNIAN
F.C.
London
Road
MEADOWBANK
RESTALRIG
Portobello
Road
A 1140
ABBEY AND PALACE
OF HOLYROODHOUSE
Willowbrae
Road
Queen's Drive
HOLYROOD PARK
ARTHUR'S
SEAT
Queen's Drive
See following page
Milton
Road
West
Road West
DUDDINGSTON
Duddingston
South
Park
Dalkeith
Road
Duddingston
Niddrie
Mains
Rd
A 6095
A 6106
Peffermill
Road
Craigmillar
Castle
Road
Lady Rd
CAMERON
TOLL
Old
Dalkeith
Road
Gilmerton
Liberton
Brae
Kingston
Av.
The
Wisp
CRAIGMILLAR
CASTLE
Braid
Burn
Braid Hills Drive
Liberton Drive
Kirkgate
NORTHFIELD
Road
Ferniehill
Drive
Road
Liberton
Gdns
GILMERTON
Drum St.
Gilmerton
Rd
FAIRMILEHEAD
Frogston Rd West
Frogston Rd East
Captain's Road
Lasswade
Rd
B 701
V
X
A 1
B 6415
A 199
A 1
BERWICK-UPON-TWEED
A 6095
B 6415
JEDBURGH
A 7
GALASHIELS
A 772
A 720
A 701
A 701
PEEBLES
B

EDINBURGH
CENTRE

Street	Grid	No.
Bernard Terrace	EZ	3
Bread Street	DZ	6
Bristo Place	EZ	7
Candlemaker Row	EZ	9
Castlehill	DZ	10
Castle Street	DY	
Chambers Street	EZ	12
Chapel Street	EZ	13
Charlotte Square	CY	14
Deanhaugh Street	CY	23
Douglas Gardens	CY	25
Drummond Street	EZ	27
Forrest Road	EZ	31
Frederick Street	DY	
Gardner's Crescent	CZ	32
George IV Bridge	EZ	33
George Street	DY	
Grassmarket	DZ	35
Hanover Street	DY	
High Street	EYZ	37
Home Street	DZ	38
Hope Street	CY	39
Johnston Terrace	DZ	42
King's Bridge	DZ	44
King's Stables Road	DZ	45
Lawnmarket	EYZ	46
Leith Street	EY	47
Leven Street	DZ	48
Lothian Street	EZ	51
Mound (The)	DY	55
North Bridge	EY	61
North St. Andrew Street	EY	66
Princes Street	DY	
Raeburn Place	CY	69
Randolph Crescent	CY	71
St. Andrew Square	EY	73
St. James Centre	EY	
St. Mary's Street	EY	75
Shandwick Place	CYZ	77
South Charlotte Street	DY	78
South St. David Street	DEY	79
Spittal Street	DZ	83
Victoria Street	EZ	84
Waterloo Place	EY	87
Waverley Bridge	EY	89
Waverley Market	EY	

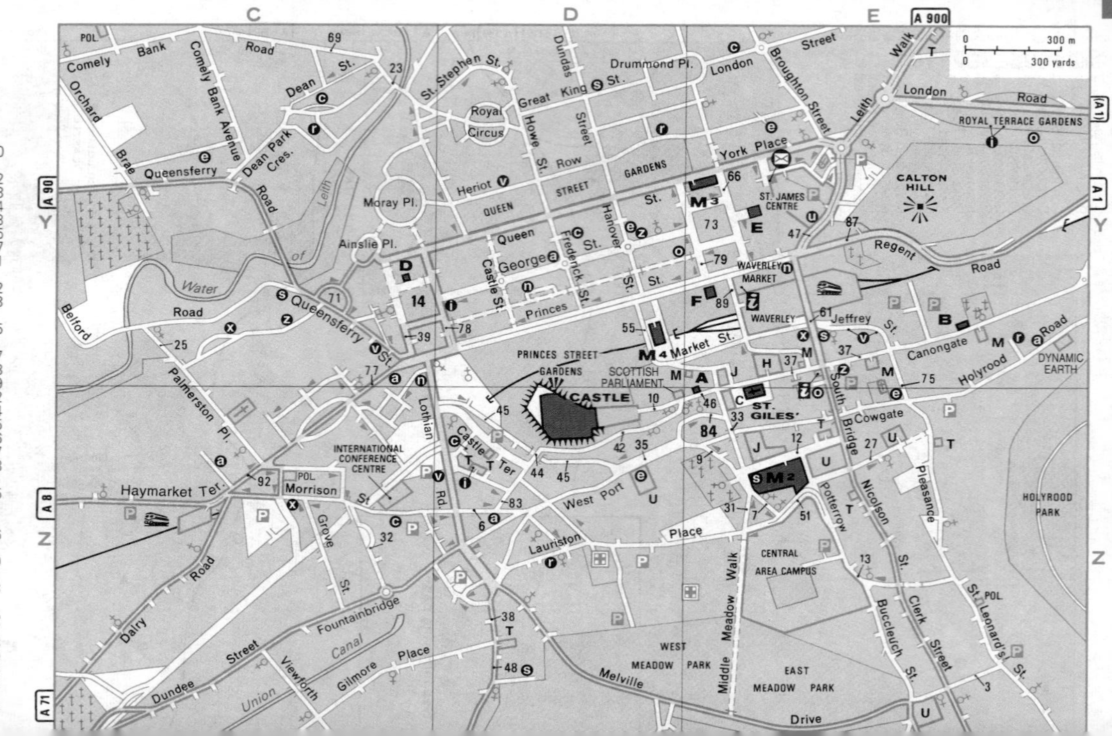

Channings, 12-16 South Learmonth Gdns, EH4 1EZ, (0131) 315 2226, *reserve@channings.co.uk, Fax (0131) 332 9631,* « Edwardian town houses » – 35. VISA. CY e
closed 23-27 December – **Meals** – (see ***Channings*** below) – **43 rm** 140.00/210.00 **t.**, 3 suites – SB.

The Bonham, 35 Drumsheugh Gdns, EH3 7RN, (0131) 226 6050, *reserve@thebonham.com, Fax (0131) 226 6080,* « Contemporary interior design » – 50. VISA. CY z
– **Meals** 12.50/15.00 (lunch) and a la carte 22.20/28.60 **t.** 14.50 – 7.50 – **46 rm** 135.00/240.00 **t.**, 2 suites – SB.

The Roxburghe, 38 Charlotte Sq, EH2 4HG, (0131) 240 5500, *roxburghe@csinn.co.uk, Fax (0131) 240 5555,* – rest, – 400. VISA. DY i
The Melrose : Meals 10.00/20.00 and a la carte 19.15/32.40 **t.** 14.25 – 12.50 – **196 rm** 145.00/195.00 **t.**, 1 suite – SB.

The Holyrood, 81 Holyrood Rd, EH8 6AE, (0131) 550 4500, *holyrood@macdonald-hotels.co.uk, Fax (0131) 550 4545,* – 180. VISA EY a
Flints : Meals a la carte 25.00/34.00 **st.** – **157 rm** 138.00/305.00 **st.** – SB.

Holiday Inn Edinburgh, Corstorphine Rd, EH12 6UA, West : 3 m. on A 8 (0870) 400 9026, *Fax (0131) 334 9237* – rm, rest, – 120. VISA JCB. AV o
Sampans : Meals - Asian - (dinner only) 18.50/22.95 and a la carte 17.95/25.40 **t.** 11.95 –
Rotisserie : Meals *(closed Saturday lunch)* (carvery rest.) a la carte 18.85/30.15 **t.** 11.95 – 13.95 – **303 rm** 140.00/165.00 **st.** – SB.

Crowne Plaza, 80 High St, EH1 1TH, (0131) 557 9797, *rescpedinburgh@allianceuk.com, Fax (0131) 557 9789,* – rm, – 250. VISA JCB. EY z
closed 24 to 27 December – **Meals** 18.95 and a la carte 20.85/38.65 **st.** 14.50 – 13.50 – **229 rm** 85.00/230.00 **st.**, 9 suites – SB.

Prestonfield House, Priestfield Rd, EH16 5UT, (0131) 668 3346, *info@prestonfieldhouse.com, Fax (0131) 668 3976,* ←, « Part 17C country house, collection of paintings », – rm, – 500. VISA JCB BX r
The Old Dining Room : Meals a la carte 21.75/29.25 **t.** 14.50 – **31 rm** 185.00/450.00 **t.** – SB.

Point, 34 Bread St, EH3 9AF, (0131) 221 5555, *info@point-hotel.co.uk, Fax (0131) 221 9929,* « Contemporary interior » – rm, – 100. VISA DZ a
closed 25-27 December – **Meals** *(closed lunch Saturday and Sunday)* 9.90/14.90 **t.** 10.95 – 10.00 – **136 rm** 120.00/160.00 **st.**, 4 suites.

Le Meridien Edinburgh, 18 Royal Terr, EH7 5AQ, (0131) 557 3222, *Fax (0131) 557 5334,* « Georgian town houses », – rest, – 80. VISA JCB. EY i
Meals (light lunch)/dinner 25.00 and a la carte 16.50/24.50 **st.** 12.50 – 10.50 – **104 rm** 120.00/170.00, 4 suites – SB.

Thistle Edinburgh, 107 Leith St, EH1 3SW, (0131) 556 0111, *Fax (0131) 557 5333* – – 250. VISA JCB EY u
Craig's : Meals *(closed Bank Holidays)* (dinner only) 10.00/19.00 12.10 – 12.50 – **139 rm** 131.00/151.00 **st.**, 4 suites – SB.

Edinburgh Marriott, 111 Glasgow Rd, EH12 8NF, West : 4 ½ m. on A 8 (0131) 334 9191, *edinburgh@marriotthotels.com, Fax (0131) 316 4507,* – rm, rest, – 300. VISA
Meals *(closed Saturday lunch)* 14.00/23.00 and a la carte 25.00/32.00 **t.** 12.95 – 12.95 – **245 rm** 125.00/145.00 **st.** – SB.

The Carlton, North Bridge St, EH1 1SD, (0131) 472 3000, *carlton@paramount-hotels.co.uk, Fax (0131) 556 2691,* squash – rm, rest, – 250. VISA. EY s
Meals 14.95/20.00 and lunch a la carte 14.85/23.85 **s.** 11.95 – 12.50 – **184 rm** 155.00/225.00 **t.**, 5 suites – SB.

Hilton Edinburgh Grosvenor, Grosvenor St, EH12 5EF, (0131) 226 6001, *reservations@edinburgh.stakis.co.uk, Fax (0131) 220 2387* – rm, – 300. VISA JCB. CZ a
Meals 8.50 (lunch) and a la carte 14.70/23.95 **st.** 12.95 – 12.75 – **187 rm** 160.00/180.00 **st.**, 2 suites – SB.

Holyrood Aparthotel without rest., 1 Nether Bakehouse (via Gentles entry), EH8 8PE, (0131) 524 3200, *reservations@holyroodaparthotel.com, Fax (0131) 524 3210,* – . VISA JCB. EY r
41 suites 145.00/170.00 **st.**

Best Western Simpson, 79 Lauriston Pl, EH3 9HZ, (0131) 622 7979, *rez@simpson hotel.com, Fax (0131) 622 7900* – . DZ
Meals *(closed 25-26 December)* 7.50/15.00 (lunch) and a la carte 16.50/27.50 **st.** 13.00 – 6.50 – **52 rm** 95.00/165.00 **st.**, 1 suite – SB.

Frederick House, 42 Frederick St, EH2 1EX, (0131) 226 1999, *frederickhouse@edne co.uk, Fax (0131) 624 7064* – . DY
Meals 12.50/18.00 **t.** 10.95 – **44 rm** 55.00/95.00 **t.**, 1 suite.

Apex International, 31-35 Grassmarket, EH1 2HS, (0131) 300 3456, *internationa apexhotels.co.uk, Fax (0131) 220 5345* – , rm, rest, – 225. DZ
Meals (bar lunch)/dinner 12.00/20.00 and a la carte 12.00/29.00 **st.** 9.95 – 9.50 **175 rm** 130.00/160.00 **t.**

Jurys Inn Edinburgh, 43 Jeffrey St, EH1 1DG, (0131) 200 3300, *jurysinnedinburg @jurydoyle.com, Fax (0131) 200 0400* – , rm, – 50. EY
closed 24-25 December – **Meals** (bar lunch)/dinner 16.00 and a la carte 15.50/20.00 **s** 12.00 – 8.00 – **186 rm** 90.00 **st.**

Holiday Inn Edinburgh North, 107 Queensferry Rd, EH4 3HL, (0131) 332 244 *Fax (0131) 332 3408*, , – , rm, – 200. AV
Meals (bar lunch)/dinner 15.95 and a la carte 16.85/18.85 **st.** 10.95 – 11.25 – **102 r** 146.00 **st.** – SB.

Maitland, 23-33 Shandwick Pl, EH2 4RG, (0131) 229 1467, *maitland@ecosse.ie.co.u Fax (0131) 229 7549* – . CY
closed 24-27 December – **Meals** (dinner only) 14.95 **st.** 9.95 – 9.75 – **65 rm** 90.0 110.00 **st.** – SB.

The Lodge, 6 Hampton Terr, West Coates, EH12 5JD, (0131) 337 3682, *thelodgehote btconnect.com, Fax (0131) 313 1700* – . AV
*closed 20-26 December***Meals** *(closed Sunday)* (booking essential) (residents only) (dinn only) 20.00/24.50 **st.** 10.50 – **11 rm** 75.00/130.00 **st.** – SB.

Kildonan Lodge, 27 Craigmillar Park, EH16 5PE, (0131) 667 2793, *kildonanlodge compuserve.com, Fax (0131) 667 9777* – . BX
closed 24-26 December – **Meals** *(closed Sunday)* 17.00/25.00 **t.** 11.90 **12 rm** 65.0 110.00 **st.** – SB.

Albany, 39 Albany St, EH1 3QY, (0131) 556 0397, *info@albanyhoteledinburgh.co.u Fax (0131) 557 6633*, « Georgian town houses » – EY
closed 24-26 December – **Meals** – (see ***Haldanes*** below) – 12.50 – **21 rm** 100.0 215.00 **t.**

Ailsa Craig, 24 Royal Terr, EH7 5AH, (0131) 556 1022, *ailsacraighotel@ednet.co.u Fax (0131) 556 6055*, « Georgian town house », – . EY
Meals (booking essential) (residents only) (dinner only) 10.50/12.50 and a la carte 12.5 17.50 **st.** 9.00 – **18 rm** 65.00/100.00 **st.**

Greenside, 9 Royal Terr, EH7 5AB, (0131) 557 0022, *greensidehotel@ednet.co.u Fax (0131) 557 0022*, « Georgian town house », – . EY
Meals (booking essential) (residents only) (dinner only) 11.50/14.50 **st.** 9.75 – **16 r** 45.00/110.00 **st.**

Premier Lodge, City Bypass, Newcraighall, EH21 8SG, East : 5 m. by A 701 on A 6095 junction with A 1 (0870) 7001372, *Fax (0870) 7001373* – , rm, rest,
Meals (grill rest.) a la carte approx. 16.95 **t.** 8.95 – **42 rm** 46.95 **t.**

Travel Inn Metro, 1 Morrison Link, EH3 8DN, (0131) 228 9819, *Fax (0131) 228 9836* , rest, . CZ
Meals (grill rest.) (dinner only) – **281 rm** 49.95 **t.**

Travelodge, 33 St Mary's St, EH1 1TA, (0131) 557 6281, *Fax (0131) 557 3681* – rm, rest, . EZ
Meals (cafe bar) – **193 rm** 69.95 **t.**

Ibis without rest., 6 Hunter Sq, EH1 1QW, (0131) 240 7000, *h2039@accor.hotels.co Fax (0131) 240 7007* – EZ
99 rm 55.00/70.00 **st.**

Travel Inn, 228 Willowbrae Rd, EH8 7NG, (0131) 661 3396, *Fax (0131) 652 2789* rm, rest, . BV
Meals (grill rest.) – **39 rm** 41.95 **t.**

Travelodge, 48 Dreghorn Link, City Bypass, EH13 9QR, (0131) 441 429 *Fax (0131) 441 4296* – rm, . AX
Meals (grill rest.) – **72 rm** 52.95 **t.**

27 Heriot Row without rest., 27 Heriot Row, EH3 6EN, (0131) 225 9474, *t.a@bl yonder.co.uk, Fax (0131) 220 1699*, « Georgian town house », – . DY
– **3 rm** 60.00/100.00.

17 Abercromby Place without rest., 17 Abercromby Pl, EH3 6LB, (0131) 557 8036, *irlys.lloyd@virgin.net, Fax (0131) 558 3453,* « Georgian town house » – . VISA. DY r
10 rm 50.00/120.00 st.

Saxe Coburg House without rest., 24 Saxe Coburg Pl, EH3 5BP, (0131) 332 2717, *birrel@zetnet.co.uk, Fax (0131) 315 3375,* « Georgian town house », – . AE VISA. BV v
5 rm 50.00/95.00 st.

19 St Bernard's Crescent without rest., 19 St Bernard's Crescent, EH4 1NR, (0131) 332 6162, *balfourwm@aol.com, Fax (0131) 332 6162,* « Georgian townhouse, antiques » – . VISA. CY c
March-October – **3 rm** 70.00/90.00 **s.**

Seven Danube Street without rest., 7 Danube St, EH4 1NN, (0131) 332 2755, *seven.danubestreet@virgin.net, Fax (0131) 343 3648,* « Georgian town house », – . VISA CY r
closed Christmas – **3 rm** 55.00/110.00 **st.**

16 Lynedoch Place without rest., 16 Lynedoch Pl, EH3 7PY, (0131) 225 5507, *susie.lynedoch@btinternet.com, Fax (0131) 226 4185,* « Georgian town house », – . VISA CY s
closed Christmas – **3 rm** 50.00/100.00.

22 Murrayfield Gardens without rest., 22 Murrayfield Gdns, EH12 6DF, (0131) 337 3569, *macnetic@dial.pipex.com, Fax (0131) 337 3803,* « Victorian house », – . VISA AV c
3 rm 45.00/80.00 **st.**

Elmview without rest., 15 Glengyle Terr, EH3 9LN, (0131) 228 1973, *marny@elmview.co.uk, Fax (0131) 229 7296,* – . VISA. DZ s
3 rm 75.00/95.00 **st.**

The Stuarts without rest., 17 Glengyle Terr, EH3 9LN, (0131) 229 9559, *gloria@the-stuarts.com, Fax (0131) 229 2226* – . AE VISA JCB. DZ s
closed 20-29 December – **3 rm** 75.00/105.00 **st.**

Kew House without rest., 1 Kew Terr, Murrayfield, EH12 5JE, (0131) 313 0700, *kew house@ednet.co.uk, Fax (0131) 313 0747* – . AE VISA JCB. AV a
6 rm 50.00/96.00 **st.**

Teviotdale without rest., 53 Grange Loan, EH9 2ER, (0131) 667 4376, *teviotdale.house @btinternet.com, Fax (0131) 667 4376* – . AE VISA JCB BX u
8 rm 30.00/90.00 **st.**

Stuart House without rest., 12 East Claremont St, EH7 4JP, (0131) 557 9030, *stuartho @globalnet.co.uk, Fax (0131) 557 0563* – . AE VISA JCB. BV x
7 rm 50.00/100.00 **t.**

Dorstan, 7 Priestfield Rd, EH16 5HJ, (0131) 667 6721, *reservations@dorstan_hotel.demon.co.uk, Fax (0131) 668 4644* – . AE VISA. BX e
closed 1 week Christmas – **Meals** (by arrangement) 17.00 **t.** – **14 rm** 48.00/82.00 **t.**

Twenty London Street without rest., 20 London St, EN3 6NA, (0131) 557 0216, *gillian-glover@lineone.net, Fax (0131) 556 6445,* « Georgian town house », – . VISA. EY c
closed 25-26 December – **3 rm** 50.00/90.00 **st.**

Classic House without rest., 50 Mayfield Rd, EH9 2NH, (0131) 667 5847, *info@classic house.demon.co.uk, Fax (0131) 662 1016* – . VISA. BX n
7 rm 30.00/60.00 **st.**

Number One (at Balmoral H.), 1 Princes St, EH2 2EQ, (0131) 622 8831, *Fax (0131) 557 8740* – . AE VISA JCB EY n
Meals 12.50/35.00 and a la carte 36.75/44.50 **st.** 24.00.

Grill Room (at Sheraton Grand H.), 1 Festival Sq, EH3 9SR, (0131) 221 6422, *Fax (0131) 229 6254* – . AE VISA JCB CDZ v
closed Saturday lunch and Sunday – **Meals** 27.50/29.00 and a la carte 31.50/44.00 **t.**

Atrium, 10 Cambridge St, EH1 2ED, (0131) 228 8882, *Fax (0131) 228 8808* – . AE VISA DZ c
closed 24-25 December, Sunday and Saturday lunch except during Festival – **Meals** 25.00 (dinner) and a la carte 24.50/34.00 **t.** 14.00.

Duck's at Le Marche Noir, 2-4 Eyre Pl, EH3 5EP, (0131) 558 1608, *bookings@ducks.co.uk, Fax (0131) 556 0798* – . AE VISA JCB BV n
closed 25-26 December, lunch Saturday and Sunday – **Meals** 15.00 (lunch) and a la carte 28.30/34.00 **t.** 9.50.

The Marque, 19-21 Causewayside, EH9 1QF, ✆ (0131) 466 6660, *themarque@claram... com, Fax (0131) 466 6661* – ⋟. MC AE VISA BX
closed Christmas, New Year and Monday – **Meals** 11.50/14.00 (lunch) and dinner a la car... 23.50/28.65 **t.** 12.95.

Channings (at Channings H.), 12-16 South Learmonth Gdns, EH4 1EZ, ✆ (0131) 315 222... *Fax (0131) 332 9631*, – ⋟. MC AE VISA CY
closed Sunday lunch – **Meals** 12.00/26.00 **t.**

Martins, 70 Rose St, North Lane, EH2 3DX, ✆ (0131) 225 3106, *martinirons@fsbdial.co.u... Fax (0131) 220 3403* – ⋟. MC AE VISA JCB DY
closed 1 week May-June, 1 week October, mid December-late January, Sunday and Mond... except during Edinburgh Festival and Saturday lunch – **Meals** (booking essential) 17.2... 25.00 and a la carte 17.75/33.25 **t.** 14.00.

Hadrian's (at Balmoral H.), 2 North Bridge, EH1 1TR, ✆ (0131) 557 50... *Fax (0131) 557 3747* – ▤. MC AE VISA JCB EY
Meals 10.50 and a la carte 15.70/23.95 **st.** 24.00.

Rhodes & Co., 3-15 Rose St (first floor), EH2 2YJ, ✆ (0131) 220 9190, *Fax (0131) 220 91...* – ▤. MC AE VISA DY
closed Sunday dinner – **Meals** a la carte 16.40/20.25 8.50.

Rogue, 67 Morrison St, EH3 8HH, ✆ (0131) 228 2700, *info@rogues-uk.co... Fax (0131) 228 3299* – MC AE VISA CZ
closed Sunday dinner – **Meals** a la carte 12.50/32.50 **st.** 12.15.

Marque Central, 30b Grindley St, EH3 9AX, ✆ (0131) 229 9859, *Fax (0131) 221 9515* – ... AE VISA DZ
closed 25-26 December, 1-2 January and Sunday – **Meals** (booking essential Bank Holiday... 11.50/14.00 and a la carte 18.40/27.95 **t.** 11.95.

Yumi, 2 West Coates, EH12 5JQ, ✆ (0131) 337 2173, *Fax (0131) 337 2818* – ⋟ P. MC ... VISA JCB AV
closed 1 week September, 2 weeks Christmas-New Year and Sunday – **Meals** - Japanese... (dinner only) 25.00/60.00 **t.** 11.00.

The Tower, Museum of Scotland (fifth floor), EH1 1JF, ✆ (0131) 225 3003, *mail@tow... restaurant.com, Fax (0131) 225 0978*, – ⋟ ▤. MC AE VISA JCB EZ
Meals a la carte 20.40/33.40 **t.** 12.00.

Iggs, 15 Jeffrey St, EH1 1DR, ✆ (0131) 557 8184, *Fax (0131) 652 3774* – MC AE V... JCB EY
closed Sunday – **Meals** 16.00/29.50 (dinner) and a la carte 16.00/29.00 **st.** 13.50.

Haldanes (at Albany H.), 39A Albany St, EH1 3QY, ✆ (0131) 556 8407, *info@haldanesrest... rant.com, Fax (0131) 556 2662*, – ⋟. MC AE VISA JCB EY
closed lunch Saturday and Sunday – **Meals** (lunch by arrangement) 13.25/16... lunch and dinner a la carte 26.00/33.00 **t.** 12.00.

Bouzy Rouge, 1 Alva St, EH2 4PH, ✆ (0131) 225 9594, *res@bouzy-rouge.co... Fax (0131) 225 9593* – ▤. MC AE VISA CY
closed 1 January – **Meals** 9.95/12.95 (lunch) and dinner a la carte 12.95/26.40 **t.** 12.95.

Nargile, 73 Hanover St, EH2 1EE, ✆ (0131) 225 5755. MC AE VISA DY
closed 25-26 December, 1-3 January and Sunday – **Meals** - Turkish - 10.45/20... and a la carte 15.95/22.45 **t.** 9.95.

Le Café Saint-Honoré, 34 North West Thistle Street Lane, EH2 1EA, ✆ (0131) 226 22... – ⋟. MC AE VISA JCB DY
closed 3 days Christmas, 3 days New Year and Sunday except during Edinburgh Festiva... **Meals** (booking essential) a la carte 18.00/32.00 10.50.

Blue, 10 Cambridge St, EH1 2ED, ✆ (0131) 221 1222, *Fax (0131) 228 8808* – ▤. MC ... VISA DZ
closed 25-26 December and Sunday – **Meals** 12.50/14.00 and a la carte 17.75/24.00 13.70.

Leith.

Malmaison, 1 Tower Pl, EH6 7DB, ✆ (0131) 468 5000, *edinburgh@malmaison.co... Fax (0131) 468 5002*, « Contemporary interior », – ▮ TV P – 55. MC AE VIS... BV
Meals - Brasserie - 11.95/12.95 **t.** 15.95 – 10.95 – **55 rm** 115.00/165.00 **t.**, 5 suites.

Express by Holiday Inn without rest., Britannia Way, Ocean Drive, EH6 6L... ✆ (0131) 555 4422, *info@hiex-edinburgh.com, Fax (0131) 555 4646* – ▮ ⋟ TV P 30. MC AE VISA BV
102 rm 62.50 **st.**

Travel Inn, 51-53 Newhaven Pl, EH6 4TX, ✆ (0131) 555 1570, *Fax (0131) 554 5994* – ... ⋟ rm, ▤ rest, TV P – 30. MC AE VISA. BV
Meals (grill rest.) – **60 rm** 41.95 **t.**

Martin Wishart, 54 The Shore, Leith, EH6 6RA, (0131) 553 3557, *info@martin-wishart.co.uk, Fax (0131) 467 7091* – . VISA BV u
closed 2 weeks January, 1 week June, Christmas, New Year, Sunday and Monday – **Meals** (booking essential) 13.50/16.50 (lunch) and dinner a la carte 30.00/34.00 **st.** 12.00
Spec. Millefeuille of langoustine and foie gras with braised fennel. Pot-roasted pork cheek, glazed vegetables, potato mousseline. Armagnac parfait with poached pear.

(fitz)Henry, 19 Shore Pl, EH6 6SW, (0131) 555 6625, *mail@fitzhenrys.com, Fax (0131) 555 0025,* « Part 17C warehouse » – AE VISA JCB BV s
closed 25-26 December, 1-16 January, Sunday and Saturday lunch – **Meals** 16.50/25.00 and a la carte 25.00/31.50 **t.** 18.00.

The Rock, 78 Commercial St, EH6 6LX, (0131) 555 2225, *Fax (0131) 337 2153* – P. AE VISA JCB BV a
closed lunch Sunday-Wednesday – **Meals** a la carte 22.95/48.65 **t.** 13.90.

Vintners Rooms, The Vaults, 87 Giles St, EH6 6BZ, (0131) 554 6767, *thevintners@thevintnersrooms.demon.co.uk, Fax (0131) 467 7130* – . AE VISA BV r
closed 2 weeks Christmas and Sunday – **Meals** 11.50/15.00 (lunch) and dinner a la carte 24.00/33.00 **t.** 12.00.

Daniels Bistro, 88 Commercial St, EH6 6LX, (0131) 553 5933, *Fax (0131) 553 3966,* – . AE VISA BV a
closed 25-26 December and 1 January – **Meals** - French - 5.85/6.85 (lunch) and a la carte 16.25/19.45 **t.** 10.85.

Bonnyrigg *(Midlothian) Southeast : 8 m. by A 7 on A 6094* – **BX** – *Edinburgh.*

Dalhousie Castle, EH19 3JB, Southeast : 1 ¼ m. on B 704 (01875) 820153, *res@dalhousiecastle.co.uk, Fax (01875) 821936,* <, « Part 13C and 15C castle with Victorian additions », – – P – 120. AE VISA JCB
closed 5-24 January – ***Dungeon :*** **Meals** (booking essential to non-residents) (dinner only) 29.50/34.50 **st.** – ***The Orangery :*** **Meals** a la carte 16.05/19.35 **st.** 13.95 – **32 rm** 115.00/275.00 **st.** – SB.

Kirknewton *Southwest : 7 m. on A 71* – **AX** – *Edinburgh.*

Marriott Dalmahoy H. & Country Club, EH27 8EB, (0131) 333 1845, *reservations.dalmahoy@marriotthotels.co.uk, Fax (0131) 333 1433,* <, « Part Georgian mansion », , , , , , , – , rest, P – 350. AE VISA.
Pentland : **Meals** *(closed Saturday lunch)* 18.00/27.50 **t.** 14.95 – ***The Long Weekend :*** **Meals** (grill rest.) a la carte 14.50/23.85 **t.** 14.95 – 12.50 – **212 rm** 175.00 **t.**, 3 suites – SB.

Edinburgh International Airport *West : 7½ m. by A 8* – **AV** – *Edinburgh.*

Hilton Edinburgh Airport, EH28 8LL, (0131) 519 4400, *Fax (0131) 519 4422,* , , – , rm, rest, P – 240. AE VISA
Meals (grill rest.) 12.00/18.00 and a la carte 15.00/28.55 **st.** 14.00 – 13.50 – **150 rm** 150.00 **st.** – SB.

Ingliston *West : 7 ¾ m. on A 8* – **AV** – *Edinburgh.*

Norton House, EH28 8LX, on A 8 (0131) 333 1275, *events.nhh@arcadianhotels.co.uk, Fax (0131) 333 5305,* , – rm, P – 200. AE VISA.
Meals *(closed Saturday lunch)* 15.00/28.00 and a la carte 18.00/38.00 **st.** 12.50 – **46 rm** 135.00/155.00 **st.**, 1 suite – SB.

DINBURGH INTERNATIONAL AIRPORT *Edinburgh City* 401 J 16 – *see Edinburgh.*

DNAM *Borders* 401 402 M 17 – *see Kelso.*

DZELL *Angus* 401 M 13 *Scotland G.* – *pop. 830.*
Env. : *Castle★ AC (The Pleasance★★★) W : 2 m.*
Exc. : *Glen Esk★, NW : 7 m.*
Edinburgh 94 – Aberdeen 36 – Dundee 31.

Glenesk, High St, DD9 7TF, (01356) 648319, *gleneskhotel@btconnect.com, Fax (01356) 647333,* , , , – rest, P – 150. AE VISA
Meals 20.00 dinner and a la carte 11.50/23.50 **st.** 8.50 – **24 rm** 60.00/98.00 **st.** – SB.

Si vous cherchez un hôtel tranquille,
consultez d'abord les cartes de l'introduction
ou repérez dans le texte les établissements indiqués avec le signe ou .

ELGIN *Moray* 401 K 11 *Scotland G.* – *pop. 11 855.*
See : *Town*★ – *Cathedral*★ *(Chapter house*★★ *)AC.*
Exc. : *Glenfiddich Distillery*★, *SE : 10 m. by A 941.*
18, 18 *Moray, Stotfield Rd, Lossiemouth* (01343) 812018 – 18 *Hardhillock, Birnie* (01343) 542338 – 18 *Hopeman, Moray* (01343) 830578.
17 High St (01343) 542666.
Edinburgh 198 – Aberdeen 68 – Fraserburgh 61 – Inverness 39.

Mansion House, The Haugh, IV30 1AW, via Haugh Rd and Murdocks Wy (01343) 548811, *Fax (01343) 547916,* – rest, – 200. VISA JCB.
Meals 15.50/25.00 and a la carte 12.00/31.00 **t.** 12.00 – **23 rm** 80.00/160.00 **t.** – SB.

Mansefield House, Mayne Rd, IV30 1NY, (01343) 540883, *reception@mansfi househotel.com, Fax (01343) 552491* – VISA.
Meals 22.50/27.50 and a la carte 23.00/30.95 **st.** 11.75 – **21 rm** 55.00/110.00 **st.** – S

Travel Inn, Linkwood Industrial Estate, East Rd, IV30 1XB, East : 1 ¼ m. on A (01343) 550747, *Fax (01343) 540635* – rm, rest, VISA
Meals (grill rest.) – **40 rm** 41.95 **t.**

Pines without rest., East Rd, IV30 1XG, East : ½ m. on A 96 (01343) 552495, *thepine talk21.com, Fax (01343) 552495,* – VISA.
closed 1 week Christmas and New Year – **6 rm** 40.00/48.00.

The Croft without rest., 10 Institution Rd, IV30 1QX, via Duff Av. (01343) 546004, *t croft-elgin@etn.org, Fax (01343) 546004,* –
3 rm 40.00/52.00.

Lodge without rest., 20 Duff Ave, IV30 1QS, (01343) 549981, *marilynspence5@hotm com, Fax (01343) 540527,* – VISA JCB
8 rm 25.00/50.00 **st.**

The Guide is updated annually so renew your Guide every year.

ELGOL *Highland* 401 B 12 – *see Skye (Isle of).*

ELIE *Fife* 401 L 15.

Bouquet Garni, 51 High St, KY9 1BZ, (01333) 330374 – . VISA
closed 2 weeks November, 2 weeks January, 25-26 December, Sunday and Monday Septe ber-May – **Meals** (booking essential) 10.50/19.50 and a la carte 19.30/27.30 **t.** 8.50.

ERBUSAIG *Highland* 401 C 12 *Scotland G.* – *Kyle of Lochalsh.*
Env. : *Wester Ross*★★★.
Skye Bridge (toll).
Edinburgh 206 – Dundee 184 – Inverness 84 – Oban 127.

Old Schoolhouse , IV40 8BB, (01599) 534369, *cuminecandj@lineone.ne Fax (01599) 534369,* – rest, VISA JCB
closed 2 weeks October and Christmas – **Meals** (booking essential) (dinner only) 16. 10.25 – **3 rm** 40.00/56.00.

ERISKA (Isle of) *Argyll and Bute* 401 D 14 – *Oban.*

Isle of Eriska , Ledaig, PA37 1SD, (01631) 720371, *office@eriska-hotel.co.u Fax (01631) 720531,* ≤ Lismore and mountains, « 19C Scottish Baronial mansion, priva island setting », 9, – rest, VISA JCB
closed 8 January-8 February – **Meals** (booking essential) (light lunch residents only)/dinn 38.50 **t.** 9.20 – **17 rm** 175.00/270.00 **t.**

ETTRICKBRIDGE *Borders* 401 402 L 17 – *see Selkirk.*

FAIRLIE *North Ayrshire* 401 402 F 16.
Edinburgh 75 – Ayr 50 – Glasgow 36.

Fins, Fencebay Fisheries, Fencefoot Farm, KA29 0EG, South : 1 ½ m. on A (01475) 568989, *fencebay@aol.com, Fax (01475) 568921* – VISA
closed 25 December, 1 January and Monday – **Meals** - Seafood - (booking essenti a la carte 19.95/36.45 **t.** 10.80.

ALKIRK *Falkirk* 401 I 16 – *pop. 42 353.*

Grangemouth, Polmonthill ℘ *(01324) 711500 – Polmont, Manuel Rigg, Maddiston* ℘ *(01324) 711277 – Stirling Rd, Camelon* ℘ *(01324) 611061 – Falkirk Tryst, 86 Burnhead Rd, Larbet* ℘ *(01324) 562415.*

2-4 Glebe St ℘ *(01324) 620244.*

Edinburgh 26 – Dunfermline 18 – Glasgow 25 – Motherwell 27 – Perth 43.

MacDonald Inchyra, Grange Rd, Polmont, FK2 0YB, Southeast : 3 m. by A 803 and Kirk Entry Bo'ness Rd ℘ (01324) 711911, *info@inchyra.macdonald-hotels.co.uk, Fax (01324) 716134*, – rest, – 700. VISA
Priory : Meals 28.50 (dinner) and a la carte 18.40/31.90 **t.** 14.95 – ***Peligrino's :*** Meals a la carte 14.85/22.65 **t.** 14.95 – 10.50 – **106 rm** 130.00/155.00 **t.**, 1 suite – SB.

Premier Lodge, Glenbervie Business Park, Bellsdyke Rd, Larbert, FK5 4EG, Northwest : 3 ¾ m. by A 803 and A 9 on A 88 ℘ (0870) 7001386, *Fax (0870) 7001387* – rest, VISA
Meals (grill rest.) a la carte approx. 14.20 **t.** 8.75 – **60 rm** 42.95 **t.** – SB.

Travel Inn, Beancross Rd, Polmont, FK2 0YS, East : 3 m. by A 904 on A 9 ℘ (01324) 720726, *Fax (01324) 716801* – rest, VISA.
Meals (grill rest.) – **40 rm** 41.95 **t.**

Glensburgh *Northeast : 2 m. by A 904 on A 905 – Falkirk.*

Grange Manor, FK3 8XJ, ℘ (01324) 474836, *info@grangemanor.co.uk, Fax (01324) 665861* – – 160. VISA JCB.
Le Chardon : Meals 13.50/25.00 and a la carte 22.50/33.40 **t.** 12.95 – ***Wallace's :*** Meals a la carte 12.45/22.65 **t.** 12.50 – **37 rm** 85.00/125.00 **t.** – SB.

ASNACLOICH *Argyll and Bute – Appin.*

Edinburgh 133 – Fort William 34 – Oban 19.

Lochside Cottage , PA38 4BJ, ℘ (01631) 730216, *broadbent@lochsidecottage.fsnet.co.uk, Fax (01631) 730216*, Loch Baile Mhic Chailen and mountains, « Lochside setting », –
Meals (by arrangement) (communal dining) 22.00 **s.** – **3 rm** 25.00/64.00 **s.**

ONNPHORT *Argyll and Bute* 401 A 15 – *Shipping Services : see Mull (Isle of).*

LODIGARRY *Highland* 401 B 11 – *see Skye (Isle of).*

ORFAR *Angus* 401 L 14 *Scotland G. – pop. 14 159.*

Env. : *Aberlemno Stones★, NE : 5 m. by B 9134.*

Exc. : *Brechin (Round Tower★), NE : 9½ m. by B 9134.*

Cunninghill, Arbroath Rd ℘ *(01307) 462120.*

40 East High St ℘ *(01307) 467876 (summer only).*

Edinburgh 75 – Aberdeen 55 – Dundee 12 – Perth 31.

Chapelbank House, 69 East High St, DD8 2EP, ℘ (01307) 463151, *themanager@chapelbank.com, Fax (01307) 461922* – VISA JCB.
closed 2 weeks January – **Meals** a la carte 13.50/21.50 **st.** 8.95 – **4 rm** 55.00/90.00 **st.**

Finavon Farmhouse, Finavon, DD8 3PX, Northeast : 5 ½ m. by B 9128 and A 90 on Milton of Finavon rd ℘ (01307) 850269, *jlr@finfarm.freeserve.co.uk, Fax (01307) 850380*, –
March-October – **Meals** (by arrangement) 10.00 **s.** – **3 rm** 26.00/44.00.

ORRES *Moray* 401 J 11 *Scotland G. – pop. 5 559.*

Env. : *Sueno's Stone★★, N : ½ m. by A 940 on A 96 – Brodie Castle★ AC, W : 3 m. by A 96.*

Exc. : *Elgin★ (Cathedral★, chapter house★★ AC), E : 10¼m. by A 96.*

Muiryshade ℘ *(01309) 672949.*

116 High St ℘ *(01309) 672938 (Easter-October).*

Edinburgh 165 – Aberdeen 80 – Inverness 27.

Knockomie , Grantown Rd, IV36 2SG, South : 1 ½ m. on A 940 ℘ (01309) 673146, *stay@knockomie.co.uk, Fax (01309) 673290*, – – 40. VISA JCB
closed 7-14 January and 25-26 December – ***Restaurant :*** Meals (dinner only) 28.50 **t.** – ***Bistro :*** Meals a la carte 13.90/23.95 **t.** 9.95 – **14 rm** 92.00/160.00 **t.**, 1 suite – SB.

Ramnee, Victoria Rd, IV36 3BN, ☎ (01309) 672410, *ramneehotel@btconnect.c* *Fax (01309) 673392*, – rest, TV P – 100. MC AE VISA JCB *closed 25-26 December and 1-3 January* – **Meals** 12.50/27.00 **st.** 8.95 – **19 rm** 67 97.50 **st.**, 1 suite – SB.

FORT WILLIAM *Highland* 401 E 13 *Scotland G. – pop. 10 391.*

See : *Town*★.

Exc. : *The Road to the Isles★★ (Neptune's Staircase (≤★★), Glenfinnan★ ≤★, Arisaig★, S Sands of Morar★, Mallaig★), NW : 46 m. by A 830 – Ardnamurchan Peninsula★★ – namurchan Point (≤★★), NW : 65 m. by A 830, A 861 and B 8007 – SE : Ben Nevis★★ (≤★ Glen Nevis★.*

North Rd ☎ (01397) 704464.

Cameron Sq ☎ (01397) 703781.

Edinburgh 133 – Glasgow 104 – Inverness 68 – Oban 50.

Inverlochy Castle, Torlundy, PH33 6SN, Northeast : 3 m. on A 82 ☎ (01397) 702 *info@inverlochy.co.uk, Fax (01397) 702953*, ≤ loch and mountains, « Victorian castl extensive parkland », – rest, TV P. MC AE VISA JCB *closed January* – **Meals** (dinner booking essential to non-residents) 28.00/50.00 **t.** 22.0 **16 rm** 180.00/380.00 **t.**, 1 suite – SB

Spec. Tian of crab with a pineapple and chilli jelly. Fillet of Angus beef, pan-fried foie g fricassée of chanterelles. Vanilla crème brûlée, caramel ice cream.

Distillery House without rest., Nevis Bridge, North Rd, PH33 6LR, ☎ (01397) 700 *disthouse@aol.com, Fax (01397) 702980*, – TV P. MC AE VISA. **7 rm** 35.00/70.00 **st.**

Travel Inn, An Aird, PH33 6AN, Northwest : ½ m. by A 82 ☎ (01397) 703 *Fax (01397) 703618* – rm, rest, TV P. MC AE VISA **Meals** (grill rest.) – **40 rm** 41.95 **t.**

The Grange without rest., Grange Rd, PH33 6JF, South : ¾ m. by A 82 and Ashb Lane ☎ (01397) 705516, *jackcampbell@grangefortwilliam.com, Fax (01397) 701595*, ≤, – TV P. MC VISA. *April-October* – **4 rm** 76.00/92.00.

Crolinnhe without rest., Grange Rd, PH33 6JF, South : ¾ m. by A 82 and Ashburn L ☎ (01397) 702709, *crolinnhe@yahoo.com, Fax (01397) 700506*, ≤, – TV P. *Easter-October* – **3 rm** 80.00/110.00.

Ashburn House without rest., 18 Achintore Rd, PH33 6RM, South : ½ m. on A ☎ (01397) 706000, *ashburn.house@tinyworld.co.uk, Fax (01397) 702024*, – TV MC AE VISA JCB. *March-November* – **7 rm** 35.00/90.00.

Lawriestone Guest House without rest., Achintore Rd, PH33 6RQ, South : ½ m. A 82 ☎ (01397) 700777, *lawriestone@btinternet.com, Fax (01397) 700777*, ≤, – P. *closed 1-2 January and 25-26 December* – **4 rm** 60.00 **s.**

Cabana House without rest., Union Rd, PH33 6RB, ☎ (01397) 705991, *veracabana@ 21.com, Fax (01397) 705991*, – TV P. *closed December-January* – **3 rm** 40.00/55.00 **s.**

Factors House with rm, Torlundy, PH33 6SN, Northeast : 3 m. on A ☎ (01397) 702177, *info@inverlochy.co.uk, Fax (01397) 702953*, – TV P. MC AE JCB *closed Sunday and Monday October-April* – **Meals** (booking essential to non-reside (dinner only) a la carte 15.00/25.00 **st.** 15.00 – 8.50 – **10 rm** 70.00/110.00 **t.**

Crannog, The Pier, PH33 7NR, ☎ (01397) 705589, *Fax (01397) 700134*, « Lochside sett ≤ Loch Linnhe » – . MC VISA. *closed 25-26 December and 1 January* – **Meals** - Seafood - (booking essential) a la ca 20.40/27.50 **t.**

at Banavie *North : 3 m. by A 82 and A 830 on B 8004 – ✉ Fort William.*

Moorings, PH33 7LY, ☎ (01397) 772797, *reservations@moorings-fortwilliam.co. Fax (01397) 772441*, ≤, – TV P – 120. MC AE VISA JCB **Meals** (bar lunch)/dinner 26.00 **t.** 9.95 – **28 rm** 60.00/100.00 **t.** – SB.

Bitte beachten Sie die Geschwindigkeitsbeschränkungen in Großbritannien
- 60 mph (= 96 km/h) außerhalb geschlossener Ortschaften
- 70 mph (= 112 km/h) auf Straßen mit getrennten Fahrbahnen und Autobahnen.

SCOTLAND

FOYERS *Highland* 401 G 12 *Scotland G.* – ✉ *Loch Ness.*

Env. : *Loch Ness*★★ – *The Great Glen*★.

Edinburgh 175 – Inverness 19 – Kyle of Lochalsh 63 – Oban 96.

Craigdarroch House ⛰, IV2 6XU, North : 1/4 m. on B 852 ☎ (01456) 486400, *dave munro@hotel_loch_ness.co.uk, Fax (01456) 486444*, ≤ Loch Ness and mountains, – TV P. MC AE VISA JCB.
Meals 12.50/19.50 and a la carte 15.00/24.00 **st.** 14.50 – **14 rm** 67.50/120.00 **st.** – SB.

Foyers Bay House, Lower Foyers, IV2 6YB, West : 1 1/4 m. by B 852 on Lower Foyers rd ☎ (01456) 486624, *panciroli@foyersbay.freeserve.co.uk, Fax (01456) 486337*, ≤, – rm, TV P. MC AE VISA JCB.
closed two weeks January **Meals** (dinner only) 9.95/15.95 and a la carte 8.45/19.00 **t.** 7.95 – **5 rm** 39.00/60.00 **t.** – SB.

GAIRLOCH *Highland* 401 C 10 *Scotland G. – pop. 2 194.*

Env. : *Wester Ross*★★★ – *Loch Maree*★★★, *E : 5 1/2 m. by A 832.*

Exc. : *Inverewe Gardens*★★★ *AC, NE : 8 m. by A 832 – Victoria Falls*★, *SE : 8 m. by A 832.*

Gairloch ☎ (01445) 712407.

Auchtercairn ☎ (01445) 712130 (April-October).

Edinburgh 228 – Inverness 72 – Kyle of Lochalsh 68.

Creag Mor, Charleston, IV21 2AH, South : 1 3/4 m. on A 832 ☎ (01445) 712068, *enquiries@ creagmor-hotel.co.uk, Fax (01445) 712044*, ≤, – rest, TV P. MC AE VISA JCB
Meals a la carte 10.65/23.45 **st.** 10.50 – **16 rm** 42.00/110.00 **st.**, 1 suite.

GALSON *Western Isles (Outer Hebrides)* 401 A 8 – *see Lewis and Harris (Isle of).*

GATEHEAD *East Ayrshire* 401 402 G 17 – ✉ *Kilmarnock.*

Edinburgh 72 – Ayr 10 – Glasgow 25 – Kilmarnock 5.

Cochrane Inn, 45 Main Rd, KA2 0AP, ☎ (01563) 570122 – P. MC AE VISA
closed 1 January – **Meals** (booking essential) a la carte approx. 15.15 **t.** 9.95.

GATEHOUSE OF FLEET *Dumfries and Galloway* 401 402 H 19 – *pop. 919.*

Gatehouse, Innisfree, Lauriestown, Castle Douglas ☎ (01557) 814766.

Car Park ☎ (01557) 814212 (Easter-October).

Edinburgh 113 – Dumfries 33 – Stranraer 42.

Cally Palace ⛰, DG7 2DL, East : 1/2 m. on B 727 ☎ (01557) 814341, *info@callypalace. co.uk, Fax (01557) 814522*, ≤, « Part 18C country mansion », 18, – , rest, TV P – 80. MC VISA.
closed 2 January-mid February – **Meals** 26.00 (dinner) and lunch a la carte 20.00/24.00 14.50 – **50 rm** (dinner included) 86.00/180.00 **t.**, 5 suites – SB.

GIFFNOCK *East Renfrewshire* 401 41 – *see Glasgow.*

GIGHA (Isle of) *Argyll and Bute* 401 C 16.

to Tayinloan (Caledonian MacBrayne Ltd) 8-10 daily (20 mn).

Edinburgh 168.

Gigha ⛰, PA41 7AA, ☎ (01583) 505254, *william@isle-of-gigha.co.uk, Fax (01583) 505244*, ≤ Sound of Gigha and Kintyre Peninsula, – , rest, TV P. MC VISA
March-November – **Meals** (booking essential to non-residents) (bar lunch)/dinner 23.00/ 26.00 **t.** 7.50 – **13 rm** (dinner included) 71.00/130.00 **t.** – SB.

GIRVAN *South Ayrshire* 401 402 F 18 – *pop. 7 719.*

Brunston Castle, Dailly ☎ (01465) 811471 – Golf Course Rd ☎ (01465) 714272.

Edinburgh 100 – Ayr 20 – Glasgow 56 – Stranraer 31.

Glendrissaig ⛰ without rest., Newton Stewart Rd, KA26 0HJ, South : 1 3/4 m. by A 77 on A 714 ☎ (01465) 714631, *fkmcintosh@waitrose.com, Fax (01465) 714631*, ≤, – P.
March-October – **3 rm** 30.00/64.00.

Wildings, 56 Montgomerie St, KA26 9HE, ☎ (01465) 713481, *info@wildingsrestaurant.co. uk, Fax (01465) 715971* –
closed October, 24 December-mid January, Monday, Tuesday and Sunday dinner – **Meals** (booking essential) 10.50/21.50 **t.** 10.50.

GLASGOW

401 402 H 16 *Scotland G. – pop. 662 853.*

Edinburgh 46 – Manchester 221.

TOURIST INFORMATION

11 George Square ✆ (0141) 204 4400.
Glasgow Airport, Tourist Information Desk, Paisley ✆ (0141) 848 4440.

PRACTICAL INFORMATION

18 *Littlehill, Auchinairn Rd ✆ (0141) 772 1916.*
18 *Rouken Glen, Stewarton Rd, Thornliebank ✆ (0141) 638 7044* **AX**.
18 *Linn Park, Simshill Rd ✆ (0141) 637 5871,* **BX**.
18 *Lethamhill, Cumbernauld Rd ✆ (0141) 770 6220,* **BV**.
9 *Alexandra Park, Dennistown ✆ (0141) 556 1294* **BV**.
9 *King's Park, 150a Croftpark Av., Croftfoot ✆ (0141) 630 1597,* **BX**.
9 *Knightswood, Lincoln Av. ✆ (0141) 959 6358* **AV**.
9 *Ruchill, Ruchill Park Brassey St. ✆ (0141) 946 7676.*
Access to Oban by helicopter.
Erskine Bridge (toll) **AV**.
Glasgow Airport : ✆ (0141) 887 1111, W : 8 m. by M 8 **AV** – **Terminal :** *Coach service from Glasgow Central and Queen Street main line Railway Stations and from Anderston Cross and Buchanan Bus Stations.*
see also Prestwick.

SIGHTS

See : *City★★★ – Cathedral★★★ (≤★)* **DZ** *– The Burrell Collection★★★* **AX M1** *– Hunterian Art Gallery★★ (Whistler Collection★★★ – Mackintosh Wing★★★) AC* **CY M4** *– Museum of Transport★★ (Scottish Built Cars★★★, The Clyde Room of Ship Models★★★)* **AV M3** *– Art Gallery and Museum Kelvingrove★★* **CY** *– Pollok House★ (The Paintings★★)* **AX D** *– Tolbooth Steeple★* **DZ A** *– Hunterian Museum (Coin and Medal Collection★)* **CY M1** *– City Chambers★* **DZ C** *– Glasgow School of Art★ AC,* **CY B** *– Necropolis (≤★ of Cathedral)* **DYZ** *– Gallery of Modern Art★.*

Env. : *Paisley Museum and Art Gallery (Paisley Shawl Section★), W : 4 m. by M 8* **AV.**

Exc. : *The Trossachs★★★, N : 31 m. by A 879 –* **BV** *–, A 81 and A 821 – Loch Lomond★★, NW : 19 m. by A 82* **AV** *– New Lanark★★, SE : 20 m. by M 74 and A 72* **BX**.

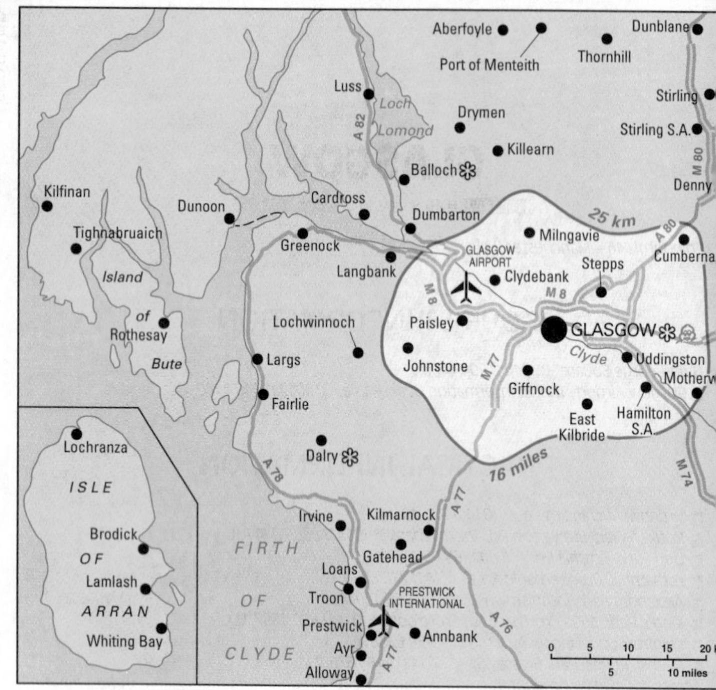

Hilton Glasgow, 1 William St, G3 8HT, (0141) 204 5555, *glahitwgm@hilton.co* *Fax (0141) 204 5004,* <, rm, – 1000.
CZ
Minsky's : Meals 17.25/24.95 **st.** 15.10 – (see also ***Camerons*** and ***Shimla Pinks*** below) 14.50 – **315 rm** 170.00 **st.**, 4 suites.

Glasgow Moat House, Congress Rd, G3 8QT, (0141) 306 9988, *cbgla@queensmo co.uk, Fax (0141) 221 2022,* <, rm, – 3000.
CZ
The Mariner : Meals *(closed Sunday)* (dinner only) a la carte 19.00/28.00 **t.** 16.00 –
Dockside : Meals *(closed lunch Saturday and Sunday)* (buffet) 16.00/12.00 **t.** 13.95 13.50 – **267 rm** 170.00/199.00 **t.**, 16 suites – SB.

One Devonshire Gardens, 1 Devonshire Gdns, G12 0UX, (0141) 339 2001, *devonshire@btconnect.com, Fax (0141) 337 1663,* « Victorian town houses » – 40.
AV
closed 6-11 January Meals – (see ***Amaryllis*** below) – 14.50 – **38 rm** 165.00/345.00 3 suites.

Glasgow Marriott, 500 Argyle St, Anderston, G3 8RR, (0141) 226 55 *Fax (0141) 221 7676,* <, rm, – 700.
CZ
Mediterrano : Meals 10.00/18.00 and a la carte 17.00/33.00 **t.** 15.00 – 13.00 – **300** 135.00/250.00 **t.**

Thistle Glasgow, 36 Cambridge St, G2 3HN, (0870) 3339154, *Fax (0870) 3339254,* rm, rest, – 1500.
DY
Gengis : Meals a la carte 16.00/28.00 **st.** 14.00 – 12.85 – **297 rm** 85.00/110.00 3 suites – SB.

Malmaison, 278 West George St, G2 4LL, (0141) 572 1000, *glasgow@malmaison.co* *Fax (0141) 572 1002,* « Contemporary interior », rm, – 30.
CY
The Brasserie *((0141) 572 1001)* **:** Meals *(closed Saturday lunch)* 10.95/12. and a la carte approx. 19.50 **st.** 12.00 – 10.95 – **64 rm** 120.00 **st.**, 8 suites.

SCOTLAND

Millennium Glasgow, 40 George Sq, G2 1DS, ☎ (0141) 332 6711, *sales.glasgow@millcop.com, Fax (0141) 332 4264,* – , rm, – 40. VISA JCB. DZ v
closed 25-26 December – ***Brasserie on George Square :*** **Meals** *(closed Sunday lunch)* 20.00 and a la carte 16.00/30.00 **st.** 17.00 – 13.95 – **112 rm** 190.00/250.00 **st.**, 5 suites – SB.

ArtHouse, 129 Bath St, G2 2SZ, ☎ (0141) 221 6789, *info@arthousehotel.com, Fax (0141) 221 6777,* « Contemporary interior » – , rm, rest, – 30. VISA DY v
closed 25 December-1 January – ***Grill :*** **Meals** 11.50 (lunch) and a la carte 21.85/49.90 **t.** 17.50 – 9.25 – **65 rm** 90.00/140.00 **st.**

Carlton George, 44 West George St, G2 1DH, ☎ (0141) 353 6373, *george@carltonhotels.co.uk, Fax (0141) 353 6263* – – 35. VISA DZ a
Windows : **Meals** 13.95 (lunch) and dinner a la carte 14.95/21.00 **t.** 13.95 – 12.95 – **64 rm** 150.00 **t.**

Hilton Glasgow Grosvenor, Grosvenor Terr, Great Western Rd, G12 0TA, ☎ (0141) 339 8811, *res@glasgrosvenor.hilton.co.uk, Fax (0141) 334 0710,* « Victorian terraced town houses » – , rm, – 450. VISA. CY s
Meals *(closed Saturday lunch)* 9.00/17.95 and a la carte 18.70/26.50 **st.** 12.30 – 14.25 – **94 rm** 120.00 **st.**, 2 suites.

Holiday Inn Glasgow City West, Bothwell St, G2 7EN, ☎ (0870) 400 9032, *Fax (0141) 221 8986,* – , rm, rest, – 1000. VISA JCB. CZ z
The Original Carvery : **Meals** (dinner only and Sunday lunch)/dinner 17.50 and a la carte 16.95/28.95 **t.** 11.95 – ***Jules :*** **Meals** *(closed Saturday lunch)* (piano at dinner) 9.95 (lunch) and a la carte 14.95/28.95 **t.** 11.95 – 13.95 – **274 rm** 99.00 **st.**, 1 suite – SB.

Sherbrooke Castle, 11 Sherbrooke Ave, Pollokshields, G41 4PG, ☎ (0141) 427 4227, *mail@sherbrooke.co.uk, Fax (0141) 427 5685,* – , rest, – 250. VISA AX r
Morrisons : **Meals** 16.00/25.00 and dinner a la carte 25.00/35.00 **t.** 11.00 – **24 rm** 65.00/85.00 **t.**, 1 suite – SB.

Ewington, Balmoral Terr, 132 Queen's Drive, G42 8QW, ☎ (0141) 423 1152, *info@countryhotels.net, Fax (0141) 422 2030* – – 80. VISA JCB BX a
Meals 9.95/16.95 and dinner a la carte 19.00/27.00 **t.** 11.00 – 10.95 – **42 rm** 79.00/99.00 **st.**, 1 suite – SB.

Langs, 2 Port Dundas Pl, G2 3LD, ☎ (0141) 333 1500, *Fax (0141) 333 5700,* « Contemporary interior », – , rm, rest, . VISA JCB. DY n
Las Brisas : **Meals** 13.95 (lunch) and a la carte 18.70/41.25 **st.** – ***Oshi :*** **Meals** - Asian specialities - a la carte 9.95/18.70 **st.** 9.95 – 12.95 – **100 rm** 125.00 **st.** – SB.

City Inn, Finnieston Quay, G3 8HN, ☎ (0141) 240 1002, *glasgow.reservations@cityinn.com, Fax (0141) 248 2754,* , , – , rm, – 50. VISA JCB CZ u
closed 24-26 and 31 December – ***City Café :*** **Meals** 15.95 and a la carte 15.95/25.95 **st.** 10.65 – 10.50 – **164 rm** 79.00 **t.** – SB.

Bewley's, 110 Bath St, G2 2EN, ☎ (0141) 353 0800, *gla@bewleyshotels.com, Fax (0141) 353 0900* – , rm, rest, . VISA. DY i
closed 24-26 December – ***Loop :*** **Meals** a la carte 15.40/23.40 **t.** 10.50 – 6.50 – **98 rm** 59.00 **st.**, 5 suites.

Holiday Inn, Theatreland, 161 West Nile St, G1 2RL, ☎ (0141) 352 8300, *info@higlasgow.com, Fax (0141) 332 7447,* – , rest, – 130. VISA DY a
closed 25-26 December and 1-2 January – ***La Bonne Auberge Brasserie :*** **Meals** 6.95/10.95 and a la carte 18.85/24.45 **st.** 10.95 – 11.95 – **110 rm** 120.00/142.50 **st.**, 3 suites – SB.

Swallow Glasgow, 517 Paisley Road West, G51 1RW, ☎ (0141) 427 3146, *glasgow.swallow@whitbread.com, Fax (0141) 427 4059,* , , – , rest, – 300. VISA AX a
Meals *(closed Saturday lunch)* (carving lunch) 9.50/21.00 and dinner a la carte 20.15/29.95 **st.** 13.50 – **117 rm** 95.00/115.00 **st.** – SB.

Theatre without rest., 27 Elmbank St, G2 4PB, ☎ (0141) 227 2772, *theatrehotel@clara.net, Fax (0141) 227 2774* – . VISA JCB CY a
58 rm 50.00/70.00 **st.**

Express by Holiday Inn without rest., Theatreland, 165 West Nile St, G1 2RL, ☎ (0141) 331 6800, *hi@holidayinn.demon.co.uk, Fax (0141) 331 6828* – . VISA JCB. DY o
88 rm 59.00 **st.**

Express by Holiday Inn without rest., Stockwell St, G1 4LT, ☎ (0141) 548 5000, *managerglasgow@expressholidayinn.co.uk, Fax (0141) 548 5048* – – 35. VISA JCB DZ x
128 rm 60.00.

GLASGOW
BUILT UP AREA

Aikenhead Road .... **BX** 3
Alexandra Parade .... **BV** 4
Balgrayhill Road .... **BV** 5
Ballater Street .... **BX** 6
Balornock Road .... **BV** 8
Balshagray Avenue .... **AV** 9
Battlefield Road .... **BX** 12
Berryknowes Road .... **AX** 15
Bilsland Drive .... **BV** 16
Blairbeth Road .... **BX** 18
Braidcraft Road .... **AX** 20
Broomloan Road .... **AV** 26
Burnhill Chapel Street ..... **BX** 28
Byres Road .... **AV** 29
Caledonia Road .... **BX** 30
Carmunnock Road .... **BX**
Cook Street .... **BV**
Cumbernauld Road .... **BV**
Edmiston Drive .... **AV**
Farmeloan Road .... **BX**
Fenwick Road .... **AX**
Glasgow Road (PAISLEY) .. **AX**
Gorbals Street .... **BX**
Grange Road .... **BX**
Haggs Road .... **AX**

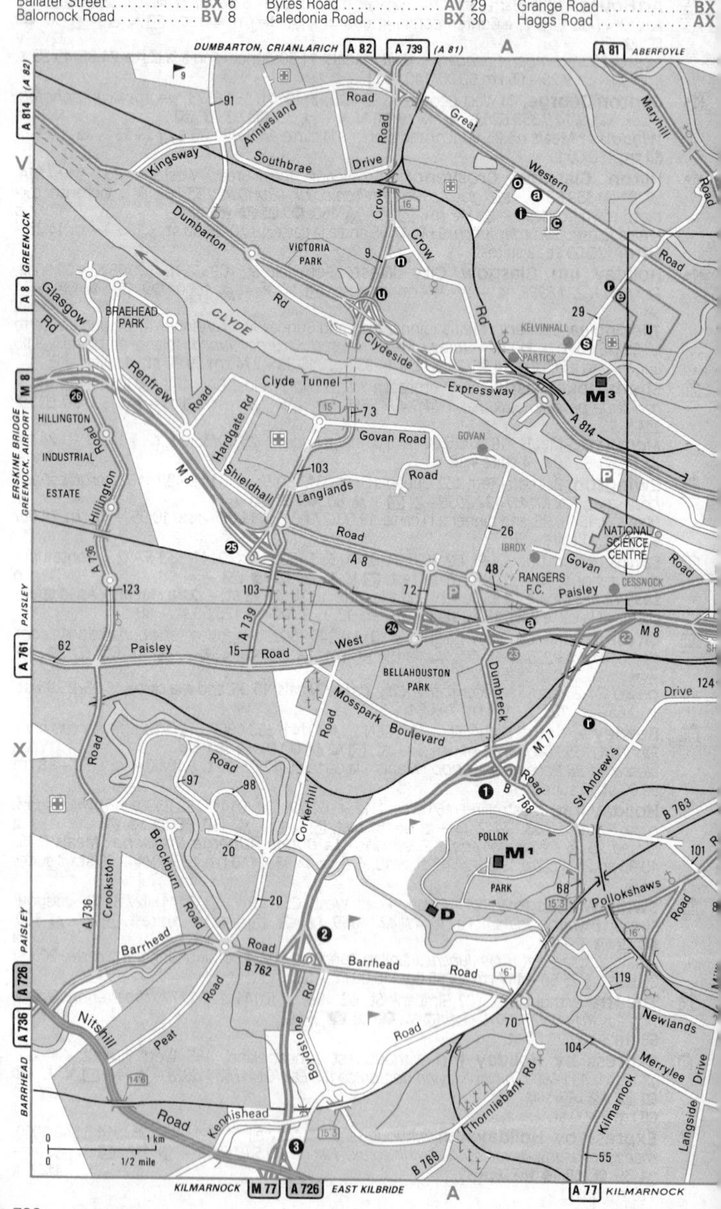

For Street Index see Glasgow p. 8

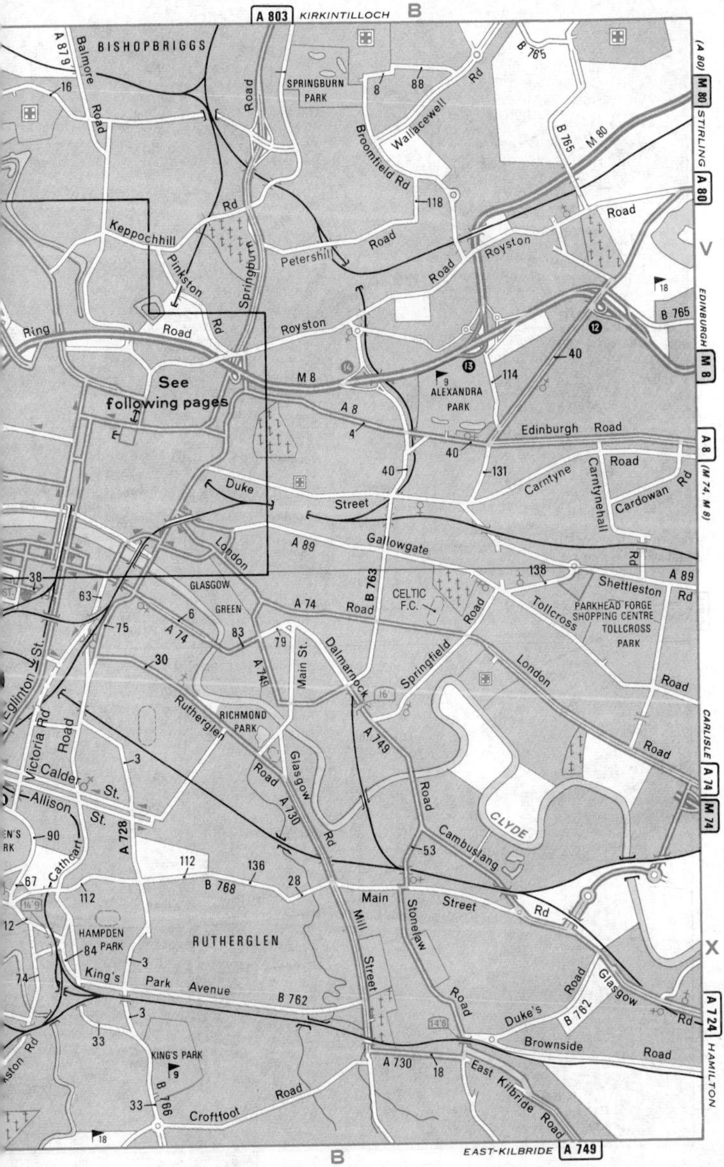

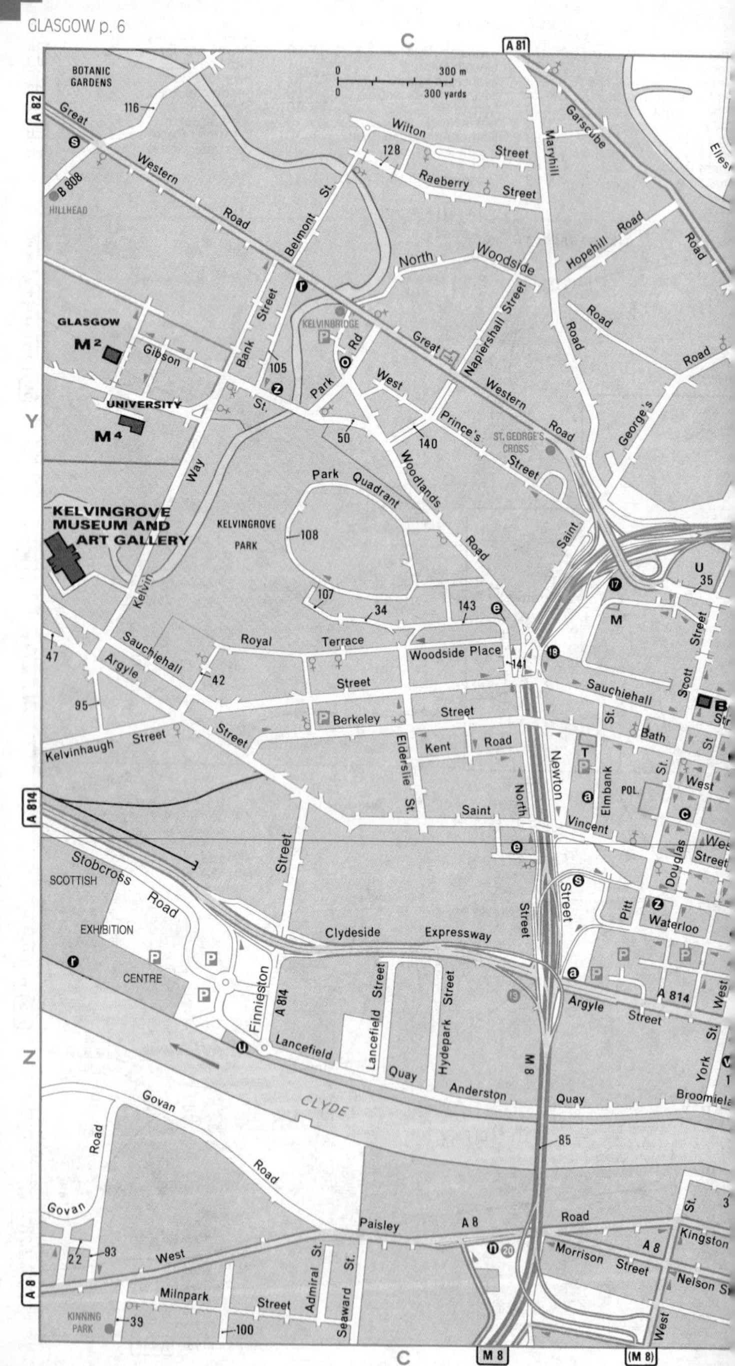
C
A 81
A 82
BOTANIC GARDENS
Great Western Road
B 808
HILLHEAD
Wilton Street
Raeberry Street
Belmont St.
North Woodside Road
Garscube Road
Maryhill Road
Hopehill Road
Napiershall Street
GLASGOW UNIVERSITY
M 2
M 4
Gibson St.
Bank Street
KELVINBRIDGE
Park Rd
West Prince's Street
ST. GEORGE'S CROSS
St. George's Road
Kelvin Way
Park Quadrant
Woodlands Road
KELVINGROVE MUSEUM AND ART GALLERY
KELVINGROVE PARK
Royal Terrace
Woodside Place
Sauchiehall Street
Argyle Street
Kelvinhaugh Street
Berkeley Street
Kent Road
Elderslie St.
North Street
Saint Vincent Street
Newton Street
Elmbank St.
Bath St.
Scott Street
West George St.
West Regent Street
Douglas St.
Pitt St.
Waterloo St.
A 814
Stobcross Road
SCOTTISH EXHIBITION CENTRE
Clydeside Expressway
Finnieston St.
Lancefield Street
Lancefield Quay
Hydepark Street
Anderston Quay
Broomielaw
York St.
Argyle Street
CLYDE
Govan Road
Paisley Road West
A 8
Morrison Street
Kingston St.
Nelson St.
Milnpark Street
Admiral St.
Seaward St.
KINNING PARK
M 8
(M 8)
Y
Z
C
0 300 m
0 300 yards

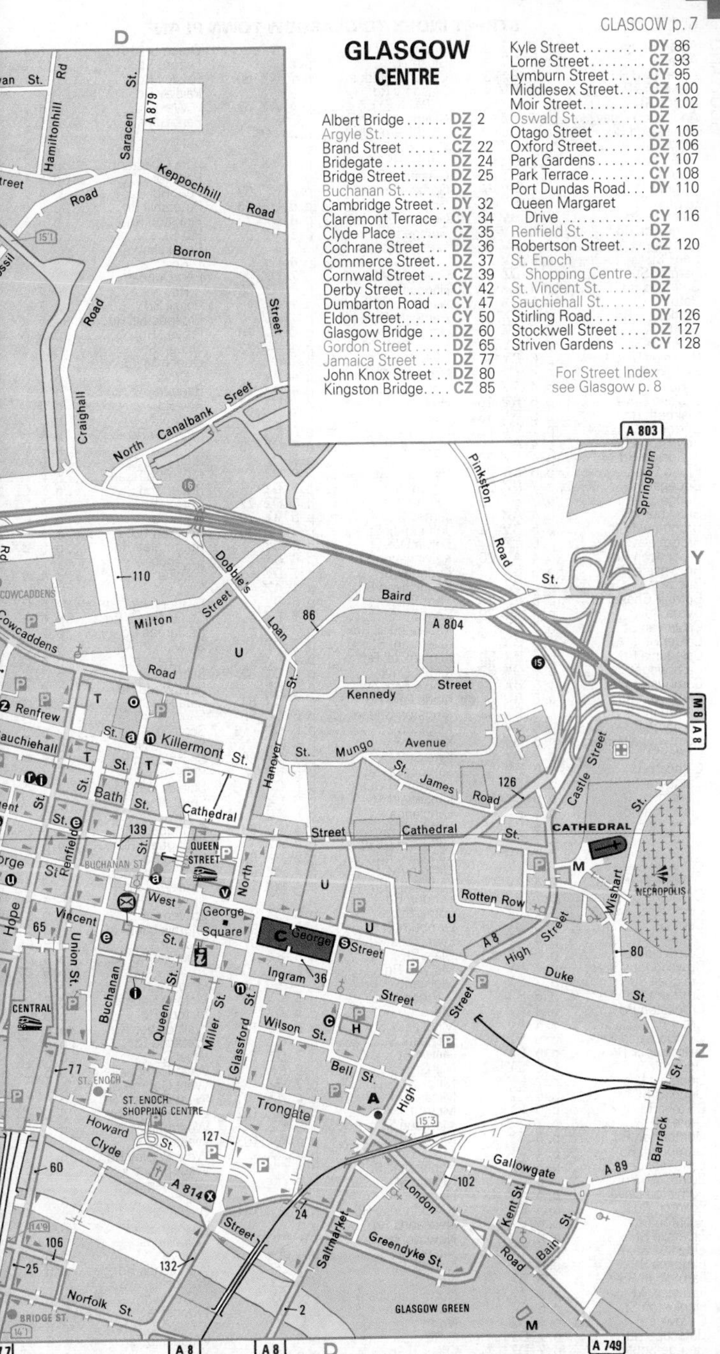
GLASGOW
CENTRE
Albert Bridge . . . . . . DZ 2
Argyle St. . . . . CZ
Brand Street . . . . . . CZ 22
Bridegate . . . . DZ 24
Bridge Street . . . . . . DZ 25
Buchanan St. . . . . . . DZ
Cambridge Street . . DY 32
Claremont Terrace . CY 34
Clyde Place . . . . CZ 35
Cochrane Street . . . DZ 36
Commerce Street . . DZ 37
Cornwald Street . . . CZ 39
Derby Street . . . . . . CY 42
Dumbarton Road . . CY 47
Eldon Street . . . . . . CY 50
Glasgow Bridge . . . DZ 60
Gordon Street . . . . . DZ 65
Jamaica Street . . . . DZ 77
John Knox Street . . DZ 80
Kingston Bridge . . . . CZ 85
Kyle Street . . . . DY 86
Lorne Street . . . . CZ 93
Lymburn Street . . . . . CY 95
Middlesex Street . . . . CZ 100
Moir Street . . . . DZ 102
Oswald St. . . . . DZ
Otago Street . . . . CY 105
Oxford Street . . . . DZ 106
Park Gardens . . . . CY 107
Park Terrace . . . . CY 108
Port Dundas Road . . . DY 110
Queen Margaret Drive . . . . CY 116
Renfield St. . . . . DZ
Robertson Street . . . . CZ 120
St. Enoch Shopping Centre . . DZ
St. Vincent St. . . . . . . DZ
Sauchiehall St. . . . . . . DY
Stirling Road . . . . DY 126
Stockwell Street . . . . DZ 127
Striven Gardens . . . . CY 128
For Street Index see Glasgow p. 8
D
Y
Z
A 879
A 803
A 804
A 8
A 814
A 89
A 749
M 8
Keppochhill Road
Borron Street
Craighall Road
North Canalbank Street
Pinkston Road
Springburn
Port Dundas Road
Baird St.
Dobbie's Loan
Milton Street
Cowcaddens Road
Kennedy Street
Mungo Avenue
St. James Road
Castle Street
Cathedral Street
CATHEDRAL
NECROPOLIS
Renfrew St.
Sauchiehall St.
Killermont St.
Bath St.
Hanover St.
North St.
QUEEN STREET
BUCHANAN ST.
West George St.
George Square
Vincent St.
Rotten Row
Wishart St.
High Street
Duke Street
Ingram Street
Wilson St.
Bell St.
Trongate
Miller St.
Glassford St.
Queen St.
Buchanan St.
Union St.
Hope St.
Renfield St.
CENTRAL
ST. ENOCH
ST. ENOCH SHOPPING CENTRE
Howard St.
Clyde Street
Gallowgate
London Road
Kent St.
Bain St.
Saltmarket
Greendyke St.
Barrack St.
Norfolk St.
BRIDGE ST.
GLASGOW GREEN
COWCADDENS
D

STREET INDEX TO GLASGOW TOWN PLAN

SCOTLAND

Travel Inn Metro, Montrose House, 187 George St, G1 1YU, (0141) 553 2700, *Fax (0141) 553 2719* – rest, – 40. VISA. DZ s
Meals (dinner only) – **254 rm** 49.95 **t.**

Travel Inn, Cambuslang Investment Park, Drumhead Pl, G32 8EY, Southeast : 5 m. by A 749 off A 74 (0141) 764 2655, *Fax (0141) 778 1703* – rm, rest, VISA.
Meals (grill rest.) – **40 rm** 41.95 **t.**

Travelodge, Hill St, G3 6PR, (0141) 333 1515, *Fax (0141) 333 1221* – rest, – 30. VISA. DY c
Meals (cafe bar) (dinner only) – **95 rm** 49.95 **t.**

Travelodge, 251 Paisley Rd, G5 8RA, (0141) 420 3882, *Fax (0141) 420 3884* – rm, rest, VISA JCB. CZ n
Meals (grill rest.) – **75 rm** 49.95 **t.**

Park House, 13 Victoria Park Gardens South, G11 7BX, (0141) 339 1559, *mail@parkhouseglasgow.co.uk, Fax (0141) 576 0915* – VISA. AV n
closed 2 weeks spring – **Meals** (by arrangement) 22.50 – **3 rm** 50.00/75.00.

Manor Park, 28 Balshagray Drive, G11 7DD, (0141) 339 2143, *manorparkhotel@aol.com, Fax (0141) 339 5842* – VISA JCB AV u
Meals (by arrangement) 16.50 **st.** 12.00 – **10 rm** 45.00/75.00.

The Town House without rest., 4 Hughenden Terr, G12 9XR, (0141) 357 0862, *hospitality@thetownhouseglasgow.com, Fax (0141) 339 9605* – VISA JCB. AV i
10 rm 60.00/72.00 **st.**

Kirklee without rest., 11 Kensington Gate, G12 9LG, (0141) 334 5555, *kirklee@clara.net, Fax (0141) 339 3828* – VISA. AV c
closed 24-26 December – **9 rm** 52.00/68.00 **t.**

Camerons (at Hilton Glasgow H.), 1 William St, G3 8HT, (0141) 204 5511, *Fax (0141) 204 5004* – VISA JCB CZ s
closed Sunday – **Meals** 21.50/28.50 **st.** 18.00.

Amaryllis (at One Devonshire Gardens), 1 Devonshire Gdns, G12 0UX, (0141) 337 3434, *info@amaryllis1.demon.co.uk, Fax (0141) 339 0047* – VISA AV a
closed Saturday lunch – **Meals** (booking essential) 18.00/40.00 **st.** 19.00
Spec. Ravioli of lobster and langoustine, pea purée. Roast duck, caramelised chicory and braised root vegetables. Cold chocolate fondant, honeycomb ice cream.

Lux, 1051 Great Western Rd, G12 0XP, (0141) 576 7576, *Fax (0141) 576 0162* – VISA AV o
closed 25-26 December, 1-2 January, Sunday and Monday – **Meals** (dinner only) 28.50 **t.** 15.00.

Eurasia, 150 St Vincent St, G2 5NE, (0141) 204 1150, *reservations@eurasia-restaurant.co.uk, Fax (0141) 204 1140* – VISA DZ u
closed 25 December, 1 January, Saturday lunch, Sunday and Bank Holidays – **Meals** 14.95/34.00 and dinner a la carte 17.95/34.00 **t.** 14.95.

Rogano, 11 Exchange Pl, G1 3AN, (0141) 248 4055, *Fax (0141) 248 2608,* « Art Deco » – VISA DZ i
Meals - Seafood - 16.50 (lunch) and a la carte 27.45/37.95 **t.** 12.00.

Buttery, 652 Argyle St, G3 8UF, (0141) 221 8188, *Fax (0141) 204 4639* – VISA CZ e
closed 25-26 December, 1-2 January, Sunday, Saturday lunch and Bank Holidays – **Meals** 17.50/19.50 (lunch) and a la carte 14.50/32.00 **t.** 10.50.

Yes, 22 West Nile St, G1 2PW, (0141) 221 8044, *Fax (0141) 248 9159* – VISA DZ e
closed 25-26 December, 1-2 January, Saturday lunch and Sunday – **Meals** 14.95/29.50 **t.** 13.95.

Rococo, 202 West George St, G2 2NR, (0141) 221 5004, *res@rococoglasgow.com, Fax (0141) 221 5006* – VISA DYZ z
closed 1 January – **Meals** 14.00/32.50 and a la carte 18.00/36.00 **t.** 16.00.

Brian Maule at Chardon d'Or, 176 West Regent St, G2 4RL, (0141) 248 3801, *info@lechardondor.com, Fax (0141) 248 3901* – VISA CY i
closed Saturday lunch, Sunday and Bank Holidays – **Meals** 15.00 (lunch) and a la carte 25.00/35.00 **st.** 13.00.

Nairns, 13 Woodside Cres, G3 7UL46, (0141) 353 0707, *info@nairns.co.uk, Fax (0141) 331 1684,* « Contemporary interior » – rest. VISA. CY e
closed Christmas, Sunday and Monday – **Meals** 9.00/29.50 **t.** 15.50.

Puppet Theatre, 11 Ruthven Lane, G12 9BG, off Byres Rd (0141) 339 8444, *puppet@bigbeat.co.uk, Fax (0141) 339 7666* – VISA AV r
closed 1-2 January, Monday and Saturday lunch – **Meals** a la carte 20.00/32.00 **t.** 15.00.

XX **The Restaurant at Corinthian,** 191 Ingram St, G1 1DA, ✆ (0141) 552 1101, *info@corinthian.uk.com, Fax (0141) 559 6826,* « Former Glasgow Ship Bank, fine Victorian architecture » – MC AE DC VISA DZ
closed lunch Saturday and Sunday – **Meals** 9.95 (lunch) and dinner a la carte 18.50/23.50 10.25.

XX **Papingo,** 104 Bath St, G2 2EN, ✆ (0141) 332 6678, *info@papingo.co.uk, Fax (0141) 332 6549* – MC AE VISA DY
closed 25-26 December, 1-2 January, Sunday lunch and Bank Holiday Mondays – **Meals** 10.95/19.95 and a la carte 17.00/28.00 **t.** 13.95.

XX **Farfelu,** 89 Candleriggs, G1 1NP, ✆ (0141) 552 5345, *Fax (0141) 400 2141* – ▤. MC AE VISA DZ
closed 25 December, 1 January and Sunday – **Meals** 10.95/13.95 (lunch) and dinner a la carte 25.85/31.25 **t.** 11.50.

XX **Ho Wong,** 82 York St, G2 8LE, ✆ (0141) 221 3550, *Fax (0141) 248 5330* – ▤. MC AE DC VISA CZ
closed 3 days Chinese New Year and Sunday lunch – **Meals** - Chinese (Peking) - 26.00 (dinner) and a la carte approx. 20.40 **t.** 12.95.

XX **Amber Regent,** 50 West Regent St, G2 2QZ, ✆ (0141) 331 1655, *Fax (0141) 353 3398* – ▤. MC AE DC VISA JCB DY
closed Chinese New Year and Sunday – **Meals** - Chinese - 9.95/34.95 and a la carte 20.90/32.50 **t.** 12.95.

XX **Shish Mahal,** 66-68 Park Rd, G4 9JF, ✆ (0870) 0725771, *reservations@shishmahal.co.uk, Fax (0141) 572 0800* – ⇿. MC AE VISA JCB CY
closed Sunday lunch – **Meals** - Indian - 5.25/6.50 (lunch) and a la carte 16.05/30.85 **t.** 8.95.

XX **Shimla Pinks** (at Hilton Glasgow H.), 1 William St, G3 8HT, ✆ (0141) 248 1951, *Fax (0141) 248 2913* – ▤ P. MC AE DC VISA CZ
closed 1 January – **Meals** - Indian - (dinner only) a la carte 10.00/18.00 **st.** 14.75.

X **Stravaigin,** 28 Gibson St, (basement), G12 8NX, ✆ (0141) 334 2665, *stravaigin@btinternet.com, Fax (0141) 334 4099* – ⇿ ▤. MC AE DC VISA CY
closed 25-26 December, 1-2 January and Monday – **Meals** (dinner only and lunch Friday-Sunday) 16.95/25.95 **t.** 12.95.

X **Groucho Saint Jude's** with rm, 190 Bath St, G2 4HG, ✆ (0141) 352 8800, *info@grouchosaintjudes.com, Fax (0141) 352 8801,* « Contemporary interior » – ▤ TV ✆ – 35. MC DC VISA CY
Meals 13.50 (lunch) and a la carte 19.00/28.00 **t.** 12.50 – **5 rm** 105.00/115.00 **st.**, 1 suite.

X **Gamba,** 225a West George St, G2 2ND, ✆ (0141) 572 0899, *info@gamba.co.uk, Fax (0141) 572 0896* – MC AE VISA DY
closed 25-26 December, 1-3 January, Sunday and Bank Holiday Mondays – **Meals** - Seafood - 14.95 (lunch) and a la carte 24.50/31.00 **t.** 13.95.

X **The Ubiquitous Chip,** 12 Ashton Lane, G12 8SJ, off Byres Rd ✆ (0141) 334 5007, *mail@ubiquitouschip.co.uk, Fax (0141) 337 1302* – MC AE DC VISA AV
closed 25 December and 1 January – **Meals** 19.95/33.95 and a la carte 9.75/24.85 **t.** 13.95.

X **La Parmigiana,** 447 Great Western Rd, Kelvinbridge, G12 8HH, ✆ (0141) 334 0686, *Fax (0141) 332 3533* – ▤. MC AE DC VISA JCB CY
closed 25-26 December, 1-2 January, Sunday and Bank Holidays – **Meals** - Italian - 9.10/11.50 and a la carte 20.90/30.15 **st.** 12.90.

X **No Sixteen,** 16 Byres Rd, G11 5JY, ✆ (0141) 339 2544 – MC VISA AV
closed first 2 weeks December and Sunday – **Meals** 11.50 (lunch) and a la carte 19.25/25.00 **t.** 12.50.

X **Bouzy Rouge,** 111 West Regent St, G2 2RU, ✆ (0141) 221 8804, *res@bouzy-rouge.com, Fax (0141) 221 6941* – ▤. MC AE DC VISA DY
closed 1 January – **Meals** 9.95/12.95 (lunch) and a la carte 12.95/26.40 **t.** 12.95.

X **Shimla Pinks,** 777 Pollokshaws Rd, G41 2AX, ✆ (0141) 423 4488, *Fax (0141) 423 2434* – ▤. MC AE DC VISA AX
closed 1 January and lunch Saturday and Sunday – **Meals** - Indian - 6.95 (lunch) and a la carte 11.10/21.85.

X **Stravaigin 2,** 8 Ruthven Lane, G12 9BG, off Byres Rd ✆ (0141) 334 7165, *stravaigin@btinternet.com, Fax (0141) 357 4785* – MC AE DC VISA AV
closed 25 December and 1 January – **Meals** 7.95/9.95 (lunch) and a la carte 15.05/24.20 **t.** 11.95.

at Stepps *(North Lanarkshire) Northeast : 5½ m. by M 8 on A 80* – BV – ✉ *Glasgow.*

Garfield House, Cumbernauld Rd, G33 6HW, ✆ (0141) 779 2111, *rooms@garfieldhotel.co.uk, Fax (0141) 779 9799* – ⇿ TV P – 100. MC AE DC VISA
closed 1-2 January – **Meals** a la carte 9.95/21.50 10.50 – **46 rm** 83.50/103.50 **t.**

t Giffnock *(East Renfrewshire) South : 5 1/4 m. by A 77 –* **AX** *– Glasgow.*

Turban Tandoori, 2 Station Rd, G46 6JF, (0141) 638 0069 – MC AE VISA JCB
closed 1 January – **Meals** - Indian - (dinner only) a la carte 11.40/21.85 **t.** 10.95.

The Cook's Room, 205 Fenwick Rd, G46 6JD, (0141) 621 1903, *Fax (0141) 621 1903* – MC VISA
closed 25 December and 1-2 January – **Meals** (dinner only and Saturday and Sunday lunch) a la carte 18.30/25.80 **st.** 12.00.

t Glasgow Airport *(Renfrewshire) West : 8 m. by M 8 –* **AV** *– Paisley.*

Holiday Inn Glasgow Airport, Abbotsinch, PA3 2TR, (0870) 400 9031, *Fax (0141) 887 3738* – rm, – 250. MC AE VISA.
The Junction : Meals *(closed Saturday lunch)* (carving rest. Friday-Sunday) 15.00/20.00 (lunch) and dinner a la carte 17.35/29.15 **t.** 12.95 – 13.95 – **296 rm** 99.00 **st.**, 2 suites – SB.

Express by Holiday Inn, St Andrews Drive, PA3 2TJ, (0141) 842 1100, *info@hiex-glasgow.com, Fax (0141) 842 1122* – rest, – 80. MC AE VISA JCB
Meals (dinner only) a la carte 10.00/16.00 **st.** 12.50 – **143 rm** 59.95 **st.** – SB.

Travel Inn Metro, Whitecart Rd, PA3 2TH, (0141) 842 1563, *Fax (0141) 842 1570* – rest, – 30. MC AE VISA.
Meals (grill rest.) (dinner only) – **104 rm** 49.95 **t.**

LASGOW AIRPORT *Renfrewshire* 401 402 G 16 – *see Glasgow.*

LENBORRODALE *Highland* 401 C 13 – *Acharacle.*
Edinburgh 190 – Inverness 116 – Oban 106.

Feorag House, PH36 4JP, (01972) 500248, *admin@feorag.demon.co.uk, Fax (01972) 500285,* Loch Sunart, « Lochside setting », – MC VISA
Meals 22.50 **st.** – **3 rm** (dinner included) 84.00/138.00 **st.** – SB.

LENSBURGH *Falkirk – see Falkirk.*

LENELG *Highland* 401 D 12.
Edinburgh 229 – Inverness 75 – Kyle of Lochalsh 25.

Glenelg Inn, IV40 8JR, (01599) 522273, *Fax (01599) 522283,* Glenelg Bay, – MC VISA JCB
Meals 25.00 (dinner) and lunch a la carte approx. 19.00 **st.** 12.00 – **6 rm** (dinner included) 144.00 **st.** – SB.

LENLIVET *Moray* 401 J 11 – *pop. 3 559 – Ballindalloch.*
Edinburgh 180 – Aberdeen 59 – Elgin 27 – Inverness 49.

Minmore House, AB37 9DB, South : 3/4 m. on Glenlivet Distillery rd (01807) 590378, *minmorehouse@ukonline.co.uk, Fax (01807) 590472,* – MC AE VISA JCB.
closed February and 2 weeks October-November – **Meals** (booking essential to non-residents) 30.00 (dinner) and lunch a la carte approx. 26.00 **st.** 13.95 – **9 rm** (dinner included) 82.50/165.00 **st.** – SB.

LENROTHES *Fife* 401 K 15 *Scotland G. – pop. 38 650.*
Env. : *Falkland★ (Village★, Palace of Falkland★ AC, Gardens★ AC) N : 5 1/2 m. by A 92 and A 912.*
18 Thornton, Station Rd (01592) 771173 – 18 Golf Course Rd (01592) 754561 – 18 Balbirnie Park, Markinch (01592) 612095 – 9 Auchterderran, Woodend Rd, Cardenden (01592) 721579 – 9 Leslie, Balsillie Laws (01592) 620040.
Edinburgh 33 – Dundee 25 – Stirling 36.

Balbirnie House, Markinch, KY7 6NE, Northeast : 1 3/4 m. by A 911 and A 92 on B 9130 (01592) 610066, *balbirnie@breathemail.net, Fax (01592) 610529,* « Part Georgian mansion in country park », 18, – rest, – 200. MC AE VISA
Orangery : **Meals** 14.50/31.50 and lunch a la carte 17.20/21.95 **t.** 13.50 – **28 rm** 125.00/245.00 **t.**, 2 suites – SB.

Express by Holiday Inn without rest., Leslie Roundabout, Leslie Rd, KY7 6XX, Wes 2 m. on A 911 ☎ (01592) 745509, *Fax (01592) 743377* – ⇔ TV ☏ & P – 🏛 30. MC AE VISA JCB. ✻
49 rm 52.50 **st.**

Travel Inn, Beaufort Drive, Bankhead Roundabout, KY7 4UJ, Southeast : 1 ¾ m. by A 9 and A 92 at junction with B 921 ☎ (01592) 773473, *Fax (01592) 773453* – ⇔, ▤ rest, TV P. MC AE ◑ VISA. ✻
Meals (grill rest.) – **41 rm** 41.95 **t.**

GRANTOWN-ON-SPEY *Highland* 401 J 12 – *pop. 2 391.*

18 Golf Course Rd ☎ (01479) 872079 – 9 Abernethy, Nethy Bridge ☎ (01479) 821305.
54 High St ☎ (01479) 872773 (April-October).
Edinburgh 143 – Inverness 34 – Perth 99.

Culdearn House, Woodlands Terr, PH26 3JU, ☎ (01479) 872106, *culdearn@globalnet.uk, Fax (01479) 873641*, – ⇔ TV P. MC AE ◑ VISA JCB. ✻
mid March-October – **Meals** (booking essential to non-residents) (dinner only) 25.00 🍷 10.95 – **9 rm** ☕ (dinner included) 75.00/150.00 **st.** – SB.

Ravenscourt House, Seafield Ave, PH26 3JG, ☎ (01479) 872286, *Fax (01479) 8732*
– ⇔ TV P.
closed 1-15 February – **Meals** (residents only) (dinner only) 17.50/19.50 **st.** 🍷 8.00 – **8 r** ☕ 35.00/80.00 **st.** – SB.

at Dulnain Bridge *Southwest : 3 m. by A 95 on A 938 – ✉ Grantown-on-Spey.*

Muckrach Lodge ⛰, PH26 3LY, West : ½ m. on A 938 ☎ (01479) 851257, *info@muckrach.co.uk, Fax (01479) 851325*, <, , – ⇔ TV & P – 🏛 35. MC AE ◑ VISA JCB
*closed2 weeks January***Meals** *(closed Sunday dinner, Monday and Tuesday lunch Novemb March)* (lunch by arrangement)/dinner 29.50 and a la carte 15.00/20.20 **st.** 🍷 11.95 – **11 r** ☕ 55.00/130.00 **st.**, 2 suites – SB.

Auchendean Lodge, PH26 3LU, South : 1 m. on A 95 ☎ (01479) 851347, *hotel@auchdean.com, Fax (01479) 851347*, < Spey Valley and Cairngorms, – ⇔ rest, TV P. MC ◑ VISA
Meals (dinner only) 27.00 **st.** 🍷 9.50 – **5 rm** ☕ 43.00/82.00 **st.** – SB.

GREENOCK *Inverclyde* 401 F 16 – *pop. 35 272.*

18, 9 Forsyth St. ☎ (01475) 720793.
Edinburgh 70 – Ayr 48 – Glasgow 24.

Howard Johnson without rest., Cartsburn, PA15 4RT, East : ¾ m. off A ☎ (01475) 786666, *greenock@howardjohnson.co.uk, Fax (01475) 786777* – ⇕ ⇔ TV ☏ P – 🏛 35. MC AE ◑ VISA JCB. ✻
☕ 6.00 **72 rm** 55.00 **st.**

Travel Inn, James Watt Dock, PA15 2AD, East : 1 m. by A 8 ☎ (01475) 7309 *Fax (01475) 730890* – ⇕ ⇔, ▤ rest, TV & P. MC AE ◑ VISA. ✻
Meals (grill rest.) – **40 rm** 41.95 **t.**

GRETNA GREEN SERVICE AREA *Dumfries and Galloway* 401 402 K 18 – ✉ *Gretna.*

Welcome Lodge, DG16 5HQ, on A 74 (M) ☎ (01461) 337566, Reservations (Freephone) 0800 0280400, *gretna.hotel@welcomebreak.co.uk, Fax (01461) 337823* – ⇔ rm, & P. MC AE ◑ VISA JCB
Meals (grill rest.) a la carte approx. 12.00 – **64 rm** 45.00 **t.**

GRIMSAY *Western Isles (Outer Hebrides)* 401 Y 11 – *see Uist (Isles of).*

GRULINE *Argyll and Bute – see Mull (Isle of).*

GULLANE *East Lothian* 401 L 15 *Scotland G.* – *pop. 2 229.*

Env. : *Dirleton★ (Castle★) NE : 2 m. by A 198.*
Edinburgh 19 – North Berwick 5.

Greywalls ⛰, Duncur Rd, Muirfield, EH31 2EG, ☎ (01620) 842144, *hotel@greywalls.co.uk, Fax (01620) 842241*, < Gardens and Muirfield golf course, « Edwardian country house designed by Sir Edwin Lutyens, gardens by Gertrude Jekyll », ✂ – ⇔ rest, TV
🏛 30. MC AE ◑ VISA
April-October – **Meals** (booking essential to non-residents) 17.50/37.50 **t.** 🍷 13.00 – 23 ☕ 115.00/230.00 **t.** – SB.

Faussetthill House without rest., Main St, EH31 2DR, ✆ (01620) 842396, *Fax (01620) 842396*, – ⅋ P. MC VISA.
March-October – **3 rm** 45.00/60.00.

Hopefield House without rest., Main St, EH31 2DP, ✆ (01620) 842191, *info@hopefieldhouse.co.uk, Fax (01620) 842191*, – P.
March-October – **3 rm** 30.00/50.00 **s.**

ADDINGTON *East Lothian* 401 L 16 *Scotland G. – pop. 7 342.*

See : *Town*★ - *High Street*★.
Env. : *Lennoxlove*★ *AC, S : 1 m – Gifford*★, *SE : 5 m. by B 6369.*
Exc. : *Tantallon Castle*★★ *(clifftop site*★★★*) AC, NE : 12 m. by A 1 and A 198 – Northern foothills of the Lammermuir Hills*★★, *S : 14 m. by A 6137 and B 6368 – Stenton*★, *E : 7 m.*
18 *Amisfield Park* ✆ *(01620) 823627.*
Edinburgh 17 – Hawick 53 – Newcastle upon Tyne 101.

Maitlandfield Country House, 24 Sidegate, EH41 4BZ, ✆ (01620) 826513, *info@maitlandfieldhouse.co.uk, Fax (01620) 826713*, – TV P – 200. MC AE VISA
Meals a la carte 13.95/24.45 **st.** 10.50 – **22 rm** 60.00/150.00 **st.** – SB.

Brown's with rm, 1 West Rd, EH41 3RD, ✆ (01620) 822254, *info@browns-hotel.com, Fax (01620) 822254*, – rest, TV P. MC AE VISA JCB.
Meals (booking essential) (dinner only and Sunday lunch)/dinner 30.00 **st.** 11.50 – **5 rm** 65.00/105.00 **st.**

ALKIRK *Highland* 401 J 8 – *pop. 1 913.*

Edinburgh 285 – Thurso 8 – Wick 17.

Bannochmore Farm without rest., Harpsdale, KW12 6UN, South : 3 ¼ m. ✆ (01847) 841216, – P.
April-October – **3 rm** 21.00/38.00.

AMILTON SERVICE AREA *South Lanarkshire* 401 H 16.

9 *Larkhall, Burnhead Rd* ✆ *(01698) 881113 –* 9 *Strathclyde Park, Mote Hill* ✆ *(01698) 429350.*
Road Chef Services, M 74 northbound ✆ *(01698) 285590.*
Edinburgh 38 – Glasgow 12.

Travel Inn without rest., ML3 6JW, M 74 between junctions 6 and 5 (northbound carriageway) ✆ (01698) 891904, *Fax (01698) 891682* – TV P – 25. MC AE VISA.
closed Christmas and New Year – **36 rm** 41.95.

ARRIS (Isle of) *Western Isles (Outer Hebrides)* 401 Z 10 – *see Lewis and Harris (Isle of).*

OWGATE *Midlothian* 401 402 K 16 – ✉ *Penicuik.*

Edinburgh 12 – Glasgow 54.

The Howgate, EH26 8PY, Southwest : ¾ m. on A 6094 ✆ (01968) 670000, *Fax (01968) 670000*, – P. MC AE VISA JCB.
closed 25-26 December and 1-2 January – **Meals** a la carte 14.20/29.45 **t.** 12.95.

GLISTON *Edinburgh City* 401 K 16 – *see Edinburgh.*

NERLEITHEN *Borders* 401 402 K 17 – *pop. 2 663 –* ✉ *Peebles.*

Edinburgh 31 – Dumfries 57 – Glasgow 60.

Caddon View, 14 Pirn Rd, EH44 6HH, ✆ (01896) 830208, *caddonview@aol.com, Fax (01896) 830104*, – TV P. MC VISA
closed 25 December and 1 month February-March – **Meals** (booking essential) (dinner only) 25.00 **t.** 10.95 – **6 rm** 48.00/70.00 **t.** – SB.

VERARAY *Argyll and Bute* 401 E 15.

9 *Inveraray, North Cromalt* ✆ *(01499) 302508.*
Front St. ✆ *(01499) 302063.*
Edinburgh 102 – Glasgow 58 – Oban 38.

Loch Fyne, PA32 8XT, Southwest : ½ m. on A 83 ✆ (01499) 302148, *lochfyne@briti trust-hotels.com, Fax (01499) 302348*, – – 50. .
Meals (bar lunch)/dinner 18.00 and a la carte 16.50/23.00 **st.** 10.95 – **80 rm** 60.(100.00 **st.** – SB.

INVERCRERAN *Argyll and Bute* 401 E 14 – ✉ *Appin.*

Edinburgh 142 – Fort William 29 – Oban 19.

Invercreran Country House, Glen Creran, PA38 4BJ, ✆ (01631) 730414, *in creran@dial.pipex.com, Fax (01631) 730532*, ≤ Glen Creran and mountains, , rest, . .
15 March-15 November – **Meals** (lunch by arrangement) 30.00 (dinner) a lunch a la carte approx. 24.00 **t.** 15.00 – **9 rm** 75.00/200.00 **t.** – SB.

INVERGARRY *Highland* 401 F 12 *Scotland G.* – ✉ *Inverness.*

Env. : *The Great Glen*★.

Edinburgh 159 – Fort William 25 – Inverness 43 – Kyle of Lochalsh 50.

Glengarry Castle, PH35 4HW, on A 82 ✆ (01809) 501254, *castle@glengarry.r Fax (01809) 501207*, ≤, , , , –
22 March-11 November – **Meals** (light lunch Monday-Saturday)/dinner 26.00/29.00 **st** **26 rm** 55.00/140.00 **st.** – SB.

Invergarry, PH35 4HJ, ✆ (01809) 501206, *hotel@invergarry.net, Fax (01809) 501400,* – rest, .
closed 3 weeks December – **Meals** (bar lunch)/dinner 19.00 **st.** 9.50 – **10 rm** 40. 70.00 **st.** – SB.

INVERKEILOR *Angus* 401 M 14 – *pop. 902* – ✉ *Arbroath.*

Edinburgh 85 – Aberdeen 32 – Dundee 22.

Gordon's with rm, 32 Main St, DD11 5RN, ✆ (01241) 830364, *gordonsrest@aol.co Fax (01241) 830364* – . .
closed 1 January and last 2 weeks January, restricted opening in winter – **Meals** *(clo Tuesday lunch)* (booking essential) (residents only Monday) 16.00/31.50 **st.** 10.95 – **3** 47.00/90.00 **st.**

INVERNESS *Highland* 401 H 11 *Scotland G.* – *pop. 62 186.*

See : *Town*★ – *Museum and Art Gallery*★ Y **M.**

Exc. : *Loch Ness*★★, *SW : by A 82* Z – *Clava Cairns*★, *E : 9 m. by Culcabock Rd, B 9006 B 851* Z – *Cawdor Castle*★ *AC, NE : 14 m. by A 96 and B 9090* Y.

Culcabock Rd ✆ (01463) 239882 Z – *Torvean, Glenurquhart Rd ✆ (01463) 711434.*

Inverness Airport, Dalcross : ✆ (01667) 464000, NE : 8 m. by A 96 Y.

Castle Wynd ✆ (01463) 234353 Y.

Edinburgh 156 – Aberdeen 107 – Dundee 134.

Plan opposite

Inverness Marriott, Culcabock Rd, IV2 3LP, ✆ (01463) 237166, *Fax (01463) 225208,* , , – , rest, – 100. Z
Meals a la carte 16.00/40.00 **st.** 12.95 – 13.00 – **75 rm** 130.00/150.00 **st.**, 7 suites –

Thistle Inverness, Millburn Rd, IV2 3TR, East : 1 m. on B 865 ✆ (0870) 3339 *inverness@thistle.co.uk, Fax (0870) 3339255*, , , – – 230.
Meals 9.75/18.95 **st.** 10.95 – 11.95 – **117 rm** 131.00/151.00 **st.**, 1 suite.

Ramada Jarvis Inverness, 33 Church St, IV1 1DX, ✆ (01463) 235181, *jiinverness jarvis.co.uk, Fax (01463) 711206*, ≤, , , – , rm, rest, – 300. Y
Waterside : **Meals** (dinner only) 17.00 and a la carte 17.25/30.75 **st.** 12.50 – ***Arts :*** **M** (lunch only) a la carte approx. 10.95 11.75 – 8.95 – **103 rm** 115.00/165.00 **st.**, 3 suit SB.

Craigmonie, 9 Annfield Rd, IV2 3HX, ✆ (01463) 231649, *info@craigmonie.c Fax (01463) 233720*, , , – – 180. . Z
closed 1-2 January, 24-26 and 31 December – ***Chardonnay :*** **Meals** - Seafood - (dinner and Sunday lunch) 22.00/26.00 and a la carte 23.00/35.45 **t.** 9.00 – ***Conservatory :*** **M** *(closed Sunday lunch)* a la carte 11.45/22.95 **t.** 7.75 – **32 rm** 80.00/118.00 **t.**, 3 suit SB.

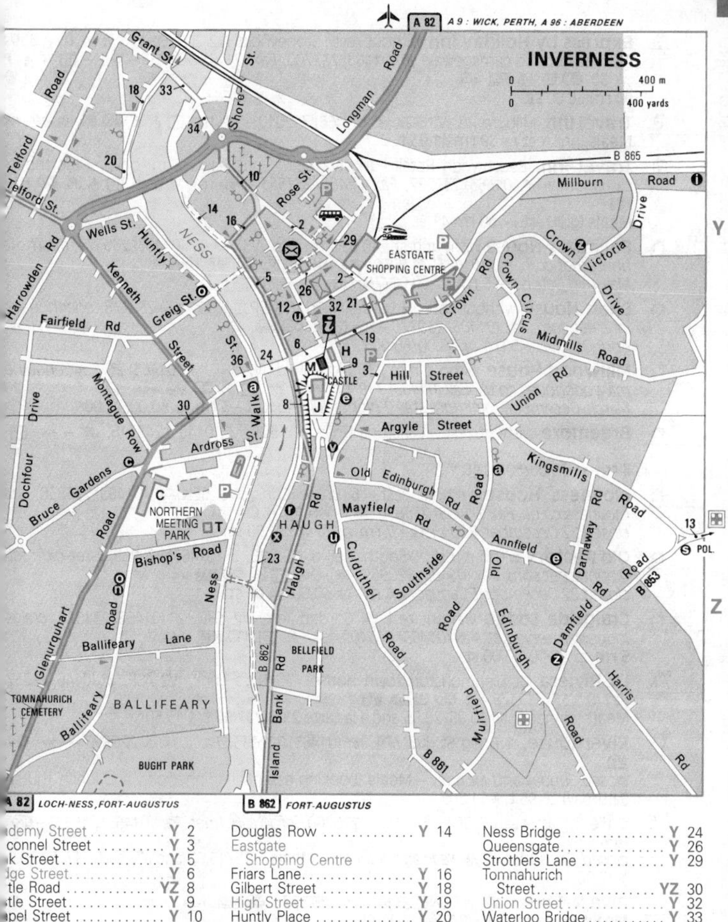

demy Street . . . . Y 2
connel Street . . . . Y 3
k Street . . . . Y 5
dge Street . . . . Y 6
tle Road . . . . YZ 8
tle Street . . . . Y 9
pel Street . . . . Y 10
rch Street . . . . Y 12
cabock Road . . . . Z 13
Douglas Row . . . . Y 14
Eastgate
Shopping Centre
Friars Lane . . . . Y 16
Gilbert Street . . . . Y 18
High Street . . . . Y 19
Huntly Place . . . . Y 20
Inglis Street . . . . Y 21
Ness Bank . . . . Z 23
Ness Bridge . . . . Y 24
Queensgate . . . . Y 26
Strothers Lane . . . . Y 29
Tomnahurich
Street . . . . YZ 30
Union Street . . . . Y 32
Waterloo Bridge . . . . Y 33
Waterloo Place . . . . Y 34
Young Street . . . . Y 36

Glenmoriston Town House, 20 Ness Bank, IV2 4SF, (01463) 223777, *glenmoriston @cali.co.uk, Fax (01463) 712378* – TV P – 30. MC AE VISA Z x
La Terrazza : **Meals** (lunch only) 10.95/15.95 and a la carte 13.50/25.00 **t.** 13.50 – (see also ***La Riviera*** below) – **15 rm** 80.00/145.00 **t.** – SB.

Glen Mhor, 9-12 Ness Bank, IV2 4SG, (01463) 234308, *glenmhor@ukonline.co.uk, Fax (01463) 713170* – rm, TV P. MC AE VISA. Z r
closed 31 December-3 January – ***Riverview :*** **Meals** *(closed in winter)* (dinner only) a la carte 11.95/27.50 **t.** 10.50 – ***Nico's :*** **Meals** a la carte 11.95/27.50 **t.** 10.50 – **42 rm** 59.00/160.00 **t.**, 3 suites – SB.

Culduthel Lodge, 14 Culduthel Rd, IV2 4AG, (01463) 240089, *Fax (01463) 240089* – TV P. MC VISA Z u
closed 3 weeks January and 2 weeks November – **Meals** (booking essential) (residents only) (dinner only) 20.00 **st.** 9.25 – **11 rm** 60.00/120.00 **st.**, 1 suite.

Glendruidh House, Old Edinburgh Rd South, IV2 6AR, Southeast : 2 m. (01463) 226499, *michael@cozzee-nessie-bed.co.uk, Fax (01463) 710745*, – TV P. MC AE VISA JCB.
closed 24-26 December – **Meals** (residents only) (dinner only) 29.50 **t.** 12.50 – **5 rm** 69.00/90.00 **t.** – SB.

SCOTLAND

Express by Holiday Inn without rest., Stoneyfield, IV2 7PA, East : 1 ½ m. by A 865 A 96 (eastbound carriageway) ☎ (01463) 732700, *Fax (01463) 732732* – 30.
94 rm 56.00 st.

Travel Inn, Milburn Rd, IV2 3QX, ☎ (01463) 712010 – rm, Y
Meals (grill rest.) – **39 rm** 41.95 **t.**

Travel Inn, Beechwood Retail Park, IV2 3BW, Southeast : 2 m. on A 9 (northbou carriageway) ☎ (01463) 232727, *Fax (01463) 231553* – rm, rest,
Meals (grill rest.) – **60 rm** 41.95 **t.**

Ballifeary House without rest., 10 Ballifeary Rd, IV3 5PJ, ☎ (01463) 235572, *ballifhote btinternet.com, Fax (01463) 717583,* – Z
May-mid October – **5 rm** 60.00/76.00 **s.**

Eden House without rest., 8 Ballifeary Rd, IV3 5PJ, ☎ (01463) 230278, *edenhouse@ internet.com, Fax (01463) 230278* – Z
April-October – **5 rm** 60.00/66.00 **t.**

Millwood House without rest., 36 Old Mill Rd, IV2 3HR, ☎ (01463) 237254, *enquirie millwoodhouse.co.uk, Fax (01463) 719400,* – Z
March-December, minimum stay 2 nights July-August – **3 rm** 60.00/78.00.

Braemore without rest., 1 Victoria Drive, IV2 3QB, ☎ (01463) 243318, – Y
3 rm 35.00/60.00 **st.**

Moyness House without rest., 6 Bruce Gdns, IV3 5EN, ☎ (01463) 233836, *sta moyness.co.uk, Fax (01463) 233836,* – Z
closed 22 December-8 January – **7 rm** 37.00/74.00 **st.**

Old Rectory without rest., 9 Southside Rd, IV2 3BG, ☎ (01463) 220969, *lister-old-rect @btinternet.com, Fax (01463) 220969,* – Z
closed 22 December-5 January – **4 rm** 30.00/44.00 **st.**

Craigside Lodge without rest., 4 Gordon Terr, IV2 3HD, ☎ (01463) 231576, *craigs lodge@amserve.net, Fax (01463) 713409,* ← – Z
5 rm 22.00/40.00 **st.**

La Riviera (at Glenmoriston Town House), 20 Ness Bank, IV2 4SF, ☎ (01463) 2237 *Fax (01463) 712378* – Z
Meals (dinner only) 10.95/29.95 and a la carte 25.70/32.95 **t.** 13.50.

Riverhouse, 1 Greig St, IV5 3PT, ☎ (01463) 222033, *Fax (01463) 220890* – Y
closed Sunday and Monday – **Meals** (booking essential) (dinner only and lunch Thursd Saturday) 26.95 **t.** 11.50.

Café 1, Castle St, IV2 3EA, ☎ (01463) 226200, *info@cafe1.net, Fax (01463) 716363* – Y
closed Christmas, New Year and Sunday – **Meals** 5.75/15.00 and a la carte 17.75/25.0 12.00.

Riva, 4-6 Ness Walk, IV3 5NE, ☎ (01463) 237377 – Y
Meals a la carte 14.95/24.70 **t.** 10.95.

at Culloden *East : 3 m. by A 96 – Y – ✉ Inverness.*

Culloden House , IV2 7BZ, ☎ (01463) 790461, *info@cullodenhouse.co. Fax (01463) 792181,* ←, « Georgian mansion », –
closed 24-28 December – **Meals** a la carte 29.00/35.00 **st.** – **22 rm** 155.00/195.00 6 suites – SB.

at Dunain Park *Southwest : 2½ m. on A 82 – Z – ✉ Inverness.*

Dunain Park , IV3 8JN, ☎ (01463) 230512, *dunainparkhotel@btinternet.c Fax (01463) 224532,* ←, « Country house, gardens », –
Meals (dinner only) a la carte 24.90/29.85 **t.** 14.50 – **5 rm** 158.00/198.00 **t.**, **8 su** 198.00 **t.** – SB.

at Bunchrew *West : 3 m. on A 862 – Y – ✉ Inverness.*

Bunchrew House , IV3 8TA, ☎ (01463) 234917, *welcome@bunchrew-invern co.uk, Fax (01463) 710620,* ←, « Part 17C Scottish mansion on the shores of Beauly Firt – rest,
closed Christmas – **Meals** 25.00/31.50 **t.** 15.50 – **14 rm** 135.00/195.00 **t.** – SB.

Die Preise Einzelheiten über die in diesem Reiseführer angegebenen Preise finden Sie in der Einleitung.

INVERURIE Aberdeenshire 401 M 12 *Scotland G. – pop. 8 647.*

Exc. : Castle Fraser★ (exterior★★) AC, SW : 6 m. by B 993 – Pitmedden Gardens★★, NE : 10 m. by B 9170 and A 920 – Haddo House★, N : 14 m. by B 9170 and B 9005 – Fyvie Castle★, N : 13 m. by B 9170 and A 947.

Blackhall Rd ☎ (01467) 620207 – Kintore, Balbithan Rd ☎ (01467) 632631 – Kemnay, Monymusk Rd ☎ (01467) 642060.

18 High St. ☎ (01467) 625800.

Edinburgh 147 – Aberdeen 17 – Inverness 90.

Thainstone House H. & Country Club, AB51 5NT, South : 2 m. by B 993 off A 96 ☎ (01467) 621643, *info@thainstonehouse.macdonald.hotels.co.uk, Fax (01467) 625084*, – 300.
Simpson's : Meals 16.50/28.50 **st.** 14.50 – **47 rm** 75.00/100.00 **t.**, 1 suite – SB.

Strathburn, Burghmuir Drive, AB51 4GY, Northwest : 1 ¼ m. by Inverness rd (A 96) ☎ (01467) 624422, *strathburn@btconnect.com, Fax (01467) 625133*, rest, – 30.
closed 25-26 December and 1-2 January – **Meals** a la carte 13.25/24.25 **st.** 8.25 – **25 rm** 68.00/90.00 **st.** – SB.

IRVINE North Ayrshire 401 F/G 17.

New St ☎ (01294) 313709.

Edinburgh 76 – Ayr 15 – Glasgow 30 – Kilmarnock 8.

Thistle, 46 Annick Rd, KA11 4LD, Southeast : 1 m. on B 7081 ☎ (01294) 274272, *irvine@thistle.co.uk, Fax (01294) 277287*, rm, – 250.
Mirage : **Meals** (dinner only) a la carte 15.70/30.20 **st.** 10.95 – ***Lagoon :*** **Meals** 12.00/18.00 **st.** 10.95 – 10.95 – **128 rm** 124.00/144.00 **st.** – SB.

ISLAY (Isle of) Argyll and Bute 401 B 16 – *pop. 3 840.*

Western Cottage, Port Ellen ☎ (01496) 302409.

Port Ellen Airport : ☎ (01496) 302022.

from Port Askaig to Isle of Jura (Feolin) (Serco Denholm Ltd) frequent services daily (approx. 4 mn) – from Port Ellen or Port Askaig to Kintyre Peninsula (Kennacraig) (Caledonian MacBrayne Ltd) 1-2 daily – from Port Askaig to Oban via Isle of Colonsay (Scalasaig) (Caledonian MacBrayne Ltd) weekly – from Port Askaig to Isle of Colonsay (Scalasaig) and Kintyre Peninsula (Kennacraig) (Caledonian MacBrayne Ltd) weekly.

at Bowmore ☎ (01496) 810254 (Easter-October).

Ballygrant.

Kilmeny Country Guest House, PA45 7QW, Southwest : ½ m. on A 846 ☎ (01496) 840668, *info@kilmeny.co.uk, Fax (01496) 840668*, ≤, « Working farm », –
closed Christmas and New Year – **Meals** (by arrangement) (communal dining) – **3 rm** (dinner included) 72.00/124.00 **s.**

Bowmore.

Harbour Inn with rm, The Square, PA43 7JR, ☎ (01496) 810330, *harbour@harbour-inn.com, Fax (01496) 810990*, ≤ –
Meals *(closed Sunday lunch)* a la carte 17.25/27.75 **st.** 10.50 – **7 rm** 45.00/85.00 **st.**

Bridgend – ✉ *Bowmore.*

Bridgend, PA44 7PQ, ☎ (01496) 810212, *bcb.islay@fonthill.co.uk, Fax (01496) 810960*, –
Meals (bar lunch)/dinner 20.00/24.00 – **10 rm** 45.00/90.00 **t.** – SB.

Port Charlotte.

Port Charlotte, Main St, PA48 7TU, ☎ (01496) 850360, *carl@portcharlottehot.demon.co.uk, Fax (01496) 850361*, ≤, –
closed 25 December – **Meals** (bar lunch)/dinner a la carte 12.90/24.95 **t.** 10.95 – **10 rm** 59.00/95.00 **t.**

Port Ellen.

Glenmachrie Farmhouse, PA42 7AW, Northwest : 4 ½ m. on A 846 ☎ (01496) 302560, *glenmachrie@lineone.net, Fax (01496) 302560*, « Working farm », –
Meals (by arrangement) 23.00 **s.** – **5 rm** 45.00/60.00 **s.**

ISLEORNSAY *Highland* 401 C 12 – *see Skye (Isle of).*

JEDBURGH *Borders* 401 402 M 17 *Scotland G.* – *pop. 4 768.*

See : *Town★ - Abbey★★* **AC** – *Mary Queen of Scots House Visitor Centre★* **AC** – *T Canongate Bridge★.*

Env. : *Waterloo Monument (※★★) N : 4 m. by A 68 and B 6400.*

Jedburgh, Dunion Rd ☎ (01835) 863587.

Murray's Green ☎ (01835) 863435.

Edinburgh 48 – Carlisle 54 – Newcastle upon Tyne 57.

Jedforest, Camptown, TD8 6PJ, South : 4 m. on A 68 ☎ (01835) 840222, *mail@jedfore hotel.freeserve.co.uk, Fax (01835) 840226,* ... TV P. MC AE VISA JCB *closed 25-26 December* – ***Bardoulets :*** **Meals** 28.00 (dinner) and lunch a la carte appro 13.90 **t.** 11.50 – **12 rm** 75.00/115.00 **t.** – SB.

Glenfriars Country House, The Friars, TD8 6BN, ☎ (01835) 862000, *bookings@ed road.demon.co.uk, Fax (01835) 862000,* ... TV P. MC VISA *closed 23 December-1 January* – **Meals** (booking essential) (dinner only) 17.50 **t.** 10.00 **6 rm** 35.00/50.00 **st.** – SB.

Hundalee House without rest., TD8 6PA, South : 1 ½ m. by A 68 ☎ (01835) 8630 *sheila.whittaker@btinternet.com, Fax (01835) 863011,* ... TV P. *March-October* – **5 rm** 25.00/46.00.

The Spinney without rest., Langlee, TD8 6PB, South : 2 m. on A 68 ☎ (01835) 8635 *thespinney@btinternet.com, Fax (01835) 864883,* ... TV P. MC VISA *mid March-mid November* – **3 rm** 35.00/48.00 **st.**

JOHN O'GROATS *Highland* 401 K 8 – *Shipping Services :* *see Orkney Islands.*

JOHNSTONE *Renfrewshire* 401 G 16 – *pop. 18 635.*

Cochrane Castle, Scott Av., Craigstone ☎ (01505) 320146.

Edinburgh 58 – Ayr 35 – Glasgow 13 – Greenock 18.

Shimla Pinks, 4 William St, PA5 8DS, ☎ (01505) 322588 – MC AE VISA *closed 1 January* – **Meals** - Indian - (dinner only) a la carte 11.10/19.85.

JURA (Isle of) *Argyll and Bute* 401 C 15 – *pop. 196.*

from Feolin to Isle of Islay (Port Askaig) (Serco Denholm Ltd) frequent services d (approx. 4 mn).

Craighouse – ✉ *Jura.*

Jura, PA60 7XU, ☎ (01496) 820243, *jurahotel@aol.com, Fax (01496) 820249,* ← Small Is Bay, ... – ... rest, P. MC AE VISA *closed 2 weeks Christmas and New Year* – **Meals** (bar lunch)/dinner a la carte 12.9 19.40 **st.** 10.65 – **16 rm** 34.00/95.00 **st.**, 1 suite.

KELSO *Borders* 401 402 M 17 *Scotland G.* – *pop. 6 167.*

See : *Town★ – The Square★★ – ←★ from Kelso Bridge.*

Env. : *Tweed Valley★★ – Floors Castle★* **AC**, *NW : 1½ m. by A 6089.*

Exc. : *Mellerstain★★ (Ceilings★★★, Library★★★)* **AC**, *NW : 6 m. by A 6089 – Waterloo Mon ment (※★★), SW : 7 m. by A 698 and B 6400 – Jedburgh Abbey★★* **AC**, *SW : 8½ m. by A – Dryburgh Abbey★★* **AC** *(setting★★★), SW : 10½ m. by A 6089, B 6397 and B 6404 – Sco View★★, W : 11 m. by A 6089, B 6397, B 6404 and B 6356 – Smailholm Tower★ (※★★), N 6 m. by A 6089 and B 6397 – Lady Kirk (Kirk o'Steil★), NE : 16 m. by A 698, A 697, A 6112 a B 6437.*

Berrymoss Racecourse Rd ☎ (01573) 23009.

Town House, The Square ☎ (01573) 223464 (Easter-October).

Edinburgh 44 – Hawick 21 – Newcastle upon Tyne 68.

The Roxburghe , Heiton, TD5 8JZ, Southwest : 3 ½ m. by A 698 ☎ (01573) 4503 *hotel@roxburghe.net, Fax (01573) 450611,* ←, ..., « Jacobean style country house », ... TV P – 60. MC AE VISA JCB **Meals** (dinner only and Sunday lunch) 27.50 **st.** 16.00 – **21 rm** 120.00/175.00 1 suite.

Ednam House, Bridge St, TD5 7HT, ☎ (01573) 224168, *ednamhouse@excite.co Fax (01573) 226319,* ←, « Part Georgian mansion on the banks of the River Tweed », ... – ... rm, TV P – 200. MC VISA *closed Christmas-8 January* – **Meals** (bar lunch Monday-Friday)/dinner 22.00 **st.** 8.5 **30 rm** 59.00/120.00 **st.** – SB.

Ednam *North : 2¼ m. on B 6461 – ✉ Kelso.*

Edenwater House , TD5 7QL, off Stichill rd ☎ (01573) 224070, *relax@edenwaterhouse.co.uk, Fax (01573) 224070,* ←, – TV P. MC VISA JCB.
closed first 2 weeks January – **Meals** *(closed Sunday-Thursday to non-residents)* (booking essential) (dinner only) (set menu only) 30.00 **st.** 12.00 – **4 rm** 60.00/80.00 **st.** – SB.

ENMORE *Perth and Kinross* 401 I 14 *Scotland G. – pop. 596.*
See : *Village*★.
Env. : *Loch Tay*★★.
Exc. : *Ben Lawers*★★, *SW : 8 m. by A 827.*
18 *Taymouth Castle, Aberfeldy ☎ (01887) 830228 – 18, 9 Mains of Taymouth ☎ (01887) 830226.*
Edinburgh 82 – Dundee 60 – Oban 71 – Perth 38.

Kenmore, PH15 2NU, ☎ (01887) 830205, *reservations@kenmorehotel.com, Fax (01887) 830262,* , , 18, , , – , rest, TV P – 35. MC AE VISA
Meals a la carte 11.75/27.15 **t.** 10.95 – **39 rm** 55.00/150.00 **st.** – SB.

ENTALLEN *Highland* 401 E 14 – ✉ *Appin (Argyll and Bute).*
Edinburgh 123 – Fort William 17 – Oban 33.

Ardsheal House , PA38 4BX, Southwest : ¾ m. by A 828 ☎ (01631) 740227, *info@ardsheal.co.uk, Fax (01631) 740342,* ←, « Part 18C country house », , – rest, P. MC AE VISA
closed mid December-mid January – **Meals** (residents only) (dinner only) (set menu only) 25.00/27.00 **st.** 12.00 – **6 rm** 48.00/96.00 **st.**

LBERRY *Argyll and Bute* 401 D 16 – *see Kintyre (Peninsula).*

LCHRENAN *Argyll and Bute* 401 E 14 *Scotland G.* – ✉ *Taynuilt.*
Env. : *Loch Awe*★★, *E : 1¼ m.*
Edinburgh 117 – Glasgow 87 – Oban 18.

Ardanaiseig , PA35 1HE, Northeast : 4 m. ☎ (01866) 833333, *ardanaiseig@clara.net, Fax (01866) 833222,* ← gardens and Loch Awe, « Country house in extensive informal gardens beside Loch Awe », , , – rest, TV P. MC AE VISA
closed 6 January-10 February – **Meals** (booking essential to non-residents) (light lunch)/dinner 38.50 **t.** 14.50 – **16 rm** 123.00/250.00 **t.** – SB.

Taychreggan , PA35 1HQ, Southeast : 1 ¼ m. ☎ (01866) 833211, *info@taychregganhotel.co.uk, Fax (01866) 833244,* ← Loch Awe and mountains, « Lochside setting », , , – P. MC AE VISA
Meals (booking essential to non-residents) (bar lunch) 35.00 **t.** 14.95 – **18 rm** 105.00/215.00 **t.**, 1 suite – SB.

LDRUMMY *Aberdeenshire* 401 L 12 *Scotland G.* – ✉ *Alford.*
See : *Castle*★ *AC.*
Exc. : *Huntly Castle (Heraldic carvings*★★★*) N : 15 m. by A 97 – Craigievar Castle*★, *SE : 13 m. by A 97, A 944 and A 980.*
Edinburgh 137 – Aberdeen 35.

Kildrummy Castle , AB33 8RA, South : 1 ¼ m. on A 97 ☎ (019755) 71288, *bookings@kildrummycastlehotel.co.uk, Fax (019755) 71345,* ← gardens and Kildrummy Castle, « 19C mansion in extensive park », – rest, TV P. MC AE VISA JCB
closed January – **Meals** 17.00/32.00 and dinner a la carte 22.00/31.00 **st.** 12.50 – **16 rm** 90.00/180.00 **st.** – SB.

LLEARN *Stirling* 401 G 15 – ✉ *Glasgow.*
Edinburgh 60 – Glasgow 19 – Perth 55 – Stirling 22.

Black Bull, 2 The Square, G63 9NG, ☎ (01360) 550215, *info@theblackbull-killearn.co.uk, Fax (01360) 550143,* , – rm, TV P. MC AE VISA
Meals 9.95/26.50 and a la carte 16.00/24.50 **t.** 14.95 – 9.95 – **14 rm** 50.00/75.00 **st.** – SB.

LLIECRANKIE *Perth and Kinross* 401 I 13 – *see Pitlochry.*

KILLIN *Stirling* 401 H 14 *Scotland G. – pop. 1 108.*

Exc. : *Loch Tay★★, Ben Lawers★★, NE : 8 m. by A 827 – Loch Earn★★, SE : 7 m. by A 827 a A 85.*

Killin ☎ (01567) 820312.

Breadalbane Folklore Centre, Main St ☎ (01567) 820254.

Edinburgh 72 – Dundee 65 – Perth 43 – Oban 54.

Dall Lodge Country House, Main St, FK21 8TN, ☎ (01567) 820217, *wilson@dallloc hotel.co.uk, Fax (01567) 820726,* – rest, VISA JCB
March-October – **Meals** (dinner only) 26.50 **st.** 9.75 – **10 rm** 49.50/99.00 **st.** – SB.

Breadalbane House, Main St, FK21 8UT, ☎ (01567) 820134, *stay@breadalbane48.f serve.co.uk, Fax (01567) 820798* – VISA JCB.
closed 15 December-February – **Meals** (by arrangement) 15.00 **st.** – **5 rm** 30.(44.00 **st.**

at Ardeonaig *(Perth and Kinross) Northeast : 6 ¾ m. – ✉ Killin (Stirling).*

Ardeonaig, South Lochtayside, FK21 8SU, ☎ (01567) 820400, *ardeonaighotel@ internet.com, Fax (01567) 820282,* – rest, VISA.
closed 22-29 December – **Meals** (dinner only) 35.00 **t.** 15.50 – **10 rm** 80.00/120.00 t SB.

KILMARNOCK *East Ayrshire* 401 402 G 17 *Scotland G.*

See : *Dean Castle (arms and armour★, musical instruments★).*

62 Bank St ☎ (01292) 678100.

Edinburgh 64 – Ayr 13 – Glasgow 25.

Travel Inn, Moorfield, KA1 2RS, Southwest : 2 m. by A 759 at junction with A ☎ (01563) 570534, *Fax (01563) 570536* – , rest, VISA.
Meals (grill rest.) – **40 rm** 41.95 **t.**

Travelodge, Kilmarnock bypass, Bellfield Interchange, KA1 5LQ, Southeast : 1 ½ m. A 735 at junction of A 71 with A 76 and A 77 ☎ (01563) 573810, *Fax (01563) 57381*
rm, VISA JCB.
Meals (grill rest.) – **40 rm** 39.95 **t.**

KILMARTIN *Argyll and Bute* 401 D 15.

Edinburgh 144 – Glasgow 99 – Oban 30 – Inverness 142.

Dunchraigaig House, PA31 8RG, South : 1 ½ m. on A 816 ☎ (01546) 605209, *dunchr @aol.com,* – VISA JCB.
Meals (by arrangement) 12.00 6.50 – **5 rm** 25.00/44.00 **t.** – SB.

KILMORE *Argyll and Bute* 401 D 14 – *see Oban.*

KILNINVER *Argyll and Bute* 401 D 14 – *see Oban.*

KINCLAVEN *Perth and Kinross* 401 J 14 – *pop. 394 – ✉ Stanley.*

Edinburgh 56 – Perth 12.

Ballathie House, Stanley, PH1 4QN, ☎ (01250) 883268, *email@ballathiehouseho com, Fax (01250) 883396,* « Country house in extensive grounds on banks of River Tay
– rest, – 60. VISA
Meals 15.00/36.50 **st.** 12.95 – **39 rm** (dinner included) 80.00/240.00 **st.**, 4 suites – S

KINCRAIG *Highland* 401 I 12 *Scotland G. – ✉ Kingussie.*

See : *Highland Wildlife Park★ AC.*

Exc. : *The Cairngorms★★ (★★★) – ★★★ from Cairn Gorm, E : 14 m. by A 9 and B 970.*

Edinburgh 119 – Inverness 37 – Perth 75.

Ossian, The Brae, PH21 1QD, ☎ (01540) 651242, *ossian@kincraig.cc Fax (01540) 651633,* – rest, VISA JCB
closed January and November – **Meals** (bar lunch)/dinner a la carte 17.45/26.45 **t.** 8.5 **9 rm** 31.00/62.00 **st.** – SB.

KINFAUNS *Perth and Kinross* 401 J 14 – *see Perth.*

SCOTLAND

INGUSSIE Highland 401 H 12 Scotland G. – pop. 1 298.

Env. : Highland Wildlife Park★ AC, NE : 4 m. by A 9.

Exc. : Aviemore★, NE : 11 m. by A 9 – The Cairngorms★★ (≤★★★) – ✻★★★ from Cairn Gorm, NE : 18 m. by B 970.

Gynack Rd ☎ (01540) 661374.

King St ☎ (01540) 661297 (May-September).

Edinburgh 117 – Inverness 41 – Perth 73.

Scot House, Newtonmore Rd, PH21 1HE, ☎ (01540) 661351, *shh@sirocco.globalnet.co.uk, Fax (01540) 661111* – ⇔ TV P. MC VISA JCB
closed January and 25 December – **Meals** (bar lunch)/dinner a la carte 20.50/29.50 **t.** 9.50 – **9 rm** (dinner included) 59.50/110.00 **t.** – SB.

Columba House, Manse Rd, PH21 1JF, ☎ (01540) 661402, *reservations@columba-hotel.co.uk, Fax (01540) 661652,* – ⇔ TV P. MC AE VISA JCB
closed 25 December – **Meals** 11.50/19.50 and a la carte 12.70/19.50 **t.** 9.00 – **10 rm** 40.00/70.00 **t.** – SB.

Hermitage, Spey St, PH21 1HN, ☎ (01540) 662137, *thehermitage@clara.net, Fax (01540) 662177,* – ⇔ rest, TV P. MC VISA.
closed 2 weeks November – **Meals** (by arrangement) 12.00 **s.** 8.00 – **5 rm** 26.00/44.00 **s.** – SB.

Avondale, Newtonmore Rd, PH21 1HF, ☎ (01540) 661731, *ray-morris@uk.ibm.com, Fax (01540) 661731,* – ⇔ TV P
closed 1 week Christmas – **Meals** (by arrangement) 10.00 **st.** – **5 rm** 35.00/44.00 **s.** – SB.

Homewood Lodge without rest., Newtonmore Rd, PH21 1HD, ☎ (01540) 661507, *homewood-lodge-kingussie.co.uk, Fax (01540) 661507,* ≤, – ⇔ TV P
4 rm 20.00/40.00.

The Cross with rm, Tweed Mill Brae, Ardbroilach Rd, PH21 1TC, ☎ (01540) 661166, *relax@thecross.co.uk, Fax (01540) 661080,* « Converted tweed mill » – ⇔ P. MC VISA.
March-November – **Meals** *(closed Tuesday)* (booking essential) (dinner only) 37.50 **st.** 14.50 – **9 rm** 160.00 **st.** – SB.

Le Grand Londres (GREATER LONDON) est composé de la City et de 32 arrondissements administratifs (Borough) eux-mêmes divisés en quartiers ou en villages ayant conservé leur caractère propre (Area).

NROSS Perth and Kinross 401 J 15 – pop. 5 047.

18, 18 Green Hotel, 2 The Muirs ☎ (01577) 863407 – 9 Milnathort, South St. ☎ (01577) 864069 – 9 Bishopshire, Kinnesswood ☎ (01592) 780203.

Heart of Scotland Visitor Centre, junction 6, M 90 ☎ (01577) 863680 (April-October).

Edinburgh 28 – Dunfermline 13 – Perth 18 – Stirling 25.

The Green, 2 The Muirs, KY13 8AS, ☎ (01577) 863467, *reservations@green-hotel.com, Fax (01577) 863180,* 18, squash – ⇔ rm, TV P – 140. MC AE VISA JCB
accommodation closed 22-30 December – **Meals** (bar lunch)/dinner 25.00/27.50 **t.** 5.60 – **46 rm** 80.00/160.00 **st.** – SB.

Windlestrae, The Muirs, KY13 8AS, ☎ (01577) 863217, *windlestrae@corushotels.com, Fax (01577) 864733,* – ⇔ rm, TV P – 200. MC AE VISA JCB
Meals (bar lunch Monday-Saturday)/dinner 18.00/28.00 **t.** 12.50 – 10.75 – **43 rm** 90.00/110.00 **st.**, 2 suites – SB.

Cleish Southwest : 4½ m. by B 996 off B 9097 – ✉ Kinross.

Nivingston House, KY13 0LS, ☎ (01577) 850216, *info@nivingstonhousehotel.co.uk, Fax (01577) 850238,* ≤, – ⇔ rest, TV P – 60. MC AE VISA
closed 2-14 January – ***Blues :*** **Meals** 13.00/25.50 **st.** 12.75 – **17 rm** 85.00/110.00 **st.** – SB.

NTORE Aberdeenshire 401 M 12.

Edinburgh 136 – Aberdeen 14 – Inverness 91.

Torryburn, School Rd, AB51 0XP, ☎ (01467) 632269, *vel@torryburn.uispa.co.uk, Fax (01467) 632271,* – ⇔ TV P – 100. MC AE VISA JCB.
closed 1 January – **Meals** (bar lunch Monday-Friday)/dinner a la carte 12.85/23.40 **t.** 8.15 – **11 rm** 39.50/62.50 **t.** – SB.

KINTYRE (Peninsula) *Argyll and Bute* 401 D 16 *Scotland G.*

See : *Carradale★ – Saddell (Collection of grave slabs★).*

18, 9 *Machrihanish, Campbeltown ✆ (01586) 810213 – 18 Dunaverty, Southend, Campbeltown ✆ (01586) 830677 – 9 Gigha, Isle of Gigha ✆ (01583) 505287.*

Campbeltown Airport : ✆ (01586) 553797.

from Claonaig to Isle of Arran (Lochranza) (Caledonian MacBrayne Ltd) frequent services daily (30 mn) – from Kennacraig to Isle of Islay (Port Ellen or Port Askaig) (Caledonian MacBrayne Ltd) 1-3 daily – from Kennacraig to Oban via Isle of Colonsay (Scalasaig) and Isle of Islay (Port Askaig) weekly.

Campbeltown.

Mackinnon House, The Pier ✆ (01586) 552056.
Edinburgh 176.

Craigard House, Low Askomil, PA28 6EP, East : ¾ m. by B 842 ✆ (01586) 554242, *info@craigard-house.co.uk, Fax (01586) 551137,* ≤, – rest, TV P. MC VISA
Meals (booking essential to non-residents) (dinner only) a la carte 16.45/23.25 **st.** 8.25 – **8 rm** 50.00/100.00 **st.** – SB.

Seafield, Kilkerran Rd, PA28 6JL, ✆ (01586) 554385, *gkennes@aol.com, Fax (01586) 552741* – rest, TV P. MC AE VISA
Meals a la carte 13.55/27.70 **t.** 8.95 – **9 rm** 45.00/75.00 **t.**

Carradale.

Dunvalanree ⛰, Port Rugh Bay, PA28 6SE, ✆ (01583) 431226, *eat@dunvalanree.com, Fax (01583) 431339,* ≤, – TV P. MC VISA JCB
Meals 18.00 **st.** 10.00 – **7 rm** (dinner included) 40.00/90.00 **st.** – SB.

Kilberry.

Edinburgh 165 – Glasgow 121 – Oban 75.

Kilberry Inn ⛰ with rm, PA29 6YD, ✆ (01880) 770223, *relax@kilberryinn.com, Fax (01880) 770223* – TV P. MC VISA
April-October – **Meals** *(closed Sunday dinner and Monday)* a la carte 12.40/19.40 **st.** 10 – **3 rm** 40.00/80.00 **st.**

Machrihanish – *pop. 5 722* – ✉ *Campbeltown.*

Edinburgh 182 – Oban 95.

Ardell House without rest., PA28 6PT, ✆ (01586) 810235, *Fax (01586) 810235,* ≤, TV P. MC VISA JCB.
March-October – **10 rm** 32.00/66.00 **t.**

Tarbert.

9 *Kilberry Rd, Tarbert ✆ (01880) 820565.*
Harbour St. ✆ (01880) 820429 (April-October).

Stonefield Castle ⛰, PA29 6YF, North : 2 m. on A 83 ✆ (01880) 820836, *enquiries@stonefieldcastle.co.uk, Fax (01880) 820929,* ≤, « 19C Scottish baronial castle, gardens », – rest, TV P. MC AE VISA JCB
Meals (dinner only) 25.00/32.50 **st.** 10.75 – **32 rm** (dinner included) 56.00/200.00 –

Columba, East Pier Rd, PA29 6UF, East : ¾ m. ✆ (01880) 820808, *columbahotel@fsdial.co.uk, Fax (01880) 820808,* ≤, « Lochside setting » – rest, TV P. MC AE VISA
closed 24-26 December – **Meals** (bar lunch)/dinner 22.50 **t.** 11.50 – **7 rm** 36.9 87.90 **t.**, 3 suites – SB.

Anchorage, Harbour St, PA29 6UD, ✆ (01880) 820881, *mail@anchoragetarbert.co.uk, Fax (01880) 820881,* « Quayside setting » – MC VISA JCB
closed January, Sunday and Monday October-May – **Meals** (dinner only) a la carte 17.2 26.15 **t.** 12.50.

KIRKCOLM *Dumfries and Galloway* 401 402 E 19 – *see Stranraer.*

KIRKCUDBRIGHT *Dumfries and Galloway* 401 402 H 19 *Scotland G.* – *pop. 4 188.*

See : *Town★.*

Env. : *Dundrennan Abbey★ AC, SE : 5 m. by A 711.*

18 *Stirling Cres. ✆ (01557) 330314.*

Harbour Sq ✆ (01557) 330494 (Easter-October).

Edinburgh 108 – Dumfries 28 – Stranraer 50.

Selkirk Arms, High St, DG6 4JG, ℘ (01557) 330402, *reception@selkirkarmshotel.co.uk, Fax (01557) 331639,* – TV P. MC AE VISA JCB
Meals (bar lunch)/dinner 22.95 **st.** 8.95 – **16 rm** 62.00/90.00 **st.** – SB.

Gladstone House without rest., 48 High St, DG6 4JX, ℘ (01557) 331734, *sue@gladstonehouse.freeserve.co.uk, Fax (01557) 331734,* – TV. MC VISA.
closed Christmas and New Year – **3 rm** 39.00/60.00 **s.**

RKMICHAEL *Perth and Kinross* 401 J 13.
Edinburgh 73 – Aberdeen 85 – Inverness 102 – Perth 29.

Cruachan Country Cottage, PH10 7NZ, on A 924 ℘ (01250) 881226, *cruachan@scot-holidays.com, Fax (01250) 881226,* – TV P. MC VISA
Meals (by arrangement) a la carte 13.05/20.40 **st.** – **3 rm** 28.50/49.00 **st.**

RKNEWTON *Edinburgh* 401 J 16 – *see Edinburgh.*

RKPATRICK DURHAM *Dumfries and Galloway* 401 402 I 18 – *see Castle Douglas.*

RKTON OF MARYCULTER *Aberdeenshire* 401 N 12 – *see Aberdeen.*

RKWALL *Orkney Islands* 401 L 7 – *see Orkney Islands (Mainland).*

RRIEMUIR *Angus* 401 K 13 – *pop. 6 347.*
St Malcolms Wynd ℘ (01575) 574097 (Easter-September).
Edinburgh 65 – Aberdeen 50 – Dundee 16 – Perth 30.

Purgavie Farm , Lintrathen, DD8 5HZ, West : 6 ¾ m. on B 951 ℘ (01575) 560213, *purgavie@aol.com, Fax (01575) 560213,* ≤ – TV P
Meals (communal dining) 13.00 **st.** – **3 rm** 30.00/50.00 **st.**

'LE OF LOCHALSH *Highland* 401 C 12 – *pop. 1 019.*
Car park ℘ (01599) 534276 (April-October).
Edinburgh 207 – Dundee 177 – Inverness 81 – Oban 123.

The Seafood, Railway Station, IV40 8AE, ℘ (01599) 534813, *jann@the-seafood-restaurant.co.uk, Fax (01599) 577230,* – rest. MC VISA
March-September – **Meals** - Seafood - (closed Sunday lunch) a la carte 14.70/32.45 9.95.

'LESKU *Highland* 401 E 9 *Scotland G.*
Env. : *Loch Assynt★★, S : 6 m. by A 894.*
Edinburgh 256 – Inverness 100 – Ullapool 34.

Newton Lodge , IV27 4HW, South : 2 m. on A 894 ℘ (01971) 502070, *newtonlge@aol.com, Fax (01971) 502070,* ≤ Loch Glencoul and mountains – TV P. MC VISA.
mid March-September – **Meals** (residents only) (dinner only) 16.00 **t.** 6.50 – **7 rm** 60.00 **t.**

DYBANK *Fife* 401 K 15 *Scotland G.* – *pop. 1 373.*
Env. : *Falkland★ – Palace of Falkland★ – Gardens★ – Village★, S : ½ m. by A 914 on A 912.*
Ladybank, Annsmuir ℘ (01337) 830320.
Edinburgh 38 – Dundee 20 – Stirling 40.

Redlands Country Lodge , Pitlessie Rd, KY15 7SH, East : ¾ m. by Kingskettle rd taking first left after railway bridge on unmarked road ℘ (01337) 831091, *redlandscountrylodge@btinternet.com, Fax (01337) 831091,* – TV P. MC VISA
closed December and January – **Meals** (by arrangement) 12.50 – **4 rm** 35.00/50.00 – SB.

IDE *Highland* 401 D 10 – ✉ *Gairloch.*
Edinburgh 233 – Inverness 75 – Kyle of Lochalsh 85.

The Old Smiddy, IV22 2NB, on A 832 ℘ (01445) 731425, *oldsmiddy@aol.com, Fax (01445) 731696,* – P. MC VISA
March-November – **Meals** (by arrangement) 25.00 **t.** – **3 rm** (dinner included) 84.00 **t.**

LAIRG *Highland* 401 G9 – *pop. 857.*

Ferrycroft Countryside Centre, Sutherland ✆ *(01549) 402160 (April- October).*
Edinburgh 218 – Inverness 61 – Wick 72.

Park House, IV27 4AU, ✆ (01549) 402208, *dwalkerparkhouse@tinyworld.co.*
Fax (01549) 402693, ≤, – rest, TV P. MC VISA JCB
closed Christmas and New Year – **Meals** 16.00 8.75 – **3 rm** (dinner included) 56.(
88.00 – SB.

LAMLASH *North Ayrshire* 401 E 17 – *see Arran (Isle of).*

LANGBANK *Renfrewshire* 401 G 16 *Scotland G.*
Env. : *Greenock (≤★★), W : 6 m. by A 8.*
Edinburgh 63 – Glasgow 17 – Greenock 7.

Gleddoch House , Old Greenock Rd, PA14 6YE, Southeast : 1 m. by B 7
✆ (01475) 540711, *reception@gleddochhouse.co.uk, Fax (01475) 540201,* ≤ Clyde a
countryside, 18, , – TV P – 40. MC AE VISA
Meals 16.00/35.00 and a la carte 18.00/41.00 **t.** 13.50 – **39 rm** 99.00/150.00 **t.** – SB.

LARGS *North Ayrshire* 401 402 F 16 *Scotland G. – pop. 11 297.*
See : *Largs Old Kirk★ AC.*
18 *Irvine Rd* ✆ *(01475) 674681.*
to Great Cumbrae Island (Cumbrae Slip) (Caledonian MacBrayne Ltd) frequent servi
daily (10 mn).
Railway Station, Main St ✆ *(01475) 689962 (April-October).*
Edinburgh 76 – Ayr 32 – Glasgow 30.

Priory House, Broomfield Pl, KA30 8DR, South : ½ m. by A 78 and Charles
✆ (01475) 686460, *enquiries@maksu-group.co.uk, Fax (01475) 689070,* ≤, – TV
60. MC AE VISA
Meals 15.00/27.00 and a la carte 13.20/26.20 **t.** 13.25 – **21 rm** 70.00/105.00 **t.** – SB.

Brisbane House, 14 Greenock Rd, Esplanade, KA30 8NF, ✆ (01475) 687200, *enquiri*
maksu_group.co.uk, Fax (01475) 676295, ≤ – TV P. MC AE VISA
Meals (bar lunch)/dinner 7.95/25.00 and a la carte 15.45/27.25 **t.** 13.00 – **23 rm** 77.
175.00 **t.** – SB.

LAUDER *Berwickshire* 401 L 16 – *pop. 2 199.*
9 *Calashiels Rd* ✆ *(01578) 722526.*
Edinburgh 27 – Berwick-upon-Tweed 34 – Carlisle 74 – Newcastle upon Tyne 77.

The Lodge, Carfraemill, TD2 6RA, Northwest : 4 m. by A 68 on A 697 ✆ (01578) 7507
enquiries@carfraemill.co.uk, Fax (01578) 750751 – TV P – 150. MC AE VISA J

Meals (grill rest.) a la carte 15.00/23.00 **t.** 8.00 – **10 rm** 48.00/70.00 **t.** – SB.

LEITH *Edinburgh* 401 K 16 – *see Edinburgh.*

LERWICK *Shetland Islands* 401 Q 3 – *see Shetland Islands (Mainland).*

LESLIE *Fife* 401 K 15 – *pop. 3 269.*
Edinburgh 35 – Dundee 26 – Perth 25 – Stirling 33.

Rescobie House, 6 Valley Drive, KY6 3BQ, ✆ (01592) 749555, *rescobiehotel@con*
serve.com, Fax (01592) 620231, – TV P. MC AE VISA JCB.
closed 24 December-5 January – **Meals** *(closed Saturday lunch and Sunday)* (book
essential) (dinner only) 9.50/26.50 and a la carte 18.90/31.90 **st.** 9.90 – **10 rm** 55.
90.00 **st.** – SB.

LEUCHARS *Fife* 401 L 14 – *pop. 5 207.*
Edinburgh 54 – Dundee 7 – Perth 29 – Stirling 52.

Drumoig, KY16 0BE, Northwest : 3 m. by A 919 off A 914 ✆ (01382) 541800, *drumoig@*
.co.uk, Fax (01382) 541122, ≤, , , 18 – TV P. MC AE VISA.
Meals 17.00 (dinner) and a la carte 10.50/17.50 **st.** 11.95 – **29 rm** 52.00/114.00 – SB.

Hillpark House without rest., 96 Main St, KY16 0HF, ✆ (01334) 839280, *enquiries@*
parkhouse.com, Fax (01334) 839280, – TV P. MC VISA
3 rm 29.00/50.00.

[L]EVERBURGH *Western Isles (Outer Hebrides)* 401 Y 10 – *see Lewis and Harris (Isle of).*

[L]EWIS and HARRIS (Isle of) *Western Isles (Outer Hebrides)* 401 A 9 *Scotland G.*

See : *Callanish Standing Stones*★★ – *Carloway Broch*★ – *St. Clement's Church, Rodel (tomb*★*).*

from Stornoway to Ullapool (Mainland) (Caledonian MacBrayne Ltd) 2 daily (2 h 40 mn) – from Kyles Scalpay to the Isle of Scalpay (Caledonian MacBrayne Ltd) (10 mn) – from Tarbert to Isle of Skye (Uig) (Caledonian MacBrayne Ltd) 1-2 daily (1 h 45 mn) – from Tarbert to Portavadie (Caledonian MacBrayne Ltd) (summer only) frequent services daily (25 mn) – from Leverburgh to North Uist (Otternish) (Caledonian MacBrayne Ltd) (1 h 10 mn).

LEWIS.

[B]reasclete.

Eshcol, 21 Breasclete, HS2 9ED, (01851) 621357, *neil@eshcol.com, Fax (01851) 621357*, ≤, – TV P
closed Christmas and New Year – **Meals** (by arrangement) 18.00 **st.** – **3 rm** 40.00/62.00.

Loch Roag, 22A Breasclete, HS2 9EF, (01851) 621357, *donald@lochroag.com, Fax (01851) 621357*, – TV P.
closed Christmas and New Year – **Meals** (by arrangement) 18.00 **st.** – **4 rm** 28.00/58.00.

[G]alson.

Galson Farm, South Galson, HS2 0SH, (01851) 850492, *galsonfarm@yahoo.com, Fax (01851) 850492*, ≤, « Working farm », – P. MO VISA.
Meals (by arrangement) (communal dining) 18.00 10.00 – **3 rm** 41.00/70.00.

[St]ornoway.

Lady Lever Park (01851) 702240.
26 Cromwell St (01851) 703088.

Cabarfeidh, Manor Park, HS1 2EU, North : ½ m. on A 859 (01851) 702604, *cabarfeidh@calahotels.com, Fax (01851) 705572* – rest, TV P – 300. MO AE VISA
closed 2 weeks January – **Meals** 22.50 (dinner) and a la carte 23.45/28.40 **st.** 8.95 – **46 rm** 75.00/98.00 **st.**

HARRIS.

[A]rdvourlie.

Ardvourlie Castle, HS3 3AB, (01859) 502307, *Fax (01859) 502348*, ≤ Loch Seaforth and mountains, « Restored Victorian hunting lodge on shores of Loch Seaforth », – rest, P.
May-September – **Meals** (residents only) (dinner only) (set menu only) 25.00 **st.** – **4 rm** (dinner included) 115.00/190.00 **st.** – SB.

[Le]verburgh.

Carminish, 1a Strond, HS5 3UD, South : 1 m. on Srandda rd (01859) 520400, *Fax (01859) 520307*, ≤ Carminish Islands and Sound of Harris, – P. MO VISA JCB.
April-September – **Meals** (by arrangement) (communal dining) 15.00 **st.** – **3 rm** 48.00 **st.**

[Sc]arista.

9 *(01859) 520236.*

Scarista House, HS3 3HX, (01859) 550238, *timandpatricia@scaristahouse.com, Fax (01859) 550277*, ≤ Scarista Bay, « Part 18C former manse », – P. MO VISA
closed 25 December and restricted opening in winter – **Meals** (booking essential for non-residents) (dinner only) (set menu only) 29.50 **t.** 11.00 – **5 rm** 75.00/130.00 **t.**

[Ta]rbert – *pop. 795* – *Harris.*

Leachin House, HS3 3AH, Northwest : 1 ¼ m. on A 859 (01859) 502157, *leachin.house@virgin.net, Fax (01859) 502157*, ≤ Loch Tarbert, – TV P. MO VISA.
closed 18 December-18 January – **Meals** (communal dining) 30.00 **st.** – **3 rm** 45.00/90.00 **st.** – SB.

Allan Cottage, HS3 3DJ, (01859) 502146, *Fax (01859) 502146* – TV
May-September – **Meals** (communal dining) 30.00 **s.** – **3 rm** 35.00/80.00 **s.**

Hillcrest, PA85 3BG, Northwest : 1 ¾ m. on A 859 (01859) 502119, ≤, – P.
Meals (by arrangement) (communal dining) 13.00 **st.** – **3 rm** 30.00/40.00 **st.**

LEWISTON *Highland* 401 G 12 *Scotland G.*

Env. : *Loch Ness*★★ – *The Great Glen*★.

Edinburgh 173 – Inverness 17.

Woodlands without rest., East Lewiston, IV63 6UJ, ✆ (01456) 450356, *drysdale@woo landsbandb.fsnet.co.uk, Fax (01456) 450199,* – TV P. MC VISA.
closed 25-26 December – **3 rm** 30.00/40.00.

Glen Rowan without rest., West Lewiston, IV3 6UW, ✆ (01456) 450235, *glenrowan lochness.demon.co.uk, Fax (01456) 450817,* – TV P. MC VISA.
closed 23-27 and 29 December-2 January – **3 rm** 45.00/50.00 **st.**

LINICLATE *Western Isles (Outer Hebrides)* 401 X/Y 11 – *see Uist (Isles of).*

LINLITHGOW *West Lothian* 401 J 16 *Scotland G.* – *pop. 13 689.*

See : *Town*★★ – *Palace*★★ *AC : Courtyard (fountain*★★*), Great Hall (Hooded Fireplace*★ *Gateway*★ – *Old Town*★ – *St. Michaels*★.

Env. : *Cairnpapple Hill*★ *AC, SW : 5 m. by A 706 – House of the Binns (plasterwork ceilings AC, NE : 4½ m. by A 803 and A 904.*

Exc. : *Hopetoun House*★★ *AC, E : 7 m. by A 706 and A 904 – Abercorn Parish Chur (Hopetoun Loft*★★*) NE : 7 m. by A 803 and A 904.*

Braehead ✆ (01506) 842585 – West Lothian, Airngath Hill ✆ (01506) 826030.

Burgh Halls, The Cross ✆ (01506) 844600 (April-October).

Edinburgh 19 – Falkirk 9 – Glasgow 35.

Champany Inn, Champany, EH49 7LU, Northeast : 2 m. on A 803 at junction with A 9 ✆ (01506) 834532, *reception@champany.com, Fax (01506) 834302,* – TV P. MC AE VISA JCB.
closed 25-26 December and 1-2 January – ***The Chop and Ale house :*** **Meals** (grill re a la carte 15.45/28.20 **t.** 13.50 – (see also ***The Restaurant*** below) – **16 rm** 115.(125.00 **st.**

The Restaurant (at Champany Inn H.), Champany, EH49 7LU, Northeast : 2 m. on A 8 at junction with A 904 ✆ (01506) 834532, *Fax (01506) 834302,* « Converted horse mill », – P. MC AE VISA JCB
closed 25-26 December, 1-2 January, Saturday lunch and Sunday – **Meals** - Beef specialit - and a la carte 30.50/45.90 **t.** 16.50.

Livingston's, 52 High St, EH49 7AE, ✆ (01506) 846565, – MC VISA.
closed 1 week June, 1 week October, first 2 weeks January, Sunday and Monday – **Me** (light lunch)/dinner 25.50/30.00 **t.** 12.00.

LIVINGSTON *West Lothian* 401 J 16 – *pop. 22 357.*

Bathgate, Edinburgh Rd ✆ (01506) 652232 – Deer Park C.C., Knightsridge ✆ (015 431037.

Edinburgh 16 – Falkirk 23 – Glasgow 32.

Jarvis International, Almondview, EH54 6QB, ✆ (01506) 431222, *j.livingston.gm@ja .co.uk, Fax (01506) 434666,* – rm, rest, TV P – 120. MC AE VISA JC
Meals *(closed Sunday lunch)* a la carte 18.25/26.25 **t.** 12.25 – 10.50 – **120 rm** 125.0 – SB.

Travel Inn, Deer Park Ave, Knightsridge, EH54 8AD, Northwest : 2 ¾ m. by A 899 junction 3 of M 8 ✆ (01506) 439202, *Fax (01506) 438912* – rm, rest, TV P. AE VISA.
Meals (grill rest.) – **83 rm** 41.95 **t.**

LOANS *South Ayrshire* 401 402 G 17 – *see Troon.*

LOCHBOISDALE *Western Isles (Outer Hebrides)* 401 Y 12 – *see Uist (Isles of).*

LOCHCARRON *Highland* 401 D 11 *Scotland G.* – *pop. 870.*

Env. : *Wester Ross*★★★ – *Loch Earn*★★.

Main St ✆ (01520) 722357 (April-October).

Edinburgh 221 – Inverness 65 – Kyle of Lochalsh 23.

Rockvilla, Main St, IV54 8YB, ✆ (01520) 722379, *rockvillahotel@btinternet.co Fax (01520) 722844,* Loch Carron – rest, TV. MC AE VISA JCB.
closed 25 December and 1 January – **Meals** (booking essential in winter) (bar lunch)/din a la carte 17.75/29.50 **t.** 7.50 – **4 rm** 34.00/60.00 **t.**

CHEARNHEAD Stirling 401 H 14 Scotland G.

Env. : Loch Earn★★.

Edinburgh 65 – Glasgow 56 – Oban 57 – Perth 36.

Mansewood Country House, FK19 8NS, South : ½ m. on A 84 ☎ (01567) 830213, *dianne@mansewood-fsbusiness.co.uk*, – rest, TV P. MC VISA.
Meals (residents only) (dinner only) 20.00 **st.** 10.00 – **6 rm** 34.00/44.00 – SB.

CHGILPHEAD Argyll and Bute 401 D 15 Scotland G. – pop. 2 421.

Env. : Loch Fyne★★, E : 3½ m. by A 83.

Blarbuie Rd ☎ (01546) 602340.

Lochnell St ☎ (01546) 602344 (April-October).

Edinburgh 130 – Glasgow 84 – Oban 38.

Empire Travel Lodge without rest., Union St, PA31 8JS, ☎ (01546) 602381, *empire-38 @lineone.net, Fax (01546) 606606* – TV P. MC VISA JCB.
closed Christmas and 1 January – **9 rm** 24.00/48.00 **s.**

Cairnbaan Northwest : 2¼ m. by A 816 on B 841 – ✉ Lochgilphead.

Cairnbaan, PA31 8SJ, ☎ (01546) 603668, *cairnbaan.hotel@virgin.net, Fax (01546) 606045*, – TV P. – 100. MC VISA
Meals (bar lunch)/dinner a la carte 15.50/29.50 **t.** 10.50 – **11 rm** 65.50/125.00 **t.** – SB.

When looking for a quiet hotel use the maps found in the introduction or look for establishments with the sign or .

CH HARRAY Orkney Islands 401 K 6 – see Orkney Islands (Mainland).

CHINVER Highland 401 E 9 Scotland G. – ✉ Lairg.

See : Village★.

Env. : Loch Assynt★★, E : 6 m. by A 837.

Kirk Lane ☎ (01571) 844330 (April-October).

Edinburgh 251 – Inverness 95 – Wick 105.

Inver Lodge, Iolaire Rd, IV27 4LU, ☎ (01571) 844496, *stay@inverlodge.com, Fax (01571) 844395*, ≤ Loch Inver Bay, Suilven and Canisp mountains, – rest, TV P. MC AE VISA JCB
April-October – **Meals** (bar lunch)/dinner 32.00/40.00 **st.** 11.25 – **20 rm** 80.00/140.00 **st.** – SB.

The Albannach, Baddidarroch, IV27 4LP, West : 1 m. by Baddidarroch rd ☎ (01571) 844407, *thealbannach@virgin.net, Fax (01571) 844285*, ≤ Loch Inver Bay, Suilven and Canisp mountains, – P. MC VISA JCB.
closed January-February – **Meals** *(closed Monday)* (booking essential) (dinner only) (set menu only) 35.00 **t.** 12.00 – **5 rm** (dinner included) 115.00/190.00 **t.**

Veyatie without rest., 66 Baddidarroch, IV27 4LP, West : 1 ¼ m. by Baddidarroch rd ☎ (01571) 844424, *veyatie@baddid.freeserve.co.uk*, ≤ Loch Inver Bay, Suilven and Canisp mountains, – P. MC VISA.
March-October – **3 rm** 36.00/52.00 **st.**

Davar without rest., Baddidarroch Rd, IV27 4LJ, West : ½ m. on Baddidarroch rd ☎ (01571) 844501, *jean@davar36.fsnet.co.uk*, ≤ Loch Inver Bay and Suilven – TV P.
March-November – **3 rm** 30.00/45.00 **st.**

CHMADDY Western Isles (Outer Hebrides) 401 Y 11 – see Uist (Isles of).

CHRANZA North Ayrshire 401 402 E 16 – see Arran (Isle of).

CHWINNOCH Renfrewshire 401 402 G 16 – pop. 4 228 – ✉ Paisley.

Edinburgh 61 – Glasgow 15 – Ayr 37 – Greenock 20.

East Lochhead Country House, Largs Rd, PA12 4DX, Southwest : 1 ¼ m. on A 760 ☎ (01505) 842610, *eastlochhead@aol.com, Fax (01505) 842610*, – TV P. MC AE VISA
Meals (by arrangement) 18.00 **st.** – **3 rm** 35.00/67.00 **st.** – SB.

SCOTLAND

LOCKERBIE *Dumfries and Galloway* 401 402 J 18 – *pop. 2 301.*

Corrie Rd (01576) 203363 – Lochmaben, Castlehill Gate (01387) 810552.

Edinburgh 74 – Carlisle 27 – Dumfries 13 – Glasgow 73.

Dryfesdale Country House, DG11 2SF, Northwest : 1 m. by Glasgow rd off B 7((01576) 202427, *reception@dryfesdalehotel.co.uk, Fax (01576) 204187,* ≤, – P. MC AE VISA JCB
Meals 11.00/30.00 and a la carte 20.50/27.00 **st.** 11.50 – **17 rm** 65.00/120.00 **st.** –

LOSSIEMOUTH *Moray* 401 K 10.

Edinburgh 181 – Aberdeen 70 – Fraserburgh 66 – Inverness 44.

Stotfield, Stotfield Rd, IV31 6QS, (01343) 812011, *reception@stotfield-hotel.co. Fax (01343) 814820,* ≤, – TV P. – 150. MC AE VISA JCB.
closed 22-27 December – **Meals** (bar lunch Monday-Saturday)/dinner 7.95/19 and a la carte 15.45/19.95 **st.** 9.50 – **45 rm** 48.00/86.00 **st.** – SB.

LUNDIN LINKS *Fife* 401 L 15.

Edinburgh 38 – Dundee 29 – Perth 31 – Stirling 46.

Old Manor, Leven Rd, KY8 6AJ, (01333) 320368, *enquiries@oldmanorhotel.co Fax (01333) 320911,* ≤, – rest, TV P. – 120. MC AE VISA JCB
closed 24-25 December – ***Aithernie :*** **Meals** (dinner only) 26.50/29.50 and a la carte 24. 33.50 **st.** 10.95 – ***Coachman's :*** **Meals** a la carte 13.25/23.95 **st.** 9.00 – **23 rm** 85. 180.00 **st.** – SB.

at Upper Largo *Northeast : 1¼ m. by A 915 on A 917 – Lundin Links.*

Scotland's Larder, KY8 6EA, (01333) 360414, *food@scotland-larder.co. Fax (01333) 360427* – P. MC VISA
closed January, lunch Friday and Saturday and Monday March-October – **Meals** (light lu only November-March) 6.95/23.50 and lunch a la carte 12.85/23.50 **t.** 10.50.

LUSS *Argyll and Bute* 401 G 15 *Scotland G. – pop. 402.*

See : *Village*★.

Env. : *E : Loch Lomond*★★.

Edinburgh 89 – Glasgow 26 – Oban 65.

Lodge on Loch Lomond, G83 8PA, (01436) 860201, *lusslomond@aol.co Fax (01436) 860203,* ≤ Loch Lomond, « Lochside setting », – TV P. – 40. MC VISA
Meals (buffet lunch Monday-Saturday)/dinner 15.95/19.95 and a la carte 19.95/26.8 12.95 – **28 rm** 99.00/135.00 **t.**, 1 suite – SB.

Inverbeg Inn, G83 8PD, North : 3 m. on A 82 (01436) 860678, *inverbeg@onyx. co.uk, Fax (01436) 860686,* ≤, – , rest, TV P. MC AE VISA
closed 25 December – **Meals** (bar lunch)/dinner 10.00/20.00 and a la carte 18.00/25.0 11.95 – **20 rm** 65.00/120.00 **t.** – SB.

LYBSTER *Highland* 401 K 9 *Scotland G.*

Env. : *The Hill o'Many Stanes*★, *NE : 3½ m. by A 9 – Grey Cairns of Camster*★, *N : 6 m. by and minor rd.*

Edinburgh 251 – Inverness 94 – Thurso 28 – Wick 14.

Portland Arms, Main St, KW3 6BS, on A 9 (01593) 721721, *info@portlandarms.co Fax (01593) 721722* – rest, TV P. – 200. MC AE VISA.
Meals (bar lunch Monday-Saturday)/dinner a la carte 13.50/18.00 **t.** 8.90 – **22** 48.00/80.00 **t.** – SB.

MACHRIHANISH *Argyll and Bute* 401 C 17 – *see Kintyre (Peninsula).*

MAYBOLE *South Ayrshire* 401 402 F 17 *Scotland G. – pop. 8 749.*

Env. : *Culzean Castle*★ *AC (setting*★★★*, Oval Staircase*★★*) W : 5 m. by B 7023 and A 719.*

Memorial Park.

Ladyburn, KA19 7SG, South : 5½ m. by B 7023 off B 741 (Girvan rd) (01655) 7405 *jh@ladyburn.demon.co.uk, Fax (01655) 740580,* ≤, , – TV P. MC AE VISA.
restricted opening in winter – **Meals** (booking essential to non-residents) 15.00/35.00 **5 rm** 115.00/175.00 **t.** – SB.

MELROSE *Borders* 401 402 L 17 *Scotland G. – pop. 2 414.*
See : *Town★ - Abbey★★ (decorative sculpture★★★) AC.*
Env. : *Eildon Hills (★★★) – Scott's View★★ – Abbotsford★★ AC, W : 4½ m. by A 6091 and B 6360 – Dryburgh Abbey★★ AC (setting★★★), SE : 4 m. by A 6091 – Tweed Valley★★.*
Exc. : *Bowhill★★ AC, SW : 11½ m. by A 6091, A 7 and A 708 – Thirlestane Castle (plasterwork ceilings★★) AC, NE : 21 m. by A 6091 and A 68.*
Melrose, Dingleton ☎ (01896) 822855.
Abbey House, Abbey St ☎ (01896) 822555 (Easter-October).
Edinburgh 38 – Hawick 19 – Newcastle upon Tyne 70.

Burts, Market Sq, TD6 9PL, ☎ (01896) 822285, *burtshotel@aol.com, Fax (01896) 822870,* – – 30. MC AE VISA JCB
Meals – (see ***The Restaurant*** below) – **20 rm** 50.00/92.00 **t.** – SB.

Dunfermline House without rest., Buccleuch St, TD6 9LB, ☎ (01896) 822148, *bestac com@dunmel.freeserve.co.uk, Fax (01896) 822148* – TV.
5 rm 25.00/50.00.

The Restaurant (at Burts H.), Market Sq, TD6 9PL, ☎ (01896) 822285, *Fax (01896) 822870* – P. MC AE VISA JCB
Meals 20.75/27.75 **t.** 11.95.

MELVICH *Highland* 401 I 8 *Scotland G. – ✉ Thurso.*
Env. : *Strathy Point★ (★★★, Ben Loyal★★), NW : 5 m. by A 836 and minor rd.*
Edinburgh 267 – Inverness 110 – Thurso 18 – Wick 40.

The Sheiling without rest., KW14 7YJ, on A 836 ☎ (01641) 531256, *thesheiling@bt internet.com, Fax (01641) 531256,* – P. MC VISA.
April-September – **3 rm** 50.00 **t.**

MEY *Highland* 401 K 8.
Edinburgh 302 – Inverness 144 – Thurso 13 – Wick 21.

Castle Arms, KW14 8XH, ☎ (01847) 851244, *info@castlearms.co.uk, Fax (01847) 851244* – TV P. MC VISA
Meals (bar lunch Monday to Saturday)/dinner a la carte 10.90/22.00 **st.** 8.50 – **8 rm** 39.00/58.00 **st.**

MILNGAVIE *Aberdeenshire* 401 L 12 – *see Aboyne.*

MILNGAVIE *East Dunbarton* 401 H 16.
Edinburgh 52 – Glasgow 8 – Dumfries 83 – Stirling 28.

Travel Inn, West Highland Gate, 103 Main St, G62 6JJ, ☎ (0141) 956 7835, *Fax (0141) 956 7839* – rm, rest, TV P. MC AE VISA JCB.
Meals (grill rest.) – **60 rm** 41.95 **t.**

MOFFAT *Dumfries and Galloway* 401 402 J 17 *Scotland G. – pop. 2 647.*
Exc. : *Grey Mare's Tail★★, NE : 9 m. by A 708.*
Coatshill ☎ (01683) 220020.
Unit 1, Ladyknowe ☎ (01683) 220620 (Easter-October).
Edinburgh 61 – Dumfries 22 – Carlisle 43 – Glasgow 60.

Auchen Castle, DG10 9SH, Southwest : 3 m. by A 701 off B 7076 (Abington rd) ☎ (01683) 300407, *reservations@auchen-castle-hotel.co.uk, Fax (01683) 300667,* – TV – 50. MC AE VISA
Meals (bar lunch Monday-Saturday)/dinner 25.00 and a la carte 12.75/23.75 **st.** 12.00 – **14 rm** 75.00/140.00 – SB.

Moffat House, High St, DG10 9HL, ☎ (01683) 220039, *Fax (01683) 221288,* – rest, TV P. MC AE VISA
Hopetoun's : Meals 9.50/24.00 and dinner a la carte 11.95/19.95 **t.** 12.00 – **21 rm** 60.00/94.00 – SB.

Beechwood Country House, Harthope Pl, DG10 9RS, North : ½ m. by A 701 ☎ (01683) 220210, *Fax (01683) 220889,* – rest, TV P. MC AE VISA
closed 1 January-15 February – **Meals** (dinner only) 22.50/26.00 **st.** 10.00 – **8 rm** 58.50/84.00 **st.** – SB.

Burnside without rest., Well Rd, DG10 9BW, East : ½ m. by Selkirk rd (A 708) taking first left turning before bridge ☎ (01683) 221900, *kate.burnside@btinternet.com, Fax (01683) 221900,* – TV P.
closed December and January – **3 rm** 30.00/50.00.

Hartfell House, Hartfell Cres, DG10 9AL, Northeast : ½ m. by Well St and Old We
(01683) 220153, *robert.white@virgin.net,* – rest,
closed Christmas and New Year and restricted opening in winter – **Meals** (by arrangem
13.50 **t.** 10.75 – **7 rm** 28.00/48.00 **t.**

Well View with rm, Ballplay Rd, DG10 9JU, East : ¾ m. by Selkirk rd (A
(01683) 220184, *info@wellview.co.uk, Fax (01683) 220088,* – VISA
closed 2 weeks February and 2 weeks October-November – **Meals** *(closed Saturday lu*
(booking essential) (set menu only) 15.00/30.00 **st.** 13.00 – **5 rm** 65.00/100.0C
1 suite – SB.

MONTROSE *Angus* 401 M 13 *Scotland G.* – *pop. 8 473.*

Exc. : *Edzell Castle★ (The Pleasance★★★) AC, NW : 17 m. by A 935 and B 966 –*
O'Mount Road★ (≤★★) N : 17 m. by B 966 and B 974 – Brechin (Round Tower★) W : 7 m
A 935 – Aberlemno (Aberlemno Stones★, Pictish sculptured stones★) W : 13 m. by A
and B 9134.

18, 18 *Traill Drive (01674) 672932.*

Bridge St (01674) 672000 (Easter-September).

Edinburgh 92 – Aberdeen 39 – Dundee 29.

Oaklands without rest., 10 Rossie Island Rd, DD10 9NN, on A 92 (01674) 672
oaklands@altavista.net, Fax (01674) 672018 – VISA
7 rm 20.00/40.00 **st.**

MOTHERWELL *North Lanarkshire* 401 I 16.

Edinburgh 38 – Glasgow 12.

Hilton Strathclyde, Phoenix Cres, Bellshill, ML4 3JQ, Northwest : 4 m. by A 721 on A
(01698) 395500, *reservations@strathclyde.stakis.co.uk, Fax (01698) 395511,*
, rest, – 400. VISA JCB.
Meals *(closed Saturday lunch)* a la carte 15.00/20.00 **st.** 11.80 – 13.50 – 10
145.00 **t.**

Express by Holiday Inn without rest., Strathclyde Country Park, Hamilton Rd,
3RB, Northwest : 4 ¼ m. by A 721 and B 7070 off A 725 (01698) 858
Fax (01698) 852375 – – 30. VISA JCB
120 rm 62.00 **st.**

Travel Inn, Edinburgh Rd, Newhouse, ML1 5SY, Northeast : 4 ¼ m. by A 723 on A
(01698) 860277, *Fax (01698) 861353* – rm, rest, – 80. VISA
Meals (grill rest.) – **40 rm** 41.95 **t.**

Travel Inn, Bellziehill Farm, Bellshill, ML4 3HH, Northwest : 3 ½ m. on A 721 at junc
with A 725 (01698) 740180, *Fax (01698) 845969* – , rm, rest,
VISA.
Meals (grill rest.) – **40 rm** 41.95 **t.**

MUIR OF ORD *Highland* 401 G 11 – *pop. 2 033.*

18 *Great North Rd (01463) 870825.*

Edinburgh 173 – Inverness 10 – Wick 121.

Dower House , Highfield, IV6 7XN, North : 1 m. on A 862 (01463) 870090, *info@*
dowerhouse.co.uk, Fax (01463) 870090, « Part 17C », – VISA
closed 2 weeks November and 25 December – **Meals** (set menu only) (booking essenti
non-residents) (lunch by arrangement)/dinner 35.00 **st.** 16.00 – **5 rm** 75.00/130.0C
1 suite – SB.

MULL (Isle of) *Argyll and Bute* 401 BC 14/15 *Scotland G.* – *pop. 2 838.*

See : *Island★ - Calgary Bay★★ – Torosay Castle* **AC** *(Gardens★ ≤★).*

Env. : *Isle of Iona★ (Maclean's Cross★, St. Oran's Chapel★, St. Martin's High Cro*
Infirmary Museum★ **AC** *(Cross of St. John★)).*

9 *Craignure, Scallastle (01680) 812487.*

from Craignure to Oban (Caledonian MacBrayne Ltd) frequent services daily (45 m
from Fishnish to Lochaline (Mainland) (Caledonian MacBrayne Ltd) frequent services
(15 mn) – from Tobermory to Isle of Tiree (Scarinish) via Isle of Coll (Arinagour) (Caledo
MacBrayne Ltd) 3 weekly (2 h 30 mn) – from Tobermory to Kilchoan (Caledonian MacBra
Ltd) 4 daily (summer only) (35 mn).

from Fionnphort to Isle of Iona (Caledonian MacBrayne Ltd) frequent services
(10 mn) – from Pierowall to Papa Westray (Orkney Ferries Ltd) (summer only) (25 mn).

The Pier, Craignure (01680) 812377 – The Pier, Tobermory (01688) 302182 (A
October).

SCOTLAND

rvaig – ✉ *Tobermory.*

Druimard Country House ⛭, PA75 6QW, on Salen rd ☎ (01688) 400345, *druimard.hotel@virgin.net, Fax (01688) 400345,* ≤, – rest, TV P. MC VISA JCB
April-October – **Meals** (booking essential to non-residents) (dinner only) (set menu only) 29.50 **t.** 8.95 – **7 rm** (dinner included) 95.00/160.00 **t.** – SB.

Balmacara, PA75 6QN, East : ¼ m. on B 8073 ☎ (01688) 400363, *balmacara@talk21.com, Fax (01688) 400363,* ≤, – rm, TV P.
Meals (by arrangement) 14.50 **st.** – **3 rm** 35.00/58.00 **st.** – SB.

uline.

Gruline Home Farm ⛭, PA71 6HR, ☎ (01680) 300581, *boo@gruline.com, Fax (01680) 300573,* ≤, – TV P. MC VISA JCB.
Meals (by arrangement) (communal dining) 23.00 **st.** – **3 rm** 62.00/74.00 **st.** – SB.

oran.

Tiroran House ⛭, PA69 6ES, ☎ (01681) 705232, *colin@tiroran.freeserve.co.uk, Fax (01681) 705240,* ≤ Loch Scridain, « Gardens », – TV P. MC VISA.
mid March-mid October – **Meals** (booking essential to non-residents) (dinner only) 25.00 **t.** 10.50 – **6 rm** 67.00/104.00 **t.**

bermory – *pop. 2 708.*

Erray Rd ☎ (01688) 302140.

Western Isles, PA75 6PR, ☎ (01688) 302012, *wihotel@aol.com, Fax (01688) 302297,* ≤ Tobermory harbour and Calve Island, – rest, TV P. MC AE VISA
closed 18-28 December – **Meals** (bar lunch)/dinner 25.00/27.50 **t.** 12.95 – **27 rm** 44.50/170.00 **t.**, 1 suite.

Tobermory, 53 Main St, PA75 6NT, ☎ (01688) 302091, *tobhotel@tinyworld.co.uk, Fax (01688) 302254,* ≤ – TV ♿. MC VISA
closed 1 week October and 1 week Christmas – ***Waters Edge :*** **Meals** (booking essential to non-residents) (dinner only) 19.50 **t.** 10.50 – **16 rm** 40.00/92.00 **t.** – SB.

Highland Cottage, Breadalbane St, PA75 6PD, via B 8073 ☎ (01688) 302030, *davidandjo@highlandcottage.co.uk, Fax (01688) 302727* – TV P. MC VISA JCB
restricted opening mid October-mid November and closed Christmas – **Meals** (booking essential to non-residents) (dinner only) 24.50 **t.** 11.50 – **6 rm** 65.00/99.00 **st.** – SB.

Fairways Lodge ⛭ without rest., Golf Course, PA75 6PS, Northeast : ½ m. by B 8073 ☎ (01688) 302238, *derekmcadam@fairwaysmull.com, Fax (01688) 302238,* ≤ Calve Island and Sound of Mull, 9, – TV P. MC VISA
5 rm 38.00/76.00.

IRCAR *Aberdeenshire* 401 N 12 – *see Murcar.*

SSELBURGH *East Lothian* 401 K 16 – *pop. 18 425.*

18 *Monktonhall ☎ (0131) 665 2005* – 18 *Royal Musselburgh, Prestongrange House, Prestonpans ☎ (01875) 810276* – 9 *Musselburgh Old Course, Balcarres Rd ☎ (0131) 665 6981.*

Old Craighall Service Area (A 1) ☎ (0131) 653 6172.

Edinburgh 6 – Berwick 54 – Glasgow 53.

Travel Inn, Carberry Rd, Inveresk, EH21 8PT, Southeast : 1 ½ m. on A 6124 ☎ (0131) 665 3005, *Fax (0131) 653 2270,* – rm, rest, TV ♿ P – 70. MC AE VISA
Meals (grill rest.) – **40 rm** 41.95 **t.**

IRN *Highland* 401 I 11 *Scotland G.* – *pop. 10 623.*

Env. : *Forres (Sueno's Stone★★) E : 11 m. by A 96 and B 9011 – Cawdor Castle★* **AC**, *S : 5½ m. by B 9090 – Brodie Castle★* **AC**, *E : 6 m. by A 96.*

Exc. : *Fort George★, W : 8 m. by A 96, B 9092 and B 9006.*

18, 9 *Seabank Rd ☎ (01667) 452103* – 18 *Nairn Dunbar, Lochloy Rd ☎ (01667) 452741.*

62 King St ☎ (01667) 452753 (April-October).

Edinburgh 172 – Aberdeen 91 – Inverness 16.

Golf View, 63 Seabank Rd, IV12 4HD, (01667) 452301, *rooms@morton-hotels.c Fax (01667) 455267,* ≤, ⛳, rest, 120. VISA
Restaurant : **Meals** (dinner only) 26.00 **st.** 12.00 – ***Conservatory :*** **Meals** 26.00 (ner) and lunch a la carte 12.00/23.00 **st.** 12.00 – **43 rm** 98.00/150.00 **st.**, 1 suite – S

Newton, IV12 4RX, (01667) 453144, *info@morton-hotels.com, Fax (01667) 454* 400. VISA
Meals (bar lunch)/dinner 26.00 **st.** 12.00 – **53 rm** 98.00/150.00 **st.**, 4 suites – SB.

Clifton House, Viewfield St, IV12 4HW, (01667) 453119, *macintyre@clara. Fax (01667) 452836,* ≤, « Antiques, memorabilia and objets d'art »,
closed mid December-mid January – **Meals** (booking essential) a la carte 25.00/31. 10.00 – **12 rm** 60.00/107.00 **t.**

Claymore House, 45 Seabank Rd, IV12 4EY, (01667) 453731, *claymorenairnscotla compuserve.com, Fax (01667) 455290,* VISA
Meals (bar lunch)/dinner a la carte 13.95/23.50 **st.** 8.95 – **13 rm** 42.50/95.0 1 suite – SB.

Boath House, Auldearn, IV12 5TE, East : 2 m. on A 96 (01667) 454896, *wendy@bo house.demon.co.uk, Fax (01667) 454896,* ≤, « Georgian mansion », VISA
closed last 3 weeks January – **Meals** *(closed Monday-Wednesday lunch)* (booking esser 24.95/35.00 **st.** 14.00 – **7 rm** 95.00/175.00 **st.** – SB.

Sunny Brae, Marine Rd, IV12 4EA, (01667) 452309, *Fax (01667) 454860,* ≤, VISA
mid March-October – **Meals** (booking essential to non-residents) (lunch residents o dinner 22.50 and a la carte 11.50/24.00 **st.** 10.00 – **9 rm** 49.00/95.00 **st.** – SB.

Links, 1 Seafield St, IV12 4HN, (01667) 453321, *linkcoop@aol.com, Fax (01667) 456* ≤, rest, VISA
February-October – **Meals** (dinner only) 15.50 and a la carte approx. 17.00 **st.** 10.0 **10 rm** 35.00/70.00 **st.** – SB.

Inveran Lodge without rest., Seabank Rd, IV12 4HG, (01667) 453731, *claymoren scotland@compuserve.com, Fax (01667) 455290,* VISA.
3 rm 60.00/70.00 **st.**

NETHERLEY *Aberdeenshire* 401 N 12 *Scotland G.* – Stonehaven.

Env. : *Muchalls Castle (plasterwork ceilings★★) AC, SE : 5 m. by B 979 – Deeside★★, N : by B 979 – Aberdeen★★, NE : 3 m. by B 979 and B 9077.*
Exc. : *Aberdeen★★, NE : 12 m. by – Dunnottar Castle★★ (site★★★) AC, S : 7 m. by B 9 Crathes Castle★★ (Gardens★★★) AC, NW : 13 m. by B 979, B 9077 and A 93.*
Edinburgh 117 – Aberdeen 12 – Dundee 54.

Lairhillock Inn, AB39 3QS, Northeast : 1 ½ m. by B 979 on Portlether (01569) 730001, *lairhillock@breathemail.net, Fax (01569) 731175* – VISA
closed 25-26 December, 1-2 January and Tuesday – **Meals** (dinner only and Sunday lu a la carte 15.00/21.50 **t.** 13.50.

NEWBURGH *Aberdeenshire* 401 N 12 *Scotland G.*

Exc. : *Pitmedden Gardens★★ AC, W : 6½ m. by B 9000 – Haddo House★ AC, NW : 14 m B 900, A 92 and B 9005.*
McDonald, Hospital Rd, Ellon (01358) 720576 – Newburgh-on-Ythan, E (01358) 789058.
Edinburgh 144 – Aberdeen 14 – Fraserburgh 33.

Udny Arms, Main St, AB41 6BL, (01358) 789444, *enquiry@udny.demon.co. Fax (01358) 789012,* 45. VISA
Meals – (see ***The Bistro*** below) – **23 rm** 68.00/85.00 **t.** – SB.

The Bistro (at Udny Arms H.), Main St, AB41 6BL, (01358) 789444, *Fax (01358) 7890* VISA
Meals (booking essential) a la carte 13.85/37.85 **t.**

NEW LANARK *Lanarkshire* 401 I 17.

Edinburgh 44 – Dumfries 55 – Glasgow 31.

New Lanark Mill, Mill One, New Lanark Mills, ML11 9DB, (01555) 667200, *hotel@ lanark.org, Fax (01555) 667222,* ≤, « Converted riverside cotton mill in restored Geor village » – 150. VISA
Meals 15.00/18.00 (dinner) and lunch a la carte 11.25/16.00 **t.** 9.00 – **38 rm** 57 75.00 **t.** – SB.

W SCONE *Perth and Kinross* 401 J 14 – *see Perth.*

WTON STEWART *Dumfries and Galloway* 401 402 G 19 *Scotland G.* – *pop. 2 543.*

Env. : *Galloway Forest Park*★, *Queen's Way*★ *(Newton Stewart to New Galloway) N : 19 m. by A 712.*

18, Kirroughtree Av., Minnigaff ☎ (01671) 402172 – 18 Wigtownshire County, Mains of Park, Glenluce ☎ (01581) 300420.

Dashwood Sq ☎ (01671) 402431 (Easter-October).

Edinburgh 131 – Dumfries 51 – Glasgow 87 – Stranraer 24.

Kirroughtree House, DG8 6AN, Northeast : 1 ½ m. by A 75 on A 712 ☎ (01671) 402141, *info@kirroughtreehouse.co.uk, Fax (01671) 402425,* ← woodland and Wigtown Bay, « 18C mansion in landscaped gardens », – rest, TV P. MC VISA
closed 2 January-mid February – **Meals** (booking essential to non-residents) 30.00 (dinner) and lunch a la carte 17.00/21.75 **t.** 14.50 – **15 rm** (dinner included) 95.00/210.00 **t.**, 2 suites – SB.

Creebridge House, Minnigaff, DG8 6NP, ☎ (01671) 402121, *info@creebridge.co.uk, Fax (01671) 403258,* – rest, TV P. MC AE VISA JCB
closed 24 and 26 December – ***Garden :*** **Meals** (dinner only and Sunday lunch) 21.00 and a la carte 14.85/26.85 **st.** 12.95 – ***Bridges Brasserie :*** **Meals** a la carte 14.85/26.85 **st.** 12.95 – **19 rm** 62.00/124.00 – SB.

Oakbank, Corsbie Rd, via Jubilee Rd off Dashwood Sq, DG8 6JB, ☎ (01671) 402822, *sheila atoakbank@aol.com,* – TV P
closed December – **Meals** (by arrangement) (communal dining) 12.00 **st.** – **3 rm** 22.00/44.00 **st.**

En saison, *surtout dans les stations fréquentées, il est prudent de retenir à l'avance. Cependant, si vous ne pouvez pas occuper la chambre que vous avez retenue, prévenez immédiatement l'hôtelier.*

Si vous écrivez à un hôtel à l'étranger, joignez à votre lettre un coupon-réponse international (disponible dans les bureaux de poste).

RTH BERWICK *East Lothian* 401 L 15 *Scotland G.* – *pop. 5 871.*

Env. : *North Berwick Law (✳★★★) S : 1 m. - Tantallon Castle★★ (clifftop site★★★) AC, E : 3½ m. by A 198 – Dirleton★ (Castle★ AC) SW : 2½ m. by A 198.*

Exc. : *Museum of Flight★, S : 6 m. by B 1347 – Preston Mill★, S : 8½ m. by A 198 and B 1047 – Tyninghame★, S : 7 m. by A 198 – Coastal road from North Berwick to Portseton★, SW : 13 m. by A 198 and B 1348.*

North Berwick, West Links, Beach Rd ☎ (01620) 895040 – 18 The Glen, East Links ☎ (01620) 892726.

Quality St ☎ (01620) 892197.

Edinburgh 24 – Newcastle upon Tyne 102.

The Marine, 18 Cromwell Rd, EH39 4LZ, ☎ (0870) 4008129, *heritagehotels_northberwick .marine@forte_hotels.com, Fax (01620) 894480,* ← golf course and Firth of Forth, heated, – TV P – 250. MC AE VISA
Meals (bar lunch Saturday) a la carte 15.70/24.95 **t.** 18.95 – 13.00 – **79 rm** 85.00/110.00 **t.**, 4 suites – SB.

Glebe House without rest., Law Rd, EH39 4PL, ☎ (01620) 892608, *jascott@tesco.net, Fax (01620) 892608,* « Georgian manse », – TV P.
closed Christmas and New Year – **3 rm** 40.00/80.00 **st.**

Beach Lodge without rest., 5 Beach Rd, EH39 4AB, ☎ (01620) 892257 – TV.
3 rm 30.00/50.00 **st.**

RTH QUEENSFERRY *Fife* 401 J 15 *Scotland G.* – ✉ *Inverkeithing.*

Env. : *Forth Bridges★★ (toll).*

Edinburgh 13 – Dunfermline 7 – Glasgow 42 – Kirkcaldy 16 – Perth 33.

Queensferry Lodge, St Margarets Head, KY11 1HP, North : ½ m. on B 981 ☎ (01383) 410000, *queensferry@corushotels.com, Fax (01383) 419708,* ← – TV P – 150. MC AE VISA
Meals a la carte 12.55/21.40 **st.** 9.95 – 10.50 – **77 rm** 89.00/105.00 **st.** – SB.

RTH UIST *Western Isles (Outer Hebrides)* 401 XY 10/11 – *see Uist (Isles of).*

OBAN *Argyll and Bute* 401 D 14 *Scotland G. – pop. 8 203.*

Exc. : *Loch Awe*★★, *SE : 17 m. by A 85 – Bonawe Furnace*★, *E : 12 m. by A 85 – Crua*
Power Station★ **AC**, *E : 16 m. by A 85 – Sea Life Centre*★ **AC**, *N : 14 m. by A 828.*

18 *Glencruitten, Glencruitten Rd* ✆ *(01631) 562868.*

Access to Glasgow by helicopter.

to Isle of Mull (Craignure) (Caledonian MacBrayne Ltd) (45 mn) – to South Uist (L boisdale) via Isle of Barra (Castlebay) (Caledonian MacBrayne Ltd) (summer only) – to Is Tiree (Scarinish) via Isle of Mull (Tobermory) and Isle of Coll (Arinagour) (Caledonian Brayne Ltd) – to Isle of Islay (Port Askaig) and Kintyre Peninsula (Kennacraig) via Is Colonsay (Scalasaig) (Caledonian MacBrayne Ltd) (summer only) – to Isle of Lismore nacroish) (Caledonian MacBrayne Ltd) 2-3 daily (except Sunday) (50 mn) – to Isle of Colc (Scalasaig) (Caledonian MacBrayne Ltd) 3 weekly (2 h).

Argyll Sq ✆ *(01631) 563122.*

Edinburgh 123 – Dundee 116 – Glasgow 93 – Inverness 118.

Manor House, Gallanach Rd, PA34 4LS, ✆ (01631) 562087, *manorhouseoban@aol.*
Fax (01631) 563053, ≤ Oban harbour and bay, – TV P. MO AE VISA
closed Sunday dinner, Tuesday lunch and Monday November-February – **Meals** (lunc arrangement)/dinner 27.50 **t.** 12.10 – **11 rm** (dinner included) 110.00/160.00 **t.** –

Dungallan House, Gallanach Rd, PA34 4PD, ✆ (01631) 563799, *welcome@dung hotel-oban.co.uk, Fax (01631) 566711,* ≤ Kerrera and Isle of Mull, – TV P. MO JCB
closed January-February – **Meals** (booking essential to non-residents) 15.00/25.00 **t.** – **13 rm** 48.00/90.00 **t.** – SB.

Kilchrenan House without rest., Corran Esplanade, PA34 5AQ, ✆ (01631) 562
kilchrenanhouse@supanet.com, Fax (01631) 562663, ≤ Oban bay, Kerrera and Isle of M
TV P. MO VISA.
March-October – **10 rm** 30.00/65.00 **t.**

The Barriemore without rest., Corran Esplanade, PA34 5AQ, ✆ (01631) 566
reception@barriemore-hotel.co.uk, Fax (01631) 566356, ≤ Oban bay, Kerrera and Is Mull – TV P. MO VISA
restricted opening in winter – **13 rm** 30.00/63.00 **st.**

Glenburnie without rest., Corran Esplanade, PA34 5AQ, ✆ (01631) 562089, *gra strachan@btinternet.com, Fax (01631) 562089,* ≤ Oban bay, Kerrera and Isle of Mull – P. MO VISA.
March-November – **13 rm** 32.00/70.00 **st.**, 1 suite.

Alltavona without rest., Corran Esplanade, PA34 5AQ, ✆ (01631) 565067, *carol@allta .co.uk, Fax (01631) 565067,* ≤ Oban bay, Kerrera and Isle of Mull – TV P. MO VISA.
February-November – **8 rm** .

Glenbervie, Dalriach Rd, PA34 5JD, via A 85 (Fort William) and Deanery
✆ (01631) 564770, *glenbervie@lineone.com, Fax (01631) 566723,* ≤ – TV P.
Meals (by arrangement) – **8 rm** 20.00/40.00 **st.**

Ee-usk, 104 George St, PA34 5NT, ✆ (01631) 565666, *eeusk.fishcafe@virgin.*
Fax (01631) 565666 – MO VISA
Meals a la carte 16.45/27.40 **t.** 9.95.

The Waterfront, No 1, The Pier, PA34 4LW, ✆ (01631) 563110, *Fax (01631) 56*
≤ Oban harbour and bay, « Quayside setting » – MO AE VISA JCB
closed 25 December-14 February – **Meals** - Seafood - a la carte 13.50/22.00 **t.** 10.75.

at Kilmore *South : 4 m. on A 816 –* ✉ *Oban.*

Invercairn without rest., PA34 4XX, East : 1 m. on Musdale rd ✆ (01631) 770
invercairn.kilmore@virgin.net, Fax (01631) 770301, ≤, – P.
April-September – **3 rm** 36.00/52.00 **s.**

at Kilninver *Southwest : 8 m. by A 816 –* ✉ *Oban.*

Knipoch House, PA34 4QT, Northeast : 1 ½ m. on A 816 ✆ (01852) 316251, *recept knipochhotel.co.uk, Fax (01852) 316249,* ≤, – rest, TV P. MO AE VISA
Meals (bar lunch)/dinner 29.50/39.50 and a la carte 12.90/27.50 **t.** 13.50 – 1
72.50/145.00 **st.**, 1 suite.

Particularly pleasant hotels and restaurants are shown in the Guide by a red symbol.

Please send us the names of anywhere you have enjoyed your stay.

Your **Michelin Guide** will be even better.

LDMELDRUM *Aberdeenshire* 401 N 11 *Scotland G.*

Exc. : *Haddo House*★, *NE : 9 m. by B 9170 on B 9005.*

Oldmeldrum, Kirkbrae ✆ *(01651) 872648.*

Edinburgh 140 – Aberdeen 17 – Inverness 87.

Meldrum House, AB51 0AE, North : 1 ½ m. on A 947 ✆ (01651) 872294, *dpmeldrum@aol.com, Fax (01651) 872464,* ←, « Part 13C baronial house », – rest, TV P – 50. MO VISA.
Meals (dinner only and Sunday lunch)/dinner 28.50/31.50 **t.** 13.25 – **9 rm** 95.00/130.00 **t.** – SB.

Cromlet Hill without rest., South Rd, AB51 0AB, ✆ (01651) 872315, *Fax (01651) 872164,* – TV P.
closed 1 week spring, 2 weeks autumn and Christmas – **2 rm** 35.00/55.00, 1 suite.

NICH *Highland* 401 E 13 – ✉ *Fort William.*

Edinburgh 123 – Glasgow 93 – Inverness 79 – Oban 39.

The Lodge on the Loch, Creag Dhu, PH33 6RY, on A 82 ✆ (01855) 821237, *reservations@freedomglen.co.uk, Fax (01855) 821463,* ← Loch Linnhe and mountains, – TV P. MO VISA
April-mid November and Christmas-New Year – **Meals** (bar lunch)/dinner 29.50 **t.** 12.00 – **17 rm** (dinner included) 73.00/210.00 **t.**, 1 suite – SB.

Allt-nan-Ros, PH33 6RY, on A 82 ✆ (01855) 821210, *reception@allt-nan-ros.co.uk, Fax (01855) 821462,* ← Loch Linnhe and mountains, – rest, TV P. MO AE O VISA
Meals (bar lunch Monday-Saturday)/dinner 29.95 **t.** 12.95 – **20 rm** (dinner included) 73.00/167.00 **t.** – SB.

Onich, PH33 6RY, on A 82 ✆ (01855) 821214, *reservations@onich-fortwilliam.co.uk, Fax (01855) 821484,* ← Loch Linnhe and mountains, « Lochside setting », – rest, TV P. MO AE O VISA
Meals (bar lunch)/dinner 28.00/26.00 and a la carte 11.10/23.00 **t.** 10.95 – **27 rm** 68.00/126.00 **t.** – SB.

***Groß-London** (GREATER LONDON) besteht aus der City und 32 Verwaltungsbezirken (Borough). Diese sind wiederum in kleinere Bezirke (Area) unterteilt, deren Mittelpunkt ehemalige Dörfer oder Stadtviertel sind, die oft ihren eigenen Charakter bewahrt haben.*

RKNEY ISLANDS *Orkney Islands* 401 KL 6/7 *Scotland G. – pop. 19 612.*

See : *Old Man of Hoy*★★★ – *Islands*★★ – *Maes Howe*★★ *AC* – *Skara Brae*★★ *AC* – *Corrigal Farm Museum*★ *AC* – *Brough of Birsay*★ *AC* – *Birsay* (←★) – *Ring of Brodgar*★ – *Unstan Cairn*★.

see Kirkwall.

service between Isle of Hoy (Longhope), Isle of Hoy (Lyness), Isle of Flotta and Houton (Orkney Ferries Ltd) – from Stromness to Scrabster (P & O Scottish Ferries) (2 h) – from Stromness to Shetland Islands (Lerwick) and Aberdeen (P & O Scottish Ferries) 2 weekly – from Kirkwall to Westray, Stronsay via Eday and Sanday (Orkney Ferries Ltd) – from Tingwall to Wyre via Egilsay and Rousay (Orkney Ferries Ltd) – from Kirkwall to Shapinsay (Orkney Ferries Ltd) (25 mn) – from Stromness to Isle of Hoy (Moness) and Graemsay (Orkney Ferries Ltd) – from Kirkwall to North Ronaldsay (Orkney Ferries Ltd) weekly (2 h 40 mn) – from Kirkwall to Invergordon (Orcargo Ltd) daily (8 h 30 mn) – from Houton to Isle of Hoy (Lyness), Flotta and Longhope (Orkney Ferries Ltd) – from Stromness to Graemsay via Isle of Hoy (Orkney Ferries Ltd).

from Burwick (South Ronaldsay) to John O'Groats (John O'Groats Ferries) 4-5 daily (45 mn).

urray.

Ankersted, KW17 2SS, East : ½ m. on A 961 ✆ (01856) 731217, *ankersted@tinyworld.co.uk, Fax (01856) 731217,* ←, – rm, TV P.
Meals (by arrangement) 12.50 **s.** – **4 rm** 18.00/36.00 **s.**

ounby.

Smithfield, KW17 2HT, ✆ (01856) 771215, *Fax (01856) 771494* – TV P. MO VISA
April-October – **Meals** 16.00 (dinner) and a la carte 7.40/20.25 **st.** 7.80 – **6 rm** 30.00/60.00 **st.** – SB.

Kirkwall *Scotland G.* – pop. 5 952.

See : *Kirkwall*★★ – *St. Magnus Cathedral*★★ – *Western Mainland*★★, *Eastern Mainland (Itali Chapel*★*)* – *Earl's Palace*★ AC – *Tankerness House Museum*★ AC – *Orkney Farm and Fo Museum*★.

Grainbank ☎ *(01856) 872457.*

Kirkwall Airport : ☎ (01856) 872421, S : 3½ m.

6 Broad St ☎ (01856) 872856.

Ayre, Ayre Rd, KW15 1QX, ☎ (01856) 873001, *ayre.hotel@orkney.com, Fax (01856) 8762* – rm, TV P – 200. MC AE VISA
closed 25 December and 1 January – **Meals** 6.95 (lunch) and dinner a la carte 11.40/22.65 8.60 – **33 rm** 66.00/100.00 **t.**

Foveran, St Ola, KW15 1SF, Southwest : 3 m. on A 964 ☎ (01856) 872389, *fover. hotel@aol.com, Fax (01856) 876430,* « Overlooking Scapa Flow », – rest, TV MC VISA JCB.
restricted opening in winter – **Meals** (lunch by arrangement)/dinner a la carte 17.4 29.40 **t.** 8.95 – **8 rm** 45.00/70.00 **t.**

Queens, Shore St, KW15 1LG, ☎ (01856) 872200, *Fax (01856) 873871* – rest, TV. VISA.
closed 25-26 December and 1-2 January – **Meals** (in bar) a la carte 11.20/22.70 **st.** 8.50 9 **rm** 35.00/50.00 **st.**

St Ola without rest., Harbour St, KW15 1LE, ☎ (01856) 875090, *Fax (01856) 875090* – TV MC VISA JCB.
closed Christmas and New Year – **6 rm** 32.00/46.00 **st.**

Lav'rockha, Inganess Rd, KW15 1SP, Southeast : 1 ¼ m. by A 960 ☎ (01856) 8761C *lavrockha@orkney.com, Fax (01856) 876103,* – TV P. MC VISA JCB.
Meals (by arrangement) 12.95 **st.** 8.00 – **5 rm** 30.00/48.00 **st.** – SB.

Polrudden, Peerie Sea Loan, KW15 1UH, West : 1 m. by Pickaquoy Rd ☎ (01856) 8747 *linda@polrudden.com, Fax (01856) 870950* – rest, TV P. MC VISA JCB.
closed 25 December and 1 January – **Meals** (by arrangement) 13.50 – **7 rm** 30.0 48.00 **st.**

Brekk-Ness without rest., Muddisdale Rd, KW15 1RS, West : ¾ m. by Pickaquoy R ☎ (01856) 874317, *sandrabews@aol.com, Fax (01856) 874317* – TV P. MC VISA JCB
closed 2 weeks December – **11 rm** 32.00/48.00.

Loch Harray.

Merkister, KW17 2LF, off A 986 ☎ (01856) 771366, *merkister-hotel@ecosse.ne Fax (01856) 771515,* ≤ Loch Harray, « Lochside setting », – rest, TV P. MC AE VI JCB
closed 24-26 and 31 December and 1-3 January – **Meals** (bar lunch Monday-Saturday dinner 20.00/24.00 and a la carte 18.00/31.00 **t.** 8.00 – **14 rm** 45.00/100.00 **t.** – SB.

St Margaret's Hope.

Creel with rm, Front Rd, KW17 2SL, ☎ (01856) 831311, *alan@thecreel.freeserve.co.uk,* ≤ TV P. MC VISA.
closed January-March and November – **Meals** (dinner only) 28.00/35.00 **t.** 11.50 – **3 r** 45.00/70.00 **t.**

Stenness.

Standing Stones, KW16 3JX, on A 965 ☎ (01856) 850449, *standingstones@sol.co.u Fax (01856) 851262,* – rm, TV P. MC AE VISA JCB
closed 22 December-7 January – **Meals** *(closed October-April)* (booking essential) (b lunch)/dinner 17.00 and a la carte 9.15/28.95 **st.** 8.50 – **17 rm** 40.00/76.00 **st.** – SB.

Stromness *Scotland G.*

See : *Town*★ - *Pier Gallery (collection of abstract art*★*).*

Stenigar without rest., Ness Rd, KW16 3DW, South : ½ m. by Main St ☎ (01856) 85043 ≤, – TV P.
restricted opening in winter – **4 rm** 50.00 **s.**

Thira, Innertown, KW16 3JP, Northwest : 1 ½ m. by Back Rd, turning right at mi roundabout, taking first right onto unmarked road and then left at two junctior ☎ (01856) 851181, *alisonsbbthira@hotmail.com, Fax (01856) 851182,* ≤ Hoy Island ar Sound, – TV P.
Meals (by arrangement) (communal dining) 10.00 – **4 rm** 24.00/48.00.

ISLEY *Renfrewshire* 401 G 16 – *pop. 43 602.*

Braehead *(0141) 884 2292.*

Edinburgh 56 – Ayr 36 – Glasgow 11 – Greenock 16 – Kilmarnock 22.

Travel Inn, Phoenix Retail Park, Linwood, PA1 2BH, West : 2 ¼ m. by A 761 (0141) 887 4865, *Fax (0141) 887 2799* – rm, rest, 30. VISA.
Meals (grill rest.) – **40 rm** 41.95 **t.**

Myfarrclan, 146 Corsebar Rd, PA2 9NA, Southwest : 1 ¾ m. on B 775 (0141) 884 8285, *myfarrclan_qwest@compuserve.com, Fax (0141) 581 1566,* – . VISA.
Meals (by arrangement) (communal dining) 18.00 **st.** – **3 rm** 60.00/70.00 **st.** – SB.

EAT INN *Fife* 401 L 15 *Scotland G.* – *Cupar.*

Exc. : *Kellie Castle*★, *SE : 7½ m. by B 940 and minor roads.*

Edinburgh 45 – Dundee 21 – Perth 28.

The Peat Inn with rm, KY15 5LH, (01334) 840206, *reception@thepeatinn.co.uk, Fax (01334) 840530,* – rest, VISA
closed 25 December, 1 January, Sunday and Monday – **Meals** (booking essential) (set menu only at lunch)/dinner 19.50/30.00 and dinner a la carte 28.00/35.50 **st.** 16.00 – **1 rm** 95.00 **st.**, **7 suites** 145.00 **st.** – SB.

EEBLES *Borders* 401 402 K 17 *Scotland G.* – *pop. 7 065.*

Env. : *Tweed Valley*★★.

Exc. : *Traquair House*★★ *AC, SE : 7 m. by B 7062 – Rosslyn Chapel*★★ *AC, N : 16½ m. by A 703, A 6094, B 7026 and B 7003.*

Kirkland St. *(01721) 720197.*

High St *(01721) 720138.*

Edinburgh 24 – Hawick 31 – Glasgow 53.

Cringletie House , EH45 8PL, North : 3 m. on A 703 (01721) 730233, *enquiries@cringletie.com, Fax (01721) 730244,* , « Victorian country house built in Scottish Baronial style in extensive grounds », , – , rest, – 30. VISA
Meals 10.95/35.00 **st.** 16.00 – **14 rm** 75.00/220.00 **st.** – SB.

Peebles Hydro, Innerleithen Rd, EH45 8LX, (01721) 720602, *reservations@peebleshotelhydro.co.uk, Fax (01721) 722999,* , , , , , , – – 450. VISA.
Meals 18.50/27.00 **st.** 13.50 – **131 rm** (dinner included) 100.25/191.00 **st.**, 2 suites – SB.

Castle Venlaw , EH45 8QG, North : 1 ¼ m. by A 703 (01721) 720384, *stay@venlaw.co.uk, Fax (01721) 724066,* , – – 35. VISA
Meals (booking essential to non-residents) (bar lunch)/dinner 25.00/28.00 **t.** 10.95 – **12 rm** 85.00/140.00 **t.**, 1 suite – SB.

Park, Innerleithen Rd, EH45 8BA, (01721) 720451, *reserve@parkpeebles.co.uk, Fax (01721) 723510,* – VISA
Meals 21.50/22.50 (dinner) and a la carte 11.90/18.50 **st.** 12.75 – **24 rm** (dinner included) 75.00/162.00 **st.** – SB.

Dilkusha House without rest., Chambers Terr, EH45 9DZ, South : ½ m. by B 7062 taking first right after bridge onto Caledonian Rd then first left onto Frankscroft (01721) 722888, *forbes_dilkusha@hotmail.com, Fax (01721) 722888,* – . VISA.
3 rm 35.00/56.00 **t.**

Woodlands without rest., EH45 8QY, North : 1 ¼ m. by A 703 (01721) 729882, *woodlands7@btinternet.com,* – rm,
closed Christmas and New Year – **3 rm** 25.00/40.00.

Rowanbrae without rest., 103 Northgate, EH45 8BU, (01721) 721630, *john@rowanbrae.freeserve.co.uk, Fax (01721) 723324* – .
3 rm 25.00/42.00.

Besonders angenehme Hotels oder Restaurants sind im Führer rot gekennzeichnet.
Sie können uns helfen, wenn Sie uns die Häuser angeben, in denen Sie sich besonders wohl gefühlt haben.
Jährlich erscheint eine komplett überarbeitete Ausgabe aller Roten **Michelin-Führer.**

... ,
XXXXX ... X,

PERTH *Perth and Kinross* **401** J 14 *Scotland G. – pop. 14 432.*

See : *City★ – Black Watch Regimental Museum★* Y **M1** *– Georgian Terraces★* Y *– Muse... and Art Gallery★* Y **M2.**

Env. : *Scone Palace★★* **AC**, *N : 2 m. by A 93* Y *– Branklyn Garden★* **AC**, *SE : 1 m. by A 85 ... Kinnoull Hill (≤★) SE : 1¼m. by A 85* Z *– Huntingtower Castle★* **AC**, *NW : 3 m. by A 85 ... Elcho Castle★* **AC**, *SE : 4 m. by A 912 –* Z *– and Rhynd rd.*

Exc. : *Abernethy (11C Round Tower★), SE : 8 m. by A 912 –* Z *– and A 913.*

18 Craigie Hill, Cherrybank ☏ (01738) 624377 Z *– 18 King James VI, Moncreiffe Isl... ☏ (01738) 625170* Z *– 18 Murrayshall, New Scone ☏ (01738) 551171* Y *– 18 North Inch, ... Perth & Kinross Council, 5 High St. ☏ (01738) 636481* Y.

Lower City Mills, West Mill St ☏ (01738) 450600.

Edinburgh 44 – Aberdeen 86 – Dundee 22 – Dunfermline 29 – Glasgow 64 – Inverness 1... Oban 94.

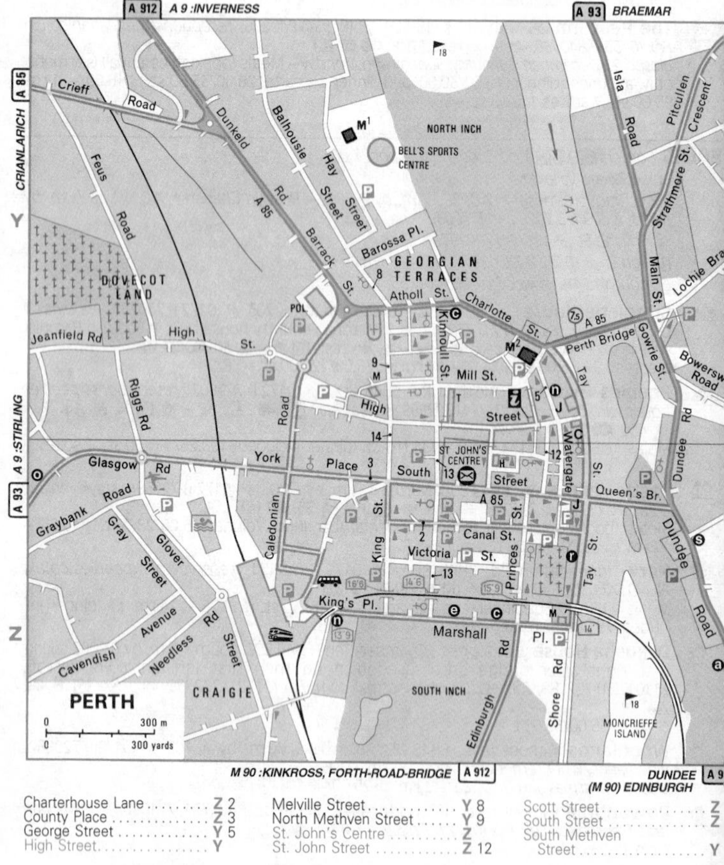

Kinfauns Castle, PH2 7JZ, East : 3 m. by A 90 ☏ (01738) 620777, *email@kinfaunscas... co.uk, Fax (01738) 620778,* ≤, « Restored 19C castle, oriental furnishings », ... rest, – 60. VISA JCB
Meals 18.50/35.00 **t.** 14.00 – **14 rm** 120.00/220.00 **t.**, 2 suites – SB.

Huntingtower, Crieff Rd, PH1 3JT, West : 3 ½ m. by A 85 ☏ (01738) 583771, *rese... tions@huntingtowerhotel.co.uk, Fax (01738) 583777,* – – 180. VISA.
Meals a la carte 13.95/28.40 **st.** 10.95 – **31 rm** 69.50/110.00 **st.** – SB.

Parklands, St Leonard's Bank, PH2 8EB, ☎ (01738) 622451, *parklands.perth@virgin.net, Fax (01738) 622046*, ⚘, ☗ – ⊭ rest, TV P – 🏱 25. MC AE ① VISA JCB Z n
Meals 8.95 (lunch) and a la carte 15.70/26.70 **st.** 🌢 10.95 – ***Ancanthus* : Meals** a la carte 15.70/26.70 **st.** 🌢 10.95 – **14 rm** ⊂ 79.00/115.00 **st.** – SB.

Dupplin Castle ⊛, PH2 0PY, Southwest : 6 ¼ m. off A 9 ☎ (01738) 623224, *dupplin@netcomuk.co.uk, Fax (01738) 444140*, ⋞, « Scottish mansion house, gardens », ⊛, ⚘ – ⊭ P. MC AE VISA JCB
Meals (booking essential) (residents only) (communal dining) (dinner only) 30.00 🌢 17.00 – **7 rm** ⊂ 70.00/140.00 **t.**

Sunbank House, 50 Dundee Rd, PH2 7BA, ☎ (01738) 624882, *reception@sunbankhouse.fsnet.co.uk, Fax (01738) 442515*, ☗ – ⊭ TV ♿ P. MC VISA JCB. ⚔ Z a
Meals (dinner only) 27.50 and a la carte 18.25/24.75 **t.** 🌢 13.50 – **10 rm** ⊂ 59.00/72.00 **t.** – SB.

Express by Holiday Inn without rest., 200 Dunkeld Rd, Inveralmond, PH1 3AQ, Northwest : 2 m. on A 912 ☎ (01738) 636666, *Fax (01738) 633363* – ⇕ ⊭ TV ☏ ♿ P – 🏱 40. MC AE ① VISA JCB
81 rm 56.00.

Beechgrove without rest., Dundee Rd, PH2 7AQ, ☎ (01738) 636147, *beechgrove.h@sol.co.uk, Fax (01738) 636147*, « Victorian manse », ☗ – ⊭ TV P. MC VISA. ⚔ Z s
8 rm ⊂ 25.00/59.00 **st.**

Kinnaird without rest., 5 Marshall Pl, PH2 8AH, ☎ (01738) 628021, *tricia@kinnaird-gh.demon.co.uk, Fax (01738) 444056*, ☗ – ⊭ TV P. MC VISA. ⚔ Z c
closed 14 December-10 January – **7 rm** ⊂ 27.00/50.00 **st.**

Park Lane without rest., 17 Marshall Pl, PH2 8AG, ☎ (01738) 637218, *stay@parklane-uk.com, Fax (01738) 643519*, ☗ – ⊭ TV P. MC AE ① VISA JCB. ⚔ Z e
closed December-20 January – **6 rm** ⊂ 25.00/50.00 **s.**

Abercrombie without rest., 85 Glasgow Rd, PH2 0PQ, ☎ (01738) 444728, *Fax (01738) 444728* – ⊭ TV P. MC VISA Z o
3 rm ⊂ 35.00/60.00 **s.**

63 Tay Street, 63 Tay St, PH2 8NN, ☎ (01738) 441451, *Fax (01738) 441461* – ⊭. MC AE VISA Z r
closed 2 weeks January, Sunday and Monday – **Meals** a la carte 15.00/25.00 **t.** 🌢 10.95.

Let's Eat, 77-79 Kinnoull St, PH1 5EZ, ☎ (01738) 643377, *enquiries@letseatperth.co.uk, Fax (01738) 621464* – ⊭. MC AE VISA Y c
closed 2 weeks July, 2 weeks January, 25-26 December, Sunday and Monday – **Meals** a la carte 16.15/25.20 **t.** 🌢 10.75.

Let's Eat Again, 33 George St, PH1 5LA, ☎ (01738) 633771, *enquiries@letseatperth.co.uk, Fax (01738) 621464* – ⊭. MC AE VISA Y n
closed 2 weeks July, 2 weeks January, 25-26 December, Sunday and Monday – **Meals** a la carte 13.95/24.40 **t.** 🌢 10.50.

t New Scone *Northeast : 2½ m. on A 94 – Y – ✉ Perth.*

Murrayshall Country House ⊛, PH2 7PH, East : 1 ¼ m. by Murraysall Rd ☎ (01738) 551171, *Fax (01738) 552595*, ⋞, Ⓛ, ≘s, ⛳18, ☗, ⚘, ✂ – ⊭ rest, TV ☏ P – 🏱 180. MC AE ① VISA JCB
***Old Masters* : Meals** (dinner only and Sunday lunch) 23.00/31.50 **st.** 🌢 12.95 – **24 rm** ⊂ 85.00/140.00 **st.**, 17 suites 150.00/170.00 **st** – SB.

t Kinfauns *East : 4 m. by A 85 – Z – off A 90 – ✉ Perth.*

Over Kinfauns, PH2 7LD, ☎ (01738) 860538, *bandb@overkinfauns.co.uk, Fax (01738) 860803*, ⋞, ☗ – ⊭ TV P
closed 25-26 December – **Meals** (by arrangement) (communal dining) 20.00 **s.** – **3 rm** ⊂ 38.00/60.00 **s.**

PETERHEAD *Aberdeenshire* **401** O 11 – *pop. 20 789.*

⛳18, ⛳9 Cruden Bay ☎ (01779) 812285 – ⛳18, ⛳9 Craigewan Links ☎ (01779) 472149 – ⛳18 Longside, West End ☎ (01779) 821558.

Edinburgh 165 – Aberdeen 35 – Fraserburgh 18.

Waterside Inn, Fraserburgh Rd, AB42 3BN, Northwest : 2 m. on A 90 ☎ (01779) 471121, *events@waterside.macdonald-hotels.co.uk, Fax (01779) 470670*, Ⓛ, ≘s, ⛆ – ⊭ TV P – 🏱 200. MC AE ① VISA
Meals 10.00/24.50 and a la carte 24.50/36.00 **st.** 🌢 14.00 – **69 rm** ⊂ 70.00/109.00 **st.** – SB.

Les prix — Pour toutes précisions sur les prix indiqués dans ce guide, reportez-vous aux pages de l'introduction.

PITCAPLE *Aberdeenshire* 401 M 12.
Edinburgh 51 – Aberdeen 21.

Pittodrie House ⛰, AB51 5HS, Southwest : 1 ¾ m. by Chapel of Garioch r
✆ (01467) 681444, *pittodrie@macdonald.hotels.co.uk, Fax (01467) 681648,* ≤, « Part 15 country house in extensive grounds », squash – ✂ rest, TV – P – 120. MC AE
VISA
Meals 17.50/31.00 ♁ 13.50 – **27 rm** ☕ 85.00/125.00 **st.** – SB.

PITLOCHRY *Perth and Kinross* 401 I 13 *Scotland G. – pop. 3 126.*
See : *Town★.*
Exc. : *Blair Castle★★ AC, NW : 7 m. by A 9* A *– Queen's View★★, W : 7 m. by B 8019* A *– Fa of Bruar★, NW : 11 m. by A 9* A.
18 *Golf Course Rd ✆ (01796) 472792.*
ℹ *22 Atholl Rd ✆ (01796) 472215.*
Edinburgh 71 – Inverness 85 – Perth 27.

PITLOCHRY

Church Road .... **AB** 2
Clunie Bridge Rd. .... **A** 3
Higher Oakfield .... **B** 4
Larchwood Rd. .... **A** 6
Port Na Craig Rd .... **A** 7
Station Road .... **A** 9
Strathview Terrace .... **A** 1
Tom Na Moan Rd. .... **B** 1
Tummel Crescent .... **A** 1

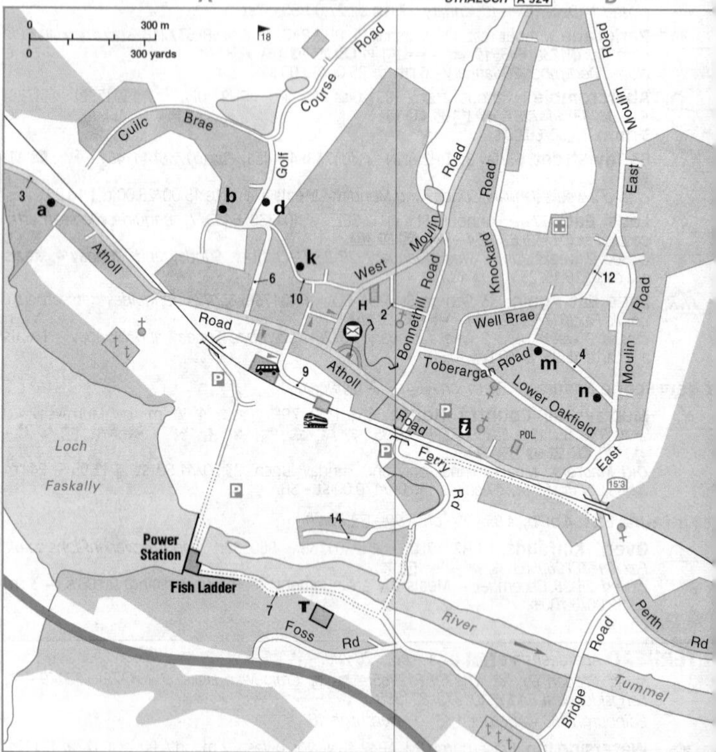

Pine Trees ⛰, Strathview Terr, PH16 5QR, ✆ (01796) 472121, *info@pinetreeshotel.co.u*
Fax (01796) 472460, ≤, – ✂ TV P. MC AE VISA JCB. – A
Meals 14.95/23.95 and a la carte 11.70/24.90 **t.** ♁ 12.95 – **20 rm** ☕ (dinner included) 99.00
198.00 **st.** – SB.

Green Park, Clunie Bridge Rd, PH16 5JY, ✆ (01796) 473248, *bookings@thegreenpark.co.uk, Fax (01796) 473520,* ≤, « Lochside setting », – TV P. MC VISA A a
Meals (booking essential to non-residents) (dinner only) 19.50 **t.** 10.00 – **39 rm** (dinner included) 65.00/130.00 **t.** – SB.

Dunfallandy House, Logierait Rd, Dunfallandy, PH16 5NA, South : 1 ¼ m. by Bridge Rd ✆ (01796) 472648, *dunfalhse@aol.com, Fax (01796) 472017,* ≤, « Georgian mansion house », – TV P. MC VISA JCB.
Easter-October – **Meals** (dinner only) 15.00/17.00 **st.** 10.95 – **8 rm** 60.00/80.00 **st.** – SB.

Knockendarroch House, 2 Higher Oakfield, PH16 5HT, ✆ (01796) 473473, *info@knockendarroch.co.uk, Fax (01796) 474068,* ≤, – TV P. MC AE VISA. B m
March-October – **Meals** (dinner only) 23.00 **t.** 12.00 – **12 rm** (dinner included) 77.00/130.00 **t.** – SB.

Balrobin, Higher Oakfield, PH16 5HT, ✆ (01796) 472901, *info@balrobin.co.uk, Fax (01796) 474200,* ≤, – rest, TV P. MC VISA B n
March-October – **Meals** (residents only) (dinner only) 18.50 **t.** 10.00 – **15 rm** (dinner included) 40.00/90.00 **t.** – SB.

Kinnaird House without rest., Kirkmichael Rd, Kinnaird, PH16 5JL, Northeast : 1 ½ m. on A 924 ✆ (01796) 472843, *kinnaird@hotmail.com, Fax (01796) 472843,* ≤, – TV P. MC VISA.
closed 3 January-Easter and November-mid December – **6 rm** 25.00/60.00 **t.**

Torrdarach, Golf Course Rd, PH16 5AU, ✆ (01796) 472136, *torrdarach@email.msn.com, Fax (01796) 473733,* « Gardens » – TV P. MC VISA. A d
March-November – **Meals** (by arrangement) 15.00 **st.** 8.95 – **7 rm** 26.00/52.00 **t.** – SB.

Dundarave, Strathview Terr, PH16 5AT, ✆ (01796) 473109, *dundarave.guesthouse@virgin.net, Fax (01796) 473109,* ≤, – TV P. MC VISA. A k
Meals (by arrangement) 12.00 – **7 rm** 18.00/50.00.

t Killiecrankie *Northwest : 4 m. by A 924 – A – and B 8019 on B 8079 – ✉ Pitlochry.*

Killiecrankie, PH16 5LG, ✆ (01796) 473220, *enquiries@killiecrankiehotel.co.uk, Fax (01796) 472451,* ≤, – TV P. MC VISA
closed January – **Meals** (bar lunch)/dinner 32.00 **t.** 13.50 – **9 rm** (dinner included) 91.00/182.00 **t.**, 1 suite – SB.

LOCKTON *Highland* 401 D 11 *Scotland G.*

See : *Village*★.
Env. : *Wester Ross*★★★.
Edinburgh 210 – Inverness 88.

Plockton, Harbour St, IV52 8TN, ✆ (01599) 544274, *sales@plocktonhotel.co.uk, Fax (01599) 544475,* ≤ Loch Carron and mountains, – rest, TV ♿. MC AE VISA
Courtyard : **Meals** a la carte 12.25/22.25 **t.** 7.25 – **14 rm** 35.00/80.00 **t.** – SB.

The Haven, 3 Innes St, IV52 8TW, ✆ (01599) 544223, *Fax (01599) 544467,* – rest, TV P. MC VISA JCB
closed 20 December-1 February – **Meals** (lunch by arrangement)/dinner 27.00 **t.** 7.95 – **13 rm** 41.00/82.00 **t.**, 2 suites – SB.

Plockton Inn with rm, Innes St, IV52 8TW, ✆ (01599) 544222, *stay@plocktoninn.co.uk, Fax (01599) 544487,* – rest, TV P. MC VISA JCB
Meals - Seafood - a la carte 10.15/22.70 **t.** 9.50 – **7 rm** 35.00/58.00 **st.** – SB.

OOLEWE *Highland* 401 D 10 *Scotland G.*

Env. : *Wester Ross*★★★ – *Inverewe Gardens*★★★, *N : 1 m. on B 8057 – Loch Maree*★★★.
Edinburgh 234 – Inverness 78 – Kyle of Lochalsh 74.

Pool House, IV22 2LD, ✆ (01445) 781272, *enquiries@poolhousehotel.com, Fax (01445) 781403,* ≤ Loch Ewe – TV P. MC AE VISA JCB.
March-December – **Meals** (bar lunch)/dinner 30.00 and a la carte **t.** 18.50 – **8 rm** 80.00/250.00 **t.**, 1 suite.

Es ist empfehlenswert, ***in der Hauptsaison*** *und vor allem in Urlaubsorten, Hotelzimmer im voraus zu bestellen. Benachrichtigen Sie sofort das Hotel, wenn Sie ein bestelltes Zimmer nicht belegen können.*

Wenn Sie an ein Hotel im Ausland schreiben, fügen Sie Ihrem Brief einen internationalen Antwortschein bei (im Postamt erhältlich).

PORT APPIN *Argyll and Bute* 401 D 14 – ✉ Appin.

Edinburgh 136 – Ballachulish 20 – Oban 24.

Airds (Allen) ⛰, PA38 4DF, ☎ (01631) 730236, *airds@airds-hotel.com, Fax (01631) 73053* ≤ Loch Linnhe and mountains of Kingairloch, « Former ferry inn », ⚓, 🌳 – ⊁ TV P. ● VISA
closed Christmas and 6-26 January – **Meals** (booking essential) (light lunch)/dinner 45.00 🕯 22.00 – **16 rm** ☕ (dinner included) 220.00/320.00 **t.** – SB
Spec. Ravioli of lobster and langoustine with tomato and cucumber. Lismore oyste smoked salmon and Champagne jelly. Pot-roasted guinea fowl, leek and truffle risotto.

Druimneil ⛰, PA38 4DQ, Southeast : ¾ m. on North Shian rd ☎ (01631) 730228, *druir eilhouse@aol.com, Fax (01631) 730668*, ≤, ⚓, 🌳, ⛵ – TV P
Meals (by arrangement) (communal dining) 25.00 **t.** 🕯 12.00 – **3 rm** ☕ 40.00/80.00 **t.**

PORT CHARLOTTE *Argyll and Bute* 401 A 16 – *see Islay (Isle of).*

PORT ELLEN *Argyll and Bute* 401 B 17 – *see Islay (Isle of).*

PORTLETHEN *Aberdeenshire* 401 N 12 – *see Aberdeen.*

PORT OF MENTEITH *Perth and Kinross* 401 H 15 – ✉ Stirling.

Edinburgh 52 – Glasgow 43 – Perth 44.

The Lake ⛰, FK8 3RA, ☎ (01877) 385258, *enquiries@lake-of-menteith-hotel.co Fax (01877) 385671*, ≤, « Lakeside setting », 🌳 – ⊁, ▤ rest, TV P. ● AE VISA
closed first 2 weeks January and 25-27 December – **Meals** *(closed Monday and Tuesd November-March)* 16.50/29.50 **t.** 🕯 12.00 – **16 rm** ☕ (dinner included) 102.00/204.00 **t.** SB.

Wenn Sie ein ruhiges Hotel suchen,
benutzen Sie zuerst die Karte in der Einleitung
oder wählen Sie im Text ein Hotel mit dem Zeichen ⛰ oder ⛰.

PORTPATRICK *Dumfries and Galloway* 401 402 E 19 – *pop. 842* – ✉ Stranraer.

⛳18, ⛳9 *Golf Course Rd* ☎ *(01776) 810273.*

Edinburgh 141 – Ayr 60 – Dumfries 80 – Stranraer 9.

Knockinaam Lodge ⛰, DG9 9AD, Southeast : 5 m. by A 77 off B 704 ☎ (01776) 810471, *reservations@knockinaamlodge.com, Fax (01776) 810435*, ≤, « Victc ian former shooting lodge in picturesque coastal setting », ⚓, 🌳, ⛵ – ⊁ rest, TV P. ● AE ● VISA
Meals (booking essential for non-residents) (set menu only) 29.00/39.00 **t.** 🕯 14.00 – **10 r** ☕ (dinner included) 145.00/340.00 **t.** – SB
Spec. Roast turbot with asparagus and truffle. Smoked foie gras with glazed white pea and sherry vinegar reduction. "Taste" of raspberries.

Fernhill, Heugh Rd, DG9 8TD, ☎ (01776) 810220, *info@fernhillhotel.co.u Fax (01776) 810596*, ≤, 🌳 – ⊁ rest, TV P. ● VISA
Meals 24.00 (dinner) and a la carte 15.70/45.95 🕯 9.00 – **23 rm** ☕ (dinner included) 70.0 164.00 **t.** – SB.

The Waterfront, North Cres, DG9 8SX, ☎ (01776) 810800, *waterfront.hotel@aol.co Fax (01776) 810850*, ≤, 🌳 – ⊁ TV P. ● AE VISA
Meals (bar lunch)/dinner a la carte 9.50/18.50 **t.** – **8 rm** ☕ 49.00/90.00 **t.** – SB.

Blinkbonnie without rest., School Brae, DG9 8LG, ☎ (01776) 810282, *Fax (01776) 8107* ≤, 🌳 – ⊁ TV P. ⊁
closed December – **6 rm** ☕ 26.00/40.00 **st.**

Campbells, 1 South Cres, DG9 8JR, ☎ (01776) 810314, *Fax (07070) 610447* – ● VISA JC
closed 2 weeks January-February and 25 December – **Meals** - Seafood specialities a la carte 15.95/29.95 **t.** 🕯 9.00.

Crown with rm, North Cres, DG9 8SX, ☎ (01776) 810261, *Fax (01776) 810551*, ≤ ⊁ rest, TV. ● AE VISA JCB
closed 25 December – **Meals** 14.95 and a la carte 13.65/28.25 **t.** 🕯 10.95 – **12 rm** ☕ 43.0 76.00 **t.** – SB.

PORTREE *Highland* 401 B 11 – *see Skye (Isle of).*

RESTWICK *South Ayrshire* 401 402 G 17 – *pop. 13 705.*

Prestwick, 2 Links Rd ✆ *(01292) 477404* – *Prestwick St. Nicholas, Grangemuir Rd* ✆ *(01292) 477608.*

Prestwick International Airport : ✆ *(01292) 479822* – BY – **Terminal :** *Buchanan Bus Station.*

see also Glasgow.

Edinburgh 78 – Ayr 2 – Glasgow 32.

Plan of Built up Area : see Ayr

Travel Inn, Kilmarnock Rd, Monkton, KA9 2RJ, Northeast : 3 m. by A 79 and A 78 at junction with A 77 ✆ (01292) 678262, *Fax (01292) 678248* – rm, TV & P – 70. MC AE VISA.

Meals (grill rest.) – **40 rm** 41.95 **t.**

UOTHQUAN *South Lanarkshire* 401 J 27 *Scotland G.* – ✉ *Biggar.*

Env. : *Biggar★ (Gladstone Court Museum★ AC – Greenhill Covenanting Museum★ AC) SE : 4½ m. by B 7016.*

Edinburgh 32 – Dumfries 50 – Glasgow 36.

Shieldhill Castle, ML12 6NA, Northeast : ¾ m. ✆ (01899) 220035, *enquiries@shieldhill.co.uk, Fax (01899) 221092,* ≤, « Part 12C fortified manor house with 16C additions », – TV P – 250. MC VISA

Meals 17.50 and a la carte 24.85/42.40 12.95 – **16 rm** 95.00/248.00 **t.**

HICONICH *Highland* 401 F 8 *Scotland G.* – ✉ *Lairg.*

Exc. : *Cape Wrath★★★ (≤★★) AC, N : 21 m. (including ferry crossing) by A 838 and minor rd.*

Edinburgh 249 – Thurso 87 – Ullapool 57.

Rhiconich, IV27 4RN, ✆ (01971) 521224, *rhiconichhotel@cs.com, Fax (01971) 521732,* ≤ Loch Inchard, – rest, TV P. MC VISA JCB

closed 25 December-2 January – **Meals** (bar lunch)/dinner 18.00/20.00 and a la carte 11.75/15.70 **t.** 7.50 – **12 rm** 36.00/74.00 **st.** – SB.

OGART *Highland* 401 H 9 – *pop. 419.*

Edinburgh 229 – Inverness 73 – Wick 63.

Sciberscross Lodge, Strath Brora, IV28 3YQ, North : 7 m. by Balnacoil rd ✆ (01408) 641246, *Fax (01408) 641465,* ≤ Brora valley and hills, – P. MC VISA

restricted opening December and January – **Meals** (booking essential) (communal dining) (dinner only) (set menu only) 27.50/47.50 **st.** – **4 rm** 47.50/95.00 **st.**

OTHESAY *Argyll and Bute* 401 402 E 16 – *see Bute (Isle of).*

OYBRIDGE *Highland* 401 F 13 – *see Spean Bridge.*

T ANDREWS *Fife* 401 L 14 *Scotland G.* – *pop. 11 136.*

See : *City★★ – Cathedral★ (✻★★) AC* B – *West Port★* A.

Env. : *Leuchars (parish church★), NW : 6 m. by A 91 and A 919.*

Exc. : *The East Neuk★★, SE : 9 m. by A 917 and B 9131* B – *Crail★★ (Old Centre★★, Upper Crail★) SE : 9 m. by A 917* B – *Kellie Castle★ AC, S : 9 m. by B 9131 and B 9171* B – *Ceres★, SW : 9 m. by B 939 - E : Inland Fife★* A.

(x4), Eden, Jubilee, New, Strathtyrum and Balgove Course ✆ *(01334) 466666* – *Duke's, Craigtoun Park* ✆ *(01334) 474371.*

70 Market St. ✆ *(01334) 472021.*

Edinburgh 51 – Dundee 14 – Stirling 51.

Plan on next page

The Old Course H. Golf Resort and Spa, Old Station Rd, KY16 9SP, ✆ (01334) 474371, *reservations@oldcoursehotel.co.uk, Fax (01334) 477668,* ≤ Championship golf course and St Andrews Bay, – rm, TV & P – 300. MC AE VISA JCB A b

closed 1 week Christmas – ***Road Hole Grill :*** **Meals** (dinner only) 38.50 and a la carte 37.50/52.00 **t.** 18.50 – ***Sands :*** **Meals** *(May-October and lunch November-April)* a la carte 20.45/32.95 **t.** 13.50 – **118 rm** 269.00/369.00 **t.**, 28 suites 425.00/520.00 **t** – SB.

ST ANDREWS

Abbey Street . . . . B 2
Abbey Walk . . . . B 3
Alexandra Place. . . . . A 5
Alfred Place . . . . A 6
Bridge Street . . . . A 7
Butts Wynd . . . . B 9
Castle Street . . . . B 10
Church Street. . . . . AB 13
Ellice Place. . . . . A 15
Gibson Place . . . . A 17
Gillespie Terrace . . . . A 18
Greenside Place . . . . B 20
Gregory Lane. . . . . B 21
Gregory Place . . . . B 22
Greyfriars Garden . . . . A 24
Hepburn Gardens . . . . A 25
Link Crescent . . . . A 27
Murray Park. . . . . A
Murray Place . . . . A
Pilmour Links. . . . . A
Pilmour Place . . . . A
Playfair Terrace . . . . A
Queen's Gardens . . . . A
Queen's Terrace . . . . B
St. Mary's Place . . . . A
Union Street . . . . B

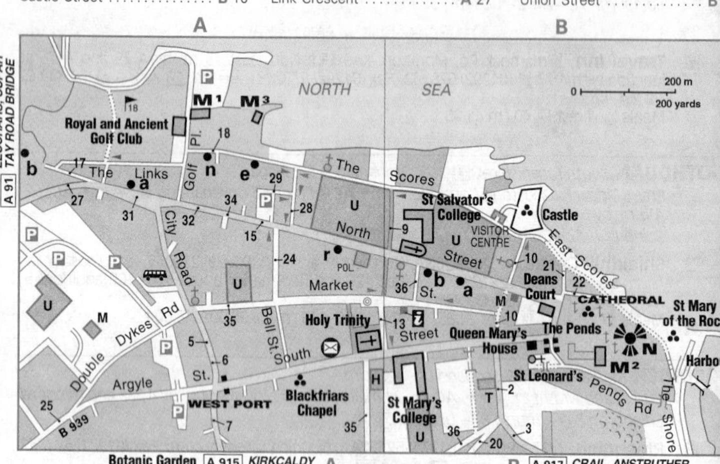

St Andrews Bay, KY16 8PN, Southeast : 3 m. on A 917 ℘ (01334) 837000, *info@ andrewsbay.com, Fax (01334) 471115,* ≤, – |‡|, rm, 700. VISA. — A
The Squire : **Meals** a la carte 19.65/27.70 **st.** 15.00 – ***Aria :*** **Meals** *(closed Sunday dinn* (dinner only and Sunday lunch)/dinner 28.00/32.00 and a la carte 24.50/34.50 **st.** 18.00
209 rm 195.00/245.00 **st.** – SB.

Rusacks, Pilmour Links, KY16 9JQ, ℘ (01334) 474321, *heritagehotel_standrews.rusacks forte-hotels.com, Fax (01334) 477896,* ≤, – |‡|, rest, – 80. JCB — A
Meals (bar lunch)/dinner a la carte 30.35/33.90 **t.** 14.70 – 15.00 – **61 rm** 130.0 290.00 **t.**, 7 suites – SB.

Rufflets Country House, Strathkinness Low Rd, KY16 9TX, West : 1 ½ m. on B 9 ℘ (01334) 472594, *reservations@rufflets.co.uk, Fax (01334) 478703,* ≤, « Country hous gardens » – VISA.
closed 3-11 January – **Meals** (bar lunch Monday-Saturday)/dinner 32.00/36.00 **st.** 14.00
22 rm 100.00/230.00 **st.** – SB.

St Andrews Golf, 40 The Scores, KY16 9AS, ℘ (01334) 472611, *reception@standrew golf.co.uk, Fax (01334) 472188,* ≤ – |‡|, rest, – 200. VISA JCB — A
Meals a la carte 27.00/35.00 **t.** 12.00 – **22 rm** 102.00/175.00 **t.** – SB.

The Scores, 76 The Scores, KY16 9BB, ℘ (01334) 472451, *office@scoreshotel.co.u Fax (01334) 473947,* ≤, – |‡|, rest, – 160. VISA. — A
closed 25 December and 1 January – **Meals** (bar lunch)/dinner 18.25 and a la carte 11.2 21.75 **t.** 9.95 – **29 rm** 93.00/179.00 **t.**, 1 suite.

Albany without rest., 56-58 North St, KY16 9AH, ℘ (01334) 477737, *enq@standre albany.co.uk, Fax (01334) 477742,* – VISA. — B
21 rm 75.00/150.00 **st.**

18 Queens Terrace without rest., 18 Queens Terr, KY16 9QF, ℘ (01334) 478849, *ji hardie@hotmail.com, Fax (01334) 470283,* « Victorian town house », – — A
3 rm 45.00/75.00.

Aslar House without rest., 120 North St, KY16 9AF, ℘ (01334) 473460, *enquiries@asl com, Fax (01334) 477540,* – VISA. — A
closed 1 week spring and 1 week autumn – **5 rm** 32.00/66.00 **s.**

Deveron House without rest., 64 North St, KY16 9AH, ℘ (01334) 473513, *angela deveron-house.co.uk, Fax (01334) 473513* – VISA. — B
6 rm 40.00/60.00.

Strathkinness West : 3 3/4 m. on B 939 – A – ✉ St. Andrews.

Fossil House and Cottage without rest., 12-14 Main St, KY16 9RU, ☎ (01334) 850639, *the.fossil@virgin.net, Fax (01334) 850639*, – TV P. MC AE VISA JCB.
4 rm 30.00/55.00 st.

BOSWELLS *Borders* 401 402 L 17 *Scotland G. – pop. 2 092.*
Env. : *Dryburgh Abbey★★ AC (setting★★★), NW : 4 m. by B 6404 and B 6356 – Tweed Valley★★.*
Exc. : *Bowhill★★ AC, SW : 11½ m. by A 699 and A 708.*
St. Boswells ☎ (01835) 823527.
Edinburgh 39 – Glasgow 79 – Hawick 17 – Newcastle upon Tyne 66.

Dryburgh Abbey, Dryburgh, TD6 0RQ, North : 3 ½ m. by B 6404 on B 6356 ☎ (01835) 822261, *enquiries@dryburgh.co.uk, Fax (01835) 823945*, ←, – rest, TV P – 150. MC AE VISA JCB
Tweed : **Meals** (bar lunch Monday-Saturday)/dinner a la carte 18.95/26.90 **st.** 12.75 – 9.95 – **36 rm** 60.00/70.00 **t.**, 2 suites.

Clint Lodge, TD6 0DZ, North : 2 ¼ m. by B 6404 on B 6356 ☎ (01835) 822027, *clintlodge@aol.com, Fax (01835) 822656*, ←, – TV P. MC VISA
closed 3 weeks February and 25-26 December – **Meals** 20.00 – **5 rm** 35.00/70.00.

FILLANS *Perth and Kinross* 401 H 14 *Scotland G.*
Env. : *Loch Earn★★.*
Edinburgh 67 – Glasgow 57 – Oban 64 – Perth 30.

Achray House, PH6 2NF, ☎ (01764) 685231, *achrayhotelsltd@btinternet.com, Fax (01764) 685320*, ← Loch Earn and mountains, – rest, TV P. MC AE VISA.
Meals (bar lunch Monday-Saturday)/dinner 19.50 and a la carte 13.00/23.00 **st.** 8.95 – **10 rm** 46.50/79.00 **st.**

MARGARET'S HOPE *Orkney Islands* 401 K 6 – *see Orkney Islands.*

MONANS *Fife* 401 L 15 – *pop. 3 965 (inc. Elie and Pinttenweem).*
Edinburgh 47 – Dundee 26 – Perth 40 – Stirling 56.

The Seafood, 16 West End, KY10 2BX, ☎ (01333) 730327, *info@theseafoodrestaurant.com, Fax (01333) 730327*, ←, – . MC AE VISA JCB
closed January, December, Sunday dinner and Monday – **Meals** - Seafood - (booking essential) 18.00 (lunch) and dinner a la carte 23.10/33.45 **t.** 12.00.

NDYHILLS *Dumfries and Galloway* 401 402 I 19 – ✉ *Dalbeattie.*
Edinburgh 99 – Ayr 62 – Dumfries 19 – Stranraer 68.

Cairngill House without rest., DG5 4NZ, ☎ (01387) 780681, *tricksharmony@virgin.net*, ←, – TV P. MC VISA JCB.
closed November-5 January – **6 rm** 25.00/58.00 **t.**

ALASAIG *Argyll and Bute* 401 B 15 – *see Colonsay (Isle of).*

ARISTA *Western Isles (Outer Hebrides)* 401 Y 10 – *see Lewis and Harris (Isle of).*

OURIE *Highland* 401 E 8 *Scotland G. – ✉ Lairg.*
Exc. : *Cape Wrath★★★ (←★★) AC, N : 31 m. (including ferry crossing) by A 894 and A 838 – Loch Assynt★★, S : 17 m. by A 894.*
Edinburgh 263 – Inverness 107.

Eddrachilles, Badcall Bay, IV27 4TH, South : 2 ½ m. on A 894 ☎ (01971) 502080, *eddrachilles@compuserve.com, Fax (01971) 502477*, ← Badcall Bay and islands, – TV P. MC VISA JCB.
15 March-18 October – **Meals** (bar lunch)/dinner 13.10 and a la carte 23.30/32.10 **st.** 5.60 – **11 rm** 60.00/90.00 **st.** – SB.

The Guide is updated annually so renew your Guide every year.

SEIL (Isle of) *Argyll and Bute* 401 D 15 – ✉ *Oban.*

Clachan Seil – ✉ *Oban.*

Willowburn ⛺, PA34 4TJ, ✆ (01852) 300276, *willowburn.hotel@virgin.r* *Fax (01852) 300597*, ≤, « Lochside setting », – TV P. MC VISA JCB
March-November – **Meals** (booking essential for non-residents) (dinner only) 27.0 10.95 – **7 rm** (dinner included) 62.00/124.00 **t.** – SB.

Easdale – ✉ *Oban.*

Inshaig Park ⛺, PA34 4RF, ✆ (01852) 300256, *inshaigparkhotel@demon.co.* *Fax (01852) 300256*, ≤ Inner Hebridean Islands, – rest, TV P
April-October – **Meals** (bar lunch)/dinner 16.50 and a la carte – **6 rm** 41.00/78.00.

SELKIRK *Borders* 401 402 L 17 *Scotland G. – pop. 6 469.*

Env. : *Bowhill★★ AC, W : 3½ m. by A 708 – Abbotsford★★ AC, NE : 5½ m. by A 7 and B 6.* *– Tweed Valley★★.*

Exc. : *Melrose Abbey★★ (decorative sculpture★★★) AC, NE : 8½ m. by A 7 and A 609* *Eildon Hills (★★★) NE : 7½ m. by A 699 and B 6359.*

The Hill ✆ (01750) 20621.

Halliwell's House ✆ (01750) 20054 (Easter-October).

Edinburgh 48 – Hawick 11 – Newcastle upon Tyne 77.

Philipburn Country House, TD7 5LS, West : 1 m. at junction of A 707 with A ✆ (01750) 20747, *info@philipburnhousehotel.co.uk*, *Fax (01750) 21690*, – r rest, TV P – 30. MC AE VISA
Restaurant 1745 **:** **Meals** (lunch by arrangement Monday-Saturday)/dinner 27.50 **t.** 11 – ***Charlies Bar and Bistro*** **:** **Meals** 15.50/26.50 and a la carte 15.95/20.95 **t.** 11.9 **12 rm** 79.50/99.50 **t.**, 3 suites – SB.

at Ettrickbridge *Southwest : 7 m. by A 707 on B 7009* – ✉ *Selkirk.*

Ettrickshaws Country House ⛺, TD7 5HW, Southwest : 1 m. on B 7(✆ (01750) 52229, *jenny@ettrickshaws.co.uk*, *Fax (01750) 52229*, ≤, , , – TV MC VISA.
Meals (booking essential for non-residents) (dinner only) 25.00 **st.** 11.00 – **5 rm** (dinner included) 60.00/110.00 **st.** – SB.

SHETLAND ISLANDS *Shetland Islands* 401 PQ 3 *Scotland G. – pop. 22 522.*

See : *Islands★ - Up Helly Aa★★ (last Tuesday in January) – Mousa Broch★★★ AC (Mo Island) – Jarlshof★★ - Lerwick to Jarlshof★ (≤★) – Shetland Croft House Museum★ AC.*

Tingwall Airport : ✆ (01595) 840306, NW : 6½ m. of Lerwick by A 971.

from Lerwick (Mainland) to Aberdeen and via Orkney Islands (Stromness) (P & Scottish Ferries) – from Vidlin to Skerries (Shetland Islands Council) booking esser 2-3 weekly (1 h 30 mn) – from Lerwick (Mainland) to Skerries (Shetland Islands Cour 2 weekly (booking essential) (2 h 30 mn) – from Lerwick (Mainland) to Bressay (Shetl Islands Council) frequent services daily (5 mn) – from Laxo (Mainland) to Isle of Wha (Symbister) (Shetland Islands Council) frequent services daily (30 mn) – from T (Mainland) to Isle of Yell (Ulsta) (Shetland Islands Council) frequent services daily (20 r – from Isle of Yell (Gutcher) to Isle of Fetlar (Oddsta) and via Isle of Unst (Belmc (Shetland Islands Council) – from Fair Isle to Sumburgh (Mainland) (Shetland Islands Cour weekly (2 h 40 mn).

from Foula to Walls (Shetland Islands Council) 2 weekly (2 h 30 mn) – from Fair Isle Sumburgh (Shetland Islands Council) weekly (2 h 40 mn).

MAINLAND.

Brae.

Busta House ⛺, ZE2 9QN, Southwest : 1½ m. by A 970 ✆ (01806) 522506, *reservati @bustahouse.com*, *Fax (01806) 522588*, ≤, « Part 16C and 18C country house », – rest, TV P. MC AE VISA
Meals (bar lunch Monday-Saturday)/dinner 28.50 10.00 – **20 rm** 75.00/95.00 **t.** – SB

erwick *Scotland G. – pop. 7 590.*

See : *Clickhimin Broch*★.

Env. : *Culber Wick (≤★), S : 2 m. by A 970.*

Shetland, Dale, Gott ☎ (01595) 840369.

The Market Cross, Lerwick ☎ (01595) 693434.

Kveldsro House, Greenfield Pl, ZE1 0AQ, ☎ (01595) 692195, *info@kgqhotels.co.uk, Fax (01595) 696595* – TV P. MC AE VISA.
closed 24 December-4 January – **Meals** (carving lunch Sunday) (bar lunch Monday-Saturday)/dinner 19.50 and a la carte 14.00/23.00 **t.** 11.50 – **16 rm** 70.00/94.00 **t.**

Grand, 149 Commercial St, ZE1 0EX, ☎ (01595) 692826, *info@kgqhotels.co.uk, Fax (01595) 694048* – TV. MC AE VISA.
closed 24 December-4 January – **Meals** 12.95/16.50 and dinner a la carte 14.00/23.00 **t.** 10.50 – **24 rm** 65.00/90.00 **t.**

Shetland, Holmsgarth Rd, ZE1 0PW, ☎ (01595) 695515, *reception@shetlandhotel.co.uk, Fax (01595) 695828,* ≤ – TV P. – 250. MC AE VISA.
closed 25 December and 1 January – **Meals** (bar lunch)/dinner 16.95/21.50 and a la carte 15.85/24.40 **t.** 9.90 – **64 rm** 69.00/89.90 **t.**, 1 suite – SB.

Glen Orchy House, 20 Knab Rd, ZE1 0AX, ☎ (01595) 692031, *glenorchyhouse@virgin.net, Fax (01595) 692031* – TV P. MC VISA JCB
Meals (residents only) (dinner only) 16.00 **st.** 9.40 – **21 rm** 40.00/66.00 **st.**

eensgarth.

Herrislea House, ZE2 9SB, ☎ (01595) 840208, *herrislea.house@zetnet.co.uk, Fax (01595) 840630,* – TV P. MC VISA JCB
closed 23 December-5 January – **Meals** *(closed Sunday)* (booking essential to non-residents) (bar lunch)/dinner 21.50 **st.** 8.75 – **13 rm** 50.00/80.00 **st.** – SB.

/hite Ness.

The Inn On The Hill, ZE2 9LJ, on A 971 ☎ (01595) 840242, *kergord@aol.com, Fax (01595) 840500,* ≤ Whiteness Voe – rest, TV P. MC VISA
Meals (residents only) (dinner only) a la carte 12.45/14.00 **t.** 8.50 – **6 rm** 40.00/75.00 **t.**

ISLAND OF UNST.

altasound.

Buness House , ZE2 9DS, East : ½ m. by A 968 ☎ (01957) 711315, *buness-house@zetnet.co.uk, Fax (01957) 711815,* ≤ Balta Sound, – P. MC VISA
closed January – **Meals** (by arrangement) (communal dining) 25.00 **st.** 7.00 – **3 rm** 36.00/63.00 **st.**

HIELDAIG *Highland* 401 D 11 *Scotland G.* – ✉ *Strathcarron.*

Env. : *Wester Ross*★★★.

Edinburgh 226 – Inverness 70 – Kyle of Lochalsh 36.

Tigh An Eilean, IV54 8XN, ☎ (01520) 755251, *tighaneileanhotel@shieldaig.fsnet.co.uk, Fax (01520) 755321,* ≤ Shieldaig Islands and Loch, « Attractively furnished inn » – rest. MC VISA
5 April-mid October – **Meals** (booking essential to non-residents) (bar lunch)/dinner 27.00 **t.** 9.95 – **11 rm** 49.50/110.00 **t.** – SB.

KYE (Isle of) *Highland* 401 B 11 /12 *Scotland G. – pop. 8 868.*

See : *Island*★★ – *The Cuillins*★★★ – *Skye Museum of Island Life*★ *AC.*

Env. : *N : Trotternish Peninsula*★★ – *W : Duirinish Peninsula*★ – *Portree*★.

Skye Bridge (toll).

– from Mallaig to Armadale (Caledonian MacBrayne Ltd) 1-2 weekly (30 mn) – from Uig to North Uist (Lochmaddy) or Isle of Harris (Tarbert) (Caledonian MacBrayne Ltd) 1-3 daily (1 h 50 mn) – from Sconser to Isle of Raasay (Caledonian MacBrayne Ltd) 9-10 daily (except Sunday) (15 mn).

from Mallaig to Isles of Eigg, Muck, Rhum and Canna (Caledonian MacBrayne Ltd) – from Mallaig to Armadale (Caledonian MacBrayne Ltd) (summer only) 1-2 weekly (30 mn).

rdvasar.

Ardvasar, IV45 8RS, ☎ (01471) 844223, *christine@ardvasar-hotel.demon.co.uk, Fax (01471) 844495,* ≤, – TV P. MC VISA
Meals (bar lunch)/dinner 26.50 **t.** – **9 rm** 50.00/100.00 **st.** – SB.

SCOTLAND

Breakish.

Rendezvous, Old School House, IV42 8PY, ☏ (01471) 822001, *Fax (01471) 822986* – MC VISA JCB
closed December-February and Tuesday – **Meals** - Seafood - (booking essential) (dinner only and Sunday lunch) a la carte 16.70/26.80 **t.** 10.75.

Broadford.

Corry Lodge, Liveras, IV49 9AA, North : 1 m. by An Acarsaid rd ☏ (01471) 82223 *Fax (01471) 822318*, ≤, « Part 18C house », – TV P. MC VISA.
April-October – **Meals** (by arrangement) (communal dining) 20.00 **st.** – **4 rm** 45.00/60.00 **st.**

Ptarmigan without rest., Harrapool, IV49 9AQ, East : ¾ m. on A 87 ☏ (01471) 82274 *info@ptarmigan-cottage.com, Fax (01471) 822745*, ≤ Broadford Bay and island « Waterside setting », – TV P. MC AE VISA
3 rm 52.00.

Earsary without rest., 7-8 Harrapool, IV49 9AQ, East : ¾ m. on A 87 ☏ (01471) 82269 *earsary@isleofskye.net, Fax (01471) 822781*, ≤, – TV P.
3 rm 25.00/48.00 **st.**

Westside without rest., Elgol Rd, IV49 9AB, on B 8083 ☏ (01471) 822320, *dolly.skye@ta 21.com, Fax (01471) 822320*, – TV P.
3 rm 22.00/44.00.

Carbost.

Talisker House, Talisker Bay, IV47 8SF, West : 4 ¼ m. on Talisker rd ☏ (01478) 64024 *jon_and_ros.wathen@virgin.net, Fax (01478) 640214*, ≤, « Part 18C country house », – P. MC VISA JCB.
April-December – **Meals** (by arrangement) 25.00 **st.** 10.00 – **4 rm** 55.00/86.00 **st.**

Culnaknock – ✉ *Portree*

Glenview Inn, IV51 9JH, ☏ (01470) 562248, *enquiries@glenview-skye.co.u Fax (01470) 562211*, ≤ – P. MC VISA
March-October – **Meals** a la carte 15.20/26.95 **t.** 10.95 – **5 rm** 60.00/70.00 **t.**

Dunvegan.

Dunorin House, Herebost, IV55 8GZ, Southeast : 2 ½ m. by A 863 on Roag r ☏ (01470) 521488, *stay@dunorin.freeserve.co.uk, Fax (01470) 521488*, ≤, – TV MC VISA.
April-mid October – **Meals** (booking essential) (dinner only) 24.00 **t.** 10.00 – **10 r** 48.00/88.00 **t.** – SB.

Kinlochfollart, IV55 8WQ, South : ¾ m. on Glendale rd ☏ (01470) 52174 *Fax (01470) 521740*, ≤, « Victorian former manse », – P. MC AE VISA JCB
closed Christmas and New Year – **Meals** (by arrangement) (communal dining) 20.00 **s.** **3 rm** 42.00/80.00 **st.**

Roskhill, Roskhill, IV55 8ZD, Southeast : 2 ½ m. by A 863 ☏ (01470) 521317, *stay@roskh demon.co.uk, Fax (01470) 521761* – P. MC AE VISA JCB
February-October – **Meals** 14.50 **s.** 9.95 – **4 rm** 40.00/70.00 **s.** – SB.

Three Chimneys & The House Over-By with rm, Colbost, IV55 8ZT, Northwest 5 ¾ m. by A 863 on B 884 ☏ (01470) 511258, *eatandstay@threechimneys.co.u Fax (01470) 511358*, ≤, « Converted Hebridean crofter's cottage » – TV P. MC VISA
closed last 2 weeks January – **Meals** - Seafood specialities - *(closed Sunday lunch and lunc in winter)* (booking essential) 17.95/35.00 and a la carte 29.00/42.00 – **6 rm** 135.00/160.00 **st.**

Elgol.

Rowan Cottage, 9 Glasnakille, IV49 9BQ, Southeast : 2 m. ☏ (01471) 866287, *rowa @rowancott.demon.co.uk, Fax (01471) 866287*, ≤ Loch Slapin and Sleat peninsula, – P.
March-October – **Meals** (by arrangement) 21.00 **s.** 9.95 – **3 rm** 35.00/50.00 **s.**

Flodigarry – ✉ *Staffin.*

Flodigarry Country House, IV51 9HZ, ☏ (01470) 552203, *info@flodigarry.co.u Fax (01470) 552301*, ≤ Staffin Island and coastline, – P. MC VISA
Meals (bar lunch Monday-Saturday)/dinner 32.00 and a la carte 19.00/35.00 **st.** 11.50 **19 rm** 59.00/110.00 **st.** – SB.

Ieornsay – ✉ *Sleat*

Kinloch Lodge ≫, IV43 8QY, North : 3 ½ m. by A 851 ☎ (01471) 833214, *kinloch@dial.pipex.com, Fax (01471) 833277*, ≤ Loch Na Dal, « 17C former shooting lodge », ≫, ≈, ⚲ – ⅹ P. MC AE VISA
closed Christmas – **Meals** (booking essential to non-residents) (dinner only) 20.00/37.00 **t.** 8.00 – **14 rm** ☐ 45.00/190.00 **t.** – SB.

Duisdale Country House ≫, IV43 8QW, North : 1 ¼ m. on A 851 ☎ (01471) 833202, *marie@duisdalehotel.demon.co.uk, Fax (01471) 833404*, ≤ Sound of Sleat and mountains, « Gardens », ⚲ – ⅹ rest, P. MC AE VISA JCB. ⅹ
Easter-October – **Meals** (booking essential to non-residents) (dinner only) 30.00 **t.** 11.00 – **17 rm** ☐ 65.00/130.00 **t.** – SB.

Eilean Iarmain ≫, IV43 8QR, ☎ (01471) 833332, *hotel@eileon-iarmain.co.uk, Fax (01471) 833275*, ≤, « 19C inn », ≫, ≈, ⚲ – ⅹ P. MC AE VISA
Meals (lunch by arrangement)/dinner 31.00 **t.** 12.00 – **12 rm** ☐ 90.00/150.00 **t.**, 4 suites – SB.

ortree – *pop. 2 126.*

Bayfield House, Bayfield Rd ☎ (01478) 612137.

Cuillin Hills ≫, IV51 9QU, Northeast : ¾ m. by A 855 ☎ (01478) 612003, *office@cuillinhills.demon.co.uk, Fax (01478) 613092*, ≤, ≈, ⚲ – ⅹ rest, TV P – 140. MC AE VISA
Meals (bar lunch Monday-Saturday) (buffet lunch Sunday)/dinner 21.00/28.00 **t.** 11.25 – **30 rm** ☐ 65.00/130.00 **t.** – SB.

Bosville, Bosville Terr, IV51 9DG, ☎ (01478) 612846, *bosville@macleodhotels.co.uk, Fax (01478) 613434*, ≤ – ⅹ TV ☎. MC AE VISA JCB
Chandlery : **Meals** - Seafood - (dinner only) 12.00/33.00 **st.** 12.00 – **15 rm** ☐ 55.00/110.00 **st.** – SB.

Rosedale, Beaumont Cres, IV51 9DB, ☎ (01478) 613131, *rosedale@achnacraig.freeserve.co.uk, Fax (01478) 612531*, ≤ harbour, ≈ – ⅹ TV P. MC D VISA
April-mid November – **Meals** (dinner only) 21.00 **t.** 11.95 – **23 rm** ☐ 42.00/102.00 **t.** – SB.

Almondbank without rest., Viewfield Rd, IV51 9EU, Southwest : ¾ m. on A 87 ☎ (01478) 612696, *jansvans@aol.com, Fax (01478) 613114*, ≤ Portree Bay, ≈ – TV P. MC VISA JCB
4 rm ☐ 37.50/60.00.

Kings Haven without rest., 11 Bosville Terr, IV51 9DG, ☎ (01478) 612290, *Fax (01478) 612290*, ≈ – TV. MC VISA. ⅹ
closed February and Christmas – **6 rm** ☐ 72.00 **st.**

'aternish.

Loch Bay Seafood ≫ with rm, 1 MacLeod Terr, Stein, IV55 8GA, ☎ (01470) 592235, *david@lochbay-seafood-restaurant.co.uk, Fax (01470) 592235* – ⅹ TV P. MC VISA. ⅹ
Easter-October – **Meals** - Seafood - *(closed Saturday lunch and Sunday)* a la carte 13.45/24.75 **t.** 9.75 – **2 rm** ☐ 34.50/55.00 **t.**

OUTH QUEENSFERRY *West Lothian* 401 J 16 – ✉ *Edinburgh.*

Edinburgh 10 – Glasgow 42 – Perth 35.

Travel Inn, Queen's Crossing, Builyeon Rd, EH30 3YJ, ☎ (0131) 331 5056, *Fax (0131) 331 4746* – |‡|, ⅹ rm, ▤ rest, TV ♿ P. MC AE D VISA. ⅹ
Meals (grill rest.) – **46 rm** 41.95 **t.**

OUTH UIST *Western Isles (Outer Hebrides)* 401 XY 11/12 – *see Uist (Isles of).*

PEAN BRIDGE *Highland* 401 F 13.

9 ☎ *(01397) 704954.*

Woollen Mill car park (01397) 712576 (April-October).

Edinburgh 143 – Fort William 10 – Glasgow 94 – Inverness 58 – Oban 60.

Corriegour Lodge, Loch Lochy, PH34 4EB, North : 8 ¾ m. on A 82 ☎ (01397) 712685, *info@corriegour-lodge-hotel.com, Fax (01397) 712696*, ≤, ≫, ≈ – ⚓ ⅹ TV P. MC AE D VISA JCB. ⅹ
closed December and January except New Year and weekends only February, March and November – **Meals** (booking essential to non-residents) (dinner only) 32.50 **t.** 12.50 – **9 rm** ☐ (dinner included) ☐ 79.50/159.00 **t.** – SB.

SCOTLAND

Corriechoille Lodge , PH34 4EY, East : 2 m. on Corriechoille rd ☎ (01397) 71200 enquiry@corriechoille.com, Fax (01397) 712002, ←, – ⊁ TV ♿ P. MC VISA JCB. ⚡
April-October – **Meals** (by arrangement) 18.00 **s.** – **5 rm** 35.00/56.00 **s.** – SB.

Coinachan, Gairlochy Rd, PH34 4EG, Northwest : 1 ¼ m. by A 82 on B 80 ☎ (01397) 712417, coinachan@supanet.com, Fax (01397) 712528, ←, – ⊁ P. ⚡
closed 25 December – **Meals** 15.00 **st.** – **3 rm** 30.00/50.00 **st.** – SB.

Springburn Farmhouse without rest., Stronaba, PH34 4DX, North : 2 ½ m. on A ☎ (01397) 712707, info@stronaba.co.uk, Fax (01397) 712707, ←, – ⊁ TV P. ⚡
4 rm 25.00/45.00 **st.**

Old Pines with rm, PH34 4EG, Northwest : 1 ½ m. by A 82 on B 80 ☎ (01397) 712324, goodfood@oldpines.co.uk, Fax (01397) 712433, ←, – ⊁ ♿ P. MC JCB. ⚡
closed 2 weeks in winter – **Meals** (closed Sunday dinner and Monday) (booking essential f non-residents) (set menu only) (light lunch) 24.50/30.00 **s.** 10.50 – **8 rm** (dinr included) 75.00/150.00 **t.** – SB.

Old Station, Station Rd, PH34 4EP, ☎ (01397) 712535, « Victorian former railway st tion » – ⊁ P. MC VISA JCB
Easter-October – **Meals** (closed Monday and dinner Sunday-Thursday) (booking essent a la carte 12.25/21.95 12.50.

at Roybridge East : 3 m. on A 86.

Glenspean Lodge, PH31 4AW, East : 2 m. on A 86 ☎ (01397) 712223, wdgsl@aol.co Fax (01397) 712660, ←, – ⊁ TV P. MC AE ① VISA. ⚡
March-October – **Meals** (bar lunch)/dinner 25.00 and a la carte 15.25/28.00 **st.** 12.00 **15 rm** 60.00/150.00 **st.** – SB.

SPITTAL OF GLENSHEE

Perth and Kinross 401 J 13 Scotland G. – ✉ Blairgowrie.

Env. : Glenshee (✳ ★★) (chairlift AC).

Edinburgh 69 – Aberdeen 74 – Dundee 35.

Dalmunzie House , PH10 7QG, ☎ (01250) 885224, dalmunzie@aol.co Fax (01250) 885225, ←, 9, , , , – |♦|, ⊁ rest, TV P. MC VISA
closed December – **Meals** (bar lunch)/dinner 24.00/26.00 **t.** 10.00 – **16 rm** 63.0 114.00 **t.**

STENNESS

Orkney Islands 401 K 7 – see Orkney Islands.

STEPPS

North Lanarkshire 401 H 16 – see Glasgow.

STIRLING

Stirling 401 I 15 Scotland G. – pop. 30 515.

See : Town★★ – Castle★★ AC (Site★★★, external elevations★★★, Stirling Heads★★, Arg and Sutherland Highlanders Regimental Museum★) B – Argyll's Lodging★ (Renaissar decoration★) B A – Church of the Holy Rude★ B B.

Env. : Wallace Monument (✳ ★★) NE : 2½ m. by A 9 – A – and B 998.

Exc. : Dunblane★ (Cathedral★★, West Front★★), N : 6½ m. by A 9 A.

ℹ Dumbarton Rd ☎ (01786) 475019 – Royal Burgh Stirling Visitor Centre ☎ (01786) 4799 – Pirnhall, Motorway Service Area, junction 9, M 9 ☎ (01786) 814111 (April-October).

Edinburgh 37 – Dunfermline 23 – Falkirk 14 – Glasgow 28 – Greenock 52 – Motherwell 3(Oban 87 – Perth 35.

Plan opposite

Stirling Highland, Spittal St, FK8 1DU, ☎ (01786) 272727, stirling@paramount-hotels .uk, Fax (01786) 272829, « Converted Victorian high school », , , , squash – |♦| rest, TV ♿ P – 100. MC AE ① VISA JCB B
Scholars : **Meals** (closed Saturday lunch) 13.95/22.50 and a la carte 19.85/30.65 **t.** 12.95 12.95 – **94 rm** 110.00/150.00 **t.**, 2 suites – SB.

Park Lodge, 32 Park Terr, FK8 2JS, ☎ (01786) 474862, info@parklodge.n Fax (01786) 449748, « Part Georgian, part Victorian house, antiques », – ⊁ TV P 100. MC VISA. ⚡ B
closed 25 December-2 January – **Meals** (closed Sunday) 10.00/21.00 and a la carte 12.3 28.80 **st.** 10.95 – **10 rm** 65.00/95.00 **st.** – SB.

Express by Holiday Inn without rest., Springkerse Business Park, FK7 7XH, East : 2 by A 905 off A 91 ☎ (01786) 449922, info@hiex-stirling.com, Fax (01786) 449932 – |♦| TV ♿ P – 30. MC AE ① VISA
80 rm 56.95.

STIRLING

rnton Street .... B 2
restone Crescent .... A 3
usewayhead Road ..... A, B 4
rn Exchange Road .... B 5
rnton Road .... A 7
xithill Road .... A 8
ummond Place .... B 9
Dumbarton Road .... B 10
Goosecroft Road .... B 12
King Street .... B 13
Leisure Centre .... B
Murray Place .... B 15
Newhouse .... A 16
Park Place .... A 18
Port Street .... B
Queen Street .... B 20
Randolph Terrace .... A 22
St. John Street .... B 23
St. Mary's Wynd .... B 24
Seaforth Place .... B 25
Shirra's Brae Road .... A 26
Spittal Street .... B 27
Thistle Centre .... B
Union Street .... B 28
Upper Craigs .... B 29
Weaver Row .... A 31

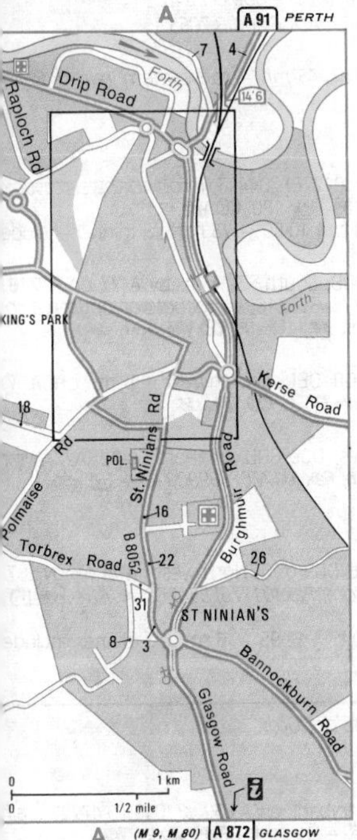

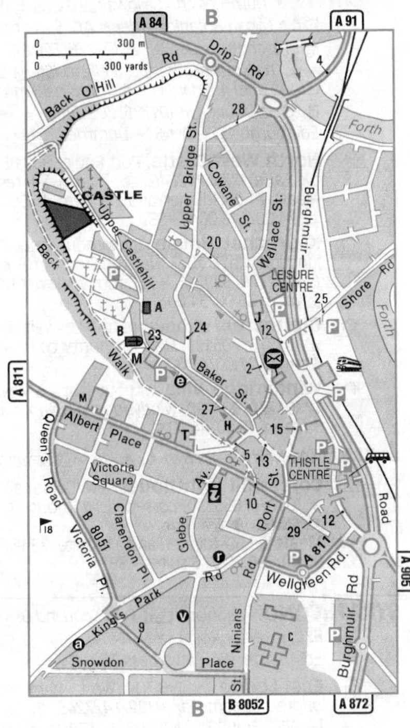

Travel Inn, Whins of Milton, Glasgow Rd, FK7 8EX, South : 3 m. by A 9 on A 872 ☎ (01786) 811256, *Fax (01786) 816415* – ❙$❙, ⇋ rm, TV ♿ P. VISA. ⚡
Meals (grill rest.) – **40 rm** 41.95 **t.**

Ashgrove House without rest., 2 Park Ave, FK8 2LX, ☎ (01786) 472640, *Fax (01786) 472640*, – ⇋ TV P. VISA. ⚡ B r
April-October – **3 rm** ☐ 40.00/55.00 **st.**

Number 10 without rest., Gladstone Pl, FK8 2NN, ☎ (01786) 472681, *cameron-10@tiny online.co.uk, Fax (01786) 472681*, – ⇋ TV. ⚡ B v
3 rm ☐ 30.00/44.00 **st.**

West Plean House without rest., FK7 8HA, South : 3 ½ m. on A 872 (Denny rd) ☎ (01786) 812208, *west.plean@virgin.net, Fax (01786) 480550*, « Working farm », – ⇋ TV P.
closed January and December – **3 rm** ☐ 34.00/54.00 **st.**

TIRLING SERVICE AREA *Stirling* 401 I 15 – ✉ *Stirling.*

Travelodge without rest., Pirnhall roundabout, Snabhead, FK7 8EU, at junction 9 of M 9 ☎ (01786) 813614, *Fax (01786) 815900* – ⇋ TV ♿ P. VISA JCB. ⚡
37 rm 39.95 **t.**

TORNOWAY *Western Isles (Outer Hebrides)* 401 A 9 – *see Lewis and Harris (Isle of).*

SCOTLAND

STRACHUR *Argyll and Bute* 401 E 15 – *pop. 628.*
Edinburgh 112 – Glasgow 66 – Inverness 162 – Perth 101.

The Creggans Inn, PA27 8BX, (01369) 860279, *info@creggans-inn.co.u* *Fax (01369) 860637,* ← Loch Fyne, « Lochside setting », – TV P. MC VISA.
Meals (bar lunch)/dinner 21.50/28.50 **t.** 11.50 – **13 rm** 100.00/136.00 **t.**, 1 suite – SB

STRANRAER *Dumfries and Galloway* 401 402 E 19 *Scotland G. – pop. 11 348.*
Exc. : *Logan Botanic Garden★ AC, S : 11 m. by A 77, A 716 and B 7065.*
18 *Creachmore, Leswalt (01776) 870245.*
to Northern Ireland (Belfast) (Stena Line) (1 h 45 mn) – to Northern Ireland (Belfa (Stena Line) 4-5 daily (1 h 45 mn/3 h 15 mn).
28 Harbour St (01776) 702595.
Edinburgh 132 – Ayr 51 – Dumfries 75.

North West Castle, Port Rodie, DG9 8EH, (01776) 704413, *info@northwestcastle.c uk, Fax (01776) 702646,* – , rest, TV P – 180. MC VISA
Meals 21.00 (dinner) and a la carte 14.50/20.00 **t.** 10.50 – **73 rm** (dinner include 74.00/148.00 **t.** – SB.

Kildrochet House without rest., DG9 9BB, South : 3 ¼ m. by A 77 on A 716 junction with B 7077 (Newton Stewart rd) (01776) 820216, *kildrochet@compuserve.cor Fax (01776) 820216,* « 18C former dower house », – P. MC VISA JCB.
3 rm 33.00/54.00.

Glenotter without rest., Leswalt Rd, DG9 0EP, Northwest : 1 m. on A 7 (01776) 703199, *lilian@glenotter.co.uk,* – TV P. MC VISA.
3 rm 27.00/44.00.

Windyridge Villa without rest., 5 Royal Cres, DG9 8HB, off Port Rodie (A77 Ayr r (01776) 889900, *windyridge-villa@hotmail.com, Fax (01776) 889900* – TV
3 rm 25.00/44.00 **st.**

at Kirkcolm *Northwest : 6 m. by A 718 – Stranraer.*

Corsewall Lighthouse , Corsewall Point, DG9 0QG, Northwest : 4 ¼ m. by B 7: (01776) 853220, *corsewall_lighthouse@msn.com, Fax (01776) 854231,* ←, – TV P. MC AE VISA JCB
Meals 29.50 (dinner) and a la carte 23.95/27.50 **t.** 12.95 – **6 rm** (dinner include 95.00/220.00 **t.**, 3 suites – SB.

STRATHCONON *Highland* 401 F 11 *Scotland G. – Muir of Ord.*
Exc. : *Wester Ross★★★.*
Edinburgh 184 – Inverness 28.

East Lodge , IV6 7QQ, West : 11 m. from Marybank off A 832 (01997) 477222, *elh btinternet.com, Fax (01997) 477243,* ←, , , – rest, TV P. MC AE VISA
Meals (bar lunch)/dinner a la carte 15.00/32.00 **t.** 7.50 – **10 rm** 45.00/90.00 **t.** – SB.

STRATHKINNESS *Fife* 401 L 14 – *see St. Andrews.*

STRATHPEFFER *Highland* 401 G 11 – *pop. 966.*
18 *Strathpeffer Spa (01997) 421219.*
The Square (01997) 421415 (April-October).
Edinburgh 174 – Inverness 18.

Craigvar without rest., The Square, IV14 9DL, (01997) 421622, *ms@gilsmith.demon.c uk, Fax (01997) 421796,* – TV P. MC VISA.
closed Christmas and New Year – **3 rm** 28.00/56.00 **st.**

STRATHYRE *Stirling* 401 H 15 *Scotland G. – Callander.*
Exc. : *The Trossachs★★★ (Loch Katherine★★) SW : 14 m. by A 84 and A 821 – Hilltc viewpoint★★★ (★★★) SW : 16½ m. by A 84 and A 821.*
Edinburgh 62 – Glasgow 53 – Perth 42.

Ardoch Lodge , FK18 8NF, West : ¼ m. (01877) 384666, *ardoch@btinternet.cor Fax (01877) 384666,* ←, , , – rest, P. MC VISA JCB
Easter-October – **Meals** (by arrangement) 24.00 **t.** – **3 rm** 38.00/72.00 **t.** – SB.

Creagan House with rm, FK18 8ND, on A 84 (01877) 384638, *eatandstay@creaga house.co.uk, Fax (01877) 384319,* ← – P. MC AE VISA
closed February and 1 week October – **Meals** (booking essential) (dinner only) 19.75 23.75 **t.** 9.90 – **5 rm** 52.50/85.00 **t.** – SB.

TROMNESS *Orkney Islands* 401 *K 7 – see Orkney Islands.*

TRONTIAN *Highland* 401 *D 13.*

Argyll ☎ (01967) 402131 (April-October).

Edinburgh 139 – Fort William 23 – Oban 66.

Kilcamb Lodge, PH36 4HY, ☎ (01967) 402257, *kilcamblodge@aol.com, Fax (01967) 402041*, ≤, « Lochside setting », – TV P. MC VISA JCB
closed January except New Year, February and December – **Meals** (light lunch) (dinner booking essential for non-residents) 20.50/29.50 **st.** 9.75 – 12.50 – **11 rm** 60.00/100.00 **st.**

TRUY *Highland* 401 *F 11.*

Edinburgh 180 – Inverness 19 – Kyle of Lochalsh 82.

The Glass at the Struy Inn, IV4 7JS, ☎ (01463) 761219, *glassrest@supanet.com* – rest, P. MC VISA JCB
closed Monday and Tuesday lunch, Tuesday dinner and Wednesday October-March – **Meals** (booking essential) a la carte 19.40/23.40 **t.** 9.50.

WINTON *Borders* 401 402 *N 16 – pop. 472 –* ✉ *Duns.*

Edinburgh 49 – Berwick-upon-Tweed 13 – Glasgow 93 – Newcastle upon Tyne 66.

The Wheatsheaf with rm, TD11 3JJ, ☎ (01890) 860257, *reception@wheatsheaf-swinton.co.uk, Fax (01890) 860688*, – TV P. MC VISA JCB
closed last 2 weeks January, 25 December, New Year and first week July – **Meals** *(closed Monday for non-residents)* a la carte 18.00/26.50 **t.** 10.95 – **7 rm** 55.00/105.00 **t.** – SB.

AIN *Highland* 401 *H 10 – pop. 4 540.*

Tain, Chapel Rd ☎ (01862) 892314 – Tarbat, Portmahomack ☎ (01862) 871512.

Edinburgh 191 – Inverness 35 – Wick 91.

Mansfield House, Scotsburn Rd, IV19 1PR, ☎ (01862) 892052, *info@mansfield-house.co.uk, Fax (01862) 892260*, – TV P – 35. MC AE VISA
Fowler's : **Meals** (bar lunch)/dinner 25.00 and a la carte 13.00/20.00 **t.** 16.00 – **19 rm** 65.00/170.00 **t.** – SB.

Morangie House, Morangie Rd, IV19 1PY, ☎ (01862) 892281, *wynne@morangiehotel.com, Fax (01862) 892872*, – rm, TV P. MC AE VISA
Meals a la carte 15.00/27.00 **t.** 11.50 – **26 rm** 75.00/120.00 – SB.

Aldie House without rest., IV19 1LZ, Southeast : 1 ½ m. by B 9174 off A 9 ☎ (01862) 893787, *info@aldiehouse.co.uk, Fax (01862) 893787*, ≤, – TV P. MC VISA.
3 rm 32.00/52.00 **st.**

Golf View House without rest., 13 Knockbreck Rd, IV19 1BN, ☎ (01862) 892856, *golfview@btinternet.com, Fax (01862) 892172*, ≤, – TV P. MC VISA.
closed January and December – **5 rm** 35.00/50.00.

t Cadboll *Southeast : 8½ m. by A 9 and B 9165 (Portmahomack rd) off Hilton rd –* ✉ *Tain.*

Glenmorangie House, Fearn, IV20 1XP, ☎ (01862) 871671, *relax@glenmorangieplc.co.uk, Fax (01862) 871625*, ≤, « Distillery owned, restored part 17C house », – TV P. MC AE VISA
Meals (booking essential to non-residents) (lunch by arrangement) (communal dining) 15.00/38.50 – **9 rm** (dinner included) 120.00/260.00 **t.** – SB.

ALLADALE *Highland* 401 *D 10 Scotland G. –* ✉ *Achnasheen.*

Env. : *Wester Ross★★★ – Loch Maree★★★ – Victoria Falls★, N : 2 m. by A 832.*

Edinburgh 218 – Inverness 62 – Kyle of Lochalsh 58.

Old Mill Highland Lodge, Loch Maree, IV22 2HL, ☎ (01445) 760271, – P
closed mid October-mid December – **Meals** 7.00 – **6 rm** (dinner included) 140.00 **st.** – SB.

ALMINE *Highland* 401 *G 8 –* ✉ *Lairg.*

Edinburgh 245 – Inverness 86 – Thurso 48.

Cloisters without rest., Church Holme, IV27 4YP, ☎ (01847) 601286, *reception@cloistertal.demon.co.uk, Fax (01847) 601286*, ≤ Rabbit Islands and Tongue Bay, – TV P
3 rm 25.00/40.00.

TARBERT *Argyll and Bute* 401 D 16 – *see Kintyre (Peninsula).*

TARBERT *Western Isles (Outer Hebrides)* 401 Z 10 – *see Lewis and Harris (Isle of).*

TARBET *Argyll and Bute* 401 F 15 – ✉ *Arrochar.*
Edinburgh 88 – Glasgow 42 – Inverness 138 – Perth 78.

Bonnie Bank without rest., Loch Lomond, G83 7DJ, South : 1 ½ m. on A 8 ℘ (01301) 702300, *info@bonniebank.f9.co.uk, Fax (01301) 702946,* ≤, « Lochside setting » – ✈ [TV] [P]. MC VISA JCB. ✻
4 rm ☕ 45.00/80.00 s.

Lomond View without rest., G83 7DG, on A 82 ℘ (01301) 702477, *lomondview@talk2 com, Fax (01301) 702477,* ≤ Loch Lomond, – ✈ [TV] [P]. MC VISA. ✻
3 rm ☕ 45.00/60.00 st.

TAYVALLICH *Argyll and Bute* 401 D 15 – ✉ *Lochgilphead.*
Edinburgh 148 – Glasgow 103 – Inverness 157.

Tayvallich Inn, PA31 8PL, ℘ (01546) 870282, *tayvallich.inn@virgin.ne Fax (01546) 870333,* ≤, , « Lochside setting » – [P]. MC VISA JCB
closed 25-26 December and 1-2 January – **Meals** - Seafood specialities - a la carte 17.85 30.35 t. 12.00.

Les prix — Pour toutes précisions sur les prix indiqués dans ce guide, reportez-vous aux pages de l'introduction.

THORNHILL *Dumfries and Galloway* 401 402 I 18 *Scotland G. – pop. 1 633.*
Env. : *Drumlanrig Castle★★ (cabinets★) AC, NW : 4 m. by A 76.*
Edinburgh 64 – Ayr 44 – Dumfries 15 – Glasgow 63.

Trigony House with rm, Closeburn, DG3 5EZ, South : 1 ½ m. on A 76 ℘ (01848) 331211, *nfo@trigonyhotel.co.uk, Fax (01848) 331303,* , , – ✈ rest, [TV] [P]. MC VISA
Meals a la carte 12.90/20.20 **t.** 10.00 – **8 rm** ☕ 40.00/80.00 **t.** – SB.

THORNHILL *Stirling* 401 H 15 – *pop. 550* – ✉ *Stirling.*
18 *Thornhill, Blacknest* ℘ *(01848) 330546.*
Edinburgh 46 – Glasgow 36.

Corshill Cottage without rest., FK8 3QD, East : 1 m. on A 873 ℘ (01786) 85027(*corshillbandb@talk21.com, Fax (01786) 850270,* – ✈ [P]. MC VISA. ✻
3 rm ☕ 30.00/52.00 s.

THURSO *Highland* 401 J 8 *Scotland G. – pop. 9 110.*
Exc. : *Strathy Point★ (≤★★★) W : 22 m. by A 836.*
18 *Newlands of Geise* ℘ *(01847) 893807.*
from Scrabster to Stromness (Orkney Islands) (P & O Scottish Ferries) (2 h).
Riverside ℘ *(01847) 892371 (April-October).*
Edinburgh 289 – Inverness 133 – Wick 21.

Forss House , Bridge of Forss, KW14 7XY, West : 5 ½ m. on A 836 ℘ (01847) 86120 *jamie@forsshouse.freeserve.co.uk, Fax (01847) 861301,* , , – ✈ rest, [TV] & [P]. MC AE VISA
closed 23 December-6 January – **Meals** (bar lunch)/dinner 22.50 **t.** 12.90 – **9 rm** ☕ 59.50 110.00 **t.**, 1 suite.

Murray House, 1 Campbell St, KW14 7HD, ℘ (01847) 895759, *angela@murrayhousebb com* – ✈ [TV] [P]. ✻
Meals 10.00 **st.** 9.00 – **4 rm** ☕ 23.00/50.00 **st.**

TIGHNABRUAICH *Argyll and Bute* 401 E 16.
Edinburgh 113 – Glasgow 63 – Oban 66.

Royal, PA21 2BE, ℘ (01700) 811239, *info@royalhotel.org.uk, Fax (01700) 811300,* ≤ « Lochside setting » – ✈ [TV] [P]. MC VISA
closed 25 December – **Meals** (bar lunch)/dinner 22.95/29.95 **t.** 10.95 – **11 rm** ☕ 87.00 144.00 **t.** – SB.

SCOTLAND

LLICOULTRY *Clackmannanshire* 401 I 15 – *pop. 4 586.*

Alva Rd ☎ *(01259) 50124.*

Edinburgh 35 – Dundee 43 – Glasgow 38.

Harviestoun Country Inn, Dollar Rd, FK13 6PQ, East : ¼ m. by A 91 ☎ (01259) 752522, *Fax (01259) 752523*, – TV P – 70. VISA.
closed 24 December-5 January – **Meals** a la carte 16.00/23.00 **t.** 10.00 – **11 rm** 50.00/75.00 **t.**

RORAN *Argyll and Bute – see Mull (Isle of).*

OBERMORY *Argyll and Bute* 401 B 14 – *see Mull (Isle of).*

ONGUE *Highland* 401 G 8 *Scotland G. – pop. 552 – ✉ Lairg.*

Exc. : *Cape Wrath★★★ (≤★★) W : 44 m. (including ferry crossing) by A 838 – Ben Loyal★★, S : 8 m. by A 836 – Ben Hope★ (≤★★★) SW : 15 m. by A 838 – Strathy Point★ (≤★★★) E : 22 m. by A 836 – Torrisdale Bay★ (≤★★) NE : 8 m. by A 836.*

Edinburgh 257 – Inverness 101 – Thurso 43.

Ben Loyal, Main St, IV27 4XE, ☎ (01847) 611216, *benloyalhotel@btinternet.com, Fax (01847) 611212*, ≤ Ben Loyal and Kyle of Tongue – rest, TV P. VISA
Meals (bar lunch)/dinner 24.00 **t.** 10.00 – **11 rm** 38.00/80.00 **t.**

Se cercate un albergo tranquillo, oltre a consultare le carte dell'introduzione, rintracciate nell'elenco degli esercizi quelli con il simbolo o .

ORRIDON *Highland* 401 D 11 *Scotland G. – ✉ Achnasheen.*

Env. : *Wester Ross★★★.*

Edinburgh 234 – Inverness 62 – Kyle of Lochalsh 44.

Loch Torridon , IV22 2EY, South : 1 ½ m. on A 896 ☎ (01445) 791242, *enquiries@lochtorridonhotel.com, Fax (01445) 791296*, ≤ Upper Loch Torridon and mountains, « 19C former shooting lodge », , , – TV P – 25. AE VISA
closed 3 weeks January and restricted opening February-March – **Meals** (booking essential) (bar lunch)/dinner 38.00/42.00 **t.** 14.00 – **18 rm** 90.00/260.00 **t.**, 2 suites – SB.

Ben Damph Lodge , IV22 2EY, South : 1 ½ m. on A 896 ☎ (01445) 791251, *bendamph@lochtorridonhotel.com, Fax (01445) 791296* – TV P. AE VISA JCB
April-October – **Meals** (grill rest.) a la carte approx. 14.00 **st.** 7.50 – **12 rm** 50.00/70.00 **t.** – SB.

ROON *South Ayrshire* 401 402 G 17 – *pop. 15 116.*

18, 18, 18 *Troon Municipal, Harling Drive* ☎ *(01292) 312464.*

to Northern Ireland (Belfast) (Sea Containers Ferries Scotland Ltd) 2 daily (2 h 30 mn).

Edinburgh 77 – Ayr 7 – Glasgow 31.

Lochgreen House , Monktonhill Rd, Southwood, KA10 7EN, Southeast : 2 m. on B 749 ☎ (01292) 313343, *lochgreen@costley-hotels.co.uk, Fax (01292) 318661*, « Edwardian house, antiques », , , – , rest, TV P – 30. AE VISA.
Meals 27.90 (dinner) and lunch a la carte 20.40/27.90 **t.** 16.50 – **14 rm** 99.00/160.00 **t.**, 1 suite – SB.

The Marine, 8 Crosbie Rd, KA10 6HE, ☎ (01292) 314444, *marine@paramount-hotels.co.uk, Fax (01292) 316922*, ≤, , , , squash – , rest, TV P – 220. AE VISA JCB
Fairways : **Meals** (restricted opening in winter) 11.00/22.50 12.95 – 12.50 – **69 rm** 110.00/160.00 **t.**, 5 suites – SB.

Piersland House, 15 Craigend Rd, KA10 6HD, ☎ (01292) 314747, *reservations@piersland.co.uk, Fax (01292) 315613*, – rest, TV P – 70. AE VISA
Meals (bar lunch Monday-Saturday)/dinner a la carte 17.85/26.85 **st.** 10.95 – **15 rm** 82.50/165.00 **st.**, **13 suites** 135.00/165.00 **st.** – SB.

t Loans *East : 2 m. on A 759 – ✉ Troon.*

XX **Highgrove House** with rm, Old Loans Rd, KA10 7HL, East : ¼ m. on Dundonald rd ☎ (01292) 312511, *highgrove@costley-hotels.co.uk, Fax (01292) 318228*, ≤, – TV P. AE VISA.
Meals a la carte 16.00/25.00 **t.** 9.95 – **9 rm** 69.00/95.00 **t.** – SB.

SCOTLAND

TURNBERRY *South Ayrshire* 401 402 F 18 *Scotland G. – ✉ Girvan.*
Env. : *Culzean Castle★ AC (setting★★★, Oval Staircase★★) NE : 5 m. by A 719.*
Edinburgh 97 – Ayr 15 – Glasgow 51 – Stranraer 36.

Turnberry, KA26 9LT, on A 719 ☎ (01655) 331000, *turnberry@westin.co* *Fax (01655) 331706,* « Part Edwardian, ≤ golf courses, bay, Ailsa Craig and Mull Kintyre », squash – |‡|, ✻ rest, ▤ rest, TV P – 150. MO AE VISA JCB
Turnberry : Meals (dinner only and Sunday lunch)/dinner 49.00 t. 25.00 – ***Terra Brasserie :*** Meals a la carte 28.35/38.35 t. 20.00 – ***Tappie Toorie Grill :*** Meals (lur only) a la carte 15.50/28.50 t. 15.00 – **202 rm** 265.00/305.00 t., 19 suites – SB.

TWYNHOLM *Dumfries and Galloway* 402 H 19 – *pop. 1 068.*
Edinburgh 107 – Ayr 54 – Dumfries 27 – Stranraer 48.

Fresh Fields, Arden Rd, DG6 4PB, Southwest : ¾ m. by Burn Brae ☎ (01557) 8602 *Fax (01557) 860221,* – ✻ P
March-October – **Meals** (by arrangement) 15.00 8.50 – **5 rm** 28.00/56.00.

UDDINGSTON *South Lanarkshire* 401 402 H 16 – *pop. 5 367 – ✉ Glasgow.*
Coatbridge, Townhead Rd ☎ (01236) 28975.
Edinburgh 41 – Glasgow 10.

Redstones, 8-10 Glasgow Rd, G71 7AS, ☎ (01698) 813774, *redstones@morris-inns.co* *Fax (01698) 815319* – ✻ rm, TV P – 30. MO AE ⓓ VISA.
closed 1 January – ***Le Papillon :*** Meals (dinner only) 22.00 and a la carte 25.00/30.00 st ***Brooklands :*** Meals a la carte 13.85/27.65 – **14 rm** 60.00/105.00 st.

Travel Inn, 601 Hamilton Rd, G71 7SA, Northwest : 2 m. by B 7071 and A 74 follow signs for Glasgow Zoo park ☎ (0141) 773 1133, *Fax (0141) 771 8354,* – |‡|, ✻ r ▤ rest, TV & P. MO AE ⓓ VISA.
Meals (grill rest.) – **66 rm** 41.95 t.

UIST (Isles of) *Western Isles (Outer Hebrides)* 401 XY 10 /11/12 – *pop. 3 510.*
see Liniclate.
from Lochboisdale to Oban via Isle of Barra (Castlebay) and Mallaig (Mainland) (Calec nian MacBrayne Ltd) (summer only) – from Lochmaddy to Isle of Skye (Uig) (Caledon MacBrayne Ltd) 1-3 daily (1 h 50 mn) – from Otternish to Isle of Harris (Leverbur (Caledonian MacBrayne Ltd) (1 h 10 mn).

NORTH UIST.

Grimsay.

Glendale without rest., 7 Kallin, HS6 5HY, ☎ (01870) 602029, *glendale@ecosse.net,* – ✻ P.
closed Christmas and New Year – **3 rm** 23.00/40.00 st.

Lochmaddy.

Lochmaddy, HS6 5AA, ☎ (01876) 500331, *info@lochmaddyhotel.co.* *Fax (01876) 500210,* ≤, – ✻ rest, TV P. MO AE VISA
Meals (bar lunch)/dinner 18.00 and a la carte 12.50/23.00 t. 9.00 – **15 rm** 42.5 80.00 t. – SB.

BENBECULA.

Liniclate.

Benbecula Airport : ☎ (01870) 602051.

Dark Island, HS7 5PJ, ☎ (01870) 603030, *Fax (01870) 602347* – TV P – 100. MO VISA
closed 26 December and 1 January – **Meals** 11.75/20.00 and a la carte 16.00/38.50 t. 8. – **42 rm** 65.00/95.00 st. – SB.

SOUTH UIST.

Lochboisdale.

Brae Lea, Lasgair, HS8 5TH, Northwest : 1 m. by A 865 ☎ (01878) 70049 *Fax (01878) 700497,* – ✻ rm, P
Meals (by arrangement) 15.00 **st.** – **6 rm** 28.00/60.00 **st.** – SB.

LLAPOOL *Highland* 401 E 10 *Scotland G. – pop. 1 231.*

See : *Town*★.

Env. : *Wester Ross*★★★ *– Loch Broom*★★.

Exc. : *Falls of Measach*★★, *S : 11 m. by A 835 and A 832 - Corrieshalloch Gorge*★, *SE : 10 m. by A 835 – Northwards to Lochinver*★★, *Morefield (*≤★★ *of Ullapool),* ≤★ *Loch Broom.*

to Isle of Lewis (Stornoway) (Caledonian MacBrayne Ltd) (2 h 40 mn).

Argyle St ℘ *(01854) 612135.*

Edinburgh 215 – Inverness 59.

Ardvreck without rest., Morefield Brae, IV26 2TH, Northwest : 2 m. by A 835 ℘ (01854) 612028, *ardvreck.guesthouse@btinternet.com, Fax (01854) 613000,* ≤ Loch Broom and mountains, – TV P. MC VISA.
– **10 rm** 26.00/56.00 **t.**

The Sheiling without rest., Garve Rd, IV26 2SX, ℘ (01854) 612947, *Fax (01854) 612947,* ≤ Loch Broom, , , – P. MC VISA.
closed Christmas and New Year – **6 rm** 35.00/52.00 **st.**

Point Cottage without rest., West Shore St, IV26 2UR, ℘ (01854) 612494, *stay@pointcottage.co.uk, Fax (01854) 613464,* ≤ Loch Broom, – TV P.
14 February-October – **3 rm** 45.00/52.00 **st.**

Dromnan without rest., Garve Rd, IV26 2SX, ℘ (01854) 612333, *dromnan@msn.com, Fax (01854) 613364,* ≤, – TV P. MC VISA.
7 rm 40.00/54.00 **st.**

The Guide is updated annually so renew your Guide every year.

NST (Island of) *Shetland Islands* 401 R 1 – *see Shetland Islands.*

PHALL *West Lothian* 401 J 16 – *pop. 14 600.*

Uphall, Houston Mains ℘ *(01506) 856404.*

Edinburgh 13 – Glasgow 32.

Houstoun House, EH52 6JS, ℘ (01506) 853831, *houston@macdonald-hotels.co.uk, Fax (01506) 854220,* « Gardens », , , , , – TV P – 400. MC AE VISA.
The Great Dining rooms : Meals *(closed Saturday lunch)* 19.50 (lunch) and dinner a la carte 28.20/39.00 **st.** 14.50 – ***The Bistro :*** Meals *(closed Sunday)* (dinner only) a la carte 15.00/29.50 **t.** 14.50 – 12.50 – **72 rm** 75.00/220.00 **st.** – SB.

PPER LARGO *Fife – see Lundin Links.*

EENSGARTH *Shetland Islands – see Shetland Islands (Mainland).*

VATERNISH *Highland – see Skye (Isle of).*

VHITE NESS *Shetland Islands* 401 Q 3 – *see Shetland Islands (Mainland).*

VHITING BAY *North Ayrshire* 401 402 E 17 – *see Arran (Isle of).*

VICK *Highland* 401 K 8 *Scotland G. – pop. 9 713.*

Exc. : *Duncansby Head*★ *(Stacks of Duncansby*★★*) N : 14 m. by A 9 – Grey Cairns of Camster*★ *(Long Cairn*★★*) S : 17 m. by A 9 – The Hill O'Many Stanes*★, *S : 10 m. by A 9.*

Reiss ℘ *(01955) 602726.*

Wick Airport : ℘ *(01955) 602215, N : 1 m.*

Whitechapel Rd ℘ *(01955) 602596.*

Edinburgh 282 – Inverness 126.

The Clachan without rest., South Rd, KW1 5NJ, South : ¾ m. on A 99 ℘ (01955) 605384, *enquiry@theclachan.co.uk,* – TV.
closed Christmas and New Year – **3 rm** 25.00/44.00 **st.**

Meadowbank House without rest., Thurso Rd, KW1 5LE, West : 1 m. on A 882 ℘ (01955) 603760 – TV P.
April-September – **3 rm** 25.00/40.00.

SCOTLAND

WIGTOWN *Dumfries and Galloway* 401 G 19 *Scotland G.* – *pop. 1 344* – ✉ *Newton Stewart.*

Exc. : *Whithorn Museum (early Christian crosses★★) S : 10 m. by A 746.*

Wigtown & Bladnoch, Lightlands Terr. ☏ *(01988) 403354.*

Edinburgh 137 – Ayr 61 – Dumfries 61 – Stranraer 26.

Corsemalzie House, DG8 9RL, Southwest : 6 ½ m. by A 714 on B 70
☏ (01988) 860254, *corsemalzie@ndirect.co.uk, Fax (01988) 860213,* –
MC AE VISA
closed 21 January-5 March and 4 days Christmas – **Meals** 24.25 (dinner) and a la car
11.00/22.70 **t.** 8.80 – **14 rm** 66.00/104.00 **t.** – SB.

WORMIT *Fife* 401 L 14 – ✉ *Newport-on-Tay.*

Scotscraig, Golf Rd, Tayport ☏ *(01382) 552515.*

Edinburgh 53 – Dundee 6 – St. Andrews 12.

Sandford Country House, DD6 8RG, South : 2 m. on B 946 ☏ (01382) 54180
sandford.hotel@btinternet.com, Fax (01382) 542136, – rest, – 45.
VISA
Meals (dinner only) 27.50 **st.** 10.00 – **16 rm** 80.00/100.00 **st.** – SB.

Wales

Place with at least

a hotel or restaurant — ● Adare
a pleasant hotel or restaurant
a quiet, secluded hotel
a restaurant with ✿, ✿✿, ✿✿✿, Meals

Localité offrant au moins

une ressource hôtelière — ● Adare
un hôtel ou restaurant agréable
un hôtel très tranquille, isolé
une bonne table à ✿, ✿✿, ✿✿✿, Meals

La località possiede come minimo

una risorsa alberghiera — ● Adare
Albergo o ristorante ameno
un albergo molto tranquillo, isolato
un'ottima tavola con ✿, ✿✿, ✿✿✿, Meals

Ort mit mindestens

einem Hotel oder Restaurant — ● Adare
ein angenehmes Hotel oder Restaurant
einem sehr ruhigen und abgelegenen Hotel
einem Restaurant mit ✿, ✿✿, ✿✿✿, Meals

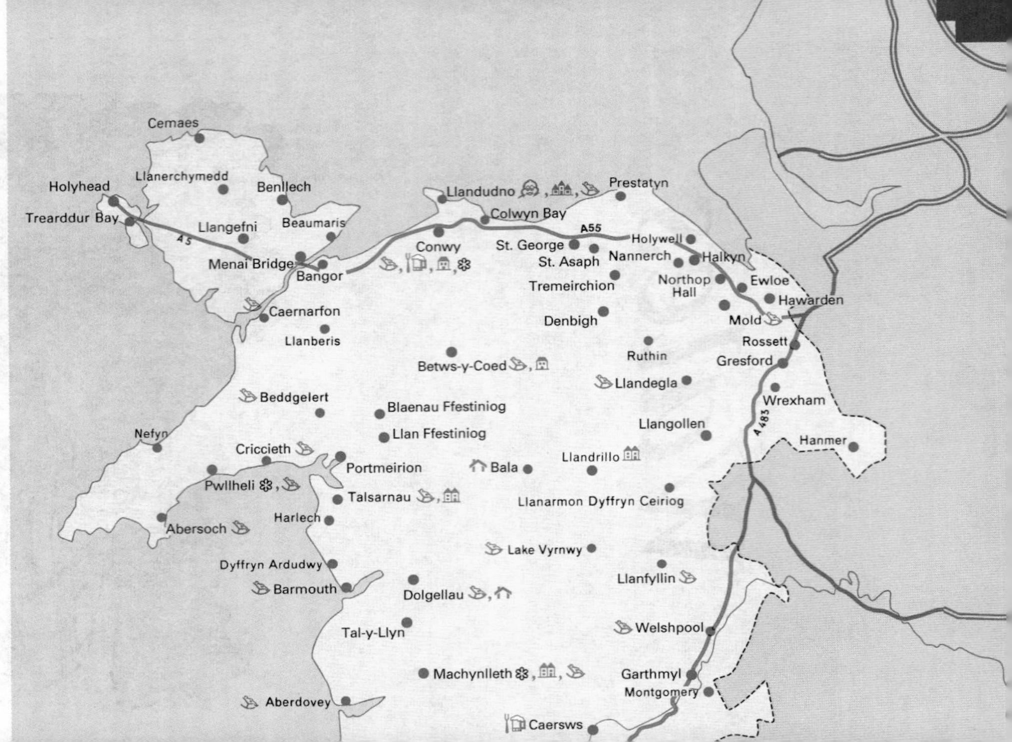

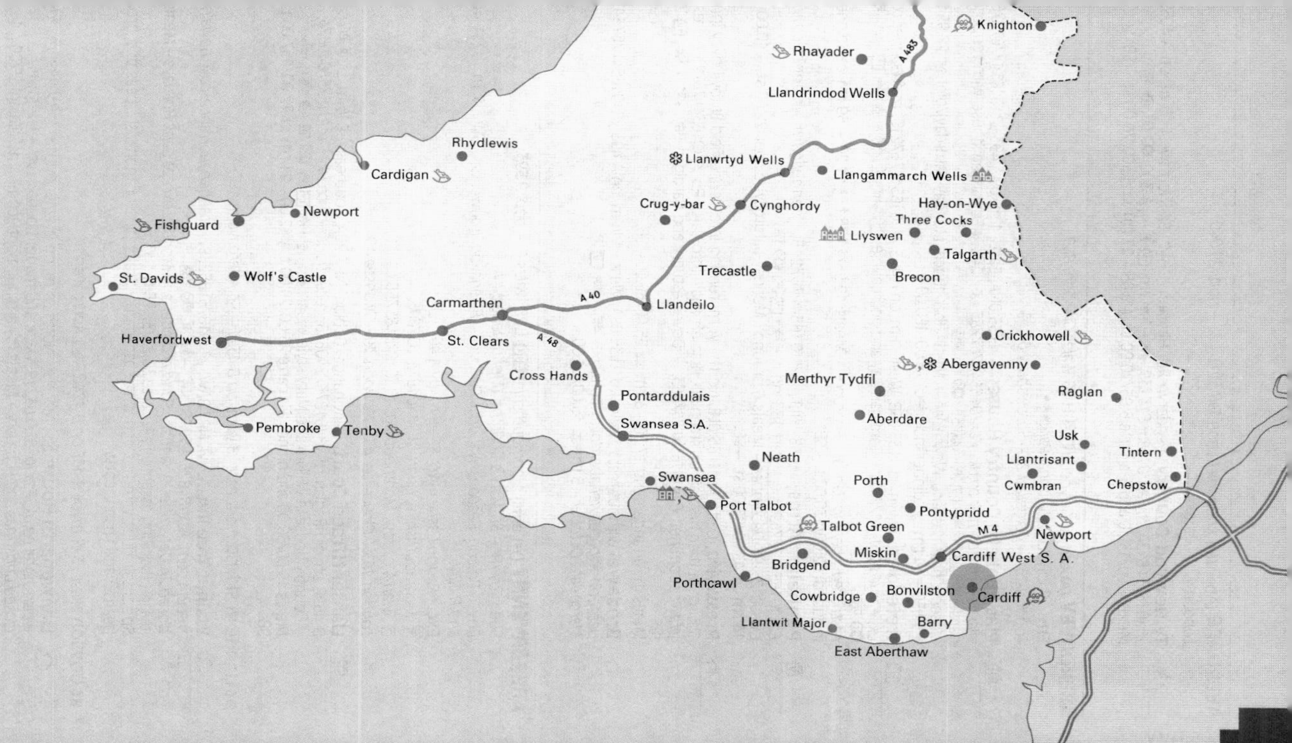
Knighton
Rhayader
A 483
Llandrindod Wells
Rhydlewis
Cardigan
Llanwrtyd Wells
Llangammarch Wells
Crug-y-bar
Cynghordy
Hay-on-Wye
Three Cocks
Newport
Fishguard
Llyswen
Talgarth
St. Davids
Wolf's Castle
Trecastle
Brecon
Carmarthen
A 40
Llandeilo
Haverfordwest
St. Clears
A 48
Crickhowell
Abergavenny
Cross Hands
Merthyr Tydfil
Raglan
Pontarddulais
Aberdare
Swansea S.A.
Pembroke
Tenby
Usk
Tintern
Neath
Llantrisant
Swansea
Porth
Cwmbran
Chepstow
Port Talbot
Pontypridd
Talbot Green
M 4
Newport
Miskin
Cardiff West S. A.
Bridgend
Porthcawl
Bonvilston
Cowbridge
Cardiff
Barry
Llantwit Major
East Aberthaw

ABERDARE **(Aberdâr)** *Rhondda Cynon Taff* 403 J 28 – *pop. 29 040.*
London 178 – Cardiff 23 – Swansea 27.

Ty Newydd Country, Penderyn Rd, Hirwaun, CF44 9SX, Northwest : 5 m. on A 405 (01685) 813433, *Fax (01685) 813139,* – rm, – 300.
Meals 5.00/13.10 and a la carte 6.95/20.90 **st.** 9.05 – **27 rm** 39.00/70.00 **st.** – SB.

ABERDOVEY **(Aberdyfi)** *Gwynedd* 403 H 26 *Wales G.* – *pop. 869.*
Env. : *Snowdonia National Park★★★.*
London 230 – Dolgellau 25 – Shrewsbury 66.

Plas Penhelig Country House , LL35 0NA, East : 1 m. by A 493 (01654) 767676 *plaspen@netcomuk.co.uk, Fax (01654) 767783,* ≤, , « Edwardian house with terraced gardens », – – 35.
closed Christmas and New Year – **Meals** (bar lunch Monday-Saturday)/dinner 28.95 12.50 – **14 rm** (dinner included) 75.00/150.00 **t.**

Trefeddian, Tywyn Rd, LL35 0SB, West : 1 m. on A 493 (01654) 767213, *tref@saqnet.co.uk, Fax (01654) 767777,* ≤ Cardigan Bay and golf course, , , , –
restricted opening January-February – **Meals** 12.95/21.75 **t.** 11.20 – **59 rm** (dinner included) 62.00/130.00 **t.** – SB.

Penhelig Arms, LL35 0LT, (01654) 767215, *penheligarms@saqnet.co.uk, Fax (01654) 767690,* ≤, « Part 18C inn » –
closed 25-26 December – **Meals** (bar lunch Monday-Saturday)/dinner 22.00 **st.** 10.00 **14 rm** 43.00/96.00 **st.** – SB.

Preswylfa, Garth Rd, LL35 0LE, North : ¼ m. turning into Copperfield St (by Dovey Inn) Church St then first left up steep hill, first left again into Garth Rd (01654) 767239, *preswylfa@cwcom.net, Fax (01654) 767983,* ≤ Dovey estuary and Cardigan Bay, –
Meals (by arrangement) 17.50 – **3 rm** 55.00/56.00 – SB.

Brodawel without rest., Tywyn Rd, LL35 0SA, West : 1 ¼ m. on A 493 (01654) 76734 *patetjohn@brodawel-aberdovey.co.uk,* ≤, –
March-late October – **5 rm** 35.00/54.00.

ABERGAVENNY **(Y-Fenni)** *Monmouthshire* 403 L 28 *Wales G.* – *pop. 9 593.*
See : *Town★ – St. Mary's Church★ (Monuments★★).*
Env. : *Brecon Beacons National Park★★ – Blaenavon Ironworks★, SW : 5 m. by A 4 and B 4246.*
Exc. : *Raglan Castle★* ***AC,*** *SE : 9 m. by A 40.*
Monmouthshire, Llanfoist (01873) 852606.
Swan Meadow, Monmouth Rd (01873) 857588.
London 163 – Gloucester 43 – Newport 19 – Swansea 49.

Llansantffraed Court, Llanvihangel Gobion, NP7 9BA, Southeast : 6 ½ m. by A 40 and B 4598 off old Raglan rd (01873) 840678, *reception@llch.co.uk, Fax (01873) 840674,* « Country house in William and Mary style », , –
Meals 15.00/35.00 and dinner a la carte 23.00/29.00 **t.** 12.00 – **21 rm** 72.00/157.00 **t.** SB.

at Llandewi Skirrid *Northeast : 3 ¼ m. on B 4521 – Abergavenny.*

Walnut Tree Inn (Terry), NP7 8AW, (01873) 852797, *stephenandfrancesco@thewalnuttreeinn.com, Fax (01873) 859764,* –
closed 24 December-2 January, Sunday dinner and Monday except Bank Holidays – **Meals** Italian - (booking essential) a la carte 30.25/37.75 **t.** 13.50
Spec. Salt duck with figs and white asparagus. Scaloppine of monkfish, peas and broad beans. Vanilla panna cotta.

at Govilon *West : 5 ¼ m. by A 465 on B 4246 – Abergavenny.*

Llanwenarth House , NP7 9SF, North : 1 m. on B 4246 (01873) 830289, *mand@welsh-hotel.co.uk, Fax (01873) 832199,* ≤, « 16C manor house », –
closed Christmas and February – **Meals** (by arrangement) (communal dining) 25.00 14. – **5 rm** 64.00/88.00 – SB.

at Llanwenarth *Northwest : 3 m. on A 40 – Abergavenny.*

Pantrhiwgoch, Brecon Rd, NP8 1EP, (01873) 810550, *info@pantrhiwgoch.co.uk Fax (01873) 811880,* ≤, –
Meals a la carte 19.85/26.85 **t.** 9.95 – **18 rm** 63.00/73.00 **t.**

ABERSOCH *Gwynedd 402 403 G 25 Wales G. – pop. 805 – ✉ Pwllheli.*

Env. : *Lleyn Peninsula★★ – Plas-yn-Rhiw★ AC, W : 6 m. by minor roads.*

Exc. : *Bardsey Island★, SW : 15 m. by A 499 and B 4413 – Mynydd Mawr★, SW : 17 m. by A 499, B 4413 and minor roads.*

18 Golf Rd ☎ (01758) 712622.

London 265 – Caernarfon 28 – Shrewsbury 101.

Neigwl, Lon Sarn Bach, LL53 7DY, ☎ (01758) 712363, *relax@neigwl.com, Fax (01758) 712544,* ← Cardigan Bay – TV P. MC AE ⓓ VISA JCB. ✻

Meals (dinner only) 20.50/26.00 **t.** 10.00 – **9 rm** (dinner included) 80.00/143.00 **t.** – SB.

at Bwlchtocyn *South : 2 m. – ✉ Pwllheli.*

Porth Tocyn ⛳, LL53 7BU, ☎ (01758) 713303, *porthtocyn.hotel@virgin.net, Fax (01758) 713538,* ← Cardigan Bay and mountains, heated, ⚘, ✕ – ✕ TV P. MC VISA

mid March-mid November – **Meals** (bar lunch Monday-Saturday) (buffet lunch Sunday)/ dinner 25.50/32.00 **st.** 12.50 – 5.25 – **17 rm** 52.50/148.00 **st.**

ABERYSTWYTH *Ceredigion 403 H 26 Wales G. – pop. 8 359.*

See : *Town★★ – The Seafront★ – National Library of Wales★ (Permanent Exhibition★).*

Env. : *Vale of Rheidol★ (Railway★★ AC) – St. Padarn's Church★, SE : 1 m. by A 44.*

Exc. : *Devil's Bridge (Pontarfynach)★, E : 12 m. by A 4120 – Strata Florida Abbey★ AC (West Door★), SE : 15 m. by B 4340 and minor rd.*

18 Bryn-y-Mor ☎ (01970) 615104.

Terrace Rd ☎ (01970) 612125.

London 238 – Chester 98 – Fishguard 58 – Shrewsbury 74.

Belle Vue Royal, 23 Marine Terrace, The Promenade, SY23 2BA, ☎ (01970) 617558, *reception@bellevueroyalhotel.fsnet.co.uk, Fax (01970) 612190,* ← – ✕ rm, ▤ rest, TV – 40. MC AE ⓓ VISA. ✻

closed 24-26 December – **Meals** 16.50/22.00 and dinner a la carte 18.50/23.00 **t.** 10.00 – **34 rm** 62.00/92.00 **t.** – SB.

Four Seasons, 50-54 Portland St, SY23 2DX, ☎ (01970) 612120, *info@fourseasonshotel.uk.com, Fax (01970) 627458* – ✕ TV P. MC VISA. ✻

closed 24 December-2 January – **Meals** (bar lunch)/dinner 16.00/21.00 **t.** 9.95 – **14 rm** 55.00/75.00 **t.** – SB.

at Chancery (Rhydgaled) *South : 4 m. on A 487 – ✉ Aberystwyth.*

Conrah Country House ⛳, SY23 4DF, ☎ (01970) 617941, *enquiries@conrah.co.uk, Fax (01970) 624546,* ←, « Part 18C mansion house », ≘s, ▢, ⚘, ✿ – |‡|, ✕ rest, TV P – 50. MC AE ⓓ VISA JCB. ✻

closed 20-30 December – **Meals** 28.00 (dinner) and lunch a la carte 16.00/22.00 **t.** 12.00 – **17 rm** 80.00/140.00 **t.** – SB.

BALA *Gwynedd 402 403 J 25 Wales G. – pop. 1 922.*

Env. : *Snowdonia National Park★★★ – Bala Lake★.*

Exc. : *Bwlch y Groes★★, SE : 11 m. by A 494, B 4403 and minor rd.*

9 Bala Lake Hotel ☎ (01678) 520344 – 9 Penlan ☎ (01678) 520359.

Penllyn, Pensarn Rd ☎ (01678) 521021.

London 216 – Chester 46 – Dolgellau 18 – Shrewsbury 52.

Fron Feuno Hall ⛳ without rest., LL23 7YF, Southwest : 1 m. on A 494 ☎ (01678) 521115, *fronfeuno@moneypennyuk.com, Fax (01678) 521151,* ← Bala Lake, ⛵, ⚘, ✕ – |‡| P

restricted opening in winter – **3 rm** 40.00/80.00 **st.**

Melin Meloch without rest., LL23 7DP, East : 1 ¾ m. by A 494 on B 4401 ☎ (01678) 520101, *theoldmill@hotmail.com,* « Part 13C converted water mill, gardens » – ✕ TV P

March-November – **4 rm** 36.00/50.00.

BANGOR *Gwynedd 402 403 H 24 Wales G. – pop. 11 173.*

Env. : *Snowdonia National Park★★★ – Penrhyn Castle★★ AC, E : 3 m. by A 5122 – Menai Bridge★, SW : 1½ m. by A 5122.*

Exc. : *Anglesey★★ – Plas Newydd★★ AC, SW : 7½ m. by A 5122 and A 4080 – Anglesey Sea Zoo★ AC, SW : 10 m. by A 5122, A 4080 and B 4419 – Llangefni (Oriel Ynys Mon★ AC), NW : 7 m. by A 5122 and B 5420.*

18 St. Deiniol, Penybryn ☎ (01248) 353098.

London 247 – Birkenhead 68 – Holyhead 23 – Shrewsbury 83.

WALES

Travel Inn, Menai Business Park, LL57 4FA, Southwest : 2 ½ m. by A 5122 and A 487 junction with A 5 ℘ (01248) 679070, *Fax (01248) 679099* – ⇔ rm, ▤ rest, TV ♿ P. MC VISA. ✻
Meals (grill rest.) – **40 rm** 41.95 **t.**

Travelodge, One Stop Services, Llandegai, LL57 4BG, Southeast : 2 ½ m. by A 5122, junction of A 5 with A 55 ℘ (01248) 370345, *Fax (01248) 370345* – ⇔ rm, ▤ rest, TV ♿ MC AE VISA JCB. ✻
Meals (grill rest.) – **62 rm** 49.95 **t.**

Country Bumpkin without rest., Cefn-y-Coed, Llandegai, LL57 4BG, South : 2 m. on A 5122 ℘ (01248) 370477, *Fax (01248) 354166*, ≤ – TV P. MC VISA
Easter-November – **3 rm** ☐ 30.00/40.00.

at Caerhun *South : 7 m. by A 5122, A 5 and B 4366 on Caerhun rd* – ✉ *Bangor.*

Penhower ⛰ without rest., LL57 4DT, ℘ (01248) 362427, ≤, ⛺ – ⇔ TV P
closed 1 week Christmas – **3 rm** ☐ 23.00/42.00 **st.**

BARMOUTH (Abermaw) *Gwynedd* 402 403 H 25 *Wales G. – pop. 2 306.*
See : *Town*★ – *Bridge*★ *AC.*
Env. : *Snowdonia National Park*★★★.
ℹ *The Old Library, Station Rd* ℘ *(01341) 280787.*
London 231 – Chester 74 – Dolgellau 10 – Shrewsbury 67.

Llwyndû Farmhouse ⛰, LL42 1RR, Northwest : 2 ¼ m. on A 496 ℘ (01341) 28014 *intouch@llwyndu-farmhouse.co.uk*, *Fax (01341) 281236*, « Part 17C farmhouse and 1 barn conversion », ⛺ – ⇔ TV P. MC VISA JCB
closed 1 week November and 25-26 December – **Meals** (by arrangement) 17.95 **t.** 🍷 9.00 **7 rm** ☐ 41.00/70.00 **t.** – SB.

BARRY (Barri) *Vale of Glamorgan* 403 K 29 – *pop. 46 368.*
⛳ *RAF St. Athan* ℘ *(01446) 751043.*
ℹ *The Promenade, Paget Rd, Barry Island* ℘ *(01446) 747171.*
London 167 – Cardiff 10 – Swansea 39.

Egerton Grey Country House ⛰, CF62 3BZ, Southwest : 4 ½ m. by B 4226 and A 4226 and Porthkerry rd via Cardiff Airport ℘ (01446) 711666, *info@egertongrey.co.* *Fax (01446) 711690*, ≤, « Part Victorian rectory », ⛺ – ⇔ rest, TV P. MC AE VISA JCB
Meals 14.50 (lunch) and a la carte 20.95/26.95 **st.** 🍷 11.50 – **10 rm** ☐ 75.00/130.00 **st.** –

Mount Sorrel, Porthkerry Rd, CF62 7XY, ℘ (01446) 740069, *reservations@mountsor. co.uk*, *Fax (01446) 746600*, ⇌s, ▢ – ⇔ rest, TV P – 🎤 150. MC AE VISA JCB
Meals (bar lunch)/dinner a la carte 16.50/20.25 **st.** 🍷 10.50 – **41 rm** ☐ 65.00/100.00 **st** SB.

Aberthaw House, 28 Porthkerry Rd, CF62 7AX, ℘ (01446) 737314, *derek@aberth. house.freeserve.co.uk*, *Fax (01446) 732376* – ⇔ rest, TV. MC AE VISA JCB. ✻
closed 25 December-1 January – **Meals** *(closed Sunday and Monday)* (bar lunch)/din a la carte 13.15/23.85 **t.** 🍷 7.95 – **8 rm** ☐ 39.50/59.50 **t.** – SB.

BEAUMARIS *Anglesey* 402 403 H 24 *Wales G. – pop. 2 050.*
See : *Town*★ – *Castle*★★ *AC.*
Env. : *Anglesey*★★ – *Penmon Priory*★, *NE : 4 m. by B 5109 and minor roads.*
Exc. : *Plas Newydd*★ *AC, SW : 7 m. by A 545 and A 4080.*
⛳ *Baron Hill* ℘ *(01248) 810231.*
London 253 – Birkenhead 74 – Holyhead 25.

Ye Olde Bull's Head Inn, Castle St, LL58 8AP, ℘ (01248) 810329, *info@bullhead. co.uk*, *Fax (01248) 811294* – ⇔ rm, TV. MC AE VISA JCB. ✻
closed 25 December and 1 January – ***The brasserie :*** **Meals** a la carte 10.50/17.80 **t.** 🍷 9 – (see also ***The Restaurant*** below) – **13 rm** ☐ 60.00/100.00 **t.** – SB.

Bishopsgate House, 54 Castle St, LL58 8BB, ℘ (01248) 810302, *hazel@johnson-ol freeserve.co.uk*, *Fax (01248) 810166* – ⇔ TV P. MC AE VISA
closed 2 January-12 February – **Meals** (booking essential for non-residents) 11.95/14 and a la carte 18.95/23.70 **t.** 🍷 9.75 – **9 rm** ☐ 43.00/80.00 **t.** – SB.

Plas Cichle ⛰ without rest., LL58 8PS, Northwest : 2 ¾ m. by B 5109 and Llanfaes ℘ (01248) 810488, ≤, « Working farm », ⛺, ✻ – ⇔ TV P. MC VISA. ✻
February-October – **3 rm** ☐ 30.00/50.00 **s.**

XX **The Restaurant** (at Ye Olde Bull's Head Inn H.), Castle St, LL58 8AP, ℘ (01248) 8103 *Fax (01248) 811294* – ⇔. MC AE VISA JCB
closed Sunday – **Meals** (dinner only) 28.75 **t.**

WALES

BEDDGELERT *Gwynedd* 402 403 H24 *Wales G. – pop. 535.*
Env. : *Snowdonia National Park*★★★ *– Aberglaslyn Pass*★, *S : 1½ m. on A 498.*
London 249 – Caernarfon 13 – Chester 73.

Sygun Fawr Country House, LL55 4NE, Northeast : ¾ m. by A 498 ☎ (01766) 890258, *sygunfawr@aol.com, Fax (01766) 890258,* ≤ Snowdon and Gwynant valley, « Part 16C stone built house », – P. VISA
restricted opening in winter – **Meals** *(closed Tuesday)* (booking essential to non-residents) (dinner only) 16.00 **st.** 9.00 – **9 rm** 47.00/64.00 **st.** – SB.

BENLLECH *Anglesey* 402 403 H 24.
London 277 – Caernarfon 17 – Chester 76 – Holyhead 29.

Hafod without rest., Amlwch Rd, LL74 8SR, ☎ (01248) 853092, – TV P.
closed 25 December – **4 rm** 30.00/50.00.

BETWS-Y-COED *Conwy* 402 403 I 24 *Wales G. – pop. 848.*
See : *Town*★.
Env. : *Snowdonia National Park*★★★.
Exc. : *Blaenau Ffestiniog*★ *(Llechwedd Slate Caverns*★ *AC), SW : 10 ½ m. by A 470 – The Glyders and Nant Ffrancon (Cwm Idwal*★*), W : 14 m. by A 5.*
Clubhouse ☎ *(01690) 710556.*
Royal Oak Stables ☎ *(01690) 710426.*
London 226 – Holyhead 44 – Shrewsbury 62.

Tan-y-Foel Country House, LL26 0RE, East : 4 m. by A 5 and A 470 on Nebo rd ☎ (01690) 710507, *enquiries@tyfhotel.co.uk, Fax (01690) 710681,* ≤ Vale of Conwy and Snowdonia, « Stylishly decorated part 16C country house », – TV P. AE VISA JCB.
closed 14 December-14 February – **Meals** (booking essential) (dinner only) 29.00 **t.** 15.00 – **6 rm** 90.00/150.00 **t.** – SB.

Henllys The Old Courthouse without rest., Old Church Rd, LL24 0AL, ☎ (01690) 710534, *henllys@betws-y-coed.co.uk, Fax (01690) 710884,* « Victorian former magistrates court and police station », – TV P. VISA JCB.
9 rm 30.00/60.00 **st.**

Pengwern Country House, Allt Dinas, LL24 0HF, Southeast : 1 ½ m. on A 5 ☎ (01690) 710480, *marilyn@pengwern49.freeserve.co.uk, Fax (01690) 710480,* ≤ Vale of Conwy, – P. VISA JCB.
closed 1 week Christmas and 1 January – **Meals** (by arrangement) (communal dining) 20.00 11.95 – **3 rm** 35.00/65.00 **st.**

Glyntwrog House, LL24 0SG, Southeast : ¾ m. on A 5 ☎ (01690) 710930, *ken@glyntwrog.freeserve.co.uk, Fax (01690) 710512,* – TV P.
Meals (by arrangement) 12.50 **st.** 6.00 – **4 rm** 32.00/54.00 **st.**

Bryn Bella without rest., Lôn Muriau, Llanrwst Rd, LL24 0HD, Northeast : 1 m. by A 5 on A 470 ☎ (01690) 710627, *brynbella@clara.net,* ≤ Vale of Conwy – TV P.
5 rm 25.00/54.00 **t.**

BLAENAU FFESTINIOG *Gwynedd* 402 403 I 25.
Unit 3, High St ☎ *(01766) 830360.*
London 237 – Bangor 32 – Caernarfon 32 – Dolgellau 23 – Chester 70.

Queen's, 1 High St, LL41 3ES, ☎ (01766) 830055, *cathy@queensffestiniog.freeserve.co.uk, Fax (01766) 830046* – rest, TV P – 100. VISA.
closed 25 December – **Meals** a la carte 10.50/16.80 **t.** 7.95 – **12 rm** 40.00/80.00 **t.**

BODUAN *Gwynedd* 402 403 G 25 – *see Pwllheli.*

BONTDDU *Gwynedd* 402 403 I 25 – *see Dolgellau.*

BONVILSTON **(Tresimwn)** *Vale of Glamorgan* 403 J 29.
London 164 – Cardiff 9 – Swansea 25.

The Great Barn without rest., Lillypot, CF5 6TR, Northwest : 1 m. by A 48 off Tre-Dodridge rd ☎ (01446) 781010, *nina@greatbarn.com, Fax (01446) 781185,* ≤, « Converted corn barn », – TV P
5 rm 38.00/55.00 **st.**

BRECON (Aberhonddu) *Powys* 403 J28 *Wales G. – pop. 7 523.*

See : *Town★ – Cathedral★ AC – Penyclawdd Court★.*

Env. : *Brecon Beacons National Park★★.*

Exc. : *Llanthony Priory★★, S : 8 m. of Hay-on-Wye by B 4423 – Dan-yr-Ogof Showcaves AC, SW : 20 m. by A 40 and A 4067 – Pen-y-Fan★★, SW : by A 470.*

Cradoc, Penoyre Park (01874) 623658 – Newton Park, Llanfaes (01874) 622004.

Cattle Market Car Park (01874) 622485.

London 171 – Cardiff 40 – Carmarthen 31 – Gloucester 65.

Peterstone Court, Llanhamlach, LD3 7YB, Southeast : 3 ¼ m. on A 4 *(01874) 665387, Fax (01874) 665376,* ‹, « Georgian manor house », heated – rm, TV P – 150. MC AE VISA
closed 26-31 December – **Meals** 10.95/25.60 and dinner a la carte approx. 23.10 **t.** 11.4 – **12 rm** 89.25/119.75 **t.** – SB.

Cantre Selyf, 5 Lion St, LD3 7AU, (01874) 622904, *cantreselyf@imaginet.co.u Fax (01874) 622315,* « 17C town house », – P.
closed January and December – **Meals** (by arrangement) 15.00 – **3 rm** 35.00/56.00.

at Llanfrynach *Southeast : 3½ m. by A 40 and B 4558 – Brecon.*

The White Swan, LD3 7BZ, (01874) 665276, *Fax (01874) 665362,* – P. MC VISA
closed 25-26 December, Monday and Tuesday – **Meals** (light lunch) a la carte 16.9 25.85 **st.** 11.95.

BRIDGEND (Pen-y-Bont) *Bridgend* 403 J 29 – *pop. 35 841.*

McArthur Glen Design Outlet Village, The Derwen, junction 36, M 4 (01656) 654906.

London 177 – Cardiff 20 – Swansea 23.

Heronston, Ewenny Rd, CF35 5AW, South : 2 m. on B 4265 (01656) 668811, *reser tions@heronston-hotel.demon.co.uk, Fax (01656) 767391,* heated, – TV P – 200. MC AE VISA
closed 25-26 December – **Meals** (bar lunch)/dinner 15.95 and a la carte 12.45/24.00 9.50 – **75 rm** 85.00/95.00 **t.**

at Pencoed *Northeast : 4½ m. by A 473.*

Travel Inn, Pantruthyn Farm, CF35 5HY, East : 1 m. by A 473 at junction 35 on M (01656) 860133, *Fax (01656) 864792* – rm, TV P. MC AE VISA.
Meals (grill rest.) – **40 rm** 41.95 **t.**

Travelodge without rest., CF3 5HU, East : 1 ¼ m. by Felindre rd (01656) 8644 *Fax (01656) 864404* – rm, TV P. MC AE VISA JCB.
40 rm 39.95 **t.**

at Coychurch (Llangrallo) *East : 2¼ m. by A 473 – Bridgend.*

Coed-y-Mwstwr, CF35 6AF, North : 1 m. by Bryn Rd (01656) 860621, *enquir @coed-y-mwstwr.com, Fax (01656) 863122,* ‹, heated, – TV P 150. MC AE VISA JCB.
Meals 7.50/22.95 and a la carte 21.00/28.50 **st.** 11.95 – **23 rm** 95.00/135.00 **st.** – SB

at Southerndown *Southwest : 5½ m. by A 4265 – Bridgend.*

Frolics, Beach Rd, CF32 0RP, (01656) 880127, *sandmartfrolics@aol.com* – MC AE
closed Sunday dinner and Monday – **Meals** (dinner only and Sunday lunch except Ju August) 12.95/15.95 and a la carte 21.95/26.75 **t.** 11.00.

at Laleston *West : 2 m. on A 473 – Bridgend.*

Great House, High St, CF32 0HP, on A 473 (01656) 657644, *enquiries@great-hou laleston.co.uk, Fax (01656) 668892,* – TV P. MC AE VISA.
restricted opening in winter – **Meals** – (see ***Leicester's*** below) – **16 rm** 90.00/165.00 t SB.

Leicester's (at Great House H.), High St, CF32 0HP, on A 473 (01656) 657644, *enquir @great-house-laleston.co.uk, Fax (01656) 668892,* – P. MC AE VISA.
restricted opening at Christmas, closed Sunday dinner and Bank Holidays – **Meals** a la ca 13.95/29.95 **t.** 10.95.

BWLCHTOCYN *Gwynedd* 402 403 G 25 – *see Abersoch.*

CAERHUN *Gwynedd* – *see Bangor.*

CAERNARFON *Gwynedd* 402 403 H 24 *Wales G. – pop. 9 695.*

See : *Town*★★★ – *Castle*★★★ *AC* – *Town Walls*★.

Env. : *Snowdonia National Park*★★★.

Aberforeshore, Llanfaglan (01286) 673783.

Oriel Pendeitsh, Castle St. (01286) 672232.

London 249 – Birkenhead 76 – Chester 68 – Holyhead 30 – Shrewsbury 85.

Seiont Manor, Llanrug, LL55 2AQ, East : 3 m. on A 4086 (01286) 673366, *Fax (01286) 672840*, – 100. VISA
Meals 13.50/23.50 t. 13.50 – 12.50 – **28 rm** 75.00/95.00 **t.** – SB.

Celtic Royal, Bangor St, LL55 1AY, (01286) 674477, *enquiries@celticroyal.wales.com*, *Fax (01286) 674139*, – 500. VISA JCB.
Meals (bar lunch)/dinner a la carte 14.95/25.65 **t.** 9.95 – **110 rm** 65.00/100.00 **s.** – SB.

Isfryn without rest., 11 Church St, LL55 1SW, (01286) 675628, *Fax (01286) 675628* – rest,
mid March-October – **6 rm** 20.00/45.00.

at Seion *Northeast : 5½ m. by A 4086 and B 4366 on Seion rd – Caernarfon.*

Ty'n Rhos Country H., Llanddeiniolen, LL55 3AE, Southwest : ¼ m. (01248) 670489, *enquiries@tynrhos.co.uk*, *Fax (01248) 670079*, VISA JCB.
closed 1 week Christmas – **Meals** *(closed Monday lunch)* (booking essential for non-residents) (restricted Sunday dinner) 12.95/19.50 and a la carte 21.45/28.40 **t.** 11.50 – **14 rm** 55.00/115.00 **t.** – SB.

at Saron *Southwest : 3¼ m. by A 487 on Saron rd – Caernarfon.*

Pengwern, LL54 5UH, Southwest : ¼ m. (01286) 831500, *pengwern@talk21.com*, *Fax (01286) 830741*, « Working farm », VISA JCB.
closed December and January – **Meals** (by arrangement) 15.00 **st.** – **3 rm** 38.00/56.00 **st.** – SB.

CAERSWS *Powys* 402 403 J 26.

London 194 – Aberystwyth 39 – Chester 63 – Shrewsbury 42.

Maesmawr Hall, SY17 5SF, East : 1 m. on A 489 (01686) 688255, *reception@maesmawr.co.uk*, *Fax (01686) 688410*, « Part 16C hunting lodge », – rest, – 120. VISA JCB
closed 26 December-3 January – **Meals** *(closed Sunday dinner and Bank Holidays)* (bar lunch Monday-Saturday)/dinner a la carte approx. 25.00 **t.** 8.50 – **17 rm** 60.00/80.00 **t.** – SB.

Lower Ffrydd, SY17 5QS, West : 2 m. by B 4569 (01686) 688269, *Fax (01686) 688269*, « 16C farmhouse, working farm »,
March-October – **Meals** (by arrangement) (communal dining) 14.00 **st.** – **3 rm** 30.00/50.00 **st.**

Upper Ffrydd Farm without rest., SY17 5QS, West : 2 m. by B 4569 (01686) 688963, « 17C farmhouse, working farm »,
April-November – **3 rm** 28.00/46.00 **s.**

Cefn-Gwyn Farm, Trefeglwys, SY17 5RF, West : 2 ½ m. on B 4569 (01686) 430648, *cefngwyn@talk21.com*, « Working farm »,
Meals (by arrangement) 16.00 **st.** – **3 rm** 25.00/48.00 **st.** – SB.

at Pontdolgoch *Northwest : 1½ m. on A 470 – Newtown.*

Ty Siarad with rm, SY17 5JE, (01686) 688919, *Fax (01686) 689134*, VISA JCB.
closed 1 week March, 1 week September and 25-26 December – **Meals** *(closed Monday lunch and Sunday)* a la carte 17.40/24.40 **t.** 11.90 – **3 rm** 65.00/95.00 **t.**

CARDIFF (Caerdydd) *Cardiff* 403 K29 *Wales G. – pop. 279 055.*

See : *City★★★ – National Museum and Gallery★★★ AC (Evolution of Wales★★, Pictur galleries★★ (Galleries 12 and 13★★), Pottery and Porcelain★)* BY – *Castle★★ AC* BZ – *Civ Centre★* BY – *Llandaff Cathedral★* AV B – *Cardiff Bay★ (Techniquest★ AC)* AX.

Env. : *Museum of Welsh Life★★★ AC, St. Fagan's, W : 5 m. by A 4161* AV – *Castell Coch★ AC, NW : 5 m. by A 470* AV.

Exc. : *Caerphilly Castle★★ AC, N : 7 m. by A 469* AV – *Dyffryn Gardens★ AC, W : 8 m. b A 48* AX.

Dinas Powis, Old Highwalls ☏ (029) 2051 2727, AX.

Cardiff (Wales) Airport : ☏ (01446) 711111, SW : 8 m. by A 48 AX – **Terminal** : *Centr Bus Station.*

16 Wood St ☏ (029) 2022 7281.

London 155 – Birmingham 110 – Bristol 46 – Coventry 124.

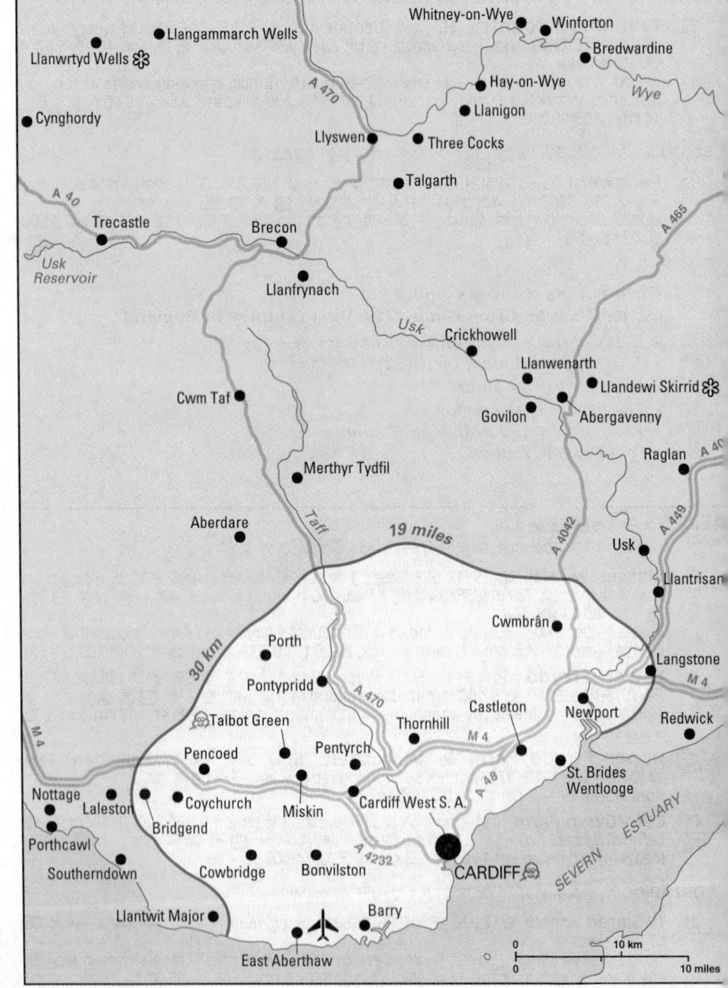

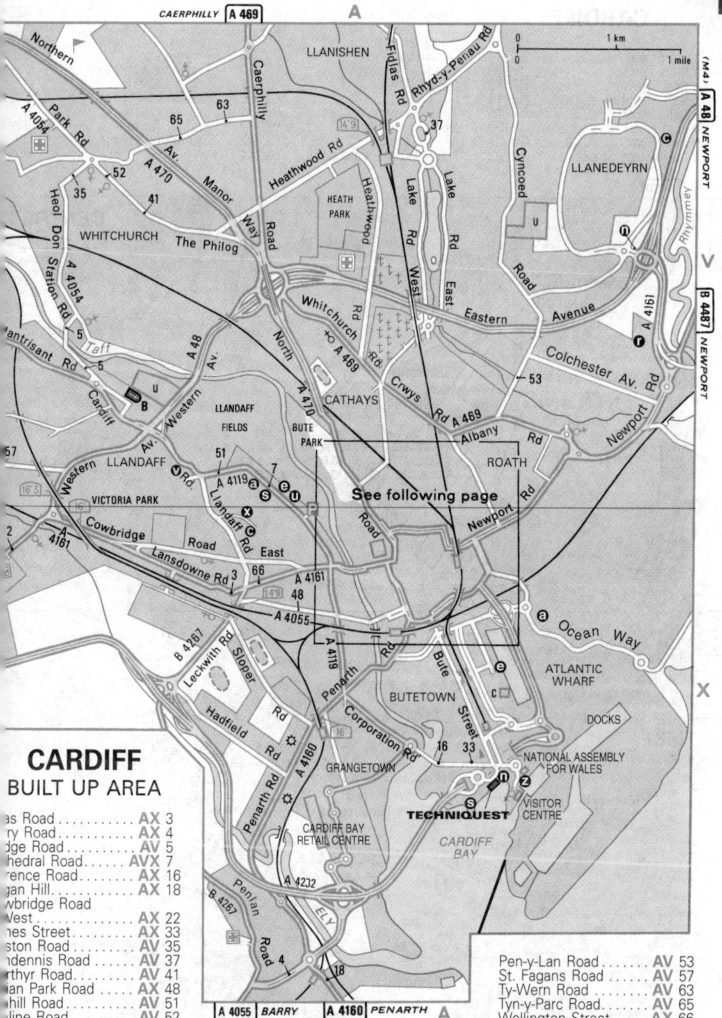

St David's Hotel & Spa, Havannah St, Cardiff Bay, CF10 5SD, South : 1 ¾ m. by Bute St ☎ (029) 2045 4045, *reservations@thestdavidshotel.com, Fax (029) 2048 7056,* ≤, « Contemporary design », Fö, ≘s, ▢ – |‡| ⋟⊭ ▤ TV ☎ ♿ P – 🏛 300. MC AE ⓘ VISA JCB. ⋟⋟
Tides : Meals 12.50/32.00 and a la carte 23.50/35.50 **t.** ♁ 14.50 – ▭ 13.50 – **120 rm** 150.00/170.00 **st.**, 12 suites. AX s

Hilton Cardiff, Kingsway, CF10 3HH, ☎ (029) 2064 6300, *gm-cardiff@hilton.com, Fax (029) 2064 6333,* Fö, ≘s, ▢ – ⋟⊭ rm, ▤ TV ☎ ♿ P – 🏛 340. MC AE ⓘ VISA JCB BZ x
Razzi : Meals 9.95/20.50 and dinner a la carte 20.50/26.65 **st.** ♁ 13.50 – **170 rm** ▭ 125.00/200.00 **t.**, 27 suites – SB.

Copthorne, Copthorne Way, Culverhouse Cross, CF5 6DH, West : 4 ¾ m. by A 4161 and A 48 at junction with A 4232 ☎ (029) 2059 9100, *sales.cardiff@mill-cop.com, Fax (029) 2059 9648,* Fö, ≘s, ▢, ⛱ – |‡| ⋟⊭, ▤ rest, TV ♿ P – 🏛 300. MC AE ⓘ VISA
Raglan's : Meals a la carte 19.90/28.30 **st.** ♁ 14.25 – ▭ 13.95 – **134 rm** 140.00/165.00 **st.**, 1 suite – SB.

CARDIFF

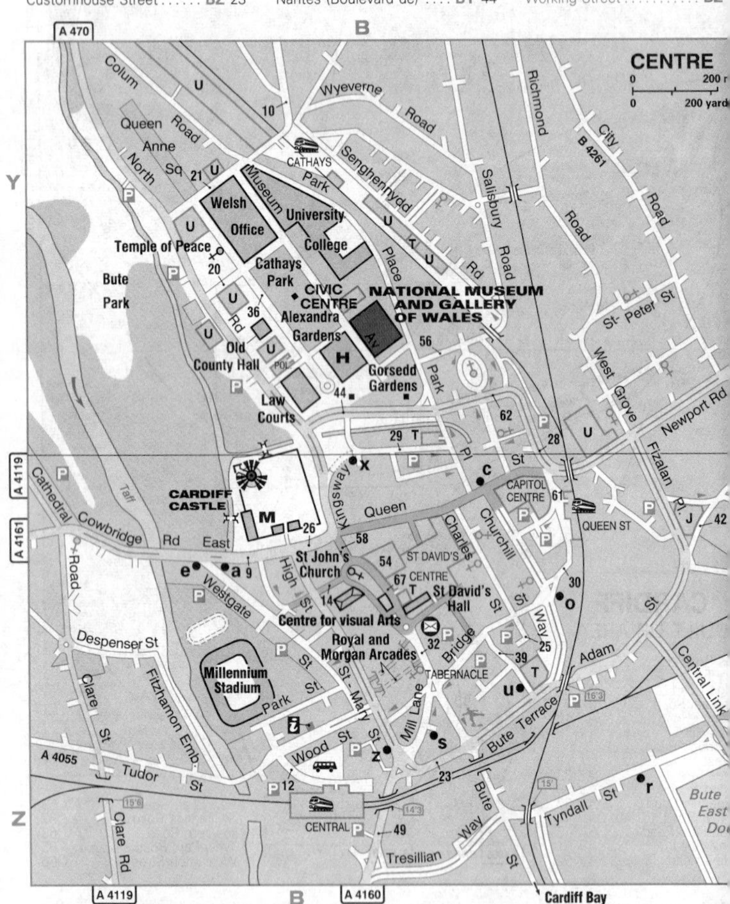

Cardiff Marriott, Mill Lane, CF10 1EZ, ✆ (029) 2039 9944, *Fax (029) 2664 4419,* ≤, BZ
Mediterrano: Meals 14.00/26.00 and a la carte 20.00/42.00 **st.** 11.95 – 13.0
178 rm 114.00/125.00 **st.**, 4 suites – SB.

Thistle Cardiff, Park Pl, CF10 3UD, ✆ (029) 2038 3471, *cardiff@thistle.co* *Fax (029) 2039 9309* – rm, rest, 300. VISA. BZ
Oval Brasserie: Meals a la carte 18.00/25.75 **st.** 12.95 – 12.00 – **132 rm** 112. 126.00 **st.**, 4 suites.

Hanover International, Schooner Way, Atlantic Wharf, CF10 4RT, ✆ (029) 2047 50 *reservations@cardiff-bay-hotel.co.uk, Fax (029) 2048 1491,* « Part Victorian warehous rm, rest, 250. VISA JCB. BZ
Halyards: Meals 12.50/21.50 and a la carte 12.50/21.50 **st.** 12.95 – 11.00 – **153** 100.00/120.00 **st.**, 3 suites – SB.

Angel, Castle St, CF10 1SZ, ☎ (029) 2064 9200, *angel@paramount-hotels.co.uk, Fax (029) 2039 6212* – 300. VISA JCB BZ a
Meals 12.00/19.50 and dinner a la carte 19.50/25.55 **st.** 12.50 – 10.50 – **100 rm** 120.00/140.00 **st.**, 2 suites – SB.

Village H. and Leisure Club, 29 Pendwyallt Rd, Coryton, CF14 7EF, Northwest : 5 m. by A 470 on A 4054 at southern side of junction 32 of M 4 ☎ (029) 2052 4300, *village.car@cybase.co.uk, Fax (029) 2052 4313,* – 250. VISA JCB.
Meals (grill rest.) a la carte 13.85/19.85 **st.** 9.75 – **98 rm** 98.00/108.00 **st.**

Jurys Cardiff, Mary Ann St, CF10 2JH, ☎ (029) 2034 1441, *cardiff@jurysdoyle.com, Fax (029) 2022 3742* – rm, rest, – 300. VISA. BZ u
Meals (bar lunch Monday-Saturday)/dinner a la carte approx. 16.95 **st.** 11.50 – 10.50 – **146 rm** 140.00 **st.**, 3 suites.

Holiday Inn, Pentwyn Rd, CF2 7XA, Northeast : 4 m. by A 48 ☎ (0870) 4008141, *reservations-cardiff@posthouse-hotels.com, Fax (029) 2054 9147,* – rest, – 120. VISA JCB
Meals 12.00/15.00 and a la carte 16.85/27.65 **st.** 11.95 – 12.95 – **142 rm** 83.00 **st.** – SB.

Holiday Inn, Castle St, CF10 1XD, ☎ (0870) 4008140, *Fax (029) 2037 1495* – rm, rest, – 150. VISA JCB BZ e
Meals 15.00 and a la carte 23.85/29.20 **t.** 14.75 – 13.95 – **155 rm** 99.00/109.00 **st.** – SB.

Cardiff Moat House, Circle Way East, Llanedeyrn, CF23 7XF, Northeast : 3 m. by A 48 ☎ (029) 2058 9988, *reservations.cardiff@moathouse.com, Fax (029) 2054 9092,* – rest, – 290. VISA. AV n
Meals (bar lunch Monday-Saturday)/dinner 16.95 and a la carte 16.25/25.10 **t.** 11.95 – 11.50 – **130 rm** 95.00/115.00 **st.**, 2 suites – SB.

Churchills, Cardiff Rd, CF5 2AD, ☎ (029) 2040 1300, *reservations@churchillshotel.co.uk, Fax (029) 2056 8347* – – 110. VISA. AV v
closed 24-26 December – **Meals** 9.95/16.50 **t.** 8.95 – **28 rm** 75.00/90.00 **t.**, 7 suites.

Lincoln House without rest., 118 Cathedral Rd, CF11 9LQ, ☎ (029) 2039 5558, *reservations@lincolnhotel.co.uk, Fax (029) 2023 0537* – . VISA JCB. AV e
23 rm 48.00/75.00 **st.**

Express by Holiday Inn without rest., Schooner Way, Atlantic Wharf, CF10 4EE, ☎ (029) 2044 9000, *sarah@cdfba.freeserve.co.uk, Fax (029) 2044 9000* – – 30. VISA JCB. AX e
87 rm 62.00 **st.**

Ibis without rest., Malthouse Ave, Cardiff Gate Business Park, Pontprennau, CF23 8RA, Northeast : 5 ¾ m. by A 48 and A 4232 at junction 30 of M 4 ☎ (029) 2073 3222, *Fax (029) 2073 4222* – – 30. VISA
78 rm 39.95 **t.**

Ibis, Churchill Way, CF10 2HA, ☎ (029) 2064 9250, *h2936@accor-hotels.com, Fax (029) 2064 9260* – rm, . VISA BZ o
Meals (grill rest.) (dinner only) a la carte approx. 12.00 – **102 rm** 49.50 **st.**

Travel Inn without rest., The David Lloyd Leisure Club, Ipswich Rd, Roath, CF23 7AQ, Northeast : 2 ½ m. by A 4161 ☎ (029) 2046 2481, *Fax (029) 2046 2482* – . VISA. AV r
70 rm 41.95 **t.**

Travel Inn, Keen Rd, CF24 5JT, ☎ (029) 2048 9675, *Fax (029) 2048 9757* – rm, rest, – 30. VISA. AX a
Meals (grill rest.) – **73 rm** 41.95 **t.**

Travel Inn, Port Rd, Nant Isaf, Wenvoe, CF5 6DD, Southwest : 5 ¾ m. by A 4161 and A 48 on A 4050 ☎ (029) 2059 3896, *Fax (029) 2059 1436* – rm, rest, – 100. VISA.
Meals (grill rest.) – **39 rm** 41.95 **t.**

Travelodge withoutrest., 65-67 St Marys St, Imperial Gate, CF10 1FA, ☎ (029) 2039 8697, *Fax (029) 2039 8737* – . VISA JCB. BZ z
100 rm 49.95 **t.**

Travelodge withoutrest., Circle Way East, Llanedeyrn, CF23 9PD, Northeast : 3 ½ m. by A 48 on Coed-y-Gores rd ☎ (029) 2054 9564, *Fax (029) 2054 9564* – . VISA JCB. AV c
32 rm 49.95 **t.**

Townhouse without rest., 70 Cathedral Rd, CF11 9LL, ✆ (029) 2023 9399, *thetownhous@msn.com, Fax (029) 2022 3214* – AV
8 rm 42.50/62.50 **st.**

Georgian without rest., 179 Cathedral Rd, CF11 9PL, ✆ (029) 2023 2594, *gmenin@georgianhotelcardiff.co.uk, Fax (029) 2023 2594* – AV
8 rm 29.00/55.00 **st.**

Annedd Lon without rest., 157 Cathedral Rd, CF11 9PL, ✆ (029) 2022 3349, *annedd.lon@ntlworld.com, Fax (029) 2064 0885* – AV
closed 24-30 December – **6 rm** 25.00/45.00.

Woods Brasserie, The Pilotage Building, Stuart St, Cardiff Bay, CF10 5BW, South 1 ½ m. by Bute St. ✆ (029) 2049 2400, *Fax (029) 2048 1998*, – AX
closed 1 week in autumn, 25-26 and 31 December, 1 January, Sunday dinner, Monday and Bank Holidays – **Meals** a la carte 18.35/32.35 **t.** 13.00.

Gilby's, Old Port Rd, Culverhouse Cross, CF5 6DN, West : 5 m. by A 4161 and A 48 off A 4050 ✆ (029) 2067 0800, *info@gilbysrestaurant.co.uk, Fax (029) 2059 4437*, –
closed 2 weeks September, 1 week Christmas, Sunday dinner and Monday – **Meals** a la carte 20.40/29.65 **t.** 11.95.

Le Gallois, 6-10 Romilly Cres, CF11 9NR, ✆ (029) 2034 1264, *le-gallois@virgin.net, Fax (029) 2023 7911* – AX
closed 3 weeks August, 1 week Christmas, Sunday and Monday – **Meals** 13.95/30.00 **t.** 11.50.

Le Cassoulet, 5 Romilly Cres, Canton, CF11 9NP, ✆ (029) 2022 1905, *lecassoulet@uonline.co.uk, Fax (029) 2022 1905* – AX
closed 3 weeks August, 2 weeks Christmas, Sunday and Monday – **Meals** - French 11.50/15.00 (lunch) and dinner a la carte 23.00/32.00 **st.**

Cutting Edge, Discovery House, Scott Harbour, CF10 4PJ, ✆ (029) 2047 078 *Fax (029) 2044 0876* – AX
closed 24 December-1 January, Saturday lunch and Sunday – **Meals** (lunch booking essential) a la carte 17.00/29.90 **t.** 15.00.

at Thornhill *North : 5¼ m. by A 470 on A 469* – AV – ✉ *Cardiff.*

New House Country, Thornhill Rd, CF14 9UA, on A 469 ✆ (029) 2052 0280, *enquiries@newhousehotel.com, Fax (029) 2052 0324*, – rest, – 200.
closed 1-2 January – **Meals** 12.50/18.50 and dinner a la carte 12.25/21.95 **t.** 11.95 – **33 rm** 92.50/115.00 **t.**, 3 suites – SB.

Manor Parc, Thornhill Rd, CF14 9UA, on A 469 ✆ (029) 2069 3723, *Fax (029) 2061 462* – – 120.
closed 24-27 December and 1 January – **Meals** *(closed Sunday dinner)* a la carte 25.50/38.50 **t.** 13.00 – **12 rm** 72.00/130.00 **t.** – SB.

at Castleton (Cas-Bach) *(Newport) Northeast : 7 m. on A 48* – AV – ✉ *Cardiff.*

St Mellons H. and Country Club, CF3 2XR, ✆ (01633) 680355, *stmellons@bestwestern.co.uk, Fax (01633) 680399*, squash – rest, – 20
*closed 1 January***Meals** *(closed Saturday lunch)* 18.00 and dinner a la carte 22.00/25.00 10.50 – **41 rm** 100.00/140.00 **t.**

Travel Inn, Newport Rd, CF3 2UQ, ✆ (01633) 680070, *Fax (01633) 681143* – rm rest,
Meals (grill rest.) – **49 rm** 41.95 **t.**

at Pentyrch *Northwest : 7 m. by A 4119* – AV – ✉ *Cardiff.*

De Courcey's, Tyla Morris Av, CF15 9QN, South : 1 m. ✆ (029) 2089 223 *Fax (029) 2089 1949*, – – 100.
closed Sunday dinner and Monday – **Meals** (dinner only and Sunday lunch) 24. and a la carte 21.00/29.00 **t.** 12.95.

CARDIFF WEST SERVICE AREA *Cardiff* 403 K 29 – ✉ *Pontycwn (Rhondda Cynon Taff).*

Travelodge, CF72 8SA, M 4 junction 33 ✆ (029) 2089 1141, *Fax (029) 2089 2497* – – 30.
Meals (grill rest.) – **50 rm** 49.95 **t.**

ARDIGAN **(Aberteifi)** *Ceredigion* 403 G 27 *Wales G. – pop. 3 758.*

Env. : *Pembrokeshire Coast National Park★★.*

Gwbert-on-Sea ☎ (01239) 612035.

Theatr Mwldan, Bath House Rd ☎ (01239) 613230.

London 250 – Carmarthen 30 – Fishguard 19.

Penbontbren Country, Glynarthen, SA44 6PE, Northeast : 9 ½ m. by A 487 ☎ (01239) 810248, *mglossop@compuserve.com, Fax (01239) 811129,* – rest, – 50.
closed Christmas – **Meals** (dinner only and Sunday lunch) a la carte 20.20/22.50 **t.** 9.95 – **10 rm** 49.00/86.00 **st.** – SB.

t St Dogmaels *West : 1½ m. by A 487 on B 4546 – ✉ Cardigan.*

Berwyn without rest., Cardigan Rd, SA43 3HS, ☎ (01239) 613555, ←, – .
closed Christmas and New Year – **3 rm** 50.00 **st.**

t Gwbert on Sea *Northwest : 3 m. on B 4548 – ✉ Cardigan.*

Gwbert, SA43 1PP, on B 4548 ☎ (01239) 612638, *gwbert@enterprise.net, Fax (01239) 621474,* ← Cardigan Bay – , – rest, .
Meals (bar lunch)/dinner 16.95 and a la carte 16.95/26.45 **t.** 7.95 – **16 rm** 41.50/127.00 **t.** – SB.

ARMARTHEN **(Caerfyrddin)** *Carmarthenshire* 403 H 28 *– pop. 12 247.*

See : *Kidwelly Castle★ – National Botanic Garden★.*

113 Lammas St ☎ (01267) 231557.

London 219 – Fishguard 47 – Haverfordwest 32 – Swansea 27.

t Nantgaredig *East : 5 m. on A 40 – ✉ Carmarthen.*

Four Seasons with rm, SA32 7NY, North : ½ m. on B 4310 ☎ (01267) 290238, *jen4seas@aol.com, Fax (01267) 290808,* , , – rm, .
closed 23 December-2 January – **Meals** *(closed Sunday and Monday)* (dinner only) 22.50 **t.** 10.50 – **6 rm** 40.00/80.00 **t.**

ASTLETON **(Cas-Bach)** *Newport* 403 K 29 *– see Cardiff.*

EMAES **(Cemais)** *Anglesey* 402 403 G 23 *Wales G.*

Env. : *Anglesey★★.*

London 272 – Bangor 25 – Caernarfon 32 – Holyhead 16.

Hafod Country House without rest., LL67 0DS, South : ½ m. on Llanfechell rd ☎ (01407) 710500, *hirst.hafod@tesco.net, Fax (01407) 710055,* ←, – .
Easter-September – **3 rm** 42.00/48.00 **st.**

HANCERY **(Rhydgaled)** *Ceredigion* 403 H 26 *– see Aberystwyth.*

HEPSTOW **(Cas-gwent)** *Monmouthshire* 403 404 M 29 *Wales G. – pop. 9 461.*

See : *Town★ – Castle★★ AC (Great Tower★★).*

Env. : *Wynd Cliff★, N : 2½ m. by A 466 – Caerwent★ (Roman Walls★), SW : 4 m. by A 48.*

Castle Car Park, Bridge St ☎ (01291) 623772.

London 131 – Bristol 17 – Cardiff 28 – Gloucester 34.

Marriott St Pierre H. & Country Club, St Pierre Park, NP16 6YA, Southwest : 3 ½ m. on A 48 ☎ (01291) 625261, *Fax (01291) 629975,* , , , , , – – 250. .
Orangery : **Meals** (booking essential) (dinner only and Sunday lunch)/dinner 25.00 **st.** 12.75 – ***Long Weekend :*** **Meals** a la carte 13.75/23.35 **st.** 11.75 – **132 rm** 122.00/135.00 **st.**, 16 suites.

George, Moor St, NP16 5DB, ☎ (01291) 625363, *george@drayton-manor-hotels.com, Fax (01291) 627418* – – 30.
Meals a la carte 12.40/19.50 **st.** 9.05 – 8.95 – **14 rm** 70.00/80.00 **st.** – SB.

Castle View, 16 Bridge St, NP6 5EZ, ☎ (01291) 620349, *mart@castview.demon.co.uk, Fax (01291) 627397,* – rest, .
Meals (bar lunch Monday to Saturday) (Sunday dinner residents only)/dinner a la carte 15.10/22.40 **s.** 8.95 – 5.95 – **13 rm** 45.95/65.95 **st.** – SB.

COLWYN BAY (Bae Colwyn) *Conwy* 402 403 I 24 *Wales G. – pop. 29 883.*

See : *Welsh Mountain Zoo★ AC (<★).*

Env. : *Bodnant Garden★★ AC, SW : 6 m. by A 55 and A 470.*

18 *Abergele, Tan-y-Goppa Rd ☎ (01745) 824034* – 9 *Old Colwyn, Woodland Av. ☎ (0149. 515581.*

Imperial Buildings, Station Sq, Princes Drive ☎ (01492) 530478 – The Promenade, Rhos on-Sea ☎ (01492) 548778 (summer only).

London 237 – Birkenhead 50 – Chester 42 – Holyhead 41.

Norfolk House, 39 Princes Drive, LL29 8PF, ☎ (01492) 531757, *booking@norfolkhous hotel.fsnet.co.uk, Fax (01492) 533781,* – TV P – 35. MC AE VISA JCB
closed 23 December-6 January – **Meals** *(closed Sunday dinner)* (bar lunch)/dinner a la car 11.00/17.00 **st.** 8.95 – **21 rm** 47.50/65.00 **st.** – SB.

Café Niçoise, 124 Abergele Rd, LL29 7PS, ☎ (01492) 531555, *Fax (01492) 531555* – MC VISA JCB
closed 1 week January, 1 week June, 25-27 December, Sunday, Monday and Tuesday lunch **Meals** 15.95 and a la carte 14.55/26.50 **t.** 9.95.

CONWY *Conwy* 402 403 I 24 *Wales G. – pop. 3 627.*

See : *Town★★ – Castle★★★ AC – Town Walls★★ – Plas Mawr★★.*

Env. : *Snowdonia National Park★★★ – Bodnant Garden★★ AC, S : 8 m. by A 55 and A 470 Conwy Crossing (suspension bridge★).*

9 *Penmaenmawr, Conway Old Rd ☎ (01492) 623330.*

Conwy Castle Visitor Centre ☎ (01492) 592248.

London 241 – Caernarfon 22 – Chester 46 – Holyhead 37.

Sychnant Pass House , Sychnant Pass Rd, LL32 8BJ, Southwest : 2 m. by A 547 an Sychnant rd, turning right at T junction ☎ (01492) 596868, *bresykes@sychnant-pass-hous co.uk, Fax (01492) 596868,* <, – TV P. MC VISA
*closed Christmas***Meals** *(closed Monday)* (booking essential to non-residents) (dinner or and Sunday lunch)/dinner 19.65 **t.** 11.95 – **9 rm** 45.00/75.00 **t.**, 1 suite – SB.

Berthlwyd Hall , Llechwedd, LL32 8DQ, Southwest : 2 ¾ m. by A 547 and Sychnant r turn right at T junction then left at National Park sign ☎ (01492) 592409, *berthlwydh @hotmail.com.net, Fax (01492) 572290,* <, « Victorian manor house », heated, – TV P. MC VISA
– **Meals** (residents only) (dinner only) (set menu only) 15.95 **st.** 8.50 – **3 rm** 50.0 80.00 **t.** – SB.

at Llansanffraid Glan Conwy *Southeast : 2½ m. A 547 and A 470 – ✉ Conwy.*

Old Rectory Country House (Wendy Vaughan) , Llanrwst Rd, LL28 5LF, on A 4 ☎ (01492) 580611, *info@oldrectorycountryhouse.co.uk, Fax (01492) 584555,* < Con estuary, « Part Georgian country house with antique furnishings », – TV P. MC JCB
closed 20 December-February and restricted opening in winter – **Meals** (booking essent to non-residents) (dinner only) (set menu only) 34.50 **st.** 15.90 – **6 rm** 129.00/169.00 – SB
Spec. Turbot with garlic potato purée, parsley and mustard sauce. Poached and roast du breast with cabbage. Double chocolate bavarois, coffee ice cream.

at Tyn-y-Groes *(Gwynedd) South : 4 m. on B 5106 – ✉ Conwy.*

Groes Inn with rm, LL32 8TN, North : 1 ½ m. on B 5106 ☎ (01492) 650545, *thegroesin btinternet.com, Fax (01492) 650855,* <, , « Part 16C », – TV P. MC AE VISA
closed 24-25 December – **Meals** 13.50/22.50 and lunch a la carte 16.00/25.00 **t.** 12.5 **14 rm** 68.00/121.00 **t.** – SB.

COWBRIDGE (Y Bont Faen) *Vale of Glamorgan* 403 J 29 – *pop. 6 167.*

London 170 – Cardiff 15 – Swansea 30.

Huddarts, 69 High St, CF71 7AF, ☎ (01446) 774645 – . MC AE VISA
closed first 2 weeks in January, Sunday dinner and Monday – **Meals** 15.95/17.95 and d ner a la carte approx. 26.00 **st.** 11.25.

COYCHURCH (Llangrallo) *Bridgend* 403 J 29 – *see Bridgend.*

CRICCIETH *Gwynedd* 402 403 H 25 *Wales G. – pop. 1 720.*

Env. : *Lleyn Peninsula★★ – Ffestiniog Railway★★.*

18 *Ednyfed Hill ☎ (01766) 522154.*

London 249 – Caernarfon 17 – Shrewsbury 85.

Mynydd Ednyfed Country House, Caernarfon Rd, LL52 0PH, Northwest : 3/4 m. on B 4411 (01766) 523269, *mynedd-ednyfed@criccieth.net, Fax (01766) 522929*, ≤, rest, TV P. VISA
closed 23 December-4 January – **Meals** (dinner only and Sunday lunch)/dinner a la carte 15.40/21.90 **t.** 9.95 – **9 rm** 30.00/75.00 **st.** – SB.

Tir-a-Môr, 1-3 Mona Terr, LL52 0HG, (01766) 523084, *Fax (01766) 523049* – VISA
closed 23 December-February and Sunday – **Meals** (dinner only) a la carte 20.75/26.70 **t.** 10.95.

CRICKHOWELL (Crucywel) *Powys* 403 K 28 *Wales G. – pop. 2 166.*

Env. : *Brecon Beacons National Park★★.*

Exc. : *Llanthony Priory★★, NE : 10 m. by minor roads.*

Beaufort Chambers, Beaufort St (01873) 812105.

London 169 – Abergavenny 6 – Brecon 14 – Newport 25.

Bear, High St, NP8 1BW, (01873) 810408, *bearhotel@aol.com, Fax (01873) 811696*, « Part 15C former coaching inn », – TV P – 50. AE VISA JCB
Meals *(closed Sunday dinner)* (lunch booking essential) a la carte 21.95/30.95 **t.** 4.95 – **31 rm** 49.50/120.00 **t.**, 1 suite.

Gliffaes Country House, NP8 1RH, West : 3 3/4 m. by A 40 (01874) 730371, *calls@gliffaeshotel.com, Fax (01874) 730463*, ≤, « Victorian country house and gardens on the banks of the River Usk », – rest, TV P – 50. AE VISA.
Meals (restricted lunch Monday to Saturday)/dinner 25.35 **st.** 12.00 – **22 rm** 55.00/145.00 **st.** – SB.

Ty Croeso, The Dardy, NP8 1PU, West : 1 1/2 m. by A 4077 off Llangynidr rd (01873) 810573, *tycroeso@ty-croeso-hotel.freeserve.co.uk, Fax (01873) 810573*, ≤, – TV P. AE VISA
closed 2 weeks January and 24-25 December – **Meals** (restricted lunch) 9.95/17.95 and a la carte 14.65/23.25 **t.** 8.50 – **8 rm** 35.00/75.00 **t.** – SB.

Glangrwyney Court, NP8 1ES, South : 2 m. on A 40 (01873) 811288, *glangrwyne@aol.com, Fax (01873) 810317*, « Georgian house », – TV P. VISA
Meals (by arrangement) (communal dining) 22.00 **s.** – **5 rm** 35.00/75.00 **s.** – SB.

Nantyffin Cider Mill Inn, Brecon Rd, NP8 1SG, West : 1 1/2 m. on A 40 (01873) 810775, *info@cidermill.co.uk, Fax (01873) 810775*, « Converted 16C cider mill », – P. AE VISA
closed 1 week October, and Monday except Bank Holidays – **Meals** a la carte 17.35/30.15 **t.** 11.95.

CROSSGATES *Powys* 403 J 27 – *see Llandrindod Wells.*

CROSS HANDS *Carmarthenshire* 403 H 28 – *pop. 9 520.*

London 208 – Fishguard 63 – Swansea 19.

Travelodge, SA14 6NW, on A 48 (01269) 845700, *Fax (01269) 845700* – rm, TV P. AE VISA JCB.
Meals (grill rest.) – **32 rm** 52.95 **t.**

CRUGYBAR *Carmarthenshire* 403 I 27 – *Llanwrda.*

London 213 – Carmarthen 26 – Swansea 36.

Glanrannell Park Country House, SA19 8SA, Southwest : 1/2 m. by B 4302 (01558) 685230, *glanparkhotel@btinternet.com, Fax (01558) 685784*, ≤, – rest, TV P. VISA
closed 24-28 December – **Meals** (booking essential to non-residents) (dinner only) 18.00 **st.** 8.50 – **8 rm** 48.00/80.00 – SB.

CWMBRAN (Cwmbrân) *Torfaen* 403 K 29 – *pop. 46 021.*

London 149 – Bristol 35 – Cardiff 17 – Newport 5.

Parkway, Cwmbran Drive, NP44 3UW, South : 1 m. by A 4051 (01633) 871199, *Fax (01633) 869160*, – rm, rest, TV P – 500. AE VISA
closed 26-30 December – **Meals** (light lunch Monday-Saturday)/dinner 20.00 and a la carte 15.00/30.00 **t.** 10.50 – 8.95 – **69 rm** 94.00/106.00 **t.**, 1 suite – SB.

CWM GWAUN *Pembrokeshire* 403 F 28 – *see Fishguard.*

CWM TAF *Merthyr Tydfil* 403 J 28 – *see Merthyr Tydfil.*

CYNGHORDY *Carmarthenshire* 403 I 27 – ✉ *Llandovery.*
London 210 – Carmarthen 31 – Swansea 41.

Llanerchindda Farm ⟡, SA20 0NB, North : 2 ½ m. by Station rd, turning right T-junction and under viaduct ☎ (01550) 750274, *nick@cambrianway.co.* *Fax (01550) 750300*, ≤ Black Mountains, « Working farm », – ⊁ TV ♿ P.
Meals (by arrangement) (communal dining) 12.00 **st.** 6.00 – **20 rm** 24.00/48.00 **st.** SB.

DEGANWY *Conwy* 402 403 I 24 – *see Llandudno.*

DENBIGH **(Dinbych)** *Denbighshire* 402 403 J 24.
London 218 – Chester 30 – Shrewsbury 53.

Berllan Bach ⟡, Ffordd Las, LL16 4LR, Southeast : 5 ¾ m. by A 543 and Llandyrnog rd Llangynhafel rd ☎ (01824) 790725, *niel.lindfield@btinternet.com*, – ⊁ TV P.
Restricted opening in winter – **Meals** (by arrangement) (communal dining) 12.50 **st.** – **3 r** 25.00/50.00 **st.**

DOLGELLAU *Gwynedd* 402 403 I 25 *Wales G.* – *pop. 2 396.*
See : *Town*★.
Env. : *Snowdonia National Park*★★★ – *Cadair Idris*★★★ – *Precipice Walk*★, *NE : 3 m. on mir roads.*
Hengwrt Estate, Pencefn Rd ☎ (01341) 422603.
Ty Meirion, Eldon Sq ☎ (01341) 422888.
London 221 – Birkenhead 72 – Chester 64 – Shrewsbury 57.

Penmaenuchaf Hall ⟡, Penmaenpool, LL40 1YB, West : 1 ¾ m. on A 493 (Tywyn ☎ (01341) 422129, *relax@penhall.co.uk*, *Fax (01341) 422787*, ≤ Rhinog mountains a Mawddach estuary, « Victorian mansion in extensive gardens », – ⊁ TV P. VISA JCB
closed 6-16 January – **Meals** 15.75/27.50 and a la carte 30.00/35.95 **t.** 12.00 – **14** 70.00/175.00 **t.** – SB.

Dolserau Hall ⟡, LL40 2AG, Northeast : 2 ¾ m. by A 494 ☎ (01341) 422522, *pk@dhh.uk*, *Fax (01341) 422400*, ≤, – ⊁ rest, TV P. VISA
closed mid November-mid February except Christmas and New Year – **Meals** (reside only) (dinner only) 21.95 **t.** 8.95 – **17 rm** (dinner included) 58.00/116.00 **t.** – SB.

George III, Penmaenpool, LL40 1YD, West : 2 m. by A 493 ☎ (01341) 422525, *recept @george-3rd.co.uk*, *Fax (01341) 423565*, ≤ Mawddach estuary and mountains, , « P 17C inn on banks of Mawddach estuary », – ⊁ rest, TV P. VISA
closed 25 December **Meals** (bar lunch Monday to Saturday)/dinner a la carte 15.50/23.7 10.95 – **11 rm** 45.00/98.00 **t.** – SB.

Abergwynant Hall ⟡, Penmaenpool, LL40 1YF, West : 3 ½ m. on A 4 ☎ (01341) 422160, *relax@abergwynant.co.uk*, *Fax (01341) 422046*, ≤, « Victorian mans in extensive parkland », – ⊁ TV P. VISA.
closed January – **Meals** (by arrangement) 25.00 14.00 – **4 rm** 100.00/150.00 **st.**

at Ganllwyd *North : 5½ m. on A 470* – ✉ *Dolgellau.*

Plas Dolmelynllyn ⟡, LL40 2HP, ☎ (01341) 440273, *info@dolly-hotel.co.* *Fax (01341) 440640*, ≤, « Part 17C manor house », – ⊁ TV P. VISA.
March-November – **Meals** (booking essential to non-residents) (bar lunch)/dinner 27.50 11.50 – **8 rm** 60.00/120.00 **st.**, 2 suites – SB.

at Llanfachreth *Northeast : 3 ¾ m.* – ✉ *Dolgellau.*

Ty Isaf Farmhouse, LL40 2EA, ☎ (01341) 423261, *raygear@tyisaf78.freeserve.co* *Fax (01341) 423261*, ≤, « 17C longhouse », – ⊁ P.
closed mid December-January – **Meals** (by arrangement) (communal dining) 17.50 s **3 rm** 35.00/50.00 **s.**

at Bontddu *West : 5 m. on A 496 (Barmouth Rd)* – ✉ *Dolgellau.*

Bontddu Hall Country House, LL40 2UF, ☎ (01341) 430661, *reservations@bont hall.co.uk*, *Fax (01341) 430284*, ≤ Mawddach estuary and mountains, , « Victorian m sion in extensive gardens » – ⊁ rest, TV P. VISA
Garden : **Meals** (carvery lunch Sunday) (dinner only and Sunday lunch) 25.00 and a la c 17.85/26.00 **st.** 13.95 – ***Brasserie :*** **Meals** a la carte 15.00/25.00 **st.** 13.95 – **17** 55.00/120.00 **st.**, 3 suites – SB.

RENEWYDD YN NOTAIS (Nottage) *Bridgend* 403 I 29 – *see Porthcawl.*

FFRYN ARDUDWY *Gwynedd* 402 403 H 25 *Wales G. – pop. 1 452 (inc. Tal-y-Bont).*
Env. : *Snowdonia National Park*★★★.
London 237 – Dolgellau 16 – Caernarfon 44.

Ystumgwern Hall Farm without rest., LL44 2DD, Northwest : 1 m. by A 496 (01341) 247249, *ynys@ystumgwern.co.uk, Fax (01341) 247171,* « Working farm », –
minimum stay 2 nights – , **5 suites** 30.00/52.00.

ST ABERTHAW (Aberddawan) *Vale of Glamorgan* 403 J 29 – ✉ *Barry.*
London 180 – Cardiff 20 – Swansea 33.

Blue Anchor Inn, CF62 3DD, (01446) 750329, *Fax (01446) 750077,* « Characterful part 14C thatched inn » – P. VISA
Meals (bar lunch Monday to Saturday) 12.95 and a la carte 16.75/22.75 **t.** 8.95.

BISTOCK *Wrexham* 402 403 L 25 – *see Wrexham.*

VLOE *Flintshire* 402 403 K 24 – *pop. 3 263.*
London 200 – Chester 8.5 – Liverpool 18 – Shrewsbury 48.

De Vere St David's Park, St David's Park, CH5 3YB, on B 5125 at junction with A 494 (01244) 520800, *reservations.stdavids@devere-hotels.com, Fax (01244) 520930,* , , 18, , – , rest, , P – 250. VISA
Fountains : **Meals** *(closed Saturday lunch)* 21.00/25.00 and a la carte 25.95/33.05 **st.** 12.50 – 11.50 – **145 rm** 118.00/128.00 **s.** – SB.

SHGUARD (Abergwaun) *Pembrokeshire* 403 F 28 *Wales G. – pop. 3 128.*
Env. : *Pembrokeshire Coast National Park*★★.
to Republic of Ireland (Rosslare) (Stena Line) 2-4 daily (1 h 40 mn/3 h 30 mn).
Town Hall, The Square (01348) 873484 – Ocean Lab, The Parrog, Goodwick (01348) 872037.
London 265 – Cardiff 114 – Gloucester 176 – Holyhead 169 – Shrewsbury 136 – Swansea 76.

Manor Town House, 11 Main St, SA65 9HG, (01348) 873260, *davis.themanor@amserve.net, Fax (01348) 873260,* , – . VISA
restricted opening in winter – **Meals** (booking essential to non-residents) (dinner only) 18.00/24.00 **st.** 9.00 – **6 rm** 32.00/65.00 **st.**

Three Main Street with rm, 3 Main St, SA65 9HG, (01348) 874275, *Fax (01348) 874017* – .
closed February – **Meals** *(closed Tuesday in winter, Sunday and Monday)* (light lunch)/dinner 30.00 **t.** 10.95 – **3 rm** 45.00/75.00 **t.**

Cwm Gwaun *Southeast : 5½ m. by B 4313 –* ✉ *Fishguard.*

Tregynon , SA65 9TU, East : 6 ¼ m. (01239) 820531, *tregynon@online-holidays.net, Fax (01239) 820808,* , – P. VISA JCB.
closed 2 weeks in winter, Sunday and Thursday – **Meals** (booking essential) (dinner only) 24.00 **t.** 11.00.

Letterston *South : 5 m. on A 40.*

Heathfield Mansion , SA62 5EG, Northwest : 1 ½ m. by B 4331 (01348) 840263, *angelica.rees@virgin.net, Fax (01348) 840263,* , , – P
April-October – **Meals** (by arrangement) 15.00 **st.** 9.00 – **3 rm** 30.00/50.00 **st.**

Welsh Hook *Southwest : 7½ m. by A 40 –* ✉ *Haverfordwest.*

Stone Hall with rm, SA62 5NS, (01348) 840212, *Fax (01348) 840815,* « Part 14C manor house with 17C additions », – P. VISA.
closed 2 weeks in winter and 25 and 31 December **Meals** (booking essential) (dinner only) 22.00 and a la carte 16.00/25.40 **t.** 11.80 – **5 rm** 50.00/80.00 **t.** – SB.

NLLWYD *Gwynedd* 402 403 I 25 – *see Dolgellau.*

RTHMYL *Powys* – *see Montgomery.*

LILYDAN *Gwynedd* – *see Llan Ffestiniog.*

GLANWYDDEN *Conwy – see Llandudno.*

GOVILON (Gofilon) *Monmouthshire – see Abergavenny.*

GRESFORD (Groes-ffordd) *Wrexham* 402 403 L 24 – *see Wrexham.*

GUILSFIELD (Cegidfa) *Powys* 402 403 K 26 – *see Welshpool.*

GWBERT ON SEA *Ceredigion* 403 F 27 – *see Cardigan.*

HALKYN (Helygain) *Flintshire* 402 403 K 24 – ✉ *Holywell.*
London 208 – Chester 22 – Liverpool 31 – Shrewsbury 48.

Travelodge, CH8 8RF, on A 55 (westbound carriageway) ☎ (01352) 7809
Fax (01352) 780952 – rm, rest, TV, P. MC AE DC VISA JCB.
Meals (grill rest.) – **31 rm** 49.95 **t.**

HANMER *Wrexham* 402 403 L 25 – *pop. 565* – ✉ *Whitchurch (Shrops.).*
London 178 – Chester 26 – Shrewsbury 27 – Stoke-on-Trent 28.

Hanmer Arms, SY13 3DE, ☎ (01948) 830532, *enquiry@thehanmerarms.freeserve.co*
Fax (01948) 830740, – rest, TV P – 80. MC AE VISA
Meals a la carte 9.30/24.30 **st.** – **21 rm** 55.00/75.00 **st.**, 6 suites.

HARLECH *Gwynedd* 402 403 H 25 *Wales G. – pop. 1 233.*
See : *Castle*★★ *AC.*
Env. : *Snowdonia National Park*★★★.
Royal St. David's ☎ *(01766) 780203.*
Gwyddfor House, High St ☎ *(01766) 780658.*
London 241 – Chester 72 – Dolgellau 21.

Hafod Wen, LL46 2RA, South : ¾ m. on A 496 ☎ (01766) 780356, *janeandreg@har*
guesthouse.co.uk, Fax (01766) 780356, ≤ Tremadoc bay and Snowdonia, – TV P
VISA
Meals 18.00 **t.** 8.00 – **7 rm** 31.00/70.00 **t.** – SB.

Gwrach Ynys, LL47 6TS, North : 2 ¼ m. on A 496 ☎ (01766) 780742, *gwynfor@tal*
com, Fax (01766) 781199, – TV P.
March-mid October – **Meals** (by arrangement) 15.00 **7 rm** 22.00/56.00 **s.** – SB.

Castle Cottage with rm, Pen Llech, LL46 2YL, off B 4573 ☎ (01766) 780479, *gh.rober*
talk21.com, Fax (01766) 780479 – . MC VISA.
closed 3 weeks February – **Meals** (booking essential) (dinner only) 24.00 **t.** 11.00 – 6
30.00/64.00 **t.** – SB.

HAVERFORDWEST (Hwlffordd) *Pembrokeshire* 403 F 28 *Wales G. – pop. 11 099.*
See : *Scolton Museum and Country Park*★.
Env. : *Pembrokeshire Coast National Park*★★.
Exc. : *Skomer Island and Skokholm Island*★, *SW : 14 m. by B 4327 and minor roads.*
Arnolds Down ☎ *(01437) 763565.*
Old Bridge ☎ *(01437) 763110.*
London 250 – Fishguard 15 – Swansea 57.

Wilton House, 6 Quay St, SA61 1BG, ☎ (01437) 760033, *wiltonhousehotel@fsbdial.co*
Fax (01437) 760297, heated – TV P. MC AE VISA.
– **Meals** *(closed Sunday)* (dinner only) a la carte 13.55/22.95 **st.** 9.95 – **10 rm** 39
59.50 **st.**

Lower Haythog Farm , Spittal, SA62 5QL, Northeast : 5 m. on B 4
☎ (01437) 731279, *Fax (01437) 731279*, « Working farm », – TV P
closed Christmas – **Meals** (by arrangement) 15.00 – **4 rm** 30.00/60.00 **s.** – SB.

HAWARDEN (Penarlâg) *Flintshire* 402 K 24.
London 205 – Chester 9 – Liverpool 17 – Shrewsbury 45.

The Brasserie, 68 The Highway, CH5 3DH, ☎ (01244) 536353, *Fax (01244) 520888* –
MC VISA
closed Saturday lunch, Sunday and Monday – **Meals** a la carte 16.20/24.45 **st.**

AY-ON-WYE (Y Gelli) *Powys* 403 K 27 *Wales G. – pop. 1 407.*

See : *Town*★.
Env. : *Brecon Beacons National Park*★★.
Exc. : *Llanthony Priory*★★, *SE : 12 m. by minor roads.*
Rhosgoch, Builth Wells ✆ *(01497) 851251.*
London 154 – Brecon 16 – Hereford 21 – Newport 62.

The Swan at Hay, Church St, HR3 5DQ, ✆ (01497) 821188, *Fax (01497) 821424*, – rest, TV P – 160. MC AE VISA JCB
Meals (bar lunch Monday-Saturday)/dinner a la carte 13.75/25.85 **t.** 10.95 – **19 rm** 50.00/90.00 **st.** – SB.

York House, Hardwick Rd, Cusop, HR3 5QX, East : ½ m. on B 4348 ✆ (01497) 820705, *roberts@yorkhouse59.fsnet.co.uk, Fax (01497) 820705*, – TV P. MC AE VISA
Meals (by arrangement) 15.00 **st.** – **4 rm** 28.00/56.00 **st.** – SB.

Old Black Lion with rm, Lion St, HR3 5AD, ✆ (01497) 820841, « Part 13C and 17C inn » – TV P. MC VISA.
Meals a la carte 16.40/26.40 **t.** 10.50 – **10 rm** 40.00/78.00 **t.** – SB.

Llanigon *Southwest : 2½ m. by B 4350 – ✉ Hay-on-Wye.*

Old Post Office without rest., HR3 5QA, ✆ (01497) 820008, « 17C house » – P
3 rm 35.00/56.00.

OLYHEAD (Caergybi) *Anglesey* 402 403 G 24 *Wales G. – pop. 11 796.*

Env. : *South Stack Cliffs*★, *W : 3 m. by minor roads.*
to Republic of Ireland (Dun Laoghaire) (Stena Line) 4-5 daily (1 h 40 mn) – to Republic of Ireland (Dublin) (Irish Ferries) 2 daily (3 h 15 mn) – to Republic of Ireland (Dublin) (Stena Line) 1-2 daily (3 h 45 mn).
Penrhos Beach Rd ✆ *(01407) 762622.*
London 269 – Birkenhead 94 – Cardiff 215 – Chester 88 – Shrewsbury 105 – Swansea 190.

Yr Hendre, Porth-y-Felin Rd, LL65 1AH, Northwest : ¾ m. by Prince of Wales Rd off Walthew Ave ✆ (01407) 762929, *rita@yrhendre.freeserve.co.uk, Fax (01407) 762929*, – TV P.
closed 13 November-1 December and 25-26 December – **Meals** (by arrangement) 12.50 **st.** – **3 rm** 30.00/50.00 **st.**

OLYWELL (Treffynnon) *Flintshire* 402 403 K 24 *Wales G. – pop. 8 770.*

See : *Town*★.
Holywell, Brynford ✆ *(01352) 710040.*
London 217 – Chester 19 – Liverpool 29.

Kinsale Hall , Mostyn Rd, Llanerch-y-mor, CH8 9DX, North : 3½ m. by B 5121 off A 548 ✆ (01745) 560001, *Fax (01745) 561298*, , , – , rest, TV P – 400. MC AE VISA.
Meals a la carte 13.00/21.00 **st.** 8.00 – **34 rm** 69.00/85.00 **st.**, 1 suite.

OWEY *Powys – see Llandrindod Wells.*

NIGHTON (Trefyclawdd) *Powys* 403 K 26 *Wales G. – pop. 2 851.*

See : *Town*★.
Exc. : *Offa's Dyke*★, *NW : 9½ m.*
Little Ffrydd Wood ✆ *(01547) 528646.*
The Offas Dyke Centre, West St ✆ *(01547) 529424.*
London 162 – Birmingham 59 – Hereford 31 – Shrewsbury 35.

Milebrook House, Ludlow Rd, Milebrook, LD7 1LT, East : 2 m. on A 4113 ✆ (01547) 528632, *hotel@milebrook.kc3ltd.co.uk, Fax (01547) 520509*, « Gardens », – TV P. MC AE VISA JCB.
Meals *(closed Monday lunch)* (bar lunch)/dinner 20.50 and a la carte 17.35/21.40 **t.** 10.50 – **10 rm** 52.50/86.00 **st.** – SB.

Llanfair Waterdine *Northwest : 4 m. by B 4355 – ✉ Knighton.*

The Waterdine with rm, LD7 1TU, ✆ (01547) 528214, *Fax (01547) 529992*, <, , « 16C inn », – TV P. MC VISA.
closed 1 week spring and winter, Monday and Sunday dinner – **Meals** (booking essential in winter) a la carte 17.25/28.00 **t.** 12.50 – **3 rm** 40.00/70.00 **t.**

LAKE VYRNWY *Powys* 402 403 J 25 *Wales G.* – ✉ *Llanwddyn.*

See : *Lake*★.

ℹ *Unit 2, Vyrnwy Craft Workshops* ✆ *(01691) 870346.*

London 204 – Chester 52 – Llanfyllin 10 – Shrewsbury 40.

Lake Vyrnwy ⛰, SY10 0LY, ✆ (01691) 870692, *res@lakevyrnwy.com*, *Fax (01691) 870259*, ≤ Lake Vyrnwy, « Victorian sporting estate », ✓, ⛪, ✓, ✓ – ✓ rest, TV P – 🏛 120. MC AE DC VISA

Meals 15.95/27.50 **st.** – **34 rm** ☕ 85.00/185.00 **st.**, 1 suite – SB.

LALESTON *Bridgend* 403 J 29 – *see Bridgend.*

LAMPHEY **(Llandyfai)** *Pembrokeshire* 403 F 28 – *see Pembroke.*

LANGSTONE *Newport* 403 L 29 – *see Newport.*

LETTERSTON **(Treletert)** *Pembrokeshire* 403 F 28 – *see Fishguard.*

LLANARMON DYFFRYN CEIRIOG *Wrexham* 402 403 K 25 – ✉ *Llangollen (Denbighshire).*

London 196 – Chester 33 – Shrewsbury 32.

West Arms, LL20 7LD, ✆ (01691) 600665, *booking@thewestarms.co.uk*, *Fax (01691) 600622*, « Part 16C », ✓, ✓ – ✓ rest, TV P – 🏛 30. MC VISA

Meals (bar lunch Monday-Saturday)/dinner 19.90/24.90 and a la carte 15.35/24.90 🍷 11.50 – **15 rm** ☕ 52.50/108.00 **t.**, 1 suite – SB.

LLANBERIS *Gwynedd* 403 H 24 *Wales G.* – *pop. 1 986.*

See : *Town*★ – *Welsh Slate Museum*★ *AC* – *Power of Wales*★.

Env. : *Snowdonia National Park*★★★ *(Snowdon*★★★, *Snowdon Mountain Railway*★★ *AC* – *panorama*★★★*).*

ℹ *41 High St* ✆ *(01286) 870765.*

London 243 – Caernarfon 7 – Chester 65 – Shrewsbury 78.

Y Bistro, 43-45 High St, LL55 4EU, ✆ (01286) 871278, *ybistro@fsbdial.co.uk*, *Fax (01286) 871278* – ✓. MC VISA JCB

closed Sunday and restricted opening in winter – **Meals** (booking essential) (dinner only) a la carte 20.50/29.50 **t.** 🍷 10.00.

LLANDEGLA *Denbighshire* 402 403 K 24 – ✉ *Wrexham.*

London 201 – Birkenhead 31 – Caernarfon 66 – Chester 22 – Liverpool 34 – Llandudno 4… – Shrewsbury 40.

Bodidris Hall ⛰, LL11 3AL, Northeast : 1 ½ m. on A 5104 ✆ (01978) 790434, *bodidris@micro-plus-web.net*, *Fax (01978) 790335*, « 15C manor of 12C origins », ✓, ⛪, ✓ – TV P – 🏛 30. MC AE DC VISA JCB. ✓

Meals 18.50/35.00 **t.** 🍷 12.75 – **9 rm** ☕ 85.00/155.00 **t.** – SB.

LLANDEGLEY *Powys* 403 K 27 – *see Llandrindod Wells.*

LLANDEILO *Carmarthenshire* 403 I 28 *Wales G.* – *pop. 850.*

See : *Town*★ – *Dinefwr Park*★ *AC.*

Env. : *Brecon Beacons National Park*★★ – *Black Mountain*★, *SE : by minor roads* – *Carreg Cennen Castle*★ *AC, SE : 4 m. by A 483 and minor roads.*

London 218 – Brecon 34 – Carmarthen 15 – Swansea 25.

Plough Inn, Rhosmaen, SA19 6NP, North : 1 m. on A 40 ✆ (01558) 823431, *enquiries@ploughrhosmaen.co.uk*, *Fax (01558) 823969*, ≤, ✓, ✓ – ✓ rm, TV ♿ P – 🏛 45. MC VISA JCB. ✓

closed 25 December – **Meals** (bar meals Sunday dinner) a la carte 18.15/25.75 **t.** 🍷 9.00 – ☕ 5.00 – **12 rm** 50.00/70.00 **t.**

LLANDEWI SKIRRID *Monmouthshire* – *see Abergavenny.*

ANDRILLO *Denbighshire* 402 403 J 25 – *pop. 1 048* – ✉ *Corwen.*

London 210 – Chester 40 – Dolgellau 26 – Shrewsbury 46.

Tyddyn Llan Country House ⨀, LL21 0ST, ✆ (01490) 440264, *tyddynllanhotel@compuserve.com, Fax (01490) 440414,* « Part Georgian country house, gardens », – rest, TV P. MC AE VISA JCB
closed 2 weeks January – **Meals** *(closed Monday lunch)* 25.00/27.00 (dinner) and a la carte 21.00/31.45 **t.** 13.50 – **10 rm** 67.50/140.00 **t.** – SB.

ANDRINDOD WELLS *Powys* 403 J 27 *Wales G.* – *pop. 4 943.*

Exc. : *Elan Valley★★ (Dol-y-Mynach and Claerwen Dam and Reservoir★★, Caban Coch Dam and Reservoir★, Carreg-ddu Viaduct★, Pen-y-Garreg Reservoir and Dam★, Craig Goch Dam and Reservoir★), NW : 12 m. by A 4081, A 470 and B 4518.*

18 *Llandrindod Wells ✆ (01597) 822010.*

Old Town Hall, Memorial Gardens ✆ (01597) 822600.

London 204 – Brecon 29 – Carmarthen 60 – Shrewsbury 58.

Metropole, Temple St, LD1 5DY, ✆ (01597) 823700, *info@metropole.co.uk, Fax (01597) 824828,* , , – , rest, TV P – 300. MC AE VISA
Meals 8.50/18.95 **t.** 10.25 – **120 rm** 71.00/94.00 **st.**, 2 suites – SB.

Charis without rest., Pentrosfa, LD1 5AL, South : 3/4 m. by A 483 ✆ (01597) 824732, *iforpat.gimson@care4free.net, Fax (01597) 824732,* – TV P
closed December and January – **3 rm** 30.00/36.00 **t.**

Crossgates *Northeast : 3½ m. on A 483* – ✉ *Llandrindod Wells.*

Guidfa House, LD1 6RF, ✆ (01597) 851241, *guidfa@globalnet.co.uk, Fax (01597) 851875,* – TV P. MC VISA.
Meals (by arrangement) 17.50 **st.** 8.50 – **6 rm** 31.80/58.00 **st.** – SB.

Llandegley *East : 7 m. by A 483 on A 44* – ✉ *Llandrindod Wells.*

Ffaldau Country House, LD1 5UD, ✆ (01597) 851421, *langstaff@ffaldau.co.uk,* « 16C origins », – P. MC VISA.
closed 5-31 January – **Meals** (by arrangement) 15.00 **s.** 9.00 – **3 rm** 38.00/55.00 **s.**

Howey *South : 1½ m. by A 483* – ✉ *Llandrindod Wells.*

Acorn Court Country House ⨀ without rest., Chapel Rd, LD1 5PB, Northeast : ½ m. ✆ (01597) 823543, *acorncourt1@btinternet.com, Fax (01597) 823543,* , – TV P.
February-October – **4 rm** 35.00/55.00 **t.**

Holly Farm ⨀, Holly Lane, LD1 5PP, off A 483 ✆ (01597) 822402, *Fax (01597) 822402,* « Working farm », , – rest, TV P. MC VISA.
Meals (by arrangement) 11.00 **st.** – **5 rm** 24.00/42.00 **st.** – SB.

ANDUDNO *Conwy* 402 403 I 24 *Wales G.* – *pop. 18 647.*

See : *Town★ – Seafront★ (Pier★)* **B** – *The Great Orme★ (panorama★★, Tramway★, Ancient Copper Mines★ AC)* **AB.**

Exc. : *Bodnant Garden★★ AC, S : 7 m. by A 470* **B.**

18 *Rhos-on-Sea, Penrhyn Bay ✆ (01492) 549641* **A** – 18 *72 Bryniau Rd, West Shore ✆ (01492) 875325* **A** – 18 *Hospital Rd ✆ (01492) 876450* **B.**

1-2 Chapel St ✆ (01492) 876413.

London 243 – Birkenhead 55 – Chester 47 – Holyhead 43.

Plan on next page

Bodysgallen Hall ⨀, LL30 1RS, Southeast : 2 m. on A 470 ✆ (01492) 584466, *info@bodysgallen.com, Fax (01492) 582519,* ≤ gardens and mountains, « Part 17C and 18C hall with terraced gardens », , , , , – TV P – 40. MC VISA JCB.
Meals (booking essential) 16.00/34.70 **st.** 14.50 – 14.50 – **19 rm** 115.00/240.00 **st.**, 16 suites 185.00/250.00 **st.** – SB.

Imperial, The Promenade, LL30 1AP, ✆ (01492) 877466, *imphotel@btinternet.com, Fax (01492) 878043,* ≤, , , – , TV P – 150. MC AE VISA **B v**
Chantrey's : **Meals** 12.00/22.00 **st.** 12.00 – **96 rm** 70.00/125.00, 4 suites – SB.

The Empire, 73 Church Walks, LL30 2HE, (see also ***The Empire (No. 72)*** below) ✆ (01492) 860555, *reservations@empirehotel.co.uk, Fax (01492) 860791,* « Collection of Russell Flint prints », , heated, – , rest, TV P – 40. MC AE VISA JCB. **A e**
closed 15 to 29 December – ***Watkins and Co. :*** **Meals** (dinner only and Sunday lunch)/ dinner 16.50/35.00 **st.** 8.00 – **43 rm** 55.00/110.00 **st.**, 7 suites – SB.

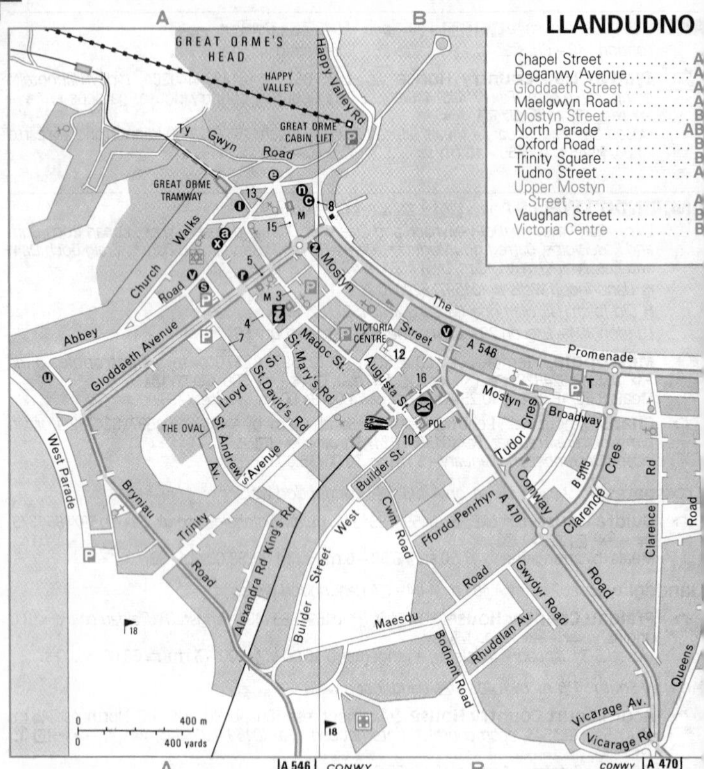

The Empire (No. 72) (at The Empire H.), 72 Church Walks, LL30 2HE, ☎ (01492) 8605 *reservations@empirehotel.co.uk, Fax (01492) 860791*, « Victoriana » – ▤ TV ☎ P. MC AE VISA JCB. ✗ A
closed 15-29 December – **8 rm** ☐ 67.50/105.00 **st.** – SB.

St Tudno, North Par, LL30 2LP, ☎ (01492) 874411, *sttudnohotel@btinternet.c Fax (01492) 860407*, ≤, ▢ – ▤ TV ⌂. MC AE ◐ VISA JCB A
Meals – (see ***Garden Room*** below) – **18 rm** ☐ 88.00/230.00 **st.**, 1 suite – SB.

Dunoon, Gloddaeth St, LL30 2DW, ☎ (01492) 860787, *reservations@dunoonhotel.dem co.uk, Fax (01492) 860031* – ▤ TV P. MC AE VISA A
mid March-mid November – **Meals** 9.00/14.50 **st.** 🍷 9.50 – **51 rm** ☐ 46.00/92.00 **t.** – SB

Bryn Derwen, 34 Abbey Rd, LL30 2EE, ☎ (01492) 876804, *brynderwen@fsbdial.co Fax (01492) 876804* – ✗ TV P. MC VISA. ✗ A
March-October – **Meals** *(closed Sunday)* (booking essential to non-residents) (dinner c 18.50 **st.** 🍷 10.50 – **10 rm** 46.00/86.00 **st.** – SB.

The Wilton, 14 South Par, LL30 2LN, ☎ (01492) 876086, *info@wiltonhotel.c Fax (01492) 876086* – TV P. MC VISA JCB AB
March-November – **Meals** (dinner only) (residents only) 13.00/15.00 **st.** 🍷 7.99 – **14** ☐ 30.00/60.00 **st.** – SB.

Tan Lan, 14 Great Orme's Rd, West Shore, LL30 2AR, ☎ (01492) 860221, *info@tanlanh co.uk, Fax (01492) 870219* – ✗ TV P. MC VISA JCB. ✗ A
closed 2 January-28 Febuary and 3 November-24 December – **Meals** (bar lunch)/dir 15.00 **st.** 🍷 6.95 – **17 rm** ☐ 37.00/54.00 **st.** – SB.

Abbey Lodge, 14 Abbey Rd, LL30 2EA, ☎ (01492) 878042, *enquiries@abbeylodg com, Fax (01492) 878042*, ⌂ – ✗ TV P. ✗ A
closed 25 December – **Meals** (by arrangement) (communal dining) 17.50 🍷 9.50 – **4** ☐ 35.00/55.00 **s.** – SB.

Lympley Lodge without rest., Colwyn Rd, Craigside, LL30 3AL, East : 1 ½ m. on B 5115 (01492) 549304, *enquiries@lympleylodge.co.uk*, – P. *closed mid December-mid January* – **3 rm** 35.00/60.00 **s.**

Epperstone, 15 Abbey Rd, LL30 2EE, (01492) 878746, *Fax (01492) 871223* – P. AE VISA A s
Meals (by arrangement) 12.00 **st.** 9.00 – **8 rm** 31.00/62.00 **st.** – SB.

The Lighthouse without rest., Marine Drive, Great Orme's Head, LL30 2XD, North : 2 ½ m. by Happy Valley Rd (01492) 876819, *enquiries@lighthouse.llandudno.co.uk, Fax (01492) 876668*, <, « Converted Victorian lighthouse » – P. VISA.
2 rm 95.00/130.00 **st.**, 1 suite.

Cranberry House without rest., 12 Abbey Rd, LL30 2EA, (01492) 879760, *cranberry house@llandudno12.fsnet.co.uk, Fax (01492) 879760* – P. VISA JCB. A a
closed Christmas and New Year – **5 rm** 35.00/50.00.

Craiglands, 7 Carmen Sylva Rd, LL30 1LZ, East : 1 m. by B 5115 (01492) 875090 – .
March-November – **Meals** 15.00 – **6 rm** 25.00/60.00 **s.**

Garden Room (at St. Tudno H.), North Par, LL30 2LP, (01492) 874411, *Fax (01492) 860407* – . AE VISA JCB A c
Meals 15.00/36.00 and dinner a la carte 29.00/36.00 **st.** 8.00.

Richard's Bistro, 7 Church Walks, LL30 2HD, (01492) 877924 – AE VISA A n
closed 3 days Christmas, 1 week June, Sunday and Monday – **Meals** (dinner only) a la carte 20.85/26.40 **st.** 10.95.

Number 1's Bistro, 1 Old Rd, LL30 2HA, (01492) 875424, *stephenrawicki@aol.com, Fax (01492) 875424* – AE VISA JCB A i
closed 25-26 December, Monday lunch and Sunday – **Meals** 15.95/19.95 (dinner) and a la carte 17.15/27.15 **st.** 11.75.

Glanwydden *Southeast : 3 m. by A 470* – **B** – *off Penthyn Bay rd* – *Llandudno.*

Queens Head, LL31 9JP, (01492) 546570, *Fax (01492) 546487* – P. VISA
closed 25 December – **Meals** a la carte 13.30/20.25 **t.** 10.90.

Llandudno Junction *Southeast : 4 m. by A 470 on A 547 at junction with A 55* – **B** – *Llandudno.*

Travel Inn, LL28 5LB, (01492) 583320, *Fax (01492) 583514* – rm, rest, P. AE VISA.
Meals (grill rest.) – **40 rm** 41.95 **t.**

Deganwy *South : 2 ¾ m. on A 546* – **A** – *Llandudno.*

Nikki Ip's, 57 Station Rd, LL31 9DF, (01492) 596611, *Fax (01492) 596600* – AE VISA JCB
closed Monday – **Meals** - Chinese - (booking essential) (dinner only) 17.50/25.00 and a la carte 17.00/23.50 **t.** 10.95.

Paysanne, Station Rd, LL31 9EJ, (01492) 582079, *Fax (01492) 583848* – . VISA
closed 25-26 December, 1 January, Sunday and Monday – **Meals** (booking essential) (dinner only) 16.00/20.50 **t.** 10.25.

ANDUDNO JUNCTION (Cyffordd Llandudno) *Conwy* 402 403 I 24 – *see Llandudno.*

ANERCHYMEDD *Anglesey* 402 403 G 24 *Wales G.*

Env. : *Anglesey*★★.
London 262 – Bangor 18 – Caernarfon 23 – Holyhead 15.

Llwydiarth Fawr , LL71 8DF, North : 1 m. on B 5111 (01248) 470321, <, « Georgian farmhouse », , , – P. VISA.
closed Christmas – **Meals** (by arrangement) 15.00 **st.** – **4 rm** 30.00/50.00 **st.** – SB.

Tre-wyn without rest., Maenaddwyn, LL71 8AE, East : 2 ¼ m. by B 5111 on Benllech rd (01248) 470875, *nia@trewyn.fsnet.co.uk, Fax (01248) 470875*, <, « Working farm », , – P.
April-September – **3 rm** 25.00/45.00.

Drws-Y-Coed without rest., LL71 8AD, East : 1 ½ m. by B 5111 on Benllech rd (01248) 470473, *Fax (01248) 470473*, <, « Working farm », , – P. VISA.
closed 25 and 26 December – **3 rm** 30.00/50.00 **s.**

ANFACHRETH *Gwynedd* 402 403 I 25 – *see Dolgellau.*

ANFAIR WATERDINE *Shrops.* – *see Knighton.*

LLAN FFESTINIOG *Gwynedd.*

Cae'r Blaidd Country House ⛰, LL41 4PH, North : ¾ m. by A 470 on Blaenau F... ✆ (01766) 762765, *info@caerblaidd.fsnet.co.uk, Fax (01766) 762765,* ≤ Vale of Ffestinio... and Moelwyn mountains, ⛱ – ⊁ TV P. ✗
closed January – **Meals** (communal dining) 14.50 **st.** 🍷 9.00 – **3 rm** ⊐ 28.00/56.00 **st.**

at Gellilydan *Southwest : 2 ¾ m. by A 470 off A 487 – ✉ Ffestiniog.*

Tyddyn du Farm, LL41 4RB, East : ½ m. by A 487 on A 470 ✆ (01766) 590281, *paula... snowdonia-farm.com, Fax (01766) 590281,* ≤, « Working farm », ⛱, ♞ – ⊁ TV P
Meals (by arrangement) 15.00 **st.** – **3 rm** ⊐ 35.00/70.00 **st.**, 1 suite.

LLANFIHANGEL *Powys* 402 403 J 25 – *see Llanfyllin.*

LLANFRYNACH *Powys* 403 J 28 – *see Brecon.*

LLANFYLLIN *Powys* 402 403 K 25 *Wales G.* – *pop. 1 267.*

Exc. : *Pistyll Rhaeadr*★, *NW : 8 m. by A 490, B 4391, B 4580 and minor roads.*
London 188 – Chester 42 – Shrewsbury 24 – Welshpool 11.

Seeds, 5 Penybryn Cottages, High St, SY22 5AP, ✆ (01691) 648604, « 16C cottages »... ⊁. MC VISA
closed 25 December, Sunday dinner and Monday, restricted opening in winter – **Mea...** 20.50 (dinner) and lunch a la carte 12.95/23.45 🍷 10.25.

at Llanfihangel *Southwest : 5 m. by A 490 and B 4393 on B 4382 – ✉ Llanfyllin.*

Cyfie Farm ⛰, SY22 5JE, South : 1 ½ m. by B 4382 ✆ (01691) 64845... *Fax (01691) 648363,* ≤ Meifod valley, « Restored 17C longhouse, working farm », ⛱, ♞... ⊁ TV P. ✗
closed Christmas and New Year – **Meals** (by arrangement) (communal dining) 16.00 **st**... **1 rm** ⊐ 28.00/64.00 **st.**, **3 suites** 60.00/64.00 **st.** – SB.

LLANGAMMARCH WELLS *Powys* 403 J 27.

London 200 – Brecon 17 – Builth Wells 8.

Lake Country House ⛰, LD4 4BS, East : ¾ m. ✆ (01591) 620202, *info@lakecoun... house.co.uk, Fax (01591) 620457,* ≤, « Victorian country house in extensive grounds », ... ⛱, ✂ – ⊁ TV P – 🎓 30. MC AE ⓓ VISA JCB
Meals 17.50/35.00 **st.** 🍷 13.50 – **9 rm** ⊐ 95.00/155.00 **st.**, **10 suites** 190.00/220.00 **st.** –...

LLANGEFNI *Anglesey* 402 403 H 24.

London 277 – Caernarfon 17 – Chester 75 – Holyhead 17.

Cefn Cwmwd without rest., Rhostrehwfa, LL77 7YL, Southwest : 2 m. by B 5109 ... B 4422 ✆ (01248) 722106, *geriant@cefncwmwd.decom.co.uk, Fax (01248) 722106,* ⛱... ⊁ TV P. MC AE ⓓ VISA. ✗
9 rm 55.00/99.00 **st.**

LLANGOLLEN *Denbighshire* 402 403 K 25 *Wales G.* – *pop. 3 267.*

See : *Town*★ – *Railway*★ *AC* – *Plas Newydd*★ *AC.*
Env. : *Pontcysyllte Aqueduct*★★, *E : 4 m. by A 539* – *Castell Dinas Bran*★, *N : by footpat... Valle Crucis Abbey*★ *AC, N : 2 m. by A 542.*
Exc. : *Chirk Castle*★★ *AC (wrought iron gates*★*), SE : 7½ m. by A 5* – *Rug Chapel*★ *AC, 11 m. by A 5 and A 494.*
18 *Vale of Llangollen, Holyhead Rd* ✆ *(01978) 860613.*
Town Hall, Castle St ✆ *(01978) 860828.*
London 194 – Chester 23 – Holyhead 76 – Shrewsbury 30.

Bryn Howel, LL20 7UW, East : 2 ¾ m. by A 539 ✆ (01978) 860331, *hotel@brynhow... co.uk, Fax (01978) 860119,* ≤, ⛨s, ⛱ – |♦|, ⊁ rest, TV ✆ P – 🎓 300. MC AE ⓓ ... JCB. ✗
Cedar Tree : **Meals** a la carte 19.45/29.50 **t.** 🍷 7.20 – ⊐ 9.00 – **35 rm** 71.50/90.00 **t.**, 1 su... – SB.

Gales, 18 Bridge St, LL20 8PF, ✆ (01978) 860089, *rgales@galesofllangollen.co... Fax (01978) 861313,* ⛱, « Part 17C and 18C » – ⊁ rm, TV P. MC AE ⓓ VISA JCB. ✗
closed 25 December-2 January – **Meals** *(closed Sunday)* (in bar) a la carte 9.70/17.1... 🍷 8.50 – **13 rm** ⊐ 45.00/60.00 **t.**, 2 suites.

Hillcrest, Hill St, LL20 8EU, ✆ (01978) 860208, *david@hillcrest-llangollen.freeserve.co... Fax (01978) 860208,* ⛱ – ⊁ TV P. ✗
Meals 12.00 🍷 7.50 – **7 rm** ⊐ 42.00/50.00 **s.**

Oakmere without rest., Regent St, LL20 8HS, on A 5 ☎ (01978) 861126, *oakmeregh@aol.com*, – 6 rm 40.00/50.00 st.

The Corn Mill, Dee Lane, LL20 8PN, ☎ (01978) 869555, *Fax (01978) 869930*, « Former corn mill on banks of River Dee » – rest. VISA
closed 25 December – **Meals** a la carte 16.50/21.50 **t.** 9.50.

LANIGON *Powys* 403 K 27 – *see Hay-on-Wye.*

LANRHIDIAN *Swansea* 403 H 29 – *see Swansea.*

LANSANFFRAID GLAN CONWY *Conwy* 402 403 I 24 – *see Conwy.*

LANTRISANT *Monmouthshire* 403 L 28 – *pop. 9 136 (inc. Pontyclun)* – Usk.
London 148 – Bristol 34 – Gloucester 43 – Newport 8.

Greyhound Inn, NP15 1LE, Northeast : ½ m. on Usk rd ☎ (01291) 672505, *enquiry@greyhound-inn.com, Fax (01291) 673255*, – VISA JCB.
closed 24-25 December – **Meals** *(closed Sunday dinner)* a la carte 14.35/20.35 **t.** 11.00 – **10 rm** 48.00/68.00 **t.**

LANTWIT MAJOR (Llanilltud Fawr) *Vale of Glamorgan* 403 J 29 – *pop. 12 909.*
London 175 – Cardiff 18 – Swansea 33.

West House Country, West St, CF61 1SP, ☎ (01446) 792406, *enq@westhouse-hotel.co.uk, Fax (01446) 796147*, – rest, VISA JCB.
Meals (lunch booking essential) 12.50/15.50 (dinner) and a la carte 19.65/28.20 **t.** 9.95 – **21 rm** 52.00/69.50 **st.** – SB.

LANWENARTH *Monmouthshire – see Abergavenny.*

LANWRTYD WELLS *Powys* 403 J 27 *Wales G.* – *pop. 649.*
Exc. : *Abergwesyn-Tregaron Mountain Road★, NW : 19 m. on minor roads.*
Ty Barcud, The Square ☎ (01591) 610666.
London 214 – Brecon 32 – Carmarthen 39.

Lasswade Country House, Station Rd, LD5 4RW, ☎ (01591) 610515, *r.stevens@messages.co.uk, Fax (01591) 610611*, – VISA JCB.
Meals (dinner only) 19.95 9.95 – **8 rm** 38.00/60.00 – SB.

Carlton House (Mary Ann Gilchrist), Dolycoed Rd, LD5 4RA, ☎ (01591) 610248, *info@carltonrestaurant.co.uk, Fax (01591) 610242* – VISA JCB
closed 9-27 December – **Meals** *(closed Sunday)* (booking essential) (dinner only) 21.00/25.00 and a la carte 27.00/34.50 **t.** 10.50
Spec. Prawn and salmon ravioli in chicken broth. Fillet of local beef, oxtail and Madeira jus. Chocolate fondant, raspberry sorbet.

YSWEN *Powys* 403 K 27 *Wales G.* – Brecon.
Env. : *Brecon Beacons National Park★★.*
London 188 – Brecon 8 – Cardiff 48 – Worcester 53.

Llangoed Hall, LD3 0YP, Northwest : 1 ¼ m. on A 470 ☎ (01874) 754525, *llangoed_hall_co_wales_uk@compuserve.com, Fax (01874) 754545*, « Edwardian mansion by Sir Clough Williams-Ellis of 17C origins », – rest, VISA JCB.
Meals *(closed 24-26, 31 December and 1 January)* (booking essential to non-residents) 16.50/42.50 **t.** 17.00 – **20 rm** 115.00/260.00 **t.**, 3 suites – SB.

ACHYNLLETH *Powys* 402 403 I 26 *Wales G.* – *pop. 2 033.*
See : *Town★ – Celtica★ AC.*
Env. : *Snowdonia National Park★★★ – Centre for Alternative Technology★★ AC, N : 3 m. by A 487.*
Ffordd Drenewydd ☎ (01654) 702000.
Canolfan Owain Glyndwr ☎ (01654) 702401.
London 220 – Shrewsbury 56 – Welshpool 37.

Ynyshir Hall, Eglwysfach, SY20 8TA, Southwest : 6 m. on A 487 (01654) 78120 *info@ynyshir-hall.co.uk, Fax (01654) 781366*, ≤, « Part Georgian country house, gardens » – rm, TV P. MC AE VISA JCB
closed 5-25 January – **Meals** (booking essential) 21.00/38.00 **st.** 15.00 – **8 rm** 110.0 195.00 **st.**, 2 suites – SB
Spec. Confit of duck, celeriac and grain mustard. Poached fillet of brill, samphire ar girolles. Consommé of summer fruits, Sauternes jelly.

MENAI BRIDGE (Porthaethwy) *Anglesey* 402 403 H 24.
London 270 – Caernarfon 10 – Chester 69 – Holyhead 22.

Wern Farm without rest., Pentraeth Rd, LL59 5RR, North : 2 ¼ m. by B 5420 c A 5025 (01248) 712421, *wernfarmanglesey@onetel.net.uk, Fax (01248) 712421*, ≤, – TV P. MC VISA JCB.
closed December and January – **3 rm** 50.00/56.00 **t.**

MERTHYR TYDFIL *Merthyr Tydfil* 403 J 28 *Wales G. – pop. 59 317.*
Env. : *Brecon Beacons National Park★★.*
Exc. : *Ystradfellte★, NW : 13 m. by A 4102, A 465, A 4059 and minor roads.*
18 Morlais Castle, Pant, Dowlais (01685) 722822 – 9 Cilsanws Mountain, Cefn Co (01685) 723308.
14a Glebeland St (01685) 379884.
London 179 – Cardiff 25 – Gloucester 59 – Swansea 33.

Tregenna, Park Terr, CF47 8RF, (01685) 723627, *reception@tregenna.co.* *Fax (01685) 721951* – rm, TV P. MC AE VISA JCB
Meals a la carte approx. 14.95 **t.** 10.95 – **21 rm** 48.00/60.00 **t.** – SB.

Travel Inn, Pentrebach, CF48 4BD, South : 2 ½ m. by A 470 (01443) 69361 *Fax (01443) 690188* – rm, TV P. – 75. MC AE VISA.
Meals (grill rest.) – **40 rm** 41.95 **t.**

at Cwm Taf *Northwest : 6 m. on A 470 – Merthyr Tydfil.*

Nant Ddu Lodge, CF48 2HY, on A 470 (01685) 379111, *enquiries@nant_ddu_lod co.uk, Fax (01685) 377088*, – rest, TV P. MC AE VISA
Meals (in bar Monday to Saturday lunch) a la carte 17.35/21.35 **t.** 8.95 – 4.95 – **28** 55.00/95.00 **t.**

MISKIN (Meisgyn) *Rhondda Cynon Taff* 403 J 29 – *Cardiff.*
London 169 – Cardiff 22 – Swansea 31.

Miskin Manor, Pendoylan Rd, Groes Faen, CF72 8ND, East : 1 ¾ m. by A 4119 (Groesfa rd) (01443) 224204, *info@miskinmanor.co.uk, Fax (01443) 237606*, ≤, « Part 17C mar house », , , , , , squash – rest, TV & P. – 170. MC AE VISA
Meals *(closed Saturday lunch)* 26.50 (dinner) and a la carte 19.00/29.50 **t.** – **42 rm** 94.0 152.50 **t.**, 1 suite.

MOLD (Yr Wyddgrug) *Flintshire* 402 403 K 24 *Wales G. – pop. 9 168.*
See : *St. Mary's Church★.*
18 Clicain Rd, Pantmywyn (01352) 740318 – 18, 9 Clicain Rd, Old Padeswood, Station (01244) 547701 – 18 Padeswood & Buckley, The Caia, Station Lane, Padeswood (012 550537 – 9 Caerwys (01352) 720692.
Library, Museum and Art Gallery, Earl Rd (01352) 759331.
London 211 – Chester 12 – Liverpool 22 – Shrewsbury 45.

Soughton Hall, CH7 6AB, North : 2 ½ m. by A 5119 and Alltami rd (01352) 8408 *info@soughtonhall.co.uk, Fax (01352) 840382*, ≤, « Early 18C Italianate mansi antiques », , – TV P. – 50. MC AE VISA
Meals – (see ***The Stables*** below) – **14 rm** 94.00/170.00 **st.** – SB.

Tower without rest., Nercwys, CH7 4EW, South : 1 m. by B 5444 and Nercwys (01352) 700220, *Fax (01352) 700220*, ≤, « 15C fortified house », , – TV P.
closed 22 December-5 January – **3 rm** 50.00/70.00 **s.**

The Stables (at Soughton Hall H.), CH7 6AB, North : 2 ½ m. by A 5119 and Alltami (01352) 840577, *info@soughtonhall.co.uk, Fax (01352) 840382*, , « Converted stables » – P. MC AE VISA
Meals (booking essential) a la carte 18.00/34.00 **st.** 10.50.

Glas Fryn, Raikes Lane, Sychdyn, CH7 6LR, North : 1 m. by A 5119 on Civic Centre rd (Theatr Clwyd) ℘ (01352) 750500, *glasfryn@brunningandprice.co.uk, Fax (01352) 751923,* , – P. MO AE VISA.
closed 25 and 26 December – **Meals** a la carte 15.95/22.95 ⚱ 9.50.

MONTGOMERY **(Trefaldwyn)** *Powys* 403 K 26 *Wales G. – pop. 1 059.*

See : *Town*★.

London 194 – Birmingham 71 – Chester 53 – Shrewsbury 30.

Dragon, Town Square, SY15 6PA, ℘ (01686) 668359, *reception@dragonhotel.com, Fax (01686) 668287,* , – rm, TV P. – 60. MO AE VISA JCB
Meals (bar lunch Monday-Saturday)/dinner 18.50 and a la carte 17.95/27.05 **t.** ⚱ 9.25 – **20 rm** 45.00/75.00 **t.** – SB.

Little Brompton Farm without rest., SY15 6HY, Southeast : 2 m. on B 4385 ℘ (01686) 668371, *gaynor.brompton@virgin.net, Fax (01686) 668371,* « Working farm », – TV P.
3 rm 25.00/50.00.

The Bricklayers Arms, Chirbury Rd, SY15 6QQ, ℘ (01686) 668177, « 15C drovers inn » – P. MO VISA
closed 26 December, 1-2 January, 2 weeks February, 1 week October, Monday, Tuesday lunch and Sunday dinner – ***Robbers :*** **Meals** (booking essential) a la carte 16.50/26.80 **st.** ⚱ 9.50.

at Garthmyl *Northwest : 3 m. by A 4385 on A 483 – ✉ Montgomery.*

Garthmyl Hall , SY15 6RS, on A 483 ℘ (01686) 640550, *Fax (01686) 640609,* ≤, « Part 18C manor house, gardens », – P. MO AE VISA JCB.
Meals *(closed Sunday and Monday)* (residents only) (dinner only) 21.50 **t.** ⚱ 10.50 – **9 rm** 45.00/105.00 **st.**

MOYLGROVE **(Trewyddel)** *Pembrokeshire* 403 F 27 – *see Newport.*

MUMBLES (The) *Swansea* 403 I 29 – *see Swansea.*

NANNERCH *Flintshire* 402 403 K 24 – *pop. 513* – ✉ *Mold.*

London 218 – Chester 19 – Liverpool 29 – Shrewsbury 52.

Old Mill without rest., Melin-y-Wern, Denbigh Rd, CH7 5RH, Northwest : ¾ m. on A 541 ℘ (01352) 741542, *welcome@old-mill.co.uk, Fax (01352) 740254,* « Converted 19C corn mill and stables », – TV P. MO AE VISA JCB
closed 2 weeks in winter – **6 rm** 47.00/67.00 **st.** – SB.

NANTGAREDIG *Carmarthenshire* 403 H 28 – *see Carmarthen.*

NEATH **(Castell-Ned)** *Neath Port Talbot* 403 I 29 *Wales G. – pop. 45 965.*

Env. : *Aberdulais Falls*★ *AC, NE : 2½ m. by B 4434 and A 4109.*

18 Swansea Bay, Jersey Marine ℘ (01792) 812198 – 18 Cadoxton ℘ (01639) 643615.

London 188 – Cardiff 40 – Swansea 8.

Cwmbach Cottages without rest., Cwmbach Rd, Cadoxton, SA10 8AH, Northwest : 1 ¾ m. by A 474 ℘ (01639) 639825, *cwmbachcottages@guesthouse25.fsnet.co.uk, Fax (01639) 639825,* ≤, – TV P.
9 rm 30.00/50.00 **t.**

NEFYN *Gwynedd* 402 403 G 25 *Wales G. – pop. 1 987.*

Env. : *Lleyn Peninsula*★★ – *Tre'r Ceiri*★, *NE : 5½ m. by B 4417 – Porth Dinllaen*★, *W : 1½ m. by B 4417.*

18, 9 Nefyn & District, Morfa Nefyn ℘ (01758) 720218.

London 265 – Caernarfon 20.

Caeau Capel , Rhodfar Mor, LL53 6EB, ℘ (01758) 720240, *caeau.capel.hotel@tinyworld.co.uk, Fax (01758) 720750,* – rest, TV P. MO VISA JCB
restricted opening in winter – **Meals** (booking essential to non-residents) (bar lunch)/dinner 17.50 **t.** ⚱ 7.55 – **18 rm** 30.00/75.00 **t.** – SB.

NEWPORT **(Casnewydd-Ar-Wysg)** *Newport* **403** L 29 *Wales G. – pop. 115 522.*

See : *Museum and Art Gallery★* **AX** – *Transporter Bridge★* **AC AY** – *Civic Centre (murals★)* **AX** – **Env. :** *Caerleon Roman Fortress★★* **AC** *(Fortress Baths★ – Legionary Museum★ – Amphitheatre★), NE : 2 ½ m. by B 4596* **AX** – *Tredegar House★★ (Grounds★ – Stables★), SW : 2½ m. by A 48* **AY**.

Exc. : *Penhow Castle★, E : 8 m. by A 48* **AX**.

Tredegar Park, Bassaleg Rd ☎ (01633) 895219 – Caerleon, Broadway ☎ (01633) 42034 – Parc, Church Lane, Coedkernew ☎ (01633) 680933.

Museum and Art Gallery, John Frost Sq ☎ (01633) 842962.

London 145 – Bristol 31 – Cardiff 12 – Gloucester 48.

NEWPORT

Allt-yr-yn Avenue . . . . . **AY** 2
Bellevue Lane . . . . . **BX** 5
Blewitt Street . . . . . **AX** 7
Caerau Crescent . . . . . **AXY** 9
Cambrian Centre . . . . . **AX**
Capel Street . . . . . **AY** 10
Clarence Place . . . . . **AX** 12
Clyffard Crescent . . . . . **AX** 13
Clytha Park Road . . . . . **AX** 14
Commercial Street . . . . . **AXY** 15
Dewsland Park Road . . . . . **AY** 17
Dock Street . . . . . **AX** 19
Godfrey Road . . . . . **AX** 21
Hereford Street . . . . . **AX** 24
High Street . . . . . **AX** 26
John Frost Square . . . . . **AX** 27
Kensington Place . . . . . **AX**
Keynsham Avenue . . . . . **AY**
Kingsway Centre . . . . . **AX**
Lower Dock Street . . . . . **AXY**
Malpas Road . . . . . **AX**
Newport Bridge . . . . . **AX**
Oakfield Road . . . . . **AX**
Queensway . . . . . **AX**
Summerhill Avenue . . . . . **AX**
Waterloo Road . . . . . **AY**

A 4042 CWMBRÂN — A — B 4596 (M 4)

CAERPHILLY B 4591 (M 4) — CARDIFF A 48 (M 4)

CARDIFF A 4042 (A 48) — A

The Celtic Manor, Coldra Woods, NP18 1HQ, East : 3 m. on A 48 ☎ (01633) 413000, *postbox@celtic-manor.com, Fax (01633) 412910,* – rm, – 1500.
Owens : Meals *(closed Sunday)* (dinner only) 38.00 and a la carte 38.00/48.00 **st.** 15.00 –
The Olive Tree : Meals (buffet lunch) 15.20/24.50 and a la carte approx. 24.40 **st.** 15.00 – 15.20 – **368 rm** 150.00/195.00 **s.**, 32 suites – SB.

Holiday Inn, The Coldra, NP18 2YG, East : 3 m. on A 48 ☎ (01633) 412777, *newport@holidayinns.co.uk, Fax (01633) 413087,* – rest, – 500.
Meals (bar lunch Monday-Saturday)/dinner a la carte 17.00/27.50 **t.** 10.35 – 10.50 – **119 rm** 99.00/125.00 **t.**

Newport Lodge, Brynglas Rd, NP20 5QN, North : ¾ m. by A 4042 off A 4051 ☎ (01633) 821818, *infor@newportlodgehotel.co.uk, Fax (01633) 856360* – rm,
Meals (dinner only) a la carte 14.40/21.25 **st.** – **27 rm** 80.00/115.00 **st.**

Kepe Lodge, 46a Caerau Rd, NP20 4HH, ☎ (01633) 262351, *Fax (01633) 262351,* – AY s
Meals (by arrangement) 9.50 **st.** – **8 rm** 25.00/50.00.

t Langstone *East : 4½ m. on A 48* – **AX** – ✉ *Newport.*

Hilton Newport, Chepstow Rd, NP18 2LX, ☎ (01633) 413737, *reservations@stakis.co.uk, Fax (01633) 413713,* – rm, rest, – 300.
Meals (bar lunch Monday to Saturday)/dinner 17.25 and a la carte 17.25/28.00 **st.** 13.50 – 9.95 – **146 rm** 130.00 **st.**, 2 suites – SB.

Travel Inn, Coldra Junction, Chepstow Rd, NP18 2NX, on A 48 (westbound carriageway) ☎ (01633) 411390, *Fax (01633) 411376* – rm, rest,
Meals (grill rest.) – **63 rm** 41.95 **t.**

t Redwick *Southeast : 9½ m. by M 4* – **AY** – *off B 4245* – ✉ *Magor.*

Brick House Country Guesthouse, North Row, NP26 3DX, ☎ (01633) 880230, *brickhouse@compuserve.com, Fax (01633) 882441,*
Meals (by arrangement) 15.00 **s.** 7.00 – **7 rm** 40.00/55.00 **s.**

t St Brides Wentlooge *Southwest : 4½ m. by A 48* – **AY** – *on B 4239* – ✉ *Newport.*

The Inn at The Elm Tree, NP10 8SQ, ☎ (01633) 680225, *inn@the-elm-tree.co.uk, Fax (01633) 681035,* – rm,
Meals 13.00 (lunch) and a la carte 19.00/28.00 **t.** 12.00 – **10 rm** 80.00/100.00 **t.**

EWPORT (Trefdraeth) *Pembrokeshire* 403 F 27 *Wales G. – pop. 1 162.*

Env. : *Pembrokeshire Coast National Park★★.*

Newport ☎ (01239) 820244.

2 Bank Cottages, Long St ☎ (01239) 820912.

London 258 – Fishguard 7.

Cnapan, East St, SA42 0SY, on A 487 ☎ (01239) 820575, *cnapan@online-holidays.net, Fax (01239) 820878,*
closed January-February and 25-26 December – **Meals** *(closed Tuesday)* (booking essential) (restricted lunch) a la carte 21.00/23.50 **t.** 9.50 – **5 rm** 37.00/60.00 **t.**

: Moylgrove *Northeast : 6 m.* – ✉ *Cardigan (Cardiganshire).*

The Old Vicarage, SA43 3BN, South : ¼ m. on Glanrhyd rd ☎ (01239) 881231, *stay@old-vic.co.uk, Fax (01239) 881341,*
restricted opening in winter – **Meals** (by arrangement) 17.00 **st.** 8.00 – **3 rm** 38.00/56.00 **st.**

ORTHOP HALL (Pentre-moch) *Flintshire* 402 403 K 24 – *pop. 4 155 (Northop).*

London 220 – Chester 9 – Liverpool 21 – Shrewsbury 52.

Holiday Inn, Gateway Services, A 55 (westbound carriageway), CH7 6HB, ☎ (01244) 550011, *info@holidayinn.a55chesterwest.i12.com, Fax (01244) 550763* – rm, – 200.
closed 24-25 December – **Meals** (bar lunch Monday-Saturday) 10.95/18.95 and a la carte 16.40/21.40 **t.** 9.95 – 8.50 – **53 rm** 69.00/90.00 **t.**

Travelodge, CH7 6HB, A 55 (eastbound carriageway) ☎ (01244) 816473 – rest,
Meals (grill rest.) – **40 rm** 49.95 **t.**

NOTTAGE (Drenewydd Yn Notais) *Bridgend* 403 *I 29 – see Porthcawl.*

PEMBROKE (Penfro) *Pembrokeshire* 403 F 28 *Wales G. – pop. 7 230.*

See : *Town★★ – Castle★★ AC.*

Env. : *Pembrokeshire Coast National Park★★ – Carew★ (Castle★ AC), NE : 4 m. by A 4075.*

Exc. : *Bosherston (St. Govan's Chapel★), S : 7 m. by B 4319 and minor roads – Stack Rocks SW : 9 m. by B 4319 and minor roads.*

18 *Military Rd, Pembroke Dock* ☎ *(01646) 621453.*

Cleddau Bridge (toll).

to Republic of Ireland (Rosslare) (Irish Ferries) 2 daily (3 h 45 mn) – to Republic of Ireland (Cork) (Swansea Cork Ferries) 2 weekly (8 h 30 mn).

Pembroke Visitor Centre, Commons Rd ☎ *(01646) 622388.*

London 252 – Carmarthen 32 – Fishguard 26.

Coach House, 116 Main St, SA71 4HN, ☎ (01646) 684602, *griffin@coachhouse-hotel.co.uk, Fax (01646) 687456* – TV P. MC AE VISA

Meals (bar lunch)/dinner 12.95/16.95 and a la carte 12.85/24.86 **st.** 7.95 – **14 rm** 55.00/70.00 **st.** – SB.

Left Bank, 63 Main St, SA71 4AD, ☎ (01646) 622333, *emmagriffith@leftbankrestaurant.co.uk, Fax (01646) 622333* – . MC AE VISA

closed 25-26 December, 3 weeks January, 1 week October, Sunday dinner and Monday – **Meals** (light lunch)/dinner 28.85/32.95 **t.** 8.90.

at Lamphey *East : 1 ¾ m. on A 4139 – Pembroke.*

Lamphey Court , SA71 5NT, ☎ (01646) 672273, *info@lampheycourt.co.uk, Fax (01646) 672480*, , , , , , , – rest, TV P. – 80. MC AE VISA.

Meals a la carte 20.30/25.70 **st.** 11.00 – **35 rm** 72.00/135.00 **st.** – SB.

Lamphey Hall, SA71 5NR, ☎ (01646) 672394, *lamphey@globalnet.co.uk, Fax (01646) 672369*, , – rest, TV P. MC AE VISA JCB.

closed 2 weeks January – **Meals** (dinner only and Sunday lunch)/dinner a la carte 13.00/27.40 **st.** 6.50 – **10 rm** 40.00/65.00 **st.**

at Stackpole *South : 5 m. by B 4319 – Pembroke.*

Armstrong Arms, SA71 5DF, ☎ (01646) 672324, – P. MC VISA JCB

closed Sunday dinner and Monday in January and February – **Meals** a la carte 12.85/22.70 7.45.

PENALLY (Penalun) *Pembrokeshire* 403 F 29 *– see Tenby.*

PENCOED *Bridgend* 403 J 29 *– see Bridgend.*

PENTYRCH *Cardiff* 403 K 29 *– see Cardiff.*

PONTARDDULAIS *Swansea* 403 H 28 *– pop. 1 634 – Swansea.*

London 203 – Fishguard 69 – Swansea 15.

The Fountain Inn with rm, 11 Bolgoed Rd, SA4 1JP, ☎ (01792) 882501, *joanne@fountaininn.com, Fax (01792) 885340* – rm, TV P. – 30. MC AE VISA.

Meals a la carte 15.23/20.95 **t.** 7.25 – **9 rm** 39.50/60.00 **st.**

PONTDOLGOCH *Powys – see Caersws.*

PONTYPRIDD *Rhondda Cynon Taff* 403 K 29 *Wales G. – pop. 28 487.*

Exc. : *Caerphilly Castle★★ AC, SE : 7 m. by A 470 and A 468 – Llancaiach Fawr Manor★ AC, NE : 6½ m. by A 4054, A 472, B 4255 and B 4254.*

Historical Centre, The Old Bridge ☎ *(01443) 490748.*

London 164 – Cardiff 9 – Swansea 40.

Llechwen Hall , Llanfabon, CF37 4HP, Northeast : 4 ¼ m. by A 4223 off A 4054 ☎ (01443) 742050, *llechwen@aol.com, Fax (01443) 742189*, – rm, TV P. – MC AE VISA JCB

closed 25-29 December – **Meals** a la carte 11.70/23.95 **t.** 8.95 – 6.95 – **20 rm** 59.50/85.00 **t.** – SB.

ORTH *Rhondda Cynon Taff* 403 J 29 *Wales G. – pop. 6 225 – ✉ Pontypridd.*
Env. : *Trehafod (Rhondda Heritage Park★), E : 1½ m. by A 4058.*
London 168 – Cardiff 13 – Swansea 45.

Heritage Park, Coed Cae Rd, Trehafod, CF37 2NP, on A 4058 ☎ (01443) 687057, *Fax (01443) 687060,* – rest, – 200. MC AE VISA JCB
Meals 13.50/15.50 and a la carte 14.90/23.35 **t.** 8.75 – **44 rm** 68.00/78.00 **t.** – SB.

ORTHCAWL *Bridgend* 403 I 29 *Wales G. – pop. 16 099.*
Env. : *Glamorgan Heritage Coast★.*
The Old Police Station, John St ☎ (01656) 786639.
London 183 – Cardiff 28 – Swansea 18.

Atlantic, West Drive, CF36 3LT, ☎ (01656) 785011, *enquiries@atlantichotelporthcawl.co.uk, Fax (01656) 771877,* ←, – MC VISA JCB.
Meals *(closed Sunday dinner)* 14.50 and a la carte 13.40/33.40 **t.** 9.50 – **18 rm** 59.00/90.00 **t.** – SB.

: Nottage *North : 1 m. by A 4229 – ✉ Porthcawl.*

Rose and Crown, Heol-y-Capel, CF36 3ST, ☎ (01656) 784850, *Fax (01656) 784296* – rest, MC AE VISA.
Meals (carving rest.) a la carte 11.95/16.85 **t.** 8.95 – **8 rm** 35.00/45.00 **t.**

ORTHGAIN *Pembrokeshire* 403 E 28 – *see St. Davids.*

The Guide is updated annually so renew your Guide every year.

ORTMEIRION *Gwynedd* 402 403 H 25 *Wales G.*
See : *Village★★★ AC.*
Env. : *Snowdonia National Park★★★ – Lleyn Peninsula★★ – Ffestiniog Railway★★ AC.*
London 245 – Caernarfon 23 – Colwyn Bay 40 – Dolgellau 24.

Portmeirion , LL48 6ET, ☎ (01766) 770000, *hotel@portmeirion-village.com, Fax (01766) 771331,* ← village and estuary, « Private Italianate village in extensive gardens and woodland designed by Sir Clough Williams-Ellis, antiques », heated – rest, – 120. MC AE VISA JCB.
closed 8 January-1 February – **Meals** *(closed Monday lunch)* (booking essential for non-residents) 10.50/35.00 and a la carte 22.00/30.00 **t.** 10.50 – 11.00 – **28 rm** 95.00/180.00 **t.**, 12 suites – SB.

Castell Deudraeth, LL48 6EN, ☎ (01766) 772400, *hotel@portmeirion-village.com, Fax (01766) 772401,* « Crenellated Victorian manor, contemporary interior design », – rest, MC AE VISA JCB.
closed 6-18 January – ***Grill :*** **Meals** - Bistro - 11.00/14.00 (lunch) and dinner a la carte 17.00/28.00 **st.** 8.50 – 11.00 – **8 rm** 145.00/230.00 **st.**, 3 suites – SB.

ORT TALBOT *Neath Port Talbot* 403 I 29 *Wales G. – pop. 37 647.*
Env. : *Margam Park★ AC (Orangery★), SE : 4 m. by A 48.*
London 193 – Cardiff 35 – Swansea 11.

Travel Inn, Baglan Rd, SA12 8ES, M 4 junction 41 (westbound) or junction 42 (eastbound) ☎ (01639) 813017, *Fax (01639) 823096* – rm, rest, MC AE VISA.
Meals (grill rest.) – **42 rm** 41.95 **t.**

RESTATYN *Denbighshire* 402 403 J 23 – *pop. 15 020.*
Offa's Dyke Centre, Central Beach ☎ (01745) 889092.
London 230 – Bangor 35 – Birkenhead 43 – Chester 35 – Holyhead 56.

Traeth Ganol, 41 Beach Rd West, LL19 7LL, ☎ (01745) 853594, *info@hotel-prestatyn.co.uk, Fax (01745) 886687* – MC AE VISA JCB.
Meals (booking essential) (dinner only) 12.50 **t.** 6.70 – **9 rm** 40.00/65.00 **t.** – SB.

WLLHELI *Gwynedd* 402 403 G 25 *Wales G. – pop. 3 974.*
Env. : *Lleyn Peninsula★★.*
18 Golf Rd ☎ (01758) 701644.
MinyDon, Station Sq ☎ (01758) 613000.
London 261 – Aberystwyth 73 – Caernarfon 21.

XXX Plas Bodegroes (Chown) with rm, LL53 5TH, Northwest : 1 ¾ m. on A 4
(01758) 612363, *gunna@bodegroes.co.uk, Fax (01758) 701247,* « Georgian count house », – TV P. MC VISA
closed 1 January-12 February December and Monday except Bank Holidays – **Meals** (booking essential) (dinner only and Sunday lunch)/dinner 30.00 **t.** 14.50 – **11 rm** 40.0 120.00 **t.** – SB
Spec. Lobster risotto with samphire. Roast loin of free-range pork with bacon and bla pudding, garlic cream. Iced prune and Armagnac parfait, prune syrup.

at Boduan *Northwest : 3 ¾ m. on A 497 – Pwllheli.*

The Old Rectory, LL53 6DT, (01758) 721519, *Fax (01758) 721519,* « Part Georgi house », – TV P
closed Christmas – **Meals** (by arrangement) 22.50 9.95 – **4 rm** 50.00/70.00 **st.**

RAGLAN *Monmouthshire* 403 L 28 *Wales G. – pop. 1 857 – Abergavenny.*

See : *Castle★ AC.*
London 154 – Gloucester 34 – Newport 18 – Swansea 58.

Travelodge without rest., NP5 4BG, Northeast : 2 m. on A 40 (eastbound carriagewa
(01600) 740455, *Fax (01600) 740329* – TV P. MC AE VISA JCB.
42 rm 39.95 **t.**

Clytha Arms, NP7 9BW, West : 3 m. on Clytha rd (old Abergavenny R
(01873) 840206, *one.bev@lineone.net, Fax (01873) 840206* – rest, P. MC AE VISA
closed 25 December – **Meals** *(closed Sunday dinner and Monday except Bank Holida* 15.95 and a la carte 14.60/28.90 **t.** 10.95.

When looking for a quiet hotel
use the maps found in the introduction
or look for establishments with the sign or .

REDWICK *Newport* 403 L 29 – *see Newport (Newport).*

RHAYADER (Rhaeadr) *Powys* 403 J 27 – *pop. 1 626.*

The Leisure Centre (01597) 810591.
London 195 – Aberystwth 39 – Carmarthen 67 – Shrewsbury 60.

Beili Neuadd without rest., LD6 5NS, Northeast : 2 m. by A 44 off Abbey-cwm-hir
(01597) 810211, *ann-carl@thebeili.freeserve.co.uk, Fax (01597) 810211,* <, , –
P
closed Christmas and New Year – **3 rm** 25.00/47.00 **st.**

RHYDLEWIS *Ceredigion* 403 G 27 *Wales G. – Llandysul.*

Exc. : *Aberaeron★, NE : 11½ m. by B 4334 and A 487.*
London 235 – Carmarthen 26 – Fishguard 38.

Broniwan , SA44 5PF, Northeast : ¼ m. by Pentregat rd, taking first turn right or unmarked road (01239) 851261, *broniwan@compuserve.com, Fax (01239) 8512*
« Working farm », , – P
Meals (by arrangement) 17.50 **st.** – **3 rm** 25.00/50.00 **st.**

ROSSETT (Yr Orsedd) *Wrexham* 402 403 L 24 – *pop. 1 986.*

London 203 – Chester 8 – Liverpool 29 – Shrewsbury 39.

Rossett Hall, Chester Rd, LL12 0DE, (01244) 571000, *reservations@rossetthallhotel.*
uk, Fax (01244) 571505, – , rest, TV P – 120. MC AE VISA.
Oscars : **Meals** 10.95 (lunch) and a la carte 16.40/24.20 **st.** 8.95 – 8.95 – **29 rm** 70.0 90.00 **st.**, 1 suite – SB.

RUTHIN (Rhuthun) *Denbighshire* 402 403 K 24 *Wales G. – pop. 5 029.*

Env. : *Llandyrnog (St. Dyfnog's Church★), Llanrhaeder-yng-Nghinmeirch (Jesse W dow★★), N : 5½ m. by A 494 and B 5429.*
Exc. : *Denbigh★ (Castle★), NW : 7 m. on A 525.*
Ruthin-Pwllglas (01824) 702296.
Ruthin Craft Centre, Park Rd (01824) 703992.
London 210 – Birkenhead 31 – Chester 23 – Liverpool 34 – Shrewsbury 46.

Ye Olde Anchor Inn, Rhos St, LL15 1DY, (01824) 702813, *hotel@anchorinn.co.uk, Fax (01824) 703050* – rest, P. VISA
Meals 16.45/19.45 and a la carte 20.70/26.40 **st.** 12.85 – **26 rm** 37.50/52.50 **t.** – SB.

Firgrove, Llanfwrog, LL15 2LL, West : 1 ¼ m. by A 494 on B 5105 (01824) 702677, *anna@firgrove.fsnet.co.uk, Fax (01824) 702677,* – P. VISA JCB.
closed 17 December-31 January – **Meals** (by arrangement) (communal dinning) 22.50/29.50 **st.** – **3 rm** 35.00/60.00 **st.**

Eyarth Station, Llanfair Dyffryn Clwyd, LL15 2EE, South : 1 ¾ m. by A 525 (01824) 703643, *eyarthstation@amserve.net, Fax (01824) 707464,* heated, – P. VISA
closed January and February – **Meals** 11.00/15.00 **s.** – **6 rm** 30.00/50.00 **s.**

T ASAPH (Llanelwy) *Denbighshire* 402 403 J 24 *Wales G. – pop. 3 399.*
See : *Cathedral★.*
Env. : *Rhuddlan Castle★★ AC, N : 2 ½ m. by A 525 and A 547 – Bodelwyddan★★ AC, W : 2 ½ m. by A 55 – Denbigh★ (Castle★), S : 6 m. by A 525 and A 543.*
London 225 – Chester 29 – Shrewsbury 59.

Plough Inn, The Roe, LL17 0LU, North : ½ m. on A 525 (01745) 585080, *Fax (01745) 585363,* – P. VISA
Meals (booking essential) a la carte 15.85/23.40 **t.** 10.95.

T BRIDES WENTLOOGE *Newport* 403 K 29 – *see Newport.*

T CLEARS (Sancler) *Carmarthenshire* 403 G 28 *Wales G. – pop. 3 014.*
Env. : *Laugharne★ (Castle★, The Boat House★), S : 4 m. on A 4066.*
London 229 – Carmarthen 9 – Fishguard 37.

Forge Lodge, SA33 4NA, East : 1 m. on A 40 (01994) 230300, *info@theforgelodge.co.uk, Fax (01994) 231577,* – P – 100. VISA
closed 25 and 26 December – **Meals** (grill rest.) a la carte 8.50/20.00 **st.** 9.00 – **18 rm** 45.00/65.00 **st.**

Travelodge, Tenby Rd, SA33 4JN, on A 40 (01994) 231227, *Fax (01994) 231227* – rm, P. VISA JCB.
Meals (grill rest.) – **32 rm** 52.95 **t.**

T DAVIDS (Tyddewi) *Pembrokeshire* 403 E 28 *Wales G. – pop. 1 959 – Haverfordwest.*
See : *Town★★ – Cathedral★★ – Bishop's Palace★ AC.*
Env. : *Pembrokeshire Coast National Park★★.*
St. Davids City, Whitesands Bay (01437) 721751.
National Park Visitor Centre, The Grove (01437) 720392.
London 266 – Carmarthen 46 – Fishguard 16.

Warpool Court, SA62 6BN, Southwest : ½ m. by Porth Clais rd (01437) 720300, *warpool@enterprise.net, Fax (01437) 720676,* – rest, P. VISA
closed January – **Meals** 25.00/37.00 **st.** 12.95 – **25 rm** 75.00/218.00 **st.** – SB.

Old Cross, Cross Sq, SA62 6SP, (01437) 720387, *enquiries@oldcrosshotel.co.uk, Fax (01437) 720394,* – rest, P. VISA JCB
closed 21 December-1 February – **Meals** (bar lunch)/dinner a la carte 16.70/22.25 **t.** 8.25 – **16 rm** 50.00/88.00 **t.** – SB.

The Waterings without rest., Anchor Drive, SA62 6QH, East : ¼ m. on A 487 (01437) 720876, *waterings@supanet.com, Fax (01437) 720876,* – P.
5 rm 45.00/65.00 **st.**

Y-Gorlan, 77 Nun St, SA62 6NU, (01437) 720837, *mikebohlen@aol.com, Fax (01437) 721148* – . VISA
Meals (by arrangement) 16.00 **st.** 10.00 – **5 rm** 27.00/54.00 **st.**

Morgan's Brasserie, 20 Nun St, SA62 6NT, (01437) 720508, *morgans@stdavids.co.uk, Fax (01437) 720508* – . VISA
closed November-February and Sunday, restricted opening March and October – **Meals** (booking essential) (dinner only) a la carte 22.00/28.00 **t.** 12.00.

t Porthgain *Northeast : 7 ¾ m. by A 487 and Llanrian rd – Haverfordwest.*

Harbour Lights, SA62 5BW, (01348) 831549, *info@wales-pembs-art.com, Fax (01348) 831193* – VISA JCB
closed Sunday-Wednesday and restricted opening October-April – **Meals** - Seafood - (booking essential) (dinner only) 21.50/25.00.

T DOGMAELS (Llandudoch) *Ceredigion* 403 G 27 – *see Cardigan.*

ST GEORGE *Conwy* – ✉ *Abergele.*
London 230 – Chester 30 – Shrewsbury 65.

Kinmel Arms, LL22 9BP, ☎ (01745) 832207, *Fax (01745) 832207* – ✂ P. MC VISA
closed 25 December – **Meals** a la carte 10.50/22.00 ♁ 6.95.

SARON *Gwynedd – see Caernarfon.*

SEION *Gwynedd* 402 403 H 24 – *see Caernarfon.*

SOUTHERNDOWN *Bridgend* 403 J 29 – *see Bridgend.*

STACKPOLE *Pembrokeshire* 403 F 29 – *see Pembroke.*

SWANSEA (Abertawe) *Swansea* 403 I 29 *Wales G.* – *pop. 181 906.*
See : *Town*★ – *Maritime Quarter*★ **B** – *Maritime and Industrial Museum*★ **B M** – *Glynn Vivia Art Gallery*★ – *Guildhall (British Empire Panels*★*).*
Env. : *Gower Peninsula*★★ *(Rhossili*★★*), W : by A 4067* **A**.
Exc. : *The Wildfowl and Wetlands Trust*★, *Llanelli, NW : 6½ m. by A 483 and A 484* **A**.
18 *Morriston, 160 Clasemont Rd* ☎ *(01792) 771079,* **A** – 18 *Clyne, 120 Owls Lodge Lan Mayals* ☎ *(01792) 401989,* **A** – 18 *Langland Bay* ☎ *(01792) 366023,* **A** – 18 *Fairwood Par Blackhills Lane, Upper Killay* ☎ *(01792) 203648,* **A** – 9 *Inco, Clydach* ☎ *(01792) 844216,* **A** 9 *Allt-y-Graban, Allt-y-Graban Rd, Pontllin* ☎ *(01792) 885757* – 9 *Palleg, Lower Cwmtwrc Swansea Valley* ☎ *(01639) 842193.*
to Republic of Ireland (Cork) (Swansea Cork Ferries) (10 h).
Plymouth St ☎ *(01792) 468321.*
London 191 – Birmingham 136 – Bristol 82 – Cardiff 40 – Liverpool 187 – Stoke-on-Trent 17

SWANSEA
BUILT UP AREA

Clase Road . . . . **A** 12
Martin Street . . . . **A** 24
Pen-y-Graig Road . . . . **A** 30
Plasmarl By-Pass . . . . **A** 32
Ravenhill Road . . . . **A** 35
Station Road . . . . **A** 37
St. Helen's Road . . . . **A** 40
Terrace Road . . . . **A** 45
Uplands Crescent . . . . **A** 49
Walter Road . . . . **A** 52
Woodfield Street . . . . **A** 60

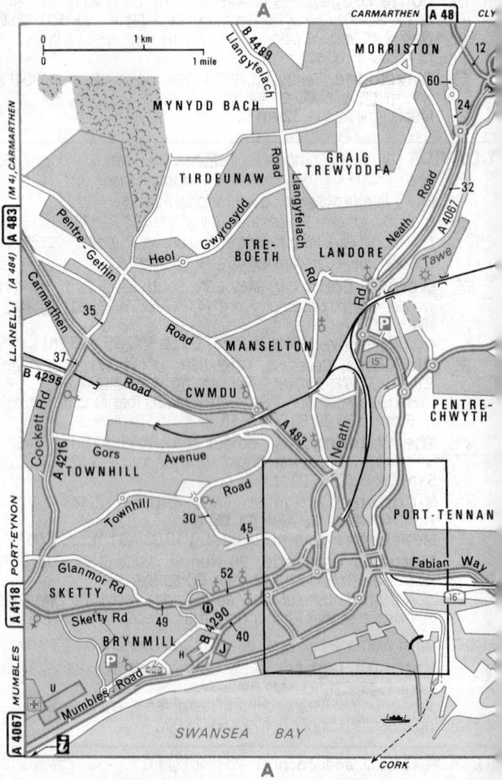

This Guide is not a comprehensive list of all hotels and restaurants, nor even of all good hotels and restaurants in Great Britain and Ireland.

Since our aim is to be of service to all motorists, we must show establishments in all categories and so we have made a selection of some in each.

SWANSEA

lexandra Road . . . . B 2
elle Vue Way . . . . B 4
armarthen Road . . . . B 7
astle Street . . . . B 8
hristina Street . . . . B 9
arence Terrace . . . . B 10
ollege Street . . . . B 13
De la Beche Street . . . . B 15
Dillwyn Street . . . . B 17
East Bank Way . . . . C 18
Grove Place . . . . B 22
Kingsway (The) . . . . B
Nearth Road . . . . B 25
Nelson Street . . . . B 26
New Cut Bridge . . . . C 27
Oxford Street . . . . B
Parc Tawe Shopping Centre . B
Princess Way . . . . B
Quadrant Centre . . . . B
St. David's Square . . . . B
St. Mary's Square . . . . B 42
Tawe Bridge . . . . C 43
Union Street . . . . B 47
Wellington Street . . . . B 54
West Way . . . . B 55

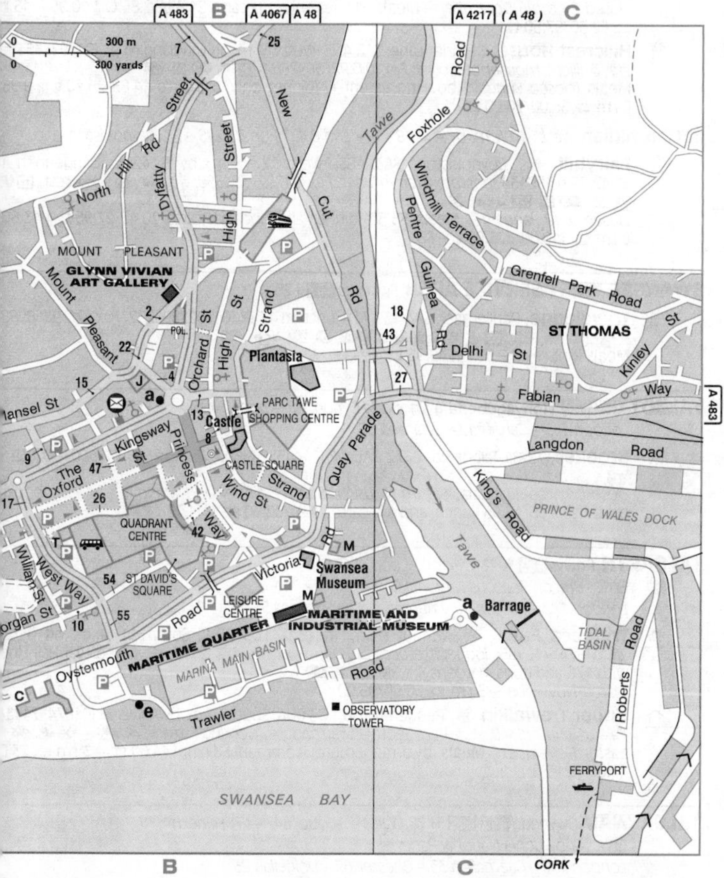

Swansea Marriott, Maritime Quarter, SA1 3SS, ☎ (01792) 642020, *Fax (01792) 650345,* ≤, ₣₆, ⊇s, ⊠ – |♦|, ⇸ ▤ TV ☏ ♿ P – 🎓 300. MC AE ⊕ VISA JCB. ✂ B e
Meals 11.95/19.95 a la carte 25.00/40.60 **st.** 🌡 13.00 – ⊇ 13.00 – **117 rm** 99.00/134.00 **st.** – SB.

Holiday Inn, 39 The Kingsway, SA1 5LS, ☎ (0870) 400 9078, *reservations-swansea@posthouse-hotels.com, Fax (01792) 456044,* ₣₆, ⊇s, ⊠ – |♦|, ⇸ rm, TV P – 🎓 270. MC AE ⊕ VISA JCB. ✂ B a
Meals (bar lunch Monday to Saturday)/dinner 15.00 and a la carte 17.35/28.85 **t.** 🌡 11.95 – ⊇ 11.95 – **100 rm** 89.00 **t.**, 6 suites – SB.

Beaumont, 72-73 Walter Rd, SA1 4QA, ☎ (01792) 643956, *info@beaumonthotel.co.uk, Fax (01792) 643044* – TV P. MC AE ⊕ VISA JCB. ✂ A n
Meals (dinner only) 10.00/15.00 and a la carte 16.95/20.70 **st.** 🌡 8.50 – **16 rm** ⊇ 60.00/90.00 **st.** – SB.

Hanson's, Pilot House Wharf, Trawler Rd, Swansea Marina, SA1 1UN, (01792) 46620 *Fax (01792) 201774* – P. VISA JCB C
closed 24-26 December and Sunday dinner – **Meals** (booking essential) 9.95/12.9 (lunch) and a la carte 18.85/26.85 **t.** 9.95.

at The Mumbles *Southwest : 7 ¾ m. by A 4067 – A – Swansea.*

Norton House, 17 Norton Rd, SA3 5TQ, (01792) 404891, *nortonhouse@btconne com, Fax (01792) 403210,* – rest, P – 25. AE VISA JCB.
closed 24 to 26 December – **Meals** (dinner only) a la carte 21.85/32.85 **t.** 10.95 – **15 r** 62.50/97.50 **t.**

Hillcrest House, 1 Higher Lane, SA3 4NS, West : ¾ m. on Langland rd (01792) 3637C *stay@hillcresthousehotel.com, Fax (01792) 363768* – P. AE VISA.
Meals *(closed Sunday)* (booking essential) (dinner only) a la carte 14.88/25.70 **t.** 9.95 **6 rm** 55.00/70.00 **t.**

at Llanrhidian *West : 10½ m. by A 4118 – A – and B 4271 on B 4295 – Reynoldston.*

Fairyhill , Reynoldston, SA3 1BS, West : 2 ½ m. by B 4295 (Llangennith r (01792) 390139, *postbox@fairyhill.net, Fax (01792) 391358,* , , – rest, P 35. AE VISA JCB.
closed 1-18 January – **Meals** 35.50 (dinner) and lunch a la carte 20.40/27.95 **t.** 13.50 **8 rm** 110.00/225.00 **t.** – SB.

SWANSEA WEST SERVICE AREA *Swansea 403 I 28.*

Travelodge, Penllergaer, SA4 1GT, M 4 junction 47 (01792) 896222, *Fax (01792) 8988* – rm, rest, P – 25. AE VISA JCB.
Meals (grill rest.) – **50 rm** 49.95 **t.**

TALBOT GREEN (Tonysguborian) *Rhondda Cynon Taff – pop. 2 405.*

London 165 – Cardiff 17 – Swansea 60.

Brookes, 79-81 Talbot Rd, CF72 8AE, (01443) 239600, *Fax (01443) 239600* – AE VISA
closed 1 week January, Saturday lunch, Sunday dinner and Monday – **Meals** (booki essential) 9.95/12.95 (lunch) and a la carte 24.90/32.90 **st.** 11.75.

TALGARTH *Powys 403 K 28 Wales G. – pop. 1 818.*

Env. : *Brecon Beacons National Park★★.*

London 182 – Brecon 10 – Hereford 29 – Swansea 53.

Trefecca Fawr without rest., Trefecca, LD3 0PW, South : 1 ¼ m. on B 45 (01874) 712195, *lodge@trefecca.zx3.net, Fax (01874) 712196,* ←, « Medieval Hall Hou with 17C additions, gardens » – P. VISA.
March-November – **3 rm** 60.00/96.00.

Upper Trewalkin , Pengenffordd, LD3 0HA, South : 2 m. by A 479 (01874) 7113 *Fax (01874) 711349,* ←, « Part Georgian farmhouse, working farm », , – P.
Easter-November – **Meals** (by arrangement) (communal dining) 14.50 **st.** – **3 rm** 23.0 46.00 **st.** – SB.

TALSARNAU *Gwynedd 402 403 H 25 Wales G. – pop. 647 – Harlech.*

Env. : *Snowdonia National Park★★★.*

London 236 – Caernafon 33 – Chester 67 – Dolgellau 25.

Maes-y-Neuadd , LL47 6YA, South : 1 ½ m. by A 496 off B 4573 (01766) 7802 *maes@neuadd.com, Fax (01766) 780211,* ←, « Part 14C country house, gardens » – P – 25. AE VISA
Meals (bar lunch Monday-Saturday) 27.00/34.00 (dinner) and lunch a la carte 14.20/18.2 12.95 – **15 rm** 116.00/180.00 **t.**, 1 suite – SB.

AL-Y-LLYN *Gwynedd* 402 403 I 25 *Wales G.* – ✉ *Tywyn.*
Env. : *Snowdonia National Park*★★★ – *Cadair Idris*★★★.
London 224 – Dolgellau 9 – Shrewsbury 60.

Tynycornel, LL36 9AJ, on B 4405 ☎ (01654) 782282, *info@tynycornel.co.uk, Fax (01654) 782679,* ⩽ Tal-y-Llyn Lake and Cadair Idris, ⇋s, ⛵, 🏞 – ⇹ TV P. MC AE VISA
Meals (bar lunch Monday-Saturday)/dinner a la carte 11.95/25.95 **t.** 🍾 10.95 – **15 rm** ⊒ 48.50/97.00 **t.**, 2 suites.

Minffordd, LL36 9AJ, Northeast : 2 ¼ m. by B 4405 on A 487 ☎ (01654) 761665, *hotel@minffordd.com, Fax (01654) 761517,* ⩽, 🏞 – ⇹ P. MC AE VISA JCB
– **Meals** (booking essential for non-residents) (dinner only and Sunday lunch) 22.00 **st.** 🍾 9.95 – **7 rm** ⊒ 47.00/78.00 **st.** – SB.

ENBY (Dinbych-Y-Pysgod) *Pembrokeshire* 403 F 28 *Wales G.* – *pop. 4 809.*
See : *Town*★★ – *Harbour and seafront*★★.
Env. : *Pembrokeshire Coast National Park*★★ – *Caldey Island*★, *S : by boat.*
18 *The Burrows* ☎ *(01834) 842787.*
The Croft ☎ *(01834) 842402.*
London 247 – Carmarthen 27 – Fishguard 36.

Waterwynch House 🐦, Narberth Rd, Waterwynch Bay, SA70 8TJ, North : 1 ¾ m. by A 478 ☎ (01834) 842464, *enquiries@waterwynchhousehotel.co.uk, Fax (01834) 845076,* ⩽, 🏞, 🌳 – ⇹ TV P. MC VISA. ✂
March-October – **Meals** *(closed Sunday dinner)* (dinner only and Sunday lunch)/dinner 15.00/20.00 🍾 10.00 – **14 rm** ⊒ 65.00/115.00 **t.**, 2 suites.

Atlantic without rest., Esplanade, SA70 7DU, ☎ (01834) 842881, *enquiries@atlantic-hotel.uk.com, Fax (01834) 842881 (ext. 256),* 🏊, 🏞 – |‡| ⇹ TV ♿ P. MC AE VISA JCB
closed 21-28 December – **42 rm** ⊒ 64.00/135.00 **st.**

Broadmead, Heywood Lane, SA70 8DA, Northwest : ¾ m. ☎ (01834) 842641, *Fax (01834) 845757,* 🏞 – ⇹ rest, TV P. MC AE VISA JCB. ✂
closed 24 December-28 February – **Meals** (dinner only) 13.00/18.00 **t.** 🍾 7.95 – **20 rm** ⊒ 32.00/64.00 **t.** – SB.

Fourcroft, North Beach, SA70 8AP, ☎ (01834) 842886, *hospitality@fourcroft-hotel.co.uk, Fax (01834) 842888,* ⩽, ⇋s, 🏊 heated – |‡| ⇹ TV – 🏛 80. MC AE ◑ VISA JCB
Meals (bar lunch)/dinner 16.00 and a la carte 13.50/25.50 **st.** 🍾 9.50 – **43 rm** ⊒ 55.00/110.00 **st.** – SB.

Myrtle House, St Marys St, SA70 7HW, ☎ (01834) 842508, *Fax (01834) 842508* – ⇹ TV 🚗. MC VISA. ✂
March-October – **Meals** (by arrangement) 10.00 **st.** – **8 rm** ⊒ 30.00/56.00 **s.**

Penally (Penalun) *Southwest : 2 m. by A 4139* – ✉ *Tenby.*

Penally Abbey 🐦, SA70 7PY, ☎ (01834) 843033, *penallyabbey@btinternet.com, Fax (01834) 844714,* ⩽, 🏞 – ⇹ rest, TV P. MC AE VISA JCB. ✂
Meals (lunch booking essential)/dinner 28.00 **st.** 🍾 12.95 – **12 rm** ⊒ 128.00/138.00 **st.** – SB.

HORNHILL *Cardiff* 403 K 29 – *see Cardiff.*

HREE COCKS (Aberllynfi) *Powys* 403 K 27 *Wales G.* – ✉ *Brecon.*
Env. : *Brecon Beacons National Park*★★.
London 184 – Brecon 11 – Hereford 25 – Swansea 55.

Three Cocks with rm, LD3 0SL, on A 438 ☎ (01497) 847215, *Fax (01497) 847339,* « Part 15C inn », 🏞 – P. MC VISA. ✂
closed December and January – **Meals** *(closed Sunday lunch and Tuesday)* (lunch booking essential)/dinner 28.00 and a la carte 21.75/32.30 **st.** 🍾 8.95 – **7 rm** ⊒ 45.00/67.00 **st.** – SB.

NTERN (Tyndyrn) *Monmouthshire* 403 404 L 28 *Wales G.* – *pop. 749* – ✉ *Chepstow.*
See : *Abbey*★★ *AC.*
London 137 – Bristol 23 – Gloucester 40 – Newport 22.

The Royal George, NP16 6SF, on A 466 ☎ (01291) 689205, *royalgeorgetintern@hotmail.com, Fax (01291) 689448,* 🏞 – ⇹ TV P – 🏛 100. MC AE ◑ VISA. ✂
Meals 8.25/22.00 and a la carte 12.25/25.00 **t.** 🍾 10.25 – **16 rm** ⊒ 62.00/88.00 – SB.

Parva Farmhouse with rm, NP16 6SQ, on A 466 ☎ (01291) 689411, *parva_hoteltintern@hotmail.com, Fax (01291) 689557* – ⇹ rest, TV P. MC AE VISA JCB
Meals (dinner only) 19.50 **st.** – **9 rm** ⊒ 55.00/80.00 **st.** – SB.

TREARDDUR BAY *Anglesey* 402 403 G 24 *Wales G.* – ✉ *Holyhead.*

Env. : *Anglesey*★★.

Exc. : *Barclodiad y Gawres Burial Chamber*★, *SE : 10 m. by B 4545, A 5 and A 4080.*

London 269 – Bangor 25 – Caernarfon 29 – Holyhead 3.

Trearddur Bay, LL65 2UN, ℘ (01407) 860301, *markdgul@trearddurbayhotel.co.u* *Fax (01407) 861181*, ▣, ⌂ – ⇹ rest, ▣ P – ⚲ 65. MC AE ◑ VISA JCB *closed 24-26 December* **Meals** (bar lunch)/dinner 23.50 **st.** ⚱ 10.00 – **42 rm** ⊒ 82.0(150.00 **st.**

TRECASTLE (Tregastell) *Powys* 403 J 28.

London 192 – Aberystwyth 60 – Cardiff 47 – Carmarthen 37 – Gloucester 81.

Castle Coaching Inn, LD3 8UH, ℘ (01874) 636354, *hotel.reservation@btinternet.co* *Fax (01874) 636457* – ⇹ rest, ▣ P. MC VISA JCB *closed 25 December* **Meals** (bar lunch)/dinner 14.95 and a la carte 17.95/24.45 **st.** ⚱ 8.95 **9 rm** ⊒ 45.00/50.00 **st.**, 1 suite – SB.

TREMEIRCHION *Denbighshire* 402 403 J 24 – ✉ *St. Asaph.*

London 225 – Chester 29 – Shrewsbury 59.

Bach-Y-Graig ⛰ without rest., LL17 0UH, Southwest : 2 m. by B 5429 off Denbigh ℘ (01745) 730627, *anwenroberts@bachygraig.fsnet.co.uk, Fax (01745) 730627*, « 16C bri built house, working farm », ⌂, ⚲ – ⇹ ▣ P. ⚔ *closed Christmas-New Year* – **3 rm** ⊒ 35.00/50.00 **s.**

TYN-Y-GROES *Gwynedd* – *see Conwy (Aberconwy and Colwyn).*

USK (Brynbuga) *Monmouthshire* 403 L 28 *Wales G.* – *pop. 2 187.*

Exc. : *Raglan Castle*★ *AC, NE : 7 m. by A 472, A 449 and A 40.*

⛳18, ⛳18 *Alice Springs, Bettws Newydd* ℘ *(01873) 880772.*

London 144 – Bristol 30 – Gloucester 39 – Newport 10.

Glen-yr-Afon House, Pontypool Rd, NP15 1SY, ℘ (01291) 672302, *enquiries@glen-afon.co.uk, Fax (01291) 672597*, ⌂ – ⇅ ⇹ ▣ ♿ P – ⚲ 200. MC AE ◑ VISA JCB **Meals** (Sunday dinner residents only) a la carte 14.00/25.70 **st.** ⚱ 9.95 – **28 rm** ⊒ 69.3 111.63 **st.** – SB.

WELSH HOOK *Pembrokeshire* 403 F 28 – *see Fishguard.*

WELSHPOOL (Trallwng) *Powys* 402 403 K 26 *Wales G.* – *pop. 5 900.*

See : *Town*★.

Env. : *Powis Castle*★★★ *AC, SW : 1½ m. by A 483.*

⛳18 *Golfa Hill* ℘ *(01938) 83249.*

ℹ *Vicarage Garden, Church St* ℘ *(01938) 552043.*

London 182 – Birmingham 64 – Chester 45 – Shrewsbury 19.

Royal Oak, The Cross, SY21 7DG, ℘ (01938) 552217, *oakwpool@aol.co* *Fax (01938) 556652* – ⇹ ▣ P – ⚲ 150. MC AE VISA **Meals** 7.95 (lunch) and a la carte 15.15/20.75 **st.** ⚱ 9.95 – **24 rm** ⊒ 58.50/85.00 **st.** – SB.

Buttington Country House, Buttington, SY21 8HD, Northeast : 2 m. by A 483 a A 458 on B 4388 ℘ (01938) 553351, *Fax (01938) 640604*, « Georgian house », ⌂ – ⇹ ⚔ *closed 24 December-mid January* – **Meals** (by arrangement) 25.00 – **3 rm** ⊒ 60.00/80.0(SB.

Moat Farm ⛰, SY21 8SE, South : 2 ¼ m. on A 483 ℘ (01938) 553179, *ewjones@free name.co.uk, Fax (01938) 553179*, « Working farm », ⌂, ⚲ – ⇹ ▣ P. ⚔ *closed December and January* – **Meals** (by arrangement) (communal dining) 14.00 **st** **3 rm** ⊒ 26.00/44.00 **st.**

at Guilsfield *North : 3 m. by A 490 on B 4392* – ✉ *Welshpool.*

Lower Trelydan ⛰, SY21 9PH, South : ¾ m. by B 4392 on unmarked ro ℘ (01938) 553105, *stay@lowertrelydan.com, Fax (01938) 553105*, « 16C farmhouse, wo ing farm », ⌂, ⚲ – ⇹ ▣ P. VISA. ⚔ *closed Christmas and New Year* – **Meals** (by arrangement) (communal dining) 13.00 ⚱ 8.00 – **3 rm** ⊒ 30.00/52.00 **t.**

WOLF'S CASTLE (Cas-Blaidd) *Pembrokeshire* 403 F 28 *Wales G.* – *pop. 616* – ✉ *Haverfordwest.*

Env. : *Pembrokeshire Coast National Park*★★.

London 258 – Fishguard 7 – Haverfordwest 8.

Wolfscastle Country H., SA62 5LZ, ☎ (01437) 741225, *enquiries@wolfcastle.com, Fax (01437) 741383,* – TV P – 150. MC AE VISA JCB
closed 24-26 December – **Meals** *(closed Sunday dinner in winter)* (lunch by arrangement Monday-Saturday)/dinner a la carte 13.90/24.40 **t.** 7.50 – **20 rm** 45.00/79.00 **t.** – SB.

WREXHAM (Wrecsam) *Wrexham* 402 403 L 24 *Wales G.* – *pop. 40 614.*

See : *St. Giles Church*★.

Env. : *Erddig*★★ *AC (Gardens*★★*), SW : 2 m – Gresford (All Saints Church*★*), N : 4 m. by A 5152 and B 5445.*

18, 9 *Chirk* ☎ *(01691) 774407* – 18 *Clays Farm, Bryn Estyn Rd* ☎ *(01978) 661406* – 9 *Moss Valley, Moss Rd* ☎ *(01978) 720518* – 9 *Pen-y-Cae, Ruabon Rd* ☎ *(01978) 810108* – 9 *The Plassey, Eyton* ☎ *(01978) 780020.*

Lambpit St ☎ *(01978) 292015.*

London 192 – Chester 12 – Liverpool 35 – Shrewsbury 28.

Llwyn Onn Hall , Cefn Rd, LL13 0NY, Northeast : 2 ½ m. by A 534 off Cefn Rd ☎ (01978) 261225, *llwynonnhallhotel@breathemail.net, Fax (01978) 363233,* ←, , – TV P. MC AE VISA JCB.
closed 26 December-2 January – **Meals** *(closed Sunday dinner to non-residents)* 10.95/14.95 and dinner a la carte 18.00/26.95 **t.** 9.95 – **13 rm** 64.00/94.00 **t.** – SB.

Travel Inn, Chester Rd, LL12 8PW, Northeast : 2 ½ m. by A 483 on B 5445 ☎ (01978) 853214, *Fax (01978) 856838* – rm, TV P. MC AE VISA.
Meals (grill rest.) – **38 rm** 41.95 **t.**

Travelodge, Croes-Foel roundabout, Rhostyllen, LL14 4EJ, Southwest : 2 m. by A 5152 at junction with A 483 ☎ (01978) 365705, *Fax (01978) 765705* – rm, rest, TV P. MC AE VISA JCB.
Meals (grill rest.) – **32 rm** 39.95 **t.**

at Gresford *Northeast : 3 m. by A 483 on B 5445.*

Pant-yr-Ochain, Old Wrexham Rd, LL12 8TY, South : 1 m. ☎ (01978) 853525, *pant.yr.ochain@brunningandprice.co.uk, Fax (01978) 853505,* , « Part 16C inn », – P. MC AE VISA
closed 25-26 December – **Meals** (booking essential) a la carte 16.15/21.70 **st.** 9.95.

at Erbistock *South : 5 ¼ m. by A 525 off A 528* – ✉ *Wrexham.*

The Cross Foxes, LL13 0DR, on A 528 ☎ (01978) 780380, *cross.foxes@brunningandprice.co.uk, Fax (01978) 780879,* , « Riverside setting », – P. MC AE VISA
Meals (booking essential) a la carte 14.15/23.40 **t.** 9.95.

Ireland

Northern Ireland

Place with at least

- a hotel or restaurant ● Tongue
- a pleasant hotel or restaurant 🏨, ⌂, ✗
- a quiet, secluded hotel 🐴
- a restaurant with ✿, ✿✿, ✿✿✿, Meals

La località possiede come minimo

- una risorsa alberghiera ● Tongue
- Albergo o ristorante ameno 🏨, ⌂, ✗
- un albergo molto tranquillo, isolato 🐴
- un'ottima tavola con ✿, ✿✿, ✿✿✿, Meals

Localité offrant au moins

- une ressource hôtelière ● Tongue
- un hôtel ou restaurant agréable 🏨, ⌂, ✗
- un hôtel très tranquille, isolé 🐴
- une bonne table à ✿, ✿✿, ✿✿✿, Meals

Ort mit mindestens

- einem Hotel oder Restaurant ● Tongue
- ein angenehmes Hotel oder Restaurant 🏨, ⌂, ✗
- einem sehr ruhigen und abgelegenen Hotel 🐴
- einem Restaurant mit ✿, ✿✿, ✿✿✿, Meals

ANNAHILT *Down* 923 N/O 4 – *see Hillsborough.*

ANNALONG **(Áth na Long)** *Down* 923 O 5 *Ireland G. – pop. 1 937.*

Exc. : *W : Mourne Mountains★★ :– Bryansford, Tollymore Forest Park★ AC – Silent Valle Reservoir★ (≤★) – Spelga Pass and Dam★ – Drumena Cashel and Souterrain★ – Kilbrone Forest Park (viewpoint★).*

Belfast 37 – Dundalk 36.

Glassdrumman Lodge ⚘, 85 Mill Rd, BT34 4RH, ☎ (028) 4376 8451, *glassdrumma @yahoo.com, Fax (028) 4376 7041,* ≤ Irish Sea and Mourne mountains, rest, TV P. MC AE VISA.
Meals (booking essential to non-residents) (dinner only) 32.50 **t.** 12.00 – **8 rm** 100.00 125.00 **t.**, 2 suites – SB.

BALLYCASTLE **(Baile an Chaistil)** *Antrim* 923 N 2.

18 *Cushendall Rd ☎ (028) 2076 2536.*

to Rathlin Island (Caledonian MacBrayne Ltd) 4 daily (40 mn).

7 Mary St ☎ (028) 2076 2024.

Belfast 55 – Ballymena 27 – Coleraine 22.

Marine, 1-3 North St, BT54 6JB, ☎ (028) 2076 2222, *mail@marinehotel.ne Fax (028) 2076 9507,* ≤ Fair Head and Rathlin Island, – TV P – 300. MC VISA.
Glass Island : **Meals** 8.50/14.00 (lunch) and dinner a la carte 14.00/22.45 **st.** 8.50 – **31 rr** 50.00/150.00 **st.** – SB.

The Guide is updated annually so renew your Guide every year.

BALLYCLARE **(Bealach Cláir)** *Antrim* 923 N/O 3.

18 *25 Springvale Rd ☎ (028) 9334 2352.*

Belfast 17 – Ballymena 14 – Larne 10.

Ginger Tree, 29 Ballyrobert Rd, BT39 9RY, South : 3 ¼ m. by A 57 on B 5 ☎ (028) 9084 8176, *Fax (028) 9084 0777* – P. MC AE VISA JCB
closed 11-13 July, 24-26 December, Saturday lunch and Sunday – **Meals** - Japanese 13.95/30.00 and a la carte 17.75/24.50 **t.** 9.50.

BALLYGALLY/BALLYGALLEY **(Baile Geithligh)** *Antrim* 923 O 3.

Ballygally Castle, Coast Rd, BT40 2QZ, ☎ (028) 2858 3212, *res@bgchastingshotels.com Fax (028) 2858 3681,* ≤, rm, TV P – 200. MC AE VISA.
Meals (bar lunch)/dinner 15.95/17.95 **st.** – **44 rm** 60.00/87.00 **st.** – SB.

BALLYMENA **(An Baile Meánach)** *Antrim* 923 N 3 *Ireland G. – pop. 28 717.*

Exc. : *Antrim Glens★★★ – Murlough Bay★★ (Fair Head ≤★★), Glengariff Forest Park★★ A (Waterfall★★), Glengariff★, Glendun★ – Antrim (Round Tower★) S : 9½ m. by A 26.*

18 *128 Raceview Rd ☎ (028) 2586 1207.*

76 Church St ☎ (028) 2563 8494.

Belfast 27 – Dundalk 78 – Larne 21 – Londonderry 51 – Omagh 53.

Galgorm Manor ⚘, 136 Fenhaghy Rd, Cullybackey, BT42 1EA, West : 3 ¾ m. by A 42 c Cullybackey rd ☎ (028) 2588 1001, *mail@galgorm.com, Fax (028) 2588 0080,* ≤, « Part 19 country house on banks of River Main », – TV P – 500. MC AE VISA.
The Restaurant : **Meals** *(closed Monday and Sunday dinner)* (bar lunch)/dinner a la car 23.75 **t.** 15.00 – **21 rm** 99.00/119.00 **t.**, 3 suites – SB.

Rosspark, 20 Doagh Rd, BT42 3LZ, Southeast : 6 m. by A 36 on B 59 ☎ (028) 2589 166 *info@rosspark.com, Fax (028) 2589 1477,* – rest, TV P – 350. MC VIS
closed 25 December – ***The Restaurant :*** **Meals** 19.95 and a la carte 10.25/14.00 **st.** 8.00 **38 rm** 85.00 **st.**, 1 suite – SB.

BALLYMONEY **(Baile Monaidh)** *Antrim* 923 M 2 – *pop. 24 198.*

Harmony Hill ⚘ with rm, Balnamore, BT53 7PS, West : 2 m. on Balnamore r ☎ (028) 2766 3459, *webmaster@harmonyhill.net, Fax (028) 2766 3740,* – TV P. MC VISA
closed 1-14 July and 25 December-6 January – **Meals** *(closed Sunday-Tuesday)* (bookir essential) (dinner only) a la carte 20.40/24.25 **t.** 9.95 – **4 rm** 39.50/65.00 **t.**

BANGOR (Beannchar) *Down* 923 O/P 4 *Ireland G.*

See : *North Down Heritage Centre*★.

Exc. : *Priory (Cross Slabs*★*) – Mount Stewart*★★★ *AC, SE : 10 m. by A 2, A 21 and A 20 – Scrabo Tower (*⩽★★*) S : 6½ m. by A 21 – Ballycopeland Windmill*★*, SE : 10 m. by B 21 and A 2, turning right at Millisle – Strangford Lough*★ *(Castle Espie Centre*★ *AC - Nendrum Monastery*★*) – Grey Abbey*★ *AC, SE : 20 m. by A 2, A 21 and A 20.*

34 Quay St ☏ *(028) 9127 0069.*

Belfast 15 – Newtownards 5.

Marine Court, The Marina, BT20 5ED, ☏ (028) 9145 1100, *admin@marinecourthotel.fsnet.co.uk, Fax (028) 9145 1200,* ⩽, ⅃₆, ⛶ – |‡|, ⇸ rm, TV ♿ P – 🏟 350. MC AE VISA. ✂
closed 25 December – ***The Stevedore :*** **Meals** *(closed Monday-Friday)* (dinner only and Sunday lunch) a la carte 14.90/21.40 **t.** 8.95 – **52 rm** ⊐ 80.00/110.00 **t.** – SB.

Clandeboye Lodge, 10 Estate Rd, Clandeboye, BT19 1UR, Southwest : 3 m. by A 2 and Dundonald rd following signs for Blackwood Golf Centre ☏ (028) 9185 2500, *info@clandeboyelodge.com, Fax (028) 9185 2772,* 18, ⛱ – |‡|, ⇸ rm, TV ✆ ♿ P – 🏟 250. MC AE ⓓ VISA. ✂
closed 24-26 December – ***Lodge :*** **Meals** (bar lunch Monday-Saturday) 19.50 and a la carte 10.50/24.25 **st.** 9.95 – **43 rm** ⊐ 70.00/90.00 **st.** – SB.

Cairn Bay Lodge, 278 Seacliffe Rd, BT20 5HS, East : 1 ¼ m. by Quay St. ☏ (028) 9146 7636, *info@cairnbaylodge.com, Fax (028) 9145 7728,* ⩽, ⛱ – ⇸ TV P. MC VISA. ✂
closed 1 week Christmas – **Meals** *(closed Sunday dinner)* 22.00 **st.** – **3 rm** ⊐ 45.00/60.00 **st.** – SB.

Shelleven House, 59-61 Princetown Rd, BT20 3TA, ☏ (028) 9127 1777, *shellevenhouse@aol.com, Fax (028) 9127 1777* – ⇸ TV P. MC ⓓ VISA. ✂
Meals (by arrangement) 25.00 **t.** 8.00 – **11 rm** ⊐ 33.00/55.00 **t.** – SB.

Shanks (Millar), The Blackwood, Crawfordsburn Rd, Clandeboye, BT19 1GB, Southwest : 3 ¼ m. by A 2 and Dundonald rd following signs for Blackwood Golf Centre ☏ (028) 9185 3313, *Fax (028) 9185 2493,* 18 – P. MC AE VISA
closed 2 weeks July, 25-26 December, Saturday lunch, Sunday, Monday and Easter Tuesday – **Meals** 19.95/35.00 **t.** 17.00
Spec. Ravioli of foie gras in chicken broth, celeriac and truffle. Local lobster with potato purée, asparagus and olive oil. Toasted marshmallow "mango mango".

BELFAST - (Béal Feirste)

Antrim 923 O 4 *Ireland G. – pop. 279 237.*

Dublin 103 – Londonderry 70.

TOURIST INFORMATION

35 Donegal Pl ☎ (028) 9024 6609.
Belfast International Airport, Information Desk ☎ (028) 9442 2888.
Belfast City Airport, Sydenham Bypass ☎ (028) 9045 7745.

PRACTICAL INFORMATION

Balmoral, 518 Lisburn Rd ☎ (028) 9038 1514, **AZ**.
Belvoir Park, Church Rd, Newtonbreda ☎ (028) 9049 1693 **AZ**.
Fortwilliam, Downview Av. ☎ (028) 9037 0770, **AY**.
The Knock Club, Summerfield, Dundonald ☎ (028) 9048 2249.
Shandon Park, 73 Shandon Park ☎ (028) 9079 3730.
Cliftonville, Westland Rd ☎ (028) 9074 4158, **AY**.
Ormeau, 50 Park Rd ☎ (028) 9064 1069, **AZ**.

Belfast International Airport, Aldergrove : ☎ (028) 9442 2888, W : 15½ m. by A 52 **AY** *– Belfast City Airport : ☎ (028) 9045 7745 –* **Terminal :** *Coach service (Ulsterbus Ltd.) from Great Victoria Street Station (40 mn).*

to Isle of Man (Douglas) (Isle of Man Steam Packet Co. Ltd) (summer only) (2 h 45 mn) – to Stranraer (Stena Line) 4-5 daily (1 h 30 mn/3 h 15 mn), (Sea Containers Ferries Scotland Ltd and Stena Line) 4-5 daily (1 h 30 mn/3 h 15 mn) – to Liverpool (Norse Irish Ferries Ltd) daily (8 h 30 mn) – to Troon (Sea Containers) 2 daily (2 h 30 mn) – to Heysham (Sea Containers) 1-3 daily (3 h 45 mn).

SIGHTS

See : *City★ - Ulster Museum★★ (Spanish Armada Treasure★★, Shrine of St. Patrick's Hand★)* **AZ M1** *– City Hall★* **BY** *– Donegall Square★* **BY 20** *– Botanic Gardens (Palm House★)* **AZ** *– St Anne's Cathedral★* **BX** *– Crown Liquor Saloon★* **BY** *– Sinclair Seamen's Church★* **BX** *– St Malachy's Church★* **BY**.

Env. : *Belfast Zoological Gardens★★ AC, N : 5 m. by A 6* **AY**.

Exc. : *Carrickfergus (Castle★★ AC, St. Nicholas' Church★) NE : 9 ½ m. by A 2 – Talnotry Cottage Bird Garden, Crumlin★ AC, W : 13½ m. by A 52.*

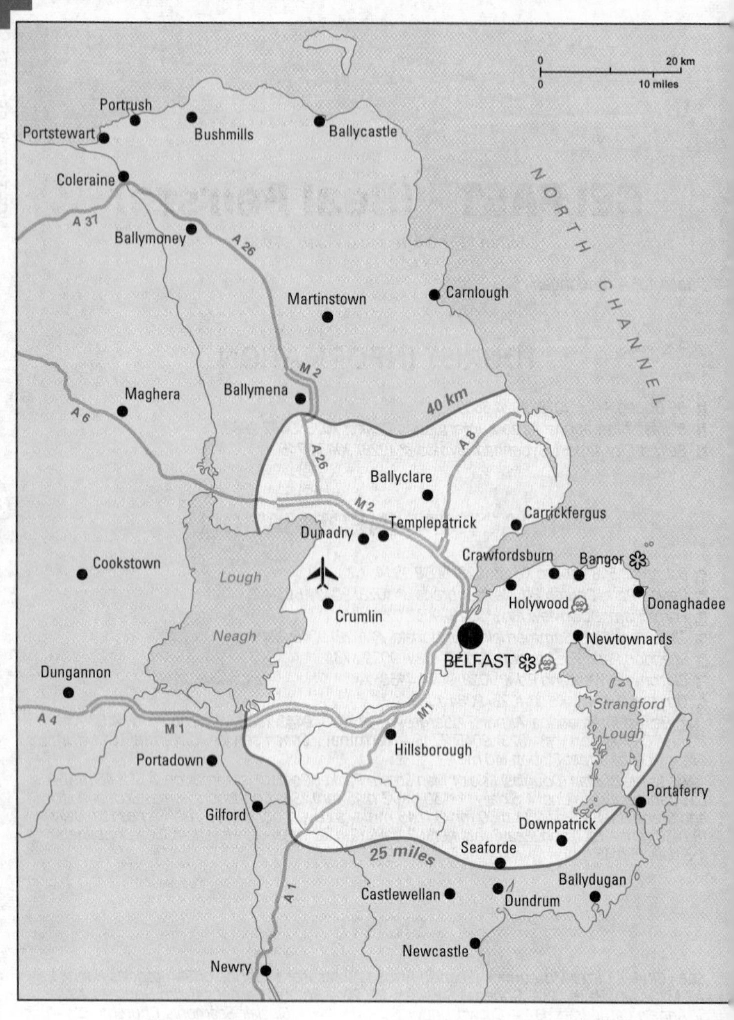

Particularly pleasant hotels and restaurants are shown in the Guide by a red symbol.

Please send us the names of anywhere you have enjoyed your stay.

Your **Michelin Guide** will be even better.

In Northern Ireland traffic and parking are controlled in the town centres. No vehicle may be left unattended in a Control Zone.

delaïde Street.......... BY
rport Road............ AY
bert Bridge Road...... AZ
lbert Bridge........... AZ 2
'bert Square........... BX 3
exandre Park Av........ AY
fred Street............ BY
nnadale Av............. AZ
nnadale Embankment .. AZ 4
nn Street.............. BY 5
ntrim Road............ AY
rdenlee Road.......... AZ
almoral Av............. AZ
edford Street.......... BY
eersdridge Road....... AZ
elmont Road........... BZ 7
otanic Avenue......... BZ
radbury Place.......... BZ 9
ridge End.............. AZ 10
ridge Street........... BY 12
astlecourt Shopping Centre............. BXY
astle Place............ BY
astle Street........... BY
astlereagh Road....... AZ
astlereagh Street...... AZ 14
avehill Road........... AY
hichester Street....... BX
ty Hospital Street...... BZ
ifton Street........... BX 15
iftonville Road......... AY
ollege Square.......... BY
orporation Square...... BX 16
orporation Street....... BX
ranmore Park.......... AZ
regagh Road........... AZ
romac Street.......... BY
rumlin Road....... AY, BX
Dargan Road............ AY
Divis Street............ BY
Donegall Park Av......... AY
Donegall Pass........... BZ
Donegall Place.......... BY
Donegall Quay.......... BXY 19
Donegall Road....... AZ, BZ
Donegall Square......... BY 20
Donegall Street......... BX
Dublin Road............ BZ
Durham Street.......... BY
East Bridge Street....... AZ 23
Falls Road............. AZ
Forestside Shopping Centre............. AZ
Frederic Street.......... BX
Galwally Road........... AZ
Garmoyle Street......... AY 24
Grand Parade........... AZ 25
Gray's Lane............ AY
Great George's Street.... BX
Great Victoria Street .. BY, BZ
Grosvenor Road...... AZ, BY
High Street............ BXY 28
Holywood Road......... AZ
Howard Street......... BY 29
Ladas Drive............ BY 31
Lagan Bridge.......... BX 32
Lansdowne Road......... AY
Lisburn Road....... AZ, BZ
Malone Road........... AZ
May Street............. BX
Middlepath Sreet........ AZ 34
Millfield Carrick Hill...... BXY
Mount Merrion Avenue ... AZ 35
Mountpottinger Road..... AZ 36
Nelson Street........... BX
Newtownards Road....... AZ 38
North Circular Road....... AY
North Queen Street....... AY
North Street............ BX
Oldpark Road........... AY
Ormeau Av.............. BZ
Ormeau Embankment..... AZ
Ormeau Road........ AZ, BZ
Oxford Street........... BY
Peters Hill............. BX
Queen Elizabeth Bridge ... BY 40
Queen's Bridge.......... BY 41
Queen's Square.......... BX 42
Queens Road............ AY
Ravenhill............... AZ
Rosemary Street......... BY 44
Rosetta Park........... AZ 45
Royal Avenue........... BXY
Saintfield Road......... AZ 47
Sandy Row............. BZ
Shankill Road.......... AZ
Shore Road............. AY
Short Strand........... AZ 48
Springfiel Road......... AZ
Stranmillis Road........ AZ
Sydenham Road......... AZ 49
Townsend Street........ BX
University Road......... BZ
University Square........ AZ 52
University Street........ BZ
Upper Knockbreda Road... AZ
Victoria Street.......... BY
Waring Street........... BX 54
Wellington Place........ BY 55
Westlink............... BY
Woodstock Road......... AZ
Woodvalle Road......... AY
York Road.............. AY
York Street............ BX

Hilton Belfast, 4 Lanyon Pl, BT1 3LP, ✆ (028) 9027 7000, *hilton_belfast@hilton.com, Fax (028) 9027 7277,* – rm, – 400. BY s
Sonoma : Meals *(closed Saturday lunch)* 14.00/18.50 **t.** 12.30 – ***Cables Bar :*** Meals a la carte 22.70/33.00 **t.** 12.30 – 16.50 – **189 rm** 140.00 **st.**, 6 suites.

Europa, Great Victoria St, BT2 7AP, ✆ (028) 9032 7000, *res@eur.hastingshotels.com, Fax (028) 9032 7800* – rm, – 750. BY e
closed 24 and 25 December – ***Gallery :*** Meals *(closed Saturday lunch and Sunday)* 13.95/23.95 and dinner a la carte 20.10/24.20 **t.** 14.00 – ***Brasserie :*** Meals a la carte 14.85/21.70 **t.** – 12.00 – **235 rm** 105.00/150.00 **st.**, 5 suites – SB.

Stormont, Upper Newtownards Rd, BT4 3LP, East : 3 ½ m. on A 20 ✆ (028) 9065 8621, *res@stor.hastingshotels.com, Fax (028) 9048 0240* – rm, rest, – 400.
closed 24 and 25 December – ***Shiraz :*** Meals *(closed Sunday)* (dinner only) 17.40/20.40 **t.** 14.00 – ***La Scala Bistro :*** Meals a la carte 15.10/20.40 **t.** 10.00 – 12.00 – **109 rm** 110.00/225.00 **st.** – SB.

The McCausland, 34-38 Victoria St, BT1 3GH, ✆ (028) 9022 0200, *info@mccauslandhotel.com, Fax (028) 9022 0220* – rm, – 60. BY v
closed 24-27 December – ***Map Room :*** Meals *(closed lunch Saturday and Sunday)* a la carte 14.40/25.40 **t.** 9.95 – 12.00 – **60 rm** 120.00/190.00 **st.** – SB.

Holiday Inn Belfast, 22 Ormeau Ave, BT2 8HS, ✆ (0870) 4009005, *reservations-belfast city@posthouse-hotels.com, Fax (028) 9062 6546,* – rm, – 140. BY u
The Junction : Meals *(closed Saturday lunch)* 11.95 (lunch) and dinner a la carte 16.85/23.65 **t.** 10.95 – 13.95 – **168 rm** 127.00 **st.**, 2 suites – SB.

Malone Lodge, 60 Eglantine Ave, BT9 6DY, ✆ (028) 9038 8000, *info@malonelodgehotel.com, Fax (028) 9038 8088,* – rm, rest, – 120. AZ n
The Green Door : Meals 15.50/25.00 and dinner a la carte 18.45/23.40 **t.** 11.50 – **51 rm** 85.00/130.00 **t.**, 8 suites – SB.

The Crescent Townhouse, 13 Lower Cres, BT7 1NR, ✆ (028) 9032 3349, *info@crescent townhouse.com, Fax (028) 9032 0646,* « Regency house » – rest, . BZ x
closed 11-13 July – ***Metro :*** Meals *(closed Sunday)* (dinner only) 12.50 and a la carte 16.85/23.85 **t.** 14.00 – **11 rm** 80.00/100.00 **t.** – SB.

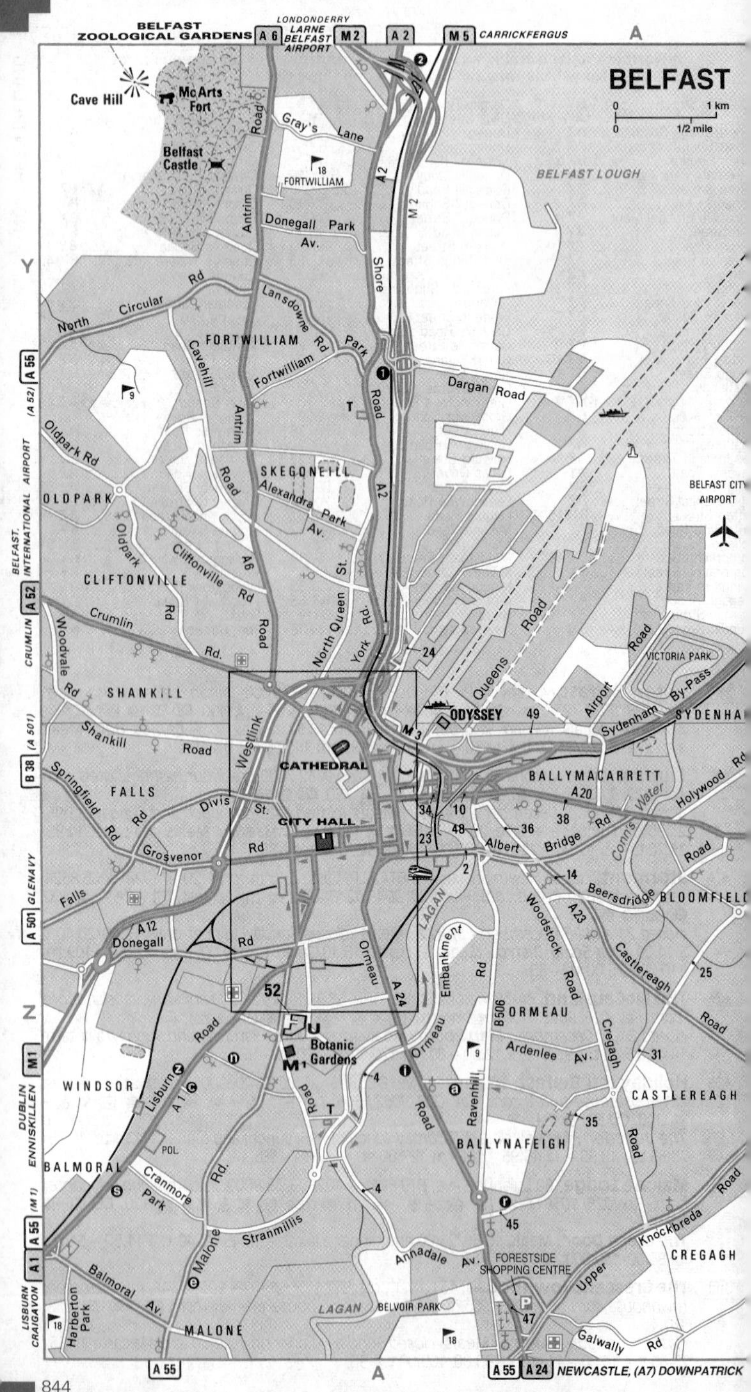
BELFAST
0 1 km
0 1/2 mile
BELFAST ZOOLOGICAL GARDENS
A 6
LONDONDERRY LARNE BELFAST AIRPORT
M 2
A 2
M 5
CARRICKFERGUS
Cave Hill
McArts Fort
Belfast Castle
FORTWILLIAM
BELFAST LOUGH
FORTWILLIAM
SKEGONEILL
OLDPARK
CLIFTONVILLE
SHANKILL
FALLS
CATHEDRAL
CITY HALL
ODYSSEY
BALLYMACARRETT
SYDENHAM
VICTORIA PARK
BELFAST CITY AIRPORT
BLOOMFIELD
ORMEAU
Botanic Gardens
WINDSOR
BALMORAL
CASTLEREAGH
BALLYNAFEIGH
CREGAGH
FORESTSIDE SHOPPING CENTRE
BELVOIR PARK
MALONE
LAGAN
A 55
(A 52)
BELFAST INTERNATIONAL AIRPORT
A 52
CRUMLIN
(A 501)
B 38
GLENAVY
A 501
M1
DUBLIN ENNISKILLEN
(M1)
A 55
A1
LISBURN CRAIGAVON
A 55
A 55
A 24
NEWCASTLE, (A7) DOWNPATRICK

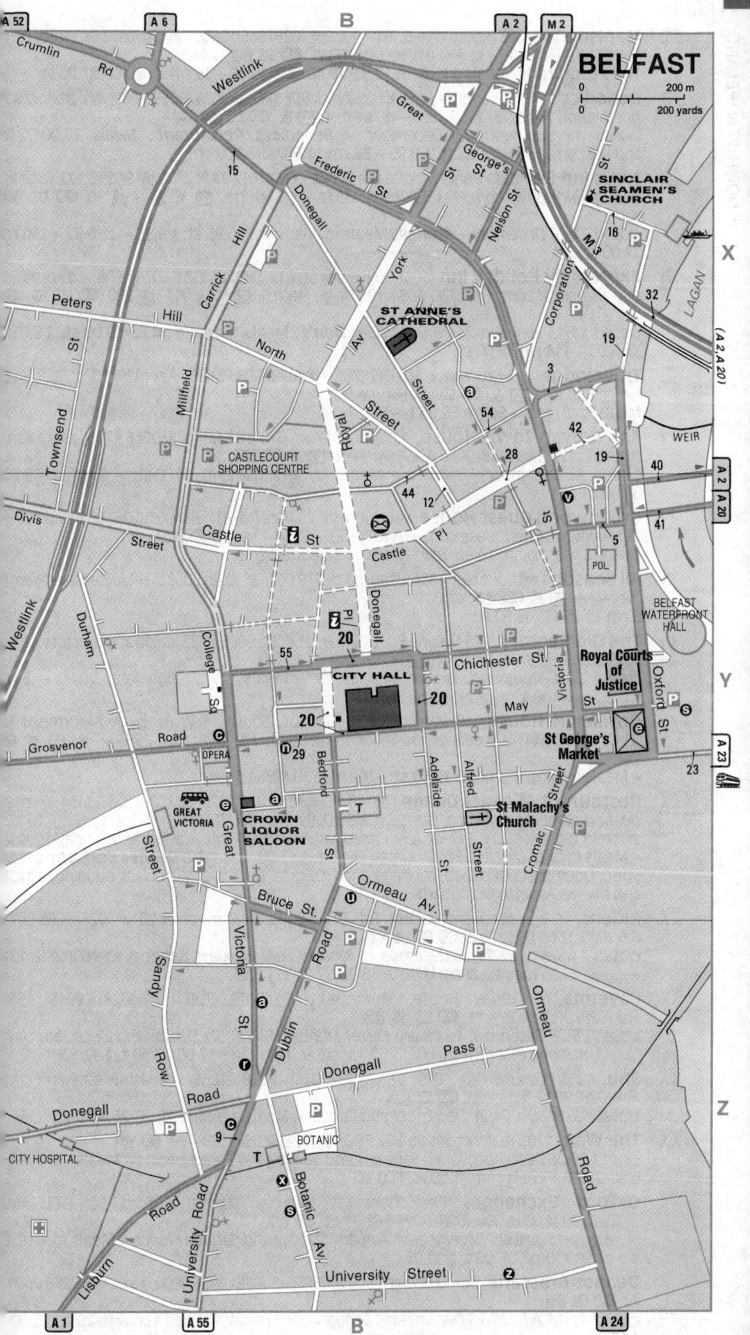
BELFAST
200 m
200 yards
A 52
A 6
A 2
M 2
B
X
Y
Z
Crumlin Rd
Westlink
Great George's St
Frederic St
Donegall St
York St
Nelson St
SINCLAIR SEAMEN'S CHURCH
M 3
LAGAN
Corporation St
Carrick Hill
Peters Hill
North Street
ST ANNE'S CATHEDRAL
York Av
Royal Av
Millfield
Townsend St
WEIR
CASTLECOURT SHOPPING CENTRE
Divis Street
Castle St
Castle Pl
Donegall Pl
BELFAST WATERFRONT HALL
POL
Durham St
College Sq
Chichester St.
Royal Courts of Justice
Oxford St
CITY HALL
May St
Victoria St
St George's Market
Grosvenor Road
OPERA
GREAT VICTORIA
Great Victoria St.
CROWN LIQUOR SALOON
Bedford St
Adelaide St
Alfred Street
St Malachy's Church
Cromac Street
Ormeau Av.
Bruce St.
Sandy Row
Dublin Road
Ormeau Road
Donegall Pass
Donegall Road
CITY HOSPITAL
BOTANIC
Botanic Av.
Lisburn Road
University Road
University Street
A 1
A 55
A 24
A 23
(A 2, A 20)
A 2
A 20

NORTHERN IRELAND

Madison's, 59-63 Botanic Ave, BT7 1JL, ℘ (028) 9050 9800, *info@madisonshotel.com* *Fax (028) 9050 9808* – rm, rest, . BZ
The Restaurant : **Meals** a la carte 12.85/19.45 **st.** 10.50 – **35 rm** 70.00/87.00 **st.**

Benedict's, 7-21 Bradbury Pl, Shaftsbury Sq, BT7 1RQ, ℘ (028) 9059 1999, *info@benedicthotel.co.uk, Fax (028) 9059 1990* – , rest, . BZ
closed 12 July and 25 December – ***Benedicts Restaurant :*** **Meals** 20.00/22.00 and a la carte 15.15/21.85 **st.** 9.95 – **32 rm** 65.00/80.00 **st.**

Jurys Inn Belfast, Fisherwick Pl, Great Victoria St, BT2 7AP, ℘ (028) 9053 3500, *jurysinnbelfast@jurysdoyle.com, Fax (028) 9053 3511* – , rm, – 30. BY
closed 24-26 December – ***Arches :*** **Meals** (dinner only) 15.95 **st.** 9.95 – 6.95 – **190 rm** 71.00 **st.**

Express by Holiday Inn, 106A University St, BT7 1HP, ℘ (028) 9031 1909, *express@holidayinn/ireland.com, Fax (028) 9031 1910* – , rm, – 200. BZ
closed 11-13 July and 24-26 December ***Don's :*** **Meals** a la carte 14.65/19.00 **st.** 8.25 – 5.95 – **114 rm** 58.00 **st.**

Travelodge, 15 Brunswick St, BT2 7GE, ℘ (028) 9033 3555, *Fax (028) 9023 2999* – , rm, rest, . BY
Meals (grill rest.) – **90 rm** 59.95 **t.** – SB.

Ash Rowan Town House, 12 Windsor Ave, BT9 6EE, ℘ (028) 9066 1758, *ashrowan@hotmail.com, Fax (028) 9066 3227,* – . AZ
closed 23 December-7 January – **Meals** (by arrangement) 30.00 **st.** – **5 rm** 48.00/84.00 **t.**

Greenwood Guest House without rest., 25 Park Rd, BT7 2FW, ℘ (028) 9020 2525, *info@greenwoodguesthouse.com, Fax (025) 9020 2530* – . AZ
closed Christmas and New Year – **7 rm** 37.50/55.00 **st.**

All Seasons without rest., 356 Lisburn Rd, BT9 6GJ, ℘ (028) 9068 2814, *allseasons@fsmail.net* – . AZ
6 rm 25.00/45.00 **st.**

The Old Rectory, 148 Malone Rd, BT9 5LH, ℘ (028) 9066 7882, *info@anoldrectory.co.uk, Fax (028) 9068 3759,* – . AZ
closed 24 December-1 January and Easter – **Meals** (by arrangement) 20.00 – **5 rm** 36.00/60.00 **s.**

Roseleigh House, 19 Rosetta Park, BT6 0DL, South : 1 ½ m. by A 24 Ormeau Rd ℘ (028) 9064 4414, *roseleighhouse@ukonline.co.uk, Fax (028) 9064 2983* – . AZ
– **Meals** (by arrangement) 17.50 **st.** – **9 rm** 38.50/54.00 **st.**

Restaurant Michael Deane, 36-40 Howard St, BT1 6PF, ℘ (028) 9033 1134, *michaeldeane@deanesbelfast.com, Fax (028) 9056 0001* – . BY
closed 1 week January, 1 week July, Christmas, New Year, Bank Holidays and Sunday-Tuesday – **Meals** (dinner only and Friday lunch) 36.50 **t.** 13.00 – (see also ***Deanes Brasserie*** below)
Spec. Open pasta of squab, cabbage and foie gras. Beef fillet with black pudding, carrot and thyme. Assiette of rhubarb.

Aldens, 229 Upper Newtownards Rd, BT4 3JF, East : 2 m. on A 20 ℘ (028) 9065 007 *Fax (028) 9065 0032* – .
closed 2 weeks July, 25-26 December, 1 January, Bank Holidays, Saturday lunch and Sunday – **Meals** 14.95 (dinner) and a la carte 18.90/27.70 **t.** 9.95.

Cayenne, 7 Lesley House, Shaftesbury Sq, BT2 7DB, ℘ (028) 9033 153 *Fax (028) 9026 1575* – . BZ
closed 25-26 December, 1 January, Easter Monday, 12-13 July, Sunday and lunch Saturday **Meals** (booking essential) 10.00/13.50 (lunch) and a la carte 17.00/23.50 **t.** 12.50.

Shu, 253 Lisburn Rd, BT9 7EN, ℘ (028) 9038 1655, *eat@shu-restaurant.com, Fax (028) 9068 1632* – . AZ
closed 12-14 July, 24-26 December and Sunday – **Meals** a la carte 20.70/26.95 **t.** 11.50.

The Wok, 126 Great Victoria St, BT2 7BG, ℘ (028) 9023 3828 – . BZ
closed 25-26 December, lunch Saturday and Sunday and Bank Holidays – **Meals** - Chinese - 6.50/20.00 and a la carte 12.50/29.00 **st.**

Oxford Exchange, First floor, St Georges Market, Oxford St, BT1 3N ℘ (028) 9024 0014, *Fax (028) 9023 5675* – . BY
closed 12-13 July, 25 December, 1 January, Sunday and Saturday lunch – **Meals** (grill rest.) a la carte approx. 26.00 **t.** 10.95.

Deanes Brasserie, 36-40 Howard St, BT1 6PF, ℘ (028) 9056 0000, *Fax (028) 9056 0001* – . BY
closed 11-13 July, 25-26 December, 1 January and Sunday – **Meals** a la carte 20.75/25.00 13.00.

Nick's Warehouse, 35-39 Hill St, BT1 2LB, ☎ (028) 9043 9690, *nicks@warehouse.dnet.co.uk, Fax (028) 9023 0514* – ▤. MC AE ⓓ VISA BX a
closed 2 days Easter, 1 May, 12 July, 25-26 December, 1 January, Saturday lunch, Monday dinner and Sunday – **Meals** a la carte 18.70/25.25 **t.** 11.40.

Ginger, 271 Ormeau Rd, BT7 3GG, ☎ (028) 9049 3143 – MC VISA AZ i
closed 2 weeks January, 2 weeks July, Sunday and Monday – **Meals** (booking essential) (unlicensed) (dinner only and Saturday lunch)/dinner a la carte 16.00/25.00 **t.**

BELFAST INTERNATIONAL AIRPORT (Aerphort Béal Feirste) *Antrim* 923 N 4 – ✉ *Aldergrove.*

✈ *Belfast International Airport, Aldergrove : ☎ (028) 9442 2888.*

Belfast 6 – Ballymena 20 – Larne 23.

Fitzwilliam International, Aldergrove, BT29 4ZY, ☎ (028) 9442 2033, *reservations@fitzwilliaminternational.com, Fax (028) 9442 3500* – |♦|, ⇔ rm, ▤ TV ☎ & P – 🏠 250. MC AE ⓓ VISA. ✂
The Terrace : **Meals** (buffet lunch)/dinner a la carte 15.00/30.00 **st.** 9.50 – ☕ 8.50 – **104 rm** 110.00 **st.**, 2 suites.

BELLEEK (Béal Leice) *Fermanagh* 923 H 4 – *pop. 550.*

Belfast 117 – Londonderry 56.

Carlton, Main St, BT93 3FX, ☎ (028) 6865 8282, *reception@hotelcarlton.co.uk, Fax (028) 6865 9005* – ⇔ rm, TV P – 🏠 200. MC AE VISA. ✂
closed 25 December – **Meals** (bar lunch Monday to Saturday)/dinner 18.95 and a la carte 16.50/19.00 **t.** 7.95 – **19 rm** ☕ 52.50/75.00 **t.** – SB.

BUSHMILLS (Muileann na Buaise) *Antrim* 923 M 2 *Ireland G.* – *pop. 1 348* – ✉ *Bushmills.*

Exc. : *Causeway Coast★★ : Giant's Causeway★★★ (Hamilton's Seat ≤★★), Carrick-a-rede Rope Bridge★★, Dunluce Castle★★ AC, Gortmore Viewpoint★ – Dunseverick Castle (≤★★), Magilligan Strand★, Downhill★ (Mussenden Temple★).*

⛳9 *Bushfoot, 50 Bushfoot Rd, Portballintrae ☎ (028) 2073 1317.*

Belfast 57 – Ballycastle 12 – Coleraine 10.

Bushmills Inn, 9 Dunluce Rd, BT57 8QG, ☎ (028) 2073 2339, *mail@bushmillsinn.com, Fax (028) 2073 2048,* « Converted 17C stables, 19C coaching inn » – ⇔ TV P – 🏠 40. MC AE VISA. ✂
The Restaurant : **Meals** (carving lunch Sunday) (bar lunch Monday to Saturday)/dinner 25.00/29.00 **t.** 10.00 – **32 rm** ☕ 78.00/128.00 **st.** – SB.

Craig Park 🐦 without rest., 24 Carnbore Rd, BT57 8YF, Southeast : 2 ½ m. by B 66 and Ballycastle rd (B 17), off Billy rd ☎ (028) 2073 2496, *jan@craigpark.co.uk, Fax (028) 2073 2479,* ≤, 🌳 – ⇔ TV P. MC VISA. ✂
closed 20 December-4 January – **3 rm** ☕ 35.00/55.00.

CARNLOUGH (Carnlach) *Antrim* 923 O 3 – *pop. 1 493.*

Belfast 36 – Ballymena 16 – Larne 14.

Londonderry Arms, 20 Harbour Rd, BT44 0EU, ☎ (028) 2888 5255, *lda@glensofantrim.com, Fax (028) 2888 5263* – |♦| ⇔ TV P – 🏠 80. MC AE ⓓ VISA. ✂
closed 25 December – ***Tapestry Room :*** **Meals** (bar lunch Monday-Saturday)/dinner 19.50 and a la carte 22.75/26.90 **t.** 9.75 – **30 rm** ☕ 55.00/95.00 **t.** – SB.

CARRICKFERGUS (Carraig Fhearghais) *Antrim* 923 O 3.

⛳18 *35 North Rd ☎ (028) 9336 3713.*

ℹ *Heritage Plaza ☎ (028) 9336 6455 (April-September).*

Belfast 11 – Ballymena 25.

Quality, 75 Belfast Rd, BT38 8PH, on A 2 ☎ (028) 9336 4556, *reservations@qualitycarrick.co.uk, Fax (028) 9335 1620* – |♦|, ⇔ rm, ▤ rest, TV ☎ & P – 🏠 350. MC AE ⓓ VISA. ✂
Meals a la carte 12.40/23.90 **st.** 10.25 – ☕ 9.50 – **68 rm** 85.00/175.00 **st.** – SB.

CARRY BRIDGE *Fermanagh* 923 J 5 – ✉ *Lisbellaw.*

Belfast 80 – Dundalk 62 – Londonderry 60.

Aghnacarra House 🐦, BT94 5HX, ☎ (028) 6638 7077, *normaensor@talk21.com, Fax (028) 6638 5811,* 🐟, 🌳 – P. MC VISA. ✂
April-mid October – **Meals** (by arrangement) 9.00 **st.** – **7 rm** ☕ 26.00/38.00 **st.**

CASTLEWELLAN *Down* 923 O 5 – *pop. 2 496.*

Slieve Croob Inn, BT31 9LA, North : 5 ½ m. by A 25 off B 175 ℘ (028) 4377 1412, *in*
@slievecroobinn.com, Fax (028) 4377 1162, ≤, – TV P – 80. MC AE VISA
closed 25 December – **Meals** (bar lunch Monday-Saturday)/dinner 17.95/22.9
and a la carte 10.60/21.40 **t.** 11.95 – **7 rm** 35.00/60.00 **t.** – SB.

COLERAINE (Cúil Raithin) *Londonderry* 923 L 2 *Ireland G.* – *pop. 20 721.*

Exc. : *Antrim Glens*** – Murlough Bay** (Fair Head ≤**), Glenariff Forest Park** A (Waterfall**), Glenariff*, Glendun* – Causeway Coast** : Giant's Causeway*** (Ham ton's Seat ≤**) – Carrick-a-rede Rope Bridge** – Dunluce Castle** AC – Dunseveri Castle (≤**) – Gortmore Viewpoint* – Magilligan Strand* – Downhill* (Mussende Temple*).*

18, 9 *Castlerock, Circular Rd ℘ (028) 7084 8314* – 9 *Brown Trout, 209 Agivey Rd ℘ (02 7086 8209.*

Railway Rd ℘ (028) 7034 4723.

Belfast 53 – Ballymena 25 – Londonderry 31 – Omagh 65.

Bushtown House, 283 Drumcroone Rd, BT51 3QT, South : 2 ½ m. on A 2
℘ (028) 7035 8367, *bushtownhousehotel@talk21.com, Fax (028) 7032 0909,* , ,
TV P – 250. MC AE VISA
closed 25-26 December – **Meals** (bar lunch Monday to Saturday)/dinner 18.50/20.0
and a la carte 14.00/21.20 **t.** 8.00 – **39 rm** 52.00/100.00 **t.** – SB.

Brown Trout Golf and Country Inn, 209 Agivey Rd, Aghadowey, BT51 4AD, South
east : 9 m. on A 54 ℘ (028) 7086 8209, *bill@browntroutinn.com, Fax (028) 7086 8878,*
9, , – rest, TV P – 40. MC AE VISA
Meals (bar lunch Monday to Saturday)/dinner a la carte 13.00/20.00 **t.** 7.95 – **15 r**
60.00/85.00 **st.**

Greenhill House, 24 Greenhill Rd, Aghadowey, BT51 4EU, South : 9 m. by A 29 c
B 66 ℘ (028) 7086 8241, *greenhill.house@btinternet.com, Fax (028) 7086 8365,* ,
rest, TV P. MC VISA.
March-October – **Meals** (by arrangement) 18.00 – **6 rm** 30.00/50.00 – SB.

COOKSTOWN (An Chorr Chríochach) *Tyrone* 923 L 4 *Ireland G.*

Env. : *Ardboe Cross*, E : 4 m. by B 73.*

18 *Killymoon, 200 Killymoon Rd ℘ (028) 8676 3762.*

The Burnavon, Burn Rd ℘ (028) 8676 6727.

Belfast 45 – Ballymena 27 – Londonderry 49.

Tullylagan Country House, 40B Tullylagan Rd, Sandholes, BT80 8UP, South : 4 r
by A 29 ℘ (028) 8676 5100, *reservations@tullylagan.fsnet.co.uk, Fax (028) 8676 1715,*
, – TV P – 150. MC AE VISA
closed 24-26 December – **Meals** *(closed Sunday dinner)* a la carte 14.40/20.40 **st.** 10.50
15 rm 49.95/90.00 **st.** – SB.

CRAWFORDSBURN (Sruth Chráfard) *Down* 923 O 4 *Ireland G.* – *pop. 572.*

Env. : *North Down Heritage Centre, Bangor*, E : 3 m. by B 20.*

Exc. : *Priory (Cross Slabs*) – Mount Stewart*** AC, SE : 12 m. by A 2, A 21 and A 20 Scrabo Tower (≤**), SW : 8 m. – Ballycopeland Windmill* AC, E : 13 m. by A 2, A 21 ar B 172 – Strangford Lough* (Castle Espie Centre* AC - Nendrum Monastery*) – Gr Abbey* AC, SE : 14 m. by A 2, A 21 and A 20.*

Belfast 12 – Bangor 3.

Old Inn, 15 Main St, BT19 1JH, ℘ (028) 9185 3255, *info@theoldinn.cor*
Fax (028) 9185 2775, – TV P – 120. MC AE VISA.
Meals 24.50/26.00 and a la carte 12.00/25.00 **t.** 11.50 – **32 rm** 70.00/150.00 **st.** – SB.

CRUMLIN (Cromghlinn) *Antrim* 923 N 4 – *pop. 2 697.*

Belfast 14 – Ballymena 20.

Caldhame Lodge, 102 Moira Rd, Nutts Corner, BT29 4HG, Southeast : 1 ¼ m. on A 2
℘ (028) 9442 3099, *info@caldhamelodge.co.uk, Fax (028) 9442 3099,* – TV P.
AE VISA JCB.
Meals (by arrangement) 17.00 – **6 rm** 35.00/60.00.

Keef Halla, 20 Tully Rd, BT29 4SW, Northeast : 3 ¾ m. by A 52 on A 26 ℘ (028) 9082 549
info@keefhalla.com, Fax (028) 9082 5940, – TV P. MC AE VISA.
Meals (by arrangement) 15.00 **st.** – **7 rm** 40.00/50.00 **st.** – SB.

DONAGHADEE (Domhnach Daoi) Down 923 P 4.

18 *Warren Rd* (028) 9188 3624.

Belfast 18 – Ballymena 44.

Grace Neill's, 33 High St, BT21 0AH, (028) 9188 4595, *stephen@graceneills.freeserve.co.uk, Fax (028) 9188 2553,* , « Oldest bar in Ireland » – P. MC AE VISA
closed 12-13 July, 25-26 December, 1 January, Sunday dinner and Monday except Bank Holidays – **Meals** a la carte 16.50/27.25 **t.** 11.95.

Pier 36, 36 The Parade, BT21 0HE, (028) 9188 4466, *info@pier36.co.uk, Fax (028) 9188 4636,* – . MC VISA
closed 25 December – **Meals** - Seafood specialities - a la carte 11.75/21.85 **t.** 8.75.

DOWNPATRICK (Dún Pádraig) Down 923 O 4/5 – *pop. 10 257.*

The Mill at Ballydugan , Drumcullen Rd, BT30 8HZ, Southwest : 2 ¼ m. by A 25 (028) 4461 3654, *info@ballyduganmill.com, Fax (028) 4483 9754,* « 18C converted flour mill », – , rm, TV P – 60. MC VISA.
closed 25 December – **Meals** (bar lunch Monday-Saturday)/dinner a la carte 9.75/22.50 **t.** 9.50 – **10 rm** 50.00 **t.**

DUNADRY (Dún Eadradh) Antrim 923 N 3 *Ireland G.*

Env. : *Antrim (Round tower★) NW : 4 m. by A 6.*

Exc. : *Crumlin : Talnotry Cottage Bird Garden★ AC, SW : 10½ m. by A 5, A 26 and A 52.*

Belfast 16 – Larne 18 – Londonderry 56.

Dunadry H. and Country Club, 2 Islandreagh Drive, BT41 2HA, (028) 9443 4343, *info@dunadry.co.uk, Fax (028) 9443 3767,* , , , – TV P – 600. MC AE VISA JCB.
closed 24-26 December – ***The Linen Mill :*** **Meals** *(closed Sunday and Monday)* (dinner only) a la carte approx. 25.00 **st.** 12.50 – ***The Bistro :*** **Meals** 10.95 (lunch) and a la carte approx. 13.40 **st.** 12.50 – 10.00 – **83 rm** 110.00/135.00 **st.** – SB.

DUNDRUM Down 923 O 5 – *pop. 2 109.*

Buck's Head Inn, 77 Main St, BT33 0LU, (028) 4375 1868, *Fax (028) 4481 1033,* , – . MC AE VISA
Meals 18.50/23.50 (dinner) and lunch a la carte 13.90/23.50 **t.** 12.00.

DUNGANNON (Dún Geanainn) Tyrone 923 L 4 *Ireland G.*

Env. : *The Argory★, S : 5 m. by A 29 and east by minor rd.*

Exc. : *Armagh★★ (St. Patrick's Cathedral★ (Anglican), St. Patrick's Cathedral★ (Roman Catholic), The Mall★, Armagh County Museum★ – Regimental Museum of the Royal Irish Fusiliers★, Navan Fort★), S : 12 m. by A 29.*

Belfast 42 – Ballymena 37 – Dundalk 47 – Londonderry 60.

Stangmore Country House, 65 Moy Rd, BT71 7DT, South : 2 m. on A 29 (028) 8772) 5600, *info@stangmorecountryhouse.com, Fax (028) 8772 6644,* – rest, TV P. MC AE VISA.
closed 24 December-2 January and 8-14 July – **Meals** *(closed Sunday)* (booking essential to non-residents) (dinner only) 15.50/17.50 **st.** 10.95 – **9 rm** 50.00/80.00 **st.** – SB.

Grange Lodge , 7 Grange Rd, BT71 7EJ, Southeast : 3 ½ m. by A 29 (028) 8778 4212, *grangelodge@nireland.com, Fax (028) 8778 4313,* – TV P. MC VISA.
closed 20 December-1 February – **Meals** (by arrangement) 24.00 **st.** 6.00 – **5 rm** 59.00/78.00 **st.**

ENNISKILLEN (Inis Ceithleann) Fermanagh 923 J 4 *Ireland G.* – *pop. 11 436.*

Env. : *Castle Coole★★★ AC, SE : 1 m.*

Exc. : *NW : Lough Erne★★ : Cliffs of Magho Viewpoint★★★ AC – Devenish Island★ AC – White Island★ – Janus Figure★ – Tully Castle★ AC – Florence Court★★ AC, SW : 8 m. by A 4 and A 32 – Marble Arch Caves and Forest Nature Reserve★ AC, SW : 10 m. by A 4 and A 32.*

18 *Castlecoole* (028) 6632 5250.

Wellington Rd (028) 6632 3110.

Belfast 87 – Londonderry 59.

Manor House Country , Killadeas, BT94 1NY, North : 7 ½ m. by A 32 on B 82 (028) 6862 2200, *info@manor-house-hotel.com, Fax (028) 6862 1545,* , , , , – , rm, TV P – 300. MC AE VISA.
The Belleck : **Meals** 12.95/23.00 and dinner a la carte 18.00/24.00 **st.** 10.95 – **81 rm** 85.00/110.00 **st.** – SB.

Killyhevlin, Killyhevlin, BT74 6RW, Southeast : 1 ¾ m. on A 4 ☎ (028) 6632 3481, *info@killyhevlin.com, Fax (028) 6632 4726,* ←, – , rm, – 500. *closed 24-26 December* – ***Regatta :*** **Meals** 13.50/24.50 and a la carte 20.00/25.00 s 10.75 – **42 rm** 75.00/110.00 **st.**, 1 suite – SB.

Rassahilly House, BT94 2FP, North : 4 ½ m. by A 32 off B 82 ☎ (028) 6632 2352, *in@rassahilly.com, Fax (028) 6632 0277,* ← Lower lough Erne, , , – VISA
Meals (by arrangement) 22.00 **st.** 9.50 – **2 rm** 38.00/66.00 **st.**, 1 suite – SB.

GILFORD (Áth Mhic Giolla) *Down* 923 M 4 – *pop. 1 639.*
Belfast 30 – Dundalk 32.

The Oriel, 2 Bridge St, BT63 6HF, ☎ (028) 3883 1543, *orielrestaurant@aol.co Fax (028) 3883 1180* – . VISA
closed 25-26 December, Saturday lunch, Sunday dinner and Monday – **Meals** a la car 19.50/26.70 **t.** 12.95.

HILLSBOROUGH (Cromghlinn) *Down* 923 N 4 *Ireland G.*
See : *Town★ – Fort★.*
Exc. : *The Argory★, W : 25 m. by A 1 and M 1.*
Courthouse ☎ (028) 9268 9717.
Belfast 12.

The Plough Inn, The Square, BT26 6AG, ☎ (028) 9268 2985, *Fax (028) 9268 2472* – P. VISA
Meals a la carte 15.00/25.00 **st.** 11.95.

at Annahilt *Southeast : 4 m. on B 177 – ✉ Hillsborough.*

Fortwilliam without rest., 210 Ballynahinch Rd, BT26 6BH, Northwest : ¼ m. on B 17 ☎ (028) 9268 2255, *fortwilliam.country.house@uk.net, Fax (028) 9268 9608,* « Workin farm », , – P. VISA
3 rm 35.00/55.00.

The Pheasant, 410 Upper Ballynahinch Rd, BT26 6NR, North : 1 m. on Lisburn r ☎ (028) 9263 8056, *pheasantinn@iol.com, Fax (028) 9263 8026* – P. VISA
closed 12-13 July, 25-26 December and Monday except Bank Holiday Mondays – **Mea** a la carte 14.35/22.35 **t.** 10.95.

HOLYWOOD (Ard Mhic Nasca) *Down* 923 O 4 *Ireland G.* – *pop. 9 252.*
Env. : *Cultra : Ulster Folk and Transport Museum★★ AC, NE : 1 m. by A 2.*
Holywood, Nuns Walk, Demesne Rd ☎ (028) 9042 2138.
Belfast 7 – Bangor 6.

Culloden, Bangor Rd, BT18 0EX, East : 1 ½ m. on A 2 ☎ (028) 9042 5223, *res@cull.hasting hotel.com, Fax (028) 9042 6777,* ←, « Part Victorian Gothic manor », , , , , squash – , rm, rest, P – 700. VISA.
Mitre : **Meals** (dinner only and Sunday lunch)/dinner 29.50 **st.** 16.00 – ***Cultra Inn :*** **Mea** (grill rest.) a la carte 11.25/16.75 **st.** 10.50 – 15.00 – **78 rm** 150.00/210.00 **st.**, 3 suites SB.

Rayanne House, 60 Demesne Rd, BT18 9EX, by High St and Downshire R ☎ (028) 9042 5859, *Fax (028) 9042 3364,* ←, – P. VISA.
closed 1 week Christmas – **Meals** (booking essential) (dinner only) 20.00 – **7 rm** 57.5 80.00.

Beech Hill without rest., 23 Ballymoney Rd, Craigantlet, BT23 4TG, Southeast : 4 ½ m by A 2 on Craigantlet rd ☎ (028) 9042 5892, *beech.hill@btinternet.co Fax (028) 9042 5892,* ←, – P. VISA
3 rm 40.00/60.00.

Braeside Country House without rest., 10 Brown's Brae, Croft Rd, BT18 0HL, East 1 ¼ m. by High St, Bangor Rd and Croft Rd ☎ (028) 9042 6665, *Fax (028) 9042 6665,* P. VISA
closed 25-26 December – **4 rm** 40.00/60.00 **st.**

Fontana, 61A High St, BT18 9AE, ☎ (028) 9080 9908, *Fax (028) 9080 9912,* – VISA
closed 25-26 December, 1 January, 12 July, Monday and Sunday dinner – **Meals** (bookin essential) 12.50 (lunch) and a la carte 20.75/25.25 **t.** 11.00.

Sullivans, Unit 5, 2 Sullivan Pl, BT18 9JF, ☎ (028) 9042 1000, *Fax (028) 9042 6664* – VISA
closed 8-14 July, 24-27 December and Monday dinner – **Meals** (light lunch) 15.00/25.0 and a la carte 15.00/25.00 **t.** 11.00.

ARNE (Latharna) *Antrim* 923 O 3 *Ireland G. – pop. 17 575.*

Env. : *SE : Island Magee (Ballylumford Dolmen★).*

Exc. : *NW : Antrim Glens★★★ – Murlough Bay★★ (Fair Head ≤★★), Glenariff Forest Park★★ AC (Waterfall★★), Glenariff★, Glendun★ – Carrickfergus (Castle★★ – St. Nicholas' Church★), SW : 15 m. by A 2.*

Cairndhu, 192 Coast Rd, Ballygally ☎ (028) 2858 3248.

to Fleetwood (P & O Irish Sea) daily (8 h) – to Cairnryan (P & O Irish Sea) 3-5 daily (1 h/2 h 15 mn).

Narrow Gauge Rd ☎ (028) 2826 0088.

Belfast 23 – Ballymena 20.

Manor Guest House without rest., 23 Olderfleet Rd, Harbour Highway, BT40 1AS, ☎ (028) 2827 3305, *welcome@themanorguesthouse.com, Fax (028) 2826 0505* – TV P. MC VISA.
closed 25-26 December – **8 rm** 25.00/40.00 **st.**

IMAVADY (Léim an Mhadaidh) *Londonderry* 923 L 2.

Benone Par Three, 53 Benone Av., Benone ☎ (028) 7775 0555.

7 Connell St ☎ (028) 7776 0307.

Belfast 62 – Ballymena 39 – Coleraine 13 – Londonderry 17 – Omagh 50.

Radisson Roe Park H. & Golf Resort, Roe Park, BT49 9LB, West : ½ m. on A 2 ☎ (028) 7772 2222, *reservations@radissonroepark.com, Fax (028) 7772 2313,* – rm, TV P – 440. MC AE VISA.
Greens : **Meals** *(closed Sunday and Monday)* (dinner only) a la carte 20.40/31.50 **st.** 10.95 – ***The Coach House :*** **Meals** a la carte 13.00/25.00 **st.** 10.50 – **63 rm** 90.00/130.00 **st.**, 1 suite – SB.

Streeve Hill, BT49 0HP, Northeast : 1 m. on A 2, turning right immediately after the estate wall finishes ☎ (028) 7776 6563, *Fax (028) 7776 8285,* ≤, « 18C country house in extensive parkland », – TV P. MC AE VISA.
closed Christmas and New Year – **Meals** (by arrangement) (communal dining) 25.00 **st.** 10.00 – **3 rm** 55.00/90.00 **st.**

Lime Tree, 60 Catherine St, BT49 9DB, ☎ (028) 7776 4300 – MC AE VISA
closed 1 week February-March, 1 week July, 1 week November, 25 December, Saturday lunch, Monday and Tuesday except December – **Meals** 7.50 and a la carte 17.00/24.00 **t.** 9.75.

ONDONDERRY (Doire) *Londonderry* 923 K 2/3 *Ireland G. – pop. 72 334.*

See : *Town★ – City Walls and Gates★★ – Long Tower Church★ – Tower Museum★.*

Env. : *Grianan of Aileach★★ (≤★★) (Republic of Ireland) NW : 5 m. by A 2 and N 13.*

Exc. : *SE : by A 6 – Sperrin Mountains★ : Ulster-American Folk Park★★ – Glenshane Pass★ (★★) – Sawel Mountain Drive★ (≤★★) – Roe Valley Country Park★ – Beaghmore Stone Circles★ – Ulster History Park★ – Oak Lough Scenic Road★.*

City of Derry, 49 Victoria Rd ☎ (028) 7131 1610.

Eglinton Airport : ☎ (028) 7181 0784, E : 6 m. by A 2.

44 Foyle St ☎ (028) 7126 7284.

Belfast 70 – Dublin 146.

Hastings Everglades, Prehen Rd, BT47 2NH, South : 1½ m. on A 5 ☎ (028) 7134 6722, *res@egh.hastingshotels.com, Fax (028) 7134 9200* – , rm, rest, TV P – 500. MC AE VISA.
Satchmo : **Meals** (dinner only and Sunday lunch) 18.00/22.00 and a la carte 20.40/23.15 **st.** 10.00 – 12.00 – **64 rm** 85.00/200.00 **st.** – SB.

Beech Hill Country House, 32 Ardmore Rd, BT47 3QP, Southeast : 3 ½ m. by A 6 ☎ (028) 7134 9279, *info@beech-hill.com, Fax (028) 7134 5366,* « 18C merchant's house », – TV P – 60. MC AE VISA.
closed 24-25 December – ***The Ardmore :*** **Meals** 17.95/23.00 and a la carte 25.85/34.85 **t.** 12.95 – **25 rm** 100.00/120.00 **t.**, 2 suites – SB.

Trinity, 22-24 Strand Rd, BT48 7AB, ☎ (028) 7127 1271, *info@thetrinityhotel.com, Fax (028) 7127 1277* – TV P – 60. MC AE VISA.
closed 24-25 December – **Meals** (carving lunch)/dinner 17.50 and a la carte approx. 20.65 **t.** 8.50 – **38 rm** 70.00/90.00 **st.**, 2 suites – SB.

Waterfoot H. & Country Club, 14 Clooney Rd, Caw Roundabout, BT47 6TB, Northeast : 3 ¾ m. on A 2 at junction with A 55 ☎ (028) 7134 5500, *info@waterfoothotel.co.uk, Fax (028) 7131 1006,* – rm, TV P – 100. MC AE VISA.
closed 25-26 December – **Meals** (grill rest.) a la carte 9.15/16.00 **t.** 8.75 – 6.00 – **48 rm** 65.00/75.00 **t.**

Quality H. Da Vinci's, 15 Culmore Rd, BT48 8JB, North : 1 m. following signs for Foy Bridge ✆ (028) 7127 9111, *info@davincishotel.com, Fax (028) 7127 9222* – ⊟, ⇎ rm, TV ♿ P. MC AE VISA. ✄
closed 25 December – ***Da Vinci's :*** **Meals** (bar lunch)/dinner a la carte 16.15/24.40 **t.** 9.9 – ☐ 6.00 – **70 rm** 59.00 **t.** – SB.

MAGHERA (Machaire Rátha) *Londonderry* 923 L 3.
Belfast 40 – Ballymena 19 – Coleraine 21 – Londonderry 32.

Ardtara Country House ⛵, 8 Gorteade Rd, Upperlands, BT46 5SA, North : 3 ¼ m. by A 29 off B 75 ✆ (028) 7964 4490, *Fax (028) 7964 5080*, « 19C », ⛟, ✕ – ⇎ rest, TV P. MC AE VISA. ✄
closed 25-26 December – ***The Restaurant :*** **Meals** (booking essential to non-residents) 14.50/23.50 and dinner a la carte **t.** – **8 rm** ☐ 80.00/150.00 **st.** – SB.

MARTINSTOWN (Baile Uí Mháirtín) *Antrim* 923 N 3 – ✉ *Ballymena.*
Belfast 36 – Dundalk 86 – Larne 28 – Londonderry 58 – Omagh 61.

Caireal Manor without rest., 90 Glenravel Rd, Glen's of Antrim, BT43 6Q ✆ (028) 2175 8465, *info@cairealmanor.co.uk, Fax (028) 2175 8465* – TV ♿ P. MC VISA. ✄
closed 24-26 December – **3 rm** ☐ 25.00/50.00.

NEWCASTLE (An Caisleán Nua) *Down* 923 O 5 *Ireland G. – pop. 7 214.*
Env. : *Castlewellan Forest Park★★ AC, NW : 4 m. by A 50 – Dundrum Castle★ AC, NE : 4 m. by A 2 – Downpatrick (Down Cathedral★ – Down County Museum★), NE : by A 2.*
Exc. : *SW : Mourne Mountains★★ : Bryansford, Tollymore Forest Park★ AC – Silent Valley Reservoir★ (≤★) – Spelga Pass and Dam★ – Kilbroney Forest Park (viewpoint★) – Struell Wells★, NE : 12 m. by A 2 – Ardglass★, NE : 18 m. by A 2.*
ℹ *Promenade ✆ (028) 4372 2222.*
Belfast 32 – Londonderry 101.

Slieve Donard, Downs Rd, BT33 0AH, ✆ (028) 4372 3681, *res@sdh.hastings.com, Fax (028) 4372 4830*, ≤, ⛹, ⛆, ⛟, ✕ – ⊟ TV ♿ P – 🪑 800. MC AE ◑ VISA. ✄
Oak : **Meals** 16.00/23.00 **st.** 14.00 – ***Percy French :*** **Meals** a la carte 16.50/28.50 **st.** 14.00 – **126 rm** ☐ 105.00/160.00 **st.** – SB.

Burrendale H. & Country Club, 51 Castlewellan Rd, BT33 0JY, North : 1 m. on A 5 ✆ (028) 4372 2599, *reservations@burrendale.com, Fax (028) 4372 2328*, ⛹, ≘s, ⛆, ⛟, ⊟ ⇎, ▤ rest, TV ♿ P – 🪑 150. MC AE ◑ VISA
Meals 19.95/23.95 and a la carte 14.85/20.95 **t.** 11.95 – **68 rm** ☐ 65.00/99.00 **t.**, 1 suite – SB.

NEWRY (An Iúr) *Down* 923 M 5 *Ireland G. – pop. 21 633.*
See : *Bernish Rock Viewpoint★★.*
ℹ *Town Hall, Bank Par ✆ (028) 3026 8877.*
Belfast 37 – Dundalk 16.

Canal Court, Merchants Quay, BT35 8HF, ✆ (028) 3025 1234, *manager@canalcourthotel.com, Fax (028) 3025 1177*, ⛹, ≘s, ⛆ – ⊟, ▤ rest, TV ☎ ♿ P – 🪑 300. MC AE ◑ VISA. ✄
closed 24-25 December – ***Old Mill :*** **Meals** 11.00/23.50 and dinner a la carte 13.50/23.95 8.50 – **50 rm** ☐ 70.00/110.00 **t.**, 1 suite – SB.

NEWTOWNARDS (Baile Nua na hArda) *Down* 923 O 4.

Edenvale House ⛵ without rest., 130 Portaferry Rd, BT22 2AH, Southeast : 2 ¾ m. on A 20 ✆ (028) 9181 4881, *edenvalehouse@hotmail.com, Fax (028) 9182 6192*, ≤, ⛟ – ⇎ TV P. MC VISA
closed 24 December-2 January – **4 rm** ☐ 35.00/55.00.

OMAGH *Tyrone* 923 K 4 – *pop. 45 809.*

Hawthorn House, 72 Old Mountfield Rd, BT79 7EN, North : ¾ m. by B 4 ✆ (028) 8225 2005, *info@hawthornhouse.co.uk, Fax (028) 8225 2005* – TV P. MC VISA. ✄
Meals 10.00/25.00 and a la carte 11.50/26.00 **t.** 11.75 – **5 rm** ☐ 40.00/60.00 – SB.

Si vous cherchez un hôtel tranquille,
consultez d'abord les cartes de l'introduction
ou repérez dans le texte les établissements indiqués avec le signe ⛵ ou ⛵

ORTADOWN **(Port an Dúnáir)** *Armagh* 923 M 4.

Seagoe, 22 Upper Church Lane, BT63 5JE, Northeast : 1 ¼ m. on A 27 ☎ (028) 3833 3076, *info@seagoehotel.com, Fax (028) 3835 0210,* – TV – 400. VISA.
closed 25 December – ***Avanti :*** **Meals** a la carte 23/36 14.66 – 9.52 – **34 rm** 114.08/156.45 **t.**

ORTAFERRY **(Port an Pheire)** *Down* 923 P 4 *Ireland G. – pop. 2 324.*

See : *Aquarium★.*

Env. : *Castle Ward★★ AC, SW : 4 m. by boat and A 25.*

Exc. : *SE : Lecale Peninsula★★ – Struell Wells★, Quoile Pondage★, Ardglass★, Strangford★, Audley's Castle★.*

Castle St ☎ (028) 4272 9882 (Easter-September).

Belfast 29 – Bangor 24.

Portaferry, 10 The Strand, BT22 1PE, ☎ (028) 4272 8231, *info@portaferryhotel.com, Fax (028) 4272 8999,* ≤, « Loughside setting » – TV. VISA.
closed 24-25 December – **Meals** (bar lunch Monday-Saturday)/dinner a la carte approx. 16.90 **t.** 12.50 – **11 rm** 57.50/95.00 **t.** – SB.

The Narrows, 8 Shore Rd, BT22 1JY, ☎ (028) 4272 8148, *info@narrows.co.uk, Fax (028) 4272 8105,* ≤, « Loughside setting », – TV – 50. VISA.
Meals – (see ***The Restaurant*** below) – **13 rm** 42.50/85.00 **t.** – SB.

The Restaurant (at The Narrows H.), 8 Shore Rd, BT22 1JY, ☎ (028) 4272 8148, *Fax (028) 4272 8105,* ≤, « Loughside setting » – . VISA
Meals a la carte 15.85/27.95 **t.** 10.95.

When looking for a quiet hotel
use the maps found in the introduction
or look for establishments with the sign *or* .

ORTRUSH **(Port Rois)** *Antrim* 923 L 2 *Ireland G. – pop. 5 703.*

Exc. : *Causeway Coast★★ : Giant's Causeway★★★ (Hamilton's Seat ≤★★) – Carrick-a-rede Rope Bridge★★ – Dunluce Castle★★ AC – Dunseverick Castle (≤★★) – Gortmore Viewpoint★ – Magilligan Strand★ – Downhill★ (Mussenden Temple★).*

18, 18, 9 *Royal Portrush, Dunluce Rd ☎ (028) 7082 2311.*

Sandhill Drive ☎ (028) 7082 3333 (March-October).

Belfast 58 – Coleraine 4 – Londonderry 35.

Magherabuoy House, 41 Magheraboy Rd, BT56 8NX, Southwest : 1 m. by A 29 ☎ (028) 7082 3507, *admin@magherabuoy.co.uk, Fax (028) 7082 4687,* ≤, – rest, TV – 200. VISA JCB.
closed 24-26 December – **Meals** a la carte 8.95/19.70 **t.** 7.95 – **40 rm** 60.00/100.00 **t.**

Glenkeen Guest House without rest., 59 Coleraine Rd, BT56 8HR, ☎ (028) 7082 2279, *glenkeen@btinternet.com, Fax (028) 7082 2279* – TV. VISA.
closed 21-27 December – **10 rm** 30.00/48.00 **s.**

Ramore Wine Bar, The Harbour, BT56 8BN, ☎ (028) 7082 4313, *Fax (028) 7082 3194,* ≤ – VISA
closed 25 December – **Meals** a la carte 13.40/18.35 **t.** 7.50.

The Harbour Bar, The Harbour, BT56 8BN, ☎ (028) 7082 2430, *Fax (028) 7082 3194,* ≤ –
closed 25 December and Monday – **Meals** a la carte 13.20/19.15 **t.** 7.50.

ORTSTEWART **(Port Stióbhaird)** *Londonderry* 923 L 2.

Cromore Halt Inn, 158 Station Rd, BT55 7PU, East : ½ m. by A 2 (Portrush rd) on B 185 (Coleraine rd) ☎ (028) 7083 6888, *info@cromore.com, Fax (028) 7083 1910* – , rest, TV – 30. VISA.
closed 24-26 December – **Meals** 12.50/16.25 **t.** 8.25 – **12 rm** 45.00/80.00 **t.**

EAFORDE **(Baile Forda)** *Down* 923 O 5 – *pop. 186* – *Downpatrick.*

Belfast 25 – Dundalk 45 – Dungannon 53.

Drumgooland House , 29 Dunnanew Rd, BT30 8PJ, North : 2 m. by A 24 ☎ (028) 4481 1956, *frank.mc_leigh@virgin.net, Fax (028) 4481 1265,* ≤, , , – TV . VISA.
Meals (by arrangement) 19.00 **st.** – **3 rm** 29.50/49.00 **st.**

TEMPLEPATRICK **(Teampall Phádraig)** *Antrim* 923 N 3 – *pop. 1 414* – ✉ *Ballyclare.*

Belfast 13 – Ballymena 16 – Dundalk 65 – Larne 16.

Hilton Templepatrick, Castle Upton Estate, BT39 0DD, North : 1 m. on B 95 (Parkga rd) ✆ (028) 9443 5500, *res.manager@park.stakis.co.uk, Fax (028) 9443 5511,* – rm, rest, 500. **Meals** 12.95/19.95 and dinner a la carte 21.40/27.25 **st.** 14.95 – 10.50 – **130 r** 150.00/210.00 **st.** – SB.

Templeton, 882 Antrim Rd, BT39 0AH, ✆ (028) 9443 2984, *Fax (028) 9443 3406,* – – 400. *closed 25-26 December* – ***Templeton :*** **Meals** *(closed Monday and Tuesday)* (dinner or and Sunday lunch)/dinner 22.50 and a la carte 18.15/24.70 **st.** 11.95 – ***Upton Grill :*** **Mea** (grill rest.) a la carte 10.00/22.40 **st.** – **24 rm** 90.00/130.00 **st.** – SB.

Republic of Ireland

Dunfanaghy
Bunbeg
Rathmullan
Gweedore
Rathmelton
Dunglow
Letterkenny
Ballybofey
N 15
Dunkineely
Killybegs
Donegal
Rossnowlagh
Bundoran
Ballyshannon
Rosses Point
Inishcrone
Sligo
N 16
Blacklion
Collooney
Crossmolina
Ballina
Riverstown
Keel
Doogort
Ballymote
Ballyconnell
ACHILL ISLAND
Swinford
Castlebaldwin
Newport
Castlebar
Carrick-on-Shannon
Kiltimagh
Westport
Knock
Roosky
Castlerea
Termonbarry
Rinvyle
Leenane
Longford
Letterfrack
Clonbur
N 17
Ballinlough
Ballynahinch
Cong
Roscommon
Clifden
Recess
Oughterard
Roundstone
Caherlistrane
Mullingar
Maam Cross
Cashel
Carna
Moycullen
Athlone
Furbogh
Galway
Ballinasloe
Inverin
Oranmore
Inishmore
Spiddal
Barna
Craughwell
Clarinbridge
Kilcolgan
Tullamore
ARAN ISLANDS
Loughrea
Kinvara
Ballyvaughan
Doolin
Gort
Birr
Lisdoonvarna
Ennistimon
N 18
Aglish
Lahinch
Borrisokane
Roscrea
Ennis
Nenagh
Spanish Point
Killaloe
Newmarket-on-Fergus
N 7
Abbeyleix
Kilkee
Bunratty
Shannon
Thurles
Bagenalstown
Cratloe
Limerick
Glin
Kilkenny
Ballybunnion
N 21
Adare
N 24
Listowel
Cashel
Graiguenamanagh
Ballingarry
Tipperary
Thomastown
Ballyheige
Bansha
Knocktopher
Ballydavid
Fethard
Inistioge
Kilcummin
Glen of Aherlow
Tralee
Caher
Ballyferriter
Camp
Clonmel
Carrick-on-Suir
Dingle
Kanturk
Dunquin
Killorglin
Glanworth
Ballymacarbry
Waterford
Caragh Lake
Fermoy
Cappoquin
VALENCIA ISLAND
Killarney
Mallow
Tallow
Tramore
Cahirsiveen
Castlelyons
Portmagee
N 22
Dungarvan
Knights Town
Kenmare
Blarney
N 25
Tahilla
Macroom
Youghal
Waterville
Cork
Killeagh
Parknasilla
Garryvoe
Castlemartyr
Caherdaniel
Shanagarry
Ballycotton
Castletownbere
Toormore

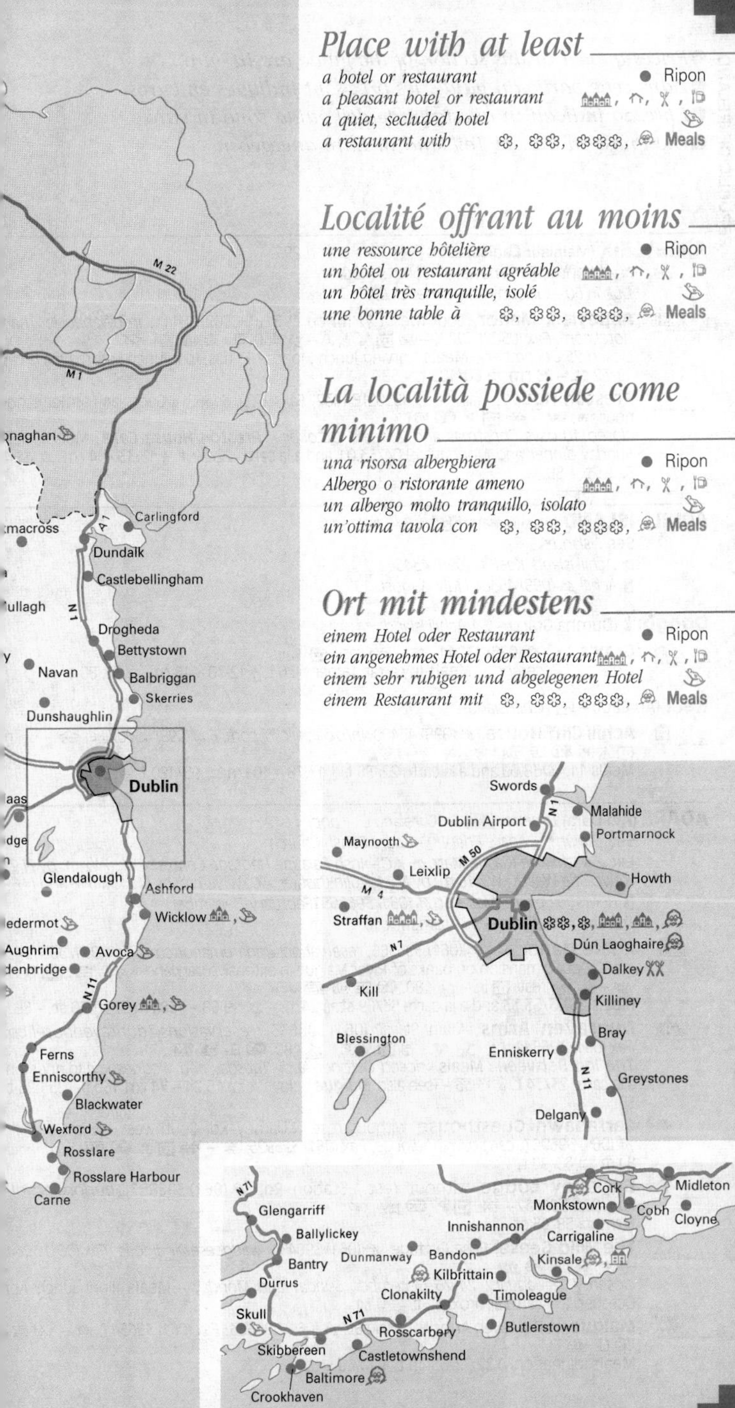
Place with at least
a hotel or restaurant ● Ripon
a pleasant hotel or restaurant
a quiet, secluded hotel
a restaurant with ✿, ✿✿, ✿✿✿, Meals
Localité offrant au moins
une ressource hôtelière ● Ripon
un hôtel ou restaurant agréable
un hôtel très tranquille, isolé
une bonne table à ✿, ✿✿, ✿✿✿, Meals
La località possiede come minimo
una risorsa alberghiera ● Ripon
Albergo o ristorante ameno
un albergo molto tranquillo, isolato
un'ottima tavola con ✿, ✿✿, ✿✿✿, Meals
Ort mit mindestens
einem Hotel oder Restaurant ● Ripon
ein angenehmes Hotel oder Restaurant
einem sehr ruhigen und abgelegenen Hotel
einem Restaurant mit ✿, ✿✿, ✿✿✿, Meals
M 22
M 1
A 1
N 1
N 11
Carlingford
Dundalk
Castlebellingham
Drogheda
Bettystown
Navan
Balbriggan
Skerries
Dunshaughlin
Dublin
Glendalough
Ashford
Wicklow
Avoca
Gorey
Ferns
Enniscorthy
Blackwater
Wexford
Rosslare
Rosslare Harbour
Carne
Swords
Malahide
Dublin Airport
Portmarnock
Maynooth
M 50
Leixlip
Howth
M 4
Straffan
Dublin ✿✿, ✿
N 7
Dún Laoghaire
Dalkey
Kill
Killiney
Bray
Blessington
Enniskerry
Greystones
Delgany
N 71
Glengarriff
Ballylickey
Bantry
Durrus
Skull
Skibbereen
Crookhaven
Baltimore
Castletownshend
Rosscarbery
Clonakilty
Dunmanway
Bandon
Kilbrittain
Innishannon
Timoleague
Butlerstown
Kinsale
Carrigaline
Monkstown
Cork
Cobh
Midleton
Cloyne

- *Prices quoted in this section of the guide are in euro*
- *Dans cette partie du guide, les prix sont indiqués en euros*
- *I prezzo indicati in questa parte dell guida sono in euro*
- *Die Preise in diesem Teil sind in Euro angegeben*

ABBEYLEIX (Mainistir Laoise) *Laois* 923 J 9 – *pop. 1 299.*

Abbeylеix, Rathmoyle ☎ (0502) 31450.
Dublin 60 – Kilkenny 22 – Limerick 67.

Abbeyleix Manor, Southwest : ½ m. on N 8 ☎ (0502) 30111, *info@abbeyleixman hotel.com, Fax (0502) 30220* – TV P – 450. MC AE VISA.
closed 25 December – **Meals** (carving lunch Monday-Friday) (bar lunch Saturday) a la car 19/32 **st.** – **23 rm** 60/105 **t.** – SB.

Preston House, Main St, ☎ (0502) 31432, *Fax (0502) 31662,* « Georgian former scho house », TV P. MC VISA
closed 10 days Christmas and 2 weeks October – ***Preston House Café :*** Meals *(clos Sunday dinner and Monday)* 19.04/33.01 and a la carte 22/32 **t.** 13.33 – **4 rm** 44.4 82.53 **t.** – SB.

ACHILL ISLAND (Acaill) *Mayo* 923 B 5/6 *Ireland G.*

See : *Island*★.
Achill Island, Keel ☎ (098) 43456.
Achill ☎ (098) 45384 (July-August).

Doogort (Dumha Goirt) – *Achill Island.*

Gray's, ☎ (098) 43244, – rest, TV P
closed 25 December – **Meals** (by arrangement) 26 **t.** 12.70 – **15 rm** 38/80 **t.**

Keel (An Caol) – *Achill Island.*

Achill Cliff House, ☎ (098) 43400, *info@achillcliff.com, Fax (098) 43007,* ←, – r
TV P. MC AE VISA.
Meals 11.43/38.09 and a la carte 22/36 **t.** 17.78 – **10 rm** 95/180 **t.** – SB.

ADARE (Áth Dara) *Limerick* 923 F 10 *Ireland G. – pop. 1 042.*

See : *Town*★ – *Adare Friary*★ – *Adare Parish Church*★.
Exc. : *Rathkeale (Castle Matrix*★ *AC – Irish Palatine Heritage Centre*★*) W : 7½ m. by N 21 Newcastle West*★*, W : 16 m. by N 21 – Glin Castle*★ *AC, W : 29 m. by N 21, R 518 and N 69*
Heritage Centre, Mains St ☎ (061) 396255 (February-December).
Dublin 131 – Killarney 59 – Limerick 10.

Adare Manor, ☎ (061) 396566, *reservations@adaremanor.com, Fax (061) 396124,* « 19C Gothic mansion on banks of River Maigue in extensive parkland », – , rest, TV P – 180. MC AE VISA JCB.
Meals 26.03/53.33 and a la carte 53/69 **st.** 24.12 – 19.68 – **138 rm** 375/670 **st.** – SB.

Dunraven Arms, Main St, ☎ (061) 396633, *reservations@dunravenhotel.co Fax (061) 396541,* , – TV P – 180. MC AE VISA.
The Inn Between : Meals *(closed October-April, Tuesday and Wednesday)* (dinner on a la carte 23/34 **t.** 13.33 – (see also ***Maigue*** below) – 15.24 – **74 rm** 139.67/253.95 **t.** SB.

Carrabawn Guesthouse without rest., Killarney Rd, Southwest : ½ m. on N ☎ (061) 396067, *carrabaw@indigo.ie, Fax (061) 396925,* – TV P. MC VISA
8 rm 60/90 **t.**

Berkeley Lodge without rest., Station Rd, ☎ (061) 396857, *berlodge@iol. Fax (061) 396857* – TV P. MC VISA.
6 rm 58/65 **st.**

The Wild Geese, Rose Cottage, ☎ (061) 396451, *wildgeese@indigo.ie, Fax (061) 3964* – . MC AE VISA
closed 7-28 January, 24-26 December, Sunday and Monday – **Meals** (light lunch Apr October) a la carte approx. 42 **t.** 20.31.

Maigue (at Dunraven Arms H.), Main St, ☎ (061) 396633, *Fax (061) 396541,* –
MC AE VISA
Meals (dinner only) 22.22/35.49 **t.** 14.60.

GLISH (An Eaglais) *Tipperary* 923 H 8 – ✉ *Borrisokane.*
Dublin 114 – Galway 53 – Limerick 43.

Ballycormac House ⛺, ✆ (067) 21129, *ballyc@indigo.ie, Fax (067) 21200,* – P. MC VISA
Meals (by arrangement) (communal dining) 31.74 **st.** 15.24 – **5 rm** 39/90 **t.**, 1 suite.

HERLOW (Eatharlach) *Tipperary* 923 H 10 – *see Glen of Aherlow.*

RAN ISLANDS (Oileáin Árann) *Galway* 923 CD 8 *Ireland G.*
See : *Islands★ – Inishmore (Dún Aonghasa★★★).*
Access by boat or aeroplane from Galway city or by boat from Kilkieran, Rossaveel or Fisherstreet (Clare) and by aeroplane from Inverin.
Aran Kilronan ✆ (099) 61263.

ishmore – ✉ *Aran Islands.*

Pier House without rest., Kilronan, ✆ (099) 61417, *pier@iol.ie, Fax (099) 61122,* ≤, – TV P. MC VISA
18 March-October – **12 rm** 69.84/76.18.

Ard Einne Guesthouse, Killeany, ✆ (099) 61126, *ardeinne@eircom.net, Fax (099) 61388,* ≤ Killeany Bay – P. MC VISA.
February-15 December – **Meals** (by arrangement) 20 **t.** 18 – **14 rm** 50/64 **t.** – SB.

Kilmurvey House, Kilmurvey, ✆ (099) 61218, *kilmurveyhouse@eircom.net, Fax (099) 61397,* ≤, – rest. MC VISA.
April-October – **Meals** (by arrangement) 25 **st.** 18 – **12 rm** 45/70 **st.**

RTHURSTOWN (Colmán) *Wexford* 923 L 11.
Dublin 103 – Cork 99 – Limerick 101 – Waterford 26.

Dunbrody Country House, ✆ (051) 389600, *dunbrody@indigo.ie, Fax (051) 389601,* ≤, « Part Georgian former hunting lodge », – TV P.
MC AE VISA JCB
closed 23-26 December – **Meals** (booking essential for non-residents) (residents only Sunday dinner) (bar lunch Monday-Saturday)/dinner 50 and a la carte 39/50 **t.** – **16 rm** 120/260 **t.**, 4 suites – SB.

SHFORD (Ath na Fuinseoge) *Wicklow* 923 N 8 – *pop. 1 215.*

Ballyknocken House, Glenealy, South : 3 m. by N 11 ✆ (0404) 44627, *cfulvio@ballyknocken.com, Fax (0404) 44696,* « Working farm », – TV P. MC VISA.
March-November – **Meals** (by arrangement) 26.50 **st.** 15.50 – **7 rm** 70/90 **st.** – SB.

THBOY *Meath* 923 L 7 – *pop. 1 172.*
Dublin 42 – Drogheda 28 – Tullamore 44.

Woodtown House, Southwest : 5 ½ m. by N 51, following obvious signage ✆ (046) 35022, *woodtown@iol.ie, Fax (046) 35022,* ≤, « Georgian country house », – P. MC VISA.
April-September – **Meals** (by arrangement) 17.00 **st.** – **3 rm** 38.10/63.50 **st.**

THLONE (Baile Átha Luain) *Westmeath* 923 I 7 *Ireland G.* – *pop. 7 691.*
Exc. : *Clonmacnois★★★ (Grave Slabs★, Cross of the Scriptures★) S : 13 m. by N 6 and N 62 – N : Lough Ree (Ballykeeran Viewpoint★, Glassan★).*
18 Hodson Bay ✆ (0902) 92073.
Athlone ✆ (0902) 94630 (April-October).
Dublin 75 – Galway 57 – Limerick 75 – Roscommon 20 – Tullamore 24.

Hodson Bay, Northwest : 4 ¾ m. by N 61 ✆ (0902) 80500, *info@hodsonbayhotel.com, Fax (0902) 80520,* ≤, « Loughside setting », 18, – TV P – 750.
MC AE VISA.
L'Escale : **Meals** 16.50/38 and dinner a la carte 29/55 **st.** 14.60 – 14.00 – **131 rm** 124/155 **st.**, 2 suites – SB.

Creggan Court, N6 Centre, Dublin Rd, Southeast : 2 ½ m. by R 446 at junction with N 6 ✆ (0902) 77777, *info@creggancourt.com, Fax (0902) 77111* – rm, TV P – 30. MC AE VISA.
closed 25-26 December – **Meals** (bar lunch) 16.45/22.86 **st.** 15.17 – **73 rm** 63.50/114.30 **st.**

Castledaly Manor ⑤, Castledaly, Southeast : 7 m. by N 6 ℘ (0902) 81221, *castleo@eircom.net, Fax (0902) 81600*, ≤, « Part 17C country mansion », ⚘, ⚘ – ⚘ rest, TV P. MC AE VISA. ⚘
closed 25 December – **Meals** (dinner only) 23.49 and a la carte approx. 25 **t.** 17.14 – **10** ⚘ 100.94/139.04 **t.**

Riverview House without rest., Summerhill, Galway Rd, West : 3 m. on N ℘ (0902) 94532, *riverviewhouse@hotmail.com, Fax (0902) 94532*, ⚘ – ⚘ rest, TV P. AE VISA. ⚘
March-mid December – **5 rm** ⚘ 32.40/50.80.

Shelmalier House without rest., Retreat Rd, Cartrontroy, East : 1 ½ m. by Dublin (N 6) ℘ (0902) 72245, *shelmal@iol.ie, Fax (0902) 73190*, ⚘ – TV P. MC VISA. ⚘
closed 20 December-1 February – **7 rm** ⚘ 39/52 **st.**

The Mill without rest., Tuam Rd, Northwest : 3 ½ m. on R 362 ℘ (0902) 92927, *oshea@iol.ie* – TV P. MC VISA. ⚘
closed 20 December-8 January – **7 rm** ⚘ 45/50 **st.**

Left Bank Bistro, Fry Pl, ℘ (0902) 94446, *leftbank@isite.ie, Fax (0902) 94509* – ⚘. MC VISA
closed 1 week Christmas, Sunday-Monday and Bank Holidays – **Meals** (light lunch) a la ca 22.10/32.45 **t.** 15.18.

at Glassan *Northeast : 5 m. on N 55 – ✉ Athlone.*

Glasson Golf H. & Country Club ⑤, West : 1 ¾ m. ℘ (0902) 85120, *info@glassgolf.ie, Fax (0902) 85444*, ≤ Golf course and Lough Ree, ⚘, ⚘ – ⚘ TV ⚘ P – ⚘ 60. MC ⚘ VISA. ⚘
closed 25 December – **Meals** a la carte 22/32 **t.** 16.44 – **29 rm** ⚘ 142.84/177.76 1 suite.

Wineport Lodge, Southwest : 1 m. ℘ (0902) 85466, *lodge@wineport Fax (0902) 85471*, « Loughside setting ≤ Lough Ree » – ⚘ P. MC AE ⚘ VISA JCB
closed 24-26 December – **Meals** (restricted lunch)/dinner a la carte 34.30/45.50 **t.** 18.

Glasson Village, ℘ (0902) 85001 – ⚘ P. MC AE ⚘ VISA. ⚘
closed 3 weeks mid October-November, 23-26 December, Good Friday, Sunday and Monc – **Meals** (dinner only and Sunday lunch) 18.41/29.84 and a la carte 29/35 **t.** 14.92.

ATHY (Baile Átha Á) *Kildare* 923 L 9 *Ireland G. – pop. 5 306.*

Exc. : *Emo Court★★, N : 20 m. by R 417 (L 18), west by N 7 (T 5) and north by R 42 Stradbally★, NW : 9 m. by R 428 (L 109) – Castledermot High Crosses★, SE : 9½ m. by R 41 Moone High Cross★, E : 12 m. by Ballitore minor rd and south by N 9 – Rock of Dunamas (≤★), NW : 12 m. by R 428 (L 109) and N 80 (T 16) – Timahoe Round Tower★, W : 10 m. R 428 (L 109) and N 80 (T 16).*
18 *Athy, Geraldine ℘ (0507) 31729.*
Dublin 40 – Kilkenny 29 – Wexford 59.

Tonlegee House ⑤ with rm, Southwest : 1 ½ m. by N 78 ℘ (0507) 31473, *marjo@tonlegeehouse.com, Fax (0507) 31473*, ≤, ⚘ – TV P. MC AE VISA
closed mid December-mid January – **Meals** *(closed Sunday and Monday)* (dinner or a la carte 30.80/36.20 **st.** – **12 rm** ⚘ 75/110 **st.** – SB.

AUGHRIM (Eachroim) *Wicklow* 923 N 9 – *pop. 745.*

The Battle of Aughrim Visitors Centre, Ballinasloe ℘ (0905) 73939 (10 April-September
Dublin 46 – Waterford 77 – Wexford 60.

Brooklodge ⑤, Macreddin Village, North : 2 m. ℘ (0402) 36444, *brooklodge@macrdin.ie, Fax (0402) 36580*, ⚘, ⚘, ⚘ – ⚘ TV ⚘ P – ⚘ 220. MC AE ⚘ VISA
closed 24-25 December – **Meals** – (see ***Strawberry Tree*** below) – **39 rm** ⚘ 137/210 s 1 suite – SB.

Lawless's, ℘ (0402) 36146, *lawhotel@iol.ie, Fax (0402) 36384*, ⚘ – ⚘ rm, TV P ⚘ 150. MC AE ⚘ VISA. ⚘
closed 23-26 December – **Meals** (bar lunch Monday-Saturday)/dinner 32 and a la car 20/37 **t.** 15.25 – **14 rm** ⚘ 91/132 **st.** – SB.

Strawberry Tree (at Brooklodge), Macreddin Village, North : 2 m. ℘ (0402) 364 *Fax (0402) 36580*, ⚘ – ⚘ P. MC AE ⚘ VISA
closed 24-25 December – **Meals** - Organic - (dinner only and Sunday lunch)/dinner 44.44 19.05.

Les prix — Pour toutes précisions sur les prix indiqués dans ce guide, reportez-vous aux pages de l'introduction.

AVOCA (Abhóca) *Wicklow* 923 N 9 *Ireland G. – pop. 490.*
Exc. : *Meeting of the Waters*★, *N : by R 752 – Avondale*★, *N : by R 752.*
Dublin 47 – Waterford 72 – Wexford 55.

Keppel's Farmhouse without rest., Ballanagh, South : 2 m. by unmarked rd ℘ (0402) 35168, *keppelsfarmhouse@eircom.net, Fax (0402) 30950,* ←, « Working farm », – ⇔ TV. MC VISA.
April-October – **5 rm** 50/64 **st.**

BAGENALSTOWN (Muine Bheag) *Carlow* 923 L 9 – *pop. 2 553.*
Dublin 63 – Carlow 10 – Kilkenny 13 – Wexford 37.

Kilgraney Country House, South : 4 m. by R 705 (Borris Rd) ℘ (0503) 75283, *kilgrany@indigo.ie, Fax (0503) 75595,* ←, « Late Georgian house with collection of Far Eastern furnishings and artefacts », – ⇔ rm, P. MC AE VISA.
closed November-February and Monday-Wednesday except July-August – **Meals** (booking essential) (residents only) (communal dining) (dinner only) 40 **st.** 18 – **6 rm** 55/140 **st.**

BALBRIGGAN (Baile Brigín) *Dublin* 923 N 7 – *pop. 5 743.*

Bracken Court, Bridge St, ℘ (01) 8413333, *info@brackencourt.ie, Fax (01) 8415118* – TV P – 200. MC AE VISA.
The Restaurant : **Meals** (carvery lunch in bar) (dinner only and Sunday lunch)/dinner 14.28/24.13 and a la carte 20.32/29.20 **t.** 15.24 – **40 rm** 76/114 **t.** – SB.

BALLINA (Béal an Átha) *Mayo* 923 E 5 *Ireland G. – pop. 6 852.*
Env. : *Mayo*★ – *Rosserk Abbey*★, *N : 4 m. by R 314.*
Exc. : *Moyne Abbey*★, *N : 7 m. by R 314 – Pontoon Bridge View* (←★), *S : 12 m. by N 26 and R 310 – Downpatrick Head*★, *N : 20 m. by R 314.*
Mossgrove, Shanaghy ℘ *(096) 21050.*
Cathedral Rd ℘ *(096) 70848 (April-September).*
Dublin 150 – Galway 73 – Roscommon 64 – Sligo 37.

Ridgepool, Barrett St, ℘ (096) 24600, *theridgepoolhotel@eircom.net, Fax (096) 24602,* « Riverside setting », – ⇔ rm, rest, TV P – 300. MC AE VISA.
Meals 9.50/31.75 and dinner a la carte **st.** 14.60 – 10.80 – **70 rm** 127/165.10 **st.**, 2 suites – SB.

Downhill Inn, Sligo Rd, East : 1 m. off N 59 ℘ (096) 73444, *thedownhillinn@eircom.net, Fax (096) 73411* – TV P. MC AE VISA.
closed 21 December-10 January – **Meals** a la carte 13.97/28.58 **st.** 8.89 – **45 rm** 85.09/93.98 **st.** – SB.

BALLINADEE (Baile na Daidhche) *Cork* 923 G 12 – *see Kinsale.*

BALLINASCARTY (Béal na Scairte) *Cork* 923 F 12 – *see Clonakilty.*

BALLINASLOE (Béal Átha na Sluaighe) *Galway* 923 H 8 *Ireland G. – pop. 5 634.*
Env. : *Clonfert Cathedral*★ *(west doorway*★★*), SW : by R 355 and minor roads.*
Exc. : *Turoe Stone, Bullaun*★, *SW : 18 m. by R 348 and R 350 – Loughrea (St. Brendan's Cathedral*★*), SW : 18 m. by N 6.*
Rossgloss ℘ *(0905) 42126* – *Mountbellew* ℘ *(0905) 79259.*
Kellar Travel ℘ *(0905) 42131 (July-August).*
Dublin 91 – Galway 41 – Limerick 66 – Roscommon 36 – Tullamore 34.

Hayden's Gateway, Dunlo St, ℘ (0905) 42347, *cro@lynchotels.com, Fax (0905) 42895,* – rest, TV P – 250. MC AE VISA.
Meals (bar lunch Monday-Saturday)/dinner 21.59/31.74 and a la carte 19.05/30.48 **st.** 15.24 – **48 rm** 117.80 **st.** – SB.

Tohers, 18 Dunlo St, ℘ (0905) 44848, *Fax (0905) 44844* – ⇔. MC VISA
closed 2 weeks October, 24-26 December, 1 January, Sunday, Monday dinner and Bank Holidays – **Meals** (light lunch) a la carte 26.66/39.36 **t.** 18.50.

Keine Aufnahme in den ***Michelin-Führer*** *durch*
- falsche Information oder
- Bezahlung!

BALLINGARRY (Baile an Gharraí) *Limerick* 923 F 10 *Ireland G. – pop. 389.*

Exc. : *Kilmallock★ (Kilmallock Abbey★, Collegiate Church★), SE : 15 m. by R 518 – Monasteranenagh Abbey★, NE : 15 m. – Lough Gur Interpretive Centre★, NE : 24 m.*

Dublin 141 – Killarney 56 – Limerick 18.

Mustard Seed at Echo Lodge ⛱, ✆ (069) 68508, *mustard@indigo... Fax (069) 68511,* ≘s, ⛱ – ⅍ TV ♿ P – 🎪 25. MC AE VISA. ⅍
closed 24-26 December and February – **Meals** *(closed Sunday and Monday in low seas...)* (booking essential for non-residents) (dinner only) 45.71 **t.** 🍷 20.31 – **14 rm** ☐ 101.... 253.94 **t.**, 3 suites.

BALLINLOUGH (Baile an Locha) *Roscommon* 923 G 6.

Dublin 114 – Galway 40 – Roscommon 24 – Sligo 51.

White House, ✆ (0907) 40112, *thewhitehousehotel@eircom.net, Fax (0907) 40993* – ▤ rest, TV ☎ ♿ – 🎪 180. MC AE ⊙ VISA
closed 25 December – ***The Blue Room :*** **Meals** (carvery lunch in bar)/dinner 31 and a la carte 23/35 **st.** 🍷 12.06 – **19 rm** ☐ 82.53/107.92 – SB.

BALLON (Balana) *Carlow* 923 L 9.

Dublin 65 – Kilkenny 36 – Wexford 35.

Ballykealey Country House ⛱, Northwest : ½ m. on N 80 ✆ (0503) 59288, *bh@io... Fax (0503) 59297,* ⛱ – TV P. MC AE ⊙ VISA. ⅍
April-18 December – **Meals** *(closed Sunday and Monday)* (booking essential to non-re... dents) 19.05/36.19 **t.** 🍷 13.33 – **12 rm** ☐ 69.84/177.76 **t.** – SB.

BALLSBRIDGE (Droichead na Dothra) *Dublin* 923 ⑩ – *see Dublin.*

BALLYBOFEY (Bealach Féich) *Donegal* 923 I 3 – *pop. 3 047 (inc. Stranorlar).*

🏌18 *Ballybofey & Stranorlar, The Glebe* ✆ *(074) 31093.*

Dublin 148 – Londonderry 30 – Sligo 58.

Kee's, Main St, Stranorlar, Northeast : ½ m. on N 15 ✆ (074) 31018, *info@keeshote... Fax (074) 31917,* 🏋, ≘s, 🏊 – ⇅ TV P. MC AE ⊙ VISA. ⅍
Looking Glass : **Meals** (dinner only and Sunday lunch)/dinner 29.14/37 and a la ca... 33/39 **t.** 🍷 16.50 – ***Old Gallery :*** **Meals** *(closed 25 December)* a la carte 16/29.50 **t.** 🍷 16.5... **53 rm** ☐ 87/178 **t.** – SB.

Jackson's, ✆ (074) 31021, *bjackson@iol.ie, Fax (074) 31096,* 🏋, ≘s, 🏊, ⛱ – ⇅, ⅍ r... ▤ rest, TV ♿ P. MC AE ⊙ VISA. ⅍
closed 25 December – **Meals** (buffet lunch) 12.00/31.11 and dinner a la carte 22.7... 41.20 **st.** 🍷 14.60 – **88 rm** ☐ 79.36/165 **t.** – SB.

Villa Rose, Main St, ✆ (074) 32266, *villarose@oceanfree.net, Fax (074) 30666* – ⇅, ⅍ r... TV ♿. MC AE VISA
Meals (bar lunch Monday-Saturday)/dinner 16.44/20.25 and a la carte 20/33 **st.** 🍷 16.5... **16 rm** ☐ 57.13/88.88 **st.** – SB.

BALLYBUNNION (Baile an Bhuinneánaigh) *Kerry* 923 D 10 *Ireland G. – pop. 1 470.*

Exc. : *Carrigafoyle Castle★, NE : 13 m. by R 551 – Glin Castle★ AC, E : 19 m. by R 5... and N 69.*

🏌18, 🏌18 *Ballybunnion, Sandhill Rd* ✆ *(068) 27146.*

Dublin 176 – Limerick 56 – Tralee 26.

Iragh Ti Connor, Main St, ✆ (068) 27112, *iraghticonnor@eircom.net, Fax (068) 277...* ⛱ – TV P. MC AE VISA. ⅍
closed 24-25 December – **Meals** a la carte 29/34 **st.** – **17 rm** ☐ 120/180 **st.** – SB.

Harty Costello Townhouse, Main St, ✆ (068) 27129, *hartycostello@eircom.n... Fax (068) 27489* – ⅍ rm, TV. MC AE VISA. ⅍
April-mid October – **Meals** *(closed Sunday)* (dinner only) 22.22 and a la carte 22.22/38.0... 🍷 16.44 – **8 rm** ☐ 63.49/114.28 **st.** – SB.

Teach de Broc Country House without rest., Link Rd, South : 1 ½ m. by Golf Club ✆ (068) 27581, *teachdebroc@eircom.net, Fax (068) 27919* – ⅍ TV ♿ P. MC VISA. ⅍
March-mid November – **10 rm** ☐ 95.23/126.97 **t.**

Manor Inn ⛱ without rest., Doon Rd, North : 1 m. on Beal rd ✆ (068) 27577, *drao@ba... bunnion-manorinn.com, Fax (068) 27757,* ⛱ – TV P. MC AE VISA. ⅍
April-November – **9 rm** ☐ 37/114 **s.**

BALLYCONNELL (Béal Atha Conaill) *Cavan* 923 J 5 – *pop. 433.*

Slieve Russell ☎ *(049) 952 6444.*

Dublin 89 – Drogheda 76 – Enniskillen 23.

Slieve Russell, Southeast : 1 ¾ m. on R 200 ☎ (049) 952 6444, *slieve-russell@quinn-hotels.com, Fax (049) 922 6474,* ←, squash – TV P – 800. AE VISA.
Conall Cearnach : **Meals** (dinner only) 39 **st.** – ***Brackley :*** **Meals** (carving lunch) 17.14 and dinner a la carte 18.34/31.68 **st.** – **151 rm** 127/216 **st.** – SB.

BALLYCOTTON (Baile Choitín) *Cork* 923 H 12 *Ireland G.* – *pop. 477.*

Exc. : *Cloyne Cathedral*★*, NW : by R 629.*

Dublin 165 – Cork 27 – Waterford 66.

Bayview, ☎ (021) 4646746, *bayhotel@iol.ie, Fax (021) 4646075,* ← Ballycotton Bay, harbour and island, – TV P – 25. AE VISA.
April-October – **Meals** (bar lunch Monday-Saturday)/dinner 43 **st.** – **33 rm** 126/192 **st.**, 2 suites – SB.

Spanish Point with rm, ☎ (021) 4646177, *spanishp@indigo.ie, Fax (021) 4646179,* ← Ballycotton Bay and Island – rest, TV P. VISA
closed 20 December-10 February – **Meals** - Seafood - (booking essential October-April) 19.05/35.55 and a la carte 17.50/35.55 **t.** 16.51 – **5 rm** 39/44 **st.**

BALLYDAVID (Baile na nGall) *Kerry* 923 A 11 – ✉ *Dingle.*

Gorman's Clifftop, Glaise Bheag, North : 1 m. ☎ (066) 9155162, *gormans@tinet.ie, Fax (066) 9155003,* ← Smerwick Harbour and Ballydavid Head, – TV P. VISA.
closed 10 January-February and 24-26 December – **Meals** (dinner only) 32/40 **t.** – **9 rm** 100/150 **t.** – SB.

Old Pier, An Fheothanach, North : 1 ½ m. ☎ (066) 9155242, *info@oldpier.com,* ← Smerwick Harbour and Ballydavid Head, – rest, TV P. VISA.
closed 25 December – **Meals** (by arrangement) 23.49 **st.** – **6 rm** 57.13/88.88 **st.** – SB.

BALLYFERRITER (Baile an Fheirtéaraigh) *Kerry* 923 A 11 – ✉ *Dingle.*

Ceann Sibeal ☎ *(066) 9156255.*

Dublin 226 – Killarney 53 – Limerick 104.

Smerwick Harbour, Gallarus Cross, East : 2 ¾ m. on R 559 ☎ (066) 9156470, *smerwickharbourhotel@eircom.net, Fax (066) 9156473,* ← – TV P. AE VISA.
restricted opening in winter – **Meals** (bar lunch)/dinner 32 and a la carte 26/36 **st.** 19.00 – **32 rm** 85/128 **st.** – SB.

BALLYHEIGE (Baile Uí Thaidhg) *Kerry* 923 C 10 – *pop. 679.*

Dublin 186 – Limerick 73 – Tralee 11.

White Sands, Main St, ☎ (066) 7133102, *whitesands@eircom.net, Fax (066) 7133357* – TV P. AE VISA
March-7 October – **Meals** (bar lunch Monday-Saturday)/dinner a la carte approx. 17 **st.** 13.33 – **81 rm** 60.95/106.66 **st.** – SB.

BALLYLICKEY (Béal Átha Leice) *Cork* 923 D 12 *Ireland G.* – ✉ *Bantry.*

Env. : *Bantry Bay*★ *– Bantry House*★ *AC, S : 3 m. by R 584.*

Exc. : *Glengarriff*★ *(Garinish Island*★★*, access by boat) NW : 8 m. by N 71 – Healy Pass*★★ *(*←★★*) W : 23 m. by N 71, R 572 and R 574 – Slieve Miskish Mountains (*←★★*) W : 29 m. by N 71 and R 572 – Lauragh (Derreen Gardens*★ *AC) NW : 27 ½ m. by N 71, R 572 and R 574 – Allihies (copper mines*★*) W : 41 ½ m. by N 71, R 572 and R 575 – Garnish Island (*←★*) W : 44 m. by N 71 and R 572.*

Bantry Bay, Donemark ☎ *(027) 50579.*

Dublin 216 – Cork 55 – Killarney 45.

Ballylickey Manor House, ☎ (027) 50071, *ballymh@eircom.net, Fax (027) 50124,* « Extensive gardens », heated, – TV P. AE VISA.
17 March-15 November – **Meals** (dinner only) 40/50 **st.** 28 – **4 rm** 220 **st.**, **5 suites** 254/341 **st.** – SB.

Sea View House, ☎ (027) 50462, *seaviewhousehotel@eircom.net, Fax (027) 51555,* – TV P. AE VISA
mid March-mid November – **Meals** (dinner only and Sunday lunch)/dinner a la carte 21/38 **st.** – **25 rm** 82/180 **st.**

Ardnagashel Lodge without rest., Northwest : 2 ½ m. on N 71 ☎ (027) 51687, P. VISA.
May-September – **3 rm** 44/68 **st.**

Larchwood House with rm, Pearsons Bridge, Northeast : 1 ¾ m. by R 5 ☎ (027) 66181, ≤, « Riverside gardens », – P. MC AE VISA.
closed 1 week Christmas and restricted opening in winter – **Meals** *(closed Sunday)* (dinner only) 36 **t.** 20 – **4 rm** 36/72 **t.**

BALLYLIFFEN (Baile Lifín) *Donegal* 923 J 2 – *pop. 299.*

Rossaor House without rest., ☎ (077) 76498, *rossaor@gofree.indigo Fax (077) 76498*, ≤, – TV P. MC VISA.
February-November – **4 rm** 45/70 **t.**

BALLYMACARBRY (Baile Mhac Cairbre) *Waterford* 923 I 11 *Ireland G. – pop. 381 –* ✉ *Clonm*
Exc. : *W : Nier Valley Scenic Route★★.*
Dublin 118 – Cork 49 – Waterford 39.

Hanora's Cottage , Nire Valley, East : 4 m. by Nire Drive rd and Nire Valley Lakes ☎ (052) 36134, *Fax (052) 36540*, – TV P. MC VISA.
closed 1 week Christmas **Meals** *(closed Sunday dinner)* (booking essential for non-residen a la carte 30/39 **st.** 15.24 – **11 rm** 107.93/215.86 **st.** – SB.

Glasha Farmhouse without rest., Northwest : 2 ½ m. by R 671 ☎ (052) 361 *glasha@eircom.net, Fax (052) 36108*, « Working farm », – TV P. MC VISA
closed December and January – **8 rm** 44.45/88.90.

Cnoc-na-Ri , Nire Valley, East : 3 ¾ m. on Nire Drive rd ☎ (052) 36239, *nharte@irela com*, ≤, – TV P. MC VISA.
closed December and January – **Meals** (by arrangement) 27.94 **st.** – **4 rm** 31.1 63.50 **st.** – SB.

BALLYMOTE (Baile an Mhóta) *Sligo* 923 G 5 – *pop. 994 –* ✉ *Sligo.*
Ballymote, Ballinascarrow ☎ (071) 83158.
Dublin 124 – Longford 48 – Sligo 15.

Mill House without rest., Keenaghan, ☎ (071) 83449, – TV P.
closed 18 December-10 January – **5 rm** 38.50/71.11.

BALLYNABOLA *Wexford* 923 L 10 – *see New Ross.*

BALLYNAHINCH (Baile na hInse) *Galway* 923 C 7 – ✉ *Recess.*
Exc. : *Connemara★★★ – Roundstone★, S : by R 341 – Cashel★, SE : by R 341 and R 340.*
Dublin 140 – Galway 41 – Westport 49.

Ballynahinch Castle , ☎ (095) 31006, *bhinch@iol.ie, Fax (095) 31085*, ≤ Owenmo River and woods, – TV P. MC AE VISA.
closed 3-28 February and 1 week Christmas – **Meals** (bar lunch)/dinner 42 and a la ca approx. 36 **t.** 18.40 – **37 rm** 120/280 **t.**, 3 suites – SB.

BALLYSHANNON (Béal Atha Seanaidh) *Donegal* 923 H 4 – *pop. 2 308.*
Dublin 33 – Donegal 169 – Letterkenny 176 – Sligo 134.

Portnason House without rest., Bundoran Rd, West : 1 m. on N 15 ☎ (072) 52016, *p nasonhouse@oceanfree.net, Fax (072) 52016*, – P. MC VISA
restricted opening in winter – **5 rm** 69.84/139.67.

Dun Na Si without rest., Bundoran Rd, West : 1 m. on N 15 ☎ (072) 52322, *dun-na-s oceanfree.net*, – TV P. MC AE VISA.
closed 21 December-5 January – **7 rm** 40/56 **t.**

BALLYVAUGHAN (Baile Uí Bheacháin) *Clare* 923 E 8 *Ireland G. – pop. 257.*
Env. : *The Burren★★ (Cliffs of Moher★★★, Scenic Routes★★, Poulnabrone Dolmen★, Aillw Cave★ AC (Waterfall★★), Corcomroe Abbey★, Kilfenora Crosses★).*
Dublin 149 – Ennis 34 – Galway 29.

Gregans Castle , Southwest : 3 ¾ m. on N 67 ☎ (065) 707 7005, *res@gregans Fax (065) 707 7111*, ≤ countryside and Galway Bay, – P. MC AE VISA.
closed Christmas-mid February – **Meals** (bar lunch)/dinner a la carte 32/50 **st.** 21 – **18 r** 176/270 **st.**, 4 suites – SB.

Hyland's, (065) 7077037, *hylands@tinet.ie, Fax (065) 7077131* – rm, TV P. MC AE D VISA.
closed December-14 February – **Meals** (bar lunch)/dinner a la carte 22/31 **st.** 12.00 – **30 rm** 91/132 **st.** – SB.

Drumcreehy House, Northeast : 1 ¼ m. on N 67 (065) 7077377, *b&b@drumcreehy house.com, Fax (065) 7077379,* ←, – TV P. MC VISA
March-October and restricted opening in winter – **Meals** (by arrangement) (set menu only) 22 **t.** 16 – **10 rm** 54/76 **t.**

Rusheen Lodge without rest., Southwest : ¾ m. on N 67 (065) 7077092, *rusheenl @iol.ie, Fax (065) 7077152,* – TV P. MC VISA.
13 February-October – **8 rm** 63.49/152.37 **st.**

Cappabhaile House without rest., Southwest : 1 m. on N 67 (065) 7077260, *cappab haile@oceanfree.net, Fax (065) 7077300,* ←, – TV P. MC VISA.
March-November – **8 rm** 59/78 **st.**

BALTIMORE (Dún na Séad) *Cork* 923 D 13 *Ireland G.* – *pop. 232.*
Exc. : *Sherkin Island★ (by ferry).*
Dublin 214 – Cork 59 – Killarney 77.

Baltimore Harbour, Lifeboat Rd, (028) 20361, *info@bhrhotel.ie, Fax (028) 20466,* , , , , – TV P – 130. MC AE D VISA.
17 March-November – **Meals** (bar lunch)/dinner 31.75 **st.** 17.78 – **58 rm** 101.60/152.40 **st.**, 6 suites – SB.

Casey's of Baltimore, East : ½ m. on R 595 (028) 20197, *caseys@eircom.net, Fax (028) 20509,* ← – rest, TV P. MC AE D VISA.
closed 2-8 March, 5-18 October and 21-27 December – **Meals** 30/35 (dinner) and a la carte 29.50/32.50 **t.** 16 – **14 rm** 91/122 **t.** – SB.

Customs House, (028) 20200 –
closed October-March, Monday and Tuesday – **Meals** - Seafood - (booking essential Sunday) (dinner only) 30 **st.** 13.

BANDON (Droichead na Bandan) *Cork* 923 F 12 – *pop. 1 697.*
18 *Bandon, Castlebernard (023) 41111.*
Dublin 174 – Cork 19.

St Anne's without rest., Clonakilty Rd, (023) 44239, *stannesbandon@eircom.net, Fax (023) 44239,* – TV P. MC VISA.
closed Christmas – **6 rm** 38.50/56 **st.**

BANSHA (An Bháinseach) *Tipperary* 923 H 10 – *pop. 288.*
Dublin 103 – Cork 55 – Limerick 30 – Waterford 48.

Bansha House , (062) 54194, *banshahouse@eircom.net, Fax (062) 54215,* , – P. MC VISA.
closed 20-28 December – **Meals** 22 **st.** 15.23 – **8 rm** 43/72 **st.** – SB.

BANTRY (Beanntraí) *Cork* 923 D 12 *Ireland G.* – *pop. 2 936.*
See : *Bantry House★ AC (Bantry Bay★).*
Exc. : *Gougane Barra Forest Park★, NE : 15 m. by R 584.*
Old Courthouse (027) 50229 (summer only).
Dublin 210 – Cork 56 – Killarney 53.

Bantry House without rest., (027) 50047, *info@bantryhouse.ie, Fax (027) 50795,* ←, « Georgian country house, antiques, formal gardens and extensive parkland », , – P. MC AE VISA.
March-October – **8 rm** 140/240 **st.**

BARNA (Bearna) *Galway* 923 E 8.
Dublin 141 – Galway 6.

Twelve Pins, on R 336 (091) 592368, *the12pinshotel@eircom.net, Fax (091) 592485,* – rest, TV P. MC AE D VISA JCB.
closed 25 December – **Meals** (bar lunch Monday-Saturday)/dinner a la carte 16/24 **t.** 8.25 – 6.29 – **18 rm** 62.22 **t.**

O'Grady's on the Pier, (091) 592223, *Fax (091) 590677* – MC AE VISA
closed 2 weeks Christmas – **Meals** - Seafood - (booking essential) (dinner only and lunch Saturday and Sunday) a la carte 23/42 **t.** 15.87.

BARRELLS CROSS *Cork – see Kinsale.*

BEAUFORT (Lios an Phúca) *Kerry* 923 D 11 – *see Killarney.*

BETTYSTOWN (Baile an Bhiataigh) *Meath* 923 N 6.

Laytown & Bettystown (041) 9827170.
Dublin 43 – Drogheda 6 – Dundalk 28.

Bacchus at the Coastguard, Bayview, (041) 9828251, *Fax (041) 9828236* ≤ Bettystown Bay, – P. VISA
closed 1-15 March, Monday in winter and Sunday dinner – **Meals** (dinner only and Sunday lunch)/dinner 25.50/38 and a la carte 35.50/44 **t.** 16.50.

BIRR (Biorra) *Offaly* 923 I 8 *Ireland G. – pop. 3 355.*

See : *Town★ – Birr Castle Demesne★★ AC (Telescope★★).*
Exc. : *Roscrea★ (Damer House★ AC) S : 12 m. by N 62 – Slieve Bloom Mountains★, E : 13 m by R 440 – Clonfert Cathedral★ (West doorway★★), NW : 15 m. by R 439, R 356 and minor roads.*
The Glenns (0509) 20082.
Main St (0509) 20110 (May-September).
Athlone 28 – Dublin 87 – Kilkenny 49 – Limerick 49.

County Arms, Railway Rd, South : ½ m. on N 62 (0509) 20791, *countyarmshotel@tinet.ie, Fax (0509) 21234,* , squash – P – 300. VISA JCB.
closed 25 December – **Meals** a la carte 23/27 **st.** 22 – **24 rm** 64/125 **st.**

Dooly's, Emmet Sq, (0509) 20032, *doolyshotel@esatclear.ie, Fax (0509) 21332* – – 300. VISA.
closed 25 December – **Meals** (bar lunch Monday-Saturday)/dinner 29.20/31.74 and a la carte 15.81/24.76 **st.** 11.00 – **18 rm** 46.98/91.42 **st.** – SB.

The Maltings, Castle St, (0509) 21345, *themaltingsbirr@eircom.net, Fax (0509) 22073* – P. VISA.
Meals 12/25 and dinner a la carte 10/19.50 **st.** 12.70 – **13 rm** 38/63.50 **st.** – SB.

Spinners Town House, Castle St, (0509) 21673, *spinners@indigo.ie Fax (0509) 21672,* , « Minimalist interior » – , rest, . VISA.
Spinners Bistro : **Meals** *(closed Monday)* (dinner only) a la carte 16/28 **st.** 12.70 – **13 rm** 44.44/63.49 **st.** – SB.

Emmet Guest House without rest., Emmet Sq, (0509) 20395, *Fax (0509) 21436* –
closed 10 December-February – **6 rm** 38.09/63.49 **s.**

at Kinnitty *East : 8¼ m. on R 440 – Birr.*

Kinnitty Castle , East : 1 m. on R 440 (0509) 37318, *kinnittycastle@eircom.net Fax (0509) 37284,* « 12C origins », , , , , – P – 200. VISA.
Meals (bar lunch Monday-Saturday)/dinner 38.09/63.49 **t.** 22.86 – 16 – **37 rm** 146/330 **t.** – SB.

BLACKLION (An Blaic) *Cavan* 923 I 5 – *pop. 153.*

Blacklion, Toam (072) 53024.
Dublin 121 – Drogheda 106 – Enniskillen 12.

Mac Nean House & Bistro with rm, (072) 53022, *Fax (072) 53404* – rest, . VISA.
closed 1 week October and 1 week Christmas – **Meals** *(closed Wednesday October-May Monday and Tuesday)* (dinner only and Sunday lunch)/dinner 21/34.65 **t.** 16.51 – **5 rm** 32/66 **t.** – SB.

BLACKROCK (An Charraig Dhubh) *Dublin* 923 N 8 – *see Dublin.*

BLACKWATER *Wexford* 923 M 10.

Dublin 73 – Kilkenny 57 – Waterfotd 47 – Wexford 13.

Blackwater Lodge, The Square, (053) 27222, *blackwaterlodge@eircom.net Fax (053) 27496* – rm, P. VISA.
Meals (bar lunch)/dinner 13.97 and a la carte 14.16/30.45 **st.** 16.44 – **12 rm** 50.79/114.28 **st.** – SB.

BLARNEY (An Bhlarna) *Cork* 923 G 12 *Ireland G. – pop. 1 963 – ✉ Cork.*
See : *Blarney Castle★★ AC – Blarney House★ AC.*
(021) 4381624.
Dublin 167 – Cork 6.

Blarney Park, (021) 4385281, *info@blarneypark.com, Fax (021) 4381506,* rm, rest, – 280. *VISA.*
closed 23-27 December – **Meals** (dinner only) 27.30 **st.** 17.78 – **91 rm** 115/180 **st.** – SB.

Killarney House without rest., Station Rd, Northeast : 1 m. (021) 4381841, *killarney houseblarney@eircom.net, Fax (021) 4381841,*
6 rm 50/62.

at Tower *West : 2 m. on R 617 – ✉ Cork.*

Maranatha Country House without rest., East : ½ m. on R 617 (021) 4385102, *info@maranathacountryhouse.com, Fax (021) 4382978,* *VISA*
15 March-November – **6 rm** 65/90 **st.**

Ashlee Lodge without rest., (021) 4385346, *info@ashleelodge.com, Fax (021) 4385726,* *VISA.*
6 rm 88.88/126.97 **st.**

BLESSINGTON (Baile Coimín) *Wicklow* 923 M 8 *Ireland G. – pop. 1 860.*
Env. : *Russborough House★★★, SW : 2½ m. by N 81.*
Dublin 19 – Kilkenny 56 – Wexford 70.

Tulfarris H. and Golf Resort, South : 6 m. by N 81 (045) 867600, *info@tulfarris.com, Fax (045) 867565,* « Part 17C », rm, rest, – 150. *VISA.*
Meals 38/45 (dinner) and a la carte 20/38 **st.** 18 – **49 rm** 109.22/139.70 **st.**, 30 suites 207.01 **st.** – SB.

Si vous cherchez un hôtel tranquille, consultez d'abord les cartes de l'introduction ou repérez dans le texte les établissements indiqués avec le signe ou .

BORRISOKANE *Tipperary* 923 H 8/9 – *pop. 850.*
Dublin 101 – Galway 53 – Limerick 37.

Dancer Cottage, Curraghmore, West : 2 m. by Ballinderry rd (067) 27414, *dcr@eircom.net, Fax (067) 27414,* *VISA.*
restricted opening in winter – **Meals** (by arrangement) (communal dining) 21.50 **st.** – **4 rm** 32/56 **st.** – SB.

BRAY (Bré) *Wicklow* 923 N 8 *Ireland G. – pop. 25 252.*
Env. : *Powerscourt★★ (Waterfall★★ AC) W : 4 m. – Killruddery House and Gardens★ AC, S : 2 m. by R 761.*
Exc. : *Wicklow Mountains★★.*
Woodbrook, Dublin Rd (01) 282 4799 – Old Conna, Ferndale Rd (01) 282 6055 – Ravenswell Rd (01) 286 2484.
Dublin 13 – Wicklow 20.

Woodland Court, Southern Cross, South : 2 ½ m. by R 761 on Greystones rd (01) 276 0258, *info@woodlandscourthotel.com, Fax (01) 276 0298* – rest, rest, – 35. *VISA.*
closed 23 December-2 January – **Meals** (bar lunch)/dinner 24.76/32.38 **st.** 17.14 – 10.79 – **65 rm** 95.23/107.93 **st.**

Tree of Idleness, Seafront, (01) 286 3498, *Fax (01) 282 8183* – *VISA*
closed 2 weeks September, 1 week Christmas and Monday – **Meals** - Greek-Cypriot - (dinner only) a la carte 31.35/42.55 **st.** 19.68.

BUNBEG (An Bun Beag) *Donegal* 923 H 2 *Ireland G. – pop. 1 400 (inc. Derrybeg).*
Exc. : *The Rosses★, S : by R 257.*
Dublin 195 – Donegal 66 – Londonderry 55.

Ostan Gweedore, (075) 31177, *ostangweedore@ireland.com, Fax (075) 31726,* Gweedore Bay, – rest, – 200. *VISA*
restricted opening in winter – **Meals** (bar lunch)/dinner a la carte 28/36 **st.** 15.24 – **36 rm** 69.84/152.37 **st.**, 3 suites – SB.

BUNDORAN (Bun Dobhráin) *Donegal* 923 H 4 – *pop. 1 707.*
Main St ☏ *(072) 41350 (March-October).*
Dublin 161 – Donegal 17 – Sligo 23.

Grand Central, ☏ (072) 42722, *Fax (072) 42656* – rm, – 200. VISA.
Meals 9.95/13.95 and dinner a la carte 4.95 – **62 rm** 50.00/90.00 **st.** – SB.

Holyrood, Main St, ☏ (072) 41232, *hrood@indigo.ie, Fax (072) 41100* – rest, – 550. VISA.
closed Christmas – **Meals** (bar lunch)/dinner 10.80/25.40 and a la carte 12.08/26.04 st 15.88 – **99 rm** 80/122 **t.** – SB.

Allingham Arms, ☏ (072) 41075, *allinghamarmshotel1@eircom.net, Fax (072) 41171* – – 400. VISA.
weekends only in January and closed 25 December – **Meals** 15.24/25.39 and dinner a la carte 17.72/26.58 **st.** – **117 rm** 66.46/107.59 **st.** – SB.

Fitzgerald's, ☏ (072) 41336, *info@fitzgeraldshotel.com, Fax (072) 42121,* ← – VISA
closed 25 November-31 December – **Meals** *(closed Monday and Tuesday)* (bar lunch)/dinner a la carte 23.40/29.40 **st.** 15 – **16 rm** 70/114 **st.** – SB.

Bay View without rest., Main St, ☏ (072) 41296, *Fax (072) 41147,* ←, – VISA
16 rm 50/65 **st.**

Leitrim House without rest., Kinlough Rd, ☏ (072) 41904, *leitrimhouse@ireland.com Fax (072) 41452,* – VISA.
March-October – **7 rm** 31.74/50.78 **st.**

Le Chateaubrianne, Sligo Rd, West : 1 m. on N 5 ☏ (072) 42160, *Fax (072) 42160* – VISA
closed January, Sunday dinner and Monday – **Meals** (dinner only and Sunday lunch)/dinner 30.00/35.00 **t.** 15.00.

BUNRATTY (Bun Raite) *Clare* 923 F 9 *Ireland G.*
See : *Town*★★ – *Bunratty Castle*★★.
Dublin 129 – Ennis 15 – Limerick 8.

Fitzpatrick Bunratty, ☏ (061) 361177, *info@bunratty.fitzpatricks.com Fax (061) 471252,* – rm, – 1200. VISA.
closed 24 to 26 December – **Meals** *(closed Saturday lunch)* 17.71/20.25 (lunch) and dinner a la carte 24.63/38.02 **t.** 16.44 – 13.33 – **115 rm** 152.36/241.25 **st.** – SB.

Bunratty Manor, ☏ (061) 707984, *bunrattymanor@eircom.net, Fax (061) 360588,* – VISA.
closed 25 December-January and February – **Meals** *(closed Monday)* (dinner only) a la carte 19.45/28.00 – **14 rm** 79.00/118.00 **t.**

Bunratty Grove without rest., Castle Rd, North : 1 ½ m. ☏ (061) 369579, *bunrattygrove@eircom.net, Fax (061) 369561,* – VISA.
April-October – **9 rm** 45.00/82.55 **st.**

Bunratty Lodge without rest., North : 1 ½ m. ☏ (061) 369402, *reservations@bunrattlodge.com, Fax (061) 369363,* – VISA.
March-October – **6 rm** 60.00/81.26 **st.**

Shannon View without rest., Northwest : 1 m. on N 18 (south-eastbound carriageway completing U-turn at junction with R 471 ☏ (061) 364056, *Fax (061) 364056,* – VISA.
April-October – **4 rm** 35.55/57.14 **st.**

Muses, Bunratty House Mews, ☏ (061) 364082, *muses@oceanfree.net, Fax (061) 364350* – VISA
closed Christmas, January, Sunday, Monday and Bank Holidays – **Meals** (dinner only a la carte 29.65/41.08 **t.** 13.34.

BUTLERSTOWN (Baile an Bhuitléaraigh) *Cork* 923 F 13 *Ireland G.* – *Bandon.*
Env. : *Courtmacsherry*★, *N : 3 m.*
Exc. : *Carbery Coast*★.
Dublin 193 – Cork 32.

Butlerstown House without rest., North : ½ m. ☏ (023) 40137, *mail@butlerstownhouse.com, Fax (023) 40137,* ←, « 18C », – VISA
March-October, Minimum 2 night stay – **4 rm** 52.50/85.00 **st.**

BUTLERSTOWN (Baile an Bhuitléaraigh) *Waterford – see Waterford.*

CAHER (An Chathair) *Tipperary* 923 I 10 – *see Cahir.*

CAHERDANIEL (Cathair Dónall) *Kerry* 923 B 12 *Ireland G.* – ✉ *Killarney.*

Exc. : *Iveragh Peninsula*** *(Ring of Kerry**)* – *Derrynane National Historic Park*** – *Staigue Fort*, E : 5 m. by N 70 and minor rd* – *Sneem*, E : 12 m. by N 70.*

Dublin 238 – Killarney 48.

Iskeroon without rest., West : 5 m. by N 70 turning right at Scarrif Inn, following signs to Bunavallla Pier taking left turn at junction then turning left onto track immediately before pier (066) 9475119, *info@iskeroon.com, Fax (066) 9475488*, ≤, – P. VISA.

March-September – **3 rm** 100.00 **s.**

Derrynane Bay House, West : ½ m. on N 70 (066) 9475404, *derrynanebayhouse@eircom.net, Fax (066) 9475436*, ≤, – P. VISA.

15 March-23 December – **Meals** 22.00 **s.** – **6 rm** 35.00/56.00 **s.**

CAHERLISTRANE (Cathair Loistreáin) *Galway* 923 E 7.

Dublin 159 – Ballina 46 – Galway 26.

Lisdonagh House, Northwest : 1½ m. by Shrule rd (093) 31163, *cooke@lisdonagh com, Fax (093) 31528*, ≤, « Early Georgian country house », – P. AE VISA.

Easter-late October – **Meals** (booking essential to non-residents) (dinner only) 40 **t.** 20.32 – **10 rm** 150/230, 2 suites.

CAHERSIVEEN (Cathair Saidhbhín) *Kerry* 923 B 12.

Dublin 221 – Killarney 40.

The Point, Renard Point, Southwest : 1 ¾ m. by N 70 (066) 9472165, *Fax (066) 9472165*, ≤ Valencia Harbour and Island, – P

closed late October-April, first Monday in August and Sunday lunch – **Meals** - Seafood - (bookings not accepted) a la carte 8/18.

CAHIR/CAHER (An Chathair) *Tipperary* 923 I 10 *Ireland G.* – *pop. 2 236.*

See : *Caher Castle** AC.*

Env. : *Swiss Cottage* AC, S : 1 m. by R 670.*

Exc. : *Clonmel* (County Museum*, St. Mary's Church*) E : 10 m. by N 24.*

Cahir Park, Kilcommon (052) 41474.

Castle St (052) 41453 (May-September).

Dublin 114 – Limerick 39 – Cork 47 – Waterford 39.

Cahir House, The Square, (052) 42727, *cahirhousehotel@eircom.net, Fax (052) 42727* – rest, P – 500. AE VISA.

closed 25 December and Good Friday – **Meals** *(closed Sunday lunch)* (bar lunch)/dinner 27.50/35 and a la carte 28/41 **st.** 13.97 – **41 rm** 80/100 **st.** – SB.

Clifford's at The Bell, First floor, 2 Pearse St, off the Square, (052) 43232 – VISA JCB

closed 2-5 January, 25 December, Sunday and Monday – **Meals** (booking essential) (dinner only) 29.20 and a la carte 34/45 **t.** 18.41.

CAMP (An Com) *Kerry* 923 C 11 – ✉ *Tralee.*

Dublin 195 – Killarney 44 – Limerick 76 – Tralee 10.

Barnagh Bridge without rest., Cappaclough, West : 2 m. on R 560 (066) 7130145, *bbguest@eircom.net, Fax (066) 7130299*, ≤, – P. AE VISA.

March-October – **5 rm** 50.00/80.00 **t.**

CAPPOQUIN (Ceapach Choinn) *Waterford* 923 I 11 *Ireland G.* – *pop. 780.*

Env. : *Lismore* (Lismore Castle Gardens* AC, St. Carthage's Cathedral*), W : 4 m. by N 72 – Mount Melleray Abbey*, N : 4 m. by R 669.*

Exc. : *The Gap* (≤*) NW : 9 m. by R 669.*

Dublin 136 – Cork 31 – Waterford 40.

Richmond House with rm, Southeast : ½ m. on N 72 (058) 54278, *info@richmondhouse.net, Fax (058) 54988*, « Georgian house », – rest, P. AE VISA.

closed 23 December-20 January – **Meals** *(closed Sunday and Monday to non-residents)* (dinner only) 43.00 **t.** 15.60 – **9 rm** 89.00/203.00 **t.** – SB.

CARAGH LAKE (Loch Cárthaí) *Kerry* 923 C 11 *Ireland G.*
See : Lough Caragh★.
Exc. : Iveragh Peninsula★★ (Ring of Kerry★★).
Dooks, Glenbeigh ✆ (066) 9768205.
Dublin 212 – Killarney 22 – Tralee 25.

Caragh Lodge, ✆ (066) 9769115, *caraghl@iol.ie, Fax (066) 9769316,* ≤, « Victorian country house in extensive gardens on shores of Lough Caragh », – rest, P. VISA.
mid April-mid October – **Meals** (booking essential to non-residents) (dinner only) a la carte 31.00/47.25 **t.** 20.00 – **14 rm** 160.00/205.00 **st.**, 1 suite – SB.

Ard-Na-Sidhe, ✆ (066) 9769105, *reception@ardnasidhe@kih.liebher.com Fax (066) 9769282,* « Elizabethan style country house on shores of Lough Caragh », – rest, P. VISA.
May-September – **Meals** (booking essential to non-residents) (dinner only) 54 **st.** 27 – 17 – **19 rm** 228/378 **st.** – SB.

Carrig House, ✆ (066) 9769100, *info@carrighouse.com, Fax (066) 9769166,* ≤ Lough Caragh, « Lough-side setting », – rm, P. VISA.
March-November – **Meals** (booking essential to non-residents) (dinner only) a la carte 20.00/33.00 14.95 – **16 rm** 90.00/250.00 **t.** – SB.

CARLINGFORD (Cairlinn) *Louth* 923 N 5 *Ireland G. – pop. 647.*
See : Town★.
Exc. : Windy Gap★, NW : 8 m. by R 173 – Proleek Dolmen★, SW : 9 m. by R 173.
Dublin 66 – Dundalk 13.

McKevitt's Village, Market Sq, ✆ (042) 9373116, *Fax (042) 9373144,* – TV. VISA.
closed 25 December – **Meals** (bar lunch)/dinner 35.00 **st.** 14.00 – **13 rm** 70.00/140.00 **st.** – SB.

Jordan's, Newry St, ✆ (042) 9373223, *jordans@iol.ie, Fax (042) 9373875* – TV. VISA.
Meals – (see ***The Restaurant*** below) – **5 rm** 69.84/114.28 **st.**

Beaufort House without rest., ✆ (042) 9373879, *michaelcaine@beauforthouse.net Fax (042) 9373878,* ≤, – TV P. VISA.
6 rm 50/185 **st.**

The Restaurant (at Jordan's), Newry St, ✆ (042) 9373223, *jordans@iol.ie Fax (042) 9373875* – VISA
Meals 17.78 (lunch) and dinner a la carte 29/32 **t.** 16.25.

CARLOW (Ceatharlach) *Carlow* 923 L 9 – *pop. 11 721.*
Carlow, Deer Park, Dublin Rd ✆ (0503) 31695.
College St ✆ (0503) 31554.
Dublin 50 – Kilkenny 23 – Wexford 47.

Seven Oaks, Athy Rd, ✆ (0503) 31308, *sevenoak@eircom.net, Fax (0503) 32155,* – TV P – 300. VISA.
closed 25 December – **Meals** (carving lunch Saturday) 17.71/35.55 and dinner a la carte **t** 13.33 – **39 rm** 139.67 **t.** – SB.

Barrowville Town House without rest., Kilkenny Rd, South : ½ m. on N 9 ✆ (0503) 43324, *Fax (0503) 41953,* – TV P. VISA.
7 rm 45.00/70.00 **st.**

Ballyvergal House without rest., Dublin Rd, North : 3 m. on N 9 ✆ (0503) 43634 *ballyvergal@indigo.ie, Fax (0503) 40386* – TV P. VISA
closed 22-31 December – **10 rm** 34.00/63.00 **st.**

CARNA *Galway* 923 C 8 *Ireland G.*
Exc. : Connemara★★★ – Cashel★, N : by R 340.
Dublin 186 – Cork 169 – Galway 48 – Limerick 112.

Carna Bay, ✆ (095) 32255, *carnabay.iol.ie, Fax (095) 32530,* ≤, – rest, TV P. VISA
closed 23-27 December – **Meals** (bar lunch Monday to Saturday)/dinner a la carte 17.00/30.00 **t.** 17.78 – **26 rm** 88.88/126.97 **st.** – SB.

The Guide is updated annually so renew your Guide every year.

CARNDONAGH (Carn Dombnach) *Donegal* 923 K 2 – *pop. 1 580.*
Dublin 163 – Donegal 68 – Letterkenny 39 – Sligo 104.

The Corncrake, Milbrae, (077) 74534 –
closed Monday and restricted opening in winter – **Meals** (booking essential) (dinner only) a la carte 25/33 **t.** 15.23.

CARNE *Wexford* 923 M 11.
Dublin 105 – Waterford 51 – Wexford 13.

Lobster Pot, (053) 31110, *Fax (053) 31401* – P. MC AE VISA
closed January, 25 December, Monday September-May except Bank Holidays – **Meals** - Seafood - (light lunch)/dinner a la carte 17.78/40.50 **st.** 15.24.

CARRICKCARNON *Louth – see Dundalk.*

CARRICKMACROSS (Carraig Mhachaire Rois) *Monaghan* 923 L 6 *Ireland G. – pop. 1 926.*
Env. : *Dún a' Rí Forest Park*★, *SW : 5 m. by R 179.*
18 *Nuremore (042) 9664016.*
Dublin 57 – Dundalk 14.

Nuremore, South : 1 m. on N 2 (042) 9661438, *nuremore@eircom.net, Fax (042) 9661853*, ≤, , , , 18, , , , squash – , rm, TV P – 600. MC AE VISA.
Meals – (see ***The Restaurant*** below) – **72 rm** 140/260 **t.** – SB.

The Restaurant (at Nuremore H.), South : 1 m. on N 2 (042) 9661438, *Fax (042) 9661853* – P. MC AE VISA
closed Saturday lunch – **Meals** 19.00/45.00 and dinner a la carte 38.00/45.00 **st.** 18.00.

CARRICK-ON-SHANNON (Cora Droma Rúisc) *Leitrim* 923 H 6 *Ireland G. – pop. 1 868.*
See : *Town*★.
Exc. : *Lough Rynn Demesne*★.
9 *Carrick-on-Shannon, Woodbrook (079) 67015.*
Old Barrel Store (078) 20170 (April-October).
Dublin 97 – Ballina 50 – Galway 74 – Roscommon 26 – Sligo 34.

The Landmark, on N 4 (078) 22222, *landmarkhotel@eircom.net, Fax (078) 22233*, ≤, , , – TV P – 500. MC AE VISA.
closed 24-25 December – **Meals** (carvery lunch)/dinner a la carte approx. 34 **st.** 19.05 – **50 rm** 115.50/208 **st.** – SB.

Hollywell without rest., Liberty Hill, (078) 21124, *holywell@esatbiz.com, Fax (078) 21124*, ≤, « Part 18C country house », – P.
closed 18 December-4 January – **4 rm** 65/102 **t.**

CARRICK-ON-SUIR (Carraig na Siûire) *Tipperary* 923 J 10 *Ireland G. – pop. 5 172.*
Env. : *Ormond Castle*★ *– Ahenny High Crosses*★, *N : by R 697.*
9 *Garravone (051) 640047.*
Dublin 95 – Cork 68 – Limerick 62 – Waterford 16.

The Bell and Salmon Arms, 95-97 Main St, (051) 645555, *bellsalmon@eircom.net, Fax (051) 641293* – TV P. MC AE VISA
closed 25 December – **Meals** (bar lunch Monday-Saturday)/dinner 22.79 and a la carte 16/26 **t.** 14.92 – **13 rm** 45/75 **st.** – SB.

CARRIGALINE (Carraig Uí Leighin) *Cork* 923 G 12 – *pop. 7 827.*
18 *Fernhill (021) 372226.*
Dublin 163 – Cork 9.

Carrigaline Court, Cork Rd, (021) 4852100, *carrigcourt@eircom.net, Fax (021) 4371103*, , , – , rest, TV P – 300. MC AE VISA.
closed 25 December – ***The Kingfisher :*** **Meals** (carvery lunch Monday-Saturday)/dinner a la carte 24.70/32.95 **t.** 14.60 – **48 rm** 82.53/165.07 **t.**, 2 suites – SB.

Glenwood House without rest., Ballinrea Rd, North : ¾ m. by R 611 (Cork rd) (021) 4373878, *glenwoodhouse@eircom.net, Fax (021) 4373878*, – TV P. MC VISA
closed 20 December-7 January – **14 rm** 55.00/90.00 **st.**

Raffeen Lodge without rest., Ringaskiddy Rd, Monkstown, Northeast : 2 ½ m. by R 61 and N 28 off R 610 ☎ (021) 4371632, *Fax (021) 4371632*, – [TV] [P]. [MC] VISA.
closed 23 December-3 January – **6 rm** 38.00/63.50 **st.**

Shannonpark House without rest., Cork Rd, North : 1 m. on R 611 ☎ (021) 437 209
– [TV] [P]. VISA.
5 rm 31.74/63.48.

CARRIGANS (An Carraigain) *Donegal* 923 J 3 – *pop. 185.*

Dublin 140 – Donegal 41 – Letterkenny 143 – Sligo 77.

Mount Royd without rest., ☎ (074) 40163, *jmartin@mountroyd.com, Fax (074) 4040*
– [TV] [P].
4 rm 38.50/50 **st.**

CASHEL (An Caiseal) *Galway* 923 C 7 *Ireland G.*

See : *Town★.*
Exc. : *Connemara★★★.*
Dublin 173 – Galway 41.

Cashel House , ☎ (095) 31001, *info@cashel-house.com, Fax (095) 31077*, ←, « Country house and gardens », , – rm, [TV] [P]. [MC] AE VISA
closed 10 January-10 February – **Meals** (booking essential to non-residents) (bar lunch) dinner 42.00/45.00 **t.** 20.25 – **32 rm** 110.00/280.00 **t.** – SB.

Zetland Country House , ☎ (095) 31111, *zetland@iol.ie, Fax (095) 31117*, ← Cashel Bay, « Gardens », , – rest, [TV] [P]. [MC] AE VISA
April-October – **Meals** (bar lunch)/dinner 45.00 **t.** 23.00 – **19 rm** 125.00/180.00 **t.** – SB

CASHEL (Caiseal) *Tipperary* 923 I 10 *Ireland G.* – *pop. 2 346.*

See : *Town★★★ – Rock of Cashel★★★ AC – Cormac's Chapel★★ – Round Tower★ – Museum★ – Cashel Palace Gardens★ – GPA Bolton Library★ AC.*
Env. : *Holy Cross Abbey★★, N : 9 m. by R 660 – Athassel Abbey★, W : 5 m. by N 74.*
Town Hall ☎ (062) 61333 (April-September).
Dublin 101 – Cork 60 – Kilkenny 34 – Limerick 36 – Waterford 44.

Cashel Palace, Main St, ☎ (062) 62707, *reception@cashel-palace.ie, Fax (062) 6152* « Former Archbishop's palace, extensive gardens », – [TV] [P] – 75. [MC] AE VISA.
closed 24-26 December – **Meals** a la carte 32/44 **t.** 15.87 – **23 rm** 152.36/349.17 **st.**

Ros Guill House without rest., Northeast : ¾ m. by R 688 on R 691 ☎ (062) 6269 *Fax (062) 61507*, – [P]. [MC] VISA.
May-late October – **5 rm** 44.00/63.50 **st.**

Chez Hans, Rockside, ☎ (062) 61177, « Converted synod hall » – [P]. [MC] VISA
closed 2 weeks January, 1 week September, Christmas, Sunday and Monday – **Meals** (dinner only) 19.68/24.70 a la carte 33.01/43.17 **t.** 20.95.

CASTLEBALDWIN (Béal Átha na gCarraigíní) *Sligo* 923 G 5 *Ireland G.* – ✉ *Boyle (Roscommon)*

Env. : *Carrowkeel Megalithic Cemetery (←★★), S : 3 m.*
Exc. : *Arigna Scenic Drive★, N : 2 m. by N 4 – Lough Key Forest Park★ AC, SE : 10 m. by N 4 – View of Lough Allen★, N : 9 m. by N 4 on R 280 – Mountain Drive★, N : 6 m. on N 4 – Boyle Abbey★ AC, SE : 8 m. by N 4 – King House★, SE : 8 m. by N 4.*
Dublin 118 – Longford 42 – Sligo 15.

Cromleach Lodge , Ballindoon, Southeast : 3 ½ m. ☎ (071) 65155, *info@cromleach.com, Fax (071) 65455*, ← Lough Arrow and Carrowkeel Cairns, , – [TV] [P]. [MC] AE VISA
February-October – **Meals** (dinner only) 55 **t.** 19 – **10 rm** 145/330 **t.** – SB.

Hillcrest , Ballindoon, Southeast : 4 ½ m. ☎ (071) 65559, ← Lough Arrow and Carrowkeel Cairns – [P]. [MC] VISA.
March-October – **Meals** (by arrangement) 16.50 – **4 rm** 30/50.

CASTLEBAR (Caisléan an Bharraigh) *Mayo* 923 E 6 *Ireland G.* – *pop. 6 585.*

Env. : *Ballintubber Abbey★★, S : 8 m. by N 84.*
Exc. : *Errew Abbey★, N : 22 m. by R 310, R 315 and minor rd.*
Castlebar, Hawthorn Av., Rocklands ☎ (094) 21649.
Linenhall St ☎ (094) 21207 (April-September).
Dublin 161 – Galway 49 – Sligo 47.

Breaffy House , Southeast : 3 m. on N 60 ☎ (094) 22033, *cro@lynchotels.com*, *Fax (094) 22276*, , , – – 300. . – **Meals** (bar lunch Monday-Saturday)/dinner 31.74/38.09 and a la carte 19.00/30.00 **st.** 17.78 – **60 rm** 117.80/317.50 **st.** – SB.

CASTLEBELLINGHAM (Baile an Ghearlánaigh) *Louth* 923 M 6 – *pop. 792 (inc. Kilsaran).*

Dublin 43 – Dundalk 8 – Drogheda 14.

Bellingham Castle , ☎ (042) 9372176, *bellinghamcastle@eircom.net*, *Fax (042) 9372766*, , – – 650.
closed 24 and 25 December – **Meals** 15.24 (lunch) and dinner a la carte 19.87/31.75 **st.** 13.90 – **21 rm** 63.50/105.00 **st.** – SB.

CASTLEDERMOT (Díseart Diarmada) *Kildare* 923 L 9 *Ireland G.* – *pop. 733.*

Env. : *Castledermot High Crosses★ – Moone High Cross★, N : by N 9.*

Exc. : *Carlow Cathedral (Marble Monument★) NE : 7 m. by N 9.*

Dublin 44 – Kilkenny 30 – Wexford 54.

Kilkea Castle , Kilkea, Northwest : 3 m. by R 418 ☎ (0503) 45156, *kilkea@iol.ie*, *Fax (0503) 45187*, ←, « Part 12C castle, gardens », , , , , , , – – 200. .
closed 24-27 December – **Meals** 30.15/52.96 26.07 – **29 rm** 195.57/260.76 **t.**, 7 suites – SB.

CASTLEKNOCK (Caisleán Cnucha) *Dublin* 923 ㊱ – *see Dublin.*

CASTLELYONS (Caisleán Ó Liatháin) *Cork* 923 H 11 – *pop. 164.*

Dublin 136 – Cork 19 – Killarney 65 – Limerick 40.

Ballyvolane House , Southeast : 3 ½ m. by Midleton rd on Britway rd ☎ (025) 36349, *ballyvol@iol.ie*, *Fax (025) 36781*, ←, « 18C Italianate mansion, extensive parklands », , – . .
closed 23 to 31 December – **Meals** (by arrangement) (communal dining) 36.00 **t.** 18.50 – **6 rm** 95.00/150.00 **t.**

CASTLEMARTYR (Baile na Martra) *Cork* 923 H 12 – *pop. 484* – ✉ *Midleton.*

Dublin 154 – Cork 19 – Limerick 76 – Waterford 55.

Old Parochial House without rest., on R 632 ☎ (021) 466 7454, *enquiries@oldparochial.com*, *Fax (021) 466 7429*, – . .
February-October – **3 rm** 45/90.

CASTLEREA (An Caisleán Riabhach) *Roscommon* 923 G 6 *Ireland G.* – *pop. 1 790.*

Env. : *Clonalis House★, W : ½ m. by N 60.*

Castlerea, Clonalis ☎ (0907) 20068.

Dublin 108 – Galway 62 – Limerick 105.

Clonalis House , West : ½ m. on N 60 ☎ (0907) 20014, *clonalis@iol.ie*, *Fax (0907) 20014*, ←, « Victorian Italianate mansion in extensive grounds », , , – . .
mid April-September – **Meals** (by arrangement) (communal dining) 31.75 – **4 rm** 73.65/147.30.

CASTLETOWNBERE (Baile Chaisleáin Bhéarra) *Cork* 923 C 13 *Ireland G.* – *pop. 926.*

Env. : *Beara Peninsula★, W : by R 572 (Allihies, mines★ - Garnish Bay ←★) – Slieve Miskish Mountains (←★).*

Berehaven, Millcove ☎ (027) 70700.

Dublin 224 – Cork 81 – Killarney 58.

The Old Presbytery without rest., Brandy Hall House, East : ¼ m. on R 572 ☎ (027) 70424, *marywrigley@midnet.net*, *Fax (027) 70420*, ←, – . .
April-September – **5 rm** 35.00/70.00 **s.**

Rodeen , East : 2 m. by R 572 ☎ (027) 70158, *taracentre@eircom.net*, *Fax (027) 70987*, ←, – . .
March-October – **Meals** (by arrangement) 25.39 **st.** – **6 rm** 38.09/63.49 **st.**

REPUBLIC OF IRELAND

CASTLETOWNSHEND (Baile an Chaisleáin) *Cork* 923 E 13.
Dublin 215 – Cork 59 – Killarney 72.

Mary Ann's, ✆ (028) 36146, *golfer@indigo.ie, Fax (028) 36377,* – MC VISA
closed last 3 weeks January, 25-26 December – **Meals** (bookings not accepted) 32.9
(dinner) and lunch a la carte 16.45/38.60 **t.** 15.38.

CAVAN (An Cabhán) *Cavan* 923 J 6 *Ireland G. – pop. 3 509.*
Env. : *Killykeen Forest Park★, W : 6 m. by R 198.*
Farnham St ✆ (049) 4331942 (March-October).
Dublin 71 – Drogheda 58 – Enniskillen 40.

Kilmore, Dublin Rd, East : 2 m. on N 3 ✆ (049) 4332288, *kilmore@quinn-hotels.com*
Fax (049) 4332458 – TV P – 550. MC AE VISA.
closed 24-25 December – **Meals** 17.50 (lunch) and dinner a la carte 24.80/29.30 **t.** 15.00
39 rm 71.00/110.00 **t.** – SB.

CHEEKPOINT (Pointe na Síge) *Waterford* 923 K/L 11 – *see Waterford.*

CLARINBRIDGE (Droichead an Chláirín) *Galway* 923 F 8.
Dublin 145 – Galway 11.

Oyster Manor, ✆ (091) 796777, *info@oystermanorhotel.com, Fax (091) 796770* – TV
– 80. MC AE VISA.
closed 24-25 December and Good Friday – **Meals** (carvery lunch Monday to Saturday)
dinner 58.57 and a la carte 24.00/41.00 **st.** 15.87 – **26 rm** 57.14/317.43 **st.** – SB.

The Old Schoolhouse, ✆ (091) 796898, *kenc@iol.ie, Fax (091) 796117* – P. MC AE VISA
closed 7 January-8 February and Monday – **Meals** (booking essential) (dinner only an
Sunday lunch)/dinner a la carte 29/32 **t.** 17.14.

CLIFDEN (An Clochán) *Galway* 923 B 7 *Ireland G. – pop. 920.*
Exc. : *Connemara★★★, NE : by N 59 – Sky Road★★ (≤★★), NE : by N 59 – Connemar
National Park★, NE : 1 m by N 59.*
Galway Rd ✆ (095) 21163 (March-October).
Dublin 181 – Ballina 77 – Galway 49.

Station House, ✆ (095) 21699, *station@eircom.net, Fax (095) 21667,* –
rest, TV P – 200. MC AE VISA.
closed 25 December – **Meals** (bar lunch)/dinner 26.66 **st.** 16.51 – ***Fire & Ice :*** **Meal**
(closed Sunday except Bank Holidays and Monday) (dinner only) a la carte 27/36 **t.** 16.51
78 rm 200.00 **st.** – SB.

Rock Glen Country House, South : 1 ¼ m. by R 341 ✆ (095) 21035, *rockglen@iol.ie*
Fax (095) 21737, ≤, « Early 19C former shooting lodge », – rest, TV P. MC A
VISA
closed mid November-mid February except 28 December-6 January – **Meals** (bar lunch)
dinner a la carte 21.00/40.00 **t.** 16.76 – **25 rm** 126.87/165.07 **t.** – SB.

Ardagh, Ballyconneely rd, South : 1 ¾ m. on R 341 ✆ (095) 21384, *ardaghhotel@
eircom.net, Fax (095) 21314,* ≤ Ardbear Bay – TV P. MC AE VISA
Easter-October – **Meals** (bar lunch)/dinner a la carte 32.00/46.00 **t.** 17.50 – **14 rm**
107.00/157.50 **t.**, 3 suites – SB.

Alcock & Brown, ✆ (095) 21206, *alcockandbrown@eircom.net, Fax (095) 21842* – rest
TV. MC AE VISA.
closed 22 to 26 December – **Meals** (bar lunch)/dinner a la carte 27.75/38.50 **st.** 16.00 –
19 rm 79.75/124.00 **st.** – SB.

The Quay House without rest., Beach Rd, ✆ (095) 21369, *thequay@iol.ie*
Fax (095) 21608, ≤ – TV. MC VISA.
12 March-7 November – **14 rm** 70.00/140.00 **t.**

Benbaun without rest., Westport Rd, ✆ (095) 21462, *benbaunhouse@eircom.net*
Fax (095) 21462, – TV P. MC VISA.
April-October – **14 rm** 30/70 **st.**

Sunnybank House, Church Hill, ✆ (095) 21437, *info@sunnybankhouse.com*
Fax (095) 21976, heated, – TV P. MC VISA.
April-October – **Meals** – (see ***O'Grady's*** below) – **8 rm** 63.50/254.00 **st.** – SB.

Buttermilk Lodge without rest., Westport Rd, ✆ (095) 21951, *buttermilk@anu.ie*
Fax (095) 21953 – TV P. MC VISA.
closed 7-31 January – **11 rm** 50.79/76.18 **t.**

Mal Dua House, Galway Rd, East : ½ m. on N 59 ✆ (095) 21171, *maldua@iol.ie, Fax (095) 21739,* – TV P. MC AE VISA.
Meals 19 **st.** 15 **14 rm** 57/114 **st.**

Dún Rí without rest., Hulk St, ✆ (095) 21625, *dunri@anu.ie, Fax (095) 21635* – TV. MC VISA.
March-October – **13 rm** 50/70 **st.**

Connemara Country Lodge without rest., Westport Rd, ✆ (095) 22122, *connemara @unison.ie, Fax (095) 21122,* – TV P.
closed 24-26 December – **10 rm** 50.79/76.18 **st.**

O'Grady's, Market St, ✆ (095) 21450, *Fax (095) 21976* – MC AE VISA
Easter-August – **Meals** *(closed Monday)* a la carte 21.78/33.20 **t.** 15.87.

High Moors, Dooneen, Southeast : ¾ m. off Ballyconneely rd ✆ (095) 21342, ← – P. MC AE VISA
April-October – **Meals** *(closed Monday-Tuesday)* (dinner only) 31.75 **st.** 16.13.

CLONAKILTY (Cloich na Coillte) *Cork* 923 F 13 *Ireland G. – pop. 2 724.*

See : *West Cork Regional Museum★ AC – West Cork Model Railway Village★.*
Env. : *Timoleague★ (Franciscan Friary★, gardens★) E : 5 m. by R 600.*
Exc. : *Carbery Coast★.*
9 Dunmore, Dunmore House, Muckross ✆ (023) 33352.
Ashe St ✆ (023) 33226.
Dublin 193 – Cork 32.

The Lodge and Spa at Inchydoney Island, South : 3 ¼ m. by N 71 following signs for Inchydoney Beach ✆ (023) 33143, *reservations@inchydoneyisland.com, Fax (023) 35229,* ←, – rm, rest, TV – 350. MC AE VISA.
The Gulfstream : **Meals** (dinner only and Sunday lunch) 44/47 **t.** 19.68 – ***The Contented Plaice :*** **Meals** a la carte 16/26 – **63 rm** 165/285 **t.**, 4 suites – SB.

Dunmore House, Muckross, South : 3 ¾ m. by N 71 off Ardfield rd ✆ (023) 33352, *dunmorehousehotel@eircom.net, Fax (023) 34686,* ←, 9, – rest, TV P – 200. MC AE VISA.
closed 25-26 December and 20 January-8 March – **Meals** (bar lunch Monday-Saturday) 21.50/40 and dinner a la carte 21.50/40 **st.** – **23 rm** 85/200 **st.** – SB.

Quality, Clogheen, West : ½ m. by N 71 (Skibbereen rd) ✆ (023) 35400, *qualityhotel@ eircom.net, Fax (023) 35404,* – rest, TV P – 160. MC AE VISA.
closed 23-27 December – **Meals** (bar lunch)/dinner 16.51/25.39 and a la carte 25/37 **t.** 19.30 – **58 rm** 95/152 **t.** – SB.

An Sugán, 41 Strand Rd, ✆ (023) 33498, *ansugan@eircom.ie, Fax (023) 33825* – MC VISA
closed 25-26 December and Good Friday – **Meals** a la carte 22/36 15.24.

at Ballinascarty *Northeast : 4 ¼ m. on N 71 – ✉ Clonakilty.*

Árd na Gréine Farm House, Northwest : 1 ¾ m. by N 71 ✆ (023) 39104, *norma walshi@eircom.net, Fax (023) 39397,* « Working farm », – TV P. MC VISA
Meals 19/27 **st.** – **5 rm** 33/66.

CLONBUR (An Fhairche) *Galway* 923 D 7.

Dublin 162 – Ballina 49 – Galway 29.

John J. Burkes, ✆ (092) 46175, *tibhurca@eircom.net, Fax (092) 46190,* – MC VISA
restricted opening in winter – **Meals** *(closed Sunday dinner)* (live music Friday-Sunday) a la carte 13.65/15.55 **t.** 14.60.

CLONDALKIN *Dublin* 923 M 8 – *see Dublin.*

CLONMEL (Cluain Meala) *Tipperary* 923 I 10 *Ireland G. – pop. 15 215.*

See : *Town★ – County Museum★, St. Mary's Church★.*
Env. : *Fethard★, N : 8 m. by R 689.*
Exc. : *Nier Valley Scenic Route★★ – Ahenny High Crosses★, E : 19 m. by N 24 and R 697 – Ormond Castle★, E : 21 m. by N 24.*
18 Lyreanearla, Mountain Rd ✆ (052) 21138.
Community Office, Town Centre ✆ (052) 22960.
Dublin 108 – Cork 59 – Kilkenny 31 – Limerick 48 – Waterford 29.

Minella, Coleville Rd, (052) 22388, *hotelminella@eircom.net, Fax (052) 24381*, ..., – rm, – 550. AE VISA.
closed 23-29 December – **Meals** 23/40 and a la carte 36/41 **t.** 18 – **68 rm** 100/165 t 2 suites – SB.

CLONTARF (Cluain Tarbh) *Dublin* 923 N 7 – *see Dublin.*

CLOYNE (Cluain) *Cork* 923 H 12 – Midleton.

Dublin 160 – Cork 20 – Waterford 60.

Barnabrow House, East : 1 ¼ m. on R 629 (021) 4652534, *barnabrow@eircom.net, Fax (021) 4652534*, ≤, « Part 17C », – VISA
closed 24-28 December – ***Trinity Rooms :*** **Meals** *(closed Sunday dinner)* (dinner only and Sunday lunch)/dinner a la carte 25/50 **t.** 17.14 – **19 rm** 62/140 **t.**

The Cross of Cloyne, Church St, (021) 465 2401, *Fax (021) 465 2853* – . VISA
closed 24-25 and 31 December and Monday-Tuesday in winter – **Meals** (dinner only) a la carte approx. 33.52 **t.** 15.17.

COBH (An Cóbh) *Cork* 923 H 12 *Ireland G. – pop. 6 468.*

See : *Town★ – St Colman's Cathedral★ – Lusitania Memorial★.*

Exc. : *Fota Island★ (Fota Wildlife Park★), N : 4 m. by R 624 – Cloyne Cathedral★, SE : 15 m. by R 624/5, N 25, R 630 and R 629.*

Ballywilliam (021) 812399.

Dublin 164 – Cork 15 – Waterford 65.

WatersEdge, (next to Cobh Heritage Centre) (021) 481 5566, *watersedge@eircom.net, Fax (021) 481 2011*, ≤ Cork harbour, – rest, AE VISA.
closed 24-27 December and 1-4 January ***Jacob's Ladder :*** **Meals** (light lunch) a la carte 32/40 **t.** 17 – **18 rm** 127/250 **t.**, 1 suite – SB.

Bella Vista Manor House without rest., Bishop's Rd, (021) 4812450, *bellavis@indigo.ie, Fax (021) 4812215*, ≤ – AE VISA.
16 rm 50.79/126.87 **t.**

Robin Hill House with rm, Rushbrooke, Northeast : 1 m. by R 624 (021) 4811395 *robinhillhouse@eircom.net, Fax (021) 4814680*, ≤, « Mid Victorian converted rectory contemporary interior », – VISA.
closed 25-27 December, 6 January-1 February and Bank Holidays – **Meals** *(closed Sunday dinner and Monday)* (dinner only and Sunday lunch) 36.19 **st.** 15.87 – **6 rm** 69.85 101.60 **st.** – SB.

COLLOONEY (Cúil Mhuine) *Sligo* 923 G 5.

Dublin 129 – Sligo 9 – Galway 82.

Glebe House with rm, West : ¾ m. off Coolaney rd (071) 67787, *glebehouse@esatbiz.com, Fax (071) 30438*, « Georgian house », – AE VISA
May-October – **Meals** (dinner only) 25/32 and a la carte 24/43 **t.** 16 – **3 rm** 50/76 – SB

CONG (Conga) *Mayo* 923 E 7 *Ireland G. – pop. 197.*

See : *Town★.*

Env. : *Lough Corrib★★.*

Exc. : *Ross Abbey★ (Tower ≤★) – Joyce Country★★ (Lough Nafooey★) W : by R 345.*

(092) 46542 (March-October).

Dublin 160 – Ballina 49 – Galway 28.

Ashford Castle, (092) 46003, *ashford@ashford.ie, Fax (092) 46260*, ≤, « Part 13C and 18C castle in extensive formal gardens on shores of Lough Corrib », ..., – , rest, – 110. AE VISA.
closed 6 January-24 February – ***George V Room :*** **Meals** (residents only) 37/55 and dinner a la carte 55 **t.** 27 – 19 – **79 rm** 352/466 **st.**, 4 suites.

Ballywarren House, East : 2 ¼ m. on R 346 (092) 46989, *ballywarrenhouse@eircom.net, Fax (092) 46989*, ≤, – AE VISA
closed 1 week in spring and 1 week in autumn – **Meals** (by arrangement) 32 16 **st.** 7.50 – **3 rm** 82/125 **st.**

Les prix — Pour toutes précisions sur les prix indiqués dans ce guide, reportez-vous aux pages de l'introduction.

CORK (Corcaigh) *Cork* 923 G 12 *Ireland G. – pop. 127 187.*

See : *City*★★ – *Shandon Bells*★★ EY, *St. Fin Bar's Cathedral*★★ AC Z, *Cork Public Museum*★ X M – *Grand Parade*★ Z , *South Mall*★ Z , *St. Patrick Street*★ Z , *Crawford Art Gallery*★ Y – *Christ the King Church*★ X D , *Elizabethan Fort*★ Z .

Env. : *Dunkathel House*★ AC, *E : 5¾m. by N 8 and N 25* X.

Exc. : *Fota Island*★ *(Fota Wildlife Park*★ *), E : 8 m. by N 8 and N 25* X – *Cobh*★ *(St. Colman's Cathedral*★, *Lusitania Memorial*★ *) SE : 15 m. by N 8, N 25 and R 624* X.

Douglas (021) 4891086, X – *Mahon, Cloverhill, Blackrock (021) 4294280* X – *Monkstown, Parkgarriffe (021) 4841376,* X – *Harbour Point, Clash, Little Island (021) 4353094,* X.

Cork Airport : (021) 4313131, S : 4 m. by L 42 X – **Terminal** : *Bus Station, Parnell Pl.*

to France (Roscoff) (Brittany Ferries and Irish Ferries) weekly (14 h/15 h) – to Pembroke (Swansea Cork Ferries) 2 weekly (8 h 30 mn) – to Swansea (Swansea Cork Ferries) (10 h).

Cork City, Grand Par (021) 4273251 – Cork Airport, Freephone facility at Arrivals Terminal.

Dublin 154.

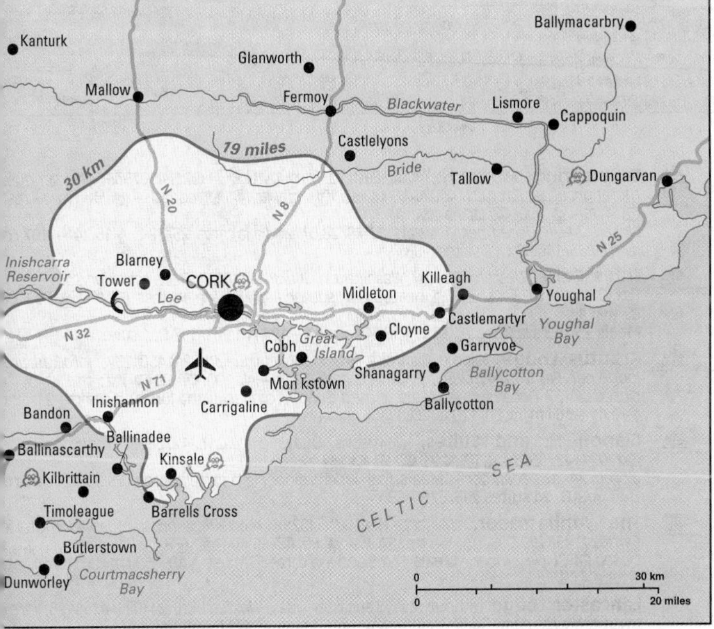

Hayfield Manor, Perrott Ave, College Rd, (021) 4845900, *enquiries@hayfieldmanor.ie, Fax (021) 4316839,* – 100. VISA. X z
The Manor Room : **Meals** *(closed Saturday lunch)* 23/30 lunch and dinner a la carte 45/60 **t.** 28 – **82 rm** 230/345 **st.**, 5 suites – SB.

Maryborough House, Maryborough Hill, Douglas, Southeast : 3 m. by R 609 (021) 4365555, *maryboro@indigo.ie, Fax (021) 4365662,* « Part 18C », rm, rest, – 500. VISA.
closed 24-26 December – ***Zing's :*** **Meals** 21.60/31.75 and a la carte 28/38 **st.** 23 – **75 rm** 138/190 **st.**, 4 suites – SB.

The Kingsley, Victoria Cross, (021) 4800500, *resv@kingsleyhotel.com, Fax (021) 4800527,* rm, – 90. VISA. X o
Otters *((021) 4800595)* : **Meals** 17.98/37.46 and dinner a la carte 25/44 **t.** 17.14 – **57 rm** 171.41/444.41 **st.** – SB.

CORK
BUILT UP AREA

Baker's Road .... X 4
Commons Road .... X 12
Curragh Road .... X 14
Gardiner's Hill .... X 20
Great William O'Brien Street X 22
Horgan Quay .... X 23
Lower Mayfield Road ...... X 3
Thomas Davis Street .... X 4
Victoria Cross Rd .... X 5
Western Road .... X 5
Wilton Road .... X 5

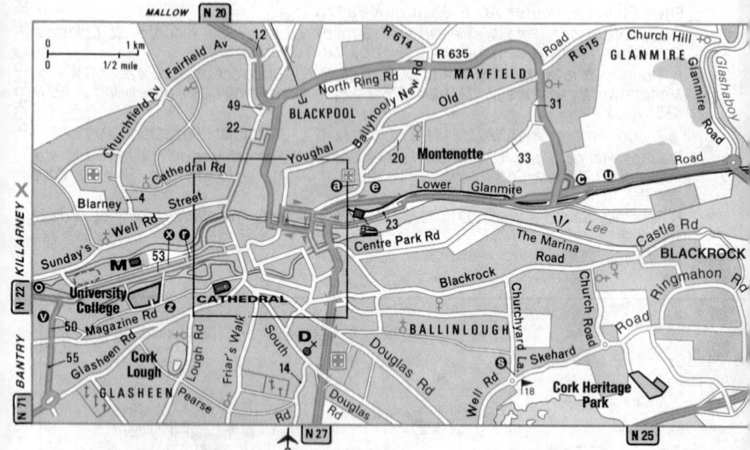

Silversprings Moran H., Tivoli, East : 2 ½ m. by N 8 ☎ (021) 4507533, *silversprings@morangroup.ie, Fax (021) 4507641,* squash – rm, rest 900. X
closed 24-26 December – **Meals** 17.78/28.57 and a la carte 25/32 **t.** 15.24 – **107 rm** 120.63/146.02 **t.**, 2 suites – SB.

Jurys Cork, Western Rd, by Washington St, ☎ (021) 4276622, *cork@jurysdoyle.com, Fax (021) 4274477,* heated, squash – rm, rest 700. Z
Meals 23 and a la carte 26/36 **t.** 16.50 – 13 – **184 rm** 171/197 **t.**, 1 suite.

Arbutus Lodge, Middle Glanmire Rd, Montenotte, ☎ (021) 4501237, *info@arbutuslodge.net, Fax (021) 4502893,* – rest, 100. X
closed 24-27 December – **Meals** *(closed Sunday dinner)* (light lunch) a la carte 21/38 **t.** 19.41 – **16 rm** 80/120 **t.** – SB.

Clarion H. and Suites, Morrisons Quay, ☎ (021) 4275858, *morisons@iol.ie, Fax (021) 4275833* – Z
closed 24-26 December – **Meals** (bar lunch)/dinner a la carte approx. 23.50 **st.** – **32 rm** 114/203, **24 suites** 215/279 – SB.

The Ambassador, Military Hill, ☎ (021) 4551996, *info@ambassadorhotel.ie, Fax (021) 4551997,* rm, 80. X
closed 24-26 December – **Meals** 17/35 and a la carte 35/45 **st.** 19 – **59 rm** 110/140 **st.**, 1 suite – SB.

Lancaster Lodge without rest., Lancaster Quay, Western Rd, ☎ (021) 4251125, *info@lancasterlodge.com, Fax (021) 4251126* – Z
closed 24-26 December – **39 rm** 76/140 **st.**

Jurys Inn Cork, Anderson's Quay, ☎ (021) 4276444, *jurysinncork@jurysdoyle.com, Fax (021) 4276144* – rm, 30. Y
closed 24-27 December – **Meals** (carving lunch)/dinner 21.50 **st.** 14 – 8.50 – **133 rm** 84 **st.**

Victoria Lodge without rest., Victoria Cross, ☎ (021) 4542233, *Fax (021) 4542572,* X
closed 24-28 December – **28 rm** 50/82.55 **st.**

Ibis Cork, Lee Tunnel roundabout, Dunkettle, East : 4 ¾ m. by N 8, following sign for Glounthaune off N 25 slip rd ☎ (021) 4354354, *h0580@accor_hotels.com, Fax (021) 4354202* – rm,
Meals (grill rest.) (dinner only) a la carte 14/23 **st.** 9.52 – **100 rm** 48.25/73.64 **st.**

Travelodge, Blackash, South : 2 ¼ m. by N 27 (south link) ☎ (021) 4310722, *Fax (021) 4310723* – rm,
Meals (grill rest.) – **40 rm** 67.95 **t.**

CORK

amden Place . . . . Y 5
oburg Street . . . . Y 10
orn Market Street . . . . Y 13
ominick Street . . . . Y 15
ason's Hill . . . . Y 17
mmet Place . . . . Y 18
erald Griffin St. . . . . Y 21
firmary Road . . . . Z 24
John Redmond Street . . . . . . Y 26
Lancaster Quay . . . . Z 28
Langford Row . . . . Z 29
Lower Glanmire Road . . . . . . Y 30
Merchant's Quay . . . . Y 32
Merchant's Quay Shopping Centre . . . . Y
Newsom's Quay . . . . Y 34
North Mall . . . . Y 35
O'Connell's Square . . . . Y 36
Oliver Plunkett Street . . . . . . Z
Parnell Place . . . . Z 38
Pembroke Street . . . . Z 39
Proby's Quay . . . . Z 40
Roman Street . . . . Y 42
St Patrick's Quay . . . . Y 44
St. Patrick's Street . . . . Z
Southern Road . . . . Z 45
South Link . . . . Z 46
South Main Street . . . . Z 47
Summer Hill . . . . Y 48
Wolfe Tone Street . . . . Y 56

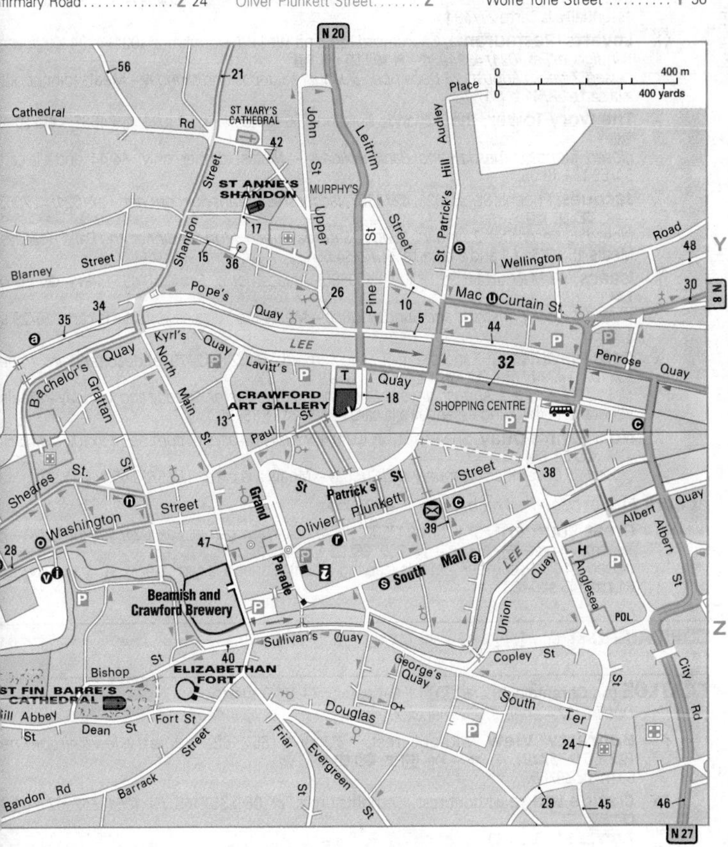

⌂ **Seven North Mall** without rest., 7 North Mall, ✆ (021) 4397191, *sevennorthmall@eircom.net, Fax (021) 4300811* – ⇔ TV P. MC VISA. ✻ Y a
closed 16 December-6 January – **7 rm** ☕ 75/120 **st.**

⌂ **Garnish House** without rest., Western Rd, ✆ (021) 4275111, *garnish@iol.ie, Fax (021) 4273872* – ⇔ TV P. MC AE DC VISA. ✻ X r
14 rm ☕ 64/114 **t.**

⌂ **Achill House** without rest., Western Rd, ✆ (021) 4279447, *info@achillhouse.com, Fax (021) 4279447* – TV P. MC VISA. ✻ Z e
6 rm ☕ 50/110 **st.**

⌂ **Killarney House** without rest., Western Rd, ✆ (021) 4270290, *killarneyhouse@iol.ie, Fax (021) 4271010* – ⇔ TV P. MC AE VISA. ✻ X x
closed 1 week Christmas – **19 rm** ☕ 76.20/88.90 **st.**

⌂ **Acorn House** without rest., 14 St Patrick's Hill, ✆ (021) 4502474, *info@acornhouse-cork.com, Fax (021) 4502474* – TV. MC VISA. ✻ Y e
closed 21 December-10 January – **9 rm** ☕ 44.44/88.88 **st.**

XXX **Flemings** with rm, Silver Grange House, Tivoli, East : 2 ¾ m. on N 8 ✆ (021) 482162' *Fax (021) 4821800*, – TV P. MC AE VISA. X
closed 23-29 December and Monday lunch – **Meals** 24.76 (lunch) and dinner a la cart 39/47 **t.** 18.41 – **4 rm** ☐ 69.84/101.58.

XX **Jacobs on the Mall,** 30A South Mall, ✆ (021) 4251530, *kingsley@eircom.ne Fax (021) 4251531*, « Contemporary Irish art collection » – ▤. MC AE VISA Z
closed 25-26 December, 1 January, Sunday and lunch Bank Holidays – **Meals** (bookin essential) a la carte 27/38 **t.**

XX **Lovetts (Restaurant),** Churchyard Lane, off Well Rd, Douglas, ✆ (021) 4294909, *lovett @indigo.ie, Fax (021) 4294024* – P. MC AE VISA X
closed 2 weeks August, 23 December-3 January, Sunday and Monday – **Meals** (dinner onl a la carte 28/51 **t.** 17.78.

X **The Ivory Tower,** The Exchange Buildings, 35 Princess St, ✆ (021) 4274665 – MC AE VISA Z
closed Monday, Tuesday and Bank Holidays – **Meals** (dinner only) 44.44 and a la cart 34/52 **t.** 19.05.

X **Jacques,** Phoenix St, ✆ (021) 4277387, *jacquesrestaurant@eircom.net, Fax (021) 427063* – ▤. MC AE VISA Z
closed 25 December-2 January, Sunday, Saturday lunch, Monday dinner and Bank Holidays **Meals** 15.10/31.61 and a la carte 22.72/34.65 **t.**

X **Isaacs,** 48 MacCurtain St, ✆ (021) 4503805, *isaacs@iol.ie, Fax (021) 4551348* – MC AE VISA Y
closed 1 week Christmas and Sunday lunch – **Meals** (booking essential) a la carte 16/29 **st** 12.50.

X **Cafe Paradiso,** 16 Lancaster Quay, Western Rd, ✆ (021) 4277939, *dpcolter@eircom.ne Fax (021) 4274973* – MC VISA Z
closed 2 weeks late August, 1 week Christmas, 4 days Easter, Sunday and Monday – **Meals** Vegetarian - (booking essential) a la carte 20/36 **st.** 15.24.

X **No 5 Fenn's Quay,** Sheares St, ✆ (021) 4279527, *polary@eircom.net, Fax (021) 427952* – ▤. MC AE VISA Z
closed 25 December, 1 January and Sunday – **Meals** a la carte 21.35/30.45 **t.** 15.90.

at Cork Airport *South : 4 m. by N 27* – X – ✉ *Cork.*

Great Southern, ✆ (021) 4947500, *res@corkairport.gsh.ie, Fax (021) 4947501*, – rm, ▤ rest, TV & P – 200. MC AE VISA.
closed 24-26 December – **Meals** (carving lunch)/dinner a la carte 19/32 **st.** 12 – ☐ 13 **81 rm** 145 **st.** – SB.

CORK AIRPORT *Cork* 923 G 12 – *see Cork.*

CRATLOE (An Chreatalach) *Clare* 923 F 9 – *pop. 557* – ✉ *Bunratty.*

Dublin 127 – Ennis 17 – Limerick 7.

Bunratty View without rest., ✆ (061) 357352, *bunrattyview@eircom.ne Fax (061) 357491*, ≤, – TV P. MC AE VISA.
6 rm ☐ 39/66.

Cratloe Lodge without rest., Setrights Cross, ✆ (061) 357168, *Fax (061) 357967* – TV P MC VISA
7 rm ☐ 31.75/50.80.

CRAUGHWELL (Creachmhaoil) *Galway* 923 F 8.

Dublin 121 – Galway 15 – Limerick 55.

St Clerans , Northeast : 3 ½ m. off N 6 taking second turning left after 1 m. the veering left after a further 2 m. ✆ (091) 846555, *stclerans@iol.ie, Fax (091) 846600*, ≤ « Part 18C country house », , , – TV & P. MC AE VISA.
Meals (dinner only and Sunday lunch) 50.79 **t.** 24.16 – **12 rm** ☐ 419.02/495.20 **t.**

CROOKEDWOOD (Tigh Munna) *Westmeath* 923 K 7 – *see Mullingar.*

CROOKHAVEN (An Cruachàn) *Cork* 923 C 13.

Dublin 237 – Cork 76 – Killarney 67 – Limerick 129.

X **Out of the Blue,** ✆ (028) 35929, *burvill@gofree.indigo.ie, Fax (028) 28305* – MC VISA
closed Monday and restricted opening in winter – **Meals** (dinner only and lunch Saturda and Sunday) a la carte 31.11/38.73 **st.** 15.87.

CROSSMOLINA (Crois Mhaoilíona) *Mayo* 923 E 5 *Ireland G. – pop. 1 103.*
Env. : *Errew Abbey★, SE : 6 m. by R 315.*
Exc. : *Broad Haven★, NW : 27 m. by N 59 and R 313.*
Dublin 157 – Ballina 6.5.

Enniscoe House, Castlehill, South : 2 m. on R 315 (096) 31112, *mail@enniscoe.com, Fax (096) 31773,* « Georgian country house, antiques », – P. VISA
April-14 December – **Meals** (booking essential to non-residents) (dinner only) 36 **st.** 13 – **6 rm** 86/172 **st.** – SB.

DALKEY (Deilginis) *Dublin* 923 N 8.
Dublin 8 – Bray 6.

Tudor House without rest., off Castle St via Kilbegnet Close (01) 285 1528, *tudorhousedalkey@hotmail.com, Fax (01) 284 8133,* « Victorian manor house », – P. VISA.
6 rm 89/138 **st.**

Kish, Coliemore Rd, Southeast : ½ m. by Convent Rd (01) 285 0377, *book@kishrestaurant.ie, Fax (01) 285 0141,* « Coastal setting, Dalkey Island and Dublin Bay » – P. VISA
closed 3 weeks January, 25 December, Monday and Tuesday – **Meals** 25.39 and a la carte 44/55 **t.** 20.32.

Munkberrys, 22 Castle St, (01) 284 7185, *info@munkberrys.com* – VISA
Meals (dinner only) a la carte 18/37 **t.** 20.32.

Le Guide change, changez de **guide Michelin** *tous les ans.*

DELGANY (Deilgne) *Wicklow* 923 N 8 – *pop. 6 682 (inc. Greystones)* – *Bray.*
18 *(01) 287 4536.*
Dublin 19.

Glenview, Glen of the Downs, Northwest : 2 m. on N 11 (01) 287 3399, *glenview@iol.ie, Fax (01) 287 7511,* – rest, P. – 250. VISA
closed 25 December – ***Woodlands :*** **Meals** 15.23/44.45 **st.** 17.14 – **73 rm** 152.40/234.90 **st.**, 1 suite – SB.

DINGLE (An Daingean) *Kerry* 923 B 11 *Ireland G. – pop. 1 536.*
See : *Town★ – St. Mary's Church★ (Presentation Convent Chapel★).*
Env. : *Gallarus Oratory★★, NW : 5 m. by R 559 – NE : Connor Pass★★ – Kilmalkedar★, NW : 5½ m. by R 559.*
Exc. : *Dingle Peninsula★★★ – Stradbally Strand★★, NE : 10½ m. via Connor Pass – Mount Eagle (Beehive Huts★), W : 9 m. by R 559 – Corca Dhuibhne Regional Museum★ AC, NW : 8 m. by R 559 – Blasket Islands★, W : 13 m. by R 559 and ferry from Dunquin.*
The Quay (066) 9151188.
Dublin 216 – Killarney 51 – Limerick 95.

Dingle Skellig, Southeast : ½ m. by N 86 (066) 9150200, *dsk@iol.ie, Fax (066) 9151501,* – P. – 250. VISA.
closed 23-26 December, Sunday and Monday in winter – **Meals** (bar lunch)/dinner 33.65/40.63 **st.** 12.70 – **110 rm** 264.10/279.34 **st.**, 2 suites – SB.

Benners, Main St, (066) 9151638, *benners@eircom.net, Fax (066) 9151412* – P. VISA.
closed 25 December – **Meals** (bar lunch)/dinner 37.46 and a la carte 26/33.50 **t.** 15 – **52 rm** 140/230 **t.** – SB.

Emlagh House without rest., off N 86 (066) 9152345, *info@emlaghhouse.com, Fax (066) 9152369,* – P. VISA.
March-November – **10 rm** 133.3/203.16 **st.**

Milltown House without rest., West : ¾ m. by R 559 (Slea Head Drive) (066) 9151372, *milltown@indigo.ie, Fax (066) 9151095,* – P. VISA.
closed December and January – **10 rm** 114.30/126.36 **t.**

Greenmount House without rest., Gortonora, by John St. (066) 9151414, *mary@greenmounthouse.com, Fax (066) 9151974,* – P. VISA.
closed 10-27 December – **12 rm** 90/125 **t.**

Heatons without rest., The Wood, West : ½ m. on R 559 (066) 9152288, *heatons@iol.ie, Fax (066) 9152324,* – P. VISA.
closed January – **16 rm** 92/164 **st.**

Doyle's Townhouse, 5 John St, ✆ (066) 9151174, *cdoyles@iol.ie, Fax (066) 9151816* TV. MC AE DC VISA. ✗
mid February-mid November – **Meals** – (see ***Doyle's Seafood Bar*** below) – **8 rm** ☐ 108 114.50 **t.**

Captains House without rest., The Mall, ✆ (066) 9151531, *captigh@eircom.ne Fax (066) 9151079,* – TV. MC AE VISA. ✗
15 March-15 November – **8 rm** ☐ 50/120 **st.**

Pax House without rest., Upper John St, Northeast : ¾ m. on John S ✆ (066) 9151518, *paxhouse@iol.ie, Fax (066) 9152461,* ←, – TV P. MC VISA
closed December and January – **12 rm** ☐ 80/140 **st.**

Cleevaun without rest., Lady's Cross, Milltown, West : 1 ¼ m. on R 559 following signs fc Slea Head Drive ✆ (066) 9151108, *cleevaun@iol.ie, Fax (066) 9152228,* ←, – TV P. VISA. ✗
mid February-mid November – **8 rm** ☐ 70/82.

Lantern Townhouse without rest., Main St, ✆ (066) 9151088, *thelantern@irelanc com,* – TV. MC VISA
February-mid December – **8 rm** ☐ 58/70, 1 suite.

Bambury's without rest., Mail Rd, East : on N 86 ✆ (066) 9151244, *berniebb@tinet.ie Fax (066) 9151786,* ← – TV P. MC VISA. ✗
12 rm ☐ 33/93 **st.**

Beginish, Green St, ✆ (066) 9151321, *dunlavin@gofree.indigo.ie, Fax (066) 9151321,* . MC VISA
closed 19 December-8 February and Monday – **Meals** (dinner only) 27.93 and a la cart 31/40 **st.** 17.71.

The Chart House, The Mall, ✆ (066) 9152255, *charthse@iol.ie, Fax (066) 9152255* – MC VISA
closed 7 January-13 February, 14-27 December and Tuesday – **Meals** (dinner only) a la cart 23.79/37.07 **t.** 16.18.

Doyle's Seafood Bar, 4 John St, ✆ (066) 9151174, *cdoyles@iol.ie, Fax (066) 9151816* . MC AE DC VISA
closed mid November-February – **Meals** (dinner only) a la carte 40/48 17.75.

The Half Door, 3 John St, ✆ (066) 9151600, *halfdoor@iol.ie, Fax (066) 9151883* – TV. MC VISA
closed mid January-mid February and Sunday – **Meals** - Seafood - 26.66 and a la cart 32/44 8.50 – **7 rm** ☐ 50.00/100.00 **t.**

DONEGAL (Dún na nGall) *Donegal* 923 H 4 *Ireland G. – pop. 2 296.*

See : *Donegal Castle★ AC.*

Exc. : *Donegal Coast★★ – Cliffs of Bunglass★★, W : 30 m. by N 56 and R 263 – Glencolmcill Folk Village★★ AC, W : 33 m. by N 56 and R 263 – Rossnowlagh Strand★★, S : 22 m. by N 1 and R 231 – Trabane Strand★, W : 36 m. by N 56 and R 263.*

Donegal Airport ✆ (075) 48284.

The Quay ✆ (073) 21148 (April-October).

Dublin 164 – Londonderry 48 – Sligo 40.

St Ernan's House, St Ernan's Island, Southwest : 2 ¼ m. by N 15 ✆ (073) 21065, *inf @sainternans.com, Fax (073) 22098,* « Wooded island setting ← Donegal Bay », , – rest, TV P. MC VISA JCB. ✗
12 April-October – **Meals** (booking essential to non-residents) (dinner only) 43 **t.** 19.05 – **9 rm** ☐ 280/380 **t.**, 2 suites.

Harvey's Point Country H. , Lough Eske, Northeast : 4 ½ m. by T 27 (Killibegs rc ✆ (073) 22208, *reservations@harveyspoint.com, Fax (073) 22352,* ←, « Loughside setting » , , , – TV P – 50. MC AE DC VISA
closed Sunday-Tuesday November-Easter – **Meals** – (see ***The Restaurant*** below) – **20 rn** ☐ 95.23/101.58 **st.** – SB.

Mill Park, The Mullans, Northwest : ½ m. by N 56 on Letterbarrow rd ✆ (073) 2288C *millparkhotel@eircom.net, Fax (073) 22640,* , , – TV P – 300. MC AE DC VISA JCB
closed 24-25 December – **Meals** 31.50/36.20 and a la carte 19/36 **st.** 15.24 – **39 rm** ☐ 80 350 **st.** – SB.

Ardeevin without rest., Lough Eske, Barnesmore, Northeast : 5 ½ m. by N 15 following signs for Lough Eske Drive ✆ (073) 21790, *seanmcginty@eircom.net Fax (073) 21790,* ← Lough Eske, – TV P. ✗
mid March-mid November – **6 rm** ☐ 40/65 **st.**

Island View House without rest., Ballyshannon rd, Southwest : 3/4 m. on N 15 ☎ (073) 22411, *dowds@indigo.ie*, ≤, – TV P.
closed 24-26 December – **4 rm** 40.63/56 **st.**

The Restaurant (at Harvey's Point Country H.), Lough Eske, Northeast : 4 ½ m. by N 56 (Killibegs rd) ☎ (073) 22208, *Fax (073) 22352*, ≤, « Loughside setting », – P. MC AE VISA
closed Sunday-Tuesday November-Easter – **Meals** 18.98/41.90 **st.** 18.41.

DONNYBROOK (Domhnach Broc) *Dublin* 923 ⑩ – *see Dublin.*

DOOGORT (Dumha Goirt) *Mayo* 923 B 5/6 – *see Achill Island.*

DOOLIN (Dúlainm) *Clare* 923 D 8 *Ireland G.*
Env. : *The Burren★★ (Cliffs of Moher★★★, Scenic Routes★★, Aillwee Cave★* AC *(Waterfall★★), Corcomrow Abbey★, Kilfenora Crosses★).*
Dublin 171 – Galway 43 – Limerick 50.

Aran View House, Coast Rd, Northeast : ½ m. ☎ (065) 7074061, *bookings@aranview.com, Fax (065) 7074540*, ≤, « Working farm », – TV P. MC AE VISA JCB
April-October – **Meals** (dinner only and Sunday lunch)/dinner 26.50/30 and a la carte 26.03/35.25 **t.** 18.41 – **19 rm** 65/120 **t.** – SB.

Doonmacfelim House without rest., ☎ (065) 7074503, *Fax (065) 7074129*, – P. MC VISA.
closed 22-28 December – **6 rm** 60/64 **t.**

DROGHEDA (Droichead Átha) *Louth* 923 M 6 *Ireland G.* – *pop. 24 460.*
See : *Town★ – Drogheda Museum★ – St. Laurence Gate★.*
Env. : *Monasterboice★★, N : 6 ½ m. by N 1 – Boyne Valley★★, on N 51 – Termonfeckin★, NE : 5 m. by R 166.*
Exc. : *Newgrange★★★, W : 3 m. by N 51 on N 2 – Old Mellifont★ – Knowth★.*
18 *Seapoint, Termonfeckin ☎ (041) 9822333* – 9 *Towneley Hall, Tullyallen ☎ (041) 42229.*
Bus Eireann Station, Donore Rd ☎ (041) 9837070 (May-September).
Dublin 29 – Dundalk 22.

Boyne Valley H. and Country Club, Southeast : 1 ¼ m. by N 1 ☎ (041) 9837737, *reservations@boyne-valley-hotel.ie, Fax (041) 9839188*, – rm, TV P – 350. MC AE VISA
Cellars Bistro : **Meals** 18.41 (lunch) and dinner a la carte 25/35 **st.** 17.78 – **37 rm** 84/153 **st.** – SB.

Tullyesker Country House without rest., Dundalk Rd, North : 3 ½ m. by N 1 ☎ (041) 9830430, *mcdonnellfamily@ireland.com, Fax (041) 9832624*, ≤, – TV P.
closed December and January – **5 rm** 50.79/66 **st.**

Boyne Haven House without rest., Dublin Rd, Southeast : 2 ½ m. on N 1 ☎ (041) 9836700, *taramcd@ireland.com, Fax (041) 9836700*, – TV P. MC VISA.
4 rm 50/76 **st.**

DRUMCONDRA (Droim Conrach) *Dublin* 923 ㊱ – *see Dublin.*

DUBLIN - (Baile Átha Cliath)

923 N 7 *Ireland G. – pop. 481 854.*

Belfast 103 – Cork 154 – Londonderry 146.

TOURIST INFORMATION

Bord Failte Offices Baggot Street Bridge, (01) 602 4000 – Suffolk St. – Arrivals Hall, Dublin Airport – The Square, Shopping Centre, Tallaght.

PRACTICAL INFORMATION

18 *Elm Park, Nutley House, Donnybrook (01) 269 3438,* GV.
18 *Milltown, Lower Churchtown Rd (01) 467 6090.*
18 *Royal Dublin, North Bull Island, Dollymount (01) 833 6346.*
18 *Forrest Little, Cloghran (01) 840 1183.*
18 *Lucan, Celbridge Rd, Lucan (01) 628 0246.*
18 *Edmondstown, Rathfarnham (01) 493 2461.*
18 *Coldwinters, Newtown House, St. Margaret's (01) 864 0324.*
Dublin Airport : (01) 814 1111, N : 5½ m. by N 1 BS – **Terminal :** *Busaras (Central Bus Station) Store St.*
to Holyhead (Irish Ferries) 2 daily (3 h 15 mn) – to Holyhead (Stena Line) 1-2 daily (3 h 45 mn) – to the Isle of Man (Douglas) (Isle of Man Steam Packet Co. Ltd) (2 h 45 mn) – to Liverpool (Merchant ferries Ltd) 2 daily (7 h 45 mn).

SIGHTS

See : *City★★★ Trinity College★★* JY – *Old Library★★★ (Treasury★★★, Long Room★★) – Dublin Castle★★ (Chester Beatty Library★★★)* HY – *Christ Church Cathedral★★* HY – *St. Patrick's Cathedral★★* HZ – *Marsh's Library★★* HZ – *National Museum★★ (The Treasury★★)* KZ – *National Gallery★★* KZ – *Newman House★★* JZ – *Bank of Ireland★★* JY – *Custom House★★* KX – *Four Courts★★* HY – *Kilmainham Gaol Museum★★* AT **M6** – *Kilmainham Hospital★★* AT – *Phoenix Park★★ – National Botanic Gardens★★* BS – *Marino Casino★★* CS – *Tailors Hall★* HY – *City Hall★* HY – *Temple Bar★* HJY – *Liffey Bridge★* JY – *Merrion Square★* KZ – *Number Twenty-Nine★* KZ **D** – *Grafton Street★* JYZ – *Powerscourt Centre★* JY – *Rotunda Hospital Chapel★* JX – *O'Connell Street★ (GPO Building★)* JX – *Hugh Lane Municipal Gallery of Modern Art★* JX **M4** – *Pro-Cathedral★* JX – *Bluecoat School★* BS **F** – *Guinness Museum★* BT **M7** – *Rathfarnham Castle★ – Zoological Gardens★* AS.

Env. : *The Ben of Howth★ (≤★).*

Exc. : *Powerscourt★★ (Waterfall★★ AC), S : 14 m. by N 11 and R 117* EV – *Russborough House★★★, SW : 22 m. by N 81* BT.

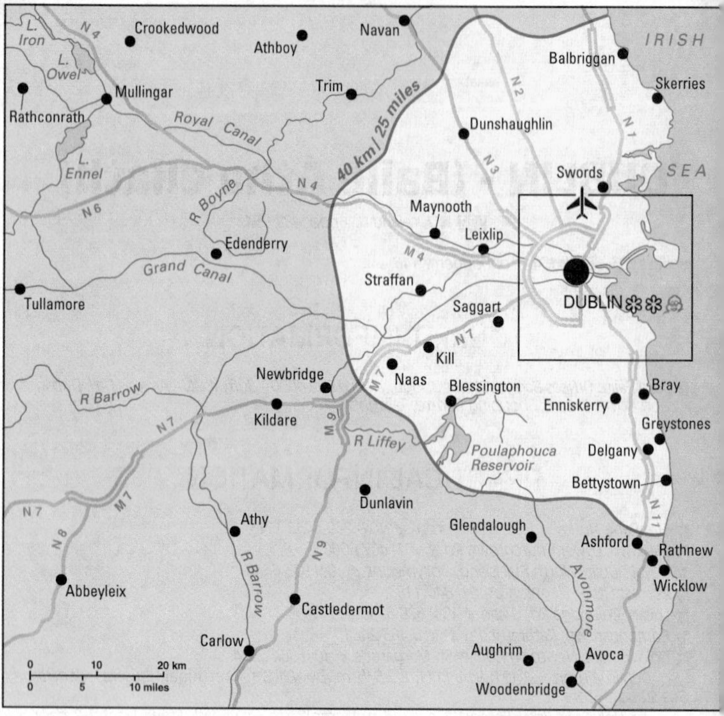

L. Iron
N 4
Crookedwood
Navan
IRISH
Athboy
L. Owel
Balbriggan
Skerries
N 2
Mullingar
Trim
Rathconrath
40 km / 25 miles
Royal Canal
N 1
Dunshaughlin
L. Ennel
N 3
SEA
Swords
N 4
R Boyne
N 6
Maynooth
Leixlip
Edenderry
M 4
Grand Canal
Straffan
Tullamore
DUBLIN
Saggart
N 7
Kill
Newbridge
Naas
M 7
R Barrow
Blessington
Bray
Kildare
Enniskerry
N 7
M 9
Greystones
R Liffey
Poulaphouca Reservoir
Delgany
Bettystown
Dunlavin
N 7
M 7
N 11
Athy
Glendalough
N 8
Ashford
Rathnew
N 9
Avonmore
Wicklow
Abbeyleix
R Barrow
Castledermot
Carlow
Aughrim
Avoca
Woodenbridge
0
10
20 km
0
5
10 miles

N 1
Malahide
N 2
Kinsaley
Portmarnock
Ireland's Eye
N 3
M 50
N 32
M 1
R 105
Howth
Castleknock
Drumcondra
Clontarf
DUBLIN
N 4
DUBLIN
Ballsbridge
Clondalkin
Merrion
Rathmines
N 7
Rathgar
Donnybrook
BAY
Blackrock
N 81
R 172
Monkstown
N 31
Dún Laoghaire
Tallaght
Stillorgan
N 11
Dalkey
Killiney
Foxrock
0
5 km
0
5 miles

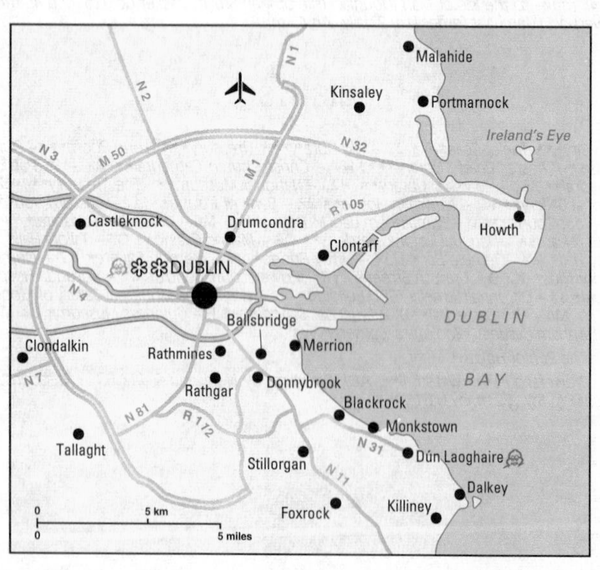

City Centre.

The Merrion, Upper Merrion St, D2, ℘ (01) 603 0600, *info@merrionhotel.com, Fax (01) 603 0700,* « Restored Georgian town houses, collection of contemporary Irish art », – rm, – 50. VISA. KZ e
Meals – (see ***Morningtons Brasserie*** and ***The Cellar Bar*** below) – 18.00 – **135 rm** 393.62 **t.**, 10 suites – SB.

Le Meridien Shelbourne, 27 St Stephen's Green, D2, ℘ (01) 663 4500, *shelbourneinfo@lemeridien-hotels.com, Fax (01) 661 6006,* – rm, – 400. VISA JCB. JZ s
No. 27 The Green : Meals *(closed Saturday lunch)* 24.76/37.47 and a la carte 36.51/62.23 **t.** 20.95 – ***The Side Door :*** Meals a la carte 33.02/36.05 **t.** 20.96 – 20.96 – **168 rm** 315/340 **t.**, 22 suites – SB.

Conrad Dublin, Earlsfort Terr, D2, ℘ (01) 676 5555, *info@conraddublin.com, Fax (01) 676 5424,* – rm, – 370. VISA JCB. JZ w
Alexandra : Meals 24.13/30.97 and a la carte 32/38 **st.** 20.32 – ***Plurabelle Brasserie :*** Meals 24.13/30.97 and a la carte 32/38 **st.** 20.32 – **191 rm** 255/380.

The Westbury, Grafton St, D2, ℘ (01) 679 1122, *westbury@jurysdoyle.com, Fax (01) 679 7078,* – rm, – 220. VISA. JY b
Russell Room : Meals 35/57 **t.** 20 – ***The Sandbank :*** Meals a la carte 22/33 **t.** 19 – 23 – **196 rm** 311/350 **t.**, 8 suites.

The Clarence, 6-8 Wellington Quay, D2, ℘ (01) 407 0800, *reservations@theclarence.ie, Fax (01) 407 0820,* « Contemporary interior design » – – 60. VISA. HY a
closed 25-26 December – **Meals** – (see ***The Tea Room*** below) – 15.00 – **45 rm** 285/305 **st.**, 4 suites.

The Fitzwilliam, St Stephen's Green, D2, ℘ (01) 478 7000, *enq@fitzwilliam-hotel.com, Fax (01) 478 7878,* « Contemporary interior » – rm, rest, – 70. VISA JCB. JZ d
Mango Toast : Meals a la carte 25/40 **st.** – (see also ***Peacock Alley*** below) – 20 – **128 rm** 275/370 **st.**, 2 suites – SB.

The Burlington, Upper Leeson St, D4, ℘ (01) 660 5222, *burlington@jurysdoyle.com, Fax (01) 660 8496* – rm, rest, – 1500. VISA. EU e
The Sussex : Meals (bar lunch)/dinner 22 **st.** 19 – 20 – **500 rm** 210/235 **t.**, 6 suites.

Stephen's Green, St Stephen's Green, D2, ℘ (01) 607 3600, *stephensgreenres@ocallaghanhotels.ie, Fax (01) 661 5663,* – rm, – 50. VISA. JZ f
closed 24 December-2 January ***The Pie Dish :*** Meals *(closed lunch Saturday and Sunday)* 24/29 and dinner a la carte 36/41 **t.** 19 – 20 – **64 rm** 315 **t.**, 11 suites – SB.

Brooks, 59-62 Drury St, D2, ℘ (01) 670 4000, *reservations@brookshotel.ie, Fax (01) 670 4455* – rm, – 50. VISA. JY r
Francesca's : Meals (dinner only) 25 and a la carte 30/50 **t.** 20 – 16.50 – **75 rm** 190.50/260 **st.**

The Alexander, Merrion Sq, D2, ℘ (01) 607 3700, *alexanderres@ocallaghanhotels.ie, Fax (01) 661 5663,* – rm, – 400. VISA. KY f
Caravaggio's : Meals *(closed lunch Saturday and Sunday)* 24/33 and dinner a la carte 34/52 **t.** 9 – 20 – **98 rm** 298 **t.**, 4 suites – SB.

The Davenport, Merrion Sq, D2, ℘ (01) 607 3500, *davenportres@ocallaghanhotels.ie, Fax (01) 661 5663,* « Part Victorian gospel hall », – rm, – 275. VISA. KY m
Lanyon : Meals *(closed Saturday lunch and Sunday)* 24/33 and dinner a la carte 35/54 **t.** 19 – 20 – **113 rm** 298 **t.**, 2 suites – SB.

Clarion H. Dublin IFSC, International Financial Services Centre, D1, ℘ (01) 433 8800, *info@clarionhotelifsc.com, Fax (01) 433 8811,* – rm, – 120. VISA JCB. CS n
closed 24-26 December – ***Sinergie :*** Meals *(closed lunch Saturday and Sunday)* 22.22/25.39 and a la carte 26/47 **t.** 20.95 – 17.77 – **147 rm** 203.15/761.84 **t.** – SB.

Morrison, Ormond Quay, D1, ℘ (01) 887 2400, *info@morrisonhotel.ie, Fax (01) 878 3185,* « Contemporary interior » – rm, VISA JCB. HY r
*closed 24-27 December*Meals – (see ***Halo*** below) – 17.15 – **90 rm** 317.50 **st.**, 4 suites.

Hilton Dublin, Charlemont Pl, D2, ℘ (01) 402 9988, *reservations_dublin@hilton.com, Fax (01) 402 9966* – rm, rest, – 400. VISA. DU b
closed 25 December ***Waterfront :*** Meals *(closed lunch Saturday and Sunday)* a la carte 26/39 **st.** 15.87 – **189 rm** 220.20/247.59 **st.** – SB.

DUBLIN

Adelaide Road .... BT 3
Bath Avenue .... CT 9
Benburb Street .... BS 15
Berkeley Road .... BS 16
Botanic Road .... BS 19
Canal Road .... BT 30
Clanbrassil Street .... BT 40
Conyngham Road .... AS 48
Denmark Street .... BS 52
Donnybrook Road .... CT 54
Dorset Street .... BS 55
Drimnagh Road .... AT 57
Eglinton Road .... CT 63
Grand Parade .... BT 72
Inchicore Road .... AT 79
Infirmary Road .... AS 81
James' Street .... BT 84
Leeson Street Upper .... BT 94
Macken Street .... BST 99
Morehampton Road .... BT 108
Mount Street Upper .... BT 112
Palmerston Park .... BT 123
Phibsborough Road .... BS 132
Rathmines Road Upper .... BT 135
Ringsend Road .... CT 139
St Agnes Road .... AT 141
St Alphonsus Road .... BS 144
St John's Road West .... AS 147
Sandford Road .... BT 151
Shelbourne Road .... CT 157
Shrewsbury Road .... CT 159
South Circular Road .... AS 162
Suir Road .... AT 168
Terenure Road East .... BT 172
Thomas Street West .... BT 174
Victoria Quay .... BS 178
Western Way .... BS 184
Wolfe Tone Quay .... BS 195

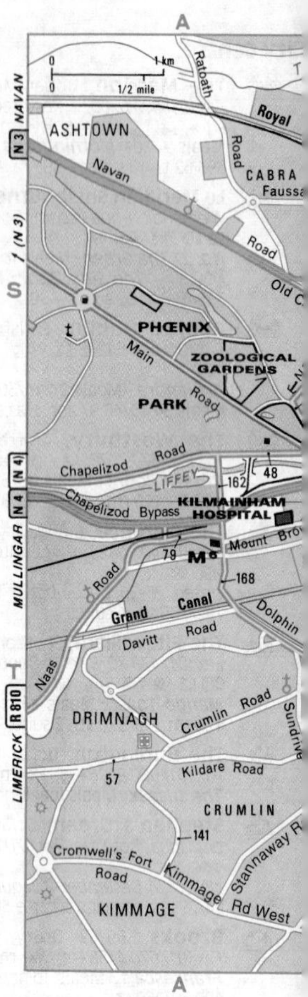

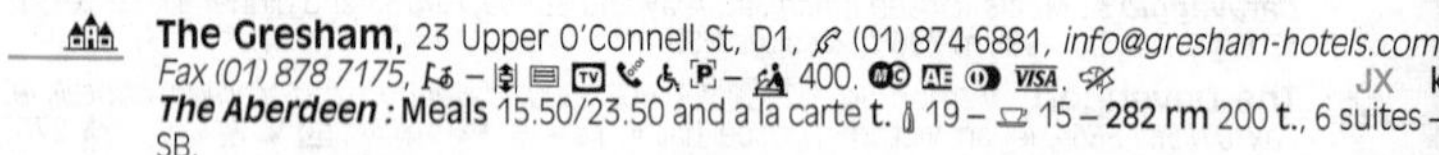

The Gresham, 23 Upper O'Connell St, D1, (01) 874 6881, *info@gresham-hotels.com, Fax (01) 878 7175,* – – 400. *VISA.* JX k
The Aberdeen : **Meals** 15.50/23.50 and a la carte **t.** 19 – 15 – **282 rm** 200 **t.**, 6 suites – SB.

La Stampa H., 35 Dawson St, D2, (01) 677 4444, *Fax (01) 677 4411* – *VISA.* JZ x
closed 25 December – **Meals** – (see ***La Stampa*** below) – 17.78 – **12 rm** 139.67/209.51, 8 suites – SB.

brownes townhouse, 22 St Stephen's Green, D2, (01) 638 3939, *info@brownesdublin.com, Fax (01) 638 3900,* « Georgian town house » – *VISA.* JZ c
closed 24 December-4 January **Meals** – (see ***brownes brasserie*** below) – **12 rm** 159/222 **st.**

Clarion Stephen's Hall, Earlsfort Centre, 14-17 Lower Leeson St, D2, (01) 638 1111, *stephens@premgroup.com, Fax (01) 638 1122* – *VISA.* JZ t
Meals *(closed Sunday)* a la carte 17/31 **t.** 15.87 – 13.97 – **3 rm** 184.11 **t.**, 28 suites 234.90 **t.**

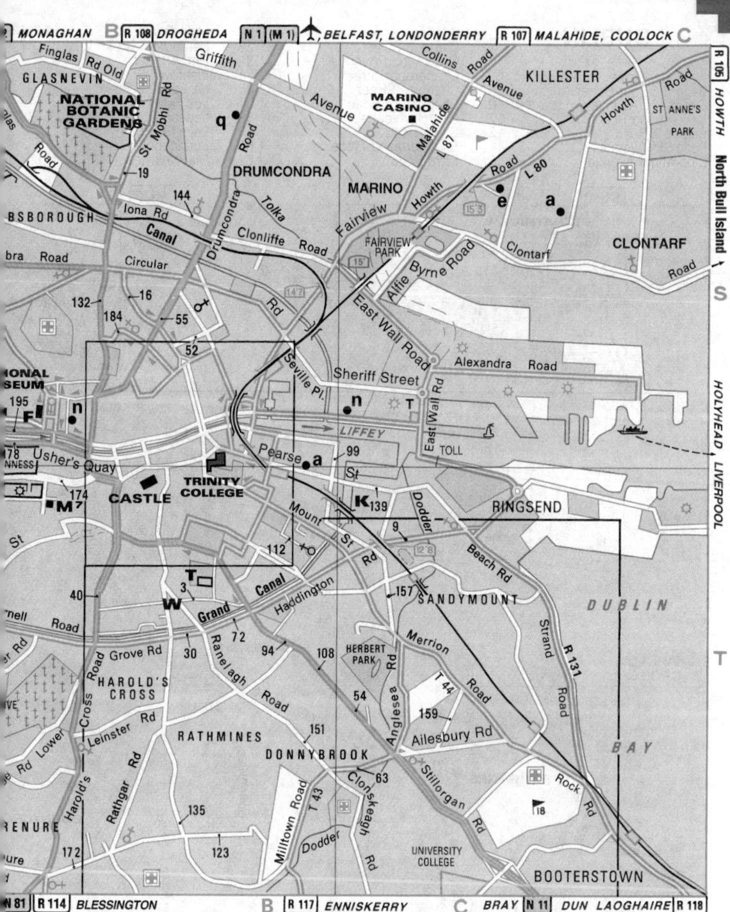

The Morgan, 10 Fleet St, D2, ☎ (01) 679 3939, *reservations@themorgan.com, Fax (01) 679 3946,* « Contemporary interior design », – |‡|, ⇔ rm, ▤ rest, TV. MC AE ◑ VISA. ✗ JY p
closed 23-26 December – ***All Sports Cafe :*** Meals (grill rest.) 10.49/17.09 and a la carte **t.** – **59 rm** 171.53/237.51 **st.**, 2 suites.

Mont Clare, Merrion Sq, D2, ☎ (01) 607 3800, *montclareres@ocallaghanhotels.ie, Fax (01) 661 5663* – |‡|, ⇔ rm, ▤ TV – 120. MC AE ◑ VISA. ✗ KY q
Goldsmiths : Meals *(closed lunch Saturday and Sunday)* 28/30 and dinner a la carte 32/38 **t.** 16.50 – 17 – **74 rm** 205 **t.** – SB.

Chief O'Neills, Smithfield Village, Smithfield, D7, ☎ (01) 817 3838, *reservations@chief oneills.com, Fax (01) 817 3839,* « Contemporary interior, interactive music centre, observation tower » – |‡|, ⇔ rm, TV ♿ P – 120. MC AE VISA. ✗ BS n
Kelly & Ping : Meals - Asian - 32.95 dinner and a la carte 23/37 **t.** 16.50 – 12.63 – **73 rm** 253.95 **st.**

Cassidys, 6-8 Cavendish Row, Upper O'Connell St, D1, ☎ (01) 878 0555, *rese@cassidys. iol.ie, Fax (01) 878 0687* – |‡| ⇔, ▤ rest, TV P – 80. MC AE ◑ VISA. ✗ JX m
closed 23-27 December – ***Number Six :*** Meals (dinner only) a la carte 19/31 **t.** 16.67 – **87 rm** 110/150 **st.**, 1 suite.

DUBLIN

Street	Grid	No.
Ailesbury Drive	FV	4
Baggot Street Upper	EU	7
Beech Hill Avenue	FV	10
Beechwood Road	EV	12
Belgrave Road	DV	13
Belleville Avenue	DV	14
Bloomfield Avenue	DU	18
Brighton Road	DV	22
Camden Street	DU	28
Castlewood Avenue	DV	31
Charlemont Street	DU	34
Charlotte Street	DU	36
Chelmsford Road	EV	37
Church Avenue	FU	39
Clyde Road	EFU	43
Eastmoreland Place	EU	61
Effra Road	DU	62
Elgin Road	EFU	6
Harrington Street	DU	7
Herbert Place	EU	7
Irishtown Road	FU	8
Lansdowne Road	FU	9
Lea Road	GU	9
Leeson Street Lower	EU	9
Leinster Road West	DV	9
Londonbridge Road	FU	9
Maxwell Road	DV	1

If you find you cannot take up a hotel booking you have made, please let the hotel know immediately.

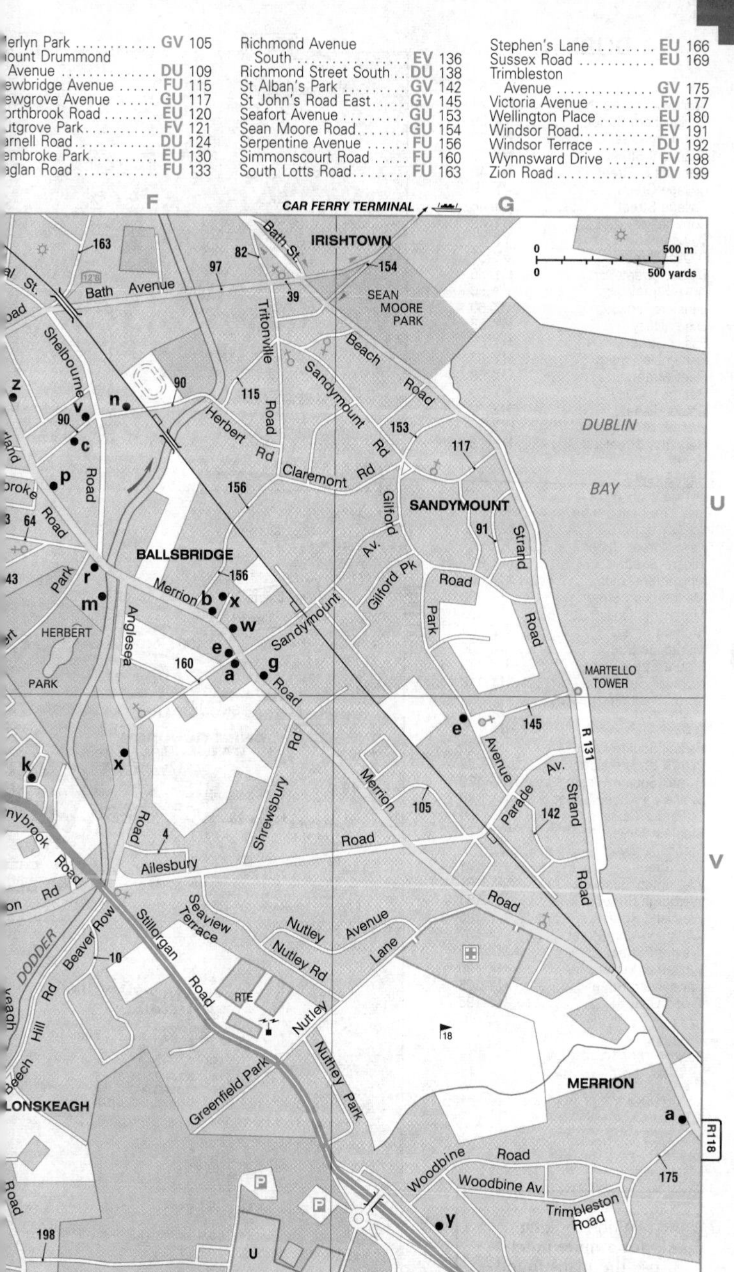

Prévenez immédiatement l'hôtelier si vous ne pouvez pas occuper la chambre aue vous avez retenue.

DUBLIN

Anne Street South . . . . JYZ 6
Brunswick Street North . . . . . HX 24
Buckingham Street. . . . . KX 25
Bull Alley. . . . . HZ 27
Chancery Street . . . . HY 33
Clanbrassil Street . . . . HZ 40
College Green . . . . JY 45
College Street . . . . JY 46
Cornmarket . . . . HY 49
Dawson Street . . . . JYZ
D'Olier Street. . . . . JY 51
Dorset Street. . . . . HY 55
Duke Street . . . . JY 58
Earlsfort Terrace. . . . . JZ 60
Essex Quay . . . . HY 65
Essex Street . . . . HY 66
Fishamble Street. . . . . HY 67
Fleet Street. . . . . JY 68
George's Quay . . . . KY 69
Golden Lane. . . . . HZ 70
Grafton Street . . . . JYZ
Henrietta Street . . . . HX 75
Henry Street. . . . . JX
High Street. . . . . HY 78
Ilac Centre. . . . . HJX
Irish Life Mall Centre. . . . . JKX
Jervis Centre. . . . . HJX
Kevin Street Upper. . . . . HZ 85
Kildare Street. . . . . JKZ 87
King Street South . . . . JZ 88
Marlborough Street. . . . . JX 100
Merchants Quay. . . . . HY 103
Merrion Street. . . . . KZ 104
Montague Street . . . . JZ 106
Mount Street Upper. . . . . KZ 112
Nicholas Street . . . . HY 118
North Great Georges's Street. JX 119
O'Connell Street . . . . JX
Parnell Square East. . . . . JX 126
Parnell Square North . . . . JX 127
Parnell Square West . . . . HJX 129
St Mary's Abbey Street. . . . . . HY 148
St Patrick Close. . . . . HZ 150
Stephen Street . . . . HJY 165
Stephens Green. . . . . JZ
Tara Street . . . . KY 171
Wellington Quay. . . . . HJY 181
Werburgh Street. . . . . HY 183
Westland Row. . . . . KY 186
Westmoreland Street . . . . JY 187
Wexford Street . . . . HZ 189
Whitefriar Street . . . . HZ 190
Winetavern Street . . . . HY 193
Wood Quay . . . . HY 196

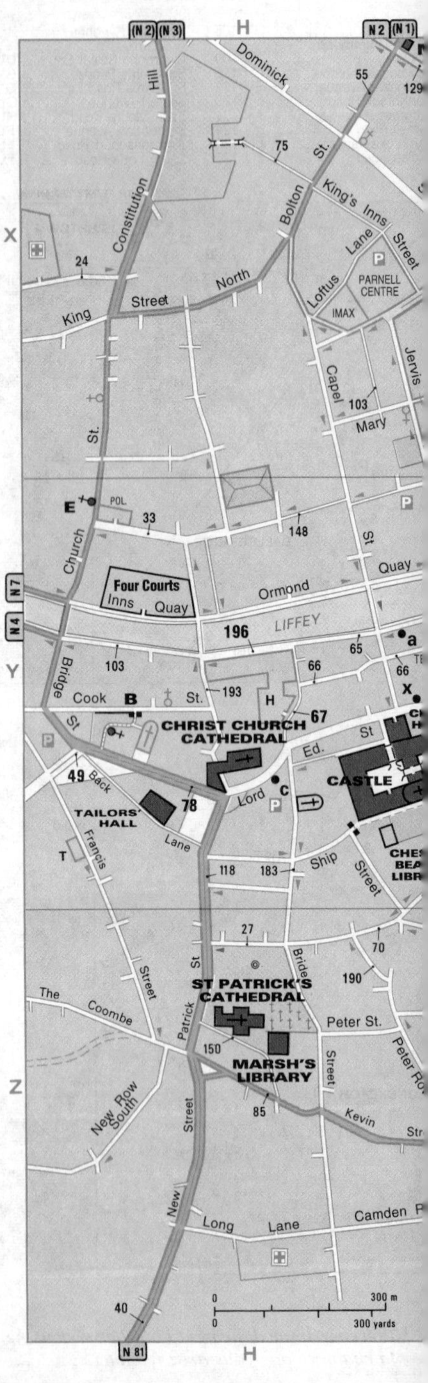

When looking for a quiet hotel use the maps found in the introduction or look for establishments with the sign or .

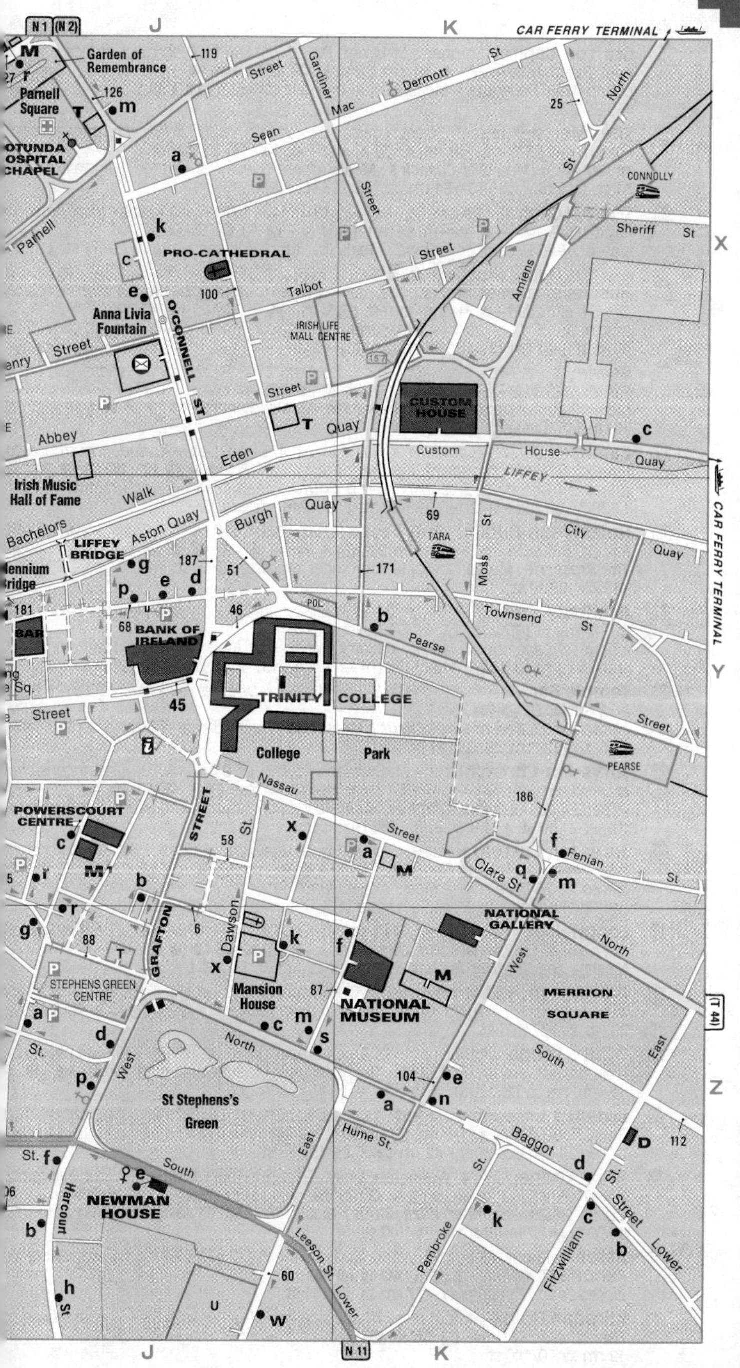
CAR FERRY TERMINAL
Garden of Remembrance
Parnell Square
ROTUNDA HOSPITAL CHAPEL
PRO-CATHEDRAL
Anna Livia Fountain
O'CONNELL ST
IRISH LIFE MALL CENTRE
CUSTOM HOUSE
CONNOLLY
Irish Music Hall of Fame
LIFFEY BRIDGE
Millennium Bridge
LIFFEY
TARA
BANK OF IRELAND
TRINITY COLLEGE
College Park
PEARSE
POWERSCOURT CENTRE
GRAFTON STREET
NATIONAL GALLERY
MERRION SQUARE
Mansion House
NATIONAL MUSEUM
STEPHENS GREEN CENTRE
St Stephens's Green
NEWMAN HOUSE
Leeson St. Lower
Baggot Street
Fitzwilliam St.
Pembroke St.
Harcourt St
Hume St.
Nassau Street
Clare St
Fenian St
Pearse Street
Townsend St
City Quay
Sheriff St
Amiens Street
Talbot Street
Abbey Street
Eden Quay
Custom House Quay
Aston Quay
Bachelors Walk
Burgh Quay
Mac Dermott St
Sean Mac Dermott Street
Gardiner Street
Dawson St.
Moss St
North St
N 1
N 2
N 11
T 44
J
K
X
Y
Z

Grafton Capital, Stephen's St Lower, D2, ✆ (01) 648 1100, *info@graftoncapital-hot com, Fax (01) 648 1122* – |‡|, ⇔ rm, TV ✆ ♿. MC AE ⊙ VISA. ✂ JZ
closed 24-26 December – **Meals** (dinner only) a la carte 23/33 **t.** 15.17 – ☕ 12.70 – **75 r** 158.83/229 **st.**

The Mercer, Mercer Street Lower, D2, ✆ (01) 478 2179, *stay@mercerhotel. Fax (01) 478 0328* – |‡|, ⇔ rm, ▤ TV ♿ 🚗 – 🎤 100. MC AE VISA. ✂ JZ
closed 24-26 December ***Cusack's :*** **Meals** *(closed Sunday dinner)* 19/38 and a la carte 2 34 **st.** 15.23 – ☕ 6.50 – **31 rm** ☕ 165/203 **st.** – SB.

Trinity Capital, Pearse St, D2, ✆ (01) 648 1000, *info@trinitycapital-hotel.co Fax (01) 648 1010* – |‡|, ⇔ rm, ▤ rest, TV ✆ ♿ – 🎤 40. MC AE ⊙ VISA. ✂ KY
closed 24-26 December – ***Siena :*** **Meals** (bar lunch)/dinner a la carte 29/31 **st.** 17.14 ☕ 12.70 – **81 rm** 152.37/222.20 **st.**

Buswells, Molesworth St, D2, ✆ (01) 614 6500, *buswells@quinn-hotels.co Fax (01) 676 2090* – |‡|, ⇔ rm, ▤ rest, TV ✆ P – 🎤 80. MC AE ⊙ VISA. ✂ KZ
closed 25-26 December – ***Brasserie :*** **Meals** (carving lunch)/dinner a la carte 26.8 39.85 **st.** – **67 rm** ☕ 146/218 **st.**, 2 suites – SB.

Bewley's, 19-20 Fleet St, D2, ✆ (01) 670 8122, *bewleyshotel@eircom.n Fax (01) 670 8103* – |‡|, ⇔ rm, ▤ TV. MC AE ⊙ VISA. ✂ JY
closed 24-26 December – ***Bewley's Café :*** **Meals** (dinner only) 20/25 **st.** 16 – ☕ 10 **70 rm** 115/144 **st.**

Camden Court, Camden St, D2, ✆ (01) 475 9666, *sales@camdencourthotel.co Fax (01) 475 9677*, 🏋, ≘s, 🏊 – |‡| ⇔, ▤ rest, TV ✆ ♿ 🚗 – 🎤 125. MC AE ⊙ VISA. ✂
closed 24 December-3 January – ***The Court :*** **Meals** (carving lunch Monday-Saturd 17.78/31.68 and a la carte 22.85/36 **st.** 19 – **246 rm** ☕ 205/255 **st.** DU

Holiday Inn Dublin, 99-107 Pearse St, D2, ✆ (01) 670 3666, *info@holidayinndublin Fax (01) 670 3636* – |‡|, ⇔ rm, ▤ rest, TV ♿ 🚗 – 🎤 100. MC AE ⊙ VISA. ✂ BST
The Brasserie : **Meals** (carvery lunch)/dinner a la carte 28/36 **st.** 15.17 – ☕ 9.95 – **92** 163.79/189.19 **st.**

Academy, Findlater Pl, D1, ✆ (01) 878 0666, *stay@academy-hotel.ie, Fax (01) 878 060* |‡|, ⇔ rm, ▤ TV ✆ P – 🎤 45. MC AE ⊙ VISA. ✂ JX
closed 23 December-2 January ***Oscar's :*** **Meals** (bar lunch Monday-Friday)/dinner 18 and a la carte 18/28 **t.** 11.36 – **96 rm** ☕ 101.57/152.36 **st.**, 2 suites – SB.

Temple Bar, Fleet St, D2, ✆ (01) 677 3333, *templeb@iol.ie, Fax (01) 677 3088* – |‡| TV ♿ – 🎤 80. MC AE ⊙ VISA. ✂ JY
closed 24-27 December – ***Citrus :*** **Meals** (bar lunch)/dinner a la carte 20.31/30.47 14.92 – **129 rm** ☕ 139.68/177.76 **st.**

Jurys Inn Christchurch, Christchurch Pl, D8, ✆ (01) 454 0000, *jurysinnchristchu @jurysdoyle.com, Fax (01) 454 0012* – |‡|, ⇔ rm, ▤ rest, TV ♿. MC AE VISA. ✂ HY
closed 24-26 December – ***Arches :*** **Meals** (bar lunch Saturday and Sunday) (carvery lunc dinner 21.50 **st.** 14 – ☕ 8.50 – **182 rm** 96 **st.**

Jurys Inn Custom House, Custom House Quay, D1, ✆ (01) 607 5000, *jurysinncust house@jurysdoyle.com, Fax (01) 829 0400* – |‡|, ⇔ rm, TV ✆ ♿ – 🎤 100. MC AE VISA. ✂
closed 24-26 December – **Meals** *(closed lunch Saturday and Sunday)* (carvery lunch Mo day-Friday)/dinner 21.50 and a la carte **st.** 14 – ☕ 8.50 – **239 rm** 96 **st.** KX

Longfield's, 10 Lower Fitzwilliam St, D2, ✆ (01) 676 1367, *info@longfields Fax (01) 676 1542*, « Georgian town house » – |‡| TV ✆. MC AE ⊙ VISA. ✂ KZ
Meals – (see ***Number Ten*** below) – **26 rm** ☕ 133.35/190.50 **t.**

Harrington Hall without rest., 70 Harcourt St, D2, ✆ (01) 475 3497, *harrington @eircom.net, Fax (01) 475 4544*, « Georgian town houses » – |‡| ⇔ TV ✆ P. MC AE VISA
28 rm ☕ 127/165 **st.** JZ

Trinity Lodge without rest., 12 South Frederick St, D2, ✆ (01) 679 5044, *trinityloc @eircom.net, Fax (01) 679 5223*, « Georgian town houses » – ▤ TV. MC AE ⊙ VISA
✂ – **10 rm** ☕ 85/220 **st.**, 3 suites. JY

Lynam's without rest., 63-64 O'Connell St, D1, ✆ (01) 888 0886, *lynamhtl@indigc Fax (01) 888 0890* – |‡|, ⇔ rm, TV ✆. MC AE ⊙ VISA. ✂ JX
closed 24-28 December – **42 rm** ☕ 95.23/152.36 **st.**

Eliza Lodge, 23-24 Wellington Quay, D2, ✆ (01) 671 8044, *info@dublinlodge.cc Fax (01) 671 8362*, ⩽ – |‡| ▤ TV ✆. MC AE VISA. ✂ JY
closed 22-28 December ***Eliza Blues :*** **Meals** 34.28/40.63 (dinner) and a la carte 26. 33.90 **t.** 17.71 – **18 rm** ☕ 70/140 **st.**

Aston without rest., 7-9 Aston Quay, D2, ✆ (01) 677 9300, *stay@aston-hotel.cc Fax (01) 677 9007*, ⩽ – |‡| TV ♿. MC AE ⊙ VISA. ✂ JY
closed 24 to 27 December – **27 rm** ☕ 75/165 **st.**

Kilronan House without rest., 70 Adelaide Rd, D2, ✆ (01) 475 5266, *info@dublinn.cc Fax (01) 478 2841* – ⇔ TV. MC AE VISA. ✂ DU
12 rm ☕ 70/140 **st.**

XXXX **Patrick Guilbaud,** 21 Upper Merrion St, D2, ✆ (01) 676 4192, *Fax (01) 661 0052*, « Georgian town house, contemporary Irish Art collection » – ▤. MC AE ◑ VISA KZ e
✿✿ *closed first week January, Sunday and Monday* – **Meals** 28/50 (lunch) and a la carte 71/122 **st.** 32.00
Spec. Lobster ravioli with coconut cream and almonds. Roast squab pigeon with fennel marmalade and spiced Madeira sauce. Rum baba.

XXXX **The Commons,** Newman House, 85-86 St Stephen's Green, D2, ✆ (01) 478 0530, *sales@thecommonsrestaurant.ie, Fax (01) 478 0551*, « Contemporary collection of James Joyce inspired Irish Art » – MC AE ◑ VISA JZ e
✿ *closed 2 weeks August, 1 week Christmas, Saturday lunch, Sunday and Bank Holidays* – **Meals** 31.74 (lunch) and a la carte 65/74 **t.** 25.39
Spec. Brochette of langoustine and asparagus. Roast loin of rabbit, morel risotto and pea purée. Assiette of chocolate.

XXX **Shanahan's,** 119 St Stephen's Green, D2, ✆ (01) 407 0939, *info@shanahans.ie, Fax (01) 407 0940*, « Georgian town house » – ⋇ ▤. MC AE ◑ VISA JZ p
closed 2 weeks Christmas and January, and Sunday – **Meals** (dinner only) a la carte 52/63 **t.** 38.02.

XXX **Peacock Alley** (Gallagher) (at The Fitzwilliam H.), 128 St Stephen's Green, D2, ✆ (01) 478 7015, *info@restaurantpeacockalley.com, Fax (01) 478 7043* – ▤ ⛟. MC AE ◑ VISA JZ d
✿ **Meals** 27.87/69.83 and a la carte 53/76 **t.** 22.85
Spec. Seared and roasted foie gras, vanilla and orange syrup. Roast turbot, pea purée, carrot and ginger. Chocolate fondant, vanilla ice cream, bitter chocolate sauce.

XXX **L'Ecrivain,** 109 Lower Baggot St, D2, ✆ (01) 661 1919, *enquiries@lecrivain.com, Fax (01) 661 0617*, ⛱ – ▤. MC AE VISA KZ b
closed Saturday lunch, Sunday and Bank Holidays – **Meals** (booking essential) 21.52/44.10 and dinner a la carte 32/48.50 **t.**

XXX **Thornton's,** 1 Portobello Rd, D8, ✆ (01) 454 9067, *Fax (01) 453 2947* – ▤. MC AE ◑ VISA DU e
✿✿ *closed 1 week August, 2 weeks Christmas, Sunday and Monday* – **Meals** (booking essential) (dinner only and Friday lunch) 31.74 (lunch) and a la carte 64/70 **t.** 22.85
Spec. Sautéed foie gras with scallops and cep jus. Roast suckling pig with stuffed trotter, poitin sauce. Pyramid of fruit parfait, orange sauce.

XXX **Chapter One,** The Dublin Writers Museum, 18-19 Parnell Sq, D1, ✆ (01) 873 2266, *chapterone@oceanfree.net, Fax (01) 873 2330*, « Contemporary Irish art collection » – ▤ P. MC AE ◑ VISA JX r
closed 25 December-9 January, Sunday, Monday, Saturday lunch and Bank Holidays – **Meals** 25.39 (lunch) and dinner a la carte 37/43 **t.** 18.41.

XX **The Tea Room** (at The Clarence H.), 6-8 Wellington Quay, D2, ✆ (01) 670 7766, *Fax (01) 670 7833* – MC AE ◑ VISA HY a
closed lunch Saturday and Sunday – **Meals** (booking essential) 19.05/49.52 and a la carte 29.20/34.28 23.49.

XX **Halo** (at Morrison H.), Ormond Quay, D1, ✆ (01) 887 2421, *Fax (01) 887 2499*, « Contemporary interior » – ▤. MC AE ◑ VISA JCB HY r
closed 24-27 December – **Meals** 25/40 (lunch) and dinner a la carte 45/59 **t.** 20.95.

XX **brownes brasserie** (at brownes townhouse H.), 22 St Stephen's Green, D2, ✆ (01) 638 3939, *info@brownesdublin.ie, Fax (01) 638 3900* – ▤. MC AE ◑ VISA JZ c
Meals (booking essential) 34.65/47.25 and a la carte 34.75/52.50 **t.** 18.95.

XX **Morningtons Brasserie** (at The Merrion H.), Upper Merrion St, D2, ✆ (01) 603 0630, *Fax (01) 603 0700* – ▤ ⛟. MC AE ◑ VISA JCB KZ e
closed lunch Saturday and Sunday – **Meals** 20.31/24.12 (lunch) and dinner a la carte 30/42 **t.** 22.85.

XX **One Pico,** 5-6 Molesworth Pl, School House Lane, D2, ✆ (01) 676 0300, *eamonnoreilly@ireland.com, Fax (01) 676 0411* – MC AE ◑ VISA JZ k
closed 25-27 December, 1 January and Sunday – **Meals** a la carte 32/44 **t.** 19.68.

XX **Les Frères Jacques,** 74 Dame St, D2, ✆ (01) 679 4555, *info@lesfreresjacques.com, Fax (01) 679 4725* – MC AE VISA HY x
closed 24 December-2 January, Saturday lunch and Sunday – **Meals** - French - 19.04/31.74 and a la carte 40/58 **t.** 15.87.

XX **Number Ten** (at Longfield's H.), 10 Lower Fitzwilliam St, D2, ✆ (01) 676 1060, *Fax (01) 676 1542* – MC AE ◑ VISA KZ d
closed lunch Saturday and Sunday) – **Meals** 17.78/36.77 **t.** 19.70.

XX **La Stampa** (at La Stampa H.), 35 Dawson St, D2, ✆ (01) 677 8611, *lastampa@eircom.net, Fax (01) 677 336*, « Former 19C ballroom, collection of Graham Nuttel paintings » – MC AE ◑ VISA JZ x
Meals (booking essential) (dinner only) 44.44/48.25 and a la carte 30/44 **t.** 18.41.

XX **Diep Le Shaker,** 55 Pembroke Lane, D2, ✆ (01) 661 1829, *Fax (01) 661 5905* – ▤. MC VISA KZ
closed 25-26 December, Saturday lunch, Sunday and Bank Holidays – **Meals** - Thai - 31.74 44.44 (dinner) and a la carte 20/60 **t.** 18.41.

XX **Saagar,** 16 Harcourt St, D2, ✆ (01) 475 5060, *saagar@iol.ie, Fax (01) 475 5741* – MC VISA JZ
closed 25 December, 1 January, Saturday and Sunday lunch – **Meals** - Indian - a la carte 20/27 **st.**

XX **Locks,** 1 Windsor Terr, Portobello, D8, ✆ (01) 4543391, *Fax (01) 4538352* – MC AE VISA DU
closed 24 December-7 January, Saturday lunch, Sunday and Bank Holidays – **Meals** 22.80 38.05 and a la carte 41.75/58.65 **t.** 17.45.

XX **Jacobs Ladder,** 4-5 Nassau St, D2, ✆ (01) 670 3865, *jaladder@gofree.indigo. Fax (01) 670 3868* – ⊁. MC AE VISA KY
closed 3 weeks Christmas-New Year, 1 week August, 17 March, Sunday and Monday – **Meals** (booking essential) 31.74 (dinner) and a la carte 32.30/48.20 **st.** 16.50.

XX **Bang Café,** 11 Merrion Row, D2, ✆ (01) 676 0898, *Fax (01) 676 0899* – ▤. MC VISA KZ
closed 1 week Christmas and Sunday – **Meals** (booking essential) a la carte 25/45.44 17.71.

X **Dobbin's,** 15 Stephen's Lane, off Lower Mount St, D2, ✆ (01) 676 4679, *dobbinswine bistro@eircom.net, Fax (01) 661 3331,* – ▤ P. MC AE VISA EU
closed 1 week Christmas-New Year, Sunday, Monday dinner, Saturday lunch and Bank Holidays – **Meals** - Bistro - (booking essential) 20.95 (lunch) and dinner a la carte 39/50 20.95.

X **Bruno's,** 21 Kildare St, D2, ✆ (01) 662 4724, *Fax (01) 662 3857* – ▤. MC AE VISA JZ
closed 25 December-2 January and Sunday – **Meals** 18.42/39.70 and dinner la carte 34.2 50.73 **t.** 18.42.

X **Bruno's,** 30 East Essex St, Temple Bar, D2, ✆ (01) 670 6767, *Fax (01) 670 8278* – ▤. MC VISA JY
closed 25 December-2 January, Saturday lunch and Sunday – **Meals** (booking essential) 18.42/43.18 and a la carte 28.08/46.67 **t.** 17.72.

X **Pearl Brasserie,** 20 Merrion St Upper, D2, ✆ (01) 661 3572, *petitepearl@eircom.net Fax (01) 661 3629* – ▤. MC AE VISA JZ
closed first 2 weeks January and Bank Holidays – **Meals** (Sunday brunch) a la carte 25/44

X **Eden,** Meeting House Sq, Temple Bar, D2, ✆ (01) 670 5372, *Fax (01) 670 3330,* – ▤. AE VISA HY
closed 25-28 December and Bank Holidays – **Meals** 20.95 (lunch) and dinner a la carte 24/37 **t.** 20.31.

X **Cooke's Café,** 14 South William St, D2, ✆ (01) 679 0536, *cookes1@iol Fax (01) 679 0546,* – ▤. MC AE VISA JY
Meals a la carte 23/40 19.40.

X **Moe's,** 112 Lower Baggot St, D2, ✆ (01) 676 7610, *moesdublin@hotmail.co Fax (01) 676 7606* – MC AE VISA KZ
closed 24-25 December, 1 January, Saturday lunch and Sunday – **Meals** a la carte 29/40 20.12.

X **Mermaid Café,** 69-70 Dame St, D2, ✆ (01) 670 8236, *Fax (01) 670 8205* – ▤. VISA HY
closed 24-26 and 31 December, 1 January and Good Friday – **Meals** (booking essential) a la carte 23/39 **t.** 17.07.

X **Cafe Mao,** 2-3 Chatham Row, D2, ✆ (01) 670 4899, *info@cafemao.com, Fax (01) 670 48* – ▤. MC VISA JZ
closed Good Friday and 25-26 December – **Meals** - South East Asian - (bookings not accepted) a la carte 18/27 **t.** 16.44.

The Cellar Bar (at The Merrion H.), Upper Merrion St, D2, ✆ (01) 603 0631, *info@merrion hotel.com, Fax (01) 603 0700,* « Restored vaulted Georgian cellars » – . MC AE VISA KZ
Meals (live music Sunday brunch) (lunch only) a la carte 20/21 **t.** 22.85.

Ballsbridge.

Dublin 4.

Four Seasons, Simmonscourt Rd, D4, ✆ (01) 665 4000, *sales.dublin@fourseasons.co Fax (01) 665 4099,* , , , – , ⊁ rm, ▤ , , , – 500. MC AE VISA FU
Seasons : Meals 32.69 (lunch) and a la carte 53/70 **t.** 31.74 – ***The Cafe :*** Meals a la carte 30/46 **t.** 31.74 – 20.95 – **192 rm** 495 **st.**, 67 suites 635/2100 **st.**

The Berkeley Court, Lansdowne Rd, D4, (01) 660 1711, *berkeleycourt@jurysdoyle.com, Fax (01) 661 7238,* – , rm, – 450. FU c
Berkeley Room : Meals *(closed Saturday lunch Sunday dinner)* 33 and a la carte 41/95 **t.** 20.00 – ***Palm Court Café :*** Meals 18 (lunch) and a la carte 28/42 **t.** 18 – 22 – **183 rm** 300 **t.**, 5 suites.

The Towers, Lansdowne Rd, D4, (01) 667 0033, *towers@jurysdoyle.com, Fax (01) 660 5324,* , , heated – . FU p
Meals 22 (lunch) and a la carte 28/42 **t.** 17 – 17 – **101 rm** 280/320 **t.**, 4 suites.

Jurys, Pembroke Rd, D4, (01) 660 5000, *ballsbridge@jurysdoyle.com, Fax (01) 660 5540,* , , heated – , rest, – 800. FU p
Raglans : Meals 22 (lunch) and a la carte 18/33 **t.** 17 – 17 – **300** 240/270 **t.**, 3 suites.

Herbert Park, D4, (01) 667 2200, *reservations@herbertparkhotel.ie, Fax (01) 667 2595,* , – , rm, – 100. FU m
The Pavilion : Meals *(closed dinner Sunday and Bank Holidays)* 23.50/25 (lunch) and dinner a la carte 31.74/45.65 **st.** 20 – 19 – **150 rm** 130/275 **st.**, 3 suites – SB.

The Hibernian, Eastmoreland Pl, D4, (01) 668 7666, *info@hibernianhotel.ie, Fax (01) 660 2655* – – 30. EU x
closed 24-27 December – ***Patrick Kavanagh Room :*** Meals *(closed Saturday and Sunday lunch and Sunday dinner to non-residents)* 17.71/22.79 (lunch) and dinner a la carte 31.04/48.82 **t.** 20.32 – 15.24 – **40 rm** 190.46/241.25 **st.** – SB.

The Schoolhouse, 2-8 Northumberland Rd, D4, (01) 667 5014, *school@schoolhousehotel.iol.ie, Fax (01) 667 5015,* « Converted Victorian schoolhouse », – , rm, . EU a
closed 24-27 December – ***Satchels :*** Meals (bar lunch Saturday) 9/38 and dinner a la carte 23.50/38 **st.** 18 – **31 rm** 159/204 **st.**

Ariel House without rest., 52 Lansdowne Rd, D4, (01) 668 5512, *reservations@ariel-house.com, Fax (01) 668 5845* – . FU n
closed 2 weeks Christmas – 12.00 – **37 rm** 95.25/228.60 **st.**

Bewley's, Merrion Rd, D4, (01) 668 1111, *bb@bewleyshotels.com, Fax (01) 668 1999,* , « Victorian facade » – rm, rest, – 30. FU a
closed 24-26 December – ***O'Connells*** *((01) 647 3400)* **:** Meals 20.32 (lunch) and dinner a la carte 25.97/37.34 **t.** 20.32 – 8.76 – **220 rm** 99 **st.**

Butlers Town House, 44 Lansdowne Rd, D4, (01) 667 4022, *info@butlers-hotel.com, Fax (01) 667 3960* – . FU v
closed 23 December-8 January – Meals (room service only) – **19 rm** 139.67/215.86 **st.**

Aberdeen Lodge, 53-55 Park Av, D4, (01) 283 8155, *aberdeen@iol.ie, Fax (01) 283 7877,* – . GV e
Meals (light meals) (residents only) a la carte 20/30.50 **t.** 12 – **17 rm** 90/130 – SB.

Pembroke Townhouse without rest., 90 Pembroke Rd, D4, (01) 660 0277, *info@pembroketownhouse.ie, Fax (01) 660 0291,* « Georgian town house » – . FU d
closed 22 December-3 January – **48 rm** 129/192 **st.**

Waterloo House without rest., 8-10 Waterloo Rd, D4, (01) 660 1888, *waterloohouse@eircom.ie, Fax (01) 667 1955,* « Georgian town house », – . EU p
closed 23 to 28 December – **17 rm** 95.25/165.10.

Merrion Hall, 54-56 Merrion Rd, D4, (01) 668 1426, *merrionhall@iol.ie, Fax (01) 668 4280,* – – 40. FU b
Meals (light meals) (residents only) a la carte 20/30.50 **t.** 12 – **23 rm** 90.00/130 – SB.

Glenogra House without rest., 64 Merrion Rd, D4, (01) 668 3661, *glenogra@indigo.ie, Fax (01) 668 3698* – . FU w
closed 20 December-20 January – **13 rm** 70/110 **st.**

Cedar Lodge Guesthouse without rest., 98 Merrion Rd, D4, (01) 668 4410, *info@cedarlodge.ie, Fax (01) 668 4533,* – . FU g
closed 24 to 29 December – **15 rm** 88/150 **st.**

Anglesea Town House without rest., 63 Anglesea Rd, D4, (01) 668 3877, *Fax (01) 668 3461* – . FV x
closed Christmas and New Year – **7 rm** 65/130 **st.**

Simmonstown House without rest., Sydenham Rd, off Merrion Rd, D4, (01) 660 7260, *info@simmonstownhouse.com, Fax (01) 660 7341* – . FU x
closed 13 December-7 January – **4 rm** 89/152 **st.**

66 Townhouse without rest., 66 Northumberland Rd, D4, (01) 660 0333, *Fax (01) 660 1051* – . FU z
closed 22 December-13 January – **8 rm** 69.83/152.36 **st.**

Roly's Bistro, 7 Ballsbridge Terr, D4, (01) 668 2611, *Fax (01) 660 8535* – . FU r
Meals (booking essential) 17.71 (lunch) and a la carte 31/35 **t.** 16.44.

Donnybrook.

Dublin 4.

Morehampton Lodge without rest., 113 Morehampton Rd, D4, ✆ (01) 283 749 *Fax (01) 283 7595* – ⇔ TV P. MC AE ◑ VISA. ✻ EV
closed 20 December-3 January – **17 rm** ☐ 89/203 st.

Eglinton Manor without rest., 83 Eglinton Rd, D4, ✆ (01) 269 3273, *Fax (01) 269 752* – ⇔ TV P. MC AE VISA EV
8 rm ☐ 126.97 st.

Ernie's, Mulberry Gdns, off Morehampton Rd, D4, ✆ (01) 269 3300, *Fax (01) 269 326* « Contemporary Irish Art collection » – ▤. MC AE ◑ VISA FV
closed 22 December-3 January, Sunday, Monday and Saturday lunch – **Meals** 16.44/36.8 and a la carte 50.14/66.01 **st.** 17.78.

Drumcondra.

Dublin 5.

Jurys Skylon, Upper Drumcondra Rd, D9, North : 2½ m. on N 1 ✆ (01) 837 9121, *skylc @jurysdoyle.com, Fax (01) 837 2778* – |♯|, ⇔ rm, TV ✆ ♿ P. MC AE VISA. ✻ BS
The Rendezvous Room : Meals 18/26 **t.** 14 – ☐ 10 – **88 rm** 149 **st.**

Merrion.

Dublin 6.

Jurys Tara, Merrion Rd, D4, Southeast : 4 m. on R 118 ✆ (01) 269 4666, *tara@jurysdoy com, Fax (01) 269 1027* – |♯| TV ✆ ♿ P – 300. MC AE VISA. ✻ GV
Meals a la carte 17.65/24.95 7.00 ***The Conservatory :*** **Meals** (dinner only and lunc Saturday and Sunday) 18/27 **t.** 18 – ☐ 12 – **113 rm** 149 **st.**

Rathgar.

Dublin 6.

St Aiden's without rest., 32 Brighton Rd, D6, ✆ (01) 490 2011, *staidens@eircom.ne Fax (01) 492 0234* – TV P. MC VISA. ✻ DV
closed 22-28 December – **8 rm** ☐ 60/100.

Poppadom, 91A Rathgar Rd, D6, ✆ (01) 490 2383, *Fax (01) 492 3900* – ▤. MC VISA DV
closed 25-26 December – **Meals** - Indian - (booking essential) (dinner only) a la car 25/34 **t.** 15.23.

Rathmines.

Dublin 6.

Rathmines Capital, Lower Rathmines Rd, D6, ✆ (01) 496 6966, *info@rathminescapit hotels.com, Fax (01) 491 0603* – |♯| TV ✆ ♿ P. MC AE ◑ VISA. ✻ DV
closed 24-26 December – ***Savannah :*** **Meals** (carvery lunch) a la carte 14/25 **t.** 13.33 **54 rm** ☐ 114.50/140 **t.** – SB.

Quality Charleville, Lower Rathmines Rd, D6, ✆ (01) 406 6100, *info@charlevillehot com, Fax (01) 406 6200* – |♯|, ⇔ rm, ▤ rest, TV ✆ ♿ 🚗. MC AE ◑ VISA. ✻ DV
Carmines : **Meals** - Italian - (bar lunch Monday-Saturday)/dinner 19.05 **t.** – **9 rm** ☐ 165.0 203.16 **st., 43 suites** 203.16 **st.**

Uppercross House, 26-30 Upper Rathmines Rd, D6, ✆ (01) 4975486, *uppercrosshote ireland.com, Fax (01) 4975361* – |♯|, ⇔ rm, TV ✆ P. MC AE ◑ VISA DV
closed 23-26 December – ***The Restaurant :*** **Meals** (dinner only and lunch Saturday ar Sunday) 15.25/31.74 and dinner a la carte 14.85/40.25 **st.** 17.15 – **49 rm** ☐ 88.2 125.70 **st.**

Zen, 89 Upper Rathmines Rd, D6, ✆ (01) 4979428 – ▤. MC AE ◑ VISA DV
Meals - Chinese (Szechuan) - (dinner only and lunch Thursday, Friday and Sunday) a la car 22.22/46.98 **t.** 16.44.

at Dublin Airport *North : 6½ m. by N 1 – BS – and M 1 – ✉ Dublin.*

Great Southern, ✆ (01) 844 6000, *dubairport@gsh.ie, Fax (01) 844 6001* – |♯|, ⇔ rm, ✆ ♿ P – 450. MC AE ◑ VISA. ✻
closed 24-26 December – ***Potters :*** **Meals** (bar lunch Monday-Saturday)/dinner 35 13. – ***Clancys Bar :*** **Meals** (carvery lunch)/dinner a la carte 13/17 **st.** 13.97 – ☐ 17 – **147 r** 190 **st.** – SB.

Holiday Inn Dublin Airport, ✆ (01) 808 0500, *reservations-dublinairport@6c.co Fax (01) 844 6002* – ⇔ rm, ▤ rest, TV ✆ ♿ P – 130. MC AE ◑ VISA. ✻
closed 24-25 December – ***Bistro :*** **Meals** *(closed Saturday lunch)* 16.75/26.60 and di ner a la carte 31/37 **t.** 6.95 – ***Sampan's :*** **Meals** - Asian - *(closed Bank Holidays)* (dinr only) a la carte 22/31 **t.** 15.17 – ☐ 16.44 – **249 rm** 177/209 **t.** – SB.

at Clontarf *Northeast : 3½ m. by R 105 – ✉ Dublin.*

Clontarf Castle, Castle Ave, D3, ✆ (01) 833 2321, *info@clontarfcastle.ie, Fax (01) 833 0418,* – , rm, – 500. CS a
closed 24-25 December – ***Templars Bistro :*** Meals (carvery lunch Monday-Saturday)/ dinner a la carte 36/44 **t.** 19.80 – 15.87 – **108 rm** 222/242 **t.**, 3 suites – SB.

Hedigan's without rest., Tullyallan House, 14 Hollybrook Park, D3, ✆ (01) 853 1663, *hedigans@indigo.ie, Fax (01) 833 3337,* – . CS e
closed 22 December-10 January – **9 rm** 57.13/101.57 **st.**

at Stillorgan *Southeast : 5 m. on N 11 – CT – ✉ Dublin.*

Radisson SAS St. Helen's, Stillorgan Rd, D4, ✆ (01) 218 6000, *info.dublin@radissonsas.com, Fax (01) 218 6010,* « Part 18C mansion, formal gardens », – – 350.
Le Panto : Meals *(closed Sunday and Monday)* (dinner only) a la carte 44.44/60.94 **st.** 24.13 – ***Tolavera :*** Meals - Italian - 29.50 (lunch) and a la carte 25.39/44.44 19 – 19 – **130 rm** 205 **st.**, 21 suites.

Stillorgan Park, Stillorgan Rd, ✆ (01) 288 1621, *sales@stillorganpark.com, Fax (01) 283 1610* – , rm, – 600.
Purple Sage : Meals (carvery lunch)/dinner a la carte 29.85/42.52 **st.** 20.30 – ***Turf Club :*** Meals 21.54/32.94 **st.** 20.30 – **129 rm** 170/195 **st.**

Jurys Montrose, Stillorgan Rd, D4, ✆ (01) 269 3311, *montrose@jurysdoyle.com, Fax (01) 269 1164* – , rm, – 70. GV y
The Belfield : Meals 17/27 **t.** 18 – 8.50 – **179 rm** 149 **st.**

at Blackrock *Southeast : 5½ m. by R 118 – CT – ✉ Dublin.*

Dali's, 63-65 Main St, ✆ (01) 278 0660, *Fax (01) 278 0661* – .
closed 25-27 and 31 December, Monday and Sunday dinner – **Meals** 13.90/17.71 (lunch) and a la carte 29.12/35.56 **t.** 17.14.

Blueberry's, 1st floor (above Jack O'Rourkes pub), 15 Main St, ✆ (01) 278 8900, *blueberrys@clubi.ie, Fax (01) 278 8903* –
closed 25-26 December, 1 January, Good Friday, Saturday lunch and Sunday dinner – **Meals** (booking essential) 16.50 (lunch) and dinner a la carte 19.60/28.00 14.50.

at Monkstown *Southeast : 6½ m. by R 118 – CT – on R 119 – ✉ Dublin.*

Siam Thai, 8a The Crescent, ✆ (01) 284 3309, *siam@eircom.net, Fax (01) 845 7178* –
on Dun Laoghaire town plan s
Meals - Thai - (dinner only) 25.41/31.74 and a la carte 28/30 **t.** 16.44.

at Foxrock *Southeast : 7½ m. by N 11 – CT – ✉ Dublin.*

Bistro One, 3 Brighton Rd, D18, ✆ (01) 289 7711, *Fax (01) 2899 858* –
closed 25 to 26 and 31 December, Sunday and Monday – **Meals** (booking essential) (dinner only) a la carte 25/47 **t.** 21.58.

at Tallaght *Southwest : 7½ m. by N 81 – BT – ✉ Dublin.*

The Plaza, Belgard Rd, D24, at junction of N 81 and R 113 ✆ (01) 462 4200, *sales@plazahotel.ie, Fax (01) 462 4600* – , rm, rest, – 300.
closed 24-30 September – ***The Olive Tree :*** Meals *(closed Sunday)* 35/44 and a la carte 33/44 **st.** 16.44 – 17.71 – **120 rm** 159 **st.**, 2 suites.

Abberley Court, Belgard Rd, D24, on R 113 ✆ (01) 459 6000, *abberley@iol.ie, Fax (01) 462 1000* – .
closed 25-30 December – ***The Leaf :*** Meals - Chinese - (dinner only and lunch Thursday, Friday, Sunday) a la carte 24.12/31.74 **t.** 15.24 – **38 rm** 100.30/124.43 **t.**

at Clondalkin *Southwest : 8 m. by N 7 on R 113 – AT – ✉ Dublin.*

Red Cow Moran, Naas Rd, D22, Southeast : 2 m. on N 7 at junction with M 50 ✆ (01) 459 3650, *info@morangroup.ie, Fax (01) 459 1588* – , rm, – 700.
closed 24-26 December – ***The Winter Garden :*** Meals 19.68/47.29 and dinner a la carte 28.18/47.29 **t.** 17.71 – **120 rm** 185/250 **t.**, 3 suites – SB.

Bewley's H. Newlands Cross, Newlands Cross, Naas Rd (N7), D22, ✆ (01) 464 0140, *res@bewleyshotels.com, Fax (01) 464 0900* – , rm, rest, .
closed 24-26 December – **Meals** (carving lunch) a la carte 15/27 **t.** – 9 – **258 rm** 75 **st.**

Ibis Dublin (without rest.), Monastery Rd, D22, Southeast : 1 ¾ m. on N 7 at junction with M 50 ✆ (01) 464 1480, *ho595@accor-hotels.com, Fax (01) 464 1484* – , rm, . – **150 rm** 62.85/75.55 **st.**

at Saggart *Southwest : 9¼ m. off N 7 – AT – ✉ Dublin.*

Citywest Conference Centre and Golf Resort, ✆ (01) 401 0500, *info@citywes hotel.ie, Fax (01) 458 8565,* ⛯, 🏊, 🏊, 🏌18 – 🛗, 🚭 rm, ▤ rest, 📺 ✆ 🅿 – 🎤 3800. 🅜🅒 AE VISA. 🐕
The Terrace : Meals 16.95/30.95 🍷 12.95 – ***The Grill Room :*** Meals (carvery res a la carte approx. 24.75 🍷 12.95 – **317 rm** ☕ 145/175 **t.**, 13 suites – SB.

Quality, Naas Rd, ✆ (01) 458 7000, *info@qualityhotel.com, Fax (01) 458 7019,* 🌳 – ▤ rest, 📺 ♿ 🅿 – 🎤 30. 🅜🅒 AE 🅓 VISA. 🐕
closed 24-27 December – ***The Westpark :*** Meals a la carte 18/29 **st.** – ☕ 8.25 – **74 r** 100.31/113.01 **st.**, **72 suites** 126.97/152.37 **st.** – SB.

at Castleknock *Northwest : 5½ m. by N 3 – AS – ✉ Dublin.*

Travelodge, Auburn Ave roundabout, D15, on N 3 ✆ (01) 820 2626, *Fax (01) 820 215* 🚭 rm, ▤ rest, 📺 ♿ 🅿. 🅜🅒 AE 🅓 VISA JCB. 🐕
Meals (grill rest.) – **100 rm** 88.95 **t.**

DUBLIN AIRPORT *Dublin* 923 N 7 – *see Dublin.*

DUNDALK **(Dun Dealgan)** *Louth* 923 M 5/6 *Ireland G. – pop. 25 762.*

Exc. : *Dún a' Rí Forest Park★, W : 21 m. by R 178 and R 179.*

🏌18 *Killinbeg, Killin Park, Bridge a Chrin ✆ (042) 9339303.*

ℹ *✆ (042) 9335484.*

Dublin 51 – Drogheda 22.

Ballymascanlon, North : 3½ m. by N 1 on R 173 ✆ (042) 9371124, *info@ballymascanlo com, Fax (042) 9371598,* ⛯, 🏊, 🏊, 🏌, 🌳, 🎾, 🍽 – 🛗 📺 ♿ 🅿 – 🎤 100. 🅜🅒 AE 🅓 VISA.
closed 24 to 25 December – Meals 19/35 **t.** 🍷 17 – **90 rm** ☕ 102/145 **t.** – SB.

Fairways, South : 3 m. on N 1 ✆ (042) 9321500, *info@fairways.ie, Fax (042) 9321511,* – 📺 🅿 – 🎤 400. 🅜🅒 AE 🅓 VISA. 🐕
closed 25 December – ***Modis :*** Meals (dinner only and Sunday lunch)/dinner a la ca 29.50/40.50 **t.** 🍷 17 – ***Fairways Grill :*** Meals a la carte 22/32 **t.** 🍷 17 – **48 rm** ☕ 95/160 t SB.

at Carrickcarnon *North : 8 m. on N 1 – ✉ Dundalk.*

Carrickdale, ✆ (042) 9371397, *Fax (042) 9371740,* ⛯, 🏊, 🏊, 🌳 – 📺 🅿 – 🎤 150. AE 🅓 VISA. 🐕
closed 25 December – Meals (carving lunch)/dinner 30.47 and a la carte 16/30 **st.** 🍷 14.6 **115 rm** ☕ 69.84/114.28 **st.** – SB.

DUNFANAGHY **(Dún Fionnachaidh)** *Donegal* 923 I 2 *Ireland G. – pop. 290 – ✉ Letterkenny.*

Env. : *Horn Head Scenic Route★, N : 2½ m.*

Exc. : *Doe Castle★, SE : 7 m. by N 56 – The Rosses★, SW : 25 m. by N 56 and R 259.*

🏌18 *Dunfanaghy, Letterkenny ✆ (074) 36335.*

Dublin 172 – Donegal 54 – Londonderry 43.

Arnold's, Main St, ✆ (074) 36208, *arnoldshotel@teircom.net, Fax (074) 36352,* ≤, 🌳 – 🅿. 🅜🅒 AE 🅓 VISA. 🐕
mid March-November – ***Tramore rest. :*** Meals (dinner only) 32/40 and a la carte 3 37.50 **t.** 🍷 16.50 – ***Garden bistro :*** Meals a la carte 26.45/32 **t.** 🍷 17.50 – **30 rm** ☕ 66/13 – SB.

Carrig Rua, Main St, ✆ (074) 36133, *carrigruahotel@eircom.net, Fax (074) 36277,* ≤ – 🅿. 🅜🅒 VISA. 🐕
closed 25 December – ***Sheephaven Room :*** Meals (dinner only) 12.70 and a la ca 17/30 **st.** 🍷 17.78 – ***The Thursday Club :*** Meals a la carte 13/22 **st.** 🍷 17.78 – **22** ☕ 63.49/114.28 **st.** – SB.

The Mill with rm, Southwest : ½ m. on N 56 ✆ (074) 36985, *themillrestaurant@oceanfr net, Fax (074) 36985,* ≤ New Lake and Mount Muckish, « Loughside setting », 🌳 – 🚭 🅿. 🅜🅒 VISA. 🐕
restricted opening in winter and closed Monday – Meals (dinner only and Sunday lun first Sunday in every month) 34.50 **t.** 🍷 13.50 – **6 rm** ☕ 44.45/76 **t.**

Les prix — Pour toutes précisions sur les prix indiqués dans ce guide, reportez-vous aux pages de l'introduction.

UNGARVAN **(Dún Garbháin)** *Waterford* 923 J 11 *Ireland G. – pop. 7 175.*

See : *East Bank (Augustinian priory, ≤★).*

Exc. : *Ringville (≤★), S : 8 m. by N 25 and R 674 – Helvick Head★ (≤★), SE : 8 m. by N 25 and R 674.*

Knocknagrannagh (058) 41605 – Gold Coast, Ballinacourty (058) 42249.

Town Centre (058) 41741.

Dublin 118 – Cork 44 – Waterford 30.

Lawlors, Bridge St, (058) 41122, *info@lawlors-hotel.ie, Fax (058) 41000* – , rest, – 300. MC AE VISA.
closed 25 December – **Meals** 14.60/25.33 and dinner a la carte 16/23 **t.** 13.90 – **89 rm** 63.49/120.63 **st.**

The Tannery, 10 Quay St, via Parnell St. (058) 45420, *tannery@cablesurf.com, Fax (058) 45518,* « 19C former tannery » – MC AE VISA
closed 3 weeks late January-first week February, Christmas, Saturday lunch, Sunday dinner except summer and Monday – **Meals** a la carte 21.10/34 17.

UNGLOW **(An Clochán Liath)** *Donegal* 923 G 3 *Ireland G. – pop. 1 042.*

Env. : *The Rosses★.*

Exc. : *Gweebarra Estuary★, S : by N 56.*

Cruit Island, Kincasslagh (075) 43296.

Lower Main St (075) 21297 (June-August).

Dublin 173 – Londonderry 51 – Sligo 76.

Ostan na Rosann, Mill Rd, (075) 22444, *ostannarosann@iol.ie, Fax (075) 22400,* ≤, , – rest, . MC AE VISA.
Meals a la carte 17/27 **st.** 15.88 – **48 rm** 82.55/125.73 **st.** – SB.

Atlantic House without rest., Main St, (075) 21061, *jcannon@iol.ie, Fax (075) 21061* – . MC VISA.
closed 20 to 30 December – **10 rm** 31.74/50.79 **st.**

The Guide is updated annually so renew your Guide every year.

UNKINEELY **(Dún Cionnaola)** *Donegal* 923 G 4 *Ireland G. – pop. 395.*

Exc. : *Donegal Coast★★ – Cliffs of Bunglass★★ – Glengesh Pass★★ – Glencolmcille Folk Village★★.*

Dublin 157 – Londonderry 56 – Sligo 50.

Castle Murray House with rm, St Johns Point, Southwest : 1 ¼ m. by N 56 and St. Johns Point rd turning left at T junction (073) 37022, *castlemurray@eircom.net, Fax (073) 37330,* ≤ McSweeney Bay – . MC VISA.
closed mid January-mid February and 25-26 December – **Meals** - French - (dinner only and Sunday lunch)/dinner 30.47/34.28 **t.** 14.60 – **10 rm** 85.07/124.43 **t.** – SB.

UN LAOGHAIRE **(Dún Laoghaire)** *Dublin* 923 N 8 *Ireland G. – pop. 55 540.*

Env. : *≤★★ of Killiney Bay from coast road south of Sorrento Point.*

Dun Laoghaire, Eglinton Park (01) 458 2622.

to Holyhead (Stena Line) 4-5 daily (1 h 40 mn).

Ferry Terminal.

Dublin 9.

Plan on next page

The Gresham Royal Marine, Marine Rd, (01) 280 1911, *info@gresham-royalmarinehotel.com, Fax (01) 280 1089,* ≤, – , rest, – 400. MC AE VISA. n
Powerscourt Room : Meals 19/28 and a la carte **t.** 19.73 – **96 rm** 150/210 **st.** – SB.

The Cumberland Lodge without rest., 54 York Rd, (01) 280 9665, *cumberlandlodge@tinet.ie, Fax (01) 284 3227,* « Regency town house », – . MC AE VISA. e
4 rm 70/90.

Duzy's Café, 1st floor (above Eagle House pub), 18 Glasthule Rd, (01) 230 0210, *duzyscafe@eircom.net, Fax (01) 230 0466* – MC AE VISA c
closed 25-27 December, 1 January, Good Friday and Saturday lunch – **Meals** (light lunch)/dinner 17.14 and a la carte 26/34 **t.** 15.24.

Cavistons, 59 Glasthule Rd, (01) 280 9245, *caviston@indigo.ie, Fax (01) 284 4054* – . MC AE VISA a
closed 22 December-4 January, Sunday and Monday – **Meals** - Seafood - (booking essential) (lunch only) a la carte 23/34 16.44.

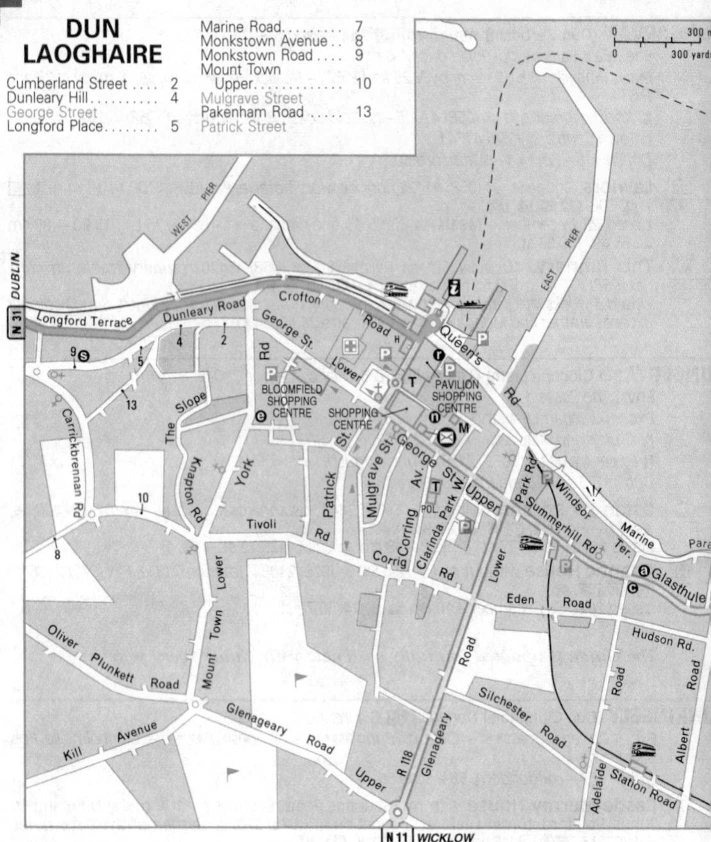

Mao Café, The Pavilion, ✆ (01) 214 8090, *info@cafemao.com, Fax (01) 214 7064* – ▤. AE
closed 25 December and Good Friday – **Meals** - South East Asian - (bookings not accepte
a la carte 21/28 **t.** 16.44.

DUNLAVIN (Dún Luáin) *Wicklow* 923 L 8 – *pop. 693.*

Rathsallagh ✆ (045) 403316.

Dublin 31 – Kilkenny 44 – Wexford 61.

Rathsallagh House, Southwest : 2 m. on Grangecon Rd ✆ (045) 403112, *inf rathsallagh.com, Fax (045) 403343*, ≤, « 18C converted stables, walled garden », – TV P. – 50. AE VISA JCB
closed 23 to 28 December – **Meals** (dinner only) 49/58 **st.** 17.78 – **28 rm** 150/270 1 suite – SB.

DUNMANWAY (Dún Mánmhaí) *Cork* 923 E 12 – *pop. 1 427.*

Dublin 191 – Cork 37 – Killarney 49.

Dún Mhuire House, Kilbarry Rd, West : ½ m. by R 586 taking first right at fork junct ✆ (023) 45162, *hayesdunmhuire@eircom.net, Fax (023) 45162*, – TV P.
closed 17 December-12 January – **Meals** *(weekends only)* (booking essential) (dinner o 30.47 **t.** 15.24 – **6 rm** 64 **t.**

UNMORE EAST (Dún Mór) *Waterford* 923 L 11 *Ireland G. – pop. 1 430 – ✉ Waterford.*
See : *Village*★.
Dunmore East ✆ (051) 383151.
Dublin 108 – Waterford 12.

Lakefield House without rest., Dunmore East Rd, Rosduff, Northwest : 5 m. by R 684 ✆ (051) 382582, *Fax (051) 382582*, ←, – rest, TV P. MO VISA
17 March-October – **6 rm** 38.10/63.50.

The Ship, Dock Rd, ✆ (051) 383141, *Fax (051) 383144* – MO AE ① VISA
closed Sunday and Monday November-March – **Meals** - Seafood - a la carte 18.41/31.68 **t.** 17.14.

UNQUIN (Dún Chaoin) *Kerry* 923 A 11 – ✉ *Dingle.*
Dublin 226 – Killarney 52 – Limerick 103.

An Portan, ✆ (066) 9156212, *donn@eircom.net, Fax (066) 9156222*, ← – P. MO VISA
restricted opening in winter – **Meals** (dinner only) a la carte 23.25/34.60 **t.** 14.60.

UNSHAUGHLIN (Dún Seachlainn) *Meath* 923 M 7 – *pop. 2 139.*
The Black Bush, Thomastown ✆ (01) 8250021.
Dublin 17 – Drogheda 19.

Old Workhouse without rest., South : 1 ½ m. on N 3 ✆ (01) 8259251, *comfort@a_vip.com, Fax (01) 825 9251*, – rm, P. MO VISA
*March-November***Meals** 35.00 – **5 rm** 88.88/101.58 **st.**

JRRUS (Dúras) *Cork* 923 D 13 – *pop. 204.*
Dublin 210 – Cork 56 – Killarney 53.

Blairs Cove with rm, Southwest : 1 m. on R 591 ✆ (027) 61127, *blairscove@eircom.net, Fax (027) 61487*, ←, « Converted 17C barn », – TV P. MO ① VISA.
17 March-October – **Meals** *(closed Sunday and Monday)* (booking essential) (dinner only) 44 **t.** 17.14 –, **3 suites** 114.27/190.46.

ENDERRY *Offaly* 923 K 7 – *pop. 3 591.*
Dublin 39 – Kilkenny 63 – Tullamore 23.

Tyrrells, Ballindoolin House, North : ½ m. ✆ (0405) 32400, *tyrrells@ballindoolin.com, Fax (0405) 32377*, « Renovated 19C coach house, gardens » – P. MO VISA.
closed 24 December-17 January, Good Friday, Sunday dinner, Monday and Tuesday – **Meals** (booking essential) 18.98 (lunch) and a la carte 27.55/34.45 **t.** 9.50.

INIS (Inis) *Clare* 923 F 9 *Ireland G. – pop. 15 333.*
See : *Ennis Friary*★ *AC.*
Exc. : *Dysert O'Dea*★, *N : 6 m. by N 85 and R 476, turning left after 4 m. and right after 1m. – Quin Franciscan Friary*★, *SE : 6½ m. by R 469 – Knappogue Castle*★ *AC, SE : 8 m. by R 469 – Corrofin (Clare Heritage Centre*★ *AC), N : 8½ m. by N 85 and R 476 – Craggaunowen Centre*★ *AC, SE : 11 m. by R 469 – Kilmacduagh Churches and Round Tower*★, *NE : 11 m. by N 18 – Kilrush*★ *(Scattery Island*★ *by boat) SW : 27 m. by N 68 – Bridge of Ross, Kilkee*★, *SW : 35½ m. by N 68 and N 67.*
Drumbiggle Rd ✆ (065) 6824074.
Arthurs Row ✆ (065) 6828366.
Dublin 142 – Galway 42 – Limerick 22 – Roscommon 92 – Tullamore 93.

Woodstock, Shanaway Rd, Northwest : 2 ¾ m. by N 85, turning left at One Mile Inn ✆ (065) 6846600, *info@woodstockhotel.com, Fax (065) 6846611*, ←, , , , , , – , rm, rest, TV & P – 200. MO AE ① VISA JCB.
closed 25-26 December – **Meals** 25.33 and a la carte 27.17/36.04 **t.** 17.71 – **67 rm** 184.11/272.99 **st.** – SB.

Temple Gate, The Square, ✆ (065) 6823300, *info@templegatehotel.com, Fax (065) 6823322* – , rm, TV P – 220. MO AE ① VISA.
closed 25 December – **Meals** (carving lunch Monday to Saturday)/dinner 28/32.50 and a la carte 24/32 **t.** 19 – **70 rm** 98/140 **st.**, 2 suites – SB.

West County, Clare Rd, Southeast : ¾ m. on N 18 ✆ (065) 6828421, Central reservations (065) 6823000, *cro@lynchotels.com, Fax (065) 6828801*, , , – , rest, TV & P – 1650. MO AE ① VISA.
Meals (carvery lunch Monday to Saturday)/dinner 20.32/33.01 and a la carte 19.68/31.78 **st.** 17.78 – **152 rm** 190.50/317.50 **st.** – SB.

Old Ground, O'Connell St, (065) 6828127, *oghotel@iol.ie, Fax (065) 6828112,* – rm, – 70. VISA.
closed 25-26 December – **Meals** 18.87/27.93 and a la carte 24/32 **st.** 15.24 – **83 r** 102/180 **st.** – SB.

Fountain Court without rest., Northwest : 2 ¼ m. on N 85 (065) 6829845, *kyrar fountain-court.com, Fax (065) 6845030,* – . VISA.
closed 20 December-2 January – **14 rm** 50/90.

Cill Eoin House without rest., Killadysert Cross, Clare Rd, Southeast : 1 ½ m. at juncti of N 18 with R 473 (065) 6841668, *cilleoin@iol.ie, Fax (065) 6841669,* , – VISA.
closed 22-28 December – **14 rm** 44.45/63.50.

at Inch *Southwest : 4 m. on R 474 (Kilmaley rd) – Ennis.*

Magowna House , West : 1 m. by R 474 (065) 6839009, *info@magowna.co Fax (065) 6839258,* , – – 350. VISA
closed 24 to 26 December – **Meals** (bar lunch Monday-Saturday) 26.50/28.50 and a la ca 14.50/28 **st.** 13.35 – **10 rm** 57.50/96 **st.** – SB.

ENNISCORTHY **(Inis Córthaidh)** *Wexford* 923 M 10 *Ireland G. – pop. 3 788.*

See : *Enniscorthy Castle★ (County Museum★).*

Exc. : *Ferns★, NE : 8 m. by N 11 – Mount Leinster★, N : 17 m. by N 11.*

Knockmarshal (054) 33191.

The Castle (054) 34699 (summer only).

Dublin 76 – Kilkenny 46 – Waterford 34 – Wexford 15.

Riverside Park, The Promenade, (054) 37800, *riversideparkhotel@tinet. Fax (054) 37900* – , rm, rest, – 800. VISA.
closed 24-25 December – ***The Moorings :*** **Meals** (carving lunch Monday to Saturda dinner 29/32 and a la carte 14.85/30.95 **st.** 17.15 – **59 rm** 96/77 **st.**, 1 suite – SB.

Treacy's, (054) 37798, *sales@treacyshotel.com, Fax (054) 37733,* , , – rest, – 350. VISA.
closed 24-25 December – **Meals** (bar lunch Monday-Saturday)/dinner 29.14/31. and a la carte 27/41 **st.** – **48 rm** 70/165 **st.** – SB.

Ballinkeele House , Ballymurn, Southeast : 6 ½ m. by unmarked road on Currac rd (053) 38105, *info@ballinkeele.com, Fax (053) 38468,* , « 19C country house », – . VISA.
March-13 November – **Meals** (by arrangement) (communal dining) 35 **t.** – **5 rm** 1 164 **t.**

ENNISKERRY **(Áth an Sceire)** *Wicklow* 923 N 8 – *pop. 1 275.*

Powerscourt, Powerscourt Estate (01) 204 6033.

Dublin 16 – Wicklow 20.

Summerhill House, Cookstown Rd, South : ½ m. (01) 286 7928, *info@summe househotel.com, Fax (01) 286 7929,* , – , rest, rest, – 220. VISA.
closed 24 to 26 December – **Meals** (dinner only and Sunday lunch)/dinner 24.76 **st.** 17 – **57 rm** 69.84/139.67 **st.** – SB.

ENNISTIMON **(Inis Díomáin)** *Clare* 923 E 9 – *pop. 920.*

Dublin 158 – Galway 52 – Limerick 39.

Grovemount House without rest., Lahinch Rd, West : ½ m. on N 67 (065) 70714 *grovmnt@gofree.indigo.ie, Fax (065) 7071823,* – . VISA.
May-October – **8 rm** 42/64 **s.**

FAHAN **(Fathain)** *Donegal* 923 J 2 *Ireland G. – pop. 284 – Inishowen.*

Exc. : *Inishowen Peninsula★★ – Grianán of Aileach★★ (★★), SE : 7 m. by R 238 and west N 13 – Dunree Fort★ AC, N : 11 m. by R 238 and coast rd – Cap of Mamore★, N : by R and coast rd.*

North West, Lisfannon (077) 61027.

Dublin 156 – Londonderry 11 – Sligo 95.

St John's Country House with rm, (077) 60289, *stjohnsrestaurant@eircom. Fax (077) 60612,* , « Loughside setting », – , rest, . VISA JCB.
closed Bank Holidays – **Meals** *(closed Monday dinner to non-residents)* (dinner only Sunday lunch)/dinner 18.77/35.55 and a la carte **t.** 19.50 – **5 rm** 44.44/190.46 **st.**

ERMOY (Mainistir Fhear Maí) *Cork* 923 H 11 – *pop. 2 310.*

Corrin ✆ (025) 32694.

Dublin 134 – Cork 24 – Killarney 59 – Limerick 42.

CastleHyde, West : 2 m. on N 72 ✆ (025) 31865, *cashyde@iol.ie, Fax (025) 31485,* « Restored 18C courtyard buildings », – rest, TV P – 30. VISA.
Meals (booking essential for non-residents) a la carte 13.50/26.20 **st.** 19.50 – **14 rm** 110/190 **st.** – SB.

ERNS (Fearna) *Wexford* 923 M 10 *Ireland G. – pop. 915 –* ✉ *Enniscorthy.*

See : *Town*★.

Exc. : *Mount Leinster*★, *NW : 17 m. – Enniscorthy Castle*★ *(County Museum*★ *AC), S : 8 m. by N 11.*

Dublin 69 – Kilkenny 53 – Waterford 41 – Wexford 22.

Clone House, South : 2 m. by Boolavogue rd off Monageer rd ✆ (054) 66113, *clone house@eircom.net, Fax (054) 66113,* « Working farm », – TV P.
April-October – **Meals** (by arrangement) (communal dining) 19.05 – **5 rm** 54.60/88.88 **st.**

ETHARD (Fiodh Ard) *Tipperary* 923 I 10 – *pop. 900.*

An-Teach, Killusty, Southeast : 3 ½ m. by R 706 (Kilsheelan rd) ✆ (052) 32088, *anteach@an teach.com, Fax (052) 32178,* – TV P. VISA
Meals (by arrangement) 19.05 **st.** 12.70 – **11 rm** 44.44/88.88 **st.** – SB.

OXROCK (Carraig an tSionnaigh) *Dublin* 923 N 7 – *see Dublin.*

URBO (Na Forbacha) *Galway* 923 E 8 – *see Furbogh.*

URBOGH/FURBO (Na Forbacha) *Galway* 923 E 8.

Dublin 142 – Galway 7.

Connemara Coast, ✆ (091) 592108, *sinnott@iol.ie, Fax (091) 592065,* ← Galway Bay, – TV P – 500. VISA.
closed 24-26 December – **Meals** (bar lunch Monday-Saturday)/dinner 30 and a la carte 30/40 **t.** 18 – **111 rm** 130/200 **st.**, 1 suite – SB.

Suan na Mara, Stripe, Northwest : ½ m. off R 336 ✆ (091) 591512, *Fax (091) 591632,* ←, – TV P. VISA.
closed 23-27 December – **Meals** (by arrangement) 26 **st.** – **4 rm** 47/70 **st.**

ALWAY (Gaillimh) *Galway* 923 E 8 *Ireland G. – pop. 57 241.*

See : *City*★★ – *Lynch's Castle*★ **BY** – *St. Nicholas' Church*★ **BY** – *Roman Catholic Cathedral*★ **AY** – *Eyre Square : Bank of Ireland Building (sword and mace*★*)* **BY D**.

Env. : *NW : Lough Corrib*★★.

Exc. : *W : by boat, Aran Islands (Inishmore – Dun Aenghus*★★★*)* **BZ** – *Thoor Ballylee*★, *SE : 21 m. by N 6 and N 18* **D** – *Athenry*★, *E : 14 m. by N 6 and R 348* **D** – *Dunguaire Castle, Kinvarra*★ *AC, S : 16 m. by N 6, N 18 and N 67* **D** – *Aughnanure Castle*★, *NW : 16 m. by N 59 – Oughterard*★ *(←★★), NW : 18 m. by N 59 – Knockmoy Abbey*★, *NE : 19 m. by N 17 and N 63* **D** – *Coole Park (Autograph Tree*★*), SE : 21 m. by N 6 and N 18* **D** – *St. Mary's Cathedral, Tuam*★, *NE : 21 m. by N 17* **D** – *Loughrea (St. Brendan's Cathedral*★*), SE : 22 m. by N 6* **D** – *Turoe Stone*★, *SE : 22 m. by N 6 and north by R 350.*

Galway, Blackrock, Salthill ✆ (091) 522033.

Carnmore Airport : ✆ (091) 752874, NE : 4 m.

Galway City Avas Failte, Forster St ✆ (091) 537700 – Salthill Promenade ✆ (091) 520500 (May-September).

Dublin 135 – Limerick 64 – Sligo 90.

Plans on following pages

Glenlo Abbey, Bushypark, Northwest : 3 ¼ m. on N 59 ✆ (091) 526666, *glenlo@iol.ie, Fax (091) 527800,* ←, « Restored part 18C house and church », – rest, TV P – 200. VISA.
River Room : **Meals** (dinner only)/dinner 35/50 and a la carte 37/54 **t.** 20.32 – ***Pullman :*** **Meals** *(closed Monday and Tuesday)* (dinner only) a la carte approx. 29/47 **t.** 21 – 18 – **41 rm** 250/310 **t.**, 5 suites – SB.

GALWAY

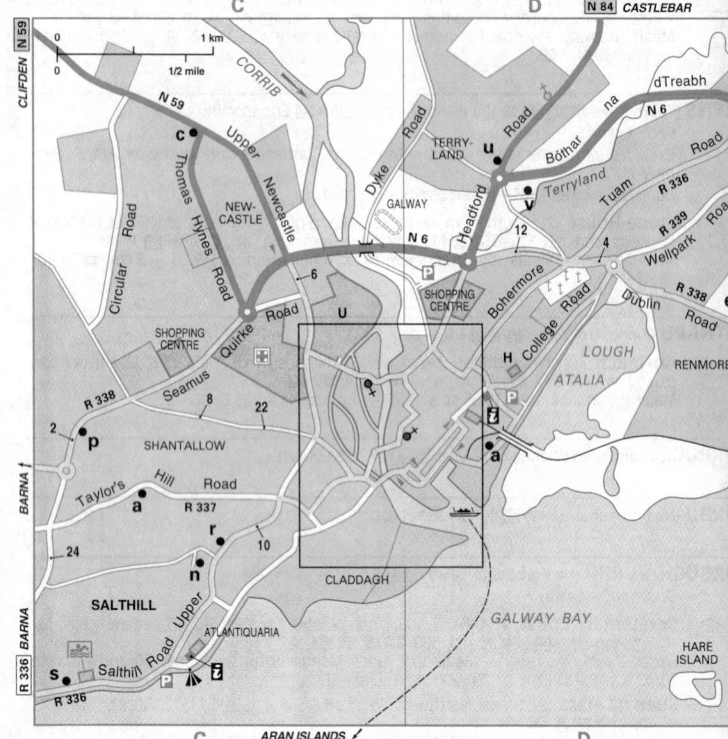

Radisson SAS, Lough Atalia Rd, ☎ (091) 538300, *sales.galway@radissonsas.co...* *Fax (091) 538380,* – – 900. D
Marinas : **Meals** (bar lunch)/dinner a la carte 20.94/37.15 **st.** 19.05 – 15.24 – **199** ... 146/190 **st.**, 3 suites – SB.

Great Southern, Eyre Sq, ☎ (091) 564041, *res@galway.gsh.ie, Fax (091) 566704,* – rm, rest, – 350. BY
closed 24 to 26 December – **Meals** (carving lunch Monday to Saturday)/dinner a la ca... 29/38 **t.** 13.97 – 13 – **107 rm** 145/230 **t.**, 1 suite – SB.

Westwood House, Dangan, Upper Newcastle, ☎ (091) 521442, *westwoodreservati... @eircom.net, Fax (091) 521400* – rm, – 350. C
closed 24-25 December – ***Meridian :*** **Meals** (dinner only and Sunday lunch) a la ca... 23/35 **t.** 15.87 – **58 rm** 125.70/227.28 **t.** – SB.

Corrib Great Southern, Renmore, East : 1 ¾ m. on R 338 ☎ (091) 755281, *res@cor... gsh.ie, Fax (091) 751390,* – rm, rest, – 750.
closed 24 to 26 December – **Meals** (carving lunch Monday to Saturday)/dinner a la ca... approx. 35 **t.** 13.97 – 13 – **176 rm** 140/220 **t.**, 4 suites – SB.

Ardilaun House, Taylor's Hill, West : 1 ½ m. on R 337 ☎ (091) 521433, *ardilaun@io... Fax (091) 521546,* – rm, – 450. C
closed 22 to 28 December – **Meals** (bar lunch Saturday) 17.78/41.27 and dinner a la ca... 27/39 **t.** 13.50 – **88 rm** 120.63/215.86 **st.**, 1 suite – SB.

Galway Harbour, The Harbour, ☎ (091) 569466, *info@galwayharbourhotel.c... Fax (091) 569455* – – 100. BZ
Meals a la carte 9/18 **t.** – 7.56 – **90 rm** 120 **st.**

GALWAY

har Uí Eithir . . . . BY 2
ddagh Bridge . . . . AZ 3
rib Shopping Centre . . . BY
ırthouse Street . . . . BZ 4
minick Street . . . . AZ 5
Father Griffin Avenue . . . . . AZ 6
Forster Street . . . . BY 7
High Street . . . . BY 8
Main Guard St. . . . . BY 9
Market Street . . . . BY 10
Mary Street . . . . BY 11
New Dock Street . . . . BZ 13
Newton Smith . . . . BY 14
O'Brien Bridge . . . . AY 15
Presentation Street . . . . AY 17
Quay Street . . . . BZ 18
St. Francis Street . . . . BY 20
St. Vincent's Avenue . . . . . . BY 21
Shantalla Road . . . . AY 22
Shop Street . . . . BY 24
William Street . . . . BY 25

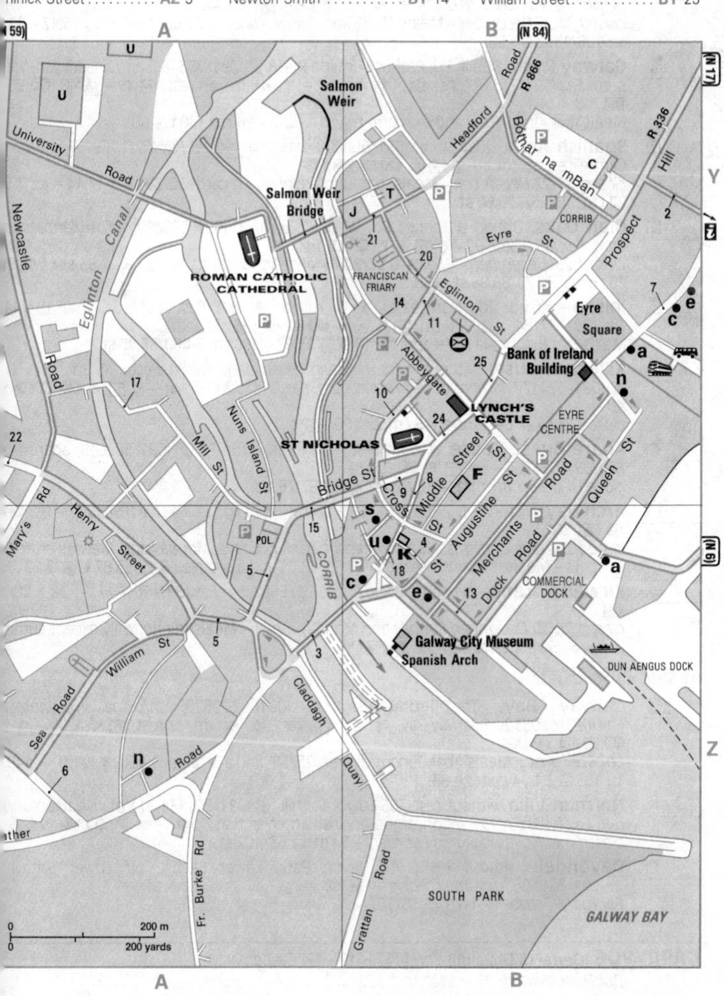

Park House, Forster St, Eyre Sq, ☎ (091) 564924, *parkhousehotel@eircom.net*, *Fax (091) 569219* – |‡|, ≡ rest, TV ☎ ♿ P – 🏛 35. MC AE ◑ VISA. ✕ — BY c
closed 24 to 26 December – **Meals** (carvery lunch)/dinner a la carte 28.13/38.22 **t.** 🍷 16.40 – **57 rm** ☕ 205 **st.** – SB.

Jurys Inn Galway, Quay St, ☎ (091) 566444, *jurysinngalway@jurysdoyle.com*, *Fax (091) 568415*, – |‡|, ⇍ rm, ≡ rest, TV ♿ P – 🏛 20. MC AE VISA. ✕ — BZ c
closed 24 to 26 December – **Meals** (carvery lunch) (bar lunch)/dinner a la carte 20/32 **st.** 🍷 14 – ☕ 8.50 – **128 rm** 94 **st.**

Brennan's Yard, Lower Merchants Rd, ☎ (091) 568166, *brennansyard@eircom.net*, *Fax (091) 568262* – |‡| TV. MC AE ◑ VISA. ✕ — BZ e
closed 23 to 28 December – **Meals** (booking essential) (bar lunch)/dinner 22.79 and a la carte 22.60/31.88 **st.** 🍷 16.44 – **45 rm** ☕ 82.55/133.35 **st.** – SB.

Forster Court, Forster St, ✆ (091) 564111, *sales@forstercourthotel.cc* *Fax (091) 539839*, – TV ✆ ♿ P. MC AE VISA. ✻ BY
closed 24-25 December – **Meals** a la carte 22/38 **st.** 18.45 – **48 rm** 120/190 **st.**

Menlo Park, Terryland, Northeast : 1 ¼ m. by N 6 (Castlebar rd) ✆ (091) 761122, *me pkh@iol.ie, Fax (091) 761222* – |♦|, ▤ rest, TV P – 160. MC AE ⓓ VISA. ✻ D
closed 24-25 December – **Meals** 15/26 and dinner a la carte 17.60/28.80 **st.** 15.17 – **64** 108/133 **st.** – SB.

Galway Ryan, Dublin Rd, East : 1 ¼ m. on R 338 ✆ (091) 753181, *enquiries@ryan-hot com, Fax (091) 753187*, |♦|, ▤ rest, TV P – 40. MC AE VISA. ✻ D
Meals (bar lunch) 9/18 and a la carte **t.** 11 – 7 – **96 rm** 130 **t.** – SB.

Spanish Arch, Quay St, ✆ (091) 569600, *emcdgall@iol.ie, Fax (091) 569191*, « Part Carmelite convent » – |♦| TV P. MC AE VISA. ✻ BZ
closed 25-27 December – **Meals** (bar lunch)/dinner a la carte 30/38 **st.** 17.14 – 7.5 **20 rm** 146.05/228.60 **st.**

Glen Oaks, Bishop O'Donnell Rd, West : 1 ½ m. ✆ (091) 589680, *info@glenoaksho com, Fax (091) 589509* – |♦| TV ♿ P. MC AE VISA. ✻ C
closed 25 December – **Meals** 6.98/22.86 and dinner a la carte 12.68/22.85 **st.** 13.9 **20 rm** 50.79/88.88 **st.** – SB.

Ibis, Headford Rd, Northeast : 1 ¼ m. by N 84 (Castlebar rd) ✆ (091) 7711 *Fax (091) 771646* – |♦|, rm, TV ✆ ♿ P. MC AE ⓓ VISA D
Meals (bar lunch) a la carte approx. 18 **st.** 13.97 – **100 rm** 54.60/83.40 **st.**

Killeen House without rest., Killeen Bushypark, Northwest : 4 m. on N ✆ (091) 524179, *killeenhouse@ireland.com, Fax (091) 528065*, – |♦| TV P. MC AE ⓓ ✻
closed 23 to 27 December – **5 rm** 100/140 **t.**

Adare Guest House without rest., 9 Father Griffin Pl, ✆ (091) 582638, *adare@io Fax (091) 583963* – TV P. MC AE VISA AZ
closed 1 week Christmas – **12 rm** 76.18/97.76 **st.**

Archway, Victoria Pl, ✆ (091) 563693, *archway@indigo.ie, Fax (091) 563074* – ▤. MC ⓓ VISA. ✻ BY
closed 2 weeks Christmas, Sunday except bank holidays, Monday and Tuesday after B Holidays – **Meals** (booking essential) 19.68/38.09 and a la carte 38.19/55.87 **t.** 22.22.

Kirwan's Lane, Kirwan's Lane, ✆ (091) 568266, *Fax (091) 561645* – ▤. MC VISA BZ
closed 25-30 December, Sunday and Monday lunch – **Meals** (dinner only except summ 22.79/63.50 a la carte 35/45 **t.** 17.71.

at Salthill *Southwest : 2 m.*

Galway Bay, The Promenade, ✆ (091) 520520, *info@galwaybayhotel. Fax (091) 520530*, ≤ Galway Bay, – |♦|, rm, ▤ rest, TV ✆ ♿ P – 5 MC AE ⓓ VISA. ✻ C
Lobster Pot : **Meals** (bar lunch)/dinner 25/35 and a la carte 30/50 12.50 – **149** 153/216 **t.**, 4 suites – SB.

Norman Villa without rest., 86 Lower Salthill, ✆ (091) 521131, *normanvilla@oceanf. net, Fax (091) 521131*, « Contemporary Irish art collection », – P. MC VISA. ✻ C
closed mid November-mid February – **5 rm** 63/102 **st.**

Devondell without rest., 47 Devon Park, Lower Salthill, off Lower Salthill ✆ (091) 528306, *devondell@iol.ie* – . ✻ C
February-October – **4 rm** 38/76.

GARRYVOE **(Garraí Uí Bhuaigh)** *Cork* 923 H 12 – ✉ *Castlemartyr.*
Dublin 161 – Cork 23 – Waterford 62.

Garryvoe, ✆ (021) 4646718, *garryvoehotel@eircom.net, Fax (021) 4646824*, ≤, rest, TV P – 300. MC AE ⓓ VISA. ✻
closed 25 December – **Meals** 16.50/29 and dinner a la carte 23/36 **st.** 16.51 – **19** 91/72 **st.** – SB.

***En saison,** surtout dans les stations fréquentées,*
il est prudent de retenir à l'avance.
Cependant, si vous ne pouvez pas occuper la chambre
que vous avez retenue, prévenez immédiatement l'hôtelier.

Si vous écrivez à un hôtel à l'étranger, joignez à votre lettre
un coupon-réponse international (disponible dans les bureaux de poste).

ANWORTH (Gleannúir) *Cork* 923 G 11 – *pop. 400.*
Dublin 136 – Cork 22 – Killarney 57 – Limerick 40.

XX **Glanworth Mill Country Inn** with rm, (025) 38555, *glanworth@iol.ie, Fax (025) 38560,* « Restored watermill on the banks of River Funcheon », – P. MC AE VISA.
closed Sunday dinner, Christmas and New Year – **Meals** 22.86 (dinner) and a la carte 20/29 **t.** 15/24 – **10 rm** 76.18/126.97 **t.** – SB.

ASLOUGH (Glasloch) *Monaghan* 923 L 5 – *see Monaghan.*

ASSAN (Glasán) *Westmeath* 923 I 7 – *see Athlone.*

ENDALOUGH (Gleann dá Loch) *Wicklow* 923 M 8 *Ireland G.*
See : *Monastic ruins★★★ – Lower Lake★★★ – Cathedral★★ – Upper Lake★★ – Round Tower★ – St. Kevin's Church★ – St. Saviour's Priory★.*
Exc. : *Wicklow Mountains★★ – Wicklow Gap★★.*
(0404) 45688 (June-September).
Dublin 28 – Kilkenny 68 – Wexford 63.

Glendalough, (0404) 45135, *info@glendaloughhotel.ie, Fax (0404) 45142,* – , rm, P – 200. MC AE VISA.
closed 2 December-2 February – **Meals** a la carte approx. 25 **t.** – **40 rm** 107/170 **st.** – SB.

ENGARRIFF (An Gleann Garbh) *Cork* 923 D 12 *Ireland G.*
See : *Town★ – Garinish Island★★.*
Env. : *Healy Pass★★ (<★★), W : by R 572 – Derreen Gardens★, W : by R 572 and north by R 574 (Healy Pass).*
(027) 63084 (seasonal).
Dublin 213 – Cork 60 – Killarney 37.

Cois Coille without rest., (027) 63202, – P.
May-September – **6 rm** 38/54 **st.**

EN OF AHERLOW (Gleann Eatharlaí) *Tipperary* 923 H 10 *Ireland G.* – *Tipperary.*
See : *Glen of Aherlow★.*
Exc. : *Caher Castle★★ AC – Swiss Cottage★ AC, SE : 7 m. by N 24 and R 670 – Clonmel★ (County Museum★, St. Mary's Church★), NE : 16 m. by N 24 – Kilmallock★ (Abbey★, Collegiate Church★), W : 27½ m. by R 664 and R 515.*
Dublin 118 – Cahir 6 – Tipperary 9.

Aherlow House , (062) 56153, *aherlow@iol.ie, Fax (062) 56212,* < Galty Mountains, – rest, P – 200. MC AE VISA.
Meals (bar lunch Monday to Saturday)/dinner 35 **st.** 17.50 – **29 rm** 97.50/164 **st.** – SB.

IN (An Gleann) *Limerick* 923 E 10 – *pop. 554.*
Dublin 152 – Limerick 32 – Tralee 32.

Glin Castle , (068) 34112, *knight@iol.ie, Fax (068) 34364,* <, « Crenellated Georgian country house, collection of antique furnishings, paintings and porcelain », , , – rest, P. MC AE VISA.
April-7 November – **Meals** (residents only) (dinner only) 45 **t.** 17 – **15 rm** 242/381 **t.**

REY (Guaire) *Wexford* 923 N 9 *Ireland G. – pop. 2 150.*
Exc. : *Ferns★, SW : 11 m. by N 11.*
Courtown, Kiltennel (055) 25166.
Main St (055) 21248.
Dublin 58 – Waterford 55 – Wexford 38.

Marlfield House , Courtown Rd, Southeast : 1 m. on R 742 (055) 21124, *info@marlfieldhouse.ie, Fax (055) 21572,* <, « Regency mansion, extensive gardens and woodland », , – P. MC AE VISA.
closed mid December-1 February – **Meals** (booking essential to non-residents) (dinner only and Sunday lunch)/dinner 51/54 **t.** 23 – **19 rm** 133/240 **t.**, 1 suite.

GORT (An Gort) *Galway* 923 F 8.
18 Castlequarter (091) 632244.
Dublin 129 – Galway 24 – Limerick 40.

The Lady Gregory, Ennis Rd, on N 18 (091) 632333, *ladygregoryhotel@tine*
Fax (091) 632332, – , rm, rest, – 400.
closed 23-27 December – **Meals** (carving lunch Monday-Saturday)/dinner 23
and a la carte approx. 27.70 **t.** 16.50 – **48 rm** 70/160 **t.** – SB.

GRAIGUENAMANAGH (Gráig na Manach) *Kilkenny* 923 L 10.
Dublin 78 – Kilkenny 21 – Waterford 26 – Wexford 16.

Waterside with rm, The Quay, (0503) 24246, *info@waterside.iol.ie, Fax (0503) 247*
, « Converted Victorian cornstore on banks of River Barrow » – .
closed 23-28 December and Tuesday – **Meals** (restricted opening in Winter) (dinner c
and Sunday lunch) a la carte 21.50/27 **st.** 7.50 – **9 rm** 60/100 **st.** – SB.

GREYSTONES (Na Clocha Liatha) *Wicklow* 923 N 8 – *pop. 9 995.*
18 Greystones (01) 287 6624.
Dublin 22.

Hungry Monk, Southview Church Rd, (01) 287 5759, *Fax (01) 287 7183* – .
closed 24-26 December, Good Friday and Monday – **Meals** (dinner only and Sunday lunc
dinner a la carte 29.20/40.63 **t.** 16.51.

When looking for a quiet hotel use the maps found in the introduction or look for establishments with the sign or .

GWEEDORE (Gaoth Dobhair) *Donegal* 923 H 2.
Dublin 173 – Donegal 45 – Letterkenny 27 – Sligo 84.

Gweedore Court, on N 56 (075) 32900, *anchvirt@eircom.net, Fax (075) 32929*,
– rest, – 80.
closed 22-26 December – **Meals** (dinner only and Sunday lunch) a la carte 20/32 **t.** 17.7
19 rm 76/152 **st.**

HOWTH (Binn Èadair) *Dublin* 923 N 7 *Ireland G.* – *Dublin.*
See : *Town★ – The Summit★ (★).*
18, 18, 9 Deer Park Hotel, Howth Castle (01) 822 2624.
Dublin 10.

Marine, Sutton Cross, D13, West : 1 ½ m. (01) 839 0000, *info@marinehote*
Fax (01) 839 0442, , , – , rm, – 175.
closed 25 to 27 December – ***The Meridian :*** **Meals** a la carte 40/44.50 **t.** 18.50 – **48**
150/235 **t.** – SB.

Inisradharc without rest., Balkhill Rd, D13, North : ½ m. (01) 8322306, *jimmcn*
free.indigo.ie, Fax (01) 8322306, , – .
closed 19 December-7 January – **3 rm** 50/66 **st.**

King Sitric with rm, East Pier, (01) 832 5235, *info@kingsitric.ie, Fax (01) 839 2442*,
rm, rest, .
closed Christmas and 2 weeks January – **Meals** - Seafood - *(closed Saturday lunch*
Sunday) 23.50/43.18 and a la carte 36.83/56.52 **t.** 18.41 – **8 rm** 85.41/190.50 **t.** – SB

INCH (An Inis) *Clare* – *see Ennis.*

INISHCRONE (Inis Crabhann) *Sligo* 923 E 5 – *pop. 692.*
Dublin 160 – Ballina 8 – Galway 79 – Sligo 34.

Ceol na Mara without rest., Main St, (096) 36351, *ceolnamara@eircom.*
Fax (096) 36642, – .
9 rm 38.10/63.49 **st.**

INISHMORE (Inis Mór) *Galway* 923 CD 8 – *see Aran Islands.*

STIOGE (Inis Tíog) *Kilkenny* 923 K 10.
Dublin 82 – Kilkenny 16 – Waterford 19 – Wexford 33.

The Motte, Plass-Newid Lodge, Northwest : 1/4 m. on R 700 ✆ (056) 58655, *atmotte@gofree.indigo.ie* – P. VISA
closed 1 week Christmas, 1 week autumn, Sunday except Bank Holidays and Monday – **Meals** (booking essential) (dinner only) 31.50 **t.** 15.

NISHANNON (Inis Eonáin) *Cork* 923 G 12 – *pop. 498* – ✉ *Cork.*
Dublin 172 – Cork 16 – Kinsale 9 – Killarney 52 – Limerick 73.

Innishannon House, South : 3/4 m. on R 605 ✆ (021) 4775121, *info@innishannon-hotel.ie, Fax (021) 4775609,* « Riverside setting », – TV P – 220. AE VISA JCB
closed 24-26 December **Meals** 21/39 and a la carte 21/39 **t.** 18.41 – **13 rm** 108/343 **st.** – SB.

VERIN (Indreabhán) *Galway* 923 D8.
Dublin 149 – Galway 17.

Tig Cualain without rest., Kilroe East, on R 336 ✆ (091) 553609, *Fax (091) 553049* – TV P.
April-October – **9 rm** 38.09/55.87.

NTURK (Ceann Toirc) *Cork* 923 F 11 *Ireland G.* – *pop. 1 666.*
See : *Town*★ - *Castle*★.
Fairy Hill ✆ *(029) 50534.*
Dublin 161 – Cork 33 – Killarney 31 – Limerick 44.

Assolas Country House, East : 3 1/4 m. by R 576 and R 580 on Cecilstown rd ✆ (029) 50015, *assolas@eircom.net, Fax (029) 50795,* ←, « Part 17C and 18C country house, gardens, riverside setting », – P. VISA.
15 March-November – **Meals** (booking essential) (residents only) (dinner only) 45 20 – **6 rm** 105/240 **st.**

Glenlohane, East : 2 1/2 m. by R 576 and R 580 on Cecilstown rd ✆ (029) 50014, *info@glenlohane.com, Fax (029) 51100,* ←, « Georgian country house, extensive parkland, working farm », – P. AE VISA.
Meals (by arrangement) (communal dining) 35 **st.** 19 – **4 rm** 100/170 **st.**

The Vintage, O'Brien St, ✆ (029) 50549, *Fax (029) 51209* – VISA
closed Good Friday, 25 December and Sunday lunch – **Meals** a la carte 13/30 **t.** 16.44.

EL (An Caol) *Mayo* 923 B 5/6 – *see Achill Island.*

NMARE (Neidín) *Kerry* 923 D 12 *Ireland G.* – *pop. 1 420.*
See : *Town*★.
Exc. : *Ring of Kerry*★★ – *Healy Pass*★★ (←★★), *SW : 19 m. by R 571 and R 574* AY – *Mountain Road to Glengarriff* (←★★) *S : by N 71* AY – *Slieve Miskish Mountains* (←★★), *SW : 30 m. by R 571* AY – *Gougane Barra Forest Park*★★, *SE : 10 m.* AY – *Lauragh (Derreen Gardens*★ AC), *SW : 14 1/2 m. by R 571* AY – *Allihies (Copper Mines*★), *SW : 35 1/2 m. by R 571 and R 575* AY – *Garnish Island* (←★), *SW : 42 1/2 m. by R 571, R 575 and R 572* AY.
Kenmare ✆ *(064) 41291.*
Heritage Centre ✆ *(064) 41233 (April-October)* AY.
Dublin 210 – Cork 58 – Killarney 20.

Plan on next page

Park, ✆ (064) 41200, *info@parkkenmare.com, Fax (064) 41402,* ← Kenmare Bay and hills, « Antiques and paintings », – TV P – 35. AE VISA. BY k
19 April-27 October and 23 December-2 January – **Meals** (dinner only) 58 and a la carte 48.50/70 **st.** 28 – **46 rm** 198/698 **st.**

Sheen Falls Lodge, Southeast : 1 1/4 m. by N 71 ✆ (064) 41600, *info@sheenfallslodge.ie, Fax (064) 41386,* « Wooded setting on banks of Sheen River and Kenmare Bay ← Sheen Falls », rm, TV P – 120. AE VISA.
closed January and weekends only for first 3 weeks December – ***La Cascade :*** **Meals** (dinner only) 60 **t.** 30 – ***Oscar's :*** **Meals** *(closed Monday-Wednesday October-Easter)* (dinner only) a la carte 22/44 **t.** 17 – 17.00 – **53 rm** 240/380 **t.**, 8 suites – SB.

KENMARE

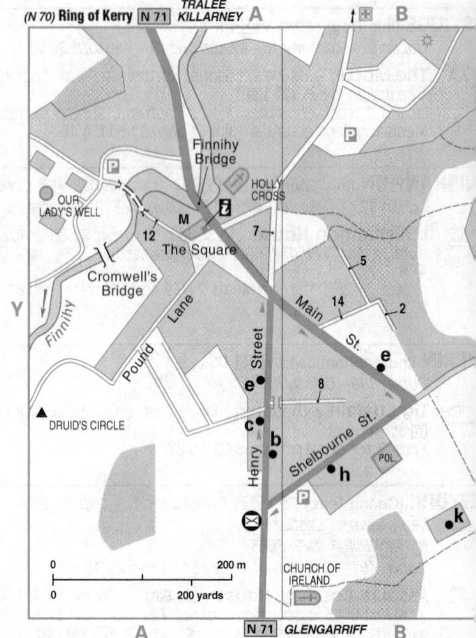

Dromquinna Manor, Blackwater Bridge P.O., West : 3 m. by N 71 on N 70 (Sneem rd) ☏ (064) 41657, *info@dromquinna.com, Fax (064) 41791*, ≤, « Situated on the shore Kenmare Bay », 🐕, 🌳, 🎾, ✂ – ⚓ TV P – 🏕 30. MC AE ⦿ VISA
March-October – **Meals** (dinner only) 32 🍷 20 – **46 rm** ☕ 57/229 **t.** – SB.

Shelburne Lodge, East : ½ m. on R 569 (Cork Rd) ☏ (064) 41013, *Fax (064) 42*
« Stylishly decorated 18C house », 🌳, ✂ – TV P. MC VISA. 🚫
March-November – **Meals** – (see ***Packies*** below) – **7 rm** ☕ 80/140 **t.**

Dunkerron, West : 2 ½ m. by N 71 on N 70 (Sneem rd) ☏ (064) 41102, *info@r cottage.ie, Fax (064) 41102*, « Ruined 12C castle in grounds », 🌳, 🎾 – P. MC VISA. 🚫
March-September – **Meals** (booking essential) (residents only) (dinner only) 19/29 **t.** 🍷 1 – **10 rm** ☕ 63.49/88.88 **t.**

The Rosegarden, West : ¾ m. by N 71 on N 70 (Sneem rd) ☏ (064) 42288, *roseg @iol.ie, Fax (064) 42305*, 🌳 – 🚭 TV P. MC AE ⦿ VISA. 🚫
April-October – **Meals** (dinner only) 19 and a la carte 26/33 **t.** 🍷 15.50 – **8 rm** ☕ 48/70 SB.

Davitt's, Henry St, ☏ (064) 42741, *davittskenmare@eircom.net, Fax (064) 42756* – 🚭 ▤ rest, TV P. MC AE VISA. 🚫 AY
closed 24-26 December – **Meals** a la carte 14/32 **t.** 🍷 15.24 – **11 rm** ☕ 50.79/76.18 **st.**

The Lodge without rest., Killowen Rd, East : ¼ m. on R 569 (Cork rd) ☏ (064) 41 *thelodgekenmare@eircom.net, Fax (064) 42724* – 🚭 TV ♿ P. MC VISA. 🚫
17 March-10 November – **10 rm** ☕ 88.90/101.60 **st.**

Sallyport House without rest., South : ¼ m. on N 71 ☏ (064) 42066, *pot@ic Fax (064) 42067*, ≤, « Antique furnishings », 🌳 – 🚭 TV P. 🚫
April-October – **5 rm** ☕ 95.33/126.98 **t.**

Mylestone House without rest., Killowen Rd, East : ¼ m. on R 569 (Cork ☏ (064) 41753, *mylestonehouse@eircom.net*, 🌳 – P. MC VISA. 🚫
March-10 November – **5 rm** ☕ 40/60.

Ceann Mara without rest., East : 1 m. on R 569 (Cork rd) ☏ (064) 41220, *ceann.m @eircom.net, Fax (064) 41220*, ≤ Kenmare Bay and hills, 🌳 – P
June-15 September – **4 rm** ☕ 38/64.

The Lime Tree, Shelbourne St, ☏ (064) 41225, *benchmark@iol.ie, Fax (064) 41* « Characterful former schoolhouse, with art gallery » – P. MC VISA BY
April-October – **Meals** (dinner only) a la carte 27.50/34.05 **t.** 🍷 17.

Packies, Henry St, ℘ (064) 41508 – MC VISA AY b
mid March-October – **Meals** *(closed Sunday and Monday)* (dinner only) a la carte 25.40/36.70 **t.** 16.50.

An Leath Phingin, 35 Main St, ℘ (064) 41559 – MC VISA BY e
closed 15 November-15 December and Wednesday – **Meals** - Italian - (dinner only) a la carte 18/28 **st.** 15.87.

Mulcahys, 16 Henry St, ℘ (064) 42383 – MC VISA AY c
closed 10 January-25 March and Tuesday except July-September – **Meals** (dinner only) a la carte 19/32 **t.** 16.44.

LBRITTAIN (Cill Briotáin) *Cork* 923 F 12.

Dublin 180 – Cork 24 – Killarney 60.

Casino House, Coolmain Bay, Southeast : 2 ¼ m. by unmarked rd on R 600 ℘ (023) 49944, *chouse@eircom.net, Fax (023) 49945,* – P. MC VISA
closed January-17 March and Wednesday – **Meals** *(weekends only November-December)* (dinner only and Sunday lunch) a la carte 30.35/40.15 **st.** 17.15.

LCOLGAN (Cill Cholgáin) *Galway* 923 F 8 – ✉ *Oranmore.*

Dublin 137 – Galway 11.

Moran's Oyster Cottage, The Weir, Northwest : 1 ¼ m. by N 18 ℘ (091) 796113, *moransthewier@eircom.net, Fax (091) 796503,* « Part 18C thatched cottage » – MC AE VISA
closed 24-25 December and Good Friday – **Meals** a la carte 20.06/36.77 **t.**

LCUMMIN (Cill Chuimín) *Kerry* 923 B 11 *Ireland G.*

Exc. : *Dingle Peninsula*★★★ *– Connor Pass*★★ *– Dingle*★*, SW : by Connor Pass.*
Dublin 203 – Killarney 34 – Limerick 85 – Tralee 21.

The Shores Country House, East : ½ m. on R 560 ℘ (066) 7139196, *theshores@eircom.net, Fax (066) 7139196,* – TV P. MC VISA.
closed December and January – **Meals** (by arrangement) 23 **st.** – **6 rm** 55/66 **st.** – SB.

Strand View House without rest., Conor Pass Rd, ℘ (066) 7138131, *strandview@eircom.net, Fax (066) 7138386,* – TV P. VISA.
4 rm 48/60.

LKEE (Cill Chaoi) *Clare* 923 D 9 *Ireland G. – pop. 1 331.*

Exc. : *Kilrush*★ *(Scattery Island*★ *by boat), SE : 10 m. by N 67 – SW : Loop Head Peninsula (Bridge of Ross*★*).*
18 *Kilkee, East End* ℘ *(065) 9056048.*
O'Connell Sq ℘ *(065) 9056112 (June-early September).*
Dublin 177 – Galway 77 – Limerick 58.

Ocean Cove, Kilkee Bay, ℘ (065) 9083100, *cro@lynchotels.com, Fax (065) 9083123,* – rm, TV P. MC AE VISA.
restricted opening in winter – ***Pan Asian's :*** **Meals** (carvery lunch Monday-Saturday)/dinner 24.13/31.74 and a la carte 22.86/29.21 **st.** 12.70 – 8.89 – **50 rm** 82.53/126.97 **st.** – SB.

Kilkee Bay, ℘ (065) 9060060, *info@kilkee-bay.com, Fax (065) 9060062* – rest, TV P – 150. MC AE VISA.
closed January and February – **Meals** (bar lunch Monday-Saturday)/dinner 15.17/31.74 and a la carte 24.12/37.41 **st.** – **40 rm** 69.84/101.58 **st.**, 1 suite – SB.

Halpin's, Erin St, ℘ (065) 9056032, *halpins@iol.ie, Fax (065) 9056317* – rest, TV P. MC AE VISA JCB.
15 March-10 November – **Meals** (bar lunch Monday-Saturday)/dinner 25/30 and a la carte 20.50/29 11 – **12 rm** 50/95 – SB.

LKENNY (Cill Chainnigh) *Kilkenny* 923 K 10 *Ireland G. – pop. 8 507.*

See : *Town*★★ *– St. Canice's Cathedral*★★ *– Kilkenny Castle and Grounds*★★ *AC – Cityscope*★ *AC – Black Abbey*★ *– Rothe House*★.
Exc. : *Jerpoint Abbey*★★ *AC, S : 12 m. by R 700 and N 9 – Dunmore Cave*★ *AC, N : 7 m. by N 77 and N 78 – Kells Priory*★*, S : 8 m. by R 697.*
18 *Glendine* ℘ *(056) 65400 –* 18 *Callan, Geraldine* ℘ *(056) 25136 –* 9 *Castlecomer, Drumgoole* ℘ *(056) 41139.*
Shee Alms House ℘ *(056) 51500.*
Dublin 71 – Cork 86 – Killarney 115 – Limerick 69 – Tullamore 52 – Waterford 29.

Kilkenny Ormonde, Ormonde St, (056) 23900, *info@kilkennyormonde.co* *Fax (056) 23977,* , , – , rest, – 400. . *closed 25 December* – ***Fredricks :*** **Meals** (dinner only) 40.00 – ***Earls Brasserie :*** **Me** (carving rest.) a la carte 30/32 **st.** – **112 rm** 152.37/241.25 **st.**, 6 suites – SB.

The Hibernean, 1 Ormonde St, (056) 71888, *info@hibernean.com, Fax (056) 7187* , rest, – 60. . *closed 24-25 December* – **Meals** (bar lunch Monday-Saturday)/dinner 25.39 and a la ca 16.82/37.96 **t.** 15.17 – **39 rm** 107.92/177.76 **t.**, 3 suites – SB.

Kilkenny, College Rd, Southwest : ¾ m. at junction with N 76 (056) 62000, *kilkenn griffingroup.ie, Fax (056) 65984,* , , , – rest, – 400. . ***Brooms Bistro :*** **Meals** 16.50/34.50 and dinner a la carte 26.59/38.25 **t.** 18 – **103** 102/190 **t.** – SB.

Newpark, Castlecomer Rd, North : 1 m. on N 77 (056) 60500, *info@newparkho com, Fax (056) 60555,* , , , , – , rm, – 600. . **Meals** (carvery lunch Monday-Saturday)/dinner a la carte 29/33 **st.** – 14 – **111 rm** 1 185 **st.** – SB.

Langton's House, 69 John St, (056) 65133, *langtons@oceanfree.n* *Fax (056) 63693,* – rest, . . *closed Good Friday and 25 December* – **Meals** 15.87/24.76 17.14 – **26 rm** 95.2 177.76 **t.** – SB.

Springhill Court, Waterford Rd, South : 1 ¼ m. on N 10 (056) 21122, *springhillcour eircom.net, Fax (056) 61600* – – 400. . **Meals** 15/27.50 and a la carte 23/31 **st.** 10 – **86 rm** 65/120 **st.** – SB.

Kilkenny River Court, The Bridge, John St, (056) 23388, *krch@iol.ie, Fax (056) 233* , – , rest, – 210. . *closed 24-27 December* – **Meals** (bar lunch Monday-Saturday)/dinner a la carte 29/38 21.27 – **90 rm** 105/350 **st.** – SB.

Butler House without rest., 15-16 Patrick St, (056) 65707, *res@butler.* *Fax (056) 65626,* – – 100. . *closed 24-29 December* – **12 rm** 85/189 **st.**, 1 suite.

Blanchville House , Dunbell, Maddoxtown, Southeast : 6 ½ m. by N 10 turning rig ½ m. after the Pike Inn (056) 27197, *info@blanchville.ie, Fax (056) 27636,* <, « Georgi country house », , – . *March-October* – **Meals** (by arrangement) (communal dining) 35 **st.** – **6 rm** 70/100 **st** SB.

Berkeley House without rest., 5 Patrick St, (056) 64848, *berkleyhouse@eircom.n* *Fax (056) 64829* – . . *closed 24-27 December* – **10 rm** 57/95 **st.**

Newlands Country House , Sevenhouses, South : 5 ¾ m. by N 10 on Callan (056) 29111, *newlands@indigo.ie, Fax (056) 29171,* – . . *closed 20-29 December* – **Meals** (by arrangement) 25.00 12.70 – **6 rm** 44.30/88.60 – SB.

Shillogher House without rest., Callan Rd, Southwest : 1 m. on N 76 (056) 632 *shillogherhouse@tinet.ie, Fax (056) 64865,* – . . **6 rm** 44.44/76.18 **t.**

Zuni with rm, 26 Patrick St, (056) 23999, *info@zuni.ie, Fax (056) 56400,* « Contempora interior » – , rm, rest, . . *closed 23-27 December* – **Meals** *(closed Monday)* a la carte 26/40 **t.** 17.71 – **13 rm** 6 150 **t.** – SB.

Ristorante Rinuccini with rm, 1 The Parade, (056) 61575, *info@rinuccini.co* *Fax (056) 51288* – . . *closed 24-28 December* – **Meals** - Italian - a la carte 30/37 **t.** 17.71 – **7 rm** 101.58 **st.** – S

KILL (An Chill) *Kildare* 923 M 8 – *pop. 1 711.*

Killeen, Killeenbeg (045) 866003.

Dublin 15 – Carlow 36.

Ambassador, on N 7 (045) 877064, *ambassador-sales@quinn-hotels.co* *Fax (045) 877515* – – 280. . **Meals** (carving lunch Monday-Saturday)/dinner a la carte 12/29 **t.** 14.60 – **36 rm** 7 134 **t.** – SB.

When looking for a quiet hotel use the maps found in the introduction or look for establishments with the sign or .

ILLALOE (Cill Dalua) *Clare* 923 G 9 *Ireland G. – pop. 972.*

See : *Town★ – St. Flannan's Cathedral★.*

Env. : *Graves of the Leinstermen (<★), N : 4½ m. by R 494.*

Exc. : *Nenagh★ (Heritage Centre★ AC, Castle★), NE : 12 m. by R 496 and N 7 – Holy Island★ AC, N : 16 m. by R 463 and boat from Tuamgraney.*

The Bridge ℘ (061) 376866 (May-September).

Dublin 109 – Ennis 32 – Limerick 13 – Tullamore 58.

Waterman's Lodge, Ballina (Tipperary), ℘ (061) 376333, *info@watermanslodge.ie, Fax (061) 375445,* – rm, P. MC AE VISA JCB.
closed 24-25 December – **Meals** (booking essential to non-residents) (dinner only and Sunday lunch)/dinner 38.10 and a la carte 36/46 **st.** 17.78 – **10 rm** 89/180 **st.** – SB.

Cherry Tree, Lakeside, Ballina, following signs for Lakeside H. ℘ (061) 375688, *Fax (061) 375689,* <, « Contemporary interior » – P. MC AE VISA
closed 24-26 December, 20 January-5 February, Sunday except Bank Holidays, Monday and Bank Holidays – **Meals** (dinner only) a la carte 32.30/38 **t.** 17.20.

t Ogonnelloe *North : 6¼ m. on R 463.*

Lantern House, ℘ (061) 923034, *Fax (061) 923139,* <, – rm, TV P. MC AE VISA.
– March-October – **Meals** (by arrangement) 21 **t.** 14 – **6 rm** 38/64 **t.**

KILLARNEY (Cill Airne) *Kerry* 923 D 11 *Ireland G. – pop. 8 809.*

See : *Town★★ – St. Mary's Cathedral★* CX – Env. : *Killarney National Park★★★ (Muckross Abbey★, Muckross House and Farms★)* AZ – *Gap of Dunloe★★, SW : 6 m. by R 562* AZ – *Ross Castle★ AC, S : 1 m. by N 71 and minor rd – Torc Waterfall★, S : 5 m. by N 71* BZ.

Exc. : *Iveragh Peninsula★★ (Ring of Kerry★★) – Ladies View★★, SW : 12 m. by N 71* BZ – *Moll's Gap★, SW : 15½ m. by N 71* BZ.

18, 18 *Mahoney's Point ℘ (064) 31034* AZ.

Kerry (Farranfore) Airport : ℘ (066) 976 4644, N : 9½ m. by N 22.

Beech Rd ℘ (064) 31633.

Dublin 189 – Cork 54 – Limerick 69 – Waterford 112.

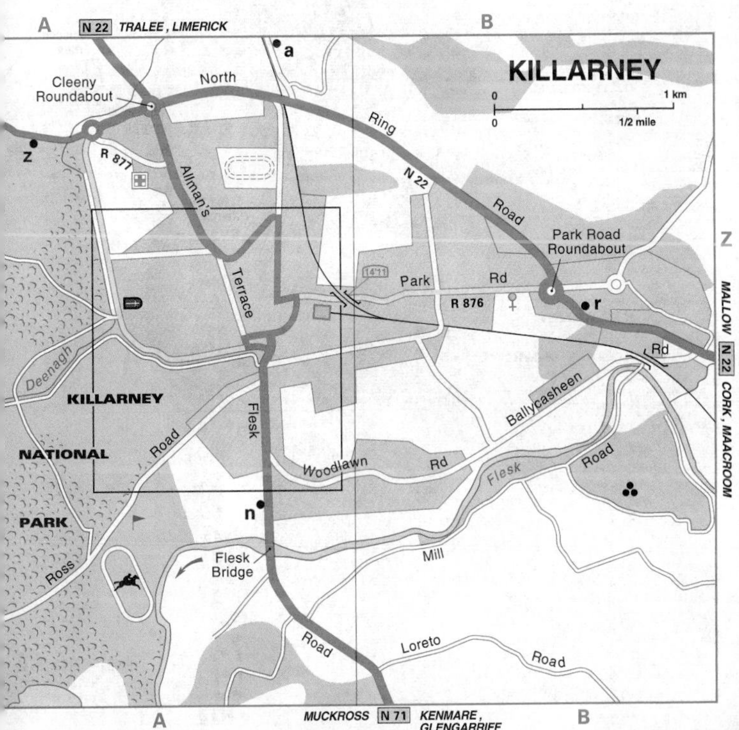

Killarney Park, Kenmare Pl, ✆ (064) 35555, *info@killarneyparkhotel.ie, Fax (064) 3526*
Ꮀ, ⛲, ⊡ – |✱|, ✕ rm, ▤ TV ✆ ♿ P – 🏛 150. MC AE ⓓ VISA. ✗ **DX**
closed 9-26 December – ***Park :*** **Meals** 45/57 (dinner) and a la carte 37.50/47.50 **t.** 🍷 27
73 rm ⊡ 335 **t.**, 3 suites – SB.

Europe 🐦, Fossa, West : 3 by R 562 on N 72 ✆ (064) 31900, *reception.europe@ki liebherr.com, Fax (064) 32118*, ← Lough Leane and Macgillycuddy's Reeks, « Loughsic setting », Ꮀ, ⛲, ⊡, ⛵, ✈, ⛵, ✕indoor – |✱| ⚓ TV P – 🏛 400. MC AE ⓓ VISA. ✗
closed January and February – **Meals** (light lunch)/dinner 54 and a la carte approx. 22.50 s 🍷 27 – ⊡ 17 – **202 rm** 228/378 **st.**, 3 suites – SB.

Killarney Royal, College St, ✆ (064) 31853, *royalhot@iol.ie, Fax (064) 34001* – |✱|, ✕ rn ▤ rest, TV ✆. MC AE ⓓ VISA. ✗ **DX**
closed 22-27 December – **Meals** (bar lunch Monday-Saturday)/dinner 22/39 and a la cart 17.85/27.85 **t.** 🍷 16 – **29 rm** ⊡ 205/385 **t.** – SB.

KILLARNEY

Bohereen Na Goun .... **CX** 3
Bohereencael .... **DX** 4
Brewery Lane .... **DX** 6
College Square .... **DX** 7
College Street .... **DX** 9
Green Lawn .... **CX** 10
Hillard's Lane .... **DX** 12
Mangerton .... **DX** 13
Marian Terrace .... **DX** 15
Muckross Drive .... **DXY** 1
O' Connell's Terrace ...... **DX** 1
O' Sullivan's Place .... **DX** 1
Plunkett Street .... **DX** 2
St. Anthony's Place .... **DX** 2

Aghadoe Heights, Northwest : 2 ¾ m. by N 22 (064) 31766, *info@aghadoeheights.com, Fax (064) 31345*, < Lough Leane, Macgillycuddy's Reeks and countryside, , , , , – , rm, rest, – 100. VISA.
closed 2 January-March – ***Fredrick's :*** Meals (bar lunch Monday-Saturday)/dinner a la carte 52/70 **t.** 31.70 – **67 rm** 174/269.50 **t.**, 2 suites – SB.

Great Southern, (064) 31262, *res@killarney.gsh.ie, Fax (064) 31642*, , , , , , – – 800. VISA. DX j
closed 1 January-3 May – ***Dining Room :*** Meals (dinner only) a la carte 29/38 **t.** 13.97 – 13 – **172 rm** 157/254 **t.**, 3 suites – SB.

Muckross Park, South : 2 ½ m. on N 71 (064) 31938, *muckrossparkhotel@eircom.net, Fax (064) 31965*, – – 200. VISA.
closed December-January – **Meals** (bar lunch)/dinner 32/45 and a la carte 30/39 **t.** 18.98 – **25 rm** 124/190 **t.**, 2 suites – SB.

Randles Court, Muckross Rd, (064) 35333, *info@randlescourt.com, Fax (064) 35206* – . VISA DY p
closed 2 weeks Christmas – ***Cleaver's :*** Meals (bar lunch)/dinner 27.93/57.14 and a la carte 42/51 26.66 – **49 rm** 158.72/292.04 **st.** – SB.

Dromhall, Muckross Rd, (064) 39300, *info@dromhall.com, Fax (064) 34242*, , , – , rm, rest, – 300. VISA DY p
closed 20-28 December – ***Abbey :*** Meals (dinner only) 33.01 **st.** – ***Kayne's :*** Meals a la carte approx. 29.84 – **72 rm** 177.76/203.16 **st.** – SB.

Holiday Inn, Muckross Rd, (064) 33000, *holidayinnkillarney@eircom.net, Fax (064) 33001*, , , – , rm, rest, . VISA AZ n
Meals (bar lunch)/dinner 22.86 **st.** 13.35 – 10.80 – **86 rm** 178.98/159.98 **st.**, 14 suites – SB.

Killarney Heights, Cork Rd, East : 1 ¼ m. by R 876 on N 22 (064) 31158, *khh@iol.ie, Fax (064) 35198* – – 300. VISA. BZ r
closed January – **Meals** (carving lunch)/dinner 21.60/31.75 and a la carte 21/36 **t.** 15.87 – **71 rm** 82.55/190.50 **st.** – SB.

Killeen House, Aghadoe, Northwest : 3 ½ m. by N 22 (064) 31711, *charming@indigo.ie, Fax (064) 31811*, – rest, . VISA
April-October – **Meals** (dinner only) 40 **t.** 18.50 – **23 rm** 110/200 **t.**

Ross, Kenmare Pl, (064) 31855, *ross@kph.iol.ie, Fax (064) 31139* – , rest, rest, . VISA. DX c
closed January, February and 4 days at Christmas – **Meals** 22.22/27.30 and a la carte approx. 37 17.14 – **32 rm** 99/129.51 **st.** – SB.

McSweeney Arms, College St, (064) 31211, *mcsweeney@eircom.net, Fax (065) 34553* – , rest, . VISA. DX n
closed 20 December-February – **Meals** 40 and a la carte 35/42 **st.** 17 – **28 rm** 85/170 **st.**

Brook Lodge, High St, (064) 31800, *brooklodgekillarney@eircom.net, Fax (064) 35001* – , rest, . VISA. CX a
15 March-27 October – **Meals** (bar lunch)/dinner a la carte 23/32 **t.** 15.87 – **18 rm** 96/140 **st.**

Foley's Townhouse, 23 High St, (064) 31217, *Fax (064) 34683* – , rest, . VISA. DX e
accommodation closed 6 November-15 March – **Meals** *(closed 23-26 December)* 15.90/44.50 and a la carte 25.10/44.65 **st.** 17.15 – **28 rm** 63.50/114.30 **t.**

Fuchsia House without rest., Muckross Rd, (064) 33743, *fuchiahouse@eircom.net, Fax (064) 36588*, – . VISA. DY u
15 March-4 November – **8 rm** 64/108 **st.**

Earls Court House without rest., Woodlawn Junction, Muckross Rd, (064) 34009, *info@killarney-earlscourt.ie, Fax (064) 34366* – . VISA. DY t
March-November – **11 rm** 100/160 **st.**

Gleann Fia Country House without rest., Old Deerpark, North : 1 ¼ m. by Emmett's Rd (064) 35035, *info@gleannfia.com, Fax (064) 35000*, – . VISA AZ a
17 rm 76.18/114.28 **st.**

Killarney Lodge without rest., Countess Rd, (064) 36499, *klylodge@iol.ie, Fax (064) 31070*, – . VISA. DX u
restricted opening in winter – **16 rm** 90/120 **st.**

Rivermere without rest., Muckross Rd, South : ½ m. on N 71 (064) 37933, *rivermereguesthouse@eircom.net, Fax (064) 37944*, – . VISA. DY e
8 March-October – **8 rm** 55/110 **st.**

Kathleens Country House without rest., Tralee Rd, North : 2 m. on N
(064) 32810, *info@kathleens.net, Fax (064) 32340*, – rm. VISA.
9 March-October – **16 rm** 110/130 **st.**

Old Weir Lodge without rest., Muckross Rd, (064) 35593, *oldweirlodge@eircom.n*
Fax (064) 35583 – VISA. DY
closed 25 December – **30 rm** 64/90 **st.**

Abbey Lodge without rest., Muckross Rd, (064) 34193, *abbeylodgekly@eircom.n*
Fax (064) 35877 – VISA. DY
closed 20-28 December – **15 rm** 101.58 **st.**

Lime Court without rest., Muckross Rd, (064) 34547, *limecrt@iol.ie, Fax (064) 3412*
VISA. DY
10 February-10 November – **16 rm** 38/127 **st.**

Redwood without rest., Rockfield, Tralee Rd, North : 3 m. on N 22 (064) 34754, *rewo*
indigo.ie, Fax (064) 34178, – .
6 rm 30/50.

Lohans Lodge without rest., North : 4 m. on N 22 (064) 33871, *Fax (064) 33871*,
VISA.
5 March-5 November – **4 rm** 52 **st.**

Naughton's Villa without rest., Muckross Rd, (064) 36025 – VISA. DY
17 March-15 November – **5 rm** 31/74.

Kingfisher Lodge without rest., Lewis Rd, (064) 37131, *kingfisherguesthouse*
eircom.net, Fax (064) 39871, – VISA. DX
closed 14 December-14 January – **9 rm** 44/70 **st.**

Hussey's Townhouse without rest., 43 High St, (064) 37454, *husseys@iol.*
Fax (064) 33144 – VISA. DX
21 March-October – **5 rm** 50.79/76.18 **st.**

Sika Lodge without rest., Ballydowney, Northwest : 1 m. on N 72 (064) 36304, *s*
lodge@eircom.net, Fax (064) 36746 – VISA. AZ
closed 24-26 December – **6 rm** 38/57 **st.**

Gaby's, 27 High St, (064) 32519, *Fax (064) 32747* – VISA DX
closed 14 February-7 March, 20 December-5 January and Sunday – **Meals** - Seafood
(dinner only) a la carte 38/67 **t.** 22.86.

The Cooperage, Old Market Lane, (064) 37716, *chezmart@iol.ie, Fax (064) 37716* –
VISA DX
closed 25 December, Sunday lunch and Monday December-March – **Meals** (light lunc
a la carte 20/37 17.71.

at Beaufort *West : 6 m. by R 562 – AZ – off N 72 – Killarney.*

Dunloe Castle , Southeast : 1 m. (064) 44111, *reception.dunloe@kil.liebherr.co*
Fax (064) 44583, Gap of Dunloe and Macgillycuddy's Reeks, , , , , , indo
– – 250. VISA.
mid March-mid November – **Meals** (dinner only) 54 and a la carte 22/54 **st.** 27 – 17
102 rm 228/378 **st.**, 1 suite – SB.

Beaufort House without rest., (064) 44764, *info@beaufortireland.co*
Fax (064) 44764, , « 18C former shooting lodge », , , – VISA.
April-September – **4 rm** 105/195 **st.**

KILLEAGH (Cill Ia) *Cork* 923 H 12 – *pop. 362.*

Dublin 151 – Cork 23 – Waterford 53.

Ballymakeigh House , North : 1 m. (024) 95184, *ballymakeigh@tinet.i*
Fax (024) 95370, « Working farm », , , – VISA.
March-October – **Meals** (by arrangement) 36 **st.** – **5 rm** 60/90 **st.**

KILLINEY (Cill Iníon Léinín) *Dublin* 923 N 8.

Killiney, Ballinclea Rd (01) 285 1983.

Dublin 8 – Bray 4.

Fitzpatrick Castle, (01) 230 5400, *info@fitzpatricks.com, Fax (01) 230 5466*, ,
, – , rm, rest, – 500. VISA.
closed 25-26 December – ***PJ's :*** **Meals** *(closed Saturday lunch)* 19.68/39.36 and din
ner a la carte 30/47 **t.** 17.14 – 14 – **107 rm** 184/222 **st.**, 6 suites – SB.

Court, Killiney Bay, (01) 285 1622, *book@killineycourt.ie, Fax (01) 285 2085*, , –
rm, – 200. VISA.
The Grill Room : **Meals** 10.16 (lunch) and a la carte 19.05/31.75 **t.** 21.52 – ***The Island***
Meals 22.86/38.10 **t.** 21.52 – **86 rm** 158.75/231 **st.** – SB.

KILLINICK (Cill Fhionnóg) *Wexford* 923 M 11 – *see Rosslare Harbour.*

KILLORGLIN (Cill Orglan) *Kerry* 923 C 11 – *pop. 1 278.*

Killorglin, Steelroe (066) 9761979.
Dublin 207 – Killarney 12 – Tralee 16.

Bianconi, Annadale Rd, (066) 9761146, *rsheeny@aol.ie, Fax (066) 9761950,* – rm, . *closed 23-29 December* – **Meals** *(closed Sunday)* (bar lunch)/dinner a la carte 25.01/33.52 **t.** 16.44 – **15 rm** 69.85/107.95 **t.**

Grove Lodge without rest., Killarney Rd, East : ½ m. on N 72 (066) 9761157, *groveldg @iol.ie, Fax (066) 9762330,* « Riverside setting », , – . *closed 22-28 December* – **10 rm** 57/110 **st.**

The River's Edge without rest., The Bridge, (066) 9761750, *coffeya@eircom.net, Fax (066) 9761750,* « Riverside setting » – . *closed 1 week Christmas* – **10 rm** 40/75 **st.**

Keine Aufnahme in den Michelin-Führer durch
- falsche Information oder
- Bezahlung!

KILLYBEGS (Na Cealla Beaga) *Donegal* 923 G 4 *Ireland G.* – *pop. 1 408.*

Exc. : *Glengesh Pass★★, SW : 15 m. by N 56 and R 263 – Glencolmcille Folk Village★★, W : by R 263 – Gweebarra Estuary★, NE : 19 m. by R 262 and R 252 – Trabane Strand★.*
Dublin 181 – Donegal 17 – Londonderry 64 – Sligo 57.

Bay View, Main St, (073) 31950, *bvhotel@iol.ie, Fax (073) 31856,* , , , – , rest, – 200. . *closed 24-29 December* – **Meals** (bar lunch Monday-Saturday)/dinner 22.90/38.10 and a la carte 20.25/38.10 – **40 rm** 83/165 **st.** – SB.

The Fleet Inn, Bridge St, (073) 31518, *fleetinn@irishmarine.com, Fax (073) 31664* – *closed Christmas, 15 February-16 March, Sunday and Monday October-May* – **Meals** - Seafood specialities - (dinner only) a la carte 30/34 **t.** 15.23.

KILMEADAN (Cill Mhíodáin) *Waterford* 923 K 11 – *see Waterford.*

KILTIMAGH (Coillte Mach) *Mayo* 923 EF 6 – *pop. 917.*

Dublin 138 – Galway 52 – Westport 26.

Cill Aodain, (094) 81761, *cillaodain@eircom.net, Fax (094) 81838* – . *closed 24-26 December* – **Meals** (carving lunch)/dinner 21.50/25 and a la carte 15/23.50 **st.** 15 – **12 rm** 44.50/83 **st.** – SB.

KINNITTY (Cionn Eitigh) *Offaly* 923 I 8 – *see Birr.*

KINSALE (Cionn tSáile) *Cork* 923 G 12 *Ireland G.* – *pop. 2 007.*

See : *Town★★ – St. Multose Church★* Y – *Kinsale Regional Museum★* ACY **M1.**
Env. : *Kinsale Harbour★ (★ from St. Catherine's Anglican Church, Charles Fort★).*
Exc. : *Carbery Coast★, W : 38 m. by R 600.*
Pier Rd (021) 4772234 (March-November).
Dublin 178 – Cork 17.

Plan on next page

Actons, Pier Rd, (021) 4772135, *info@actonshotelkinsale.com, Fax (021) 4772231,* , , , , – – 300. . Z p
closed 24-26 December – **Meals** (bar lunch Monday-Saturday)/dinner a la carte 32/45 **t.** 18 – **75 rm** 127/238 **t.** – SB.

Perryville House without rest., Long Quay, (021) 4772731, *sales@perryville.iol.ie, Fax (021) 4772298,* « Late Georgian house overlooking Kinsale harbour » – . Y f
2 April-October – 15 – **27 rm** 200/380.

KINSALE

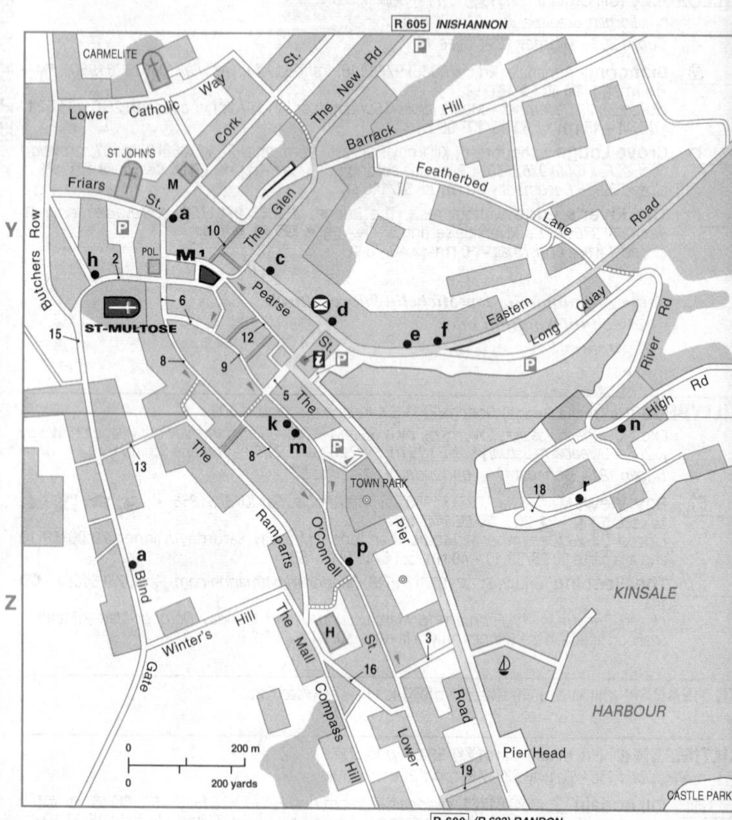

Blue Haven, 3 Pearse St, (021) 4772209, *bluehaven@iol.ie, Fax (021) 4774268,* – rm, rest, . . — Y
closed 24-26 December – **Meals** - Seafood - (bar lunch)/dinner 31.50 and a la carte 25.50.80 12.70 – **17 rm** 120/170 **st.** – SB.

Old Bank House without rest., 11 Pearse St, (021) 4774075, *oldbank@indigo.ie* *Fax (021) 4774296* – . — Y c
closed 1 week Christmas – **17 rm** 155/250 **st.**

The Old Presbytery without rest., 43 Cork St, (021) 4772027, *info@oldpres.com* *Fax (021) 4772166* – . — Y a
closed December-12 February – **16 rm** 76.20/178 **st.**

Long Quay House without rest., Long Quay, (021) 4774563, *Fax (021) 4774563* – . — Y e
closed 16 November-27 December – **7 rm** 65/95 **st.**

Blindgate House without rest., Blindgate, (021) 4777858, *info@blindgatehouse.com, Fax (021) 4777868,* – . — Z a
closed 23 December-March – **11 rm** 100/120 **st.**

Harbour Lodge without rest., Scilly, (021) 4772376, *relax@harbourlodge.com* *Fax (021) 4772675,* ≤ Kinsale harbour – . — Z
8 rm 204/330 **st.**

Colneth House without rest., Cappagh, Northwest : 1 m. by Bandon rd (R 605) ☎ (021) 4772824, *colnethhouse@tinet.ie, Fax (021) 4773357*, – TV P. MC AE VISA.
March-October – **8 rm** 57.14/114.23 **st.**

Kilcaw Guesthouse without rest., East : 1 m. on R 600 ☎ (021) 4774155, *info@kilcawhouse.ie, Fax (021) 4774755*, – TV P. MC AE VISA.
7 rm 57.14/63.49 **st.**

The Vintage, Main St, ☎ (021) 4772502, *info@vintagerestaurant.ie, Fax (021) 4774828* – MC AE DC VISA JCB. Z k
closed 1 January-13 February, Sunday and Monday in winter – **Meals** (dinner only) 31/48.50 and a la carte 41/58.30 **t.** 22.

Max's, Main St, ☎ (021) 4772443 – . MC AE VISA Z m
closed November-March and Tuesday – **Meals** 16.38 (lunch) and a la carte 20/34 **t.** 15.24.

Fishy Fishy Cafe (at The Gourmet Store), Guardwell, ☎ (021) 4774453, – Y h
closed 1 week Christmas and Sunday October tillmarch – **Meals** - Seafood - (bookings not accepted) (lunch only) a la carte 18/29 **t.** 17.71.

at Barrells Cross *Southwest : 3½ m. on R 600 – Z – ✉ Kinsale.*

Rivermount House without rest., Northeast : ½ m. ☎ (021) 4778033, *rivermnt@iol.ie, Fax (021) 4778225*, – TV P. MC VISA.
February-November – **6 rm** 55/70 **st.**

at Ballinadee *West : 7½ m. by R 600 – Z – ✉ Kinsale.*

Glebe Country House , ☎ (021) 4778294, *glebehse@indigo.ie, Fax (021) 4778456*, « Georgian rectory », – P. MC DC VISA
closed Christmas and New Year – **Meals** *(closed Sunday and Monday)* (residents only) (dinner only) 30 **st.** – **4 rm** 57/90 **st.**

KINSALEY *Dublin* 923 N 7 – *see Malahide.*

KINSEALEY *Dublin* 923 N 7 – *see Malahide.*

KINVARRA (Cinn Mhara) *Galway* 923 F 8 – *pop. 432.*
Dublin 142 – Galway 17 – Limerick 37.

Merriman Inn without rest., Main St, ☎ (091) 638222, *merrimanhotel@eircom.net, Fax (091) 637686* – TV P. MC AE DC VISA.
closed 23-28 December and 3 January-8 February – **32 rm** 75/140 **st.**

KNIGHTS TOWN *Kerry* 923 B 12 – *see Valencia Island.*

KNOCK (An Cnoc) *Mayo* 923 F 6 *Ireland G. – pop. 575.*
See : *Basilica of our Lady, Queen of Ireland*★.
Knock (Connaught) Airport : ☎ (094) 67222, NE : 9 m. by N 17.
Knock Airport ☎ (094) 67247 (June-September) – Knock ☎ (094) 88193 (May-September).
Dublin 132 – Galway 46 – Westport 32.

Hotels see : **Cong** *SW : 36 m. by N 17, R 331, R 334 and R 345.*

KNOCKTOPHER *Kilkenny.*
Dublin 87 – Kilkenny 12 – Waterford 18 – Wexford 45.

Carroll's, ☎ (056) 68082, *info@carrollshotel.com, Fax (056) 68290* – rest, TV P. MC AE VISA.
closed 25 December – **Meals** (bar lunch) 11.62/31.75 and a la carte 9/14 **t.** 12.64 – **10 rm** 50/100 **t.** – SB.

LAHINCH (An Leacht) *Clare* 923 D 9 *Ireland G. – pop. 580.*
Env. : *Cliffs of Moher*★★★.
18, 18 *Lahinch ☎ (065) 7081003* – 9 *Spanish Point, Miltown Malbay ☎ (065) 7084198.*
Dublin 162 – Galway 49 – Limerick 41.

Quality Aberdeen Arms, Main St, ☎ (065) 7081100, *aberdeenarms@eircom.net, Fax (065) 7081228*, – rest, TV P – 200. MC AE DC VISA.
closed January-February – **Meals** (bar lunch)/dinner 24.13 and a la carte 16/26 **st.** 15.87 – **55 rm** 82.53/139.67 **st.** – SB.

Moy House, Southwest : 2 ½ m. on N 67 (Milltown Malbay rd) ✆ (065) 7082800, *moyhouse@eircom.net, Fax (065) 7082500*, ≤ Lahinch Bay, « Early 19C country house », – TV P. MC AE VISA.
closed 24-27 December and 30 December-14 January – **Meals** (residents only) (dinner only) 38.10 **t.** 22.22 – **8 rm** 127/228.60 **t.**

Greenbrier Inn without rest., Ennistymon Rd, ✆ (065) 7081242, *gbrier@indigo.ie, Fax (065) 7081247* – TV P. MC VISA.
closed 7 January-7 March and 25-26 December – **14 rm** 65/115 **st.**

LEENANE (An Líonán) *Galway* 923 C 7 *Ireland G.* – ✉ *Clifden.*

See : *Killary Harbour*★.

Env. : *Joyce Country*★★ – *Lough Nafooey*★, *SE : 6 ½ m. by R 336* – *Aasleagh Falls*★, *NE : 2 ½ m.*

Exc. : *Connemara*★★★ – *Lough Corrib*★★, *SE : 10 m. by R 336 and R 345* – *Doo Lough Pass*★, *NW : 9 m. by N 59 and R 335.*

Dublin 173 – *Ballina 56* – *Galway 41.*

Delphi Lodge, Northwest : 8 ¼ m. by N 59 on Louisburgh rd ✆ (095) 42222, *delfish@iol.ie, Fax (095) 42296*, ≤, « Georgian sporting lodge, loughside setting », – P 25. MC VISA.
closed 15 December-10 January – **Meals** (residents only) (communal dining) (dinner only) (set menu only) 45 **t.** 20 – **12 rm** 135/240 **t.** – SB.

There is no paid advertising in this Guide.

LEIXLIP (Léim an Bhradáin) *Kildare* 923 M 7 – *pop. 13 451.*

Dublin 14 – *Drogheda 39* – *Galway 125* – *Kilkenny 73.*

Springfield, Leixlip Rd, ✆ (01) 458 1100, *reception@springfieldhotel.ie, Fax (01) 458 1142*, – rest, TV P – 200. MC AE VISA.
closed 25-26 December – **Meals** (carving lunch)/dinner a la carte 23/40 **st.** 15.17 – **52 rm** 82.53/184.11 **st.**

Leixlip House, Captain's Hill, ✆ (01) 624 2268, *manager@leixliphouse.com, Fax (01) 624 4177*, « Georgian house » – TV P – 100. MC AE VISA.
closed 25 December – **Meals** – (see ***The Bradaun*** below) – **19 rm** 133/165 **st.** – SB.

The Bradaun (at Leixlip House H.), Captain's Hill, ✆ (01) 624 2268, *Fax (01) 624 4177* – P MC AE VISA
closed 25 December – **Meals** (dinner only and lunch Saturday and Sunday) 22.22/31.75 and dinner a la carte 31.05/36.01 **st.** 17.75.

LETTERFRACK (Leitir Fraic) *Galway* 923 C 7 *Ireland G.*

Env. : *Connemara*★★★ – *Sky Road*★★ (≤★★) – *Connemara National Park*★ – *Kylemore Abbey*★, *E : 3 m. by N 59.*

Dublin 189 – *Ballina 69* – *Galway 57.*

Rosleague Manor, West : 1 ½ m. on N 59 ✆ (095) 41101, *rosleaguemanor@eircom.net, Fax (095) 41168*, ≤ Ballynakill harbour and mountains, – rest, TV P MC AE VISA
April-October – **Meals** 41.91 **t.** 17.14 – **20 rm** 120.65/215.90 **st.** – SB.

Diamond Lodge without rest., Kylemore Rd, ✆ (095) 41380, *paulineconroy@eircom.net, Fax (095) 41205*, – P. MC VISA
16 March-20 November – **4 rm** 50/76 **t.**

LETTERKENNY (Leitir Ceanainn) *Donegal* 923 I 3 *Ireland G.* – *pop. 7 606.*

Exc. : *Glenveagh National Park*★★ *(Gardens*★★*), NW : 12 m. by R 250, R 251 and R 254* – *Grianan of Aileach*★★ (≤★★) *NE : 17 ½ m. by N 13* – *Church Hill (Glebe House and Gallery*★ *AC) NW : 10 m. by R 250.*

18 *Dunfanaghy* ✆ *(074) 36335.*

Derry Rd ✆ *(074) 21160.*

Dublin 150 – *Londonderry 21* – *Sligo 72.*

Holiday Inn Letterkenny, Derry Rd, Southeast : 1 ¾ m. on N 14 at junction with N 13 ✆ (074) 24369, *info@holidayinnletterkenny.net, Fax (074) 25389*, – rm TV P – 700. MC AE VISA.
closed 24-26 December – **Meals** (carvery lunch) 13.97/31.68 and dinner a la carte 25/46 **st.** 13.90 – 10.09 – **120 rm** 95.23/196.80 **st.** – SB.

Castlegrove House, Ramelton Rd, Northeast : 4 ½ m. by N 13 off R 245 ℘ (074) 51118, *marytsweeney@hotmail.com, Fax (074) 51384*, ≤, « Late 17C country house », –, P. VISA. *closed 22-28 December* – **Meals** *(closed Sunday)* (dinner only) 25.39/44.44 **t.** 12.70 – **13 rm** 63.49/190.46 **t.**, 1 suite – SB.

Quality Court, Main St, ℘ (074) 22977, *sales@qualitydonegal.com, Fax (074) 22928* – rm, rest, P. VISA. *closed 25 December* – **Meals** (bar lunch) 10.09/12.63 and a la carte 18/25 **t.** 13.90 – **58 rm** 76/139 **st.**, 25 suites – SB.

Gleneany House, Port Rd, ℘ (074) 26088, *Fax (074) 26090* – rest, rest, P. VISA. *closed 23-31 December* – **Meals** 31.40 and a la carte 13/21 **t.** 19.05 – **22 rm** 50/100 **t.**

Pennsylvania House without rest., Curraghleas, Mountain Top, North : 2 ¼ m. by N 56 ℘ (074) 26808, *pennsylvania.house@indigo.ie, Fax (074) 28905*, ≤, – P. VISA. *closed Christmas* – **7 rm** 38.10/101.60.

Ballyraine Guesthouse without rest., Ramelton Rd, East : 1 ¾ m. by N 14 on R 245 ℘ (074) 24460, *ballyraineguesthouse@eircom.net, Fax (074) 20857* – P. VISA. **8 rm** 27.93/57.13 **st.**

LIMERICK (Luimneach) *Limerick 923 G 9 Ireland G. – pop. 52 039.*

See : *City★★ - St Mary's Cathedral★★ Y – Limerick Museum★ Z* **M2** – *King John's Castle★ AC Y – John Square★ Z* **20** – *St. John's Cathedral★ Z.*

Env. : *Hunt Museum★★ AC, E : 2 m. by N 7 Y – Cratloe Wood (≤★) NW : 5 m. by N 18 Z.*

Exc. : *Castleconnell★, E : 7 m. by N 7 – Lough Gur Interpretive Centre★ AC, S : 11 m. by R 512 and R 514 Z – Clare Glens★, E : 13 m. by N 7 and R 503 Y – Monasteranenagh Abbey★, S : 13 m. by N 20 Z.*

Shannon Airport : ℘ (061) 471444, W : 16 m. by N 18 Z – **Terminal** : *Limerick Railway Station.*

Arthur's Quay ℘ (061) 317522 Y.

Dublin 120 – Cork 58.

Plan on next page

Castletroy Park, Dublin Rd, East : 2 ¼ m. by N 7 ℘ (061) 335566, *sales@castletroy-park.ie, Fax (061) 331117*, – rm, P – 450. VISA. *closed 24-26 December* – ***McLaughlin's :*** **Meals** *(closed Sunday dinner and Monday)* (dinner only and Sunday lunch)/dinner 20/38 and a la carte 30.50/43.50 **st.** 18 – **105 rm** 195/220 **st.**, 2 suites – SB.

South Court, Raheen Roundabout, Southwest : 2 ¾ m. on N 20 ℘ (061) 4874870, *c/o@lynchotels.com, Fax (061) 4874999*, – rm, rest, P – 200. VISA. ***Seasons :*** **Meals** (dinner only and Sunday lunch)/dinner 25.39/31.74 **st.** 17.78 – ***Boru's :*** **Meals** (dinner only) a la carte 20.32/29.21 **st.** 15.24 – **124 rm** 139.70/165.10 **st.** – SB.

Limerick Ryan, Ennis Rd, Northwest : 1 ¼ m. on R 587 ℘ (061) 453922, *ryan@indigo.ie, Fax (061) 326333*, – rm, rest, P – 120. VISA. **Meals** 10.16/25.39 and dinner a la carte 16.17 – 11.60 – **179 rm** 154.83/203.72 **st.**, 2 suites – SB.

Jurys Limerick, Ennis Rd, ℘ (061) 327777, *limerick@jurysdoyle.com, Fax (061) 326400*, – rm, rest, P – 200. VISA. Y z *closed 24-26 December* – ***Sorrels :*** **Meals** 18/26 **t.** 18 – 12 – **94 rm** 147/184 **t.**, 1 suite.

Limerick Inn, Ennis Rd, Northwest : 4 m. on N 18 ℘ (061) 326666, *limerick-inn@limerick-inn.ie, Fax (061) 326281*, – rest, P – 600. VISA. *closed 24-25 December* – **Meals** (bar lunch Monday-Saturday)/dinner 36 – 11 – **150 rm** 145/190 **st.**, 3 suites.

Jurys Inn Limerick, Lower Mallow St, ℘ (061) 207000, *jurysinnlimerick@jurysdoyle.com, Fax (061) 400966* – rm, rest, – 30. VISA. Z a *closed 24-26 December* – **Meals** (dinner only) 21.50 14 – 8.50 – **151 rm** 75 **st.**

Greenhills, Ennis Rd, Northwest : 2 ¼ m. on R 587 ℘ (061) 453033, *info@greenhillsgroup.com, Fax (061) 453307*, – rm, P – 600. VISA. *closed 25 December* – **Meals** (carvery lunch)/dinner a la carte approx. 30 **st.** 15.87 – **58 rm** 107.93/165.07 **st.** – SB.

Kilmurry Lodge, Dublin Rd, Castletroy, East : 3 ¼ m. by N 7 ℘ (061) 331133, *info@kilmurrylodge.com, Fax (061) 330011* – P – 300. VISA. *closed 25-26 December* – **Meals** 16/37 and dinner a la carte **st.** 14.60 – **99 rm** 83/153 **st.**

LIMERICK

Arthur Quay .... Y 2
Arthur Quay Shopping Centre .... Y
Baal's Bridge .... Y 4
Bank Place .... Y 5
Barrington Street............ Z 6
Bridge Street .... Y 7
Broad Street................ Y 8
Castle Street .... Y 10
Cathedral Place .... Z 12
Charlotte's Quay .... Y 13
The Crescent .... Z 14
Cruises Street .... Z 15
Gerald Griffen St. .... Z 16
Grattan Street .... Y 17
High Street.................. Z 18
Honan's Quay .... Y 19
John Square................. Z 20
Lock Quay .... Y 21
Lower Cecil Street .... Z 22
Lower Mallow St............. Z 23
Mathew Bridge .... Y 24
Mount Kenneth .... Z 26
Newtown Mahon .... Z 28
North Circular Rd............ Z 29
O'Connell Street .... Z
O'Dwyer Bridge .... Y 30
Patrick Street .... YZ
Penniwell Road .... Z
Roches Street .... Z
Rutland Street .... Y
St Alphonsus St............. Z
St Gerard St. .... Z
St Lelia Street.............. YZ
Sarfield Street .... Y
Sexton Street North .... Y
Shannon Street .... Z
South Circular Rd............ Z
Thomond Bridge .... Y
Wickham Street.............. Z
William Street .... Z

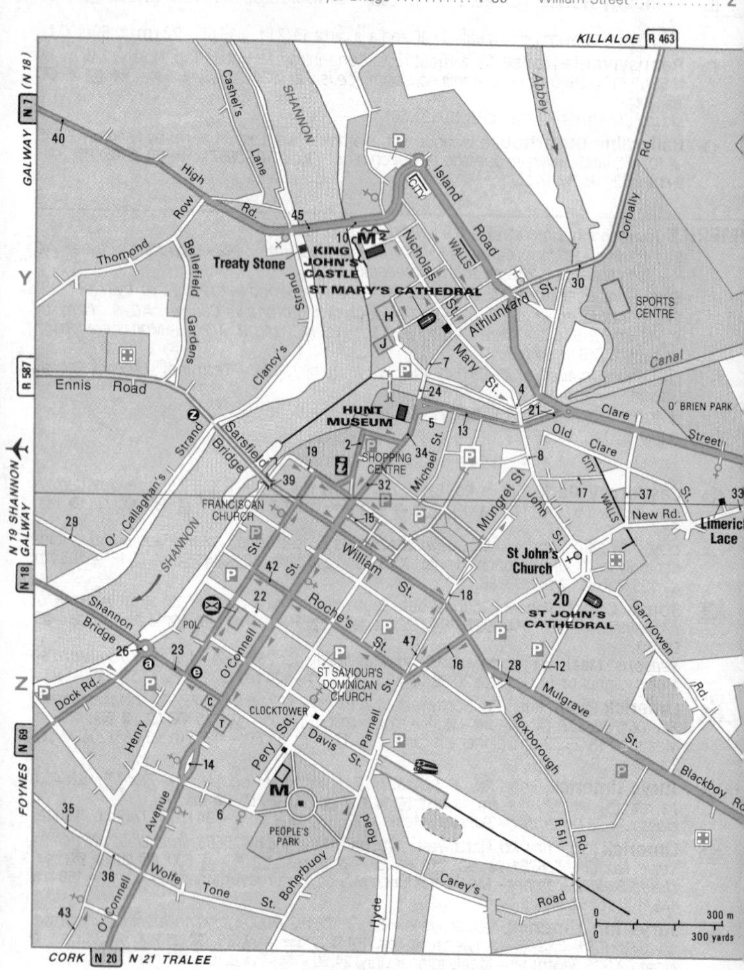

Les hôtels ou restaurants agréables
sont indiqués dans le guide par un signe rouge.
Aidez-nous en nous signalant les maisons où,
par expérience, vous savez qu'il fait bon vivre.
Votre guide Michelin sera encore meilleur.

Clifton House without rest., Ennis Rd, Northwest : 1 ¼ m. on R 587 ℘ (061) 451166, *cliftonhouse@eircom.net, Fax (061) 451224,* – TV P. MC VISA.
closed 21 December-2 January – **16 rm** 45/64 **t.**

Travelodge, Coonagh roundabout, Ennis Rd, Northwest : 2 ½ m. by R 587 at junction with N 18 ℘ (061) 457000, *Fax (061) 457000* – rm, rest, TV P. MC AE VISA JCB.
Meals (grill rest.) – **40 rm** 67.95 **t.**

Clonmacken House without rest., Clonmacken Rd, off Ennis Rd, Northwest : 2 m. by R 587 ℘ (061) 327007, *clonmac@indigo.ie, Fax (061) 327785,* – TV P. MC AE VISA.
closed 21 December-2 January – **10 rm** 45/64 **st.**

Acacia Cottage without rest., 2 Foxfield, Dooradoyle Rd, Southwest : 2 m. by N 20 off Ballykeefe roundabout ℘ (061) 304757, *acaciacottage@iolfree.ie, Fax (061) 304757,* – TV P. MC VISA.
4 rm 40/58.

Brûlées, Corner Mallow/Henry St, ℘ (061) 319931 – MC AE VISA Z e
closed 1 week Christmas, Sunday and Monday – **Meals** (dinner only) a la carte 18.41/32.29 **t.** 15.88.

LISDOONVARNA (Lios Dúin Bhearna) *Clare* 923 E 8 *Ireland G. – pop. 890.*

Env. : *The Burren★★ (Cliffs of Moher★★★, Scenic Routes★★, Aillwee Cave★ AC (Waterfall★★), Corcomroe Abbey★, Kilfenora Crosses★).*
Dublin 167 – Galway 39 – Limerick 47.

Ballinalacken Castle Country House , Coast Rd, Northwest : 3 m. by N 67 (Doolin rd) on R 477 ℘ (065) 7074025, *ballinalackencastle@eircom.net, Fax (065) 7074025,* – rest, TV P. MC VISA
mid April-October – **Meals** *(closed Tuesday)* (dinner only) a la carte approx. 41 **t.** 17.78 – **12 rm** 101.58/203.16 **t.**

Carrigann, ℘ (065) 7074036, *carrigannhotel@eircom.net, Fax (065) 7074567,* – rest, TV P – 70. MC VISA.
March-October – **Meals** (bar lunch)/dinner a la carte 27.30/36.05 **t.** 14 – **20 rm** 50/100 **t.** – SB.

Sheedy's Country House, Sulphir Hill, ℘ (065) 7074026, *enquiries@sheedyscountryhouse.com, Fax (065) 7074555,* – TV P. MC VISA.
mid April-mid October – **Meals** – (see ***The Restaurant*** below) – **11 rm** 88/128 **t.**

Woodhaven without rest., Doolin Coast Rd, West : 1 m. by N 67 (Doolin rd) off R 477 ℘ (065) 7074017, – P. MC VISA.
4 rm 38.50/54.

The Restaurant (at Sheedy's H.), Sulphir Hill, ℘ (065) 7074026, *Fax (065) 7074555* – P. MC AE VISA
mid April-mid October – **Meals** (dinner only) a la carte 28.90/47.60 **s.** 16.50.

LISTOWEL (Lios Tuathail) *Kerry* 923 D 10 – *pop. 3 393.*

St John's Church ℘ (068) 22590 (June-September).
Dublin 168 – Killarney 34 – Limerick 47 – Tralee 17.

Allo's with rm, 41-43 Church St, ℘ (068) 22880, *allosbar@eircom.net, Fax (068) 22803* – TV. MC AE VISA
closed Good Friday, 25 December and 1 January – **Meals** *(closed Sunday and Monday)* (dinner only) a la carte approx. 31.74 **t.** 17.78 – (see also below) – **3 rm** 76.18/114.28 **t.**

Allo's Bar, 41-43 Church St, ℘ (068) 22880 – MC AE VISA
closed Good Friday, 25 December, 1 January, Sunday and Monday – **Meals** (booking essential) a la carte 15/32 **t.** 17.78.

LONGFORD (An Longfort) *Longford* 923 I 6.

Market Sq ℘ (043) 46566 (May-September).
Dublin 77 – Drogheda 75 – Galway 70 – Limerick 109.

Cumiskey's Farmhouse , East : 5 ½ m. by R 194 off Aghnacliffe Rd ℘ (043) 23320, *kc@iol.ie, Fax (043) 23516,* – P. MC VISA.
restricted opening November-February – **Meals** (by arrangement) 32 **st.** 12 – **5 rm** 40/120 **st.**, 1 suite.

Les prix — Pour toutes précisions sur les prix indiqués dans ce guide, reportez-vous aux pages de l'introduction.

LOUGHREA (Baile Locha Riach) *Galway* 923 F 8 – *pop. 3 335.*
Dublin 112 – Galway 22 – Limerick 57 – Sligo 106.

Meadow Court, Northwest : 1 ½ m. by N 6 ✆ (091) 841051, *meadowcourthotel@eircom.net, Fax (091) 842406* – 🛗 TV ♿ P – 🎪 400. MC AE VISA. ✂
closed 25-26 December – **Meals** a la carte 14/26 **t.** – **21 rm** ☕ 53.96/114.27 **st.**

MAAM CROSS *Galway* 923 D 7.
Dublin 163 – Galway 27 – Westport 33.

Peacockes, ✆ (091) 552306, *peacockes@eircom.net, Fax (091) 552215,* – 🛗, 🚭 rest TV ✆ ♿ P – 🎪 100. MC AE VISA. ✂
closed 23-26 December – **Meals** 29.20 (dinner) and a la carte 15/27 **t.** 🍷 15.24 – **25 rm** ☕ 150 **t.** – SB.

MACROOM (Maigh Chromtha) *Cork* 923 F 12 – *pop. 2 457.*
18 *Lackaduve ✆ (026) 41072.*
Dublin 186 – Cork 25 – Killarney 30.

Castle, Main St, ✆ (026) 41074, *castlehotel@eircom.net, Fax (026) 41505,* 🏋, 🏊, 🚭 rest, ▤ rest, TV ✆ P – 🎪 60. MC AE DC VISA. ✂
closed 24-28 December – **Meals** 10.16/33.01 and a la carte 25.37/31.74 **st.** 🍷 16.51 – **42 rm** ☕ 91/132 **st.** – SB.

MALAHIDE (Mullach Íde) *Dublin* 923 N 7 *Ireland G.* – *pop. 13 539.*
See : *Castle★★.*
Env. : *Fingal★.*
18, 9 *Beechwood, The Grange ✆ (01) 846 1611.*
Dublin 9 – Drogheda 24.

Grand, ✆ (01) 845 0000, *info@thegrand.ie, Fax (01) 845 0987,* 🏋, ≘s, 🏊 – 🛗, 🚭 rm, TV ✆ ♿ P – 🎪 500. MC AE DC VISA. ✂
closed 25-26 December – ***Colonnade :*** **Meals** 19/44 and a la carte 35/44 **st.** 🍷 17 – **147 rm** ☕ 190/265 **st.**, 3 suites – SB.

Cruzzo, Marina Village, ✆ (01) 845 0599, *info@cruzzo.ie, Fax (01) 845 0602,* ≤, 🏠, « Marina setting » – 🛗 ▤ P. AE DC VISA
closed 25 December, Saturday lunch and Sunday dinner – **Meals** (light lunch)/dinner a la carte approx. 35.55 **t.**

Siam Thai, Gas Yard Lane, off Strand St ✆ (01) 845 4698, *siames@eircom.net, Fax (01) 8457178* – ▤. MC AE DC VISA
closed 25-26 December and Good Friday – **Meals** - Thai - (booking essential) (dinner only) 27.95/30.47 and a la carte 24.66/28.52 **t.** 🍷 16.44.

at Kinsaley *Southwest : 2½ m. by R 106 on R 107* – ✉ *Malahide.*

Belcamp Hutchinson without rest., Carrs Lane, Balgriffin, D17, South : 1 m. by R 107 ✆ (01) 846 0843, *belcamphutchinson@eircom.net, Fax (01) 848 5703,* « Georgian house », – TV P. MC VISA
closed 21 December-1 February – **8 rm** ☕ 65/126.97 **st.**

Liscara without rest., Malahide Rd, D17, South : ½ m. on R 107 ✆ (01) 848 375 *Fax (01) 848 3751,* – 🚭 P. ✂
March-October – **6 rm** ☕ 44.44/63.49.

MALLOW (Mala) *Cork* 923 F 11 *Ireland G.* – *pop. 6 434.*
See : *Town★ – St. James' Church★.*
Exc. : *Doneraile Wildlife Park★ AC, NE : 6 m. by N 20 and R 581 – Buttevant Friary★, N : 7 m. by N 20 – Annes Grove Gardens★, E : 11 m. by N 72 and minor rd.*
18 *Ballyellis ✆ (022) 21145.*
Dublin 149 – Cork 21 – Killarney 40 – Limerick 41.

Longueville House 🐦, West : 3 ½ m. by N 72 ✆ (022) 47156, *info@longuevillehouse.ie, Fax (022) 47459,* ≤, « Part Georgian mansion in extensive grounds, working farm », 🎣, – 🚭 TV ✆ P – 🎪 30. MC AE DC VISA. ✂
14 March-4 November – ***Presidents :*** **Meals** (booking essential) (bar lunch)/dinner 47/61 🍷 21 – **20 rm** ☕ 85/336 **t.** – SB.

Springfort Hall 🐦, North : 4 ¾ m. by N 20 on R 581 ✆ (022) 21278, *stay@springforthall.com, Fax (022) 21557,* « Part 18C », , 🌳 – TV ♿ P – 🎪 300. MC AE VISA. ✂
Meals 21/41 and dinner a la carte 28/41 **st.** 🍷 19 – **49 rm** ☕ 80/127 **st.** – SB.

MAYNOOTH (Maigh Nuad) *Kildare* 923 M 7 *Ireland G. – pop. 8 528.*
Env. : *Castletown House*★★ *AC, SE : 4 m. by R 405.*
Dublin 15.

Moyglare Manor ⑤, Moyglare, North : 2 m. ℘ (01) 628 6351, *info@moyglaremanor.ie, Fax (01) 628 5405*, ≤, « Georgian country house, extensively furnished with antiques », ⁂, – P. MC AE ⓓ VISA. ✂
closed 24-27 December – **Meals** *(closed Saturday lunch)* 28.50/45.65 and dinner a la carte 30/48 **t.** 20.25 – **16 rm** ☐ 140/230 **t.**

Glenroyal, Straffan Rd, ℘ (01) 629 0909, *glenroyal@hotel.ie, Fax (01) 629 0919*, ⅓, ≘s, ☐ – |♦|, ≡ rest, TV ✆ ♿ P – 🔧 450. MC AE ⓓ VISA. ✂
closed 25 December – **Meals** *(closed Sunday dinner)* (carving lunch Monday-Saturday)/dinner a la carte 25.69/35.79 **t.** 15.23 – **57 rm** ☐ 95.23/146.01 **t.** – SB.

MERRION (Muirfin) *Dublin – see Dublin.*

MIDLETON (Mainistir na Corann) *Cork* 923 H 12 – *pop. 3 266.*
East Cork, Gortacrue ℘ (021) 4631687.
Jameson Heritage Centre ℘ (021) 4613702.
Dublin 161 – Cork 12 – Waterford 61.

Midleton Park, Old Cork Rd, ℘ (021) 4635100, *info@midletonpark.com, Fax (021) 4635101*, ⅓, ≘s, ☐, ⁂ – |♦| TV ✆ ♿ P – 🔧 300. MC AE ⓓ VISA. ✂
closed 25 December – **Meals** (bar lunch)/dinner a la carte 19.05/33.01 **t.** 15.87 – **76 rm** ☐ 139.67/190.46 **t.**, 1 suite – SB.

MONAGHAN (Muineachán) *Monaghan* 923 L 5 – *pop. 5 628.*
Market House ℘ (047) 81122 (April-October).
Dublin 83 – Belfast 43 – Drogheda 54 – Dundalk 22 – Londonderry 75.

Hillgrove, Old Armagh Rd, Southeast : ¾ m. by N 2 ℘ (047) 81288, *hillgrove@quinn-hotels.com, Fax (047) 84951* – |♦|, ≡ rest, TV ♿ P – 🔧 800. MC AE ⓓ VISA. ✂
Cavendish : **Meals** 18/38 **st.** 16.50 – ***Bracken :*** **Meals** (carving lunch)/dinner 8.25/20 **st.** 16.50 – **44 rm** ☐ 85/165 **st.** – SB.

Four Seasons, Coolshannagh, North : 1 m. on N 2 ℘ (047) 81888, *info@4seasons hotel.ie, Fax (047) 83131*, ⅓, ☐, ⁂ – TV P. MC AE ⓓ VISA. ✂
closed 25 December – **Meals** 20/40 and a la carte 19/38 **st.** 18 – **38 rm** ☐ 60/140 **st.**, 6 suites – SB.

Andy's, Market St, ℘ (047) 82277, *andysrestaurant@eircom.net, Fax (047) 84195* – MC VISA
closed 2 weeks July, 25 and 31 December and Monday dinner – **Meals** 25.39 (dinner) and a la carte 20/29 **t.** 14.60.

at Glaslough *Northeast : 6½ m. by N 2 and R 168 – ✉ Monaghan.*

Castle Leslie ⑤, ℘ (047) 88109, *info@castleleslie.com, Fax (047) 88256*, ≤, « 18C castle in extensive parkland », ⑤, ⁂, ✂ – ⇎ rest, P. MC VISA
Meals (dinner only) 28.57/60.95 **st.** 20.32 – **14 rm** ☐ 95/133 **st.** – SB.

MONKSTOWN (Baile na Mhanaigh) *Cork* 923 G/H 12.
Parkgarriffe ℘ (021) 841376.
Dublin 162 – Cork 9 – Waterford 75.

The Bosun, The Pier, ℘ (021) 4842172, *Fax (021) 4842008*, ≤, ⁂ – |♦|, ≡ rest, TV. MC AE ⓓ VISA. ✂
closed 24-26 December – **Meals** (bar lunch Monday-Saturday)/dinner 33.65 and a la carte 20/34 **t.** 16.51 – **15 rm** ☐ 50.79/88.88 **t.**

MONKSTOWN (Baile na Mhanaigh) *Dublin* 923 ⑩ *– see Dublin.*

MOYCULLEN (Maigh Cuilinn) *Galway* 923 E 7 – *pop. 601.*
Dublin 139 – Galway 7.

Knockferry Lodge ⑤, Knockferry (on Lough Corrib), Northeast : 6 ½ m. by Knockferry rd ℘ (091) 550122, *knockferrylodge@eircom.net, Fax (091) 550328*, ≤, ⑤, ⁂ – ⇎ rest, P. MC AE ⓓ VISA. ✂
March-October – **Meals** *(restricted opening in winter)* (dinner only) 28 16.50 – **10 rm** ☐ 50/70 **t.** – SB.

XX **Moycullen House** with rm, Southwest : 1 m. by Spiddle rd (091) 555621, *info moycullen.com, Fax (091) 555566*, – P. MO AE VISA.
closed 8 January-10 March and 24-26 December – **Meals** *(closed Wednesday)* (dinner or and Sunday lunch)/dinner 33 and a la carte 33/45 **t.** 18 – **3 rm** 80/144 **st.** – SB.

MULLAGH **(Mullach)** *Cavan* 923 L 6 – *pop. 403.*
Dublin 47 – Drogheda 34 – Dundalk 39.

Ardlo, 48 Main St, (046) 42201 – TV P. MO VISA.
Meals (bar lunch Monday-Saturday) a la carte 16/29 **t.** 15.18 – **10 rm** 44.45/82.56 **t.**

MULLINAVAT **(Muileann an Bhata)** *Kilkenny* 923 K 10 – *pop. 275.*
Dublin 88 – Kilkenny 21 – Waterford 8.

Rising Sun, Main St, (051) 898173, *therisingsun@eircom.net, Fax (051) 898435* – TV MO AE VISA
closed 24-28 December – **Meals** (carving lunch)/dinner 20/23 and a la carte 17.85/26.50 17 – **10 rm** 50/80 **st.**

MULLINGAR **(An Muileann gCearr)** *Westmeath* 923 JK 7 *Ireland G. – pop. 8 040.*
Env. : *Belvedere House and Gardens★ AC, S : 3½ m. by N 52.*
Exc. : *Multyfarnhan Franciscan Friary★, N : 8 m. by N 4 – Tullynally Castle★ AC, N : 13 m. N 4 and R 394 – Fore Abbey★, NE : 17 m. by R 394.*
Market House (044) 48650.
Dublin 49 – Drogheda 36.

Austin Friar, Austin Friar St, (044) 45777, *reception@austin-friar.com, Fax (044) 458* – TV – 50. MO AE VISA
closed 24-26 December – **Meals** *(closed Sunday dinner)* (dinner only and Sunday lunch dinner a la carte 21/25 **st.** 12.50 – **19 rm** 60/115 **st.** – SB.

Hilltop Country House without rest., Delvin Rd, Rathconnell, Northeast : 2 ½ m. N 52 (044) 48958, *hilltopcountryhouse@eircom.net, Fax (044) 48013*, – TV P. VISA.
closed December and January – **5 rm** 40/60 **t.**

at Crookedwood *North : 6½ m. on R 394 – Mullingar.*

Crookedwood House, East : 1 ½ m. on Delvin rd (044) 72165, *info@crook woodhouse.com, Fax (044) 72166*, – TV P. MO AE VISA
closed 24-27 December – **Meals** – (see ***The Restaurant*** below) – **8 rm** 69.85/139.70 **t** SB.

XX **The Restaurant** (at Crookedwood House H.), East : 1 ½ m. on Delvin rd (044) 721 *Fax (044) 72166*, « Cellars of 18C rectory », – P. MO AE VISA
closed 24-27 December, Sunday dinner and Monday – **Meals** (dinner only and Sunc lunch)/dinner 34.29 and a la carte 32/40 **t.** 15.88.

at Rathconrath *West : 7¾ m. on R 392 – Mullingar.*

Mearescourt House, Northwest : 3 ¾ m. by R 392, Ballnacarrigy rd on Moyvore (044) 55112, *Fax (044) 55112*, « Georgian mansion in parkland », – P. MO VISA.
closed 20 December-10 January – **Meals** (by arrangement) 32 **st.** – **4 rm** 50.79/76.18

NAAS **(An Nás)** *Kildare* 923 L/M 8 – *pop. 14 074.*
Kerdiffstown, Naas (045) 874644.
Dublin 19 – Kilkenny 52 – Tullamore 53.

Killashee House, South : 1 m. on R 448 (045) 879277, *reservations@killash house.com, Fax (045) 879266*, – rm, TV P – 2000. MO AE VISA.
closed 25 December – ***Turners :*** **Meals** 23/38.09 and dinner a la carte 34/48 **t.** 17.78 **78 rm** 150/425 **t.**, 6 suites – SB.

XX **Les Olives,** 10 South Main St, (above Joseph Kavanagh pub), (045) 894788, *lesoliv indigo.ie* – MO VISA
closed Good Friday, 25-26 December and Monday – **Meals** (booking essential) (dinner or a la carte 31/52 **t.** 18.01.

X **Lemongrass,** Abbey St, off South Main St by the Town Hall (045) 8715 *Fax (045) 874876* – . MO VISA
closed 25-26 December and Good Friday – **Meals** - Asian specialities - (booking essent a la carte 23/33 **t.**

NAVAN (An Uaimh) *Meath* 923 L 7 *Ireland G. – pop. 3 447.*

Env. : *Bective Abbey★, S : 4 m. by R 161.*

Exc. : *Trim★ (castle★★), SW : 8 m. by R 161 – Kells★ (Round Tower and High Crosses★★, St. Columba's House★), NW : by N 3 – Tara★, S : 6 m. by N 3.*

Moor Park, Mooretown ☎ (046) 27661 – Royal Tara, Bellinter ☎ (046) 25244.

Dublin 30 – Drogheda 16 – Dundalk 32.

Newgrange, Bridge St, ☎ (046) 74100, *info@newgrangehotel.ie, Fax (046) 73977* – rm, rest, – 550. VISA. *closed 25 December* – ***Bridge Brasserie :*** **Meals** (carvery lunch Monday-Saturday) 17.14/31.74 and dinner a la carte 19/33 **st.** 13.27 – **36 rm** 89/127 **st.** – SB.

Ardboyne, Dublin Rd, South : 1 m. on N 3 ☎ (046) 23119, *ardboyne@quinn-hotels.com, Fax (046) 22355,* – rest, – 350. VISA. *closed 24-25 December* – **Meals** (carvery lunch Monday-Saturday) 16/28 and dinner a la carte 28.49/33.81 **t.** 15 – **29 rm** 77/116 **t.** – SB.

Ma Dwyers without rest., Dublin Rd, South : ¾ m. on N 3 ☎ (046) 77992, *Fax (046) 77995* – VISA. *closed 24-26 December* – **9 rm** 45/80 **st.**

Killyon without rest., Dublin Rd, South : 1 m. on N 3 ☎ (046) 71224, *killyonguesthouse.navan@eircom.net, Fax (046) 72766* – VISA. *closed 25-26 December* – **6 rm** 50.79/76.18.

Southbank Bistro, 1 Ludlow St, ☎ (046) 72406, *dine@southbankbistro.com, Fax (046) 76824* – VISA *closed 25-26 December and Good Friday* – **Meals** (dinner only and Sunday lunch)/dinner a la carte 23.40/37.35 **t.** 15.20.

NENAGH (An tAonach) *Tipperary* 923 H 9 *Ireland G. – pop. 5 645.*

See : *Town★ – Heritage Centre★ – Castle★.*

Nenagh, Birchwood ☎ (067) 31476.

Connolly St ☎ (067) 31610 (mid May-mid September).

Dublin 96 – Galway 63 – Limerick 26.

Nenagh Abbey Court, Dublin Rd, East : ¼ m. on N 7 ☎ (067) 41111, *abycourt@indigo.ie, Fax (067) 41022* – rm, rest, – 450. VISA. – **Meals** *(closed dinner Sunday and Monday)* (carvery lunch Monday to Saturday)/dinner 21/31 and a la carte 14/36 **st.** 15 – **76 rm** 63.50/114.30 **st.** – SB.

Ashley Park House, Ardcrony, Northeast : 4 m. on N 52 ☎ (067) 38223, *margaret@ashleypark.com, Fax (067) 38013,* ←, « 18C country house on the shores of Lough Orna », – Meals (by arrangement) 38.09 **st.** 19.05 – **6 rm** 44.44/88.88 **st.** – SB.

NEWBRIDGE (An Droichead Nua) *Kildare* 923 L 8 *Ireland G. – pop. 12 970.*

Env. : *Irish National Stud★★ AC (Japanese Gardens★★ AC) SW : 6 m. by N 7 – Kildare★ (Cathedral★★) SW : 5½ m. by N 7.*

Curragh ☎ (045) 441238.

Dublin 28 – Kilkenny 57 – Tullamore 36.

Keadeen, Curragh Rd, Ballymany, Southwest : 1 m. ☎ (045) 431666, *keadeen@iol.ie, Fax (045) 434402,* – rest, – 800. VISA. *closed 24-27 December* – ***The Derby Room :*** **Meals** (bar lunch Monday-Saturday)/dinner a la carte 23/38 **st.** – **54 rm** 153/229 **st.**, 1 suite – SB.

NEWMARKET-ON-FERGUS (Cora Chaitlín) *Clare* 923 F 7 *– pop. 1 542.*

Dromoland Castle ☎ (061) 368444.

Dublin 136 – Ennis 8 – Limerick 15.

Dromoland Castle, Northwest : 1½ m. on N 18 ☎ (061) 368144, *sales@dromoland.ie, Fax (061) 363355,* ←, « Converted castle », – rest, – 450. VISA. ***Earl of Thormond :*** **Meals** (dinner only and Sunday lunch) 26/100 and a la carte – ***Fig Tree*** *(at Dromoland Golf & Country Club) (☎ (061) 368444)* **: Meals** 26/100 a la carte – 19 – **93 rm** 352/495 **st.**, 6 suites.

Clare Inn, Northwest : 2 m. on N 18 ☎ (061) 368161, *cro@lynchotels.com, Fax (061) 368622,* – rest, – 400. VISA. **Meals** 15.24/31.74 and a la carte 19.05/31.75 **st.** 17.78 – 10.16 – **181 rm** 95.23/317.50 **st.** – SB.

NEWPORT (Baile Uí Fhiacháin) *Mayo* 923 D 6 *Ireland G. – pop. 567.*

Env. : *Burrishoole Abbey*★, *NW : 2 m. by N 59 – Furnace Lough*★, *NW : 3 m. by N 59.*

George St ☎ (098) 41895 (summer only).

Dublin 164 – Ballina 37 – Galway 60.

Newport House ⑤, ☎ (098) 41222, *kjt1@anu.ie, Fax (098) 41613,* « Antique furnishe country house », ⑤, ⑤, ⑤ – ⑤ rest, ⑤ P. ⑤ ⑤ ⑤ VISA. ⑤
19 March-5 October – **Meals** (dinner only) 46 and a la carte approx. 37 **st.** 11.50 – **18 r** 126/252 **st.**

NEW ROSS (Ros Mhic Thriúin) *Wexford* 923 L 10 *Ireland G. – pop. 5 012 – ✉ Newbawn.*

See : *St. Mary's Church*★.

Exc. : *Kennedy Arboretum, Campile*★ *AC, S : 7½ m. by R 733 – Dunbrody Abbey*★, *S : 8 r by R 733 – Inistioge*★, *NW : 10 m. by N 25 and R 700 – Graiguenamanagh*★ *(Duiske Abbey*★ *AC), N : 11 m. by N 25 and R705.*

The Quay ☎ (051) 421857 (June-August).

Dublin 88 – Kilkenny 27 – Waterford 15 – Wexford 23.

Clarion Brandon House ⑤, South : ¾ m. on N 25 ☎ (051) 421703, *brandonhou @tinet.ie, Fax (051) 421567,* ⑤, ⑤, ⑤, ⑤, ⑤ – ⑤ rest, ⑤ ⑤ P – ⑤ 250. ⑤ ⑤ ⑤ VI ⑤
Meals (dinner only and Sunday lunch)/dinner 31.74 and a la carte 18.41/31.74 **st.** 15.87 **60 rm** 100.31/158.72 **st.** – SB.

Riversdale House without rest., Lower William St, ☎ (051) 422515, *riversdalehouse@ com.net, Fax (051) 422800,* ⑤ – ⑤ ⑤ P. ⑤ VISA. ⑤
March-November – **4 rm** 39/54 **st.**

at Ballynabola *Southeast : 6 m. on N 25 – ✉ New Ross.*

Cedar Lodge, Carrigbyrne, East : 3 m. on N 25 ☎ (051) 428386, *cedarlodge@tinet. Fax (051) 428222,* ⑤ – ⑤ P. ⑤ ⑤ ⑤ VISA. ⑤
closed 26 December-February – **Meals** (bar lunch)/dinner 40 **st.** 17 – **28 rm** 11 180 **st.** – SB.

OGONNELLOE (Tuath Ó gConaíle) *Clare* 923 G 9 – *see Killaloe.*

ORANMORE (Órán Mór) *Galway* 923 F 8 *Ireland G. – pop. 1 410.*

Env. : *Galway*★★ *(St. Nicholas Church*★, *Lynch's Castle*★, *Roman Catholic Church*★, *E Square, Bank of Ireland Building, sword and mace*★*), NW : 5 m. by N 6.*

Exc. : *Athenry*★, *NE : 7 m. by N 6 and R 348 – Dunguaire Castle*★, *SW : 12 m. by N 18 a N 67 – Thoor Ballylee*★, *S : 15 m. by N 18 and minor rd – Coole Park*★, *S : 15 m. by N 18 a N 66 – Loughrea (St. Brendan's Cathedral*★*), SE : 17 m. by N 6 – Knockmoy Abbey*★, *N 17 m. by N 18, N 17 and N 63 – Tuam (St. Mary's Cathedral*★*), N : 18 m. by N 18 and N 1 Turoe Stone*★, *SE : 20 m. by N 6 and north by R 348.*

Dublin 131 – Galway 7.

Galway Bay Golf & Country Club ⑤, Southwest : 3 ½ m. by Tawin rd ☎ (091) 7905(*cro@lynchhotels.com, Fax (091) 790510,* ⑤ Galway Bay and City, ⑤18, ⑤ – ⑤ ⑤ ⑤ P ⑤ 120. ⑤ ⑤ ⑤ VISA. ⑤
Meals (bar lunch Monday-Saturday)/dinner 29.20/28.09 and a la carte 17.78/29.21 15.24 – 10.16 – **39 rm** 139/165 **st.**, **53 suites** 159/185 **st.** – SB.

Quality, North : ¾ m. on N 6 ☎ (091) 792244, *qualityhotelgalway@eircom.n Fax (091) 792246,* ⑤, ⑤, ⑤ – ⑤, ⑤ rm, ⑤ rest, ⑤ ⑤ P – ⑤ 60. ⑤ ⑤ ⑤ VISA. ⑤
closed 25-26 December – **Meals** (carvery lunch)/dinner 24.06 and a la carte 13/28 10.15 – 7.55 – **93 rm** 148.55 **st.** – SB.

Oranmore Lodge, ☎ (091) 794400, *orlodge@eircom.net, Fax (091) 790227,* ⑤, ⑤, – ⑤ ⑤ P – ⑤ 300. ⑤ ⑤ ⑤ VISA. ⑤
closed 24-25 December – **Meals** a la carte 9/34 **st.** 19.04 – **56 rm** 114.27/203.15 **st** SB.

Mooring's, Main St, ☎ (091) 790462, *themoorings1@eircom.net, Fax (091) 790462* – P – ⑤ 30. ⑤ ⑤ VISA. ⑤
Meals *(closed Sunday)* (dinner only) a la carte 20.95/36.19 **t.** 19.68 – **6 rm** 63.4 88.88 **st.**

The Bistro, Main St, ☎ (091) 792600, *fhels@gofree.indigo.ie, Fax (091) 792606* – ⑤ VISA
closed 7-31 January, 24-26 December and Monday – **Meals** (booking essential) (dinner o and Sunday lunch) 18.95/24 and a la carte 29/41 **t.** 17.70.

OUGHTERARD (Uachtar Ard) *Galway* 923 E 7 *Ireland G. – pop. 751.*

See : *Town*★.

Env. : *Lough Corrib*★★ *(Shore road – NW – ≤★★) – Aughnanure Castle*★ *AC, SE : 2 m. by N 59.*

Gortreevagh ℘ (091) 552131.

Community Office ℘ (091) 552808.

Dublin 149 – Galway 17.

Ross Lake House, Rosscahill, Southeast : 4 ½ m. by N 59 ℘ (091) 550109, *rosslake@iol.ie, Fax (091) 550184,* – P. VISA
15 March-October – **Meals** (dinner only) 37 **st.** 17.77 – **12 rm** 102/180 **st.**, 1 suite – SB.

Currarevagh House, Northwest : 4 m. on Glann rd ℘ (091) 552312, *currarevagh@ireland.com, Fax (091) 552731,* ≤, « Victorian manor on the shores of Lough Corrib », – rest, P. VISA.
April-21 October – **Meals** (booking essential) (dinner only) (set menu only) 32 **t.** 15.19 – **15 rm** 78/156 **t.** – SB.

River Run Lodge, Glann Rd, Northwest : ½ m. ℘ (091) 552697, *rivrun@indigo.ie, Fax (091) 552669,* – P. VISA
restricted opening in winter – **Meals** (dinner only) a la carte 30/40 **t.** 17.71 – **8 rm** 57/110 **st.** – SB.

Boat Inn, The Square, ℘ (091) 552196, *info@theboatinn.com, Fax (091) 552694* – . VISA.
closed 25 December – **Meals** a la carte 14/21 **st.** 13.90 – **10 rm** 38/76 **st.**

Waterfall Lodge without rest., ℘ (091) 552168, *kdolly@eircom.net,* « Riverside setting », – P.
closed 23-28 December – **6 rm** 40/64 **st.**

The Guide is updated annually so renew your Guide every year.

PARKNASILLA (Páirc na Saileach) *Kerry* 923 C 12 *Ireland G.*

Env. : *Sneem*★, *NW : 2½ m. by N 70.*

Exc. : *Iveragh Peninsula*★★ *(Ring of Kerry*★★*) – Derrynane National Historic Park*★★, *W : 16 m. by N 70 – Staigue Fort*★, *W : 13 m. by N 70.*

Dublin 224 – Cork 72 – Killarney 34.

Parknasilla Great Southern, ℘ (064) 45122, *res@parknasilla.gsh.ie, Fax (064) 45323,* ≤ Kenmare River and Caha mountains, « Collection of Irish art », 9, – rest, P – 80. VISA.
Pygmalion : Meals (dinner only) a la carte approx. 40 **st.** 13.97 – 13 – **84 rm** 176/292 **st.**, 1 suite – SB.

PORTMAGEE (An Caladh) *Kerry* 923 A 12 *Ireland G.*

Exc. : *Iveragh Peninsula*★★ *(Ring of Kerry*★★*).*

Dublin 227 – Killarney 45 – Tralee 51.

Moorings, ℘ (066) 9477108, *moorings@iol.ie, Fax (066) 9477220,* ≤, – rest, P. VISA.
March-October – **Meals** *(closed Monday dinner except Bank Holidays)* (bar lunch)/dinner a la carte 28.82/46.03 **t.** 6.95 – **14 rm** 54.60/88.88 **t.**

PORTMARNOCK (Port Mearnóg) *Dublin* 923 N 7 *Ireland G. – pop. 9 145.*

Env. : *Fingal*★.

Dublin 5 – Drogheda 28.

Portmarnock H. and Golf Links, ℘ (01) 846 0611, *reservations@portmarnock.com, Fax (01) 846 2442,* ≤, 18, – rm, rest, P – 250. VISA JCB.
The Links : Meals a la carte 21/39 **st.** 18.70 – (see also ***The Osborne*** below) – **101 rm** 210/280 **st.**, 2 suites – SB.

XXX **The Osborne** (at Portmarnock H. and Golf Links), ℘ (01) 846 0611 – P VISA JCB
closed Sunday and Monday – **Meals** (dinner only) a la carte 45/61 **st.** 20.

RATHCONRATH (Ráth Conarta) *Westmeath* 923 J 7 – *see Mullingar.*

RATHGAR (Ráth Garbh) *Dublin* – *see Dublin.*

RATHMELTON (Ráth Mealtain) *Donegal* 923 J 2 *Ireland G.*

See : *Town*★.

Dublin 154 – Donegal 37 – Londonerry 27 – Sligo 76.

Ardeen without rest., (074) 51243, *ardeenbandb@eircom.net, Fax (074) 51243*, – . *Easter-October* – **4 rm** 35/70 **s.**

RATHMINES (Ráth Maonais) *Dublin* 923 ⑳ – *see Dublin.*

RATHMULLAN (Ráth Maoláin) *Donegal* 923 J 2 *Ireland G. – pop. 491 – Letterkenny.*

Exc. : *Knockalla Viewpoint*★, *N : 8 m. by R 247 – Rathmelton*★, *SW : 7 m. by R 247.*

Otway, Saltpans (074) 58319.

Dublin 165 – Londonderry 36 – Sligo 87.

Rathmullan House, North : ½ m. on R 247 (074) 58188, *rathhse@iol.ie, Fax (074) 58200*, ≤, « Part 19C country house, gardens », – rest, . *closed 2 January-15 February and 23 to 28 December* – **Meals** 42.50 (dinner) and a la carte 30/42.50 **t.** 9.50 – **24 rm** 90/180 **t.** – SB.

Fort Royal, North : 1 m. by R 247 (074) 58100, *fortroyal@eircom.net, Fax (074) 58103*, ≤, squash – rest, *22 March-October* – **Meals** (bar lunch)/dinner 30/35 **st.** 15 – **15 rm** 80/160 **st.** – SB.

Prices — For notes on the prices quoted in this Guide, see the introduction.

RATHNEW (Ráth Naoi) *Wicklow* 923 N 8 – *see Wicklow.*

RECESS (Sraith Salach) *Galway* 923 C 7 *Ireland G.*

Exc. : *Connemara*★★★ – *Cashel*★, *SW : by N 59 and R 340.*

Dublin 173 – Ballina 72 – Galway 36.

Lough Inagh Lodge, Northwest : 4 ¾ m. by N 59 on R 344 (095) 34706, *inagh@iol.ie, Fax (095) 34708*, ≤ Lough Inagh and The Twelve Bens, « Part 17C former fishing lodge », – *closed 9 December-14 March* – **Meals** (booking essential to non-residents) (bar lunch)/dinner a la carte approx. 33 **t.** 19.04 – **12 rm** 130/190 – SB.

RENVYLE (Rinn Mhaoile) *Galway* 923 C 7 – *see Rinvyle.*

RINVYLE/RENVYLE (Rinn Mhaoile) *Galway* 923 C 7 *Ireland G.*

Exc. : *Connemara*★★★.

Dublin 193 – Ballina 73 – Galway 61.

Renvyle House, (095) 43511, *renvyle@iol.ie, Fax (095) 43515*, ≤ Atlantic Ocean, heated, – 120. *closed 6 January-14 February and 25 November-22 December* – **Meals** (bar lunch)/dinner 38.09 and a la carte approx. 38.09 **st.** 18.41 – **63 rm** 133/204 **st.**, 2 suites – SB.

RIVERSTOWN (Baile idir Dhá Abhainn) *Sligo* 923 G 5 – *pop. 266.*

Dublin 123 – Sligo 13.

Coopershill, (071) 65108, *ohara@coopershill.com, Fax (071) 65466*, ≤, « Georgian country house », *April-October* – **Meals** (booking essential to non-residents) 38.09/43.17 and a la carte 38.09/43.17 **st.** 12.06 – **8 rm** 100.31/187.92 **st.**

ROOSKY (Rúscaigh) *Roscommon* 923 I 6.

Dublin 83 – Drogheda 81 – Galway 76 – Limerick 115.

Shannon Key West, The River Edge, (078) 38800, *shnkywst@iol.ie, Fax (078) 3881*... rest, – 300. *closed 24-26 December* – **Meals** (carvery lunch)/dinner a la carte 25/31.50 **t.** 15.80 – **39 rm** 74/128 **t.** – SB.

REPUBLIC OF IRELAND

ROSCOMMON (Ros Comáin) *Roscommon* 923 H 7 *Ireland G. – pop. 1 432.*
See : *Castle★.*
Exc. : *Castlestrange Stone★, SW : 7 m. by N 63 and R 362 – Strokestown★ (Famine Museum★ AC, Strokestown Park House★ AC), N : 12 m. by N 61 and R 368 – Castlerea : Clonalis House★ AC, NW : 19 m. by N 60.*
Moate Park ✆ (0903) 20068.
Harrison Hall ✆ (0903) 26342 (June-August).
Dublin 94 – Galway 57 – Limerick 94.

Abbey, on N 63 (Galway rd) ✆ (0903) 26240, *cmv@indigo.ie, Fax (0903) 26021,* – 200.
closed 25-26 December – **Meals** 18.40/31.75 and dinner a la carte 17.78/34.92 **t.** 15.87 – **25 rm** 88.90/139.70 **t.**

ROSCREA (Ros Cré) *Tipperary* 923 I 9 *Ireland G. – pop. 4 170.*
See : *Town★ – Damer House★.*
Roscrea, Derryvale ✆ (0505) 21130.
Dublin 76 – Kilkenny 37 – Limerick 95.

Monaincha House without rest., Monaincha, East : 1 ½ m. on N 7 ✆ (0505) 23181, « Georgian house, working farm »,
April-October – **3 rm** 40.63/71.10 **s.**

ROSSCARBERY (Ros Ó gCairbre) *Cork* 923 E 13 *Ireland G. – pop. 406.*
Env. : *Drombeg Stone Circle★, SW : 2m. by R 597 – Glandore★, SW : 4 m. by R 597.*
Exc. : *Carbery Coast★.*
Dublin 194 – Cork 39 – Killarney 75.

Celtic Ross, ✆ (023) 48722, *info@celticrosshotel.com, Fax (023) 48723,* – 250.
Meals (bar lunch Monday-Saturday)/dinner 22 and a la carte 13.50 – **66 rm** 90/160 **t.**, 1 suite – SB.

ROSSES POINT (An Ros) *Sligo* 923 G 5 – *pop. 799.*
County Sligo ✆ (071) 77134.
Dublin 139 – Belfast 132 – Sligo 6.

Yeats Country H., ✆ (071) 77211, *yeatscountry@eircom.net, Fax (071) 77203,* rm,
closed January – **Meals** (bar lunch)/dinner 18/22 and a la carte 14 – **98 rm** 65/150 **st.** – SB.

ROSSLARE (Ros Láir) *Wexford* 923 M 11 – *pop. 929.*
Rosslare Strand ✆ (053) 32203.
Kilrane ✆ (053) 33232 (May-September).
Dublin 104 – Waterford 50 – Wexford 12.

Kelly's Resort, ✆ (053) 32114, *kellyhot@iol.ie, Fax (053) 32222,* indoor/outdoor, squash – rest,
closed 9 December-22 February – ***Kelly's :*** Meals 19/36 **t.** 17.80 – ***La Marine :*** Meals a la carte 24.10/33.40 **t.** 17.80 – **99 rm** 76/190 **t.** – SB.

Crosbie Cedars, ✆ (053) 32124, *info@crosbiecedars.iol.ie, Fax (053) 32243,* – rest, – 250.
closed 25 December – **Meals** (bar lunch Monday to Saturday)/dinner 18 and a la carte 19.87/29.17 **t.** 14.60 – **34 rm** 83/128 **t.** – SB.

ROSSLARE HARBOUR (Calafort Ros Láir) *Wexford* 923 N 11 – *pop. 1 023.*
to France (Cherbourg and Roscoff) (Irish Ferries) (18 h/15 h) – to Fishguard (Stena Line) 2-4 daily (1 h 40 mn/3 h 30 mn) – to Pembroke (Irish Ferries) 2 daily (3 h 45 mn).
Kilrane ✆ (053) 33232 (April-October).
Dublin 105 – Waterford 51 – Wexford 13.

Great Southern, St Martins Rd, ✆ (053) 33233, *res@rosslare.gsh.ie, Fax (053) 33543,* – rest, – 230.
closed 2 January-mid February – **Meals** (bar lunch)/dinner 23/32 and a la carte approx. 32 **st.** 12.70 – 12 – **100 rm** 105/150 **st.** – SB.

Euro Lodge without rest., on N 25 ✆ (053) 33118, *eurolodge@eircom.net, Fax (053) 33120* –
Closed January and February – 7 – **38 rm** 58 **st.**

REPUBLIC OF IRELAND

Ferryport House without rest., on N 25 ℘ (053) 33933, *thh@iol.ie* – TV P. MC VISA. 🚫
17 rm ☕ 80 st.

St Martin's without rest., St Martin's Rd, ℘ (053) 33133, *thh@iol.ie, Fax (053) 33133* – P. MC AE VISA
closed 24-26 December – **8 rm** ☕ 39/52 **st.**

at Tagoat *West : 2½ m. on N 25* – ✉ *Rosslare.*

Churchtown House 🐎, North : ½ m. on Rosslare rd ℘ (053) 32555, *churchtow rosslare@indigo.ie, Fax (053) 32577,* « Part 19C », – TV ♿ P. MC AE VISA. 🚫
March-3 November – **Meals** *(closed Sunday and Monday)* (booking essential) (resider only) (dinner only) 35 **st.** 23 – **12 rm** ☕ 80/150 **st.** – SB.

at Killinick *West : 5¾ m. off N 25* – ✉ *Rosslare.*

Assaly Lodge without rest., ℘ (053) 58300, *sales@wexford.irl.com, Fax (053) 58300,* – TV P. MC VISA. 🚫
closed 15 December-15 January – **6 rm** ☕ 44.44/63.48 **st.**

ROSSNOWLAGH **(Ros Neamhlach)** *Donegal* 923 H 4 *Scotland G.*
See : *Rossnowlagh Strand*★★.
Dublin 153 – Donegal 14 – Sligo 31.

Sand House 🐎, ℘ (072) 51777, *info@sandhouse_hotel.ie, Fax (072) 52100,* ≤ b beach and mountains, – rm, TV P. MC AE VISA
Easter-November – **Meals** (bar lunch Monday-Friday)/dinner 36/40 25 – **45 rm** 85/25(– SB.

ROUNDSTONE **(Cloch na Rón)** *Galway* 923 C 7 *Ireland G. – pop. 241.*
See : *Town*★.
Exc. : *Connemara*★★★.
Dublin 193 – Galway 47.

Eldon's, ℘ (095) 35933, *eldonshotel@tinet.ie, Fax (095) 35722,* ≤, – TV P. MC AE VISA. 🚫
13 March-4 November – ***Beola :*** **Meals** - Seafood specialities - (bar lunch)/dinner 29.2 38.09 and a la carte 20/36 **t.** 17.14 – **18 rm** ☕ 44.44/114.27 – SB.

SAGGART **(Teach Sagard)** *Dublin* 923 M 8 – *see Dublin.*

SALTHILL **(Bóthar na Trá)** *Galway* 923 E 8 – *see Galway.*

SCHULL **(An Scoil)** *Cork* 923 D 13 – *see Skull.*

SHANAGARRY **(An Seangharraí)** *Cork* 923 H 12 *Ireland G. – pop. 230* – ✉ *Midleton.*
Env. : *Cloyne Cathedral*★*, NW : 4 m. by R 629.*
Dublin 163 – Cork 25 – Waterford 64.

Ballymaloe House 🐎, Northwest : 1¾ m. on L 35 ℘ (021) 4652531, *res@ballymal ie, Fax (021) 4652021,* ≤, « Part 16C, part Georgian country house », heated, – rest, P. MC AE VISA. 🚫
closed 22 to 26 December – **Meals** (booking essential) (buffet dinner Sunday) 25.39/5 20 – **33 rm** ☕ 100/260 **t.**

SHANNON **(Sionainn)** *Clare* 923 F 9 – *pop. 7 811.*
18 *Shannon Airport ℘ (061) 471020.*
Shannon Airport : ℘ (061) 471444.
Shannon Airport, Arrivals Hall ℘ (061) 471664.
Dublin 136 – Ennis 16 – Limerick 15.

Oak Wood Arms, on N 19 ℘ (061) 361500, *reservations@oakwoodarms.cc Fax (061) 361414,* – rm, TV P – 400. MC AE VISA. 🚫
closed 25 December – **Meals** (carving lunch Monday to Saturday)/dinner a la carte 18/3 13.50 – **99 rm** ☕ 58/76 **st.**, 2 suites – SB.

Quality, Ballycasey Rd, on N 19 ℘ (061) 364588, *sales@qualityshannon.cc Fax (061) 364045* – , rm, rest, TV ♿ P. MC AE VISA. 🚫
closed 25 December – **Meals** (carvery lunch Monday to Saturday)/dinner a la carte 21/34 15.87 – **54 rm** ☕ 114.28/126.97 **st.** – SB.

t **Shannon Airport** *Southwest : 2½ m. on N 19 – ✉ Shannon.*

Great Southern, ✆ (061) 471122, *res@shannon.gsh.ie, Fax (061) 471982* – lift, ⊭ rm, ▤ rest, TV P – 🎪 150. MC AE ⓓ VISA. ✂
closed 24 to 26 December – **Meals** *(closed lunch Saturday, Sunday and Bank Holidays)* (carvery lunch)/dinner a la carte approx. 28 **st.** 🍷 13.97 – ☕ 12 – **115 rm** 130 **st.** – SB.

HANNON AIRPORT *Clare* 923 F 9 – *see Shannon.*

KERRIES **(Na Sceirí)** *Dublin* 923 N 7 *Ireland G. – pop. 7 339.*
Env. : *Fingal★.*
Skerries ✆ (01) 849 1204.
Skerries Mills ✆ (01) 849 5208.
Dublin 19 – Drogheda 15.

Redbank Lodge, 12 Convent Lane, ✆ (01) 849 0439, *redbank@eircom.net, Fax (01) 849 1598,* ⛱ – TV. MC AE ⓓ VISA
closed 25-26 December – **Meals** – (see ***Redbank*** below) – **5 rm** ☕ 65/100 **t.** – SB.

Redbank with rm, 7 Church St, ✆ (01) 849 1005, *redbank@eircom.net, Fax (01) 849 1598* – ⊭ TV ✆. MC AE ⓓ VISA. ✂
closed 24-27 December – **Meals** - Seafood - *(closed Sunday dinner)* (dinner only and Sunday lunch)/dinner a la carte 35/40 **t.** 🍷 19 – **7 rm** ☕ 60/100 **t.** – SB.

KIBBEREEN *Cork* 923 E 13 – *pop. 1 926.*
North St ✆ (028) 21766.
Dublin 210 – Cork 53 – Killarney 65.

West Cork, Ilen St, on N 71 ✆ (028) 21277, *info@westcorkhotel.com, Fax (028) 22333* – TV P. MC AE ⓓ VISA
closed 1 week Christmas – **Meals** 18/33 and dinner a la carte 15.23/27.30 **st.** 🍷 16 – **29 rm** ☕ 82/152 **st.**, 1 suite – SB.

Eldon, Bridge St, ✆ (028) 22000, *welcome@eldon-hotel.ie, Fax (028) 22191,* ⛱ – ⊭ rm, TV P. MC ⓓ VISA
– ***Potters :*** **Meals** a la carte 28/31 **st.** 🍷 15.87 – **19 rm** ☕ 80/160 **t.** – SB.

Ty ar Mor, 46 Bridge St, ✆ (028) 22100, *tyarmor@iol.ie* – MC VISA. ✂
closed Monday-Tuesday in winter – **Meals** - Seafood - (dinner only) 36/39.50 and a la carte approx. 36 **t.** 🍷 17.70.

KULL/SCHULL **(An Scoil)** *Cork* 923 D 13 *Ireland G. – pop. 595.*
See : *Town★.*
Exc. : *Sherkin Island★ (by ferry) – Mizen Peninsula (≤★★ from pass).*
Coosheen, Coosheen, Schull ✆ (077) 28182.
Dublin 226 – Cork 65 – Killarney 64.

Grove House without rest., Colla Rd, ✆ (028) 28067, *billyoshea@yahoo.com, Fax (028) 28069,* ⛱ – ⊭ TV P. MC AE VISA. ✂
March-October – **5 rm** ☕ 69.83/114.27 **st.**

Corthna Lodge Country House without rest., West : ¾ m. by R 592 ✆ (028) 28517, *Fax (028) 28032,* ≤, ⛱ – ⊭ P. MC VISA
9 rm ☕ 50/120 **st.**

LIEVEROE **(Sliabh Rua)** *Waterford – see Waterford.*

LIGO **(Sligeach)** *Sligo* 923 G 5 *Ireland G. – pop. 17 786.*
See : *Town★★ – Abbey★.*
Env. : *SE : Lough Gill★★ – Carrowmore Megalithic Cemetery★ AC, SW : 3 m. – Knocknarea★ (≤★★) SW : 6 m. by R 292.*
Exc. : *Drumcliff★, N : by N 15 – Parke's Castle★ AC, E : 9 m. by R 286 – Glencar Waterfall★, NE : 9 m. by N 16 – Creevykeel Court Cairn★, N : 16 m. by N 15.*
Rosses Point ✆ (071) 77134.
Sligo Airport, Strandhill : ✆ (071) 68280.
Avar Reddan, Temple St ✆ (071) 61201.
Dublin 133 – Belfast 126 – Dundalk 106 – Londonderry 86.

REPUBLIC OF IRELAND

Sligo Park, Pearse Rd, South : 1 ¼ m. on N 4 ✆ (071) 60291, *sligopk@leehotels.* *Fax (071) 69556,* – rm, rest, – 🚶 400.
Meals *(closed Saturday lunch)* 19.04/31.74 and dinner a la carte 18/32 **st.** 13.90 – 8
110 rm 69.75/70.78 **st.** – SB.

Tree Tops without rest., Cleveragh Rd, South : ¼ m. by Dublin rd ✆ (071) 60160, *treetc* *@iol.ie, Fax (071) 62301,* – VISA.
closed 15 December-8 January – **5 rm** 53/59 **t.**

Benwiskin Lodge without rest., Shannon Eighter, North : 2 m. by N 15 ✆ (071) 410 *pquigley@iol.ie, Fax (071) 41088,* – VISA.
closed 22 December-2 January – **5 rm** 33/58.

Ard Cuilinn Lodge without rest., Drumiskabole, Southeast : 3 m. by N 4 off R 2 ✆ (071) 62925, *ardcuiln@esatclear.ie,* – VISA.
March-October – **4 rm** 31/54 **st.**

Lisadorn without rest., Donegal Rd, North : 2 m. by N 15 ✆ (071) 43417, *Fax (071) 464* – VISA
7 rm 38.01/57.14 **st.**

SPANISH POINT (Rinn na Spáinneach) *Clare* 923 D 9 – ✉ *Milltown Malbay.*
Dublin 171 – Galway 65 – Limerick 52.

Burkes Armada, ✆ (065) 708 4110, *armada@iol.ie, Fax (065) 708 4632,* ← – 🚶 300. VISA JCB.
Meals (bar lunch Monday to Saturday)/dinner 30.41 **st.** 14.60 – **60 rm** 63.49/139.67 – SB.

Le Guide change, changez de ***guide Michelin*** *tous les ans.*

SPIDDAL/SPIDDLE (An Spidéal) *Galway* 923 E 8.
Dublin 143 – Galway 11.

An Cruiscin Lan, ✆ (091) 553148, *info@cruiscinlanhotel.com, Fax (091) 553712* rm, VISA.
closed 24-26 December – **Meals** 22.80/31.70 (dinner) and a la carte 16/31 **t.** 14.60
14 rm 82.53/215.85 **t.**

Ardmor Country House without rest., West : ½ m. on R 336 ✆ (091) 553145, *ardm* *@ireland.com, Fax (091) 553596,* ←, –
March-December – **7 rm** 40/60.

SPIDDLE (An Spidéal) *Galway* 923 E 8 – *see Spiddal.*

STILLORGAN *Dublin* 923 N 8 – *see Dublin.*

STRAFFAN (Teach Srafáin) *Kildare* 923 M 8 – *pop. 341.*
Naas, Kerdiffstown ✆ (045) 874644.
Dublin 15 – Mullingar 47.

Kildare H. & Golf Club ✆ (01) 601 7200, *resortsales@kclub.ie, Fax (01) 601 7298,*
« Part early 19C country house overlooking River Liffey, riverside gardens and arboretum indoor/outdoor, squash – 🚶 130. VISA.
Byerley Turk **:** **Meals** (booking essential to non-residents) 25/63 and a la carte appro 63 **st.** 23 – ***Legends*** (in K Club) **: Meals** 31/44 and a la carte approx. 44 **st.** 23 – 24
60 rm 410/445 **st.**, 9 suites – SB.

Barberstown Castle, North : ½ m. ✆ (01) 628 8157, *castleir@iol.ie, Fax (01) 627 70* ←, « Part Elizabethan, part Victorian house with 13C castle keep », – rest, 🚶 30. VISA.
closed 6 January-4 February and 24-29 December – **Meals** (booking essential) (dinner o a la carte 41/60 **t.** 23.49 – **21 rm** 126.97/198.08 **t.**, 1 suite – SB.

SWINFORD (Béal Atha na Muice) *Galway.*
Dublin 132 – Galway 57 – Sligo 37.

Gateway, Main St, ✆ (094) 52156, *gathotel@ie, Fax (094) 51328* – – 🚶 300. VISA.
closed 24-26 December – **Meals** a la carte 13/27 **st.** 12.06 – **15 rm** 34.93/82.55 **st.**

SWORDS (Sord) *Dublin* 923 N 7 *Ireland G. – pop. 22 314.*
Env. : *Fingal★ – Newbridge House★, N : by N 1 and east by R 126.*
Exc. : *Malahide Castle★★, SE : by N 1 and R 106.*
Balheary Av. (01) 840 9819.
Dublin 8 – Drogheda 22.

Travelodge, Miltons Field, South : ½ m. on N 1 (01) 840 9233, *Fax (01) 840 9235* – rm, rest, VISA JCB.
Meals (grill rest.) – **100 rm** 88.95 **t.**

Old Schoolhouse, Well Rd, on Brackenstown rd (01) 840 4160, *Fax (01) 840 5060,* – VISA.
closed Christmas and New Year, Saturday lunch, Sunday dinner and Bank Holidays – **Meals** 18/42 and a la carte 37.75/50.25 **t.** 21.

TAGOAT (Teach Gót) *Wexford* 923 M 11 – *see Rosslare Harbour.*

TAHILLA (Tathuile) *Kerry* 923 C 12 *Ireland G.*
Exc. : *Iveragh Peninsula★★ (Ring of Kerry★★) – Sneem★, NW : 4 m. by N 70.*
Dublin 222 – Cork 70 – Killarney 32.

Tahilla Cove , (064) 45204, *tahillacove@eircom.net, Fax (064) 45104,* Coongar Cove and Caha Mountains, « Waterside setting », rest, VISA
April-mid October – **Meals** (bar meals lunch and Tuesday dinner)/dinner 25 **st.** – **9 rm** 75/100 **st.** – SB.

TALLAGHT (Tamhlacht) *Dublin* 923 N 8 – *see Dublin.*

TALLOW (Tulach an Iarainn) *Waterford* 923 H 11 – *pop. 802.*
Dublin 145 – Cork 29 – Killarney 70 – Limerick 40.

Buggys Glencairn Inn with rm, North : 3 ¾ m. by N 72 on Glencairn rd (058) 56232, *buggysglencairninn@tinet.ie, Fax (058) 56232,* – rm, VISA.
Meals (booking essential) (dinner only) a la carte approx. 30 **t.** – **5 rm** 63.49/101.58 **st.**

TERMONBARRY *Longford* 923 I 6 *Ireland G.*
Exc. : *Strokestown★ (Famine Museum★ AC, Strokestown Park House★ AC), NW : by N 5.*
Dublin 81 – Galway 85 – Roscommon 22 – Sligo 62.

Shannonside House, (043) 26052, *info@keenans.ie, Fax (043) 26332* – VISA.
closed 24-25 December – **Meals** (by arrangement) 31.55 **t.** – **9 rm** 44.44/69.84 **t.**

THOMASTOWN (Baile Mhic Andáin) *Kilkenny* 923 K 10 *Ireland G. – pop. 1 581 – Kilkenny.*
Env. : *Jerpoint Abbey★★, SW : 1½ m. by N9.*
Dublin 77 – Kilkenny 11 – Waterford 30 – Wexford 38.

Mount Juliet , West : 1 ½ m. (056) 73000, *info@mountjuliet.ie, Fax (056) 73019,* « 18C manor and sporting estate, River Nore and park », – VISA.
Lady Helen McCalmont : **Meals** (dinner only) 60 **t.** 34.50 – (see also ***Hunters Yard at Mount Juliet*** below) – 20 – **45 rm** 250/520 **st.**, 18 suites 409.53/520 – SB.

Hunters Yard at Mount Juliet, West : 1 ½ m. (056) 73000, *info@mountjuliet.ie, Fax (056) 73019,* « Converted 18C stables », – rest, 90. VISA.
Kendals : **Meals** (dinner only and Sunday lunch)/dinner 44.44/50.79 a la carte 29/38 **t.** – 15.87 – **16 rm** 228.25 **st.** – SB.

Abbey House without rest., Jerpoint Abbey, Southwest : 1 ¼ m. on N 9 (056) 24166, *Fax (056) 24192,* – VISA
closed 23 to 30 December – **7 rm** 50.74/88.88 **t.**

Carrickmourne House without rest., New Ross Rd, Southeast : 2 m. by R 700 (056) 24124, *Fax (056) 24124,* – VISA.
closed 15 December-15 January – **5 rm** 36/76 **st.**

Silks, Marshes St, (056) 54400, *Fax (056) 58780* – VISA
closed 25-26 December and Monday – **Meals** (dinner only and lunch Sunday) a la carte 29/40 **t.** 17.71.

THURLES (Durlas) *Tipperary* 923 I9 – *pop. 6 603.*

18 *Turtulla* ✆ *(0504) 21983.*

Dublin 92 – Cork 71 – Kilkenny 30 – Limerick 47 – Waterford 58.

Anner, Dublin Rd, ✆ (0504) 21799, *info@annerhotel.com, Fax (0504) 22111,* – rest, – 250. *VISA.*
closed 24-27 December – **Meals** 17.80/34.50 and dinner a la carte approx. 31.35 **t.** 17.14 – **64 rm** 70/285.75 **t.** – SB.

The Munster, Cathedral St, ✆ (0504) 22305, *info@munsterhotel.com, Fax (0504) 26281,* – rest, – 600. *VISA.*
closed 25 December – **Meals** 15.87/23.49 and dinner a la carte 11/28 **st.** 14.60 – **18 rm** 53.96/88.88 **st.** – SB.

Inch House, Northwest : 4 m. on R 498 ✆ (0504) 51348, *inchhse@iol.ie, Fax (0504) 51754,* « Georgian manor house, working farm », – rest, *VISA.*
closed 23-29 December – **Meals** *(closed Sunday and Monday)* (dinner only) 35.55/38.09 **st** – **5 rm** 57.14/101.58 **st.**

TIPPERARY (Tiobraid Arann) *Tipperary* 923 H 10.

9 *Rathanny* ✆ *(062) 51119.*

✆ *(062) 51457 (summer only).*

Dublin 113 – Cork 60 – Limerick 35 – Waterford 52.

Ballyglass Country House, Glen of Aherlow Rd, South : 2 m. turning off Main S following signs for Glen of Aherlow ✆ (062) 52104, *ballyglasshouse@eircom.net Fax (062) 52229,* – *VISA*
closed 24-25 December – **Meals** *(closed Sunday dinner)* (bar lunch Monday to Saturday) dinner 21.50 and a la carte 15.30/25.90 **t.** 12.65 – **10 rm** 35.50/73.60 **t.** – SB.

TIMOLEAGUE (Tigh Molaige) *Cork* 923 F 13.

Dublin 186 – Cork 29.

Lettercollum House, West : ¾ m. by R 600 ✆ (023) 46251, *conmc@iol.ie Fax (023) 46270,* – *VISA.*
April-October – **Meals** *(closed Sunday dinner and Monday)* (dinner only and Sunday lunch) dinner 40 **t.** 17.78.

TOORMORE (An Tuar Mór) *Cork* 923 D 13 – ✉ *Goleen.*

Dublin 221 – Cork 68 – Killarney 65.

Fortview House without rest., Gurtyowen, Northeast : 1 ½ m. on Durrus rd (R 591 ✆ (028) 35324, *Fax (028) 35324,* –
March-October – **5 rm** 40/80 **st.**

TOWER *Cork* 923 G 12 – *see Blarney.*

TRALEE (Trá Lí) *Kerry* 923 C 11 *Ireland G.* – *pop. 19 056.*

Env. : *Blennerville Windmill★ AC, SW : 2 m. by N 86 – Ardfert Cathedral★, NW : 5 ½ m. b R 551.*

Exc. : *Banna Strand★, NW : 8 m. by R 551 – Crag Cave★ AC, W : 13 m. by N 21 – Rattc Round Tower★, N : 12 m. by R 556.*

Ashe Memorial Hall ✆ *(066) 7121288.*

Dublin 185 – Killarney 20 – Limerick 64.

Ballyseede Castle, Southeast : 3 ¼ m. by N 21 ✆ (066) 7125799, *ballyseedee eircom.net, Fax (066) 7125287,* ←, « Late 18C crenellated country house in parkland », *VISA.*
Meals *(closed Monday)* (booking essential for non-residents) (dinner only) 32/3 and a la carte 30/35.50 **t.** 16.50 – **12 rm** 95.50/210.

Abbey Gate, Maine St, off Rock St, ✆ (066) 7129888, *abbeygat@aol.ie, Fax (066) 712982* – rm, rest, – 350. *VISA.*
closed 25 December – **Meals** (carvery lunch Monday to Saturday)/dinner 21.53/29. and a la carte 24/37.91 **t.** 13.34 – **100 rm** 133.90/153.90 **t.** – SB.

The Meadowlands, Oakpark, Northeast : ¾ m. on N 69 ✆ (066) 718 0444, *medlan @iol.ie, Fax (066) 718 0964,* – – 30. *VISA.*
closed 24-26 December – **Meals** *(closed Sunday dinner)* (bar lunch Monday to Saturday dinner 28.57/34.92 and a la carte 26.47/40.57 **st.** 18.41 – **27 rm** 95.23/241.25 **st.** – SB

The Grand, Denny St, (066) 7121499, *info@grandhoteltralee.com, Fax (066) 7122877* – rest, – 250. .
Meals 13/24 and a la carte 15/30 **st.** 8.89 – **44 rm** 50/125 **st.** – SB.

Ballygarry House, Killarney Rd, Southeast : 2 m. on N 21 (066) 712 3322, *ballygarry@eircom.net, Fax (066) 712 7630,* – – 500. .
closed 20-26 December – **Meals** (bar lunch)/dinner 31.75 and a la carte 35/45 19 – **48 rm** 95/160 **t.** – SB.

Brook Manor Lodge without rest., Fenit Rd, Spa, Northwest : 2 ¼ m. by R 551 on R 558 (066) 7120509, *brookmanor@eircom.net, Fax (066) 7127552,* – . .

7 rm 57.14/126.97 **t.**

Tralee Townhouse without rest., High St, (066) 7181111, *townhouse@iolfree.net, Fax (066) 7181112* – . .
closed 26-29 December – **19 rm** 38/76 **st.**

The Forge without rest., Upper Oakpark, Northeast : 1 ½ m. on N 69 (066) 7125245, *Fax (066) 7125245,* – . .
closed 8 December-8 January – **6 rm** 39/64 **st.**

Barnakyle without rest., Clogherbrien, Northwest : 1 ½ m. on R 551 (066) 7125048, *barnakyl@iol.ie, Fax (066) 7181259,* – . .
April-October – **4 rm** 38.09/55.86 **s.**

TRAMORE (Trá Mhór) *Waterford* 923 K 11 – *pop. 6 536.*

(051) 281572 (June-August).

Dublin 106 – Waterford 6.

Glenorney without rest., Newtown, Southwest : 1 m. by R 675 (051) 381056, *glenoney@iol.ie, Fax (051) 381103,* <, – . .
closed 1 week Christmas – **6 rm** 40/55 **st.**

***Le Grand Londres** (GREATER LONDON) est composé de la City et de 32 arrondissements administratifs (Borough) eux-mêmes divisés en quartiers ou en villages ayant conservé leur caractère propre (Area).*

TRIM (Baile Átha Troim) *Meath* 923 L 7 *Ireland G.* – *pop. 1 740.*

See : *Trim Castle★★ – Town★.*

Env. : *Bective Abbey★, NE : 4 m. by R 161.*

County Meath, Newtownmoynagh (046) 31463.

(046) 37111 (May-September).

Dublin 27 – Drogheda 26 – Tullamore 43.

Highfield House without rest., Maudlins Rd, on Kilcock rd (046) 36386, *highfieldhouseaccom@eircom.net, Fax (046) 38182,* « 19C former maternity home », – .
closed 23 December-5 January – **7 rm** 38.09/63.49 **t.**

Crannmór without rest., Dunderry Rd, North : 1 ¼ m. (046) 31635, *cranmor@eircom.net, Fax (046) 38087,* – . .
closed 21 December-7 January – **4 rm** 38.10/63.50 **st.**

TULLAMORE (Tulach Mhór) *Offaly* 923 J 8 – *pop. 9 221.*

Tullamore, Brookfield (0506) 21439.

Tullamore Dew, Heritage Centre (0506) 52617.

Dublin 65 – Kilkenny 52 – Limerick 80.

Tullamore Court, on N 80 (Portlaoise rd) (0506) 46666, *info@tullamorecourthotel.ie, Fax (0506) 46677,* , , – , rm, rest, – 750. .
closed 24-25 December – **Meals** 19 (lunch) and dinner a la carte 29.79/44.11 **st.** 15.18 – **72 rm** 150/265 **st.** – SB.

Bridge House, off Main St. (0506) 22000, *info@bridgehouse.com, Fax (0506) 41338,* , , – , rest, rest, – 550. .
closed 24-26 December – **Meals** (bar lunch)/dinner 20/33 and a la carte 23.25/35 **st.** 11 – **70 rm** 85/280 **st.**

VALENCIA ISLAND (Dairbhre) *Kerry* 923 A/B 12.

Dublin 237 – Killarney 55 – Tralee 57.

Knights Town.

Glanleam House, Glanleam, West : 1 ¼ m. taking right fork at top of Market St *(066) 9476176, Fax (066) 9476108*, « Part 17C and 18C country house in extensive sub-tropical gardens », – P. VISA.
mid March-October – **Meals** (booking essential to non-residents) (communal dining) (dinner only) 40 20 – **6 rm** 55/240 **st.** – SB.

VIRGINIA (Achadh an Iúir) *Cavan* 923 K 6 *Ireland G. – pop. 811.*

Exc. : *Kells★ (Round Tower and High Crosses★★, St. Columba's House★), SE : 10 m. by N 3 – Loughcrew Passage Graves★, S : 10 m. by R 195, turning right into L 3.*

Virginia, Park Hotel (049) 8548066.

Dublin 51 – Drogheda 39 – Enniskillen 60.

Sharkey's, Main St, (049) 8547561, *sharkeys@destination_ireland.com, Fax (049) 8547761*, – P – 250. VISA.
Meals (carving lunch) 16.50/31.74 and dinner a la carte 25.08/36.45 **st.** – **13 rm** 50.15/95.25 **st.** – SB.

WATERFORD (Port Láirge) *Waterford* 923 K 11 *Ireland G. – pop. 42 540.*

See : *Town★ – City Walls★.*

Env. : *Waterford Crystal★, SW : 1½ m. by N 25 Y.*

Exc. : *Duncannon★, E : 12 m. by R 683, ferry from Passage East and R 374 (south) Z – Dunmore East★, SE : 12 m. by R 684 Z – Tintern Abbey★, E : 13 m. by R 683, ferry from Passage East, R 733 and R 734 (south) Z.*

Newrath (051) 874182.

Waterford Airport, Killowen : (051) 875589.

41 The Quay (051) 875788 Y – Waterford Crystal Visitor Centre (051) 358397 – The Granary, Merchants Quay (051) 875823.

Dublin 96 – Cork 73 – Limerick 77.

Plan opposite

Waterford Castle H. and Golf Club, The Island, Ballinakill, East : 2 ½ m. by R 683, Ballinakill Rd and private ferry (051) 878203, *info@waterfordcastle.com Fax (051) 879316*, « Part 15C and 19C castle, river island setting », – rest, P. VISA.
Meals (bar lunch Monday-Friday)/dinner 52/60 and a la carte 38/42 **t.** 23 – 22 – **14 rm** 230/420 **st.**, 5 suites – SB.

Granville, Meagher Quay, (051) 305555, *stay@granville-hotel.ie, Fax (051) 305566* – rm, rest, – 250. VISA. Y a
closed 25 and 26 December – **Meals** *(closed Saturday lunch)* 18/35 and dinner a la carte 22/30 **st.** 20 – **98 rm** 110/190 **st.** – SB.

Woodlands, Dunmore Rd, Southeast : 3 m. on R 683 (Dunmore East rd) (051) 304574 *woodhl@iol.ie, Fax (051) 304575*, – , rest, P – 400. VISA
*closed 25-2 December***Meals** (carving lunch Monday-Saturday) 16.44/38.09 14.60 – **46 rm** 95.23/165.07 **st.** – SB.

Dooley's, The Quay, (051) 873531, *hotel@dooleys-hotel.ie, Fax (051) 870262* – rm, – 300. VISA. Y
closed 25-28 December – **Meals** (carvery lunch Monday-Saturday)/dinner 20 and a la carte 26/37 **t.** 17 – 12 – **112 rm** 102/152 **t.** – SB.

Quality H. Waterford, Canada St, The Quays, (051) 856600, *marinagm@gofree indigo.ie, Fax (051) 856605*, « Riverside setting », – P – 45. VISA. Z
closed 23 December-3 January – **Meals** (bar lunch Monday to Saturday)/dinner 21.5 19.05 – **80 rm** 69.84/152.37 – SB.

Bridge, The Quay, (051) 877222, *bridgehotel@treacyhotelsgroup.com Fax (051) 877229* – , rest, P – 400. VISA JCB. Y
closed 25 December – **Meals** (carvery lunch Monday to Saturday)/dinner 19.05/31.7 and a la carte 13/31 **t.** 13.90 – **127 rm** 76.18/152.78 – SB.

Jurys, Ferrybank, (051) 832111, *waterford@jurysdoyle.com, Fax (051) 832863*, City, – , rm, P – 800. VISA. Y
closed 24-26 December – **Meals** (carving lunch)/dinner 24 **t.** 18 – 15 – **97 rm** 126. 152 **t.**, 1 suite.

WATERFORD

Alexander Street . . . . Y 2
Arundel Square . . . . Y 3
Bachelors Walk . . . . Y 4
Bailey's New Street . . . . Z 5
Ballybricken Green . . . . Y 6
Barronstrand Street . . . . Y 7
Blackfriars Street . . . . Y 8
Broad Street . . . . Y 9
Brown's Lane . . . . Y 10
Carrigeen Park . . . . Y 13
Cathedral Square . . . . Z 14
City Square Shopping Centre YZ
Coal Quay . . . . Y 15
Colbeck Street . . . . Z 16
Five Alley Lane . . . . Y 17
George Street . . . . Y 20
Gladstone Street . . . . Y 19
Greyfriar's Street . . . . Z 21
Hanover Street . . . . Y 23
Henrietta Street . . . . Z 24
High Street . . . . YZ 25
Jenkin's Lane . . . . Y 27
Keiser Street . . . . Z 28
King's Terrace . . . . Y 29
Lady Lane . . . . YZ 30
Lombard Street . . . . Z 31
Mayors Walk . . . . Y 32
Meagher's Quay . . . . Y 33
Newgate Street . . . . Y 35
New Street . . . . Y 36
Palace Lane . . . . Z 37
Penrose Lane . . . . Y 38
Railway Square . . . . Y 39
St. Patrick Terrace . . . . Y 40
Sally Park . . . . Y 41
Scotch Quay . . . . Z 42
Shortcourse . . . . Y 43
Trinity Square . . . . Y 44
Vulcan Street . . . . Y 45
Water Side . . . . Z 46

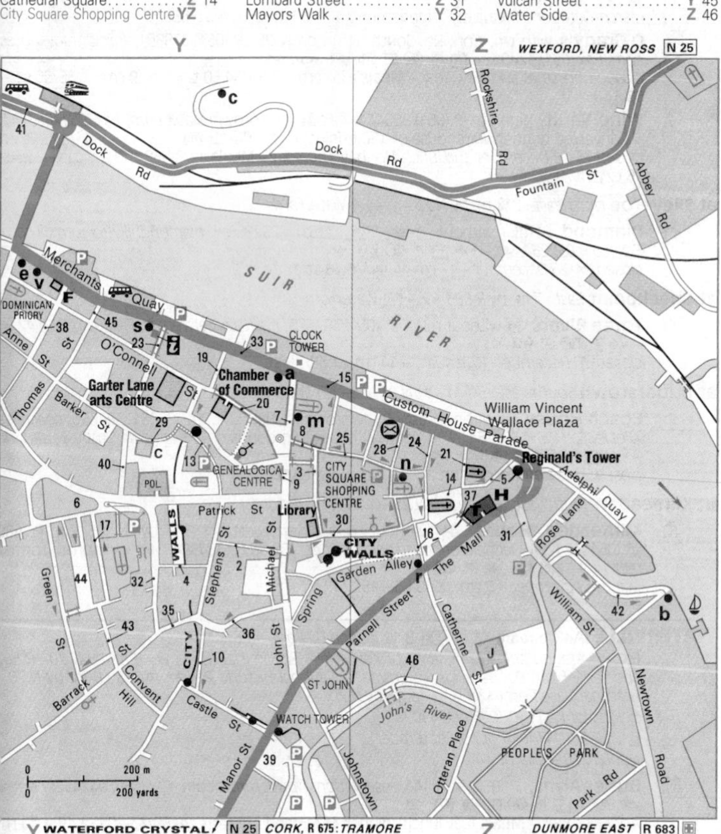

The Belfry, Conduit Lane, ✆ (051) 844800, *info@belfryhotel.ie, Fax (051) 844814* – ⫶, ▤ rest, TV ✆. MC AE VISA. ✻ Y m
closed 24-28 December – **Meals** (bar lunch)/dinner a la carte 19.30/29.15 **t.** ▯ 15.87 – **49 rm** ⌓ 80/160 **st.** – SB.

Ivory's, Tramore Rd, South : 1 ¼ m. by N 25 on R 675 ✆ (051) 358888, *info@ivorys-hotel.ie, Fax (051) 358899,* ⛱ – ⇹ rm, TV ♿ P. MC AE ⓓ VISA
Meals *(closed Sunday dinner)* (carvery lunch) 19/22.25 and a la carte 23.50/34.25 **t.** ▯ 15.17 – **40 rm** ⌓ 90/135 **st.**

Travelodge, Cork Rd, Southwest : 1 ¼ m. on N 25 ✆ (051) 358885, *Fax (051) 358890* – ⇹ rm, ▤ rest, TV ♿ P. MC AE ⓓ VISA JCB. ✻
Meals (grill rest.) – **32 rm** 67.95 **t.**

The Anchorage without rest., 9 The Quay, ✆ (051) 854302, *anchors@indigo.ie, Fax (051) 856979* – ⅍ TV. MC VISA Y v
12 rm ☕ 44.44/76.18 **st.**

Avondale without rest., 2 Parnell St, ✆ (051) 852267, *info@staywithus.net* – TV. MC VISA. ✻ Z r
closed 23-30 December – **6 rm** ☕ 50.18/76.20 **st.**

Foxmount Country House ⛰, Passage East Rd, Southeast : 4 ½ m. by R 683, off Cheekpoint rd ✆ (051) 874308, *foxmount@iol.ie, Fax (051) 854906*, ←, « Working farm », ⛰, ⛰, ⛰ – ⅍ rest, P. ✻
March-October – **Meals** (by arrangement) 30 – **5 rm** ☕ 60/90 – SB.

XX **O'Grady's** with rm, Cork Rd, South : 1 m. on N 25 ✆ (051) 378851, *info@gradyshotel.com, Fax (051) 374062* – TV P. MC AE ① VISA JCB. ✻
closed Christmas and New Year – **Meals** a la carte 17.80/34.60 **t.** 🍷 17 – **9 rm** ☕ 35/90 **st.** – SB.

X **Wine Vault,** High St, ✆ (051) 853444, *info@waterfordwinevault.com, Fax (051) 853444*, « Converted bonded warehouse of 15C origins » – ▤. MC AE VISA Z n
closed 25-26 December and lunch Monday-Thursday – **Meals** 12/31.68 and a la carte 23.36/36 **t.** 🍷 17.78.

at Slieveroe *Northeast : 2 ¼ m. by N 25* – Z – ✉ *Waterford.*

Diamond Hill without rest., ✆ (051) 832855, *diamondhill29@hotmail.com, Fax (051) 832254*, ⛰ – ⅍ TV P. MC VISA. ✻
closed 24-26 December – **17 rm** 44.44/76.18 **st.**

at Cheekpoint *East : 7 m. by R 683* – Z – ✉ *Waterford.*

Three Rivers ⛰ without rest., ✆ (051) 382520, *mail@threerivers.ie, Fax (051) 382542*, ← – ⅍ P. MC AE VISA. ✻
closed 20 December-10 January – **14 rm** ☕ 38/76 **st.**

at Butlerstown *Southwest : 5 ¼ m. by N 25* – Y – ✉ *Waterford.*

Coach House ⛰ without rest., Butlerstown Castle, Cork Rd, ✆ (051) 384656, *coachhse@iol.ie, Fax (051) 384751*, ←, « Victorian house in grounds of Butlerstown Castle », ⛰, ⛰ – ⅍ TV P. MC AE ① VISA. ✻
closed 21 December-1 February – **9 rm** ☕ 57/89 **st.**

at Kilmeadan *Southwest : 6 ¾ m. on N 25* – Y – ✉ *Waterford.*

Kilmeaden House ⛰ without rest., Northwest : 1 m. by N 25 on R 680 ✆ (051) 384254, *kilmeadenhouse@eircom.net, Fax (051) 384884*, ←, « Victorian former rectory », ⛰, ⛰ – ⅍ P. MC VISA. ✻
March-September – **5 rm** ☕ 101.58/152.37.

WATERVILLE (An Coireán) *Kerry* 923 B 12 *Ireland G. – pop. 466.*

Exc. : *Iveragh Peninsula★★ (Ring of Kerry★★) – Skellig Islands★★, W : 8 m. by N 70 , R 567 and ferry from Ballinskelligs – Derrynane National Historic Park★★ AC, S : 9 m. by N 70 – Leacanabuaile Fort (←★★), N : 13 m. by N 70.*

⛳18 *Ring of Kerry ✆ (066) 9474102.*

ℹ *✆ (066) 9474646 (June-September).*

Dublin 238 – Killarney 48.

Butler Arms, ✆ (066) 9474144, *reservations@butlerarms.com, Fax (066) 9474520*, ←, ⛰, ⛰, ⛰ – TV P. MC AE ① VISA. ✻
April-October – **Meals** (bar lunch)/dinner 38/45 and a la carte 28.60/43.20 **t.** 🍷 19 – **40 rm** ☕ 166/320 **t.** – SB.

Waterville House and Golf Links without rest., South : ¾ m. on N 70 ✆ (066) 9474244, *Fax (066) 9474567*, ←, ⛰, ⛰ heated, ⛳18, ⛰, ⛰ – ⅍ TV P. MC AE VISA ✻
6 rm ☕ 126.97/190.46 **t.**, 4 suites.

Brookhaven House without rest., New Line Rd, North : ¾ m. on N 70 ✆ (066) 9474431 *brookhaven@esatclear.ie, Fax (066) 9474724*, ⛰ – ⅍ TV P. ✻
closed 25 December, January and February – **5 rm** ☕ 60/101.58 **st.**

En saison, *surtout dans les stations fréquentées,*
il est prudent de retenir à l'avance.
Cependant, si vous ne pouvez pas occuper la chambre
que vous avez retenue, prévenez immédiatement l'hôtelier.
Si vous écrivez à un hôtel à l'étranger, joignez à votre lettre
un coupon-réponse international (disponible dans les bureaux de poste).

WESTPORT **(Cathair na Mart)** *Mayo* 923 D 6 *Ireland G. – pop. 4 253.*

See : *Town★★ (Centre★) – Westport House★★ AC.*

Exc. : *SW : Murrisk Peninsula★★ – Ballintubber Abbey★, SE : 13 m. by R 330 – Croagh Patrick★, W : 6 m. by R 335 – Bunlahinch Clapper Bridge★, W : 16 m. by R 335 – Doo Lough Pass★, W : 24 m. by R 335 – Aasleagh Falls★, S : 22 m. by N 59.*

The Mall ✆ (098) 25711.

Dublin 163 – Galway 50 – Sligo 65.

Knockranny House, Knockranny, East : ½ m. by N 5 ✆ (098) 28600, *info@khh.ie, Fax (098) 28611*, ≤ – |‡|, ▤ rest, TV ♿ P – 500. MC AE VISA. ✂
closed 22-28 December – ***La Fougère :*** **Meals** (bar lunch Monday-Saturday)/dinner 45 19 – **54 rm** ☐ 175/230 **t.** – SB.

Atlantic Coast, The Quay, West : 1 m. on R 335 ✆ (098) 29000, *achotel@iol.ie, Fax (098) 29111*, Lδ, ≘s, ☒ – |‡|, ⇹ rm, TV ✆ ♿ P – 150. MC AE VISA. ✂
closed 24-28 December – ***Blue Wave :*** **Meals** (bar lunch Monday-Saturday)/dinner 31.75/36 and a la carte 25/32 **t.** 16.50 – **82 rm** ☐ 108/178 **t.**, 1 suite – SB.

Westport, The Demesne, Newport Rd, ✆ (098) 25122, *reservations@hotelwestport.ie, Fax (098) 26739*, Lδ, ≘s, ☒, ♣ – |‡| TV P – 400. MC AE ◑ VISA. ✂
Meals (bar lunch Monday-Saturday)/dinner 33 **t.** 9 – **129 rm** ☐ 102/369 **t.** – SB.

Ardmore Country House, The Quay, West : 1 ½ m. by R 335 ✆ (098) 25994, *ardmore@anv.ie, Fax (098) 27795*, ≤, ♣ – ⇹ rm, TV P. MC AE VISA. ✂
closed February and 21-28 December – **Meals** *(closed Sunday dinner for non-residents)* (dinner only) a la carte 31.38/39.83 **t.** 16.44 – **13 rm** ☐ 120.65/203.20 **t.** – SB.

Westport Woods, Quay Rd, West : ½ m. ✆ (098) 25811, *info@westportwoodshotel.com, Fax (098) 26212*, Lδ, ≘s, ☒, ♣, ✂ – TV P – 300. MC AE ◑ VISA. ✂
Meals (bar lunch Monday-Saturday)/dinner 25.40/32 **t.** 15.87 – **111 rm** ☐ 133/266 **t.** – SB.

Augusta Lodge without rest., Golf Links Rd, North : ½ m. off N 59 ✆ (098) 28900, *info@augustalodge.ie, Fax (098) 28995* – ⇹ TV P. MC VISA. ✂
closed 1 week February, 1 week November and 23-28 December – **10 rm** ☐ 51/76 **st.**

*Es ist empfehlenswert, **in der Hauptsaison** und vor allem in Urlaubsorten, Hotelzimmer im voraus zu bestellen. Benachrichtigen Sie sofort das Hotel, wenn Sie ein bestelltes Zimmer nicht belegen können.*

Wenn Sie an ein Hotel im Ausland schreiben, fügen Sie Ihrem Brief einen internationalen Antwortschein bei (im Postamt erhältlich).

WEXFORD **(Loch Garman)** *Wexford* 923 M 10 *Ireland G. – pop. 9 533.*

See : *Town★ – Main Street★* YZ *– Franciscan Friary★* Z *– St. Iberius' Church★* Y **D** *– Twin Churches★* Z.

Env. : *Irish Agricultural Museum, Johnstown Castle★★ AC, SW : 4 ½ m.* X *– Irish National Heritage Park, Ferrycarrig★ AC, NW : 2½ m. by N 11* V *– Curracloe★, NE : 5 m. by R 741 and R 743* V.

Exc. : *Kilmoer Quay★, SW : 15 m. by N 25 and R 739 (Saltee Islands★ - access by boat)* X *– Enniscorthy Castle★ (County Museum★ AC) N : 15 m. by N 11* V.

18 *Mulgannon ✆ (053) 42238.*

Crescent Quay ✆ (053) 23111.

Dublin 88 – Kilkenny 49 – Waterford 38.

Plans on following pages

Ferrycarrig, Ferrycarrig Bridge, Northwest : 2 ¾ m. on N 11 ✆ (053) 20999, *ferrycarrig@griffingroup.ie, Fax (053) 20982*, ≤ River Slaney and estuary, Lδ, ≘s, ☒, 18, ♣ – |‡|, ⇹ rm, ▤ rest, TV ✆ P – 400. MC AE ◑ VISA. ✂ V a
Tides : **Meals** *(closed Sunday-Monday) (restricted opening in winter)* (dinner only) a la carte 33.50/45.40 **t.** 15.90 – ***Boathouse Bistro :*** **Meals** 40.50/43.18 (lunch) and a la carte 26.90/34.80 **t.** 15.90 – **94 rm** ☐ 152.40/266.70 **t.**, 4 suites – SB.

Talbot, Trinity St, ✆ (053) 22566, *talbotwx@eircom.net, Fax (053) 23377*, Lδ, ≘s, ☒ – |‡|, ⇹ rm, ▤ rest, TV ✆ ♿ P – 400. MC AE ◑ VISA. ✂ Z b
Meals (carving lunch) 7.62/33.01 and a la carte 22.22/35.87 **t.** 8.89 – **99 rm** ☐ 87.61/149.83 **t.** – SB.

Whitford House, New Line Rd, West : 2 ¼ m. on R 733 ✆ (053) 43444, *whitford@indigo.ie, Fax (053) 46399*, ☒, ♣, ✂ – TV P. MC AE VISA. ✂ V d
closed 23 December-7 January – **Meals** (carvery lunch Monday-Saturday)/dinner 33.65 and a la carte 26/39 **t.** 16.25 – **36 rm** ☐ 69.84/165.06 **t.** – SB.

Slaney Manor ⊗, Ferrycarrig, West : 3 m. on N 25 ✆ (053) 20051, *slaneymanor@eircom.net, Fax (053) 20510*, ≤, 🐕 – ⊬ TV P. ⊕ AE ⊙ VISA. ✂ V c
closed 20-28 December – **Meals** *(closed Sunday lunch)* (booking essential) (residents only) (bar lunch)/dinner 20/30 **st.** 13 – **18 rm** ☐ 90/170 **st.**

Farmers Kitchen, Drinagh, South : 2 ½ m. on Rosslare Rd ✆ (053) 43295, *Fax (053) 45827*, ≤ – TV P. ⊕ AE VISA. ✂ X f
closed 25 December – **Meals** 15.25/25.40 and a la carte 17.20/27.43 **st.** 12.69 – **21 rm** ☐ 44/114.28 **st.** – SB.

Clonard House ⊗ without rest., Clonard Great, Southwest : 2 ½ m. by R 733 ✆ (053) 43141, *khayes@indigo.ie, Fax (053) 43141*, ≤, « Georgian country house, working farm », ≤, 🐕 – ⊬ TV P. ⊕ VISA. ✂ X n
April-5 November
9 rm ☐ 38/66 **st.**

McMenamin's Townhouse without rest., 3 Auburn Terr, Redmond Rd, ✆ (053) 46442, *mcmem@indigo.ie, Fax (053) 46442* – ⊬ TV P. ⊕ VISA. ✂ Y r
closed 20-30 December
5 rm ☐ 45/70 **st.**

Rathaspeck Manor ⊗ without rest., Rathaspeck, Southwest : 4 m. by Rosslare Rd off Bridgetown rd ✆ (053) 42661, « Georgian country house », 18, ≤, ✂ – TV P. ✂ X k
20 June-October
6 rm ☐ 63.50 **st.**

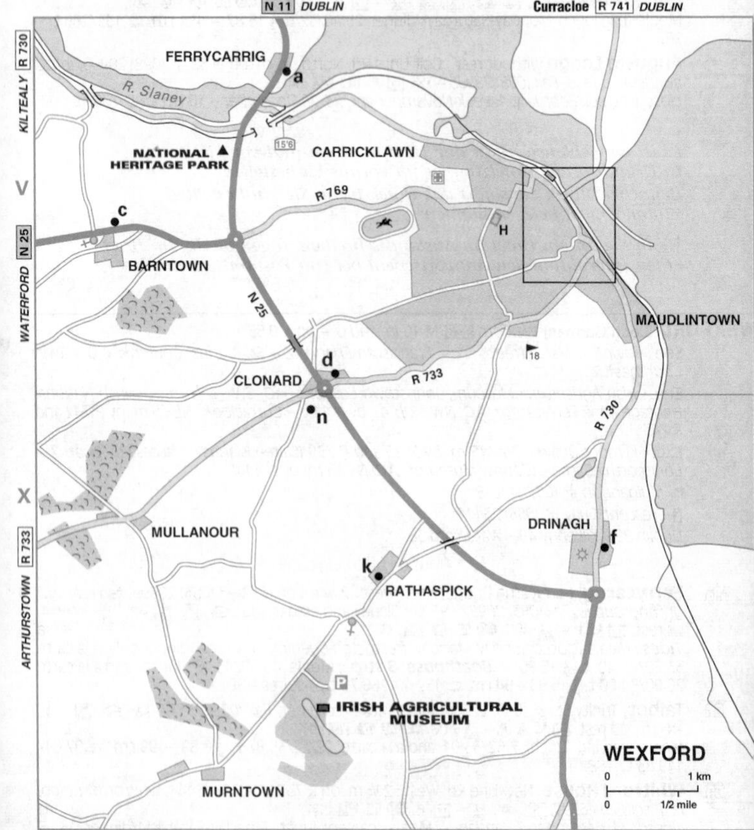

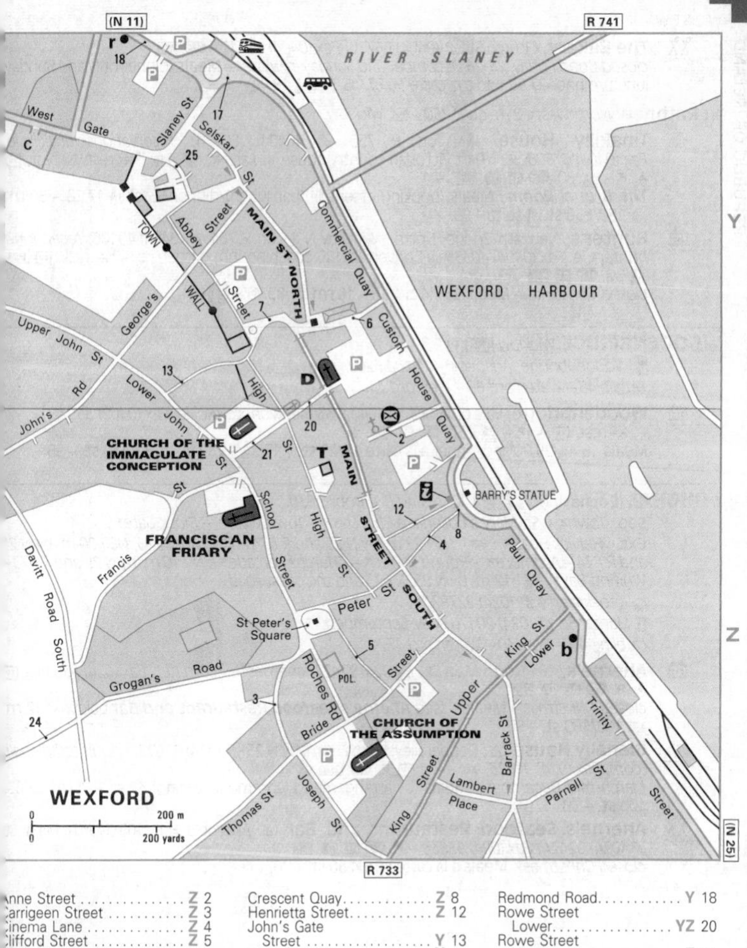

nne Street . . . . Z 2	Crescent Quay. . . . . Z 8	Redmond Road. . . . . Y 18
arrigeen Street . . . . Z 3	Henrietta Street. . . . . Z 12	Rowe Street Lower. . . . . YZ 20
inema Lane . . . . Z 4	John's Gate Street . . . . Y 13	Rowe Street Upper . . . . Z 21
lifford Street . . . . Z 5	Main St. North. . . . . Y	Summerthil Road . . . . Z 24
ommon Quay Street . . . . Y 6	Main St. South . . . . Z	Temperance Row. . . . . Y 25
ornmarket . . . . Y 7	Redmond Place. . . . . Y 17	

Bitte beachten Sie die Geschwindigkeitsbeschränkungen in Großbritannien
- 60 mph (= 96 km/h) außerhalb geschlossener Ortschaften
- 70 mph (= 112 km/h) auf Straßen mit getrennten Fahrbahnen und Autobahnen.

WICKLOW (Cill Mhantáin) *Wicklow* 923 N 9 *Ireland G. – pop. 6 416.*

Env. : *Mount Usher Gardens, Ashford★ AC, NW : 4 m. by R 750 and N 11 – Devil's Glen★, NW : 8 m. by R 750 and N 11.*

Exc. : *Glendalough★★★ (Lower Lake★★★, Upper Lake★★, Cathedral★★, Round Tower★, St. Kevin's Church★, St. Saviour's Priory★), – W : 14 m. by R 750, N 11, R 763, R 755 and R 756 – Wicklow Mountains★★ (Wicklow Gap★★, Sally Gap★★, Avondale★, Meeting of the Waters★, Glenmacnass Waterfall★, Glenmalur★, – Loughs Tay and Dan★).*

(0404) 69117.

Dublin 33 – Waterford 84 – Wexford 67.

XX **The Bakery,** Church St, ℘ (0404) 66770, *Fax (0404) 66717* – MC VISA
closed Good Friday, 24-26 December and Sunday in winter – **Meals** (dinner only and Sunday lunch)/dinner 27.72 and a la carte 30.87/45.36 **t.** 18.41.

at Rathnew *Northwest : 2 m. on R 750 – ✉ Wicklow.*

Tinakilly House ⑤, on R 750 ℘ (0404) 69274, *reservations@tinakilly.ie, Fax (0404) 67806*, ≤, « Part Victorian country house », Ls, ⊼, ✗ – |♣|, ⊁ rest, ▤ rest, TV ♿ P – 🏃 80. MC AE ⓓ VISA. ✗
The Brunel Room : **Meals** (booking essential) (bar lunch)/dinner 55 **st.** 17.78 – **50 rm** ⊐ 180/238 **st.**, 1 suite – SB.

Hunter's, Newrath Bridge, North : ¾ m. by N 11 on R 761 ℘ (0404) 40106, *reception@hunters.ie, Fax (0404) 40338*, « Converted 18C coaching inn, gardens » – ⊁ rest, TV P – 🏃 30. MC AE VISA JCB. ✗
closed Christmas – **Meals** 25/44 **t.** 16 – **16 rm** ⊐ 89/178 **t.**

WOODENBRIDGE *Wicklow* 923 N 9.

18 *Woodenbridge, Arklow* ℘ *(0402) 35202.*
Dublin 46 – Waterford 68 – Wexford 41.

Woodenbridge, Vale of Avoca, ℘ (0402) 35146, *wbhotel@iol.ie, Fax (0402) 35573*, ≤, ⊼ – ⊁ rest, TV ♿ P – 🏃 250. MC AE VISA. ✗
Meals 16.44/29.20 and dinner a la carte 17/29 **st.** 15.24 – **23 rm** ⊐ 82/140 **st.** – SB.

YOUGHAL **(Eochaill)** *Cork* 923 I 12 *Ireland G.* – *pop. 5 630.*

See : *Town★ – St. Mary's Collegiate Church★★ – Town Walls★ – Clock Gate★.*
Exc. : *Helvick Head★ (≤★), NE : 22 m. by N 25 and R 674 – Ringville (≤★), NE : 20 m. by N 25 and R 674 – Ardmore★ – Round Tower★ – Church★ (arcade★), N : 10 m. by N 25 and R 673 – Whiting Bay★, SE : 12 m. by N 25, R 673 and the coast road.*
18 *Knockaverry* ℘ *(024) 92787.*
ℹ *Market Sq* ℘ *(024) 20170 (May-September).*
Dublin 146 – Cork 30 – Waterford 47.

Aherne's, 163 North Main St, ℘ (024) 92424, *ahernes@eircom.net, Fax (024) 93633* – TV ♿ P. MC AE ⓓ VISA. ✗
closed Christmas – **Meals** – (see ***Aherne's Seafood Restaurant and Bar*** below) – **12 rm** ⊐ 110/180 **st.** – SB.

Glenally House ⑤, Copperalley, North : 1 m. by N 25 ℘ (024) 91623, *enquiries@glenally.com, Fax (024) 91623*, ⊼ – ⊁ TV P. MC VISA. ✗
March-mid December – **Meals** (by arrangement) (communal dining) 32 **st.** – **4 rm** ⊐ 63/100 **st.** – SB.

XX **Aherne's Seafood Restaurant and Bar** (at Aherne's H.), 163 North Main St ℘ (024) 92424, *Fax (024) 93633* – P. MC AE ⓓ VISA
closed Christmas – **Meals** a la carte 19/54.50 **st.** 20.

Die im **Michelin-Führer**
verwendeten Zeichen und Symbole haben
- **fett** oder dünn gedruckt, rot oder **schwarz** -
jeweils eine andere Bedeutung.
Lesen Sie daher die Erklärungen aufmerksam durch.

Distances

All distances in this edition are quoted in miles. The distance is given from each town to other nearby towns and to the capital of each region as grouped in the guide.
To avoid excessive repetition some distances have only been quoted once – you may therefore have to look under both town headings.
The distances in miles quoted are not necessarily the shortest but have been based on the roads which afford the best driving conditions and are therefore the most practical.

Distances en miles

Pour chaque région traitée, vous trouverez au texte de chacune des localités sa distance par rapport à la capitale et aux villes environnantes.
La distance d'une localité à une autre n'est pas toujours répétée aux deux villes intéressées : voyez au texte de l'une ou de l'autre.
Ces distances ne sont pas nécessairement comptées par la route la plus courte mais par la plus pratique, c'est-à-dire celle offrant les meilleures conditions de roulage.

Dublin - Sligo: 135 Miles

	Belfast	Cork	Dublin	Dundalk	Galway	Killarney	Limerick	Londonderry	Omagh	Sligo	Tullamore
Cork	259										
Dublin	105	155									
Dundalk	54	206	52								
Galway	195	124	134	155							
Killarney	298	55	194	245	137						
Limerick	228	59	124	175	66	71					
Londonderry	73	296	143	102	173	301	230				
Omagh	68	262	110	69	157	258	187	34			
Sligo	123	208	135	106	91	220	149	83	67		
Tullamore	137	124	63	84	83	144	74	161	128	99	
Waterford	204	74	100	151	143	119	78	241	208	183	84

Distanze in miglia

Per ciascuna delle regioni trattate, troverete nel testo di ogni località la sua distanza dalla capitale e dalle ditta circostanti.
Le distanza da una località all'altra non è sempre ripetuta nelle due città interessate : vedere nel testo dell'una o dell'altra.
Le distanza non sono necessariamente calcolate seguendo il percorso più breve, ma vengono stabilite secondo l'itinerario più pratico, che offre cioè le migliori condizioni di viaggio.

Entfernungsangaben in meilen

Die Entfernungen der einzelnen Orte zur Landeshauptstadt und zu den nächstgrößeren Städten in der Umgebung sind im allgemeinen Orstext angegeben.
Die Entfernung zweier Städte voneinander können Sie aus den Angaben im Ortstext der einen oder der anderen Stadt ersehen.
Die Entfernungsangaben gelten nicht immer für der kürzesten, sondern für den günstigsten Weg.

Distances between major towns

Distances entre principales villes

Distanze tra le principali città

Entfernungen zwischen den größeren Städten

432 Miles — *Edinburgh - Southampton*

	Aberdeen	Ayr	Birmingham	Blackpool	Brighton	Bristol	Cambridge	Cardiff	Carlisle	Coventry	Dover	Dumfries	Dundee	Edinburgh	Glasgow	Inverness	Ipswich	Kingston-upon-Hull	Leeds	Leicester	Liverpool	London	Manchester	Middlesbrough	Newcastle	Norwich	Nottingham	Oban	Oxford	Plymouth	Portsmouth	Sheffield	Southampton	Stoke-on-Trent	Swansea
Ayr	189																																		
Birmingham	437	295																																	
Blackpool	329	186	130																																
Brighton	606	463	168	298																															
Bristol	521	378	91	213	162																														
Cambridge	471	358	99	222	122	155																													
Cardiff	540	398	110	232	193	42	186																												
Carlisle	234	92	205	96	374	288	268	308																											
Coventry	454	311	23	146	159	98	79	123	221																										
Dover	591	493	205	328	107	200	123	232	404	184																									
Dumfries	213	57	238	129	407	321	301	341	35	254	437																								
Dundee	68	117	357	249	526	440	404	460	154	373	523	133																							
Edinburgh	123	85	298	190	467	381	346	401	95	314	466	74	56																						
Glasgow	150	37	302	193	470	385	365	404	99	318	500	77	78	47																					
Inverness	110	213	462	353	631	545	508	565	259	478	660	237	130	160	174																				
Ipswich	526	413	154	277	128	209	58	241	323	134	129	356	459	401	420	563																			
Kingston-upon-Hull	363	250	146	144	266	238	148	258	160	127	267	193	296	238	257	400	163																		
Leeds	327	214	124	89	267	216	155	236	124	123	275	157	260	202	221	364	210	62																	
Leicester	418	316	44	151	169	121	72	153	226	24	189	259	350	292	323	483	127	103	104																
Liverpool	363	220	103	55	271	186	196	167	130	119	301	164	283	224	227	387	251	131	76	124															
London	554	411	123	246	58	123	58	155	321	101	77	354	474	403	418	578	73	202	206	107	219														
Manchester	358	215	90	54	259	173	183	193	125	106	288	158	278	219	222	382	238	100	44	111	35	206													
Middlesbrough	273	189	182	125	326	274	208	294	91	181	328	132	205	148	196	309	263	90	64	154	146	265	115												
Newcastle	231	149	215	136	359	308	241	327	60	214	360	92	163	105	156	267	295	133	97	187	179	297	147	40											
Norwich	492	379	161	245	169	231	64	263	289	141	170	322	424	367	386	529	44	142	176	119	225	111	191	229	263										
Nottingham	398	285	54	135	197	146	91	165	195	53	218	228	330	272	292	434	146	90	76	28	108	136	76	134	168	121									
Oban	185	128	402	293	570	485	465	505	199	418	600	177	119	124	101	116	520	357	321	423	327	518	322	270	228	486	392								
Oxford	506	364	68	198	108	71	85	103	274	59	147	307	426	367	371	531	138	178	175	76	172	59	159	233	267	146	105	471							
Plymouth	639	496	209	331	217	120	275	156	406	216	295	439	559	500	503	663	313	356	334	239	304	227	291	393	427	335	264	603	195						
Portsmouth	590	447	152	282	49	100	138	153	357	143	143	390	510	451	454	614	165	262	258	159	255	80	242	317	351	198	188	554	86	176					
Sheffield	364	251	87	97	231	179	130	199	161	86	252	194	296	239	258	401	185	71	35	67	77	170	43	101	135	151	39	358	138	298	222				
Southampton	571	429	133	263	62	79	133	119	339	124	144	372	491	432	435	596	170	243	240	141	237	84	224	298	332	192	169	536	68	154	22	203			
Stoke-on-Trent	393	250	48	85	217	131	141	151	160	64	247	193	312	253	257	417	196	136	92	67	58	165	45	162	196	176	50	357	117	250	201	47	182		
Swansea	525	383	137	217	229	78	222	40	293	159	268	326	445	386	389	550	277	284	224	180	172	191	183	321	355	299	192	490	138	193	189	226	155	178	
Wick	218	321	569	461	738	652	615	672	366	586	768	345	238	268	282	109	670	507	471	591	495	686	490	417	375	636	542	225	638	771	722	508	703	524	657

Birmingham	Cardiff	Dublin	Glasgow	London	
430	456	597	726	302	**Amsterdam**
920	866	1094	1223	901	**Barcelona**
623	649	789	918	495	**Basel**
783	809	949	1078	654	**Berlin**
682	708	848	977	553	**Bern**
567	519	741	870	616	**Bordeaux**
1067	1093	1233	1362	938	**Bratislava**
1455	1481	1621	1750	1326	**Brindisi**
327	353	493	622	198	**Bruxelles-Brussel**
166	117	310	468	117	**Cherbourg**
535	561	709	838	516	**Clermont-Ferrand**
450	476	616	745	322	**Düsseldorf**
576	602	742	871	448	**Frankfurt am Main**
668	694	834	963	539	**Genève**
677	704	844	492	550	**Hamburg**
872	898	469	1165	744	**København**
268	294	435	564	140	**Lille**
1322	1273	1496	1625	1371	**Lisboa**
459	485	625	754	330	**Luxembourg**

Birmingham	Cardiff	Dublin	Glasgow	London	
668	694	834	963	539	**Lyon**
1006	958	1181	1310	1056	**Madrid**
1336	1288	1510	1639	1385	**Málaga**
863	889	1029	1158	734	**Marseille**
832	858	998	1127	703	**Milano**
799	825	965	1094	670	**München**
362	314	536	665	313	**Nantes**
1319	1345	1486	1615	1191	**Palermo**
379	405	545	674	251	**Paris**
1195	1147	1370	1499	1245	**Porto**
884	910	1050	1179	756	**Praha**
1193	1219	1359	1488	1064	**Roma**
717	669	891	1020	766	**San Sebastián**
585	611	751	880	457	**Strasbourg**
704	670	877	1006	685	**Toulouse**
1096	1014	1270	1399	1077	**Valencia**
1129	1155	1296	1424	1001	**Warszawa**
1016	1042	1182	1311	888	**Wien**
1138	1164	1304	1433	1010	**Zagreb**

For distances refer to the colour key in the table
Les distances sont indiquées dans la couleur du point de passage
Le distanze sono indicate con il colore del punto di passaggio
Die Entfernungen sind angegeben in der Farbe des betroffenen Passagepunktes

- FOLKESTONE (CHANNEL TUNNEL)
- SOUTHAMPTON
- TYNEMOUTH

Glasgow - Barcelona 1223 Miles

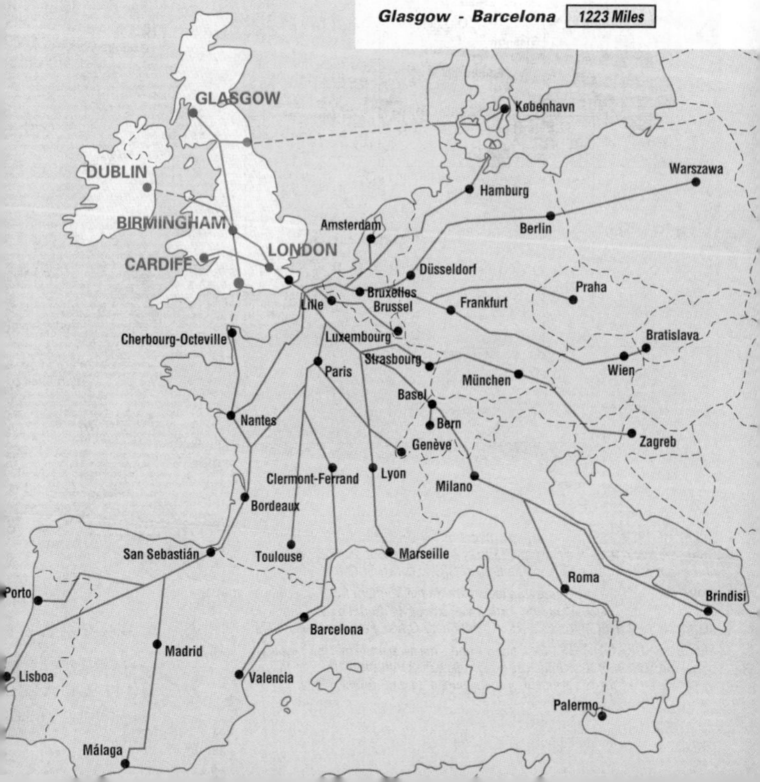

Major roads and principal shipping routes

Motorway

Road number . . . . . . A 4. T 35. N 2

Mileage 20

Principales routes et liaisons maritimes

Autoroute

N° de route . . . . A 4. T 35. N 2

Distance en miles 20

Principali strade e itinerari marittimi

Autostrada

Numero di strada . . . A 4. T 35. N 2

Distanza in miglia 20

Hauptverkehrsstrassen und Schiffsverbindungen

Autbahn

Straßennummer . . . . A 4. T 35. N 2

Entfernung in Meilen . . 20

SHETLAND ISLANDS
Unst
Yell
Whalsay
Mainland
Lerwick
Scalloway
Bergen
Aberdeen
Stromness
Lerwick
Westray
Sanday
Rousay
Stronsay
Mainland
Stromness
Kirkwall
ORKNEY ISLANDS
Hoy
Durness
Thurso
Tongue
Wick
MINCH
Loch Shin
Brora
Ullapool
Garve
Elgin
Banff
Fraserburgh
Nairn
Keith
Inverness
Kyle of Lochalsh
Loch Ness
Spey
Lerwick
Torshavn
ABERDEEN
Invergarry
Kingussie
Dee
Braemar
Stonehaven
Fort William
SCOTLAND
NORTH SEA
Loch Tay
DUNDEE
Arbroath
Oban
Crianlarich
Perth
Lochearnhead
St.Andrews
Tarbet
Stirling
Firth of Forth
Kirkcaldy
Lochgilphead
Dunfermline
Greenock
Falkirk
GLASGOW
EDINBURGH
Rothesay
Largs
Motherwell
Berwick upon Tweed
Ardrossan
Peebles
Brodick
Galashiels
Kilmarnock
Arran
Ayr
Abington
Hawick
Alnwick
New Galloway
Dumfries
Bergen
Stavanger
Hirtshals
Amsterdam
Tynemouth
Cairnryan
NEWCASTLE UPON TYNE
Stranraer
Carlisle
Sunderland
Durham
Penrith
Hartlepool
Workington
Whitehaven
Keswick
Darlington
Middlesbrough
Isle of Man
Kendal
Scarborough
ENGLAND
Douglas
Barrow-in-Furness

NORTHERN IRELAND
IRISH SEA
Isle of Man
ST GEORGE'S CHANNEL
WALES
ENG
Bristol Channel
ENGLIS
Ballymena
Larne
Belfast
Bangor
Lough Neagh
Strangford Lough
Ballygawley
Armagh
Banbridge
Newcastle
Monaghan
Dundalk / Dun Dealgan
Kells
Drogheda/ Droichead Átha
DUBLIN/ BAILE ÁTHA CLIATH
Dún Laoghaire
Naas
Bray
Wicklow
Carlow
Arklow
Enniscorthy
Wexford
Rosslare
Cairnryan
Stranraer
Douglas
Carlisle
Penrith
Workington
Whitehaven
Keswick
Kendal
Barrow-in-Furness
Heysham
Lancaster
BLACKPOOL
Blackburn
Preston
Southport
Wigan
LIVERPOOL
Birkenhead
Bolton
MANCHES
Warrington
Chester
Holyhead/ Caergybi
Colwyn Bay/ Bae Colwyn
Bangor
Caernarfon
Mold/ Yr Wyddgrug
Wrexham/ Wrecsam
Dolgellau
Shrewsbury
Welshpool/ Y Trallwng
Wolverhampton
Dudley
BIRMINGHAM
Aberystwyth
Llangurig
Ludlow
Llandrindod Wells
Worcester
Hereford
Fishguard/ Abergwaun
Carmarthen/ Caerfyrddin
Brecon/ Aberhonddu
Ross
Gloucester
Milford Haven/ Aberdaugleddau
Merthyr Tydfil
Pembroke Dock/ Doc Penfro
Newport/ Casnewydd
Swansea/ Abertawe
CARDIFF/ CAERDYDD
BRISTOL
Bath
Ilfracombe
Minehead
Wells
Barnstaple
Bridgwater
Taunton
Salisbury
Yeovil
Bude
EXETER
Honiton
Dorchester
Exmouth
Weymouth
BOURNEMO
Newquay
Bodmin
PLYMOUTH
Torquay Torbay
Truro
Penzance
Falmouth
Isles of Scilly
Santander
Roscoff
St-Malo
Rosslare
Alderney
Guernsey
Sark
St.Peter-Port
Jersey

2

Hartlepool
Middlesbrough
Scarborough
York
KINGSTON UPON HULL
Immingham
Rotterdam
Zeebrugge
Scunthorpe
Great Grimsby
Doncaster
Rotherham
Lincoln
Skegness
Boston
NOTTINGHAM
Cromer
King's Lynn
Wisbech
NORWICH
Great Yarmouth
LEICESTER
Stamford
Peterborough
Lowestoft
Ely
Rugby
Bury St.Edmunds
Northampton
Bedford
CAMBRIDGE
Ipswich
Felixstowe
Esbjerg
Göteborg
Hoek van Holland
Hamburg
Stevenage
Colchester
Harwich
Luton
Aylesbury
Harlow
Chelmsford
OXFORD
Tilbury
Southend-on-Sea
Reading
Windsor
LONDON
Margate
Ramsgate
Newbury
Basingstoke
Sheerness
Canterbury
Deal
Guildford
Maidstone
Crawley
Royal-Tunbridge Wells
Dover
Winchester
Folkestone
Channel Tunnel
SOUTHAMPTON
BRIGHTON
Hastings
Chichester
Worthing
Eastbourne
PORTSMOUTH
Newhaven
Newport
Isle of Wight
St-Malo
CHANNEL
Rosslare
LE HAVRE
NORTH SEA
THAMES
Ouse
Trent
Swale
Kingston upon Hull
Zeebrugge
OOSTENDE
BRUGGE
BELGIË
BELGIQUE
Dunkerque
Calais
St-Omer
Boulogne
LILLE
Arras
Cambrai
Abbeville
Somme
Dieppe
AMIENS
St-Quentin
FRANCE
Beauvais
Compiègne
ROUEN
Senlis

3

ATLANTIC OCEAN
NORTH CHANNEL
CELTIC SEA
ST GEORGE'S
IRELAND
NORTHERN IRELAND
Tiree
Mull
Colonsay
Jura
Port Askaig
Islay
Port Ellen
Coleraine
Waterfoot
Londonderry
Letterkenny
Ballymena
Larne
Strabane
Donegal
Omagh
Lough Neagh
BELFAST
Ballygawley
Enniskillen
Sligo/
Sligeach
Armagh
Banbridge
Newcastle
Monaghan
L. Allen
Ballina
Boyle
Cavan
Dundalk /
Dun Dealgan
Westport
Castlebar
L. Mask
Longford
Kells
Drogheda/
Droichead Átha
Clifden
L. Corrib
Roscommon
L. Ree
Mullingar
Boyne
Galway/
Gaillimh
Athlone
Ballinasloe
DUBLIN/
BAILE ÁTHA CLIATH
Tullamore
Lisdoonvarna
River Shannon
Naas
Dún Laoghaire
Bray
Ennis/
Inis
Roscrea
Wicklow
Kilkee
Thurles
Suir
Carlow
Arklow
LIMERICK/
LUIMNEACH
Kilkenny /
Cill Chainnigh
Cashel/
Caiseal
Barrow
Tralee
Enniscorthy
Dingle
Caher
Carrick on Suir
Wexford
Killarney/
Cill Airne
Fermoy
R. Blackwater
Lismore
Waterford/
Port Lairge
Rosslare
CORK/
CORCAIGH
Cobh
Youghal
Glengarriff
Bantry

Major hotel groups

Central reservation telephone numbers

Principales chaînes hôtelières

Centraux téléphoniques de réservation

Principali catene alberghiere

Centrali telefoniche di prenotazione

Die wichtigsten Hotelketten

Zentrale für telefonische Reservierung

ACCOR HOTELS (IBIS, MERCURE & NOVOTEL)	*0208 2834500*
CHOICE HOTELS	*0800 444444 (Freephone)*
CORUS & REGAL HOTELS	*08457 334400*
DE VERE HOTELS PLC	*01925 639499*
HILTON HOTELS	*08705 515151*
HOLIDAY INN WORLDWIDE	*0800 897121 (Freephone)*
HYATT HOTELS WORLDWIDE	*08457 581666*
INTERCONTINENTAL HOTELS LTD	*0800 0289387 (Freephone)*
JURYS/DOYLE HOTELS	*0870 9072222*
MACDONALD HOTELS PLC	*08457 585593*
MARRIOTT HOTELS	*0800 221222 (Freephone)*
MILLENNIUM & COPTHORNE HOTELS PLC	*0845 3020001*
PREMIER LODGES	*08702 010203*
QUEENS MOAT HOUSES PLC	*0500 213214 (Freephone)*
RADISSON EDWARDIAN HOTELS	*0800 33333333 (Freephone)*
RAMADA JARVIS HOTELS	*08457 581811*
SHERATON HOTELS	*0800 353535 (Freephone)*
THISTLE HOTELS	*0800 181716 (Freephone)*
TRAVEL INNS	*0870 2428000*
TRAVELODGES	*08700 850950*

International Dialling Codes

Note: when making an international call, do not dial the first «0» of the city codes (except for calls to Italy).

Indicatifs Téléphoniques Internationaux

Important : pour les communications internationales, le zéro (0) initial de l'indicatif interurbain n'est pas à composer (excepté pour les appels vers l'Italie).

from / to	A	B	CH	CZ	D	DK	E	FIN	F	GB	GR
A Austria		0032	0041	00420	0049	0045	0034	00358	0033	0044	0030
B Belgium	0043		0041	00420	0049	0045	0034	00358	0033	0044	0030
CH Switzerland	0043	0032		00420	0049	0045	0034	00358	0033	0044	0030
CZ Czech Republic	0043	0032	0041		0049	0045	0034	00358	0033	0044	0030
D Germany	0043	0032	0041	00420		0045	0034	00358	0033	0044	0030
DK Denmark	0043	0032	0041	00420	0049		0034	00358	0033	0044	0030
E Spain	0043	0032	0041	00420	0049	0045		00358	0033	0044	0030
FIN Finland	0043	0032	0041	00420	0049	0045	0034		0033	0044	0030
F France	0043	0032	0041	00420	0049	0045	0034	00358		0044	0030
GB United Kingdom	0043	0032	0041	00420	0049	0045	0034	00358	0033		0030
GR Greece	0043	0032	0041	00420	0049	0045	0034	00358	0033	0044	
H Hungary	0043	0032	0041	00420	0049	0045	0034	00358	0033	0044	0030
I Italy	0043	0032	0041	00420	0049	0045	0034	00358	0033	0044	0030
IRL Ireland	0043	0032	0041	00420	0049	0045	0034	00358	0033	0044	0030
J Japan	00143	00132	00141	001420	00149	00145	00134	001358	00133	00144	00130
L Luxembourg	0043	0032	0041	00420	0049	0045	0034	00358	0033	0044	0030
N Norway	0043	0032	0041	00420	0049	0045	0034	00358	0033	0044	0030
NL Netherlands	0043	0032	0041	00420	0049	0045	0034	00358	0033	0044	0030
PL Poland	0043	0032	0041	00420	0049	0045	0034	00358	0033	0044	0030
P Portugal	0043	0032	0041	00420	0049	0045	0034	00358	0033	0044	0030
RUS Russia	81043	81032	810420	6420	81049	81045	*	810358	81033	81044	*
S Sweden	0043	0032	0041	00420	0049	0045	0034	00358	0033	0044	0030
USA	01143	01132	01141	001420	01149	01145	01134	01358	01133	01144	01130

** Direct dialling not possible*

** Pas de sélection automatique*

Indicativi Telefonici Internationali

Importante: per le comunicazioni internazionali, non bisogna comporre lo zero (0) iniziale dell'indicativo interurbano (escluse le chiamate per l'Italia)

Telefon-Vorwahlnummern international

Wichtig: bei Auslandgesprächen darf die Null (0) der Ortsnetzkennzahl nicht gewählt werden (ausser bei Gesprächen nach Italien).

H	I	IRL	J	L	N	NL	PL	P	RUS	S	USA	
0036	0039	00353	0081	00352	0047	0031	0048	00351	007	0046	001	**A Austria**
0036	0039	00353	0081	00352	0047	0031	0048	00351	007	0046	001	**B Belgium**
0036	0039	00353	0081	00352	0047	0031	0048	00351	007	0046	001	**CH Switzerland**
0036	0039	00353	0081	00352	0047	0031	0048	00351	007	0046	001	**CZ Czech Republic**
0036	0039	00353	0081	00352	0047	0031	0048	00351	007	0046	001	**D Germany**
0036	0039	00353	0081	00352	0047	0031	0048	00351	007	0046	001	**DK Denmark**
0036	0039	00353	0081	00352	0047	0031	0048	00351	007	0046	001	**E Spain**
0036	0039	00353	0081	00352	0047	0031	0048	00351	007	0046	001	**FIN Finland**
0036	0039	00353	0081	00352	0047	0031	0048	00351	007	0046	001	**F France**
0036	0039	00353	0081	00352	0047	0031	0048	00351	007	0046	001	**GB United Kingdom**
0036	0039	00353	0081	00352	0047	0031	0048	00351	007	0046	001	**GR Greece**
	0039	00353	0081	00352	0047	0031	0048	00351	007	0046	001	**H Hungary**
0036		00353	0081	00352	0047	0031	0048	00351	*	0046	001	**I Italy**
0036	0039		0081	00352	0047	0031	0048	00351	007	0046	001	**IRL Ireland**
00136	00139	001353		001352	00147	00131	00148	001351	*	00146	0011	**J Japan**
0036	0039	00353	0081		0047	0031	0048	00351	007	0046	001	**L Luxembourg**
0036	0039	00353	0081	00352		0031	0048	00351	007	0046	001	**N Norway**
0036	0039	00353	0081	00352	0047		0048	00351	007	0046	001	**NL Netherlands**
0036	0039	00353	0081	00352	0047	0031		00351	007	0046	001	**PL Poland**
0036	0039	00353	0081	00352	0047	0031	0048		007	0046	001	**P Portugal**
81036	*	*	*	*	*	81031	81048	*		*	*	**RUS Russia**
0036	0039	00353	0081	00352	0047	0031	0048	00351	007		001	**S Sweden**
01136	01139	011353	01181	011352	01147	01131	01148	011351	*	011146		**USA**

**Selezione automatica impossibile*

**Automatische Vorwahl nicht möglich*

Index of towns
Index des localités
Indice delle località
Ortsverzeichnis

B

C

D

E

H

L

N

O

P

Q

R

S

In the same series

Dans la même collection

Altri titoli della collezione

Weitere Titel

Benelux
Deutschland
España & Portugal
Europe Main cities
France
Ireland
Italia
London
Paris
Portugal
Suisse/Schweiz/Svizzera

Manufacture française des pneumatiques Michelin

Société en commandite par actions au capital de 304 000 000 EUR.
Place des Carmes-Déchaux – 63 Clermont-Ferrand (France)
R.C.S. Clermont-Fd B 855 200 507

Michelin et Cie, Propriétaires-Éditeurs 2002

Dépôt légal Janvier 2002 – ISBN 2-06-100175-0

Printed in Germany 12-01

Photocompositeur : A.P.S. - Tours (France)
Imprimeur-Relieur : NEEF STUMME - Wittingen (Allemagne)

Illustrations Cécile Imbert/MICHELIN : pages 4 à 56
Narratif Systèmes/Geneclo : pages 58 à 66
Autres illustrations : Rodolphe Corbel.